ALBERT SCHATZ, 1839-1910.

LIBRARY OF CONGRESS

CATALOGUE

OF

OPERA LIBRETTOS

PRINTED BEFORE 1800

PREPARED BY

OSCAR GEORGE THEODORE SONNECK

CHIEF OF THE DIVISION OF MUSIC

VOLUME I

TITLE CATALOGUE

WASHINGTON
GOVERNMENT PRINTING OFFICE
1914

L. C. card, 13—35009

This work in two volumes is for sale by the
SUPERINTENDENT OF DOCUMENTS
Government Printing Office
Washington, D. C.

Price, $2.00 per set

PREFACE

Applied to musical dramas like Wagner's "Tristan und Isolde," the term libretto sounds absurd, but it would be difficult to substitute for the purely practical purpose of naming a catalogue an equally convenient, an equally generic, and at the same time equally specific term. By international consent libretto has come to mean a text that is intended for musical composition, whether it be a text for musical tragedy, comedy or farce, oratorio, sacred or secular cantata. Exactly therein lies the value of this somewhat artificial traditional term for purposes of modern phraseology that it circumscribes without necessity of further definition one distinctive field of literature, just as opera, a similarly artificial term, possesses an unmistakable significance. Certainly the combination of the two—opera-libretto— can not be surpassed in terseness of self-explanatory meaning.

At any rate, the term libretto has here been used without any of the current aspersions on the esthetic value of texts for dramatic music. The term opera-libretto is usually coupled with the idea of a type of drama hardly to be dignified by the name of drama or even literature. Unfortunately this contempt is justified in very many individual cases; but a sweeping condemnation of opera-librettos would be just as unfair as a sweeping condemnation of "legitimate" dramas, though most of these, too, suffer from artificiality, conventionality, and insipidity of theme and treatment. The difference is this, that the defects of the average opera-libretto are not hidden from view so easily by the clever drapery of language. A libretto is not an art work complete in itself and self-sufficient as literature. It requires to be complemented by music. To use Mr. Forsyth's witty phrase, it is but one-half of the scissors of opera. A libretto is practically useless without the music, and *vice versa*. Thus, while working with the tools of dramatic craft, the librettist molds something with all the attributes of a play, yet not a play self-sufficient on the stage or in the closet. He is handicapped from the beginning by imperative consideration of the technical problems of the composer, the limitations and possibilities of musical art. At his best he delivers into the hands of his partner the perfect half of an art work. The difficulty of his peculiar art, therefore, is to prepare and to facilitate the amalgamation of two different arts, and this is a difficulty not always fully appreciated by those who criticize librettos from a literary standpoint and who, over the occasional absurdities of an "Alfred Bunn, Esq.," forget the accomplishments of men like Zeno, Metastasio, Goldoni, Quinault, Favart, Wagner, Boito, Gilbert, Maeterlinck, and many others.

Whatever the place of librettos is in the history of literature, the libretto has its distinct place in the history of music, more especially in the history of opera. This has been recognized for centuries, and none of the fairly numerous treatises on the dramaturgics of opera omits a more or less convincing consideration of the function and art of the librettist. For this very reason it is astonishing that so far no serious attempt should have been made to give us a comprehensive history of libretto. It would be, of course, a difficult and a very complicated task, one that could be undertaken only by a scholar equally intimate with the history and technique of dramatic music and of dramatic literature, not to forget an indispensible intimacy with "Kulturgeschichte" and the economic as well as purely commercial currents underflowing the development of both arts; but it would be a fascinating task, indeed, fascinating to both the author and the reader. There are signs—I refer to the recent book on Zeno's librettos by Mr. Fehr—that the interest in the history of librettos is being revived, and if this interest continues the history of opera can not but profit by it. One result would be a clearer understanding of the share progressive librettists had in the shaping of the art form of opera. One hears much of the suggestions offered by composers to their librettists, one hears less of the outspoken or latent suggestions offered to composers by their librettists. It was Burney, I believe, who first made the observation that composers and librettists like to travel in pairs; that is, one composer preferably setting librettos by one author to music. If that observation is correct, it stands to reason that under the circumstances the influence of thoughtful librettists on the evolution of opera as an art form must have been very considerable. To decide, for instance, whether Verdi's "Falstaff," as a combined effort in the right direction, owes more to Verdi than to Boito, would be difficult, indeed, just as it would be to establish a perfect balance between our indebtedness to Wagner, the dramatist, and to Wagner, the composer. Earlier periods were not different in this respect. In the case of Calsabigi and Gluck, for instance, we have known for some time that Calsabigi had at least an equal share in certain reforms generally attributed to Gluck alone. If we turn to Metastasio, his letters to Hasse and others prove that he was by no means a willing tool in the hands of composers. He submitted to certain traditional conventionalities perhaps because it would have been useless in his time to offer stubborn resistance, but he resented the idea that the librettist had no problems of his own and should be a mere servant to the composer. "The play is the thing" was his maxim, too, and he plainly gave to the dramaturgics of opera deep and continued thought. With something like a mild monopoly on the art of writing "grand opera" librettos for eighty years in the "eroicamente erotico" manner, as one reformer put it, his influence on opera as an art form clearly must have been remarkable. It is not lessened by the fact that he excelled where most of the composers of his time failed because of fossilized conventionality, namely, in the dialogue, which stamps him, from the purely literary standpoint, too, a great playwright. What is true of Metastasio is true also *mutatis mutandis* of Goldoni, of Zeno, and the earlier musical playwrights that really count. Indeed, the very foundations of opera were laid, I dare say, by Rinuccini as much as by Jacopo Corsi, Peri, or Caccini.

If, therefore, the importance of librettos is clear for the history of musical dramaturgics and esthetics, in short of opera in general, still more so is their importance for the history of individual operas. The truth of this statement is perhaps not fully appreciated by those who use only modern librettos with the object of preparing themselves by a better acquaintance with the text for a better understanding of the opera to be heard, a function of the libretto which our libraries should begin to value more highly. Lexicographers and historians, especially local historians of opera, would have been greatly handicapped in their compilations without the direct or indirect help of the librettos which, in innumerable cases, furnish the only available clue as to the composer and author of older operas, the casts, which means biographical data on the singers, and the year-dates of performance, very often of first performance. Beyond such invaluable clues, however, librettos furnish information of a very different and equally important kind. Every student of Wagner's life, for instance, knows that his "Tannhäuser" was performed in the earliest days at Dresden with several different endings, but in just what these differences consisted was not accurately known before Tappert carefully compared the several editions of the "Tannhäuser" librettos first used at Dresden. If we go back to the eighteenth century the importance of librettos for the solution of similar textual problems becomes even greater, indeed perplexingly so if we are interested in early Italian operas.

This is primarily due to the well-known fact that an opera was hardly ever performed exactly alike as to text and *therewith as to music* in different cities. The original version of an opera only in rare cases coincided with that of replicas. The *pasticcio* and *rifacimento* tendency of the age, fostered by the demands of the singers for "thankful" numbers and the commercial risks of the managers, undermined the respect for the mental property of author and composer. The custom to substitute at will arias in the opera to be performed by arias from other operas by other composers and authors, or to replace them by such composed for the occasion, and all this very often without the slightest notice to the audience, grew into a chronic disease, into a system before which authors and composers bowed resignedly and which lasted until the latter part of the eighteenth century. There are cases on record in which out of a total of about thirty arias only about half a dozen had been retained from the original version of the opera by the author and composer under whose names the opera continued to sail.

Supposing, therefore, that a library possesses the score of an old Italian opera and that the score bears the name of a certain composer. The inexperienced would look up the date of first performance of the opera in some standard reference work, would attach that date to the score, would accredit the whole score, irrespective of incongruity of style, to one author and one composer and would hold them responsible for the merits or demerits of text and music in detail without further misgivings. This conclusion would be unsound from the first to the last, as may be inferred from the manner in which the expert would study the score. He would locate in the first place a copy of the libretto as actually used at the first performance of the composer's opera. If the text in the score and the text in the opera agree, with only irrelevant differences, he would conclude correctly that presumably this was a copy of the score as originally composed by the composer. If the name of the composer had been added by a later hand, he would also conclude that the score had been correctly attributed to him. If, however, the text of the score and of the libretto disagree, he would know immediately, first, that the score in this form was not used for the original performance; secondly, that the score contains ingredients for which the composer named is not responsible. Only by finding an edition of the libretto coinciding fully with the score under question would he be able to date it correctly, and only by a comparison of the original edition of the composer's opera with the edition of the established replica would he be able to determine what belongs to the original author and composer of the opera and what not. Other reconstructive possibilities any reader may find for himself by applying, as it were, the rules of permutation.

Cursory as these remarks are on the different uses to which librettos may be put, they suffice to illustrate the importance of a libretto collection in any well-equipped musical library. Its importance will increase in the same ratio as the library's collection of opera scores increases, and the need of an adequate libretto collection will become imperative should a library attempt to develop its collection of opera scores organically, to build up, as it were, a museum of operatic history. At any rate, this was the standpoint of the Library of Congress when the project of assembling a comprehensive, representative collection of operas began to assume definite shape. The ideal solution of the problem would be to have every opera represented also by its libretto. Whether such an ideal solution is possible of attainment or not, it is clearly the course which every systematic effort would have to take. That it would be futile to start such a collection *ab ovo* by the painfully slow process of acquiring one desirable libretto after the other was realized from the beginning. Even the gradual purchase of small, though fine, collections like that of Mr. James E. Matthew could hardly accomplish the desired result. The Library of Congress, therefore, abided its time until one of the large collections known to be in private hands would be within reach. The supreme opportunity came when in the fall of 1908 one of the most famous of all libretto collections, that of Mr. Albert Schatz, of Rostock, was offered us. The Library of Congress lost no time in acquiring this collection, the formation of which had taken Mr. Schatz not less than forty years.

As Mr. Schatz was in feeble health, and as the Library of Congress quite naturally wished to possess for future use an authoritative statement on the origin and history of his great collection before it might be too late, he was requested to furnish such a statement himself. With characteristic promptness he complied with our request and wrote the following autobiographical sketch under date of Rostock, March 17, 1909:

"Meine Sammlung von Operntexten, wie sie jetzt die Library of Congress in Washington erworben hat, ist das Ergebnis eigener Sammeltätigkeit von über 42 Jahren. Bereits in frühster Jugend entwickelte sich bei mir ein besonderes Interesse für die Oper und ihre Geschichte, das durch ältere Freunde nicht bloss wach gehalten, sondern lebhaft gefördert wurde. Als der kaufmännische Beruf mich zunächst nach Hamburg und dann 7 Jahre nach San Francisco führte, ruhte zwar mein Sinn für dies Gebiet. Kaum war ich indessen im Herbst 1873 nach Rostock zurückgekehrt und Besitzer der noch jetzt hier bestehenden Musikalienhandlung Ludwig Trutschel Nachfolger geworden, als die alte Neigung von neuem erwachte und zu dem Plan erstarkte, selbst eine Geschichte der Oper zu schreiben. Dieser Plan ist, trotz bis heute fortgesetzter Arbeit daran, noch nicht zur Vollendung gekommen; denn der Stoff nahm bei der von mir angewandten Methode ungeahnte Dimensionen an. Es stellte sich heraus, dass die bisherigen Darstellungen der Operngeschichte als Quellen völlig unzureichend und unzuverlässig waren, da sie in der Hauptsache nicht unmittelbar auf den Quellen aufgebaut, sondern ohne Kenntnis dieser, einander nachgeschrieben sind. So kam ich zu dem Schluss, dass eine korrekte Darstellung ein unmittelbares Studium der Grundquellen vernotwendige, und sah mich genötigt, da sämmtliche grossen Bibliotheken dies Quellenmaterial nur unvollständig enthielten, selbst an das Aufspüren und Sammeln derselben zu gehen. So ist im Laufe der Jahre meine Textsammlung und meine Bibliothek entstanden, von denen in Sonderheit erstere von kaum einer anderen Sammlung gleicher Art übertroffen werden dürfte und unter allen ernsten Arbeitern auf gleichem Gebiet weit und breit bekannt geworden ist. Sie führte mich mit einer Reihe anderer Musikhistoriker zusammen, mit denen ich korrespondiert habe und zum Teil noch korrespondiere. Diese Sammlung, sowie die Bestände der Bibliotheken Europas, förderten meine Geschichte der Oper so weit, dass das statistische Material in circa 80,000 Zetteln ziemlich abgeschlossen vorliegt. Diese Zettel enthalten jeder den Titel einer Oper, Namen des Komponisten und Dichters, Ort, Theater und Zeit, nicht bloss der ersten Aufführung, sondern auch der erstmaligen Wiederholungen in andern Städten oder Theatern. Sie sind chronologisch und alphabetisch geordnet, lassen sich ohne grosse Schwierigkeit, aber auch nach Komponisten, Dichtern, Städten und Theatern zusammen stellen und ergeben den vollständigen Stoff für eine Bibliographie der Oper. Zu dem fertigen Material gehört insbesondere das über die Komponisten D. Cimarosa, B. Galuppi, C. W. von Gluck, K. H. Graun, P. Guglielmi, G. F. Händel, J. A. Hasse, N. Jommelli, J. S. Mayr, F. Paër, G. Paësiello, N. Piccini, A. M. G. Sacchini, und G. Sarti. Es liegt vor in 36 Bänden und bedarf zur Veröffentlichung nur einer Schlussrevision. Das Werk im ursprünglichen Plan zur Ausführung zu bringen, ist mir, da ich in wenigen Wochen das 70. Lebensjahr erreiche, wohl nicht mehr beschieden. Soweit ich selbst nicht noch zu Einzeldarstellungen gelange oder eine andere Verwertung sich mir anbietet, beabsichtige ich dieses Material mir bekannten Fachgenossen zur Veröffentlichung oder Benutzung bei anderen Arbeiten zu übergeben. Das unfertige Material soll dagegen nach meinem Tode der Vernichtung anheim fallen.''

[Translation.]

''My collection of opera-librettos, now in possession of the Library of Congress, is the result of more than forty-two years of collecting. Since early youth I took a particular interest in opera and the history of opera, and this interest was kept alive by older friends and encouraged. When a commercial career took me first to Hambourg and then for seven years to San Francisco, my mind was concentrated on other matters, but hardly had I returned in the fall of 1873 to Rostock, to become the owner of the still existing firm

'Musikalienhandlung Ludwig Trutschel Nachfolger,' when my old passion awoke and I conceived the plan of writing a history of opera. This project, though I have worked at it until now, has not been completed, inasmuch as it reached unsuspected dimensions, owing to the method of procedure employed by me. I found that previous histories of operas were absolutely insufficient and unreliable, since in the main they are not based on primary sources, but were copied one from the other without the knowledge of these sources. I became convinced that a correct history would necessitate the study of the primary sources, and since none of the large libraries contained the material sufficiently complete, that I would have to trace and collect it myself.

"In this manner my libretto collection and my library gradually came into existence, of which especially the former is hardly surpassed by any other. At any rate, it became known everywhere to scholars interested in the same subject, and through my collection I was brought into contact with quite a few other musical historians with whom I corresponded and still correspond. My own collection and librettos in other European collections furthered my history of opera to the point that the statistical part may be considered fairly finished on about 80,000 cards. Each card contains the title of an opera, name of composer and author, place, theatre, and date of the first performance not only, but of the first repetitions in other cities or theatres. The cards are arranged chronologically, subarranged alphabetically, but without much difficulty could be rearranged by composer or author or cities and theatres. They represent the complete material for a bibliography of opera. I mention especially the material on the composers D. Cimarosa, B. Galuppi, C. W. von Gluck, K. H. Graun, P. Guglielmi, G. F. Händel, J. A. Hasse, N. Jommelli, J. S. Mayr, F. Paër, G. Paësiello, N. Piccini, A. M. G. Sacchini, and G. Sarti. These thirty-six volumes need but a final revision for the purpose of publication. (To write my history of opera, according to the original plan, is hardly allotted to me, since in a few weeks I reach my seventieth year.) If I am not able to at least write some monographs, or unless an opportunity arises for disposing of it otherwise, I intend to entrust this material to colleagues of my acquaintance to be published or to be used by them for other works. The incomplete material, on the other hand, shall be destroyed after my death."

Beyond the pride in the possession of the Albert Schatz collection, the Library of Congress takes a sentimental interest in it because, as the reader will have noticed, Mr. Schatz spent some of the best years of his life in America. After his return to Rostock he lived there until his death, October 18, 1910 (he was born there May 19, 1839), active in the musical affairs of his city in several honorary positions, quietly and with self-sacrifice and at great expense amassing his libretto collection, industriously collecting and digesting material for his colossal chronological statistics of operas, his opera-dictionary and kindred works, and ever ready to spend liberally from his wonderful store of knowledge to all—and they were many—who sought his advice.

The total number of librettos in the Albert Schatz collection, not counting duplicates, is in round figures 12,240. Of these 12,000 are opera librettos, the remainder librettos of oratorios and cantatas.

These appear to have come into his possession incidentally through the purchase of miscellaneous lots of librettos, such as are offered quite frequently by dealers, who only recently have shown a disposition to give to individual librettos that attention which they deserve and for which collectors and librarians have been sighing. In the same manner he appears to have acquired many librettos of unimportant replicas, which he otherwise would hardly have cared to add to his collection. Not that they are valueless—at least they have a decided value for local history—but, as might be expected from a connoisseur like Albert Schatz, his plan seems to have been to collect first editions, i. e., librettos printed for the first performance of an opera; in other words, librettos in their original state in preference to those used for replicas with the customary alterations, additions, interpolations, etc. This accounts for the presence of such an extraordinary number of first editions of seventeenth and eighteenth century librettos, and exactly herein lies the great value of the Albert Schatz collection for historical purposes. If in many cases even a patient collector like Mr. Schatz had to content himself with more or less important replica librettos, it merely serves to show how difficult, not to say impossible, a task it was and still is to form a comprehensive, representative collection of librettos by systematic and organic development. At no time, of course, can Mr. Schatz have entertained the notion to acquire every libretto of the more than 30,000 operas performed since 1597. Furthermore, it stands to reason that he knew intimately the weak spots in his, as every expert will agree, formidable collection. There are such weak spots the plenty, as in every collection of books, pictures, coins, or what not. If Mr. Schatz, for instance, turned to a master like Agostino Steffani, he must have felt keen disappointment at his inability to make a better showing. Presumably he consoled himself with the knowledge, born of long experience, that the find of a particularly rare libretto is practically a matter of luck, and presumably he tendered his silent good wishes to some competitor luckier or speedier than he. Moreover, though in innumerable instances his showing may well excite the envy of some specialist, some collector especially interested in the operas of a particular master or performed in a particular city, Mr. Shatz unmistakably was forming a *general* collection. If he had concentrated his efforts on particular masters to the neglect of others, probably the result would sometimes have been more satisfactory for the purposes of specialists with a limited sphere of interest, but it certainly would have been less satisfactory for the purposes of a general library. While weak spots, as conceded above, have their explanation in peculiar obstacles over which a collector is not master, another aspect of the Schatz collection is rather puzzling. Though cosmopolitan in his tendencies, Mr. Schatz did not collect French librettos with the same planful zeal as he did German and Italian. For reasons unknown to us, he preferred at first German translations to the French originals, and though he evidently in later years paid more attention to the latter, he did not quite succeed in reversing the balance in their favor. In other words, the Schatz collection, *relatively speaking*, was not as strong in French librettos as it might have been. A similar estimate applies to Russian, Scandinavian, Bohemian, Hungarian, Spanish, English, and American librettos in the *original* language. That it was not a lack of linguistic ability which prompted Mr. Schatz to leave his collection more or less underdeveloped in these fields is proven by the curious (and sometimes embarrassing) fact that he invariably entered librettos in his own catalogue in the language written, whether that be Hungarian, Norwegian, Portuguese, or any other, and in case of Russian librettos he even made his catalogue entries and notes in Russian script.

After a study of Mr. Schatz' "Hand-Katalog," which accompanied the purchase, had established the character and relative strength and weakness of his collection, the Library of Congress gradually entered on a campaign of filling in gaps. Not, of course, recklessly and without discrimination. The campaign was based on the fundamental idea of deepening and facilitating the study of opera scores in our possession by putting at the student's disposal also the librettos of the operas. For administrative reasons the want lists were based on our collection of full scores, now more than 2,500, and not on the collection of about 7,000 vocal scores. And in view of the fact that the publication of the catalogue of our seventeenth and eighteenth century librettos was likely to precede that of nineteenth century librettos by several years, emphasis was laid on the earlier period. This was the theory, but for actual results we were subject to the caprices of the market. Still, the Schatz collection was strengthened by many hundreds of librettos, including very many French. It further happened that the remarkable Longe collection of minor English dramatists, acquired by the Library of Congress, included some four hundred English librettos, mostly before 1800. As to American librettos, the Library of Congress is practically in a *status quo;* this means that the eighteenth and the early nineteenth centuries are not yet represented with that completeness which one would like to consider characteristic of a national library. This deficiency is due to the exasperating scarcity of early American librettos. On the other hand, by dint of the broadening stream of copyright deposits, the Library of Congress may point to a collection of later American librettos which it would be extremely difficult to duplicate by other means. That these copyright deposits include many foreign librettos of recent date may be mentioned in passing. It is a safe estimate that the total number of librettos accrued to the Library of Congress by purchase, copyright, gift, or otherwise now reaches, if it not surpasses, 17,000. That the publication of a complete catalogue of this huge collection will stimulate assistance to fill in disagreeable gaps is confidently expected. Perhaps in course of time even the so strangely scarce collected works of certain early librettists like Morselli, and others may come our way and we may be able to make a better showing of the Italian librettos published at London in Händel's time, as also in certain other fields now comparatively barren.[1]

Immediately after purchase of the Albert Schatz collection the plan was conceived of making access to our collections easier by publication of a catalogue, thereby enhancing the practical value of the collections themselves immeasurably. Quite naturally we turned to Mr. Schatz' own catalogue of his collection as a suitable basis for further operations, but the plan of publishing his catalogue as it stood, merely incorporating with it our own librettos, soon had to be abandoned. Much to our regret this idea of a memorial to Mr. Schatz' patience, energy, and enthusiasm was found to be impracticable. Some of the chief obstacles will readily appear from a perusal of the facsimile of a page or rather sheet from his catalogue.

Painstaking and valuable, indeed invaluable, as his entries are for the names of composers and authors, date, and place of first performance, etc., they deal with a system of abbreviations, which, simple, uniform, and understandable to a linguist though it be, would not be quite convenient in an American publication. It will also be noticed that the bibliographical description of the librettos is restricted to a minimum, sufficient undoubtedly for Mr. Schatz' own special purposes, but not for ours. In addition, the alphabet under individual composers was found to overlap, i. e., to start anew two, three, and more times with annoying frequency—an irregularity easily explained by the gradual growth of Mr. Schatz' collection. Finally, his catalogue is prepared throughout by entry under composers with neither author nor title index, and without the latter his catalogue soon proved of

---

[1] Occasion is here taken to inform those interested that it is the practice of the Library of Congress to acquire librettos only, if they are not represented at all in our collections, or, if they antedate the editions in our possession, preference being given to the *original* libretto of an opera.

too limited usefulness, as, for obvious reasons, will be any libretto catalogue without a title index. The editorial and mere·clerical labor in dissecting, realphabeting, copying, standardizing Mr. Schatz' in its way, of course, splendid catalogue for our purposes, would have been very much greater than those uninitiated in library perplexities and drudgery might expect, and too great for practical consideration. In short, as a list his catalogue is too full, as a catalogue too meager.

Instead of reducing his catalogue after incorporation of our other librettos to a mere list, the preparation and publication of which would not have consumed more than one or two years, but the *permanent* value of which for reference and research would have been doubtful and the cost not commensurate with its usefulness, a decision was reached to prepare a new and full-entry catalogue, which would answer all purposes except perhaps those of bibliographical anatomists. That for this new catalogue Mr. Schatz' own catalogue would have to be utilized to the fullest possible extent was, of course, understood, as was also our obligation to consider him, whom no less a scholar than Friedrich Chrysander in his review of Taddeo Wiel's "Catalogo delle opere in musica rapresentate nel secolo XVIII in Venezia" (Vierteljahrschrift für Musikwissenschaft, v. 10, 1894) had called "mein Orakel in solchen Dingen" as prime authority in all matters usually embodied in the best kind of opera dictionaries. This obligation became all the more apparent after the Library of Congress acquired, in 1911, from the heirs of Mr. Schatz all the manuscripts alluded to in his autobiographical sketch. Now Mr. Schatz' industry in keeping abreast of current literature is well illustrated by the fact that the date for the same opera does not always tally in his several compilations apparently made at different times. Consequently I felt obliged to consult them all. Not because this entailed much and tedious labor is the fact mentioned here, but because quite likely now and then I overlooked discrepancies and thereby missed the opportunity to profit by Mr. Schatz' final historical data. These data frequently do not coincide with those in the published standard reference works. In most such cases I felt methodically justified in accepting without question his data instead of those of his predecessors, because Mr. Schatz had worked his way through practically all the available standard dictionaries, catalogues, bibliographies, etc., of his time, such as those by Groppo, Allacci, Wotquenne, Wiel, Piovano, von Weilen, Parke, Baker, Grove, Parfaict, Clément and Larousse, Fétis, Goedicke, Riemann, Salvioli, and possibly Eitner, besides many biographies and purely historical works. Furthermore, his own extensive researches and his libretto collection as primary source had enabled him to rectify many errors which had been inherited by one lexicographer from the other, to add new and to suppress antiquated data, or, at any rate, to throw the weight of his authority in favour of one date as against the other—and the catalogue itself is the best proof for this assertion.

Nevertheless, my respect for Mr. Schatz' accomplishments did not render me immune against the necessity of spending off and on many hours in consultation of books that had either escaped his attention or which I interpreted differently or which have appeared during the last few years. These remarks refer, of course, mainly to purely historical data. That there is still ample room for improvement I fully realize, and I realize it all the more because my experience has taught me that the time for an absolutely comprehensive and accurate opera-dictionary has passed forever. The task is altogether too formidable and too complicated. Even the most conscientious effort in this direction will suffer from the breed of ingrown, inherited errors in books otherwise full of new information, but growing too numerous for critical perusal by any one man or set of men. After all, this is a catalogue, not an opera-dictionary (in concept and purpose two distinctly different types of works). All purely historical data that ordinarily come within the province of lexicographers, but not of the cataloguer, are here intended and offered as an accidental, not as *the* essential feature, though under the circumstances their value for reasonably accurate reference can not be gainsaid.

Originally the plan had been to enter our entire libretto collection alphabetically by composer in one catalogue, undivided by periods. By the time about 2,500 librettos of the Schatz collection had been catalogued on this plan, its feasibility had become questionable. Not only did the question of expense assume grave aspects, but the entry by composer of early librettos proved to have very considerable disadvantages. Almost invariably modern librettos mention both composer of the music and author of the text and therewith leave nothing to be desired for main entry under either, though main entry of opera-librettos under author is undesirable for obvious reasons. The chief reason is that in ninety-nine out of a hundred cases the inquirer neither knows nor takes interest in the author, but almost invariably he will know the composer. Library economy, therefore, would seem to suggest a compromise between cataloguing maxims and actual conditions and that in libretto entries the author be subordinated to the composer. It is quite different with the earlier librettos, especially Italian. Often only the author is mentioned, often only the composer, and in many hundreds of cases neither. In these cases the composer either remains unknown, or the opera is attributed to a certain composer on the strength of direct or circumstantial historical evidence, in most cases simply on the strength of Allacci's authority. If it is the function of a sensible catalogue to let the books (in this case, librettos) speak as much as possible for themselves and to avoid a confusion in the mind of the user of the catalogue between facts contained in the book and facts furnished by the cataloguer, then the entry of anonymous librettos under composer will inevitably lead to endless explanations, complications, contradictions, or worse. No such drawbacks attach to main entry of early librettos under title. The cataloguer occupies neutral ground, and whether anonymous or not, the librettos fall in line readily. Therefore, it was decided to continue to catalogue modern librettos under composer, but earlier librettos under title. The year 1800 was selected somewhat arbitrarily for the parting of the ways, so that the complete catalogue of our libretto collection will consist of two independent parts, the first, here presented, of librettos printed before 1800, the second of librettos printed after 1800, perhaps with supplemental volumes treated in the same manner.[1]

To my knowledge Alfred Wotquenne's splendidly gotten up and lavishly illustrated catalogue of seventeenth century Italian librettos (inclusive of oratorios) in the Royal Conservatory Library of Brussels has been the only libretto catalogue available in print, with exception of catalogues and lists of limited importance, such as those by Scheurleer, Bergmans, Walter, von Weilen, Carvalhaes. Since Wotquenne's catalogue, too, is arranged by title, the question arose in how far it might otherwise be followed as a model. One feature of his book is the publication of casts. Their value, of course, lies mainly in the direction of biographical data on the lives of opera singers of the seventeenth century. Commendable as is Mr. Wotquenne's idea, his task was not very irksome. Burney was, of course, mistaken if he dated the origin of the custom to print the cast in librettos about 1680, since a cast may be found at least as early as 1654 in the libretto (Lucca) of Cesti's and Bigongiari's "Alessandro il vincitor di se stesso," but generally speaking, casts were printed very seldom during the seventeenth century and they occur with anything like frequency only toward its very end. Consequently, it would have been easy and comparatively inexpensive to imitate Mr. Wotquenne in our catalogue so far as seventeenth century librettos are concerned. On the other hand, it would have been too expensive and too laborious to apply the same principle to the eighteenth century when casts became the rule. One need but turn to Wiel's volume on eighteenth century operas performed at Venice, in which conscientiously every cast is given with the indispensable index to the names in these casts at the end of the volume, to realize the labor, cost of printing, consumption of space that would have been involved by a similar scheme covering several thousand eighteenth century librettos with casts. Conse-

---

[1] The change from composer's entry to title entry obliged me to reconsider hundreds of early librettos among the 2,500 already catalogued by composer. More likely than not, this change of front has sometimes led to inconsistencies in treatment, or inconsistencies were not detected by me, but it is hoped that they are in no case of a serious nature.

quently, as there is no valid reason for discriminating against the
eighteenth century in favor of the seventeenth in an otherwise uniform catalogue, no casts have been copied from the librettos, but
every entry states whether the libretto contains a cast or not.   No
such note has been attempted for the presence of the list of characters, because there exists practically no libretto without the *dramatis
personae*.   The so-called and often ludicrous "protesta" in old Italian
librettos I have disregarded as unnecessary.   Maybe it was also
unnecessary to note the presence of what I have called, for want of a
better term, the scenario, I mean the "mutazioni," or other such
indications of the scenery, but I preferred to be on the safe side in
this respect, in order to make identification of a libretto through
enumeration of contents as easy as possible.   For this reason the
arguments, prefatory notes, dedicatory remarks, and the absence or
presence of the name of the author or composer have always been
noted, just as was done by Mr. Wotquenne.   His plan was also
adopted to quote from the preliminary contents of the libretto whatever threw light on the history of the libretto, resp. the opera, on the
esthetic and dramaturgic creed of either author or composer, on their
technique, or on special customs of the time.   Sometimes such a
quotation has been limited by me to a mere repetition of statement
that the opera was the second of the season, but often enough the
quotations consume quite a bit of printer's ink, and in some instances
the user of this catalogue is practically treated to full or partial
reprints of interesting essays.   On the whole, I have been inclined
to liberality in the space devoted to such quotations, just as now
and then, particularly in the case of "La Dafne" and "Il giocatore",
my "notes" were allowed to grow into "articles."   Of course, the
catalogue would be complete in itself without them, but there can
be no hard and fast rule as to what a cataogue should contain.
This depends entirely on the subject matter, and the fact that early
librettos are scarce and not accessible in many libraries, justified
the inclusion of nonbibliographical matter in a form that would suggest further study of the libretto at least to the specialist.

On these grounds he might expect to find an exhaustive index to
the arias contained in the librettos, something that might have been
called an "Aria-Repertorium."   Unquestionably, whoever has done
work in early operatic history has felt handicapped by the want of
such a compilation which would help to trace the migration of arias
from one opera to the other, to reduce the innumerable librettos (and
scores!!) of the pasticcio type into their, as it were, chemical elements
and to reconstruct the opera as originally written and composed.
For this Bertillon method of analysis, again Mr. Wotquenne has pointed
the way by the publication of his so useful "Zeno, Metastasio
and Goldoni, Alphabetisches Verzeichnis," but it would have been a
rather quixotic attempt to treat five or six thousand librettos in the

same manner. At the low average of twenty arias to a libretto this would have meant an "appendix" to the catalogue with more than one hundred thousand first-line ("*incipit*") entries. It is one thing to devote a lifetime to the compilation of such an "Aria-Repertorium," quite another to expect a public library to embark on its publication. Yet the mere recital that the Library possesses the Rome 1740 and the Parma 1745 edition of a libretto means little and conveys no definite suggestion along lines which would interest the historian, and it is he, no less than the librarian, bibliographer, collector, to whom a catalogue of librettos of early operas should appeal. His interest centers more in the textual than in the purely bibliographical differences between two librettos of the same opera. I therefore made it a point to set forth in the briefest manner possible textual distinctions between at least the original edition, if we had it, and editions used for replicas. As a rule, such an attempt to call the historian's attention to telling textual differences between replica librettos only, was not made, since the relationship between replica editions without the original edition as a basis for textual comparison will not permit of sound deductions for reconstructive or analytical purposes. Furthermore, these comparative hints, as a rule, do not go beyond the year 1780, because toward the end of the eighteenth century it came to be more and more the custom to follow the original text for replicas, excepting, of course, cuts and similar unimportant alterations that are customary and perhaps locally necessary even in present-day operatic life. No guarantee is offered that the plan outlined above has been carried out in every single case, as there is a limit to human endurance, and as a musical librarian in a great public library has other duties to perform besides preparing unconventional catalogues. This means that the absence of comparative comment in any given case does not imply textual identity. On the contrary, for the period of about 1700 to 1770 it should be taken for granted without special danger signals of mine that almost invariably replica editions show considerable differences from the original. (If the specialist requires further information, the Library of Congress will feel only too glad to furnish it promptly.)

Careful attention was paid to ballets, pantomimes, etc., mentioned in the librettos (principally Italian of the later eighteenth century) either by characteristic title or more or less fully described in a separate synopsis of plot and often with cast, argument, scenario, etc., and even separate imprint and invariably with the name of the ballet master as author who "composed" the ballet, as the then technical term was, very much less frequently with the name of the actual composer of the music. In the case of Gaspero Angiolini and others the identity of "composer" and composer often is probable, but it is never certain, unless attested to by some such phrase as

"Musica composta da." This distinction has been lost sight of occasionally by recent writers with the result that ballet-masters have sometimes but erroneously been credited with the music of ballets merely "composed" or "invented" by them. Care was taken not to add to the confusion in this catalogue and a composer of the music has not been entered unless so recorded in the libretto. But even at that, the activity of certain composers now assumes a different aspect from that in Eitner and elsewhere, and certain men like Canavasso, Le Messier, and Trento appear to have been astonishingly prolific as ballet composers, though of slight importance as opera composers. It would have been simple enough to suppress all data pertaining to ballets, pantomimes, etc., and thereby to have saved much space, but the history of this once so flourishing form of musical dramatic art is still in its infancy, and the data made accessible through this catalogue for such a history will be welcome. It is no secret that the modern dramatic ballet and pantomime, whether allegorical, symbolical, mythological, historical, realistic, and with designations running from tragic to burlesque through the whole gamut of possible shadings, are at least contemporary in their origin with opera, and that opera from the beginning borrowed from the art of dancing for the support of interest, but of course a catalogue can not very well be expected to reflect the evolution as long as the dances—be it even characteristic dances with or without relationship to the opera—continued to be incidental without titles specific enough to afford a grip on them for catalogue entry. Toward the middle of the eighteenth century, however, the ballets ceased to be incidental, or rather incidental dancing receded in favor of a juxtaposition of generally in theme not connected operas and ballets for the same evening, a kind of double-headed entertainment, often with first the act of an opera, then a ballet followed by the second act of the opera, which in turn was followed by another ballet, and so forth. In other words, the ballet was no longer considered an inferior but an equal dramatic art, since in the hands of thoughtful and imaginative ballet "composers," it had received a highly developed technique and offered esthetic and dramatic possibilities which soon a genius like Noverre was to gather into a dramaturgic system. Most of the ballets of this period until the end of the century, when the *genre* fast deteriorated, necessarily had characteristic and specific titles, and it is with these and these only that this catalogue deals.[1]

---

[1] Perhaps certain specialists will regret that no attention, as a rule, has been paid to the architect, artists, and engineers who devised the ingenious machines, designed or painted the gorgeous scenery, or acted as stage directors. I appreciate the fact that the history of stage management in all its ramifications is very interesting and instructive, and that at the end of the seventeenth and the beginning of the eighteenth century often the spectacular features of an opera interested the public more than the musical. Indeed, the art of a Balbi or Bibiena was often considered so much more important than that of the composer that the public was not even taken into the impresario's or publisher's confidence as to his name. However, the line had to be drawn somewhere if the catalogue was to be kept within reasonable limits.

As to the year and place of publication of undated librettos (marked in the collation for reasons of convenience, though somewhat at variance with the regular practice of the Library of Congress, *n. d.* (no date), *n. pl.* (no place), or *n. i.* (no imprint) if neither place nor publisher are given, and *n. publ.* if the name of the publisher is absent), the date and place of performance given in the title should be assumed to coincide with the actual date and place of publication. Attention of the uninitiated, however, may be called to a fine point of distinction. Many undated librettos were scheduled for the beginning of the carnival season, and since carnival in certain cities began at the end of December we often have the choice between two years for the year of publication. For instance, if an undated libretto was to have been performed at Turin during carnival of 1800, the libretto may have been published in December, 1799, or early in 1800. In every case the place and year given in the title or in the imprint should be assumed to be the place and year of first performance, unless otherwise stated in a note, and such notes, to repeat it, are generally based on Schatz. If a libretto contained a dated dedication, Mr. Schatz, unless previous performances in the same city or elsewhere were known to him, took the date of dedication to be the date of first performance. Mr. Piovano has questioned the absolute correctness of this procedure on the grounds that often the date of dedication must have preceded the actual date of performance, and I agree with him, but at any rate the date of dedication may be considered the most approximate available in absence of further information. That certain earlier librettos lead to chronological perplexities from local preference of either the Julian or the Gregorian calendar I mention here, without going into detail.

The librettos have been entered, as a rule, first by the original title, and then by the title of the replicas and translations. In every case reference is made from the alternative title (abbreviated A. T.), which often became the better known title, from the later (L. T.) and the translated title (Tr. T. or Tr.) to the original title (O. T.). Librettos of the same title by unknown composers precede those by known composers and are in turn preceded by neutral librettos. By this I mean librettos entered from the collected works, for instance, of Metastasio, with or without the name of any particular composer (usually the first to set the text) as the composer of the libretto in the version of the text in that particular edition. If, for instance, the Paris, 1780–82, edition of Metastasio works mentions in the title of each libretto the name of the original composer, it by no means follows that he used the text as then published. On the contrary, it can often easily be proven that he did not. It would therefore be methodologically incorrect to assign the text as given in that particular edition exclusively to the composer mentioned, and still more incorrect, if no composer is mentioned, to assign it to any one of several composers who are known to have set it to music. Generally speaking, therefore, the "Artaserse" text as published at Paris, 1780–82, would belong with equal right to any of the more than fifty composers who composed it, and for this reason should precede all individual "Artaserse" librettos with or without composer's name. The text of the titles, with elision of irrelevant matter, has been copied as printed in the libretto with retention of the original orthography, but without imitation of the typographical picture. In this respect there has been a certain amount of modernization which, at times, looks odd if coupled with the original orthography. In the use of capital letters, the rules of the Library of Congress have been followed, now and then for practical reasons with slight inconsistencies and generally regardless of my personal likes and dislikes in the matter. Furthermore, the remark appears necessary that the catalogue deals only with librettos which are either in the custody of the Music Division or are not in its custody for purely administrative reasons, such as the librettos in special collections like the Goethe, or miscellaneous collections like the Longe collection. The inclusion of librettos contained in the collected writings (published before 1800) of all authors who happened to write a few librettos has not been attempted, because this would have led entirely too far into literature in general, and because the idea itself from the very nature of things is altogether too pedantic for serious consideration. Exceptions to this rule were of course deemed desirable, but they have been restricted to authors like Goldoni, Quinault, Piron, Panard, whose importance for the history of libretto writing is so obvious as to have rendered their exclusion in the present state of our libretto collection just as pedantic as would have been the inclusion of many others.

For the addition of the brief-entry lists by composers and authors and of the index to arias incidentally mentioned no lengthy explanation is needed, since they obviously are necessary to complete the circle of possible inquiry. That no attempt was made to furnish year of birth and death of authors may perhaps be regretted by those who wish to consult the author list for purposes of literary bibliography. My principal reason for this omission was the knowledge that with all possible diligence the result would not have been in keeping with the labor of research involved.

Finally, a word of explanation as to the method of dealing with author and composer names. Somewhere in this catalogue the full names of authors and composers had to be given if repetition *ad nauseam* in the title catalogue was to be dispensed with. The proper places, it seemed to me, were the composer and author lists; and these lists should be consulted in case of doubt. In whatever form author and composer names appear in the titles themselves the rule has been not to repeat them in full in the editorial matter except to avoid confusion and to facilitate identification. If they appear elsewhere in the libretto, usually in some once current, condensed form (for instance, Ferdinando Bertoni instead of Ferdinando Giuseppe), the editorial matter of the title catalogue records them, as a rule, in full, and in some more or less generally accepted form without comment, and with disregard of harmless differences of spelling. But no display has been made of full names in the title catalogue. A person with a modicum of culture need not be told every time in a title-catalogue that Goethe is Johann Wolfgang von Goethe, and even the most punctilious adherent of uniformity and consistency will admit that Cherubini was too much of a master and still is too well known as such to be put down every time religiously as Maria Luigi Zenobio Carlo Salvatore Cherubini.

O. G. Sonneck
Chief of the Division of Music

Herbert Putnam
Librarian of Congress, Washington, D. C.
November 1, 1913.

Gluck, Christoph Willibald, Ritter von.

3885   1. <u>Alceste</u>. Trag: p. in 3 a. di Ranieri di Calsabigi. Wien, K.K. priv. Hoftheater, 26/XII 1767. Ed. orig. 8°. Wien 1767.

3886   a, <u>Alceste — Alceste</u>. Trag: p. in 3 a. di Ranieri di Calsabigi, rif. di Antonio di Filistri di Caramondani. Berlin, Kgl. Opern Theater, 17/I 1804. Ed. 8°. ital. u. deutsch. May (Berlin, K.O.H. 4/XII 1796)

3887   b, <u>Alceste — Alceste</u>. Trag: p. in 3 a. di Ranieri di Calsabigi. Wien, K.K. Hoftheater nächst Kärntnerthor, 7/X 1810. Ed. 8°. ital. u. deutsch. Wien 1810.

3888   c, <u>Alceste</u>. Tragédie Opéra 3 a., paroles françaises du Bailli Du Rollet. Paris, Théâtre de l'Académie royale de musique / 23/IV 1776. Ed. 4°. Paris 1779. (Paris, d. d. d. 23/IV 1776)

3889   d, <u>Alceste</u>. Ernsthafte O. 3 a., deutsch Heinrich Gottlieb Schmieder. Vollst. Buch. 12°. Mannheim 1792. (Mainz National Theater, 7/X 1791.)

3890   e, <u>Alceste</u>. Gr. O. 3 a., deutsch Carl Alexander Herklots. Berlin, Kgl. Opernhaus 15/X 1817. Vollst. Buch 8°. f. d. Aufführung. Berlin o. J.

3891   f, <u>Alceste</u>. Gr. O. 3 a., deutsch H. G. Schmieder, neue Bearb. Leipzig, Stadttheater 13/XII 1853. Text 8° f. d. Vorstellung. Leipzig o. J.

3892   g, <u>Alceste</u>. Musikal. Drama 3 a., deutsch Carl August Peter Cornelius. Vollst. Text 8°. Ausg. Bres. u. Leipzig o. J. (Hannover, H. Theater, 26/IX 1883.)

3893   2. <u>Armide</u>. Trag. 5 a. de Philippe Quinault. Paris, Théâtre de l'Académie royale de musique 23/IX 1777. Ed. orig. 4°. Paris 1777.

3894   a, <u>Armide</u>. Heldengedicht y Singspiel 5 a., deutsch ? Vollst. Buch 8°. Köln 1786.

3895   b, <u>Armide</u>. Grosse O. 5 a., deutsch Julius von Voss. Wien, K.K. priv. Theater a. d. Wien, 7/X 1808. Vollst. I. Buch. 8° Wien 1808. (Berlin, N. Stadt Theater 20/X 1805)

3896   c, <u>Armida</u>. Gr. O. 5 a., deutsch neu bearb. a. d. Übers. Jul. v. Voss u. a. d. Franz. v. J. Meinen Esser. Wien, K.K. Hof Opern Theater, 2/II 1869. Vollst. Buch. 8°. Wien o. J.

3897   3. <u>Le Feste d'Apollo</u>. Spettacolo diviso in 1 prol. y 3 atti diversi, cioè Bauci e Filemone — Aristeo, e Orfeo. Poesia di Carlo Innocente Frugoni e Ranieri di Calsabigi (Orfeo). Parma, Teatro Ducale, 24/VIII 1769. Ed. orig. 4° con incisioni. Parma 1769.

  4.

3898   5. <u>Iphigénie en Aulide</u>. Trag. Opéra 3 a. de Marie François Louis Bault Gélone du Rollet. Paris, Académie royale de musique 19/IV 1774. Ed. orig. 4°. Paris 1774.

3899   a, <u>Iphigénie en Aulide — Iphigenia in Aulis</u>. Gr. Tragödie 3 a., deutsch Johann Daniel Sander. Berlin, Kgl. Opernhaus, 25/IX 1809. Vollst. Buch franz. u. deutsch. Berlin 1809. 8°.

3900   b, <u>Iphigenia in Aulis</u>. O. 3 a., deutsch ? Darmstadt, Grossh. Hoftheater 16/XII 1827. Vollst. Buch. 8°. Darmstadt 1827.

3901   c, <u>Iphigenia in Aulis</u>. Gr. O. 3 a., deutsch Joh. David Sander nach Bearb. Richd. Wagner. Vollst. Buch 8°. Leipzig o. J. (Dresden, K. s. Hoftheater, 24/II 1847)

3902   d, <u>Iphigenie in Aulis</u>. Gr. Trag. 3 a., deutsch Carl Aug. Peter Cornelius. Vollst. Buch. 8°. Aug. Bres? Leipzig o. J.

3903   6. <u>Iphigénie en Tauride</u>. Tragédie 4 a. par Nicolas François Guillard. Paris, Théâtre de l'Académie royale de musique 18/V 1779. Ed. orig. 4°. Paris 1779.

3904   a, <u>Iphigenia in Tauris</u>. Sing Spiel 4 a., deutsch Johann von Alxinger. Wien, K.K. National Theater 4/d Burg, 23/X 1781. Vollst. Buch. 8°. Wien 1781.

FACSIMILE OF ENTRY SHEET IN MR. SCHATZ' CATALOGUE OF HIS COLLECTION.

TITLE CATALOGUE

TITLE CATALOGUE

L'abate Collarone. O. T. of Trinchera's text Le chiajese cantarine.

Abduramel, ballet. *See* Nasolini's Melinda.

Der abend im walde, eine operette in zween aufzuegen. Die musik ist vom hrn. capellmeister Wolf.

Weimar, Carl Ludolf Hoffmann, 1774. 124 p. 15½^{cm}.

Two acts. By Gottlob Ephraim Heermann, who is not mentioned. Composed by Ernst Wilhelm **Wolf**.

First performed at Weimar, Schlosstheater, Wilhelmsburg, December 10, 1773.

SCHATZ 11075

Die abenteurer. Tr. of Paisiello's Gli avventurieri.

Die abgeredete zauberey. Tr. of Grétry's La fausse magie.

Das abgeschaffte herkommen. Ein westphaelisches schauspiel mit gesang in drey aufzuegen dem herrn justiz-rath Moeser gewidmet.

Ossnabrueck, n. publ., 1783. 92 p. 16½^{cm}.

Not recorded in Deutsches Anonymen Lexikon. ML 50.2.A19

Abraham auf Moria, ein religiöses drama fuer die musik, von A. H. Niemeyer.

n. i., 1779. 32 p. 16^{cm}.

Two acts. The composer, Johann Heinrich **Rolle,** is not mentioned. First performed 1777.

SCHATZ 11392

Abroad and at home. A comic opera in three acts. Now performing at the Theatre-Royal, Covent-Garden. By J. G. Holman.

London, George Cawthorn, 1796. 92 p. 21½^{cm}.

Cast. The composer, William **Shield,** is not mentioned. Originally "*The King's bench*" (Tufts.)

First performed November 19, 1796. (Genest.) LONGE 237

L'académie bourgeoise, opera-comique en un acte; représenté pour la première fois sur le Théâtre de la Foire, en 1735.

Charles François Pannard, Théâtre, Paris, Duchesne, 1763, v. 2, [445]*-504 p. 17*^{cm}.

In prose and vaudevilles. Composer not mentioned and not recorded by Parfaict, etc.

First performed as indicated, February 3, 1735. PQ 2019.P3

Acajou, opera comique, par Monsieur Favart. Représenté pour la premiere fois sur le Théatre du Fauxbourg Saint-Germain, le 18. mars 1744.

Paris, Prault fils, 1744, 52 p. 18^{cm}.

Three acts. No music printed with the text. In prose and couplets. (*Comp.* next entry.)

ML 50.2.A23

23

Acajou—Continued.

—**Acajou,** opera comique en trois actes, en vaudevilles.   Par le Sr Favart.

Paris, Prault fils, 1753.   72 p.   19^{cm}.   (Theatre de M. Favart, Paris, Duchesne, 1763–77, t. vii.)

No music printed at the end or in the text.   On p. [2] the following note:
"Cette pièce est tirée du conte d'Acajou, de Mr. Duclos, elle fut jouée d'abord en prose & couplets à Paris le 18 mars 1744 sur le Théâtre de la Foire St. Germain.   Après la défense faite à l'Opera comique de parler, on la représenta toute en vaudevilles a la Foire St. Laurent suivante, & sur le Théâtre de l'Académie royale de musique au mois d'Octobre de la même année."
Font does not mention Favart's musical collaborator.   ML 49.A2F1

L'accademia di musica e La conversazione.   Divertimenti teatrali per musica da rappresentarsi nel Real Teatro di Salvaterra nel carnovale 1775.

[Lisbona], Stamperia reale, n. d.   37 p.   14½^{cm}.

One act each.   The second divertimento on p. 23–37.   Cast and name of Niccolò **Jommelli** as composer of both.   Authors not mentioned and unknown to Schatz, who says that the text of "La conversazione" is the same as of "Il giuoco di picchetto," which *see* for further details.   SCHATZ 4887

Accampamento o sia La lotteria militare, ballet.   *See* Anfossi's Armida.

Accampamento di Micheletti, ballet.   *See* Bosi's La figlia obbediente.

Gli accidenti della villa.   Cantata di Saverio Zini da rappresentarsi nel Teatro de' Fiorentini nel carnevale di quest' anno 1797.

Napoli, n. publ., 1797.   31 p.   15^{cm}.

Cast.   Pierre **Dutillieu** is mentioned as the composer.
First performed at Vienna, Hoftheater n. d. Burg, Sept. 19, 1794.   SCHATZ 2877

The **accomplish'd maid.**   Tr. of Piccinni's La buona figliuola.

L'accorta cameriera.   L. T. of Martin y Soler's In amor ci vuol destrezza.

Achille et Deidamie, tragedie représentée par l'Académie royale de musique l'an 1735.   Paroles de M. Danchet.   Musique de M. Campra.   CXXI. opera.

n. i., n. d.   front., 431–496 p.   14^{cm}.   (Recueil général des opéra, Paris, 1739, t. xv.)

Detached copy.   Five acts with prologue.
First performed, as indicated, February 24, 1735.   SCHATZ 1539
          Second copy.   ML 48.R4

— **Achille et Deidamie,** tragedie.

[359]–412 p.   17½^{cm}.   (Antoine Danchet, Théâtre, Paris, 1751, t. iii.)

Prologue and five acts.   The composer, André **Campra,** is not mentioned.
          PQ 1972.D2

Achille et Polixene, tragedie en musique, representée par l'Academie royale de musique.   Suivant la copie imprimée à Paris.

[Amsterdam, Antoine Schelte], 1687.   57 p. (incl. front.)   13½^{cm}.

Prologue and five acts.   Author and composer not mentioned.   ML 49.A2L9

Achille et Polixene—Continued.

— **Achille et Polixene,** tragedie en musique, representée par l'Academie royale de musique.

Amsterdam, Henry Schelte, 1701. 57 p. (incl. front.) 14^{cm}.

Reprint of the 1687 edition.

ML 50.2.A25L9

— **Achille et Polixene,** tragedie representée par l'Academie royale de musique, l'an 1688. Les paroles de M. Capistron, & la musique de M. Collasse. XXII. opera.

n. i., n. d. 14^{cm}. front., 223–280 p. (Recueil général des opèra, t. iii, Paris, 1703.)

Detached copy. Five acts and prologue. The score, Amsterdam, 1688, informs us that the first act was composed by Jean Baptiste de **Lully.**
First performed, as indicated, November 7, 1687.

SCHATZ 5781
Second copy. ML 48.R4

Achille in Aulide. Dramma per musica da rappresentarsi nel carnevale dell' anno 1739. Nel Teatro a Torre Argentina . . .

Roma, Antonio de' Rossi, n. d. 67 p. 15^{cm}.

Three acts. Author not mentioned and unknown to Schatz. Dedication by Gius. Polvini Faliconti, argument, cast, name of Geminiano **Giacomelli** as composer and scenario. The libretto mentions also the cast of intermezzi with the characters "Golpone" and "Birina." It would seem as if these intermezzi were also composed by Giacomelli. Their text does not appear in the libretto. ML 50.2.A26G3

Achille in Sciro. Commedia drammatica per musica fedelmente, ed eroicamente tradotta, e ridotta dall' antico stato allo stato presente da Publio Quintiliano Settimio da Sarmacanda.

Hisphahan, l'anno passato. 59 p. 15^{cm}.

Three acts. Printer's dedication "al suo caro M. Timocrato," sonnet by "Clonico Nasposi" to the reader and "dicharamento." The character of this carnivalesque effort may be judged from the fact that Achilles figures in the list of characters as "Ermafrodito vulgo detto femminella spassatiempo di Deidamia." ML50.2.A27

Achille in Sciro.

64 p. 19^{cm}. (Pietro Metastasio, Opere drammatiche, Venezia, Giuseppe Bettinelli, 1733–37, v. 4.)

Three acts. Argument. No composer mentioned. ML 49.A2M4

—**Achille in Sciro.**

[87]–185 p. (Metastasio, Poesie, Parigi, vedova Quillau, 1755, t. iv) 16^{cm}.

Three acts. Argument. ML 49.A2M42

— **Achille in Sciro.** Dramma immaginato, e disteso dall' autore nel prescritto termine di giorni diciotto, e rappresentato con musica del Caldara in Vienna la prima volta, nell' interno gran teatro della Cesarea corte, . . . il dì 13 febbrajo 1736, per festeggiare le felicissime nozze delle AA. RR. di Maria Teresa . . . e di Stefano Francesco, duca di Lorena . . .

pl., [3]–110 p. 26^{cm}. (Metastasio, Opere, t. v, Parigi, vedova Herissant, 1780.)

Three acts. Argument. ML 49.A2M44

Achille in Sciro. Dramma per musica e festa teatrale da rappresentarsi nel Regio Teatro di Berlino per le nozze delle Altezze Loro reali il prencipe di Prussia, nipote di S. M. il Rè con la principessa Elisabetta Christina Ulrica di Brunswico, per commando di Sua Maestà il rè . . .

> *Berlino, Haude e Spener, 1765. 2 p. l., 113, [3] p. 16ᶜᵐ.*

Three acts. By Pietro Metastasio. Argument, scenario, and name of the composer, Johann Friedrich **Agricola.** German title "Achilles in Scirus" and text face Italian. First performed, as indicated, July 16, 1765.   SCHATZ 66

Achille in Sciro. Dramma per musica da rappresentarsi nel nobilissimo Teatro la Fenice l' autunno dell' anno 1794.

> *Venezia, Modesto Fenzo, 1794. 62 p. 18ᶜᵐ.*

Three acts. Argument, cast, scenario, and name of (Marcello di Capua) **Bernardini** as composer, but not of the author Metastasio. On p. 27–33 argument, cast, and detailed description of "Andromeda e Perseo, ballo eroico pantomimo d' invenzione e composizione del Signor Onorato Viganò." The composer of the music is not mentioned.   SCHATZ 829

Achille in Sciro. Dramma per musica da rappresentarsi nel nuovo Teatro Tron in S. Cassiano il carnovale dell' anno MDCCLXIV . . .

> *Venezia, Paolo Colombani, 1764. 54 p. 16½ᶜᵐ.*

Three acts. Impresario's dedication, argument, cast, scenario, and name of Ferdinando Giuseppe **Bertoni** as composer, but not of the author Metastasio. The "primo ballo" (p. 27) is described in form of a sonnet. At the end of the libretto the words of "Porto in sen libero" and "Vanne dal caro bene," two arias which were to be interpolated "dopo brevi sere" for the primadonnas "che resteranno pienamente contente."   SCHATZ 903

Achille in Sciro. Dramma per musica, da rappresentarsi nel Gran Teatro dell' imperial corte . . . in occasione delle felicissime nozze de' serenissimi principi Maria Teresa, arciduchessa d'Austria e Francesco III, duca di Lorena. L' anno MDCCXXXVI. La poesia è del Sig. abbate Pietro Metastasio . . . La musica è del Sig. Antonio Caldara . . .

> *Vienna d'Austria, Gio. Pietro Van Ghelen, n. d. 2 p. l., 76 p. 15½ᶜᵐ.*

Three acts. Argument and scenario. The ballet music at the end of the acts was composed by Niccola Matteis. First performed at Vienna, February 12, 1736.   SCHATZ 1476

— Achilles in Scyro . . . Bey gelegenheit der hoechstbeglueckten vermaehlung der durchleuchtigsten ertz-hertzogin Mariae Theresiae mit Francisco dem dritten, hertzogen in Lothringen. In dem grossen Theatro der kaiserlichen burg in einer welschen opera vorgestellet anno 1736. Poësi des herrn abbate Pietro Metastasio . . . Von herrn Antonio Caldara . . . in die music verfasset. In das teutsche versetzet von herrn Antonio Prokoff . . .

> *Wien, Johann Peter Ghelen, 1735. 2 p. l., 75 p. 15ᶜᵐ.*

Imprint on preliminary title-page.   SCHATZ 1477

Achille in Sciro. Dramma per musica da rappresentarsi nel Teatro di S. Angelo nel carnovale del 1739 . . .

> *Venezia, Marino Rossetti, 1739. 46 p. 15½ᶜᵐ.*

Three acts. By Metastasio. Impresario's dedication, argument, cast, scenario, and name of the composer, Pietro **Chiarini.**   SCHATZ 1852

Achille in Sciro. Dramma per musica del celebre Sig. abate Pietro Metastasio, Poeta Cesareo. Da rappresentarsi nel Teatro Grimani in S. Gio. Grisostomo per la fiera dell' Ascensione dell' anno 1766 . . .

Venezia, Modesto Fenzo, 1766. 54 p. 17½cm.

Three acts. Dedication, argument, cast, scenario, and name of the composer, Florian Leopold **Gassmann**. SCHATZ 3607

L'Achille in Sciro. Favola dramatica da rappresentarsi in musica nel Teatro à S. Stefano in Ferrara l' anno 1663 . . .

Venetia, n. publ., 1663. 104, [2] p. 14cm.

Three acts and prologue. Dedication signed by Michiel Colombo mentioning Giovanni **Legrenzi** as the composer, publishers' notice to the reader, argument. The author, marchese Ippolito Bentivoglio, is not mentioned. The text is followed by a fly leaf with two inside pages of errata. SCHATZ 5532

— L'Achille in Sciro. Favola dramatica da rappresentarsi in musica nel Teatro à S. Salvatore per l' anno 1664 . . .

Venetia, Steffano Curti, 1664. 96 p. 14cm.

Prologue and three acts. Publisher's dedication dated Venice, January 29, 1664, argument, and notice to the reader with apologies for typographical errors as "l' autore non hà permesso, che si legga il suo nome in questi fogli, nè meno ha voluto pigliarsi la briga di rivedere queste minutie."

Neither the composer, Giovanni **Legrenzi**, is mentioned nor the author, marchese Ippolito Bentivoglio. SCHATZ 11720

Achille in Sciro. Dramma per musica da rappresentarsi nel Regio Teatro di Torino nel carnovale del 1785 . . .

Torino, Onorato Derossi, n. d. viii, 54, [1], 15 p. 17½cm.

Three acts. By Metastasio, who is not mentioned. Argument, cast, scenario, and names of Gaetano **Pugnani** as composer of the opera, of Vittorio Amedeo Canavasso as composer of the music for Paolino Franchi's three ballets, a description of two of which is printed on the last 15 p. with separate imprint, argument, and cast. The titles were "La Galzeuca ossia Golconda liberata dalla tirannide di Scour-Malou, ballo eroico, tragico pantomimo in quattro atti," and "Il matrimonio per concorso." SCHATZ 8505

Achille in Sciro. Drama per musica da rappresentarsi nel Teatro Grimani a S. Samuele per la fiera dell' Ascens^ne l' anno 1747.

n. i. n. d. 48 p. 15cm.

Three acts. By Metastasio, who is not mentioned. Dedication, argument, scenario, cast, and name of Giovanni Battista **Runcher** as the composer. SCHATZ 9151

Achille in Sciro. Drama per musica da rappresentarsi sul famosissimo Theatro di Braunsviga nella fiera d' estate l' anno MDCCXXXXVI. —Achilles in Sciro . . .

Wolffenbüttel, C. Bartsch wittwe, n. d. Unpaged. 18½cm.

Three acts. By Metastasio, who is not mentioned. German text faces Italian. Argument, scenario, and name of Giovanni **Verocai** as composer.

First performed in August, 1746, as indicated. SCHATZ 10717

Achille placato. Tragedia per musica da rappresentarsi nel Teatro Tron di S. Cassano l' anno 1707. Impressione seconda.

Venezia, Marino Rossetti, 1707. 72 p. 15cm.

Five acts with "intramezzi ridicoli." By Urbano Rizzi, who is not mentioned. Argument, cast, scenario, notice about the intermezzi, and name of Antonio **Lotti** as composer. SCHATZ 5713

Achille riconosciuto. Introdutione di un balletto fatto dalla Ser^{ma.} Arcid^{a.} Marianne d'Austria: per il giorno natal^{o.} della Ser^{ma.} Arcid^{a.} Leonora d'Austria. Attione dramatica di Teofilo messa in musica dal Sig. Antonio Draghi . . .

Vienna, Joan. Jacobo Kürner, 1668.   1 p. l., 55 p.   12^{cm}.

One act.   Dedication by the author (real name unknown to Wotquenne), notice to the reader mentioning the archduchess Marianne as "il personaggio principale," and on p. 52–55 cast (Marianne having the principal part) of the ballet and remark:
"All' armonia del canto seguì il rimbombo degli strumenti, che diedero segno all ballo il quale fù per l' aria composta dall Signore Smelzer [Johann Heinrich **Schmelzer**, 1630–1700], e per i passi inventati dal Sign. Santo . . ."
Was to be performed on May 21, 1668, but performance was canceled.   (von Weilen).

ML50.2.A29D7

Achilles. An opera. As it is perform'd at the Theatre-Royal in Covent-Garden . . . Written by the late Mr. Gay. With the musick prefix'd to each song.

London, J. Watts, 1733.   4 p. l., 68,[3] p.   20^{cm}.   [Bound with his Beggar's opera.   London, 1728]

Three acts with prologue.   Ballad opera.   Cast and table of the 54 songs.   The airs are given in the text with their titles.   The text is followed by a [3] p. publisher's list, first page of which is dated February 28, 1733.
First performed, as indicated, February 10, 1733.   ML50.5.B3

— . . . **Achilles.** An opera. As written by John Gay. Distinguishing also the variations of the theatre, as performed, in two acts, at the Theatre Royal in Covent-Garden. Regulated from the prompt-book, by permission of the managers, by Mr. Wild, prompter.

London, John Bell, 1777.   60 p.   17^{cm}.

Prologue, cast, and at end table of the 58 songs, of which only three are marked as having been introduced for these performances.   The text is printed in three acts, but according to a note on p. 38 act III became act II, the two others apparently being performed in one.   At head of title: "Bell's edition."   SCHATZ 11469

Achilles.   *See* Keiser's Das zerstoerte Troja.

Achilles in petticoats. An opera. As it is performed at the Theatre Royal, in Covent-Garden . . . Written by Mr. Gay, with alterations. The music entirely new by Dr. Arne.

London, W. Strahan, T. Lowndes [etc.], 1774.   4 p. l., 38 p.   20^{cm}.

Two acts.   Table of the 25 songs, cast, and Advertisement according to which this is Gay's "Achilles" "now revived with no very essential changes from the original piece; the chief alterations consisting of abridgement and transposition . . ."   They were made by George Colman.
First performed at London, Covent Garden, December 16, 1773.   LONGE 26

Achilles in Sciro.   Tr. of Verocai's Achille in Sciro.

Achilles in Scirus.   Tr. of Agricola's Achille in Sciro.

Achilles in Scyro.   Tr. of Caldara's Achille in Sciro.

Achilles und Ulysses auf der insel Scyros, ballet.   *See* Bach's Lucius Silla.

Achills zuernender schatten, ein tragisches singspiel in fuenf aufzuegen von Traugott Benjamin Berger, allen musicalischen schauspielern gewidmet.

Leipzig, Christian Gottlob Hilscher, 1777.   74, [6] p.   15½^{cm}.

The last [6] p. contain a sale's list of the publisher.   No composer or performance recorded by Schatz.   SCHATZ 11595

Achmet et Almanzine. Piece en trois actes. Par Mrs le S * * e d'Or * * Les couplets des divertissemens sont de M. F * * * Representée à la Foire Saint Laurent 1728.

Le Théâtre de la foire, Paris, 1728, t. vi, pl., [373]–493 p. 17cm.

By Le Sage, d'Orneval, and Fuzelier. Largely *en vaudevilles*. The airs, selected or composed and arranged by Jean Claude **Gillier**, the "compositeur" of the company, are printed at the end of the volume in the "Table des airs."
First performed June 30, 1728. ML48.L2 VI

Achmet und Almanzine. Ein singspiel in zwei aufzuegen. Nach dem franzoesischen der herrn le Sage und d'Ormeville [!]. Aufgefuehrt auf den K. K. Hof-Theatern in Wien.

[Wien], mit von Kurtzbekischen schriften, 1795. 100 p. 15½cm.

Johann Baptist **Schenck** is mentioned as the composer. In the preface the unknown author says of his "gaenzliche umarbeitung" of the French original:
"Hier musste man freylich den gang der handlung haeufig veraendern, und noch haeufiger die nicht selten, muthwillige laune der verfasser dem anstande, und der sittlichkeit aufopfern, so, dass von dem franzoesischen originale wenig mehr, als der hauptumriss uebrig geblieben ist."
First performed, as indicated, July 17, 1795. SCHATZ 9591

Aci, e Galatea. Dramma per musica da rappresentarsi nel nobilissimo Teatro Venier in San Benedetto l'autunno dell' anno 1792.

Venezia, Modesto Fenzo, 1792. 48 p. 17cm.

Two acts. Impresario's dedication, cast, scenario, and names of the composer, Francesco **Bianchi**, and Giuseppe Foppa, the author.
First performed October 13, 1792, as indicated. SCHATZ 993

Aci e Galatea, ballet. *See* Cimarosa's Il fanatico burlato.

Aci e Galatea, ballet. *See* Curcio's Solimano.

Aci e Galatea, ballet. *See* Tarchi's Il matrimonio per contrattempo.

Aci e Galatea, ballet. *See* Traetta's Le feste d'Imeneo.

Acis et Galatée, pastorale heroique en musique, representée pour la premiere fois dans le Château d'Anet devant Monseigneur le Dauphin. Par l'Academie royale de musique. Suivant la copie imprimée à Paris.

[Amsterdam, Antoine Schelte], 1686. 43 p. (incl. front.) 13½cm.

Prologue and three acts, without name of composer or author. ML49.A2L9

— Acis et Galatée, pastorale heroique representée par l'Academie royale de musique l'an 1686. Les paroles de M. Capistron & la musique de M. de Lully. XXI. opera.

n. i., n. d. 14cm. front., 179–222 p. (Recueil général des opéra, t. iii, Paris, 1703.)

Detached copy. Three acts and prologue.
First performed, as indicated, September 17, 1686; at Anet, at the palace of the Duke of Vendôme, September 6, 1686. SCHATZ 5756
Second copy. ML48.R4

Acis et Galatée—Continued.

—Tircis et Doristée, pastorale; parodie d'Acis et Galatée; représentée pour la premiere fois par les Comédiens italiens ordinaires du roi, le 4 septembre 1752. Nouvelle édition.

> *Paris, N. B. Duchesne, 1759. 60, [4] p. 19ᶜᵐ. (Theatre de M. Favart, Paris, Duchesne, 1763–77, t. ii.)*

> One act. Cast. En vaudevilles, many of the airs being printed in the text. The [4] p. contain a catalogue of plays and a "Catalogue de musiques nouvelles relatives aux pieces de théâtres de M. Favart, & autres." The arranger of the music is not mentioned by Font.   ML 49.A2F1

— Acis und Galatée. In einem hochteutschen sing-spiel auf dem hoch-fuerstl. Wuertemb. Schauplatz aufgefuehret.

> *Stuttgart, Paul Treuen, 1698. 43 p. 15ᶜᵐ.*

> Three acts and prologue (located at Stuttgart!) Argument. On p. 41–43 seven additional arias. Neither the author is mentioned, nor the translator, nor **Lully**.
> First performed 1698, as indicated.   SCHATZ 5757

Acis och Galatea. Heroisk-ballet i tre acter upförd på den Kongl. Svenska theatren. Första gången den 10 maji 1773.

> *Stockholm, Anders Jacobsson Nordström, 1773. 6 p. l., 30 p. 20ᶜᵐ.*

> Dedication, argument, cast, notice to the reader, and statement that the poetry is by Lars Samuel Lalin (translated from John Gay's "Acis and Galatea"?) and that the music of the ballet-opera is "dels ny, dels af **Hendels** opera Acis och Galatéa samt andre beroemde måstares arbeten utsökt och i ordning satt afven" by the author. The prefatory note gives further information on the history of this curious pasticcio product, especially that the recitatives and some of the choruses were composed or adjusted by Henrick Filip **Johnsen**, the court conductor.   SCHATZ 4494

Acis und Galatea, ballet by Toeschi. *See* Bach's Lucius Silla.

[L'Acomate]

> *3–38 p. 16½ᶜᵐ.*

> Two acts. Argument, cast, scenario. Title-page wanting, but impresario's dedication to the nobility and "Popolo Pisano" says "Fa la sua prima comparsa su queste scene l'ACOMATE." Giuseppe **Giordani** is mentioned as the composer, and on p. 38 the date of first performance is given as April 21. Consequently this is an imperfect copy of the original Pisa edition by unknown author of Giordani's opera performed at Pisa, Teatro Nuovo, 1783.   ML 48.A5 v.7

— L'Acomate. Dramma per musica da rappresentarsi in Firenze la primavera dell' anno 1784 nel nuovo Regio Teatro degl' Intrepedi detto La Palla a Corda . . .

> *Firenze, Stamperia Bonducciana, 1784. 34 p. 16½ᶜᵐ.*

> Two acts. Author not mentioned and unknown to Schatz. Argument, cast, scenario, and name of Giuseppe **Giordani** as the composer. ("La musica è tutta nuova.")   SCHATZ 3832

— Elpinice. Dramma serio per musica da rappresentarsi in Bologna nel Teatro Zagnoni l'autunno dell' anno 1783 . . .

> *Bologna, Sassi, n. d. 62, [1] p. 17ᶜᵐ.*

> Though in three acts, and in part radically different, plainly based on "L'Acomate." Impresario's dedication, argument, cast, scenario, and name of Giuseppe **Giordani** as the composer. On p. 27–37 argument, cast, and description of fratelli Ricciardi's ballo eroitragico pantomimo in five acts "La morte di Arrigo Sesto, rè d'Inghilterra." music by Mattia Stabingher.   SCHATZ 3843

L'acteur dans son ménage, tableau anecdotique, mêlé de vaudevilles, par M^in. J^h. Boullault. Représenté, pour la première fois,
sur le Théâtre de l'Ambigu-comique, le 6e jour complémentaire,
an 7. [Sept. 22, 1799]

*Paris, chez le libraire, au Théâtre du Vaudeville, an viiie [1799–1800]
55 p. 20^cm.*

Cast. Prefatory note. On p. 53–54 the unaccompanied "Air nouveau du C. **St.-
Amans,** membre du Conservatoire: Je quitte à regret." Not recorded by Cl. & L. or
Schatz. ML 48.M2L

L'Adalinda. A. T. of Gl' inganni innocenti.

L'Adaloaldo furioso. Drama per musica da rappresentarsi nel
Teatro Giustiniano di S. Moise nel carnovale 1727.

Venezia, Carlo Buonarrigo, n. d. 45 p. 14½^cm.

Three acts. By Antonio Maria Lucchini, who is not **mentioned.** Argument,
scenario, and name of Giacomo **Macari** as composer.
First performed, as indicated, December 26, 1726. **Schatz** 5807

Adela of Ponthieu. A tragy-pantomime ballet.

*Noverre, Jean George, Works. Tr. from the French, London, 1783,
v. 3, p. [53]–91. 21½^cm.*

Five acts. Noverre's dedication and dedicatory poem, "preliminary discourse,"
argument, detailed scene by scene description, and note to the effect that this ballet
was first represented at the King's Theatre, London, in 1782. GV 1787.N8

Adelaide. Drama per musica da recitarsi nel Teatro delle Dame
pe'l carnevale dell' anno 1743 . . .

Roma, Bernabò e Luzzarini, 1743. 71 p. 15½^cm.

Three acts. By Antonio Salvi (not mentioned). Dedication, argument, scenario,
cast, and name of the composer, Gioacchino **Cocchi.** Schatz 2052

Adelaide, dramma per musica. Adelheid, ein musicalisches
schauspiel.

*Hamburg, gedruckt mit Spieringischen schrifften, n. d. 2 p. l.,
75 p. 18^cm.*

Three acts. Cast, scenario, and argument. German text faces Italian. Neither
the author, Antonio Salvi, nor the composers, **Finazzi,** Filippo, **Scalabrini,** Paolo,
etc., are mentioned.
First performed at Hamburg, Opernhaus b. Gänsemarkt, July 23, 1744.
Schatz 3101

Adelaide. Dramma per musica da rappresentarsi nel Teatro
Tron di S. Cassano nel carnovale 1729 . . .

Venezia, Marino Rossetti, 1729. 59 p. 15½^cm.

Three acts. By Antonio Salvi, who is not mentioned. Impresario's dedication
dated Venice, February 6, 1729, argument, cast, scenario, and name of Giuseppe
Maria **Orlandini** as the composer. **Schatz** 7326

— Adelaide. Drama per musica, da rappresentarsi nell' Arciducale
Teatro di Mantova nel carnovale dell' anno MDCCXXXI . . .

Mantova, Alberto Pazzoni, n. d. 60 p. 16^cm.

Three acts. Dedication dated Mantova, December 26, 1730, argument, cast,
scenario and note: "La musica è del Signor Giuseppe **Orlandini** . . . e d'altri
autori." Salvi is not mentioned. The differences between the text of Venice,
1729, and this ed. are considerable. For instance, "Ricordati, cor mio" (I, 7) has
become "Conservati fedele" and "La tua fortuna, o bella" (I, 9) has become "Se

Adelaide—Continued.

brami mia bella.'' ''La pietà del core augusto'' has been added to I, 10, as also ''Va superba, ed ostinata'' to I, 15, whereas ''Prendi uno sposo'' has been dropped from I, 14. Scene I, 16, now consists of ''Ma pur da te dipende (Rec.)—*Ciel più tranquillo—Palido il Sole*,'' including the original recitative ''Quanto più sien tenaci,'' but excluding the original aria ''Scherza in mar la navicella.'' It is reasonable to conjecture that the differences in the texts give a clue to the music ''d'altri autori.''
ML 50.2.A31O7

Adelaide, ballet. *See* Paisiello's Il Sismano nel Mogol.

Adelaide. Drama per musica da recitarsi nel Teatro Alibert pe'l carnevale dell' anno 1723. Presentato alla Maestà di Clementina, regina della Gran Bretagna, etc.

   Roma Bernabò, 1723. 72 p. 15^{cm}.

Three acts. By Antonio Salvi, who is not mentioned. Dedication, argument, cast, scenario, and name of Nicolà Antonio **Porpora** as the composer.
First performed, as indicated, January 23, 1723.   Schatz 8376

— Adelaide. Dramma per musica.

   Roma, Pietro Ferri, 1723. 72 p. 14½^{cm}.

Three acts. Neither Salvi is mentioned, nor **Porpora**. Argument. The arias in this edition differ noticeably from those in the Bernabò edition. For instance, in the latter I, 1, has no aria, whereas the Ferri edition has ''Contro l'idolo adorato.'' In the Ferri ed. I, 5, has ''Ornò la mia diletta,'' in the Bernabò ed. ''Per salvarti, idolo mio,'' etc., etc.   ML 50.2.A31P6

Adelaide, ballet. *See* Portugal's Fernando nel Messico.

L'Adelaide. Drama per musica da rappresentarsi nel Teatro Vendramino à San Salvatore. L'anno MDCLXXII . . .

   Venetia, Francesco Nicolini, 1672. 72 p. 14½^{cm}.

Three acts. By Pietro Dolfino, who is not mentioned. Publisher's dedication, with the name of Antonio **Sartorio** as the composer, and dated Venice, February 19, 1672. Argument and scenario.   Schatz 9488

Adelaide di Ghesclino, ballo eroico. *See* V. Fabrizj's opera L'amore per interesse.

Adelaide di Guesclin, ballet. *See* Cafaro's Il natal d'Apollo.

L'Adelaide, regia principessa di Susa. Dramma musicale da Gio. Batista Rodoteo, Veneto.

   Venetia, n. publ., 1670. 48 p. 14^{cm}.

Three acts. Argument, and notice to the reader alluding to the first performances of the opera at Munich, Hoftheater, 1669. Giulio **Riva,** the composer, is not mentioned.   Schatz 8833

Adelasia, ballet. *See* Zingarelli's Il mercato di Monfregoso.

Adelasia riconosciuta, ballet. *See* Cherubini's Mesenzio rè d'E-truria.

Adelasia riconosciuta, ballet. *See* Mayr's Che originali.

Adele di Ponthieu, ballet. *See* Borghi's Artaserse.

Adelheid. Tr. of Finazzi and Scalabrini's Adelaide.

Adelheid, in einem sing-spiele auf dem Hamburgischen Schauplatze vorgestellet im jahr 1727.

[Hamburg], Gedruckt mit Stromerschen Schrifften, n. d. Unpaged. 18½*cm*.

Three acts. Author not mentioned and unknown to Schatz. Georg Philipp **Telemann** is mentioned as the composer.

First performed at Bayreuth, Hochfuerstl. Theater, 1724, as "Adelheid, oder Die ungezwungene liebe."

SCHATZ 10254

Adelheit von Veltheim. Ein schauspiel mit gesang in vier akten.
Leipzig, Dykische buchhandlung, 1781. 6 p. l., 130, [2] p. 17cm.

Dedication signed by the author Gustav Friedrich Wilhelm Grossmann and the composer Christian Gottlob **Neefe.** This is followed by prefatory remarks of Grossmann's addressed "An herrn magister Dyk" and dated September 10, 1780. To the same is addressed Neefe's preface dated "Frankfurt am Mayn, den 10. Sept. 1780." In this preface we are told:

"Ich hätte diese arbeit schon laengst geendiget, wenn mein lieber Grossmann nicht bisweilen einen anfall von traegheit bekommen und mich gehemmt hätte.—Pfui! was ich da für verleumdungen geschrieben habe!—Nicht traegheit, sondern veraenderung der umstaende, die viele andre geschaefte von ihm erheischten, sezten ihn ausser stand, an seiner oper fortzuarbeiten. Ich muss ihnen das sagen, um gewisser kritischer spione willen, die einige gesaenge darinne finden werden, die sie irgendwo schon gelesen haben, und die sich weidlich lustig machen moechten, etwas ausgespaeht zu haben, das sie berechtige, ihn eines plagiats zu beschuldigen. Aber die herren wuerden sich nur umsonst freuen: denn eben diese gesaenge hatte er vom anfange her fuer Adelheit von Veltheim gefertigt! Umstände . . . machten es unwahrscheinlich, dass diese oper je zu stande kommen wuerde. Ich nahm daher einige gesaenge in eine fremde operette auf . . . Mein freund ging aufs neue an seine oper, und die ausgelehnten gesaenge wurden wieder eingeloest. Das Vossische lied: *Bey meinem lieben topf voll Reiss* u. s. w. gefiel meinem freunde Grossmann so sehr und passte so gut fuer einen seiner sklaven, dass er es fast unveraendert beybehielt . . ."

First performed at Frankfurt a. M., Theater am Junghof, September 23, 1780.

SCHATZ 7068

— **Adelheit von Veltheim.** In vier akten. Komponirt vom herrn hoforganist Neefe zu Bonn.
n. i., n. d. 1 p. l., 136 p. 17cm.

The author, Grossmann, is not mentioned.

SCHATZ 11734

Adelia e Roberto. A. T. of La selvaggia.

Adelina Senese o sia L'amore secreto. Dramma giocoso per musica da rappresentarsi nel Teatro in S. Samuele per la prima opera d'autunno 1797.

Venezia, Stamperia Valvasense, n. d. 71 p. 17cm.

Two acts. Author not mentioned and unknown to Schatz. Prefatory note, cast, and name of Gaspare **Spontini** as composer. ("La musica del tutto nuova"). On p. [37]–44 argument, cast and description without name of the composer of the music of Antonio Berti's "Duglas ed Ernestina, ballo di mezzo carattere." SCHATZ 9991

Arien und gesaenge zum trauerspiel **Adelstan und Roeschen** von Schink. Die musik von herrn Hiller.
n. i., n. d. [8] p. 16½cm.

Two acts. Composed by Friedrich Adam **Hiller.**
First performed at Güstrow, Theater im Rathhause, September 6, 1792.

SCHATZ 4714

34

Ademira. Dramma per musica da rappresentarsi nel Real Teatro di S. Carlo nel di 30 di maggio 1789 festeggiandosi il glorioso nome di Ferdinando IV . . .

Napoli, Vinzenzo Flauto, 1789. 56 p. 15½ᶜᵐ.

Three acts. By Ferdinando Moretti who is not mentioned. Impresario's dedication, dated Naples, May 30, 1789, argument, scenario and name of Pietro **Guglielmi** as the composer. A footnote states that for brevity's sake the "recita" in the third act would be omitted and its music transferred to I, 7. On p. 9–20 cast and description of Sebastiano Gallet's "Amor può tutto, ossia Il trionfo del valore, ballo pantomimo in tre atti," music by "diversi autori." SCHATZ 4231

Ademira. Dramma per musica da rappresentarsi nel nobilissimo Teatro di S. Benedetto per la fiera dell' Ascensione dell' anno 1784.

Venezia, Modesto Fenzo, 1784. 56 p. 17ᶜᵐ.

Three acts. Author not mentioned and unknown to Schatz. Argument, cast, scenario and name of Andrea **Luchesi**, as composer. On p. 21–34 description, argument, cast, but not name of the composer of the music of Paolino Franchi's "Hurtado e Miranda, ballo tragico-pantomimo."
First performed May 2, 1784, as indicated. SCHATZ 5739

Ademira. Dramma per musica da rappresentarsi nel nobilissimo Teatro Venier in San Benedetto l'autunno dell' anno 1787.

Venezia, Modesto Fenzo, 1787. 59 p. 17½ᶜᵐ.

Two acts. Author not mentioned and unknown to Schatz. Argument, cast, scenario and note "La musica è del Sig. Angelo **Tarchi,** e d'altri rinomati autori." On p. [47]–59 prefatory note, argument, cast without name of the composer of the music and description of Domenico Ballon's "La conquista del Perù ossia Amazili e Telesco, ballo eroico tragico tratto dall' Incas del Sig. Marmontel." His second ballet is called "La vedova ingegnosa ossiano Le bizzarie del bel sesso."
First performed at Milan, Teatro alla Scala, December 27, 1783. SCHATZ 10211

Admeto. Dramma per musica di Giuseppe Palomba. Da rappresentarsi nel Real Teatro del Fondo di Separazione per second opera di quest' anno 1794 . . .

Napoli, Vinzenzo Flauto, 1794. 43 p. 15ᶜᵐ.

Two acts. Impresario's dedication dated Naples, October 5, 1794, cast and name of Pietro **Guglielmi** as the composer. On p. 6–13 argument, cast and description of Giovanni Battista Giannini's, "La fata benefica, ballo persiano favoloso," music by Giuseppe Ercolani. SCHATZ 4286

Admeto.

Three act opera by Georg Friedrich **Händel.** Text an altered version of Aurelio Aureli's "L'Antigona delusa da Alceste."
First performed at London, Haymarket, January 31, 1727.
Not in L. of C.

— Admetus, koenig in Thessalien. In einer opera auf dem Hamburgischen Schau-Platze vorgestellet. Im jahr 1730.

[Hamburg], Gedruckt mit Stromerschen schriften, n. d. Unpaged. 18ᶜᵐ.

Three acts. Argument and scenario. Neither C. G. Wendt, the translator of "Admeto," nor Georg Friedrich **Händel,** the composer is mentioned.
First performed at Hamburg, Theater beim Gänsemarkt, January 23, 1730. SCHATZ 4470

— Admetus, koenig in Thessalien, in einer opera auf dem Hamburgischen Schau-Platze vorgestellet. Im jahr 1731.

Hamburg, mit Piscators schriften, n. d. Unpaged. 18ᶜᵐ.

Three acts. Scenario and "Historischer bericht" (argument) with names of Wend as translator, and Georg Friedrich **Händel** as composer. The Italian text of the arias is added to the German. SCHATZ 11713

Admeto ed Alceste. A. T. of the ballet La maggior impresa d'Ercole.

Admeto ed Alceste, ballet. *See* Jommelli's L'Olimpiade.

Admeto rè di Tessaglia. Melodrama da recitarsi nel Regio Teatro di Milano . . .

Milano, Marc' Antonio Pandolfo Malatesta, 1702. 67 p. 15^{cm}.

Three acts. Dedication by the author Pietro d'Averara, argument, scenario, and notice to the reader with name of Paolo **Magni** as the composer, compliment to the impresarios Piantanida for their generosity in staging the opera and remark:
"Mi son ristretto ne' recitativi, e nelle agnizioni tediose, massime nel fine . . . In somma hò cercato il tuo diletto, chè e la regola principale della Drammatica, e l'oggetto della mia attezione . . ."   SCHATZ 5839

Admetus, koenig in Thessalien. Tr. of Händel's Admeto.

Adolphe et Clara, ou Les deux prisonniers, comédie en un acte et en prose, mélée d'ariettes. Paroles de B. J. Marsollier. Musique du citoyen d'Aleyrac. Représentée, pour la première fois, à Paris, sur le Théâtre de l'Opéra-comique-national, rue Favart, le 22 pluviôse, an 7 [February 10, 1799].

Paris, Cailleau, An septième [1799]. 46 p. 19½^{cm}
Cast.   ML 50.2.A33D2

L'Adone, tragedia musicale del clarissimo Signor Paolo Vendramino. Rappresentata in Venezia l' anno 1639. All' illustrissimo Sig. Antonio Grimani fù dell' illustrissimo Signor Vettor.

Venetia, Sarzina, 1640. 71 p. 13½^{cm}.

Five acts with prologue. The dedication is signed by Francesco Manelli and dated Venice, December 21, 1639. It is followed by a "Lettera del Signor Vendramino al Manelli," dated Bologna, December 16, 1639, in which the author says:
"Intendo, che V. S. vuol porre alle stampe l'Adone. Me ne rincresce altretanto, quanto m'hà già doluto la sua risoluzione di farlo recitare, non ostante la mia lontananza, ch' è à dire, senza i lumi più necessarii dell' apparenze, co'quali doveva illustrarsi l'azione . . ."
The letter is followed by the argument. **Monteverdi,** the composer, is not mentioned.   SCHATZ 6594

Adone e Venese, ballet. *See* Pugnani's Demofoonte.

Adone in Cipro. Drama per musica da rappresentarsi nel famosissimo Teatro Vendramino di S. Salvatore. L'anno MDCLXXVI. Inventato dal dottor Giannini . . .

Venetia, Francesco Nicolini, 1676. 60 p. 14^{cm}.

Three acts. Publisher's dedication, dated Venice, December 18, 1675, argument, and note that all the "versi appuntati sono dell' inventore di questo drama," which implies that the others were not. According to Schatz, Tebaldo Fattorino retouched Giannini's original text. The composer, Giovanni **Legrenzi,** is not mentioned.
                                                    SCHATZ 5540

Adone rè di Cipro. Drama per musica di Filippo Vanstryp romano, da rappresentarsi nella sala degl' illustrissimi Signori Capranica nel carnevale dell' anno 1731 . . .

Roma, Rossi, n. d. 64 p. 16^{cm}.

Three acts. Impresario's dedication, argument, scenario, cast, and name of the composer, Michele **Caballone.**   SCHATZ 1446

The **adopted child,** a musical drama, in two acts. As it is performed at the Theatre Royal, Drury-Lane. By Samuel Birch.

London, C. Dilly, 1795. 2 p. l., 41 p. 20ᶜᵐ.

Cast and prefatory note. The composer, Thomas **Attwood,** is not mentioned. In Longman & Broderip's vocal score "Woman is curious" is headed as "Selected by Mrs. Bland" and added in pencil is the name of the air "Boded no good."
First performed May 1, 1795.   LONGE 230

Adrast und Isidore, oder Die nachtmusik. Eine komische oper in zween aufzuegen. Nach Molière. Aufgefuehrt im K. K. National-Theater.

Wien, beym Logenmeister, 1780. 52 p. 15ᶜᵐ.

By Christoph Friedrich Bretzner. Neither he nor the composer, Franz Adam, ritter von **Mitscha,** is mentioned.
First performed at Vienna, Nationaltheater n. d. Burg, April 26, 1781.

     SCHATZ 6535

Arien aus **Adrast und Isidore.** Eine komische oper, in zween akten. Nach Moliere.

n. i., 1787. 16 p. 15½ᶜᵐ.

Neither the author, Christoph Friedrich Bretzner, is mentioned, nor the composer, von **Kospoth.**
First performed at Berlin, Döbbelinsches Theater, October 16, 1779; at Dresden, Hoftheater, February 22, 1779.   SCHATZ 5217

Adrast und Isidore, oder Die serenate. Eine komische oper in zween akten. Nach Moliere. [silhouette] Componirt vom herrn Preu in Leipzig.

[193] -254 p. (C. F. Bretzner, Operetten, bd. I, Leipzig, 1779.) 16ᶜᵐ.

The silhouette is a portrait of M. Bauser. In the Vorbericht Bretzner says of this play:
"Das dritte stueck ist posse, und als solche betrachtet, schluepft es vielleicht mit durch. In Wien erhielt es eine premie, und wird vermutlich von dort aus, unter dem titel: die *Nachtmusik,* gedruckt erscheinen. Ich habe seitdem vershiedne veraenderungen darinn gemacht, und haette gern in den liedern noch mehrere gemacht, wenn es nicht bereits componirt gewesen waere . . ."
First performed at Dresden, Hoftheater, February 22, 1779.   SCHATZ 11680
Second copy. SCHATZ 8462.

Adrasto rè d'Egitto. Dramma per musica da rappresentarsi nel Teatro alla Scala il carnevale dell' anno 1792 . . .

Milano, Gio. Batista Bianchi, n. d. 96 p. 16ᶜᵐ.

Three acts. Impresario's dedication dated Milan, February 4, 1792, author's notice to the reader, argument, cast, scenario and names of Giovanni de Gamerra as author, of Angelo **Tarchi** as composer.   SCHATZ 10233
Second copy. ML 50.A5 v. 8

Adrasto rè degli Argivi. Dramma per musica da cantarsi nella Real villa di Queluz per celebrare il felicissimo giorno natalizio di S. M. . . . D. Pietro III . . . li 5. luglio, 1784.

[Lisboa], Nella stamperia reale, n. d. 30 p. 15ᶜᵐ.

One act. By Gaetano Martinelli. Argument, cast, and names of the composer, João de Sousa **Carvalho,** and the author.   SCHATZ 1670

Adrian in Syrien. Tr. of Bernasconi's Adriano in Siria.

L'Adriano. Dramma per musica da rappresentarsi nel Teatro Tron di S. Cassiano il carnovale dell' anno MDCCXLVIII.

n. i. 66 p. 15^{cm}.

Three acts. By Metastasio ("Adriano in Siria"). Argument, cast, scenario and name of the composer Vincenzo Legrenzio **Ciampi.**
First performed at Venice as indicated. Schatz 1875

· **Adriano en Syria.** Tr. of Conforto's Adriano in Siria.

L'Adriano in Siria.

[75]–147 p. 19^{cm}. (Pietro Metastasio, Opere drammatiche, Venezia, Giuseppe Bettinelli, 1733–37, v. 1.)

Three acts and Licenza. Argument. No composer is mentioned.
This belongs to those texts which exist in different versions by Metastasio himself. Some of the telling differences are as follows:
The original version (as here represented) has in I, 8, the aria "È vero che oppresso." Its scene I, 13, begins "E nessuno sa dirmi," its scene I, 14, begins "Misera, dove fuggo?" and has the aria "Se non ti moro allato."
The later versions (as below 1755, t. I and 1780, t. I) do not have the aria in I, 8. Their I, 13, begins "Se quel folle si perde" and their I, 14, begins "Senti. Come mi lascia" and has no aria. ML 49.A2M4

— Adriano in Siria.

Metastasio, Poesie, Parigi, vedova Quillau, 1755, t. I, [111]-204 p. 16^{cm}.

Three acts and licenza. Argument.
"Nella forma in cui sono stati ridotti dall' autore." (*See* note on p. 169 of v. vi.)
———— *Same, t. VI, [171]-280 p. 16^{cm}.*
"Come . . . nell' altre edizioni." ML 49.A2M42

— Adriano in Siria. Rappresentato con musica del Caldara la prima volta in Vienna nell' interno gran Teatro della Corte Cesarea alla presenza degli augustissimi sovrani, il di 4 novembre 1731, per festeggiare il nome dell' imperator Carlo VI . . .

p. l., [113]-212 p. 26^{cm}. (Pietro Metastasio, Opere, Parigi, vedova Herissant, t. I, 1780.)

Three acts and licenza. Argument. ML 49.A2M44

—– Adrien.

Metastasio, Tragedies-opera, Vienne, 1751, t. ii, 123 p. 14^{cm}.
Three acts. Richelet's translation of Adriano in Siria. ML49.A2M47

Adriano in Siria. Dramma per musica da rappresentarsi nel nobilissimo Teatro di S. Benedetto il carnovale dell' anno 1780.

Venezia, Modesto Fenzo, 1780. 56 p. 16½^{cm}.

Three acts. By Pietro Metastasio. Argument, cast, scenario, and name of Felice **Alessandri** as composer. Schatz 153

Adriano in Siria, ballet. *See* Bertoni's Eumene.

Adriano in Siria. Dramma per musica da rappresentarsi nel Nuovo Teatro di corte . . . nel carnevale dell' anno 1755. La poesia è del Sig. abbate Pietro Metastasio . . . La musica è del Sig. Andrea de Bernasconi . . .

Monaco, Giov. Giac. Vötter, n. d. 151 p. 19^{cm}.

Three acts. Argument, cast and scenario. German title-page "Adrian in Syrien" and text face Italian. Schatz 854

Adriano in Siria, rappresentato e recitato nel nuovo Teatro Ducale in Stuggarda, 1737.

n. i., n. d.   237 p., 1 l.   16ᶜᵐ.

Three acts. By Metastasio, followed by the *licenza,* p. 190–195 and the three act intermezzo "Pollastrella & Parpagnocco" (text by Pariati), p. 196–237. Argument, cast and scenario. German title-page "Der in Syrien triumphirende Kayser Hadrianus" and text face Italian. Riccardo **Broschi's** name is not mentioned but, as he was then the first conductor at the Stuttgart court, it stands to reason that he composed this opera.   SCHATZ 1338

Adriano in Siria.   Dramma per musica da rappresentarsi nel nuovo Teatro Grimani di S. Benedetto il carnovale dell' anno MDCCLVII.

Venezia, Modesto Fenzo, 1757.   58 p.   14½ᶜᵐ.

Three acts. By Metastasio. Argument, cast, and scenario but without name of the composer, Francesco **Brusa.**   SCHATZ 1376

Adriano in Siria.   Drama per musica da rappresentarsi nella Cesarea corte per il nome gloriosissimo della Sac.ᵃ Ces.ᵃ e Catt. Real Maestà di Carlo VI . . . L'anno MDCCXXXII. La poesia è del Sig. abbate Pietro Metastasio . . . La musica è del Sig. Antonio Caldara . . .

Vienna d'Austria, Gio. Pietro Van Ghelen, n. d.   4 p. l., 78 p. 15½ᶜᵐ.

Three acts and licenza. Argument and scenario. The ballet music at the end of the acts was composed by Niccola Matteis.

First performed as indicated, November 9, 1732.   SCHATZ 1478

Adriano in Siria.   Opera drammatica da rappresentarsi nel Regio Teatro del Buon-Ritiro. Festeggiandosi il gloriosissimo giorno natalizio di sua Maestà Cattolica il re nostro Signore D. Ferdinando VI . . . anno MDCCLVII.

(At end) Madrid, Michele Scrivano. n. d. 13 p. l., 157 p.   20½ᶜᵐ.

Three acts. By Metastasio and somewhat reduced by him as a note informs the reader. With dedication signed by Carlo Broschi Farinelli and dated "Madrid, 20. settembre 1757," argument, cast, scenario and name of the composer Niccolò **Conforto.** Spanish title "Adriano en Syria" and text face the Italian.   SCHATZ 2121

Adriano in Siria.   Dramma per musica da rappresentarsi nel Teatro Vendramin di S. Salvatore nella fiera dell' Ascensíone dell' anno 1760.

Venezia, Modesto Fenzo, 1760.   56 p.

Three acts. By Metastasio who is not mentioned. Argument, cast, scenario and name of Baldassare **Galuppi** as composer. "La musica tutta nuova," consequently his second setting of the text.   SCHATZ 3473

Adriano in Siria.   Dramma per musica di Pietro Metastasio trà gli Arcadi Artino Corasio, da rappresentarsi nel famosissimo Teatro Grimani di S. Gio. Grisostomo. Il carnovale dell' anno 1733 . . .

Venezia, Carlo Buonarrigo, 1733.   72 p.   14½ᶜᵐ.

Three acts. By Metastasio with alterations indicated in the libretto. Impresario's dedication, argument, cast, scenario and name of Geminiano **Giacomelli** as the composer.   SCHATZ 3805

Adriano in Siria.   Dramma per musica da rappresentarsi nel famosissimo Teatro Grimani di S. Gio. Grisostomo il carnovale dell' anno 1740 . . .

Venezia, Marino Rossetti, 1740.   60 p.   15ᶜᵐ.

Three acts. By Metastasio who is not mentioned. Impresario's dedication, argument, cast, scenario and name of Giovanni Antonio **Giai** as the composer.

SCHATZ 3819

Adriano in Siria. Dramma per musica da rappresentarsi nel Teatro nobile di S. Benedetto il carnovale dell' anno MDCCLXVI.

Venezia, Giorgio Fossati, n. d.   55 p.   17^{cm}.

Three acts. By Metastasio who is not mentioned. Argument, cast, scenario and name of Pietro **Guglielmi** as the composer. The last page contains the additional aria for II, 6 "Alla tua bella face."

First performed, as indicated, December 26, 1765.   SCHATZ 4232

Adriano in Siria, dramma per musica, da rappresentarsi nel Teatro della Regia elettoral corte di Dresda, nel carnevale dell' anno MDCCLII.

Dresda, la vedova Stössel, n. d.   4 p. l., 89 p.   19½^{cm}.

Three acts. Argument, scenario, cast and names of Metastasio as author, of Johann Adolph **Hasse** as composer.

First performed, as indicated, Jan. 17, 1752.   SCHATZ 4503

— Adriano in Siria, dramma per musica, da rappresentarsi nel Teatro della Regia elettoral corte di Dresda, nel carnovale dell' anno MDCCLII

Dresda, la vedova Stössel, n. d.   7 p. l., 89, 89 p.   19^{cm}.

Three acts. The same as Schatz 4503, except that German title "Adrianus in Syrien" and text face Italian.   SCHATZ 4504

Adriano in Siria. Dramma per musica da rappresentarsi alla corte elettorale palatina in occasione delle felicissime nozze di Sua Altezza Serenissima Federigo Augusto elettore di Sassonia etc. etc. e di Sua Altezza Serenissima Amalia Augusta contessa palatina de' Due Ponti l'anno MDCCLXIX.

Mannheim, Stamperia elettorale, n. d.   100, [7] p.   15½^{cm}.

Three acts. Argument, cast, scenario, and names of Metastasio as author, of Ignaz **Holzbauer** as the composer. The 7 additional pages contain Mattia Verazi's Licenza. Performed, as indicated, at Mannheim, Hoftheater, January 1769; first performed there November 4, 1768.   SCHATZ 4778

— Hadrian in Syrien. Ein musicalisches trauerspiel, welches an dem hoechsten namensfeste Ihro Churfuerstlichen Durchlaucht zu Pfalz . . . bey Hof aufgefuehret worden.

Mannheim, mit Academischen schriften, 1768.   1 p. l., 111, 20 p. 18^{cm}.

German translation for the above performance. Argument, cast, scenario, and names of Metastasio and **Holzbauer.** The 20 additional pages contain casts and descriptions of Bouqueton's ballets "Cephal und Procris" and "Reinald und Armide," music by "Cannabich und Toeschi."   SCHATZ 4779

Adriano in Siria. Dramma per musica da rappresentarsi nel Teatro Grimani di S. Samuel nella fiera dell' Ascensione dell' anno 1760.

Venezia, Modesto Fenzo, 1760.   56 p.   14¼^{cm}.

Three acts. By Metastasio, who is not mentioned. Argument, cast, scenario, and name of the composer Antonio Maria **Mazzoni** ("La musica sarà nuova.")

First performed May 14, 1760.   SCHATZ 6225

Adriano in Siria. Dramma per musica da rappresentarsi nel Nuovo Teatro in proprietà de' quattro cavalieri patrizi della Regio-inclita città di Pavia nella primavera dell' anno 1777 . . .

Pavia, Porro e Bianchi, n. d.   52 p.   14½^{cm}.

Three acts. By Metastasio, who is not mentioned. Argument, cast, scenario, and name of Joseph **Misliweczek** as the composer.   SCHATZ 6533

L'Adriano in Siria. Dramma per musica da rappresentarsi nel Ducal Teatro di corte il carnovale dell' anno 1775 . . .

Modena, gli eredi di Bartolomeo Soliani, n. d.   48 p.   18^{cm}.

Three acts. By Metastasio, who is not mentioned. Argument, scenario, cast, and name of Gaetano **Monti** as the composer. On p. 48 the reader is informed that after publication of the libretto scenes 8 and 10, act II were cancelled, Sabina's aria "Non ha ragione ingrato" transferred from II, 8, to I, 111, etc.

First performed, as indicated, January 31, 1775.   SCHATZ 6605

Adriano in Siria. Dramma per musica da rappresentarsi nel Teatro alla Scala il carnevale 1790 . . .

Milano, Gio. Batista Bianchi, n. d.   58, [10] p.   16½^{cm}.

Three acts. By Metastasio, who is not mentioned. Impressario's dedication, dated Milan, December 26, 1789, argument, cast, scenario, and name of Sebastiano **Nasolini,** maestro della Capella, e della Direzione Teatrale di Trieste, as the composer.

With the opera were performed Francesco Clerico's ballets "La morte d'Ercole" and "La superba innamorata a suo dispetto" (argument on the 10 unnumbered p.). The composer of the music is not mentioned.   SCHATZ 6998

Second copy.   ML 48.A5   v. 9

Adriano in Siria. Dramma per musica da rappresentarsi nel nobil Teatro di Torre Argentina il carnovale dell' anno 1758.

Roma, Fausto Amidei, n. d.   72 p.

Three acts. By Metastasio, who is not mentioned. Argument, cast, scenario, and name of **Rinaldo di Capua** as composer.

First performed at Rome, Teatro Argentina, January 2, 1758.   ML 50.2.A36R4

Adriano in Siria. Dramma per musica da rappresentarsi nel Regio Teatro di Torino nel carnovale del 1782 . . .

Torino, Onorato Derossi, n. d.   viii, 64 p.   15½^{cm}.

Three acts. By Metastasio, who is not mentioned. Argument, cast, scenario, and name of Giacomo **Rust** as the composer. With the opera were performed, music by Vittorio Amedeo Canavasso, Sebastiano Gallet's ballets "Lauso e Lidia," "Il manescalco," and "Popoli della Siria."

First performed December 26, 1781.   SCHATZ 9166

Adriano in Siria. Dramma per musica da rappresentarsi nel nobilissimo Teatro di San Benedetto la fiera dell' Ascensione dell' anno 1771.

Venezia, Modesto Fenio, 1771.   61 p.   17^{cm}.

Three acts. By Metastasio, who is not mentioned. Argument, cast, scenario, and name of Antonio **Sacchini** as the composer   SCHATZ 9204

Adriano in Siria. Dramma per musica da rappresentarsi nel nobil Teatro a Torre Argentina nel carnevale dell' anno 1779 . . .

Roma, Luigi Bendio, 1779.   48 p.   16^{cm}.

Three acts. By Metastasio, to whom this typical note refers:

"Tuttociò, chi si è tolto, aggiunto, o sconnesso nel presente dramma, si e fatto per adattarsi alle circostanze del moderno teatro, e non mai per correggere il celeberrimo Poeta Cesareo, alle opere di cui si protesta tutta la stima e la venerazione."

Argument, cast, scenario, and name of Giuseppe **Sarti** as the composer. On p. 7 argument without name of the composer of the music of Paolino Franchi's ballet "Gustavo Vaza." Second ballet called "La cappricciosa."

First performed, as indicated, December 28, 1778.   SCHATZ 9470

L'Adriano in Siria. Drama per musica da rappresentarsi nel Teatro Tron di S. Cassiano nel carnovale dell' anno MDCCLII.

[Venezia], n. publ.   1 p. l., 60 p.   15½^{cm}.

Three acts. By Metastasio (not mentioned), with acknowledged alterations "per comodo del teatro, e per le convenienze degl' attori." Argument, cast, scenario, and name of Giuseppe. **Scarlatti** as the composer.   SCHATZ 9540

Adriano in Siria. Dramma per musica da rappresentarsi nel Teatro di S. Samuelle il carnevale dell' anno MDCCLIV.

Venezia, Angiolo Geremia, n. d. 58, [1] p. 16^{cm}.

Three acts. By Metastasio, who is not mentioned. Argument, cast, scenario, and name of Giuseppe **Scolari** as the composer. SCHATZ 9802

Adrianus in Syrien. Tr. of Hasse's Adriano in Siria.

Adrien. Tr. of Metastasio's text Adriano in Siria.

Adrien, opéra en trois actes, représenté pour la première fois, sur le Théâtre de la République et des Arts, le 16 Prairial, an VII.

Paris, Ballard, An vii de la République, [1799]. 1 p. l., 79 p. 26^{cm}.

"Paroles du citoyen Hoffmann. Musique du citoyen **Méhul**." Cast. First performed June 4, 1799. SCHATZ 6276

An **adventure at Margate.** A. T. of Arnold's Summer amusement.

Adventures of twelve hours. A. T. of Love in the East.

Aeneas in Latium. Tr. of Righini's Enea nel Lazio.

Der **aepfeldieb.** A. T. of Gaertner's Ich heisse Theiss.

Der **aepfeldieb.** Ein originalsingspiel in einem aufzuge. Vom herrn Bretzner. Aufgefuehrt auf dem k. k. Hof-Nationaltheater von der in der schauspielkunst sich uebenden jugend. Die musik dazu ist neu, vom herrn Jast.

Wien, beym logenmeister, 1781. 45 p. 16^{cm}.

At end imprint of Joseph, edler von Kurzbeck. Composer F. **Jast**, also known as Jost. SCHATZ 4979

Der **aepfeldieb,** oder Der schatzgraeber. Eine operette in einem akte. [silhouette] Componirt vom herrn Kaffka, Schauspieler beym Churfuerstl. Saechs. Theater.

16^{cm}. [255]-298 p. (C. F. Bretzner, Operetten, bd. I, Leipzig, 1779.)

The silhouette is that of the composer, J. C. Kaffka. Of this piece Bretzner says, in his Vorbericht:

"Der aepfeldieb war als lustspiel bereits in meinen ersten Beytraegen ['Neue theatralische beytraege,' 1771] gedruckt; hier habe ich nichts davon als den plan beybehalten; den dialog aber gaenzlich umgearbeitet."

First performed at Berlin, Döbbelin'sches Theater, June 26, 1780.
SCHATZ 11680
Second copy, detached. SCHATZ 4982

Der **aerndtekranz.** Eine komische oper, in drey aufzuegen.

Leipzig, in der Dyckischen buchhandlung, 1771. 214 p. 15^{cm}.

Neither the author, Christian Felix Weisse, nor the composer, Johann Adam **Hiller**, is mentioned.

First performed at Leipzig, Theater am Rannstaedter Thore, 1771.
SCHATZ 4718

— Der **aerntekranz.** Eine komische oper in drey aufzuegen.

C. F. Weisse, Komische opern, Carlsruhe, 1778, th. iii, p. [135]-264 p. 18½^{cm}.

The composer, Johann Adam **Hiller**, is not mentioned. ML 49.A2W2

Aesopus bey hofe, in einem singspiele auf dem Hamburgischen Schau-platze vorgestellet im jahr 1729.

[Hamburg], Gedruckt mit Stromerischen schrifften, n. d.   Unpaged. 18½ᶜᵐ.

Five acts. Argument and scenario. Neither Johann Mattheson, the author, (resp. translator), nor Georg Philipp **Telemann,** the composer, is mentioned.
First performed, as indicated, February 28, 1729.   SCHATZ 10255.

Aetius.   Tr. of Metastasio's text Ezio.

Aetius.   Tr. of Graun's Ezio.

Aetius.   Tr. of Jommelli's Ezio.

Gli affetti generosi.   A. T. of Metastasio's text L'Atenaide.

Gli affetti più grandi, vinti dal più giusto.   Drama per musica nel felicissimo giorno natalizio della S. R. Mᵗᵃ di Giuseppe I. rè de' Romani . . . l'anno MDCCI. Posto in musica dal Sigʳ Giovanni Bononcini . . . con l'arie per li balletti del Sigʳ Gio. Gioseffo Hoffer . . .

Vienna d'Austria, Susanna Cristina, vedova di Matteo Cosmerovio, n. d.   77 p.   14½ᶜᵐ.

Three acts and *licenza.* Dedication, signed and dated by the author, Donato Cupeda, Vienna, July 26, 1701, argument, and scenario.   SCHATZ 1199

Aftenen.   Et syngespil i een akt.   Ved Frederik Høegh Guldberg. Sat i musik af hr. koncertmester Schall.

Kjøbenhavn, Niels Christensen, 1795.   78 p.   16ᶜᵐ.

Dedicatory poem and preface.
First performed at Copenhagen, Royal Theatre, April 23, 1795.   SCHATZ 9581

Agamemnon vengé.   Ballet tragique en cinq actes par M. Noverre. Exécuté sur les théatres de Vienne 1771.

[Vienne], de Ghelen, n. d.   42 p.   17ᶜᵐ.

Scene by scene description preceded by Noverre's highly interesting "Réflexions justificatives, sur le choix et l'ordonnance du sujet" on p. 3–13, in which Noverre outlines his entire bold system of ballet of which the leading thought is:
"Un balet n'est pas un drame . . . une production de ce genre ne peut se subordonner aux règles étroites d'Aristote . . . c'est toujours en grand que la pantomime doit peindre . . ."
No composer mentioned.   ML 52.2.A2

— **Agamemnon revenged.**   A tragic ballet in five acts.

Noverre, Jean George, Works.   Tr. from the French, London, 1783, v. 3, p. [183]–262.   21½ᶜᵐ.

"Remarks in justification of the author's choice and management of the subject" and detailed scene by scene description.   GV 1787.N8

Agaton und Psiche, ein drama mit gesang, vor. Friedrich Christian Schlenkert.

Leipzig, Paul Gotthelf Kummer, 1780.   86 p.   15ᶜᵐ.

No composer or performance recorded by Schatz.   SCHATZ 11598

L'age viril ou L'amour coquet. Entrée in Campra's Les ages, ballet.

Les **ages,** ballet, representé par l'Academie royale de musique, l'an 1718. Paroles de M. Fusilier. Musique de M. Campra. XCV. opera.

n. i., n. d. pl., 317-376 p. 14^{cm}. *(Recueil général des opera, Paris, 1734, t. xii, no. 6.)*

Detached copy. Prologue and three entrées called "La jeunesse ou L'amour ingenu," "L'age viril ou L'amour coquet," "La vieillesse ou L'amour enjoué." In his Avertissement the author says:

"Je n'ai prétendu donner qu'un tissu de maximes enjouées, liées par une intrigue légere, qui pût occasionner des airs gracieux & des danses variées. C'est ce me semble, ce qui doit constituer le fonds d'un ballet."

First performed, as indicated, October 9, 1718.   SCHATZ 1540
                              Second copy.   ML 48.R4

Agesilao. Dramma per musica da rappresentarsi nel nobilissimo Teatro Venier in San Benedetto il carnovale dell' anno 1788.

Venezia, Modesto Fenzo, 1787. 64 p. 17^{cm}.

Three acts. Cast, argument, scenario, and name of Gaetano **Andreozzi** as composer but not of librettist, who is unknown to Schatz. On p. 47-64 the argomento and detailed description of "Sardanopalo, rè degli Assirj ballo eroico tragico, tratto dall' Istoria del regno assiro, d'invenzione, e composizione di Monsieur Domenico Ballon." The composer of the music is not mentioned.   SCHATZ 221

— L'**Agesilao.** Dramma per musica da rappresentarsi nel magnifico Teatro dell' Accademia Filarmonica di Verona il carnevale dell' anno 1792.

Verona, Dionigi Ramanzini, n. d. 37 p. 17$\frac{1}{2}$^{cm}.

Two acts. Author not mentioned and unknown to Schatz. Impresario's dedication, argument, cast, scenario and name of **Andreozzi** as composer.   ML 50.2.A38A5

Agesilao. O. T. of Francesco Ballani's text Lisandro.

Agide rè di Sparta. Dramma per musica di Luisa Bergalli da rappresentarsi nel Teatro Giustiniano di San Moisè l'anno MDCCXXV . . .

Venezia, Marino Rossetti, n. d. front., 57 p. 15^{cm}.

Three acts. Argument, cast, scenario, name of Giovanni **Porta** as the composer, and author's dedication, in which she calls this "mio debole primo componimento."
                                          SCHATZ 8387

Aglae eller Støtten. Comedie i een act af hr. de Sivry . . . oversat af det franske og forøget med arier hvortil musiquen er sat af hr. Sarti.

n. i., n. d. 50 p. 15$\frac{1}{2}$^{cm}.

By Claus Fasting and A. G. Carstens, who are not mentioned.
First performed at Copenhagen, Hoftheater, February 16, 1774.   SCHATZ 9423

Songs, chorusses, etc., in the new musical farce called the **Agreeable surprise,** as it is performed at the Theatre Royal in the Hay-Market.

London, T. Cadell, 1781. 24 p. 20^{cm}.

Two acts. By John O'Keefe, who is not mentioned. The overture and all the airs in the libretto are indicated as by Samuel **Arnold,** except airs IV, VI, XI, XII, XIII, for which popular tunes (mostly Irish) were used. According to Biog. Dr. the opera was originally produced at Dublin as "The secret enlarged, in 1776, but Lawrence found no trace of this."

First performed at London, Haymarket, September 3, 1781.   ML 50.2.A4A7

Agreeable surprise—Continued.

— Songs, chorusses etc. in the new musical farce called the **Agreeable surprise**. As it is performed at the Theatre Royal in the Hay-Market. Fourth edition.

London, T. Cadell, 1782. 24 p. 21ᶜᵐ.

Two acts. Cast. The author, John O'Keefe, is not mentioned. The overture and most of the songs are headed as composed by **Arnold**. LONGE 91

— The **agreeable surprise**. A comic opera, in two acts. By Mr. O'Keefe. The music composed by Dr. Arnold.

Dublin, W. Wilson, 1786. 48 p. 17½ᶜᵐ.

Cast. LONGE 149

— The **agreeable surprise**. A comic opera.

[117]–148 p. 16ᶜᵐ. (A volume of plays, Dublin, Printed for the booksellers, 1791.)

Without name of author or composer. PR 1269.V6

Agrippina. Drama per musica. Da rappresentarsi nel famosissimo Teatro Grimani di S. Gio. Grisostomo l'anno MDCCIX.

Venezia, Marino Rossetti, 1709.

Three acts. Argument, cast, scenario. Neither the author, Vincenzo Grimani, nor Georg Friedrich **Händel**, the composer, is mentioned.
First performed, as indicated, December 26, 1709. SCHATZ 4471

— **Agrippina.** Drama per musica da rappresentarsi nel Teatro d'Hamburgo l'anno 1718.—Agrippina in einer opera vorgestellet . . .

Hamburg, Caspar Jakhel, n. d. Unpaged. 18½ᶜᵐ.

Three acts. German text faces Italian. Neither Grimani nor **Händel** is mentioned. The Italian text follows the original closely, though with some differences. For instance, I, 3 "A cenni tuoi sovrani" has become "Ah Pallante, Pallante," and I, 4 "Or che Pallante è vinto" has become "Di occulto arcano." SCHATZ 4472

L'Agrippina, moglie di Tiberio. Dramma per musica di Guido Riviera Piacentino da rappresentarsi nel Regio-Ducal Teatro di Milano nel carnovale dell' anno 1743 . . .

Milano, Giuseppe Richino Malatesta, 1743. 6 p. l., 70 p. 15ᶜᵐ.

Three acts. Dedication, argument, scenario, cast, and name of Giovanni Battista San Martino (**Sammartini**) as composer. It is said on 5th p. l. that the character of Emilio was added for these performances.
First performed in January, 1743, as indicated. ML 48.A5 v.18

Ahtor ed Erma, ballet. *See* G. Nicolini's Artaserse.

Ahtor ed Erma, ballet. *See* Prota's I studenti.

Aiglé. *See* Lagarde's Eglé.

L'Ajace. Dramma per musica del Signor A. D. Averara [!].

Napoli, Dom. Ant. Parrino e Michele Luigi Mutio, 1697. 76 p. 13½ᶜᵐ.

Three acts. Dedication by Nicola Serino as impresario, argument, cast, scenario, and notice to the reader:
"Eccoti un drama, ch' havendo alcuni anni sono riportato nel Teatro di Milano un sommo applauso, & in quello delli Signori Capranica in Roma [1697] estremo gradimento, uscendo per la terza volta alla luce in questa fedelissima città di Napoli aspira al tuo gradimento . . . Hora ti si aggiunge, che secondo la prima impressione, il

L'Ajace—Continued.

riconoscimento, che Idraspe sia figlio del rè, e fratello di Ajace si faceva per mezzo di Zelta vecchia nutrice di corte, ed essendosi dovuta sostituire una damigella giovanetta è convenuto per salvar parte dell' improprietà supporre, che questa sia figlia della medesima nutrice informata di tutto. L'opera troverai mutata quasi in tutte l'ariette con l'aggiunta di alcune scene ridicole, e ciò si è fatto per più compiacerti . . ."

Schatz records as composers Carlo Ambrogio **Lonati** and Paolo **Magni**. He also records, in accordance with the title page, A. D. Averara as author, but the title page of the Rome, 1697 ed. (Brussels Conservatory) has "signor A. d'Averara," which Wotquenne reads to mean "l'abbé Pietro d'Averara," who is of some note as librettist, whereas an A. D. Averara has not otherwise come to my notice. Probably Wotquenne's conjecture is correct.

First performed at Milan, Teatro al Ducale Palazzo, 1694.   Schatz 5682

Ajace e Cassandra, ballet. *See* Borghi's Ricimero.

Ajax, tragédie, representée pour la premiere fois par l'Académie royale de musique, le lundi 20. avril 1716. Les paroles de M. Mennesson & la musique de M. Bertin. LXXXIX opera.

n. i., n. d.   pl., [419]–472, [4] p.   14^{cm}.   (Recueil general des opera, t. xi, Paris, 1720.)

Detached copy. Prologue and five acts.   Schatz 878

         Second copy.   ML 48.R4

— **Ajax,** tragedie representée pour la premiere fois, par L'Academie royale de musique, de Lyon en l'année 1742.

Lyon, Aimé Delaroche, 1742.   67 p.   23^{cm}.

Five acts. Cast. Neither the author, Mennesson, is mentioned, nor the composer, T. **Bertin de la Doué.**   Schatz 11668

Al fatto ci vuol pazienza. Intermezzi per musica a quattro voci da rappresentarsi nell' antico Teatro di Tordinona, nel carnevale dell' anno 1753 . . .

Roma, Giuseppe Agazzi, 1753.   22 p.   15^{cm}.

Two parts. Publisher's dedication and cast. The characters are Polimante, Dorilla, Fumantino, and Scrulletta. Neither author nor composer mentioned and both unknown to me.   ML 50.2.A42

Alarbas. A dramatick opera. Written by a gentleman of quality . . .

London, Printed by M. J. for J. Morphew, 1709.   3 p. l., 51, [1] p. 21½^{cm}.

Three acts with prologue and epilogue. In his preface the unknown author says: ". . . The poem being some time since drawn according to the model of our English dramatick opera's, any person that is the least acquainted with the late performances, will easily account for its appearing in this manner before it had pass'd the stage, if they will be pleas'd to observe, that the nature of the play will not admit of its representation in either house. The opera-theatre being wholly taken up with Italian airs, and the other totally excluding the musical part."   Longe 132

L'Alarico. Drama per musica da rappresentarsi nel Teatro Formagliari l'estate dell' anno 1716 . . .

Bologna, Giampietro Barbiroli, n. d.   59 p.   13^{cm}.

Three acts. Dedication signed by Francesco Antonio Novi and dated Bologna, June 5, 1716, argument, scenario, cast, and notice to the reader. Neither the author, Borso Buonacossa, is mentioned, nor the composer, Giov. Battista **Bassani.**

First performed, as indicated, June 7, 1716; at Ferrara, Teatro del conte Pinamonte Buonacossi in 1685.   Schatz 633

Alarico il Baltha, cioè l'Audace, rè de Gothi. Drama per musica comandato dall' Altezza Serenissima di Massimiliano Emanuele duca dell' una e l'altra Baviera . . . per celebrare il dì natalzio dell' Augustissima consorte . . . l'anno 1687. Composto da Luigi Orlandi . . . e posto in musica dal S. Agostino Steffani . . . con l'arie per i balletti del S. Melchior d'Ardespin maestro di concerti e ajutante di camera di S. A. E.

Monaco, Giovanni Jecklino, n. d. 4 p. l., 74 p. 19½^{cm}.

Three acts. Author's dedication dated Munich, January 14, 1687, argument, scenario, and names of the "cavalieri" who danced Francisco Rodier's three incidental ballets on this occasion, January 18, 1687, at the Hoftheater.   SCHATZ 10036

Alba Cornelia, musicalische opera, welche auf dem Teatro zu Bresslau anno 1726 in der fastnacht vorgestellet . . . wie auch . . . zu den heurigen fuersten-tag dediciret wird . . .

n. i., n. d. Unpaged. 18^{cm}.

Three acts. By Pietro Pariati. Impresario's dedication, argument, scenario, and names of the author and the composer, Francesco Bartolomeo **Conti.** German text faces Italian, which Schatz attributes to Silvio Stampiglia!

According to Schatz the opera was first performed at Milan, Regio Ducal Teatro, carnival 1704 and at Vienna, February, 1714.   SCHATZ 2203

L'Albagia in fumo, ballet. *See* Tarchi's La congiura Pisoniana.

L'albergatrice vivace. Dramma giocoso per musica da rappresentarsi in Parma nel R. D. Teatro di Corte il carnevale dell' anno MDCCLXXXI . . .

Parma, Filippo Carmignani, n. d. 3 p. l., 62 p. 17½^{cm}.

Two acts. Author unknown to Schatz. Impresario's dedication, cast, and name of the composer, Luigi **Caruso.**

First performed at Venice, Teatro di S. Samuele, carnival 1780.   SCHATZ 1655

L'Albergia smascherata o sia Il cittadino rinnobilito. Dramma giocoso per musica da rappresentarsi ne' Teatri privilegiati di Vienna nel carnovale dell' anno 1767.

Vienna, Ghelen, n. d. 95 p. 17^{cm}.

Three acts. Author not mentioned and unknown to Schatz. Prefatory poem by the publisher, cast, and name of Giuseppe Pasqua (**Pasque**) as the composer.

First performed, as indicated, February 23, 1767.   SCHATZ 7782

Albert der Dritte von Bayern. Im originale. Ein singspiel in fuenf aufzuegen. Mit musik von Georg Vogler . . .

n. i., 1781. 88 p. 16^{cm}.

"Vorerinnerung" signed "Th. T***r." (Karl Theodor von Traiteur).

First performed at Stuttgart, National schaubühne im kleinem theater, December, 1781.   SCHATZ 10791

Albion and Albanius: an opera. Perform'd at the Queens theatre, in Dorset Garden. Written by Mr. Dryden . . .

London, J. Tonson, 1685. 6 p. l., 30 p. 28^{cm}.

Three acts. Prologue, Epilogue, description of "the frontispiece," and Dryden's extraordinary, esthetical, historical, polemical preface, with postscript. The opera was first performed at the Theatre Royal, in Dorset Garden, June 6, 1685 (Grove).

As specimens of Dryden's opinions, may be quoted from the preface:

". . . An *opera* is a poetical tale, or fiction, represented by vocal and instrumental musick, adorn'd with scenes, machines, and dancing. The suppos'd persons of this musical *drama*, are generally supernatural, as Gods and Goddesses, and Heroes, which at least are descended from them, and are in due time, to be adopted into their number.

Albion and Albanius—Continued.

The subject therefore being extended beyond the limits of humane nature, admits of that sort of marvellous and surprizing conduct, which is rejected in other plays. Humane impossibilities are to be receiv'd, as they are in Faith; because where Gods are introduc'd, a Supreme Power is to be understood, and second Causes are out of doors: Yet propriety is to be observ'd even here . . .

"The recitative part of the *Opera* requires a more masculine beauty of expression and sound: the other, which (for want of a proper English word) I must call *the Songish Part*, must abound in the softness and variety of numbers; its principal intention, being to please the hearing, rather than to gratifie the understanding . . . I have probable reasons, which induce me to believe, that some Italians having curiously observ'd the gallantries of the *Spanish Moors* at the *Zambra's*, or royal feasts, where musick, songs and dancing were in perfection; together with their machines . . . may possibly have refin'd upon those Moresque divertisements, and produc'd this delightful entertainment, by leaving out the warlike part of the carousels, and forming a poetical design for the use of the machines, the songs, and dances . . .

". . . The Italian . . . seems indeed to have been invented for the sake of poetry and musick . . . their very speaking has more of musick in it than Dutch poetry and song . . . the French, who now cast a longing eye to their country, are not less ambitious to possess their elegance in poetry and musick; in both of which they labour at impossibilities . . . The English has yet more natural disadvantages than the French; our original Teutonick consisting most in monosyllables, and those incumbred with consonants, cannot possibly be freed from those inconveniences. The rest of our words, which are deriv'd from the Latin chiefly, and the French, with some small sprinklings of Greek, Italian and Spanish, are some relief in poetry and help us to soften our uncouth numbers; which together with our *English genius*, incomparably beyond the trifling of the French, in all the nobler parts of verse, will justly give us the preheminence. But, on the other hand, the effeminacy of our pronunciation, (a defect common to us, and to the Danes,) and our scarcity of female rhimes, have left the advantage of musical composition for songs, though not for recitative, to our neighbours.

"Through these difficulties, I have made a shift to struggle, in my part of the performance of this *opera;* which, as mean as it is, deserves at least a pardon, because it has attempted a discovery beyond any former undertaker of our nation . . . Yet I have no great reason to despair; for I may with out vanity, own some advantages, which are not common to every writer; such as are the knowledge of the Italian and French language, and the being conversant with some of their best performances in this kind; which have furnish'd me with such variety of measures, as have given the composer Monsieur [Louis] **Grabut** what occasions he cou'd wish, to shew his extraordinary talent . . . And let me have the liberty to add one thing; that he has so exactly express'd my sense, in all places, where I intended to move the passions, that he seems to have enter'd into my thoughts, and to have been the poet as well as the composer. This I say, not to flatter him, but to do him right; because amongst some English musicians and their scholars, (who are sure to judge after them) the imputation of being a *Frenchman*, is enough to make a party, who maliciously endeavour to decry him. But the knowledge of Latin and Italian poets, both which he possesses, besides his skill in musick, and his being acquainted with all the performances of the French opera's, adding to these the good sense to which he is born, having rais'd him to a degree above any man, who shall pretend to be his rival on our stage. When any of our Country-men excell him, I shall be glad, for the sake of old England, to be shewn my errour; in the mean time, let vertue be commended, though in the person of a stranger . . .

"The same reasons which depress thought in an opera, have a stronger effect upon the words; especially in our language: for there is no maintaining the purity of *English* in short measures, where the rhime returns so quick, and is so often female, or double rhime, which is not natural to our tongue, because it consists too much of monosyllables, and those too, most commonly clogg'd with consonants; for which reason I am often forc'd to coin new words, revive some that are antiquated, and botch others; as if I had not serv'd out my time in poetry, but was bound 'prentice to some doggrel rhimer, who makes songs to tunes, and sings them for a livelihood. 'Tis true, I have not been often put to this drudgery; but where I have, the words will sufficiently shew, that I was then a slave to the composition, which I will never be again: 'Tis my part to invent, and the musician's to humour that invention. I may be counsell'd, and will always follow my friend's advice, where I find it reasonable; but will never part with the power of the *militia* . . .

"It [this opera] was originally intended only for a prologue to a play, of the nature of the *Tempest*; which is a tragedy mix'd with *opera;* or a *drama* written in blank

Albion and Albanius—Continued.

verse adorn'd with scenes, machines, songs and dances: so that the fable of it is all spoken and acted by the best of the comedians; the other part of the entertainment to be perform'd by the same singers and dancers who are introduc'd in this present *opera* . . . But some intervening accidents having hitherto deferr'd the performance of the main design, I propos'd to the actors, to turn the intended prologue into an entertainment by itself, as you now see it, by adding two acts more to what I had already written. The subject of it is wholly allegorical . . . The descriptions of the scenes and other decorations of the stage, I had from Mr. Betterton, who has spar'd neither for industry, nor cost, to make this entertainment perfect, nor for invention of the ornaments to beautifie it . . ."

In the "Post-Script" Dryden says that though the whole preface was written before the death of Charles II., he found himself so satisfied with it even after the King's death, that he saw no reason for alterations except "for the addition of twenty or thirty lines in the Apotheosis of Albion" to "save" the piece "from a botch'd ending." He also says that by the late King's command the opera, especially the first and third acts of it, had been "practis'd before him" to his entire satisfaction with opera. He died just before the first performance.   ML 50.2.A43

— **Albion and Albanius:** an opera. Perform'd at the Queens Theatre in Dorset-Garden. Written by Mr. Dryden . . .

> *London, Jacob Tonson, 1691. 7 p. l., 34 p. 21^{cm}.*
>
> P. 32–33 incorrectly numbered 24–25.
> Three acts. Text and contents as in the 1685 edition.   SCHATZ 4060

Albion restored, or Time turned oculist: a masque.

> *London, J. Seymour, 1758. 22 p. 20^{cm}.*
>
> One act. Dedicated "To the Grand President . . . of the Laudable Order of Anti-Gallicans . . . by the author, a true Anti-Gallican." No further data in Clarence's "The Stage," except that the masque was produced in 1757. "Not acted and probably never set to music" (Squire).   ML52.2.A3

L'Alboino in Italia. Drama per musica da rappresentarsi nel famo-sissimo Teatro Grimano di SS. Gio. e Paolo l'anno 1691 . . .

> *Venetia, Nicolini, 1691. 57 p. 14^{cm}.*
>
> Three acts. Dedication signed with the initials of Giulio Cesare Corradi, argument, scenario, and notice to the reader, speaking of this as: "due miracoli di musica, prodotti da due gran maestri, e publicati da sette voci canore tutte ammirabili nel loro essere." These two composers were Giuseppe Felice **Tosi** and Carlo Francesco **Pollaroli.**   SCHATZ 1038?

Albumazar. Drama per musica da rappresentarsi nel Teatro Ven-dramini a S. Salvatore la primavera dell' anno MDCCXXVII.

> *Venezia, Marino Rossetti, 1727. 48 p. 14½^{cm}.*
>
> Three acts. By the composer, Giuseppe Maria **Buini** (Schatz). Argument.
> First performed at Bologna, Teatro Formagliari, carnival 1727.   SCHATZ 1387

L'Alcate. Drama di Marc' Antonio Tirabosco. Rappresentato in musica nel Teatro novissimo di Venetia l'anno 1642 . . .

> *Venetia, Gio. Battista Suriano, 1642. 96 p. 14^{cm}.*
>
> Prologue and three acts. Author's dedication dated Venice, February 13, 1642, with name of Francesco **Manelli** as composer, his notice to the reader and argument.
>   SCHATZ 5890

L'Alcatrasso geloso. Drama per musica di D. Carlo Antonio Mar-chesini Mantovano . . .

> *Vicenza, Giacomo Amadio, 1672. 72 p. 14^{cm}.*
>
> Three acts. Impresario's dedication, notice to the reader, scenario, and argument. The composer, Alessandro **Spinazzari,** is not mentioned.
> First performed at Vicenza, Teatro di Piazza, 1672.   SCHATZ 9975

Alceste.   Tragedia per musica.

Vienna, Ghelen, 1767.   54 p.   16^{cm}.

Three acts. By Ranieri de 'Calsabigi, who signed the dedication.   Argument
and scenario, but no cast, and **Gluck,** the composer, is not mentioned.
First performed at Vienna, December 26, 1767. (Wotquenne incorrectly substitutes December 16 in his Thematic catalogue without giving his reasons.)

SCHATZ 3885

— Alceste.   Tragedia per musica da rappresentarsi in Bologna nel
Nuovo Pubblico Teatro nella p.imavera dell' anno MDCCLXXVIII.

Bologna, Sassi, n. d.   60, [2] p.   19½^{cm}.

Three acts. Argument, cast, and names of Calsabigi as author, of **Gluck** ("Sig.
cavaliere Gluk frà gli Arcadi Armonide Terpsicoreo") as composer.
First performed, as indicated, May 9, 1778.   ML48.A5 v. 29

— Alceste, tragédie-opera, en trois actes, représentée pour la premiere fois par l'Académie-royale de musique, le mardi 16 avril 1776.
Et rimise au théâtre le vendredi 22 octobre 1779.

*Paris, aux dépens de l'Académie. de l'imprimerie de P. de Lormel,
1779. 52 p.   24½^{cm}.*

Three acts. Cast. By Du Roullet, who in the unsigned Avertissement comments
on the liberties which he took with Calsabigi's text. **Gluck** is mentioned as the
composer.
Originally performed at Paris, Académie royale de musique, April 23, 1776 (deferred from April 16, the date of the original libretto), and not on April 30, as the
printed score has it. (Comp. Wotquenne.)   SCHATZ 3888

— Alceste, tragédie-opéra en trois actes; représentée devant Leurs
Majestés, à Fontainebleau, le 13 octobre 1785, et remise à Paris, sur
le Théatre de l'Académie royale de musique, le vendredi 24 février
1786.

Paris, P. de Lormel, 1786.   47 p.   24½^{cm}.

Three acts. By Du Roullet, who is not mentioned.   Cast and name of **Gluck** as
the composer.   SCHATZ 3940
Second copy.   ML48.M2B

— Alceste.   Eine ernsthafte oper in drey akten von Schmieder.   Die
musik ist von Ritter Gluck.

n. i., 1792.   48 p.   13^{cm}.

First performed at Mayence, Nationaltheater, April 9, 1791.   SCHATZ 3889

— La bonne femme, ou Le Phénix, parodie d'Alceste, en deux
actes, en vers, mêlés de vaudevilles et de danses; représentée pour
la premiere fois par les Comédiens italiens ordinaires du Roi, le
dimanche 7 juillet 1776.

Paris, Chardon, 1776.   47 p.   19^{cm}.

Neither author nor composer recorded by Schatz.   SCHATZ 11484

Alceste.   Dramma tragico da rappresentarsi nel Regio-Ducal Teatro
di Milano nel carnovale dell' anno 1769 . . .

Milano, Giuseppe Richino Malatesta, 1768.   6 p. l., 46, [1] p.   14½^{cm}.

Three acts. By Ranieri de' Calsabigi, who is not mentioned. Dedication, argument, cast, scenario, and name of Pietro **Guglielmi** as the composer. Pasted on the
p. following the (unnumb.) p. 46 the aria "Veggo la sposa, oh Dio" as substitute for
"So, che morir dovrei," III, 2.
First performed, as indicated, December 26, 1768.   SCHATZ 4233

Alceste. Tragedia per musica del Signor Antonio Simon Sografi A. V. Poeta del nobilissimo Teatro La Fenice. Composta per il teatro stesso pel carnovale 1799.

Venezia, Stamperia Valvasense, n. d. 64 p. 17^{cm}.

Three acts. Cast, scenario, and name of Marcos **Portugal** as the composer ("La musica tutta nuova"). On p. 63 a substitute scene for III, 1. On p. [53]–62 Argument, cast, description, and name of Luigi Gianella as composer of "la musica tutta nuova" of Onorato Viganò's "La morte di Geta, ballo eroico tragico pantomimo" in five acts.

First performed, as indicated, December 26, 1798.   Schatz 8396

Alceste. Ein singspiel in fuenf aufzuegen.

n. i., 1773. 48 p. 18½^{cm}.

Cast. Neither Wieland, the author, is mentioned nor Anton **Schweitzer**, the composer.

First performed at Weimar, Kleines Schlosstheater, May 28, 1773. Schatz 9768

— **Alceste.** Ein singspiel in fünf aufzuegen. In musik gesetzt von dem kapellmeister Anton Schweitzer, und in den jahren 1773 und 74 auf dem damahligen Weimarischen Hoftheater aufgeführt.

n. i. 58 p. 26^{cm}. (Wielands Sämmtl. werke, xxvi. bd.)

Before 1800?   Schatz 9768a

Alceste ou Le triomphe d'Alcide, tragedie. Representée devant Sa Majesté à Fontainebleau. Suivant la copie imprimee à Paris.

[Amsterdam, Antoine Schelte], 1688. 68 p. (incl. front.) 13½^{cm}.

Prologue and five acts. Cast and dedicatory poem to the king. Neither author nor composer mentioned.   ML 50.2.A49L9

— **Alceste,** ou Le triomphe d'Alcide, tragedie representée par l'Academie royale de musique l'an 1674. Les paroles sont de M. Quinault e la musique de M. de Lully. V. opera.

n. i., n. d. 14^{cm}. front., 205-272 p. (Recueil général des opéra, t. i, Paris, 1703.)

Detached copy. Dedicatory poem, prologue, and five acts.
First performed, as indicated, January 19, 1674.   Schatz 5758
                                          Second copy. ML 48.R4

— **Alceste,** ou Le triomphe d'Alcide, tragedie. Representée par l'Academie royale de musique, en 1674.

Quinault, Théatre, t. iv, Paris, 1739. pl., p. [143]-189. 17^{cm}.

Prologue and five acts. **Lully** is not mentioned.   PQ1881.A1739

— **Alceste,** parodie. Par les Srs. Dominique & Romagnesi . . . Representée pour la premiere fois, par les Comédiens italiens ordinaires du roi, le 28 juin 1728.

Les parodies du Nouveau théâtre italien, Nouv. éd., Paris, Briasson, 1738, t. iv, [121]-182 p. 16½^{cm}.

One act. The airs and vaudeville used are printed at end of the volume in the "Table des airs" (92 p.).   ML 48.P3

— **La noce interrompue,** parodie d'Alceste, representée pour la premiere fois; par les Comédiens italiens, ordinaires du roi, le jeudi 26 janvier 1758.

Paris, la veuve Delormel & fils, 1758. 2 p. l., 64 p. 19^{cm}. (Theatre de M. Favart, Paris, Duchesne, 1763–77, t. iv.)

Three acts. Cast. No music printed in the text! Composer, resp. arranger, not known to Font.   ML 49.A2F1

Alceste; or, The triumph of conjugal love. A tragic ballet.

Noverre, Jean George, Works. Tr. from the French, London, 1783, v. 3, p. [301]–330. 21½ᶜᵐ.

Detailed description of the nine scenes. GV 1787.N8

Alceste e Admeto, ballet. *See* Monza's Cleopatra.

Alceste ed Admeto. A. T. of the ballet La discesa d' Ercole all' inferno.

Alcesti, o sia L'amor sincero. Tragedia musicale, nelle seconde nozze della Reale Altezza di Savoia. L'anno 1665.

Torino, Bartolomeo Zavatta, 1665. 76, [1] p. 17½ᶜᵐ.

Prologue and five acts. Argument. Not recorded by Schatz. ML 50.2.A5

Der alchymist. *See* Meissner's text Der liebesteufel oder Der alchymist.

L'Alciade overo La violenza d'amore, opera tragicomica da rappresentarsi in Bergamo nella partenza . . . dell' illustriss., e eccellentiss. Sigʳ Francesco Donaldo . . .

Milano, Giuseppe Pandolfo Malatesta, 1709. 52 p. 14ᶜᵐ.

Three acts. By Marc' Antonio Gasparini, who is not mentioned, and whose original alternative title was "L'eroico amore." The one quoted above is pasted over the original. Argument, scenario, cast, and names of the composers, Carlo Francesco **Gasparini,** act I; Carlo Francesco **Polaroli,** act II; Francesco **Ballarotti,** act III.

SCHATZ 3597

— **L'amante impazzito.** Drama per musica, da rappresentarsi nel Teatro di S. Fantino l'autunno dell' anno 1714 . . .

Venetia, Girolamo Albrizzi, n. d. 46 p. 14ᶜᵐ.

Three acts. Merely a later version of "L'Alciade overo La violenza d'amore." The dialogue not so different in the two versions as the arias. For instance, the opening aria of third act "Sento che a poco a poco" has been dropped, "Qui la vipera soggiorna" (III, 5) has become "Sul mio crin di sdegno armato," "Come sento in un momento" (III, 7) has become "T' intendo sì mio cor," etc. Neither author nor the composers are mentioned. Dedication, notice to the reader, and scenario.

SCHATZ 3598

L'Alciade. Drama decimo quarto di Giovanni Faustini. Da rappresentarsi in musica nel famoso Theatro Grimano di SS. Gio. e Paolo l'anno MDCLXVII . . .

Venetia, Francesco Nicolini e Steffano Curti, 1667. 83 p. 15ᶜᵐ.

Prologue and three acts. Nicolini's dedication, argument, scenario, and this notice to the reader:

"Il Signor Giouanni Faustini nell' età sua più giouenile per diletto proprio applicò l'ingegno alle compositioni Dramatiche Musicali, nelle quali riuscì ammirabile nell' invétione in particolare; Onde nel corso di soli anni nove (essendo stato troppo prematuramente rapito dalla morte l'anno 1651., nel trigesimo secondo dell' età sua) si viddero rappresentare nei Theatri di questa Città con gli applausi maggiori la Virtù de Strali d'Amore, L'Egisto, L'Ormindo, il Titone, La Doriclea, L'Ersilda, L'Euripo, L'Oristeo, La Rosinda, La Calisto, L'Eritrea, & doppo la di lui morte ancora l'Eupatra, poi L'Elena rapita da Teseo, vestita col manto di Poesia da sublime virtuoso, tutte poste in Musica, ò dalla virtù singolare del Signor Francesco Cavalli dignissimo Organista della Serenissìma Republica, ò dal Signor Don Pietro Andrea Zianni hora Maestro di Capella della Maestà dell' Imperatrice, incontrarono non solo nel genio, & nella sodisfattione di questa Città tanto delicata nell' vdire simili rappresentationi; mà di molte altre principali dell' Italia, nelle quali, più, e più volte sono state rappresentate con ogni pienezza d'applauso; anzi che con l'Inuentioni multiplici, &

L'Alciade—Continued.

varie d' esse quasi come di cose obliate si sono addobbate, & arrichite altre compositioni. Restano ancora tre fatiche di questo virtuoso: La Medea placata, L'Alciade, & il Meraspe, overo il Tiranno humiliato d'Amore: L'anno presente comparianno nel Nobilissimo Theatro Grimano prima l'Alciade, & poi il Meraspe, promessi dall' Auttore nelle sue stampe l'anno 1651., che passò ad altra vita; L'inventioni saranno nuove, curiose, & dilettevoli, havendo procurato d'allontanarsi da introdurvi in esse femine in habito virile datesi à credere per huomeni, & altre cose ancora, più, & più volte vedute, rappresentate; Onde si può credere, che anco queste siano per incontrare nella sodisfattione della Città. Nell' Alciade si sono aggionte alcune cose, composte da virtùoso soggetto per favorire, & à richiesta di chi fà rappresentare il DRAMA. La compositione della Musica d'Esso è del Signor Zianni [Pietro Andrea **Ziani**], che conforme al suo solito hà fatto cose mirabili; Viui in tanto lieto, & tatendi alla favela." Schatz 11211

Alcibiade. Dramma per musica da rappresentarsi nel Teatro Tron di S. Cassano l'autunuo dell' anno MDCCXLVI.

n. i., n. d. 72 p. 15ᶜᵐ.

Three acts. By Gaetano Roccaforte. With argument, cast, scenario, and name of the composer, Giuseppe **Carcano**, but not of librettist.
First performed at Venice, as indicated. Schatz 1621

L'Alcibiade. Drama per musica nel famosissimo Teatro Grimano à SS. Gio. e Paolo. Di Aurelio Aurelii. Opera XX. . . .

Venetia, Francesco Nicolini, 1680. 72 p. (incl. front.) 14ᶜᵐ.

Three acts. Author's dedication, argument, scenario, and notice to the reader, with name of Marc' Antonio **Ziani** as the composer.
First performed, as indicated, carnival 1680. Schatz 11177
Second copy. ML 48.M2

Alcide, tragedie representée par l'Academie royale de musique l'an 1693. Les paroles de M. Capistron, & la musique de Mʳ Louis de Lully, & de Mʳ Marais. XXIX. opera.

n. i., n. d. 14ᶜᵐ. front., 229-280 p. (Recueil général des opéra, t. iv, Paris, 1703.)

Detached copy. Five acts and prologue.
First performed, as indicated, February 3, 1693. Schatz 5785
Second copy. ML 48.R4

— La **mort d'Hercule**, tragedie, représentée pour la premiere fois par l'Academie royale de musique, sous le titre d'Alcide, le [blank] d'avril 1693. Remise au theatre le 23 juin 1705.

Paris, Christophe Ballard, 1705. 6 p. l., 48, [1] p. 23 p.

Prologue and five acts. Cast. Neither Campistron nor the composers, Louis de **Lully** and Marin **Marais**, are mentioned. ML 50.2.A51L9

Alcide al Bivio. Questa festa teatrale, tutta allusiva ai sicuri segni d'indole generosa dati fin dalla prima sua adolescenza dal gran principe per cui è scritta, fu d'ordine sovrano composta in Vienna, e rappresentata con musica dell' Hasse nella Cesarea corte . . . per le nozze delle AA. RR. di Giuseppe II . . . e della principessa Isabella di Borbone, l'anno 1760.

pl., [207]–248 p. 26ᶜᵐ. (Metastasio, Opere, t. viii, Parigi, vedova Herissant, 1781.)

One act. Argument. ML 49.A2M44

Alcide al bivio. Festa teatrale da rappresentarsi in musica per le felicissime nozze delle LL. AA. RR. l'arciduca Giuseppe d'Austria e la principessa Isabella di Borbone . . . In Vienna l'anno MDCCLX.

n. i., n. d. Unpaged. 21½ᶜᵐ.

The ornamental engraved title page is preceded by a frontispiece engraved by Ant. Tischler and followed by exquisite head and tail pieces by the same artist.

One act. Argument, cast, and name of Johann Adolph **Hasse** as the composer. The author, Metastasio, is not mentioned.

First performed at Vienna, Grosser Redontensaal, October 8, 1760.   SCHATZ 4505

— **Alcides an der doppel-strasse.** Ein theatralisch-musicalisches schauspiel, so bey dem glorreich begangenen vermaehlungs-feste Ihrer Koenigl. Hoheiten des Durchleuchtigsten erz-herzogens Joseph von Oesterreich, und der Durchleuchtigsten prinzessin Isabella von Bourbon . . . in Wien aufgefuehret worden, im jahr 1760. Verfasset von herrn abbate Metastasio . . . und in das teutsche uebersetzt von J. A. E. v. G.

[Wien], Gedruckt mit von Ghelischen schriften, n. d. Unpaged. 15½ᶜᵐ.

One act. Translated by Johann Anton, edler van Ghelen. Argument, cast, and name of Johann Adolph **Hasse** as composer.   SCHATZ 4506

— **Alcide al bivio.** Dramma per musica, da rappresentarsi nel Regio Teatro.—Alcides ved te to veie . . .

Kiøbenhavn, H. J. Graae, 1774. 79, [3] p. 17ᶜᵐ.

One act and licenza. Argument, cast, and name of Johann Adolph **Hasse** as the composer. Danish text faces Italian.

First performed, as indicated, February 2, 1774.   SCHATZ 4507

Alcide negli orti Esperidi, ballet. *See* P. Guglielmi's Tomiri.

Alcides an der doppel-strasse. Tr. of Hasse's Alcide al bivio.

Alcides ved te to veie. Tr. of Hasse's Alcide al bivio.

Alcimena principessa dell' Isole Fortunate o sia L'amore fortunato ne' suoi disprezzi. Dramma per musica da rappresentarsi nel Teatro Tron di San Cassiano il carnovale dell' anno 1750.

Venezia, Modesto Fenzo, 1750. 39 p. 16½ᶜᵐ.

Modern transcript. By Pietro Chiari, who is not mentioned. Argument, cast, and name of **Galuppi** as composer.

First performed, as indicated, December 26, 1749 (Pavan).   SCHATZ 3479

Alcina. An opera: as it is perform'd at the Theatre Royal in Covent-Garden. The third edition.

London, T. Wood, 1736. 48 p. 17ᶜᵐ.

Three acts. Argument and cast. Neither the author, Antonio Marchi, nor the composer, Georg Friedrich **Händel**, is mentioned. An English translation faces Italian, which is an altered version of Marchi's "Alcina delusa da Ruggiero."

First performed, as indicated, April 16, 1735.   SCHATZ 4496

Alcina delusa da Rugero. Drama per musica da rappresentarsi nel Teatro Tron di S. Cassan l'autunno dell' anno MDCCXXV. Di Antonio Marchi.

Venezia, Marino Rosetti, 1725. 58 p. 14½ᶜᵐ.

Three acts. Notice to the reader, cast, scenario, and name of Tommaso **Albinoni** as composer.   SCHATZ 113

Alcina delusa da Rugero—Continued.

— **Gl' evenimenti di Rugero.** Drama per musica da rappresentarsi nel Teatro Giustiniano di S. Moisé il carnevale dell' anno MDCCXXXII. Di Antonio Marchi . . .

Venezia, Steffano Valvasense, 1732. 46 p. 13½^{cm}.

Three acts. Cast, scenario, and notice to the reader. Merely a somewhat altered version of **Albinoni's** "Alcina delusa da Rugero." For instance, the opening four lines of the first scene "Care spiaggie, amato lido," were dropped.   Schatz 93

Alcina e Leone, ballet. *See* Rust's Alessandro nell' Indie.

Alcina e Ruggero. Dramma per musica da rappresentarsi nel Regio Teatro di Torino nel carnovale del 1775 alla presenza delle Maestà Loro.

Torino, Onorato Derossi, n. d.   viii, 68 p.   15½^{cm}.

Three acts. Notice to the reader, scenario, cast, and names of Vittorio Amedeo Cigna-Santi as author, Felice **Alessandri** as composer. The ballet music was composed by "Paolo Ghebart," of Vienna.   Schatz 141

Alcina ed Astolfo, ballet. *See* Zingarelli's Annibale in Torino.

Alcine, tragedie. Représentée par l'Academie royale de musique l'an 1705. Les paroles de M. Danchet & la musique de M. Campra. LXIII. Opera.

n. i., n. d. front., 333–392 p. 14^{cm}. (Recueil général des opera, Paris, 1706, t. viii, no. 7.)

Detached copy. Five acts, with prologue.   Schatz 154
          Second copy. ML 48.R4

— **Alcine,** tragedie, représentée par l'Academie royale de musique le quinzième jour de janvier 1705.

Amsterdam, Henri Schelte, 1707.   69 (incl. front.), [3] p.   14^{cm}.

Five acts with prologue. Cast. Neither **Campra** nor Danchet mentioned. On the [3] p. a "Catalogue de tous les opera" published by Schelte.   ML 50.2.A512C2

— **Alcine,** tragédie.   Représentée par l'Académie royale de musique, l'an 1705.

[335]–398 p.   17½^{cm}.   (Antoine Danchet, Théâtre, t. ii, Paris, 1751)

Prologue and five acts. The composer, André **Campra,** is not mentioned.
          PQ 1972.D2

Alcines oe.   Tr. of Gazzaniga's L'isola d'Alcina.

Alcione. Dramma per musica per celebrare il felicissimo giorno natalizio della serenissima Signora Donna Maria Francesca Benedetta principessa del Brasile li 25 luglio 1787.

[Lisbona], Nella stamperia reale, n. d.   28 p.   15^{cm}.

One act. By Gaetano Martinelli. Argument, cast and names of the author and the composer, João de Sousa **Carvalho.**   Schatz 1674

Alcione, tragedie, representée par l'Academie royale de musique le jeudy dix-huitième fevrier 1706.

Amsterdam, Henri Schelte, 1707.   57 (incl. front.), [3] p.   14^{cm}.

Five acts with prologue. Cast. Neither the author, La Motte, nor the composer, **Marais,** mentioned. On the [3] p. "Catalogue de tous les opera" published by Schelte.   ML 50.2.A513M2

Alcione—Continued.

—**Alcione,** tragédie représentée par l'Académie royale de musique l'an 1706. Les paroles de M. de la Mothe & la musique de M. Marais. LXVI. Opera.

n. i., n. d. pl., p. 65–114 (Recueil général des opéra, Paris, 1710, t. ix) 14^{cm}.

Detached copy. Five acts and prologue.   SCHATZ 5919
Second copy.   ML 48.R4

A **Aldeana em corte.** Tr. of Rust's La contadina in corte.

Aldiso. Drama per musica da rappresentarsi nel famosissimo Teatro Grimani a S. Gio. Grisostomo. Nel carnovale dell' anno 1726.

Venezia, Marino Rossetti, 1726. 59 p. 14½^{cm}.

Three acts. By conte Claudio Nicola Stampa, who is not mentioned. Argument, cast, scenario and name of Giovanni **Porta** as the composer.   SCHATZ 8383

Alessandro.

Metastasio, Poesie, Parigi, vedova Quillau, 1755, t. iv, 85 p. 16^{cm}.

Three acts. Argument. Same as his "Alessandro nell' Indie."
"Nella forma in cui sono stati ridotti dall' autore." (*See* note on p. 169 of v. VI.)
This revised version is easily identified from the first scene, which has no aria and has the lines in Poro's monologue "Della spoglia più grande / Il trionfo a costui . . . Ma la mia sposa." Also its III, 1 begins "Ma lasciami, Erissena" and has the aria "Se troppo crede al ciglio."

——*Same, t. vii, 117 p. 16^{cm}.*

["Come . . . nell' altre edizioni." (Note, VI, 169.) This original version has in I, 1 the aria "È prezzo leggiero" and the lines in Poro's monologue "Della spoglia più grande / Il trionfo a costui. Già visse assai;" also its III, 1 begins "Erissena / Che miro" and has the aria "Risveglia lo sdegno."   ML 49.A2M42

Alessandro.

[221]–258 p. 17^{cm}. (Rolli, Componimenti poetici, Nuova edizione, Verona, G. Tumermani, 1744.)

Three acts. Argument. The composer, **Händel,** is not mentioned.
First performed at London, Haymarket, May 5, 1726.   ML 49.A2R7

— Der **hochmuethige Alexander,** in einem sing-spiele auf dem Hamburgischen schau-Platze vorgestellet im jahr 1726.

Hamburg, Gedruckt mit Stromerschen schrifften, n. d. Unpaged. 18^{cm}.

Three acts. German version by C. G. Wendt of "Alessandro" by Rolli, neither of whom mentioned. Argument, scenario and name of Hendel (Georg Friedrich **Händel**) as the composer. Italian text of the arias added to the German.
         SCHATZ 4473

Alessandro. Dramma per musica in due atti, con balli analoghi. Da rappresentarsi nei Teatri di S. M. I. nel 1799.

S. Pietroburgo, Stamperia imperiale, 1799. 35 p. 19^{cm}.

Author not mentioned and unknown to Schatz. Argument (in Italian and French), cast and name of Friedrich Heinrich **Himmel** as the composer.   SCHATZ 4741

L'Alessandro amante. Drama per musica da rappresentarsi nel Teatro di San Moise l'anno MDCLXVII . . .

Venetia, Francesco Nicolini & Steffano Curti, 1667. 5 p.l., 69 p. 14^{cm}.

Three acts with prologue. Impresario's dedication, dated January 28, 1667, notice to the reader, and scenario.
According to the preface, in which Giovanni Antonio **Boretti** is mentioned as composer, the libretto was finished after the death of the author, Giacinto Andrea

L'Alessandro amante—Continued.

Cicognini, "da altro virtuoso soggetto." For these performances at Venice in 1667 the libretto was considerably altered by an (anonymous) "virtuoso ingegno" to conform to the tastes of the time. Cicognini's libretto was originally called "Gli amori di Alessandro e di Rossane" and as such was performed at Venice in 1651 with Fr. Luzzo's music. With music by Benedetto Ferrari the libretto was performed at Bologna in 1656 and in 1663 Lupardi published a new edition at Rome under the title "La Rosane, con gli Amori di Alessandro Magno." Both of these editions are preserved at Brussels and described by Wotquenne.   SCHATZ 1215

Alessandro e Campaspe, ballet. *See* Mayr's Un pazzo ne fa cento.

Alessandro e Poro. Dramma per musica da rappresentarsi nel Regio Teatro di Berlino per ordine di Sua Maestà.

   Berlino, A. Hande, 1744.   187, [3]   16½^{cm}.

Three acts. Metastasio (original title: "Alessandro nell' Indie") is mentioned as author and Carl Heinrich **Graun** as the composer. Argument and scenario. German title page "Alexander und Porus" and text face Italian.
   First performed as indicated, December 21, 1744.   SCHATZ 4087

Alessandro e Timoteo. Dramma per musica da rappresentarsi nel R. D. Teatro di corte nella primavera dell' anno MDCCLXXXII.

   Parma, Stamperia reale, n. d.   8 p. l., 37 p.   28^{cm}.

One act. Dedicatory poem signed by the author, conte Gastone della Torre di Rezzonico. Argument, cast, scenario and name of Giuseppe **Sarti** as the composer. ("La musica sarà.")
   First performed as indicated, April 6, 1782.   SCHATZ 9424

Alessandro fra' le Amazoni. Drama per musica da rappresentarsi nel Teatro di S. Angelo l'anno 1715 . . .

   Venezia, Marino Rossetti, 1715.   60 p.   15^{cm}.

Three acts. By Grazio Braccioli. Author's dedication, notice to the reader, cast, scenario and name of the composer, Fortunato **Chelleri.**   SCHATZ 1812

Alessandro il vincitor di se stesso. Tragicomedia musicale. Di Francesco Sbarra in questa terza impressione ridotta all' intera sua forma . . .

   Lucca, Francesco Marescandoli, 1654.   177, [1] p.   13½^{cm}.

Three acts, with two prologues, author's dedication dated Lucca, Feb. 1, 1654, notice to the reader, argument, and at end (p. 170–177) source of plot, *allegoria*, cast, and names of the two composers. ("La musica fù per la maggior parte del Sig. Antonio **Cesti** . . . et il resto del Sig. Marco **Bigongiari** . . .") The one additional page contains a sonnet by Dalli to Sbarra. The one prologue is that "recitato in Venetia," 1651, with Cavalli's music, the other that "rappresentato in Lucca." The author's notice to the reader is in substance similar to that in the Venice, 1651, ed. of the text (*see infra*), but special emphasis is laid on the fact that the original version "precipitato dalla mia penna, si portò à Venetia per le poste, ove per accomodarsi alla brevità, che in simili funtioni si desidera, fù ridotto in forma molto minore di quella, che portò dalla sua nascita, ricoperto in gran parte questo defetto dalla magnificenza delle scene, e machine, dalla vaghezza, e bizzarria delle comparse, e de balli, e sopra tutto dall' eccellenza della musica, e dall' esquisitezza de gl' attori; hoggi però che s'espuone sopra il nostro teatro non potendo farsi vedere con quegl' addobbi, de i quali fù arricchito in Venetia, comparisce se non vagho, almeno intero, e con tutte le sue parti . . ."
   The differences between the two editions are quite noticeable. For instance, I, 9 of the Venice ed., "Più celar non si può," is I, 11 in the Lucca ed.; I, 9 of the Lucca ed., "Alessandro, che pensi," is I, 10 in the Venice ed.; I, 14 in the Lucca ed., "Ohimè, dov'è," is I, 12 in the Venice ed.   SCHATZ 1786

Alessandro in Armenia. Dramma per musica da rappresentarsi nel nobilissimo Teatro di S. Benedetto l'autunno dell' anno 1768.

Venezia, Modesto Fenzo, 1768. 48 p. 17^{cm}.

Three acts. Dedicatory sonnet addressed by "Dolenio, P. A." to the author, argument, cast, and names of the composer Giovanni Battista **Borghi**, and the librettist, "Cleofonto Doriano P. A. Accademico Quirino, Infecondo ec. ec. ec." Wotquenne does not mention this Arcadian name in his "Essai d'un dictionnaire des noms académiques . . ." (Brussels Catalogue, Annexe I.), but Schatz identifies him with conte Antonio Papi.

First performed, as indicated, November 26, 1768.   SCHATZ 1226

Alessandro in Sidone.

Apostolo Zeno, Poesie drammatiche, Venezia, 1744, t. ix, p. [293]-416 p. 19^{cm}.

Five acts. Argument. Written in collaboration with Pietro Pariati. No composer is mentioned. In the "Catalogo" at end of t. x, date and place of first ed. are given as Vienna, 1721.   ML 49.A2Z3

— Alessandro in Sidone. Pubblicato per la prima volta in Vienna 1721.

Apostolo Zeno, Poesie drammatiche, Orleans, 1785-86, t. xi, p. 223-347. 21^{cm}.

Five acts. Argument. No composer is mentioned. Written in collaboration with Pietro Pariati.   ML 49.A2Z4

Alessandro in Sidone. Tragicommedia per musica, da rappresentarsi nella Cesarea corte . . . nel carnevale dell' anno MDCCXXI. La musica è del Sig. Francesco Cor.ti . . .

Vienna d'Austria, Gio. Van Ghelen, n. d. 4 p. l., 88 p. 14$\frac{1}{2}$^{cm}.

Five acts. By Apostolo Zeno and Pietro Pariati, who are not mentioned. Argument and scenario. Niccola Matteis is mentioned as the composer of the ballet music.

First performed at Vienna, Hoftheater, February, 1721.   SCHATZ 2192

— Alessandro in Sidone. Tragicomedia per musica da rappresentarsi sul famosissimo Teatro di Braunsviga nella fiera d'estate l'anno 1726.—Alexander in Sidon . . .

Wolffenbüttel, Christian Bartsch, n. d. Unpaged. 18^{cm}.

Three acts. Scenario and name of Francesco **Conti** as composer. The argument is in German. Text in Italian and German. The first act exactly like the first act in the Vienna, 1721, five-act ed. The first nine scenes of the second also identical, but then the differences begin, owing to the contraction of the text into three acts. For instance, the scene "Tu, Addolonimo, sei" (II, 11) has been dropped, also "Come pensi schernirle" (III, 1) and "Due soli di nostr' alma" (III, 2) has become II, 12.

                    SCHATZ 2193

Alessandro in Susa. Tragicomedia da rappresentarsi in musica nel famosissimo Teatro Grimano di S. Gio. Grisostomo l'anno 1708 . . .

Venezia, Marino Rosetti, 1708. 60 p. 14$\frac{1}{2}$^{cm}.

Five acts. By conte Girolamo Frigimelica Roberti, who is not mentioned. Printer's notice to the reader, dedication in form of argument, "fondamento istorico, e poetico," cast, scenario. Luigi **Manza**, the composer, is not mentioned. (Schatz records a Carlo Manza as composer, Eitner, perhaps more correctly, the above.)

                    SCHATZ 5916

Alessandro Magno in Sidone. Drama per musica. Da rappresentarsi nel famoso Teatro Grimano à SS. Gio. Paolo di Aurelio Aureli. Opera XIX . . .

Venetia, Francesco Nicolini, 1679. 70, [1] p. 14ᶜᵐ.

Three acts. Dedication, argument, scenario, and author's notice to the reader, in which he mentions the "giovinetto Signor Marc' Antonio **Ziani**," and says:
"Amico, sò che ti sembrera stravagante successo il veder la mia Musa, che dopo haver nel corso di due lustri esule pellegrina dal famoso Teatro Grimano, ora conosciuta, ora mascherata, ed occulta passeggiato sovra altri teatri, ritorni in quest' anno à calcar quella scena dove tra pomposi e dorati coturni campeggiò fortunata ne la rappresertatione di undici continuati miei drami . . ."
First performed, as indicated, carnival, 1679.   Schatz 11178

— **Alessandro Magno in Sidone.** Drama in musica, rappresentato in Venetia nel famosissimo Teatro Grimano di S. S. Giovanni e Paolo. Hora da rappresentarsi con alcune aggionte in Vicenza . . .

Vicenza, gl' H. di Giacomo Amadio, 1681. 68 p. 14ᶜᵐ.

Three acts. Dedication, argument, scenario. Neither Aureli, nor **Ziani** mentioned.   ML 50.2.A515Z3

— **La virtù sublimata dal grande,** ovvero Il Macedone continente. Drama per musica. Da rappresentarsi nel Teatro di Canal regio l'anno MDCLXXXIII.

Venetia, Francesco Nicolini, 1683. 60 p. 14½ᶜᵐ.

Three acts. Argument, scenario, and prefatory notice to the reader with apologies for this replica of "Alessandro Magno in Sidone" in a small theatre with an inferior cast. Neither the author, Aurelio Aureli, nor the composer, Marc' Antonio **Ziani**, is mentioned.
First performed under the new title, as indicated, carnival 1683. Schatz 11209

L'Alessandro nell' Indie.

[243]–322 p. 19ᶜᵐ. (Pietro Metastasio, Opere drammatiche, Venezia, Giuseppe Bettinelli, 1733–37, v. 2.)

Three acts. Argument. No composer mentioned. (*Comp.* next entry.)
ML 49.A2M40

—**Alessandro nell' Indie.** Rappresentato con musica del Vinci la prima volta in Roma nel Teatro detto delle Dame, il 26 decembre dell' anno 1729.

pl., [263]–356 p. 26ᶜᵐ. (Pietro Metastasio, Opere, t. 4, Parigi, vedova Herissant, 1780.)

Three acts. Argument. The revised version of his "Alessandro," which *see* for telling differences between the versions.   ML 49.A2M44

Alessandro nell' Indie. Drama per musica da rappresentarsi nel teatro di Torre Argentina nel carnevale dell' anno 1772 . . .

Roma, Archangelo Casaletti, n. d. 71 p. 15ᶜᵐ.

Three acts. Impresario's dedication with indication of Metastasio as author, argument, cast, scenario, and name of Pasquale **Anfossi** as composer.
First performed January 7, 1772, as indicated.   Schatz 282

Alessandro nell' Indie. Dramma per musica da rappresentarsi in Oranienbaum . . . La poesia è del celebre Signor abbate Pietro Metastasio . . . La musica è del Signor Francesco Araja . . .

St. Pietroburgo, nella Stamperia dell' Accademia imperiale delle scienze, 1759. 125 p. 18ᶜᵐ.

Three acts. Cast and scenario. French text faces Italian.
First performed at St. Petersburg, Court opera, Dec. 8 (19), 1743. Schatz 304

Alessandro nell' Indie. Dramma serio per musica da rappresentarsi in Bologna nel Teatro Zagnoni l'autunno dell' anno 1787 . . .

Bologna, Sassi, n. d. 51, [2] p. 17½^{cm}.

Imprimatur dated October 8, 1787. Impresario's dedication, argument, cast, scenario and name of Francesco **Bianchi** as composer. Metastasio is not mentioned.

ML 50.2.A517B25

—Alessandro nell' Indie. Dramma per musica da rappresentarsi nel nuovo e nobilissimo Teatro detto La Fenice l'autunno dell' anno 1792.

Venezia, Modesto Fenzo, 1792. 64 p. 16½^{cm}.

Three acts. Argument, cast, scenario, and name of Francesco **Bianchi** as composer, but not of the librettist, Pietro Metastasio. On p. 29–32 argument and cast of the "Ballo primo. Giulio Sabino . . . composto e diretto dal Signor Onorato Viganò." Neither of this nor of his second ballet "La follia e la saggiezza" is the composer of the music mentioned.

First performed at Venice, Teatro di S. Benedetto, January 28, 1785

SCHATZ 974

Alessandro nell' Indie, ballet. *See* Cimarosa's Circe.

[Alessandro nell' Indie] Alexander in Indien, ein musicalisches schauspiel, aufzufuehren auf dem grossen hochfuerstl. Braunschw. Theatro im Opern-hause in der Winter-Messe 1752.

Braunschweig, Keitel, n. d. Unpaged. 18^{cm}.

Three acts. By Metastasio. German text faces Italian. Argument, scenario, cast, and name of the composer "Ignazio **Fiorillo,** maestro di capella di corte." ("di nuova composizione")

Accordingly "È prezzo leggero" was added to I, 1, and "Se vuol mirarti esangue" to II, 8. The latter is not by Metastasio.

Second setting, first performed at Stuttgart, Hochfürstl. Theatre, in February, 1752. The first setting was first performed at Mantova, Nuovo Arciducale Teatro, carnival 1738 (Piovano). SCHATZ 3198

Alessandro nell' Indie. Dramma per musica da rappresentarsi nel Teatro di San Samuelle per la fiera dell' Ascensione dell' anno MDCCLV.

Venezia, Angiolo Geremia, n. d. 60 p. 15½^{cm}.

Three acts. By Metastasio. Argument, scenario, cast, and name of Baldassare **Galuppi** as composer. Between p. 6–7 one page of "Arie aggiunte e mutate."

SCHATZ 3430

— Alessandro nell' Indie. Dramma per musica da rappresentarsi nel nuovo Teatro di corte per comando di S. A. S. E. Massimiliano Gioseppe . . . nel giorno glorioso di suo nome li 12. ottobre 1755. La poesia è del Sig. abbate Pietro Metastasio . . . La musica è del Signor Baldassare Galuppi . . .

Monaco, Gio. Giac. Vötter, n. d. 131, [1] p. 19^{cm}.

Three acts. Argument, scenario, and cast. German title "Alexander in Indien" and text face Italian. At end, one page of Errata. SCHATZ 3431

Alessandro nell' Indie. Dramma per musica da rappresentarsi nel Real Teatro di S. Carlo nel dì 4 di novembre 1789 per festeggiarsi il glorioso nome di Sua Maestà la regina . . .

Napoli, Vincenzo Flauto, 1789. 70 p. 14½^{cm}.

Two acts. By Metastasio, who is not mentioned. Impresario's dedication dated, Naples, November 4, 1789, cast, argument, scenario, and name of Pietro **Guglielmi** as the composer. On p. 9–28 cast and description of Sebastiano Gallet's "Telemaco nell' isola di Calipso, ballo eroico pantomimo in cinque atti," music by Pietro Dutillieu. On p. 29–31 synopsis of the ballet "Di rado l'uom sa giudicar se stesso," also by Gallet. SCHATZ 4234

Alessandro nell' Indie, ballet.   *See* P. Guglielmi's Enea e Lavinia.

L'Alessandro nell' Indie.   Dramma per musica da rappresentarsi nel famosissimo Teatro Grimani di S. Gio. Grisostomo nel carnovale dell' anno 1736 . . .

Venezia, Marino Rossetti, 1736.   72 p.   15½cm.

Three acts. By Metastasio. Dedication by Domenico Lalli, argument, cast, scenario, and name of Johann Adolph **Hasse** as the composer. Mennicke lists this as a second version, numbering the "Cleofide" of 1731, whose text was based on "Alessandro nelle Indie" as the first version.   SCHATZ 4508

— Alessandro nell' Indie.   Dramma per musica, da rappresentarsi nel Nuovo Teatro di Prespurgo nell' estate del' anno 1741 . . .

Presburgo, Eredi Royeriani, n. d.   103 p.   18½cm.

Three acts. Dedication by Pietro Mingotti, argument, cast, scenario, and name of Franz Joseph Pirker as the translator of the German text, which faces the Italian. Neither the author, Metastasio, nor the composer, Johann Adolph **Hasse**, is mentioned. The text is somewhat different from that in the original Venice edition of 1736. For instance, I, 5 has now the aria "Scherza il nocchier tal' ora" instead of "O su gli estivi ardori," and the scene, I, 12, "Non condannarmi, amico," has become I, 9.   SCHATZ 4509

— Alessandro nell' Indie.   Dramma per musica da rappresentarsi nel famosissimo Teatro Grimani di Sⁿ. Giõ. Grisostomo nel carnevale 1743 . . .

n. i., n. d.   1 p. l., 67 p.   15cm.

Three acts. Argument, cast, scenario, and name of Joh. Ad. **Hasse** as the composer. The text is somewhat different from the Dresden ed of 1741 and the Venice ed. of 1736. For instance, their aria at end of I, 2, "Vedrai con tuo periglio," has been dropped, and their aria, "Vil trofeo d'un' alma imbelle," in I, 3, has become "Vadan li rei felloni." In this Venice, 1743 ed., the original aria, "O su gli estivi ardori," for I, 5, has been restituted, as also the scene "Non condannarmi, amico," as I, 12. Indeed, the Venice, 1743, ed., as might be expected, is more like the Venice, 1736, ed. than like the Dresden, 1741, ed.   SCHATZ 4593

L'Alessandro nell' Indie.   Dramma per musica da rappresentarsi nel Teatro ducale di Stutgart festeggiandosi il felicissimo giorno natalizio di Sua Altezza Serenissima Carlo, Duca regnante di Wirtemberg e Teck, etc., etc. La poesia è del Signor abbate Pietro Metastasio . . . La musica è nuovamente composta dal Signor Nicolò Jommelli . . .

Stutgart, Cristofero Frederico Cotta, 1760.   201 p.   19cm.

Three acts. Argument, scenario, cast. German title page "Alexander in Indien" and text face Italian. The ballets have no specific titles.
First performed at Stuttgart, as indicated, February 11, 1760.   SCHATZ 4841

— Prologo da recitarsi avanti l'opera **Alessandro nell' Indie** nel Teatro ducale di Stutgart nel solenne giorno natalizio di Sua Altezza Serenissima Carlo, duca regnante di Wirtemberg e Teck, etc etc.

Stutgart, Cristofero Frederico Cotta, 1760.   15 p.   18½cm.

Cast. German title, "Prologus," and text face Italian.   SCHATZ 11754

— Alessandro nell' Indie.   Dramma per musica da rappresentarsi nel Real Teatro dell' Ajuda nel felicissimo giorno natalizio del fedelissimo monarca D. Giuseppe I . . . nel di 6 giugno 1776.

[Lisbona], Stamperia reale, n. d.   79 p.   15cm.

Three acts. Argument, cast, scenario, and names of Metastasio as author, of Niccolò **Jommelli** as composer. The text is somewhat different from that of 1760, as it, for instance, jumps from the aria "Se mai turbo il tuo riposo" (I, 7) to the former I, 10 "Principessa adorata" as I, 9, interpolating as I, 8 the scene "Dei, che tormento è questo."   SCHATZ 4899

Alessandro nell' Indie. Dramma per musica da rappresentarsi nel Teatro Tron di San Cassiano. Il carnovale dell' anno 1753 . . .

Venezia, Modesto Fenzo, 1753. 60 p. 15^{cm}.

Three acts. By Metastasio, who is not mentioned. Dedication by "Li virtuosi," who had assumed the management of the theatre, argument, cast, scenario, and note that the music was "in gran parte" by Gaetano **Latilla**, the rest by "altri bravi autori."

SCHATZ 5455

L'Alessandro nell' Indie. Dramma per musica da rappresentarsi nel nobilissimo Teatro di S. Benedetto la fiera dell' Ascensione dell' anno 1778.

Venezia, Modesto Fenzo, 1778. 64 p. 17½^{cm}.

Three acts. By Metastasio, who is not mentioned. Argument, cast, scenario, and name of Luigi **Marescalchi** as the composer ("La musica è tutta nuova").

On p. 27–40 cast, argument, and description of Onorato Viganò's "Il Rinaldo, ballo tragico eroico pantomimo di lieto fine," in six parts. The composer of the music is not mentioned.

First performed as indicated, May 27, 1788. SCHATZ 5946

Alessandro nell' Indie. Dramma per musica del Signore abate Pietro Metastasio, Poeta Cesareo da rappresentarsi nel pubblico Teatro di Lucca nell' autunno dell' anno MDCCLXXXIII.

Lucca, Francesco Bonsignore, n. d. 68 p. 14½^{cm}.

Three acts. Argument, cast, scenario, and name of Michele **Mortellari** as the composer.

First performed at Siena, Teatro degl' Intronati, July 22, 1778; at Lucca, August 9, 1783. SCHATZ 6683

Alessandro nell' Indie, dramma per musica da rappresentarsi nel gran teatro nuovamente eretto alla real corte di Lisbona, nella primavera dell' anno MDCCLV. Per festeggiare il felicissimo giorno natalizio di Sua Maestà fedelissima D. Maria Anna Vittoria . . . La poesia del dramma è del . . . Pietro Metastasio . . . La licenza è del Sig^r Giuseppe Bonechy . . . La musica è del Sig^r David Perez . . .

Lisbona, Regia stamperia Sylviana, 1755. front., 4 p. l., 53, [2] p., 9 folded pl. 19^{cm}.

Three acts. Argument, cast, and scenario. The plates are by I. Berardi, Le Bouteux, J. B. Dourneau. The front. by S. Manelli.

First performed, as indicated, March 31, 1755; at Genova, Teatro di Sant' Agostino, December 26, 1745. SCHATZ 7882

Alessandro nell' Indie. Dramma per musica di Pietro Metastasio frà gli Arcadi Artino Corasio. Da rappresentarsi nel Teatro di S. Angelo nel carnovale dell' anno 1732.

Venetia, Carlo Buonarrigo, n. d. 70 p. 14½^{cm}.

Three acts. Argument, cast, scenario, and name of Giovanni Battista **Pescetti** as the composer. SCHATZ 7960

Alessandro nell' Indie. Dramma per musica da rappresentarsi nel Teatro di via della Pergola nel carnevale del MDCCLXXVII . . .

Firenze, Gio. Risaliti, n. d. 39 p. 15½^{cm}.

Three acts. By Metastasio, who is not mentioned. Argument, scenario, cast, and name of Niccolò **Piccinni** as the composer. Schatz calls this his second setting of the text.

First performed at Naples, Teatro di S. Carlo, January 12, 1774. SCHATZ 8137

Alessandro nell' Indie. Dramma per musica del Sig. abate Pietro Metastasio . . . Da rappresentarsi nel nobil Teatro di S. Samuel la fiera dell' Ascensione l'anno 1775 . . .

Venezia, Gio. Battista Casali, 1775. 36 p. 17ᶜᵐ.

Three acts. Dedication by Giacomo **Rust**, who is mentioned as the composer, cast, and scenario.
With the opera was performed Antonio Pitrot's ballet "Alcina e Leone," music by Piombanti, a description of which is said to have been published separately.
SCHATZ 9175

Alessandro nell' Indie. Dramma per musica da rappresentarsi nel Teatro Vendramino di San Salvatore nella fiera dell' Ascensione dell' anno 1763.

Venezia, Francesco Valvasense, 1763. 48 p. 15ᶜᵐ.

Three acts. By Metastasio, who is not mentoined. Cast, scenario, and name of Antonio **Sacchini** as the composer. ("La musica sarà tutta nuova.")
SCHATZ 9243

— Alessandro nell' Indie. Dramma per musica da rappresentarsi nel Regio Teatro di Torino nel carnovale del 1766 . . .

Torino, Stamperia reale, n. d. viii, 62 p., [2] l.

Three acts. By Metastasio, who is not mentioned. Argument, cast, scenario, and name of Antonio **Sacchini** as composer. Giuseppe Antonio Le Messier composed the ballet music. The [2] l. contain the aria "Se vedi il caro bene" substituted for "Tu, che il tenor già sai" (II, 8), and the imprimatur.   SCHATZ 11746

Alessandro nell' Indie. Dramma per musica del celebre Sig. abate Pietro Metastasio . . . Da rappresentarsi nel Nuovo Pubblico Teatro di Bologna la primavera dell' anno 1764 . . .
Bologna, Lassi, n. d. 68, [2] p. 16ᶜᵐ.

Three acts. By Metastasio, who is not mentioned. On the last page the additional aria "Se possono tanto" (I, 9). Impresario's dedication, argument, cast, scenario, and name of Gregorio **Sciroli** as the composer. ("La musica è tutta nuova.")
First performed May 31, 1764, as indicated.   SCHATZ 9781

Alessandro nell' Indie. Dramma per musica da rappresentarsi nel famoso Teatro Vendramin di S. Salvatore per la solita fiera dell' Ascensione dell' anno 1759 . . .

Venezia, Modesto Fenzo, 1759. 56 p. 15½ᶜᵐ.

Three acts. By Metastasio, who is not mentioned. Impresario's dedication, scenario, cast, and name of Giuseppe **Scolari** as composer.   SCHATZ 9786

Alessandro nell' Indie. Dramma serio per musica da rappresentarsi nel Regio Teatro dell' Accademia degli Avvalorati in Livorno l'autunno dell' anno 1791 . . .

[Livorno], Tommaso Masi e comp., n. d. 48 p. 18ᶜᵐ.

Two acts. By Metastasio, who is not mentioned. Impresario's dedication, cast, scenario, and name of Angelo **Tarchi** as the composer. On p. [26]–34 argument and description without name of the composer of the music of Francesco Clerico's "Amleto, ballo tragico pantomimo, in quattro atti." His second, a "ballo comico," was called "I due vedovi."
Schatz distinguishes this opera, first performed at London, Haymarket, spring of 1789, as first setting of the text, from the opera of the same title, first performed at Torino, Regio Teatro, carnival 1798, which he, without giving his reasons, calls the second setting.   SCHATZ 10228

Alessandro nell' Indie. Dramma per musica da rappresentarsi nel rinovato Teatro di Piazza di Vicenza il carnevale dell' anno MDCCL . . .

Vicenza, Pierantonio Berno, 1750. 52 p. 15cm.

Three acts. By Metastasio, who is not mentioned. Impresario's dedication, argument, cast. Note: "La musica sarà diretta dal Sig. Antonio **Tiraboschi**, maestro di cappella," whom Schatz calls the composer of this opera. Schatz 10355

Alessandro nell' Indie. Drama per musica di Pietro Metastasio fra gli Arcadi Artino Corasio. Da rappresentarsi nel Teatro detto delle Dame nel carnevale dell' anno 1730 . . .

Roma, Zempel e il de Mey, n. d. 83 p. 15cm.

Three acts. Impresario's dedication, argument, scenario, cast, and name of Leonardo **Vinci** as composer.

First performed, as indicated, December 26, 1729. Schatz 10742

— Alessandro nell' Indie. Drama per musica da rappresentarsi nel Teatro di S. A. S. E. di Baviera nel carnevale dell' anno 1735.

Monaco, Giovanni Giacomo Vötter, n. d. 82, [1] p. 15cm.

Three acts. Argument and cast. By Metastasio, who is not mentioned. The composer unknown to Schatz, but the name of [Leonardo] **Vinci** is written in pencil on the title page. Schatz 11297

Alessandro Severo.

Apostolo Zeno, Poesie drammatiche, Venezia, 1744, t. vi, p. [271]-355. 19cm.

Three acts. Argument. No composer is mentioned. In the "Catalogo" at end of t. x, date and place of first ed. are given as Venice, 1717. (*See* below.) ML 49.AZ3

— Alessandro Severo. Pubblicato per la prima volta in Venezia 1717.

Apostolo Zeno, Poesie drammatiche, Orleans, 1785-86, t. iv, p. 353-430. 21cm.

Three acts. Argument. No composer is mentioned. ML 49.A2Z4

Alessandro Severo. Dramma per musica da rappresentarsi nel famoso Teatro Grimani di S. Gio. Grisostomo nel carnovale del 1739 . . .

Venezia, Marino Rossetti, 1738. 58 p. 15cm.

Three acts. By Apostolo Zeno. Dedication by Dom. Lalli. Argument, scenario, cast, and name of librettist, but not of composer, Andrea **Bernasconi**.

First performed at Venice, as indicated, December 27, 1738. Schatz 867

— Salustia. Dramma per musica da rappresentarsi nel Teatro Vendramin di San Salvatore per l'occasione della fiera dell' Ascensione dell' anno MDCCLIII . . .

Venezia, Modesto Fenzo, n. d. 58 p. 14½cm.

Three acts. Impresario's dedication, cast, scenario, and name of Andrea **Bernasconi** as composer, but not of author of libretto, which is a condensation and otherwise altered version of Zeno's "Alessandro Severo." In this the three acts have 15, 15, 11 scenes, in "Salustia" 12, 12, 11. Schatz 866

Alessandro Severo. Drama per musica, da rappresentarsi nel famosissimo Teatro Grimani di S. Giovanni Grisostomo . . .

Venezia, Marino Rossetti, 1717. 60 p. 15cm.

Three acts. Dedication signed by the author, Apostolo Zeno, with his initials, argument, cast, scenario, and name of Antonio **Lotti** as composer.

First performed, as indicated, December 26, 1716. Schatz 5714

Alessandro Severo. Dramma per musica da rappresentarsi nel Teatro Grimani di S. Benedetto il carnovale dell' anno 1763.

Venezia, Paolo Colombani, 1763. 48 p. 13½^{cm}.

Three acts. Argument, cast, scenario, and name of Antonio **Sacchini** as the composer. Text by Apostolo Zeno, who is not mentioned.

First performed, as indicated, December 26, 1762.   SCHATZ 9241

Alessandro Severo. Drama per musica da rappresentarsi nel Teatro di S. Bartolomeo nel maggio del 1719 . . .

Napoli, Michele Luigi Muzio, 1719. 60 p. 16^{cm}.

Three acts. By Apostolo Zeno, who is not mentioned. Dedication dated Naples, May 14, 1719, argument, scenario, cast, and name of Domenico **Sarro** as composer.

      SCHATZ 9412

Alessandro trionfante nell' Indie, ballet. *See* Salieri's La scuola de' gelosi.

Alessandro vincitor di se stesso. Dramma musicale del Signor Francesco Sbarra, gentilhuomo Lucchese. Dedicato all' Altezza Sereniss. di Leopoldo Guglielmo da Gio. Battista Balbi, inventore degli apparati di scena, machine, e balli. Rappresentato in Venezia nel Theatro di S. Gio. e Paolo.

Venetia, Giacomo Batti, 1651. 11 p. l., 72 p. 15^{cm}.

Three acts, with prologue. Dedication dated Venice, January 20, 1651, a "Lettera dell' autore al Signor Michel' Angelo Torcigliani " dated Lucca, December 29, 1650, and argument.

In his "Lettera" Sbarra says:

"Il Padre Cesti, miracolo della musica, con altri virtuosi rappresentò nel passato autunno un gentilissimo dramma nella città nostra; io se bene all' hora relegato in letto da una lunga, e pericolosa indispositione, a dispetto del male, che voleva trà l'altre miserie, che seco adduce, privarmi ancora della vista di questa virtuosa attione, mi portai a vederla: il gusto, ch'io ne retrassi, fù riconosciuto da me per l'unico mio rimedio . . . Per sodisfare all' istanze di questi virtuosi, da' quali riconosceva la ricuperata salute, intrapresi, e ultimai un dramma, in quei pochi giorni, che d'otio mi concesse la mia convalescenza, tempo maggiore, e più opportuno non venendomi permesso dalla necessità, che tenevano di rappresentarlo prontamente in Venetia. I parti, che sono concepiti in stato simile di non intera sanità, sono sēpre imperfetti: ma questi è più d'ogni altro, non havendo havuto ben minimo tempo di rivederlo, necessitato dall' angustia del tempo a lasciarlo metter sotto le note nella stessa forma, che alla giornata l'andava abbozzādo. S'aggiunge, che per esser riuscito troppo lungo per la musica, è convenuto a i medesimi d'accorciarlo, si che e impossibile, che qualche storpiatura non apparisca, & in questa maniera mi avvisano, che sono necessitati à stamparlo . . ."

He further calls this "quest'opera, prima che si stampi, che in questa conformità scrivo." In his notice to the "spettatori del dramma" Sbarra remarks:

"Sò che l'ariette cantate da Alessandro, & Aristotile, si stimerāno cōtro il decoro di personaggi si grādi; ma sò ancora, ch'è improprio il recitarsi in musica, non imitandosi in questa maniera il discorso naturale, e togliendosi l'anima al cōponimēto drāmatico, che nō deve esser altro, che un' imitatione dell' attioni humane, e pur questo difetto non solo è tolerato dal secolo corrente; ma ricevuto con applauso; questa specie di poesia hoggi non hà altro fine che il dilettare, onde conviene accommodarsi all' uso de i tempi; se lo stile recitativo non venisse intermezzato con simili scherzi, porterebbe più fastidio, che diletto . . . se in questo spettacolo ritroverai con che appagare il tuo gusto, il tutto riconosci dall' esquisitissime inventioni del mirabile Sig. Gio. Battista Balbi, autore non meno de' balli, e delle machine, che d'ogni altro scenico apparato."

It will be noticed that the composer, in this case no less a master than Francesco **Cavalli,** is mentioned nowhere.

First performed carnival 1651, as indicated.

(For further data, *see* Cesti's Alessandro il vincitor di se stesso, Lucca, 1654.)

      SCHATZ 1715

Alessandro vincitor di se stesso—Continued.

— **Alessandro vincitor di se stesso.** Dramma musicale del signor Francesco Sbarra, gentiluomo lucchese . . .

Bologna, Giacomo Monti, 1655. front., 92 p. 13ᶜᵐ.

Prologue and three acts. Dedication by Pietro Antonio Cerva, notice to the reader, argument. The composer, Francesco **Cavalli,** is not mentioned.
First performed at Bologna, Teatro Guastavillani, 1655.   SCHATZ 11681

Alessio ed Eloisa o sia Il disertore, ballet. *See* Astaritta's Ipermestra.

Alexander in Indien.   Tr. of Fiorillo's Alessandro nell' Indie.

Alexander in Indien.   Tr. of Galuppi's Alessandro nell' Indie.

Alexander in Indien.   Tr. of Jommelli's Alessandro nell' Indie.

Alexander in Sidon.   Tr. of Fr. Conti's Alessandro in Sidone.

Alexander und Porus.   Tr. of Graun's Alessandro e Poro.

Alexandre aux Indes, opéra en trois actes, représenté, pour la première fois, sur le Théâtre de l'Académie-royale de musique, le mardi 26 août 1783.

Paris, P. de Lormel, 1783.   vi, 43 p.   24ᶜᵐ.

By Etienne Morel de Chefdeville, who is not mentioned. On p. ii Jean Nicolas Le Froid de **Méreaux** is mentioned as the composer. Cast.   SCHATZ 6310

Alexandre et Thalestris, ballet-heroïque en trois actes.

Venard de La Jonchère, Théâtre lyrique, Paris, 1772, t. i, p. [289]-343.   18½ᶜᵐ.

"Avant-propos" (p. 291–302). No composer mentioned, and none recorded by Cl. & L.   ML 49.A2L2

Alexis, ou L'erreur d'un bon père. Comédie, en un acte, et en prose, mélée d'ariettes. Paroles du citoyen Marsollier, musique du citoyen Daleyrac. Représenté sur le théâtre Feydeau, le 5 pluviose, an 6 de la République [January 24, 1798].

Paris, Barba, (1798). An vi.   40 p.   19½ᶜᵐ.

Cast.   ML 50.2.A52D2

Alexis et Justine, comédie-lyrique, en deux actes et en prose, mêlée d'ariettes; représentée pour la premiere fois, à Versailles, devant Leurs Majestés, le vendredi 14 janvier 1785; & à Paris, sur le Théâtre de la Comédie italienne, le lundi 17. Paroles de M. de Monvel, musique de M. De Zede.

Toulouse, Broulhiet, 1785.   40 p. 22ᶜᵐ.

Cast.   ML 50.2.A53D3

Alfonso di Castiglia, ballet. *See* Paër's Tegene e Laodicea.

Alfea reverente. Rappresentata nella seconda venuta della Serenissima Vittoria della Rovere gran duchessa di Toscana in essa città l'anno 1639.

[*Atend*] *In Pisa, appresso Francesco delle Dote, 1639. 20 p. 20*^*cm*^.

Historical-allegorical "funzione," "sovra pomposo carro, tirato da sei bianchi e generosi destieri" fully described on p. 3–12 preceding the text. On p. 20: "*Li noue gentil' huomini à cauallo furono* . . . [follow the names, as ninth that of] Il Sig. cav. Pietro Cascina. Del quale sono l'inventioni, e le compositioni.

Il carro fù disegno del Sig. Alfiere Giovanni Navarretti, la direzione del quale operò molto in questa funzione.

Le musiche furono del Sig. Antonio **Pisani** organista della Chiesa de Cavalieri di S. Stefano di Pisa.

Il musico che rappresentò *Alfea* fu il Sig. Luca Angeletti, musico di S. A. S.

Quello che fece la prima ninfa del coro, e doppo rappresentò la *Fama*, fù il Sig. Christofano Bastini, musico dell' eccell. Repub. di Lucca, condotto per questa funzionze dalli suddetti nove gentil' huomini, li quali fecero anche il rimanente di tutta la spesa.

Le ninfe dell' Arno erano musici delle due Cappelle della Chiesa Primatiale, e di S. Stefano, con l'assistenza del Sig. Lorenzo Brunelli maestro di capella della medesima Chiesa di S. Stefano, in assenza del medesimo Sig. Pisani." SCHATZ 8191

Alfonso, dramma per musica rappresentato per regio comando in Dresda in occasione delle auguste nozze di Carlo rè delle Due Sicilie, e Amalia, principessa reale di Polonia, duchessa di Sassonia, MDCCXXXVIII.

n. i., n. d. 4 p. l., 68, 22 p. 18½^*cm*^.

At end of opera the imprint of "la vedova Stössel."

Five acts. Dedication by the author Stefano Benedetto Pallavicini, argument, cast, and name of Johann Adolph **Hasse** as the composer.

The 22 additional pages contain text (by unknown author) and cast of **Hasse's** "Il *tutore.* Intermezzi . . . In Dresda, l'anno 1738," first performed at Naples, Teatro di S. Bartolomeo, 1730.

"Alfonso" was first performed as indicated, May 11, 1738. SCHATZ 4510

— **Alfonso,** dramma per musica rappresentato per regio comando in Dresda . . . MDCCXXXVIII.

Dresden, verwittibte Hof-buchdr. Stoessel, n. d. 135 p. 16½^*cm*^.

Five acts. Argument, cast, scenario, names of Pallavicini as author, of **Hasse** as the composer. The same as Schatz 4510, except that German title "Alfonso" and text face Italian and that the intermezzi do not appear in this edition, issued in honor of the same nuptial festivities. SCHATZ 4511

Alfonso Primo. Drama per musica. Da recitarsi nel Teatro Vendramino di S. Salvatore. L'anno 1694. Di Matteo Noris . . .

Venetia, Nicolini, 1694. 84 p. 14^*cm*^.

Three acts. Author's dedication, brief argument, and scenario. The composer, Carlo Francesco **Pollaroli,** is not mentioned. SCHATZ 8268

Alfred: a masque. Represented before Their Royal Highnesses the prince and princess of Wales, at Cliffden, on the first of August, 1740.

London, Printed for A. Millar, 1740. 44 p. 19½^*cm*^.

Two acts. Cast. Neither authors nor composer mentioned. (*See* next entry.) On p. 42–43 "An ode. *When Britain, first, at heaven's command.*" AC 901.M5v.596

— **Alfred,** a masque. As it is now revived at the Theatre-Royal, in Drury Lane, by His Majesty's servants.

London, T. Cadell and T. Becket [*etc.*], *1773. 4 p. l., 72,* [*2*] *p. 19½*^*cm*^.

Three acts and "Prologue, by a friend. Spoken by Mr. Garrick, when it was first acted." Cast, argument, and this prefatory note:

"Alfred, a masque, was written by Mr. [James] Thompson, in conjunction with Mr. [David] Mallet, at the request of his Royal Highness Frederick Prince of Wales,

Alfred—Continued.

before their Royal Highnesses, on the first of August, 1740. Ten years after it was adapted for the stage by Mr. Mallet and was received with great applause. Mr. Mallet, in his advertisement (after giving an account of his joining with Mr. Thompson in the performance) goes on—

" 'But to fit it for the stage, I found it would be necessary to new plan the whole, as well as write the particular scenes over again; to enlarge the design, and make Alfred what he should have been at first, the principal figure in his own masque. This I have done; but, according to the present arrangement of the fable, I was obliged to reject a great deal of what I had written in the other, neither could I retain of my friend's part, more than three or four single speeches, and a part of one song; I mention this expressly, that whatever faults are found in the present performance, they may be charged, as they ought to be, entirely to my account.

" '*D. Mallet.*"

The note then goes on to say:

"It is now revived with some few alterations, and with some new music; the favourite airs of Dr. **Arne,** as they stood in the masque altered by Mallet, are reserved; there are some few alterations, which are now published."

David Garrick is supposed to have been responsible for this second revision. The last [2] p. contain "When Britain first, at heav'n's command," with first refrain line "Rule, Britannia, rule the waves" and headed by note: "The following song was altered by the author, and is now printed as it is sung."

First performed at Cliefden, August 1, 1740; at Dublin, Theatre Royal in Smock Alley, March 10, 1744; at London, Drury Lane, March 20, 1745, in an altered version and further altered at London, Drury Lane, February 23, 1751. The above version was first performed, as indicated, October 9, 1773.   LONGE 36

Alfredo il grande, rè degli Anglo-Sassoni, ballet by Trento. *See* Bianchi's Seleuco.

Alfsol. Plan eines singspieles von fünf acten, in einem briefe an den herausgeber.

16^cm. p. 205-229. (Cramer's Musik, Copenhagen, 1789.)
Signed by Sander.   ML 4.M3

Aline, dronning i Golconda, en opera i tre acter. Oversat af det franske til hr. capellmester Schulzes musik ved Thomas Thaarup . . . Andet oplag.

Kiøbenhavn, Johan Frederick Schultz, 1789. 46 p. 16^cm.

Prefatory note by the translator, "Udtog af den franske fortaelling," and cast. Johann Abraham Peter Schulz' "Aline, reine de Golconde," text by Sedaine, was first performed before Prince Henry of Prussia at Rheinsberg in 1787, and in this Danish version at the Royal Theatre, Copenhagen, January 30, 1789.   SCHATZ 9717

— Aline, königinn von Golconda. Eine oper in drey acten.

16^cm. p. [298]-346. (Cramer's Musik, Copenhagen, 1789.)

Carl Friedrich Cramer's own translation, with "vorbericht" of Sedaine's text, as composed by **Schulz.**   ML 4.M3

Aline, reine de Golconde.

Three acts, text by Sedaine, music by **Monsigny.**
First performed at Paris, Académie royale de musique, April 15, 1766.
Not in L. of C.
This title appears on the original score as published by Hérissant and appears to be the O. T. of the following:

— La reine de Golconde, opera en trois actes, représenté, pour la première fois, par l'Académie-royale de musique, en 1766. Et remis au Théâtre le mardi 26 mai 1772.

Paris, de Lormel, 1772. 59 p. 25^cm.

Sedaine is mentioned as author, but **Monsigny** not as composer. Argument and cast.   SCHATZ 6587

Aline, reine de Golconde. O. T. of Schulz's Aline, dronning i Golconda and Aline, königinn von Golconda.

Alisbelle, ou Les crimes de la féodalité, opera en trois actes, en vers, par le citoyen Desforges, musique du citoyen Louis Jadin.

*Paris, Prault l'aîné, ventose l'an II. [1794]. 48 p. 20½*cm.

First performed at Paris, Théâtre National, rue de la Loi, February 27, 1794.
SCHATZ 4949

Le allegrezze per le vittorie di Scipione, ballet. *See* Galuppi's Sofonisba.

L'allegria della campagna. Commedia per musica da rappresentarsi nel Teatro Nuovo sopra Toledo per prim' opera di questo corrente anno 1791.

*Napoli, Vincenzo Flauto, n. d. 47 p. 15½*cm.

Two acts. Cast and name of **Marcello di Capua** as composer. Librettist not mentioned, and unknown to Schatz.   SCHATZ 839

Alles aus liebe. Tr. of Naumann's Tutto per amore.

L'alliance de Romulus et de Tatius.—Der fried zwischen Romulo und Tatzio, ballet. *See* Sacchini's Scipione in Cartagena.

L'allure. Piece en un acte. Representée à la Foire Saint Laurent. 1732.

*Le Théâtre de la foire, Paris, 1737, t. ix, 2, pl., [169]-215 p. 17*cm.

By Carolet. The airs, probably selected or composed and arranged by Jean Claude **Gillier**, are printed at the end of the volume in the "Table des airs."
First performed September 27, 1732.   ML 48.L2

L'Almadero. Drama per musica, da rappresentarsi nel Teatro di Castello; composto . . . dal marchese Annibale Lanzoni . . .

*Mantova, gli Osanna, 1667. 86 p. 15*cm.

Three acts. Author's dedication, dated Mantova, April 30, 1667, argument. The composer is not mentioned, and is unknown to Schatz.   SCHATZ 11298

Almansore o sia Il pregindizio che nasce dal mancare di parola. O. T. of Pollaroli's Almansore in Alimena.

L'Almansore in Alimena. Drama per musica. Da recitarsi nel Teatro di Sant' Angelo l'anno 1703 . . .

*Venetia, Girolamo Albrizzi, n. d. 60 p. 15*cm.

Three acts. By Giov. Matteo Giannini, who is not mentioned. Impresario's dedication, argument, scenario, and notice to the reader, with the name of Carlo [Francesco] **Pollaroli** as the composer. If the impresario, Giovanni Orsato, says that "questo drama . . . nel Teatro di Reggio di Modona hà saputo riportarne i primi applausi," he refers to the performances there of the opera in 1696, under the title of "Almansore o sia Il pregiudizio che nasce dal mancar di parola."
First performed at Bologna, Teatro Pubblico della Sala, carnival, 1690.
SCHATZ 8269

Almena: an English opera. As it is performed at the Theatre-Royal in Drury-Lane. Written by Mr. Rolt . . . The music composed by Mr. Arne and Mr. Battishill.

*London, T. Becket and P. A. de Hondt, 1764. 4 p. l., 32 p. 19½*cm.

Three acts. Cast and argument. The last p. l. a publishers' book-list. The Arne mentioned is Michael, not Thomas Augustine. Thompson's vocal score mentions only **Battishill** as composer.
First performed November 2, 1764, as indicated.   LONGE 37

L'Almeria. Nuovo dramma per musica da rappresentarsi in Livorno nel Teatro da S. Sebastiano la primavera dell' anno 1761.

Livorno, Gio. Paolo Fantechi, 1761. port., xvi, 88 p. 17^{cm}.

Three acts. By Marco Coltellini, whose port. adorns the book. Coltellini's dedicatory poem to Metastasio, cast, scenario, name of Giovanni Francesco de **Majo** as composer, and notice to the reader, containing argument, statement that certain indicated lines, for brevity's sake, were not composed, and this remark:

"Il pubblico, che è il giudice più competente delle opere di teatro, quando mi metta in conto anche le angustie, in cui è ridotta la tragedia dalle leggi della musica, non potrà a meno di accordarmi un cortese compatimento per un primo parto . . ."

ML 50.2.A54M3

L'Almerico in Cipro. Drama per musica di Girolamo Castelli. Da recitarsi nel Teatro di S. Moisè l'anno 1675 . . .

Venetia, Francesco Nicolini, 1675. 66, [1] p. 14^{cm}.

Three acts. Author's dedication dated Venice, November 30, 1674, notice to the reader with name of Antonio dal (del) **Gaudio** as the composer, argument and scenario.

SCHATZ 3635

L'Almerinda. Drama per musica da rappresentarsi nel Teatro di San Casciano l'anno 1691 . . .

Venetia, Girolamo Albrizzi, 1691. 68 p. 13½^{cm}.

Three acts. Impresario's dedication dated Venezia, January 20, 1690, author's notice, argument, scenario, and name of the composer, Giuseppe **Boniventi**. The author, Giulio Pancieri, who is not mentioned by name, informs the reader that this is the totally changed version of a previous libretto which he does not mention by title.

SCHATZ 1187

L'Almira. Drama per musica da rappresentarsi nel famosissimo Teatro Grimani di S. Giovanni e Paolo l'anno 1691 . . .

Venetia, Girolamo Albrizzi, 1691. front., 68 p. 14^{cm}.

Three acts. Impresario's dedication, dated Venice, November 22, 1691, author's notice, argument, scenario, and name of the composer, Giuseppe **Boniventi**, but not of the librettist, Giulio Pancieri.

SCHATZ 1188

Almira, koenigin in Castilien. A. T. of Keiser's Der durchlauchtige secretarius.

Almira, koenigin von Castilien. A. T. of Händel's Der in krohnen erlangte glueckswechsel.

Alonso e Cora. Dramma per musica da rappresentarsi nel nobilissimo Teatro di S. Benedetto il carnovale dell' anno 1786.

Venezia, Modesto Fenzo, 1786. 55 p. 18½^{cm}.

Two acts. Notice to the reader, argument, cast, scenario, and name of composer, Francesco **Bianchi**, but not of the librettist, Giuseppe Foppa. On p. [25]–34 argument and full description of "Gli amori di Clodio e Pompea, ballo eroico pantomimo," in five acts by Antonio Muzarelli, "esposto per la prima volta," music ("tutta nuova") by Vittorio Trento.

First performed February 7, 1786, as indicated.

SCHATZ 994

Alonso e Cora, ballet. *See* Bianchi's Piramo e Tisbe.

Alonzo e Cora. A. T. of the ballet La vergine del Sole.

Alonzo e Cora, ballet. *See* Bianchi's Aspard.

Die als magd gewordene frau. Tr. of Pergolesi's La serva padrona.

Alsinda. Dramma per musica da rappresentarsi nel Teatro alla Scala il carnevale dell' anno 1785 . . .

Milano, Gio. Batista Bianchi, n. d. 72 p. 16^{cm}.

Three acts. By Ferdinando Moretti, who is not mentioned. Dedication, argument, cast, scenario, and name of Nicola Antonio **Zingarelli** as the composer. With the opera were performed, composers of the music not mentioned, Sebastiano Gallet's ballets "Il signore benefico," "Il maniscalco francese" and "Mascherata." Descriptions of these are remarked to have been published separately.

First performed, as indicated, February 22, 1785. SCHATZ 11264

Der alte freyer, eine komische oper in einem aufzuge. Verfertigt und in musik getzt von Johann André.

Frankfurt am Mayn, Johann Christian Gebhard, 1775. 72 p. 15½^{cm}.

André characterizes in a prefatory note as "dumme Beschuldigungen" the report: "ich hätte meine musick zum Töpfer aus französischen operetten genommen."

First performed at Berlin, Döbbelinsches Theater, October 2, 1775. SCHATZ 178

Der alte ueberall und nirgends. Erster theil. Ein schauspiel mit gesang in fünf aufzügen, nach der geistergeschichte des herrn Spiess bearbeitet von Karl Friedrich Hensler. Die musik ist von herrn Wenzel Müller . . .

Wien, Joh. Bapt. Wallishausser, 1796. 96 p. 16^{cm}.

"Aufgefuehrt zum erstenmale auf der k. k. priv. Marinellischen Schaubühne in Wien," June 10, 1795. SCHATZ 6906

— **Der alte ueberall und nirgends.** Zweyter theil . . .

Wien, Joh. Bapt. Wallishauser, 1796. 102 p. 16^{cm}.

"Aufgefuehrt zum erstenmale auf der k. k. priv. Marinellischen schaubühne in Wien," December 16, 1795 (Schatz), December 10 (Krone). SCHATZ 6907

Arien und gesänge aus der komischen oper: **Alter schützt für thorheit nicht.** In einem aufzuge.

Hamburg, J. M. Michaelsen, 1781. 16 p. 17^{cm}.

By Friedrich Ludwig Wilhelm Meyer. Neither he nor the composer, Johann **André,** mentioned.

First performed at Hamburg, Theater beim Gänsemarkt, June 14, 1781; at Mannheim, Churf. deutsche Schaubühne, June 20, 1779. SCHATZ 179

L'Alvilda. Dramma per musica. Da rappresentarsi nel nobilissimo Teatro Grimani di S. Samuele in tempo della fiera dell' Ascensione l'anno 1737.

Venezia, Marino Rossetti, 1737. 48 p. 16^{cm}.

Three acts. "L'amor generoso" by Apostolo Zeno, retouched by Dom. Lalli, neither mentioned. Lalli's dedication, argument, cast, and name of **Galuppi** as composer.

First performed, as indicated, May 29, 1737. SCHATZ 3480

L'Alvilda, regina de Goti. A. T. of Pallavicino's L'Amazone corsara.

Alzira. Dramma per musica da rappresentarsi nel Teatro da S. Agostino il carnovale dell' anno 1797 . . .

Genova, Stamperia Gesiniana, n. d. 55, [1] p. 14½^{cm}.

Two acts. The author is not mentioned, and is unknown to Schatz. Cast, scenario, and names of Giuseppe **Nicolini** as composer of the opera ("affatto nuova"), and of Santi Trento, of the ballet music. SCHATZ 7153

Ama chi t'ama. Dramma per musica fatto recitare da' SS. Consiglieri nel Teatro di Siena, l'anno 1682.

Siena, Stamparia del pubblico, n. d. 45 p. 13½^{cm}.

Prologue and three acts. Dedication of this "operetta," dated Siena, February 6, 1682. Unknown to Schatz. ML 50.2.A57

Ama più chi men si crede. Melodrama pastorale da rappresentarsi nel famosissimo Teatro Grimani di S. Gio. Grisostomo nell' autunno MDCCIX . . .

Venezia, Marino Rossetti, 1709. 71, [1] p. 14½^{cm}.

The add. p. contains a list of "Opere musicali sin' ora stampate in Venezia da Antonio Bortoli."
Three acts. Dedication signed by the author, Francesco Silvani, and dated Venice, November 20, 1709, argument, notice to the reader, cast, scenario, and name of Antonio **Lotti** as the composer. SCHATZ 5715

Amadi. Tragedia per musica di Filippo Quinault. Traduzione dell' abate Gaetano Sertor.

Venezia, Nuova Stamperia, 1793. xi, 72 p. 12½^{cm}.

Five acts. Argument, "Giudizi ed aneddoti sopra l'Amadi" (p. vii–xi), without even hinting at a composer. SCHATZ 11666

Amadigi di Gaula.

Three-act opera by Georg Friedrich **Händel**. Text supposedly by John James Heidegger.
First performed at London, Haymarket, May 25, 1715.
Not in L. of C.

— Oriana. [vignette.] Wurde in einem singe-spiel auf dem Hamburgischen Schau-Platz vorgestellet im monath september 1717.

Hamburg, gedruckt mit sel. Friedrich Conrad Greflingers schrifften, n. d. Unpaged. 18^{cm}.

Three acts. German version by Joachim Beckau of Heidegger's "Amadigi di Gaula." Neither they nor the composer, Georg Friedrich **Händel**, are mentioned. The Italian text of the arias is added to the German. SCHATZ 4474

Amadis, tragedie en musique, representée par l'Academie royale de musique. Suivant la copie imprimée à Paris.

[Amsterdam, Antoine Schelte], 1687. 60 p. (incl. front.) 14^{cm}.

Prologue and five acts. Neither Quinault nor **Lully** mentioned.
ML 50.2.A59L9

— Amadis, tragedie representée par l'Academie royale de musique l'an 1684. Les paroles de M. Quinault, e la musique de M. de Lully. XVI. opera.

n. i., n. d. 14^{cm}. front., 431-491 p. (Recueil général des opéra, t. ii, Paris, 1703.)

Detached copy. Five acts and prologue.
First performed, as indicated, January 18, 1684. SCHATZ 5759
Second copy. ML 48.R4

— Amadis, tragedie en musique. Representée par l'Academie royale de musique, le 15. janvier 1684.

Philippe Quinault, Théâtre, Paris, 1739, t. v, pl., p. [249]-311. 17^{cm}.

Prologue and five acts. **Lully** is not mentioned. PQ 1881.A1 1739

Amadis de Grece, tragedie representée par l'Academie royale de musique.

Amsterdam, les héritiers d'Antoine Schelte, 1699. 60 p. (incl. front.) 15ᶜᵐ.

Prologue and five acts, with Houdar[!] De La Motte's dedicatory poem to the King. **Destouches** is not mentioned.   ML 50.2.A595D2

— **Amadis de Grece.** Tragedie representée par l'Academie royale de musique l'an 1699. Les paroles de M. de la Mothe, e la musique de M. Destouches. XLVII. opera.

n. i., n. d. front., p. 355-412. (Recueil général des opéra, t. vi, Paris, 1703.) 14ᶜᵐ.

Detached copy. Prologue and five acts, with laudatory poem to the King. First performed, as indicated, March 26, 1699.   SCHATZ 2543
Second copy. ML 48.R4

— **Amadis de Grece.** Tragedie representée par l'Academie royale de musique de Paris, les vingt-six mars 1699, trois novembre 1711 & deux mars 1724. Et par L'Academie royale de musique de Lyon en 1742.

Lyon, Aimé Delaroche, 1742. 60 p. 23½ᶜᵐ.

Cast.   SCHATZ 2543A

— **Amadis le cadet.** Parodie d'Amadis de Grece. Representée pour la premiere fois par les Comédiens italiens ordinaires du roi, le 24. mars 1724.

Les parodies du Nouveau théâtre italien, Nouv. éd., Paris, 1738, t. ii, [279]-328 p. 16½ᶜᵐ.

One act. By Fuzelier (*see* t. I). The airs and vaudeville used are printed at the end of the volume in the "Table des Airs" (60 p.).   ML 48.P3

Amage, regina de' Sarmati. Dramma per musica da rappresentarsi nel Teatro di S. Angelo. L'anno 1694. Di Giulio Cesare Corradi . . .

Venetia, Nicolini, 1694. 60 p. 14ᶜᵐ.

Three acts. Author's dedication, argument, and scenario. The composer, Carlo Francesco **Pollaroli,** is not mentioned.
This libretto would seem to contradict Allacci, Wotquenne, Schatz, etc., who give the date of first performance as fall of 1693, at the same theatre.   SCHATZ 8270

Amalasunta. Drama per musica da rappresentarsi nel Teatro di S. Angelo nel Carnevale dell' anno 1719 . . .

Venezia, Marino Rossetti, 1719. 60 p. 15ᶜᵐ.

Three acts. By G[iacomo] G[abrieli]. Author's dedication dated Venice, December 24, 1718, argument, cast, scenario, and name of the composer, Fortunato **Chelleri.**
SCHATZ 1811

L'amalato per amore. A. T. of Astaritta's Il medico parigino.

Les amans brouillés, comédie en un acte, et en vers, melée d'ariettes. Par M. D. L. * * *. Mise en musique par M. D. . . .

Paris, veuve Duchesne, 1776. 30, [1] p. 19ᶜᵐ.

Author, composer and date of first performance unknown to me. ML 50.2.A62

Les amans inquiets. Parody of Colasse's Thetis et Pelée.

Les amans réunis—Die wieder vereinigten freier, ballet. *See* Sacchini's Scipione in Cartagena.

Les amans trompés, piece en un acte mêlée d'ariettes, par Mrs. Anseaume & de Marcouville. Représentée pour la premiere fois á l'Opera-comique, sur le Théâtre du Fauxbourg St. Laurent le lundi 26. juillet 1756.

Paris, Duchesne, 1756. 86 p. 19½^{cm}.

Cast. On p. 64–86 the same airs as in next entry. The arranger and composer of the music is not recorded by Schatz, whereas Towers attributes the music to **Laruette.**

ML 50.2.A63

— **Les amants trompés,** pièce en un acte, mélée d'ariettes, représentée pour la premiere fois à l'Opéra-comique, sur le Théâtre du Fauxbourg Saint Laurent, le lundi 26 juillet 1756. Par Mr. Anseaume.

Paris, veuve Duchesne, 1756. 84 p. 19^{cm}.

On p. 62–84 the "Airs des Amants trompés": "Revenez cher amant," "Pour l'objet qui règne," "Lorsque deux coeurs," "Dans l'excès de sa tendresse," "Quelle cruauté! Si l'inconstant," "L'amant délicat," "Ma vive tendresse," "Vous ne devez rien ménager," "C'est pour jamais," "Loin d'imiter son inconstance," "Ne me parle plus d'Emilie," "N'est-il, n'est-il donc."

Schatz 11478

L'amant déguisé ou Le jardinier supposé, comédie en un acte, mêlée d'ariettes; représentée pour la premiere fois par les Comediens italiens ordinaires du roi, le samedi 2 septembre 1769. La musique est de M. Philidor.

Paris, la veuve Duchesne, 1769. iv, 48 p. 19^{cm}. (Theatre de M. Favart, Paris, Duchesne, 1763–77, t. x.)

Cast. On p. 46–47 the air of the final vaudeville "Pour les amans & les belles." The authors, Favart and Voisenon, are not mentioned. Text preceded by this Avertissement:

"Cette bagatelle fut représentée au Théâtre italien au mois de Juin 1756, sous le titre de la *Plaisanterie de campagne:* elle fut reçue avec plaisir; son succès fut interrompu par la maladie & la mort de Mademoiselle Silvia. On a cru pouvoir remettre cette piece au théâtre, en y ajoûtant des ariettes pour se conformer au goût dominant. M. Philidor a bien voulu se prêter à cette tentative, & nous esperons que le public aura assez de bonté pour nous savoir gré des efforts que nous avous faits pour contribuer à son amusement."

ML 49.A2F1

— **L'amant déguisé,** ou Le jardinier supposé, comédie en un acte, mêlée d'ariettes, représentée pour la premiere fois par les Comédiens italiens ordinaires du roi, le 2 septembre 1769. La musique est de M. Philidore.[!]

Paris, La veuve Duchesne, 1772. 35 p. 18^{cm}.

By Charles Simon Favart and Claude Henri Fusée de Voisinon, who are not mentioned. Cast and air (on p. 34–35) of the *vaudeville* "Pour les amants & les belles."

Schatz 8005

Second copy. Yudin PQ

— **L'amant déguisé,** ou Le jardinier supposé, comedie en un acte, mêlée d'ariettes. Représentée pour la premiere fois par les Comédiens italiens ordinaires du roi, le 2 septembre 1769. La musique est de M. Philidor.

Paris, la veuve Duchesne, 1785. 36 p. 19^{cm}.

Cast. On p. 11–14 the ariette "Que la campagne est un séjour" and on p. 36–37 the vaudeville "Pour les amans & les belles." The authors, Favart and Voisenon, are not mentioned.

Schatz 11735

— Der **verkleidete liebhaber** oder Der verstellte gaertner, ein sing-spiel in einem aufzuge aus dem franzoesischen uebersetzt mit musik.

Frankfurt am Mayn, mit Andreaeischen schriften, 1774. 55 p., 16 p. (folded music) 17^{cm}.

Translated by Johann Heinrich Faber. Neither he nor the composer, **Philidor,** is mentioned. The music (voice and bass) consists of: "Ein gärtner ist" (I, 2) ["Un jardinier est un grand homme"], "Nur in der stadt" (I, 3) ["J'aime la ville"], "Lustig seyn die Schwobemaidle" (I, 5) ["Toute fille en Provence"]. Cast of Theob. Marchand's company.   SCHATZ 8006

L'amant jalouz. A. T. Grétry's Les fausses apparences.

L'amant statue, comédie en un acte et en prose, mêlée d'ariettes. Représentée, pour la premiere fois, par les Comédiens italiens ordinaires du roi, le jeudi 4 août 1785.

Paris, Brunet, 1786. 52 p. 19½^{cm}.

Neither the author, Desfontaines, nor the composer, **Dalayrac,** is mentioned.
                                        ML 50.2.A64 D2

— De **minnaer standbeeld:** zangspel. Gevolgd naar het fransch, door W. van Ollefen [vignette].

Amsterdam, J. Helders en A. Mars, 1794. 40 p. 19½^{cm}.

Vignettes. Translator's "Opdragt aan den heere B. Ruloffs," dated Amsterdam, March 15, 1794, and privilege notice, dated Amsterdam, March 20, 1794.
                                        SCHATZ 2388

L'amante cabala. Intermezzo.

(Carlo Goldoni, Opere drammatiche giocose, t. iv, Torino, 1757.) [110]–152 p. 16½^{cm}.

Three parts. Original composer unknown to Schatz, who dates first performance Venice, Teatro di S. Samuele, fall 1736.   ML 49.A2G6

— **L'amante cabala.** Intermezzo di tre parti per musica.

Carlo Goldoni, Opere teatrali, Venezia, Zatta e figli, 1788–95, t. 35, [95]–140 p. 18½^{cm}.   PQ

L'amante che spende. O. T. of Tassi's libretto Il cavalier magnifico.

L'amante che spende. Dramma giocoso per musica da rappresentarsi nel Teatro Giustiniani di S. Moisè l'autunno dell' anno 1770.

Venezia, Antonio Graziosi, 1770. 54 p. 18½^{cm}.

Three acts. Dedication, cast, scenario, and names of Niccolò Tassi as author, of Pietro **Guglielmi** as composer.   SCHATZ 4309

L'amante combattuto dalle donne di punto. Commedia per musica di Giuseppe Palomba da rappresentarsi nel Nuovo Teatro de' Fiorentini per prima opera di quest' anno 1781.

Napoli, n. publ., 1781. 71 p. 15^{cm}.

Three acts. Cast and name of the composer, Domenico Nicola **Cimarosa.**
                                        SCHATZ 1994

L'amante confuso. Commedia per musica di Saverio Zini. Da rappresentarsi nel Teatro de' Fiorentini nell' autunno de corrente anno 1772.

Napoli, Raffaele Lanciano, 1772. 3 p. l., 68 p. 15^{cm}.

Three acts. Argument, scenario, cast, and name of Pasquale **Anfossi** as composer.   SCHATZ 258

L'amante contrastata. Dramma giocoso del Signor D. Giacomo Lendenesi da rappresentarsi nel Teatro Giustiniani di S. Moisè l'autunno dell' anno 1768.

Venezia, Modesto Fenzo, 1768. 60 p. 15½ᶜᵐ.

Three acts. Cast, scenario, and name of the composer, Alessandro **Felici.**

SCHATZ 3053

L'amante del cielo. Dramma sacro per musica da rappresentarsi nel Collegio Nazzareno per le vacanze dell' anno 1699 . . .

Roma, Gioseppe Vannacci, 1699. 71 p. 13ᶜᵐ.

Three acts. Author not mentioned and unknown to Schatz. Dedication signed by Erasino de Silvestris and dated Rome, February 13, 1699, argument, and scenario. The composer, Francesco **Minissari,** is not mentioned.

On p. 68–69 "Drammi stampati da Carlo Giannini," on p. 70 "Drammi che si vendono dall' istesso," and on p. 71 "Opere in prose, che si vendono dal medesimo."

SCHATZ 6520

L'amante del studio, ballet. *See* Bianchi's L'orfano cinese.

L'amante democratico. Dramma giocoso da rappresentarsi nel Teatro Carignano nella primavera dell' anno 7° Rep° [1799].•

Torino, Giacomo Fea, n. d. 4 p. l., 54 p. 15½ᶜᵐ.

Two acts. By Gian. Domenico Boggio. Cast. Names of the author and the composer, Stefano **Cristiani.** With the opera were performed two ballets, one of which was called "L'Italia rigenerata," by Luigi Dupen. The composer of the music is not mentioned.

SCHATZ 2293

L'amante di tutte. Drama giocoso per musica di Ageo Liteo Da rappresentarsi nel Teatro della Fama de' nobili Signori di Gubbio ne' mesi di maggio, e giugno 1761 . . .

Urbino, Nella stamperia camerale, 1761. 61 p. 15ᶜᵐ.

Three acts. By Antonio Galuppi. Impresario's dedication, cast, and name of Baldassare **Galuppi** as composer.

First performed at Venice, Teatro di S. Moisè, fall of 1760.

SCHATZ 3432

— L'amante di tutte. Dramma giocoso per musica da rappresentarsi in Firenze nel Teatro di via del Cocomero, nella primavera dell' anno 1764 . . .

Firenze, Anton Giuseppe Pagani, 1764. 58 p. 15ᶜᵐ.

Three acts. By Antonio Galuppi, who is not mentioned. Cast and name of Baldassare **Galuppi** as composer. With the opera were performed (composers of the music not mentioned) Vincenzio Monari's ballets "Il giardiniere convinto da Amore" and "Il quadro movibile."

ML 48.A5 v. 20

— L'amante di tutte. Dramma giocoso per musica. Di Ageo Liteo. Da rappresentarsi nel Piccolo Teatro di S. A. E. di Sassonia. Dresda, l'anno 1770.

n. i., n. d. 139 p. 15½ᶜᵐ.

Three acts. Scenario and name of the composer, **Galuppi.** German title: "Der liebhaber von allen," and text face Italian.

SCHATZ 3433

— La moglie bizzarra. Operetta comica, da rappresentarsi sul Regio Teatro Danese, nell' autunno dell' anno 1763.—Den flanevurne kone. . . . Oversadt paa dansk, af R. Soelberg . . .

Kiφbenhavn, Lars Nielsen Svare, n. d. 71 p.

Two acts. Cast and names of **Galuppi,** as composer, and of Pietro Chiari, as author, but comparison proves that this is only a very much altered version in two acts of "L'amante di tutte," leaving most of the arias intact.

SCHATZ 3434

L'amante di tutte—Continued.

— **Il vecchio geloso,** dramma giocoso per musica da rappresentarsi ne' Teatri privilegiati di Vienna l'anno 1767.

[*Vienna*], *Ghelen, n. d. 66 p. 16^{cm}.*

Three acts. By Antonio Galuppi, who is not mentioned. Cast, scenario and name of **Galuppi** as composer. Slightly altered version of his "L'amante di tutte." For instance, the latter does not contain the aria (I, 2) "Quando vedi il Damerino," but "Qualora un galantuomo."   SCHATZ 3510

— **Der liebhaber von allen,** ein singspiel aus dem italiaenischen welches an dem churpfaelzischen hof in dem carneval des jahres 1770 aufgefuehret worden.

Mannheim, Akademische buchdruckerei, n. d. 58 p. 15$\frac{1}{2}$^{cm}.

Three acts. Scenario and cast. **Galuppi** is not mentioned.   SCHATZ 3435

L'amante eroe. Drama per musica di Domenico David, da rappresentarsi nel Teatro Vendramino di San Salvatore l'anno 1691 . . .

Venetia, Nicolini, 1691. front., 71 p. 14$\frac{1}{2}$^{cm}.

Three acts. Author's dedication, argument, scenario, and notice to the reader, with the name of Marc' Antonio **Ziani** ("che nel giorno d'oggi è la delizia dei teatri di Venezia") and remark:

"Il poco tempo, che nell' uso d'oggidì si permette alle scene di Venezia, ed il soverchio numero delle canzoni, desiderate anche fuori dalle loro nicchie non mi ha lasciato in libertà l'ingegno di amplificar nei recitativi, e di fedelmente eseguire i buoni precetti della Poetica."

First performed, as indicated, carnival 1691.   SCHATZ 11198

L'amante fortunato per forza. Dramma per musica; da recitarsi nel Teatro di Sant' Angiolo, l'anno MDCLXXXIV . . .

Venetia, Francesco Nicolini, 1684. 60 p. 14^{cm}.

Three acts. By Pietro d'Averara, who is not mentioned. Dedication dated Venice, November 30, 1684, argument, scenario, and notice to the reader:

" . . . per addattarmi all' uso di questo paese [the text was based on 'un' historietta, scritta in francese'], (nel quale li signori musici vogliono havere più canzoni, che parole, e dove à chi scrive viene prescritta, non solo la quantità mà anco la qualità de' personaggi), hò convenuto alterare l'inventione, l'intreccio, e quasi tutti gl' episvodii; e perciò, se vi trovi qualche cosa d'aggradevole, (che pur sarà puoco) è d'altri: tutto l'imperfetto è mio. E questo basti, perche tu sappia, ch'io non vado à caccia di lode. Se però sarò compatito, l'havrò à caro. Quanto al verso havrei forse potuto tenerlo più sollevato, mà anche in questo mi son accommodato al genio universale, & al soggetto, ch'è più tosto comico. Vivi felice.

"La musica è compositione del Signor Giovanni **Varischini**, le di cui note ti riuscirono tanto gradite nel famoso Odoacre."   SCHATZ 10594

L'amante generosa, ballet. *See* Bertoni's Telemaco ed Eurice.

L'amante impazzito. L. T. of Gasparini, Polaroli, and Ballarotti's L'Alciade overo La violenza d'amore.

L'amante imprudente. A. T. of Caruso's La sposa volubile.

L'amante in cimento, ballet. *See* Fioravanti's L'amor per interesse.

L'amante in cimento, ballet. *See* Portugal's Non irritare le donne.

L'amante in statua. A. T. of La scuola olandese, ballet.

L'amante per bisogno. Dramma giocoso per musica accomodato
e riscritto da Egisippo Argolide P. A. della Colonia Arfèa da rappresentarsi nel nobile Teatro di San Samuele nel carnovale dell' anno
1781. La musica è d'un nobile Accademico filarmonico Veronese.

Venezia, Modesto Fenzo, 1781.

Two acts. By Carlo Giuseppe Lanfranchi Rossi, music by Giuseppe **Gazzaniga.**
Cast and scenario. SCHATZ 3689

L'amante ridicolo deluso. Farsetta per musica a quattro voci dell'
abate Alessandro Pioli da rappresentarsi nella real Villa di Queluz
del serenissimo Signore infante Don Pietro. L'anno MDCCLXIII.

Lisbona, Stamperia Ameniana, n. d. 2 p. l., 42 p. 17ᶜᵐ.

Two acts. Niccolò **Piccinni** is mentioned as the composer.
First performed at Rome, Capranica, January, 1762, according to Schatz; at
Naples, 1757, under the title of "L'amante ridicolo" according to Cametti, who refers
to Florimo II, 260, but Florimo enters this there on mere second-hand information and
has no such entry in his fourth volume. SCHATZ 8063

L'amante servitore. Commedia per musica del Signor Sografi,
poeta del nobilissimo Teatro La Fenice e del Teatro Comico Sant'
Angelo. Composta per il nobilissimo Teatro Giustiniani in San Moisè
il carnovale dell' anno 1797.

Venezia, Modesto Fenzo, 1796. 64 p. 18½ᶜᵐ.

Two acts. Argument, cast, scenario, and name of Ferdinando Per (Ferdinando
Francesco **Paër**) as the composer.
First performed December 26, 1796, as indicated. SCHATZ 7478

L'amante statua. Farsa da rappresentarsi nel nobile Teatro Vero-
nese in San Cassano il carnovale dell' anno 1794. Poesia del tenente
Antonio Valli, posto in musica dal celebre Signor maestro Luigi
Piccini.

Venezia, Casali, 1794. 28 p. 18ᶜᵐ.

One act. With the opera were performed the ballets "I Veneziani a Costantinopoli" and "Il Chinese." SCHATZ 8062

L'amante travestita, ballet. *See* G. M. Rutini's Sicotencal.

Gli amanti alla prova. O. T. of Caruso's Gli amanti dispettosi.

Gli amanti alla prova. Dramma giocoso per musica da rappresentarsi nel Teatro di S. A. E. di Sassonia.

Dresda, 1784, n. publ. 103 p. 15½ᶜᵐ.

Two acts. By Giovanni Bertati, who is not mentioned. Francesco **Piticchio** is
mentioned as the composer. German title "Die liebhaber auf der probe" and text
face Italian.
First performed January 4, 1785, as indicated. SCHATZ 8201

Gli amanti canuti. Dramma giocoso per musica del nobile Signore
Carlo Lanfranchi Rossi gentiluomo toscano fra gli Arcadi Egisippo
Argolide. Da rappresentarsi nel nobile Teatro di San Samuele l'au-
tunno dell' anno 1781.

Venezia, Modesto Fenzo, 1781. 68 p. 17ᶜᵐ.

Two acts. Cast, scenario, and name of Pasquale **Anfossi** as composer. After the
first act, on p. 38–43, argomento, cast, and description of Onorato Viganò's new "Ninias tranno di Babilonia punito da Zoroastro o sia Piramo e Tisbe. Ballo eroico
tragico pantomimo." The composer of this is not mentioned, but of the "secondo
ballo Li sposi ridicoli burlati" it was Luigi Marescalchi. SCHATZ 223

Gli **amanti canuti**—Continued.

— Gli **amanti canuti.** Dramma giocoso per musica da rappresentarsi nel Piccolo Teatro Elettorale.

Dresda, n. publ. 1783.   131 p.   16^{cm}.

Two acts. **Anfossi** is mentioned as composer. German title-page "Die liebenden greise" and text face Italian. The text differs only slightly from that of the original libretto. For instance, I, 9 has now the aria "Dice benissimo" instead of "State zitte, non parlate."
The second act appears also in the libretto of Anfossi's "Il disprezzo."

SCHATZ 224

Li **amanti comici** o sia La famiglia in scompiglio.   Dramma giocoso per musica da rappresentarsi nel Teatro di S. A. S. il Signor principe di Carignano nella primavera dell' anno 1797.

Torino, Onorato Derossi, n. d.   59 p.   14½^{cm}.

Two acts. By Giuseppe Petrosellini (not mentioned), with cast, scenario, and name of the composer, Domenico Nicola **Cimarosa**. On p. 57–69 [recte 59] substitute scene with aria "No, figlia, con più forza ciò va detto—*Orso, bifolco, ingrato*" for II, 5. The ballets were entitled "Il marito umiliato ossia La moglie di spirito" and "Carlo e Carolina." They were by Urbano Garzia. The composer of the music is not mentioned.
First performed at Naples, Teatro de' Fiorentini, 1778.   SCHATZ 2003

Gli **amanti comici** o sia D. Anchise Campanone.   Commedia per musica di G. B. L. P. A.   Da rappresentarsi nel Teatro Nuovo sopra Toledo per quarta commedia del corrente anno 1794.

Napoli, n. publ., 1794.   60 p.   15^{cm}.

Three acts in Napolitan dialect. By Giambattista Lorenzi, whose title originally was "Fra i due litiganti il terzo gode." Cast and name of Giovanni **Paisiello** as the composer.
First performed at Naples, Teatro Nuovo, fall of 1772.   SCHATZ 7588

— **Don Anchise Campanone.** Dramma giocoso per musica da rappresentarsi ne' Teatri privilegiati di Vienna nell' anno 1775.

[Vienna], Giuseppe Kurzböck, n. d.   89, [1] p.   16½^{cm}.

Three acts. Name of Giovanni **Paisiello** as the composer.
The text is in Italian, but so little of it can be traced in the text by Lorenzi that we have practically two operas, so far as the text is concerned, and it stands to reason that the music can not have been the same.
First performed at Vienna, December 12, 1775, as indicated, and with the same title at Venice, Teatro di S. Samuele, fall 1774.   SCHATZ 7589

Gli **'amanti della dote:** *See* Bernardini's L'ultima che si perde è la speranza.

Gli **amanti della dote:** Farsa seconda per musica da rappresentarsi nel Reggio Teatro di S. Carlo della Principessa nel carnovale dell' anno 1794 . . .

Lisbona, Simone Taddeo Ferreira, 1794.   87 p.   14½^{cm}.

One act. Author not mentioned and unknown to Schatz. Impresario's dedication, cast, and name of Pietro **Guglielmi** as the composer. Portuguese text faces Italian. With the opera were performed, composers of the music not mentioned, Pietro Angiolini's ballets "Ciro in Timbraja" and "Gli finti filosofi." The original title of Zini's text was "L'ultima che si perde è la speranza."   SCHATZ 4293

Gli amanti della dote. Dramma giocoso per musica da rappresentarsi per la second' opera in Cremona nel Teatro della Nob. Associazione il carnovale dell' anno 1794.

Cremona, Giuseppe Feraboli, n. d. 47 p. 15½^{cm}.

Two acts. By Saverio Zini, who is not mentioned. Impresario's dedication, cast, scenario, and name of Silvestro di **Palma** as the composer. ("La musica è tutta nuova.") With the opera was performed Antonio Maraffi's ballet, "Il principe di Lago Nero ossia La contadina in corte." The composer of the music is not mentioned.

First performed at Florence, Teatro dei Risoluti, summer, 1791.   SCHATZ 7747

Gl'amanti delusi, ballet.   *See* Sarti's Cleomene.

Gli amanti dispettosi. Commedia per musica da rappresentarsi nel Real Teatro del Fondo di Separazione per terz' opera di quest' anno 1787 . . .

Napoli, n. publ., 1787. 52 p. 14½^{cm}.

Two acts. By Bertati, who is not mentioned. Impresario's dedication, cast, and name of the composer, Luigi **Caruso.** The two ballets by Giambattista Giannini, "Le reclute villane" and "Il quacquero burlato," were performed with the opera. The composer of the ballet music is not mentioned.

First performed as "Gli amanti alla prova" at Venice, S. Moisè, December 26, 1783.   SCHATZ 1653

Gli amanti folletti. Dramma giocoso per musica, da rappresentarsi nel Teatro Elettorale.

Dresda, n. publ., 1794. 148 p. 15½^{cm}.

Two acts. German title page, "Die verliebten poltergeister," and text face Italian. **Mozart** is mentioned as the composer, but it is not mentioned who selected the music from his operas, "Il dissoluto punito," "Le nozze di Figaro," and "La clemenza di Tito," nor who wrote the libretto.

The pasticcio was first performed, as indicated, 1794.   SCHATZ 6748

Gli amanti generosi. Drama per musica da rappresentarsi nel Teatro di Sant' Angelo l'anno 1703 . . .

Venetia, Marino Rossetti, n. d. 69 p. 14½^{cm}.

Three acts. Scenario, argument, dedication by the author, Giovanni Pietro Caudi, and his notice to the reader, in which he says:

"Comparisce novello quest' anno il mio nome sù i Veneti teatri. Questo drama, già diversi anno, a solo motivo di divertimento da me composto, è stato lavorato sul serio, & sopra il gusto della tragedia. Ora non sò come habbia havuto la sorte di doversi esser rappresentato in questo teatro; nel quale non ricercandosi tanta gravità, e richiedendo più tosto lusinga d'orecchio col gaio di qualche scena comica, & col brio delle ariete, che solletico al cuore con la mozione degli affetti; sono stato costretto ad accomodarmi à questa necessità, & à togliergli molto di quel grave, e patetico, che il tragico accompagna, levando, aggiungendo molte cose, & situando delle ariete in loco non totalmente proprio, & fuori del loro nicchio . . . Restano pure levate molte apparenze all quali non può accomodarsi la ristrezza della scena . . . Rimane solo, che la tua bell' anima . . . tolleri con generosità anco le mie imperfezioni; l' avvantaggio delle quali sarà il non comparire così difformi, perche mascherate, & abbellite dalle virtuose, e spiritose note del Sig. maestro il Sig. cavalier **Vinacese,** come pure dalla singolare abilità de virtuosi soggeti, che lo rappresentano.

"Protestando il sig. maestro medesimo haver intrapresa la composizione musicale di questo drama à solo mottivo d'obbedire ad' un commando de cavalieri à quali non ha potuto negarlo, mentre era fuori d'ogni sua intenzione il far più musiche per drami; esprimendosi in oltre d' aver in molte arie secondato più il gusto commune, che il proprio genio."   SCHATZ 10739

Gli **amanti in puntiglio.** Commedia per musica di G. M. D. da rappresentarsi nel Teatro Nuovo sopra Toledo per terza commedia del corrente anno 1794.

Napoli, n. publ., 1794. 40 p. 15ᶜᵐ.

Two acts. By Giuseppe Maria Diodati. Cast and name of Giacomo **Tritto** as the composer.   Schatz 10465

Gli **amanti in Tempe.** Azione pastorale con cori e balli analoghi da rappresentarsi in Firenze nel Regio Teatro degli Intrepidi detto della Palla a Corda . . .

Firenze, Ant. Gius. Pagani e comp., 1792. 23 p. 17½ᶜᵐ.

Two acts. By Giovanni de Gamerra. Cast and names of composer, Gaetano **Andreozzi,** and librettist.

First performed at Florence, as indicated, summer, 1792.   Schatz 216

Gli **amanti protetti da Amore,** ballet. *See* Traetta's Cavaliere errante.

Gli **amanti protetti dall' Amore,** ballet. *See* Borghi's Siroe.

Gli **amanti ridicoli.** Commedia per musica da rappresentarsi nel Teatro de' Fiorentini per terz' opera del corrente anno 1797.

Napoli, n. publ., 1797. 67 p. 15ᶜᵐ.

Two acts. By Giambattista Lorenzi, who is not mentioned. Cast and name of Silvestro di **Palma** as the composer.   Schatz 7746

Gli **amanti ridicoli** ossia La capricciosa umiliata, ballet. *See* Tritto's Le avventure galanti.

Gli **amanti riuniti.**   A. T. of Tritto's La donna sensibile.

L'**amanti schiavi,** ballet.   *See* Piccinni's Ercole al Termedonte.

Les **amants inquiets.**   Parody of Colasse's Thetis et Pelée.

Les **amants trompés.**   *See* Les amans trompés.

Amar per vendetta.   L. T. of Ruggeri's La Clotilde.

L'**amar per virtù.** Drama per musica da rappresentarsi, nel Teatro Vendramino di S. Salvatore. L' autunno dell' anno MDCIC . . .

Venezia, Nicolini, 1699. front., 60 p. 14½ᶜᵐ.

Three acts. By Donato Cupeda, but retouched. Neither he nor Antonio **Draghi,** the principal composer of this pasticcio, is mentioned. Dedication, argument, notice to the "Saggio lettore," cast and scenario.

First performed, in its original form, Vienna, June 9, 1697.   Schatz 2806

L'**amar per virtù.**   A. T. of Graupner's Berenice e Lucilla.

Amarillis.   *See* Campra's ballet Les Muses.

L'**amateur de musique,** comédie en prose et en un acte, mêlée d'ariettes. Paroles & musique de M. B. L. Raymond. Représentée pour la première fois sur le Théâtre des Petits Comédiens de Monseigneur le comte de Beaujolois, au Palais-Royal, le 3 juillet 1785.

Paris, Cailleau, 1785. 40 p. 19ᶜᵐ.

Dedicatory poem, cast and long preface (p. 3–7) which begins:

"Cette petite pièce fut primitivement faite pour être jouée par les *Bamboches.* Le caractère de Monsieur Piano était beaucoup plus développé. Certaines scènes

L'amateur de musique—Continued.

plus filées. J'y avais placé des vaudevilles, ou plutôt des *Pont-Neufs*, comme je l'avais vu pratiquer par les autres auteurs. MM. les entrepreneurs de ce spectacle, ayant substitué des petits enfans plein d'intelligence à des figures de bois inanimées, j'élaguai le dialogue autant qu'il me fut possible, parce qu'en prose surtout, il est très difficile à rendre par le *pantomime*. J'ôtai tous mes vaudevilles, à l'exception d'un seul, qui finit en trio, & qui a produit de l'effet. Je regrette de ce que j'ai coupé, les phrases qui caractérisaient mes premiers personnages, & motivaient leur conduite.''

He then, with quotations from the original version, defends himself against criticism leveled at his character of Monsieur Piano and makes this confession:

"C'est moi qui me suis peint dans Monsieur Piano & Monsieur Crescendo. C'est moi qui brulais du desir de me produire au grand jour dans la Capitale.''

SCHATZ 8617

Amazili e Telesco. A. T. of the ballet La conquista del Perù.

L'Amazone corsara, overo L'Alvilda regina de Goti, drama da rappresentarsi in musica nel famoso Teatro Grimano di SS. Gio. e Paolo, l'anno 1686. Di Giulio Cesare Corradi . . .

Venetia, Francesco Nicolini, 1686. 72 p. 14^{cm}.

Three acts. Author's dedication, notice to the reader with Carlo **Pallavicini's** name as the composer, argument and scenario.
The imprimatur is dated February 1, 1686. SCHATZ 7716

Le Amazoni nell' Isole Fortunate. Drama per musica del dottor Piccioli da rappresentarsi in Piazzola, nel nobilissimo Teatro dell' ill. et eccell. Sig. Marco Contarini . . . l'anno MDCLXXIX.

Padova, Pietro Mar. Frambotto, n. d. 14^{cm}.

Incomplete, ending with p. 48. Prologue and three acts. Dedication by Francesco Maria Piccioli, dated Piazzola, November 11, 1679, argument, notice to the reader and scenario. The composer, Carlo **Pallavicino,** is not mentioned.
SCHATZ 7717

Le Amazzoni, ballet. *See* Zingarelli's Il conte di Saldagna.

L'ambigu de la folie ou Le ballet des dindons. O. T. of Favart's Les Indes dansantes.

L'ambizione castigata. Comi-drama da rappresentarsi in musica nel Teatro di San Fantino. Il carnovale 1717.

Venezia, Antonio Bortoli, 1717. 43 p. 14½^{cm}.

Pages 3–6 wanting, containing presumably argument, cast, and perhaps name of the composer, though he is unknown to Wiel. Schatz considers this a pasticcio which was known also as "Umor di principessa, o sia L'ambizione castigata," text by Francesco Mazzarà. SCHATZ 11299

L'ambizione delusa. *See* La commedia in commedia.

L'ambizione delusa. O. T. of Barlocci's text Il vecchio amante, not to be confused with the L. T. of his Madama Ciana.

L'ambizione delusa. L. T. of Latilla's Madama Ciana.

L'ambizione delusa. Dramma giocoso per musica da rappresentarsi nel Teatro di S. A. Serenissima il Signor principe di Carignano nella primavera dell' anno 1780.

Torino, Onorato Derossi, n. d. 42 p. 15^{cm}.

Two acts. Author unknown to Schatz. Cast, scenario, and name of Giuseppe **Sarti** as the composer.
First performed at Rome, Teatro Capranica, February, 1779. SCHATZ 9471

L'ambizione depressa. Dramma per musica da rappresentarsi nel Teatro di Sant' Angelo nella fiera dell' Ascensione l' anno 1733 . . .

Venezia, Marino Rossetti, n. d. 60 p. 15^{cm}.

Three acts. Dedication, signed by Giuseppe Grandini, probably as impresario, argument, scenario, cast, and name of Baldassare **Galuppi** as composer. The text is attributed by Schatz and others to Grandini, but according to Piovano it is by Giuseppe Papis, and was originally composed by A. Scarlatti for Naples, 1714, under the title of "L'amor generoso." For the Venice version the character of *Despina* was suppressed.   SCHATZ 3477

Ambleto.

Apostolo Zeno, Poesie drammatiche, Venezia, 1744, t. ix, p. 100. 19^{cm}.

Three acts. Argument. Written in collaboration with Pietro Pariati. No composer is mentioned. In the "Catalogo" at end of t. x, date and place of first ed. are given as Venezia, 1706.   ML 49.A2Z3

— **Ambleto.** Pubblicato per la prima volta in Venezia 1706.

Apostolo Zeno, Poesie drammatiche, Orleans, 1785-86, t. ix, p. 185-278. 21^{cm}.

Three acts. Argument. No composer is mentioned. Written in collaboration with Pietro Pariati.   ML 49.A2Z4

Ambleto. Drama per musica da rappresentarsi nel Teatro di Sant' Angelo il carnovale dell' anno MDCCXLII . . .

Venezia, Gasparo Girardi, 1742. 55 p. 15½^{cm}.

Three acts. By Zeno and Pariati (not mentioned), with alterations. Impresario's dedication, argument, scenario, cast, and name of the composer, Giuseppe **Carcano**.   SCHATZ 1620

Ambleto. Drama per musica da rappresentarsi nel Teatro Tron di S. Cassano il carnovale dell' anno MDCCV . . .

Venezia, Marino Rossetti, 1705. 72 p. 14½^{cm}.

Three acts. By Apostolo Zeno and Pariati. Neither they nor Carlo Francesco **Gasparini**, the composer, are mentioned. Impresario's dedication, argument, cast, and scenario.   SCHATZ 3556

Ambroise, ou Voilà ma journée, comédie en un acte et en prose, mêlée d'ariettes. Par le citoyen Monvel.

Paris, Barba, An septième [1798-99]. 36 p. 19^{cm}.

Cast. The composer, Nicolas **Dalayrac,** is not mentioned.
First performed at Paris, Opéra-comique, January 12, 1793.   SCHATZ 2328

Amelia. A musical entertainment of two acts . . .

London, T. Becket, 1771. 2 p. l., 32 p. 20½^{cm}.

Cast and note that "the songs composed by Mr. [Charles] **Dibdin,** are new." The other composers figuring in the headings of the songs of this pasticcio are **Piccinni, Potenza, Cocchi,** [Joh. Chr.] **Bach, Stanley, Arnold, Richter.** Comparison proved clearly that "Amelia" is taken from Richard Cumberland's three-act "The summer's tale," some scenes having been lifted verbatim (dialogue and songs) into "Amelia," which was first performed under this title at London, Drury Lane, December 14, 1771. Not to be confused, it appears, with another alteration called *Amelia* and first performed at Covent Garden April 12, 1768.   LONGE 105

Amelia. A new English opera, as it is perform'd at the New Theatre in the Hay-Market, after the Italian manner. Set to musick by Mr. John Frederick Lampe.

London, J. Watts, 1732. 4 p. l., 29, [3] p. 19½^{cm}.

The [3] p. contain a book-list by the publisher.
Three acts. Cast and argument. By Henry Carey, who is not mentioned.
First performed March 13, 1732, as indicated. LONGE 105

— **Amelia**: an opera. Set to musick by Mr. John Frederick Lampe.
2 p. l., 46 p. 22^{cm}. (Henry Carey, Dramatick works, London, 1743.
Three acts. Argument. ML 49.A2C2

Amelia ed Ottiero. Dramma per musica da rappresentarsi nel Ces. Reg. Teatro di Trieste nell' autunno 1797.

[Trieste], Cesarea regia privilegiata stamperia governale n. d. 40 p. 18^{cm}.

Two acts by Carlo Sernicola, who is not mentioned. Impresario's dedication dated Trieste, November 7, 1797, argument, scenario, cast, and name of Gaetano **Andreozzi** as composer. With the opera was performed (composer of the music not mentioned) Niccolò Ferlotti's ballet "Nina pazza per amore." SCHATZ 201

The **American adventurers.** A. T. of The coup de main.

The **American Indian;** or, Virtues of nature. A play. In three acts. With notes. Founded on an Indian tale. By James Bacon . . .

London, Printed for the author, 1795. xvi, [8], 44 p. 21¼^{cm}.

List of subscribers, dedication, dated Lincoln's Inn, October 12, 1795, preface stating that this play (which was rejected by Drury-Lane) is based on Mrs. Morton's "Ouâbi, or, the virtues of nature," and note that "The Death Song" ("Rear'd midst the war-empurpled plain") was literally copied from her poem. LONGE 270

L'Americana in Europa, ballet. *See* Gazzaniga's La disfatta de' Mori.

L'Americana in Olanda. Dramma giocoso per musica in due atti di Nunzio Porta da rappresentarsi nel nobil Teatro di San Samuele l'autunno dell' anno 1778.

Venezia, Modesto Fenzo, 1778. 17^{cm}.

Cast and name of Pasquale **Anfossi** as composer. SCHATZ 264

L'Americana in Scozia, ballet. *See* Nasolini's Eugenia.

L' Americano. Intermezzo per musica da rappresentarsi nel Teatro di S. Gio. Grisostomo dell' eccellentissima casa Grimani l' autunno dell' anno 1779.

Venezia, Pietro Sola, 1779. 48 p. 17½^{cm}.

Two acts. The author not mentioned and unknown to Schatz. Cast, scenario, and name of Niccolo **Piccinni** as the composer.
First performed at Rome, Teatro Capranica, February 22, 1772. SCHATZ 8064

— Der **Amerikaner,** ein vierstimmiges singspiel. In musik gesetzt von herrn Nikolaus Piccini . . .

Bamberg, n. publ., 1791. 80 p. 15^{cm}.

Two acts. The translator is not mentioned and is unknown to Schatz. SCHATZ 8065

L'ami de la maison, comédie en trois actes et en vers, mêlés d'ariettes; représentée devant Sa Majesté à Fontainebleau le 26 octobre 1771, & sur le Théatre de la Comédie italienne, le 2 décembre suivant. Par Mr. Marmontel . . . La musique de M. Gretry.

Paris, Vente, 1772. 52 p. 18½^{cm}.

Cast. On p. 46–52 the music of the "Airs" "Je suis de vous très mécontente" and "Ah! dans ces fêtes." The full score gives the first Parisian performance correctly as on May 14, 1772. So does evidently a libretto printed by Vente, 1772, as reprinted by Wotquenne in Grétry's Oeuvres. The odd feature is that our libretto, too, was printed by Vente in 1772. SCHATZ 4132

Second copy. Yudin PQ.

— **L'ami de la maison,** comédie en trois actes et en vers, mêlée d'ariettes; représentée devant Sa Majesté, à Fontainebleau, le 26 Octobre 1771. Les paroles sont de M. Marmontel . . . & la musique est de M. Grétry.

Paris, Ruault, 1776. 36 p. 19½^{cm}. ML 48M2M

— Der **hausfreund,** ein singspiel in drey aufzuegen aus dem franzoesischen uebersetzt, mit musik.

Frankfurt am Mayn, mit Andreaeischen schriften, 1774. 88 p., 11 p. (folded music, dated 1775). 15½^{cm}.

Translation by Johann Heinrich Faber, who is not mentioned. The music (voice and bass) consists of "Mit Ihnen bin ich unzufrieden" ("Je suis de vous très mécontente" and "Neigt sich ein hitziger Tag" ("Dans la brûlante saison").

SCHATZ 4133

Gli amici. Pastorale per musica nel Teatro Malvezzi l'estate dell' anno MDCIC.

(At end) Bologna, per l'erede del Benacci, n. d. front., 70, [1] p. 12½^{cm}.

Three acts. By Pietro Jacopo Martelli, who is not mentioned. Cast, argument, and name of conte Pirro **Albergati** as composer.

First performed, as indicated, August 16, 1699. SCHATZ 77

Gl' amici rivali. L. T. of C. F. Pollaroli's L' enigma disciolto.

Aminta.

Apostolo Zeno, Poesie drammatiche, Venezia, 1744, t. vi, p. [357]-447 p. 19^{cm}.

Three acts. Argument. No composer is mentioned. First composed by Tommaso **Albinoni,** according to Schatz. In the "Catalogo" at end of t. x, date and place of first ed. are given as Florence, 1703. ML 49.A2Z3

— **Aminta.** Pubblicato per la prima volta in Firenze 1703.

Apostolo Zeno, Poesie drammatiche, Orleans, 1785-86, t. ii, p. 305- 384. 21^{cm}.

Three acts. Argument. No composer is mentioned. ML 49.A2Z4

Amintas. L. T. of Rush's The royal shepherd.

L'amitié à l'épreuve, comédie en deux actes et en vers, meslée d'ariettes; représentée, devant Sa Majesté, à Fontainebleau, le 13 novembre 1770. Les paroles sont de MM. ***, & Favart . . . La musique est de M. Grétry.

Paris, la veuve Simon & fils, 1771. 46, [1] p. 18^{cm}.

Cast. Favart's collaborator is not known. The additional page contains a description of the "*Divertissement*" and p. 45–46 the air of the "*Romance,* A quels maux il me livre."

First performed at Paris, Comédie italienne, January 24, 1771 (Schatz); January 17, 1771 (Wotquenne, also the date given in the score).

In 1786 revised, with an additional third act. SCHATZ 4134

— **L'amitié a l'épreuve,** comédie en un acte et en vers, mêlie d'ariettes; tirée des Contes moraux de M. de Marmontel . . . Les paroles sout de MM * * *, & Favart. La musique est de M. Grétry.

Paris, la veuve Duchesne, 1776. 2 p. l., 45 p. 19^{cm}. (Theatre de M. Favart, Paris, Duchesne, 1763–77, t. x.)

Font claims that this one-act reduction was by "Favart seul," *i. e.,* did not contain matter by Voisenon. It should be noted that a three-act version "par Favart seul" was printed in 1786.

Cast. No music printed in the text. Dedication to "Madame la Dauphine," and the prefatory note:

"Cette pièce fut représentée en deux actes [by Voisenon and Favart] sur le Théâtre de la cour à Fontainebleau, le 13 novembre 1770, & à Paris, le 24 janvier 1771.

"M. Favart l'ayant réduite en un acte, elle fut jouée devant Leurs Majestés, à Versailles, le 29 décembre 1775 ; & à Paris, le premier janvier 1776."

ML 49.A2F1

— **L'amitié a l'épreuve,** comédie en deux actes et en vers. Melée d'ariettes. Représentée, devant Sa Majesté, à Fontainebleau le 13 Novembre 1770. Les paroles sont de MM. *** & Favart . . . La musique est de M. Grétry.

Paris, Didot, 1777. 35 p. 19½^{cm}. ML 48M2M

— Die **freundschaft auf der probe,** ein singspiel in zween aufzuegen aus dem franzoesischen uebersetzt, mit musik.

Frankfurt am Mayn, mit Andreaeischen schriften, 1772. 84 p., 8 p. (folded music.) 16½^{cm}.

Translation by Joh. Heinr. Faber, who is not mentioned. Cast. The music (voice and bass) consists of "Denken hast Du mich gelehret" (I, 4, "Si je pense, c'est votre ouvrage"), "Nelson flieht, mich zu verlassen" ("Nelson part, Nelson me laisse," II, 1), and "Siehst Du, wie ich mich quäle" (II, 3, "A quels maux il me livre"). SCHATZ 4135

— Die **freundschaft auf der probe.** Eine operette in zween aufzeugen. Aufgefuehrt in k. k. Nationaltheater.

Wien, zu finden beym Logenmeister, 1780. 64 p.. 16½^{cm}.

The translator is not mentioned and unknown to Schatz.

First performed, as indicated, January 22, 1781. SCHATZ 4136

Amleto. Dramma per musica da rappresentarsi nel nobilissimo Nuovo Teatro di Padova nella fiera del Santo l'anno 1792 . . .

Padova, Conzatti A. S. Lorenzo n. d. 51 p. 17½^{cm}.

Two acts. By Giuseppe Foppa. Dedication, prefatory note, cast, scenario, and name of Gaetano **Andreozzi** as composer but not of librettist. The libretto was based on the tragedy Amleto by Ducis. With the opera these ballets were per-

Amleto—Continued.

formed: "La distruzione di Cartagine, ballo eroico-tragico-pantomimo" by Domenico Ballou, music composed for the occasion by Vittorio Trento and Il sonambolo. Argomento, cast, and detailed description of the former on p. 26–36.   SCHATZ 212

Amleto, ballet.   *See* Tarchi's Alessandro nell' Indie.

Amleto, ballet.   *See* Zingarelli's Apelle e Campaspe.

L'ammalato immaginario. Intermezzi musicali da rappresentarsi in Perugia nel Teatro de' Nobili nel carnevale dell' anno 1727.

Perugia, Costantini, n. d.   16 p.   14½ cm.

Three intermezzi.   The composer, Francesco Bartolomeo **Conti,** is not mentioned. The author is unknown to Schatz.

First performed at Vienna, Teatro di Corte, February, 1713.   SCHATZ 2204

L'amor artigiano.   Dramma giocoso per musica da rappresentarsi nel Teatro Giustiniani di San Moisè l' autunno dell' anno 1776.

n. i., n. d.   68, xiv p.   18 cm.

Three acts.   By Carlo Goldoni, who is not mentioned.   Cast, scenario, and name of Joseph **Schuster** as the composer.   ("La musica è nuovamente composta.")   The xiv p. (after p. 32) contain prefatory note, argument, cast, and description, but not name of the composer of the music of Antonio Terrades' "Apelle e Campaspe, ballo eroico-pantomimo."   SCHATZ 9759

L'amor bizzaro o sia La gelosa di se stessa.   Dramma giocoso per musica di Giovanni Bertati da rappresentarsi nel Teatro Giustiniani di San Moisé nel carnovale dell' anno 1775.

Venezia, Antonio Graziosi, 1775.   54 p.   17 cm.

Three acts.   Cast, scenario, and name of Giacomo **Rust** as the composer.   ("La musica sarà.")   SCHATZ 9167

O amor conjugal.   Dramma para ser representado no Theatro do Salitre, no felicissimo dia no nascimento da Senhora D. Maria Francisca Benedicta . . .

Lisboa, José de Aquino Bulhoens, 1789.   27 p.   15½ cm.

Cast and names of José Procopio Monteiro as author, of Marcos **Portugal as** composer.

First performed July 25, 1789, as indicated (Schatz), July 27, 1784 (Carvalhaes).

SCHATZ 8434

Amor contadino.   Dramma giocoso per musica di Polisseno Fegejo P. A.   Da rappresentarsi nel Teatro di Sant' Angelo l' autunno dell' anno 1760.

Venezia, Modesto Fenzo, 1760.   69 p.   15 cm.

Three acts.   By Goldoni.   Cast, scenario, and name of Giovanni Battista **Lampugnani** as the composer.

First performed, as indicated, November 12, 1760.   SCHATZ 5386

— **L'amor contadino.**   Operetta comica, da rappresentarsi sul Teatro Reale danese, nell' autunno dell' anno 1763.—Bφnderfolks elskov . . .   Oversadt paa dansk, af R. Soelberg.

Kiφbenhavn, Lars Nielsen Svare, n. d.   71 p.   15½ cm.

Three acts.   Cast and names of Goldoni as author, of **Lampugnani** as composer.

SCHATZ 5387

L'amor contrastato. Commedia per musica di Giuseppe Palomba da rappresentarsi nel nobile Teatro Giustiniani in San Moisè il carnovale dell' anno 1789.

Venezia, Modesto Fenzo, 1788. 72 p. 17^{cm}.

Three acts. Cast, scenario, and name of Giovanni **Paisiello** as the composer. The third act of this version consists of three scenes not to be found in our other librettos.
First performed at Naples, Teatro dei Fiorentini, summer, 1788. SCHATZ 7590a

— **L'amor contrastato.** Dramma giocoso per musica, da rappresentarsi nel Teatro di S. A. E. di Sassonia.

Dresda, n. publ., 1790. 143 p. 15$\frac{1}{2}$^{cm}.

Two acts. **Paisiello** is mentioned as the composer. German title page "Die streitig gemachte liebschaft" and text face Italian. SCHATZ 7591

— **La molinara** o sia L'amor contrastato. Drama giocoso . . .

Berlino, Haude e Spener, n. d. 125 p. 15$\frac{1}{2}$^{cm}.

Two acts. **Paisiello** is mentioned as the composer. German title page "Die müllerin oder Die streitig gemachte liebe" and text face Italian. SCHATZ 7593

— Arien und gesaenge aus dem komischen singspiel: **Die schoene muellerim.** In zwey aufzuegen. Mit musik von Paesiello.

Berlin, n. publ., n. d. 40 p. 16^{cm}.

Cast. Published before 1800? German version by Christoph Friedrich Bretzner.
First performed at Berlin, Kgl. Nationaltheater, Oct. 16, 1793. SCHATZ 7594

— Gesaenge aus dem singspiele: **Die muellerin,** nach dem italienischen, in zwey akten. Die musik ist von Paisiello.

Hamburg, Friedrich Hermann Nestler, n. d. 39 p. 15$\frac{1}{2}$^{cm}.

Two acts. Published before 1800?
First performed at Hamburg, Theater C. Gänsemarkt, April 26, 1793.
SCHATZ 7595

Amor corsaro, ballet. *See* Monza's Oreste.

L'amor costante. Dramma giocoso per musica da rappresentarsi nel Real Teatro di Salvaterra nel carnovale dell' anno 1785.

[Lisboa] Stamperia reale, n. d. 67 p. 15^{cm}.

Two acts. Scenario, cast, and name of composer, Domenico Nicola **Cimarosa.** Author unknown to Schatz.
First performed at Rome, Teatro Valle, carnival, 1782. SCHATZ 1927

— **Giulietta ed Armidoro.** Dramma giocoso in due atti da rappresentarsi nel Teatro di S. A. E. di Sassonia.

Dresda, n. publ., 1790. 99 p. 15$\frac{1}{2}$^{cm}.

Two acts, with name of the composer, **Cimarosa.** German title, "Julie und Armidor," and text face Italian. The same as "L'amor costante," but with modifications, for instance, "Laura" has become "Giulia," and the second act begins with what was the second scene, "Si, Giulia sarà mia."
First performed at Dresden March 13, 1790. SCHATZ 1928

Amor d'un ombra, e gelosia d'un aura. Dramma per musica da rappresentarsi nel nuovo teatro eretto di sotto Monte Calvario, in questa primavera del corrente anno 1725 . . .

Napoli, Angelo Vocola, 1725. 56 p. 14$\frac{1}{2}$^{cm}.

Three acts by Carlo Sigismondo Capeci, with alterations by Carlo de Palma.
Dedicatory preface by the impresario Angelo Carasale, notice to the reader, names of the authors and the composer, Giuseppe **Sellitti,** argument, cast, scenario. The new arias are marked by an asterisk, for instance: "Ne bell' occhi le Grazie ed Amore" (I, 14). From the dedication it appears that the libretto was originally given at Rome "nel Teatro domestico della Maestà di Maria Casimira, regina di Polonia," but it is not stated with whose music. SCHATZ 9829

Pequeno dramma intitulado o **Amor da patria,** para se representar no Theatro do Salitre, em aplauso das felicissimas melhorias do serenissimo Senhor D. Joaõ princepe do Brazil.

Lisboa, José de Aquino Bulhoens, 1789. 15 p. 15½cm.

One prose scene with two choruses, an aria and a duet.   Neither author nor composer mentioned.   Not recorded by Schatz.   ML 50.2.A65

L'amor della patria, superiore ad ogn'altro.   Dramma musicale del Signor Francesco Sbarra.

Venetia, Nicolò Pezzana, 1668.   104 p.   14cm.

Three acts.   Printer's dedication, argument, and scenario.   Composer not mentioned and unknown to Schatz.

First performed, according to Schatz, at Munich, Hoftheater, April, 1665.

Schatz 11301

L'amor di Curzio per la patria.   Drama da rappresentarsi in musica nel famosissimo Teatro Grimano di SS. Gio. e Paolo l' anno 1690 di Giulio Cesare Corradi . . .

Venetia, Nicolini, 1690.   68 p.   15½cm.

Three acts.   Argomento, author's dedication, scenario, and notice to the reader with name of [Francesco] Paris **Algisi** as composer.   Schatz 160

L'amor di figlia.   Drama per musica da recitarsi nel Teatro di S. Angelo nell' autunno dell' anno 1718 . . .

Venezia, Marino Rossetti, 1718.   60 p.   15½cm.

Three acts.   Argument, cast, scenario, name of Giovanni **Porta** as the composer, dedication signed by Domenico Lalli, who says in a prefatory notice to the reader: "Questo presente drama fù composto dal Signor Gio. Andrea Moniglia . . . (come appare in stampa, nelle sue dramatiche poesie Parte seconda) con il titolo della Pietà di Sabina. Io l' hò ridotto nella miglior forma che hò potuto all' uso odierno de Teatri Dramatici, avendovi lasciato buona parte de' versi dell' autore, a' quali hò procurato di far consimili i miei, per quanto mi è stato possibile."   Schatz 8395

L'amor di figlio non conosciuto.   Dramma per musica da rappresentarsi nel Teatro di Sant' Angelo nel carnovale dell' anno 1715. Di Domenico Lalli . . .

Venezia, Carlo Buonarigo, 1715.   5 p. l., [13]-70 p.   15cm.

The supplementary leaf contains the aria "Dirai per mè" in full with four stanzas, instead of only two stanzas as on p. 38.   Two of the unnumbered pages preceding p. 13 lacking.   They contained probably cast, scenario, and name of Tommaso **Albinoni** as composer.   Three acts.   Argument and dedication.   Schatz 102

Amor, e dover.   Drama per musica di Domenico David.   Da recitarsi nel Teatro Grimani di S. Gio. Grisostomo . . .

Venezia, Nicolini, 1697.   72 p.   14½cm.

Three acts.   Author's dedication, argument, notice to the reader, and scenario. Carlo Francesco **Pollaroli**, the composer, is not mentioned.

First performed carnival 1697, as indicated.   Schatz 8271

Amor fa l'uomo cieco.   Intermezzo di due parti per musica.

Carlo Goldoni, Opere teatrali, Venezia, Zatta e figli, 1788–95, v. 35, [141]-157 p.   18½cm.   PQ

In his "Verzeichnis" Wotquenne dates this 1731.   As a matter of fact, intermezzi of this title were performed at Naples, Teatro di S. Bartolomeo, winter 1731 with Pergolesi's "La Salustia."   According to Radiciotti there is in the libretto at end of the first intermezzo the remark "Tutto il recitativo di quest' intermezzo è di Domenico Carcajus."   Goldoni does not seem to be mentioned; at least Radiciotti is silent on his authorship.   The music is attributed by him and Schatz to **Per-**

Amor fa l' uomo cieco—Continued.

golesi, whose score has not been located.   Radiciotti gives in the second part of his book an outline of the plot mentioning as characters Nerina and Nibbio.   Neither plot nor characters are those of the intermezzi in Goldoni's Opere teatrali, which fact complicates matters!   Goldoni's characters are "Livietta," "Cardone suo amante" and "Mingone servo che non parla."   One is instantly reminded, upon reading the text, of Mariani's "Livietta e Tracollo," composed by **Pergolesi** and first performed at the same theatre on October 25, 1734.   Indeed, both librettos contain the arias "Vi sto ben? Vi comparisco" and "Non si move, non rifiata."   Here, then, is a puzzle, which does not as yet seem to have aroused the attention of biographers and opera-historians.   If the text published in Goldoni's works really dates from 1731, the natural explanation would be that Mariani in 1734 incorporated Pergolesi's two arias of 1731 in "Livietta e Tracollo."   And yet how is it possible that Pergolesi composed in 1731 this "Amor fa l'uomo cieco" text, if it does not agree with the text which, according to Radiciotti, is that of the libretto printed in 1731?   Yet these two texts appear to have at least one aria in common: "La carozza ci sarà," and this aria was listed in Breitkopf's catalogue of 1770.

It will simplify further research, if the arias in Goldoni's text follow here:
(Int. I)—
Vi stò ben?   Vi comparisco?
Per pietà, chi mai m'insegna.
La carozza ci sarà.
Gioja mia, devo partire.
Parto dunque, o mia diletta (duet).
(Int. II)—
Quanto mi vien da ridere.
Non si move, non rifiata.
Oh come sei bello.
Oh che sorte, oh che piacere (duet).

L'amor fra gl' impossibili.   Dramma per musica da recitarsi nel Teatro della Fenice d'Ancona nell' anno 1727.

Ancona, Belelli, 1727.   62 p.   14^{cm}.

Three acts.   Girolamo Gigli is mentioned as author, Giovanni Battista **Mastini** as the composer.   Argument and scenario.   SCHATZ 6095

L'amor geloso.   Azione teatrale comica per musica da rappresentarsi nel Real Teatro del Fondo di Separazione per seconda opera di questo corrente anno 1782.

Napoli, n. publ., 1782.   43 p.   15$\frac{1}{2}$^{cm}.

Two acts.   The author is not mentioned and is unknown to Schatz.   Cast and name of "Vincentio Martinez" (**Martin y Soler**) as the composer.   SCHATZ 6026

L'amor geloso.   Azione teatrale comica per musica in due parti.

Vienna, di Ghelen, 1770.   Unpaged.   19^{cm}.

Two acts.   Author not mentioned and unknown to Schatz.   Giuseppe **Scarlatti** is mentioned as the composer.
First performed at Vienna, Burgtheater, 1770.   SCHATZ 9560

L'amor generoso.

Apostolo Zeno, Poesie drammatiche, Venezia, 1744, t. vi, p. [105]–182.
19^{cm}.

Three acts.   Argument.   No composer is mentioned.   In the "Catalogo" at end of t. x, date and place of first ed. are given as Venice, 1707.   (*See* below). ML 49.A2Z3

— L'amor generoso.   Pubblicato per la prima volta in Venezia 1707.

Apostolo Zeno, Poesie drammatiche, Orleans, 1785–86, t. iii, p. 277–348.   21^{cm}.

Three acts.   Argument.   No composer is mentioned.   ML 49.A2Z4

L'amor generoso.   Drama per musica da rappresentarsi nel Teatro degl' illustrissimi signori Capranica l'anno 1727 . . .

Roma, Rossi, n. d.   62 p.   15ᶜᵐ.   •

Three acts.   By Apostolo Zeno, who is not mentioned.   Argument, cast, scenario, and name of the composer, Giovanni **Costanzi**.   SCHATZ 2276

L'amor generoso.   Drama da rappresentarsi per musica nel Teatro Tron di S. Cassano, l'autunno dell' anno MDCCVII . . .

Venezia, Marino Rossetti, n. d.   59, [1] p.   15ᶜᵐ.

Three acts.   By Apostolo Zeno, who signs the dedication with his initials.   Argument, cast, scenario, and name of (Carlo) Francesco **Gasparini** as the composer.   On the additional page a list of Antonio Bortoli's musical publications.   SCHATZ 3557

— **La fede in cimento.**   Drama per musica da rappresentarsi nel Teatro Tron di S. Cassiano.   Il carnovale dell' anno 1730 . . .

Venezia, Carlo Buonarrigo, 1730.   48 p.   15ᶜᵐ.

Three acts.   By Apostolo Zeno, who is not mentioned.   Impresario's dedication, argument, cast, scenario.   The composers Carlo Francesco **Gasparini** and Santo **Lapis** are not mentioned.   In reality this is a later version of Gasparini's "L'amor generoso," Venice, 1707.   The dialogue follows fairly closely that of the original, but many arias are different, and it was for these that Lapis wrote the music.   For instance, "Anche da te lontano" (I, 2) has supplanted "Il mio cor non si spaventa," "Son amante, e non son figlia" (I, 3) the aria "Sparger non vo più lagrime," etc. etc.

SCHATZ 3596

L'amor guerriero.   Drama per musica, rappresentato nel famosissimo Teatro Grimano.   L'anno 1663 . . .

Venetia, Francesco Nicolini, 1663.   92 p. (incl. front.)   15ᶜᵐ.

Pages 1–24, 73–92 not numbered.

Prologue and three acts.   Argument, scenario, dedication by the author, Cristoforo Ivanovich, and his notice to the reader, in which he says:

"Ecco il mio primo drama . . .   Troverai inserita qualche machina, non attaccata dal capriccio, ma introdotta dall' arte.   Queste sono le primitie del mio ingegno, che nato di diverso linguaggio, à pena si è innestato à più bassi rami della Tosana Facondia . . .   La musica è del Signor Don Pietro **Ziani** . . .   Le voci saranno de i cigni più famose, che volano per l' italico cielo . . ."

First performed, as indicated, carnival, 1663.   SCHATZ 11220

Amor indovino, favola pastorale in musica da rappresentarsi nel Teatro Giustinian à S. Moisè.   Nel mese di ottobre, l' anno 1726 . . .

Venezia, Marin Rossetti, 1726.   36 p.   14½ᶜᵐ.

Three acts.   By Giov. Battista Neri.   Impresario's dedication dated October 26, 1726, argument, and cast.   Neither the composer, Antonio **Cortona**, is mentioned, nor the author.   SCHATZ 2263

Amor l'astuzia insegna.   Dramma giocoso per musica di Giovanni Bertati, poeta al servizio di S. M. I. R. A. etc., da rappresentarsi nel nobilissimo Teatro Giustiniani in San Moisè il carnovale dell' anno 1797.

Venezia, Modesto Fenzo, 1797.   48 p.   17ᶜᵐ.

Two acts.   Cast, scenario, and name of Francesco **Gardi** as composer.

First performed, as indicated, February 18, 1797.   SCHATZ 3536

Amor lunatico.   Dramma giocoso per musica da rappresentarsi nel Teatro Giustiniani di San Moisè il carnovale dell' anno 1770.   Dell' abbate Pietro Chiari . . .

Venezia, Modesto Fenzo, 1770.   54 p.   16½ᶜᵐ.

Three acts.   Dedicatory poem by the impresario, cast, scenario, and name of Baldassare **Galuppi** as the composer.   SCHATZ 3436

L'amor marinaro. Dramma giocoso per musica in due atti da rappresentarsi nel Teatro elettorale di Sassonia.

Dresda, n. publ., 1798. 183 p. 15½ᶜᵐ.

Three acts. By Giovanni di Gamerra, who is not mentioned. German title-page "Die liebe im matrosenkleide," and text face Italian. Joseph **Weigl** is mentioned as the composer.

First performed at Vienna, Hoftheater, October 15, 1797; at Dresden, July 18, 1798, as indicated. SCHATZ 10926

L'amor nell' inganno. Intermezzi per musica tra Merlina e Falchetto. Da rappresentarsi per la prima volta nel Teatro de' Convittori del Seminario di Mantova nel carnovale dell' anno 1745.

n. i., n. d. 22 p. 15½ᶜᵐ.

Four intermezzi. Both author and composer unknown to Schatz. SCHATZ 11300

Amor non ha riguardi e Le convulsioni. Farse in musica di Giuseppe Palomba da rappresentarsi nel Teatro de' Fiorentini per quart' opera dell' anno 1787.

Napoli, n. publ., 1787. 48 p.

One act. (The second farce, music by Gius. Curcio, on p. 26–48.) Cast and name of Luigi **Platone** as the composer. SCHATZ 8218

L'amor per interesse. Commedia per musica di Gaetano Gasbarri, P. A. da rappresentarsi nel Real Teatro del Fondo di Separazione per second' opera del corrente anno 1797 . . .

Napoli, n. publ., 1797. 52 p. 15½ᶜᵐ.

Two acts. Impresario's dedication dated Nov. 15, 1797, cast, and name of Valentino **Fioravanti** as composer. On p. [46]–52 cast, argument, and description of "Berilowitz in Tartaria, ballo eroico pantomimo, diviso in cinque atti d'invenzione, ed esecuzione di Giuseppe Cajani," who also is mentioned as the composer of the music. The second ballet, also by Cajani, was called "L'amante in cimento." The composer of the music is not mentioned. SCHATZ 3112

Amor per oro. Dramma giocoso per musica di Cerilo Orcomeno P. A. da rappresentarsi nel nobile Teatro in San Samuele l'autunno dell' anno 1782 . . .

Venezia, Modesto Fenzo, 1782. 72 p. 17ᶜᵐ.

Two acts. Impresario's dedication, cast, scenario, and name of Giuseppe **Gazzaniga** as the composer. With the opera were performed Onorato Viganò's ballets, "Diana al bagno" and "La capanna incantata." The composers of the music are not mentioned. SCHATZ 3690

Amor per oro. Dramma giocoso, da rappresentarsi nel Teatro di S. A. E. di Sassonia.

Dresda, n. publ., 1790. 143 p. 15ᶜᵐ.

Two acts. By Cerilo Orcomeno, P. A., who is not mentioned. Franz **Seydelmann** is mentioned as the composer. German title-page "Liebe aus haabsucht," and text face Italian.

First performed April 7, 1790, as indicated. SCHATZ 9840

L'amor per rigiro. Intermezzo in musica a cinque voci da rappresentarsi nel nobil Teatro Tron di San Cassiano nel carnevale dell' anno MDCCLXXXI.

Venezia, Pietro Sola, n. d. 44 p. 17½ᶜᵐ.

Two acts. Nicolò Tassi is mentioned as author, Angiolo **Gagni** as the composer. Cast, scenario, and titles of Alberto Cavos's ballets, "Il matrimonio per gratitudine," and "Il sargente burlato." The composers of the music are not mentioned. SCHATZ 3411

L'amor perfetto.   A. T. of Piccinni's Il servo padrone.

L'amor perfetto.   A. T. of Schuster's Il servo padrone.

Amor piaga ogni core.   Comedia per musica d'Agostino Donati da rappresentarsi nella Sala dell' illustrissimo, & eccellentissimo Sig. marchese Bentivoglio.

Ferrara, Bernardino Pomatelli, 1691.   64 p.   15½ᶜᵐ.

Three acts.   Argument and notice to the reader with name of "Sabastiano **Chierici,** Mastro di cappella dell' illustriss.   Accademia dello Spirito Santo" as composer.   Not recorded by Allacci or Schatz.   ML 50.2.A66C3

L'Amor prigioniero.

Metastasio, Poesie, Perigi, vedova Quillau, 1755, t. vii, [377]-389 p. 16ᶜᵐ.

One act.   ML 49.A2M42

— **L'amor prigioniero.**   Questo componimento drammatico fu scritto d'ordine sovrano dall' autore in Vienna, e cantato con musica del Reütter in corte privatamente l'anno 1741.

[417]-428 p.   26ᶜᵐ.   (Pietro Metastasio, Opere, t. ii, Parigi, vedova Herissant, 1780.)

One act.   ML 49.A2M44

L'amor puo tutto.   Da cantarsi nel Teatro privilegiato da S. M. C. e Cat. in Vienna.   Nell' anno MDCCXXXVI. nel mese di febbraio.— Die lieb kan alles . . .

Wien, Johann Peter v. Ghelen, n. d.   64 p.   16ᶜᵐ.

Three acts.   Argument.   Author and composer not mentioned and unknown to Schatz.   Not recorded by von Weilen.   . SCHATZ 11302

Amor può tutto, ossia Il trionfo del valore, ballet.   *See* P. Guglielmi's Ademira.

L'amor sincero.   A. T. of Alcesti.

L'amor tirannico.   Drama per musica di Domenico Lalli da rappresentarsi nel Teatro Grimani di S. Samuele nel maggio dell' anno 1722.   E per la prima volta rappresentato nel Teatro Tron di S. Cassano l'autunno dell' anno 1710 . . .

Venezia, Marino Rossetti, 1722.   48 p.   16ᶜᵐ.

Three acts.   Author's dedication, argument, cast, scenario, and names of the composers, Fortunato **Chelleri** and Giovanni **Porta** (for the third act).
                                                      SCHATZ 1819

L'amor tirannico.   Drama per musica da rappresentarsi nel Teatro Tron di S. Cassano l'autunno dell' anno 1710.   Di Domenico Lalli . . .

Venezia, Marino Rossetti, 1710.   71 p.   14½ᶜᵐ.

Five acts.   Author's dedication, argument, and scenario.   Carlo Francesco **Gasparini,** the composer, is not mentioned.   SCHATZ 3558

Amor tiranno.   Accademia fatta in casa dell' illustrissimo Sig. Senator Fantuzzi.   Composta in musica da Domenico Pellegrini Accad. Filomuso all' illustrissima Signora Sulpizia Orsi Grimaldi.

Bologna, Per gli Hh. del Dozza, 1649.   36 p.   19ᶜᵐ.

By Domenico Gisberti, who is not mentioned.   Dedication signed by the composer and dated "Bologna li 6. febraro 1649."   On p. 25-33:

"Il Sig. Pietro Mengoli col seguente discorso provò, che l'armonia della musica, non è dissimile dell' armonia che unite formano le parti, che constituiscono un bel sembiante."   SCHATZ 7859

Amor tra le vendemmie. Commedia per musica di Giuseppe Palomba da rappresentarsi nel Teatro Nuovo sopra Toledo per terz' opera di questo corrente anno 1792.

Napoli, Vincenzo Flauto, 1792. 52 p. 15^cm.

Two acts. Cast and name of Pietro **Guglielmi** as the composer. Schatz 4287

Amor und Psyche. Tr. of the ballet Amore e Psiche.

L'amor vendicativo. Intermezzo per musica a quattro voci da rappresentarsi nel Teatro Nuovo nel carnevale del corrente anno 1783 . . .

Napoli, n. publ., n. d. 32 p.

Two acts. Dedication by "La Comica Società napolitana," dated February 14, 1783, cast, and name of the composer, Giuseppe **Coppola.** The author is unknown to Schatz.

First performed at Rome, Teatro di Tor di Nona, carnival, 1780. Schatz 2212

L'Amor vince Fortuna. Dramma per musica dedicato all' Altezza Serenissima Elettorale Massimiliano Emanuele duca di Baviera, etc. . . . in occasione delle di lui augustissime nozze con la Serenissima Maria Antonia arciduchessa d'Austria. Composto da Carlo Sigismondo Capece, e rappresentato in casa del medesimo.

Roma, Gio. Battista Bussotti, 1686. 62 p. 16^cm.

Prologue and three acts. Dedication by the author, name spelled Capeci. The composer is not mentioned and is unknown to Schatz. ML 50.2.A67

Amor vince tutto, ballet. *See* P. Guglielmi's La Morte di Cleopatra.

L'amor vincitor ossia Dianna ed Endimione, ballet. *See* P. Guglielmi's L'impostore punito.

L'amor vincitore ossia Diana ed Endimione, ballet. *See* Bianchi's La villa nella rapita.

L'amor vincitore, ballet. *See* Salieri and Rust's Il talismano.

L'amor volubile e tiranno. A. T. of A. Scarlatti's La Dorisbe.

Amor vuol sofferenza. O. T. Federico's libretto Li matti per amore.

Amore aguzza l'ingegno. Commedia per musica da rappresentarsi nel Real Teatro del Fondo di Separazione nel carnevale di questo corrente anno 1792.

Napoli, n. publ., 1792. 48 p. 15½^cm.

Two acts. Author not mentioned and unknown to Schatz. Cast and name of Gaetano **Marinelli** as the composer. With the opera were performed Giov. Battista Giannini's ballet "Il moro di corpo bianco o sia Lo schiavo del proprio onore." The composer of the music is not mentioned. Schatz 5958

L'amore ammalato. Die kranckende liebe. Oder: Antiochus und Stratonica. Musicalisches schau-spiel, auf dem grossen Hamburgischen theatro vorgestellet. Im jahr 1708.

n. i., n. d. Unpaged. 18½^cm.

Three acts. Neither the author, Barthold Feind, nor the composer, Christoph **Graupner,** is mentioned in the "Vorbericht." Some arias have Italian text in addition to the German. Schatz 4120

L'amore ammalato—Continued.

— **L'amore ammalato.** Die kranckende liebe. Oder: Antiochus und Stratonica. Musicalisches schau-spiel.

Barth. Feind's Deutsche gedichte, Stade, 1708, p. [393]–454. 17cm.

Three acts, with "Vorbericht." The composer, Christoph **Graupner,** is not mentioned. ML49.A2F2

Amore artigiano. Dramma di tre atti per musica. Rappresentato per la prima volta in Venezia il carnovale dell' anno MDCCLXI con musica del Lattilo [!].

Carlo Goldoni, Opere teatrali, Zatta e figli, 1788–95, v. 37, [137]–204 p. 18½cm. PQ

L'amore artigiano. Intermezzo per musica a quattro voci da rappresentarsi nel Teatro di Tordinona nel carnevale dell' anno 1778.

Roma, Ottavio Puccinelli, 1788. 28 p. 15½cm.

Two acts. By Goldoni, who is not mentioned. Cast, scenario, and name of Agostino **Accorimboni** as composer. SCHATZ 16

L'amore artigiano. Dramma giocoso per musica da rappresentarsi in Firenze nel Teatro di via del Coromero, nell' autunno dell anno 1770 . . .

[Firenze], Si vende da Ant. Giuseppe Pagani, n. d. 80 p.

By Goldoni, who is not mentioned. Scenario and name of Florian Leopold **Cassmann** as the composer.

First performed at Vienna, Burgtheater, April 26, 1767. SCHATZ 3608*

— **L'amore artigiano.** Dramma giocoso per musica da rappresentarsi nel Teatro grande alla Scala di Milano, la primavera dell' anno 1782 . . .

Milano, Gio. Batista Bianchi, n. d. 82 p. 16cm.

Three acts. By Goldoni, who is not mentioned. Dedication and name of the composer, Florian Leopold **Gassmann.** With the opera were performed Gaspero Angiolini's (also the music by him) ballets, "I geni riuniti," "Il Solimano secondo," "Il diavolo a quattro, ossia La doppia metamorfosi," and "La Lauretta." SCHATZ 3608

— **L'amore artigiano.** Drama giocoso da rappresentarsi nel Teatro di Ratisbona . . . Die liebe bey den handwerkern . . .

Regensburg, gedruckt mit Zunkelischen schuften, n. d. 199 p. 15½cm.

Three acts. By Goldoni, who is not mentioned. Cast, scenario, and name of Florian Leopold **Gassmann** as the composer.

Date of performance unknown to Schatz. SCHATZ 3610

— Die **liebe unter den handwerksleuten.** Ein lustiges singespiel, von dem herrn advocat, Carl Goldoni, aufgefuehret, auf dem kleinen Churfl. Saechs. Schauplatze, Dresden, im jahre 1770.

n. i., n. d. 182 p. 16cm.

Three acts. Slightly altered German version, with Italian text facing the German, of "L'amore artigiano," by **Gassmann,** whose name as composer is given. SCHATZ 3609

— Die **liebe unter den handwerksleuten.** Ein singspiel, aus dem italienischen des hrn. Goldoni, in drey aufzuegen. Aufgefuehrt auf dem K. K. Nationaltheater.

Wien, beym Logenmeister, 1779. 116 p. 16½cm.

Three acts. German translation totally different from the above. **Gassmann** is mentioned as the composer.

First performed as indicated, September 29, 1779. SCHATZ 3611

L'amore artigiano—Continued.

— Arien und gesaenge aus der oper: **Die liebe unter den handwerksleuten.** In drey aufzuegen. Die musik ist von Florian Gassmann.

Hamburg, J. M. Michaelsen, 1782. 36 p. 17ᶜᵐ.

Three acts. German version by Christian Gottlob Neefe, and totally different from the other translations.

First performed at Hamburg, Theater C. Gänsemarkt, August 28, 1782.

Schatz 3612

— Die **liebe unter den handwerksleuten,** eine operette, aus dem italiaenischen des herrn Goldoni, aufgefuehret am Churpfaelzischen hof in jahr 1772.

Mannheim, Hof- und Akademie-Buchdruckerei, n. d. 96 p. 15½ᶜᵐ.

Three acts. This German version again different from the others. Cast and name of **Gassmann** as the composer.

First performed, as indicated, at Schwetzingen, August, 1772. Schatz 3620

L'amore artigiano. Dramma giocoso per musica di Polisseno Fegejo Pastor Arcade, da rappresentarsi nel Teatro di S. Angelo il carnevale dell' anno 1761.

Venezia, Modesto Fenzo, 1761. 70 p. 15ᶜᵐ.

Three acts. By Goldoni. Cast, scenario, and name of Gaetano **Latilla** as composer.

Schatz 5442

— **L'amore artigiano.** Operetta comica, da rappresentarsi sul Regio Teatro Danese, il carnovale dell' anno 1762.—De forelskte haandverksfolk . . .

Kiøbenhavn, Lars Nielsen Svare, n. d. 115 p. 14½ᶜᵐ.

Three acts. Cast and names of Goldoni and **Latilla.** Danish text faces Italian.

Schatz 5443

Amore contadino. Dramma di tre atti per musica. Rappresentato per la prima volta in Venezia l'autunno dell' anno MDCCLX con musica del Lampugnani.

Carlo Goldoni, Opere teatrali. Venezia, Zatta e figli, 1788–95, v. 37, [205]–267 p. 18½ᶜᵐ.
PQ

L'amore costante. Commedia per musica in quattro atti di Giovanni Bertati da rappresentarsi nel nobilissimo Teatro Giustiniani di San Moisè per la prima opera il carnovale dell' anno 1787.

Venezia, Antonio Casali, n. d. 64 p. 18½ᶜᵐ.

Four acts. Cast and name of Giuseppe **Gazzaniga** as the composer.

First performed as indicated, December 26, 1786. Schatz 3683

— La **costanza in amor, rende felice.** Commedia per musica in quattro atti da rappresentarsi nel Ces. Reg. Teatro della città e porto-franco di Trieste il carnovale 1787.

Trieste, Stamperia dell' eccelso governo, n. d. 56 p. 17½ᶜᵐ.

Four acts. Cast and name of Giuseppe **Gazzaniga** as the composer. Slightly different text from the original of Bertati, who is not mentioned. For instance, I, 5 now begins "Pandolfino mio ben!" with the aria "La donna che è amante," instead of "Con questo maledetto can da guardia," with the aria "Oh quanto è mai felice."

Schatz 3686

Amore custode del giardino di Armida, ballet. *See* Anfossi's Armida.

L'amore della patria. *See* M. Curzio.

Amore di sangue. L. T. of Porta's Amore e fortuna.

Amore dottorato, con le Conclusioni difese da lui nel Tempio della Virtù . . . Invenzione drammatica intrecciata alla commedia dell' Amor virtuoso nel nobil collegio Tolomei per il carnevale di quest' anno 1691.

> *Siena, Stamperia del Pubblico, n. d.   3 p. l., 22 p.   13½ cm.*

Prologue and two intermezzi.   Dedication signed by "L' Economico Intronato," Arcadian name of Girolamo Gigli, as author.   Argument and note:
"Così, non per aggiungnere ornamento all' opera, che n' hà sortito a bastanza dalla penna ingegnosa dell' autore, ma per empire tutto quel tempo, che è destinato al trattenimēto dell' otio d'una sera virtuosa, si sono fraposte quest' invēzioni musicali; dove per alludere all' Amor virtuoso dell' azione, si mostra l'Amore in cattedra, che difende i suoi principij.   Le Conclusioni sono de' più accreditati autori in poesia italiana e premettēdosene una avāti ciascheduno atto della commedia, si mostrano nelle difese di quelle l'azioni virtuose de i primi personaggi dell' opera."
Not listed by Schatz.   Composer unknown to me.   ML 48.A5   v. 46

Amore e fortuna.   Drama da rappresentarsi in musica nel Teatro Giustinian di San Moisè il carnovale dell' anno 1727.

> *Venezia, Steffano Valvasense, 1727.   45 p.   15 cm.*

Three acts.   By Francesco Passarini, who is not mentioned.   Argument, scenario, and reader's notice with name of Giovanni **Porta** as the composer and the remark that this is a replica.
First performed at Rovigo, Teatro Campagnella, fall of 1712.   Schatz 8385

— **Amore di sangue.**   Drama per musica da rappresentarsi in Bergamo il carnevale dell' anno 1729 . . .

> *Venezia, Andrea Pippari, n. d.   48 p.   15 cm.*

Three acts.   Dedication, notice to the reader with Giovanni **Porta**'s name as the composer, argument, cast, and scenario.   This is Francesco Passarini's "Amore e fortuna" text with the customary modifications.   Schatz 8386

L' amore e l' azzardo, ballet.   *See* Rust's Gli antiquari in Palmira.

Amore e maestà o sia L'Arsace.   O. T. of Salvi's Arsace.

Amore e maestà.   Drama per musica da rappresentarsi in Bologna nel Teatro Marsiglj Rossi il carnovale dell' anno MDCCXXII.

> *Bologna, Costantino Pisarri, 1721.   59 p.   12°.*

Three acts.   By Antonio Salvi.   Notice to the reader, scenario, and cast, but without the names of the librettist and the composer.
First performed, as indicated, December 26, 1721.   Schatz 3384

Amore e magia, ballet.   *See* Portugal's Fernando nel Messico.

Amore e musica.   Intermezzi da rappresentarsi nel Teatro alla Valle degl' illustrissimi Sig. Capranica nel carnevale dell' anno 1773.

> *Roma, Lorenzo Corradi, n. d.   60 p.   16 cm.*

Two parts.   Author not mentioned and unknown to Schatz.   Dedication by Ang. Lungi, cast and name of Marcello di Capua (**Bernardini**) as composer.
                                   ML 50.2.A68B3

Amore e Psiche, ballet by Le Messier.   *See* Bertoni's Tancredi.

Amore e Psiche, ballet.   *See* Bianchi's Nitteti.

Amore e Psiche, ballo eroico. *See* Fischietti's La molinara.

Amore e Psiche. Opera rappresentata nell' Imperial Regio Teatro festeggiandosi i felicissimi sponsali di Ferdinando IIII di Borbone . . . e di Maria Giuseppa d'Austria l' anno MDCCLXVII.

Vienna, Ghelen, 1767. Unpaged. 23ᶜᵐ.

Three acts. Argument, cast, and name of Marco Coltellini as author, of Florian Leopold **Gassmann** as the composer.

First performed, as indicated, October 5, 1767. SCHATZ 3626

Amore e Psiche—Amor und Psyche, ballet. *See* Jommelli's Semiramide.

Amore e Psiche, ballet. *See* Robuschi's Briseide.

Amore e sdegno. Drama per musica da rappresentarsi nel Teatro Tron di S. Cassano nel carnevale dell' anno MDCCXXVI . . .

Venezia, Marino Rossetti, 1726. 48 p. 14½ᶜᵐ.

Three acts. Argument, cast, notice to the reader, and dedication signed by cav. Michiel Angelo Boccardi di Mazzera, who altered Francesco Silvani's (not mentioned) "La moglie nemica" under the above title. The composer, Luigi **Tavelli,** is not mentioned. SCHATZ 10253

Amore ed innocenza. A. T. of the ballet La fata Alcione.

L' amore eroico. Drama per musica da rappresentarsi nel Teatro Grimani di S. Samuele per la fiera dell' Ascensione l' anno 1725 . . .

Venezia, Marino Rossetti, 1725. 47 p. 14ᶜᵐ.

Three acts. According to Schatz a later version of "Zenobia in Palmira" by Apostolo Zeno and Pietro Pariati, but I find no such text in their works. Publisher's dedication, who speaks repeatedly of "il mio drama," argument, scenario, cast, and name of Giovanni Francesco **Brusa** as composer. SCHATZ 1373

L'amore figlio del merito. Drama per musica da recitarsi nel Teatro di Sant' Angelo l'anno 1694. Di Matteo Noris . . .

Venetia, Nicolini, 1694. 69 p. 14ᶜᵐ.

Three acts. Publishers dedication, argument, scenario. Marc' Antonio **Ziani,** the composer, is not mentioned.

First performed, as indicated, carnival 1694. SCHATZ 11179

Amore figlio della gratitudine. A. T. of Badia's La Rosaura.

L'amore fortunato ne' suoi disprezzi. A. T. of Galuppi's Alcimena principessa dell' Isole Fortunate.

Amore fra gl' Impossibili. Dramma per musica, di Amaranto Sciaditico, pastore Arcade.

Roma & Siena, Bonetti, 1693. 82 p. 13½ᶜᵐ.

Three acts. By Girolamo Gigli. Argument and scenario. The composer, Carlo **Campelli,** is not mentioned.

This ed. differs distinctly from the one at the Brussels Conservatoire, which has on the t.-p. "dedicato all' illustriss. Signora duchessa di Zagarolo e da lei fatto rappresentare nel suo teatro," has 4 p. l., with a dedication dated Rome, January 2, 1693, and signed by the poet Girolamo Gigli, and the text on only 76 p. SCHATZ 1532

Amore gastigato. Dramma musicale.

Girolamo Bartolommei Smeducci, Drammi musicali morali, Firenze, 1656, v. I, p. [183]–231. 23ᶜᵐ.

Prologue and three acts. Argument and allegoria. No composer recorded by Schatz. ML 49.A2B3

Amore giustificato. Festa teatrale in occasione delle felicissime nozze di S. A. S. il principe Massimiliano, duca di Sassonia etc. e di S. A. R. La principessa Carolina di Parma etc.

Dresda, Stamperia elettorale, 1792. 53 p. 21ᶜᵐ.

One act. Caterino Mazzolà is mentioned as the author, Johann Gottlieb **Naumann** as the composer. German title page, "Die gerechtfertigte liebe," and text face Italian.

First performed, as indicated, May 12, 1792.   SCHATZ 7037

Amore guerriero per la Rocca incantata. *See* Trattenimento musicale d'Apollo con il Reno.

L'amore immaginario. Commedia per musica da rappresentarsi nel Teatro Nuovo sopra Toledo per seconda commedia del corrente anno 1794.

Napoli, n. publ., 1794. 48 p. 15ᶜᵐ.

Two acts. Author not mentioned and unknown to Schatz. Cast, and name of the composer, Valentino **Fioravanti**.   SCHATZ 3114

L'amore in ballo. Dramma giocoso per musica da rappresentarsi nel Teatro Giustiniani di San Moisè il carnovale dell' anno 1765.

Venezia, Modesto Fenzo, 1765. 60, [1] p.

The additional p. contains the substitute aria I, 10, "Infelice meschinella."

Three acts. Antonio Bianchi, the author, is not mentioned. Cast, scenario, and name of Giovanni **Paisiello** as the composer.   SCHATZ 7587

L'amore in campagne. O. T. of Borghi's Le villanelle innamorate.

Amore in caricatura. Dramma di tre atti per musica. Rappresentato per la prima volta in Venezia il carnovale dell' anno MDCCLXI con musica del Ciampi.

Carlo Goldoni, Opere teatrali, Venezia, Zatta e figli, 1788–95, v. 37, [268]–313 p. 18½ᶜᵐ.   PQ

Amore in caricatura. Dramma per musica di Polisseno Fegejo Pastor Arcade, da rappresentarsi nel Teatro di S. Angelo il carnovale dell' anno 1761 . . .

Venezia, Modesto Fenzo, 1761. 48 p. 14½ᶜᵐ.

Three acts. By Goldoni. Impresario's dedication, cast, scenario, and name of the composer, Vincenzo Legrenzio **Ciampi**.   SCHATZ 1888

L'amore in contrasto, ballet. *See* Anfossi's Zemira.

L'amore in maschera. Commedia per musica di Antonio Palomba da rappresentarsi nel Teatro de' Fiorentini nel carnevale di quest' anno 1748 . . .

Napoli, Domenico Langiano, 1748. 4 p. l., 70 p. 14½ᶜᵐ.

Three acts. Impresario's dedication, cast, and name of Niccolò **Jommelli** as composer.   SCHATZ 4875

L'amore in musica. Dramma giocoso da rappresentarsi nel Teatro Giustiniani di S. Moisè il presente autunno MDCCLXIII.

Venezia, Francesco Valvasense, n. d. 71 p. 15ᶜᵐ.

Three acts. By Carlo Goldoni, according to Schatz, but not to be found in his works. Cast, scenario, and name of composer, Antonio **Boroni**.   SCHATZ 1244

L'amore in musica—Continued.

— L' amore in musica, opera comica da rappresentarsi nel Teatro della Solitudine per ordine di Sua Altezza Serenissima il regnante duca di Wirtemberg et Teck etc. La musica è del Signor Antonio Boroni . . .

[*Stuttgart*], *Nella stamperia di Cotta, 1770. 207 p. 16*cm.

Cast. French title, "L'amour en musique," and text face Italian.
First performed, as indicated, at Ludwigsburg in 1770. Schatz 1245

— L'amore in musica.

*89 p. 15*cm.

Title page wanting; has half-title only. Three acts. Cast, scenario, and name of Antonio **Boroni** as composer. Goldoni is not mentioned. ML 50.2.A69B6

Amore in puntiglio. Farsa per musica da rappresentarsi nel Teatro di S. Cassiano l'anno 1773.

*Venezia, n. publ., 1773. 52 p. 15*cm.

Three acts. Author not mentioned and unknown to Schatz. Michiel Pfeiffer di Franconia (Jean Michel **Pfeiffer**) is mentioned as the composer. Schatz 8001

Amore in tarantola. Dramma giocoso per musica da rappresentarsi nel Teatro Giustiniani di S. Moisè nell' autunno dell' anno MDCCL.

*Venezia, Modesto Fenzo, 1750. 60 p. 14*cm.

Three acts. By Vaccina who is not mentioned. Argument, cast, scenario, and name of Gaetano **Latilla** as composer. Schatz 5444

Amore in trappola. Dramma giocoso per musica del Sig. ab. Pietro Chiari da rappresentarsi nel Teatro Giustiniani di S. Moisè il carnovale dell' anno 1768.

*Venezia, Modesto Fenzo, 1768. 72 p. 15½*cm.

Three acts. Cast, scenario, and name of composer, Tommaso **Traetta**.

Schatz 10405

L'amore in villa. Componimento per musica a cinque voci da rappresentarsi nel Teatro domestico del cittadino Sforza Cesarini dagli Accademici Intrepidi.

*Roma, Salomoni, anno VI. dell' era repubblicana, [1797]. 47 p. 17*cm.

Two acts. Cast and names of Giuseppe Petrosellini as author, and of Pietro **Guglielmi** as composer. Schatz 4308

Amore inamorato. Drama per musica nel famoso Teatro Grimani di S. Gio. Grisostomo. L'anno MDCLXXXVI. Di MatteoNoris . . .

Venetia, Francesco Nicolini, 1686. 70, [1] p.

Three acts. Publisher's dedication, argument, scenario, and list of machines. The composer, Carlo **Pallavicino,** is not mentioned. The imprimatur is dated January 10, 1686. Schatz 7718

L'amore industrioso. Dramma giocoso per musica del celebre Signore Casori. Da rappresentarsi nel Piccolo Teatro di S. A. E. di Sassonia.

*Dresda, n. publ., 1769. 151 p. 15½*cm.

Three acts. Bernardino (Bernardo) **Ottani** is mentioned as the composer. German title page "Die scharfsinnige liebe" and text face Italian.
First performed Nov. 21, 1769, as indicated. Schatz 7357

L'amore industrioso. Dramma giocoso per musica da rappresentarsi nel Teatro Tron di S. Cassano nell' autunno dell' anno 1765. Del Signor abbate Casori.

Venezia, Modesto Fenzo, 1765.   62 p.   17½^{cm}.

Three acts.   Cast, scenario, and name of Gio. Marco **Rutini** as the composer.

SCHATZ 9186

Amore ingegnoso, o sia La giovane scaltra.   Dramma giocoso per musica da rappresentarsi nel Teatro Obbizzi il carnovale dell' anno 1775 . . .

Padova, Stamperia Penada n. d..   32 p.   19^{cm}.

Two acts.   Author not mentioned and unknown to Schatz.   Music by **Paisiello,** who is not mentioned.   Impresario's dedication and cast.   Originally known as "La cantata e disfida di Don Trastullo" and as such composed by Jommelli for Rome, 1746.

SCHATZ 7694

— L'amore ingegnoso.   Intermezzo in musica a cinque voci da rappresentarsi nel Teatro Valle degl' illustriss.   Sigg. Capranica nel carnevale dell' anno 1785 . . .

Roma, Agostino Palombini, n. d.   50 p.   15^{cm}.

Two acts.   Author not mentioned and unknown to Schatz.   Cast and name of **Paisiello** as composer.

ML 50.2.A693P2

— L'amore ingegnoso.   Dramma per musica da rappresentarsi nel Real Teatro di Salvaterra nel carnovale dell' anno 1790.

[Lisbona], Stamperia reale, n. d.   74 p.   15^{cm}.

Two acts.   Author not mentioned and unknown to Schatz.   Cast, scenario, and name of Giovanni **Paisiello** as the composer.

SCHATZ 7596

— L'amore ingegnoso.   Intermezzo in musica da rappresentarsi nel Teatro di S. A. E. di Sassonia.

Dresda, n. publ., 1786.   141 p.   15½^{cm}.

Two acts.   **Paisiello** is mentioned as the composer.   German title page "Die erfinderische liebe" and text face Italian.

First performed, as indicated, November 18, 1786.

SCHATZ 7597

Amore innamorato.   Favola da rappresentarsi in musica nel Teatro di S. Moisè l'anno 1642 . . .

Venetia, Battista Surian, 1642.   81 p.   13½^{cm}.

Five acts with prologue.   Dedication signed by the author Giovanni Battista Fusconi and dated January 1, 1642; argument, scenario, and name of **Francesco Cavalli** . . . creduto l'Anfione de' nostri giorni" as composer in the notice to the reader.

SCHATZ 1734

Amore innamorato.   A. T. of Scarlatti's La Psiche.

L'amore maestro di scuola, ballet.   *See* Rispoli's Ipermestra.

Amore per amore.   L. T. of M. A. Bononcini's Il trionfo di Camilla.

L'amore per forza.   Drama per musica da rappresentarsi nel Teatro Giustiniano di S. Moisè l'autunno dell' anno 1721.

Venezia, Marino Rossetti, 1721.   45 p.   14½^{cm}.

Three acts.   By Bartolomeo Pavieri, who is not mentioned.   Notice to the reader with argument, cast, scenario, and names of Girolamo **Bassani** as composer of the first act, of Matteo **Lucchini** of second and third.

SCHATZ 636

Amore per incanto. Commedia per musica da rappresentarsi nel Real Teatro del Fondo di Separazione per quart' opera di questo corrente anno 1791.

Napoli, Vincenzo Flauto, n. d. 52 p. 15½ᶜᵐ.

Two acts. Cast and name of **Marcello di Capua** as composer. Librettist not mentioned and unknown to Schatz. On p. 5–9 cast and description of "Il trionfo de' Spagnoli, o sia La disfatta de' Marrocchini. Ballo composto, e diretto dal Sig. Gio. Battista Giannini." Pietro Dutilieu is mentioned as composer of the music.

SCHATZ 838

L'amore per interesse. Drama giocoso per musica da rappresentarsi in Parma nel R. D. Teatro di corte il carnevale dell' anno MDCCLXXXVIII . . .

Parma, Carmignani, n. d. viii, 63, [1] p. 17ᶜᵐ.

Two acts. A later version of "Mirandolina" by Bertati, who is not mentioned. Imprimatur dated Dec. 19, 1786. Dedication by the impresario, Angelo Bentivoglio, cast, scenario, and name of the composer, Vincenzo **Fabrizj.** ("La musica è tutta nuova espressamente composta.") In two acts by Giovanni Bertati. On p. 51–63 pref., cast, and description of the five-act "Adelaide di Ghesclino. Ballo eroico, composto e diretto dal Signor Giuseppe Banti . . . La musica . . . è del Signor Domenico Rava, Napoletano." The second ballet was called "La Ghinghetta." First performed December 26, 1786, as indicated.

SCHATZ 2971

L'amore politico. A. T. of the ballet La donna bizzarra.

Amore premiato, ballet. *See* Paisiello's Il tamburo notturno.

L'amore rammingo. Dramma giocoso per musica in due atti d'Antonio Piazza Veneziano da rappresentarsi nel nobilissimo Teatro di S. Samuele nel carnovale dell' anno 1777.

Venezia, Gio. Battista Casali, 1777. 78 p. 17ᶜᵐ.

Two acts. Cast, scenario, and name of Francesco **Salari** as the composer. On p. [33]–44 dedication, scenario, cast, description, and name of Baldassare Filippo Mattei as the composer of the music of Innocenzo Gambuzzi's "Medonte, ballo eroico;" on p. [69]–78 the same without name of the composer of his ballet, "Il seguito tra l'armi o sia La donna militare."

SCHATZ 9266

L'amore secreto. A. T. of Spontini's Adelina Senese.

L'amore senza malizia. Dramma giocoso per musica del Sig. ab. Pietro Chiari da rappresentarsi nel Teatro Giustiniani di S. Moisè il carnovale dell' anno 1768.

Venezia, Modesto Fenzo, 1768. 72 p. 16ᶜᵐ.

Three acts. Cast, scenario, and name of Bernardo **Ottani** as the composer.

SCHATZ 7358

— L'amore senza malizia. Dramma giocoso per musica del Signore abb. Pietro Chiari da rappresentarsi nel Piccolo Teatro di S. A. E. di Sassonia.

Dresda, n. publ., 1768. 157 p. 15½ᶜᵐ.

Three acts. Cast, scenario, and name of Bernard(in)o **Ottani** as the composer. German title page, "Die liebe ohne bossheit," and text face Italian, which seems to follow the original closely.

SCHATZ 7359

L'amore senza malizia—Continued.
— L'amore senza malizia. Dramma giocoso per musica da rappresentarsi in Lisbona nel Teatro della Rua dos Condes nell' estate dell' anno 1774.

> [Lisbona], Stamperia reale, n. d.   87 p.   15ᶜᵐ.

Three acts. Cast, scenario, and name of Bernardino **Ottani** as composer. Chiari is not mentioned.   ML 48.C6I

L'Amore soldato. Dramma giocoso per musica da rappresentarsi nel Teatro Giustiniani di S. Moisè l'autunno dell' anno 1769.

> Venezia, Modesto Fenzo, 1769.   48 p.   17ᶜᵐ.

Three acts. Cast, scenario, names of the author, Niccolò Tassi, and of the composer, Alessandro **Felici**.   SCHATZ 3054

L'amore soldato ou L'amour soldat.   Opera-comique italien.   En trois actes; musique, del Signor Sacchini.   Représenté par l'Académie-royale de musique, le jeudi 8 juillet 1779.

> Paris, P. de Lormel, 1779.   85 p.   21ᶜᵐ.

Cast.   Italian text (by Nicola Tassi, not mentioned) and French text on opposite pages.
First performed at London, Haymarket, 1777.   ML 50.2.A697S2

Amore spesso inganna. A. T. of Sartorio's (?) Orfeo a torto geloso.

Amore trionfator della magia, ballet.   See Marescalchi's Il tutore ingannato.

L'amore trionfante della vendetta.   A. T. of Francesco Rossi's La Corilda.

Amore vendicato, ballet.   See Caruso's Antigono.

L'amore verso la patria.   Die liebe gegen das vaterland oder Der sterbende Cato. [vignette.] Musicalisches schau-spiel, auf dem grossen Hamburgischen Schau-platz aufgefuehret im jahr 1715.

> Hamburg, Friedrich Conrad Greflinger, n. d.   Unpaged.   19ᶜᵐ.

Three acts. In the "Vor-bericht" with argument it is stated that this is a translation from Matteo Noris [his "Catone Uticense"]. Neither Barthold Feind, the translator, nor Reinhard **Keiser**, the composer, is mentioned. Some arias have the Italian text added to the German.   SCHATZ 5075

L'amore vince l'inganno, drama pastorale d'ordine di sua Altezza Serᵐᵃ il Sigʳ duca regnante di Sassonia-Gotha ed Altenburgo, etc., rappresentato nel Theatro di Friedenstein.   Ai [blank] d'Aprile 1736.

> n. i., n. d.   34 p.   18ᶜᵐ.

Three acts. Author not mentioned and unknown to Schatz. Gottfried Heinrich **Stoelzel** is mentioned as the composer.   SCHATZ 10076

Amore vincitore dell' indifferenza, ballet.   See Jommelli's L'isola disabitata.

L'amore vinto dall' amicizia, ballet.   See G. F. de Majo's Catone in Utica.

L'amore volubile. Dramma giocoso per musica. Opera nuova del Signor abbate Serafino Bellini, poeta romano da rappresentarsi nel Teatro Zagnoni il carnevale dell' anno 1779 . . .

Bologna, Sassi, n. d.. 70, [1] *p.* 15*cm.*

Two acts. Imprimatur dated December 22, 1778. On p. 70 a list of errata, on the additional page a substitute aria for act II, sc. 10. With impresario's dedication, cast, scenario, and name of the composer, Luigi **Caruso** ("musica tutta nuova").

SCHATZ 1666

Os amores de Sisbe e Selene. A. T. of Calimedonte, rei do Epiro.

Gli amori d'Apollo e di Dafne di Gio. Francesco Busenello. Rappresentati in musica nel Teatro di S. Casciano, in Venetia nell' anno 1640.

Venetia, Andrea Giuliani, MDCLVI [!]. *4 p. l. (incl. front.), 64 p.* 15*cm.* *("Delle hore ociose di Gio. Francesco Busenello. Parte prima," Venetia, Andrea Giuliani, 1656.)*

Three acts with prologue. Author's dedication dated Venice, September 10, 1656, argument. The composer, Francesco **Cavalli,** is not mentioned. SCHATZ 1716

Gl' amori d'Apollo e di Leucotoe. Drama per musica di Aurelio Aureli, favola undecima. Rappresentato in Venetia nel famoso Teatro Grimano l'anno 1663 . . .

Venetia, Francesco Nicolini, 1663. *6 p. l. (incl. front.), 57 p.* 13½*cm.*

Three acts. Author's dedication dated Venice, January 8, 1663, argument and notice to the reader with the name of **Rovettino** as composer. SCHATZ 9107

Gli amori d'Igor primo Czar di Moscovia, ballet. *See* Cimarosa's L'impresario in angustie, (Milano, 1789).

Gli amori d'Igor, primo Zar di Moscovia, ballet. *See* Tarchi's Ifigenia in Tauride.

Gl' amori di Alessandro Magno e di Rossane. Dramma musicale posthumo del dottor Hiacint' Andrea Cicognini Academico Instancabile . . .

Venetia, Gio. Pietro Pinelli, 1651. *108 p.* 13½*cm.*

Three acts and prologue. Dedication by Giovanni Burnacini, dated Venice, January 24, 1651, and notice to the reader stating: "La famosa penna del dottor Hiacint' Andrea Cicognini, ordì quasi come quì vedi l'argomento, e tessutone il prologo; il primo atto, & due scene del secondo, cedè alla vita, & alla opera" and that the work was finished by an author who forbade to mention his name. Burnacini continues by saying that to him "che per i diletti dell' architettura, e di macchine posso con verità dirmi il primo, quanto al tempo, c'habbia ornate scene ò fatte macchine in questa città . . . è toccato di porre sul mio, benche picciolo theatro, un Alessandro grande; sproportione la conosco; e per il sito, e per l'opera, e per le mie forze . . ."

Composed by Francesco **Luccio** according to Schatz. It should be noted that (comp. Wotquenne Catalogue) the same text in the Bologna 1656 ed. mentions Benedetto Ferrari as composer. SCHATZ 5745

Gli amori di Alessandro e di Rossane. O. T. of Cicognini's text L'Alessandro amante.

Gli amori di Angelica e Medoro, ballet. *See* Paër's La Rossana.

Gli amori di Circe con Ulisse.   Opera italiana rappresentata sopra il Teatro di Dresda . . . composta in Italiano per il Sig. Gio. Batta. Ancioni & tradotta in francese . . . per il Sig. Angelo de Constantini Veron . . .   Dresda gli 22 maggio 1709.

[Dresden], Stampata per Giacomo Harpeter, n. d.   6 p. l., 87, [1] p. 19cm.

In twenty-two scenes. Cast, translator's dedication, and name of Carlo Agostino **Badia** as composer. Entirely different from "La costanza d'Ulisse," attributed by Schatz to Ancioni (1700). The French title "Les amours d'Ulisse & de Circe" and text face Italian. The argument at the end of the libretto.   SCHATZ 543

Gli amori di Clodio e Pompea, ballet. *See* Bianchi's Alonso e Cora.

Gli amori di Clodio e Pompea.   A. T. of Draghi's Chi più sà manco.

Gli amori di Giasone, e d' Isifile.   Festa teatrale di Oratio Persiani posta in musica dal Sign. Marco Marazzoli . . .

Venetia, Antonio Bariletti, 1642.   80 p.   13½cm.

Three acts and prologue. Author's dedication dated Venice, February 22, 1642, and argument.
First performed at Venice, Teatro Grimani a S. S. Gio. e Paolo, February 22, 1642.
SCHATZ 5923

Gli amori di Mirtillo con Silvanzia, ballet. *See* Antonelli's Catone in Utica.

Gli amori di Mirtillo e con Silvanzia, ballet. *See* Giordani's Osmane.

Gli amori di Rinaldo con Armida.
Three acts. Text by Girolamo Colatelli, music by Teofilo **Orgiani.**
First performed at Brescia, Teatro dell' Accademia degl' Erranti, 1697.
Not in L. of C.

— L'honor al cimento.   Opera musicale.   Da rappresentarsi nel Teatro di S. Fantino l'anno 1703 . . .

Venezia, Gio. Francesco Valvasense, 1703.   48 p.   14½cm.

Three acts. Dedication signed by the author Girolamo Colatelli, scenario, and notice to the reader with Teofilo Organi's (**Orgiani**) name as the composer, and remark:
"Si avvertisce, che si sono accorciate alcune scene, & aggionti alcuni versi, onde non è il drama in quel primo essere, in cui fù posto dall' autore."
In fact, it was a retouched version of "Gli amori di Rinaldo con Armida" as was also: SCHATZ 7295

— Armida regina di Damasco.   Drama per musica da rappresentarsi nel Teatro di Verona in questo autunnale 1711 . . .

Verona, n. publ., 1711.   45 p.   14cm.

Three acts. Impresario's dedication, practically the same notice to the reader as in Schatz 7295, but referring to **Orgiani** as "maestro della catedrale di Udine" and alluding to the addition of some verses "a causa della staggione autunale."
SCHATZ 7296

Li amori di Tirsi ed Eurilla interrotti dalla maga Falsirena, ballet. *See* Galuppi's Cajo Mario.

Gl' amori fatali. L. T. of Pistocchi's Il Leandro.

Gl' amori infruttosi di Pirro. Drama per musica di Aurelio
Aureli, favola ottava. Nel Teatro Ass. Gio. e Paulo. Per l'anno
1661 . . .

Venetia, Francesco Nicolini, 1661. 72 p. 14ᶜᵐ.

Three acts. Author's dedication dated Venice, January 4, 1661, argument, and
notice to the reader:
"Averti, che la scena nona và doppo la scena quinta nel terzo atto . . . Sappi
di più, che per essere il Signor Clemente arrivato in tempo, ch'erano già dispensate le
parti del drama, m' è convenuto inserirlo nell' uno, e nell' altro al meglio, che hà
potuto permettere la brevità del tempo; havendo havuto un solo riguardo, di non
privarti del godimento della voce di un virtuoso si insigne nel rimanente compatisci,
e stà sano."
Antonio **Sartorio**, the composer, is not mentioned. SCHATZ 9480

Gl' amori ministri della fortuna. Drama per musica da rappresentarsi nel Regio Teatro di Milano l' anno MDLXCIV. Del Signor
abbate Francesco Silvani . . .

*Milano, Marc' Antonio Pandolfo Malatesta, n. d. 6 p. l., 88 p.
14½ᶜᵐ.*

Three acts. Impresario's dedication dated Milan, January 9, 1694, argument, cast,
scenario, and notice to the reader with name of Marc' Antonio **Ziani** as composer. A
contemporary ms. note on 2d p. l. says: "Mai fatta à Venezia sotto alcun altro
titolo." SCHATZ 11208

Gl'amori politici della libertà raminga. *See* M. Curzio.

Gl' amori tra' gl' odii, o sia Il Ramiro in Norvegia. Drama per
musica da rappresentarsi nel Teatro Tron di S. Cassiano l'anno 1699.

Venetia, Nicolini, 1699. 68 p. 15ᶜᵐ.

Three acts. Argument, "supposti," scenario, and notice to the reader with the
name of Marc' Antonio Remena as author, and of Marc' Antonio **Ziani** as the composer.
First performed, as indicated, carnival 1699. SCHATZ 11199

L'amorosa libertà. Dramma musicale del Signor Carlo Barbetta
. . . e recitata nella città di Senegaglia l' anno 1647.

Macerata, Filippo Camacci, 1647. 12 p. l., 137 p. 13ᶜᵐ.

Five acts with prologue. Author's dedication dated "Senegaglia, 10. Febraro
1647," notice to the reader, Imprimatur, poem, sonett by "L'autore dell' opera al
Signor Francesco **Ferrari**, maestro di cappella, & musico di camera dell' eminentissimo Fachinetti. Per la compositione musicale dell' Amorosa libertà," argument,
and characters without cast. SCHATZ 3076

Amors gukkasten. Eine operette in einem aufzuge, von J. B.
Michaelis.

Leipzig, Dyckische buchhandlung, 1772. 54 p. 17ᶜᵐ.

Christian Gottlob **Neefe**, the composer, is not mentioned.
First performed at Königsberg, Ackermann'sches Schauspielhaus, August 1772.
SCHATZ 7069

L'amour au village, opera-comique en un acte, et en vaudevilles,
représenté pour la premiere fois sur le Théâtre du Fauxbourg S.
Germain, le 3 février 1745. Nouvelle édition.

*Paris, Duchesne, 1762. 48 p. 19ᶜᵐ. (Theatre de M. Favart,
Paris, Duchesne, 1763–77, t. vii.)*

Many of the airs printed in the text. Favart's musical collaborator not mentioned
by Font. ML 49.A2F1

L'amour clairvoyant—Der sehende Cupido, ballet. *See* Bernasconi's La Clemenza di Tito.

L'amour conjugal. A. T. of Gaveaux's Léonore.

L'amour conjugal. A. T. of Grétry's Céphale et Procris.

L'amour coquet. A. T. of Campra's L'âge viril.

L'amour desoeuvré, ou Les vacances de Cythère. Pièce en un acte. Composée pour être représentée à la Foire S. Laurent 1734 sur le Théâtre de l'Opéra comique.

   Le Théâtre de la foire, Paris, 1737, t. ix, 2, [489]–534 p.   17ᶜᵐ.

   By Carolet. Largely *en Vaudevilles.* The airs are printed at the end of the volume in the "Table des airs." A prefatory note on p. [90] informs the reader that this piece which was commenced in August, 1734, and was scheduled for performance in the same month, was not performed at the Opéra-comique.   ML 48L2X

L'amour en musique.   Tr. of Boroni's L'amore in musica.

L'amour enjoué. A. T. of Campra's La vieillesse.

L'amour enjoué. *See* Fragments, composés . . . de l'acte de . . .

L'Amour et Psyché. *See* Mondonville's Les festes de Paphos.

L'amour filial, opéra en un acte. Par C. A. Demoustier.

   Paris, Huet [etc.], L'an second [1793–94].   port., 48 p.   20ᶜᵐ.

   The colored port. is that of Juliet who played Germon in the opera, according to the cast. The composer, Pierre **Gaveaux,** is not mentioned. An Avertissement with compliments to the actors reads in part:

   "Au moment où l'on imprime cet ouvrage, il est à sa cent-quatrième représentation . . ."

   The title had been originally "Les deux Suisses," but the political events necessitated a change.

   First performed at Paris, Théatre Feydeau, March 7, 1792.   ML 50.2.A7G2

— Arien und gesaenge aus dem singspiel: **Kindliche liebe,** in einem akt, aus dem franzoesischen. Die musick ist von Gavaux.

   Frankfurt am Main, n. publ., 1798.   19 p.   16ᶜᵐ.

   German version by Carl Alexander Herklots.

   First performed at Frankfurt a. M., Nationaltheater, 1798; at Berlin, Kgl. Nationaltheater, October 16, 1796.   Schatz 3637

L'amour impromptu.   Parody of an entrée in Rameau's Les fêtes d'Hébé.

L'amour ingenu. A. T. of Campra's La jeunesse.

[L'Amour malade].   Vers du Ballet du roy.

   n. i., n. d.   15 p.   21½ᶜᵐ.

   Half title, title page evidently wanting. Ten entries, with names of the dancers. This is clearly the same as the entry by De La Vallière: "Amour malade, ballet du loi à dix entrées, dansé par Sa Majesté le 17 janvier 1675 [! instead of 1657]. Les paroles sont de Benserade. Paris, Robert Ballard, 1657."

   From the words in the fifth entrée, "Baptiste, compositeur de la musique du ballet, représentant Scaramouche," it follows that the music was composed by Jean Baptiste de **Lully.**   ML 52.2.B15

L'amour marin. *See* L'indifférence.

L'amour maternel. A. T. of Grétry's Elisca.

L'amour peintre, ou Le jaloux dupé. Opéra comique en deux actes, tiré de Molière.

Cassel, Griesbach, 1794. 52 p. 20^cm.

Two acts. Text and music by David Philipp von **Apell,** according to Schatz, who does not record a performance. Schatz 292

Intermèdes d'**Amour pour amour,** comédie en trois actes et en vers, représentée devant Leurs Majestés à Versailles le 23 janvier 1765.

[Paris], Christophe Ballard, 1765. 15 p. 20½^cm. (Journal des spectacles, t. i, 1766.)

Three intermèdes. Cast and name of François **Rebel** as responsible for "l'arrangement de la musique," but on p. 7 of the Journal he is also said to have selected the words. ML 48 J7

L'amour quêteur, comédie en deux actes et en vers, mêlée d'ariettes et de vaudevilles. Par Mr. Maillé de Merencour. Représenté pour la premiere fois par la troupe des Petits comédiens de Sa Majesté, le 14 octobre 1777. Nouvelle edition.

Paris, Delalain, 1782. 32 p. 20½^cm.

Cast. Arranger of the music not mentioned. Not recorded by Schatz. ML 50.2.A702

L'amour saltinbanque. Entrée in Campra's Les festes vénitiennes.

L'amour soldat. Tr. of Sacchini's L'amore soldato.

L'amoureux de quinze ans, ou La double fête, comédie en trois actes et en prose, mêlée d'ariettes. Les paroles sont de M. Laujon; la musique de M. Martiny. Représentée pour la premiere fois par les Comédiens italiens ordinaires du roi, le 18 avril 1771.

Paris, la veuve Duchesne, 1771. 68 p. 21^cm.

Cast. On p. 65–68 the "*Ariettes*" "Que j'avions d'impatience" (II, 7), "Ah! Ah! Ah! v'là tous nos bouquets" (II, 8), and the "*Vaudeville.* Note d'moiselle a dit. (Divertissement.)" Schatz 6034

— **L'amoureux de quinze aus,** ou La double fête, comedie en trois actes et en prose, meslée d'ariettes . . . Représentée pour la premiere fois par les Comédiens italiens ordinaires du roi, le jeudi 18 avril 1771. Les paroles sont de M. Laujon. La musique de M. Martiny.

Paris, la veuve Duchesne, 1771. 64 p. 17½^cm.

Cast. On p. 63–64 the airs of "Que j'avions d'impatience" and "Ah! ah! v'là ous nos bouquets." Yudin PQ
t

— Der **liebhaber von funfzehn jahren,** ein singspiel in drey aufzuegen nach dem franzoesischen. Die musik ist vom herrn Martiny. Aufgefuehrt auf dem k. k. Nationaltheater.

Wien, beym logenmeister, 1778. 77 p. 17^cm.

By Gottlieb Stephanie d. jüng.
First performed, as indicated, December 29, 1778. Schatz 6035

Les amours champêtres, pastorale, par Monsieur F . . . Représentée pour la premiere fois par les Comédiens italiens ordinaires du roi, le jeudi 2 septembre 1751. Troisième édition.

 Paris, N. B. Duchesne, 1759. 47 [1] p. 19ᶜᵐ. (Theatre de Favart, Paris, Duchesne, 1763–77, t. i.)

One act. Cast. Several airs are printed in the text. The arranger of the music is not mentioned. The unnumb. p. contains a "Catalogue de parodies & opera comiques." ML 49.A2F1

Les amours d'Arion & de Léucosie—Die lieb des Arion gegen die Leucosie, ballet. *See* Bernasconi's Demofoonte.

Les amours d'été, divertissement en un acte & en vaudevilles, par MM. de Piis & Barré; représenté pour la première fois, à la Muette, devant Leurs Majestés, le jeudi 20 septembre 1781; & à Paris, le mardi 25 du même mois, par les Comédiens italiens ordinaires du roi.

 Paris, Vente, 1784. 32 p. 19ᶜᵐ.

Printed in the text is the air "Avec les yeux, dans le village," scene 1. The arranger of the vaudevilles not recorded by Schatz. SCHATZ 11480

Les amours d'Ulisse & de Circe. Tr. of Badia's Gli amori di Circe con Ulisse.

Les amours de Bastien et Bastienne. Parody of Rousseau's Le devin du village.

Les amours de Gonesse. A. T. of de La Borde's Le Mitron et la Mitronne.

Les amours de Mars et de Venus, ballet représenté par l'Academie royale de musique l'an 1712. Les paroles de M. Danchet & La musique de M. Campra. LXXIX. opera.

 n. i., n. d. pl., 447–480 p. 14ᶜᵐ. (Recueil général des opéra, Paris, 1714, t. x, 7.)

Detached copy. Three *entrées* with prologue.
First performed, as indicated, Sept. 6, 1712. SCHATZ 1543
            Second copy. ML 48.R4

— **Les amours de Venus,** ballet.

 [183]–216 p. 17½ᶜᵐ. (Antoine Danchet, Théâtre, Paris, 1751, t. iii.)

Prologue and three entrées. **Campra,** the composer, is not mentioned.
            PQ 1972.D2

Ballet des **Amours de Momus,** en musique, dansé par l'Academie royale de musique. Suivant la copie imprimée à Paris.

 Amsterdam, Antoine Schelte, 1696. 43 p. (incl. front.) 14ᶜᵐ.

Prologue and three acts. Neither the author, Joseph François Duché, nor Henri **Desmarets** is mentioned.
First performed, as indicated, May 25, 1695. ML 52.2.A4D2

— **Les amours de Momus,** ballet representé par l'Academie royale de musique l'an 1695. Les paroles sont de M. Duché, & la musique de M. Desmarets. XXXV. opera.

 n. i., n. d. front., p. 135–184. (Recueil général des opéra, t. v, Paris, 1703. 14ᶜᵐ.

Detached copy. Prologue and three acts.
First performed, as indicated, May 25, 1695. SCHATZ 2529
            Second copy. ML 48.R4

Les **amours de Nanterre.** Piéce d'un acte. Par Mrs. le S**. & D'Or**. Représenté à la Foire de Saint Laurent 1718. Et pendant le cours de la même foire, sur le Théâtre de l'Opéra, par ordre de S. A. Royale Madame.

Le Théâtre de la foire, Paris, 1737, t. iii, pl., [269]–329 p. 17^{cm}.

By Le Sage and d'Orneval. Largely *en vaudevilles.* The airs, selected or composed and arranged by Jean Claude **Gillier,** the "compositeur" of the theatre, are printed at the end of the volume in the "Table des airs." Parfaict's Dictionnaire gives as authors "Autreau en société avec messieurs Le Sage & d'Orneval."

ML 48.L2 III

Les **amours de Protée,** ballet, représenté par l'Academie royale de musique, l'an 1720. Paroles de M. Lafonds. Musique de M. Gervais. XCIX. opera.

n. i., n. d. pl., p. 65–116. (Recueil général des opéra, t. xiii, Paris, 1734.) 14^{cm}.

Detached copy. Three acts and prologue. Avertissement.
First performed, as indicated, May 16, 1720. SCHATZ 3790a
Second copy. ML 48.R4

— Les **amours de Protée,** ballet. En trois actes. Representé par l'Academie royale de musique, de Lyon. En l'année 1742.

Lyon, Aimé Delaroche, 1742. 58 p. 23½^{cm}.

Three acts and prologue. By Joseph de Lafont, who is not mentioned. Avertissement and cast. Composed by Charles Hubert **Gervais,** who is not mentioned.

SCHATZ 3790b

— Les **amours de Protée.** Parodie de l'opera. Par M^{rs.} le S** & d'Or** Representée à la Foire Saint Laurent 1728.

Le Théâtre de la foire, Paris, 1731, t. vii, pl., [85]-120 p. 17^{cm}.

By Le Sage and d'Orneval. Largely *en vaudevilles.* The airs, selected or composed and arranged by Jean Claude **Gillier,** the "compositeur" of the company, are printed at the end of the volume in the "Table des airs."
First performed, as indicated, September 24, 1728. ML 48.L2 v. 11

Les **amours de Ragonde,** comédie en musique, en trois actes.

n. i., n. d. 1 p. l., 30 p. 23^{cm}.

Neither the author, Philippe Néricault Destouches, nor the composer, Jean Joseph **Mouret,** is mentioned. Cast and at end the "Permission," dated Lyon, March 15, 1739, as given to the Académie Royale de musique de Lyon.

First performed there 1742; previously at Sceaux, at the palace of the duke du Maine under the title "Le mariage de Ragonde" as also at Paris, Académie royale de musique, January 30, 1742. The score was published as "Ragonde ou La soirée de village." SCHATZ 6738

Les **amours de Venus.** L. T. of Campra's Les amours de Mars et Vénus.

Les **amours deguisez.** *See* Les comediens corsaires.

Les **amours déguisez,** ballet representé par l'Académie royale de musique l'an 1713. Les paroles de M. Fuselier et la musique de M. Bourgeois. LXXXII. opera.

n. i., n. d. 48 p., pl. (Recueil général des opéra, Paris, 1720, t. xi) 14^{cm}.

Detached copy. Three acts with prologue. Avertissement.
First performed, as indicated, August 22, 1713. SCHATZ 1272
Second copy. ML 48.R4

Les amours des déesses, ballet heroique, representé par l'Academie royale de musique, l'an 1729.   Paroles de M. Fuselier.   Musique de M. Quinault.   CXII. opera.

n. i., n. d.   pl., p. [345]-396.   14*cm*.   (*Recueil général des opéra, Paris, 1734, t. XIV.*)

Detached copy.   Prologue and three acts, to which was added as *quatrième entrée,* text also by Louis Fuzelier (p. 387–396), "L'Aurore et Céphale," on August 25, 1729. The other entrées have titles "Venus et Adonis," "Diane et Endimion". and "Melpomene et Linus."   The introduction of the latter subject the author defends in the *avertissement* (p. 347–348).

First performed, as indicated, August 9, 1729.   Schatz 8530
Second copy.   ML 48.R4

Les amours des dieux, ballet heroique, representé par l'Academie royale de musique, l'an 1727.   Paroles de M. Fuselier.   Musique de M. Mouret.   CVIII. opera.

*n. i., n. d.   p. 123-188, pl.   (Recueil général des opéra, t. xiv, Paris, 1734.)   14*cm*.

Detached copy.   Prologue and four entrées, called "Neptune et Amymone," "Jupiter et Niobe," "Apollon et Coronis," and "Bacchus et Ariane."   Schatz 6739
Second copy.   ML 48.R4

— Les amours des dieux, ballet-heroique, représenté par l'Academie-royale de musique, pour la premiere fois, le dimanche quatorze septembre 1727.   Remis au Théâtre le mardi 18 juin 1737, le jeudi 12 may 1746, et le mardi 16 août 1757.

Paris, Aux dépens de l'Académie, chez la v. Delormel & fils, 1757.
*51 p.   22½*cm*.*

Prologue and three entrées, with titles "Neptune et Amymone," "Apollon et Coronis," "Ariane et Bacchus."   Casts, avertissement and names of Fuzelier as author and of **Mouret** as composer.   ML 52.2.A5

Amours des dieux.   *See also* Fragments, composés du prologue des . . .

Les amours grivois, opera comique-ballet.   Divertissement flamand, en un acte.   Par M. Favart.   Derniere edition, augmentée des couplets nouveaux.

*n. i., 1751.   56 p.   19*cm*.   (Theatre de M. Favart, Paris, Duchesne, 1763–77, t. vii.)*

En vaudevilles.   On p. 41–56 seventeen airs headed "L'ecole des amours grivois," which title appears to have been the original title.   Font mentions Lagarde and Lesueur as Favart's collaborators, and says that he composed one of the airs.   He does not mention Favart's musical collaborator.

First performed at Paris, Foire St. Laurent, July 16, 1744.   ML 9.A2F1

The amours of the great.   A. T. of Vanelia.

The amours of Venus; or Vulcan's revenge.   An episodical ballet.

Noverre, Jean George, Works.   Tr. from the French, London, 1783,
v. 3, p. [285]-299.   21½*cm*.

Argument and detailed description of the four scenes.   GV 787.N8

Amphion.   Entrée in Grenet's Le triomphe de l'harmonie.

Amphion.   Eine oper, in musik gesetzt vom herrn oberkapellmeister Naumann.

Leipzig, Breikopf, n. d.   24 p.   18^{cm}.

Three acts.   The author, Johann Leopold Neumann, is not mentioned.   Not the original German edition as used for the first performance at Schwedt (Brunswick) Hoftheater, 1788.   Previously performed with Swedish text in one act by Gudmund Göran Adlerbeth at Stockholm, January 26, 1778 (Schatz), January 1, 1778 (Norlind).

SCHATZ 7038

Amphitryon: or, the two Sosia's.   A comedy.   As it is acted at the Theatre Royal.   Written by Mr. Dryden.   To which is added, the musick of the songs.   Compos'd by Mr. Henry Purcell.

London, J. Tonson and M. Tonson, 1691.   4 p. l., 57, [3] p.   21½^{cm}.

—— The songs in **Amphitryon.**   The musick.   Composed by Mr. Henry Purcell.

London, Jacob Tonson, 1690.   1 p. l., 13 p.   21½^{cm}.

The comedy was advertised early in November 1690 as published.   The first edition had in the title the misprint "Socia's" instead of "Sosia's."   Our copy of the text belongs to the corrected, second edition, in which the misprint has disappeared from the title page, but was retained in the caption title on p. 1.   This second edition, as follows from Dryden's "epistle dedicatory" to Sir William Levison Gower, Bar, of date October 24, 1690, must have been printed after the "third day," which fixes the date of performance approximately.

First edition of the music (voice and partly figured bass) including "Celia, that I once was blest," "For Iris I sigh," "Fair Iris and her swain" (dialogue) and chorus "Thus at the height we love."

Five acts, prologue and epilogue, followed by a catalogue of John Dryden's works. Cast and Dryden's dedication dated October 24, 1690, in which he acknowledges his indebtedness to Plautus and Molière and says:

"But what has been wanting on my part, has been abundantly supplyed by the excellent composition of Mr. **Purcell**, in whose person we have at length found an English-man, equal with the best abroad.   At least my opinion of him has been such, since his happy and judicious performances in the late opera; and the experience I have had of him, in the setting my three songs for this *Amphitryon:* To all which, and particularly to the composition of the *Pastoral dialogue*, the numerous quire of fair ladies gave so just an applause on the third day . . ."

ML 50.2.A705P9

— **Amphitryon:** or, The two Sosias.   A comedy, alter'd from Dryden.   As it is perform'd at the Theatre-Royal in Drury-Lane. With a new interlude of music, an occasional prologue, and some account of the alterations.

London, Printed and sold by J. Payne, 1756.   4 p. l., 56 p.   29¼^{cm}.

Five acts.   Cast.   In his préface, John Hawkesworth (not mentioned) gives as his main reason for the alterations "the profaneness and immodesty" of the original which would have made its revival impossible.   He has dropped all the songs which gave Purcell his inning.   Consequently Purcell's music can not have been used in this revival.   All the music has been relegated to the end of the fourth act and consists of Mercury's song "Away with the fables philosophers hold," a song by a nymph "in the character of wit" and a duet by the two.   The composer of this is not mentioned.

PR 3415.A5   1756

Amphitryon, ballet héroï-comique, en trois actes.

Venard de La Jonchère, Théâtre lyrique, Paris, Barbou, 1772, t. I, p. [179]–228 p.   18¼^{cm}.

In the interesting "Avant-propos" (p. 181–190) the author calls this his "coup d'essai."   No composer mentioned and none recorded by Cl. & L.   ML 49.A2L2

Amphytrion.   Tr. with additions of Gasparini's Anfitrione.

Amulio e Numitore. Drama per musica da recitarsi nel famoso Teatro Grimano di S. Gio. Grisostomo l'anno 1689 . . .

Venetia, Nicolini, 1689. front., 72 p. 15^{cm}.

Three acts. Dedication signed with the initials of the author Adriano Morselli, brief notice to the reader with name of [Giuseppe Felice] **Tosi** as the composer, argument and scenario.   SCHATZ 10375

Anacréon. Entrée in Les fêtes liriques.

Anacréon chez Polycrate, opéra en trois actes, représenté pour la première fois, à Paris, sur le Théatre des arts, le 28 nivose, an cinqui- ème. Seconde édition. Paroles de J. H. Guy. Musique de Grétry.

Paris, Tiger, an vii de la République [1798-99] 74, [1] p. 19½^{cm}.

Cast. First performed, as indicated, January 17, 1797.   SCHATZ 4137

Anacreonte tiranno. Drama per musica nel famoso Teatro Ven- dramino di San Salvatore. L'anno MDCLXXVIII. Del Bus- sani . . .

Venetia, Francesco Nicolini, 1678. 72 p. 14½^{cm}.

Three acts. Author's dedication, argument, scenario and notice to the reader: "Eccoti l'Anacreonte. In questo drama tù godrai il diletto de recitanti animato dalla musica sempre più maravigliosa e singolare del Signor Antonio **Sartorio** . . .
SCHATZ 9490

Anagilda. Dramma per musica da rappresentarsi nel Teatro Giustinian di S. Moisè. Nel carnovale dell' anno 1749.

Venezia, Modesto Fenzo, 1749. 15^{cm}. 36^{cm}.

Three acts. Argument, cast, scenario. Author (Girolamo Gigli) and composer not mentioned, and the latter unknown to Schatz.   SCHATZ 11302

L'Anagilda. Dramma per musica da rappresentarsi nel Teatro domestico dell' illustrissimo ed eccellentissimo Signor principe di Cerveteri pel carnovale del 1711.

Roma, Antonio de' Rossi, n. d. 86 p. 15^{cm}.

Three acts. By Girolamo Gigli, who is not mentioned. Cast, scenario, name of Antonio **Caldara** as composer, and argument, which reads, in part:

"Quest' opera, che tante volte è comparsa in diversi teatri d'Italia, si fa vedere adesso in Roma con qualche piccola mutazione, e giunta di ariette colle quali ha stimato di ravvivarla, e meglio addattarla all' uso d'oggidì il suo medesimo primo autore. Egli, per commandamento del generoso personaggio che la fa rappresentare, ed a cui si fa pregio di servire attualmente, ci ha tramezzate due parti ridicole affatto sciolte dal nodo del dramma (siccome oggi si pratica nelle scene di Venezia, ed altrove) colle quali s'intrecciano gli stessi intermedj, di piacevoli invenzioni di danze, e com- parse, al maggior divertimento composti."

The two intermezzi are called "Dorina e Grullo," but were also known as "Grullo e Dorina."   SCHATZ 1491

L'Anagilda. Drama per musica da rappresentarsi nel famoso Teatro Tron di San Cassiano nel carnovale dell' anno 1735 . . .

Venezia, Marino Rossetti, 1735. 44 p. 15½^{cm}.

Three acts. By conte Antonio Zaniboni, who figures only as "un pastore d'Ar- cadia." Impresario's dedication, cast, argument, and name of [Gaetano] Antonio **Pampino [Pampani?]** as the composer.   SCHATZ 7756

Anagilda, azione drammatica, da rappresentarsi nel Regio Teatro Danese.—Anagilda, et synge-spil . . .

Kiøbenhavn, H. J. Graae, 1772. 63 p. 17^{cm}.

One act. Author not mentioned and unknown to Schatz. Cast and name of Paolo **Scalabrini** as the composer. ("La musica è tutta nuova.") Italian and Danish texts.

First performed December 18, 1772, as indicated.   SCHATZ 9514

L'anarchia dell' imperio. Drama per musica da rappresentarsi nel famosissimo Teatro Vendramino à San Salvatore. L'anno MDCLXXXIV. Di Tomaso Stanzani. Seconda impressione con nove aggiunte . . .

Venetia, Francesco Nicolini, 1684. 60 p. 14½cm.

Three acts. Stanzani's dedication, dated Venice, January 1, 1684, argument, and scenario. Giovanni **Legrenzi**, the composer, is not mentioned.
First performed, according to Schatz, fall of 1683. SCHATZ 5541

L'Andromaca. Drama per musica da rappresentarsi in Firenze nel Teatro di via della Pergola nel prossimo carnevale dell' anno 1728 . . .

Firenze, Domenico Ambrogio Verdi, n. d. 70 p. 15cm.

Three acts. Argument, cast, scenario. Author and composer not mentioned and unknown to Schatz. Text based on Racine's "Andromaque." SCHATZ 11305

Andromaca. Drama per musica da rappresentarsi nel Regio Teatro di Milano . . .

Milano, Marc' Antonio Pandolfo Malatesta, 1701. 6 p. l., 60 p. 15cm.

Three acts and prologue. Dedication signed by the author Pietro d'Averara, argument and scenario. Composer not mentioned and unknown to Schatz.
First performed 1701 as indicated. SCHATZ 11304

Andromaca.

Apostolo Zeno, Poesie drammatiche, Venezia, 1744, t. ii, 85 p. 19cm.

Five acts and licenza. Argument. No composer is mentioned. In the "Catalogo" at end of t. x., date and place of first ed. are given as Vienna, 1724 (first performed August 28 with music by **Caldara**). ML 49.A2Z3

— Andromaca. Pubblicata per la prima volta in Vienna, 1724.

Apostolo Zeno, Poesie drammatiche, Orleans, 1785-86, t. vi, p. 78. 21cm.

Five acts and licenza. Argument. No composer is mentioned. ML 49.A2Z4

Andromaca. Dramma per musica da rappresentarsi nel nobilissimo Teatro di S. Benedetto nell' carnovale dell' anno MDCCLXXII.

Venezia, Modesto Fenzo, n. d. 54 p. 17½cm.

Three acts. Argument, cast, scenario, and name of Ferd. Gius. **Bertoni** as composer, but not of librettist, Antonio Salvi. On p. 24–26, cast and description of the ballet, "Inca il tiranno," by Giovanni Antonio Sacco (composer not mentioned), and, by the same ballet master, on p. 42–43, description of the ballet, "La pietà inaspettata."
First performed at Venice, as indicated, December 26, 1771. SCHATZ 904

Andromaca, drama per musica da rappresentarsi nel Nuovo Teatro del Signor Domenico Valle nel carnevale dell' anno 1730 . . .

Roma, Zempel e de Mey, n. d. 59 p. 15½cm.

Three acts. By Apostolo Zeno, who is not mentioned, but "Ridotta oggi all' uso delle Romane scene" (p. 4). Impresario's dedication, argument, cast, scenario, and name of Francesco **Feo** as the composer.
First performed as indicated, February 5, 1730. SCHATZ 3062

L'Andromaca. Dramma per musica da rappresentarsi nel Real Teatro di S. Carlo nel dì 4. novembre di quest' anno 1742. Per festeggiare il glorioso nome di Sua Maestà.

Napoli, Francesco e Cristoforo Ricciardo, n. d.   2 p. l., 60 p.   14^{cm}.

Three acts. By Antonio Salvi, who is not mentioned. Dedication, argument, cast, scenario, and name of Leonardo **Leo** as composer. According to the dedication by barone di Liveri, "L'Andromaca, . . . altra volta col titolo di Astianatte videsi in questa città . . ." which leaves it open whether this applies to the text only or also to Leo's music.   SCHATZ 5556

Andromaca. Dramma per musica da rappresentarsi nel Regio Teatro di Torino nel carnovale del 1781. Alla presenza delle Maestà Loro.

Torino, Onorato Derossi, n. d.   viii, 63 p.   16^{cm}.

Three acts. By Antonio Salvi, who is not mentioned. Argument, cast, scenario, and names of Vincenzo Martin (**Martin y Soler**) as the composer of the opera, of Vittorio Amedeo Canavasso as composer of Filippo Beretti's ballets, "La bella Arsene," "Il teatro italiano alla China," and "Marinari di nazioni diverse."
First performed, as indicated, December 26, 1780.   SCHATZ 6027

Andromaca. Dramma per musica da rappresentarsi nel nobilissineo Teatro di San Samuele il carnovale dell' anno 1790.

Venezia, Modesto Fenzo, 1790.   46 p.   17^{cm}.

Three acts. Antonio Salvi, the author, not mentioned. Argument, cast, and name of Sebastiano **Nasolini** as the composer.   SCHATZ 6999

L'Andromaca. Dramma per musica da rappresentarsi nel Teatro La Fenice per il solito tempo dell' Ascensione dell' anno 1798.

Venezia, Stamperia Valvasense, n. d.   55 p.   17^{cm}.

Two acts. Author not mentioned and unknown to Schatz. Argument, cast, scenario, and name of the composer, Giovanni **Paisiello**.
First performed at Naples, Teatro S. Carlo, fall 1797.   SCHATZ 7598

L'Andromaca. Dramma per musica da rappresentarsi nel Teatro dell' illustrissima città di Lodi nel carnovale dell' anno 1757 . . .

Milano, Carlo Ghiolandi, n. d.   6 p. l., 48 p.   15^{cm}.

Three acts. Dedication signed by the author Giuseppe Maria Viganò and dated Lodi, January 20, 1757. Argument, scenario, cast, and name of Giuseppe **Scolari** as the composer.   SCHATZ 9803

Andromaca in Epiro, ballet. *See* Gazzaniga's Tullo Ostilio.

Andromaca in Epiro, ballet. *See* Sarti's Farnace.

Andromaque, tragédie-lyrique, en trois actes, représentée pour la premiére fois, par l'Académie-royale de musique le mardi 6 juin 1780.

Paris, P. de Lormel, 1780.   66 p.   22½^{cm}.

Based by Louis Guillaume Pitra (who is not mentioned) on Racine's tragedy. As the "Avertissement" says on p. 7:
"On a conservé les vers de ce grand homme, autant que la coupe des scènes, la forme des airs & du récitatif, l'ont permis. Il a fallu malheureusement mêler souvent d'autres vers avec les siens pour former la contexture de l'action."
Cast and name of **Grétry** as the composer.   SCHATZ 4138

Andromeda. Poemetto drammatico nel giorno del gloriosissimo nome della Sac. Ces. R. Maestà dell' imperadrice Amalia Willelmina.

Bernardoni, Pietro Antonio, Poemi drammatici, parte terza, Vienna, van Ghelen, 1707, p. 137–147.   16½^{cm}.

The composer is not mentioned by von Weilen.
First performed at Vienna, as indicated, July 10, 1702.   ML 49.A2B4

Andromeda. Dramma per musica da rappresentarsi nel Regio Teatro di Torino nel carnevale del 1755 . . .

Torino, Zappata ed Avondo, n. d. xi, [1], 55 p. 15½ᶜᵐ.

Three acts. By Vittorio Amadeo Cigna-Santi (not mentioned). Argument, cast, scenario, and name of the composer, Gioacchino **Cocchi**. Rocco Gioannetti is mentioned as the composer of the ballet music. SCHATZ 2051

Andromeda. Dramma per musica da rappresentarsi nel Regio Teatro di Torino nel carnovale del 1772 alla presenza di S. S. R. M.

Torino, Onorato Derossi, n. d. viii, 54, [1] p. 16½ᶜᵐ.

Three acts. By Vittorio Amadeo Cigna-Santi, who is not mentioned. Argument, cast, scenario, and name of the composer, Giuseppe **Colla**. On p. 52–54 description of the allegorical ballets "Il ritorno della primavera," "Le nozze americane" and "Feste in onore di Bacco." The ballets were by Giacomo Favier, their music by Giuseppe Antonio Le Messier.

First performed as indicated, December 26, 1771. SCHATZ 2106

L'Andromeda del Signor Benedetto **Ferrari**. Rappresentata in musica in Venetia l'anno 1637 . . .

Venetia, Antonio Bariletti, 1637. 70, [2] p. 13½ᶜᵐ.

Three acts. Publisher's dedication dated Venice, May 6, 1637, sonnet by Alfonso Pucinelli "all' autore, poeta, musico, e sonator di tiorba eccellentissimo," sonnets by Bartolameo Angarani and Gio. Francesco Busenello to the author, on p. 5–12 a very interesting preface by the publisher with name of Francesco **Manelli** as composer and describing in detail the scenes, costumes, machines, etc., giving the names of the singers. Following the text of the opera on p. 61–68 "Sonetti del Signor Benedetto Ferrari in lode de signori musici più celebri, ch' intervennero nell' Andromeda," a sonnet by Carlo Federici to Ferrari, one by Donato Milcetti, "per l'Andromeda," latin ode by Bartolameo Angarani to Ferrari, and on last page the errata. From the publisher's preface and from the sonnets it appears that Annibale Graselli da Città di Castello represented Mercurio, Perseo and Ascalà, Francesco Angeletti da Assisi represented Giunone, Giovanni Battista Bisucci Bolognese represented Protheo and Giove, Anselmo Marconi Romano represented Venere, Madelena Manelli Romana represented Andromeda and Francesco Manelli da Tivoli, the composer, Nettuno and Astarco Mago and Girolamo Medici Romano represented Astrea. Enthusiastic praise is also bestowed on Gio. Battista Balbi Venetiano, ballarino celebre, and on Ferrari's several tiorba accompaniments. From the dedication the date of performance may be fixed since Bariletti says:

"Andromeda che su le scene rinacque già son due mesi; su le glorie de' suoi natali, esce ad acrescersi negl' applausi dell' universo." SCHATZ 5887

Andromeda. Dramma per musica da rappresentarsi nel Regio Teatro di Berlino il carnovale dell' anno 1788. Composto con li balli analoghi da Antonio Filistri de' Caramondani . . . e messo in musica dal Sigr. Giov. Feder. Reichardt . . .

Berlino, Haude e Spener, n. d. 167, [1] p. 15½ᶜᵐ.

One act. Argument and cast. German title and text face Italian, and it is stated on p. 19 that the translation is not by the translator "der mehresten vorhergehenden opern." On p. 160–167 "die umstaendliche anzeige von dem urspruenglichen entwurf des Schlussballets bey dessen ausfuehrung jedoch ein theil der details vielleicht wegbleiben duerfte."

First performed January 11, 1788, as indicated. SCHATZ 8634

L'Andromeda. Dramma del cavalier Carlo Bassi posto in musica dal Sig. Isidoro Tortona, e rappresentato nel Teatro Ducale di Piacenza l'anno 1662 . . .

Piacenza, Giovanni Bazachi, n. d. 8 p. l., 72 p. 14ᶜᵐ.

Prologue and three acts. Author's dedication dated May 17, 1662. Argument, cast and somewhat stilted notice to the reader in which Bassi says:

"a simil genere di componiměto, questa è la prima volta, ch'io ci hò lasciata incorrere la penna." SCHATZ 10374

Andromeda. Melodramma in due atti a tre personaggi. Rappresentato nell' anno 1796 nel Teatro di S. E. il Signor conte Carlo di Breünner ambasciatore Cesareo regio presso la serenissima repubblica di Venezia, ec. ec. ec.

n. i., n. d.   18 p.   20cm.

Argument, cast (aristocratic amateurs), names of Giovanni Bertati as author, of Nicola Antonio **Zingarelli** as composer.   Schatz 11265

Andromeda e Perseo, ballet.   *See* Bernardini's Achille in Sciro.

Andromeda e Perseo, ballet.   *See* Mortellari's Le astuzie amorose.

Andromeda und Perseus. Ein schauspiel mit musik. Aufgefuehrt im Kais. Koenigl. National theater.

Wien, beym Logenmeister, 1780.   32 p.   17cm.

One act.   Neither the author, Kempel, nor the composer, Anton **Zimmermann,** is mentioned.
First performed, as indicated, April 23, 1781.   Schatz 11234

Andronico e Ramira, ballet.   *See* Borghi's Egilina.

Andronico e Ramira, ballet.   *See* Nasolini and Trento's Gli innamorati.

Andronico e Ramira, ballet.   *See* Sarti's I pretendenti delusi.

Andronico e Ramira, ballet.   *See* Winter's I fratelli rivali.

L'âne d'or d'Apulée, opéra-comique en deux actes, mêlé de prose & de vaudevilles. Joué sur le Théâtre du Fauxbourg Saint-Laurent en 1725.

Alexis Piron, Oeuvres complettes, Liege, 1776, v. 3, [285]–346 p. 17½cm.

In a foot-note on p. 287 the editor says: "Cette pièce eut 40 représentations consécutives pendant 40 jours."   Composer not recorded.   PQ 2019.P6

L'anello incantato. Dramma giocoso per musica da rappresentarsi nel Teatro della rua dos Condes in Lisbona nell' estate dell' anno 1772.

[Lisbona], nella Stamperia reale, n. d.   83 p.   17cm.

Three acts.   Cast, scenario, and names of Ferdinando Giuseppe **Bertoni** as composer and of the author, Giovanni Bertati.   The first ballet, "Diana e Endimione," was by Vinceslao de Rossi.   The composer is not mentioned.
First performed at Venice, Teatro di S. Moisè, fall of 1771.   Schatz 929

Anfitrione. Tragicommedia per musica da rappresentarsi nel Teatro Tron di S. Cassano, l'autunno dell' anno MDCCVII . . .

Venezia, Marino Rossetti, 1707.   70 p.   14½cm.

Five acts with prologue.   Dedication, signed by Pietro Pariati, the author, argument, cast, scenario and name of Carlo Francesco **Gasparini** as the composer.   Fehr attributes the text jointly to Zeno and Pariati, but the text does not appear so in Zeno's works.   Schatz 3559

Anfitrione—Continued.

— **Amphytrion,** in einem sing-spiele, auf dem Hamburgischen Schauplatze im jahr 1725 vorgestellet.

[*Hamburg*], *Gedruckt mit Stromerischen schrifften, n. d.   Unpaged.* 18½ᶜᵐ.

Three acts and prologue. The "Vorbericht an den leser" informs us wherein the condensation of Pariati's original text consists.   The end of this curious preface reads: "An der musique hat der beruehmte Francesco **Gasparini** keinen geringen antheil, doch sind die meisten arien wohlgerathene kinder einer illustren persohn [Johann von **Wich**, according to Schatz], welche die von ihren hohen verrichtungen abgemuessigte stunden einem so edlen zeit-vertreibe zu widmen kein bedencken traeget. Da nun das Recitativ auch von einem beruehmten manne verfertiget worden, so mag die schoenheit der musique, der unvollkommenen uebersetsung zu statten kommen. Es ist dieselbe ein poëtisches kinder-werck von J. P. Praetorius."
Scenario and cast.   German text faces Italian, but not throughout.   Some scenes and arias have German text only.   Schatz 3560

L'Angelica, serenata.

[*379*]–*424 p.   19ᶜᵐ.*   (*Pietro Metastasio, Opere drammatiche, Venezia, Giuseppe Bettinelli, 1733–37, v. 3.*)
Two parts.   No composer mentioned.   ML 49.A2M4
First performed with music by **Porpora** at Vienna, November 19, 1720.

— **L'Angelica.**   Serenata.

Metastasio, Poesie, Parigi, vedova Quillau, 1755, t. ix, [181]–238 p. 16ᶜᵐ.
Two parts with licenza.   ML 49.A2M42

— **L'Angelica.**   Serenata.

pl., [199]–250 p.   26ᶜᵐ.   (Metastasio, Opere, t. x, Parigi, vedova Herissant, 1782.)
Two parts with licenza.   ML 49.A2M44

La Angelica.   Serenata da rappresentarsi sopra il Teatrino della ducal corte in Wolfenbuttell, per festeggiare il giorno natalizio della Altezza Serenissima di Antonetta Amalia, duchessa di Bronsevigo et Luneburgo etc li 22. aprile MDCCLI.

n. i., n. d.   Unpaged.   19ᶜᵐ.
Two parts.   Author (Metastasio) and composer (unknown to Schatz) not mentioned.   Schatz 11306

L'Angelica.   Serenata per musica da cantarsi nella Real villa di Queluz . . . per celebrare il felicissimo giorno natalizio della Serenissima Signora D. Maria Francesca Benedetta, principessa del Brasile, li 25. lug. 1778.

[*Lisbona*], *Stamperia reale, n. d.   28 p.   16ᶜᵐ.*
Two parts.   Cast and names of Metastasio as author, of Giovanni de Sousa Caravalho (**Carvalho**) as composer.   ML 50.2.A71C2

Angelica.   Dramma per musica da rappresentarsi nel Teatro Grimani di S. Samuele nella fiera dell' Ascensione dell' anno 1738 . . .

Venezia, Marino Rossetti, 1738.   47 p.   14½ᶜᵐ.
Three acts.   Dedication signed by Domenico Lalli, cast, scenario, argument, name of Giovanni Battista **Lampugnani** as the composer and statement, that this is the first drama of the author (Carlo Vedoa, not mentioned by name) and that it was written in eight days.
First performed May 11, 1738, as indicated.   Schatz 5391

Angelica e Medoro. Dramma per musica da rappresentarsi in Firenze nel Regio Teatro degli Intrepidi detto della Palla a Corda nella primavera dell' anno 1792 . . .

Firenze, Ant. Gius. Pagani e comp., 1792. 36 p. 18^{cm}.

Two acts. By Gaetano Sertor, based on Metastasio's "Serenata l'Angelica e Medoro." Cast, argomento, and name of Gaetano **Andreozzi**, as composer, but not of librettist. At Florence the opera was followed by "La turca in cimento. Ballo-eroi-comico pantomimo diviso in due atti composto dal Sig. Luigi Dupen" and the libretto contains on p. 7–10 the plot of this ballet. Composer of the music not mentioned.

First performed at Venice, Teatro di S. Benedetto, carnival 1791.   SCHATZ 194

[Angelica e Medoro] Angelica und Medorus, ein singspiel welches auf Sr. Koenigl. Majestaet in Preussen allergnaedigsten befehl an dem hoechsterfreulichen geburts-feste Ihro Majestaet der koenigl. frau mutter frauen Sophien Dorotheen koeniginn in Preussen etc etc etc auf dem Berlinischen schauplatze soll aufgefuehret werden.

Berlin, Haude und Spener, 1749. 128 p. 15½^{cm}.

Three acts. Leopoldo de Villati is mentioned as author and Carl Heinrich **Graun** as the composer. Argument and scenario. German text faces Italian.

First performed at Berlin, Kgl. Operntheater, March 27, 1749.   SCHATZ 4088

Angelica e Wilton, ballet. *See* Isola's La conquista del vello d'oro.

Angelica in India. Istoria favoleggiata con drama musicale dal co. Pietro Paolo Bissari. K.

Vicenza, gli heredi Amadii, 1656. 82 p. 14^{cm}.

Three acts and prologue. Author's dedication, argument. On p. 79–82 "Registro delle istorie figurate nel drama" and "Auttorità della lingua in Antello." Composer not mentioned and unknown to Schatz.   SCHATZ 11307

Angelica und Medorus. Tr. of Graun's Angelica e Medoro.

Die **Angelsachsen.** A. T. of Schulz's Minona.

Der **angenehme betrug,** oder Der carneval von Venedig, in einem sing-spiele auf den grossen Hamburgischen schau-platze vorgestellet im jahr 1707.

n. i., n. d. Unpaged. 18½^{cm}.

The last leaf contains "Was im druck ausgelassen worden."

Three acts. The "Vorbericht" by the author, resp. translator, Barthold Feind (not mentioned) says in part:

"Unterschiedliches ist aus den frantzösischen und anderen authoren genommen und vor hiesigen zustand accommodiret . . . Was die music betrifft, moegen diejenigen kenner rahten, welche von dem herrn capell-meister **Keiser** sey, die in die 12. jahr dessen arbeit bereits gehoeret."

To some arias the Italian text has been added.

First performed, as indicated, February, 1707.   SCHATZ 5076

— Der **angenehme betrug** oder Der carneval von Venedig. In einem sing-spiele auf dem Grossen Hamburgischen Schau-platze vorgestellet.

Hamburg, Friderich Conrad Greflinger, 1716. Unpaged. 19^{cm}.

Three acts. Scenario and "vor-bericht" with name of Reinhard **Keiser** as the composer and statement that this is a "veraenderung" of the opera as performed three years ago. The author, Barthold Feind, is not mentioned. Some of the arias have the Italian text added to the German. The text is practically the same as in the version of 1707, except that the burlesque scene III, 10, has been doubled in length, everything after the words "So kann ich bym olden een jungen erwarven" being added.

First performed, as indicated, 1716.   SCHATZ 5118

Der **angenehme betrug**—Continued.

— Der **angenehme betrug,** oder Der carneval von Venedig. Auf dem Hamburgischen Schau-platze in einer opera vorgestellet, im jahr 1723.

Hamburg, Caspar Jakhel, n. d. Unpaged. 18ᶜᵐ.

Three acts. Third version of this opera. Neither Feind is mentioned nor **Keiser.** The Italian text is added to many of the arias. The text is somewhat different from the 1716 version. For instance, I, 1, now begins "Lungi da me vagha beltà—Schoenheit entferne dich von mir" instead of "Liebste freyheit, du allein," I, 1–I, 5 are the same, also dialogue of I, 6, but the aria "Unsre liebe bleibt bestaendig" has become "Mio tesoro. Mio diletto—Mein Schatz! Mein ergoetzen," the seventh scene now begins "Quanto è dolce, quanto piace—Wie angenehm und vergnuegt ist es" instead of "Amor, te'l giorno a fè—O Liebe! ich schwoere dir," etc., etc.   Schatz 5119

Les **animaux raisonnables.** Pièce d'un acte. Par messieurs F** & Le G**. Représentée à la Foire de S. Germain 1718.

Le théâtre de la foire, Paris, 1737, t. III, pl., 35 p. 17ᶜᵐ.

By Louis Fuzelier and Alexandre Le Grand. The airs, selected or composed and arranged by Jean Claude **Gillier,** are printed at the end of the volume in the "Table des airs."

First performed, according to Parfaict, end of February, 1720.   ML48.L2ɪɪɪ

L'**anneau perdu** et retrouvé, opera comique en deux actes, mêlée de morceaux de musique. Par M. Sedaine. La musique de M. B. * * * Représenté pour la première fois par les Comédiens italiens ordinaires du roi, le lundi 20 août 1764.

Paris, Claude Herissant, 1764. [vi], [2], 56 p. 20ᶜᵐ.

Page 1 is preceded by two pages (numbered 75, 58) with list of Sedaine's works, the contents of the "Théâtre de la Foire & des Boulevards," etc. Cast and "avertissement," in which Sedaine says:

"Le 5 mars 1761 on a donné a l'Opera Comique de la Foire S. Germain, une pièce intitulée: les Bons compères, ou Les bons amis, qui, comme dit le Dictionnaire des Théâtres, n'eut pas de succès. L'auteur de la musique qui m'honore de son amitié [Jean Benjamin de **La Borde**], me pria de vouloir y faire des changemens, je les fis du jour au lendemain. Je retranchai les scènes, & j'en fis des neuves pour joindre les scènes divisées, mais tous mes efforts ne purent retarder la chute de la pièce: la musique cependent avoit fait plaisir, & sur-tout une des ariettes. Séduit par elle, je me mis en tête de mettre cette pièce en état d'être rejouée . . . il s'est trouvé à la fin que j'avois fait une maison neuve: cela a obligé le musicien de faire toute musique nouvelle, à l'exception d'un morceau qui, par le plus grand hazard, s'est rencontré ajusté sur mes paroles, & de cette ariette en question que j'a vois parodiée. Mais le musicien a exigé de moi que je laissasse les anciennes paroles; & de fait elles sont plus conformes à la musique qui avoit été faite pour elles. Je les ai donc conservées, du consentement du propriétaire de l'ancienne pièce" . . .

He then points out some differences between the new and the old piece, and says that he used two verses by La Fontaine.   Schatz 5350

Annetta e Fierillo, ballet. *See* Millico's La Zelinda.

Annette and Lubin, pantomime. *See* The fable of the pantomime dances.

Annette and Lubin: A comic opera in one act. As it is performed at the Theatre-Royal in Covent-Garden.

London, G. Kearsley, 1778. 24 p. 21ᶜᵐ.

Cast and the author-composer, Charles **Dibdin**'s, "Advertisement," which he published with all of his imitations of one act French comic operas.

First performed October 2, 1778, as indicated.   Longe 102

Annette et Lubin, comédie en un acte en vers; mêlée d'ariettes & de vaudevilles. Par Madame Favart & Mr. * * *. Représentée pour la premiere fois par les Comédiens italiens ordinaires du roi, le 15 février 1762.

Paris, Duchesne, 1763. 78, [2] p. 19^{cm}. (Theatre de M. Favart, Paris, Duchesne, 1763–77, t. v.)

One act. Cast. At the time of its appearance the play was attributed to Voisenon, but Font argues that he had nothing to do with it, and that the text was written by Mad. Favart in collaboration with her husband and Lourdet de Santerre for the wedding festivities of M. de Mailly and Mlle de Périgord. It was first privately performed in January, 1762, according to Favart's Corresp. Font incorrectly attributes the music to Martini, but the music was arranged and partly composed by **Blaise.** Many of his ariettes appear printed in the text (the duo "Lorsqu' Annette est avec Lubin" expressly bears his name), whereas no vaudeville air is so printed. "Mes trois femmes étoient veuves" was to be sung to "Air: de M: *Sodi.*" ML 49.A2F1

—Annette et Lubin. Comédie en un acte en vers; mêlée d'ariettes & de vaudevilles. Par Madame Favart, & Mr. * * * Représentée pour la premiére fois par les Comédiens italiens ordinaires du roi, le 15 février 1762.

Paris, Duchesne, 1763. 78 p. 18½^{cm}.

The composer, Adolphe **Blaise,** is not mentioned. Most of the airs are printed in the text. SCHATZ 1063

— Annette et Lubin, comédie en un acte, en vers, mêlée d'ariettes & de vaudevilles; par madame Favart, & Mr. * * *. Représentée pour la premiere fois par les Comédiens italiens ordinaires du roi, le 15 février 1762.

Paris, la veuve Duchesne, 1770. 48 p. 19^{cm}.

On p. 15 the air of "Il étoit une fille, une fille d'honneur," on p. 45–46 the vaudeville "Que tout le hameau s'apprête," and on p. 47 the ronde "Lubin aime sa bergere." **Blaise,** the composer, is not mentioned. SCHATZ 11675

— Annette et Lubin, comédie en un acte et en vers libres, mêlée d'ariettes & de vaudevilles par Madame Favart, & M * * * Représentée pour la première fois par le Comédiens italiens ordinaires du roi, le 15 Février 1762.

Avignon, Louis Chambeau, 1774. 40 p. 19½^{cm}.

Blaise, the composer, is not mentioned. ML 48.M2M

— Annette et Lubin, Comédie.

p. 5-55. 16^{cm}.

Title page, etc., missing. SCHATZ 11676

Annibale. Dramma per musica da rappresentarsi nel Teatro di S. Angelo nell' autunno.

Venezia, Carlo Buonarrigo, 1731. 1 p. l., 60 p. 15^{cm}.

Three acts. By Filippo Vanstryp, who is not mentioned. Argument, cast, scenario, and name of Nicolà Antonio **Porpora** as the composer. SCHATZ 8368

L'Annibale in Capua. Melodrama rappresentato in Venetia nel famoso Teatro Grimano l'anno MDCLXI . . .

Venetia, Giacomo Batti, 1661. 2 p. l. (incl. front.), 94 p. 15^{cm}.

Prologue and three acts. By conte Nicolo Beregani, who is not mentioned by name. Publisher's dedication, argument, scenario, and notice to the reader, informing him that this drama was prepared for performance in twenty days, and that the music was composed by Pietro [Andrea] **Ziani.**

First performed, as indicated, carnival, 1661. SCHATZ 11225

Annibale in Torino. Dramma per musica da rappresentarsi nel Regio Teatro di Torino nel carnovale del 1771 . . .

    Torino, Onorato Derossi, n. d. xi, 52 p. 16^{cm}.

Three acts. By Jacopo Durandi, who is not mentioned. Argument, cast, scenario, and names of **Paisiello** as the composer of the opera, of Giuseppe Antonio Le Messier of the ballet music.   Schatz 7692

Annibale in Torino, ballet. *See* Tarchi's Bacco ed Arianna.

Annibale in Torino. Dramma per musica da rappresentarsi nel Regio Teatro di Torino nel carnovale del 1792 . . .

    Torino, Onorato Derossi, n. d. viii, 55, [1] p. 15^{cm}.

Three acts. By Jacopo Durandi, who is not mentioned. Argument, cast, scenario, and name of Nicola Antonio **Zingarelli** as the composer. With the opera were performed Domenico Le Fèvre's ballets "Il finto giardiniere," "Alcina ed Astolfo," and "La cuccagna," the music selected by Le Fèvre from "diversi celebri autori."   Schatz 11239

The anniversary of St. Patrick. A. T. of The shamrock.

L'annore resarciuto. Commedeja napoletana de lo dottore Nicola Gianni da rappresentarese a lo Tiatro de li Shiorentine nchist' anno 1727 . . .

    Napole, Pe lo soleto [mutilated], 1727. 48 p. 14½^{cm}.

Three acts. Dedication, cast and name of Antonio Arefice (**Orefice**) as composer.   ML 50.2.A715O7

Antigona. Dramma per musica da rappresentarsi nel nobilissimo Teatro La Fenice per seconda dell' autunno 1799.

    Venezia, Valvasense, 1799. 39 p. 17½^{cm}.

Two acts, based on an English drama with additions by Gaetano Rossi. Cast and names of librettist and Francesco **Basili** as composer.   Schatz 630

Antigona. Tragedia per musica da rappresentarsi nel Teatro grande alla Scala il carnevale dell' anno 1789 . . .

    Milano, Gio. Batista Bianchi, n. d. 6 p. l., 13-56 p. 16½^{cm}.

Three acts, based on a libretto by Marco Coltellini written for St. Petersburg in 1772, as is stated in the argomento. This is preceded by a dedication and followed by cast, scenario, and name of Vincenzo **Campobasso d'Alessandro** as composer. With the opera were performed Gaspero Angiolini's ballets (also the music) "Fedra" and "Lorezzo."

First performed, as indicated, December 26, 1788.   Schatz 1538

Antigona. Dramma per musica da rappresentarsi nel Regio Teatro di Torino nel carnovale del 1752 . . .

    Torino, Pietro Giuseppe Zappata e figliuolo, 1752. 69 p. 15½^{cm}.

Three acts. By Gaetano Roccaforte (not mentioned). Argument, scenario, cast, and name of the composer, Giovanni Battista **Casali**. With the opera were performed Pietro Alovar's ballets, composer of the music not mentioned, "Armida" and "Le nozze di Perseo e d'Andromada."   Schatz 1678

Antigona. Drama per musica da rappresentarsi in Roma nel Teatro delle Dame nel carnevale dell' anno MDCCLI . . .

    Roma, Fausto Amidei, n. d. 66 p. 14½^{cm}.

Three acts. Dedication, argument, scenario, cast and names of Gaetano Roccaforte as author, of Baldassare **Galuppi** as composer.

First performed as indicated, January 9, 1751 (Piovano).   ML 50.2.A718G3

Antigona—Continued.

— **Antigona.** Dramma per musica da rappresentarsi nel Teatro Giustinian di S. Moisè l'autunno dell' anno 1754.

Venezia, Modesto Fenzo, 1754. 58 p. 15½^{cm}.

Three acts. By Gaetano Roccaforte, who is not mentioned. Argument, scenario, cast, and name of Baldassare **Galuppi** as composer.
First performed at Rome, Teatro delle Dame, Jan. 9, 1751 (Piovano).

SCHATZ 3437

— **Antigona.** Ein musicalisches schauspiel so an dem churfuerstl pfaeltzischen hof auf den erfreulichen hoechsten geburts-tag der durchlaeuchtigssten frauen churfuerstin den 17 Januarii 1752 . . . aufgefuehret worden.

Mannheim, Nicolaus Pierron, n. d. 86 p.

Three acts. Argument, scenario, cast, and names of the author, Gaetano Roccaforte, and the composer, Bald. **Galuppi.** Text in German only. SCHATZ 3438

Antigona. Dramma per musica da rappresentarsi nel nobilissimo Teatro delle Dame il carnevale dell' anno 1768. Dedicato a Sua Eccellenza la Signora D. Matilde Bentivoglio Erizzo, ambasciatore di Venezia.

Roma, Ottavio Puccinelli, n. d. 58 p. 15½^{cm}.

Three acts. Dedication, argument, scenario, cast, and names of Gaetano Roccaforte as author, of Giovanni Francesco de **Majo** as composer. SCHATZ 5862

Antigona. Dramma per musica da rappresentarsi nel nobilissimo Teatro di San Benedetto per la fiera dell' Ascensione dell' anno 1776.

Venezia, Modesto Fenzo, 1776. 70 p. 17½^{cm}.

Three acts. Gaetano Roccaforte is mentioned as the author, Michele **Mortellari** as the composer. Argument, cast, and scenario. On p. [25]–39 argument and description of Giuseppe Canziani's "Linceo, ballo tragico in cinque atti." The composer of the music is not mentioned.
First performed as indicated, May 11, 1776. SCHATZ 6679

Antigona. Tragedia da cantarsi nel Teatro Tron nel carnovale dell' anno MDCCXVIII offerita à G. A. G. da Merindo Fesanio Past. Arc.

Venezia, Marino Rossetti, 1718. front., 1 p. l., 71 p. 16^{cm}.

Five acts. Author's real name, Benedetto Pasqualigo. Dedicatory poems, argument, cast, scenario, and name of Giuseppe Maria **Orlandini** as the composer.

SCHATZ 7327

— **La fedeltà coronata.** Drama per musica da rappresentarsi in Bologna nel Teatro Malvezzi la state dell' anno MDCCXXVII.

(At end) *Bologna, Clemente Maria Sassi, 1727. 59 p. 16½^{cm}.*

Three acts. Imprimatur dated May 19, 1727, scenario, cast, name of Giuseppe Maria **Orlandini** as composer and notice to the reader with argument and apologies for the alterations in the "presente *Libretto*" by Benedetto Pasqualigo, who is not mentioned. It is remarked: "Questa è la sorte, che incontrano i drami fatti per musica, primieramente di doversi agli altrui vari, e discordi giudicj, più che a quello del poeta accomodare; e poi di essere in nuove maniere riordinati, e rivestiti."
In this *rifacimento*, for instance, the aria "Se vaporetto in nuvoletto" has been dropped from I, 1, and moved to I, 3; "Fu di rè comando allora" in I, 2, has been replaced by "Il padre amante contro un' ingrato"; scene V, 6, "Ti vendichi, e ti salvi," has become III, 11, and indeed this three act version is so different from the original five act version as to be almost a different opera.
"La fedeltà coronata" was first performed as indicated, June 14, 1727.

ML 50.2.A718O7

L'Antigona delusa da Alceste. Drama per musica di Aurelio Aureli. Favola settima . . .

Milano, Stampa archiepiscopale, 1662. 84 p. 13ᶜᵐ.

Three acts. Dedication dated Milan, April 15, 1662, argument, scenario, and notice to the reader with name of Pietro Andrea **Ziani** as the composer:

". . . La mia debolezza costretta à obedire à i commandi di quella autorità, che non è avvezza à ricever negative da chi conosce di poter restare servita, quando 'l desidera, si è veduta questa volta necessitata à produrti nel corso d'un mese non dirò un parto, mà un' abhorto d'ingegno, ed ad amareggierti la soavità di quel gusto, che haveresti provato fino al fine del carnevale corrente dalle contuate recite del virtuosissimo drama dell' illustrissimo Signor Pietro Angelo Zaguri, mio riverito signore e padrone . . . Avverti di più, che per la strettezza del tempo mi è convenuto aggiustare il drama sopra le scene (trattane sol una) sopra i medesimi balli, e sù parte delle machina inventate dall' illustrissimo Signore Zaguri, onde se tu credi, che da questa mia fatica io sia per acquistare alcuna portione di gloria, io tutta voluntariamente la cedo all' illustrissimo Signor Zaguri, sudetto, come à quello, che mi hà prestato la base per fondamentare la machina di questo mio drama."

First performed at Milan, Teatro del Palazzo Ducale, April 15, 1662; at Venice,. Teatro di S. Gio. e Paolo, carnival 1660. SCHATZ 11212

Antigono.

Metastasio, Poesie, Parigi, vedova Quillau, 1755, t. v, [173]–263 p. 16ᶜᵐ.

Three acts and licenza. Argument. ML 49.A2M42

— Antigono. Dramma scritto dall' autore in Vienna l'anno 1744 per la reale, ed elettoral corte di Dresda: dove nel carnevale fu rappresentato la prima volta con musica dell' Hasse.

pl., [181]-274 p. 26ᶜᵐ. (Metastasio, Opere, t. vi, Parigi, vedova Herissant, 1780.)

Three acts, with licenza. Argument. ML49.A2M44

Antigono. Dramma per musica da rappresentarsi nel nobilissimo Teatro di S. Benedetto nella fiera dell' Ascenzione dell' anno MDCCLXXIII.

Venezia, Modesto Fenzo, 1773. 48 p. 17ᶜᵐ.

Three acts. By Pietro Metastasio. Cast, scenario, argomento, and name of Pasquale **Anfossi** as composer, but not of librettist. The libretto of the opera is followed by the "Programma delli due balli" (on 30 p.). The first is called "Semiramide, ballo tragico pantomimo . . . inventato e composto dal Signor Gasparo Angiolini," who is also mentioned in the cast as the composer of the music. He was also the inventor, author, and composer of the other *ballo pantomimo* "Il disertore francese." SCHATZ 225

Antigono. Dramma per musica da rappresentarsi nel Teatro grande alla Scala di Milano nel carnevale dell' anno 1781.

Milano, Gio. Batista Bianchi, n. d. 62, [1] p. 16ᶜᵐ.

Three acts. The added page contains the additional aria for II, 7, "Scherno degli astri, e gioco." By Metastasio, who is not mentioned. Argument, scenario, cast, and note, "musica nuova in parte del Sig. maestro Pasquale **Anfossi,** e nella maggior parte del Sig. maestro abate Luigi **Gatti.**" With the opera were performed Gasparo Angiolini's ballets (also the music), "Attila," "Il castigo de' bonzi," and a Divertimento. First performed, as indicated, February 3, 1781. SCHATZ 283

Antigono. Dramma per musica da rappresentarsi nel nobilissimo Teatro La Fenice la fiera dell' Ascenzione dell' anno 1794.

Venezia, Modesto Fenzo, 1794. 60 p. 18ᶜᵐ.

Three acts. By Metastasio. Argument, cast, scenario, and name of the composer, Luigi **Caruso.** On p. 21–33, argument, cast, and detailed description of the first

Antigono—Continued.

ballet, music by Luigi Marescalchi, "La morte d'Egisto ossia Le furie d'Oreste, ballo tragico pantomimo d'invenzione e direzione del Sig. Onorato Viganò." The second ballet was called "Amore vendicato."

First performed at Rome, Teatro Alibert, carnival, 1788. SCHATZ 1659

Antigono. Dramma per musica da rappresentarsi nel Teatro Grimani di S. Benedetto il carnovale dell' anno 1762.

Venezia, Paulo Colombani, 1762. 58 p. 14^{cm}.

Three acts. By Metastasio. Argument, cast, scenario, and name of Baldassare **Galuppi** as composer.

First performed at London, Haymarket, 13/24 May, 1746. SCHATZ 3439

Antigono. Drama per musica da rappresentarsi in Roma nel Teatro di Torre Argentina nel carnevale dell' anno 1756 . . .

Roma, Fausto Amidei, n. d. 59 p. 14$\frac{1}{2}$^{cm}.

Three acts. Dedication ("la prima volta sù questo teatro"), argument, scenario, cast and names of Metastasio as author, of **Gluck** as composer.

First performed as indicated, February 9, 1756. ML 50.2.A72G5

Antigono, dramma per musica da rappresentarsi nel Regio elettoral Teatro alla corte di Dresda nel carnovale dell' anno MDCCXLIV.

n. i., n. d. 70, [1] p. 15$\frac{1}{2}$^{cm}.

Three acts and licenza. Argument, cast, scenario, and names of Metastasio as author, of Johann Adolph **Hasse** as composer.

First performed at Hubertusburg, October 10, 1743; at Dresden, January 20, 1744. ML50.2.A72H2

— Antigono. Dramma per musica rappresentata nel Regio elettoral Teatro alla corte di Desdra [!] l'anno MDCCXLIV del Signor abbate Pietro Metastasio.

Lucca, Domenico Ciuffetti, e Filippo Maria Benedini, 1744. 60 p. 19$\frac{1}{2}$^{cm}.

Three acts. Composed by **Hasse**, who is not mentioned. Argument and scenario. The text is the same as in the Dresden edition, except that the licenza has not been reprinted. ML 48.M2M7

Antigono. Dramma per musica da rappresentarsi nel nobilissimo Teatro di S. Benedetto il carnovale dell' anno 1768 . . .

Venezia, Modesto Fenzo, 1768. 62 p. 16$\frac{1}{2}$^{cm}.

Three acts. By Metastasio, who is not mentioned. Prefatory poem by Michele dall' Agata, argument, cast, scenario, and name of Francesco de **Majo** as composer

First performed as indicated, December 26, 1767. SCHATZ 5854

Antigono. Drama per musica da rappresentarsi nel Teatro di Torre Argentina nel carnevale dell' anno 1772 . . .

Roma, Arcangelo Casaletti, n. d. 60 p. 15^{cm}.

Three acts. By Metastasio. Argument, scenario, cast, name of Carlo **Monza** as the composer, and impresario's dedication, in which he says:

"Si rappresenta per la terza volta sù le scene romane L'Antigono, opera dell' insigne poeta Cesareo."

On p. 10 the note:

"Tuttociò, che si trova cangiato nel dramma si è dovuto fare per adattarsi alle circostanze presenti del Teatro; si è procurato per altro di servirsi dei sentimenti medesimi del primo autore sparsi nell' altre opere da lui composte."

Consequently, this version was a pasticcio from Metastasio's works. SCHATZ 6620

Antigono. Dramma per musica da rappresentarsi nel Nuovo Teatro di corte . . . nel carnevale dell' anno MDCCLXIX. La poesia è dell' abbate Pietro Metastasio . . . La musica è del Sig. Pietro Pompeo Sales . . .

*[Monaco, Maria Maddalena Mayrin], n. d. 205, [3] p. 14½*cm*.*

Three acts. Argument, cast, and scenario. German title, "Antigonus," and text face Italian. The 3 unnumb. p. contain the argument of the ballet, "Antoine & Cleopatre."

SCHATZ 9269

Antigono. Dramma per musica da rappresentarsi nel Nuovo Teatro in Padova per la solita fiera di giugno 1764 . . .

*Padova, n. publ., 1764. 56 p. 17*cm*.*

Three acts. Impresario's dedication, argument, cast, scenario, and name of composer, Tomaso **Traetta**, but not of librettist, Pietro Metastasio. The music is called "tutta nuova."

SCHATZ 10406

L'Antigono. Dramma per musica dell' incomparabile Signor abate Pietro Metastasio Poeta Cesareo da rappresentarsi in questo Regio-Ducal Teatro Nuovo la primavera dell' anno 1786 . . .

*Mantova, l'erede di Alberto Pazzoni, n. d. 45, 20 p. 17½*cm*.*

Two acts! Dedication dated April 13, 1786 (when the stagione began), argument, cast, scenario and name of Niccola **Zingarelli** as composer. On the 20 additional p., argument, cast, scenario and detailed description without name of composer of music of Antonio Muzzarelli's five-act "Ines de Castro, ballo tragico pantomimo."

ML 50.2.A72Z4

Antigono tutore di Filippo rè della Macedonia. Tragedia da cantarsi nel Teatro Giustiniano in S. Moisè. Il carnovale dell' anno 1724.

*Venezia, Carlo Buonarrigo, 1724. 48 p. 14½*cm*.*

Five acts. Argument, scenario, cast. Neither the author, Giovanni Piazzon, is mentioned, nor the composers Tommaso **Albinoni** and Giovanni **Porta**.

SCHATZ 133

Antigonus. Tr. of Sales' Antigono.

Antiochus und Stratonica. A. T. of Graupner's Die kranckende liebe.

Antioco. O. T. of Zeno and Pariati's Seleuco.

Antioco.

*Apostolo Zeno, Poesie drammatiche, Venezia, 1744, t. x, p. [289]–382. 19*cm*.*

Three acts. Argument. Written in collaboration with Pietro Pariati. No composer is mentioned. In the "Catalogo" at end of vol. x date and place of first edition are given as Venice, 1705.

ML 49.A2Z3

— Antioco. Pubblicato per la prima volta in Venezia 1705.

*Apostolo Zeno, Poesie drammatiche, Orleans, 1785–86, t. ix, p. 95–184. 21*cm*.*

Three acts. Argument. No composer is mentioned. Written in collaboration with Pietro Pariati.

ML 49.A2Z4

Antioco. Drama per musica nel Teatro a San Cassano per l'anno 1658 . . .

*Venetia, Andrea Giuliani, 1658. 5 p. l., 72 p. 13½*cm*.*

Three acts with prologue. By conte Niccolò Minato. Author's dedication dated Venice, January 21, 1658, notice to the reader, and argument, but without name of the composer, Pietro Francesco **Cavalli**.

SCHATZ 1717

Antioco. Drama per musica da rappresentarsi nel Teatro Tron di S. Cassano l'autunno dell' anno MDCCV . . .

Venezia, Marino Rossetti, 1705. 72 p. 16ᶜᵐ.

Three acts. By Apostolo Zeno and Pietro Pariati, who are not mentioned. Impresario's dedication, dated Venice, October 30, 1705, argument, cast, and scenario. Carlo Francesco **Gasparini**, the composer, is not mentioned.   Schatz 3561

Antioco. Dramma per musica da rappresentarsi nel Teatro alla Scala il carnevale dell' anno 1788 . . .

Milano, Gio. Batista Bianchi, n. d. 64 p. 17ᶜᵐ.

Three acts. By Ferdinando Moretti, who is not mentioned. Dedication, argument, cast, scenario, and name of Angelo **Tarchi** as the composer. With the opera were performed, composers of the music not mentioned, Filippo Beretti's "ballo pantomimo eroico-tragico Giulietta e Romeo," "ballo eroico-comico Lilla e Lubino, ossia Una cosa rara." Of these, a note informs us, special librettos were published. First performed December 26, 1787, as indicated.   Schatz 10234

Antioco il Grande. Drama per musica da rappresentarsi l'anno MDCLXXXI nel famoso Teatro Grimano di S. Gio. Grisostomo . . .

Venetia, Francesco Nicolini, 1681. 72 p. 14ᶜᵐ.

Three acts. Dedication dated Venice, December 17, 1681, and signed by the author, Girolamo Frisari, argument, scenario, and name of the composer, Giovanni **Legrenzi**, "che à nostri tempi è la vera norma della musica; & il vivo oracolo dell' armonia."

The libretto contains a list of errata, due to the sickness of the author while it was being printed, and for which he apologizes in the dedication.   Schatz 5533

Antioco principe della Siria, dramma per musica da recitarsi nel Teatro del Falcone l'anno 1690 . . .

Genova, Gio. Battista & Antonio Scionici, n. d. 79 p. 13ᶜᵐ.

Three acts. Dedication by the scenery painter, Tomaso Aldrovandini, argument, cast. The composer, Carlo Ambrogio **Lonati**, who also wrote the text, is not mentioned.   Schatz 5681

Antiope. Ballet héroique en trois actes, avec un prologue.

Venard de La Jonchère, Théâtre lyrique, Paris, 1772, t. I, p. [229]– 288. 18½ᶜᵐ.

"Avant-propos" (p. 231–244). No composer mentioned, and none recorded by Cl. & L.   ML 49.A2L2

Gli antiquari in Palmira. Commedia per musica da rappresentarsi nel Teatro grande alla Scala l'autunno dell' anno 1780 . . .

Milano, Gio. Batista Bianchi, n. d. 86 p. 16ᶜᵐ.

Three acts. By Giuseppe Carpani, who is not mentioned. Dedication, cast, scenario, and name of Giacomo **Rust** as the composer ("musica nuova"). With the opera were performed Gaspero Angiolini's ballets, "La morte di Cleopatra" and 'L'amore e l'azzardo," for which he also composed the music.   Schatz 9176

L'Antiquario fanatico. A. T. of Bernardini's La finta Galatea, the O. T. of his Le donne bisbetiche o sia L'antiquario fanatico.

Antoine e Cleopatre, ballet. *See* Sales' Antigono.

Antoine Masson. O. T. of Philidor's Le bon fils.

Anton der dumme gärtner oder Der name thut nichts sur sache. O. T. of Schack's Die beiden Antone and Der dumme gärtner.

Anton und Antonette. Tr. of Gossec's Toinon et Toinette.

Antonino e Pompeiano. Drama per musica nel famosissimo Teatro Vendramino di S. Salvatore. L'anno MDCLXXVII. Del Bussani . . .

> *Venetia, Francesco Nicolini, 1677. 68, [1] p. (incl. front.) 15cm.*
> Three acts. Author's dedication, argument, scenario, and notice to the reader, with the name of Antonio **Sartorio** as the composer. Schatz 9491
> Second copy. ML 48.M2O

Antonino e Pompejano. O. T. of Bussani's text La tirannide punita.

Antonius und Cleopatra. Ein duodrama mit gesang, in zwey aufzuegen, von d'Arien. In musik gesetzt von J. C. Kaffka. (Zum erstenmal vorgestellt auf der hiesigen schaubühne den 15. dieses monats.)

> *p. 753-761, 769-773. (Litteratur und Theater Zeitung, Berlin, 1779, 2ter jahrg., 4ter t.) 18½cm.* Schatz 4772

L'antre de Trophonius, opéra-comique en un acte. 1722.
> *Alexis Piron, Oeuvres complettes, Liege, 1776, v. 3, [47]-97 p. 17½cm.*
> In his Avertissement Piron says:
> "Cette pièce fut representée la dernière semaine de Carême, sur le Théâtre du Sieur Francisque, après *Deucalion.* Alors, tous les théâtres étant fermés, & le privilège des Comédiens n'ayant plus lieu, tous les acteurs parloient. Après mon premier essai théâtral, dans un monologue, je voulus voir ce que je saurois faire en dialogue, dans une pièce d'intrigue telle quelle . . ."
> Composer not recorded by Parfaict, etc. PQ 2019.P6

L'ape. Componimento drammatico, scritto dall' autore in Vienna, l'anno 1760, per uso della Real corte cattolica.
> *[149]-162 p. 26cm. (Metastasio, Opere, t. xi, Parigi, vedova Herissant, 1782.)*
> One act. ML 49.A2M44

L'ape musicale rinnuovata. Comedia per musica in tre atti. Da rappresentarsi la quadragesima dell' anno MDCCLXXXIXI. [!] Lel [!] Teatro di corte a benefizio di alcuni virtuosi.
> *Vienna, Giuseppe nob. de Kurzbek, n. d. 61 p. 16cm.*
> Three acts. By Lorenzo da Ponte, who is not mentioned. Cast and notice to the reader:
> "Questo è una spezie di comediola, dove ora parodiando, ora cangiando, ed ora conservando le originarie parole, si sono introdotti i migliori pezzi di musica, che si sentiron fin' ora nelle nostre opere, e quelli particolarmente che più sono stati amati e favoriti dal pubblico questi due ultimi anni . . ."
> First performed, as indicated, Vienna, Burgtheater, March 23, 1791.
> Schatz 11308

Apelle. Dramma per musica da rappresentarsi nel nobilissimo Teatro della Fenice del Signor Antonio Simon Sografi . . . in Venezia l'autunno 1793.
> *n. i., n. d. 64 p. 19½cm.*
> Three acts. Cast, scenario, name of Nicola Antonio **Zingarelli** as composer, and dedication, dated Venezia, November 18, 1793, in which Sografi says:
> "Ho sempre creduto, che bello sia quello spettacolo in questo genere, dove le belle arti per modo vi figurano, che non lasciano molto a desiderare. Nel caso mio la poesia

Apelle—Continued.

si è adoperata per questo, invitando a concorrere nel lavoro la musica, l'architettura, la pittura, la declamazione, la danza, somministrando ad esse i mezzi onde potessero sfoggiare la loro piacevole attività . . .''

On p. [53]–64, cast and description, without name of the composer of the music of Giacomo Onorati's "L'eroe castigliano o sia Rodrigo Ecimene, gran ballo eroico pantomimo,'' in five acts.   SCHATZ 11266

— **Apelle e Campaspe.** Dramma serio per musica da rappresentarsi in Bologna nel Nuovo Publico Teatro la primavera dell' anno 1795 . . .

Bologna, Sassi, n. d.   64 p.   17½cm.

Three acts. Impresario's dedication and prefatory note, cast, scenario, argument, and name of Nicola Antonio **Zingarelli** as the composer. This is Sografi's "Apelle" text, but with numerous alterations. For instance, the third act now begins, "Dove, ahi dove mi trovo,'' instead of "Ministri, il sacrifizio,'' which now opens the second scene in the act. On p. [55]–64, argument, cast, and description, without name of the composer of the music of Francesco Clerico's "Amleto, ballo tragico pantomimo.''

First performed, as indicated, May 24, 1795.   SCHATZ 11267

Apelle e Campaspe. A. T. of the ballet La generosità d'Alessandro.

Apelle e Campaspe, ballet. *See* Schuster's L'amor artigiano.

Apelle e Campaspe. Dramma per musica da rappresentarsi nel Teatro alla Scala il carnevale dell' anno 1796 . . .

Milano, Gio. Batista Bianchi, n. d.   50, [6] p.   16cm.

Three acts. By Simone Sografi, who is not mentioned. Impresario's dedication, dated December 26, 1795, argument, cast, scenario, and name of Giacomo **Tritto** as the composer. On the six unnumb. pages, casts and brief descriptions, without names of the composers of the music of Gaspare Ronzi's "ballo eroico tragico pantomimo La Didone'' and "ballo comico pantomimo Le reclute d'amore.''

SCHATZ 10452

Apelle e Campaspe. L. T. of Zingarelli's Apelle.

Apelle et Campaspe, opéra en un acte, par le citoyen Demoustier, musique du citoyen Eler; représenté pour la première fois sur le Théâtre de la République et des Arts, le 24 messidor, an 6.

Paris, Huet, an VI [1797–98]:   54 p.   20cm.

With cast. Correct date of first performance is 26 messidor, or July 14, 1798, according to Schatz. Clément and Larousse give July 12.   SCHATZ 2912

Apelles and Campaspe, or, The self-conquest of Alexander. An heroic pantomimical ballet.

Noverre, Jean George, Works.   Tr. from the French, London, 1783, v. 3, p. 263–283.   21½cm.

Argument and detailed description of the five scenes.   GV 1787.N8

Le api riverite. Azzione dramatica all' illustriss. e reverendiss. Sig. Card. Francesco Barberini di Bernardino Mariscotti nell' Academia de' Gelati il Notturno.

Bologna, Clemente Ferroni, 1628.   51 p.   19cm.

Five acts, preceded by a dedicatory "Canzone" by the author and his dedication, dated Bologna, June 2, 1628. Mariscotti says that the Academia de' Gelati wished to honor the cardinal after his return to Rome from a successful diplomatic mission in France and Spain and decided for the purpose on

"qualche azzione academica, appropriata, quanto per noi si potesse il meglio, all' occorrenza, con machinare invenzione vistosa per varièta confacevole per argomento,

Le api riverite—Continued.

e significante per allegoria. Fu lavorato di scrittura, e di pittura, e già erano imparate le musiche, e dato l'intiero compimento alla scena, e all' apparenze. Ma dipoi al mancar della cagione, venne à mancar l'effetto; non ci fù la persona, svanì l'azzione, rimase l'invenzione . . ."

Placed in this embarrassing situation the Academy finally decided not to perform the work in the cardinal's absence, but to have at least the text printed. The composer of the music is not mentioned. The work is not recorded by Ricci.

ML 48.M2 I

Apio Claudio. Drama per musica da rappresentarsi nel Teatro di Sant' Angelo. L'anno MDCLXXXIII . . .

Venetia, Francesco Nicolini, 1683. front., 56 p. 14^{cm}.

Three acts. By Adriano Morselli, who is not mentioned. Impresario's dedication, argument, scenario, and notice to the reader, in which he complains: "Hanno alcuni havuto la bontà di levar certe arie dell' auttore per mettervi le proprie senza sua notitia."

These have been printed in quotation marks. The notice begins: "L'auttore del Temistocle in bando ti presēta questo nuovo drama."

The composer, Giovanni Marco **Martini,** is not mentioned. SCHATZ 6033

Apollo deluso, drama per musica rappresentato nel giorno natale dell' augustissimo e sempre invitto Leopoldo . . . Musica di Gio. Felice Sances . . . Poesia di Antonio Draghi . . .

Vienna, Matteo Cosmerovio, 1669. Unpaged. 19½^{cm}.

Three acts and licenza. Author's dedication of date Vienna, July 9, 1669, argument, and notice to the reader informing him that this drama "nel suo nascimento egli non hebbe più d'una settimana per comparire alla luce . . . Sono concorsi à coprire la sua nudità con adobbi preziosi, il Signor Felice **Sances,** maestro di capella di S. Maestà Ces: quale con la soavità della sua armonia hà reso con mirabile artificio dolce l'amarezza del verso."

Not a single hint will be found in the libretto that Leopold I composed part or all of the score. This is the more noteworthy, because, according to Adler, the title page of the second act of the score at the Hofbibliothek, Vienna, reads: "Atto 2do Apollo deluso. Musica di **Sua M^{ta} Ces^a** Anno 1669" and the binding of the first act says "Di S. M. C." (this, however, probably meaning "property of" not "by"). In view of this libretto, however, it would be unsafe to agree with Adler that "probably the music of all three acts with exception of the licenza" is by Leopold I. Presumably the libretto was published with Sances' name as composer, though Leopold I, as he often did, had contributed more or less music to the score of his court conductor. Adler published in his "Musikalische Werke der Kaiser" as by Leopold I the arias "Aurimena, la tua pena" (II, 10), Recitativ "In oscura prigion" and aria "Pensieri non v'atterrite" (II, 11), "Se non basta" (II, 11), and "Sù, che fate" (II, 11).

ML 48.M2 D

Apollo e Dafne. A. T. of the ballet Cupido trionfatore.

Apollo e Dafne, ballet. *See* G. Giordani's Atalanta.

Apollo geloso. Pastorale per musica da rappresentarsi nel Teatro di Lugo in occasione della Fiera d' Agosto dell' anno 1720 . . .

Bologna, Costantino Pisarri, n. d. 47 p. 15½^{cm}.

Three acts. Argument and dedication dated Lugo, August 17, 1720, and signed by Giuseppe Maria **Buini,** "compositore della musica," who says "l'Apollo geloso, che sotto la mia debole direzzione dee rappresentarsi su queste scene." Not recorded by Allacci, Schatz or Dent. Author unknown to me. ML 50.2.B727A9

Apollo in Tessaglia. Cantata a tre voci per festeggiar la solenne apertura dell' Accademia degl' Ingegnosi nel Teatro del Corso de' Tintori la sera de' 12 marzo 1769.

Firenze, Giuseppe Allegrini, e comp., 1769. 15 p. 19½^{cm}.

Two parts. By Luigi Semplici. With argument, "Attori," and names of author and composer, Alessandro **Felici** ("musica nuova"). SCHATZ 3052

Apollo in Tessaglia. Drama per musica da rappresentarsi nel nuovo famoso Teatro Formagliari l'anno 1679 . . .

Bologna, per l'erede di Vittorio Benacci, n. d.   5 p. l., 92, [1] p. 14cm.

Three acts and prologue. By Tommaso Stanzani, who dates his dedication Bologna, May 27, 1679.   Printer's notice to the reader with the name of Petronio **Franceschini** as composer, and argument.   Schatz 3316

Apollo placato, ballet.   *See* Salieri's Europa riconosciuta.

Apollo turn'd stroller; or, Thereby hangs a tale.   A musical pasticcio.   In two parts.   As performed, with the most unbounded applause, at the Royalty-Theatre.

London, S. Bladon, 1787.   2 p. l., 28 p.   21cm.

Cast.   Neither the author, Sir John Oldmixon, nor the composers, G. F. **Händel** and others, are mentioned.
First performed December 3, 1787, as indicated.   Longe 102

Apollo unter den hirten. Ein vorspiel mit arien.   An dem geburtsfeste Ihro Majestaet des koenigs aufgefuehrt von der Hannoeverischen Gesellschaft koeniglicher schauspieler den 4ten Juni 1770.

n. i., n. d.   31 p.   17cm.

Neither Johann Georg Jacoby, the author, nor Anton **Schweitzer**, the composer, is mentioned.   Schatz 9769

Apollon et Coronis.   *See* Mouret's Les amours des dieux.

Apollon et Daphné, divertissement mis en musique par Monsieur de Lully . . .   Chanté devant Sa Majesté, à Fontainebleau le [*blank*] octobre 1698.

Amsterdam, les héritiers d'Antoine Schelte, 1699.   22 p. (incl. front.). 14cm.

Prologue and one act.   By Danchet.   Composed, probably, by Louis de **Lully** in his capacity as "compositeur de la chambre du roi."   Not recorded by Schatz or Cl. & L.   ML 50.2.A73L9

— Apollon et Daphné, divertissement mis en musique par M. de Lully, . . . chanté devant Sa Majesté à Fontainebleau, le [*blank*] octobre 1698.

[13]-26 p.   17½cm.   (Antoine Danchet, Théâtre, t. ii, Paris, 1751.)
One act.   PQ 1972.D2

Apollo's mask.   *See* Stapylton's text Diana's mask.

L'apoteosi d'Ercole.   Dramma per musica da rappresentarsi nel nobilissimo Teatro Venier in San Benedetto il carnovale dell' anno 1791.

Venezia, Modesto Fenzo, 1790.   54 p.   17½cm.

Three acts.   By Mattia Butturini, who is not mentioned.   Cast, scenario, and name of Angelo **Tarchi** as the composer.   On p. 49–54, scenario and prefatory note to Gaspero Angiolini's (who composed also the music) "Tito o La partenza di Berenice, ballo eroico pantomimo in cinque atti."   Schatz 10212

De **Apothecar en de doctor.**   Tr. of Dittersdorf's Der apotheker und der doktor.

Die apotheke, eine komische oper in zwey aufzuegen. [vignette]

Leipzig, Dyckische buchhandlung, 1772. xv, [1], 96 p. 17ᶜᵐ.

Preface addressed to J. F. Bause by the author [Johann Jakob Engel] and dated Leipzig, November 10, 1771. The preface is interesting as containing Engel's views of the esthetics of the "Possenspiel." On p. vii, this shrewd remark:

"Ich denke uebrigens, man wuerde gutthun, wenn man aus allen possenspielen operetten machte. Unser publikum sieht diese possen gerne, und moechte doch gerne das ansehen haben, als wenn es sie verachtete; es lacht von herzen ueber die Goldonischen stuecke, und zuckt die achseln darueber, wenn sie aus sind."

On p. vi, this remark on the origin of this libretto:

"Ein tonkuenstler [**Hiller**] . . . bat mich um eine oper, worinn nicht der naive ton, sondern zur abwechslung der eigentlich komische herrschte . . . Mein freund wurde krank, und konnte lange zeit an keine komposition denken. Er hatte aber die ersten arien, so wie sie fertig geworden waren, einem jungen tonkuenstler, von viel versprechendem genie [**Neefe**], uebergeben, der sie sogleich in musik setzte; und ich schrieb hernach weiter, damit dieser nicht moechte umsonst gearbeitet haben."

First performed at Berlin, Koch'sches Theater in der Behrenstrasse, December 13, 1771.   SCHATZ 7070

Die apotheke. Ein originalsingsspiel in zween aufzuegen. Die musik ist vom herrn Umlauf. Aufgefuehrt auf der K. K. Nationalschaubuehne.

Wien, bey dem logenmeister, 1778. 35 p. 15½ᶜᵐ.

By Johann Jakob Engel, who is not mentioned.
First performed, as indicated, June 20, 1778.   SCHATZ 10523

Der apotheker. Tr. of Pallavicini's and Fischietti's Lo speziale.

Der apotheker und der doktor. Ein komisches singspiel in zwey aufzuegen. Nach dem franzoesischen des grafen von N . . . l'Apoticaire de Murcie von Stephani dem juengern. Die musik ist neu vom herrn Ditters v. Dittersdorf.

n. i., 1788. 128 p. 16ᶜᵐ.

First performed at Vienna, Nationaltheater n. d. Burg, July 11, 1786, as "Doctor und apotheker."   SCHATZ 2585

— The **doctor and the apothecary.** A musical entertainment in two acts. As performed at the Theatre-Royal, Drury-Lane.

London, C. Dilly, 1788. 1 p. l., 44 p. 20ᶜᵐ.

Cast. The preliminary half-title is missing. By James Cobb, adapted to Dittersdorf's music with additions by Stephen **Storace.** In Longman & Broderip's vocal score "This marriage article" is headed as composed by **Paisiello.**
First performed as indicated, October 25, 1788. (Genest).   SCHATZ 2586
                              Second copy (2 pl., 44 p. 21ᶜᵐ.)   LONGE 164

— De **apothecar en de doctor,** zangspel. Gevolgd naar het hoogduitsch van Stephani door I. J. A. Gogel.

Amsteldam, J. Heiders, 1796. 108 p. 16½ᶜᵐ.

First performed at Amsterdam, Stads Schouwburg, 1796.   SCHATZ 2611

The **apotheosis of Punch;** a satirical masque: With a monody on the death of the late Master Punch. As now performing at the Patagonian Theatre, Exeter-'Change, with universal applause . . .

London, J. Wenman, F. Newberg and W. Thompson, 1779. 42, [2] p. 21ᶜᵐ.

Dedication by "Plunder" to Richard Brinsley Sheridan. The first unnumb. p. contains advertisement of the opera "Retaliation. By the same author," therefore, Leonard Mac Nally, whose idea was to ridicule Sheridan's monody on the death of Garrick. The composer, if any, is not recorded by Clarence or Schatz. LONGE 102

L'apparenza inganna o sia La villeggiatura. Commedia in due atti per musica di Giambattista Lorenzi P. A. da rappresentarsi nel Teatro de' Fiorentini nella primavera del corrente anno 1784.

Napoli, n. publ., 1784. 58 p. 15^{cm}.

Two acts. Cast and name of the composer, Domenico Nicola **Cimarosa.**

SCHATZ 1980

The **apparition!** A musical dramatic romance, in two acts, as performed with universal applause at the Theatre-Royal, Hay-Market. By J. C. Cross . . . [vignette]

London, J. Barker, 1794. 35, [1] p. 21½^{cm}.

Cast, dedication dated Theatre-Royal, Hay-Market, Sept. 9, 1794, and prefatory note. The composer, William **Reeve,** is not mentioned.
First performed Sept. 3, 1794.   LONGE 239

The **apparition of the cliffs.**   A. T. of Reeve's The Sicilian romance.

L'apprensivo raggirato. Commedia per musica di G. M. D. da rappresentarsi nel Teatro de' Fiorentini per terz' opera del corrente anno 1798.

Napoli, n. publ., 1798. 64 p. 15^{cm}.

Two acts. By Giuseppe Maria Diodati. Cast and name of the composer, Domenico Nicola **Cimarosa.** On p. 58–59 cast, argument, and detailed description of Giov. Battista Giannini's ballet "La Ginevra degli Almieri." The composer of the music is not mentioned.   SCHATZ 1904

April-Day, a burletta, in three acts. Written by the author of Midas. As it is performed at the Theatre Royal in the Hay-Market. The music composed by Dr. Arnold.

London, G. Kearsly, 1777. vii, [1], 44 p. 20½^{cm}.

Cast. In his prefatory "Extract of a letter . . . to his friend in London"the author, Kane O'Hara, says:
"The interlude of the *Magic girdle* which Mr. Barthelemon left in my hands for correction, furnished me with the first hint of this drama. I send you the original, that you may see my great reserve in borrowing from it; at the same time, humbly begging pardon of the gentleman, unknown, with whose hasty sketch I have taken so many liberties. This plot is here totally changed, and his personages thrown into a different cast of character: I have availed myself but very sparingly of his words; scarce at all of his poetry . . . I adopt the laconic dialogue of Italian burletta, in order to comprise my fable within the narrow limits of late prescribed by the taste of your audiences . . ."
This letter is dated Dublin, January 12, 1775.
First performed at London, Hay-market, August 22, 1777.   LONGE 126

L'Arabo cortese. Commedia per musica di Pasquale Mililotti da rappresentarsi nel Teatro Nuovo sopra Toledo nell' autunno del corrente anno 1776.

Napoli, n. publ., 1776. 59 p. 15½^{cm}.

Three acts. Scenario, cast, and name of **Paisiello** as the composer, with exception of the following starred arias by Domenico **Cimarosa:** "Dint'a st'uocchie appassionate" (I, 6), "Qual colomba innamorata," (III, 3).
First performed at Naples, Teatro Nuovo, winter 1769.   SCHATZ 7665

Arato in Sparta. Drama per musica da rappresentarsi nel Teatro di Sant' Angelo il carnovale dell' anno 1709 . . .

Venezia, Gio. Battista Zuccato, 1709. 72 p. 15^{cm}.

Three acts. Argument, cast, scenario, and dedication in which this is called "questa picciola operetta, parto di miei primi genii" over the signature of *N. M.,* which stands for Benedetto Marcello (Schatz). The composer, Giovanni Maria **Ruggeri,** is not mentioned.   SCHATZ 9130

L'Arbace. Dramma per musica da rappresentarsi in Firenze nel nuovo Regio Teatro degl' Intrepidi detto La Palla a Corda nella primaver del 1785 . . .

> *Firenze, Stamperia Bonducciana, 1785. 32 p. 16½^{cm}.*

Two acts. By Gaetano Sertor (not mentioned). Cast, argomento, scenario, and name of Gaetano **Andreozzi** as composer. The music for the "ballo serio pantomimo Giasone e Medea" by Domenico Ricciardi was by Giuseppe Horban.
First performed at Livorno, Teatro di S. Sebastiano, 1781. Schatz 214

Arbace. Dramma per musica da rappresentarsi nel nobilissimo Teatro di S. Benedetto il carnovale dell' anno 1782.

> *Venezia, Modesto Fenzo, 1782. 61 p. 17^{cm}.*

Three acts. By Gaetano Sertor. Argument, cast, scenario, and names of the librettist and the composer, Giovanni Battista **Borghi.** On p. 27–34 cast, argument, and detailed description of Paolino Franchi's "Tito e Berenice, ballo eroico pantomimo." The composer of the music is not mentioned. Schatz 1239

L'arbore di Diana. Dramma giocoso per musica da rappresentarsi nel Teatro grande alla Scala l'autunno dell' anno 1788 . . .

> *Milano, Gio. Batista Bianchi, n. d. 72 p. 16^{cm}.*

Two acts. Lorenzo da Ponte is mentioned as author, Vincenzo Martini (**Martin y Soler**) as composer. Dedication, argument, cast, and scenario. With the opera were performed Domenico Le Fevre's ballets, "Giasone e Medea" and "Le feste florali." The composers of the music are not mentioned.
First performed, as indicated, October 1, 1788; at Vienna, Nationaltheater nächst der Burg, October 1, 1787. Schatz 5999

— **Der baum der Diana.** Ein singspiel in zwey aufzuegen. Aufzufuehren bei der ankunft I. K. Hoheit Maria Theresia, erzherzoginn von Oesterreich, braut des prinzen Anton von Sachsen.

> *Wien, n. publ., 1787. 67 p. 15½^{cm}.*

With names of Lorenzo da Ponte as author and Vincenz Martini (**Martin y Soler**) as the composer. Schatz 6000

— Text der beliebtesten arien, einiger duetten, terzetten und quartetten aus dem **Baum der Diana** samt den plan dieses singspiels, nach der uebersetzung des herrn Eberls wie er auf dem Leopoldstaedtertheater aufgefuehrt worden. Den schoenen stimmen artiger maedchen gewidmet vom berausgeber.

> *Wien, Hochleiter, 1788. 37 p. 15½^{cm}.*

Cast, "Vorrede," and "Nachrede." Schatz 6001

— Gesaenge aus dem singspiele: **Der baum der Diana,** in zwey aufzuegen, nach dem italienischen des abbt da Ponte, von d'Arien. In musik gesezt vom kapellmeister Vincenz Martin.

> *Hamburg, Joh. Matthias Michaelsen, 1792. 40 p. 16^{cm}.*

First performed at Hamburg, Opernhaus am Gänsemarkt, November 10, 1788. Schatz 6002

— **Der baum der Diana.** Eine komische oper in zwey aufzuegen. Nach der musik des kapellmeisters Martini aus dem italienischen ins deutsche übersetzt von C. H. Necse [! Neefe].

> *Oels, Samuel Gottlieb Ludwig, n. d. 72 p. 17½^{cm}.*

First performed at Oels, Hoftheater, May 2, 1795. Schatz 6003

Arcadia; or, The shepherd's wedding. A dramatic pastoral. As it is performed at the Theatre-Royal in Drury-Lane. The music composed by Mr. Stanley . . .

London, J. and R. Tonson, 1761. 20 p. 19^{cm}.

One act. By Robert Lloyd, who is not mentioned.
First performed October 26, 1761, as indicated (Genest).   LONGE 52

— Arcadia; or, The shepherd's wedding. A dramatic pastoral, as it is performed at the Theatre-Royal in Drury-Lane. By Mr. Lloyd. The music composed by Mr. Stanley . . .

London, Printed for J. and R. Tonson; Dublin, Re-printed for R. Watts [etc.] 1761. 1 p. l., [5]-21 p. 17^{cm}.

Bound with: Thompson, James. Edward and Eleonora. [n. p., 17—]

L'Arcadia in Brenta.

[117]-172 p. (Carlo Goldoni, Opere drammatiche giocose, t. ii, Torino, 1757.) 16½^{cm}.

Three acts. Argument.   ML 49.A2G6
First performed, with music by Vincenzo Legrenzio **Ciampi** at Bassano, fall 1747.

L'Arcadia in Brenta. Dramma di tre atti per musica. Rappresentato per la prima volta in Bassano l'anno MDCCLVII.

Carlo Goldoni, Opere teatrali, Venezia, Zatta e figli, 1788-95, v. 43, [5]-61 p. 18½^{cm}.

PQ

L'Arcadia in Brenta. Dramma comico per musica da rappresentarsi nel Regio-ducal Teatro di Milano nella primaviera dell' anno 1750 . . .

Milano, Giuseppe Richino Malatesta, 1750. 4 p. l., 52, [1] p. 14½^{cm}.

Three acts. By Goldoni, who is not mentioned. Dedication, argument, cast. Bald. **Galuppi**, the composer, is not mentioned. Following the argument is this note:
"Siccome quest' operetta fu tagliata la prima volta sul dosso degl' attori, che l'hanno rappresentata a Venezia, cosi dovendosi ora rappresentare in questo teatro da personaggi diversi, è stata dall' autore medesimo in qualche parte variata per uniformarsi al preciso carattere de' nuovi attori."
The additional page contains the substitute aria (I, 9), "Fabrizio amabile, Io parto, addio."
First performed at Venice, Teatro di S. Angelo, May 14, 1749.   SCHATZ 3440

— L'Arcadia in Brenta. Dramma giocoso per musica da rappresentarsi in Monaco di Baviera. l'anno 1759.

[Monaco], Gio. Giac. Vötter, n. d. 51 p. 16½^{cm}.

Condensation of Goldoni's libretto to two acts. Neither he nor the composer, **Galuppi**, is mentioned.   SCHATZ 3518

L'Arcadia in Brenta. Dramma giocoso per musica di Polisseno Fegejo Pastor Arcade. Da rappresentarsi nel Real Teatro di Salvaterra nel carnovale dell' anno 1764.

Lisbona, Stamperia Ameniana, n. d. 4 p. l., 77 p. 16^{cm}.

Three acts. By Goldoni, who is not mentioned. Cast, scenario, and name of "Giovanni Cordeiro " (João Cordeiro da **Silva**) as composer.   SCHATZ 9885

Archelao. Dramma per musica da cantarsi nella Reál Villa di Queluz per celebrare il felicissimo giorno natalizio del serenissimo Signore Don Giuseppe, principe del Brasile li 21 agosto 1785.

[*Lisboa*] *Stamperia Reale, n. d.   32 p.   16½ᶜᵐ.*

One act and licenza.   Argument, cast, and names of Gaetano Martinelli as author, João Cordeiro da **Silva** as composer.   SCHATZ 9887

The **Archers,** or Mountaineers of Switzerland; an opera, in three acts, as performed by the Old American Company, in New York; to which is subjoined a brief historical account of Switzerland . . .

New York, T. & J. Swords, 1796.   viii, [9]-94 p.   22½ᶜᵐ.

Prologue, cast, and preface by the author, William Dunlap, dated New York, April 10, 1796, which reads, in part:

"In the summer of the year 1794, a dramatic performance, published in London, was left with me, called *Helvetic Liberty.* I was requested to adapt it to our stage. After several attempts, I gave it up, as incorrigible, but, pleased with the subject, I recurred to the history of Switzerland, and composed the piece now presented to the public . . ."

The composer, Benjamin **Carr,** is not mentioned.

First performed at New York, April 18, 1796.   ML 50.6.A72

Second copy.   PR 1241.D7   v. 14

L'Archetiello, commedia per musica da rappresentarsi nel carnovale di quest' anno 1778 nel Real Conservatorio della Pietà de' Turchini.

Napoli, Vincenzo Mazzola-Vocola, 1778.   72 p.   15ᶜᵐ.

Three acts.   Author not mentioned and unknown to Schatz.   Cast and name of Angelo **Tarchi** as the composer.   SCHATZ 10223

Archidamia.   A. T. of Hasse's La Spartana generosa.

Archidamia.   Festa teatrale per musica, da rappresentarsi nell'Imperial corte festeggiandosi il glorioso e felicissimo nome della Sac. Ces. Catt. e Real Maestà di Elisabetta Cristina   . . .   l'anno MDCCXXVII.   La poesia è del Sig. abate Giovan Claudio Pasquini . . .   La musica è del Sig. Giorgio Reuter il giovine.

Vienna d'Austria, Gio. Pietro Van Ghelen, n. d.   Unpaged.   18½ᶜᵐ.

One act.   Argument.

First performed, as indicated, November 22, 1727.   SCHATZ 8695

L'Arcifanfano.   Dramma giocoso per musica da rappresentarsi nel Teatro di rua Dos Condes . . .

Lisbona, Pietro Ferreira, n. d.   3 p. l., 106, [1] p.   14½ᶜᵐ.

Three acts.   By Goldoni, who is not mentioned.   Dedication to David Perez signed by the composer, Giuseppe **Scolari.**

First performed 1768, as indicated.   SCHATZ 9801

Arcifanfano, re de' matti.

[*215]-260 p.   16½ᶜᵐ.   (Carlo Goldoni, Opere drammatiche giocose, t. i, Torino, 1757.)*

Three acts.   ML 49.A2G6

— **Arcifanfano rè dei matti.** Dramma di tre atti per musica. Rappresentato per la prima volta in Roma l'anno MDCCLVIII. [!]

Carlo Goldoni, Opere teatrali, Venezia, Zatta & figli, 1788-95, t. 40, [171]-217 p.   18ᶜᵐ.   PQ

Arcifanfano, rè dei matti. Dramma comico per musica di Polis-seno Fegejo Pastor Arcade. Da rappresentarsi nel Teatro Giusti-niani di S. Moisè nell' autunno dell' anno 1750.

  Venezia, Modesto Fenzo, 1750. 46 p. 14½ᶜᵐ.

  Three acts. By Goldoni. The composer, Baldassare **Galuppi,** is not mentioned. Scenario and cast.

  First performed at Venice, same theatre, carnival 1750.   Schatz 3442

— Arcifanfano, rè dei matti. Dramma giocoso per musica di Polisseno Fegejo, Pastor Arcade da rappresentarsi nel Teatro di S. A. serenissima il Signor Principe di Carignano nell' autunno dell' anno MDCCLIX. In quest' ultima impressione dall' autore ricorretta e migliorata.

  Torino, Giacomo Giuseppe Avondo, n. d. 46 p. 14ᶜᵐ.

  Three acts. Cast, scenario, and remark:

  "La musica è la maggior parte del celebre maestro Sign. Baldassare **Galuppi** detto Buranello, ed altri celebri autori."

  The text of this version is conspicuously different from that of Venice, 1750. Not even the first scene of the first act has been left untouched. Venice has "Con un colpo di terza, e di quarta," Torino has "Non teme la spada"; Venice has "Il mio core poverino," Torino has "Sordidon, che cosa hai fatto," etc.   Schatz 3497

L'Ardelinda. Drama da rappresentarsi nel Teatro di S. Angelo l'autunno dell' anno 1732. Del Signor Bortolamio [!] Vitturi citta-dino Veneto.

  Venezia, Stamparia Nova à S. Moisè, n. d. 57, [1] p. 12º.

  Three acts. Argument, notice to the reader, cast, scenario, and name of **Tom-**maso **Albinoni** as composer.

  The supplementary page contains the aria "Da più affetti combattuta" as sub-stitute for "Vò che cada trafitto" on p. 25. Pages 3–4 lacking in our copy. Pages 5–6 contain several substituted arias.   Schatz 106

Arethuse, ballet representé par l'Academie royale de musique l'an 1701. Les paroles de M. Danchet & la musique de M. Campra. LII. Opera.

  n. i., n. d. front., 167–214 p. 14ᶜᵐ. (Recueil général des opera, Paris, 1703, t. vii.)

  Detached copy. Three acts with prologue.

  First performed, as indicated, July 14, 1701.   Schatz 1544

                                        Second copy. ML 48.R4

— Arethuse, ballet. Représenté par l'Académie royale de musique, le 14 juillet 1701.

  [83]–124 p. 17½ᶜᵐ. (Antoine Danchet, Théâtre, t. ii, Paris, 1751.)

  Prologue and three acts. The composer, **Campra,** is not mentioned.

                                        PQ 1972.D2

L'Aretusa. Melo-drama da' recitarsi nel Teatro di S. Fantino l'anno 1709 . . .

  Venezia, Gio. Battista Zuccato, 1709. 48 p. 14½ᶜᵐ.

  Three acts. By Pietro d'Averara, who is not mentioned. Publisher's dedication, argument, scenario, and notice to the reader that this drama had been performed on the famous stages of Italy, but that

  "l'angustie del teatro non permettono, che ti venga rappresentato con quel gran-dioso apparato, con cui, & altre volte egli comparve."

  Clemente **Monari,** the composer, is not mentioned.

  First performed at Milan, Regio Ducal Teatro, 1703.   Schatz 6549

Argea. Dramma per musica da rappresentarsi nel Teatro nazionale di Torino nel carnovale del 1799 anno settimo della Repubblica francese, primo della libertà piemontese.

Torino, Onorato Derossi, n. d. 64 p. 15½ᶜᵐ.

Three acts. Giandomenico Boggio is mentioned as author, Gaetano **Andreozzi** as composer. Argument, cast, scenario.

The ballets by Gaetano Gioja, composer of music not mentioned, were entitled: "La disfatta di Abdurahamel, tiranno di Trabacca, ballo eroico pantomimo," "Nina pazza per amore," and "La volubile." The detailed description of the first ballet on p. 65 *et seq.* missing in this copy. Sᴄʜᴀᴛᴢ 215

L'Argene. Trattenimento per musica. Da rappresentarsi nell' Academia à il Saloni l'anno 1689. dell' abbate Paolo Emilio Badi . . .

Venetia, Gio. Maria Rossi, 1689. 40 p. 16ᶜᵐ.

Three acts. Argument, scenario, Badi's dedication and prefatory note, in which he says:

"Questa non è opera, non è drama, non è di quei parti, che richiede l'Alcmene per madri, ò che s'impregnino i monti per concepirlo: è un trattenimento di delitia, un passatempo disinteressato di gentilezza, una ricreatione ideata, per assicurare nell' hore calde le matrone dell' Adria da gl' insulti di quel Sole, che sdegnoso di vedersi diviso ne' loro volti, imprime in quelle faccie serene, ma con rossore, i segni chiarissimi della sua fervida gelosia . . . Bene non sò, per che in trè mamattine, che sono state assegnate a questo componimento, non può il mio debole ingegno ritrovar di perfetto altro, che il numero . . . Tutto l'affanno, che possano ricevere gli occhi nel leggere, sarà contrapesato dall' udito, che ascolterà armoniose le meraviglie nella musica del Sig. Antonio **Caldara** il quale dalle viscere più amorose delle sua viola loquace ha filate le dolcezze per allacciare gli applausi . . ." Sᴄʜᴀᴛᴢ 1492

Argenide. Dramma per musica da rappresentarsi nel Teatro di S. Angelo nell' autunno dell' anno 1738 . . .

Venezia, Marino Rossetti, 1738. 60 p. 15ᶜᵐ.

Three acts. By Alvise Giusti (not mentioned). Argument, scenario, and cast. The composer, Pietro **Chiarini,** is not mentioned. Sᴄʜᴀᴛᴢ 1853

Argenide. Dramma per musica da rappresentarsi nel Teatro S. Angelo nel carnovale dell' anno 1733 . . .

Venezia, Marino Rossetti, 1733. 60 p. 14½ᶜᵐ.

Three acts. By Alvise Giusti, who is not mentioned. Dedication, argument (p. 6. "S'aggiungono gl'infrascritti verissimili"), cast, scenario, and name of **Galuppi** as composer.

First performed, as indicated, January 15, 1733 (Piovano). Sᴄʜᴀᴛᴢ 3481

Argeno. Dramma per musica di Domenico Lalli tra gli Arcadi Ortanio: Da rappresentarsi nel famosissimo Teatro Grimani di S. Gio. Grisostomo il carnovale dell' anno 1728 . . .

Venezia, Marino Rossetti, 1728. 70 p. 15½ᶜᵐ.

Three acts. Lalli's dedication, dated Venice, January 17, 1728, argument, scenario, cast, and name of Leonardo **Leo** as composer. Sᴄʜᴀᴛᴢ 5552

L'Argia, dramma musicale, rappresentato à Insprugg alla Maestà della serenissima Cristina, regina di Suezia, etc.

Insprugg, per Hieronymo Agricola, anno 1655. 6 p. l., 94 p. 19½ᶜᵐ.

Three acts, with prologue. Argument, scenario, and list of machines, but neither the composer, presumably Marc' Antonio **Cesti,** is mentioned, nor the author Apollonio Apolloni. (For further data *see* Wotquenne's libretto catalogue.)

First performed at Innsbruck, at the Ducal Palace, November 4, 1655. Sᴄʜᴀᴛᴢ 1777

L'Argia—Continued.

— **L'Argia.**   Drama per musica da rappresentarsi nel Teatro a San Salvatore l'anno 1669 . . .

Venetia, Francesco Nicolini, 1669.   front., 81 p.   14ᶜᵐ.

Three acts, without prologue. By Apollonio Apolloni, with considerable alterations of the original libretto, as acknowledged in the notice to the reader:

"Quest' opera hà fatto stupire di se stessa le scene più famose, & hora si conduce a farsi freggio del tuo eroico compiacimento. Vi dovrai ammirare la virtù di due penne famose; una nella parte poetica, l'altra nell' armonica. Basta che io ti dinoti esser ella figlia di quei genitori de' quali applaudesti alla Dori [text by Apolloni, music by **Cesti**]. Vi sentirai alcune ariette udite in altra occasione: mà perche sià noto, che furon prese da questo drama vi si hanno lasciate sì per essere di pochissimo numero, come anco di singolare esquisitezza. E stato ancora abbreviato, e fattavi qualche alteratione, à solo ogetto d'accomodarsi alla brevità, & alle congionture delle parti . . ."

Accordingly, for instance, the aria, "Vendetta, vendetta" (I, 15), was replaced by "Amori fuggite" (I, 16, of the Venice ed.), the aria, "Ecco Alceo guerrier novello" (II, 5), by "Io pensavo innamorarmi" (II, 5); and the original final scene (III, 18), the quartet, "Alle gioie, a i diletti," was dropped. On the whole, the alterations were numerous, but not radical. The notice to the reader is followed by the argument and the scenario. It is preceded by the publisher's dedication, dated Venice, January 13, 1669.   SCHATZ 1777a

Argiope.   Favola musicale di N. e di Gio. Battista Fusconi. Consacrata al chiaro merito della Signora Anna Renzi.

Venetia, Gio. Pietro Pinelli, 1649.   96 p.   14ᶜᵐ.

Three acts and prologue. G. B. Fusconi's dedication is dated Venice, December, 1645 [!]. Argument, cast, and important notice to the reader giving the odd history of the libretto, which according to Schatz was written by Pietro Michieli and Giov. Battista Fusconi. The notice reads:

"L'orditura di questa favola venne a preghiere d'amici più tosto precipitata, che tessuta in quatordici sere dalla penna di quel famosissimo Cigno dell' Adria, che mantiene al nostro secolo in vita la poesia italiana: poiche essendo egli allhora di partenza, e in aspettatione della discretione de' venti, che gli aprissero la strada per un lungo viaggio maritimo non potè applicarvisi, che a momenti rubati al sonno. Partitosi adunque nell sconciatura di quest' opera, me la lasciò con amplissima licenza . . . Operai per tanto quello che seppi, e che potei rimettendola insieme nella fretta, che mi facevano gl'Interessati, che volevano recitarlo. Ma delusi da vari accidenti di fortuna che ne impedì la recita i loro desideri, si compiacque l'inventore dell' opera di rivederla, e di rimutarla; perche a me ancora tocasse questo secondo fastidio, e mi reuscì la facenda in guisa, che non vi resto quasi più vestigio alcuno dell' effigie datale dal primo schizzo. Con qual mio rammarico l'altri l'imagini mentre mi convenne ritoccar con rozzo pennello le linee eccellentissime d'un Apelle . . . Spero nondimeno che la diversità pur troppo apparente dello stile verrà resa uniforme dalla musica impareggiabile (ancorche diversa) delli Signori Gio. **Rovetta**, & Alessandro **Leardini**, prencipi de musici moderni, e che l'eccellenza delle più famose voci del secolo coprirà i mancamenti della mia penna . . ."

Accordingly this is merely G. B. Fusconi's *advance* notice, and though Schatz, etc., actually enter "Argiope" under the two composers mentioned, the libretto itself would seem to furnish evidence that their setting, if at all composed, was not performed, and that an explanation of the remarkable discrepancy between the date of performance (1649) on the title page and the date of the dedication (1645) may be found in this notice, which follows the end of the text on p. 96:

"*A chi haverà letto.* Gli errori, che avvengono nella stampa, sono figli d'una madre, che pur troppo ne sà esser feconda. Perciò nel medesimo tempo, che quegli doveano venire da te emendati saranno stati ancora compatiti. Gli accidenti, che mutano l'essere alle cose in un istante, havendo privato della seconda gloria il nostro dramma, la quale sarebbe stata la musica del Sig. Rovetta, unita a quella del Sig. Leardini, ti lasceranno godere dell' armonia d'un solo Orfeo, mentre io te ne havea apparecchiata quella di due."   SCHATZ 9106

L'Argippo. Drama per musica da rappresentarsi nel Regio ducal Teatro di Milano in occasione di celebrarsi il giorno natalizio della Cesarea Cattolica Maestà di Elisabetta Cristina imperatrice, regina delle Spagne etc etc.

Milano, Giuseppe Richino Malatesta, 1722. 6 p. l., 44 p. 14ᶜᵐ.

Three acts. Domenico Lalli's "Il Gran Mogol," retouched by Claudio Nicola Stampa, who signs the preface. Impresario's dedication, dated August 27, 1722, cast, scenario, and name of the composer, Stefano Andrea **Fiorè**. SCHATZ 3191

L'Argippo. Drama per musica da rappresentarsi nel Teatro di San Cassiano l'autunno dell' anno MDCCXVII. Di Domenico Lalli . . .

Venezia, Marino Rossetti, 1717. 60 p. 14½ᶜᵐ.

Three acts. Dedication by Lalli, a later title of whose "Il Gran Mogol" this is, argument, cast, scenario, and name of Giovanni **Porta** as the composer. SCHATZ 8388

Gli argonauti in Colco o sia La conquista del vello d'oro. Dramma per musica del Signor A. S. Sografi da rappresentarsi nel nobilissimo Teatro di San Samuele il carnovale dell' anno 1790.

Venezia, Modesto Fenzo, 1789. 62 p. 22ᶜᵐ.

Three acts. Author's dedication, cast and name of the composer, Giuseppe **Gazzaniga**.
First performed at Venice, December 26, 1789. SCHATZ 3657

Ariadne. *See* Keiser's Die betrogene und nachmals vergoetterte . . .

Ariadne auf Naxos. Ein duodrama mit musick.

Gotha, n. publ., 1775. 4 p. l., 12 p. 18¼ᶜᵐ.

One act. The "Vorbericht" by the author, Joseph Jacob Christian Brandes (not mentioned) of date Gotha, January 3, 1775, contains the argument and the following remarks, with name of Georg **Benda** as composer in a foot-note:
"Die bekannte cantate des herrn von Gerstenberg, *Ariadne auf Naxos*, ist zur grundlage dieses duodrama genommen und vieles daraus woertlich beybehalten worden. Der ausdruck so mannigfaltiger leidenschaften, die vortreflichen gemaehlde dieses dichters sind ursache, dass der verfasser es gewagt hat, jene so wohl klingende poesie in prosa aufzuloesen, sie mittelst einiger veraenderungen auch fuer die buehne brauchbar zu machen und zugleich durch diesen weg einem unsrer besten meister in der musik gelegenheit zu geben, an einem so reichhaltigen stoffe sein grosses talent zu zeigen. Der umstand, dass dies duodrama zur musikbegleitung geschrieben ist, wird dem leser leicht die ursache der oeftern absaetze im text erklaeren."
First performed at Gotha, Schlosstheater, January 27, 1775. SCHATZ 768

— **Ariadne auf Naxos.** Ein duodrama von Joh. Christian Brandes.

Leipzig, Dykische buchhandlung, 1790. 1 p. l., 21 p. 18½ᶜᵐ.

One act. On p. [1] the note "Verfertigt in jahr 1774." The Vorbericht the same as in the 1775 ed. ML 50.2.A737

Ariadne et Bachus. *See* Marais' Ariane et Bachus.

Ariadne und Theseus, ballet. *See* Piccinni's Cato in Utica.

Ariane, tragedie representée pour la premiere fois par l'Académie royale de musique, le mardy 6. avril 1717.

Paris, Pierre Ribou, 1717. xiv, [50] p. 25½ᶜᵐ.

Last 2 p. incorrectly numbered 7 and 5.
Prologue and five acts. Cast. Neither authors nor composer mentioned. (*See* next entry.) ML 50.2.A739M6

Ariane—Continued.

— **Ariane,** tragedie représentée par l'Academie royale de musique, l'an 1717. Paroles de Messieurs Roy & de Lagrange. Musique de M. Mouret. XCII. opera.

n. i., n. d. p. 132-186, 1 pl. (Recueil général des opéra, t. xii, Paris, 1734.) 14ᶜᵐ.

Detached copy.   Five acts and prologue.   SCHATZ 6694
                                     Second copy.   ML 48.R4

Ariane dans l'isle de Naxos, drame lyrique, représenté pour la pre-mère fois, par l'Académie royale de musique, le mardi 24 septembre 1782.

Paris, P. de Lormel, 1792.   12 p.   22ᶜᵐ.

One act.   Argument, cast, and names of [Pierre Louis] Moline as author, of [Johann Friedrich] **Edelmann** as composer.   ML 50.2.A74E3

Ariane et Bachus, tragedie.   Representée par l'Academie royale de musique.

Amsterdam, les héritiers d'Antoine Schelte, 1699.   front., 52 p.   14ᶜᵐ.

Prologue and five acts.   Neither the author, Saint-Jean, nor the composer, Marin **Marais,** is mentioned.
First performed, as indicated, March 8, 1696.   ML 50.2.A742M2

— **Ariadne et Bachus,** tragedie représentée par l'Académie royale de musique l'an 1696.   Les paroles sont de M. S. Jean. & La musique de M. Marais. XXXVIII. opera.

n. i., n. d.   front., p. 291-352 (Recueil général des opéra, t. v, Paris, 1703).   14ᶜᵐ.

Detached copy.   Five acts and prologue.   SCHATZ 5920
                                     Second copy.   ML 48.R4

Ariane et Bacchus.   *See* Mouret's Les amours des dieux.

Arianna, ballet.   *See* Colla's Sicotencal.

Arianna.   Drama per musica, da rappresentarsi nel Regio Teatro di Torino, l'anno 1728. alla presenza delle Loro Sacre Reali Maestà, e delle Loro Altezze Reali.

Torino, Gio. Battista Valetta, n. d.   50 p.   15½ᶜᵐ.

Three acts.   By Pietro Pariati, who is not mentioned.   Argument, scenario, cast, and name of the composer, "Leonardo **Feo,** mastro di cappella di Napoli."
                                         SCHATZ 3061

L'Arianna.   Tragedia del Sig. Ottavio Rinuccini, gentilomo della camera del Rè Cristianissimo.   Rappresentata in musica nelle reali nozze del sereniss. principe di Mantova, e della serenissima infanta di Savoia.

Mantova, presso gli heredi di Francesco Osanna, 1608.   2 p. l., 46 p. 16ᶜᵐ.

Monteverdi, the composer, is not mentioned.
Wotquenne claims that the original edition was published at Florence in 1606. This is evidently a misprint for 1608, when Giunti, of Florence, published Rinuccini's text. The Brussels catalogue lists neither this edition nor ours, but one published at Venice in the same year. Schatz claims our edition to be the original. This opera (of which the music is lost, except the famous Lamento) was first performed, as indicated, on May 28, 1608.
Neither this edition is divided into acts, nor the following.   SCHATZ 6595

L'Arianna—Continued.

— **L'Arianna** del Sig. Ottavio Rinuccini. Posta in musica dal Sig. Claudio Monteverdi. [!] Rappresentata in Venetia l'anno 1640. Al molto illustre Signore il Sig. Bortolo Stacio.

Venetia, Bariletti, 1640.   64 p.   13½ cm.

This is apparently the text as used in the winter of 1639 at Venice for the opening of the Teatro di San Moisè.   On p. 5 Antonio Bariletti says in his dedication:
". . . Hora dunque che l'Arianna, componimento, che fra' Drammatici ha riportati i primi vanti da' theatri italiani, ritorna à veder le scene in Venetia, per opra del Signor Claudio **Monte Verdi** [!] celebratissimo Apollo del secolo, e prima intelligenza del cielo armonico, prendo occasione di non tenerle i miei più lungamente celati; ma con offerirla al nome di V. S. di manifestargli al mondo per mezzo della sua nuova ristampa . . ."
This dedication is followed, on p. 8–9, by the "Sonetto del Signor Benedetto Ferrari dalla Tiorba: al Sig. Claudio Monteverdi oracolo della musica."
Since the dedication begins on p. 5, since the verso of the title-page is blank and unnumbered, and since the signatures A3–A6 are in twos, it is clear that either p. 3–4 are missing or that the title-page was intended as p. 3, and was preceded, perhaps, by a frontispiece.
A line-by-line comparison of the Venice (1640) and the Mantova (1608) edition reveals exceedingly few differences.   The verbal differences are indeed entirely negligible, except, perhaps, in Apollo's opening address, where, in the third stanza—
" Di strali armato, e non di face, o d'arco
Gran Rè, c'hai sovra l'alpi e scettro, e regno "
has become—
" Di pace armato, e non di strali, o d'arco
A te, c'hai sovra l'acque scettro, e regno."
Also, the "Odi Carlo immortal" has now become "Odi Duce immortal."   It is further noticeable that in the 1640 version "Uno del C." [oro] was often employed instead of the chorus, so that, for instance, the last three lines of the chorus, "Miseri peregrin quietar nō ponno," were now sung only by "uno del c."
The Venetian version, finally, is, toward the end, slightly condensed, as on p. 42 the chorus lines, "Bell'è il tacer," etc. and on p. 62 (Amore) the lines "Soave e dolce nume," etc., before Arianna's "Gioite al gioir mio," and her lines, "Felice il martir mio," before the chorus, have been dropped.   The repeated spelling of the name as Monteverd*i*, not Monteverd*e*, is interesting, since it strengthens Emil Vogel's contention, based on the composer's manuscripts, that his name was Monteverdi, and not Monteverde, as many Italian and other writers still insist on spelling it.

SCHATZ 6592

Arianna. Azione scenica per musica, rappresentata nella Regia elettoral villa di Sant' Uberto per solennizzare il giorno natalizio della Maestà di Augusto III . . . l'anno MDCCXXXVI.

Dresda, la vedova Stössel, n. d.   Unpaged.   18½ cm.

One act.   Argument.   Neither the author, Stefano Benedetto Pallavicini, nor the composer, Giovanni Alberto **Ristori,** is mentioned.
First performed, as indicated, October 7, 1736.   SCHATZ 8816

Arianna abbandonata. Drama per musica da rappresentarsi nel Teatro Giustiniano di San Moisè l'autunno dell' anno MDCCXIX.

Venezia, Marino Rossetti, 1719.   48 p.   14 cm.

Three acts.   Argument and scenario, but without names of the composer, Giuseppe **Boniventi,** and the librettist, conte Angelo Schietti.   SCHATZ 1189

Arianna abbandonata da Teseo, e soccorsa da Bacco. A. T. of the ballet Il trionto d'Arianna.

Arianna abbandonata da Teseo e soccorsa da Bacco, ballet. *See* Rust's L'idolo cinese.

Arianna e Teseo. Dramma per musica da rappresentarsi nel famo-sissimo Teatro Grimani di S. Gio. Grisostomo nel carnovale dell' anno MDCCLI [vignette]

Venezia, In merceria all' insegna della scienza, n. d.   52 p.   15½^{cm}.

Three acts. Cast, scenario, name of Girolamo **Ab(b)os** as composer. Librettist unknown to Schatz.
First performed at Rome, Teatro delle Dame, December 26, 1748.   SCHATZ 9

Arianna e Teseo. Dramma per musica da rappresentarsi nel nobi-lissimo Teatro di S. Benedetto il carnovale dell' anno 1769.

Venezia, Modesto Fenzo, 1769.   54, [7] p.   17^{cm}.

Three acts. By Pietro Pariati, who is not mentioned. Argument, cast, scenario, and name of Baldassare **Galuppi** as composer. The additional seven pages contain a "Descrizione dei balli."
First performed at Padua, Teatro Nuovo, June 12, 1763.   SCHATZ 3441

Arianna e Teseo. Dramma per musica da rappresentarsi nel Regio Teatro di Torino nel carnovale del 1764 . . .

Torino, Gaspare Bayno, n. d.   viii, 48 p.   16^{cm}.

Three acts. By Pietro Pariati, who is not mentioned. Argument, cast, and name of Giuseppe **Pasque** as the composer. On p. 45–48 description of Augusto Huss' ballets, "Il giuoco dell' arco," "Le fontane incantate," and "Le donne Ateniesi, e i loro compagni," music by Giuseppe Antonio Le Messier.
First performed, as indicated, December 26, 1763.   SCHATZ 7781

Arianna e Teseo. Dramma per musica da rappresentarsi nel Teatro Grimani di San Gio. Grisostomo nell' autunno MDCCXXVII.

Venezia, Marino Rossetti, 1727.   60 p.   15^{cm}.

Three acts. By Pietro Pariati, who is not mentioned. Argument, cast, scenario, and name of Nicolà Antonio **Porpora** as the composer.
First performed at Vienna, Hoftheater, October 1, 1714.   SCHATZ 8369

Arianna e Teseo. A. T. of P. v. Winter's I sacrifizi di Creta.

Arianna in Naxo.

[259]–293 p.   17^{cm}.   (Rolli, Componimenti poetici, Nuova edizione, Verona, G. Tumermani, 1744.)

Three acts. Argument. The composer, Nicolò **Porpora**, is not mentioned.
First performed at London, Lincoln's Inn Fields, December 29, 1733.

ML 49.A2R7

Arianna nell' isola di Nasso, ballet. *See* Naumann's Armida.

Ariarate. Dramma per musica da rappresentarsi nel Regio Teatro di Torino nel carnovale del 1789 . . .

Torino, Onorato Derossi, n. d.   viii, 67 p.   16^{cm}.

Three acts. By Ferdinando Moretti, who is not mentioned. Argument, scenario, cast, and name of Giuseppe **Giordani** as the composer. On p. 59–67 description of Giuseppe Banti's ballets, "Il riconoscimento di Teseo ossia Teseo e Medea (4 acts) and "Il disertore francese," music for both by Vittorio Amedeo Canavasso.
First performed, as indicated, December 26, 1788.   SCHATZ 3842

Ariarate. Dramma per musica in due atti da rappresentarsi nel R. Teatro di S. Cecilia per la primavera dell' anno 1787 . . .

Palermo, Solli, n. d.   48 p.   15½^{cm}.

Three acts. By Ferdinando Moretti, who is not mentioned. Dedication, argu-ment, cast, and name of Angelo **Tarchi** as the composer.
First performed at Milan, Teatro alla Scala, January, 1786.   SCHATZ 10213

Ariberto e Flavio, regi de Longobardi. Drama per musica da rappresentarsi nel ristaurato famoso Teatro Vendramino di San Salvatore l'anno MDCLXXXV. Di D. Rinaldo Cialli . . .

Venetia, Francesco Nicolini, 1684 [!]. *69 (incl. front), [1] p. 14ᶜᵐ.*

Three acts. Cialli's dedication, dated Venice, December 9, 1685, argument, scenario, and notice to the reader, with name of Carlo Ambrogio **Lonati** as the composer. SCHATZ 5680

Aricie, ballet representé par l'Academie royale de musique l'an 1697. Les paroles sont de M. Pic & la musique de M. la Coste. XLII. opera.

n. i., n. d. 14ᶜᵐ. pl., 63–120 p. (Recueil général des opéra, t. vi, Paris, 1703.)

Detached copy. Five entries and prologue.
First performed at Paris, Académie royale de musique, June 9, 1697.
SCHATZ 5351
Second copy. ML 48.R4

Ariodante. Drama per musica. Del dottore Antonio Salvi, Fiorentino, da rappresentarsi nel famosissimo Teatro Grimani di San Giovanni Grisostomo . . .

Venezia, Marino Rossetti, 1716. 58 p. 14½ᶜᵐ.

Three acts. Dedication by the impresario, argument, cast, scenario, name of Carlo Francesco **Pollaroli** as the composer, and this notice to the reader:
"Nella ristampa, che io ho dovuto fare di questo drama, in occasione che egli si dee rappresentare in questa città di Venezia, mi corre l'obbligo di avvertirti, che in esso tu non ricerchi tutto quell' ordine, e tutti que' versi con cui l'insigne autore l'ha composto e pubblicato. Si è dovuto troncarlo, e accrescerlo, e alterarlo in molte parti. Diverso è'l numero degli attori, delle scene, delle mutazioni, e così dell' altre parti costitutive del drama. Ciò tuttavolta non è stato fatto con animo di migliorarlo, ma solo ad oggetto di adattarlo al bisogno. L'autore è pregato a prendere questo cangiamento in buona parte, e ciò con l'esempio, o sia più tosto con l'abuso, che in oggi corre per tutti i teatri d'Italia in simili componimenti, dove ognuno ha l'autorità e'l privilegio di porci mano, e di cangiarne infino i titoli, come pure in questo si è fatto."
First performed fall of 1716, as indicated. SCHATZ 8272

Ariodante. Drama per musica da rappresentarsi nel famosissimo Teatro Grimani a S. Gio. Grisostomo l'autunno 1745 . . .

[Venezia], n. i., n. d. 1 p. l., 48 p. 15ᶜᵐ.

Three acts. Dedication, scenario, cast, name of Georg Christoph **Wagenseil** as the composer, and notice to the reader, who is informed that in this version of Antonio Salvi's text (who is not mentioned):
"Si è dovuto troncarlo, accrescerlo, e alterarlo in molte parte, e particolarmente in buona parte dell' arie introdotevi a maggior comodo della nuova musica. Diverso è il numero delle scene, delle mutazioni, e cosi dell' altre parti costitutive del drama. Ciò tutta volta non è stato fatto con animo di migliorarlo, ma solo ad' oggetto di adattarlo al bisogno, e ciò con l'esempio, o sia più tosto con l'abuso, che in oggi corre per tutti teatri d'Italia in simili componimenti, dove ogn' uno a l'autorità e'l privileggio di porci màno e di cangiarne infino i titoli." (*Comp.* preceding entry.)
SCHATZ 10816

Arion. Tragedie representée pour la première fois par l'Académie royale de musique, le mardy 10. avril 1714. Les paroles de M. Fuzelier & la musique de M. Mattau. LXXXIII. opera.

n. i., n. d. pl., p. [50]–109. (Recueil général des opéra, t. xi, Paris, 1720.) 14ᶜᵐ.

Detached copy. Five acts and prologue. Composed by Jean Baptiste **Matho.**
SCHATZ 6097
Second copy. ML 48.R4

Aristeo. Second act of Gluck's Le feste d'Apollo.

L'Aristeo. Drama per musica. Da rappresentarsi nel Teatro Tron di S. Cassiano l'anno 1700 . . .

Venezia, Nicolini, 1700. 69 p. 14ᶜᵐ.

Three acts. By Giulio Cesare Corradi, who is not mentioned. Impresario's dedication, argument, cast, scenario, and notice to the reader, with the name of Antonio Polaroli (**Pollaroli**) as the composer. SCHATZ 8260

Aristide.

[285]–300 p. 16½ᶜᵐ. (Carlo Goldoni, Opere drammatiche giocose, t. iii, Torino, 1757.)

Two parts. *(See below.)* ML 49.A2G6

— **Aristide.** Intermezzo di due parti per musica.

Carlo Goldoni, Opere teatrali, Venezia, Zatta e figli, 1788–95, v. 35, [271]–287 p. 18½ᶜᵐ.

PQ

Aristide. Drama eroi-comico per musica da rappresentarsi nel Teatro Grimani di S. Samuel dalla Compagnia de. Comici l'autunno dell' anno 1735. Di Calindo Grolo . . .

Venezia, Alvise Valvasense, 1735. 30 p. 14½ᶜᵐ.

One act. By Carlo Goldoni. Dedicatory sonnet, argument, cast, scenario, and name of Lotavio **Vandini** as composer. The latter would seem to be a fictitious name for Giacomo **Macari**, since Schatz claims that all the names in the libretto are fictitious. Wiel does not mention the opera at all. SCHATZ 5808

Aristo, e Temira e Orfeo, ed Euridice. Drammi per musica da rappresentarsi nel nobilissimo Teatro di S. Benedetto il carnovale dell' anno MDCCLXXVI . . .

Venezia, Modesto Fenzo, 1776. 48 p. 17¼ᶜᵐ.

Both in one act, with argument, cast, and name of Ferdinando Giuseppe **Bertoni** as composer, but not of the librettists. "Aristo e Temira" was by *conte* de Salvioli, "Orfeo ed Euridice" (p. 23–48) by Ranieri de' Calsabigi. Bertoni's "Orfeo ed Euridice" was revived at the same theatre. *(See* libretto.) The impresario says in his dedication that "Orfeo" had been first performed at Vienna, but this remark refers to Calsabigi's text, as composed by Gluck, Vienna, 1762. SCHATZ 934–935

Aristo e Temira, text by conte De Salvioli, music by Carlo Monza. *See* Gluck's Orfeo ed Euridice (Schatz 3934).

Aristomene Messenio. Drama per musica nel giorno natalitio della Sac. R. M.ᵗᵃ Mariana d'Austria . . . l'anno MDCLXX. Posto in musica dal Sᵣ Felice Sances . . .

Vienna d'Austria, Matteo Cosmerovio, n. d. 78 p. 15½ᶜᵐ.

Three acts and licenza. Dedication by the author, conte Nicolò **Minato**, dated Vienna, December 20, 1670, notice to the reader, argument, and scenario.

First performed, not as indicated in the dedication, but December 22, 1670 (Schatz). SCHATZ 9367

Aristote amoureux; ou Le philosophe bridé, opéra-comique, en un acte & en vaudevilles: Représenté pour la premiere fois par les Comediens italiens ordinaires du roi, le vendredi 11 août 1780.

Paris, Vente, 1780. 33, [1] p. 20ᶜᵐ.

Cast. The authors, de Piis and Barré, are not mentioned. Arranger of the music unknown to Schatz. ML 50.2.A746

Arkadien. L. T. of Schmittbauer's Lindor und Ismene.

Arlequin Atys, parody. *See* Lully's Atys.

Arlequin Bellérophon, parody. *See* Lully's Bellérophon.

Arlequin Colombine. A. T. of Colombine Arlequin.

Arlequin défenseur d'Homère. Pièce d'un acte. Par Monsieur F***. Representée à la Foire de S. Laurent 1715 . . .

> *Le Théâtre de la foire, Paris, 1737, t. ii, pl., 43 p. 17ᶜᵐ.*

By Fuzelier. *En vaudevilles,* selected or composed by Jean Claude **Gillier,** the "compositeur" of the theatre and printed in the "Table des airs" at the end of the volume. A note on the title page reads:
"Cette pièce a été composée à l'occasion de la fameuse querelle qu'il y avoit dans ce tems là entre les auteurs au sujet d'Homère."
First performed, as indicated, July 25, 1715.   ML 48.L2 I

Arlequin-Deucalion, monologue en trois actes. Donné à l'Opéra-comique en 1722.

> *Alexis Piron, Oeuvres complettes, Liege, 1776, v. 3, 45 p. 17½ᶜᵐ.*

Composer not recorded by Parfaict, etc.
First performed, as indicated, February 25, 1723.   PQ 2019.P6

Arlequin Endymion. *See* Prologue des deux pièces . . .

Arlequin Hulla, ou La femme repudiée. Pièce d'un acte. Par Messieurs le S***. & D'Or**. Representée à la Foire de S. Laurent 1716.

> *Le Théâtre de la foire, Paris, 1737, t. ii, pl., [353]–397 p. 17ᶜᵐ.*

By Le Sage & d'Orneval. Music composed by **Aubert.** according to Parfaict.
            ML 48.L2 II

Arlequin invisible. Pièce en un acte. Par Monsieur le S**. Representée à la Foire de S. Laurent 1713.

> *Le Théâtre de la foire, Paris, 1737, t. i, pl., [85]–104 p. 17ᶜᵐ.*

By Alain René Le Sage. A *pièce par écriteaux, en vaudevilles.* The melodies are printed in the "Table des airs" at the end of the volume. They were selected or composed and arranged by the "compositeur" of the theatre, Jean Claude **Gillier.**
Parfaict gives as title "Arlequin invisible chez le roi de la Chine." ML 48.L2 I

Arlequin Mahomet, et Le tombeau de Nostradamus. Pièces chantées par les acteurs, d'une acte chacune, liées par un prologue intitulé: La foire de Guibray. Par M. le S**. Representées à la Foire de S. Laurent 1714.

> *Le Théâtre de la foire, Paris, 1737, t. i, 3 pl., [105]–199 p. 17ᶜᵐ.*

By Alain René Le Sage. *En vaudevilles.* The melodies are printed in the "Table des airs" at the end of the volume. They were selected or composed and arranged by the "compositeur" of the theatre, Jean Claude **Gillier.**
First performed, as indicated, July 25, 1714.   ML 48.L2 I

Arlequin Persée. Parody of Lully's Persée.

Arlequin Phaëton, parody. *See* Lully's Phaëton.

Arlequin, roi des Ogres, ou Les bottes de sept lieues. *See* Le diable d'argent.

Arlequin Roland. Parody of Lully's Roland.

Arlequin, roy de Serendib. Pièce en trois actes. Par M. le S*** representée à la Foire de Saint Germain 1713.

Le Théâtre de la foire, Paris, 1737, t. i, pl., p. 17–63. 17*cm*.

By Alain René Le Sage. A *pièce par écriteaux, en vaudevilles.* The melodies are printed in the "Table des airs" at the end of the volume. They were selected or composed and arranged by the "compositeur" of the theatre, Jean Claude **Gillier**.

ML 48.L2 I

Arlequin, sultane favorite. Pièce en trois actes. Par Monsieur le T**. Representée à la Foire de S. Germain 1715.

Le Théâtre de la foire, Paris, 1737, t. i, pl., [202]-285 p. 17*cm*.

By Le Tellier. *En vaudevilles.* The melodies are printed in the "Table des airs" at the end of the volume. They were selected or composed and arranged by the "compositeur" of the theatre, Jean Claude **Gillier**.

First performed, as indicated, February 3, 1719 (Parfaict). ML 48.L2 I

Arlequin Thétis. Pièce en un acte. Par Monsieur le S**. Representée à la Foire de S. Laurent 1713.

Le Théâtre de la foire, Paris, 1737, t. i, pl., [65]-83 p. 17*cm*.

By Alain René Le Sage. A *pièce par écriteaux, en vaudevilles.* The melodies are printed in the "Table des airs" at the end of the volume. They were selected or composed and arranged by the "compositeur" of the theatre, Jean Claude **Gillier**.

ML 48.L2 I

Arlequin traitant. Pièce en trois actes. Par M. D'or **. Représentée à la Foire de Saint Germain 1716 . . .

Le Théâtre de la foire, Paris, 1737, t. ii, pl., [133]-225 p. 17*cm*.

By d'Orneval. The airs, selected or composed and arranged by Jean Claude **Gillier**, are printed at the end of the volume in the "Table des airs." A note on the t.-p. reads:

"Cette pièce fut faite à l'occasion de la déroute des Traitans, causée par la Chambre de justice qui fut établie dans ce tems-là."

First performed, as indicated, March, 1716. ML 48.L2 II

L'Armida. Dramma per musica del tenente de Gamerra . . . Aprile N. 4. 1771.

*Milano, Giuseppe Galeazzi, n. d. 48 p. 15*cm*.*

Three acts. Author's dedication, prefatory poem, argument. Composer not mentioned and unknown to Schatz. On p. 44-48, "Osservazioni sull' opera in musica," which are noteworthy, and which culminate in Gamerra's contention that, contrary to current notions, "dovrebbe essere al poeta di precisa necessità la total nozion della musica . . ." SCHATZ 11309

Armida. Cantata a quattro voci per il benefizio di Gaetano Neri, da rappresentarsi nel Regio Teatro di S. Carlo della Principessa, la sera dei 16 novembre 1798.

*Lisboa, Simone Taddeo Ferreira, 1798. 35 p. 14*cm*.*

One act. Portuguese text faces Italian. Cast and name of Angelo Talassi as author. The composer is not mentioned. Under date of November 16, 1798, Schatz records a performance of Talassi's text at Lissabon, with music by Sacchini, but Sacchini's "Armida" (1772) had three acts. The text was by Giovanni de Gamerra, and Sacchini died 1786. ML 50.2.A75

Second copy. SCHATZ 9247

Armida. Dramma per musica da rappresentarsi nel Regio Teatro di Torino nel carnovale del 1770 . . .

*Torino, Onorato Derossi, n. d. viii, 72 p. 16½*cm*.*

Three acts. By Jacopo Durandi. Argument, cast, scenario, and name of Pasquale **Anfossi** as composer, but not of librettist.

The ballets, invented by Augusto Huss, the music by Giuseppe Antonio Le Messier, were entitled, "Amore custode del Giardino di Armida," "Accampamento, o sia la Lotteria militare," and "Di Furie." SCHATZ 226

Armida. Dramma per musica da rappresentarsi nel Teatro Giustiniani di San Moisè nella fiera dell' Ascensione dell' anno 1777.

[*Venezia*], *n. publ., n. d. 39 p. 17*^{cm}*.

Two acts. By Giannambrogio Migliavacca. Impresario's dedication, with name of author, argument, scenario, cast, and name of Gennaro **Astaritta** as composer.

SCHATZ 367

Armida. Dramma per musica da rappresentarsi nel Teatro di S. Angelo il carnovale dell' anno 1747.

Venezia, Modesto Fenzo, 1747. 48 p. 16^{cm}*.

Three acts. Scenario, cast, and name of Ferdinando Giuseppe **Bertoni** as composer, but not of librettist, Bartolomeo Vitturi.

SCHATZ 925

Armida, ballet. *See* Casali's Antigona.

L'Armida del Ferrari.

n. i., n. d. 75 p. 15^{cm}*.

According to Schatz, lacks a front. Dedication signed by the author-composer, Benedetto **Ferrari,** argument, "Prologo. La fortuna. Poesia d'Incerto.," characters, and three sonnets addressed to the author.
First performed at Venice, Teatro de' S. S. Gio. e Paolo, carnival, 1639.

SCHATZ 3065

— **L'Armida** di Benedetto Ferrari dalla tiorba. Rappresentata in musica in Venetia. Posta in musica dall' istesso autore.

n. i., n. d. 13^{cm}*. [109]-163 p. (B. Ferrari, Poesie drammatiche, Milano, 1644.)*

Detached copy. Three acts and prologue. Three sonnets by conte Giuseppe Theodoli, Michel Angelo Botti, Giuliano Bezzi to the author, argument.

SCHATZ 11699

Armida. Dramma per musica da rappresentarsi nel nobil Teatro a Torre Argentina nel carnevale dell' anno 1773 . . .

Roma, Lorenzo Capponi e Gio. Bartolomicchi, n. d. 61, [1] p. 16^{cm}*.

Three acts. Impresario's dedication, argument, scenario, cast, and name of Giuseppe **Gazzaniga** as composer. The author (unknown to Schatz) is not mentioned.

ML 50.2.A75G2

Armida. Dramma per musica da rappresentarsi nel Regio Teatro di Berlino per il felicissimo giorno natalizio della Sacra Real Maestà di Sofia Dorotea Regina madre . . .

Berlino, Haude e Spener, 1751. 89, [5] p. 16^{cm}*.

Three acts. Leopoldo de Villati is mentioned as author, Carl Heinrich **Graun** as the composer. Argument and scenario. German title page and text face Italian.
First performed, as indicated, March 27, 1751.

SCHATZ 4089

Armida. Dramma per musica del Signor avvocato Giacomo Duranti Torinese da rappresentarsi in Verona nel Teatro dell' illustrissima Accademia Filarmonica nel carnovale 1771.

Verona, Dionisio Ramanzini, n. d. 52, [5] p. 17½^{cm}*.

Three acts. Dedication, argument, cast, scenario, and name of Vincenzo **Manfredini** as composer. With the opera was performed, composer of the music not mentioned, Jean Favier's ballet "Zefiro e Flora."
First performed at Bologna, Teatro Comunale, May 1770.

SCHATZ 5893

Armida. Dramma per musica da rappresentarsi nel Teatro grande alla Scala il carnovale dell' anno 1780 . . .

Milano, Gio. Batista Bianchi, n. d.   61 p.   16ᶜᵐ.

Three acts. Dedication, cast, scenario, and name of Giuseppe **Misliweczek** as composer ("La musica nuova"). A note on p. [11] says of the text by Giannambrogio Migliavacca, who is not mentioned:
"La poesia è una versione dell' Armida di Quinault, di cui si sono esattamente seguite le tracce a differenza della semplice libera imitazione, che, per l'angustia del tempo, in Vienna, anni sono, ne fu già prodotta dal traduttore. Per maggior brevità però sono stati ommessi alcuni versi del dramma francese, e sostituiti o aggiunti altri colla scena, prima e terza dell' atto secondo, nell' italiano, per accomodarsi all' uso nostro."
The ballet music was composed by Gaspero Angiolini.
First performed, as indicated, December 26, 1779.   ML 48.A5   v. 9

Armida. Dramma per musica da rappresentarsi nel nobilissimo Nuovo Teatro di Padova nella fiera dell' anno MDCCLXXIII.

Venezia, Modesto Fenzo, 1773.   48 p.   17ᶜᵐ.

Three acts. By Giovanni Bertati, who is not mentioned. Impresario's dedication, argument, cast, scenario, and note: "La musica tutta nuova del . . . Giovanni Amadeo Neumann Sassone" (Johann Gottlieb **Naumann**).
With the opera was performed Gaspero Angiolini's ballet "Arianna nell' isola di Nasso," the composer of the music not being mentioned.
First performed in June, 1773, as indicated.   Schatz 7039

— Armide. Ein singspiel in drey aufzuegen. Nach einem italienischen Texte, aus Tasso's Goffredo entlehnt, von Bock. Die komposition ist von herrn kapellmeister Naumann.

n. i., n. d.   p. [79]–146 (Komische opern der Italiener, th. ii, no. 2, Leipzig, 1782).   16½ᶜᵐ.

Detached copy. First performed at Leipzig, Theater b. Rannstädter Thore, July 6, 1780.   Schatz 7040

Armida. Dramma del Signor Coltellini da rappresentarsi nel Gran Teatro Reale di Berlino nel febbraio 1797. Con musica del Signor Vicenzo Righini . . .

Berlino, Haude e Spener, n. d.   71, [1] p.   16½ᶜᵐ.

Two acts. Argument and cast. German title "Armide" and text face Italian. On last unnumb. p. title of "La figlia dell' aria o sia L'innalzamento di Semiramide, ballo tragico-pantomimo in cinque atti composto dal Sign. Onorato Viganò e rimesso sulle scene dal Sign. Salvatore Viganò. La musica è delli Sign. Giulio e Salvatore Viganò."
First performed at Berlin, Kgl. Opern-Theater, February 21, 1797; at Vienna, private theatre of prince A. Auersperg, July 23, 1782, and at Aschaffenburg, September 1788.   Schatz 8778

Armida. Dramma per musica da rappresentarsi nel Regio-ducal Teatro di Milano nel carnovale dell' anno 1772 . . .

Milano, Gio. Battista Bianchi, n. d.   70 p.   15ᶜᵐ.

Three acts. Dedication, argument, cast, name of Antonio **Sacchini** as the composer, and this "Protesta":
"Nell' atto I. alla scena 3. l'aria Rinaldo col recitativo, che la precede, e tutta la scena 12. col duetto, non meno che nell' atto II. alla scena 4. il recitativo avanti l'aria cantabile, e l'ultimo recitativo della scena 9. quando Armida è svenuta con tutta la scena 10. che segue col rondeau, come pure nell' atto III. alla scena 9. il minuetto col suo recitativo sono que' pochi, e soli cambiamenti, che in tutta l'opera il rispettoso poeta ha fatti, cosi richiedendo le convenienze degli attori, e le circostanze della scena, dichiarandosi però di professare la più perfetta stima in riguardo al valente autore di questo drammo."
The author was Giovanni de Gamerra, who is not mentioned.   Schatz 9205

Armida—Continued.

— Armida. Dramma per musica da rappresentarsi nel R. Duc. Teatro nella città della Piacenza nelle primavera dell' anno MDCCLXXXVI.

Piacenza, Salvoni, n. d.   47 p.   17^{cm}.

Three acts. Argument, cast, and name of Antonio **Sacchini** as composer. The author, Giovanni de Gamerra, is not mentioned. With the opera were performed, composers of the music not mentioned, Domenico Rossi's ballets "La vittoria di Tamerlano contro Bajazette ossia La Rossana" and "La contadina in corte." First performed May 27, 1786, as indicated.   SCHATZ 11745

— Renaud . . Tragedie-lyrique en trois actes, représentée, pour la premiere fois, par l'Académie-royale de musique, le mardi 25 février 1783.

Paris, P. de Lormel, 1783.   55 p.   22½^{cm}.

Three acts. Cast, names of Jean Joseph Leboeuf as author and of **Sacchini** as the composer and "avertissement," in which the author says that he based the text on Pellegrin, but

"je n'ai ni pu, ni dû suivre le plan tracé par Pellegrin; mais j'avoue que je m'en suis rapproché avec plaisir, autant qu'il m'a été possible. Je ne dissimulerai pas même, que trouvant qu'il avoit heureusement traduit plusieurs morceaux du Tasse, & désespérant de les traduire mieux, je ne me suis point fait scrupule de me les approprier, & de me servir quelquefois des vers de l'auteur français."

The published score has the same date as this libretto, but according to Cl. & L. and Schatz the first performance was on February 28. As the L. of C. does not possess the score of Sacchini's "Armida," I do not know to what extent the score of "Renaud" is based on that of "Armida." Leboeuf is said by Lajarte to have had Framery's assistance in adapting the French version to the Italian score.

    SCHATZ 9206

— Renaud. Tragédie-lyrique, en trois actes: représentée pour la première fois sur le Théâtre de l'Opéra, le 25 février 1783. Le poëme est de M. Le Boeuf. La musique est de M. Sacchini.

Bruxelles, n. publ., 1783.   21 p.   21^{cm}.

    ML 50.2.R38 S2

— Renaud, tragédie lyrique en trois actes, représentée, pour la premiere fois, par l'Académie royale de musique, le vendredi 28 février 1783. Le poëme est de M. Le Boeuf. La musique est de M. Sacchini.

Paris, P. de Lormel, 1786.   34 p.   21^{cm}.

Text is the same as in the 1783 ed.   ML 50.2.R38 S3

Armida. Eine oper, von Salieri.

n. i., n. d.   [1]–40 p.   15½^{cm}.

Three acts. By Marco Coltellini, who is not mentioned. In this libretto the German translation does not face the Italian, but follows it in segments, which must have been very confusing for the reader. *Comp.* Cramer's Tr. in his "Magazin der Musik," 1783. (ML 4.M2) First performed at Vienna, Burgtheater, June 2, 1771.   SCHATZ 9274

— Armida. Eine tragische oper von Carlo [!] Cotellini [!] und Antonio Salieri. Herausgegeben von C. S. Cramer.

Lueneburg, Joh. Fried. Wilh. Lemke, 1786.   62 p.   15½^{cm}.

Three acts. "Vorrede" with the argument.   SCHATZ 9275

Armida.   Azione teatrale per musica.   [vignette.]

Vienna, Ghelen, 1760.   Unpaged.   Vignettes.   22½^{cm}.

One act.   Avvertimento that this is a modified Italian version of Quinault's "Armide," and the author resp. translator's Giannambrogio Migliavacca's dedication to conte Giacomo Durazzo, "supremo direttore della musica delle Maestà Loro I. I. R. R.," in which he says:

"A Parigi vi nacque la voglia d'imitare in versi toscani, e di far eseguire con musica italiana l'Armida di Quinault. Ritornato in seno dell' inclita vostra patria, ne cominciaste, fra le delizie di Pegli, voi medesimo il lavoro, in compagnia d'illustre amico . . . Portatovi in appresso a questa Augustissima Corte, vi degnaste eccitarmi a proseguire, ed a condurre l'opera al suo termine, e se nel restarmene il desiderio, non mi fosse allora il tempo mancato di secondare i vostri impulsi, avrei, mercè vostra, io forse avuto il vantaggio, di essere il primo a produrre fra noi codesta nuova specie di spettacolo, come a voi la gloria non può negarsi, d'essere stato il primo a proccurarlo.   Finalmente, dopo tanti anni, voi avete costantemente voluto, che la sorte di mettere al giorno la da voi ideata imitazione, fosse a me riservata . . . acciò lo stile riuscisse tutto uniforme, voi, con generosità senza pari, non vi siete primieramente curato, di sacrificare la stessa egregia fatica, già da voi fatta, e di permettermi, che ad ordir la mia io incominciassi da capo . . . essendo destinata quest' opera a festeggiare il giorno natalizio di S. A. R. la serenissima arciduchessa sposa, principessa di Parma, sole poche settimane appena avanti tal giorno, per l'angustia del tempo, è convenuto, di mano in mano, che andavo scrivendo la poesia, passarla al compositore della musica, il che fu poi causa, che della già seguita edizione di questo libro io non rimanessi soddisfatto intieramente.   Colla presente più corretta ristampa," etc., etc.

This seems to be the libretto for Tommaso **Traetta**'s "Armida," first performed at Vienna, Saturday, January 3, 1761.   SCHATZ 11382

Armida.   Azione teatrale da rappresentarsi nel Teatro Vendramin di S. Salvatore nell' occasione della fiera dell' Ascensione dell' anno 1767 . . .

Venezia, Modesto Fenzo, 1767.   xlviii p.

One act.   Unsigned dedicatory poem by the author, Giannambrogio Migliavacca, argument, cast, and name of Tommaso **Traetta** as composer, but not of librettist, who professes to have based his "Armida" on Quinault's Armide, though in the Italian taste.   Of the music it is said "sarà tutta nuova;" consequently the identity with Traetta's "Armida," first performed at Vienna, Jan. 3, 1761, becomes doubtful.

First performed at Venice May 27, 1767.   SCHATZ 10407

Armida abbandonata.   Dramma per musica da rappresentarsi nel Teatro da S. Agostino il carnovale dell' anno 1786 . . .

Genova, Stamperia Gesiniana, n. d.   44 p.

Three acts.   Impresario's dedication, argument, cast, scenario, and name of Ferdinando Giuseppe **Bertoni** as composer.   The librettist is unknown to Schatz.

First performed at Venice, Teatro di S. Benedetto, December 26, 1780.

     SCHATZ 931

Armida abbandonata.   Dramma per musica da rappresentarsi per seconda nell' autunno MDCCXXIII nel Teatro Giustiniano di San Moisè.

Venezia, Carlo Buonarrigo, n. d.   47 p.   14½^{cm}.

Three acts.   By Francesco Silvani.   Notice to the reader, cast, scenario, and name of the composer, Giuseppe Maria **Buini**, but not of the librettist.

First performed at Bologna, Teatro Formagliari, Aug. 16, 1716.   SCHATZ 1388

Armida abbandonata.   Dramma per musica da rappresentarsi nel Real Teatro dell' Ajuda in occasione di festeggiarsi il felicissimo giorno natalizio di Sua Reale Maestà . . . D. Marianna Vittoria . . . nella primavera dell' anno 1773.

[Lisbona], Stamperia reale, n. d.   78 p.   16^{cm}.

Three acts.   By Francesco Saverio di Rogatis, who is not mentioned.   Argument, scenario, cast, and name of Niccolò **Jommelli** as the composer.   The text seems to be practically the same as in the Naples ed. of 1780.

First performed, as indicated, March 31, 1773; at Naples, same theatre, May 30, 1770.

     SCHATZ 4901

Armida abbandonata—Continued.

— **Armida abbandonata.** Dramma per musica da rappresentarsi nel Real Teatro di S. Carlo nel dì 13. agosto 1780 per festeggiarsi la nascita di S. M. la regina . . .

Napoli, Vincenzo Flauto, 1780. 71 p. 18^{cm}.

Three acts. By Francesco Saverio de Rogatis, who is not mentioned. Dedication, argument, cast, scenario, and name of Nicola **Jommelli** as the composer, and of Giuseppe Gazzaniga as conductor, who was probably responsible for alterations, if any, in the score, as first performed there May 30, 1770. On p. 9–17, description of Carlo Lepicq's ballet, "La Semiramide." The second ballet was Domenico Rossi's "Il disertore francese." The composers of the ballet music are not mentioned.

SCHATZ 4842

Armida abbandonata. Opera seria da rappresentarsi nel Teatro Nuovo di corte . . . nel carnavale.

n. i., 1785. 95 p. 16^{cm}.

Two acts. Argument, cast, scenario, and names of Gaetano Sertor as author, of sig. Hey as translator, and of Alessio **Prati** as the composer. German title-page, "Die verlassene Armide," and text face Italian.
First performed 1785, at Munich, as indicated.

SCHATZ 8450

Armida abbandonata. Drama per musica da rappresentarsi nel Teatro di Sant' Angelo l'autunno dell' anno 1707 . . .

Venezia, Zuccato, 1707. 60 p. 14½^{cm}.

Three acts. Dedication dated Venice, November 8, 1707, cast, scenario, and notice to the reader by the author, Francesco Silvani (not mentioned), who names Giovanni Maria **Ruggeri** as the composer, and defends himself for having used Tasso for "un drama intieramente amoroso."

SCHATZ 9133

— **Armida abbandonata.** Dramma per musica da rappresentarsi nel Teatro di Mantova il carnevale del MDCCXI . . .

Mantova, Alberto Pazzoni, n. d. 51 p. 15½^{cm}.

Three acts. Impresario's dedication dated Mantova, January 3, 1711, and notice to the reader, in which this is called a slightly altered version of Silvani's text, accommodated "alla contingenza del luogo, ed al genio de virtuosi cantanti." **Ruggeri,** the composer, perhaps mentioned on p. 7–8, which are missing. ML 48.A5 v. 3

Armida al campo. Drama per musica da rappresentarsi nel Teatro di Sant' Angelo il carnovale dell' anno 1707. M. V. . . .

Venezia, Zuccato, 1707. 70 [2] p. 14½^{cm}.

Three acts. Impresario's dedication, dated Venice, January 19, 1707, argument, cast, and name of the composer, Giuseppe **Boniventi,** but not of the librettist, Francesco Silvani. At the end a list of the "opere musicali sin' ora stampate in Venezia da Antonio Bortoli a S. Maria Formosa in Calle longa." SCHATZ 1184

Armida al campo. Drama per musica da rappresentarsi nel Teatro di S. Bartolomeo nel carnevale dell' anno 1718 . . .

Napoli, Michele Luigi Muzio, 1718. 67 p. 13½^{cm}.

Three acts. By Francesco Silvani, who is not mentioned. Impresario's dedication, dated Naples, February 13, 1718, notice to the reader, scenario, cast, and name of Domenico **Sarro** as the composer. SCHATZ 9413

Armida al campo d'Egitto. Drama per musica da rappresentarsi nel Teatro Giustiniano di San Moisè il carnovale dell' anno MDCCXVIII . . .

Venetia, Marino Rossetti, 1718. 60 p. 15½^{cm}.

Three acts. By Giovanni Palazzi, who is not mentioned. Publisher's dedication, argument, cast, scenario, and name of Antonio **Vivaldi** as the composer.

SCHATZ 10759

Armida delusa. Drama per musica da rappresentarsi nel Teatro di S. Angelo. Il carnovale dell' anno 1720.

Venezia, Marino Rossetti, 1720. 58 p. 15^{cm}.

Three acts. Argument, notice to the reader, cast, scenario, and name of the composer, Giuseppe Maria **Buini,** who also wrote the text (Schatz). SCHATZ 1389

Armida e Rinaldo, ballet. *See* Cimarosa's Giunio Bruto.

Armida e Rinaldo, ballet. *See* Cimarosa's Il pittor parigiuo.

Armida in Damasco. Drama per musica da rappresentarsi nel Teatro di S. Angelo l'autunno dell' anno 1711. Del dottor Grazio Braccioli . . .

Venezia, Marino Rossetti, 1711. 64 p. 14^{cm}.

Three acts. Author's dedication dated Venice, October 17, 1711, cast, scenario, name of Giacomo **Rampini** as the composer, and notice to the reader, in which Braccioli as much as begs pardon for having had the temerity to select the same subject as Francesco Silvani, "gentile poeta dramatico de nostri tempi" of "Armida abbandonata" and "Armida al Campo." SCHATZ 8595

Armida regina di Damasco. L. T. of Orgiani's Gli amori di Rinaldo con Armida.

Armida und Rinaldo. Ein nach Tasso frey bearbeitetes melodrama in vier aufzeugen, mit choeren und taenzen vermischt. Fuer das K. K. Nationalhoftheater.

Wien, Johann Baptist Wallishausser, 1793. 43 p. 16^{cm}.

Neither Franz Joseph Marius von Babo, the author, is mentioned, nor Peter von **Winter,** the composer.

First performed September 7, 1793, under this title, but as "Reinold und Armida," at Munich, Altes Opernhaus, March 30, 1780. SCHATZ 11050

Armide, tragédie en cinq actes donnée pour la première fois par l'Académie royale de musique, en 1686, 1746, 1761, 1764; et remise au Théâtre, le mardi 23 septembre 1777.

Paris, Aux dépens de l'Académie, chés P. de Lormel, 1777. 66 p. 22½^{cm}.

Cast. Quinault is mentioned as the author, and **Gluck** as the composer.

SCHATZ 3893

— Armide. Ein heldengedicht, und singspiel in fünf aufzeugen. In musik gesetzt vom ritter Gluck. Aufgefuehrt unter der direktion des herrn Boehm.

Koeln am Rhein, Johan Godschalk Langen, 1786 39 p. 17^{cm}.

SCHATZ 3894

— L'opéra de province, nouvelle parodie d'Armide, en deux actes et en vers. Melés de vaudeville; Représentée pour la premiere fois, à Paris, le mercredi 17 décembre 1777; & à Versailles, devant Leurs Majestés, le vendredi suivant, par les Comédiens italiens ordinaires du roi.

Paris, Didot l'ainé, 1778. 34 p. 19½^{cm}.

Cast. The authors, Piis and Barré, are not mentioned. ML 50.2.A76G5

Armide, tragedie en musique. Représentée par l'Academie royale de musique. Suivant la copie imprimée à Paris.

[*Amsterdam, Antoine Schelte*], 1686. 57 p. (incl. front.) 14*cm*.
Prologue and five acts. Neither Quinault nor **Lully** mentioned.

ML 50.2.A76 L9

— **Armide**, tragedie représentée par l'Academie royale de musique l'an 1686. Les paroles sont de M. Quinault, & la musique de M. de Lully, XX. opera.

n. i., n. d. 14cm. front., 121-178 p. (Recueil général des opéra, t. iii, Paris, 1703.)
Detached copy. Five acts and prologue.
First performed, as indicated, February 15, 1686. Schatz 5760
Second copy. ML 48.R4

— **Armide**, tragedie en musique. Representée par l'Academie royale de musique, le 15 fevrier 1686.

Quinault, Théatre, Paris, 1739, t. v. pl., p. [409]-459. 17cm.
Prologue and five acts. **Lully** is not mentioned. PQ 1881.A1 1739

— **Armide**, tragedie. Mise au Theatre de l'Academie royale de musique de Lyon, en l'année 1742.

Lyon, Aymé Delaroche, 1742. 55 p. 23cm.
Five acts. Cast. Neither Philippe Quinault, the author, is mentioned nor Jean Baptiste de **Lully**, the composer. The text is the same as in the 1703 ed., except that the fourth act has two scenes only, scenes third and fourth and half of the second having been dropped. Schatz 5760a

— **Armida.** Opera musicale tradotta dal francese, senza mutar le note del famoso Gio. Battista Lulli.

Roma, Angelo Bernabò, 1690. 4 p. l., 87 p. 16cm.
Five acts and prologue. In a prefatory note the unknown translator first apologizes for having, as a Frenchman, made this translation into Italian:
"Cantar in questa lingua alcune arie dell' opere francesi, è stato caso fortuito, e bizarria d'un amatore della musica e della lingua italiana. La vaghezza del componimento musicale gli ha fatto poi tentare di tradurre opere intiere: ed ora il farne cantare, e stampare una in Roma, è stato atto di compiacenza per questi signori Francesi. La musica è parto d'un gran soggetto, nato in Italia, mà allevato da giovanne in Parigi, ed è il famoso Giovanni Battista **Lulli**, ornamento di Toscana, e ristauratore dell' armonia in Francia . . ."
He then interestingly dwells on the great difficulties of making exact metric translations from French into Italian and concludes by saying:
"dall' opera di *Fetonte* [Phaeton] in quà, egli hà di man in mano tradutto per diporto, e nell' ore di divertimento dagli studij più serij, sei altre opere composte successivamente dal medesimo Lulli, sin alla sua morte."
In the libretto the original French text faces the Italian.
First performed at Rome, Teatro di Tor di Nona, 1690. Schatz 4779

— **Armide**, parodie, par M. B*** Représentée pour la premiere fois par les Comédiens italiens ordinaires du roi, le 21 mars 1725.

Les parodies du Nouveau théatre italien, Nouv. éd., Paris, Briasson, 1738, t. III, 51 p. 16½cm.
One act. By Jacques Bailly (Parfaict). The airs and vaudeville used are printed at the end of the volume in the "Table des airs" (84 p.) ML 48.P3

Armide. Tr. of Naumann's Armida.

Armide. Tr. of Righini's Armida.

Armide. Ein singspiel in drey aufzuegen. Nach einem italienischen texte, [by Bertati], aus Tasso's Goffredo entlehnt, von Bock. Die composition ist von herrn Rudolph Zumsteeg.

Stuttgart, Druckerei der herzogl. Hohen Carlsschule, n. d. 62 p. 16ᶜᵐ.

First performed at Stuttgart, Kleines Schauspielhaus auf der Planie, August 30, 1786.   SCHATZ 11292

Arminio. Drama per musica da rappresentarsi in Firenze nel Teatro di via della Pergola nel estate dell' anno MDCCXXV . . . [vignette]

Firenze, Fabio Benedetto Maria Verdi, 1725. 62 p. 14ᶜᵐ.

Three acts. Notice to the reader, cast and scenario. Neither the author, Antonio Salvi, is mentioned, nor the composer. According to Schatz this was a pasticcio by unknown composers.   ML 48.A5   v. 16

L'Arminio. Dramma per musica da rappresentarsi nel Teatro Tron di S. Cassiano l'autunno dell' anno MDCCXLVII.

n. i., n. d. 67 p. 15ᶜᵐ.

Three acts. By Antonio Salvi, who is not mentioned. Argument, cast, scenario, and name of **Galuppi** as composer.
First performed at Venice, as indicated, November 26, 1747 (Pavan). SCHATZ 3482

Arminio. Drama da rappresentarsi nel Regio ducal Teatro di Milano in occasione di celebrarsi il giorno natalizio . . . di Elisabetta Cristina, imperadrice, regina delle Spagne etc.

Milano, Giuseppe Richino Malatesta, 1730. 5 p. l., 52 p. 14ᶜᵐ.

Three acts. By Antonio Salvi, who is not mentioned. Impresario's dedication, argument, cast, scenario, and name of Johann Adolph **Hasse** as the composer.
First performed, as indicated, August 28, 1730.   SCHATZ 4575

Arminio. Dramma per musica da rappresentarsi in Dresda festiggiandosi il felicissimo giorno natalizio di S. R. M. Augusto III . . . La poesia è del Sigʳᵉ abᵉ Gio. Claudio Pasquini, la musica è del Sigʳᵉ Gio Adolfo Hasse . . .

n. i., n. d. 8 p. l., 99, 99, [2] p. 17ᶜᵐ.

Three acts and licenza. Argument and scenario. German title page "Arminio . . . Dresden, gedruckt . . . bey der verw. . . . Stoesselin, 1745" and text face Italian. Mennicke calls this Hasse's second version of "Arminio," though he correctly gives Salvi as the author of the one text and Pasquini of the other. As a matter of fact the two texts have nothing in common except the subject, and consequently the two operas "Arminio" are two different operas, not the one an altered version of the other.
First performed, as indicated, October 7, 1745.   SCHATZ 4512

Arminio. Dramma per musica da rappresentarsi nel Regio Teatro di Torino nel carnovale del 1781 . . .

Torino, Onorato Derossi, n. d. viii, 48 p. 16½ᶜᵐ.

Three acts. A later version of "Germanico in Germania" by Niccolò Coluzzi, who is not mentioned. Argument, cast, scenario, and name of Bernard(in)o **Ottani** as the composer. With the opera were performed three ballets by Filippo Beretti, music by Vittorio Amedeo Canavasso, the first of which was called "Il volubile assodato."   SCHATZ 7363

Arminio. Dramma per musica, da rappresentarsi sopra il Teatro di S. M. B.

London, G. Woodfall, 1760. 57, [1] p. 19½ᶜᵐ.

Three acts. Argument, cast, and note, "La musica è di varj autori." English translation faces Italian. The last (unnumb.) p. contains the aria, "Care luci, che regnate," substituted for "Se al labbro mio" (II, 3). Burney (IV, 472) says: "All the airs in *Arminio* that Mattei sung, were composed by **Perez**." This would apply to "Il fuggir, cara mia vita" (I, 1), "Ah, padre adorato" (I, 2), "Fuggi dagli occhj miei" (I, 5), "Nel pensar al gran cimento" (I, 6), "Padre, tiranno, barbaro" (II, 2), "Caro sposo, amata speme" (II, 5), "Ah non più gelar mi sento" (III, 4). In Walsh's "Favourite songs," however, I, 1, and II, 5, are printed without Perez' names, whereas "Se l'amor tuo" (III, 4), not sung by Mattei, but by Cornacchini, is there attributed to Perez. The text is by Antonio Salvi, with interpolations from Metastasio.

First performed at London, Hay-Market, March, 1760. ML 50.2.A77

L'Arminio. Drama per musica da rappresentarsi nel Teatro di Sant' Angelo nell' autunno 1722 . . .

Venezia, Marino Rossetti, 1722. 60 p. 15½ᶜᵐ.

Three acts. Impresario's dedication dated Venice, November 10, 1722, cast, scenario, name of Carlo Francesco **Pollaroli** as the composer, and notice to the reader, informing him that this is a somewhat altered version of the drama as originally performed at Pratolino. The performances took place 1703 there in the Teatro di Villa Medici. The author of the text, Antonio Salvi, is not mentioned. SCHATZ 8273

Arminio. Drama per musica da recitarsi nella Sala dell' illᵐᵒ Sign. Federico Capranica nel carnevale dell' anno 1722 . . .

Roma, Bernabò, 1722. 72 p. 15ᶜᵐ.

Three acts. By Antonio Salvi, who is not mentioned. Dedication, cast, scenario, name of Alessandro **Scarlatti** as composer, and notice to the reader, in which the alterations in Salvi's text are acknowledged in this manner:

"Se poi colla licenza, che dal moderno uso si permette a chi di nuovo fà comparire in teatro opere altre volte recitate, si è mutato, o scemato in qualche parte per comodo della musica, o per la brevità tanto in oggi desiderata, cio si è procurato di fare in guisa tale, che non resta alterata parte alcuna essenziale del drama; onde sicome non potrà alcuno dolersi di non ritrovarvi tutta l'antica sua bellezza, cosi si spera, che l'istesso autore sia per condonare le piccole accidentali variazioni, che per la detta necessità vi si sono indotte."

First performed at Naples, Teatro San Bartolomeo, November 15, 1714.

ML 50.2.A77S2

L'Arminio. Dramma per musica da rappresentarsi in questo Regio-ducal Teatro Nuovo la primavera dell' anno MDCCLXXXV . . .

Mantova, per l'erede di Alberto Pazzoni, n. d. 51 p. 17ᶜᵐ.

Two acts. By Ferdinando Moretti, who is not mentioned. Dedication dated Mantova, May 8, 1785, argument, cast, scenario, and name of Angelo **Tarchi** as the composer. On p. 10, schedule of the season's performances. With the opera were performed, the composers of the music not mentioned, Filippo Beretti's ballets, "Giulietta e Romeo, fatto patrio Veronese" and "Una festa villereccia."

SCHATZ 10230

L'Arminio. Dramma per musica da rappresentarsi nel nobil Teatro di Torre Argentina il carnevale dell' anno 1786.

Roma, Arcangelo Casaletti, 1786. 46 p. 15ᶜᵐ.

Three acts. Author not mentioned and unknown to Schatz. Argument, cast, scenario, and name of Giacomo **Tritto** as the composer. With the opera were performed Onorato Viganò's ballets, "Cefalo e Procri," music by Salvatore Viganò, and "La donna di spirito," composer not mentioned. SCHATZ 10454

L'**Armoire** ou La piece a deux acteurs.　*See* the A. T.

Arneris ou Les Isies.　Entrée in Rameau's Les fêtes de l'Himen et de l'Amour.

Arrenione.　Drama per musica da rappresentarsi nel Teatro di Sant' Angelo . . .

　Venezia, Gio. Battista Zuccato, 1708.　58 p.　15^{cm}.

Three acts.　Dedication dated Venice, November 8, 1708, and signed with the initials of the author, Francesco Silvani, argument, cast, and scenario.　The composer, Giovanni Maria **Ruggeri,** is not mentioned.　　　　　　SCHATZ 9131

— **Arrenione.**　Dramma per musica da rappresentarsi nell' Imperial Teatro di Mantova la primavera del MDCCXI . . .

　Mantova, Alberto Pazzoni, n. d.　55 p.　15½^{cm}.

Three acts.　By Silvani, who is not mentioned.　Dedication by Christoforo Frigeri, dated Mantova, April 10, 1711, argument, cast, scenario.　**Ruggeri** is not mentioned as the composer.　The text is slightly different from that of the above ed. For instance, the aria'"Se par ch'io serbi in petto" (I, 12) replaced "Merope bella."
　　　　　　ML 50.2.A775R9

Der **arrestant.**　Tr. of Della Maria's Le prisonnier.

Les **arrests de l'amour.**　Pièce d'un acte.　Par. M. D'Or**.　Representée à la Foire de Saint Germain 1716.

　Le Théâtre de la foire, Paris, 1737, t. ii, pl., [227]-258 p.　17^{cm}.

By d'Orneval.　*En vaudevilles,* selected or composed and arranged by Jean Claude **Gillier,** the "compositeur" of the theatre, and printed at the end of the volume in the "Table des airs."　According to Parfaict, composed by **Aubert.**

　First performed February 3, 1716, as third act of "Arlequin gentilhomme malgré lui;" under its own title, in a revised form, July 17, 1726.　　　　ML 48.L2 I

Arrived at Portsmouth.　An operatic drama, in two acts, performed at the Theatre-Royal, Covent-Garden.　Written by the author of Hartford-Bridge　. .

　London, T. N. Longman, 1794.　2 p. l., 43, [1] p.　20^{cm}.

Cast and dedication, dated November 22, 1794, to Sir Alan Gardner, vice-admiral of the Blue for his conduct in the naval engagement of June 1, 1794, to which victory this "temporary drama . . . slightly relates."　By William Pearce.　William **Shield,** the composer, is not mentioned.

　First performed October 30, 1794.　　　　　　　　LONGE 228

L'**arrivo d'Enea nel Lazio.**　Componimento drammatico in decorazione di una mostra di esercizi cavallereschi dall' Instuto de' Nobili presentata alle Loro Altezze Reali . . . Pietro Leopoldo d'Austria . . . e . . . Maria Louisa di Borbone . . . nella faustissima occasione della Loro venuta in Firenze ed eseguita nel Teatro dell' Accademia degl' Immobili la sera de' 25 novembre MDCCLXV giorno del gloriosissimo nome di S. A. R. il serenissimo Gran Duca.

　Firenze, Moücke, 1765.　lix, [ii] p.　26^{cm}.

One act.　By marchese Vincenzio Alamanni.　Argument, lists of founders, members, etc., of the Instituto de' Nobili, note on the pictures exhibited, half-title with author's name, list of characters without cast, text of the libretto with names of the participants in the dances, the giuochi and abbattimenti, name of Baldassare **Galuppi** as composer, colophon, list of errata, cast, and note that the terzetto was composed by Pietro **Bizzarri** of Florence.　　　　　　SCHATZ 3443

L'**arrivo d'Europa nell' isola di Creta,** ballet.　*See* Bertoni's Ifigenia in Aulide.

L'arrivo del Burchello da Padova in Venezia. Farsa per musica in due atti, a cinque voci di Gaetano Fiorio Comico da rappresentarsi nel nobil Teatro Grimani di S. Gio. Grisostomo il carnovale dell, anno 1780 . . .

Venezia, Pietro Sola, 1779. 40 p. 18^{cm}.

Two acts. Author's dedication, cast, scenario, and name of the composer, Luigi **Caruso** ("musica nuova"). SCHATZ 1660

L'arrivo di Venere nell' isola di Cipro, ballet. *See* Radicchi's Medonte rè di Epiro.

L'arrivo opportuno, ballet. *See* Zingarelli's Il mercato di Monfregoso.

Arsace. Dramma per musica da rappresentarsi nel nobilissimo Teatro di S. Benedetto il carnovale dell' anno 1768.

Venezia, Modesto Fenzo, 1768. 54 p. 17$\frac{1}{2}$^{cm}.

Three acts. A later version of "Amore e maestà o sia L'Arsace" by Antonio Salvi, who is not mentioned. Notice to the reader, cast, scenario, and name of Carlo **Franchi** as composer. SCHATZ 3326

Arsace. Drama per musica da rappresentarsi nel famosissimo Teatro Grimani di San Gio. Grisostomo il carnovale dell' anno MDCCXVIII. Del dottore Antonio Salvi, Fiorentino . . .

Venezia, Marino Rossetti, 1718. 71 p. 15^{cm}.

Three acts. A later version of "Amore e maestà o sia L'Arsace" by Antonio Salvi, who is not mentioned. Publisher's dedication, notice to the reader informing him that this is a retouched version of the text for local purposes, cast, scenario, and name of Michel Angelo **Gasparini** as the composer. SCHATZ 3599

L'Arsace. Dramma per musica da rappresentarsi nel nobile **Teatro** Tron di S. Cassiano nel carnovale dell' anno 1737.

Venezia, Giuseppe Betinelli, n. d. 7 p. l., 48 p. 15^{cm}.

Three acts. By Antonio Salvi with alterations of his original text "Amore e maestà o sia L'Arsace," possibly by Domenico Lalli, who signs the dedication. Then the notice to the reader, cast, scenario, and name of Geminiano **Giacomelli** as the composer.

First performed at Prato, Teatro pubblico, 1736. SCHATZ 3810

Arsace. Dramma per musica da rappresentarsi nel nobilissimo Teatro Venier in San Benedetto il carnovale dell' anno 1789.

Venezia, Modesto Fenzo, 1788. 48 p. 16$\frac{1}{2}$^{cm}.

Three acts. By Giovanni de Gamera, who is not mentioned. Argument, cast, scenario, and name of Pietro **Guglielmi** as the composer. On p. [22]–29 argument, cast, and description of Francesco Clerico's "Il ritorno d'Agamenone, ballo tragico in cinque atti," composer of the music not mentioned. Gamerra's text was originally called "Medonte rè di Epiro."

First performed, as indicated, December 26, 1788. SCHATZ 4297

Arsace. Dramma per musica da rappresentarsi nel nobilissimo Nuovo Teatro di Padova la fiera dell' anno 1775.

Venezia, Modesto Fenzo, 1775. 61 p. 17$\frac{1}{2}$^{cm}.

Three acts. By Giovanni de Gamerra, who is not mentioned. The original title of his text was "Medonte, rè d'Epiro." Impresario's dedication, argument, cast, scenario, and name of Michele **Mortellari** as the composer. ("La musica tutta nuova.")

On p. [27]–35 cast, argument, and description of Giuseppe Canziani's "Pigmalione, ballo eroico pantomimo." The composer of the music is not mentioned. SCHATZ 6685

Arsace. Drama per musica da rappresentarsi in Firenze nel Teatro di Via della Pergola nel carnevale dell' anno 1732 . . .

Firenze, Domenico Ambrogio Verdi, n. d.   56 p.   14½^{cm}.

Three acts. A later version of "Amore e maestà o sia L'Arsace" by Antonio Salvi, who is not mentioned. Impresario's dedication, argument, cast, scenario, and name of Giuseppe Maria **Orlandini** as composer.

First performed at Turin, Teatro delle Feste, carnival 1726 (Schatz) but on February 1, 1721, there was performed at the Haymarket, London, an "Arsace" by Orlandini with added arias by Filippo Amadei.   ML 48.A5.   v 18

Arsace. Dramma per musica da rappresentarsi nel Real Teatro di S. Carlo il di 30. maggio 1754.   In cui ricorre il nome del gran monarca delle Spagne, e del nostro real terzogenito . . .

Napoli, Domenico Lanciano, 1754.   iv, 47 p.   19½^{cm}.

Three acts. A later version of "Amore e maestà o sia L'Arsace by Antonio Salvi, who is not mentioned. Impresario's dedication, argument, cast, scenario, and name of Nicolò **Sabatini** as the composer.   SCHATZ 9201

Arsace. Dramma per musica da rappresentarsi nel Teatro di S. Bartolomeo l'inverno dell' anno 1718.   Del dott. Antonio Salvi . . .

Napoli, Michele Luigi Muzio, 1718.   64 p.   16^{cm}.

Three acts. A later version of Salvi's "Amore e maestà o sia L'Arsace." Impresario's dedication, dated Naples, December 10, 1718, scenario, cast, name of Domenico **Sarro** as the composer and notice to the reader which reads in part:

"Questo soggetto è lo stesso, che già espose su le scene di Francia il famoso Tomaso Cornelio, sotto il nome del Conte di Essex; ma dovendo questo servire alla musica, ed al Teatro italiano, si è cambiata la scena in Persia . . . conservando però i caratteri de' personaggi principali . . .

"Il fine dell' autore fù di formare una tragedia in musica col fine veramente tragico (novità non più veduta, almeno su le scene d'Italia) e di avere il preggio d'essere il primo a farti sortir dal teatro con le lagrime, frà le dolci armonie della musica, lo che è facile, che ottenga se attendi alla forza del soggetto, e se riguardi alla perfezione de' rappresentanti.

"Vi è stato in altro teatro in qualche parte variato il fine, per non renderlo totalmente funesto; come ancora in questo con non poca pena di chè l'hà diretto vi si sono variate alcune arie, & accresciuti, ò diminuiti alcuni recitativi, come altresì vi si sono dovute ponere le parti buffe, mà in modo, che nõ interrompino il dramma, mà solo minorino la mestizia con un poco di allegria."   SCHATZ 9414

L'Arsacide. Drama per musica da rappresentarsi nel Teatro Giustiniano di S. Moisè il carnovale dell' anno 1721.   Poesia d'Antonio conte Zaniboni . . .

Venezia, Marin Rossetti, 1721.   48 p.   15^{cm}.

Three acts. Author's dedication dated Venice, December 28, 1720, argument, cast and scenario. The composer Fortunato **Chelleri** is not mentioned. SCHATZ 1810

Arsene. Nach Favart. Singspiel von A. G. Meissner [vignette].

Leipzig, Dykische buchhandlung, 1778.   3 p. l., 73 p.   16½^{cm}.

Four acts. In his "Vorbericht" Meissner says:

"Die schauspieldirektion der stadt, wo ich fuer jetzt lebe, ersuchte mich, die gesaenge dieser operette zu verfertegen, da man die, so in der bereits 1778 erschienenen uebersetzung der franzoesischen musik unterliegen, nicht nuetzen koenne. Diese bitte . . . und der zusatz, dass ein wuerdiger tonkuenstler [Franz **Seydelmann**] meine neuen gesaenge su setzen bereit sey, machten, dass ich versprach, alles zu thun, was ich thun koenne."

Instead of utilizing the dialogue in the "ueber alle maasen steife Frankfurter uebersetzung" ["Die schoene Arsene," by J. H. Faber], he preferred to translate Favart's "La belle Arsene" anew. He ends his remarks with this:

"Uebrigens ist diess das letzte singspiel, das ich nach dem franzoesischen bearbeite; darauf geb' ich mein wort."

The Ms. score at Dresden has the title "Die schöne Arsene" (Cahn-Speyer).

First performed at Dresden, Churfuerstl. Kleines Theater, March 3, 1779 (Schatz); Leipzig, April 15, 1779, and Dresden, 1781 (Cahn-Speyer).   SCHATZ 9841

Arsene—Continued.

— **Arsene.** In vier akten. Komponirt vom herrn Kapellmeister Seydelmann zu Dresden.

n. i., n. d. 3 p. l., 73 p. 17^{cm}.

The same as above. Schatz' entry "Txtb. m. Recitativen, anstatt des dialoges für concert aufführungen" is incorrect, as the dialogue is the same as in the Leipzig 1778 ed.   SCHATZ 9842

— **Arsene.** Ein singspiel in drey akten nach Favart, von A. G. Meissner. In musik gesetzt von Franz Seydelmann . . .

n. i., n. d. 23 p. 16^{cm}.

The t.-p. contains also the list of characters.   SCHATZ 11748

— **Arsene.** In vier akten. Nach Favart.

A. G. Meissner, Operetten, Leipzig, 1778. 3 p. l., 73 p. 17^{cm}.

Forms the third libretto in the collection, and is the same as the other ed. of 1778.
ML49.A2M3

L'Arsiade. Drama per musica da rappresentarsi in Mantova l'anno 1700 . . .

[Mantova], Gio. Batt. Grana, n. d. 84 p. 15½^{cm}.

Three acts. By Pietro d'Averara, who is not mentioned. Dedication, argument, cast, scenario. The composer, Antonio Francesco **Martinengo,** is not mentioned. I, 2, has the aria "Frà tue ritorte" (duet); II, 2, has no aria.   ML 50.2.A778M2

— **Arsiade,** drama per musica da rappresentarsi nel Regio Teatro di Torino . . .

Torino, Gio. Battista Zappata, 1703. 88 p. 14½^{cm}.

Three acts. By Pietro d'Averara who is not mentioned. Impresario's dedication, argument, scenario, and cast. Composed by Antonio Francesco **Martinengo,** who is not mentioned. I, 2 has the aria "La luce del mio foco"; II, 2 has the aria "Taci crudel."

First performed at Milan, Regio ducal Teatro, carnival 1700.   SCHATZ 6032

Arsilda, regina di Ponto. Drama per musica. Da rappresentarsi nel Teatro di S. Angelo nell' autunno dell' anno 1716 . . .

Venezia, Marino Rossetti, 1716. 60 p. 14^{cm}.

Three acts. By Domenico Lalli who is not mentioned. Argument, cast, scenario, name of the "celebre virtuoso di violino il signor D. Antonio **Vivaldi**" as composer, and dedication in which the author says that just as a man who has built himself a house, is not satisfied with the marble exterior but seeks to adorn it with beautiful tapestries, statuettes, etc., he, the author, needs the adornment of D. Giacomo Brivio, conte di Brochles for his drama (to whom it is dedicated) "cosi per l'insuffienza del suo maestro che la compose, come per il gusto di coloro, li quali han voluto in essa, non già quello che ragionevole appariva, mà tutto ciò che apertamente non si doveva, à tale che per mia non la riconosco, per che rossore n'averia in veggendola cosi affatto cangiata dal mio primo disegno, e per l'arie, e per la sua giusta sceneggiatura."
SCHATZ 10760

L'Arsinoe, drama da rappresentarsi nel Teatro del Seren. elettore di Sassonia l'anno MDCXCIII—Arsinoe . . .

Dresden, Hoff-Buchdruckerey durch Immanuel Bergen, n. d. Unpaged. 28½^{cm}.

Three acts. Argument. German text faces Italian, which is not that by Stanzani. Neither author nor composer mentioned and both unknown to Fürstenau.
ML 50.2.A779

Arsinoe. Drama per musica di M. R. da rappresentarsi nel Real Teatro di S. Carlo nel dì 13. di Agosto 1795 festeggiandosi la nascita di S. M. la Regina . . .

Napoli, Vincenzo Flauto, 1795.   47 p.   15½cm.

Two acts. Author unknown to Schatz. Dedication signed by Andrea di Benedetto, and dated Naples, August 13, 1795, cast, scenario, notice to the reader and name of Gaetano **Andreozzi** as composer. With the opera were performed the ballets, "La costanza premiata o sia Il genio tutelare, ballo eroicopantomimo composto, e diretto dal Signor Gaetano Gioja" (detailed description on p. 9–16) and "La semplice burlata." The composers of the music are not mentioned.   Schatz 206

L'Arsinoe. Drama per musica da rappresentarsi nel Teatro Formagliari l'anno MDCLXXVII . . .

Bologna, per l'erede del Benacci, n. d.   6 p. l., 69, [1] p.   13½cm.

Three acts. By Tommaso Stanzani, who dates his dedication Bologna, December 26, 1676. Printer's notice to the reader naming Petronio **Franceschini** as composer, argument and scenario.   Schatz 3317

— **Arsinoe.** Drama in musica recitata nel Theatro Grande d'Insprugg, avanti la Maestà della regina di Polonia . . . li 12. gennaro, l'anno MDCLXXXVI.

[Insprugg], Giacomo Christoforo Wagner, n. d.   59 p.   13½cm.

Three acts. Argument and scenario. Neither author nor composer mentioned, but the text is clearly an altered version of Tommaso Stanzani's "Arsinoe" as composed for Bologna by **Franceschini.** For instance, Stanzani's first scene "O regina del ombre" is now second and is preceded by the scene "Or che mi chiama al trono" with the arias "Bella dea, che al sol nascente" and "Aurette cortesi." Whether these and the other alterations were by Francesco Santurini, who modified Stanzani's text for Venice, 1677, is unknown to me.   ML 50.2.A779F7

Arsinoe. A. T. of Keiser's La grandezza d'animo.

Arsinoe e Breno. Altered version of Pietro Guglielmi's Debora e Sisara.

Arsinoe, queen of Cyprus. An opera, after the *Italian* manner: All sung. As it is perform'd at the Theatre Royal in Drury-Lane, by Her Majesty's servants.

London, Jacob Tonson, 1705.   2 p. l., 48 p.   22cm.

Three acts. Cast and preface, signed by Thomas Clayton, who says:
"The design of this entertainment being to introduce the Italian manner of musick on the English stage, which has not been before attempted; I was oblig'd to have an Italian opera translated: In which the words, however mean in several places, suited much better with that manner of musick, than others more poetical would do.
"The stile of this musick is to express the passions, which is the soul of musick: And though the voices are not equal to the Italian, yet I have engag'd the best that were to be found in England, and I have not been wanting, to the utmost of my diligence, in the instructing of them.
"The musick being recitative, may not, at first, meet with that general acceptation, as is to be hop'd for from the audience's being better acquainted with it: But if this attempt shall, by pleasing the nobility and gentry, be a means of bringing this manner of musick to be us'd in my native country, I shall think all my study and pains very well employ'd."
According to Hawkins (IV, 136) "Clayton had brought with him a collection of Italian airs . . . these he mangled and sophisticated, and adapting them to the words of an English drama, entitled Arsinoe Queen of Cyprus, called it an opera, composed by himself." Burney, on the other hand (IV, 199), quotes Clayton's words from the preface of the printed book that he "was obliged to have an Italian opera translated" and Burney names that written by Tomaso Stanzani in 1676 and

Arsinoe, queen of Cyprus—Continued.

first performed at Bologna with Petronio Franceschini's music. Mr. Husk in Grove's Dictionary sides with Hawkins and claims that Clayton used "an English piece, written by Peter Motteux, called "Arsinoe, Queen of Cyprus." The Dict. of National Biography goes still further and attributes to Motteux an opera libretto of the same title, printed in 1707 [!] As a matter of fact, a comparison between the English libretto, printed in 1705 anonymously, the preface signed by Clayton, and Stanzani's libretto (both in L. C.) proves that the English libretto is a free *translation* of the latter. Motteux' name is not mentioned. Consequently, if he was connected at all with "Arsinoe," it can have been only as translator, not as author.

The title page of the score published by Walsh reads: "Songs in the new opera, call'd Arsinoe, Queen of Cyprus, *compos'd by Mr. Tho. Clayton.*"

Until Hawkins' supposition (shared by Burney) is proved that Clayton simply utilized a collection of Italian airs which he brought with him from Italy, it will be fairer to consider Clayton the actual composer.

First performed at London, Drury-Lane, Jan. 16, 1705.   ML 50.2.A78

—Arsinoe, queen of Cyprus. An opera, after the *Italian* manner. As it is perform'd at the Theatre Royal in Drury-Lane, by Her Majesty's servants.

London, Jacob Tonson, 1707. 2 p. l., 40 p. 21½^{cm}.

Same cast, preface and text as in the 1705 edition.   LONGE 106
Second copy.   LONGE 177

Arsinoe vendicata. Drama per musica. Da rappresentarsi nel Teatro di S. Angelo il carnevale del 1712. Del dottor Grazio Braccioli . . .

Venezia, Marino Rossetti, 1712. 56 p. 13½^{cm}.

Three acts. Author's dedication dated Venice, February 1, 1712, argument, cast, scenario and name of Gio. Maria Rugieri (**Ruggeri**) as the composer.

SCHATZ 9134

Artabene rè di Persia. L. T. of Vivaldi's La costanza trionfante degl' amori e degl' odii.

Artamene. Dramma per musica di Bartolomeo Vitturi da rappresentarsi nel Teatro di S. Angelo il carnovale dell' anno 1740 . . .

Venezia, Marino Rossetti, n. d. 60 p. 14½^{cm}.

Three acts. Dedication, argument, scenario, cast and notice to the reader in which the author calls this "uno de miei drammi intieramente nuovo." The composer, Tommaso **Albinoni,** is not mentioned.

First performed as indicated December 26, 1740.   SCHATZ 87

Artanaganamenone. Tragichissimissimo dramma per musica da rappresentarsi nel Teatro Giustininan a San Moisè. In occasione della fiera dell' Ascensione. L'anno MDCCXXXI.

Venezia, Carlo Buonarrigo n. 'd. 48 p. 14^{cm}.

Three acts. Attributed by Schatz and Wiel to the composer, Giuseppe Maria **Buini,** who is not mentioned. Argument, scenario and notice to the reader.

First performed at Bologna, Teatro Marsigli Rossi, carnival 1728, as "Malmosor."

SCHATZ 1397

L'Artaserse. Tragedia drammatica per musica fedelmente, ed eroicamente tradotta e ridotta dall' antico stato allo stato presente da P. Quintiliano Settimio da Sarmacanda, dottore a due doppj.

Pekin, l'anno che corre. 48 p. 16^{cm}.

Three acts. Argument and dedication, from which it appears that the initials of the author's real name are *G. B. G.* The piece is a carnevalesque parody.

ML 50.2.A8

L'Artaserse.
74 p.   19ᶜᵐ.   (Pietro Metastasio, Opere drammatiche, Venezia, Giuseppe Bettinelli, 1733–37, v. 1.)
Three acts.   Argument.   No composer mentioned.   ML 49.A2M4

—Artaserse.
Metastasio, Poesie, Parigi, vedova Quillau, 1755, v. I, 110 p.   16ᶜᵐ.
Three acts.   Argument.   ML 49.A2M42

— Artaserse.   Rappresentato con musica del Vinci la prima volta in Roma, il carnevale dell' anno 1730, nel Teatro detto delle Dame.
pl., 112 p.   26ᶜᵐ.   (Pietro Metastasio, Opere, Parigi, vedova Herissant, 1780, t. I.)
Three acts.   Argument.   ML 49.A2M44

Artaserse.
Apostolo Zeno, Poesie drammatiche, Venezia, 1744, t. x, p. [107]-204 p.   19ᶜᵐ.
Three acts.   Argument.   Written in collaboration with Pietro Pariati.   No composer is mentioned.   At the end of vol. X in the "Catalogo" date and place of first ed. are given as Venice, 1705.   ML 49.A2Z3

— Artaserse.   Publicato per la prima volta in Vienna 1705.
Apostolo Zeno, Poesie drammatiche, Orleans, 1785-86, t. ix, p. 94. 21ᶜᵐ.
Three acts.   Argument.   No composer is mentioned.   Written in collaboration with Pietro Pariati.   ML 49.A2Z4

Artaserse.   Drama per musica da rappresentarsi nel Teatro di Livorno l'anno 1706 . . .
Livorno, Jacopo Valfisi, 1706.   4 p. l., 64 p.   14½ᶜᵐ.
Three acts.   Dedication, argument, scenario.   Authors (Zeno and Pariati) and composer not mentioned, and latter unknown to Schatz.   SCHATZ 11383

Artaserse.   Dramma per musica dell' abate Pietro Metastasio da rappresentarsi nel Teatro di Cagliari festeggiandosi le reali nozze di Vittorio Amadeo duca di Savoia, e di Maria Antonia, infante di Spagna . . .
Cagliari, Bonaria, 1750.   59 p.   15ᶜᵐ.
Three acts.   Impresario's dedication, argument, scenario, cast.   Composer not mentioned and unknown to Schatz.   SCHATZ 11310

Artaserse.   Dramma per musica del sig. ab. Pietro Metastasio . . . Da rappresentarsi in Pisa nel Teatro del Pubblico la primavera dell' anno 1770 . . .
Pisa, Pompeo Pollonj e comp., 1770.   56 p.   15ᶜᵐ.
Three acts.   Impresario's dedication, argument, cast, scenario, and note, "La musica è di diversi eccellenti autori."   ML 48.A5   v. 30

Artaserse.   Drama per musica da rappresentarsi nel Regio Teatro di Torino nel carnovale del 1741 . . .
Torino, Pietro Giuseppe Zappata e figliuolo, n. d.   74, [1] p.   14ᶜᵐ.
Three acts.   By Metastasio, who is not mentioned.   Argument, scenario, cast, and name of Giuseppe **Arena** as composer.   Contemporary ms. note on t.-p.: "Opera seconda dopo l'appertura del nuovo teatro."   SCHATZ 308

Artaserse. Dramma per musica da rappresentarsi nel Regio Teatro di Torino nel carnevale del MDCCLXI . . .

Torino, Giacomo Giuseppe Avondo, n. d. viii, 72 p. 16^{cm}.

Three acts. By Metastasio. Argument, cast, scenario, and name of Johann Christian **Bach** as composer. The music of the ballets was composed by Giuseppe Antonio Le Messier. The ballets were invented by Vincenzo Saunier, and the first was called "La morte, ed il rinascimento del pastore Adone."

First performed, as indicated, December 26, 1760. SCHATZ 532

Artaserse. Dramma per musica da rappresentarsi nel Teatro Interinale di Milano il carnovale dell' anno 1777 . . .

Milano, Gio. Batista Bianchi, n. d. 60 p. 14½^{cm}.

Three acts. Impresario's dedication, argument, cast, scenario, and name of Ferd. Gius. **Bertoni** as composer, but not of librettist, Metastasio. On a fly-leaf *Megabise's* added aria (I, 6), "Sogna'l guerrier le schiere." This is Bertoni's first setting of the text.

First performed at Forli, Teatro della Città, spring of 1775. SCHATZ 905

— Artaserse; a new serious opera; as performed at the King's Theatre in the Hay-Market. The music entirely new, by Signor Ferdinando Bertoni. The translation by Mistress Rigaud.

London, G. Bigg, 1779. 63 p. 19^{cm}.

Three acts. Argument, cast, Italian and English text. Schatz lists this with Bertoni's first setting of Metastasio's "Artaserse," but the librettos are so different from each other in the third act, where Metastasio has been tampered with very considerably, that the same music can hardly have been used throughout for both. Therefore, at least part of the opera must have been newly composed, or it was "entirely new," as the t.-p. states. In that case this would be the second setting of the text by Bertoni.

First performed at London, as indicated, in 1779. SCHATZ 906

— Artasèrse. Dramma per musica da rappresentarsi in Genova nel Teatro da S. Agostino il carnovale del 1788 . . .

Genova, Stamperia Gesiniana, n. d. 55 p. 13½^{cm}.

Three acts. Argument, cast, scenario, and name of composer, **Bertoni**. Practically the same text as that of the Milan 1777 ed., therefore, especially in the third act, very unlike the London 1779 ed. Schatz lists this 1788 Genoa ed. as Bertoni's second setting of the text. This can be correct only if it was not a revival of the setting of 1775 and if the music for London, 1779 was not "entirely new." Unless Schatz had evidence to the contrary, just as likely as not Bertoni composed the text only once, but made additions and changes to suit the circumstances. SCHATZ 907

Artaserse. Drama per musica da rappresentarsi nel nobilissimo Teatro di S. Benedetto il carnovale dell' anno MDCCLXXVI.

Venezia, Modesto Fenzo, 1776. 1 p. l., 80 p. 17½^{cm}.

Three acts. By Metastasio. Argument, cast, scenario, and name of the composer, Giovanni Battista **Borghi**, but not of the librettist. On p. 25–38, cast, argument, and detailed description of "Adele di Ponthieu, ballo tragico in cinque atti di Mons. Noverre dato in Venezia dal signor Franchi," p. 55–68 of "La prima età dell' innocenza o sia La Rosaja di Salency, ballo pantomimo." The composers of these ballets are not mentioned.

First performed December 26, 1775, as indicated. SCHATZ 1227

Artaserse. Dramma per musica del Sig. abate Pietro Metastasio da rappresentarsi in Verona nel Teatro dell' illustrissima Accademia Filarmonica nel carnovale dell' anno 1770.

Verona, Dionisio Ramanzini, n. d. 58 p. 17^{cm}.

Three acts. Impresario's dedication, argument, cast, scenario, and name of the composer, Antonio **Boroni**. "Il Ratto della sposa," by Giuseppe Anelli, was one of the ballets performed with the opera. The composer of the ballet is not mentioned.

First performed at Prague, Kgl. Theater i. d. Kotzen, 1767. SCHATZ 1250

Artaserse. Dramma per musica da rappresentarsi nel Teatro Obizzi in Padova nella primavera dell' anno 1738 . . .

Padova, Giovambatista Conzatti, 1738. 4 p. l., 64 p. 17½ cm.

Three acts. By Metastasio. Dedication dated Padova, May 20, 1738, argument, scenario, and name of the composer, Giuseppe Ferdinando **Brivio**. Schatz 1325

L'Artaserse. Dramma per musica da rappresentarsi in Firenze nella primavera del 1780 nel nuovo Regio Teatro degl' Intrepidi detto della Palla a corda . . .

n. pl., Ant. Giuseppe Pagani, n. d. 44 p. 17½ cm.

Three acts. By Metastasio. Argument, cast, and name of the composer, Luigi **Caruso** ("la musica è tutta nuova"). On p. 6–10 cast and detailed description of Antonio Pitrot's four-act "Enea e Lavinia, ballo eroico-pantomimo," music by Francesco Piombanti. Schatz 1656

Artaserse. Dramma per musica da cantarsi in Verona nel Teatro dell' Accademia Filarmonica nel carnovale 1741 . . .

Verona, Dionigi Ramanzini, n. d. 54 p.

Three acts. By Metastasio. Dedication, argument, scenario, cast, and name of the composer, Pietro **Chiarini**. Schatz 1854

Artaserse. Dramma per musica da rappresentarsi nel Regio Teatro di Torino nel carnovale del 1785 . . .

Torino, Onorato Derossi, n. d. 64 p. 18½ cm.

Three acts. By Metastasio. Argument, cast, scenario, and name of the composer, Domenico Nicola **Cimarosa**. On p. 56–64 argument, cast, and description of Paolino Franchi's "La Tusnelda o sia La disfatta di Vario, ballo eroico in cinque atti." His other two ballets were called "Gli Sposi delusi dalle astuzie di Crespino" and "Gioconda." The music was composed by Vittorio Amedeo Canavasso.

First performed at Turin, as indicated, December 26, 1784. Schatz 1905

L'Artaserse. Dramma per musica, da rappresentarsi nel Nuovo privilegiato Imperial Teatro in Vienna nel carnevale l'anno MDCCXLIX.

[Vienna], Giov. Pietro v. Ghelen, n. d. 60 p. 16 cm.

Three acts. By Metastasio, who is not mentioned. Argument, cast, scenario, and name of Baldassare **Galuppi** as composer. Schatz 3444

Artaserse. Dramma per musica da rappresentarsi nel Teatro Ducale di Stutgart nel carnovale dell' anno 1751 . . . La poesia è del Signore abbate Pietro Metastasio . . . La musica è del Signore Graun . . .

Stutgart, Giovanne Georgio Cotta, n. d. 83 p. 19 cm.

Three acts. Argument and scenario. German title-page "Artaxerxes" and text face Italian.

First performed, as indicated, in January, 1751, previously at Stuttgart, Lusthaussaal, August 30, 1750; at Berlin, Kgl. Operntheater, December 2, 1743. Schatz 4090

Artaserse. Dramma per musica da rappresentarsi in Bologna nel Teatro Zagnoni il carnevale dell' anno 1789 . . .

Bologna, Sassi, n. d. 56 p. 17 cm.

Two acts! By Metastasio, who is not mentioned. Impresario's dedication, argument, cast, scenario, and name of Pietro **Guglielmi** as the composer.

First performed at Rome, Teatro di Torre Argentina, January 29, 1777. Schatz 4298

Artaserse. Dramma per musica da rappresentarsi nel famosissimo Teatro Grimani di S. Gio. Grisostomo nell' carnevale dell' anno MDCCXXX . . .

Venezia, Carlo Buonarigo, n. d. 1 p. l., 69, [1] p. 15ᶜᵐ.

Three acts. Dedication in which this is called the "ultimo carnesalescho divertimento" of the season, argument, scenario, cast, names of Metastasio as the author and of Joh. Adolph **Hasse** as the composer, and note:

"Si avverte, che siccome per accommodarsi alle circostanze del teatro fù di bisogno, abbreviare tutto quello, che con virgole segnato si vede così d'aliena penna è tutto cio ch'è con stellette contrasegnato."

To the omitted parts "con virgole" belong about one-half of the first scene beginning with "Cresceste insieme di fama e di virtù," "Tutto si versi," etc. (I, 3), "Inutile accortezza," etc. (I, 9), "Mio ben, mia vita," etc. (I, 14), "Le tue richieste. Ah voglia," etc. (II, 1), "Basta mostrarti," etc. (II, 2), "Perchè tarda è mai la morte," (opening of III, 1), and other parts of scenes to the end. To the starred parts, as of "d'aliena penna" belong the arias "Lascia cadermi in volto" (II, 2), "Per questo dolce amplesso (II, 11), the entire scene II, 15, "Eccomi al fine in libertà," and the whole scene III, 2 "Ch'io parta? E in faccia al mondo," also the aria "Pensa, che l'amor mio" (III, 1). SCHATZ 4576

— **Artaserse,** dramma per musica rappresentato alla Regia elettorale corte di Dresda, nell' anno MDCCXL.

n. i., n. d. (double) 95 p. 15½ᶜᵐ.

Three acts. Argument, scenario, cast, and names of Metastasio as author, of Johann Adolph **Hasse** as the composer. German title page "Artaxerxes . . . Dresden . . . bey der verwitt. . . . Stoesselin" and text face Italian, which follows the Venetian ed. of 1730 closely, including the there starred parts, but excluding *all those con virgole*, dropping the aria "Non conosco in tal momento" (II, 14) and adding "Deh respirar lasciatemi" (I, 11 at end) which is by Metastasio and in fact forms part of "Artaserse" as published in the 1733 edition of his works. Schatz and Mennicke call the 1740 Dresden "Artaserse" Hasse's second version.

First performed, as indicated, Dresden, September 9, 1740. SCHATZ 4513

— **Artaserse.** Dramma per musica da rappresentarsi in Ferrara nel Teatro Bonacossi da S. Stefano il carnovale dell' anno 1765 . . .

Ferrara, Bernardino Pomatelli, n. d. 63 p. 15ᶜᵐ.

Three acts. Dedication, argument, cast, scenario, and name of Johann Adolph **Hasse** as the composer. The text differs both from Dresden, 1740, and from Venice, 1730. For instance, these two editions do not have at end of I, 3, the aria "Su le sponde del torbido Lete" and their scene I, 7, "Voi della Persia, voi" with the aria "Bramar di perdere" has been dropped. However, since this "Artarserse" (Hasse's third version, according to Schatz, in which view Mennicke concurs with a reservation) was first performed at Naples, Teatro di San Carlo, January 20, 1760 (according to Schatz. At Warsaw, August 3, 1760, according to Mennicke), it is impossible to tell from the Ferrara, 1765 ed. just what the Naples 1760 ed. contained.

SCHATZ 4590

Artaserse. Dramma per musica da rappresentarsi nel Teatro Ducale di Stugart festeggiandosi il felicissimo giorno natalizio di Sua Altezza Serenissima Elisabetta Sofia Federica duchessa regnante di Wirtemberg e Tech . . . La poesia è del Signore abbate Pietro Metastasio . . . La musica è del celebre Signore Nicolò Jommelli . . .

Stutgart, Cotta, 1756. 143 p. 18ᶜᵐ.

Three acts. Argument, cast, and scenario. German title page "Artaxerxes" and text face Italian.

First performed, as indicated, August 30, 1756; at Rome, Teatro di Torre Argentina, February 4, 1749. SCHATZ 4843

Artaserse. Dramma per musica da rappresentarsi nel Teatro Grimani di San Benedetto il carnovale dell' anno 1762.

Venezia, Paolo Colombani, 1762.   59 p.   15^{cm}.

Three acts. By Metastasio, who is not mentioned. Argument, cast, scenario, and name of Giovanni Francesco de **Majo** as composer.
First performed, as indicated, January 30, 1762.   Schatz 5861

Artaserse. Dramma per musica da rappresentarsi nel nobilissimo Teatro di S. Benedetto nel carnovale dell' anno MDCCLXXII.

Venezia, Modesto Fenzo, n. d.   48 p.   17^{cm}.

Three acts. By Metasatsio, who is not mentioned. Argument, cast, scenario, and name of Vincenzo **Manfredini** as composer.
First performed in January, 1772, as indicated.   Schatz 5892

Artaserse. Dramma per musica da rappresentarsi nel nobilissimo Teatro della Fenice l'autunno dell' anno 1795.

Venezia, Stamperia Valvasense, n. d.   72 p.   18^{cm}.

Three acts. By Metastasio, who is not mentioned. Cast and name of Giuseppe **Nicolini** as the composer. On p. [23]–36 preface, cast, argument, and description of Lauchlin Duquesny's "Ahtor ed Erma, ballo eroico in cinque atti," music ("tutta nuova ed espressamente scritta") by Vittorio Trento.
First performed, as indicated, November 17, 1795.   Schatz 7140

Artaserse. Drama per musica da rappresentarsi nel Teatro di S. Bartolomeo nell' està dell' anno 1708 . . .

Napoli, Michele Luigi Mutio, 1708.   5 p. l., 50 p.   14^{cm}.

Three acts. Impresario's dedication dated Naples, June 7, 1708, notice to the reader, argument, cast, scenario, and note:
"La musica è del Sig. Giuseppe Maria **Orlandini**. Le scene buffe, e tuttle le arie con il presente signo * sono del Sig. Francesco **Mancini** . . . come anche molte altre accomodazioni."
The starred arias or parts of arias are: "Vinse Marte pugnando col brando" (I, 2), "Basti a lei, che per suo vanto" (I, 6), "Grida vendetta Amor" (I, 17), "Un'alma fedele ti chiama al rigore" (II, 4), "Scherza l'ape sù del fiore" (II, 10), "La smarrita Tortorella" (II, 11), "Il Dio d'amore" (II, 12), "Sento nel petto mio" (II, 15), "Combattono a vicenda" (II, 20), "Spesso in un core" (III, 9), "La signorina mia" (III, 16), "Sò che non hò fortuna" (III, 18).
Schatz attributes the text to Zeno and Pariati, with alterations and additions by Andrea del Pò, but the notice to the reader says:
"L'Artaserse di Giulio Agosti Reggiano, dopo esser comparso sopra molte scene d'Italia, viene avanti i lumi dell' erudita Partenope in qualche parte diverso dalla sua prima impressione, essendo stato di bisogno toglierne il meno necessario per adattarsi alla stagione, nella quale si rappresenta, ed aggiungervi il ridicolo per conformarsi all' uso della città, nella quale è recitato . . .
"Le scene buffe, e alcune arie col segno § sono dell' A. P. . . ."
The arias or parts of arias with the sign § are:
"Che del cor. son dolce amore" (II, 5), "Fugge, e vola ad altro fior" (II, 10), "Sarai contento" (II, 13), "Tutta rigore" (II, 15), "Un avanzo di pietà" (II, 19), "Sdegno, pietade, e amor" (II, 20). Comparison with Wotquenne's "Zeno, Metastasio and Goldoni" list proves that many of the arias actually belong to Zeno and Pariati's "Artaserse," but just as many do not, not to mention those with the sign §.
It would seem, therefore, that this opera was a pasticcio both in text and music.
                                                                   Schatz 7328

Artaserse. Dramma per musica da rappresentarsi nel famoso Teatro di S. Salvatore la fiera dell' Ascensione dell' anno 1742 . . .

Venezia, Marino Rossetti, n. d.   46 p.   14½^{cm}.

Three acts. Metastasio is mentioned as the author and (by a contemporary hand) Giuseppe Antonio **Paganelli** as the composer. Impresario's dedication, dated Venice, May 1, 1742, argument, cast, and scenario.
First performed, as indicated, May 2, 1742; at Brunswick, in February, 1737.
                                                                   Schatz 7572

Artaserse. Dramma per musica da rappresentarsi (nel famosissimo Teatro Grimani di S. Gio. Grisostomo) nel carnevale dell' anno 1750.

Venezia, In Merceria, n. d. 60 p. 15^{cm}.

The words in parenthesis are printed on a mounted slip. Originally the title page contained the name of the same theater. This was then crossed out and substituted in ms. by Teatro di S. Benedetto before Teatro Grimani was printed again as above.

Three acts. By Metastasio, who is not mentioned. Argument, cast, scenario, and name of Antonio Gaetano **Pampani** as the composer. SCHATZ 7754

Artaserse. Dramma per musica da rappresentarsi nel Teatro Nobile di S. Benedeto il carnovale dell' anno MDCCLXVI.

Venezia, Giorgio Fossati, n. d. 63 p. 17½^{cm}.

Three acts. By Metastasio, who is not mentioned. Argument, cast, scenario, and name of Giuseppe **Ponzo** as the composer. SCHATZ 8355

Artaserse. Dramma per musica da rappresentarsi in Perugia nel Nuovo Teatro Civico del Verzaro l'autunno dell' anno MDCCLXXXI . . .

Perugia, Mario Riginaldi, n. d. 64 p. 18^{cm}.

Three acts. By Metastasio, who is not mentioned. Argument, cast and name of Giacomo **Rust** as composer. ("La musica è nuova.") ML 50.2.A8R8

— **Artaserse.** Dramma per musica da rappresentarsi nel Regio Teatro di via della Pergola nel carnevale del MDCCLXXXIII . . .

Firenze, Giovanni Risaliti, 1783. 48 p. 17^{cm}.

Three acts. By Metastasio, who is not mentioned. Argument, cast, and name of Giacomo **Rust** as the composer. On p. 19–23 description of Antonio Muzzarelli's ballet "La guerra del MDCLXXXIII fra i Turchi e gli Austriaci," on p. 39–41 of his ballet "Assedio e liberazione di Vienna," the composers of the music not being mentioned. SCHATZ 9165

Artaserse. Drama per musica da rappresentarsi nel nobil Teatro a Torre Argentina il carnevale dell' anno 1768 . . .

Roma, Ottavio Puccinelli, n. d. 60 p. 15^{cm}.

Three acts. Impresario's dedication ("comparisce di nuovo su le nostre scene l'Artaserse"), argument, scenario, cast and names of Metastasio as author, of **Sacchini** as composer. In a note, Metastasio's text is called "in qualche parte . . . alterata" because of the "dura necessità di averlo dovuto accomodare al teatro presente." But it is not clear why it was necessary, for instance, to contract Metastasio's scenes I, 5, and I, 6, into one dropping both arias "Per pietà, bell' idol mio" and "Sogna il guerrier."

First performed in January, 1768, as indicated. ML 50.2.A8S2

Artaserse, drama da rappresentarsi in musica.

Copenhagen, Ernesto Enrico Berling, n. d. 95 p. 19½^{cm}.

Three acts. By Metastasio, who is not mentioned. Cast, scenario, argument, and name of Paolo **Scalabrini** as the composer "à risserva di alcune arie, di diversi auttori." Italian and German texts.

First performed at Copenhagen, Theater paa Kongens Nytorv, November 28, 1752; at Hamburg, Theater beim Gänsemarkt, November 13, 1743. SCHATZ 9515

Artaserse. Dramma per musica da rappresentarsi nel Teatro di Ratisbona . . .

[Ratisbona], Nella Stamperia Breitfeldiana, n. d. 2 p. l., 143 p. 16^{cm}.

Three acts. By Metastasio, with acknowledged alterations. Argument, names of the author and of the composer, Theodor, freiherr von **Schacht**, and his dedication (preceding the title page), in which he says:

"Encouragé par l'acceuil gracieux qu'elle [Altesse Serenissime, the prince of Thurn und Taxis] à daigné faire aux differentes pieces de musique que j'ai ajouté

Artaserse—Continued.

aux operettes qu'on à representé ici pendant quatre années et persuadé du grand effet que font sur Votre Altesse Serenissime les comedies et tragedies allemandes qu'on represente ici avec toutes les regles du costume, ainsi qu'avec toute l'exactitude, j'ai osé faire cet essai par cette magnifique tragedie du celebre Metastase."
German title "Artaxerxes" and text face Italian.
First performed at Ratisbon, carnival, 1785.   SCHATZ 9562

Artaserse. Dramma per musica da rappresentarsi nel Teatro Vendramin di S. Salvatore nella fiera dell' Ascensione dell' anno 1758.

Venezia, Modesto Fenzo, 1758. 37 p. 15ᶜᵐ.

Three acts. By Metastasio, who is not mentioned. Argument, scenario, cast, and name of Giuseppe **Scolari** as the composer.   SCHATZ 9787

Artaserse. Dramma per musica da rappresentarsi nel famosissimo Teatro Grimani di Sⁿ Gio. Grisostomo nel carnevale 1744 . . .

[Venezia], n. publ., n. d. 1 p. l., 59 p.   15ᶜᵐ.

Three acts. By Metastasio, who is not mentioned. Arg⸺ ⸏, cast, scenario, and name of Domingo **Terradellas** as the composer.   SCHATZ 10283

Artaserse. Drama per musica di Pietro Metastasio Romano fra gli Arcadi Artino Corasio. Da rappresentarsi nel Teatro detto delle Dame nel Carnevale dell' anno 1730 . . .

Roma, Zempel e de Mey, n. d. 79 p. 15ᶜᵐ.

Three acts. Impresario's dedication, scenario, argument, cast, and name of Leonardo **Vinci** as composer.
This fact obviously was unknown to Mr. Edward J. Dent when he wrote his "Notes on Leonardo Vinci" (Musical Antiquary, July 1913, p. 199). Otherwise this distinguished English scholar hardly would have written:
"From the *Diario ordinario di Roma* quoted by F. Piovano [Sammelbände d. I. M. G. 1906/7, v. 8, p. 76] it would seem that *Artaserse* was not produced with Vinci's music until after the composer's death. An *Artaserse* was produced at the Teatro delle Dame (Teatro d'Alibert) in February, 1730, but it was possibly by another composer. Vinci died suddenly on Sunday, May 28, 1730. His *Artaserse* was described as new in June, 1731, when produced at the same theatre."
As a matter of fact, the *Diario*, as quoted by Piovano, says under date of June 16, 1731:
"l'altro dramma che deve andare in scena nel medesimo teatro [delle Dame] intitolato *Artaserse*, composto dal Signor abbate Pietro Metastasio, e posto in musica dal fu [!] Signor Maestro di Cappella Leonardo Vinci."
and under June 23, 1731, the *Diario* says, referring to this revival on June 19, 1731: "*già recitato nel medesimo teatro l'anno* 1730." These words make it absolutely clear that the *Diario* referred to Vinci's "Artaserse" as second opera of the season, when on February 11, 1730, it wrote, without mentioning the composer:
"Sabbato sera [=February 4, 1730], nel Teatro detto delle Dame, andò in scena il secondo dramma intitolato *Artaserse*."
These quotations, together with the fact that Vinci's name appears in the 1730 libretto, leave no doubt, I think, that Vinci's "Artaserse" was actually performed for the first time at Rome, Teatro delle Dame, February 4, 1730.   SCHATZ 10743

— **Artaserse,** dramma per musica, rappresentato nel Nuovo Real Teatro privilegiato. L'anno MDCCXLVI. In Dresda.

n. i., n. d. 95, 95 p. 16ᶜᵐ.

Three acts. Argument, scenario, cast, and names of Metastasio as author, of Leonardo **Vinci** as composer. German title "Artaxerxes" and text face Italian, which is practically the same as in the Rome, 1730 ed., though, for instance, "Per pietà, bell' idol mio" has been dropped from I, 5.   SCHATZ 10744

Artaserse. Drama per musica da rappresentarsi nel Teatro di Sant' Angelo l'anno MDCCV . . .

Venezia, Marino Rossetti, 1705. 72 p. 15½cm.

Three acts. By Apostolo Zeno and Pietro Pariati, who are not mentioned. Dedication dated Venice, January 8, 1705, argument, cast, scenario, name of Antonio Giannettini (**Zannettini**) as composer, and notice to the reader informing him that this is an operatic version of Giulio Agosti's L'Artaserse, 1700, which accounts for the liberties taken with his drama. SCHATZ 11141

Artaserse. Dramma per musica da rappresentarsi nel Teatro alla Scala il carnevale dell' anno 1794 . . .

Milano, Gio. Batista Bianchi, n. d. 68 p. 16cm.

Three acts. By Metastasio, who is not mentioned. Impresario's dedication dated Milan, December 26, 1793, argument, cast, scenario, and name of Nicola Antonio **Zingarelli** as composer. The descriptions of the ballets "Elfrida, ballo eroico pantomimo" and "Il feudatorio pentito, ballo comico pantomimo" announced to be "in fine" are not there. The ballets were by Gaetano Gioja, the composers of the music not being mentioned.

First performed at Trieste, Teatro di S. Pietro, March 19, 1789. SCHATZ 11240

Artaserse Longimano. Dramma per musica da rappresentarsi nel Teatro di S. Angelo. Nel carnovale dell' anno 1737 . . .

Venezia, Marino Rossetti, 1737. 68 p. 15cm.

Three acts. Impresario's dedication, notice to the reader with apologies to Metastasio for the liberties taken with his "Temistocle." Argument, scenario, cast, and name of Antonio Gaetano Pampino (**Pampani?**) as the composer. SCHATZ 7753

Artaserse rè di Persia. L. T. of Lotti's Il tradimento traditore di se stesso.

L'Artaxerse ovvero L'Ormonda costante. Drama per musica nel famoso Teatro Grimano l'anno MDCLXIX. Di Aurelio Aureli. Opera decimaquinta . . .

Venetia, Francesco Nicolini, 1669. front., 65, [1] p. 14cm.

Three acts. Author's dedication dated Venice, December 28, 1668, argument, scenario. The composer, Carlo **Grossi**, is not mentioned. On the additional page is a list of "Drammi per musica composti da Aurelio Aureli," and opposite, on a blank page, Schatz has written the years of first performance and composers, as follows:

L'Erginda. 1652. Gaspare Sartorio.
L'Erismena. 1655. Francesco Cavalli.
La Rodope e Damira. 1657. P. A. Ziani.
Il Medoro. 1658. Francesco Luzzo.
La costanza di Rosmonda. 1659. G. B. Rovettini.
La virtù guerriera rappresentata in Vienna. 1659. Without music.
L'Antigona delusa da Alceste. 1660. P. A. Ziani.
Il Pirro. 1661. Antonio Sartorio.
Gli scherzi di Fortuna. 1662. P. A. Ziani.
Le fatiche d'Ercole per Deianira. 1662. P. A. Ziani.
Gl'amori d'Apollo e Leucotoe. 1663. G. B. Rovettini.
La Rosilena. 1664. G. B. Rovettini.
Il Perseo. 1665. A. Mattioli.
L'Eliogabalo. 1668. T. Orgiani.
L'Artaserse. 1668. Carlo Grossi.

In the dedication to the brothers Grimani, Aureli, referring to his "Eliogabalo," performed during the previous carnival at their theatre, says it was his intention to rest this year, but at the instance of the Grimani brothers he changed his mind, and wrote "L'Artaxerse," "anco trà la perdita funesta del padre, e d'un unico figlio." He then continues:

"So, che questa inusitata stravaganza di due titoli, desterà stupore non meno, che curiosità ne' lettori di saperne la causa: Mà basta à me che VV. SS. Illustrissime la sappino. Spero, che non si sdegneranno di recevere quello, ch'Elle medesime si sono contentate di scegliere." SCHATZ 4216

Artaxerxes. An English opera. As it is performed at the Theatre-Royal in Covent-Garden. The musick composed by Tho. Aug. Arne, Mus. Doc.

London, J. and R. Tonson, 1763. 47, [1] p. 20^{cm}.

Three acts. Cast, argument, and same preface as in next entry.
First performed at Covent Garden, February 2, 1762.   ML 50.2.A81A7

— **Artaxerxes.** An English opera. As it is performed at the Theatres Royal in Drury Lane, and Covent Garden. The musick composed by Tho. Aug. Arne, Mus. Doc. A new edition.

London, T. Lowndes and J. Condell, n. d. 47 p. 20½^{cm}.

Three acts. Casts, argument, and preface, in which Arne (not mentioned) submits his translation of Metastasio's "Artaserse" as "this first attempt of the kind." "As the narrative part of this drama may seem too barren of forcible epithets, which in reading or speaking dignify the style," he quotes Dryden's and Lord Lansdown's sentiments on the subject of opera librettos. He further quotes Metastasio's own recipe for the poetry of an opera, and finally comments on
"the necessity of sometimes departing from the author, on account of the different idioms of our language; and of leaving out many beauties in the narrative part of the drama, for the sake of brevity."   LONGE 308

— **Artaxerxes,** an English opera. As it is performed at the Theatre Royal, Covent-Garden. Corrected from the prompt-book, by James Wild, prompter.

London, Scatcherd and Whitaker, 1792. 31, [1] p. 18^{cm}.

Last (unnumb.) page contains announcement of "The Miser." Three acts. Cast.
Arne is not mentioned.   LONGE 218

Artaxerxes. Ein musicalisches schau-spiel, welches aus hoechstem befehl . . . auf den churfuerstlichen neuen Theater in der carnevalszeit anno 1763 ist aufgefuehret worden. Die poesie ist von . . . Peter Metastasio . . . Die music ist von . . . Andreas von Bernasconi . . .

Muenchen, Frantz Joseph Thuille, n. d. 15 p. p. (double), 70 p., [8] p. 15^{cm}.

German translation faces Italian of Metastasio's "Artaserse." Cast, argument, and scenario.   SCHATZ 863

Artaxerxes. Tr. of Grann's Artaserse.

Artaxerxes. Tr. of Hasse's Artaserse (second setting).

Artaxerxes. Tr. of Jommelli's Artaserse.

Artaxerxes. Ein musicalisches schau-spiel, aufgefuehret auf der hiesigen Hof-Schaubuehne naechst der Kaiserl. Burg, zur fassnachts-zeit, im jahr 1763. In das teutsche gebracht von J. A. E. v. G.

Wien, mit von Ghelischen schriften, n. d. Unpaged. 16^{cm}.

Three acts. Joh. Anton edler van Ghelen's transl. of Metastasio's "Artaserse." Argument, cast, and name of Giuseppe **Scarlatti** as the composer. On the last 2 p.: "Beschreibung der taenze," by Gaspero Angiolini; music by Joseph Starzer.
First performed at Lucca September, 1747.   SCHATZ 9541

Artaxerxes. Tr. of Vinci's Artaserse.

L'arte in garra con l'arte. Drama per musica da rappresentarsi nel Teatro Tron di S. Cassiano. L'anno 1702. Poesia di Francesco Silvani, servitore di S. A. Sereniss. di Mantoua.

Venezia, Marino Rossetti, n. d. 81 p. 14½^{cm}.

Three acts. Argument, scenario, notice to the reader. The composer, Tommaso **Albinoni,** is not mentioned.   SCHATZ 88

Artemisia. Dramma per musica da rappresentarsi nel nobilissimo
Teatro di S. Benedetto l'Ascensione dell' anno 1782.

Venezia, Modesto Fenzo, 1782. 50 p. 17^{cm}.

Three acts. By "Sig. conte N. N." Argument, cast, scenario, and name of the
composer, Giuseppe **Calegari**. On p. 23–27 the argument of the ballets "Il Suffi e
lo schiavo" and "Il diavolo a quatro, ossia La doppia metamorfosi" by Gaspero Angiolini, who also composed the music.   SCHATZ 1510

Artemisia. Drama per musica nel Teatro a SS. Gio. e Paolo per
l'anno MDCLVI . . .

Venetia, Andrea Giuliani, 1656. 6 p. l. (incl. front.), 72 p. 14$\frac{1}{2}$^{cm}.

Three acts, with prologue. Dedication, signed with Niccolò Minato's initials as
author and dated January 10, 1656, argument, and scenario. The composer, Pietro
Francesco **Cavalli**, is not mentioned. The "Ariette aggionte" (8 p.) of the Brussels
copy not in ours.   SCHATZ 1730

Artemisia. Dramma per musica, da rappresentarsi nel Teatro della
Regia elettoral corte di Dresda, nel carnevale dell' anno MDCCLV.
La poesia è del Sigr Giannambrogio Migliavacca . . . La musica è
del Sigr Gio. Adolfo Hasse . . .

*Dresda, la vedova Stössel, e . . . Giov. Carlo Krause, n. d. 7 p. l.,
(double) 80 p. 20^{cm}.*

Three acts. Argument, cast, scenario. German title page "Artemisia" and text
face Italian.
First performed, as indicated, February 6, 1754.   SCHATZ 4514

Artemisia. [vignette] In einem musicalischen schau-spiele auf
dem grossen Hamburgischen Theatro vorgestellet im jahr 1715.

Hamburg, Friderich Conrad Greflinger, n. d. Unpaged. 19^{cm}.

Three acts. Scenario and Vorbericht (argument) at end of which this is called
the sixty-fourth opera by Reinhard **Keiser**. Author unknown to Schatz.
                                                            SCHATZ 5077

Artemisia regina di Caria. Dramma serio per musica dell' avv.
D. Marcello Marchesini da rappresentarsi nel Real Teatro di S. Carlo
in occasione delle faustissime nozze . . . di Francesco Borbone . . .
e di Maria Clementina . . .

Napoli, Stamperia Flautina, 1797. 64 p. 15$\frac{1}{2}$^{cm}.

Two acts. Dedication dated June, 1797, argument, scenario, cast, and name of
the composer, Domenico Nicola **Cimarosa**. On p. 56–64 argument, description, and
cast of Gaspare Ronzi's "Le nozze di Peleo e Teti, ballo pantomimo" in five acts.
As second ballet was performed his "Giannina, e Bernadone ossia Il geloso sincerato,
ballo buffo in tre atti." The composers of the music are not mentioned.
    This first setting of the text by Cimarosa, as Schatz calls it, was first performed on
June 25, 1797, as indicated.   SCHATZ 1990

Artemisia regina di Caria. Dramma per musica da cantarsi nel
Real Palazzo dell' Ajuda per celebrare il felicissimo giorno natalizio
di Sua Maestà fedelissima l'augusta Donna Maria I. regina di Portogallo . . . li 17. dec. 1787.

n. pl., n. d., Nella stamperia reale. 31 p. 15^{cm}.

One act. Gaetano Martinelli is mentioned as author, Antonio Leal **Moreira**,
"maestro del Real Seminario di Lisbona," as the composer. Argument and cast.
First performed at Lisbon, as indicated.   SCHATZ 6629

L'Artenice. Dramma per musica da rappresentarsi nel Real Teatro di S. Carlo nel dì 13 agosto 1784 per festeggiarsi la nascita di S. M. la regina . . .

Napoli, Vincenzo Flauto, 1784. 55 p. 15ᶜᵐ.

Three acts. Author not mentioned and unknown to Schatz. Dedication, argument, cast, scenario, and name of Giacomo **Tritto** as the composer. On p. 9–18 cast and description of Domenico Lefevre's "Colombo nell' Indie, ballo tragico pantomimo in cinque atti," music ("tutta nuova") by Antonio Rossetti, on p. 19–25 description of Gasparo Angiolini's ballet "Lauretta," composer of the music not mentioned.

SCHATZ 10455

The artifice: a comic opera. In two acts. As it is performed at the Theatre Royal Drury Lane. Written by William Augustus Miles.

London, T. Cadell, 1780. 4 p. l., 54 p. 21½ᶜᵐ.

Cast, dedication to Sheridan, dated London, April 14, 1780, and prefatory advertisement in which Miles reproaches the dramatic writers for "having exhibited sea officers on the stage in caricature." He says that the theatres "are not in possession of one natural marine character" and trusts that his own sea characters "will be found similar to those that are met with in real life."

The composer Michael **Arne** is not mentioned.

First performed April 14, 1780.

LONGE 239

Die artige schaefer. Ballet. *See* Piccinni's Das gute maedgchen.

Die artigen zufaelle zwischen liebe und eifersucht. Tr. of Galuppi's Li vaghi accidenti fra amore e gelosia.

Gli artigiani. Dramma giocoso per musica da rappresentarsi nel Teatro alla Scala l'autunno dell' anno 1795 . . .

Milano, Gio. Batista Bianchi, n. d. 72 p. 17ᶜᵐ.

Two acts. Attributed by Schatz to Carlo Goldoni, who is not mentioned. Dedication by the impresario, dated Milan, August 12, 1795 ("il primo spettacolo del corrente autunno"), scenario, cast, and name of Pasquale **Anfossi** as composer. With the opera were performed the ballets, invented by Gaspare Ronzi, (composer of music not mentioned), entitled "Il re pastore" and "La fanciulla mal custodita" and described with cast on p. 69–72.

First performed at Venice, Teatro di S. Moisè, carnival 1794.   SCHATZ 227

L'artigiano gentiluomo. *See* also Il bottegaro gentiluomo: Orlandini (?).

L'artigiano gentiluomo. L. T. of Hasse's Larinda e Vanesio.

Arvire et Evelina, tragédie-lyrique en trois actes; représentée, pour la premiere fois, sur le Théatre de l'Académie-royale de musique, le mardi 29 avril 1788.

Paris, P. de Lormel, 1788. viii, 62 p. 22ᶜᵐ.

Cast, names of Nicolas François Guillard as author, of **Sacchini** as the composer, and "avertissement" which reads in part:

"M. William Mason a traité à Londres ce sujet. Il a été joué en 1776, sur le Théâtre de Covent Garden, sous le titre de Caractacus. [with music by Th. Aug. Arne]. Ceux qui liront l'ouvrage anglais, seront peut être surpris des changements considérables que je me suis permis. La conduite de la piéce, le dénouement, jusqu'aux noms sont ici différents . . .

"Le poëme ne faisant gueres que moitié de la tâche que nous avons à remplir, le prix que celui ci a obtenu au concours me rassure moins que les talens du celebre compositeur qui a cousacré a cet ouvrage les derniers élans d'un génie fécond qui étoit encore dans toute sa force, lorsq'une mort aussi funeste qu'imprévue l'a enlevé aux plaisirs du public, & a porté le désespoir dans l'ame de ses amis."

Sacchini did not live to finish the score. The last act was completed by J. B. **Rey,** who successfully selected pieces from Sacchini's works for the purpose. The score was published with the title "Evelina."   SCHATZ 9207

Arvire et Evelina—Continued.

— Arvire og Evelina. Oper i tre akter. Oversat af fransk og underlagt Sacchinis musik, af Dr. Frankenau.

Kiøbenhavn, J. F. Morthorstes enke, n. d. 56 p. 17^{cm}.

First performed at Copenhagen, Kongl. Theater, January 30, 1799.

SCHATZ 9208

Arvire og Evelina. Tr. of Sacchini's Arvire et Avelina.

L'Ascanio, drama per musica da rappresentarsi nel carnovale del 1686 . . . Posto in musica dal S. D. Giuseppe Antonio Bernabei . . . con l'arie per i balletti del S. Melchior Dardespin . . .

Monaco, Giovanni Jecklino, n. d. 5 p. l., 118 p. 14½^{cm}.

Three acts and three ballets. Argument, scenario, and dedication signed by Ventura Terzago. For this reason evidently Schatz attributes the libretto to him, but Terzago says "toccando a me la sorte di presentare alle S. S. A. A. V. V. E. E. l'Ascanio del S^r. Barone Filippo Renato Sbarra gran maestro di cucina di sua M^{ta} l'Imp^{ce} Ved^a. abbraccio quest'onore con tanto maggior sodisfazione, quãto considero quella che sono per ricavare le S. S. E. E. A. A. V. V. dalla lettura di questo bel poema, che valerà a ristorar la noja reccata dal mio Servio Tullio, che a giorni a dietro passeggiò queste scene . . ." SCHATZ 824

Ascanio. Drama per musica da recitarsi nel Regio Teatro di Milano . . .

Milano, Marc' Antonio Pandolfo Malatesta, 1702. 71, [1] p. 15½^{cm}.

Three acts. Dedication by the author Pietro d'Averara, his preface to the reader with the names of [Carlo Francesco] **Pollaroli** as composer of the opera, and of Monteclair as composer of the *balli*, argument, and scenario.

First performed 1702, as indicated. SCHATZ 8274

Ascanio in Alba. Dramma per musica da cantarsi nella Real Villa di Queluz per celebrare il felicissimo giorno natalizio di S. M. Fedelissima l'augusto D. Pietro III. Rè di Portogallo . . . li 5 luglio 1785.

n. pl., n. d., Nella stamperia reale. 28 p. 14½^{cm}.

Two acts. Argument and cast. Claudio Niccolo Stampa is mentioned as author of the text, altered by Gins. Parini. Antonio Leal **Moreira** as the composer.

SCHATZ 6633

L'Asiatico generoso, ballet. *See* Galuppi's L'Ipermestra

L'asilio d'amore.

[449]–480 p. 19^{cm}. (Pietro Metastasio, Opere drammatiche, Venezia, Giuseppe Bettinelli, 1733–37, v. 2.)

One act. No composer mentioned. On p. 451 note: "La seguente festa teatrale fu rappresentata in Lintz il di 28. agosto dell' anno 1732 festeggiandosi il giorno natalizio dell' augustissima imperadrice, alla presenza della medema." Performed 1765 in a revised version as "Il trionfo d'amore." ML 49.A2M40

— L'asilio d'amore.

Metastasio, Poesie, Parigi, vedova Quillau, 1755, t. v, [427]–463 p. 16^{cm}.

One act. ML 49.A2M42

L'asilio d'amore—Continued.

— **L'asilio d'amore.**   Festa teatrale scritta dall' autore in Vienna
l'anno 1732, ed eseguita alla presenza de' regnanti, con sontuosa
magnificenza, la prima volta con musica del Caldara nella gran
Piazza di Lintz, capitale dell' Austria Superiore; dove trovandosi
allora con tutta la Cesarea Corte l'imperator Carlo VI per ricever
l'omaggio di quella provincia, si festeggiò il 28 d'agosto, giorno di
nascita dell' imperatrice Elisabetta . . .

[*336*]–*368 p. 26*^{cm}*. (Pietro Metastasio, Opere, t. iii, Parigi,
vedova Herissant, 1780.)

One act.   ML 49.A2M44

L'Asmiro rè di Corinto.   Dramma musicale da rappresentarsi nel
famosissimo Teatro di S. S. Gio. e Paolo l'anno MDCXCVI . . .
Composto in musica dal Sig. D. Pietro Romolo abbate Pignatta.

Venetia, Nicolini, 1696. 4, 3-59 p. 14^{cm}*.*

Three acts.   Composer's dedication signed, Venice, February 15, 1696, his notice
to the reader, in which he appears as the author of the text, too, and scenario.

Schatz 8168

Asmodeus der krumme teufel.   Ein opera comique von zwey
aufzuegen.

Wien, Johann Thomas edl. von Trattnern, 1770. 44 p. 16½^{cm}*.*

Two acts.   Neither the author, Johann Joseph Felix von Kurz (*called* Bernardon),
nor the composer, Franz Joseph **Haydn,** is mentioned.

First performed at Vienna, Theater naechst dem Kärnthnerthore, November 24,
1770; previously there, as "Der neue Krumme teufel," in 1752.   Schatz 4609

Aspard.   Dramma per musica da rappresentarsi nel nobilissimo
Teatro delle Dame il carnevale dell' anno 1784 . . .

Roma, Gioacchino Puccinelli, n. d. 45 p. 15½^{cm}*.*

Three acts.   Publisher's dedication dated "Dalla stamperia 31. [!] del 1784",
argument, scenario, names of Gaetano Sertor as author, of Francesco **Bianchi** as
composer.   With the opera were performed two ballets, "Alonzo e Cora," musica
tutta nuova," by Antonio Capuzzi and "L'assedio di Belgrado. Fatto da Mao-
metto II, soccorso e liberato da Giovanni Unniade governatore dell' Ungheria,"
music by Antonio Bisoni, "detto il Rossetto."   ML 50.2.A82B3

Aspasia.   Dramma per musica da rappresentarsi nel nobilissimo
Teatro Venier in San Benedetto il carnovale dell' anno 1790.

Venezia, Modesto Fenzo, 1790. 59 p. 17^{cm}*.*

Three acts.   Gaetano Sertor, the author not mentioned.   Argument, cast, scenario,
and name of Giuseppe **Giordani** as the composer.   On p. 47–59, cast and description
of "Giulio Villenvelt, osia L'assassino di Scozia, ballo pantomimo d'invenzione . . .
del signor Giuseppe Trafieri."   The composer of the music is not mentioned.

Schatz 3833

L'assedio di Belgrado, ballet.   *See* Bianchi's Aspard.

L'assassino di Scozia, ballet.   *See* Giulio Villenvelt.

Assedio e liberazione di Vienna, ballet.   *See* Rust's Artaserse.

L'assemblée.   Entrée in Bourgeois' Les plaisirs de la paix.

L'assemblée des dieux pour le mariage d'Alcide & d'Hebé,
ballet.   *See* Bernasconi's Demofoonte.

Astarbea, ballet. *See* Zingarelli's Giulietta e Romeo.

Astarbea ossia Pimmalione vendicato, ballet. *See* Anfossi's I matrimoni per fanatisimo.

Astarto.

Apostolo Zeno, Poesie drammatiche, Venezia, 1744, t. x, p. 106. 19ᶜᵐ.

Three acts. Argument. Written in collaboration with Pietro Pariati. No composer is mentioned. In the "Catalogo" at end of vol. x, date and place of first ed. are given as Venice, 1708. ML 49.A2Z3

— **Astarto.** Pubblicato per la prima volta in Venezia, 1708.

Apostolo Zeno, Poesie drammatiche, Orleans, 1785–86, t. x, p. 97–198. 21ᶜᵐ.

Three acts. Argument. No composer is mentioned. Written in collaboration with Pietro Pariati. ML 49.A2Z4

Astarto. Drama per musica da rappresentarsi nel Teatro Tron di S. Cassano l'autunno dell' anno MDCCVIII . . .

Venezia, Marino Rossetti, 1708. 6 p. l., 60 p. 15ᶜᵐ.

Three acts. By Zeno and Pariati, who are not mentioned. Dedication, argument, cast, scenario, and name of Tommaso **Albinoni** as composer. Bound with this is the libretto of his intermezzi, "Pimpinone" (*see* under title), performed with the opera.

Schatz 110

— **L'Astarto.** Dramma per musica da rappresentarsi nel Teatro arciducale di Mantova nel carnovale·dell' anno 1714 . . .

Mantova, Alberto Pazzoni, n. d. 58 p. 16ᶜᵐ.

Three acts. By Zeno and Pariati, who are not mentioned. Dedication dated Mantova, February 8, 1714, argument, cast, scenario, name of Tommaso **Albinoni** as composer. ML 50.2.A83A4

L'Astarto. Drama per musica, da rappresentarsi nel Teatro d'Hamburgo, l'anno MDCCXXI.—Astartus in einer opera, vorgestellet auf dem hamburgischen Theatro im jahr 1721.

[Hamburg], Caspar Jakhel, n. d. Unpaged. 18½ᶜᵐ.

Three acts. Originally by Apostolo Zeno and Pietro Pariati, rewritten by Paolo Antonio Rolli. German text faces Italian. Imperfect copy, lacking all preliminary matter. The composer, Giovanni Battista **Bononcini,** is not mentioned.

Schatz 120

Astartus. Tr. of G. B. Bononcini's L'Astarto.

Asteria, favola pastorale per musica, rappresentata alla Real corte di Dresda l'anno MDCCXXXVII nel giorno del nome della Maestà del rè . . .

n. i., n. d. Unpaged. 18ᶜᵐ.

Pagination possibly cut off by binder. At end: "Dresda . . . la vedova Stössel."

Three acts. Johann Adolph **Hasse** is mentioned as the composer on an additional leaf, with the chorus, "Rive d'Elba oggi più liete." The author, Stefano Benedetto Pallavicini, is not mentioned.

First performed, as indicated, August 3, 1737. Schatz 4516

Astiage. Drama per musica nel famoso Teatro Grimani di SS. Gio. e Paolo l'anno MDCLXXVII . . .

Venetia, Frencesco Nicolini, 1677. 71 p. 14½ᶜᵐ.

Three acts. Dedication by Matteo Noris, who informs the reader in a prefatory note that he was engaged to modernize and partly rewrite Apollonio Apolloni's original text; that the opera was composed by "Gio. Bonaventura **Viviani,** maestro di capella di S. M. C. in Ispruch, and sung "da i primi e più celebri canori cigni d'Europa," which was the customary formula in absence of the cast. Argument and scenario.

Schatz 10783

Astianatte. Drama per musica da rappresentarsi in Monaco nel Teatro della corte, nel verno dell' anno MDCCXVII . . .

[*Monaco*], *apud Mariam Susannam Jaecklinin, n. d. 67 p. 14½ᶜᵐ.*

Three acts. Argument (both in Italian and German) and scenario. Neither the composer, Marc 'Antonio **Bononcini**, nor the librettist, Antonio Salvi, is mentioned. First performed at Pratolino, Teatro della Villa Medici, 1701.   Schatz 1204

Astianatte. O. T. of Leo's Andromaca.

Astianatte. Dramma per musica da rappresentarsi nel Teatro Giustiniani di S. Moise. il carnovale dell' anno 1755.

Venezia, Modesto Fenzo, 1755. 48 p. 14½ᶜᵐ.

Three acts. By Antonio Salvi, who is not mentioned. Argument, cast, scenario, and name of Antonio Gaetano **Pampani** as the composer   Schatz 7755

L'astratto ovvero Il giocator fortunato. Dramma giocoso per musica del Sig. abbate Giuseppe Petrosellini P. A. da rappresentarsi nel Teatro di San Samuel il carnovale dell' anno 1772.

Venezia, Modesto Fenzo, 1772. 64 p. 18½ᶜᵐ.

Three acts. Cast, scenario, and name of Nicolò **Piccinni** as the composer.
    Schatz 8066

— **L'astratto** ovvero Il giuocatore fortunato. Dramma giocoso per musica da rappresentarsi nel Nuovo Teatro della città di Pisa il carnevale dell' anno 1773 . . .

Pisa, Francesco Picraccini, 1773. 78 p. 17ᶜᵐ.

Three acts. Impresario's dedication, cast, and name of **Piccinni** as the composer. Petrosellini is not mentioned. This Pisa version deviates noticeably from the Venetian original. For instance, the latter has the arias, "Con fiemma io ve lo dico" (I, 1), "Io mi sento in mezzo al core" (I, 4), whereas Pisa has "Voglio un marito" and "Nocchier che al porto in seno," resp. the substitute aria on p. 78, "Fra dubbiosi affetti miei."   Schatz 8066a

Astrea placata.

Metastasio, Poesie, Parigi, vedova Quillau, 1755, t. vii, [307]–335 p. 16ᶜᵐ.

One act.   ML 49.A2M42

— **Astrea placata.** Componimento drammatico, scritto dall' autore l'anno 1739 . . . ed eseguito con musica del Predieri la prima volta nella Galleria dell' Imperial Favorita . . . per festeggiare il di 28 d'Agosto, giorno di nascita dell' augustissima imperatrice Elisabetta.

[*381*]–*404 p. 26ᶜᵐ.* (*Metastasio, Opere, t. v., Parigi, vedova Herissant, 1780.*)   ML 49.A2M44

Astrea placata; ovvero La felicità della terra. Festa teatrale . . . all' occasione del guibileo in cui compisce il secolo, che i fortunati popoli di Danimarc felicemente deferirono la sovranità alla loro augustissima casa regnante da rappresentarsi sul Regio Teatro Danese.

Copenhagen, L. N. Svare, 1760. Unpaged. 16½ᶜᵐ.

One act. Impresario's dedication, cast, and name of Giuseppe **Sarti** as the composer ("La musica è tutta nuova"), and of Erasmo Soelberg as the translator of (not mentioned) Metastasio's text. Danish title, "Astrea tilfredsstillet; eller Jordens lyksalighed," and text face the Italian.
First performed, as indicated, October 17, 1760.   Schatz 9426

Astrea placata ovvero La felicità della terra. Componimento drammatico da cantarsi il dì V. settembre MDCCLIII per festeggiare il giorno natalizio di S. A. R. Federico Cristiano elettoral principe di Sassonia.

Dresda, vedova Stössel, n. d. 1 p. l., 23 p. 23ᶜᵐ.

One act. Neither Metastasio, the author, nor Johann Georg **Schürer**, the composer, is mentioned.

First performed at Dresden, Churfürstl. Kleines Theater, October 7, 1746.

SCHATZ 9730

Astrea tilfredsstillet eller Jordens lyksalighed. Tr. of Sarti's Astrea placata.

Astrée. Tragedie par Monsieur de La Fontaine, representée par l'Academie royale de musique. Suivant la copie imprimée à Paris.

[Amsterdam, Antoine Schelte], 1692. 46 p. (incl. front.) 13½ᶜᵐ.

Prologue and three acts. The composer, **Colasse**, is not mentioned.

ML 50.2.A86 C6

— **Astrée,** tragedie representée par l'Academie royale de musique l'an 1691. Les paroles de M. de la Fontaine & la musique de M. Collasse. XXVIII. opera.

n. i., n. d. front., p. 155-206. 14ᶜᵐ. (Recueil général des opéra, Paris, 1703, t. 4.)

Detached copy. Three acts with prologue.

First performed, as indicated, Nov. 28, 1691.

SCHATZ 2097
Second copy. ML 48.R4

L'astrologa. Commedia per musica da rappresentarsi nel Real Teatro del Fondo di Separazione per terza opera del corrente anno 1782.

Napoli, n. publ., 1782. 66 p. 15ᶜᵐ.

Three acts. Argument, cast, scenario, and name of the composer, Francesco **Bianchi.** The author is not mentioned and is unknown to Schatz. SCHATZ 988

L'astrologa. Dramma giocoso per musica dell' abate Pietro Chiari da rappresentarsi nel Teatro di S. A. Serenissima il Signor principe di Carignano nell' autunno dell' anno MDCCLXII.

Torino, Gaspare Bayno, n. d. 56 p. 15ᶜᵐ.

Three acts. Cast, scenario, and name of Niccolò **Piccinni** as the composer.

First performed at Venice, Teatro di S. Moisè, carnival 1762. SCHATZ 8147

Gli **astrologi imaginari.** O. T. of Paisiello's I filosofi imaginari.

L'astrologo. L. T. of Gasparini's Parpagnacco.

L'astuta in amore. Dramma giocoso per musica da rappresentarsi nel Teatro grande alla Scala l'autunno 1796 . . .

Milano, Gio. Batista Bianchi, n. d. 63, [1] p. 17ᶜᵐ.

Three acts. Censor's date "Le Iʳ fructidor an 4.ᵐᵉ" (Aug. 18, 1796). Cast, scenario, and name of Valentino **Fioravanti** as composer. The author, Giuseppe Palomba, is not mentioned. On p. 61–63 argument and dedication and on the unnumb. p. cast of Filippo Beretti's ballet "Lucrezia ossia L'espulsione dei rè da Roma." His second ballet was called "La calzolaja." The composers of the music are not mentioned.

First performed at Naples, Teatro Nuovo sopra Toledo, 1795. ML 48.A5 v. 2

L'astuta in amore—Continued.

— Il furbo malaccorto: Dramma per musica in due atti da rappresentarsi nel Regio Teatro di S. Carlo della Principessa l'autunno dell' anno 1797.

Lisbona, Simone Taddeo Ferreira, 1797.   163 p.   14½ᶜᵐ.

Cast and name of the composer.   Portuguese text faces Italian.   SCHATZ 3161

L'astuzia felice.   Dramma di tre atti per musica.

Carlo Goldoni, Opere teatrali, Venezia, Zatta e figli, 1788-95, t. 41,
[181]–237 p.   18ᶜᵐ.

First performed, according to Schatz, with music by Gaetano **Latilla** and others at Turin, Teatro Carignano, spring of 1750.   PQ

L'astuzia felice.   Dramma giocoso per musica del Signor dottore Carlo Goldoni ridotta in sei personaggi, e addattata all'uso del Teatro Giustiniani di S. Moisè l'autunno dell' anno 1767.

Venezia, Modesto Fenzo, 1767.   60 p.   14½ᶜᵐ.

Three acts.   Cast, scenario, and name of Filippo **Gherardesca** as the composer.
SCHATZ 3800

Le astuzie amorose.   Drama giocoso per musica da rappresentarsi nel nobile Teatro di San Samuele nell' autunno dell' anno 1775.

Venezia, Stamperia Carcani, n. d.   63 p.   18ᶜᵐ.

Three acts.   By Francesco Cerlone, who is not mentioned.   Cast and name of Michele **Mortellari** as the composer.   On p. 30–35 argument and description of Onorato Viganò's "Andromeda e Perseo, ballo eroico pantomimo."   The composer of the music is not mentioned nor of Viganò's second ballet "Il giocatore."
SCHATZ 6688

Le astuzie amorose.   Dramma giocoso per musica da rappresentarsi nel Teatro di via della Pergola nella primavera del MDCCLXXVII . . .

Firenze, Gio. Risaliti, 1777.   55 p.   16½ᶜᵐ.

Three acts.   By Francesco Cerlone, who is not mentioned.   Cast and name of **Paisiello** as the composer.
First performed at Naples, Teatro Nuovo, spring, 1775.   SCHATZ 7675

L'astuzie di Bettina.   Dramma giocoso per musica da rappresentarsi nel Teatro Giustiniani in San Moisè per la seconda opera del carnovale 1784.

Venezia, Modesto Fenzo, 1784.   63, [1] p.   17½ᶜᵐ.

Two acts.   Author not mentioned and unknown to Schatz.   Dedication signed by the impresario, Antonio Dian, cast, scenario, and name of Mattia **Stabingher** as the composer.   With the opera were performed Federico Terrades' ballets, composers of the music not mentioned, "La forza delle donne" and "Il veglione."
First performed at Genoa, Teatro di S. Agostino, spring of 1780.   SCHATZ 10019

Le astuzie in amore.   Commedia per musica di G. M. D.   Da rappresentarsi nel Teatro Nuovo sopra Toledo per terz' opera di quest' anno 1790.

Napoli, Vincenzo Flauto, 1790.   46 p.   15ᶜᵐ.

Two acts.   By Giuseppe Maria Diodati.   Cast and name of Giacomo **Tritto** as the composer.   SCHATZ 10460

L'astuzie villane. Commedia per musica di Giuseppe Palomba da rappresentarsi nel Teatro de' Fiorentini per second' opera in quest' anno 1786.

Napoli, n. publ., 1786. 60 p. 15ᶜᵐ.

Three acts. Argument, cast, and name of Pietro **Guglielmi** as the composer.

SCHATZ 4235

Atalanta. Dramma per musica da rappresentarsi nel Regio Teatro di Torino nel carnovale del 1792 . . .

Torino, Onorato Derossi, n. d. viii, 52 p. 15½ᶜᵐ.

Three acts. By Cesare Olivieri. Argument, cast, scenario, and name of Giuseppe **Giordani** as the composer. On p. 47–52 cast and description of Domenico Le Fevre's ballets "Il Pigmalione," "Le sultane," (4 acts) and "Apollo e Dafne." The composers of the music are not mentioned.

First performed, as indicated, December 26, 1791. SCHATZ 3834

Atalanta e Meleagro. Festa teatrale che introduce ad un ballo allegorico scritta da Antonio de' Filistri . . . da rappresentarsi con musica del Sign. Vicenzo Righini . . . nel Gran Teatro Reale di Berlino il giorno 15 febbraio 1797 in occasione delle felicissime nozze dell' Altezza Reale di Federica Cristina Augusta principessa di Prussia con l'Altezza Serenissima di Guglielmo principe ereditario di Assia-Cassel.

Berlino, Haude e Spener, n. d. 63 p. 16ᶜᵐ.

One act, with ballets. Argument and cast. German title-page, "Athalante und Meleager," and text face Italian. SCHATZ 8779

— Atalanta e Meleagro. Festa teatrale scritta con balli analoghi da Antonio de' Filistri . . . da rappresentarsi con musica del Sign. Vicenzo Righini . . . nel gran Teatro Reale di Berlino il carnevale dell' anno 1799.

Berlino, Haude e Spener, n. d. 71 p. 16ᶜᵐ.

One act. Argument and cast. German title-page, "Athalante und Meleager," and text face Italian.

First performed, as indicated, January 14, 1799. SCHATZ 8780

Atalanta ed Ippomene—Atalante et Hippomène, ballet. *See* Jommelli's Demofoonte.

Atalo. Dramma per musica da rappresentarsi nel famoso Teatro Tron a S. Cassiano il carnovale dell' anno 1742.

Venezia, Bonifacio Viezzeri, 1742. 48 p. 14½ᶜᵐ.

Three acts. By Francesco Silvani, altered from the first edition, published in 1713 under the title of "La verità nell' inganno," to which fact the *argument* alludes. Scenario, cast, and name of the composer, **Chinzer,** "Giovanni Chintzer di Firenze." SCHATZ 1866

Atamo huomo vecchio e Palandra giovine, intermezzo. *See* Caldara's L'inganno tradito dall' amore.

L'Atanagilda, regina di Gottia. A. T. of M. A. Ziani's L'inganno regnante.

Ataulfo rè de' Goti, ovvero La forza della virtù. Dramma da recitarsi nella Sala de' Sigⁿ Capranica nel carnevale dell' anno 1712 . . .

Roma, Bernabò, 1712. 71 p. 15½ᶜᵐ.

Three acts. Author not mentioned and unknown to Schatz. Impresario's dedication, argument, cast, scenario, and name of Giuseppe Maria **Orlandini** as the composer.

SCHATZ 7349

Atenaide.

Apostolo Zeno, Poesie drammatiche, Venezia, 1744, t. i, p. [357]- 448   19^{cm}.

Three acts and licenza. Argument. No composer is mentioned. In the "Catalogo" at the end of t. x, date and place of first ed. are given as Vienna, 1714, but, according to Schatz, first performed at the court, Vienna, 1709, music of the first act by Andrea **Fiorè**, of the second by Ant. **Caldara**, and of the third by C. F. **Gasparini**. According to Fehr first performed in 1709 at Barcelona. Both agree that in 1714 the first act was composed by M. A. **Ziani**, the second by Ant. **Negri**, and the third by **Caldara**.   ML 49.A2Z3

— **Atenaide.**   Pubblicata per la prima volta in Vienna 1714.

Apostolo Zeno, Poesie drammatiche, Orleans, 1785-86, t. iv, p. 267- 352.   21^{cm}.

Three acts and licenza. Argument. No composer is mentioned.   ML 49.A2Z4

L'Atenaide o vero Gli affetti generosi.   Azione teatrale, scritta dall' autore in Vienna l'anno 1762 . . . e posta in musica dal Bonno, per doversi rappresentare privatamente negl' interni appartamenti del palazzo cesarea dalle Altezze Reali di cinque arciduchesse d'Austria . . .   Ma non ne permise la già disposta esecuzione l'inaspettata ultima infermità della soprannominata arciduchessa Isabella di Borbone.

pl., [5]-56 p.   26^{cm}.   (Metastasio, Opere, t. xi, Parigi, vedova Herissant, 1782.)

Two parts.   ML 49.A2M44

Athalanta und Meleager.   Tr. of Righini's Atalanta e Meleagro.

Athalia.   Ein trauerspiel mit chören.   Nach Racine von Carl Friedrich Cramer.   Die musik vom herrn capellmeister Schulz.

Kiel, bey dem verfasser, n. d.   [xxviii], 179, [1] p.   15^{cm}.

On p. 141–179, Cramer's "Anmerkungen," some of which are equally interesting, as his "Vorrede," in which he first (and charmingly) gives the history of Racine's "Athalie" in France; then the history of Schulz' setting and this translation; then his reasons for taking some liberties with Racine—his ambition was "mein original nicht allein zu erreichen, sondern auch, wo möglich zu übertreffen," and with this in view, he busied himself with the "Flecken im originale, die abgewischt werden konnten und-mussten"—and, finally, Racine's preface. As to Schulz' setting, Cramer says:

"Se. Königliche Hoheit, der Prinz Heinrich, der seinem grossen bruder wie an heldeneigenschaften, so auch an liebe zu den dichtern Frankreichs gleicht, trug seit verschiedenen jahren dem componisten, seinem capellmeister [1780–1787], auf, für sein Privat-Theater, das während seines sommeraufenthalts in Reinsberg seine liebste erholung ausmacht, die chöre dieser tragödie in musik zu setzen. Schulz erfüllte diesen befehl, und Athalia (ein vorzug, dessen sich die glänzende hauptstadt Frankreichs selber nicht rühmen kann), ward in Deutschland, auf dieser zwar kleinen, aber ihres geschmacks wegen merkwürdigen bühne, zum erstenmal *vollständig*, wie es ihre würde erforderte, aufgeführt. Die beschaffenheit der composition, ihr genauer musicalischer vortrag durch eine zureichende und gewählte capelle, so wie ihr dramatischer, in der die hauptrollen von einem manne, welcher, ob's sein beruf gleich nicht ist, dennoch desto rühmlicher die dreyfachen talente eines einsichtsvollen componisten, sängers und schauspielers in sich vereinigt, und von einer braven actrize, Madame d'Orceville, gemacht wurden, erwarben sich bey mehrmaligen vorstellungen den beyfall des prinzen und aller kenner, die es aufführen sahen. Durch das gerücht davon gereizt, suchte ich, da ich die Athalie immer sehr geliebt, und schon früher mit Madame Seyler von ihrer verpflanzung auf die deutsche bühne geredet hatte, die schulzische composition näher kenner su lernen . . ."

Cramer's German translation, first performed at Berlin, Concertsaal des Corsicaischen Hauses, 1786, and at Hamburg, Theater beim Gänsemarkt, March 30, 1789.
                                                                SCHATZ 9719

Athalia—Continued.

— Athalia. Tragedie af Racine i fem akter, med mellemsange componerede af hr. capelmester Schultz.

Kiøbenhavn, Johan Frederik Schultz, 1790. *100 p.* *17½ᶜᵐ.*
First performed at Copenhagen, Royal Theatre, March 24, 1790. Sᴄʜᴀᴛᴢ 9720

Athaliah. Tr. of Racine's Athalie.

Athaliah. A tragedy. Translated from the French of Monsieur Racine. By Mr. Duncombe. The third edition, revised and corrected.

London, J. Watts, 1746. *8 p. l. (incl. front.), 64 p.* *16½ᶜᵐ.*
Five acts. William Duncombe's dedication dated November, 1722, his prefatory note, and Racine's preface. This transl. was first published in 1724. Lᴏɴɢᴇ 70

Athalie. O. T. of Schulz' Athalia.

Ati e Sangaride. Serenata per musica da cantarsi nella Real Villa di Queluz . . . per celebrare il felicissimo giorno natalizio della serenissima Signora D. Maria Francesca Benedetta, principessa del Brasile li 25 luglio 1779.

[Lisboa], Stamperia Reale, n. d. *30 p.* *16ᶜᵐ.*
One act. Gaetano Martinelli is mentioned as author, Luciano Xavier dos **Santos,** as composer. Argument and cast. Sᴄʜᴀᴛᴢ 9398

Atide. Drama per musica da rappresentarsi nel nuovo famoso Teatro Formagliari l'anno 1679 Di Tomaso Stanzani . . .

Bologna, per l'herede di Vittorio Benacci, n. d. *6 p. l., 71, [1] p.* *14ᶜᵐ.*
Three acts. Author's dedication dated, Bologna, June 23, 1679, cast, scenario, and argument with the names of the composers, Giuseppe Felice **Tosi** (act I), Pietro degli **Antoni** (act II), and Giacomo Antonio **Perti** (act III) in this "garra virtuosa." Sᴄʜᴀᴛᴢ 10381

Atis. Parody of Lully's Atys.

Attalo rē di Bitinia. Dramma per musica da rappresentarsi nel nobil Teatro di Torre Argentina il carnovale dell' anno 1790.

Roma, Gioacchino Puccinelli, n. d. *48 p.* *15½ᶜᵐ.*
Two acts. By Antonio Salvi (not mentioned). Publisher's dedication, argument, scenario, cast, and name of the composer, Luigi **Caruso.** Vittorio Trento is mentioned as the composer of the second ballet, which is not named by title. Sᴄʜᴀᴛᴢ 1661

Attalo rē di Bitinia. Dramma per musica da rappresentarsi nel Regal Teatro di S. Carlo a dì 20. gennajo 1752 . . .

Napoli, Domenico Lanciano, 1752. *48 p.* *14ᶜᵐ.*
Three acts. By Francesco Silvani (not mentioned), originally with the title "La verità nell' inganno." Impresario's dedication dated Naples, January 20, 1751 (=1752), argument, cast, and name of Giuseppe **Conti** as composer. Sᴄʜᴀᴛᴢ 2206

Attalo rē di Bitinia. Dramma per musica da rappresentarsi in Ferrara nel Teatro Bonacossi da S. Stefano il carnevale dell' anno 1739 . . .

Ferrara, Giuseppe Barbieri, n. d. *52 p.* *15ᶜᵐ.*
Three acts. Impresario's dedicatory sonnet, argument, cast and name of Johann Adolph **Hasse** as the composer. The text is Francesco Silvani's "La verità nell' inganno."
First performed at Naples, Teatro di San Bartolomeo, spring of 1728. Sᴄʜᴀᴛᴢ 4517

Attalo rè di Bitinia. Dramma per musica da rappresentarsi nel Real Teatro dell' Ajuda nel felicissimo giorno natalizio di Sua Maestà Fedelissima l'augusta Donna Maria I regina di Portogallo . . . li 17 decembre 1791.

[Lisboa], Stamperia reale, n. d. 60 p. 16½ᶜᵐ.

Two acts. By Antonio Salvi, who is not mentioned. Argument, cast, scenario, and name of Ferdinando **Robuschi** as the composer.
First performed at Padua, Teatro Nuovo, June, 1788. 　　　Schatz 8842

Attalo rè di Bitinia. Dramma per musica da rappresentarsi nel nobilissimo Teatro in S. Benedetto il carnovale dell' anno 1783.

Venezia, Modesto Fenzo, 1783. 56 p. 17ᶜᵐ.

Three acts. By Antonio Salvi, who is not mentioned. Argument, cast, scenario, and name of Giuseppe **Sarti** as composer. ("La musica è nuovamente composta") On p. [23]–31 argument, cast, name of Vincenzo Martini as composer of the music ("tutta nuova") and description of Domenico Ricciardi's "Cristiano II., rè di Danimarca, ballo eroico in quattr' atti."
First performed, as indicated, December 26, 1782. 　　　Schatz 9472

Attila, ballet. *See* Anfossi's Antigono, 1781.

Attila. Drama per musica, da rappresentarsi nel Teatro Grimano à SS. Gio. e Paolo. L'anno MDCLXXII. Di Matteo Noris . . .

Venetia, Francesco Nicolini, 1672. 6 p. l. (incl. front.), 67, [1] p. 13½ᶜᵐ.

Three acts. Author's dedication, dated Venice, February 12, 1672, argument, scenario, and notice to the reader in which Noris says:
"Spero, che sia per dilettarti, comparendoti nel Grimano Teatro, Reggia, della scenica maestà; ed' io non ribellandomi al genio, hò praticato nel comporlo gli soliti sforzi d'equivoco & forze di scena, usate da pochi. Hò scritto per obligo, Tu vieni, e compatisci per gentilezza."
The composer, Pietro Andrea **Ziani,** is not mentioned. 　　　Schatz 11213

Attilio Regolo.

Metastasio, Poesie, Parigi, vedova Quillau, 1755, t. vi, [77]–168 p. 16ᶜᵐ.

Three acts. Argument. 　　　ML 49.A2M42

— **Attilio Regolo.** Dramma scritto dall' autore in Vienna . . . per doversi produrre in occasione di festeggiare il prossimo giorno di nome dell' augustissimo . . . Carlo VI, il dì 4 novembre 1740. Ma, avendo egli cessato di vivere prima della preparata solennità, rimase occulto il dramma per lo spazio di anni dieci: dopo i quali mandato dall' autore a richiesta di Augusto III ré di Polonia, fu nella corte di Dresda . . . la prima volta rappresentato con musica dell' Hasse . . . nel carnevale dell' anno 1750.

pl., [3]–104 p. 26ᶜᵐ. (Metastasio, Opere, t. viii, Parigi, vedova Herissant, 1781.)

Three acts. Argument. 　　　ML 49.A2M44

— **Regulus . . .**

Metastasio, Tragedies-opera, Vienne, 1751, t. v, p. [105]–213. 14ᶜᵐ.

Three acts. Richelet's translation. Below the title the note:
"Cet opéra est le dernier qu'a composé l'abbé Metastasio. Il a été representé cette année (1750) à la Cour de Naples, & à celle de Dresde." 　　　ML 49.A2M47

Attilio Regolo. Dramma per musica rappresentato nel Teatro della Regia elettoral corte di Dresda nel carnovale dell' anno MDCCL. La poesia è del Sig. abbate Pietro Metastasio . . . la musica è del Sig. Gio. Adolfo Hasse . . .

Friedrichstadt, la vedova Harpeter, n. d. 4 p. l., 82 p. 19^{cm}.

Three acts. Argument, cast, scenario.
First performed, as indicated, January 12, 1750. SCHATZ 4518

— Attilio Regolo. Dramma per musica rappresentato nel Teatro della Regia elettoral corte di Dresda, nel carnovale dell' anno MDCCL . . .

Friedrichstadt, la vedova Harpeter, n. d. 5 p. l., (double) 82 p. 18½^{cm}.

Same as Schatz 4518, except that German title page "Attilius Regulus" and text have been added. SCHATZ 4519

Attilio Regolo. Drama per musica da rappresentarsi in Roma nel Teatro delle Dame nel corrente carnevale dell' anno MDCCLIII . . .

Roma, Marcello Silvestri, n. d. 69 p. 14½^{cm}.

Three acts. Impresario's dedication, argument, cast, scenario, and names of Metastasio as author ("in qualche piccola parte diversa dalla prima impressione") and of Niccolò **Jommelli** as the composer.
First performed, as indicated, January 8, 1753. Abert says, on p. 3 of his Jommelli biograghy, 1751, but on p. 54 he says 1752, both dates apparently incorrect.
SCHATZ 4844

Attilius Regulus. Tr. of Hasse's Attilio Regolo.

Atys, tragedie en musique. Ornée d'entrées de ballet, de machines, & de changements de theatre. Representée devant Sa Majesté à Saint Germain en Laye, le dixième jour de janvier 1676.

Paris, Christophe Ballard, 1676. 6 p. l., 70 p. 22^{cm}.

Prologue and five acts. Cast. Neither Quinault nor **Lully** mentioned.
First performed at Saint-Germain en Laye before the king, as indicated, at Paris August, 1676 (Schatz), April, 1677 (Prunières). ML 50.2.A9L8

— Atys. Tragedie en musique ornée d'entrées de ballet, de machines, & de changemens de theatre. Suivant la copie imprimée à Paris.

[Amsterdam, Antoine Schelte], 1687. 79 p. (incl. front.) 13½^{cm}.

Prologue and five acts. Cast. Neither Quinault nor **Lully** mentioned.
ML 50.2.A9L9

— Atys, tragedie representée par l'Academie royale de musique l'an 1676. Les paroles de M. Quinault, & la musique de M. de Lully, VIII. opera.

n. i., n. d. 14^{cm}. front., 371–444 p. (Recueil général des opéra, t. i, Paris, 1703.)

Detached copy. Five acts and prologue. SCHATZ 5761
Second copy. ML 48.R4

— Atys, tragedie représentée devant Sa Majesté, a Saint-Germain-en Laye, ès années 1676 & 1682 et depuis par L'Academie royale de musique, en 1679, en 1690, en 1699, en 1709, en 1725. Remise au théâtre le mardy 7. janvier 1738.

[Paris], Jean Baptiste Christophe Ballard, 1738. xii, 67, [1] p. 24^{cm}.

Prologue and five acts. Cast. Neither Quinault nor **Lully** mentioned.
ML 50.2.A9L93

Atys—Continued.

— **Atys,** tragedie en musique. Ornée d'entrées de ballet, de machines & de changemens de théatre. Représenté devant Sa Majesté à Saint Germain en Laye, le 10 février 1676.

Quinault, Théatre, Paris, 1739, t. iv, pl., p. [267]–335. 17ᶜᵐ.

Prologue and five acts. **Lully** is not mentioned.   PQ 1881.A1 1739

— **Atys,** tragedie representée devant Sa Majesté, a Saint-Germain-en-Laye, ès années 1676 & 1682. Et depuis par l'Academie royale de musique de Paris, en 1679, en 1690, en 1699, en 1709, en 1725, & en 1738. Et par l'Académie royale de musique de Lyon en décembre 1742.

Lyon, Aimé Delaroche, 1743. 79 p. 23ᶜᵐ.

Five acts. Cast. Neither the author, Quinault, is mentioned nor the composer, **Lully.** The text is practically the same as that of 1703, except that the last scene has been cut down to consist only of "Que cet arbre sacré," etc.   Schatz 5761a

— **Arlequin Atys,** représentée pour la premiere fois, par les Comédiens italiens ordinaires du roi, le 22. janvier, 1726.

Les parodies du Nouveau théâtre italien, Nouv. éd., Paris, 1738, t. iii, [163]-218 p.   16½ᶜᵐ.

One act. Parody of "Atys" by Pontau (*see* t. I). The airs and vaudeville used are printed at the end of the volume in the "Table des airs" (84 p.).   ML 48.P3

— **Atis,** parodie en un acte; précédée d'un prologue; représentée sur le Théâtre de l'Opéra-comique, en février 1726.

Alexis Piron, Oeuvres complettes, Liege, 1776, v. 5, [257]–319 p. 17½ᶜᵐ.

Prose and vaudevilles. Composer not recorded. Parody of Lully's opera, attributed by Parfaict to Fuzelier.
First performed, as indicated, Feb. 19, 1720.   PQ 2019.P6

— La **grand-mere amoureuse.** Parodie d'Atys. En trois actes. Par Mʳˢ F***. & D'Or***. Representée à la Foire de S. Germain 1726.

Le Théâtre de la foire, Paris, 1731, t. viii, pl., 1 p. l., 65 p.   17ᶜᵐ.

By Fuzelier and d'Orneval. Largely *en vaudevilles.* The airs, selected or composed and arranged by Jean Claude **Gillier,** the "compositeur" of the company, are printed at the end of the volume in the "Table des airs."
First performed, as indicated, March 18, 1726.   ML 48.L2 VIII

Atys, tragedie-lyrique, en trois actes, représentée, pour la premiere fois, par l'Académie-royale de musique, le mardi 22 février 1780.

[Paris], Aux depens de l'Académie de l'imprimerie de P. de Lormel, 1780. 60 p. 23ᶜᵐ.

Cast. Quinault is mentioned as the author, Niccolò **Piccinni** as the composer, but the text is really more or less by Marmontel.   Schatz 8067

— **Atys,** tragedie-lyrique en trois actes, représentée, pour la premiere fois, par l'Académie royale de musique, le mardi 22 février 1780. Et remise au Théâtre, le mardi 14 janvier 1783.

Paris, P. de Lormel, 1783. 60 p. 23ᶜᵐ.

Cast and name of Quinault as author, of **Piccinni** as composer.   Schatz 11743

Aucassin et Nicolette, ou Les moeurs du bon vieux tems, comédie remise en trois actes et en vers, dont une partie est en musique; représentée, pour la premiere fois, devant Leurs Majestés à Versailles, le 30 décembre 1779, par les Comédiens italiens ordinaires du roi, & à Paris, le 3 janv. 1780, & reprise le 7 janv. 1782. Le drame est de M. Sedaine. La musique de M. Grétry.

Paris, Brunet, 1782. 63, [1] p. 19^{cm}.

Cast.　　　　　　　　　　　　　　　　　　　　　　ML 50.2.A92G7

— **Aucassin et Nicolette,** ou Les moeurs du bon vieux temps, comédie en trois actes, en vers, dont une partie est en musique: Représentée pour la première fois par les Comédiens italiens ordinaires du roi, le 7 janvier 1782. Le drame est de M. Sédaine. La musique de M. Grétry.

Paris, Brunet, 1784. 48 p. 18$\frac{1}{2}$^{cm}.

Cast. On p. 39–42, the air of the "*Ariette.* Que de pièces d'or."
The date of performance on the title page refers only to the three-act version. The original four-act version was first performed at Versailles December 30, 1779, and at Paris, Comédie italienne, January 3, 1780.　　　　　　SCHATZ 4139

— Gesaenge aus dem singspiele: **Ferdinand und Nicolette,** oder Liebe erhaelt den sieg, in drey aufzuegen. Aus dem franzoesischen uebersetzt von André. In musik gesetzt von Grétry.

Hamburg, J. M. Michaelsen, 1787. 24 p. 16$\frac{1}{2}$^{cm}.

First performed at Hamburg, Theater am Gaensemarkt, April 17, 1787.

SCHATZ 4140

L'audacia fortunata. Commedia per musica da rappresentarsi nel Real Teatro del Fondo di Separazione per terza commedia del corrente anno 1793.

Napoli, n. publ., 1793. 48 p. 15^{cm}.

Two acts. Author not mentioned and unknown to Schatz. Cast and name of the composer, Valentino **Fioravanti.**　　　　　　　　SCHATZ 3117

— **L'audacia fortunata**: Dramma giocoso per musica per celebrare l'augusto nome di Sua Altezza Reale la serenissima Signora D. Carlotta Gioacchina . . . per eseguirsi nel Regio Teatro di S. Carlo, l'autunno dell'anno 1796.

Lisbona, Simone Taddeo Ferreira, 1796. 173 p. 14$\frac{1}{2}$^{cm}.

Two acts. Cast and name of the composer **Fioravanti,** but not of the author. Portuguese text faces Italian.　　　　　　　　　　SCHATZ 3173

Les audiences de Thalie. Piece en un acte. Representée sur le Théatre de l'Opéra comique à la Foire S. Germain, le 7 avril 1734.

Le Théâtre de la foire, Paris, 1737, t. ix, 2 pl., [385]-427 p. 17^{cm}.

By Carlolet, who has this to say in a prefatory note:
"Ce petit acte est moins une piece qu'une description fidelle de l'état où se trouvoit alors le Théatre de l'Opera comique. L'entrepreneur conseillé par des associés, ausquels la tête ne tournoit pas moins qu' à lui, se livroit, comme eux, à l'ignorance & à la prévention. Les bons acteurs murmuroient hautement de se voir forcés de representer sans cesse de mauvaises pieces, & de contribuer avec des acteurs aussi pitoyables que neufs, à écarter le public d'un spectacle qui sçut toujours sous d'autres chefs & sous d'autres auteurs, charmer son attente & ses plus chers loisirs."
Largely *en vaudevilles.* The airs, a few of which with name of **Corrette** as composer, are printed at the end of the volume in the "Table des airs." ML 48. L2X

Auf dem land kennt man die rache nicht. A. T. of Kauer's Der unschuldige betrug.

Das **aufgeboth.** A. T. of Wenzel Müller's Die getreuen Oesterreicher.

Augusta's triumph. A. T. of Daniel Purcell's Brutus of Alba.

Les **Augustales,** divertissement, représentée par l'Academie royale de musique le [*blank*] novembre 1744.

> *Paris, Jean Baptiste Christophe Ballard, 1744. 15 p. 24cm.*

> One act. Cast and name of Pierre Charles Roy as author, of François **Rebel** and François **Francoeur** as the composers.
> First performed on November 15, 1744, as indicated.   SCHATZ 8621

Auguste et Théodore, ou Les deux pages. Comédie en deux actes, en prose et mêlée de chant. Par MM. Dezède & B. D. M. Représentée, pour la première fois, à Paris par les Comédiens français ordinaires du roi, le 6 mars 1789, & à Versailles, devant Leurs Majestés, le 12 du même mois.

> *Paris, Brunet, 1790. vi, 7–48 p. 19cm.*

> Incomplete copy.
> Dezède's collaborator was Ernest, baron de Mantauffeld. With cast and "Costumes" (p. iii–vi).   SCHATZ 2525

Auld Robin Gray: a pastoral entertainment, in two acts. As performed at the Theatre-Royal, Hay-Market. Written by S. Arnold, jun. The music by Dr. Arnold.

> *London, Geo. Goulding, 1794. 55 p. 21½cm.*

> Cast and prefatory note. The vocal score published by Preston & Son says: "The music (with a Scotish overture) selected & composed." The ballad airs utilized by Arnold are indicated in the vocal score. "The shipwreck" is there headed as by "Dr. **Haydn.**"
> First performed July 29, 1794.   LONGE 239

L'Aureliano. Drama per musica di Giacomo dall' Angelo da rappresentarsi nel Teatro di S. Moisè l'anno 1666 . . .

> *Venetia, Francesco Nicolini, 1666. 7 p. l. (incl. front.), 72 p. 14½cm.*

> Prologue and three acts. Author's dedication dated Venice, February 25, 1666, argument, "fintioni," and scenario. The composer, Carlo **Pallavicino,** is not mentioned.   SCHATZ 7719

Aurelio and Miranda: a drama. In five acts. With music. First acted at the Theatre Royal, Drury-Lane, on Saturday, December 29, 1798. Written by James Boaden. Third edition . . .

> *London, J. Bell, 1799. 2 p. l., 67 p. 21½cm.*

> Cast. The composer is not mentioned.   LONGE 266

Auretta e Masullo ossia Il contratempo. Dramma giocoso per musica da rappresentarsi nel Teatro da S. Agostino la primavera del 1792 . . .

> *Genova, Stamperia Gesiniana, n. d. 60 p. 14cm.*

> Two acts. Impresario's dedication speaking of the composer as "un talente nascente," cast, scenario, and name of Francesco **Gnecco** ("La musica sarà tutta nuova"). Schatz also attributes the text to him.   SCHATZ 3958

Aurora. A. T. of Keiser's Der morgen des europaeischen glueckes.

L'Aurora in Atene. Drama per musica nel Teatro Grimani di S. S. Gio. e Paolo. L'anno 1678. Del dottor Frisari . . .

Venetia, Francesco Nicolini, 1678. 56 p. 14ᶜᵐ.

Three acts. Author's dedication, dated Venice, February 10, 1678, argument, scenario, and notice to the reader who is informed that Antonio **Zannettini** composed the music and that the text is based on conte Berni's "Il ratto di Cefalo." This copy does not contain the frontispiece and woodcut in the Brussels copy. (*See* Wotquenne.)   SCHATZ 11146

L'Aurora ingannata.

Prologue and four intermedii. Forms part (p. 6–10, 38–41, 77–79, 97–99, 147–150) of "FILARMINDO. Favola pastorale del Sig. Co. Ridolfo Campeggi. In questa quinta impressione arricchita con *L'Aurora ingannata.* Favoletta per gl'intermedij in musica . . . In Venetia, MDCXXVIII. Apresso Gio. Battista Cioti." (178 p. 13½ᶜᵐ.)

Date slightly mutilated. Allacci, without mentioning a composer, says: "In alcune delle suddette edizioni si vede l'*Aurora ingannata* dello stesso autore . . . udita in musica la prima volta nell' anno 1615." Schatz says under "Filarmindo" (not under "Aurora ingannata," which he does not seem to know): "Musik von Girolamo **Giacobbi**. Bologna, Sala Zoppia, 1605," but "Filarmondo" was merely a *favola pastorale* with no music, except perhaps by the *choro*. Corradi says that the intermezzi of "L'Aurora ingannata" were added in 1615.   PQ

L'Aurora vendicata, ballet. *See* P. Guglielmi's La pastorella nobile.

L'Aurore et Céphale, fourth entrée in Quinault's Les amours des Déesses.

Einem hoch-edlen und hochweisen Rath der Stadt Hamburg, wurde mit gehorsamsten respect und schuldigster danckbarkeit wegen erzeigter gnade in einer action Der eiserne Koenig, nebst vorhergehender musicalischen serenata. Betitult: **Die aus Bellonens reich vertriebene und an dem Elbe-strande frohlockende vergnuegung.** Dedicirt und unterthaenig vorgestellet von denen anwesenden Koenigl. pohlnischen und churfuerstl. saechsischen privilegierten hof-comoedianten.

Hamburg, Philip Ludwig Stromer, 1719. Unpaged. 19ᶜᵐ.

One act. Dedication, avertissement, and at end "Summarischer innhalt der action an sich selbst," note that this "haupt-action" would be followed by "eine lustige nachcomoedie" and note: "Der schau-platz ist in der Neustadt in der Fuhlen Twiet ueber dem Bremer-Schluessel." Author and composer not mentioned and unknown to Schatz.   SCHATZ 11448

Die aus der einsamkeit in die welt zurueckgekehrte opera, ward bey neuer eroeffnung des Hamburgischen Schau-Platzes in einem vor-spiele aufgefuehret im monath octobris, anno 1729.

[Hamburg], Gedruckt mit Stromerschen schrifften, n. d. Unpaged. 18ᶜᵐ.

Cast. Neither the author, Christ. Gottl. Wendt, is mentioned, nor the composer, Georg Philipp **Telemann.**

First performed as indicated, October 10, 1729.   SCHATZ 10269

Die aus-schweifenden. Tr. of Piccinni's La schiava riconosciuta·

L'auteur dans son ménage, comédie en un acte, en prose; mêlée d'ariettes. Paroles du C. Gosse; musique du C. Bruni: Représentée pour la première fois sur le théâtre Feydeau, le 8 germinal an sept [March 28, 1799] de la République:

Paris, Huet [etc.], an vii. 44 p. 21ᶜᵐ.   ML 50.2.A93B8

Arien und gesänge der operette: Der **authomat**.   In einem aufzuge.
Nach dem französischen des Cuinet Dorbeil.   Die musik ist vom
herrn Joh. André.

Hamburg, J. M. Michaelsen, 1783.   16 p.   16ᶜᵐ.

Text by the composer.
First performed at Hamburg, Theater beim Gänsemarkt, 1783.   SCHATZ 180

— Arien und gesänge der operette: Das **automat**.   In einem aufzuge.   Nach dem franzoesischen des Cuinet Dorbeil.   Die musik ist
vom herrn Joh. André.

Lübeck, Gedruckt mit Greenischen schriften, 1784.   16 p.   16ᶜᵐ.

First performed at Lübeck, Theater in der Bäckergrube, 1784.   SCHATZ 181

The **author's farce**; and the pleasures of the town.   As acted at the
Theatre in the Hay-Market.   Written by Scriblerus Secundus.   The
second edition.

London, J. Watts, 1730.   4 p. l., 59, [4] p.   19ᶜᵐ.

Prologue, three acts, and epilogue.   Cast.   The first and second acts contain only
one song each, but the third act, a puppet-show in form of a ballad opera, contains
twenty-five, the airs of which are indicated.   The text is by Henry Fielding.
First performed at the "little" Haymarket Theatre, March 1730.   ML 50.5.A82

Das **automat**.   L. T. of André's Der authomat.

Gli **avantaggi della concordia**.   *See* M. Curzio.

Gli **avari in trappola**.   Dramma giocoso per musica da rappresentarsi nel Teatro di S. A. E. di Sassonia, composto da **Caterino Mazzolà** . . .

Dresda, n. publ., 1787.   135 p.   15½ᶜᵐ.

Two acts.   Joseph **Schuster** is mentioned as the composer.   German title "Die
geizigen in der falle" and text face Italian.
First performed, as indicated, January, 1787.   SCHATZ 9743

L'**avaro**.   Dramma giocoso per musica da rappresentarsi nel Teatro
di via S. Maria nel carnevale dell' anno 1777 . . .

Firenze, nella Stamperia in borgo de' Greci, n. d.   56 p.   16½ᶜᵐ.

Three acts.   By Giovanni Bertati.   Cast and name of Pasquale **Anfossi** as composer, but not of librettist.
First performed at Venice, Teatro di S. Moisè, fall of 1775.   SCHATZ 228

— L'**avaro**, dramma giocoso per musica; da rappresentarsi nel Regio
Teatro.   Den Giaerrige, et lystigt synge-spil; til at opfores paa den
kongelige skueplads.   Oversadt paa dansk af R. Soelberg.

Kiobenhavn, H. J. Graae, 1776.   109 p.   16½ᶜᵐ.

Three acts.   Bertati is not mentioned.   Cast and name of **Anfossi** as composer.
Italian and Danish text on opposite pages.
First performed at Copenhagen, as indicated, January 31, 1777.   SCHATZ 229

— L'**avaro**.   Dramma giocoso per musica da rappresentarsi nel
piccolo Teatro elettorale in Dresda, 1780.—Der Geizige.   Ein scherzhaftes singspiel . . .

n. i., n. d.   147 p.   16ᶜᵐ.

Three acts.   Italian and German text on opposite pages.   **Anfossi** mentioned as
composer.   SCHATZ 230

L'avaro. Dramma giocoso per musica da rappresentarsi in Ferrara nel Teatro Bonacossi il carnovale dell' anno 1776 . . .

Ferrara, Bernadino Pomatelli, n. d. 60 p. 14½cm.

Three acts. By Giovanni Bertati. Cast, scenario, and name of Gennaro **Astaritta** ("musica tutta nuova") as composer, but not of librettist. Schatz 381

L'avaro, ballet. *See* Curcio's Emira e Zopiro.

L'avaro. Intermezzi per musica da rappresentarsi nel Teatro di S. Angelo l'autunno dell' anno 1720.

Venezia, Marin Rossetti, 1720. 20 p. 14½cm.

Three intermezzi. Neither the author, Antonio Salvi, nor the composer, Carlo Francesco **Gasparini**, is mentioned.

First performed at Florence in the same year; at Venice, between the acts of Vivaldi's "La verità in cimento." Schatz 3594

L'avaro burlato. Operetta comica, da rappresentarsi sul Regio Teatro Danese, l'autunno dell' anno 1762—Den beskaemmede guier . . .

Kiøbenhavn, Lars Nielsen Svare, n. d. 103 p. 16cm.

Three acts. Schatz enters the text under Bartolomeo Vitturi's "Chi tutta abbraccia nulla stringe," music by Scolari, but, as a matter of fact, from the third scene of the first act on the texts become so different as to have very little in common.

Cast and note: "La musica è la più parte del signor **Scolari**." Schatz 9792

L'avaro burlato, ballet. *See* Zingarelli's Carolina e Mexicow.

L'avaro deluso. L. T. of Paisiello's La discordia fortunata.

L'avaro deluso, a new comic opera; as performed at the King's Theatre in the Haymarket. The poetry by Signor Bertati, with alterations and additions by Signor Antonio Andrei; the music entirely new by Signor Antonio Sacchini; the translation by Mrs. Rigaud.

London, G. Bigg, 1778. 87 p. 19cm.

Three acts. Cast. Bertati's text originally had the title, "Calandrano."

First performed 1778, as indicated. Schatz 9209

— Il Don Calandrano. Dramma giocoso per musica da rappresentarsi in Firenze nell' autunno dell' anno 1781. Nel Regio Teatro degl' Intrepidi detto della Palla a Corda . . .

Firenze, Anton Giuseppe Pagani e comp., 1781. 44 p. 16cm.

Two acts. By Giovanni Bertati, with alterations by Antonio Andrei, neither of whom is mentioned. Antonio **Sacchini**'s name is given as that of the composer.

Schatz 9245

L'aveugle de Palmyre, comédie-pastorale, en deux actes, en vers, mêlée d'ariettes. Représentée pour la premiere fois par les Comédiens italiens ordinaires du roi, le jeudi 5 mars 1767. Par M. Desfontaines. La musique de M. Rodolphe . . .

Paris, la veuve Duchesne, 1767. 1 p. l., 54 p. 21cm.

Cast. On p. 50–51, the air of the vaudeville, "La lumière la plus pure." On p. 53–54, the air of "L'espoir qui t'enflamme" (I, 3). The text is the same as in the other 1767 edition. Schatz 11752

L'aveugle de Palmyre—Continued.

— L'aveugle de **Palmyre,** comedie-pastorale, en deux actes, en vers, mêlée d'ariettes. Réprésentée pour la premiere fois par les Comediens italiens ordinaires du roi, le jeudi 5 mars 1767. Par M. Desfontaines. La musique de M. Rodolphe . . .

Paris, la veuve Duchesne, 1767. 39 p. 19^{cm}.

Cast.   SCHATZ 8851

— L'aveugle de **Palmyre,** comédie pastorale en deux actes et en vers; mêlée d'ariettes. Par Monsieur Desfontaines. Nouvelle édition.

Paris, N. B. Duchesne, 1776. 32 p. 19$\frac{1}{2}$^{cm}.

Rodolphe is not mentioned.   ML 48M2M

Les **aveux indiscrets,** opera comique mêlé d'arietes; par M. de la Ribardiere; représenté pour la premiere fois à la Foire Saint-Germain, le mercredi 7 février 1759.

Paris, Michel Lambert, 1759. 36, 4 p. 19^{cm}.

The 4 p. at end contain six "Airs des Aveux indiscrets," unaccompanied. An Avertissement on p. [3] reads:
"Cet ouvrage a été fait en vers, & mis en musique il y a quatre ans; on a été obligé, pour le donner au public, de substituer de la prose à la place du récitatif. L'auteur de la musique a cru devoir le faire graver en grande partition, & laisser subsister les récitatifs tels qu'ils avoient été faits. Il paroîtra vers le 25 de ce mois . . ."
The composer, **Monsigny,** is not mentioned.   ML 50.2.A95M7

Aviso aos casados. Tr. of Isouard's L'avviso ai maritati.

Gl'avvanzi fortunati del mondo naufragente. *See* M. Curzio.

Gli avvenimenti d'Erminia e di Clorinda sopra il Tasso. Drama per musica da rappresentarsi nel famosissimo Teatro Grimano di Sr. Giovanni e Paulo l'anno MDCXCIII. Di Giulio Cesare Corradi . . .

Venetia, Nicolini, 1693. 67 p. 14$\frac{1}{2}$^{cm}.

Three acts. Author's dedication, scenario, and notice to the reader which reads in part:
"T'invito solo ad udire la musica del Sig. Carlo Francesco Polarolo [**Pollaroli**], che per essere l'ultima faticha delle cinque opere, vestite quest' anno, nel giro di tre mesi, delle sue spiritosissime, & impareggiabili note, ti farà certamente stupire . . ."
                                                         SCHATZ 8275

Gl' avvenimenti d'Orinda. Drama per musica per il Teatro Grimani a SS. Gio. e Paolo, rappresentato l'anno 1659 di Pietr' Angelo Zaguri . . .

Venetia, Giacomo Batti, 1659. front., 6 p. l., 64 p. 14$\frac{1}{2}$^{cm}.

Three acts. Impresario's dedication, dated Jan. 3, 1659, notice to the reader, argument, but without name of the composer, Daniele **Castrovillari.** SCHATZ 1690

Le avventure d'Ircana, ballet. *See* Salieri's La fiera di Venezia.

Le avventure del carnovale, ballet. *See* Rispoli's Idalide.

Le avventure di Cleomede. Dramma serio-comico per musica da rappresentarsi nel Real Teatro dell'Ajuda nel felicissimo giorno natalizio del fedelissimo monarca D. Giuseppe I . . . nel di 6. giugno 1772.

Lisbona, Stamperia reale, n. d. 100 p. 15^{cm}.

Three acts. Argument, cast, scenario, and names of Gaetano Martinelli as author, of Niccolò **Jommelli** as composer ("nuova composizione"). This work seems to have escaped Abert.   SCHATZ 4889

Le avventure di Milord Wilver e di Miledi sua sposa, ballet. *See* Giordani's Ines de Castro.

Le avventure galanti. L. T. of Tritto's Le vicende amorose.

Gli avventurieri. Dramma giocoso per musica, da rappresentarsi nel Teatro elettorale, di Caterino Mazzolà, poeta dell' elettore di Sassonia.

*Dresda, n. publ., 1791. 141 p. 15½*cm.

Two acts. German title page "Die abenteurer" and text face Italian. **Paisiello** is mentioned as the composer.

Schatz enters this opera as a replica of Paisiello's "Il re Teodoro" with a new text by Mazzolà. It is a fact that both operas have a few arias in common, as for instance, "Figlia, il cielo ti destina" (I, 7 resp. I, 11); "Dov' e Dorina" (I, 19) resp. "Ov' è Lisetta" (I, 14), and "Voi semplici amanti" (II, 5), but most of the arias are not identical and the characters and the dialogue are absolutely different.

SCHATZ 7654

L'avviso ai maritati. Dramma giocoso per musica, da rappresentarsi nel Teatro elettorale.

*Dresda, n. publ., 1795. 119 p. 15½*cm.

Three acts. Niccolò **Isouard** is mentioned as composer. German title page "Die schule der ehemaenner" and text face Italian, which is by Francesco Gonella, who is not mentioned.

First performed at Florence, Teatro di via della Pergola, spring of 1794.

SCHATZ 4908

— Aviso aos casados. Drama jocoso em musica em hum só acto para se representar no Real Theatro de S. Carlos, offerecido ao respectavel publico de Lisboa por Domingos Caporalini no dia do seu beneficio.

*Lisboa, Simão Thaddeo Ferreira, 1796. 93 p. 16½*cm.

Notice to the reader and name of Niccolo **Isouard** as composer. Italian text faces Portuguese.

SCHATZ 4944
Second copy. ML 48.C6 II

Avviso ai maritati. Dramma giocoso per musica da rappresentarsi nel Teatro in S. Samuele il carnavale 1798.

*Venezia, Stamperia Valvasense, n. d. 70 p. 18*cm.

Two acts. Francesco Gonella, the author, is not mentioned. Cast and name of Joh. Simon **Mayr** as the composer. On p. [35]–44 argument, cast, and description of Antonio Berti's five act "La fata Alcinoe ossia Amore ed innocenza." The composer of the music is not mentioned. SCHATZ 6188

Axur, koenig von Ormus. Tr. of Salieri's Axur, rè d'Ormus.

Axur, rè d'Ormus. Italian version of Salieri's Tarare.

Azakia. Ein singspiel in drei aufzeugen von C. F. Schwan. Die musik ist von hrn. direktor Cannabich.

*Mannheim, C. F. Schwan, 1778. 56 p. 17*cm.

First performed at Mannheim, Churfürstl. deutsche Schaubühne, 1778.

SCHATZ 1573

Azémia, ou Les sauvages, comédie, en trois actes, en prose, mêlée d'ariettes. Représentée à Fontainebleau, devant Leurs Majestés, le 17 octobre 1786, & à Paris, le 3 mai 1787.

*Paris, Brunet, 1787. 1 p. l., viii, 72 p. 20*cm.

Azémia—Continued.

Cast. The viii p. contain an "Epitre dedicatoire à Monsieur **Dalayrac**" as composer, by the author, de la Chabeaussière (not mentioned by name), and his Avertissement, which is directed against the criticism of his work in the Mercure by le Vacher de Charnois.   He says:
"C'étoit après de mûres & profondes réflexions sur l'art dramatique, & ses différentes branches, que je regardois comme permis & peut-être nécessaire, d'étendre les ressources du genre borné de l'opéra-comique, en admettant, de préférence, les situations romanesques, lors-qu'elles pouvoient se concilier avec la vraisemblance . . ."
ML 50.2.A98D2

— **Azémia,** ou Les sauvages, comédie en trois actes, en prose, mêlée d'ariettes; représentée à Fontainebleau, devant Leurs Majestés, le 17 octobre 1786, & à Paris, le 3 mai 1787. Les paroles sont de M. de la Chabeaussière, la musique de M. le chevalier d'Alayrac.

Toulouse, J. B. Broulhiet, 1787. 43 p. 22^{cm}.
Cast.   Without the dedication and Avertissement.   ML 50.2.A98D22

— **Azémia,** ou Les sauvages, comédie en trois actes, en prose, mêlée d'ariettes; représentée à Fontainebleau . . . le 17 octobre 1786, & à Paris, le 3 mai 1787. Les paroles sont de M. de la Chabeaussiere, la musique de M. le chevalier d'Alayrac.
Paris, Brunet, 1788. 48 p. 20^{cm}.   ML 48.M2L

— Die **Wilden.**   Singspiel in drei akten, nach dem französischen von Dr. Schmieder.   Die musik ist von d'Alayrac.   Zuerst aufgefuehrt auf dem Mainzer Nationaltheater.

Frankfurt am Main, bei Johann Gottlob Pech, 1791. 96, [1] p. 14½^{cm}.
Dedication, cast, and prefatory note:
"Schon durch die oefteren vorstellungen im manuscript, ist dies singspiel in Deutschland bekannt.   Fuer den druck hab'ich noch bei einigen stellen naiver unschuldiger liebe im dialog Shakespears Sturm benutzt, bei den gesaengen ist die fessel der musik zu beschraenkend . . ."
First performed, as indicated, May 26, 1789.   SCHATZ 2371

Azor, rè di Kibinga. Dramma giocoso per musica di Giovanni Bertati da rappresentarsi nel Teatro Giustiniani in S. Moisè l'autunno dell' anno 1779.

Venezia, n. publ., n. d. 62, [2] p. 18½^{cm}.
Two acts. Cast and name of Pasquale **Anfossi** as composer. On p. 31–34 "programma del ballo primo," without title of the ballet, invented by Antonio Marliani.   The second ballet was entitled, "Il tutore in gannato."   SCHATZ 265

L'Azzardo. Commedia per musica da rappresentarsi nel Real Teatro del Fondo di Separazione per terz' opera di questo corrente anno 1790.

Napoli, Vincenzo Flauto, n. d. 54 p. 15^{cm}.
Three acts.   Argument, cast, and name of Pietro **Guglielmi** as the composer. Author not mentioned and unknown to Schatz. On p. 7–9, cast and synopsis of Giovanni Battista Giannini's "Magia contro magia, ballo eroico favoloso," music ("tutta nuova") by Pietro Dutillieu.
First performed, as indicated, October 9, 1790.   SCHATZ 4236

I baccanali, ballet.   *See* Bianchi's Il disertore.

Les bacchanales.   Entrée in Colin de Blamont's Les festes grecques et romaines.

I bacchanali, ballet. *See* Farinelli's Seldano.

Bacchus. Intermède in Bourgeois' Les plaisirs de la paix.

Bacchus et Ariane. *See* Les amours des dieux.

Bacchus et Ariane, ballet héroique par M. Gallet; musique de M. Rochefort, second maitre de musique de l'Orchestre, représenté pour la première fois sur le Théâtre de l'Académie royale de musique, le dimanche 11 décembre 1791.

Paris, L'imprimérie civique, n. d. 24 p. 19½ cm.

One act. Detailed argument, cast, and prefatory note, in which Gallet says:
"L'administration de l'Opéra, jalouse sans doute de ménager la santé d'un sujet qui lui est aussi recommandable à titre de premier danseur, que comme compositeur, étoit occupée du soin de se procurer une personne pour partager la fatigue des ballets avec celles qui en sont chargées. Ramené à cette époque dans le sein de ma patrie, je me suis offert.

"Chargé, depuis que j'ai quitté l'Opéra, de cet emploi dans les premiers théâtres de l'Europe, je n'ai cessé de m'occuper d'un art qui s'est ouvert la plus vaste carrière, en remontant à son origine, et joignant la pantomime à la danse . . ."

He continues by saying that he was obliged to select a simple subject, like "Bacchus & Ariane," because the repertoire of new works did not permit the selection of one of his "grands ballets." ML 52.2.B1R6

Second copy. ML 48.B2

Bacchus et Érigone. *See* Mondonville's Les festes de Paphos.

Bacco ed Arianna, ballet. *See* Insanguine's Motezuma.

Bacco ed Arianna. Festa teatrale per musica da rappresentarsi nel Regio teatro di Torino nella primavera del 1784 . . .

Torino, Onorato Derossi, n. d. viii, 48 p. 20 cm.

Two acts. Argument, cast, scenario, and names of Cesare Oliveri as the author and Angelo **Tarchi** as the composer. On p. [41]–47 argument, cast, and description of Sebastiano Gallet's ballet, music by Vittorio Amedeo Canavasso, "Annibale in Torino, ballo eroico pantomimo." Schatz 10226

Bacco e Arianna, ballet. *See* Sarti's I due litiganti.

Die baeurinn bey hofe. Tr. of Sacchini's La contadina in corte.

I bagni d'Abano.

[161]–216 p. 16½ cm. (*Carlo Goldoni, Opere drammatiche giocose, t. iii, Torino, 1757.*)

Three acts. ML 49.A2G6

— **I bagni d'Abano.** Dramma di tre atti per musica.

Carlo Goldoni, Opere teatrali, Venezia, Zatta e figli, 1788–95, v. 44, [339]–394 p. 18½ cm. PQ

I bagni d'Abano. Dramma giocoso per musica da rappresentarsi nel Teatro Nuovo di S. Samuele il carnovale dell' anno 1753 . . .

Venezia, Modesto Fenzo, 1753. 56 p. 17 cm.

Three acts. By Goldoni. Neither he nor the composers, Baldassare **Galuppi** and Ferdinando Giuseppe **Bertoni,** are mentioned. Impresario's dedication, dated Venice, February 10, 1753, cast, and scenario. Schatz, Wotquenne, and Piovano attribute the music to the above, whereas Wiel merely says under no. 556: "Musica: Baldassare Galuppi?" Schatz 3519

I bagni d'Abano o sia La forza delle prime impressioni. Commedia del Sig. Antonio S. Sografi . . . posta in musica dal Signor maestro Antonio Capuzzi per il nobilissimo Teatro Venier in San Benedetto il carnovale dell' anno 1794.

Venezia, Casali, 1793.　87 p.　18ᶜᵐ.

Two acts.　Author's dedication, dated December 26, 1793, and scenario.

SCHATZ 1597

Baiazet. Dramma per musica da rappresentarsi nel famosissimo Teatro Grimani di Sⁿ. Giõ. Grisostomo l'autuno 1742 . . .

n. i., n. d.　1 p. l., 54 p.　15½ᶜᵐ.

Three acts.　Argument, cast, scenario, and name of Andrea **Bernasconi** as composer but not of author of libretto, conte Agostino Piovene.　Originally it was called "Tamerlano."

First performed as Baiazet at Venice, as indicated.　　SCHATZ 868

Baiocco et Serpilla.　L. T. and parody of Il marito giogatore.

Le baiser donné et rendu, comédie en un acte et en prose, mêlée d'ariettes.　Représentée à Paris, sur le Théâtre des Amis de la patrie, le 27 pluviôse, l'an 4ᵉ [Feb. 16, 1796].　Par J. H. Guy.　Musique du citoyen Gresnich.

Paris, Barba, 1796, l'an IVᵉ. ix, 2–31, [1] p.　21ᶜᵐ.

The ix p. contain list of errata, preface, in which Guy takes issue with his critics, and a "Programme du role de Nicolas."　ML 50.2.B2G7

Il Bajazet.　L. T. of Gasparini's Tamerlano.

Bajazet. Dramma per musica da rappresentarsi nel Regio Teatro di Torino nel carnovale del 1754 . . .

Torino, Zappata ed Avondo, n. d.　4 p. l., 51 p., [1] l.　16½ᶜᵐ.

Three acts.　The same as "Tamerlano" by conte Agostino Piovene, who is not mentioned.　Argument, cast, scenario, and names of Niccolò **Jommelli** as the composer of the opera, of Rocco Gioanetti of the three ballets "Le feste di Flora," etc. On the additional leaf the aria "Va dal crudel tiranna," which replaced "Digli, che peni, e frema" in I, 6.

First performed, as indicated, December 26, 1753.　　SCHATZ 4878

Bajazet. Dramma per musica da rappresentarsi in Verona nel Nuovo Teatro dell' Accademia Filarmonica il carnovale dell' anno 1765 . . .

Verona, Dionisio Ramanzini, n. d.　45 p.　17ᶜᵐ.

Three acts.　Text is the "Tamerlano," by conte Agostino Piovene, who is not mentioned.　Impresario's dedicatory poem, argument, cast, scenario, and name of Giuseppe **Scarlatti** as the composer.　("La musica sarà.")　　SCHATZ 9558

Il Bajazette. Dramma per musica da rappresentarsi nel Regioducal Teatro di Parma la primavera del MDCCLXV.

Parma, Monti, n. d.　56 p.　20ᶜᵐ.

Three acts.　Dedicatory poem by the author conte Jacopo Antonio San-Vitale, argument, scenario, cast, and name of the composer, Ferdinando Giuseppe **Bertoni.** With the opera were performed the ballets "Telemaco nell' isola di Calipso" and "I Tartari generosi," described on p. 26–27, 44 without name of the composer of the music.　　SCHATZ 936

Le Bal.　Entrée in Campra's Les festes venitiennes.

Le **bal bourgeois,** opera-comique, en un acte, meslé d'ariettes, par M. Favart: représenté pour la premiere fois sur le Théâtre de l'Opéra-comique de la Foire St. Laurent, le 13 mars 1738. Imprimé en 1762.
Paris, Duchesne, 1762. 76, [4] p. 19ᶜᵐ. (Theatre de M. Favart, Paris, Duchesne, 1763–77, t. viii.)
One act. Cast. Prose, vaudevilles and ariettes. Some of the airs printed in the text. According to Favart's Correspondence, he composed several of them. His musical collaborator is not mentioned by Font.
First performed as indicated, end of August, 1761, for the opening of the Foire St. Laurent. ML 49.A2F1

Le **bal champetre.** Entrée in Duplessis' Les festes nouvelles.

Le **bal de Strasbourg,** divertissement allemand, au sujet de la convalescence du roy. Opera comique ballet. Par Mrs. F . . . D. L. G . . . & L. S . . .
Paris, Prault fils, 1744. 32, 4, 4, 4 p. 18ᶜᵐ.
The one-act opera is *toute en vaudevilles,* i. e., the dialogue is sung to popular airs. The 12 p. following the text contain the "Airs du Bal de Strasbourg": "Reviens amour," "Je vous aimois," "Je me mets à peine," "Notre bonheur nous fait," and separately the "Pʳ vaudeville": "Tout ici partage" and "IIᵉ vaudeville": "Notre bonheur nous fait." The authors of this piece were, as indicated, Charles Simon Favart, de La Garde, and Lesueur. Their musical collaborator is not mentioned by Font.
First performed at Paris, Foire Saint-Laurent, September 13, 1744. ML 48.P2

— Le **bal de Strasbourg,** divertissement allemand, au sujet de la convalescence du roi, opera comique ballet. Par Mrs. F . . . D. L. G . . . & L. S . . .
Paris, Prault fils, 1744. 32, 4 p. 19ᶜᵐ. (Theatre de M. Favart, Paris, Duchesne, 1763–77, t. vii.)
Exactly like the original edition, except that the two vaudevilles are not at end.
ML 49.A2F1

Le **bal interrompu.** *See* Campra's Trois nouvelles entrées.

Le **bal interrompu.** Entrée in Fragments de Monsieur Lully.

Le **bal masqué,** opéra-comique en un acte et en prose. Mêlé d'ariettes; mises en musique par M. d'Arcis, âgé de 12. ans, eleve de M. Gretry. Nouvelle édition.
Paris, Didot l'aîné, 1773. 24 p. 19ᶜᵐ.
Author unknown to me.
First performed at Paris, Comédie italienne, April 1, 1772. ML 50.2.B21G7

Baldassarre punito. Dramma sacro per musica da rappresentarsi nel Regio Teatro di via della Pergola la quadragesima del 1796 . . .
Firenze, Stamperia Albizziniana, 1796. 39 p. 16½ᶜᵐ.
Two parts. Cast and name of Gaetano **Marinelli** as composer. Author unknown to Schatz.
First performed at Naples, Teatro del Fondo di Separazione, quadragesima 1792.
ML 48.A5 v. 14

Balders død. Et heroisk syngespil i tre handlinger af Johan Evald.
n. i., n. d. 104 p. 15½ᶜᵐ.
On p. 100–104 "Forklaring" of the mythological names in the piece. The composer, Johann Ernst **Hartmann,** is not mentioned.
First performed at Copenhagen, Royal Theater, February 7, 1778. Schatz 4463

Balders død—Continued.

— Balders tod. Ein trauerspiel mit gesang von J. Ewald. Aus dem daenischen. Nach der musik des herrn concertmeister Hartmann. Zweyte aufl. mit 3 kupf. v. Chodowieki.

Kopenhagen, Christ. Gottlob Proft, 1785. 112 p. 14½^{cm}.

The plates are missing.   SCHATZ 4464

La ballerina amante. Dramma giocoso per musica da rappresentarsi nel Teatro di S. A. E. di Sassonia.

Dresda, n. publ., 1786. 141 p. 15½^{cm}.

Two acts. By Giuseppe Palomba (not mentioned.) Cast and name of the composer Domenico Nicola **Cimarosa**. German title "Die verliebte taenzerin" and text face Italian.

First performed at Dresden in 1786; at Naples, Teatro de' Fiorentini in 1782.
                                                                    SCHATZ 1912

Ballet auf das erfreulichste vermaehlungs-fest in des Durchlauchtigen fuersten und herrn Friedrich Ferdinands hertzogen zu Wuertemberg und Teck . . . und . . . princessin Elisabeth . . . welches . . . den 19. monats-tag septembr. des 1689tzigsten jahres celebriret wurde.

Oelss, Heinrich Bockshammer, n. d. Unpaged. 32^{cm}.

Twenty-one entrées with arias. Cast. On last page a "Beschluss-Sonnet." Neither author nor composer mentioned in the libretto. Not recorded by Sittard.
                                                                    ML 52.2.B107

Ballet dansé a Ville-Neuve-Saint-George devant Monseigneur le premier septembre 1692. Par l'Académie royale de musique et remis au Théatre de ladite Academie avec le Carnaval, mascarade. Les paroles sont de M. Banzy, & la musique de M. Colasse.

n. i., n. d. 206–228 p. 13½^{cm}. (Recueil général des opéra, Paris, 1703, t. iv.)

Detached copy. *A note on p. 208 reads:

"Ce ballet n'est pas compté au nombre des opera, parce qu'il ne peut former une representation complete & ordinaire. On l'a neanmoins placé dans ce volume ainsi qu'il est annoncé au Prologue du Carnaval, mascarade [by Lully], afin de ne rien omettre de tout ce qui s'est representé sur le Théatre de l'Academie royalle de musique."   SCHATZ 2104

Second copy. ML 48.R4

Le ballet de Flore. *See* Campra's Les festes venitiennes.

Ballet de la jeunesse, divertissement meslé de comedie & de musique. Représenté devant La Majesté à Versailles le [*blank*] janvier 1686 . . . Suivant la copie imprimée à Paris.

[Amsterdam Antoine Schelte], 1686. 24 p. (incl. front.) 13½^{cm}.

Prologue and the three intermèdes for the comedy. The names of the performers in the text. Neither the author, Dancourt, nor the composer, Michel Richard de **La Lande,** is mentioned.

First performed January 28, 1686, as indicated.   ML 49.A2L9

Ballet des ages. *See* Campra's Les ages.

Ballet des Parnasses. *See* Bontempi's Il Paride.

Ballet des saisons. Representé par l'Academie royale de musique. Suivant la copie imprimée à Paris.

Amsterdam, Antoine Schelte, 1696. 40 p. 14½^{cm}.

Four entrées and prologue. Neither author nor composer mentioned. *Comp.* next entry.   ML 52.2.B115

Ballet des saisons—Continued.

— **Ballet des saisons,** representé par l'Academie royale de musique l'an 1695. Les paroles sont de M. Picque, & la musique de M. Collasse. XXXVI. opera.

n. i., n. d. 14ᶜᵐ. front., 185-232 p. (Recueil général des opéra, t. v, Paris, 1703.)

Detached copy. Four entrées and prologue. Text by the abbé Pic. The second edition (1700) of Colasse's score bears this statement on the title page: "augmentée de toute la musique de feu Monsieur de **Lully** qui manquoit dans la premiere." Which Lully did he mean? Louis de Lully and Jean Baptiste de Lully, the younger, certainly not, because they were both still alive. To be considered, therefore, is only Jean Louis de Lully, who died 1688, about one year after his great father Jean Baptiste. Now, the son is not known to have collaborated with Colasse, whereas it is known that Colasse, as amanuensis of the elder Lully, saved and utilized in his own scores airs that had been discarded by Lully, who, moreover, on July 23, 1661, performed his own "Ballet des Saisons." SCHATZ 5782
Second copy. ML 48.R4

Le **ballet des sens,** représenté par l'Académie royale de musique, l'an 1732. Paroles de M. Roy. Musique de M. Mouret. CXVI. opera. Tom. xv.

n. i., n. d. front., p. 121-204. (Recueil général des opéra, Paris, 1739.) 14ᶜᵐ.

Detached copy. Prologue and five *entrées* entitled: "L'odorat," "Le toucher," "La vue," "L'ouie," and "Le goût." At the first performance, May 29, 1732 (so the score. Schatz gives June 5, 1732), the ballet consisted only of the prologue and the first three *entrées.* On July 8, 1732, "L'ouië" replaced "Le toucher," and August 14, 1732, "Le goût" replaced "La vue" before the ballet assumed its final form. As "Le triomphe des sens" the score was published by Mouret's widow.
SCHATZ 6744–6746
Second copy. ML 48.R4

Le **ballet des XXIV heures,** ambigu comique répresenté devant Sa Majesté à Chantilly, le 5 nov. 1722. Par l'Academie royale de musique, les comediens francois & italiens.

Paris, Jean Pepingué & la veuve Guillaume, 1723. 2 p. l., 123, [3] p. 16½ᶜᵐ.

Prologue and four parts, called "La nuit," "La matinée," "L'apresdinée" and "La soirée." On p. 6 "Monsieur D. L. F * *" [de la Font?] is mentioned as author of the prologue, "Le Grand, Comedien du roy" as author of "l'idée du ballet, les paroles qui se chantent, & les diverses petites comedies & scenes détachées" and [Jacques] **Aubert** as composer of the music, which was practically restricted to the ballet entrées. Casts and preface:
"Ce ballet a été ordonné, inventé, composé, apris & représenté en moins de trois semaines, & quoique l'execution dépendit de plus de deux cens personnes de differens talens, ella été des plus regulieres. Cette espece d'ambigu-comique a fort réjoui le roy & toute la cour: & c'est sur-tout ce qu'avoit recommandé à l'auteur le prince magnifique qui a donné ce divertissement à Sa Majesté."
The [3] p. at end contain the imprimatur, dated November 22, 1722, and Le Grand's privilege. ML 52.2.B11

Ballet du Dereiglement des passions. De l'Interest, de l'Amour, & de la Gloire.

n. i., n. d. 19 p. 22½ᶜᵐ.

Title page missing?
Three parts, with 10, 9, and 10 entries, each briefly described, with names of the dancers. Each part opens with a "recit," and the whole is preceded by "Le ballet au spectateur. Sonnet," and argument. Text by Berthaud, who is not mentioned. According to de La Vallière, the ballet was danced before the King and Queen of France on January 23, 1648, and the text was printed in the same year. Music by Michel **Lambert?** ML 52.2.B17

Ballet du Temps. Dansé par le roy le dernier jour de novembre 1654. [printer's mark].

Paris, Robert Ballard, 1654. 1 p. l., 1, 4-11 [!] p. 21½cm.

Perfect copy. Error in pagination.

Two parts of 12, resp. 11 entries. The names of the dancers are given. Neither the author of the text, Isaac de Benserade, is mentioned, nor Jean Baptiste de **Lully**, who composed some of the music. The air "Bien que nous courrions" was composed by Jean de **Cambefort.**   ML 52.2.B17

Componimento drammatico che introduce ad un **Ballo cinese** rappresentato in musica nell' imperial córte nel carnevale del 1735.

[25]–36 p. 19cm. (Pietro Metastasio, Opere drammatiche, Venezia, Giuseppe Bettinelli, 1733–37, v. 4.)

One act. No composer mentioned for whom *see* better known L. T. "Le Cinesi."
                          ML 49.A2M4

Il ballo de' segni celesti.

p. 317–326. 15½cm. (Ottavio Tronsarelli, Drammi musicali, Roma, Francesco Corbelletti, 1632.)

One act. Argument. No composer mentioned.   ML 49.A2T7

Songs, duetts, trios, chorusses, etc etc in the comic opera of the **Banditti;** or, Love's labyrinth. As it is performed at the Theatre Royal in Covent-Garden. The music by Dr. Arnold.

London, T. Cadell, 1781. 27 p. 20cm.

Two acts. Cast. John O'Keefe, the author, is not mentioned.
First performed November 28, 1781.
Better known in the altered version as: ML 50.2.B23A7

— Songs, duets, trios, etc. in the comic opera of the **Castle of Andalusia.** As performed at the Theatre-Royal, in Covent-Garden. The ninth edition.

London, T. Cadell, 1783. 27 p. 21cm.

Three acts. Neither the author, John O'Keefe, is mentioned, nor the composer and compiler of the music, Samuel **Arnold.** Bland's vocal score says: "The selected airs by **Handel, Vento, Giordani, Bertoni,** Giardini, Dr. **Arne,** and **Carolan,** the Irish bard. The overture, choruses, new airs, etc., composed by Doctor **Arnold.**"
First performed under the above title November 2, 1782.   LONGE 91

— The **castle of Andalusia,** a comic opera. In three acts. As it is performed at the theatres in London and Dublin. By John O'Keefe, Esq. With additional songs by Sig. Tenducci.

Dublin, Sold by the booksellers, 1783. 72 p. 16½cm.

Cast.   LONGE 148

Bannian day, a musical entertainment, in two acts, performed at the Theatre Royal, Hay-market. Written by George Brewer.

London, T. N. Longman, 1796. 4 p. l., 35 p. 21cm.

Cast, preface, and note that "The words (with a very few alterations) and the music of the duet at the end of the first act were borrowed from the musical piece, called The apparition; written by Mr. Cross."
The composer, Samuel **Arnold,** is not mentioned.
First performed June 11, 1796.   LONGE 234

The banquet. Tr. of Bertoni's Il convito.

The banquet-gallery. A. T. of Kelly's Feudal times.

I barbari sacrifizi distrutti, ballet. *See* Rispoli's Idalide.

La barbarie del caso. Tragedia di Domenico Gisberti . . . dall' Academia delli Sigg. Angustiati rappresentata in Murano nel MDCLXIV.

*[At end] Venetia, Francesco Valvasense, 1664. 166, [1] p. 13½*cm.

Three acts and prologue. Dedication and argument in verse. Pietro **Molinari** is mentioned as the composer. SCHATZ 6548

The barber duellist. A. T. of Modern honour.

The barber of Seville, or The useless precaution; a comedy in four acts. With songs, etc. By the author of Eugenie, or the School for rakes. Addressed to R. B. Sheridan, Esq.

*London, Printed for the author, 1776. 1 p. l., iv, [2], 70 p. 21*cm.

In his dedication the publisher calls this a translation of Beaumarchais' "Le barbier de Seville," and he mentions his reasons for publishing, "contrary to usual custom, a piece before it has been acted in London." Necessary corrections he leaves to be made by the author of the *Duenna*, "as being most fit to correct its faults." Clarence records Mrs. Griffiths as the translator.
Not performed. LONGE 318

Le barbier de Séville. Parody of Paisiello's Il barbiere di Siviglia.

Il barbier di Siviglia, ballet. *See* Il Demetrio, Livorno, 1785.

Der barbier von Sevilla oder Die unnütze vorsicht. Tr. of Paisiello's Il barbiere di Seviglia.

Der barbier von Seville, oder Die vergebliche vorsicht. Ein lustspiel.des herrn von Beaumarchais, in vier akten: mit untermischten gesaengen. Aus dem franzoesischen.

*Leipzig, Dykische Buchhandlung, 1784. 8 p. l., [81]-216 p. 15½*cm

The "Vorbericht" reads in part:
"Ursprünglich kommen in diesem stücke wohl einige gesaenge vor; aber der plan desselben ist gar nicht zu einer komischen operette angelegt. Warum es auf den meisten deutschen theatern aber als operette aufgefuehrt wird, ruehrt daher, weil Herr Seiler, fuer dessen theater herr [Gustav Friedrich Wilhelm] Grossmann das stueck zuerst uebersetzte, gern eine operette daraus wollte gemacht haben . . . Die von herrn Grossmann eingeschobenen gesaenge, welche herr [Friedrich Ludwig] **Benda** in musik gesezt hat, moegen hier ihren platz einnehmen; desto bequemer kann man sie bey der vorstellung uebersehen."
They are printed on the 8 p. l.
First performed at Dresden, Neues Theater vor dem Schwarzen Thore, August, 1776; at Leipzig, September, 1776; at Gotha, Hoftheater, October 18, 1776.
SCHATZ 764

Il barbiere di Siviglia, ballet. *See* Bianchi's La villanella rapita.

Il barbiere di Siviglia, ovvero La precauzione inutile, dramma giocoso per musica tradotto liberamente dal francese, da rappresentarsi nel Teatro Imperiale di corte, l'anno 1782. La musica è del Signor Giovanni Paisiello . . .

*Pietroburgo, Breitkopf, n. d. 5 p. l., 75 p. 20*cm.

Four acts. Cast, scenario, "protesta del traduttore" [Giuseppe Petrosellini, not mentioned] and Paisiello's dedication to Catherine II in which he says:
"Le barbier de Séville [by Beaumarchais] ayant été gouté par Votre Majesté Imperiale, j'ai pensé que cette même pièce en opera italien pourroit ne pas Lui déplaire; en conséquence j'en ai fait faire un extraît, que je me suis appliqué à rendre aussi court que possible, en conservant (autant que le génie de la poesie italienne peut le permettre) les expressions de la pièce originale sans y rien ajouter . . ."
M 50.2.B25P2

Il barbiere di Siviglia—Continued.

— Le **barbier de Séville**, opéra comique, en quatre actes; mis en musique sur la traduction italienne par le celebre Seigneur Paisiello. Et remis en français, d'après la pièce de Mr. de Beaumarchais, et parodié sur la musique, par Mr. Framery . . . Représenté devant Leurs Majestés à Trianon, sur le Théâtre de la reine, le 14 septembre, et à Versailles le 28 octobre, 1784 . . .

*Amsterdam, Cesar Noël Guerin, 1786. front. (a portrait of Beaumarchais), 111 p. 16½*cm.

Dedication to the queen and "*Avis:* Sans avoir égard à la verification, on a copié les paroles, comme elles sont placées sous la musique, pour la commodité des personnes qui aiment à suivre le chanteur." SCHATZ 7600

— Der **barbier von Sevilla** oder Die unnütze vorsicht. Ein singspiel in vier akten nach dem franzoesischen des herrn von Beaumarchais von G. F. W. Grossmann. Die komposition der musik ist von herrn Paisiello.

*Koeln am Rhein, Joh. Godschalk Langen, 1786. 104 p. 15½*cm.

First performed at Mannheim, Nationaltheater, Nov. 20, 1785. SCHATZ 7601

— **L'inutile precauzione.** Dramma giocoso per musica da rappresentarsi nel nobile Teatro di San Samuele il carnovale dell' anno MDCCLXXXVII.

*Venezia, Modesto Fenzo, 1787. 56 p. 18*cm.

Cast, name of **Paisiello** as the composer, scenario, and notice to the effect that, though printed in four acts, the opera was really performed in two parts, first and second, resp. third and fourth acts together. The author, Giuseppe Petrosellini, is not mentioned. SCHATZ 7602

— **Figaro als barbier zu Sevilla,** ein lustspiel mit gesang in 4 akten. Text nach Beaumarchais, musik von Johann Paisiello.

*Passau, Ambrosi, 1796. 108 p. 16*cm.

At end [32] p. "Buecher Anzeiger." SCHATZ 7603

Der barbier von Sevilien, oder Die unnütze vorsicht; ein lustspiel in vier akten. Aus dem französischen des herrn von Beaumarchais, und mit neuer musik von Johann André.

*Offenbach am Mayn, Ulrich Weiss, 1776. 136 p. 17*cm.

First performed at Berlin, Döbbelinsches Theater, October 2, 1776. SCHATZ 182

Barillotto. Intermezzi da rappresentarsi nel Teatro di Sant' Angelo l'autunno dell' anno 1712. Poesia del Sig. dott. Francesco Salvi di Firenze. Musica del Sig. Domenico Saro [!] . . .

*Venezia, Marino Rossetti, 1712. 12 p. 15*cm.

Three parts. Cast. SCHATZ 942

Barilotto e Slapina, intermezzi. L. T. of Salvi's text Barillotto.

Le **Barnevelt françois.** A. T. of Duni's L'école de la jeunesse.

Il baron di Lago Nero. Dramma giocoso per musica da rappresentarsi nel nobile Teatro Tron di San Cassiano nell' autunno dell' anno 1776.

*Venezia, Gio. Battista Casali, 1776. 54 p. 17½*cm.

Three acts. The author is not mentioned and is unknown to Schatz. Cast, scenario, and names of Michele **Mortellari** as the composer of the opera and of "Santo Trento" of the ballet music ("tutta nuova"). SCHATZ 6689

Il baron di Terra Asciuta. Dramma giocoso per musica da rappresentarsi nel Nobile Teatro di San Samuele il carnovale dell' anno 1776.

Venezia, Gio. Battista Casali, 1776. 40 p. 17cm.

One act. Author not mentioned and unknown to Schatz. Cast, name of Giacomo **Rust** as the composer, and this *avviso:*

"... s'è pensato in luogo d'un' opera buffa di far rappresentare due operette, come costumano i Francesi. Una delle quali, per la ristrettezza del tempo, non ha potuto esser pronta, ma lo sarà dopo i tre primi dì dell' anno. Intanto si supplirà col primo atto dell' opera passata."

On p. [29]–40, argument and description of Onorato Viganò's "Oreste o sia La morte di Clitennestra, ballo tragico pantomimo," without name of the composer of the music.

First performed at Venice, December 26, 1775, as indicated. SCHATZ 9168

The baron Kinkvervankotsdorsprakingatchdern. A new musical comedy. As performed at the Theatre Royal in the Hay-market. By Miles Peter Andrews, Esq.

London, T. Cadell, 1781. xi, [5], 71, [1] p. 20cm.

Three acts, prologue, and epilogue. Cast and preface, in which the author protests against the charges of "many low and gross indecencies" resulting in the removal of his successful play from the stage after three performances. The composer of the music is not mentioned. The music, perhaps partly compiled, has been ascribed to Dr. **Arnold.** LONGE 196

First performed as indicated, July 9, 1781.

Der baron vom Vesten thurme. Ein singspiel in zween aufzuegen. Ein freye uebersetzung aus dem italienischen von C.[arl] J. F.[örg] Aufgefuehrt auf dem Churfuerstl. deutschen Theater in Muenchen.

[Muenchen], Gedruckt bey Franz Joseph Thuille, 1777. Unpaged. 14½cm.

Joseph **Michl** is mentioned as the composer. The original Italian title was, "Il barone di Torre Forte."

First performed at Munich, Opernhaus b. St. Salvator, March 23, 1772.

SCHATZ 6488

Der baron von Alten Felss. Tr. of Franchi and Anfossi's Il barone di Rocca Antica.

Der baron von Starckenthurm. Tr. of Piccinni's Il barone di Torreforte.

Il barone a forza, o sia Il trionfo di Bacco. Farsetta per musica da rappresentarsi nel Teatro Pallacorda [!] di Firenze nel carnevale dell' anno 1786.

Roma, Michele Puccinelli, n. d. 68 p. 15½cm.

Two acts. Author not mentioned and unknown to Schatz. Cast and name of **Marcello di Capua** as composer. ML 50.2.B29B2

— **Il barone a forza** o sia Il trionfo di Bacco. Dramma giocoso per musica da rappresentarsi in Bologna nel Nuovo publico teatro il carnevale dell' anno 1788 . . .

Bologna, Sassi, n. d. 79 p. 17cm.

Two acts. Dedication, cast, scenario, and name of **Marcello di Capua** as composer. Librettist not mentioned and unknown to Schatz. The *imprimatur* dated December 16, 1787.

First performed at Bologna, December 26, 1787. SCHATZ 845

Il barone burlato. L. T. of Cimarosa's Il pittor parigino.

Il **barone di Moscabianca.**   A. T. of Caruso's Oro non compra amore.

Il **barone di Rocca Antica.**   Intermezzo per musica a quattro voci da rappresentarsi in Lisbona nel Teatro della rua dos Condes nell' estate dell' anno 1773.

[Lisbona], Nella Stamperia reale, n. d.   71 p.   16½^{cm}*.*

Two parts. By Giuseppe Petrosellini, who is not mentioned. Cast, scenario, and name of the composer, Carlo **Franchi.**
First performed at Rome, Teatro delle Dame, February 4, 1771.   Schatz 3327

— Il **barone di Rocca Antica.**   Azzione comica per musica da rappresentarsi nel Piccolo Teatro di S. A. E. di Sassonia.

Dresda., 1772, n. publ.   143 p.   16½^{cm}*.*

Two acts. German title-page, "Der baron von Alten Felss. Eine lustige musical-ische handlung," and text face Italian. Carlo **Franchi** is named as the composer of the first and Pasquale **Anfossi** of the second act in this version.   Schatz 3330

Il **barone di Torre Forte.**   O. T. of Michl's Der baron vom Vesten thurme.

Il **barone di Torreforte.**   Azzione comica in musica, da rappresen-tarsi nel Piccolo Theatro di S. A. E. di Sassonia.

Dresda, n. publ., l'estate del 1766.   93 p.   16^{cm}*.*

Two acts. The author is not mentioned and unknown to Schatz. Cast and name of Niccolò **Piccinni** as the composer. German title-page, "Der baron von Starcken-thurm," and text face Italian.
First performed at Rome, Teatro Capranica, January 10, 1765.   Schatz 8068

— Il **barone di Torreforte.**   Dramma giocoso per musica da rap-presentarsi nel Teatro di via S. Maria nell' estate dell' anno 1768 . . .

Firenze, Stamperia in Borgo de' Greci, n. d.   Unpaged.   17^{cm}*.*

Two acts. Dedicatory poem by the impresario, Antonio Fabbrini, cast, and name of Niccolò **Piccinni** as composer.
Previously performed at Florence, Teatro via del Cocomero, spring of 1766.
ML 48.A5   v. 24

Il **barone in angustie.**   Commedia per musica di Giuseppe Palomba da rappresentarsi nel Real Teatro del Fondo di Separazione per quart' opera del corrente anno 1797 . . .

Napoli, n. publ., 1797.   43 p.   15^{cm}*.*

Two acts. Impresario's dedication dated Naples, February 1, 1797, cast, and name of Giacomo **Tritto** as the composer. With the opera was performed (composer of the music not mentioned) Lauchlin Dusquesney's ballet, "L'inutile precauzione."
Schatz 10459

Il **barone Spazzacamino.**   L. T. of Portugal's Spazzacamino principe.

La **baronessa Stramba.**   *See* Cimarosa's Il credulo.

Barsina.   Dramma per musica da rappresentarsi nel famoso Teatro Tron a S. Cassiano. L'autunno dell' anno MDCCXLII.

Venezia, Milosco, 1742.   48 p.   15½^{cm}*.*

Three acts. By Francesco Silvani, who is not mentioned. Argument, scenario, cast, and name of Giuseppe Antonio **Paganelli** as the composer.   Schatz 7573

Le **baruffe chiozzote,** ballet. *See* Robuschi's Castrini, padre e figlio.

Basilio rè Doriente [!]. Dramma per musica da recitarsi nel Teatro à S. Cassano, novamente riaperto à uso d'opere l'anno 1696 . . .

Venetia, Nicolini, 1696. 66 p. 15^{cm}.

Three acts. Dedication signed by the author, Giovanni Battista Neri, and dated Venice, December 31, 1695, argument and "A chi legge discretamente" with name of Francesco **Navara** as the composer, source of the story, the usual complaint about brevity of time, and the remark:

"Sarebbe ben stato di bisogno il poter da dovero con arte magica ingrandir la capacità del Teatro, che non sarei io stato costretto a restringere, e quasi annichilare le operazioni della mia scena: oltre il comando inviolabile della brevità, che con più tirannia di quella hò sofferto dall' angustia del sito, mi ha violentato à levar molte scene di quelle che sono chiamate di forza, e cangiar la più parte de frutti in pochi fiori di nulla fragranza . . ." Schatz 7065

Basilio und Quiteria, ein singgedicht.

n. i., n. d. p. [365]–386. 18^{cm}.

Detached copy. One act. Neither Daniel Schiebeler, the author, is mentioned nor Georg Philipp **Telemann,** the composer.

First performed at Hamburg, 1735. Schatz 10256

Il bassa generoso. Intermezzo per musica a cinque voci da rappresentarsi nel Piccolo Teatro di S. A. E. di Sassonia.

Dresda, n. publ., 1782. 19 p. 15½^{cm}.

Two acts, with name of composer, **Marcello di Capua,** but not of librettist, who is unknown to Schatz. German title-page "Der grossmuethige bassa" and text face Italian.

First performed, as indicated, February 9, 1782; at Rome, Teatro Capranica, carnival 1780. Schatz 830

Der bassa von Tunis, eine komische operette in einem aufzuge, von K. F. H. Die musik ist von herrn Holly in Prag.

Berlin und Leipzig, n. publ., 1774. 56 p. 15^{cm}.

By Carl Franz Henisch.

First performed at Berlin, Koch'sches Theater in der Behrenstrasse, January 6, 1774. Schatz 4768

Bassiano, overo Il maggior impossibile. Drama per musica da rappresentarsi nel famoso Teatro Grimano in SS. Giovanni e Paolo. L'anno MDCLXXXII. Di Matteo Noris . . .

Venetia, Francesco Nicolini, 1682. 62 p. 13½^{cm}.

Three acts. Author's dedication, argument, and scenario. The composer, Carlo **Pallavicino,** is not mentioned. Schatz 7720

Bassiano overo Il maggior impossibile. Melodrama da rappresentarsi nel Teatro di S. Bartolomeo di Matteo Noris . . .

Napoli, Perrino e Mutii, 1694. 6 p. l., 60 p. 13½^{cm}.

Three acts. Impresario's dedication, argument, scenario, and notice to the reader which begins:

"Viddero altrove i teatri rappresentar questo drama [with music by Carlo Pallavicino] da qualche tempo con applausi; hora viene sù questo di Partenope. Il tempo breve, la staggione, e l'uso l'han fatto variare in qualche parte non essentiale, ti si dice acciò, se à caso vedessi impresso quello, che prima rappresentossi, non giudichi, che si è fatto il correttore all' autore, che tanto celebre è nel mondo. E stato poi posto in musica dal . . . Sig. Alessandro **Scarlatti** in cosi breve tempo che è parso un miracolo . . ."

This notice followed by the restituted arias, etc., "Voi che tanto ne vedete" (II, 10), "El io più nõ appare" (III, 6), and "Questo di logore" (III, 11).

Mentioned by Dent?

First performed, as indicated, in the spring of 1694. Schatz 9533

The **Bastille:** a musical entertainment of one act: As performed at the Royal Circus, in Saint George's Fields. Written by John Dent . . . The second edition.

London, W. Lowndes, 1790. 3 p. l. (incl. pl.), viii, 24 p. 21^{cm}.

The plate (a scene from the opera) is dated December 15, 1789. Author's dedication dated November 31, 1789, and Address narrating the difficulties in the way of the production of this piece which ran for seventy-nine nights consecutively after having been "actually got up and represented within seven days after it had been first conceived, and determined on." Composer not recorded by Clarence or Schatz.

                                                                    LONGE 318

Les **bateliers de Saint Cloud,** opera comique de m. F * * *.

Bruxelles, n. publ., 1744. 44 p. 19^{cm}. (Theatre de M. Favart, Paris, Duchesne, 1763–77, t. vi.)

One act. Prose and vaudevilles. No music printed in text or added.
First performed as "La fête de Saint Cloud" at Paris, Opéra comique, Foire Saint Laurent, August, 1741, revived under the above title and with alterations, August, 1744.   ML 49.A2F1

— Les **bateliers de Saint Cloud,** opéra-comique en un acte.

Paris, la veuve Duchesne, 1766. 72 p. 19^{cm}.

On p. 43–74 twenty-three "Airs des Bateliers de S. Cloud," unaccompanied. Neither the author, Favart, is mentioned, nor the arranger of the popular airs.

                                                                    SCHATZ 11483

Bathile. *See* Floquet's L'union de l'amour et des arts.

The **battle of Hexham.** A comedy. In three acts, as performed at the Theatre-Royal, Crow-street.

Dublin, P. Byrne, 1790. 58 p. 17½^{cm}.

London and Dublin casts. Considerably interspersed with songs, etc. Neither the author, George Colman, the younger, is mentioned, nor Samuel **Arnold,** the composer.
In Longman and Broderip's vocal score the glee "When Arthur first" is headed as composed by **Calcott** and the catch "Lurk, lurk, o'er the green sword" as by Dr. **Arne.**
First performed August 11, 1789.   LONGE 233

The **battle of the poets;** or, The contention of the laurel. As it is now acting at the New Theatre in the Hay-market; introduced as an entire new act to the comical tragedy of Tom Thumb. Written by Scriblerus Tertius . . .

London, W. Trott and T. Astley, 1731. 24 p. 17½^{cm}.

Cast and prologue. Interspersed with songs, the airs of which are indicated by title. By some attributed to Thomas Cooke.   LONGE 321
First performed, as indicated, January 1, 1731 (Genest)

Bauce e Palemone. Dramma per musica per celebrare il felicissimo giorno natalizio della serenissima Signora Donna Carlotta Gioacchina . . . li 25 aprile 1789.

[Lisboa], Stamperia reale, n. d. 23 p. 15^{cm}.

One act. Argument, cast, and names of João Cordeiro da **Silva** as composer, of Gaetano Martinelli as author.   SCHATZ 9883

Bauci e Filemone. First act of Gluck's Le feste d'Apollo.

Das **bauern-maegdchen am hofe.** A. T. of Hiller's Lottchen.

Der **baum der Diana.** Tr. of Martin y Soler's L'arbore di Diana.

Das **bauren-maedgen.** Tr. of Sacchini's La contadina in corte.

Il **Bayram de' Turchi,** ballet. *See* Salieri and Rust's Il talismano.

Bayes no poetaster. A. T. of The two queens of Brentford.

Bays in petticoats. A. T. of The rehearsal.

Bays's opera. As it is acted at the Theatre-Royal, by His Majesty's servants. Written by Mr. Odingsells . . .

London, printed: and sold by J. Roberts, 1730. 4 p. l., 70 p. 20ᶜᵐ.

Lacks the "Epilogue," [2] p. after p. 70.

Three acts. Ballad opera. The tunes (49) not printed—merely indicated. Cast and preface, which reads, in part:

"When the town thought fit to pass sentence on this trifling piece, corrected by their judgment, I determin'd to finish the execution, and bury it in oblivion: lest by setting it in open light, I shou'd be thought presumptuous enough to think of confronting and expostulating with their resentment. But my too partial friends, who first seduc'd me by their approbation to exhibit it to the publick, over-rul'd my resolution; and thought it incumbent on me to publish it, in order to clear up some disadvantages it labour'd under in the representations, which made it obscure, and perhaps unintelligible, and to confute some insinuations scatter'd about, injurious to my private character . . .

"The only view of this performance was to expose the folly and absurdities of a prevailing (and, as I thought, vitiated) taste; which seem'd to prefer farce and buffoonery, as well as the unprofitable, immoral and unnatural representations of poetical fiction, to the more polite and instructive entertainments of dramatick poetry and musick.

"As the design is carried on in one continu'd allegory, all persons of taste (and to such only I make my humble appeal,) well know that an allegory, to be rightly understood in all its parts, requires an exact attention from the beginning to the end . . .

"For the judicious this piece was, tho' unhappily, calculated; and therefore not intended to entertain by ballad-singing; which was only accidental to the design; or rather a means to enliven the burlesque scheme. It was my view to alarm men of sense to a care of the liberal arts, which seem to languish, and, at their last gasp, invoke their assistance to raise them . . .

"I cou'd take notice of some invidious reflections industriously spread by a certain author, who has claim'd to himself the invention of this scheme; (tho' I doubt neither of us have any great reason to boast of it;) but as it is not the turn of my ambition to aspire at, much less to rival any man in the character of author, I shall readily give him up any thing but truth, I shall therefore only observe, that it was impossible for me to steal any hints from him, because this was wrote, and known to many gentlemen above a year before he dates the theft . . .

"It has been urg'd, in a place where I cou'd wish scandal and defamation might never enter, that this performance was aim'd to expose the celebrated author of the Beggar's Opera and his works; but to clear me from this abhorr'd aspersion, I shall want no other vindication than what I am sure to find from the candid judgment of that ingenious gentleman . . ."

First performed at Drury Lane, March 30, 1730. ML 50.5.B19

Second copy, complete with the "Epilogue," [2] p. after p. 70. Longe 78

Beau in the sudds. A. T. of The female parson.

The **beau metamorphos'd.** A. T. of The happy lovers.

Den **bedragne formynder** eller De under masken sluttede giftermaale. Tr. of G. M. Rutini's I matrimoni in maschera.

Die **befreyte sklavinn.** Tr. of Schuster's La schiava liberata.

The **beggar's opera.** As it is acted at the Theatre-Royal in Lin-colns-Inn-Fields. Written by Mr. Gay . . . To which is added, the musick engrav'd on copper-plates.

London, J. Watts, 1728.   58, [2] p., 16 p. (music).   20^{cm}.

Three acts with introduction. Cast. At end of text [2] p. of a list of "Books lately publish'd," the heading of the second page reading "Books printed for J. Tonson and J. Watts. Feb. 10, 1727." In third act there are by error two "Scene X," one on p. 50, the other on p. 51. The airs are numbered consecutively for each act: 18, 22, 28, total 68 *not* 69. The airs, by no means only ballad-airs, are printed separately following the text, but without titles, merely with number corresponding to that in the text, where the tunes are indicated by title. John Christopher **Pepusch,** who composed the overture and arranged the music, is not mentioned. *First edition.*

First performed, as indicated, January 29, 1728.   ML 50.5.B3

— The **beggar's opera.** As it is acted at the Theatre-Royal in Lincolns-Inn Fields. Written by Mr. Gay . . . 3d ed.: with the ouverture in score, the songs, and the basses, (the ouverture and basses compos'd by Dr. Pepusch) Curiously engrav'd on copper plates.

London, J. Watts, 1729.   4 p. l., 60 p., 46 p. (music).   23^{cm}.

Three acts and introduction. Ballad opera. Cast and table of the sixty-nine [!] songs numbered consecutively. The corresponding airs are printed in the text with their titles.   ML 50.5.B33

— The **beggar's opera.** Written by Mr. Gay. The fifth edition: to which is prefix'd the ouverture in score and the musick to each song.

London, John Watts, 1742.   4 p. l., 8, 76 p.   20½^{cm}.

Three acts. The 4 p. l. contain a table of the 69 songs, advertisements, cast and first page of the "Introduction" followed on the 8 p. by the "Ouverture in score. Compos'd by Dr. *Pepusch.*"   AC 901.M5v.519

— The **beggar's opera.** Written by Mr. Gay. To which is pre-fixed the overture in score: and the musick to each song.

London, J. and R. Tonson, 1765.   94 p. (incl. front.)   21½^{cm}.

Title vignette: port.
Three acts and introduction. Cast and table of the songs. On p. 11–18 the "Overture in score. Composed by Dr. Pepusch." The airs (69) are printed in the text, numbered consecutively.   ML 50.5.B35

Second copy.   LONGE 46

— The **beggar's opera.** As written by John Gay. Distinguishing also the variations of the theatre, as performed at the Theatre-Royal in Drury-Lane. Regulated from the prompt-book, by permission of the managers, by Mr. Hopkins, prompter.

London, John Bell, 1777.   65 p.   17½^{cm}.

At head of title: "Bell's edition." On p. 63–65: "A Table of the songs." **Pepusch** is not mentioned. Following the text 2 unnumb. p. of "Books published by J. Bell." On p. 3 the Drury-Lane and Covent-Garden casts.

The Drury Lane cast in this libretto is not the same as given by Genest for November 8, 1777.   SCHATZ 7864

— The **beggar's opera.** A comic opera. By John Gay. Adapted for theatrical representation, as performed at the Theatre-Royal, Drury-Lane. Regulated from the prompt-book, by permission of the managers.

London, John Bell, 1791.   2 pl., ix, [4], 14–99, [3] p.   15^{cm}.   (J. Bell, British theatre, London, 1791–1797, t. 2.)

The beggar's opera—Continued.

The first pl. represents Mrs. Crouch as Polly and is dated February 2, 1791. The second pl. is an added pictorial title page and is dated January 20, 1791. Biographical sketch of John Gay, editorial note on the "Beggar's Opera." A table of the songs on the [3] p. at end. PR 1241.B4

— **The beggar's opera.** A comic opera. By John Gay. Adapted for theatrical representation, as performed at the Theatres-Royal, Drury-Lane & Covent-Garden. Regulated from the prompt-book, by permission of the managers . . . Cooke's edition. Embellished with superb engravings.

London, C. Cooke, n. d. 2 pl. x, [11–13], 14–72 p. 14½cm.

Plates and contents the same as in preceding entry, except that there is no table of the songs. Published before 1800? PR 3473.B4C6

The beggar's wedding. A new ballad opera. As it is acted at the theatre in Dublin, with great applause; and at the theatre in the Haymarket. To which are added the new prologue and epilogue. By Mr. Char. Coffey . . . 5th ed.

London, Printed by J. D., 1733. 58 p. 16cm.

Three acts. The airs are not printed, merely indicated. They are numbered consecutively in each act: 20, 15, 19, total 54.

Under the above title (prose and songs, in three acts) "The beggar's wedding" was first published with music at London in 1729. This and the second edition, 1729 (without music) and a third edition, 1729 (with music) are at the British Museum, as well as the fourth edition, 1731. Genest says under Haymarket 1729 of the "Beggar's wedding": "it seems to have come out at Dublin and then to have been acted at this theatre." Under Drury Lane, July 4, 1729 he then enters the first performance of the reduced version as "Phebe or Beggar's wedding."

ML 50.5.B4

First performed at Dublin, Smock Alley, March 24, 1729. (Lawrence).

— **The beggar's wedding.** An opera. As it is acting with great applause at the Theatre-Royal, in Drury-Lane. With the prologue and epilogue. By Mr. Char. Coffey . . .

London, R. Horsfield and T. Lownds, 1763. 64 p. 21cm.

Cast. The 56 (20, 15, 21) airs are indicated in the text by title. LONGE 102

— **Phebe;** or, The beggar's wedding. An opera.

47 p. 19cm.

Title page wanting. The British Museum lists an edition of London, 1729. One act. By Charles Coffey who is not mentioned. Cast. Ballad opera, the 32 airs of the songs being indicated by title. LONGE 151

Il Begliar-Bey di Caramania. Dramma in musica da rappresentarsi nel Piccolo Teatro Elettorale l'anno 1780.

Dresden, Stamperia elettorale, n. d. 119 p. 15½cm.

German title ("Der Begjlerbey in Caramanien") and text face Italian. Two acts. With name of Giuseppe **Amendola** as composer, but not that of the librettist, Girolamo Tonioli.

First performed at Dresden, Churf. sächs. Kleines Theater, November 22, 1780.

SCHATZ 173

Der Begjlerbey in Caramanien. Tr. of Amendola's Il Begliar-Bey di Caramania.

Der **beglueckte Florindo**. In einem singe-spiel auf dem Hamburgischen Theatro vorgestellet.

[*Hamburg*], *n. publ., 1708. Unpaged. 18½*cm.

Three acts. German version by Hinsch of unknown Italian work. Neither he nor the composer, Georg Friedrich **Händel**, are mentioned. The "Vorrede" contains the argument and statement that because "die vortrefliche music, womit diese opera gezieret, etwas gar zu lang ausgefallen," the work would be divided in two parts, the first as above, the second as "Die verwandelte Daphne." Italian text of the arias added to the Italian.
First performed, as indicated, January, 1708.   SCHATZ 4476

— Die **verwandelte Daphne**. In einem singe-spiel auff dem Hamburgischen Theatro vorgestellet. Im jahr 1708.

*n. i., n. d.   Unpaged.   18½*cm.

Three acts. Some arias have Italian, others German, text only. To some the Italian text has been added.
First performed in January, 1708, as indicated.   SCHATZ 4493

Die **beiden angefuehrten thoren**. A. T. of Portugal's Die schlaue wittwe.

Die **beiden Antone** oder Der name thut nichts zur sache. Eine komische oper in zwei akten. Nach dem ungedruckten Schikanederschen originale, mit beibehaltung der musik von Schack, neu bearbeitet.

*Leipzig, Friedrich August Leo, 1797.   88 p.   15*cm.

The prefatory note, signed, "Geschrieben in der Leipziger Michaelmesse, 1796, **Z.**," reads, in part:
"Gegenwaertiges singspiel gefiel seit zehn jahren auf den oesterreichischen buehnen und in der dortigen nachbarschaft so sehr, dass es noch immer mit neuem beifall wiederholt wird . . . In dessen war sein provinzieller anstrich wohl auch immer ein hinderniss, dass man es ausser seinem vaterlande nicht auch auffuehrte . . . Hier ist ein versuch, worinn die originalität dieses stuecks, so weit es nur thunlich war, beibehalten wurde, und der schon in Sachsen, bei der J. Secondaschen Gesellschaft, schmeichelhaften beifall erhielt . . ."
First performed at Leipzig, Theater am Rannstädter Thore, 1797; at Vienna, Theater a. d. Wieden, 1789, as "Anton der dumme gârtner oder Der name thut nichts sur sache."   SCHATZ 9566

— Arien aus den [!] **Dummen gaertner**. Ein komisches singspiel in zwey aufzeugen, von Emanuel Schickaneder. Aufgefuehrt von der Mihuleschen Gesellschaft.

*Augsburg, n. publ., 1793.   23 p.   16*cm.

The same as "Die beiden Antone."
First performed at Augsburg, National Theater, 1793.   SCHATZ 9567

Die **beiden geizigen**. Tr. of Grétry's Les deux avares.

Die **beiden militzen**. Tr. of Fridzeri's Les deux miliciens.

Il **Beiram** o sia Il carnovale turco, ballet. *See* Curcio's Solimano.

Belisa ossia La fedeltà riconosciuta. Dramma in due atti da rappresentarsi nel Teatro di Monza l'autunno 1795 . . .

*Milano, Gaetano Motta, n. d.   4 p. l., 56, [1] p.   16½*cm.

Two acts. By conte Alessandro Pepoli, who is not mentioned. Impresario's dedication, cast, scenario, and name of Peter von **Winter** as the composer. With the opera were performed Paolino Franchi's ballet, "Raol de Crequi" (music by Winter and Wenzeslaus Pichl), and Carlo Biancardi's ballet, "Le preziose umiliate"; composer not mentioned.
First performed at Venice, Teatro di S. Benedetto, carnival, 1794.
                                                                SCHATZ 11020

La bella Arsena. Tr. of Monsigny's La belle Arsène.

La bella Arsene, ballet. *See* Martin y Soler's Andromaca.

La bella Girometta. Dramma giocoso per musica da rappresentarsi nel Teatro Giustiniani di S. Moisè l'autunno dell' anno MDCCLXI dell' abate Pietro Chiari . . .

> *Venezia, Modesto Fenzo, 1761. 58 p. 15ᶜᵐ.*

Three acts. Cast, scenario, and name of composer, Ferdinando Giuseppe **Bertoni.**

SCHATZ 937

La bella incognita e **La maga Circe.** Farsette per musica di una sola parte a 5. voci da rappresentarsi nel Teatro Valle degl' illustrissimi Signori Capranica il carnevale dell' anno 1788.

> *Roma, Gioacchino Puccinelli, n. d. 55, [1] p. 15ᶜᵐ.*

Casts and names of Francesco **Basili** as composer of the first farce, of Pasquale **Anfossi** of the second. Authors unknown to Schatz. The second farce stands on p. 28–55.

ML 50.2.B28B2

La bella Lauretta. Dramma giocoso per musica di Giovanni Bertati, poeta pensionato di S. M. I. R. A. etc. etc. da rappresentarsi nel nobilissimo Teatro Giustiniani in S. Moisè per la seconda opera del carnovale 1795.

> *Venezia, Valvaseuse, 1795. 62 p. 18½ᶜᵐ.*

With name of Francesco **Gardi** as the composer.

SCHATZ 3537

La bella pescatrice. Commedia per musica di Saverio Zini. Da rappresentarsi nel Teatro Nuovo sopra Toledo per second' opera di quest' anno 1789.

> *Napoli, n. publ., 1789. 48 p. 15½ᶜᵐ.*

Two acts. Cast and name of Pietro **Guglielmi** as the composer.

SCHATZ 4237

— La bella pescatrice. Dramma giocoso per musica, da rappresentarsi nel Teatro di S. A. E. di Sassonia.

> *Dresda, n. publ., 1791. 127 p. 16ᶜᵐ.*

Two acts. Zini's text, with alterations. For instance, the aria, "Sposina più vezzosa," has been dropped from I, 3. Pietro **Guglielmi** is mentioned as the composer. German title-page, "Das schoene fischermaedchen," and text face Italian. First performed, as indicated, November 5, 1791.

SCHATZ 4238

— La pescatrice. Commedia per musica di Saverio Zini da rappresentarsi nel Real Teatro del Fondo di Separazione per prim' opera di questo corrente anno 1790.

> *Napoli, n. publ., 1790. 46 p. 15ᶜᵐ.*

Two acts. Pages 3–6, 19–22 missing, containing, probably, also Pietro **Guglielmi**'s name as composer. Cast. The text seems to follow that of 1789.

SCHATZ 4281

— Arien und gesaenge aus Dem fischermaedchen. Eine operette in zwey aufzuegen. Die musick ist von Guglielmi . . .

> *Frankfurt am Main, n. publ., 1794. 24 p. 16ᶜᵐ.*

The translator is not mentioned.

First performed at Frankfurt a/M, Nationaltheater, 1794.

SCHATZ 4239

Bella und Fernando, oder Die satire, in einem aufzuge.   In musik gesezt von herrn Preu.

n. i., n. d.   p. [111]-176.   14½ᶜᵐ.   (C. A. Vulpius, Operetten. bd. I. Baireuth, 1790.)

Detached copy.
First performed at Bayreuth, Privattheater Gesellschaft, May 20, 1789.

           Sᴄʜᴀᴛᴢ 8463

La bella verità.   Dramma di tre atti per musica.   Rappresentato per la prima volta in Bologna l'estate dell' anno MDCCLXII con musica del Piccini.

Carlo Goldoni, Opere teatrali, Venezia, Zatta e figli, 1788-95, t. 39., [67]-126 p.   18ᶜᵐ.   PQ

First performed as indicated, at the Teatro Marsigli Rossi, June 12, 1762.
           Second, detached copy.   Sᴄʜᴀᴛᴢ 8069

La belle Arsène, comédie-féerie, en quatre actes, mêlée d'ariettes. Les paroles de M. Favart; la musique de M. de Monsigny.   Représentée devant Sa Majesté, à Fontainebleau, le 6 novembre 1773, & à Paris, le 14 août 1775.

Paris, la veuve Duchesne, 1775.   ix, 10-61 p.   18ᶜᵐ.

Cast.   On p. [iii]-ix Voltaire's poem "La béguele" and prefatory note saying that this poem had furnished the sujet for the opera, that the verses in *guillemets* (quotation marks) have been borrowed more or less literally from the poem and that the opera as performed originally at Fontainebleau had only three acts.   Sᴄʜᴀᴛᴢ 6562

— **La belle Arsène,** coméaie-féerie, en quatre actes.   Mêlée d'ariettes.

n. i., n. d.   xv, [1], 77, [1] p.   19ᶜᵐ.   (Theatre de M. Favart, Paris, Duchesne, 1763–77, tx.).

At end: "De l'imprimerie de C. Simon . . . 1775."
Cast, Favart's dedication to the duc de Richelieu and Voltaire's poem "La béguele" on which the opera is founded, precede the text.   No music printed in the text.   The composer, **Monsigny,** is not mentioned.   ML 49.A2F1

— Die **schoene Arsene,** ein singspiel in vier aufzuegen aus dem franzoesischen uebersetzt mit musik.

Frankfurt am Mayn, mit Andreäischen schriften, 1776.   100 p. 17ᶜᵐ.

No music.   Neither Johann Heinrich Faber, the translator, nor **Monsigny** is mentioned.   This version, according to Schatz, was used by Th. Marchand's Churpfälz. deutsche Hofschauspielgesellschaft.   Sᴄʜᴀᴛᴢ 6563

— Gesaenge aus der romantischen oper: Die **schoene Arsene.**   In vier aufzuegen.   Die musick ist von Monsigny.

Hamburg, J. M. Michaelsen, 1780.   16 p.   17ᶜᵐ.

Johann André's version, who is not mentioned.
First performed at Hamburg, Theater b. Gänsemarkt, Oct. 27, 1780.

           Sᴄʜᴀᴛᴢ 6564

— La **bella Arsena.**   Ein singspiel in vier aufzuegen.

[At end] Augsburg, mit Brinhausserischen schriften, 1781.   84 p. 16ᶜᵐ.

Version of Johann Heinrich Faber.   Sᴄʜᴀᴛᴢ 6565

La belle Arsène—Continued.

— Den **skiønne Arsene**; et syngestykke i fire handlinger af Favart, med musik af M * * *, til samme musik oversat af Adam Gottlob Thoroup.

n. i., n. d. 76 p. 16½ cm.

First performed at Copenhagen, Kongel. Theater paa Kongens Nytorv, December 10, 1781. Schatz 6566

— De **schoone Arsène**, zangspel met balletten. Naar het fransch gevolgd van Favart, door Bartholomeus Ruloffs.

Amsteldam, J. Helders en A. Mars, 1789. 4 p. l., 71, [1] p.

Dedicatory poem by the translator dated 1789.
First performed at Amsterdam, Stads Schouwburg, October, 1788. Schatz 6586

La belle esclave, ou Valcour et Zéila, comédie en un acte et en prose, mêlée d'ariettes. Par M. Dumaniant. Musique de M. Philidor. Jouée à Paris, sur le Théâtre des Petits comédiens de Mgr. le comte de Beaujolais, le 18 septembre 1787, & publiée au profit du Sieur Morel.

Paris, Prault, 1787. 2 p. l., 38, [3] p. 21 cm.

On first p. l. the note:
"Le Sieur Morel est le jeune acteur qui a eu la main blessée par l'explosion d'un pistolet qui devoit lui servir dans un de ses rôles, & au profit duquel on a déjà donné une représentation." The [3] p. contain: "Couplets de la scène iv, mis en musique." ("Riches de la terre.") ML 50.2.B3P3

Belle et Bonne, ou Les deux soeurs, comédie en un acte, en prose et vaudevilles. Représentée, pour la première fois, à Paris, sur le Théâtre du Vaudeville, le 5 frimaire, an 6, samedi 25 novembre 1797 (v. st.) par F. P. A. Leger.

Paris, Au Théatre du Vaudeville, an VIe. 1798 (v. st.) 54 p. 20 cm.

Cast. Many of the airs are printed in the text and some of them are marked as new by **Leger**. A new air was also contributed by **Bruni**. Not recorded by Cl. & L. or Schatz. ML 48.M2L

La belle fermière. A. T. of Candeille's Catherine.

La belle-mère. A. T. of Fay's Clémentine.

Bellerofon, ein ernsthaftes singspiel in drei aufzuegen, aufgefuehrt bei der ankunft Sr. Durchlaucht des herrn kurfuersten zu Pfalzbaiern auf der Kurfuerstl. Nationalschaubuehne. Verfasst von Johann Friedrich, des H. R. R. frei und pannerherrn Binder von Krieglstein. In musik gesezt von herrn Peter Winter . . .

Muenchen, n. publ., 1785. 64 p. 16 cm.

Cast, argument.
First performed at Munich, July 29, 1785. Schatz 11022

Il Bellerofonte. Dramma per musica da rappresentarsi nel Teatro dell' Accademia degl' Intronati nella primavera dell' anno 1767 in occasione del felice arrivo in Siena delle Altezze Loro reali Pietro Leopoldo, arciduca d'Austria . . . e Maria Luisa, infanta di Spagna . . .

n. i., n. d. 8 p. l., 48 p. 20 cm.

Three acts. The author is not mentioned and is unknown to Schatz. Impresario's dedication, dated Siena, May 6, 1767, argument, scenario, cast, poem of welcome, name of Giuseppe **Misliweczek** as the composer and "avvertimento":

Il **Bellerofonte**—Continued.

"Tronco, ed alterato in gran parte troverassi l'originale, ch'è parto di non ignota penna; ma tal'è, quasi sempre, il destino de i drammi musicali, qualora nuova rappresentazione se ne intraprende."

The first ballet, by Francesco Turchi, was called "Orfeo ed Euridice." The composer of the music is not mentioned.

First performed at Naples, Teatro di San Carlo, January 20, 1767.   SCHATZ 6532

Il **Bellerofonte**.   Drama musicale del Signor Vincenzo Nolfi da rappresentarsi nel Teatro Novissimo di Venetia l'anno 1642 . . .

Venetia, Gio. Battista Surian, 1642.

Three acts with prologue.   Author's notice to the reader, with Francesco **Sacrati**'s name as the composer, argument.   "Ode" to Nolfi on his "Bellerofonte," sonnet by him, "Per le due sublimi cantatraci del Teatro Novissimo nel Bellerofonte" (not mentioned by name) and "Sonetto in lode del Signor Francesco Sacrati, compositore della musica," by conte Paolo Feretti d'Ancona.   SCHATZ 9252

Bellerophon.   Theatralisches singspiel, so zu Oranienbaum auf befehl Sr. Kayserl. Hoheit des gross-fuersten etc aufgefuehret worden. Die poesie is vom hrn. doctor J. Bonechi . . . die musick vom hrn. Fr. Araya . . .

St. Petersburg, Kayserl. Academie der wissenschaften, 1757.   11 p. 26cm.

Two parts.   Argument, cast and synopsis of the plot without the text.   "Bellerofonte" was first performed at St. Petersburg, Court Theater, April 10/21, 1741.

ML 50.2.B35A7

Bellerophon.   Tragedie reresentée [!] par l'Academie royale de musique.

Paris, Christophe Ballard, 1679.   front., 54, [4] p.   23cm.

The [4] p. contain **Lully**'s "Permission pour tenir Academie royale de musique." Prologue and five acts.   The prefatory note contains argument and same note as below.   Corneille, the author, is not mentioned.

First performed, as indicated, January 31, 1679.   ML 50.2.B35L7

— **Bellerophon**.   Tragedie, représentée par l'Academie royale de musique.   Suivant la copie imprimée, a Paris.

[Amsterdam, Antoine Schelte], 1679.   56 (incl. front.), 4 p.   13cm.

Contents as in next entry.   ML 50.2.B35L8

— **Bellerophon**.   Tragedie, representee par l'Academie royale de musique.   Suivant la copie imprimée. à Paris.

[Amsterdam, Antoine Schelte], 1682.   56 (incl. front.), [4] p.   13½cm.

The [4] p. contain Lully's "Permission pour tenir Academie royale de musique." Prologue and five acts.   The prefatory note contains argument and remark:

"Le roy ayant donné la paix à l'Europe, l'Academie royale de musique a creu devoir marquer la part qu'elle prend à la joye publique par un spectacle, où elle pust faire entrer les témoignages de son zele pour la gloire de cet auguste monarque."

Without name of Corneille or **Lully**.   ML 49.A2L9

— **Bellerophon**, tragedie representée par l'Academie royale de musique l'an 1679.   Les paroles sont de M. Corneille & la musique de M. de Lully, XI. opera.

n. i., n. d.   14cm.   pl., 135–196 p.   (Recueil général des opéra, t. II, Paris, 1703).

Detached copy.   Five acts and prologue.   The text is said to have been a collaboration of Thomas Corneille, Fontenelle (and Boileau?)   (For a digest of the contrversy see Clément and Larousse.)   The prologue is preceded by the same note as above.   SCHATZ 5762

Second copy.   ML48.R4

Bellerophon—Continued.

— **Arlequin Bellerophon.** Parodie. Par Messieurs Dominique & Romagnesi . . . Representée pour la premiere fois par les Comédiens italiens ordinaires du roi, le 7. May 1728.

Les parodies du Nouveau théâtre italien, Nouv. éd., Paris, Briasson, 1738, t. iv, 36 p. 16½^{cm}.

One act. The airs and vaudeville printed at end in the "Table des airs" (92 p.).

ML 48.P3

Bellerophon, oder: Das in die preussische krone verwandelte wagengestirn, an dem frohen vermaehlungsfeste Sr. Koeniglichen Majestaet von Preussen Friderici I . . . zu unterthaenigster freuden-bezeugung in einer operetta, auf dem Grossen Hamburgischen Schau-platz aufgefuehret. Im jahr 1708. den 28. Novembr.

n. i., n. d. Unpaged. 18½^{cm}.

Three acts with prologue and epilogue. Neither Barthold Feind, the author who based his text on Corneille, nor Christoph **Graupner**, the composer, is mentioned in the "Vorbericht." Some of the arias and the choruses have both Italian and German text.

SCHATZ 4118

Bellezza ed onestà. A. T. of Martin y Soler's Una cosa rara.

La bellezza sopra d'un carro. *See* Scipione Affricano.

La Bellinda. Commedia per musica di Francesco Cerlone da rappresentarsi nel Teatro Nuovo sopra Toledo nel carnevale di quest' anno 1781.

Napoli, n. publ., 1781. 68 p. 15^{cm}.

Three acts. Cast and name of Giacomo **Tritto** as the composer. SCHATZ 10461

Belmira in Creta. Drama per musica da rappresentarsi nel Teatro Giustiniano di S. Mosè l'autuno corrente MDCCXXIX . . .

Venezia, Alvise Valvaseuse, 1729. 47 p. 15^{cm}.

Three acts. By Girolamo Giusti, who is not mentioned. Dedication, notice to the reader, argument, scenario, cast, and name of the composer, Antonio **Galeazzi**.

SCHATZ 3419

Belmont und Constanze, oder: Die entfuehrung aus dem serail. Eine operette in drey akten von C. F. Bretzner. Componirt vom herrn kapellmeister André in Berlin.

Leipzig, Carl Friedrich Schneider, 1781. 72 p. 15½^{cm}.

First performed at Berlin, Döbbelinssches Theater, May 25, 1781. SCHATZ 183

Belmont und Constanze oder Die entfuehrung aus dem serail. Eine operette in drey akten von C. F. Bretzner. Componirt vom herrn. hofmusikus Dieter in Stuttgart.

Stuttgart, Druckerey der herzoglichen Hohen Karls-Schule, 1784. 72 p. 16^{cm}.

First performed at Stuttgart, herzogl. Kl. Theater, 1784. SCHATZ 2574

Belmonte und Konstanze. L. T. of Mozart's Die entführung aus dem serail.

. . . Die **belohnte rechtschaffenheit,** ein schauspiel mit gesang in einem akt. Verfasst und in musik gesezt von herrn Wagenseil.

n. i., n. d. [6] *p. 16ᶜᵐ.*

At head of title: "Von der Kleinen Liebhaber gesellschaft wird den 23 und 26 maymonats 1785 aufgefuehrt," at Kaufbeuren. It was followed by the two act "Das wunsch huetchen. Ein lustspiel."   SCHATZ 10814

Belphegor; or, The wishes. A comic opera: as it was acted at the Theatre Royal, Smoke-Alley.

[*Dublin*], *Printed for the booksellers, 1788. 29 p. 15½ᶜᵐ.*

Neither the author, Miles Peter Andrews, is mentioned nor the composer François Hippolyte **Barthélémon.**
First performed at London, Drury Lane, March 17, 1778.   LONGE 223

Belsazer. A. T. of Telemann's Das ende der Babylonischen monarchie.

The **benevolent planters.** A dramatic piece, as performed at the Theatre Royal, Haymarket. Written by Thomas Bellamy. [vignette]

London, J. Debrett, 1789. 3 p. l., 14, [2] p. 20ᶜᵐ.

One act and prologue. Cast. A slavery abolition play in which there are a few songs, one to the tune of "Rule Britannia." The [2] p. contain publisher's booklists.
First performed August, 1789, as "The friends, or, the benevolent planters."   LONGE 195

Benevolent tar. A. T. of Reeve's The purse.

Berengario rè d'Italia. Drama per musica. Da rappresentarsi nel Teatro di Sant' Angelo il carnovale dell' anno 1709. Di Matteo Noris . . .

Venezia, Marino Rossetti, 1709. 69, [1] p. 15ᶜᵐ.

The additional p. contains a list of "Opere musicali" publ. by Antonio Bortoli.
Three acts. Dedication, argument, author's prefatory remarks, and scenario. Girolamo **Polani,** the composer, is not mentioned.   SCHATZ 8248

Berenice. O. T. of Antonio Salvi's text "Le gare di politica e d'amore."

Berenice. Dramma per musica da rappresentarsi nel famosissimo Teatro Grimani di S. Gio. Grisostomo. Nel carnovale dell' anno MDCCXXXIV . . .

Venezia, Marino Rossetti, 1734.

Three acts. By Antonio Salvi who is not mentioned. Dedication by Domenico Lalli, cast, argument, scenario, and name of Francesco **Araya** as composer.
First performed at Pratolino Teatro della Villa Medici, 1730.   SCHATZ 305

Berenice, in einem singenden schau-spiele auff dem Hamburgischen Schau-platze vorgestellet.

[*Hamburg*], *Conrad Neumann, 1702. Unpaged. 18½ᶜᵐ.*

Three acts. Neither Hinsch, the author, is mentioned nor Georg **Bronner,** the composer. Text based on Zeno's "Lucio Vero."   SCHATZ 1332

Berenice. Dramma per musica da rappresentarsi nel Teatro di S. Angelo il carnovale dell' anno 1741 . . .

Venezia, Marino Rossetti, n. d. 58 p. 15½ᶜᵐ.

Three acts. Author not mentioned and unknown to Schatz. Impresario's dedication, argument, scenario, cast, and name of **Galuppi** as composer. On a fly leaf preceding the title page the substitute aria (I, 12) "Il fiero mi tormenta."
First performed, as indicated, January 27, 1741 (Piovano).   SCHATZ 3483

Berenice. Dramma da cantarsi nel Teatro celebre Grimani in S. Gio. Grisostomo il carnovale MDCCXXV.

Venezia, Marino Rossetti, n. d. 66 p. 15½^{cm}.

Three acts. By Benedetto Pasqualigo, who is not mentioned. Argument, cast, scenario, and name of Giuseppe Maria **Orlandini** as the composer. Schatz 7329

La Berenice. Drama per musica da rappresentarsi in Verona nel Nuovo Teatro dell' Accademia Filarmonica nel carnovale dell' anno 1762 . . .

Verona, Dionisio Ramanzini, 1762. 48 p. 17^{cm}.

Three acts. Dedication with name of Apostolo Zeno as the author (an alteration of whose "Lucio Vero" this is), argument, cast, scenario, and name of David **Perez** as the composer. Schatz 7879

Berenice. Dramma per musica da rappresentarsi nel Teatro d. S. Angelo per la solita fiera dell' Ascensione dell' anno 1759 . . .

Venezia, Modesto Fenzo, 1759. 48 p. 15^{cm}.

Three acts. By Bartolomeo Vitturi, who is not mentioned. Impresario's dedication, argument, cast, scenario, and name of Salvatore **Perillo** as the composer. ("La musica tutta nuova.")
First performed, as indicated, May 23, 1759. Schatz 7925

Berenice. Dramma per musica da rappresentarsi nel Regio Teatro di Torino nel carnovale del 1771 . . .

Torino, Mairesse, n. d. viii, 60 p. 17^{cm}.

Three acts. By Jacopo Durandi, who is not mentioned. Argument, cast, scenario, and names of Ignazio **Platania** as the composer of the opera, of Giuseppe Antonio Le Messier of the ballet music.
First performed, as indicated, December 26, 1770. Schatz 8214

Berenice e Lucilla overo L'amar per virtù.—Berenice und Lucilla, oder Das tugendhaffte lieben, meistens aus dem italianischen genommen, und zu Darmstadt in einem sing-spiel vorgestellet den [*blank*] Februarii im jahr 1710.

Darmstadt, Hoff-Buch-druckerey, n. d. 83 p. 18½^{cm}.

Three acts. Argument. Neither Osiander, the author, nor Christoph **Graupner**, the composer, is mentioned. Schatz 4119

Berenice und Lucilla oder Das tugendhaffte lieben. *See* Graupner's Berenice e Lucilla.

La bergère des Alpes. Pastorale en trois actes, et en vers, melée de chants. Par M. Marmontel, de l'Académie françoise.

Avignon, Louis Chambeau, 1766. 32 p. 19^{cm}.

The composer, Joseph **Kohault**, is not mentioned.
First performed at Paris, Comédie italienne, February 19, 1766. ML 48.M2 I

— **La bergere des Alpes,** pastorale en trois actes, et en vers, mêlée de chant. Par M. Marmontel . . .

Bruxelles, J. J. Boucherie & compagnie, 1770. 44 p. 18^{cm}.

The composer, Joseph **Kohault,** is not mentioned. On p. 39–44: "Airs de la Bergere des Alpes;" "C'est dans le bois" (I, 1); "Oui, la nature est la mère" (I, 9); "Si les talents & les graces" (?); "Sous ces gazons depuis deux ans" (III, 4). Schatz 5204

La bergerie. Entrée in Niel's Les romans.

Die **bergknappen,** ein originalsingspiel in einem aufzug. Aufgefuehrt auf der hochfuerstl. Thurn und Taxischen Schaubuehne. Die
musik ist vom hrn.   Paul Kuerzinger.

Regensburg, mit Breitfeldischen schriften, 1773.   24 p.   15ᶜᵐ.

Text by Paul Weidmann, who is not mentioned.
First performed 1773, as indicated.   Schatz 5337

Die **bergknappen,** ein originalsingspiel von einem aufzuge.   Aufgeführt auf der K. K. Nationalschaubühne.   Die musik ist vom herrn
Umlauf.

Wien, bey dem Logenmeister, 1778.   26 p.   16ᶜᵐ.

By Paul Weidmann, who is not mentioned.
First performed, as indicated: privately, for Joseph II, on January 16, 1778; pub-
licly, on February 17, 1778.   (Haas has this date on p. xii of his ed. of the opera, 1911;
on p. x he has February 18)   Schatz 10524

Berilowitz in Tartaria, ballo eroico pantomimo. *See* Fioravanti's
L'amor per interesse.

Il **Bertarido, rè de Longobardi.**   Drama per musica da rappresentarsi in Venezia nel Teatro Tron di S. Cassiano l'autuno dell' anno
MDCCXXVII.

Venezia, Marino Rossetti, 1727.   59 p.   14ᶜᵐ.

Three acts.   Argument, preface, cast, and names of the composer of the opera,
Giuseppe **Boniventi,** and of the ballet airs, Giacomo Mioto Antonio Salvi. The
unmentioned author is Antonio Salvi, whose altered "Rodelinda, regina de' Longobardi" this is.   Schatz 1185

Bertholde à la ville.   Parody of Ciampi's Bertoldo, Bertoldino e
Cacasenno.

Bertoldo.   Drama tragicomico da rappresentarsi nel Teatro di San
Fantino il carnovale dell' anno 1717.

Venezia, Christoforo Bortoli, 1717.   43 p.   14½ᶜᵐ.

Three acts.   Prefatory note and scenario.   Neither the librettist, Francesco Passarini, is mentioned, nor the composer, Girolamo **Bassani.**   Schatz 635

Il **Bertoldo.** Dramma giocoso per musica da rappresentarsi nel Regio Teatro di via della Pergola nel carnevale del
MDCCLXXXVIII . . .

Firenze, Stamperia già Albizziniana, n. d.   64 p.   16½ᶜᵐ.

Two acts.   By Lorenzo da Ponte, with his name and that of the composer, Antonio
Brunetti. ("La musica è tutta nuova.") With the opera were performed Le
Fevre's ballets, "Il Cristoforo Colombo nell' Indie, ballo eroico tragico" and "Le
figlie astute."   The composers of the music are not mentioned.   Schatz 1363

— **Bertoldo e Bertoldino.**   Dramma giocoso per musica da rappresentarsi in Genova nel Teatro da S. Agostino l'estate del 1791 . . .

Genova, Stamperia Gesiniana, n. d.   68 p.   13½ᶜᵐ.

Two acts.   A much-condensed version of "Il Bertoldo."   The first act, for instance,
has only 25 scenes, instead of 28, the opening chorus, "Di re si possente," the fifth
scene, "Ah me la pagnerai," the tenth, "Quanti diversi affetti," etc., being suppressed.   Impresario's dedication, cast, scenario, and name of Antonio **Brunetti** as
composer.   Schatz 1364

Bertoldo.   *See* Ciampi's Bertoldo, Bertoldino e Cacasseno.

Bertoldo, ein lustiges singspiel in zwey aufzuegen. Aufgefuehrt im K. K. Hoftheater.

Wien, n. publ., 1787. 79 p. 16^{cm}.

Two acts. German text only. Lorenzo da Ponte is mentioned as the author, Francesco **Piticchio** as the composer. The translator is not mentioned.
First performed, as indicated, June 22, 1787. Schatz 8202

Bertoldo, Bertoldino e Cacasenno.

[155]-214 p. 16½^{cm}. (Carlo Goldoni, Opere drammatiche giocose, t. i, Torino, 1757.)

Three acts. In his humorous prefatory note on the text Goldoni says:
"A proposito del poeta, fa egli la sua protesta . . . e che, se ha fatto un cattivo libro in dieci giorni, non l'ha saputo far meglio. Circa le arie, alcune sono figlie legittime, e naturali del libro, alcune adattate, altre spurie, ed altre adulterine per comodo, e compiacimento de' virtuosi, onde ec." ML 49.A2G6

— **Bertoldo, Bertoldino e Cacasenno.** Dramma di tre atti per musica.

Carlo Goldoni, Opere teatrali, Venezia, Zatta e figli, 1788-95, t. 39, [189]-248 p. 18^{cm}. PQ

Bertoldo, Bertoldino, e Cacasenno, dramma comico per musica da rappresentarsi nel Teatro Giustiniano di S. Moisè il carnovale dell' anno 1749.

Venezia, Modesto Fenzo, 1749. 60 p. 14½^{cm}.

Three acts. Neither the author, Carlo Goldoni, is mentioned, nor Vincenzo Legrenzio **Ciampi,** the composer. Goldoni's witty notice to the reader ends:
"Circa le arie, alcune sono figlie legitime, e naturali del libro, alcune addotate, altre spurie, ed altre adulterine per commodo, e compiacimento de virtuosi, onde, ec."
This is the real and original title of Goldoni's famous libretto. All statements that Ciampi composed another opera called "Bertoldo in (or alla) corte," first performed at Parma are incorrect, because a comparison of the librettos (all in three acts) in the L. C. proves that "Bertoldo in corte" is practically identical with "Bertoldo, Bertoldino e Cacasseno." The opera became known also simply as "Bertoldo," but "Bertoldo in (or alla) corte" appears to have become the most popular title, and as such Ciampi's opera was first performed at Paris on November 22, or November 9, 1753, as a *pasticcio.* For instance (*compare* De La Laurencie's essay mentioned below) "Grandi, e ver son" was from **Leo**'s "Olimpiade" and "Quando sento spirarmi" was parodied from his "Se mai senti spirarti" in his "Clemenza di Tito." "La donna onorata" does not appear in the original Venice, 1749 libretto of Ciampi's opera, though in the Brunswick and Strassburg librettos analized by me. "Cosi fugge e spaventosa" is not in Goldoni's text. For a detailed comparison of these different editions *see* the author's study on Ciampi's opera and Favart's "Ninette à la cour" in the Sammelbánde d. I. M. G. 1910/11, p. 525-564.
To this essay I wish to add here that there exist two collections of "Favourite Songs . . . Bertoldo," not only one, as I presumed. The Royal College of Music in London possess both, with this ms. note on the title page, as Mr. Squire informed me: "Published originally in 1749 and republished with no. 1 in 1762." The L. of C. copy is identical with No. 2. The contents of No. 1 are:

1. *Sive Bertoldo mio garbato.* Ciampi
   (Text not by Goldoni.)
2. *Sono allegra[, son contenta].* Ciampi
   (Text from Goldoni's La buona figliuola maritata.)
3. *Ciascun mi dice.* Ciampi
   (Text not in the original Venice, 1749, libretto, but in the Brunswick and Ferrara eds.)
4. *Se nessuno ora non c' è.* anonymous
   (Text from Goldoni's Il mercato di Malmantile.)
5. *Ah poi che pietà.* Galuppi
   (Text not by Goldoni.) Schatz 1882

Bertoldo, Bertoldino, e Cacasenno—Continued.

— **Bertoldo, Bertoldino e Cacasenno.** Dramma giocosa [!] per musica da rappresentarsi nel Nuovo Teatro dell' Opera-pantomima di Bronsevico.

*n. i., [1750?] 147 p. 18½*cm.

Three acts. Scenario and name of the composer, Vincenzo **Ciampi**, German title page "Bertoldus, Bertoldinus und Cacasennus" and text face the Italian.

                                      Schatz 1879

— **Bertoldo.** Dramma comico per musica da rappresentarsi nel Teatro Nuovo di Argentina.

*Argentina, Giovanni Henrico Heitz, 1751. 46 p. 15*cm.

Three acts. Notice to the reader, cast, and name of the composer, Vincenzo **Ciampi**.

First performed at Strassburg (Argentina) in 1751, as indicated.   Schatz 1876

— **Bertoldo in corte.** Dramma giocoso per musica da rappresentarsi nel Teatro Bonacossi da S. Stefano il carnevale dell' anno 1755 . . .

*Ferrara, Giuseppe Rinaldi, n. d. 48 p. 14½*cm.

Three acts. Impresario's dedication, Goldoni's original "Bertoldo, Bertoldino e Cacasenno" preface (with exception of the last paragraph), cast, and name of the, composer, Vincenzo **Ciampi**. The parts of "Aurelia, sorella del rè" and "Lisaura, figlia del rè, e della regina," have been dropped and the whole libretto has been considerably condensed and modified. For purposes of identification may be mentioned that the opening chorus "Amor discenda" has been dropped and that the opera now begins with the words "Amico, in questa alpestre," that its third act has only eight scenes instead of eleven, the second fifteen instead of eighteen, etc.

                                      Schatz 1887

— **Bertholde a la ville,** opera-comique, en un acte. Représenté pour la premiere fois sur le Théâtre [!] de la Foire S. Germain le 9 mars 1754.

*Paris, Duchesne, 1754. 55, [1] p. 19½*cm.

Cast. On p. 31–55 the same airs as in the 1766 ed., which compare for authors and composer. On last p. is a list of "Opera-comiques nouveaux."

                                      ML 50.2.B37C31

— **Bertholde a la ville,** opera-comique en un acte. Représenté pour la premiere fois sur le Théâtre de la Foire S. Germain, le 9 mars 1754.

*La Haye, Jean Neaulme, 1755. 28 p. · 19*cm.

Neither authors nor composer mentioned. (*See* next entry.)   ML 48.A4

— **Bertholde à la ville.** Opéra-comique, en un acte. Représenté pour la premiere fois sur le Théatre de la Foire S. Germain le 9 mars 1754.

*Paris, la veuve Duchesne, 1766. 55 p. 18½*cm.

Cast. On p. 31–55 the "Airs de Bertholde," "Quand le hasard ensemble," "Tel qu'un petit oiseau," "Votre coeur en vain," "A tant de charmes," "Dieu! quel paix," "Le Ciel va rendre." As authors of this parody *en vaudevilles* of Ciampi's opera are mentioned by different authorities Anseaume alone, or de Lattaignan and Anseaume, or Vadé, Anseaume and Hautemer. All mention **Lasalle d'Offemont** as composer, resp. arranger of the music, which was selected from French vaudevilles and the six ariettes from Ciampi's opera and Cocchi's "La mascherata."

                                      Schatz 1883

— Le **caprice amoureux,** ou Ninette a la cour. Comédie en trois actes, melée d'ariettes, parodiées de Bertolde a la court. Par

Bertoldo, Bertoldino, e Cacasenno—Continued.

Favart. Représenté pour la premiere fois par les Comédiens françois ordinaires du roi le 12 février 1757 [!]

Paris, N. B. Duchesne, 1758. 48 p. 19½^{cm}.

The date of performance should be 1755. (*See* next entry.)   ML 50.2.B37C33

— Le **caprice amoureux** ou Ninette à la cour, comédie en deux
actes, mêlée d'ariettes, parodiées de Bertolde à la cour par Monsieur
Favart. Représentée pour la premiere fois par les Comédiens italiens ordinaires du Roi, le mercredi 12 mars 1756 et ci-devant en
trois actes le 12 février 1755. Nouvelle édition corrigée & conforme
à la réprésentation.

Paris, N. B. Duchesne, 1759. 86 p. 18^{cm}.

Cast. On p. 81–82 "Table des ariettes de Ninette à la cour, gravées en quatre
parties" with the foot-note "Les ariettes marquées dans la table par une S, ne se
chantent point à la Représentation; mais se trouvent gravées dans la musique."
These are in *partie* I, no. 9, "En tourbillon, un papillon," in *partie* II, no. 18, "Au
sein des alarmes," and no. 21, "Qu'il a de gentillesse," in *partie* III, no. 23, "Je
veux tirer vengeance," no. 24, "Assise sur le bord d'une onde," no. 25 "Non, non,
je n'ai peur," and no. 27 "Quatuor." On p. 83–86 "Catalogue des pièces des comé-
dies françoise & italienne, & opera comiques qui se vendent détachés." The text
is a close parody of Goldoni's "Bertoldo," but the music is a pasticcio from Ciampi's
opera, and operas by Latilla, Cocchi, Selitti, Jommelli, Vinci, etc. Duni is said by
some authorities to have arranged the score for Favart, but this is not certain. The
whole complicated matter of text and music has been investigated by the author in
the study mentioned above. Compare also De La Laurencie's article on "Les
bouffons," S. I. M., 1912, nos. 6–8. The music of the "O dell' Egitto," final chorus
in Rinaldo di Capua's La Zingara" and his "Toute mon âme" is, as I since learned,
borrowed from Hasse's "Leucippo."   SCHATZ 1877

— Le **caprice amoureux,** ou Ninette a la cour, comédie en deux
actes, meslée d'ariettes, parodiées de Bertolde a la cour; par M.
Favart: Représentée pour la premiere fois par les Comédiens italiens
ordinaires du roi, le mercredi 12 mars 1756.

n. i., n. d. 120 p. 19^{cm}. (*Theatre de M. Favart, Paris, Duchesne,
1763–77, t. iii.*)

No cast. No composer mentioned. No music printed in the text, but the text
is followed on p. [81]–98 by twenty-seven "Ariettes de Ninette a la cour, parodie . . .
Nouvelle édition corrigée, et conforme aux représentations" and on p. [97]–120 by
six "Ariettes, pour servir de supplément . . ." with foot-note: "Ces ariettes ne se
chantent point à la représentation; mais elles ont toujours été gravées dans la
musique." They are "En tourbillon, un papillon," "Au sein des alarmes," "Qu'il
a de zentillesse," "Je veux tirer vengeance," "Assise sur les bords," "Non, non, je
n'ai point peur." Of these only the words of "Qu'il a de zentillesse" appear in the
present text (II, 10) and the same air is printed as no. 21 of the "Ariettes." The
others are remnants of the three-act version.   ML 49.A2F1

— Der **verliebte eigensinn,** oder Nannerl bei hofe, eine komische
oper in zween aufzuegen. Aus dem franzoesischen des herrn Favart
uebersetzt [vignette].

Pressburg, Anton Loewe, 1778. 1 p. l., 70 p. 16½^{cm}.

German version by Carl Ludwig Reuling, with cast.
First performed at Pressburg, Neues Theater, in 1778.   SCHATZ 1878

— **Bondepigen ved hoffet.** En lyrisck comedie i to handlinger, af
Favart. Musiken af Duny; til samme musik oversat af Niels Krog
Bredal.

n. i., n. d. 112 p. 16^{cm}.

Duni did not compose the music, but possibly arranged the score for Favart.
First performed at Copenhagen, Hoftheater i Christiansborg Slot, March 12, 1776.
     SCHATZ 2852

Bertoldo in corte. *See* Ciampi's Bertoldo, Bertoldino e Cacasseno.

Die **besaenftigte mitbuhlerinnen.** Tr. of Le rivali placate.

Gesaenge in dem nachspiel Der **beschaemte geizhals.** Verfertigt und in musik gesezt von herrn Wagenseil.

    Kaufbeuren, Dorn, 1787. [*12*] *p.* 16^{cm}.

One act. A contemporary hand has written on the title page: "Aufgefuert d. 30 oct. 1ten und 6ten nov. 1787"; on p. [2] the cast and the receipts. The performances were given at the Theater der bürgerlichen Agenten Gesellschaft AC.

                                                      SCHATZ 10815

Der **beschluss des carnevals.** Opera comique auf dem Hamburgischen Schau-platze vorgestellet im monat februarii anno 1724.

    [*Hamburg*], *Caspar Jakhel, n. d.*   *Unpaged.* 18^{cm}.

A pasticcio in three acts, of which the first two have French text, and the last German. In the anonymous German *avertissement* we are informed that the first act is based on "L'Europe galante," composed by **Campra.**

    "Weil darinnen ein türckischer aufzug vorkommt, der bey einer ansehnlichen menge von personen so viel fremdes als laecherliches in sich haelt."

    The third act consists "aus einer neu-verfertigten *operette comique,*" which Schatz attributes to **Telemann** (text by Schwemschu), under the title "Il capitano." The second act is Montfleury's comedy "La fille capitaine," and is spoken (in French!) throughout. Surely, one of the oddest mixtures imaginable!   SCHATZ 1564

Der **besiegte zauber.** Tr. of Süssmayer's L'incanto superato.

Den **beskaemmede gnier.** Tr. of Scolari's L'avaro burlato.

Den **besnaerede Cadi.** Tr. of Monsigny's Le cadi dupé.

Die **bestaendigkeit besieget den betrug.** German title of Graupner's La costanza vince l'inganno.

Die **beständigkeit in der liebe.** A. T. of Anfossi's Isabella und Rodrigo.

Das **beste komt zulezt.** A. T. of Kaffka's Der guckkasten.

Die **bestrafte eifersucht.** Tr. of Cimarosa's Il marito disperato.

Gesaenge aus dem singspiele: Der **bestrafte hochmuth,** oder: Liebe macht alle staende gleich, in drey aufzuegen. Die musik ist von Gerl.

    Hamburg, Rabe und Freystatzky wittwe, 1798. *40 p.* 16$\frac{1}{2}$^{cm}.

Text by Franz Joseph Fransky after Coltellini's "La contessina."

First performed at Hamburg, Theater beim Gänsemarkt, September 10, 1798; previously as "Graf Balbarone oder Die maskerade" at Brünn, National-theater, May, 28, 1796.

                                                      SCHATZ 3785

Der **bestuerzte und wieder erhoehte Nebucadnezar,** koenig zu Babylon, unter dem grossen propheten Daniel, in einem singespiel auf dem grossen Hamburgischen Schau-platze vorgestellet im jahr 1704.

    [*Hamburg*], *mit Greflingischen schrifften, n. d.* *Unpaged.* 18$\frac{1}{2}$^{cm}.

Three acts. Neither the author, Christian Friedrich Hunold (Menantes) is mentioned, nor the composer, Reinhard **Keiser.** Scenario and "Vorrede" with argument.

                                                      SCHATZ 5092

Die **betrogene arglist.** *See* Weigl's Das unnütze bestreben.

Der **betrogene geizhals.** Tr. of Paisiello's L'avaro deluso.

Der **betrogene geizige,** oder Wer das glueck hat. **Tr.** of Paisiello's
La discordia fortunata.

Die **betrogene staats-liebe,** oder Die unglueckselige Cleopatra,
koenigin von Egypten, in einem singespiel auf dem Hamburgischen
Schau-Platz vorgestellet.

> *Hamburg, Nicolaus Spieringks wittwe, 1704. Unpaged. 19^{cm}.*
> Three acts. The "Historische einleitung" is not signed by the author, Friedrich
> Christian Feustking, nor is the composer, Johann **Mattheson,** mentioned.
> First performed, as indicated, October 20, 1704.   SCHATZ 6101

Die **betrogene und nachmals vergoetterte Ariadne,** in einem
singe-spiele auff dem Hamburgischen Schau-platze im jahr 1722 vorgestellet.

> *[Hamburg], Casper Jakhel, n. d. Unpaged. 18½^{cm}.*
> Three acts and prologue. Cast, scenario, and name of Reinhard **Keiser** as the
> composer. The last page contains two substitute arias. Many arias have Italian
> text added to the German. The author, resp. translator, Christian Heinrich Postel,
> is not mentioned. According to Schatz the title of the text originally was "Die
> schöne und getreue Ariadne."   SCHATZ 5079

Der **betrogene vormund** oder Das einfaeltige maedgen. Tr. of von
Schacht's Il tutore deluso o La semplice.

Die **betrogenen kastellane.** Tr. of Fabrizj's Li castellani burlati.

Der **betrug aus liebe,** oder Der schuss von Gaensewiz. Ein komisches singspiel in drey aufzeugen. Durch den eleve Rudolph
Zumsteeg im musik gesezt.

> *Stuttgart, Christoph Gottfried Maentler, 1780. 63 p. 14½^{cm}.*
> Author not mentioned and unknown to Schatz.
> First performed at Stuttgart, Hoftheater, 1780.   SCHATZ 11293

Betrug durch aberglauben. Ein komisches singspiel in zwey
aufzeugen vom F. Eberl. Die musik dazu ist ganz neu von herrn
Karl Ditters, edlen von Dittersdorf. Aufgeführt im K. K. National-
Hoftheater.

> *[Vienna], Zu finden beym logenmeister, n. d. 93 p. 15^{cm}.*
> Bound in with this "Arien aus . . . Una cosa rara . . . von Vinzenz Martini,
> Wien, 1787."
> First performed, as indicated, October 3, 1786.   SCHATZ 2587

Der **bettelstudent,** oder Das donnerwetter. Ein originallustspiel
in zwey aufzeugen mit gesaengen. Die musik ist von herrn Peter
Winter . . .

> *n. i., 1789. [405]–458 p. 17^{cm}.*
> Detached copy. By Paul Weidmann, who is not mentioned.
> First performed at Munich, National Schaubuehne, February 2, 1785.
>   SCHATZ 11023

Il **Beverlei o sia Il giouocatore inglese,** ballet. *See* Gardi's Il
nuovo convitato di pietra.

Il bevitore, intermezzi per musica, da rappresentarsi nel Regio Teatro alla corte di Dresda.   L'anno 1747.

   n. i., n. d.   79 p.   16^{cm}.

   Three parts.   Cast.   Neither the author (unknown to Schatz) nor the composer, Joh. Ad. **Hasse,** is mentioned.   German title page, "Der saeuffer," and text face Italian.
   First performed, as indicated, January, 1747.   SCHATZ 4520

Der bey dem allgemeinen welt-friede von dem grossen Augustus geschlossene tempel des Janus auf dem lang-gewuenschten friedenfeste welches im jahr 1698 in Hamburg gefeiret ward in einem singespiel vorgestellet.   [vignette.]

   Hamburg, Nicolaus Spieringk, n. d.   Unpaged.   18$\frac{1}{2}$^{cm}.

   Three acts.   Lengthy historical preface, delving even into numismatics, by the author Christian Heinrich Postel.   Neither he is mentioned, nor the composer, Reinhard **Keiser.**   The text of the opera is followed by 4 p. of text with title: "Nach geendigter opera faehret Fama in einer wolcke herab und singet dem grossen kayser Leopold zu ehren nachfolgendes.   Auff dessen beschluss folget das feuer-werck. Hamburg, Gedrucktbey Nicolaus Spieringk, 1698."
   First performed at Hamburg Opernhaus beim Gänsemarkt, June 9, 1698.
                                                                SCHATZ 5120

— **Der bey dem allgemeinen welt-frieden von dem grossen Augustus geschlossene tempel des Janus,** in einer opera auf dem Hamburgischen Schau-platze aufs neue aufgefuehret im monath octobris anno 1729.

   [Hamburg], mit Stromerschen schrifften, n. d.   Unpaged.   18$\frac{1}{2}$^{cm}.

   Three acts.   Neither the author, Christian Heinrich Postel, nor the composer, Reinhard **Keiser,** is mentioned.   The text is the same as in the edition of 1698 except that the dialogue of the scene III, 13, was suppressed, the final aria "Edler friede sey willkommen" now forming part of III, 12.   SCHATZ 5078

Die beyden barons von Rocca Azura.   Tr. of Cimarosa's I due baroni di Rocca Azurra.

Die beyden eifersuechtigen.   Tr. of Martin y Soler's Li sposi in contrasto.

Die beyden fluechtlinge.   Tr. of Paisiello's Le gare generose.

Die beyden kleinen Savoyarden.   Tr. of Dalayrac's Les deux petits Savoyards.

Die bezauberte insel.   A. T. of P. Ritter's Der sturm.

Der bezauberte kranz, ballet.   *See* Piccinni's Das gute maegdchen.

Die bezauberten.   Eine komische oper in einem aufzuge.   Nach dem französischen der Madame Favart.   Verfertigt und in musik gesetzt von Johann André.

   Berlin, Christian Friedrich Himburg, 1777.   70 p.   15^{cm}.

   Based on "Les ensorcelés ou Jeannot et Jeannette," parody of "Les surprises de l'amour" by de Marivaux.
   First performed at Berlin, Döbbelinssches Theater, October 18, 1777.
                                                                SCHATZ 184

Bezestan o Mercato di schavi, ballet.   *See* M. A. Valentini's Solimano.

Bianca de' Rossi, ballet. *See* P. Guglielmi's La pupilla scaltra.

Bianca de' Rossi, ballet. *See* Tarchi's Dorval e Virginia.

Bianca de' Rossi. Dramma nuovo per musica da rappresentarsi nel nobilissimo Teatro Venier in San Benedetto il carnovale dell' anno 1797.

Venezia, Modesto Fenzo, 1797. 43 p. 18ᶜᵐ.

Three acts. By Mattia Botturini, who is not mentioned. He makes this curious remark in a prefatory note:

"L'unico avviso, ch' egli [l'autore] avanza al pubblico, è ch' esiste su questo soggetto una tragedia del Signor abbate Pier Antonio Meneghelli, intitolata anch' essa *Bianca de' Rossi,* uscita in Padova dalla stamperia di Gio. Antonio Gonzati, e rappresentata in questa Dominante e in altre città d'Italia, nonchè un ballo pantomimo composto dal Signor Giuseppe Trafieri ed eseguito nel nobilissimo Teatro di San Benedetto il carnovale dell' anno 1793."

Cast, scenario and name of Vittorio **Trento** as the composer. Whether or not he used the music of the 1793 ballet which he composed is not mentioned. On p. 21–25 cast and description of Maria de' Caro's "Oscar e Malvina, ballo eroico pantomimo," "musica tutta nuova . . . del Sig. Giuseppe Nucci;" and on p. 39–40, brief description, without name of the composer, of Giuseppe Domenico de Rossy's ballet, "Mysis ed Eufrasia ossia I due gemelli."

First performed, as indicated, January 14, 1797.   SCHATZ 10418

Biblis, tragedie, représentée par l'Académie royale de musique, l'an 1732. Paroles de M. Fleury. Musique de M. La Coste. CXVII. opera.

n. i., n. d. 14ᶜᵐ. pl., 205–264 p. (Recueil général des opéra, t. xv, Paris, 1739.)

Detached copy. Five acts and prologue.
First performed, as indicated, November 6, 1732.   SCHATZ 5352
Second copy. ML 48.R4

Bickerstaff's Unburied dead. A moral drama. As acted at the Theatre-Royal in Lincoln's-Inn-Fields . . .

London, J. Watts, 1743. 4 p. l., 30, [2] p. 21½ᶜᵐ.

Two acts and epilogue. Cast and preface. Interspersed with songs, the composer of which is not mentioned. Author unknown to Clarence.   LONGE 271
First performed as indicated, January 14, 1743 (Genest).

Gesaenge aus dem schauspiele: Biondetta.

n. i., n. d. [8] p. 16½ᶜᵐ.

Four acts. Neither the author, Karl Christian Engel, nor the composer, Friedrich Adam **Hiller,** is mentioned.

First performed at Schwerin, Theater im Ballhause, July 14, 1790.   SCHATZ 4715

La birba. Intermezzo.

[210]–230 p. 16½ᶜᵐ. (Carlo Goldoni, Opere drammatiche giocose, t. iv, Torino, 1757.)

Two parts. Original composer unknown to Schatz.   ML 49.A2G6

—**La birba.** Intermezzo di due parti per musica. Rappresentato per la prima volta in Venezia il carnovale dell' anno MDCCXXXIV.

Carlo Goldoni, Opere teatrali, Venezia, Zatta e figli, 1788–95, t. 35, [71]–93 p. 18½ᶜᵐ.   PQ

Li birbi. Intermezzi da rappresentarsi in musica nel Teatro di S. Angelo nel carnevale 1732.

Venezia, Carlo Buonarrigo, 1732. 12 p. 15ᶜᵐ.

Two intermezzi. By Antonio Zanetti, who is not mentioned. Michele **Fini** is mentioned as the composer. Cast.   SCHATZ 3105

Li birbi. Intermezzo da rappresentarsi in musica nel Theatro nuovo dell' Opera pantomima, de piccoli Hollandesi di Nicolini.—Die schelmen, ein musicalisches zwischenspiel. Vorgestellet auf dem neuen Theater in der Opera pantomima von denen hollaendischen kindern des herrn Nicolini.

Braunschweig, Keitel, n. d.   Unpaged.   19½^{cm}.

Two parts. By Antonio Zanetti, who is not mentioned. German text faces Italian. Cast and name of the composer, "Ignatio **Fiorillo** Napoletano." First performed as indicated, 1749; at Hamburg, Neumarkt by the same company, December 2, 1748; at Prague, by the same company in the same year.   Schatz 3199

The birth-day, or, The prince of Arragon. A dramatick piece, with songs. In two acts. As performed at the Theatre-Royal, Hay-Market. Written by J. O'Keefe.

London, T. Cadell, 1783.   2 p. l., iv, [4], 38 p.   21 p.

Prologue, cast, and O'Keefe's dedication to the Prince of Wales, dated London, August 26, 1783. Of the nine songs, etc., the music of six is indicated as being by Samuel **Arnold,** of two as by **Piccinni.** The finale-chorus of the second act is without composer's name.

First performed August 12, 1783, as indicated.   Longe 164

The birth of the Prince of Wales. A. T. of Attwood's Caernarvon Castle.

Die biss in und nach dem todt unerhoerte treue des Orpheus. L. T. of Keiser's Orpheus.

Bitten und erhoerung. Ein singspiel womit das geburtstagsfest des koenigs am 24sten januar dieses jahres von der Waeserschen gesellschaft zu Breslau gefeiert worden.

p. 273–281.   18½^{cm}.   (Litteratur und Theater Zeitung, Berlin, 1783).

Footnote by the editor: "Hat den herrn kammer-referendarius Berger in Breslau zum verfasser, und die musik ist vom herrn [Johann Christian] **Kaffka** dazu verfertigt worden."   .   Schatz 4772

La bizarra contadina. Commedia per musica di Giuseppe Palomba da rappresentarsi nel Teatro Nuovo sopra Toledo per second' opera di quest' anno 1790.

Napoli, n. publ., 1790.   47 p.   15½^{cm}.

Two acts. Cast and name of Gaetano **Marinelli** as the composer.   Schatz 5959

La bizzarria degli umori. Farsetta per musica a cinque voci da rappresentarsi nel Teatro Capranica nel carnevale dell' anno 1777 . . .

Roma, Ottavio Puccinelli, 1777.   47 p.   15^{cm}.

Two acts. Author is not mentioned and is unknown to Schatz. Impresario's dedication, cast, and name of Giuseppe **Gazzaniga** as the composer.   Schatz 3684

Le bizzarie del bel sesso. A. T. of the ballet La vedova ingegnosa.

Blaise et Babet ou La suite des Trois fermiers. Comédie en deux actes, mêlée d'ariettes, par M. Monvel; représentée pour la première fois par les Comédiens italiens ordinaires du roi, devant Leurs Majestés, à Versailles, le 4 avril, & à Paris le 30 juin 1783.

Paris, Brunet, 1784.   56 p.   18½^{cm}.

Cast. **Dezède,** the composer, is not mentioned. The melodies of the "Chanson. Lise chantoit dans la prairie" (I, 5) and of the "Romance. Entends ma voix" (II, 5) are printed in the text   Schatz 2514

Blaise et Babet—Continued.

— Gesaenge aus dem singspiele: **Toeffel und Dortchen,** in zwey aufzuegen, nach Monvell. In musik gesetzt von Desaides.

Hamburg, J. M. Michaelsen, 1788. 20 p. 16½cm.

The translator is not mentioned.

First performed at Hamburg, Theater b. Gànsemarkt, Oct. 13, 1788; at Mannheim, Nationaltheater, Aug. 10, 1788.   SCHATZ 2515

Blaise le savetier, opera comique, suivi de La nôce de Nicaise, intermède mêlé de chants & de danses; par Monsieur S. . . . La musique de M. Phillidor. Représenté pour la première fois sur le Théâtre de l'Opéra comique de la Foire Saint Germain, le 9 mars 1759.

Paris, N. B. Duchesne, 1759. 31 p. 19½cm.

Imprimatur of date, June 27, 1759, cast and Avertissement by Sedaine, the author. (*See* next entry.)   ML 50.2.B39P4

—**Blaise le savetier,** opéra comique, suivi de La noce de Nicaise; intermède mêlé de chants & de danses: par M. S. . . . La musique de M. Philidor. Représenté pour la premiere fois sur le Théatre de l'Opéra-comique de la Foire Saint-Germain, le neuf mars mil sept cent cinquante-neuf.

Paris, la veuve Duchesne, 1769. 38 p. 19cm.

By Michel Jean Sedaine (not mentioned), who says in his *avertissement:*

"Si quelqu' un me reproche l'attention avec la quelle j'ai écrit la pantomime de cette farce, qu'il fasse réflexion que le grand défaut de la plupart des ariettes au théatre, est de se voir dénuées d'action: soit que ce défaut vienne des paroles & de la situation théatrale; soit que l'acteur, seulement musicien, ne sçache point les revêtir des gestes & du sentiment vrais."   SCHATZ 8007

— **Blaise le savetier,** opera comique, mêlé d'ariettes, par Monsieur S. . . . La musique de M. Philidor.

Paris, Duchesne, 1771. 29 p. 19cm.

Sedaine's Avertissement not in this ed.   SCHATZ 11736

—**Hanns der schuhflicker,** ein singspiel in einem aufzuge aus dem franzoesischen uebersetzt mit musik.

Frankfurt am Mayn, mit Andrealischen schriften, 1772. 61 p, 9 p. (music) 16cm.

Cast. Neither Joh. Heinr. Faber, the translator, nor **Philidor**, the composer, is mentioned. Version used by Theob. Marchand's company. The music (voice and bass) consists of: "Um vergnügt zu leben" (I, 4. "Tiens, tu me fais pitié"), "Nur das geld kann" (I, 5. "L'argent seul fixe le caprice").   SCHATZ 8008

Blanche et vermeille, comédie pastorale, en deux actes et en prose, mêlée de musique. Représentée pour la premiere fois par les Comédiens italiens ordinaires du roi, le lundi 5 mars 1781.

Paris, Thomas Brunet, 1781. 28 p. 21cm.

Neither Jean Pierre Claris de Florian, the author, is mentioned, nor Henri Joseph **Rigel**, the composer.   ML 50.2.B4R3

Der blaue schmetterling, oder Der sieg der natur ueber die schwaermerey. Ein komisches singspiel in drey aufzuegen. Nach Wieland. Sowohl die worte, als die musik, sind vom hrn. Maximilian Ulbrich. Aufgefuehrt im K. K. Nationalhoftheater.

Wien, beym Logenmeister, 1782. 70 p. 15½cm.

First performed, as indicated, April 2, 1782.   SCHATZ 10522

Das **blendwerk.**   Tr. of Grétry's La fausse magie.

The **blind beggar of Bethnal Green.**   By R. Dodsley [vignette].
London, Printed for R. Dodsley, 1741.   44 p.   20ᶜᵐ.
On p. [5], advertisement of Dodsley's "Publick register."
One act.   Cast.   The composer, Thomas Augustine **Arne**, is not mentioned.
First performed at London, Drury-Lane, April 3, 1741 (Genest).   LONGE 124
                                                         Second copy.   AC901 M5 v. 596

Blue-beard; or, Female curiosity! A dramatick romance; first
represented at the Theatre Royal Drury-Lane, on Tuesday, January
16, 1798.   Written by George Colman, the younger . . .
London, Cadell and Davies, 1798.   vi, [1], 54, [1] p.   21ᶜᵐ.
Two acts.   Cast and preface, with name of Michael **Kelly** as composer and compiler of the music, and statement that the piece is not a translation from the French
or any other language.   In Corri, Dussek & co's vocal score "And silence reigns
within the walls" is headed as by **Paesiello.**   LONGE 246

The **airs, glees, choruses,** etc. in the new pantomime of **Blue Beard;**
or, The flight of Harlequin.   As performed at the Theatre-Royal,
Covent-Garden.   Third edition.
London, T. Cadell, 1791.   20 p.   18ᶜᵐ.
Two acts.   Cast.   The airs, "That all ride their hobbies" and "My name's Tippy
Bob," are headed as composed by William **Reeve.**   LONGE 218

Blunders at Brighton,   A. T. of Shield's The Irish mimic.

Die **blut-durstige rache,** oder Heliates und Olympia, in einem
singspiel auf den Hamburgischen Schau-platze vorzustellen.
[Hamburg], Spiering, 1709.   Unpaged.   18½ᶜᵐ.
Three acts.   Text and music by Reinhard **Keiser,** who is not mentioned.   Scenario
and argument.   A few arias have Italian text added to the German.   SCHATZ 5080

The **boarding-school:** or, The sham captain.   An opera.   As it is
perform'd at the Theatre Royal in Drury-Lane, by His Majesty's
servants.   Written by the author of the Beggar's wedding and The
Devil to pay.   With the musick prefix'd to each song.
London, J. Watts, 1733.   44 p. 19ᶜᵐ.
One-act ballad opera.   Cast, dedication signed by the author, Charles Coffey, and
table of the 23 songs, the airs of which are printed in the text with their titles, except
airs 1, 2, 12, which are headed, "set by Mr. **Seedo.**"
First performed January 29, 1733, as indicated.   LONGE 50

— The **boarding school:** or, The sham captain.   An opera.   By
C. Coffey, Esq.
*[185]–215 p.   19ᶜᵐ.   (Collection of the most esteemed farces and en-
tertainments, t. v., Edinburgh, 1792.)*
Drury-Lane cast.   Ballad opera, with the airs "set by Mr. **Seedo.**"
                                                         SCHATZ 11753E

Die **boese frau.** Komisches original-singspiel in zwey aufzuegen.
1791.
*n. i., n. d.   [297]–392 p.   16ᶜᵐ.   (Herklots' Operetten, iv, Berlin,
1792.)*
Detached copy.   The composer, Ignatz **Walter,** is not mentioned.
First performed at Bremen, Theater an der Bastion beim Osterthore, November 3,
1794.   SCHATZ 10858

La **Bohémienne.** *See* La Zingara, by Rinaldo di Capua.

La **boîte de Pandore.** *See* La faussefoire.

Le **bon fils,** opéra en un acte. Paroles de Louis Hennequin, musique de L. S. Lebrun . . . Représenté, pour la premiere fois, sur le Théâtre de la rue Feydeau, le premier jour complémentaire de la troisième année républicaine (17 septembre 1795, vieux style).

Paris, Huet, an quatrième de la République, [1795–96]. 23 p. 20ᶜᵐ.

Cast. Between p. 22–23 in contemporary ms. the added couplet for Lise's "Vous jugérez de mon ivresse."
ML 50.2.B7L3

Le **bon fils,** comédie, en un acte et en prose, mêlée d'ariettes; par M. de Vaux. La musique, de M. Philidor. Représentée, pour la première fois, par les Comédiens italiens ordinaires du roi, le lundi, 11 janvier 1773.

Paris, la veuve Duchesne, 1773. iv, [6]–80, p. 4 p. (*music*) 17ᶜᵐ.

The music consists of the *vaudeville:* "Enfans voilà votre." In his *avertissement* the author repudiates the charge of plagiarism because of the great similarity of a scene with one in Grétry's "Silvain." His own piece, he says,
"faite dans son origine pour un théâtre de société, avoit été lue à ceux qui devoient la jouer & à quelques gens de lettres plus d'un an avant la représentation de Silvain. C'est donc le hasard qui a fait naître la même idée à deux poëtes qui ne se connoissoient pas." Nevertheless, he says, he has done all in his power to weaken the resemblance. Further on he states, that the piece was at first called "Antoine Masson," but "le public, après la seconde représentation, prévint l'acteur qui l'annonçoit & prononça *le bon fils.*"
SCHATZ 8009

Il **bon ton.** Dramma giocoso per musica da rappresentarsi nel Teatro Giustiniani in S. Moisè il carnovale dell' anno 1780.

Venezia, n. publ., n. d. 78 p. 18ᶜᵐ.

Two acts. Author not mentioned and unknown to Schatz. Cast and name of Joseph **Schuster** as the composer. ("La musica sarà.")
SCHATZ 9761

Le **bon vivant,** oder Die Leipziger messe, in einem singe- und lustspiel auff dem Hamburgischen Schau-Platz vorgestellet. Im jahr 1710.

Hamburg, Johan Niclas Gennagel, n. d. Unpaged. 19ᶜᵐ.

Three acts. Preface in form of a commentary on his own piece by Weidemann, the author. Neither he nor the composer, Reinhard **Keiser,** is mentioned.
SCHATZ 5121

Bondehovmod eller Kiøbmanden som adelsmand, og bondepigen som frøken. Tr. of Picinni's Il fumo villano.

Bondepigen ved hoffet. Tr. of Ciampi's Le caprice amoureux, ou Ninette à la cour.

Bønderfolks elskov. Tr. of Lampugnani's L'amor contadino.

Bonduca: or, The British heroine. A tragedy. Acted at the Theatre Royal. By His Majesty's servants. With a new entertainment of musick, vocal and instrumental. Never printed or acted before.

London, Printed for Richard Bentley, 1696. 4 p. l., 53, [3] p. 21½ᶜᵐ.

Three acts, prologue, and epilogue. Last (unnumb.) page contains Bentley's book list. Cast, dedication by Geo. Powell, and his notice to the reader. Powell

Bonduca—Continued.

says that a friend of his, name not given, is responsible for this revision and modernization of (Beaumont ? and) Fletcher's "Bonduca," that

"the whole play was revised quite through, and likewise studied up in one fortnight."

In the dedication he says:

"'Tis a fabrick of antiquity; a foundation of that celebrated poetical architect, the
famous Fletcher; but with several alterations, besides the two first acts new writ. . . .
it has this further advantage, as being an English story; that the glory of worthies
and heroes sounds sweetest, where the musick is tuned at home . . .'"

This last is, of course, an allusion to Henry **Purcell**.

First performed 1695 (Squire).   LONGE 208

Le **bonheur de l'illussion**.   A. T. of Piron's text Les chimeres.

La **bonne amie**.   A. T. of Desbrosses' Les deux cousines.

La **bonne femme**.   Parody of Gervais' Hipermnestre.

La **bonne femme** ou Le Phénix.   Parody of Gluck's Alceste.

Le **bonne homme misère**.   A. T. of Gaveaux Le diable couleur de
rose.

Les **bons et les méchans**, ou Philémon et Baucis, pantomime, en
deux actes; par M. Audinot.   Représentée, pour la première fois,
sur le Théâtre de l'Ambigu-comique, le premier janvier 1783.

Paris, Cailleau, 1783.   18 p.   18½^{cm}.

Two acts.   Scene by scene description of the action.   The composer of the music
is not mentioned.   In an Avertissement the publisher says:

". . . Grand peintre & grand machiniste, le chevalier Servandoni porta à sa
perfection la Pantomime à Machines.   Personne ne poussa plus loin que ce fameux
artiste, l'art de faire jouer les décorations, d'en multiplier les effets, de les varier,
de les opposer avec autant de rapidité.

"Ne pouvant employer aucun de ces grands moyens, le directeur de l'Ambigu-
Comique puisa dans la nature même un nouveau genre de pantomime.   Une action
simple & suivi, des situations intéressantes, agréables, des tableaux pittoresques,
variés & multipliés, qui tiennent toujours au sujet, voilà la tâche que cet entrepreneur s'est imposée.

"La *Belle au bois dormant*, fut le premier & l'un des plus agréables ouvrages
qu'il ait offert au public, & le succés constant que cette pantomime a eu toutes les
fois qu'on l'a remise au théâtre, dispense d'entrer, à cet égard, dans de plus grands
détails.

"Bientôt les *quatre Fils Aymon & Pierre de Provence*,, qui succédèrent à la Belle
au bois dormant, obtinrent les applaudissemens les plus encourageans.

"Enfin, *le Prince Noir & Blanc & Dorothée*, semblent avoir réunis tous les suffrages
d'un public, qui donne toujours une nouvelle preuve d'indulgence & d'intérêt à
chaque effort nouveau que l'on fait pour lui plaire. . . .

"L'effet de ces sortes d'ouvrages, est de parler d'abord aux yeux, & de n'arriver
au coeur ou à l'esprit, que par le secours de cet organe, & d'une musique destinée à
remplacer le dialogue.   On pense que leurs programmes n'en doivent être que la
description . . ."   ML48.B2

Both sides of the water.   A. T. of Reeve's The raft.

Il **bottanico novellista**.   Dramma giocoso per musica da rappresentarsi la primavera dell' anno 1770 nel Teatro Dolfino in Treviso . . .

Venezia, Giambattista Casali, 1770.   48 p.   15½^{cm}.

Three acts.   By Goldoni, originally called "Lo speziale."   Impresario's dedication, cast, and name of the composer, Domenico **Fischietti**.   SCHATZ 3241

Il **bottaro**, ballet.   *See* P. Guglielmi's Arsinoe e Breno.

Il **bottaro di Svezia,** ballet. *See* Paisiello's Le gare generose.

La **bottega da caffè,** commedia.

[5]–44 p. 16½^{cm}. (*Carlo Goldoni, Opere drammatiche giocose, t. iv, Torino, 1757.*)

Three parts. Original composer unknown to me. ML 49.A2G6

— La **bottega del caffè.** Intermezzo di tre parti per musica. Rappresentato per la prima volta in Venezia l'anno MDCCXXXV.

Carlo Goldoni, Opere teatrali, Venezia, Zatta e figli, 1788–95, v. 35, [289]–331 p. 18½^{cm}. PQ

Il **bottegaro gentiluomo.** Intermezzo a' due voci.

Venezia, Domenico Lovisa, 1739. 12 p. 14½^{cm}.

Two parts. By Antonio Salvi, who is not mentioned. In the brief entry catalogue of his libretto collection Schatz attributed the music to Giuseppe Maria **Orlandini,** but in the manuscript of his Opera-dictionary he attributes it to Joh. Adolf **Hasse,** remarking that the intermezzo is also known as "Larinda e Vanesio," and originally, for the first performances at Naples, Teatro di San Bartolomeo, December, 1726, was called "L'artigiano gentiluomo." Florimo makes no mention of such a performance. Mennicke (p. 511) says that the Royal Library at Dresden possesses Hasse's "Cajo Fabricio," Dresden, 1734, with his intermezzi, "L'artigiano gentiluomo (=Larinda e Vanesio), and that a German edition of the text of these is in the Schatz collection. On p. 495 of his book he enters under "Intermezzi": "1726. L'artigiano gentiluomo, Neapel, Datum der Aufführung: ?, Exemplar: Dresden, Librettist: ?"

It is quite clear that this information was partly derived from Schatz himself, whose libretto collection, indeed, contains "Der handwerksmann als edelmann," Dresden, 1734.

To add to the confusion, Schatz, in his ms. work (in L. of C.), "Chronologische folge der von Johann Adolph Hasse in musik gesetzten dramatischen werke," enters as no. 6:

"*Larinda e Vanesio.* Intermezzi per musica in 2 parti. Text ursprüngl. m. d. titel "L'artigiano gentiluomo," von Antonio Salvi, verändert von [blank], Neapel, Teatro di S. Bartolomeo. xii, 1726."

"Besetzung

"Larinda   Sig^a Celeste Reste
"Vanesio   Sig. Gioacchino Corrado
"NB. Dieses werk wurde als zwischenspiel z. d. dramma per musica "L'Astarto" aufgeführt."

He then quotes from the libretto (which is not in his collection):

"Se l'intermezzi li vedrai tutti diversi dal loro primo essere, e da quella forma, che si sono rappresentati in Torino, Fiorenza, ed altri capitoli, sappi, che si è fatto per adattarli al costume di questa città."

As 6a. Schatz enters—

"*L'artigiano gentiluomo* (Larinda e Vanesio) . . . Dresden, 8/vii, 1734 . . . Textbuch in deutscher prosa, am textbuch der oper "Cajus Fabritius" angeheftet . . .

"NB. Dieses werk wurde als zwischenspiel z. d. dramma per musica "Cajo Fabrizio" aufgeführt."

Schatz means, of course, that both the opera and the intermezzi were performed in Italian.

As 6^b he enters:

"Il *bottegaro gentiluomo* (Larinda e Vanesio) . . . Venedig, Teatro di S. Angelo, carnevale 1739 . . . Aufgeführt als zwischenspiel zu dem Dr. p. m. "Achille in Sciro" v. P. Chiarini."

"Il bottegaro gentiluomo" was indeed performed at Venice, 1739, with Chiarini's opera, "Achille in Sciro," and Wiel adds this note:

"Con questa opera furono rappresentati gli intermezzi: Un *bottegaro gentiluomo,* in due parti; e: *Pandolfo* (musica di G. A. Hasse)."

It will be noticed that Wiel attributes only the music of "Pandolfo" to Hasse, not of "Un bottegaro gentiluomo," whose composer he did not know. This point Schatz overlooked, and he (incorrectly), on Wiel's authority, attributed "Il bottegaro gentiluomo," Venice, 1739, to Hasse, after first having attributed it to Orlandini.

To sum up, while Hasse apparently composed Salvi's altered text under the title of "L'artigiano gentiluomo" or "Larinda e Vanesio," for Naples, 1726, used also later

Il bottegaro gentiluomo—Continued.

on in 1734, at Dresden, there is nothing to show that his music was also used at Venice, 1739, for another version of Salvi's text under the title of "Il bottegaro gentiluomo." I therefore prefer Orlandini as composer, though his connection with the work is made doubtful by the following entry: SCHATZ 7350

— **Le bourgeois gentilhomme**; or, Vanesio and Larinda. An interlude. Performed by Sig. Anna Maria Faini, and Signor Antonio Lottini, at the King's Theatre in the Haymarket. The music is composed by Signor Orlandini.

     London, J. Chrichley, 1737. 15 p. 17^{cm}.

Two parts. This is *not* Salvi's text, as Schatz would have found on comparison. Salvi begins his with "Un Marte furibondo," for instance, whereas the London libretto begins, "Sotto mentite spoglie;" act second in this begins, "La, la, la, la, etc., Fate largo o Ganimede," instead of "Levamiti davanti."

First performed, as indicated, 1737.   SCHATZ 7353

Les bottes de sept lieues. A. T. of Arlequin, roi des Ogres.

Le bouquet du roi, opera comique, en un acte, représentée sur le Théatre de l'Opéra comique, le 24 août 1752 [!]

     La Haye, Pierre Gosse, 1760. 32 p. 16^{cm}. (Vadé, Oeuvres, La Haye, 1760, t. i.)

One act, *en vaudevilles.* Cast. From footnotes it would appear that only scenes 4 and 6 were by Vadé. The musical arranger of the vaudevilles, etc., is not mentioned.   ML 49.A2V2

— **Le bouquet du roi,** opéra-comique, en un acte, représenté sur le Théatre de l'Opéra-comique, le 24 août 1753.

     Paris, la veuve Duchesne, 1766. 32 p. 18½^{cm}.

Cast. On p. 30–32 the "Airs": "De tes pleurs, tendre Aurore," "Les jolis, les petits marquis." Neither Vadé nor the arranger of the music is mentioned.

1753 appears to be the correct date. (*Comp.* Parfaict.)   SCHATZ 11485

Le bourgeois gentil-homme. Tr. of Orlandini's Il bottegaro gentiluomo.

The Bow-street opera, in three acts. Written on the plan of the Beggar's opera; all the most celebrated songs of which are parodied; and the whole piece adapted to modern times, manners and characters . . . The fourth edition.

     London, Printed for the author, 1776. iv, 44 p. 21^{cm}.

An everything-but-complimentary dedication to David Garrick, whose refusal "to suppress the exhibition of the Beggar's opera, at the requisition of the Bowstreet magistrates" gave rise to this anonymous "whim," which is in three acts and utilizes 32 ballad airs, indicated by title. First edition published in 1773.   LONGE 251

La Bradamante del Co. Pietro Paolo Bissari. Drama per musica nel Teatro Grimano.

     Venetia, Valvasense, 1650. 84 p. 13½^{cm}.

Last page incorrectly paged 82. Our copy lacks the front, which should form p. [1–2]. Three acts, with prologue. Author's dedication, argument, and scenario. The composer, Pietro Francesco **Cavalli**, is not mentioned.

First performed, as indicated, carnival 1650.   SCHATZ 1731

Bradamante, tragedie représentée par l'Academie royale de musique l'an 1707. Les paroles de M. Roy, & la musique de M. La Coste. LXIX. opera.

n. i., n. d. *14*^{cm}*.* *pl., 227–278 p.* (*Recueil général des opéra, t. ix, Paris, 1710.*)

Detached copy. Five acts with prologue. "Avertissement."
First performed, as indicated, May 2, 1707. Schatz 5353
Second copy. ML 48.R4

Bradamante e Ruggero, ballet. *See* Monza's Oreste.

Bradamante nell' isola d'Alcina. Drama da rappresentarsi in Parma nel novo Teatro di S. A. S. il carnovale dell' anno 1729 . . .

Parma, Eredi di Paolo Monti, 1729. *xii, 46, [1] p.* *15*^{cm}*.*

Three acts. By Antonio Fanzaglia (Schatz). Author's dedication, argument, cast, scenario, and name of the composer, Riccardo **Broschi**. It appears from the dedication that the opera had previously been performed at Rome in 1728. The title originally was "L'isola d'Alcina." Schatz 1342

Der braeutigam ohne braut. A. T. of Cimarosa's Die vorgeblichen grafen.

Il bravo burlato. Intermezzo per musica da rappresentarsi nel Teatro de' Nobili di Gubbio il carnevale del MDCCLVII.

Gubbio, gli eredi del Mattioli, n. d. *[16] p.* *18½*^{cm}*.*

Two acts. By Antonio Pavoni. Neither he nor the composer, **Rinaldo di Capua,** is mentioned.
First performed at Rome, Teatro di Palla a Corda, carnival 1746. Schatz 8801

Brenno. O. T. of Reichardt's Brennus.

Brenno, dramma per musica composto con cori, e balli analoghi da Ant. Filistri de 'Caramondani . . . e messo in musica da Giov. Federico Reichardt . . . da rappresentarsi nel Regio Teatro di Berlino . . .

Berlino, Haude e Spener, 1789. *155 p.* *16*^{cm}*.*

Three acts. Cast. Argument. German t.-p. "Brennus" and text face Italian.
Comp. below. ML 50.2.B8R3

— Brennus. Ein musikalisches drama, nach der italiaenischen poesie des herrn Filistri de' Caramondani fuer das Koenigl. Opern theater zu Berlin zum carneval des jahres 1789 in musik gesetzt von Johann Friederich Reichardt. Am 24 Januar 1798 im Königl. Opernhause von den Koenigl. saengern und saengerinnen und dem Koenigl. orchester mit deutscher poesie concertmaessig aufgefuehrt. Den beschluss macht eine neue composition nach Ramlers poesie, zur gedaechtnissfeier des grossen koenigs Friedrichs des Zweiten.

Berlin, Johann Friedrich Unger, 1798. *3 p. l., 34 p.* *15*^{cm}*.*

Three acts. Cast and prefatory note according to which only so much of the opera (as first performed on October 16, 1789) was retained
"als zum verstaendniss der haupthandlung und fuer den effekt der arien und mehrstimmigen singesätze nothwendig war." Schatz 8637

Brenno in Efeso. Drama per musica da rappresentarsi nel famoso Teatro Vendramino di S. Salvatore l'anno 1690 . . .

Venetia, Nicolini, 1690. *60 p.* *14*^{cm}*.*

Three acts. Dedication signed by the author, Antonio Arcoleo, notice to the reader with name of Giacomo Antonio **Perti** as the composer, argument, and scenario.
Schatz 7947

Bretislaus oder Die siegende bestaendigkeit auf die hoechst-glueck-liche verbindung Seiner Koenigl. Hoheit . . . Carl Friedrich, erben zu Norwegen, hertzogen zu Schlesswig-Holstein etc etc. mit der . . . prinzessin Anna Petrowna an deroselben hohen gebuhrts-feste den 7 febr:/27 jan. anno 1725 in einem sing-spiele, nebst einer illumina-tion und einem feuer-wercke auf dem Hamburgischen Schauplatze vorgestellet.

Hamburg, Caspar Jakhel, n. d.   Unpaged.   20cm.

Three acts and prologue. Cast, scenario, and statement that the music "ausser einigen eingerueckten italiaenischen arien" is by Reinhard **Keiser.** The author, Johann Philipp Praetorius, is not mentioned.   SCHATZ 5133

Briseide. Dramma per musica da rappresentarsi nel Regio Teatro di Torino nel carnovale del 1784 alla presenza delle Maestà Loro.

Torino, Onorato Derossi, n. d.   viii, 62 p.   8°.

Three acts. Argument, cast, scenario, and names of the composer, Francesco **Bianchi,** and the librettist, Francesco Sebastiano Gambino. The three ballets by Sebastiano Gallet, music by Vittorio Amedeo Canavasso, were called "Enea e Turno," "La viaggiatrice osia Le circostanze imbarazzanti," and "Di Greci festeggianti la riconciliazione d'Achille e d'Agamennone," and separate librettos are said to have been printed.

First performed, as indicated, December 26, 1783.   SCHATZ 1002

Briseide. Dramma per musica da rappresentarsi nel Real Teatro di S. Carlo nel dì 13. di agosto 1791. Festeggiandosi la nascita di S. M. la regina . . .

Napoli, Vincenzo Flauto, 1791.   44 p.   16cm.

Two acts. Impresario's dedication, with same date as in the title, argument, cast, scenario, and names of Angelo Pocobelli as the author, of Ferdinando **Robuschi** as composer of the opera, of Giuseppe Maria Curcio as composer ("musica tutta nuova") of Michele Fabiani's "Amore e Psiche, ballo eroico pantomimo in cinque atti," described on p. 10–14.   SCHATZ 8839

Britain's glory; or, A trip to Portsmouth. A musical entertain-ment, in one act, as performed at the Theatre Royal, in the Hay-Market, with universal applause. By the late Mr. Benson . . .

London, J. Wallis, n. d.   1 p. l., 32 p.   21cm.

Cast and dedication. The composer, Samuel **Arnold,** is not mentioned.
First performed, August 20, 1794.   LONGE 246

Britannia and Batavia: a masque. Written on the marriage of the princess royal with His Highness the prince of Orange. By the late Mr. Lillo.

London, J. Gray, 1740.   1 p. l., 5–15 p.   20cm.

One act. Of the 12 "airs" (songs), two were to be sung to popular airs, indicated by title. The composer (and author?) of these songs, Henry **Carey,** is not mentioned. Perhaps identical with "Britannia or the royal lovers," Covent Garden, February 11, 1734.   ML 52.2.B86

Britannico. Tragedia per musica da rappresentarsi nel Regio Teatro di Berlino . . . l'anno 1751.

Berlino, Haude e Spener, n. d.   91, [4] p.   16cm.

Three acts. Carl Heinrich **Graun** is mentioned as the composer, and Leopoldo de Villati as the author. ("La presente tragedia è stata tirata dal francese [Racine's 'Britannicus'] e composta ad uso di musica.") Argument and scenario. German title-page, "Britannicus," and text face Italian.

First performed, as indicated, February 17, 1751.   SCHATZ 4091

Britannicus.   Tr. of Graun's Britannico.

The **British enchanters**;   or, No magick like love.   A dramatick poem.   [port. vignette.]

London, J. Tonson, 1732.   71 p.   16^cm^.

Five acts and prologue.   Cast and notice to the reader:

"Upon the separation of the houses, when musical performances were confin'd to one theatre, and dramatick to the other [this regulation went in force about January, 1708!], it became necessary to lengthen the representation of the ensuing poem with several alterations and additions, and some entire new scenes, to fill up the spaces occasion'd by the necessity of leaving out the mixture of musical entertainment. Which additions are herewith printed, having never been publish'd before."

The text is by George Granville (Lord Lansdowne), and was written as an attempt to improve on opera librettos.   It was first performed, evidently with "musical entertainments," at the Haymarket Theatre, February 21, 1706, and again with alterations on March 22, 1707 (Genest).   The composer not recorded by Schatz or Clarence.

LONGE 75

British fortitude, and Hibernian friendship;   or, An escape from France.   A musical drama in one act by J. C. Cross.   As performed with universal applause at the Theatre Royal Covent Garden. [vignette]

London, Printed by & for J. Roach, Sept. 3, 1794.   1 p. l., 31, [1] 20½^cm^.

Cast, dedication, and author's prefatory note, according to which the piece was originally written for Mr. Johnstone's benefit (as Capt. O'Leary), who introduced "songs . . . the production of gentlemen well known in the literary world, and . . . sung by him . . . previous to their introduction in British fortitude . . ."

The composer, William **Reeve,** is not mentioned.

First performed, March 29, 1794.

LONGE 308

The **British heroine.**   A. T. of Purcell's Bonduca.

British heroism.   A. T. of The death of captain Faulknor.

The **British recruit.**   A. T. of To arms!

The **British stage**;   or, The exploits of Harlequin: a farce.   As it is performed by a company of wonderful comedians at both theatres, with wonderful applause; with all its original songs, scenes, and machines.   Design'd as an after-entertainment for the audiences of Harlequin Doctor Faustus, and The Necromancer . . .

London, T. Warner, 1724.   1 p. l., v–vii, [1], 24 p.   19^cm^.

One act.   Preface.   Obviously a satire by unknown author.

LONGE 152

The **British worthy.**   A. T. of H. Purcell's King Arthur.

Britons, strike home: or, The sailor's rehearsal.   A farce.   As it is acted at the Theatre-Royal, by His Majesty's servants.   Written by Mr. Edward Phillips.   With the musick prefix'd to each song.

London, J. Watts, 1739.   3 p. l., 30, [2] p.   17½^cm^.

Cast.   One act, prologue, epilogue.   Though the fact that the eight airs are printed in the text without titles would permit the inference that they were composed for the occasion, the piece is nevertheless a ballad-opera, as Mr. Squire has proven.

First performed at Drury Lane, December 31, 1739.

LONGE 321

— **Britons strike home**:   or, The sailors rehearsal.   A farce.   As it is acted at the Theatre-Royal by his Majesty's servants.   By Mr. Edward Phillips.

Glasgow, n. publ., 1761.   25, [3] p.   17^cm^.

One act, prologue and epilogue.   Cast and on last (unnumb.) page table of the eight songs, the airs of which are not indicated.

LONGE 118

Die **brueder als nebenbuhler.** Tr. of P. v. Winter's I fratelli rivali.

Bruto. *See* M. Curzio.

Bruto costante. *See* M. Curzio.

Il **Bruto milanese** ossia La congiura contro Galeazzo Maria Sforza Visconti, ballet. *See* Nasolini's Il trionfo di Clelia.

A new opera; called, **Brutus of Alba:** or, Augusta's triumph. As it is acted at the Theatre, in Dorset-Garden, by His Majesty's servants.
>   *London, Printed by W. Olney, for S. Briscoe, 1697. 2 p. l., 63, [1] p. 21½cm.*

> No. 6 and 7 repeated in paging, making an actual total of 61 p.
> Imperfect, wanting p. 35–48.
> Five acts. The "epistle dedicatory" of date "Monday, Octob. 16, 1699" [!] is signed by the authors George Powell and John Verbruggen. Daniel **Purcell,** the composer, is not mentioned.   ML 50.2.B85

Le bucheron, ou Les trois souhaits, comédie en un acte, mélée d'a-riettes. Représentée pour la premiere fois par les Comédiens italiens ordinairès du roi, le lundi 28 février 1763. La musique par M. Philidor.
>   *Paris, Claude Herissant, 1763. 56 p. 19cm.*

> By Jean François Guichard and Castet, who are not mentioned. Perrault's "Conte" on which the play is based, precedes the text.   SCHATZ 8010

—— Le **bucheron,** ou Les trois souhaits. Comedie en un acte, mêlée d'ariettes; par Mr. Guichard. La musique de Mr. Philidor. Repré-sentée sur le Théâtre de la cour par les Comédiens françois ordinaires du roi, le [*blank*] 1767.
>   *Copenhague, Cl. Philibert, 1767. 64 p. 19cm.*

> Cast.   YUDIN PQ

—— Le **bucheron,** ou Les trois souhaits comédie en un acte, meslée d'ariettes. Représentée pour la premiere fois par les Comédiens italiens ordinaires du roi, le lundi 28 février 1763. La musique par M. Philidor.
>   *Paris, la veuve Duchesne, 1771. 50 [3] p. 19cm.*

> Cast. The [3] p. contains "Conte de feu Mr. Perrault, qui a donné lieu à la pièce." The authors, Jean François Guichard and Castet, are not mentioned.   SCHATZ 11736

—— Le **bucheron,** ou Les trois souhaits comédie en un acte, mêlée d'ariettes; représentée pour la première fois par les Comédiens italiens ordinaires du roi, le lundi 28 février 1763. La musique par M. Philidor.
>   *Paris, la veuve Duchesne, 1782. 55 p. 19cm.*

> Cast. In this ed. Perrault's "Conte" on p. 3–6. Authors not mentioned.   SCHATZ 11737A

—— Der **holzhauer** oder Die drey wuensche, ein singspiel in einem aufzuge aus dem franzoesischen uebersetzt mit musik.
>   *Frankfurt am Mayn, mit Andreaeischen schriften, 1773. 88 p., 8 p. (folded music) 16½cm.*

Le bucheron—Continued.

Cast. Version for Theob. Marchand's company by Johann Heinrich Faber. Neither he is mentioned nor **Philidor,** the composer. The music (voice and bass) incorrectly bound in with this copy belongs to Fridzeri's "Die beiden militzen," whereas the 8 p. of music belonging to the "Holzhauer" are incorrectly bound in with "Die beiden militzen." It consists of "Sieh doch den schmerz" (I, 1 "Annette au bois") "Colins augen sind sehr schön (I, 10 "Colin a des yeux charmants"), "Ihr männer, die ihr immer schmälet" (last scene. "Maris, qui querrellez sans cesse.") SCHATZ 8011

— Skovhuggeren eller De tre ønsker. Et syngespil i een act af Guichard hvortil musiken er componeret af Philidor. Oversat af Lars Knudsen.

n. i., n. d. 78 p. 15½^{cm}*.*

First performed at Copenhagen, December 3, 1782.   SCHATZ 8013

Die **buckeligen.** A. T. of Portugal's Die taeuschende aehnlichkeit.

Buergerfreuden! Ein oesterreichisches buergergemaehlde mit choeren in einem aufzug. Von Karl Friedrich Hensler. Aufgefuehrt by der gluecklichen zurueckkunft unsers tapfern erzherzogs Karl. Am 2. maerz 1797. Die musik ist von Wenzel Müller . . .

Wien, gedruckt mit Schmidtischen schriften, n. d. 56 p. 17^{cm}*.*

First performed as indicated on the Marinelli'sche Schaubuehne.

SCHATZ 6914

Le bugie hanno le gambe corte. A. T. of Moneta's Il conte Policronio.

Bund ueber eck. A. T. of Ruprecht's Die dorfhaendel.

La buona figliuola. Dramma di tre atti per musica. Rappresentato per la prima volta in Parma il carnovale dell' anno MDCCLVI.

Carlo Goldoni, Opere teatrali, Venezia, Zatta e figli, 1788–95, v. 38, [165]–217 p. 18½^{cm}*.*   PQ

La buona figliuola. Dramma giocoso per musica di Polisseno Fegejo, Pastor Arcade. Da rappresentarsi nel Teatro di S. A. Serenissima il Signor principe di Carignano nell' autunno dell' anno MDCCLVIII.

Torino, Gaspare Bayno e Giuseppe Avondo, n. d. 52, [1] p. 14^{cm}*.*

Three acts. By Goldoni. The unnumbered page contains "Arie cangiate . . ." Se del fiume altera l'onda [I, 14] "Alla selva, al prato, al rio" [II, 9] "Misera rondinella" [III, 4].

Cast and name of the composer, "Egidio **Duni** Napolit. Maestro di capella di S. A. R. di Parma."

First performed at Parma, Teatro Ducale, carnival, 1757 not 1756. SCHATZ 2834

La buona figliuola. Dramma giocoso per musica di Polisseno Fegejo Pastor Arcade recitato nel Teatro Giustinian di S. Moisè il carnovale dell' anno 1760. Seconda edizione.

Venezia, n. publ., 1760. 48 p. 15^{cm}*.*

Three acts, p. 45–48, incorrectly headed "atto quarto." By Goldoni. Salvatore **Perillo** is mentioned as the composer.   SCHATZ 7921

La **buona figliuola.** Dramma giocoso per musica di Polisseno Fegejo, Pastore Arcade.

Roma, n. publ., 1760. 52 p. 16ᶜᵐ.

Three acts. By Carlo Goldoni. Niccolò **Piccinni** is mentioned as the composer. First performed at Rome, Teatro delle Dame, February 6, 1760, and again summer, 1768 (Schatz).   ML 50.2.B9P4

— La **buona figliuola.** Dramma giocoso per musica del . . . Carlo Goldoni . . . da rappresentarsi ne' Teatri privilegiati di Vienna l'estate dell' anno 1768.

Vienna, Ghelen, n. d. 63, [1] p. 17ᶜᵐ.

Three acts. Niccolò **Piccinni** is mentioned as the composer. On the last p. the substitute aria for "Son tradita" (II, 9), "In tanti affanni miei," which does not appear to have been written by Goldoni.
First performed at Vienna, 1764.   SCHATZ 8070

— La **buona figliuola,** dramma giocoso per musica del celebre Sign. Carlo Goldoni, da rappresentarsi nel Regio Teatro Danese—Den fromme pige . . .

Kiøbenhavn, L. N. Svare, 1770. 115 p. 17ᶜᵐ.

Three acts. Italian and Danish texts. Cast and name of **Piccinni** as the composer. First performed 1769, as indicated.   SCHATZ 8071

— La **buona figliuola.** Commedia per musica da rappresentarsi nel Teatro Nuovo per second' opera del corrente anno 1778.

Napoli, n. publ., 1778. 64 p. 15ᶜᵐ.

Three acts. By Goldoni. Cast and name of Niccolò **Piccinni** as the composer.
     SCHATZ 8131

— La **buona figliuola.** Dramma giocoso per musica, di Polisseno Fegejo, P. A. da rappresentarsi nel Piccolo Teatro di S. A. E. di Sassonia.

Dresda, n. publ., 1781. 127 p. 15½ᶜᵐ.

Three acts. German title, "Das gute maedel," and text face Italian. **Piccinni** is mentioned as the composer.   SCHATZ 8074
First performed at Dresden, November 16, 1765.

— The **accomplish'd maid:** A comic opera. As it is performed at the Theatre-Royal in Covent-Garden. The music by Sigⁿʳ Niccolo Piccini . . .

London, W. Griffin [etc.], 1767. 1 p. l., ii, 59, [1] p. 19½ᶜᵐ.

Three acts. Cast and preface by the translator, Edward Toms (not mentioned), who says, in part:
". . . This translation is attempted, so as to be sung to the original music, as performed in Italy . . . As the music of this opera, has always been esteemed the most capital work of that great composer Piccini, the translator thought it more just, to give up the claim to poetical harmony, rather than make the least infringement on the musical accent. He likewise flatters himself, that it will not be less acceptable to an English audience, by the dialogue's being without the incumbrance of recitative. All other alterations, are made only to adapt it to the English stage . . . Should this first attempt of bringing an entire Italian musical composition on the English stage, by applying our language to the harmony of their most eminent composer, prove acceptable to the public, the translator's intention is fully answered, as it may be the means of exciting some abler genius to tread the same path."
The last (unnumb.) p. contains the "Table of the songs," with note that "Bring, ye tedious hours," "Some men with artful praise," and "Thus the sun at morn" "were not originally" in *La Buona figliuola,* "but are the composition of the same master." In Randall & Abel's, vocal score the air "Oh! (Off), my lord, pray forbear" is headed as by "Sigʳ Pirillo, Napolitano." (Salvatore *Perillo*.)

La **buona figliuola**—Continued.

First performed, as indicated, December 3, 1766; in Italian at the Haymarket, December 9, 1766 (Burney). LONGE 32

— The **accomplish'd maid.** A new comic opera. As it is performed at the Theatre-Royal in Covent-Garden. The music by Signior Niccolo Piccini . . .

Philadelphia, Printed and sold by Robert Bell, 1777. **61,** [1] *p.* 20½*cm.*

Three acts. London cast.
Not performed in America. ML 50.6.A2

— La **buona figliuola,** opéra comique, en trois actes; parodiée en français sur la musique du célebre Piccini. Représentée pour la premiere fois par les Comédiens italiens ordinaires du roi, le 17 juin 1771.

Paris, Didot l'aîné, 1771. 48 p. 19cm.

Cast and anonymous preface, with Goldoni's name, and that of Domenico Baccelli as the musician either responsible for the musical side of the parody or indeed partly for the parody itself, since the author says: "Baccelli . . . me proposa de la faire connoître en France, en parodiant les paroles italiennes sur la quelle elle étoit composée." The preface contains also some observations on the difficulty of making *parodies.* The text is attributed to Jean François Cailhava d'Estandoux. On p. 45, a note to the effect that the piece was already half printed when the Comédiens italiens substituted the following ariettes, "Dans ces floeurs je vois l'image" (I, 1) and "La tendresse et la sagesse" (III, 5), for "Quel plaisir, quelle volupté" and "Dans mon coeur." Both substituted airs were by Piccinni, but not from "La buona figliuola. On p. 47–48, the air of the ariette, "Pauvre Annette, quelle pitié" (I, 4).
SCHATZ 8073

— La **buona figliuola,** opéra comique, en trois actes; parodiée en François sur la musique du célèbre Piccini. Représentée pour la première fois par les Comédiens italiens du roi le 17 juin 1771.

Paris, Didot laîné, 1771. 48 p. 19½cm.

Cast. Cailhava d'Estandoux is not mentioned. On p. 47–48 the text of the substituted arias. This ed. of 1771 contains no music. ML 48.M2M

— La **buona figliuola,** opera comique en trois actes, parodiée en françois sur la musique du célébre Piccini, représenté pour la premiere fois par les Comédiens italiens ordinaires du roi le 17 juin 1771.

Paris, la veuve Duchesne, 1772. 56 p. 17½cm.

Cast. On p. 47–56 the two "Airs de la Buona Figliuola" "Par le trou de la serrure" and "Je suis d'une bonne pâte." YUDIN PQ

— Das **gute maegdchen,** ein scherzhaftes musicalisches schauspiel aus dem italiaenischen, welches an dem Churpfaelzischen Hof bei gelegenheit des hoechst beglueckten namensfestes Sr. Churfuerstl. Durchlaucht . . . aufgefuehret worden. Im jahr 1769.

Mannheim, Akademische buchdruckerei, n. d. 55 p. 16½cm.

Cast, scenario, and name of **Piccinni** as the composer. On p. 51–53 the titles of Legrand's ballets "Die artige schaefer" and "Die eifersuechtige Faunen" and a description of Fabiani's ballet "Der bezauberte kranz." The composers of the music are not mentioned.
First performed November 4, 1769, as indicated. ,SCHATZ 8072

— Das **gute maedchen.** Eine operette in drey akten. Nach der musik der Buona figliuola von Nic. Piccini.

Leipzig, Carl Friedrich Schneider, 1783. 56 p. 16cm.

Transl. by Johann Joachim Eschenburg, who is not mentioned.
First performed at Berlin, Döbbelinsches Theater, Sept. 8, 1777. SCHATZ 8075

La **buona figliuola**—Continued.

— Gesaenge aus dem singspiele: Das **gute maedchen,** in zwey aufzuegen, nach der Buona figliuola von Piccini.

Hamburg, Joh. Matthias Michaelsen, 1791. 24 p. 17^cm.

Eschenburg's translation.
First performed at Hamburg, Theater b. Gänsemarkt, January 14, 1779.

SCHATZ 8076

La **buona figliuola maritata.** Dramma di tre atti per musica.
Rappresentato per la prima volta in Venezia l'autunno dell' anno
MDCCLXII.

*Carlo Goldoni, Opere teatrali, Venezia, Zatta e figli, 1788–95, v. 38,
[219]–269 p. 18½^cm.*

First performed at Bologna, 1761. (*See* below.)   PQ

La **buona figliuola maritata.** Dramma giocoso per musica da
rappresentarsi l'anno 1764.

Vienna, Ghelen, n. d. 56 p. 16^cm.

Three acts. By Goldoni (who is not mentioned) as sequal to his "La buona figliuola." Cast, scenario, and name of Niccolò **Piccinni** as the composer.
First performed at Bologna, Teatro Formagliari, May, 1761.   SCHATZ 8135

— La **buona figliola maritata.** Farzetta a sei voci, ridotta dalla
burletta in musica di Polisseno Fegejo, P. A. da rappresentarsi nel
Teatro degli Accerbi de' nobili d'Urbania nel carnevale dell' anno
1769 . . .

Roma ed in Fano, Andrea Donati, n. d. 39 p. 39^cm.

Two acts. Dedication and name of Niccolò **Piccinni** as the composer.

SCHATZ 8136

Buovo d'Antona. Dramma di tre atti per musica. Rappresentato per la prima volta in Firenze l'anno MDCCL.

*Carlo Goldoni, Opere teatrali, Venezia, Zatta e figli, 1788–95, v. 41,
[5]–59 p. 18^cm.*

See next entry.   PQ

Buovo d'Antona. Dramma giocoso per musica di Polisseno Fegejo,
Pastor Arcade, da rappresentarsi nel Teatro Giustinian di S. Moisè
il carnovale dell' anno 1759.

Venezia, Modesto Fenzo, 1759. 58 p. 14½^cm.

Three acts. By Carlo Goldoni. Cast, scenario, and name of Tommaso **Traetta**
as composer.
First performed, as indicated, December 27, 1758, unless previously at Florence,
1750.   SCHATZ 10388

Il burbero di buon cuore. Dramma giocoso per musica da rappresentarsi nel nobile Teatro Giustiniani in San Moisè nell' autunno dell'
anno 1789.

Venezia, Modesto Fenzo, 1789. 68 p. 16^cm.

Two acts. By Lorenzo da Ponte, who is not mentioned. Cast and name of Vincenzo Martini (**Martin y Soler**) as the composer.
First performed at Vienna, Burgtheater, Jan. 4, 1786.   SCHATZ 6005

Il **burbero di buon cuore**—Continued.

— Il **burbero di buon cuore.** Dramma giocoso per musica da rappresentarsi nel Teatro di S. A. E. di Sassonia.

Dresda, n. publ., 1789. 157 p. 15½ᶜᵐ.

Two acts. By Lorenzo da Ponte with few if any changes. German title page "Der gutherzige polterer" and text face Italian. Vincenz Martini (**Martin y Soler**) is mentioned as composer.

First performed at Dresden, Churf. Theater, October 3, 1789. Schatz 6006

Die **burg Hymens.** Tr. of Naumann's La reggia d'Imenèo.

La **burla di D. Pacconio a Parigi,** ballet. *See* Anfossi's La maga Circe.

Le **burle per amore.** Dramma giocoso per musica da rappresentarsi nel nobile Teatro di San Samuele il carnovale dell' anno 1784.

Venezia, Giov. Battista Casali, n. d. 62 p. 17½ᶜᵐ.

Two acts. By Marcello Bernardini, who is not mentioned. Cast and name of Vincenzo Martini (**Martin y Soler**) as the composer. With the opera was performed Francisco Clerico's "Il convalescente innamorato, ballo comico pantomimo." The composer of the music is not mentioned. Schatz 6007

Il **cabalista ne sa' men del caso.** A. T. of Auletta's Il marchese di Spartivento.

La **caccia d'Enrico Quarto,** ballet. *See* Anfossi's Demofoonte.

La **caccia d'Enrico IV,** ballet. *See* P. Guglielmi's Le due gemelle.

La **caccia d'Enrico IV.** Dramma giocoso per musica da rappresentarsi nel Teatro Giustiniani in San Moisè l'autunno dell'anno 1783 . . .

Venezia, Modesto Fenzo, 1783. 76 p. 17ᶜᵐ.

Three acts. Cast, scenario, name of Giacomo **Rust** as the composer, and dedication by Antonio Dian, which reads, in part:

"A prima vista potrebbe forse sembrar quello [drama] stesso, che a tempi addietro venne in altre scene di questa Dominante rappresentato; ma, toltone un aria sola della prima buffa nell' atto secondo, che siè desiderato di conservare, egli è tutto nuovo. La dotta pena, che quello scrisse, valendosi d'arbitrio non conteso ai poeti, immaginò combinazioni di personaggi, di nazione, di caratteri, e di episode diverse da quelle che ci somministra il Teatro comico francese, e ciò forse per addattarsi allo stile delle drammatiche rappresentazioni musicali di quei dì, assai diverso dall' odierno. Io ho bramato che si concilino possibilmente uniformità colla commedia francese e condotta di dramma musicale, il che si è fatto, per quanto disparità di circostanze fra questo, e quella, e massime per la distribuzion delle arie, e per la combinazion de' finali, non l'abbia impedito."

With the opera were performed Antonio Mauro's ballets "Dove entrò cervo, esce donna, o sia Il curioso accidente della caccia" and "La serietà in conflitto," the composers of the music not being mentioned. Schatz 9177

La **caccia d'Isabella, regina di Spagna,** ballet. *See* Tarchi's Ezio.

Caccia di Diana, ballet. *See* Gius. Scarlatti's Partenope.

La **caccia in Etolia.** O. T. of Valeriani's libretto Gl'inganni fortunati.

La **caccia in Etolia,** pastorale per musica da recitarsi nel Teatro Bonacossi à S. Stefano l'anno 1715 . . .

Ferrara, Eredi di Bernardino Pomatelli, 1715. 62 p. 16½ᶜᵐ.

Three acts. By Belisaro Valeriani. Author's dedication, notice to the reader, argument, cast, name of Fortunato **Chelleri** as composer, and imprimatur dated May 28, 1715. Schatz 1817

Il **cacciatore deluso.**   Dramma serio-comico per musica da rappresentarsi nel Real Teatro di Salvaterra nel carnovale dell' anno 1771.

Lisbona, Stamperia reale, n. d.   86 p.   16^{cm}.

Three acts.   Argument, cast, scenario, and name of Gaetano Martinelli as author,
of Niccolò **Jommelli** as composer.   Known also as "Semiramide in bernesco."
First performed at Tübingen, Neues theater, November 11, 1767.   SCHATZ 4897

I **cacciatori burlati,** ballet.   *See* Hasse's L'Olimpiade.

Le **cadi dupé,** opera-comique en un acte, mêlé d'ariettes, de la composition de M. le chevalier Gluck.

Vienne, Ghelen, 1768.   32 p.   16^{cm}.

By Pierre Réné Lemonnier, who is not mentioned.
First performed at Vienna, Burg theater, 1761, and again at Laxenburg, Favorita,
May 28, 1764.   SCHATZ 3924

Le **cadi dupé,** opera-comique en un acte; par l'auteur du Maître en
droit: représenté pour la premiere fois sur le Théâtre de l'Opera-
comique de la Foire S. Germain, le 4 février 1761.

Paris, Duchesne, 1761.   50, [6] p.   19^{cm}.

Cast.   By Pierre Réné Lemonnier.   **Monsigny,** the composer, is not mentioned.
On the [6] p. catalogues of plays, operas, etc.   On 43–50 the same ariettes as in the
1782 ed., with exception of the sixth, which is not in this ed.   ML 50.2.C2M7

—Le **cadi dupé,** opéra-comique, en un acte, par l'auteur du Maître en
droit.   Représenté, pour la premiere fois, sur le Théâtre de l'Opéra-
comique de la Foire Saint Germain.

Paris, la veuve Duchesne, 1766.   32 p.   19^{cm}.

Neither the author, Pierre Réné Lemonnier, is mentioned, nor the composer
Pierre Alexandre **Monsigny.**   SCHATZ 11725

— Le **cadi dupé,** opéra comique en un acte, par l'auteur du Maître
en droit; représenté pour la première fois sur le Théâtre de l'Opéra
comique de la Foire Saint-Germain, le 4 février 1761.

Paris, la veuve Duchesne, 1782.   40 p. 19^{cm}.

Cast.   On p. 33–40, "Ariettes du Cadi dupé.   No. 1. Vous, qu'amour brûle.   2. Si
votre flamme est trahie.   3. Amant fidelle & sensible.   4. Toi, que mon coeur adore.
5. Non, ma reine, sois certaine.   6. Ah! que le sort d'une femme."   **Monsigny** is
not mentioned.   SCHATZ 6567

— Den **besnaerede Cadi.**   Et syngespil i en act af Monnier.
Hvortil musikken er componeret af Monsigny.   Oversat af Lars
Knudsen.

n. i., n. d.   46 p.   16^{cm}.   SCHATZ 6568

Cadmo.   Dramma per musica da cantarsi nella Real villa di Queluz
per celebrare il felicissimo giorno natalizio del serenissimo Signore Don
Giuseppe principe del Brasile li 21 agosto 1784.

[Lisboa], Stamperia reale, n. d.   31 p.   15^{cm}.

One act and licenza.   Cast and names of Gaetano Martinelli as author, of Antonio
da **Silva** as composer.   SCHATZ 9881

Cadmo ed Ino, ballet.   *See* Piccinni's Tigrane.

Cadmus, in einem musicalischen schau-spiele, auf dem Hamburg-ischen Schau-platze vorgestellet im jahr MDCCXXV.

Hamburg, Caspar Jakhel, n. d. Unpaged. 19^{cm}.

Three acts. Cast, scenario, and "vorbericht" with names of Johann Ulrich Koenig as author, of Johann Paul Kunz (**Kuntze**) as composer, and remark that the aria "Kan dem mein hertze widerstehen" and "zwo andere, welche bey den originalien in italiaenisch gedruckt worden, gewisser ursachen willen in selbiger sprache gesungen werden."

First performed at Brunswick, Fuerstl. Opernhaus, February, 1720.   SCHATZ 5314

Cadmvs et Hermione. Tragedie. Representée par l'Academie royale de musique.

Paris, Imprimée aux dépens de ladite Academie, par R. Baudry, 1674. front., 4 p. l., 68 p. 23^{cm}.

Prologue ("Le serpent Python") and five acts. Neither the author, Philippe Quinault, nor the composer, Jean Baptiste **Lully**, is mentioned, but the latter's "Permission pour tenir Academie royale de musique" and "Privilege" follows the text.   ML 50.2.C22L9

— **Cadmus et Hermione,** tragedie. En musique. Suivant la copie imprimée à Paris.

[Amsterdam, Antoine Schelte], 1687. 64 p. (incl. front.) 13½^{cm}.

Prologue and five acts. Cast. Neither Quinault is mentioned, nor **Lully**.
ML 50.2.C22L92

— **Cadmus et Hermione,** tragedie representée par l'Academie royale de musique l'an 1674. Les paroles sont de M. Quinault & la musique de M. de Lully. IV. opera.

n. i., n. d. front., 143–204 p. 14^{cm}. (Recueil général des opéra, t. i, Paris, 1703.)

Detached copy. Laudatory poem, prologue, and five acts.

First performed, as indicated, April 27, 1673 (Schatz), February, 1673 (Prunières).
SCHATZ 5763
Second copy.   ML 48.R4

— **Cadmus et Hermione,** tragedie representée par l'Academie royale de musique, pour la premiere fois sur le Théatre de Bel-Air, & ensuite sur celui du Palais Royal, au mois d'Avril 1672.

Quinault, Théatre, Paris, 1739, t. iv, pl., p. [53]–118. 17^{cm}.

Prologue and five acts. **Lully** is not mentioned.   PQ 1881.A1   1739

La caduta d'Amulio. Dramma per musica del dr. Carlo Gandini da rappresentarsi nel Teatro di S. Angelo il carnovale dell' anno 1747.

Venezia, Modesto Fenzo, 1747. 59 p. 15^{cm}.

Three acts. Cast, argument, scenario, and name of Antonio Gaetano **Pampani** as the composer.   SCHATZ 7757

La caduta de decemviri. Drama per musica da rappresentarsi nel Regio Ducal Teatro di Milano l'anno 1723 . . .

Milano, Giuseppe Richino Malatesta, 1723. 5 p. l., 58 p. 14^{cm}.

Three acts. By Silvio Stampiglia, who is not mentioned. Impressario's dedication dated Milan, December 26, 1723, argument, cast, scenario, and name of Giovanni **Porta** as the composer.   SCHATZ 8389

La caduta de' decemviri. Drama per musica di Silvio Stampiglia tra gl'Arcadi Palemone Licurio . . .

Napoli, Dom. Ant. Parrino e Michele Luigi Mutio, 1697. 5 p. l., 72 p. 14^{cm}.

Three acts. Dedications by the author and the impressario, argument, cast, and scenario. The composer, Alessandro **Scarlatti**, is not mentioned.

First performed at Naples, Teatro di S. Bartolomeo, November, 1697. SCHATZ 9523

La caduta de' decemviri. Drama per musica da rappresentarsi nel Teatro di S. Bartolomeo il di primo ottobre di questo corrente anno 1727. Festeggiandosi il felicissimo giorno natalizio della Sac. Ces. Catt. Real Maestà di Carlo Sesto imperador regnante . . .

Napoli, Francesco Ricciardi, 1727. 60 p. 14½^{cm}.

Three acts. By Silvio Stampiglia, who is not mentioned. Impresario's dedica--tion, argument, scenario, cast and name of Leonardi **Vinci** as composer.

First performed as indicated, October 1, 1727.　　　　ML 50.2.C23V4

La caduta di Elio Seiano. Drama per musica nel Teatro à S. Salvatore l'anno MDCLXVII . . .

Venetia, per gli eredi Leni, 1667. front., 70 p. 14^{cm}.

Three acts. Dedication by the author, conte Niccolò Minato, and dated, Venice, February 3, 1667, argument, scenario, and notice to the reader, with name of Antonio **Sartorio** as the composer. The opera was a sequel to his "La prosperità di Elio Seiano." SCHATZ 9492

La caduta di Gelone. Drama per musica da rappresentarsi nel Teatro di S. Angelo l'autunno dell' anno 1719.

Venezia, Marino Rossetti, 1719. 57 p. 15^{cm}.

Three acts. By Francesco Rossi. Notice to the reader signed by the author, cast, scenario, and name of the composer, Giuseppe Maria **Buini**. SCHATZ 1390

La caduta di Leone, imperator d'Oriente. Drama per musica da recitarsi nel Teatro di Sant' Angelo l'autunno MDCCXXXII . . .

Venezia, Alvise Valvasense, n. d. 47 p. 14^{cm}.

Three acts. By Carlo Paganicesa, who is not mentioned. Impresario's dedication, dated Venice, December 3, 1732, argument, cast, and name of Giuseppe Antonio **Paganelli** as the composer. SCHATZ 7571

La caduta di Troia, ballet. *See* Monza's Erifile.

La caduta di Troja, ballet. *See* Pio's Medonte.

Caernarvon castle; or, The birth of the Prince of Wales: an opera in two acts. First performed at the Theatre-Royal, Hay-Market, August 12th, 1793 . . .

London, William Lane, 1793. 3 p. l., 39 p. 21½^{cm}.

Cast and dedication. Neither the author, John Rose, is mentioned, nor the composet, Thomas **Attwood**. LONGE 239

Il caffè di campagna. Dramma giocoso per musica da rappresentarsi nel Teatro di S. A. serenissima il Signor principe di Carignano nell' autunno dell' anno MDCCLXII.

Torino, Gaspare Boyno, n. d. 52 p. 15½^{cm}.

Three acts. By Pietro Chiari (not mentioned). Cast, scenario, and name of the composer, Ignazio **Celoniat**. SCHATZ 1772

Il **caffè di campagna.** Dramma giocoso da rappresentarsi in musica nel Teatro Giustiniani di San Moisè l'autunno dell' anno MDCCLXI. Dell' abate Pietro Chiari . . .

> *Venezia, n. publ., 1761. 57 p. 15½ᶜᵐ.*

Three acts. Cast, scenario, and name of **Galuppi** as composer.
First performed, as indicated, Nov. 18, 1761. SCHATZ 3501

La **caffettiera bizzarra.** Dramma giocoso in tre atti. Da rappresentarsi nel Teatro Elettorale.

> *Dresda, n. publ., 1796. 21 p. l. 65 p. 16ᶜᵐ.*

Two acts. By Lorenzo da Ponte who is not mentioned. German title "Die launige kaffeeschenkinn" faces Italian. A scene by scene synopsis in German precedes the Italian text. Joseph **Weigl** is mentioned as the composer.
First performed 1796 as indicated, at Vienna, Burgtheater, September 15, 1790.
SCHATZ 10930

Le **cahos.** *See* Destouches and Lalande's ballet Les élémens.

Caio Gracco. Dramma per musica rappresentato alle Sac. Ces. Reali Maestà nel carnevale dell' anno MDCCX. Poesia del Sig. Silvio Stampiglia, trà gli Arcadi Palemone Licurio . . . musica del Sig. Gio. Bononcini . . .

> *Vienna d'Austria, gli heredi Cosmeroviani, n. d. 88 p. 14½ᶜᵐ.*

Three acts. Argument and scenario.
First performed as indicated, in February, 1710. SCHATZ 1203

Caio Marzio Coriolano. Dramma per musica da rappresentarsi nel Teatro Tron di San Cassiano il carnovale dell' anno MDCCXLVII.

> *Venezia, n. publ., n. d. 5 p. l. (incl. port.), 78 p. 16½ᶜᵐ.*

The port., by Raf. Bachi, represents Maria Teresa Cibo d'Este.
Three acts. By Zaccaria Seriman, who is not mentioned. Argument, cast, scenario, and name of Pietro **Pulli** as the composer.
First performed at Reggio, Teatro del Pubblico, 1741. SCHATZ 8513

Caio Ostilio. Dramma per musica da rappresentarsi nel Regio Teatro di via della Pergola il carnevale del MDCCXCV . . .

> *Firenze, Pietro Fantosini, 1794. 35 p. 17ᶜᵐ.*

Two acts. By Eustacchio Manfredi. Neither he nor the composer Giuseppe **Giordani** is mentioned. Cast. On p. 5–9 the description of Giacomo Ricciardi's four-act "Dorcis e Cleobisa, ballo eroico pantomimo," whose ballet "Gli sposi per inganno" was also performed. The composers of the music are not mentioned.
First performed as indicated, December 27; 1794; at Faenza, Nuovo Teatro Comunale, for its opening May 12, 1788. SCHATZ 3850

Il **Cajetto.** Dramma per musica da rappresentarsi nel nuovo famosissimo Teatro di S. Girolamo nel carnovale dell' anno 1746. Dedicata a Madama Gramatica.

> *Venezia, Luigi Pavini, 1746. 80 p. 11ᶜᵐ.*

Three acts. With whimsical dedication, argument, cast, scenario and name of composer, Ferdinando **Bertoni,** but not of author, Antonio Rigo (*called* Gori).
SCHATZ 908

C. Fabbrizio.

> *Apostolo Zeno, Poesie drammatiche, Venezia, 1744, t. i, p. [173]–270. 19ᶜᵐ.*

Three acts with licenza. Argument. No composer is mentioned. In the "Catalogo" at end of t. x, date and place of first ed. are given as "in Vienna. 1729 [November 4, music by *Caldara*] 1730."
ML 49.A2Z3

C. Fabbrizio—Continued.

— **C. Fabbrizio.** Pubblicato per la prima volta in Vienna 1729.

Apostolo Zeno, Poesie drammatiche, Orleans, 1785–86, t. vii, p. 249–342. 21^{cm}.

Three acts and licenza. Argument. No composer is mentioned. ML 49.A2Z4

Cajo Fabricio. Dramma per musica di Apostolo Zeno da rappresentarsi nel Teatro di corte . . . Musica del Sig. Giovanni Adolfo Hasse . . .

Salisburgo, Giovanni Gioseppe Mayr, 1737. 71, [1] p. 15^{cm}.

Three acts. Argument.
First performed at Salzburg, Hoftheater, 1737; at Rome, Teatro Capranica, January 12, 1732. Schatz 4522

— **Cajo Fabricio.** Drama per musica da rappresentarsi nel Teatro di S. Angelo il carnovale dell' anno 1735 . . .

Venezia, Marino Rossetti, 1735. 60 p. 14^{cm}.

Three acts. Impressario's dedication, argument, cast, scenario, and name of 'Adolfo Asse detto il Sassone" (Joh. Ad. **Hasse**) as composer. On p. 8 the substitute aria "No, nò non ti lagnar" (III, 2) instead of "Misera tortorela." In the Salzburg 1737 ed. the corresponding aria is "Volgi à me gli affetti tuoi" and numerous other differences are noticeable, as for instance III, 1 having the aria "Sarà vezzosa, e bella" instead of as Venice "Richezza non chiede," which is not by Zeno at all.
Schatz 4522a

— **Cajus Fabritius,** ein sing und trauer spiel, vorgestellt aufn Koenigl. pohln. und churfuerstl. saechss. Schauplatz zu Dresden. Ins deutsche aus dem italienischen uebersetzt.

Dresden, bey Gottlob Christian Hilschern, 1734. 88 p. 16½^{cm}.

Three acts in prose. In his dedication addressed to the "Annehmliches frauenzimmer" the translator gives as *raison d'être* of his translation:
"Das sinnliche vergnuegen, so Sie bei vorstellung dieses stueckes durch die ohren, und augen geniessen, suche ich vollkommener zu machen, wenn ich auch Ihrem verstande was dabei zu thun gebe."
and in his "Vorbericht" he expresses the same idea:
"Der uebersetzer hat auf nichts dabei geseben, als dieses trauerspiel in rein deutsch zu bringen, um es einigen zuschauern verstaendlich zu machen."
He does not mention **Hasse**, the composer, whose "Cajo Fabricio" was first performed at Dresden, July 8, 1734, Mennicke adding "2 Fassg.?" (2d version?). Two intermezzi have been added on p. 81–88 under the title "Der handwercks-mann ein edelmann." This is a translation of "L'artigiano gentiluomo," under which title the intermezzi were performed at Dresden simultaneously with "Cajo Fabricio." It is the title of Antonio Salvi's original text, but when it was first performed in an altered version with Hasse's music, at Naples, Teatro di S. Bartolomeo, December 1726, it was called "Larinda e Vanesio." Schatz 4523

— **Cajo Fabricio.** Dramma per musica da rappresentarsi nel Regio Teatro di Berlino per ordine di Sua Maestà . . .

Berlino, Haude et Spener, 1766. 111, [3] p. 16^{cm}.

Three acts. Argument, scenario, and names of Joh. Ad. **Hasse** as the composer and Apostolo Zeno as the original author, which note refers to the numerous alterations of his text. German title page "Cajus Fabricius" and text face Italian.
First performed, as indicated, September 1766. Schatz 4524

Cajo Fabricio. Dramma per musica da rappresentarsi nell Sala degl' illm̄i Signori Capranica nel carnevale dell' anno MDCCLV . . .

Roma, Fausto Amidei, n. d. 66 p. 15^{cm}.

Three acts with intermezzi. By Apostolo Zeno, who is not mentioned. Impresario's dedication, argument, cast, scenario, and name of Giuseppe **Scolari** as the composer. Schatz 9804

Il Cajo Mario. Dramma per musica da rappresentarsi nel Nuovo Teatro de nobili Sig. fratelli Prini della città di Pisa la primavera dell' anno 1779.

Pisa, Francesco Pieraccini, 1779. 48 p. 17cm.

Three acts. Author not mentioned and unknown to Schatz. Cast, scenario, argument, and note: "La musica è di vari celebri autori." SCHATZ 11311

Cajo Mario. Dramma per musica da rappresentarsi nel Teatro di S. Benedetto nell' autunno dell' anno MDCCLXX.

Venezia, Modesto Fenzo, n. d. 54 p. 18cm.

Three acts. By Gaetano Roccaforte. Argument, cast, name of composer, Pasquale **Anfossi**, but not of librettist. SCHATZ 231

Il Cajo Mario. Dramma per musica da rappresentarsi nel nobilissimo Teatro di S. Benedetto nella fiera dell' Ascensione dell' anno 1781.

Venezia, Modesto Fenzo, 1781. 55 p. 16½cm.

Three acts. Argument, cast, scenario, and name of composer, Ferdinando **Bertoni**, but not of librettist, Gaetano Roccaforte. On p. 21–30, 43–49, cast and *ristretto* (synopsis) of "L'orfano della China, ballo tragico in cinque atti," and "Lauretia, ballo eroicomico in tre atti, inventati e composti dal Signor Gaspero Angiolini." The composers are not mentioned. SCHATZ 909

Cajo Mario. Dramma per musica da rappresentarsi nel real Teatro di S. Carlo nel dì 30 maggio 1784, festeggiandosi il glorioso nome di Ferdinando IV . . .

Napoli, Vincenzo Flauto, 1784. 24, 35 p. 15cm.

Three acts. Dedication, dated May, 30, 1784, argument, scenario, cast, and name of the composer, Francesco **Bianchi**, but not of the librettist, Gaetano Roccaforte. On p. 12–22, argument, cast, and full description of "Il ritorno di Rinaldo presso Armida, o sia, La vendetta di Armida vinta dall' amore, ballo eroico in tre atti," by Domenico Le Fèvre, music ("tutta nuova") by Antonio Rossetti. SCHATZ 995

Cajo Mario. Dramma per musica da rappresentarsi nel Teatro da S. Agostino il carnovale dell' anno 1782 . . .

Genova, Stamperia Gesiniana, n. d. 59 p. [1 l.] 13½cm.

Three acts. By Gaetano Roccaforte (not mentioned). Dedicatory poem, argument, cast, and name of the composer, **Cimarosa**.
First performed at Rome, Teatro delle Dame, carnival, 1780. SCHATZ 1991

Cajo Mario. Dramma per musica del Signor abate Gaetano Roccaforte Romano. Da rappresentarsi nel Teatro Grimani in S. Gio. Grisostomo la fiera dell' Ascensione dell' anno 1764.

Venezia, Modesto Fenzo, 1764. 54 p. 17½cm.

Three acts. Argument, cast, and name of **Galuppi** as composer. ("La musica tutta nuova.") With the opera were performed the ballets, "Il giudizio di Paride" and "Li amori di Tirsi ed Eurilla interrotti dalla maga Falsirena," both by Gaetano Cesari, the composers of the music not being mentioned.
First performed, as indicated, May 31, 1764. (Piovano) SCHATZ 3502

Cajo Mario. Dramma per musica da rappresentarsi nel Teatro alla Canobiana l'estate dell' anno 1791 . . .

Milano, Gio. Batista Bianchi, n. d. 43 p. 16½cm.

Two acts. By Gaetano Roccaforte, who is not mentioned. Impresario's dedication, argument, cast, scenario, and name of Giuseppe **Giordani** as the composer. With the opera was performed Urbano Garzia's ballet, "La villeggiatura in scompiglio ossia Il falso amico." The composer of the music is not mentioned.
First performed at Lodi, Nuovo Teatro, August, 1789. SCHATZ 3835

Cajo Mario.　Drama per musica da rappresentarsi in Verona nel Nuovo Teatro dell' Accademia Filarmonica nel carnovale dell' anno 1762 . . .

　Verona, Dionisio Ramanzini, 1761.　54 p.　16½ᶜᵐ.

Three acts.　Argument, cast, scenario, name of Niccolò **Jommelli** as composer, and dedication, with remark that this is the first performance of Gaetano Roccaforte's drama at Verona.

　First performed at Rome, Teatro di Torre Argentina, February 6, 1746.

SCHATZ 4896

Cajo Mario.　Dramma per musica da rappresentarsi nel nobilissimo Teatro di S. Benedetto nella fiera dell' Ascensione dell' anno MDCCLXXVII.

　Venezia, Modesto Fenzo, 1777.　62 p.　17ᶜᵐ.

Three acts.　By Gaetano Roccaforte.　Argument, cast, scenario, and name of Carlo **Monza** as the composer.　("La musica tutta nuova.")　On p. [23]–32, cast and description of Paolo Franchi's ballet, "Lauso e Lidia, ballo eroico pantomimo in cinque atti."　The composer of the music is not mentioned.　SCHATZ 6617

Cajo Mario.　Dramma per musica da rappresentarsi nel Regio-Ducal Teatro di Milano nel carnovale dell' anno 1765 . . .

　Milano, Giuseppe Richino Malatesta, 1765.　6 p. l., 48 p.　14ᶜᵐ.

Three acts.　Dedication, argument, scenario, cast, and names of Gaetano Roccaforte as the author, of Giuseppe **Scolari** as the composer.　SCHATZ 9788

Cajus Fabricius.　Tr. of Hasse's Cajo Fabricio.

Cajus Fabricius.　Ein musicalisches schau-spiel welches an dem glorreichen hoechsten nahmens-tag Ihro Churfuerstl. Durchleucht zu Pfaltz . . . aufgefuehret worden im jahr 1760.　Die poesie ist von dem herrn Mathias Verazj . . .　Die music ist eine neue composition von dem beruehmten herrn Nicolaus Jommelli . . . ausser denen mit einem sternlein, in dem italiaenischen buechlein bezeichneten arien, so von dem herrn Joseph Colla Parmesanischen capell-meister neu componiret worden.

　Mannheim, Hof-buchdruckerey, n. d.　7 p. l., 117 p.　15ᶜᵐ.

The translator is not mentioned.　Argument, cast, scenario.
"Cajo Fabricio" was first performed at Mannheim, Hoftheater, November 4, 1760.

SCHATZ 4846

Cajus Fabritius.　Tr. of Hasse's Cajo Fabricio.

La calamita de' cuori.

　[103]–153 p.　16½ᶜᵐ.　(*Carlo Goldoni, Opere drammatiche giocose, t. i, Torino, 1757*).

Three acts.　　　　　　　　　　　　　　　　　　　　ML 49.A2G6

— **La calamita de' cuori.**　Dramma di tre atti per musica.

　Carlo Goldoni, Opere teatrali, Venezia, Zatta e figli, 1788–95, v. 43, [241]–293 p.　18ᶜᵐ.　　　　　　　　　　　　　　PQ

　See next entry.

La calamita de' cuori.　Dramma giocoso per musica da rappresentarsi nel Teatro Nuovo di S. Samuele il carnovale dell' anno 1753 . . .

　Venezia, Modesto Fenzo, 1753.　56 p.　16½ᶜᵐ.

Three acts.　By Goldoni, who is not mentioned.　Impresario's dedication dated Venice, December 26, 1752, cast, but without the name of the composer, Baldassare **Galuppi.**　(Read: calamíta, not calamità.)　SCHATZ 3476

La calamita de cuori. Dramma giocoso. Da rappresentarsi ne' Teatri privilegiati di Vienna nell' anno 1774.

[Vienna], Giuseppe Kurzbök, n. d. 70 p. 15½^{cm}.

Three acts. By Giovanni de Gamerra, who is not mentioned. Scenario, name of Antonio **Salieri** as the composer and cast added in red pencil to the list of characters.
First performed, as indicated, January 1, 1774. Schatz 9276

— **La calamita de cuori.** Dramma giocoso per musica da rappresentarsi nel Piccolo Teatro di S. A. E. di Sassonia.

Dresda, n. publ., 1776. 135 p. 16½^{cm}.

Three acts. Giov. de Gamerra, the author, is not mentioned. Scenario and name of Antonio **Salieri** as the composer. German title page "Der magnetstein der herzen" and text face the Italian, which is with very few differences the same as that in the Vienna, 1774, edition. For instance, "Questa del sesso nostro" (I, 2) has become "Contro di quell' audace." Schatz 9277

Calandrano. Dramma giocoso per musica di Giovanni Bertati da rappresentarsi nel Teatro di San Samuel l'autunno dell' anno 1771.

Venezia, Modesto Fenzo, n. d. 61 p. 18^{cm}.

Three acts. Cast, scenario, and name of Giuseppe **Gazzaniga** as the composer. Schatz 3658

La Calciope. Drama per la musica di me Ercole Bonacossi.

Author's autograph, 16—. [53] l. 19^{cm}.

Prologue and three acts. Argument. Not recorded by Schatz or Allacci.

ML 95.B6

Caleb Quotem and his wife. *See* Throw physick to the dogs!

Calfurnia. Drama per musica. Da rappresentarsi nel Teatro di Sant' Angelo il carnovale dell' anno 1713 . . .

Venezia, Marino Rossetti, 1713. 59 p. 14¼^{cm}.

Three acts. Dedication by the author, Grazio Braccioli, dated Venice, January 26, 1713, argument, cast, scenario, and name of "Giovanni Heyninghen di Sassonia" (Johann David **Heinichen**) as composer. Schatz 4701

— **Die roemische grossmuht,** oder Calpurnia. In einem musicalischen schau-spiele im monath februar. 1716 auf dem Hamburgischen Theatro aufgefuehret.

Hamburg, Friedrich Conrad Greiflinger, n. d. Unpaged. 16¼^{cm}.

Scenario and "Vorbericht" by the translator, Johann Ulrich König, in which he mentions **Heinichen** as the composer, and remarks that the translation was made from the score, because he does not know the name of the Italian author and never saw a printed copy of the Venetian libretto of 1713. He also states that he has done nothing
"als nebst der uebersetzung hin und wieder einige stellen den hiesigen liebhabern zu gefallen, geaendert und hin und wieder etliche taentze, arien, decorationen oder auftritte eingerueckt . . ."
Such arias appear with German text only, and their composer is not mentioned. The other arias have the Italian text added to the German. Schatz 4702

Il Caligola. L. T. of Pagliardi's Caligula delirante.

Caligula delirante. Melodrama da rappresentarsi in musica, nel Teatro famoso Grimano di SS. Giovanni e Paolo, l'anno MDCLXXII . . .

Venetia, Francesco Nicolini, 1672. front., 84, [1] p. 14¼^{cm}.

Three acts. By Domenico Gisberti, who is not mentioned, and whose title originally was "La pazzia in trono ovvero Caligola delirante." Publisher's dedication,

Caligula delirante—Continued.

dated Venice, December 18, 1672, argument, notice to the reader, scenario, and name of "Giovanni Maria **Pagliardi**, mastro di capella del sereniss. Gran Duca di Toscana," as the composer.   SCHATZ 7582

— Il **Caligola**. Dramma per musica, rappresentato in Roma nel nuovo Teatro di Tor di Nona nel presente anno 1674 . . .

Roma, Stamparia della Rev. C. A., 1674. 63 p. 13½^{cm}.

Three acts. Gisberti's text, with noticeable differences from the version of Venice, 1672. For instance, I, 2 now begins, "O Di quanto il Sol vede," instead of "Su ! mia figlia corraggio;" I, 6, "Nesbo di regal ceppo," has been dropped and I, 7, "De la vaga Teosena," has become I, 6, etc., etc.   SCHATZ 7586

Calimedonte, rei do Epiro, ou Os amores de Sisbe e Selene: baile heroico-pantomimo em quatro actos para se executar no Real Theatro de S. Carlos em beneficio de Theresa Mellazzi em 9 de janeiro de 1796.

Lisboa, Simão Thaddeo Ferreira, 1796. 21 p. 15^{cm}.

Argument and detailed description of the single acts. Neither the composer of the music is mentioned nor the "composer" of the ballet. Not recorded by Schatz.
                                                                    ML 52.2.C2

Calipso. Dramma per musica. Da rappresentarsi nel Real Teatro di S. Carlo nel di 30 maggio 1782 festeggiandosi il glorioso nome di Ferdinando IV . . .

Napoli, Vicenzo Flauto, 1782. 56 p. 16^{cm}.

Three acts. Author not mentioned, and unknown to Schatz. According to a foot-note on p. 20, the text had been greatly changed to adapt it to this theatre. Dedi-cation dated May 30, 1782, argument, scenario, and name of Giacomo **Insanguine,** called Monopoli, as composer. On p. 10–18, argument, cast, and description of Paolo Franchi's "La principessa di Tingi, ballo eroico pantomimo in cinque atti." The second ballet was Giuseppe Trafieri's comic ballet, "La vendemia ossia La conta-dina impertinente." Giuseppe Giordani is mentioned as composer of both ballets.
                                                                    SCHATZ 4839

Calipso. Dramma per musica da rappresentarsi nel Regio Teatro di Torino nel carnovale del 1777 . . .

Torino, Onorato Derossi, n. d. viii, 58 p. 16½^{cm}.

Three acts. By Donzel (who is not mentioned), with a few alterations. Argument, cast, scenario, and name of Bernard(in)o **Ottani** as the composer. Vittorio Amedeo Canavasso is mentioned as the composer of the music for the ballets, a description of which was to follow on p. 59.

First performed December 26, 1776, as indicated.   SCHATZ 7360

Calipso abbandonata, ballet. *See* Mortellari's Troja distrutta.

Calista. An opera. As it was designed to have been perform'd at one of the theatres . . .

London, C. Davies, 1731. 6 p. l., 60 p. 18½^{cm}.

Three acts and introduction. Anonymous dedication and table of the 39 tunes used in this ballad-opera. Author not recorded.   LONGE 322

La Calisto. Drama per musica di Giovanni Faustini. Favola decima.

Venetia, Giuliàni, 1651. 82 p. 13½^{cm}.

Three acts with prologue. Author's preface and argument. The composer, Pietro Francesco **Cavalli,** is not mentioned.

First performed at Venice, Teatro di S. Apollinare, fall of 1651.   SCHATZ 1744

La **Calisto.** Intermezzi printed with Sarro's Candaule rè di Lidia.

Calisto: or, The chaste nimph. The late masque at court, as it was frequently presented there, by several persons of great quality. With the prologue, and the songs betwixt the acts. All written by J. Crowne.

London, Printed by Tho. Newcomb, for James Magnes and Richard Bentley, 1675. 12 p. l., 81, [1] p. 21½cm.

Five acts, prologue and epilogue (last, unnumb. p.). Cast of "The persons of the play," not of the singers. John Crowne's dedication and his preface in which he states that he was—

"invaded, on the sudden, by a Powerful Command, to prepare an entertainment for the court, which was to be written, learnt, practised, and performed, in less time than was necessary for the writing alone. True, it was not performed, till some months after the time first decreed, but that hapned from the discretion of those on whom the dancing and musical parts depended, who found it required time to do any thing in perfection; but I not knowing it would be so deferred, finished my part within time first alotted me, which was scarce a month; not only for the play, but the prologue, and songs, the nature of which I was wholly a stranger to, having never seen any thing of the kind; and by these means, I was forced upon a brisk dullness, writing quick, but flat. I was also confined in the number of the persons; I had but seven allow'd me, neither more nor less: those seven to be all ladies, and of those ladies, two onely were to appear in men's habits. Next, for my subject, it was not, I confess, imposed upon me by command, but it was for want of time to find a better: For I had but some few hours allow'd me to choose one . . .

"Having made this little vidication of my self, I were now bound in gratitude, (before I conclude) to record the due praises of those whose admirable performances in their several kinds, lent this entertainment much of the praise it had; namely, the singers, and the composer of all the musick both vocal and instrumental Mr. [Nicholas] **Staggins** . . . if the judgments of others, and those the most skilful too, be not mistaken, Mr. Staggins has not only delighted us with his excellent composition, but with the hopes of seeing in a very short time a master of musick in England, equal to any France or Italy have produced . . ."

The singers evidently were professionals in the king's service; their names are not mentioned.

Performed 1675, as indicated. LONGE 106

Callias, ou Nature et patrie, drame héroïque en un acte et en vers, mêlé de musique. Représenté, pour la première fois, sur le Théâtre de l'Opéra comique national, le deuxième jour complémentaire, l'an second de la République [September 18, 1794]. Paroles du citoyen Hoffman, musique du cit. Grétry.

Paris, Maradan, Troisième année de la République, 1794–95. 2 p. l., 31 p. 21½cm. SCHATZ 4202

Callirhoé, tragedie representée par l'Academie royale de musique l'an 1712. Les paroles sont de M. Roy. & La musique de M. Destouches. LXXX. opera. Tome x.

n. i., n. d. pl., p. 481–544 (Recueil général des opéra, Paris, 1714). 14cm.

Detached copy. With argument. Five acts with prologue.
First performed, as indicated, December 27, 1712. SCHATZ 2544
Second copy. ML 48.R4

Calliroe. Dramma per musica da rappresentarsi nel nuovo Regio Ducal Teatro di Milano il carnovale dell' anno 1779 . . .

Milano, Gio. Batista Bianchi, n. d. 62 p. (incl. h.-t.), [1] p. (errata). 16½cm.

Three acts. Dedication, scenario, cast, names of Mattia Verazi as author (on h.-t.), of Felice **Alessandri** as composer, and argument, at end of which this is called a com-

Calliroe—Continued.

pletely remodeled and adapted version of "quest' opera stessa . . . già . . . la prima volta esposta sul Ducal Teatro di Wirtemberg." This evidently refers to Sacchini's setting of Verazi's "Calliroe," first performed at Stuttgart January 10, 1779. With Alessandri's opera was performed the ballet, "Porzia," by either Giuseppe Canziani or Sebastiano Gallet.

First performed, as indicated, December 26, 1778.   SCHATZ 142

La Calliroe. Dramma per musica da rappresentarsi nel Regio Teatro di via della Pergola il carnevale del MDCCXCII . . .

Firenze, Stamperia Albizziniana, 1792. 44 p. 16½ᶜᵐ.

Two acts. Argument, cast, and name of Sebastiano **Nasolini** as composer. The author, Mattia Verazi, is not mentioned. On p. 5–12, argument, cast, and description. without name of the composer of the music of Domenico Ballon's "Ino e Temisto, ballo eroico tragico pantomimo." The second ballet was by Carlo Taglioni, and was called "La pazza per amore."   ML 48.A5   v. 22

La Calliroe. Dramma per musica da rappresentarsi nel nobile Teatro di Padova la fiera di giugno dell' anno 1776 . . .

Venezia, n. publ., n. d. 56p. 17ᶜᵐ.

Three acts. By Mattia Verazi, who is not mentioned. Onorato Viganò's dedication as impresario, argument, cast, scenario, and name of Giacomo **Rust** as the composer. ("La musica sarà tutta nuova.")   SCHATZ 9173

Calliroe. Dramma per musica da rappresentarsi nel Gran Teatro Ducale di Louisbourg festeggiandosi il felicissimo giorno natalizio di Sua Altezza Serenissima Carlo duca regnante di Wirtemberg et Teck etc etc. La musica è nuovamente composta dal Signor Antonio Sacchini . . .

[Stuttgart], Cotta, 1770. 167 p. 18ᶜᵐ.

On half-title Mattia Verazi is mentioned as the author. Argument, scenario, cast. French t.-p. "Calliroe," and text face Italian. On p. 162–167, cast and description of a "ballo allegorico" for this February 11, 1770, the duke's birthday. SCHATZ 9210

Calpurnia. A. T. of Heinichen's Die roemische grossmuht.

Calto. Dramma per musica da rappresentarsi nel nobilissimo Teatro Venier in San Benedetto il carnovale dell' anno 1788.

Venezia, Modesto Fenzo, 1788. 40 p. 17½ᶜᵐ.

Two acts. Preface by the author, Giuseppe Foppa, who calls this his second drama written for this theatre, argument, cast, scenario, and name of the composer, Francesco **Bianchi**. The first ballet was called "Le ninfe di Diana, ballo anacreontico." It was by Domenico Ballon. The composer is not mentioned. The music is called "tutta nuova."   SCHATZ 996

Calypso; a masque: In three acts. As it is performed at the Theatre-Royal in Covent-Garden. Written by Richard Cumberland, Esq. The music composed by T. Butler . . .

London, T. Evans, 1779. v, [1], 48, [2] p. 21ᶜᵐ.

The [2] p. contain publisher's book-list.
Cast and dedication.
First performed March 20, 1779.   LONGE 102

Calypso oder Sieg der weissheit ueber die liebe. In einem sing-spiele auf dem Hamburgischen Schau-Platze im jahr 1727 vorgestellet.

[Hamburg], Gedruckt mit Stromerschen schrifften, n. d. Unpaged. 19^{cm}.

Cast, names of Johann Philipp Praetorius as author, of Georg Philipp **Telemann** as composer, and noteworthy "Vorbericht" (incl. argument), which reads, in part:

"Nachfolgendes sing-spiel ist einigermassen ein versuch zur verbesserung der theatralischen musick in teutscher sprache, nach dem model der Italiaener . . . Unser schau-platz hat von einigen jahren her einen grossen theil der musick von ihnen entlehnet; verschiedene ihrer beruehmtesten opern sind bey uns nicht allein aufgefuehret worden, sondern es haben auch bestaendig einige ihrer geschickten landes-leute in selbigen gesungen . . .

"Nimmermehr ist der vorsatz derjenigen, welche die italiaenische opern erstlich bey uns eingefuehrt, dahin gerichtet gewesen, dass selbige den gaentzlichen besitz unsers theatri, mit ausschliessung aller ahrten, so wir selbst hervorbringen moechten, einnehmen solten. Ich weiss auch nicht wie einige unter uns neulicher zeit zu den gedancken gekommen, dass die teutschen worte zur musick untauglich seyn: Dass die teutsche sprache nicht so weibisch, und mit vocalen angefuellet sey, als die italiaenische, solches gestehe ich gern; aber damit ist es noch lange nicht ausgemacht, dass sie zur harmonie untuechtig sey . . .

"Es est gewiss von viel groesserer folge bey schau-spielen, dass sie in einer dem auditorio verstaendlichen sprache aufgefuehret werden. Dieser satz, deucht mich, braucht eben nicht viel beweises. Das groesste vergnuegen, so man bey der vocal-music hat, entstehet aus der vereinigung der idéen, welche zu gleicher zeit von den worten und dem klange herruehren . . ." SCHATZ 10257

Il **calzettaro** ossia Tanto va la gatta al lardo chi si lascia lo zampino, ballet. *See* Paisiello's Gli schiavi per amore.

La **calzolaja tedesca,** ballet. *See* Fioravanti's Le cantatrici villane.

Il **calzolajo,** ballet. *See* Cristiani's La città nuova.

Camaide, imperatore della China o vero Li figliuoli rivali del padre. Dramma per musica, da rappresentarsi nel Teatro di corte . . . Poesia del Sig. Domenico Lalli. Musica del Sig. Antonio Caldara . . .

Salisburgo, Giovanni Gioseppe Mayr, n. d. 4 p. l., 100, [2] p. 16^{cm}.

Three acts and licenza. Argument and scenario. On pages 23–29, 59–65 Domenico Lalli's intermezzo in two parts, "LA MARCHESINA DI NANCHIN ED IL CONTE DI PELUSIO," which were performed together with "Camaide" at Salzburg, Hoftheater, May 9, 1722. SCHATZ 1479

Il **cambio felice** o sia Pulcinella sposo deluso, ballet. *See* Curcio's La Nitteti.

Cambise. Dramma per musica di Domenico Lalli. Da rappresentarsi nel Teatro di S. Bartolomeo nel carnevale dell' anno 1719 . . .

Napoli, Michele Luigi Muzio, 1719. 72 p. 13½^{cm}.

Three acts. Impresario's dedication dated Naples, February 4, 1719, argument, cast, scenario, and name of Alessandro **Scarlatti** as the composer. SCHATZ 9526

Cambro-Britons, an historical play, in three acts. First performed at the Theatre Royal, Haymarket, on Saturday, July 21, 1798. With a preface. Written by James Boaden . . .

London, G. G. and J. Robinson, 1798. vi, [2], 88 p. 21^{cm}.

Cast. The preface, *inter alia*, repudiates the charge of plagiarism of Lewis' "Castle Spectre" and says that of the songs two are by George Colman, the younger. The composer, Samuel **Arnold,** is not mentioned. LONGE 248

Second copy. LONGE 266

La **cameriera astuta.** A new comic opera in two acts. As performed at the King's Theatre in the Hay-Market. The music entirely new by Mr. Storace.

London, D. Stuart, 1788. 1 p. l., 91 p. 18ᶜᵐ.

Cast. English prose translation faces Italian by author, who is not mentioned. First performed March 4, 1788, as indicated.   SCHATZ 10078

La **cameriera per amore.** Dramma giocoso per musica da rappresentarsi nel Real Teatro di Salvaterra nel carnovale dell' anno 1776.

[Lisbona], nella Stamperia reale, n. d. 88 p. incl. h.-t. 14½ᶜᵐ.

Three acts. By Filippo Livigni, who is not mentioned. Cast, scenario, and name of Felice **Alessandri** as composer.
First performed at Turin, Teatro Carignano, fall of 1774.   SCHATZ 152

Camilla. Tr. of M. A. Bononcini's Il trionfo di Camilla.

Camilla ossia La sepolta viva. Tr. of Dalayrac's Camille ou Le souterrain.

Camilla, regina de' Volsci. Dramma per musica da rappresentarsi nel Teatro Tron di Cassiano. Il carnovale dell' anno 1749.

Venezia, Modesto Fenzo, 1749. 36 p. 15ᶜᵐ.

Three acts. By Silvio Stampiglia, who is not mentioned. Argument, cast, scenario. Composers not mentioned and unknown to Schatz, who records this as a pasticcio.   SCHATZ 11312

Camilla, regina de' Volsci. L. T. of M. A. Bononcini's Il trionfo di Camilla, regina de' Volsci.

Camille, reine des Volsques, tragédie representée pour la premiere fois par l'Académie royale de musique le mardi neuf novembre 1717.

Paris, Pierre Ribou, 1717. xviii, 60 p. 25ᶜᵐ.

Five acts with prologue and author's Avertissement. Neither Danchet nor **Campra** mentioned. Cast.   ML 50.2.C253C2

— **Camille, reine des Volsques,** tragedie, représentée par l'Academie royale de musique, l'an 1717. Paroles de Monsieur Danchet. Musique de M. Campra. XCIII. Opera.

n. i., n. d. 187–258p. 14ᶜᵐ. (Recueil général des opéra, Paris, 1734, t. xii.)

Detached copy. Five acts with prologue and author's Avertissement.

First performed as indicated, November 9, 1717.   SCHATZ 1546
Second copy. ML 48.R4

— **Camille, reine des Volsques,** tragedie.

[281]–350 p. 17½ᶜᵐ. (Antoine Danchet, Théâtre, Paris, 1751, t. iii.)

Prologue and five acts. Preface. The composer, André **Campra,** is not mentioned.   PQ 1972.D2

Camille ou Le souterrain, comédie en trois actes, en prose, mêlée de musique, par M. Marsollier, représentée par les Comédiens italiens, le 19 mars 1791.

Paris, Brunet, 1791. 60 p. 19ᶜᵐ.

Label of Vente pasted over imprint.
Cast. The composer, **Dalayrac,** is not mentioned.   ML 50.2.C25D2

Camille—Continued.

— **Camille,** ou Le souterrain, comédie en trois actes et en prose, mêlée de musique. Par M. Marsollier. Représentée par les Comédiens italiens, le 19 mars 1791.

Paris, Delalain, 1793. 37 p. 22ᶜᵐ.

Cast. **Dalayrac** is not mentioned.   ML 50.2.C25D22

— **Camille,** of Het onderaardsch gewelf. Zangspel. Gevolgd naar het fransch. Door N. C. Brinkman, wed C. Van Streek [vignette]

Amsterdam, J. Helders en A. Mars, 1796. 87 p. 17ᶜᵐ.

Two acts. Neither Marsollier nor **Dalayrac** mentioned.
First performed at Amsterdam, Stads Schouwburg, 1796.   Schatz 2392

— **Camilla** ossia La sepolta viva. Commedia tradotta dal francese con musica da rappresentarsi nel Regio Teatro di S. Carlo . . . nel giorno 29 novembre dell' anno 1799.

Lisbona, Simone Taddeo Ferreira, 1799. 151 p. 15ᶜᵐ.

Translated from Marsollier by Giuseppe Carpani. Three acts. Cast, names of the author, and the composer, **Dalayrac.** Portuguese and Italian text. Schatz 2332

Camillo generoso, drama per il Teatro del Serenissimo elettore di Sassonia l'anno MDCXCIII—Camillus der Gross-muethige . . .

Dresden, Hoff-buchdruckerey, gedruckt durch Immanuel Bergen, n. d. Unpaged. 29ᶜᵐ.

Three acts. Argument, scenario. German text faces Italian. Neither author nor composer mentioned and both unknown to Fürstenau. The "Dekorationsbilder" mentioned by him are not in this copy, which does not appear to lack any.

           ML 50.2.C256

The **camp,** a musical entertainment, as performed at the Theatre Royal, Drury Lane. By R. B. Sheridan, Esq.

London, n. publ., 1795. 28 p. 17½ᶜᵐ.

Two acts. Cast. The composer, Thomas **Linley,** is not mentioned.
In S. and A. Thompson's vocal score of the opera Linley printed a note to the effect that many of the airs, trios, etc., in the The Camp were taken from his comic opera of "The Royal merchant," "some of the musick of which was found particularly applicable to the subject of this piece." Also we know from the vocal score that the "March spiritoso" in the opera was not by Linley but by **Parke.**
First performed October 15, 1778.   Longe 233

I **campi Elisi** ossia Le spose ricuperate. Dramma giocoso per musica da rappresentarsi nel Teatro alla Scala la primavera dell' anno 1788 . . .

Milano, Gio. Batista Bianchi, n. d. 72 p. 16ᶜᵐ.

Two acts. By Giovanni Bertati. Impresario's dedication, cast, scenario, and name of the composer, Luigi **Caruso,** but not of the author.
First performed at Venice, Teatro di San Samuele, fall of 1785.   Schatz 1662

Candace. Dramma per musica da rappresentarsi nel famosissimo Teatro Grimani di S. Gio. Grisostomo l'autunno dell' anno 1740 . . .

Venezia, Marino Rossetti, n. d. 59 p. 14½ᶜᵐ.

Three acts. Dedication signed by Domenico Lalli, who, according to Schatz, altered "I veri amici," by Francesco Silvani (not mentioned), argument, cast, scenario, and name of Giovanni Battista **Lampugnani** as composer. Schatz 5392

La **Candace** o'siano Li veri amici. Drama per musica da rappresentarsi nel Teatro Arciducale di Mantova nel carnovale dell' anno MDCCXX . . .

Mantova, Alberto Pazzoni, n. d. 60 p. 16^{cm}.

Three acts. Lalli's version of Francesco Silvani's "I veri amici" (neither of whom mentioned). Argument, cast, scenario and name of Antonio **Vivaldi** as composer.
ML 50.2.C26V3

Candalide. Dramma per musica di Bartolomeo Vitturi da rappresentarsi nel Teatro di Sant' Angelo. Nel carnovale dell' anno MDCCXXXIV.

Venezia, Marino Rossetti, 1734. 59 p. 15^{cm}.

Three acts. Argomento, cast, and name of Tommaso **Albinoni** as composer, whose eightieth opera this is called.
SCHATZ 174

Candaspe, regina de Sciti. Dramma per musica da rappresentarsi nel Teatro di San Angelo il carnovale dell' anno 1740.

Venezia, Marino Rossetti, 1740. 48 p. 14^{cm}.

Three acts. By Bartolomeo Vitturi (not mentioned). Argument, scenario, cast, and name of the composer, Giovanni Battista **Casali**.
SCHATZ 1677

Candaule. Drama per musica da rappresentarsi nel Teatro di S. Casciano l'anno 1680 . . .

Venetia, Francesco Nicolini, 1680. 64 p. 14½^{cm}.

Three acts. Dedication, argument, and scenario. Neither the author, Adriano Morselli, nor the composer, Pietro Andrea **Ziani**, is mentioned.
First performed, as indicated, fall of 1679.
SCHATZ 11219

Candaule re di Lidia. Drama per musica da rappresentarsi nel Nuovo Teatro di S. Giovanni de' Fiorentini . . .

Napoli, Michele Luigi Mutio, 1706. 5 p. l., 50 p. 13½^{cm}.

Three acts. By Adriano Morselli, who is not mentioned. At end of second act, on p. 28–35, apparently as intermezzo, is printed the text of the one act "La **CALISTO** Scherzo dramatico."

Impresario's dedication, argument of "Candaule" and of "La Calisto," cast, scenario, and name of Domenico **Sarro** as composer of "Candaule," list of characters, without cast and without name of composer of "La Calisto," and after the dedication a notice to the reader, which says, in part:

"L'autore del presente drama è incerto, fù però rappresentato in questa medesima città nell' anno 1679, mà con qualche diversità da quel ch'oggi si rappresenta solamente intorno alla locuzione, essendo rimasto in tutto l'intrico dell' antica favola.

"Lo scherzo dramatico è nuova poesia, mà se conoscerai, che il personaggio del Pastor Napoletano sia fuor di costume, compatisci con la tua bontà il mio desiderio di rendere il drama più allegro."

Neither the author nor the composer of this is mentioned; but Schatz attributes the music to Sarro. The point is not of much consequence, in view of this note, printed at end of the third act:

"Lo scherzo dramatico intitolato La Calisto, che dovea rappresentarsi nella fine dell' atto secondo non si rappresenta per render più breve il drama, ed invece di detto scherzo si vedrà altro trattenimento curioso."
SCHATZ 9417

Canente, tragedie representée par l'Academie royale de musique l'an 1700. Les paroles de M. de la Mothe, & la musique de M. Collasse. L. opéra.

n. i., n. d. p. 49–108. 14^{cm}. (Recueil général des opéra, Paris, 1703, t. 7.)

Detached copy. Five acts, with prologue.
First performed, as indicated, Nov. 4, 1700.
SCHATZ 2098
Second copy. ML 48.R4

Canope. Entrée in Rameau's Les fêtes de l'Himen et de l'Amour.

La cantarina. Commeddea pe mmuseca da rappresentarese a lo Tiatro de li Sciorentine nchisto carnevale de lo 1728.

Napole, n. publ., 1728. 59 p. 14½cm.

Three acts. Author not mentioned and unknown to Schatz. Notice to the reader, cast and names of Mechele **Caballone** as composer of act I, of Costantino Ruberto (**Roberto**) of acts II–III. ML 50.2.C265C2

La cantata e disfida di D. Trastullo. Intermezzi per musica a tre voci da rappresentarsi nel Teatro di Tordinona nel carnevale dell' anno 1756 . . .

Roma, Ottavio Puccinelli, 1756. 24 p. 15cm.

Two parts. Author not mentioned and unknown to Schatz. Dedication by Angelo Lungi, cast and name of Niccolò **Jommelli** as composer.
Performed with same title in the same year at Bologna, Teatro Marsigli Rossi; first performed, perhaps with same title, at Rome, Teatro della Pace, carnival 1746. ML 50.2.C266J6

— **Il Don Trastullo.** Intermezzi per musica a tre voci da rappresentarsi nel Pubblico Teatro di Lucca nel carnevale dell' anno 1762. In occasione delle recite in prosa da farsi dall' Accademia de' dilettanti della Comica . . .

Lucca, Filippo Maria Benedini, 1762. 24 p. 14½cm.

Two parts. Cast and name of Niccolò **Jommelli** as composer. Author not mentioned, and unknown to Schatz. Text the same as in the Rome, 1756 ed. Schatz 4882

Le cantatrici villane. Commedia per musica di Giuseppe Palomba da rappresentarsi nel Teatro de' Fiorentini per quart' opera del corrente anno 1798.

Napoli, n. publ., 1798. 47 p. 15cm.

Two acts. Cast and name of the composer Valentino **Fioravanti**. With the opera was performed "La calzolaja tedesca, ballo comico, composto . . . dal Sig. Gio. Battista Giannini." The composer of the music is not mentioned. Schatz 3122

La capanna incantata, ballet. *See* Gazzaniga's Amor per oro.

Il capitan Galoppo. Intermezzi comici musicali da rappresentarsi nel Teatro di Sant' Angelo l'autunno dell' anno MDCCXLI.

Venezia, Marino Rossetti, 1741. 21 p. 16cm.

Two parts. Cast. Neither the author, Bernardo Saddumene, is mentioned, nor the composer, Johann Adolph **Hasse**. Originally performed as "La Fantesca" at Naples, Teatro di S. Bartolomeo, January 29, 1729. Schatz 4588

Il capitan Tenaglia, o sia La muta per amore. Dramma giocoso per musica da rappresentarsi in Firenze l'autunno dell' anno 1784 nel nuovo Regio Teatro degl' Intrepidi detto La Palla a Corda . . .

Firenze, Stamperia Bonducciana, 1784. 68 p. 16½cm.

Two acts. By Cerilo Orcomeno, P. A., who is not mentioned and whose real name is unknown to Schatz. (Wotquenne does not mention this P. A. at all.) Cast and name of Giuseppe **Moneta** as the composer. According to Schatz the O. T. of the libretto was the present A. T. Schatz 6556

Il capitano. Operette comique aus dem beschluss des carnevals auf dem Hamburgischen Schau-Platze abermahl vorgestellet. Im monaht Mertz, anno 1726.

[Hamburg], Gedruckt mit Stromerschen schrifften, n. d. Unpaged. 18cm.

Cast. Neither the author, Schwemschu, nor the composer, Georg Philipp **Telemann**, is mentioned.
First performed, as indicated, February, 1724. Schatz 10270

Il capitano Cook all' isola Ottaiti, ballet. *See* Cimarosa's L'impresario in angustie, (Milano, 1789).

Capocchio and Dorina. *See* The happy captive and The temple of dullness.

Il cappellaro, ballet. *See* Tarchi's La Virginia.

La cappricciosa, ballet. *See* Sarti's Adriano in Siria.

La cappricciosa ravveduta. Dramma giocoso per musica da rappresentarsi nel nobilissimo Teatro Giustiniani in San Moisè l'autunno dell' anno 1794.

    Venezia, Modesto Fenzo, 1794.   59 p.   17½^{cm}.

Two acts. Scenario and name of composer, Francesco **Bianchi.**
Schatz says that the text is a later version of Caterino Mazzolà's "Il Turco in Italia." On p. 31–34 description of the three act ballet "I riti della Baja Duchy, composta dal Sig. Lorenzo Panzieri." The composer of the music is not mentioned.
                                            SCHATZ 976

La cappricciosa umiliata. A. T. of the ballet Gli amanti ridicoli.

La cappriciosa umiliata, ballet. *See* Anfossi's Le gelosie fortunate.

I capricci. Farsa per musica di Giuseppe Foppa da rappresentarsi nel nobilissimo Teatro Venier in San Benedetto il carnovale dell' anno 1795.

    [Venezia], n. publ., n. d.   30 p.   18^{cm}.

One act. Prefatory note by the author, cast, and name of Vittorio **Trento** as the composer. Schatz says that this libretto was published together with the farce "I raggiri fortunati," Venice, 1795.
                                            SCHATZ 10442

I capricci di Galatea, ballet. *See* Jommelli's L'Olimpiade.

I capricci in amore. Dramma giocoso per musica da rappresentarsi nel nobilissimo Teatro della nobil Donna Tron Veronese in San Cassiano l'autunno dell' anno 1791.

    Venezia, Modesto Fenzo, 1791.   55 p.   17^{cm}.

Two acts. Cast, scenario, and name of Gennaro **Astaritta** as composer. Librettist unknown to Schatz, who says that the title of the libretto originally was "La contadina semplice."
                                            SCHATZ 384

Il capriccio corretto. Dramma per musica da rappresentarsi nel Piccolo Teatro Elettorale, composto da Caterino Mazzolà . . .

    Dresda, n. publ., 1783.   125 p.   15½^{cm}.

Two acts. Franz **Seydelmann** is mentioned as the composer. German title page "Der eigensinn der liebe" and text face Italian.
First performed 1783, as indicated.
                                            SCHATZ 9843

Il capriccio drammatico. Rappresentazione per musica di Giovanni Bertati per la seconda opera da rappresentarsi nel Teatro Giustiniani di S. Moisè il carnovale dell' anno 1787.

    Venezia, Antonio Casali, n. d.   71 p.   17½^{cm}.

Two plays in one of one act each. The second is (on p. 31–71) Bertati's "Don Giovanni o sia Il convitato di pietra." No cast is given of this, nor is Giuseppe **Gazzaniga,** the composer of the music, mentioned, whereas of the first act the cast is given, and a note reads: "La musica è tutta nuova di varj signori maestri." Schatz, following Wiel, attributes, nevertheless, the "Capriccio dramatico" to Giovanni **Valentini.**
                                            SCHATZ 10580

La **capricciosa.** Drama giocoso per musica da rappresentarsi nel Teatro delle Dame nel carnevale dell' anno 1776 . . .

Roma, Ciovanni Bartolomicchi, 1776. 67 p. 15½ᶜᵐ.

Three acts. Author not mentioned and unknown to Schatz. Cast, scenario and name of Nicolà **Piccinni** as composer.

First performed as indicated, February 8, 1776. ML 50.2.C267P4

— La **capricciosa.** Dramma giocoso per musica da rappresentarsi nel Piccolo Teatro di S. A. S. E. di Sassonia l'anno 1777.

Dresda, Stamperia elettorale, n. d. 133 p. 16ᶜᵐ.

Three acts. German title page "Die eigensinnige," and text face Italian. N. **Piccinni** is mentioned as the composer. The author is not mentioned, and is unknown to Schatz. SCHATZ 8077

La **capricciosa corretta.** Dramma giocoso per musica da rappresentarsi nel Teatro di S. A. E. di Sassonia.

Dresda, n. publ., 1796. 20 p. l., 64 p. 16ᶜᵐ.

Two acts.. By Lorenzo da Ponte, who is not mentioned. German title-page, "So bessert sie sich," faces Italian. The p. l. contain also a detailed description of the "Inhalt," which precedes the Italian text. Vincenz Martini (**Martin y Soler**) is mentioned as the composer.

First performed at London, Haymarket, May 17, 1794. SCHATZ 6008

La **capricciosa e il credulo,** intermezzi. Die geliebte eigensinnige und der leicht-glaeubige liebhaber, in einem zwischen-spiele, auf dem Hamburgischen-Platze fuergestellet anno 1725.

[Hamburg], Gedruckt mit Stromerschen schrifften, n. d. Unpaged. 18ᶜᵐ.

Three parts. Cast, names of the author, resp. translator, Johann Philip Praetorius, and of the composer, Georg Philipp **Telemann,** and notice to the reader, in which Praetorius protests that his frequent use of "auslaendische woerter" ("gegen meine bis herige gewohnheit") is not to be construed as an admission of the German language's poverty for operatic purposes. On the contrary: "Ich bin der unvorgreifflichen meinung, die sprach-vermengung sey unserer mund-arth eben so anstaendig, als ein buntes pickel-haerings-kleid einem ehrbaren und ansehnlichen manne," but the use of foreign technical terms, as in this libretto, he considers quite proper.

The author of the Italian original is not mentioned, and is unknown to Schatz. The Italian words of the arias are added to the German. SCHATZ 10271

Le **caprice.** L. T. of Piron's text Le mariage du caprice.

Le **caprice amoureux** ou Ninette à la cour. Parody of Ciampi's Bertoldo, Bertoldino e Cacasenno.

The **capricious lovers.** O. T. of Phillis at court.

The **capricious lovers:** A musical entertainment: Taken from the opera of that name. Written by the late Mr. R. Lloyd. The music composed by Mr. Rush.

London, R. Withy, W. Griffin [etc.], 1765. 2 p. l., 27 p. 20ᶜᵐ.

Two acts. Cast. After Favart's "Le caprice amoureux ou Ninette à la cour."

First performed at London, Drury Lane, November 28, 1764. LONGE 26

The **captive,** a comic opera; as it is perform'd at the Theatre-Royal in the Hay-Market.

London, W. Griffin, 1769. vi, [2], 23 p. 19½ᶜᵐ.

Two acts. Cast and prefatory note, with remark:

"The dialogue of this trifle is taken [by Isaac Bickerstaffe?], with some alterations, from a play of Dryden's [Don Sebastian] . . . The songs . . . have been selected with great care . . ."

The captive—Continued.

This is followed by a "Table of the songs, with the composers' names:" **Ciampi, Cocchi, Duni, Galuppi, Perez, Vento, Vinci,** and Charles **Dibdin,** who composed for the piece the songs, "Ah, how sweet the rural scene," "Poor panting heart," "In emblem I am like a cat," "But pr'ythee spare me," and "Now, now, my fairest, let us go."

First performed 1769, as indicated.   Longe 37

The captive of Spilburg. In two acts, as performed at the Theatre Royal, Drury Lane, altered from the favourite French drama called Le Souterrain, with a preface by the translator. The music by Dussek . . .

London, Machell Stace and J. Hatchard, 1799.   x, 46 p.   21cm.

Last page numbered 47 by mistake. Cast, dedication, and preface, with sensible remarks on the difficulties of a librettist, as, for instance:

"The principal alteration consists in the airs, which, when new music is to be composed, it is seldom of any advantage to translate."

This translation of Marsollier's "Camille, ou, Le souterrain" is generally attributed to Prince Hoare.

First performed November 14, 1798.   Longe 249

Caractacus, a dramatic poem: written on the model of the ancient Greek tragedy. By the author of Elfrida . . . The scond edition.

London, J. Knapton and R. and J. Dodsley, 1759.   vii, [1], 96 p. 19cm.

Dedication by the author, William Mason, dated March 20, 1759. Not this, but the following dramatized version was composed by Thomas Augustine **Arne** and first performed at Covent Garden, December 6 (*not* December 1) 1776. (The anonymous "Caractacus" music generally attributed to Arne, is certainly *not* his work.)

       Longe 42

— Caractacus. A dramatic poem. Written on the model of the ancient Greek tragedy. First published in the year 1759, and now altered for theatrical representation. By W. Mason . . .

York, Printed by A. Ward, and sold by R. Horsfield and J. Dodsley, in London, 1777.   4 p. l., 76 p.   19½cm.

Five acts. Cast, author's dedicatory poem dated Aston, Nov. 12, 1776, and "Letter to Thomas Harris, Esq.," the manager, dated September 10, 1776, in which Mason appreciates Harris' "very fair and candid behaviour towards me, in not only asking my permission to bring *Caractacus* upon the stage, but in thinking me capable of making the alterations in it."

(This is a rebuke between the lines directed at George Colman for his unauthorized dramatization of Mason's "Elfrida.")

Mason continues:

"As I have endeavoured, in fitting it for the stage, not to leave it totally unfit for the closet, I suspect it may still be too long for representation. If, therefore, upon rehearsal with the music, you should find this to be the case, I will send you a second copy, in which several other lines and passages shall be mark'd with inverted commas, which you may either omit, or retain, as shall then seem expedient. But, if I print the tragedy, these passages will not be so marked, for the above reason . . ."

It should be noted, that this York edition of the text appeared later than the libretto printed for the performances. **Arne** is not mentioned by Mason.

       PR 3548.M2A65

— Caractacus. A dramatic poem. By W. Mason . . . Adapted for theatrical representation, as performed at the Theatre-Royal, Covent-Garden. Written on the model of the ancient Greek tragedy . . .

London, George Cawthorn, 1796.   front., 1 p. l., 9, [2], 12–106 p. 15cm.   (J. Bell, British Theatre, London, 1791–1797, v. 34.)

Caractacus—Continued.

The front. represents Mr. Caulfield as Arviragus and is dated October 29, 1796. The p. l. (with same date) is an added engraved title page with a scene from the play.

Five acts. "Life of William Mason" with editorial comments on his works. His elegy to Rev. Hurd, March 20, 1759, and cast. PR 1241.B4

La caravana del Cairo. Tr. of Grétry's La caravane du Caire.

La caravane du Caire, opera en trois actes, représentée devant Leurs Majestés à Fontainebleau.

[Paris], P. R. C. Ballard, 1783. 5 p. l., 46 p. 19^{cm}.

Cast and "Avertissement." **Grétry** is mentioned as the composer. Schatz attributes the text to the comte de Provence (Louis XVIII) and Etienne Morel de Chefdeville.

First performed, as indicated, Oct. 30, 1783; at Paris, January, 1784.

SCHATZ 4141

— **La caravana del Cairo.** Grand' opera in tre atti e per musica, tolta dal francese. Da rappresentarsi nel Teatro di Monza l'autunno 1795 . . .

Milano, Gaetano Motta, n. d. 4 p. l., 40 p. 16$\frac{1}{2}$^{cm}.

Three acts. Italian version by Giuseppe Carpani, who is not mentioned. Dedication, short notice to the public, cast, scenario, and names of **Grétry** as composer and of Wenceslao **Pichel** as composer of the added numbers. SCHATZ 4200

Cariselli. *See* Lully's Fragments.

Carlo e Carolina, ballet. *See* Cimarosa's Li amanti comici.

Carlo il Grande. Drama per musica da rappresentarsi nel famosissimo Teatro Grimano di S. Gio. Grisostomo l'anno 1688 . . .

Venetia, Francesco Nicolini, 1688. 72 p. 14^{cm}.

Three acts. By Adriano Morselli, who is not mentioned. Publisher's dedication, author's notice to the reader with Domenico **Gabrieli's** name as composer, argument, and scenario. SCHATZ 3397

Carlo Magno, festa teatrale in occasione della nascita del Delfino offerta alle Sacre Reali Maestà Cristianissime del Re, e Regina di Francia dal cardinale Ottoboni, Protettore degl' affari della corona.

Roma, Antonio de' Rossi, 1729. front., 11 p. l., 64 p., lxii pl. 24$\frac{1}{2}$^{cm}.

Three acts. By cardinal Pietro Ottoboni himself, with "notizia istorica," resp. "avertissement historique," scenario, and name of the composer, Giovanni **Costanzi.** The *sixty-two* plates were designed by cav. Nicolò Michetti and engraved by different artists. They represent the scenes of the opera as arranged by Michetti. The engr. front., not numb. as a pl., also by Michetti, is interesting as it contains a picture of the opera orchestra of the time with two cembalists and ten other players. On p. 61–64 the text of the "Machina che termina il dramma," a kind of *licenza.*

First performed at Rome, Palazzo Ottoboni, October, 1729. SCHATZ 2277

Carlo re d'Italia. Drama per musica da rappresentarsi nel famosissimo Teatro Grimano in S. Gio. Grisostomo. L'anno MDCLXXXII. Di Matteo Noris . . .

Venetia, Francesco Nicolini, 1682. 82 p. 14^{cm}.

Three acts. Author's dedication and preface, argument, and scenario. The composer, Carlo **Pallavicino,** is not mentioned. SCHATZ 7733

Le carnaval, mascarade representée par l'Academie royale de musique l'an 1675. Les paroles de differents auteurs, & la musique de M. de Lully. VII. opera.

n. i., n. d.   14ᶜᵐ.   pl., 347–370 p.   (Recueil général des opéra, t. I, 1703.)

Detached copy. Nine entrées. On p. 348 the note:
"Lorsque cette mascarade a été représentée sur le Theatre de l'Opera, elle a toûjours eté precedé de quelque autre divertissement; le plus souvent de *l'eglogue de Versailles,* & une fois seulement du *ballet de Ville-Neuve-Saint-Georges.* Ce dernier divertissement occupera sa place dans le iv. tome de ce recueil, sous l'année 1692. Pour *l'eglogue de Versailles,* elle suivra immediatement *l'Ydille de la Paix,* dans le iii. volume: Car c'est dans cet ordre qu'en 1685 Monsieur de Lully l'a fait imprimer en musique."

As authors are mentioned by Schatz: Molière, Quinault, and Lully.
First performed at Saint-Germain en Laye, before the King, 1675, and at Paris, as indicated, October 17, 1675.   SCHATZ 5765
                                                    Second copy.   ML 48.R4

Le carnaval de Venise, ballet represente par l'Academie royale de musique.

Amsterdam, chez leş héritiers d'Antoine Schelte, 1699.   72 p.   15ᶜᵐ.

Contents same as below. Neither Renard nor **Campra** mentioned.
First performed, as indicated, February 28, 1699.   ML 52.2.C23C3

— **Le carnaval de Venise,** ballet. Representé par l'Academie royale de musique l'an 1699. Les paroles sont de M. Renard & la musique de M. Campra. XLVI. opera.

n. i., n. d.   291–354 p.   14ᶜᵐ.   (Recueil général des opéra, Paris, 1703, t. vi.)

Detached copy. Three acts, with prologue and an interpolated miniature opera in one act of eight scenes, called "Orfeo ne'll inferi," *scil.* "Orphée aux enfers," French title and text facing Italian.   SCHATZ 1547
                                                    Second copy.   ML 48.R4

Le carnaval et la folie, comedie-ballet, représentée par l'Académie royale de musique l'an 1704. Les paroles de M. de la Mothe & La musique de M. Destouches. LX. opera.

n. i., n. d.   front., p. 181–232.   (Recueil général des opéra, t. viii, Paris, 1706.)   14ᶜᵐ.

Detached copy. Prologue and four acts. The "Avertissement" ends:
"La premiere impression de cette piece est dattée du 27. décembre 1703, neanmoins elle n'a été représentée que le 3. janvier 1704."
This date refers to the first performance at Paris; at Fontainebleau, in the King's private theatre, it was performed October 14, 1703.   SCHATZ 2545
                                                    Second copy.   ML 48.R4

— **La rupture du carnaval et de la folie.** Parodie du ballet des Amours du carnaval, & de la folie. Représentée pour la premiere fois par les Comédiens italiens ordinaires du roi, le 6. juillet 1719.

Les Parodies du Nouveau théatre italien, Nouv. ed., Paris, Briasson, 1738, t. ii, 40 p.   16½ᶜᵐ.

One act. The airs used are printed at the end of the volume in the "Table des airs" (melodies only. 60 p.). By Fuzelier, who is not mentioned.

— **L'enfant gâté,** ou Folette et Roger-Bontems, parodie du Carnaval et de la folie. Mêlée d'ariettes, représentée sur le Théâtre de l'Opéra-comique, le 6. septembre 1755. Nouvelle édition.

Paris, Aux dépens de la Communanté des imprimeurs-libraires, 1758. 38, [1] p.   19ᶜᵐ.

Le **Carnaval et la folie**—Continued.

On the [1] p. the approbation of 1755. On cover of our copy the music is attributed to "F. **Krafft**" (François Krafft, b. 1733?). The note is probably based on Fétis, whose data are corroborated by this libretto of an opera, which was unknown to Fétis. (*See* next entry.) ML 50.2.E45

— **Folette** ou L'enfant gâté, parodie du Carnaval & la folie. Par M. Vadé. Représenté pour la premiere fois, sur le Théâtre de l'Opéra-comique de la Foire S. Laurent, le 6 septembre 1755.

La Haye, Pierre Gosse junior, 1759. 62 p. 16^{cm}. (Vadé, Oeuvres, La Haye, 1759, t. iii.)

One act, *en vaudevilles.* Cast. On p. 58–62 the *ariette notée,* "Une jeune danseuse." ML 49.A2V2

Der **carneval von Venedig.** A. T. of Keiser's Der angenehme betrug.

Carolina e Mexicow, ballet. *See* Sarti's Giulio Sabino.

Carolina e Mexicow. Tragedia per musica di Gaetano Rossi da rappresentarsi nel Teatro La Fenice il carnovale dell' anno 1798.

Venezia, Stamperia Valvaseuse, n. d. 94 p. 18^{cm}.

Three acts. Cast and name of Nicola Antonio **Zingarelli** as the composer. On p. [33]–46, argument, cast, and description of Lauchlin Duquesney's "Orlina ossia La famiglia riunita, ballo pantomimo in cinque atti," music ("tutta nuova") by Ercolani. On p. 79–88 cast and description, without name of the composer of the music of the comic ballet "L'avaro burlato." SCHATZ 11268

Carolus V. A. T. of Keiser's Die oesterreichische grossmuht.

Carrousel des quatre elemens. Tr. of Li quattro elementi, with music by Lotti.

Il **Cartesiano fantastico.** Commedia per musica di G. M. D. Da rappresentarsi nel Teatro Nuovo sopra Toledo per prima opera di quest' anno 1790.

Napoli, n. publ., 1790. 48 p. 15^{cm}.

Two acts. By Giuseppe Maria Diodati. Cast and name of Giacomo **Tritto** as the composer. SCHATZ 10467

O **casamento inesperado.** A. T. of Paisiello's O marquez de Tulipano.

La **Cascina.** Dramma di tre atti per musica. Rappresentato per la prima volta in Venezia il carnovale dell' anno MDCCLVI con musica dello Scolari.

Carlo Goldoni, Opere teatrali, Venezia, Zatta e figli, 1788–95, t. 41, [299]–358 p. 18^{cm}.

La **cascina.** Dramma giocoso per musica di Polisseno Fegejo P. A. Da rappresentarsi nel Teatro di S. Samuele il carnevale dell' anno MDCCLVI.

Venezia, Angiolo Geremia, n. d. 52 p. 15^{cm}.

Three acts. By Goldoni. Cast, scenario and name of Giuseppe **Scolari** as the composer. SCHATZ 9789

La **cascina**—Continued.

— La **cascina**. Dramma giocoso per musica da rappresentarsi nel Regio Teatro di Berlino . . .

> *Berlino, Haude e Spener, 1763. 85, [3] p. 18^{cm}.*

Three acts. Scenario and name of Giuseppe **Scolari** as the composer. German title-page "Der meyerhof" and text face Italian, which is strikingly different from the Venetian original, in which the first act has eleven scenes and the third nine whereas the Berlin ed. has only five in either act.   SCHATZ 9790^a

First performed 1763 as indicated.

— La **cascina**. Dramma giocoso per musica di Polisseno Fegejo, Pastore Arcade. Da rappresentarsi nel Real Teatro di Salvaterra nel carnovale dell' anno 1766.

> *Lisbona, Michele Manescal da Costa, n. d. 78 p. 16^{cm}.*

Three acts. By Goldoni. Cast, scenario and name of Giuseppe **Scolari** as the composer.   ML 50.2.C27S2

Cassandra: or, The virgin prophetess. An opera, as it is now perform'd at the Theatre Royal by His Majesty's servants. The musical entertainments being inserted in their proper places.

> *London, A. Roper and R. [?] 2 p. l., 42 p. 21½^{cm}.*

Imprint mutilated in binding. Five acts. Cast. A play interspersed with some songs, etc., the composers not being mentioned. Clarence dates the work 1692 and mentions Lagrange as author of the text. Is this an English version of Lagrange-Chancel's "Cassandre"?   LONGE 180

La **Cassandra indovina**. Drama per musica da rappresentarsi nel nuovo Teatro de Fiorentini . . . Poesia di Nicola Giuvo fra Pastori di Arcadia detto Eupidio.

> *Napoli, Michele Luigi Muzio, 1713. 5 p. l., 68 p. 13½^{cm}.*

Three acts. Author's dedication, argument, cast, scenario, and name of composer "Nicolò **Fago** detto il Tarantino."   SCHATZ 2980

Cassandre, tragedie. Représentée pour la première fois par l'Academie royale de musique le vingtdeuxième jour de juin 1706.

> *Amsterdam, Henri Schelte, 1707. 60 p. (incl. front.) 14^{cm}.*

Five acts and prologue. Cast. Neither author, La Grange nor composers, **Bou**vard and **Bertin de la Doué**, mentioned.   ML 50.2.C28B6

— **Cassandre**, tragedie représenteé par l'Academie royale de musique l'an 1706. Les paroles de M. de la Grange. la musique de Mrs. Bouvard Bertin. LXVII. opéra.

> *n. i., n. d. p. 115–168. 14^{cm}. (Recueil général des opéra, Paris, 1710, t. ix.)*

Detached copy. Prologue and five acts.   SCHATZ 1275
Second copy.   ML 48.R4

Li **castellani burlati**. Dramma giocoso per musica da rappresentarsi nel Teatro di S. A. E. di Sassonia.

> *Dresda, n. publ., 1788. 141 p. 16^{cm}.*

Two acts. By Filippo Livigni, who is not mentioned. Vincenzo **Fabrizj** is mentioned as the composer. German text and title-page: "Die betrogenen kastellane" face Italian.

First performed at Bologna, Teatro Marsigli, Rossi, fall of 1785 under the following title: SCHATZ 2967

Li castellani burlati—Continued.

— **Li due castellani burlati.** Dramma giocoso per musica in un solo atto da rappresentarsi nel Regio Teatro di S. Carlo della Principessa l'estate dell' anno 1797.

Lisbona, Simone Taddeo Ferreira, 1797. 95 p. 15^{cm}.

Cast, scenario, and name of Vincenzo **Fabrizi** as composer. The author, Filippo Livigni, is not mentioned. Portuguese text faces Italian.   ML 50.2.D7F2

I castellani burlati. Dramma giocoso per musica di Filippo Livigni da rappresentarsi nel nobile Teatro Giustiniani in S. Moisè il carnevale dell' anno 1785 . . .

Venezia, Antonio Casali, n. d. 71 p. 17½^{cm}.

Two acts. Dedication, cast, scenario, and name of Giovanni **Valentini** as the composer.   SCHATZ 10581

Il castello d'Atlante. Dramma giocoso per musica da rappresentarsi da' signori dilettanti di Desenzano per il secondo nel carnovale 1791.

Brescia, Pasini, n. d. 59 p. 16½^{cm}.

Two acts. By Angelo Anelli, who is not mentioned. Dedication, notice to the spectators, cast, and remark on p. 5:
"La musica è novissima del celebre Sig. Martini d'Asturies autor della *Cosa rara*, [**Martin y Soler**] eccetto alcuni pezzi aggiunti, che sono del Sig. **Paisiello**, ed altri più celebri maestri."   SCHATZ 6029

Il castigo de' bonzi, ballet. *See* Anfossi's Antigono, 1781.

The castle of Andalusia. L. T. of Arnold's The banditti.

The castle of Sorrento. A comick opera in two acts. First represented at the Theatre Royal Haymarket, on Saturday July 13th, 1799. Altered from the French, and adapted to the English stage, by Henry Heartwell, Esq.

London, Cadell and Davies, 1799. iv, [2], 66 p. 21^{cm}.

Cast, dedication, and prefatory note, stating that the piece is based on the one-act French opera "Le prisonnier, ou La resemblance" (text by Duval, music by Della Maria, Paris, 1798). He alludes to his own translation, which was published in one act as "The prisoner, or, The resemblance," 1799, by the same publishers (*see* title), if he says:
"The translation was too simple for an English stage, and to produce effect, numerous changes appeared indispensible."
He mentions George Colman as responsible "for many happy alterations," but not Thomas **Attwood,** who composed (and adapted) the music.   LONGE 256

Castor et Pollux, tragedie représentée pour la prémiere fois, par l'Academie royale de musique; le vingt-quatrième jour d'octobre 1737.

[Paris], Jean Baptiste Christophe Ballard, 1737. xii, 43, [1] p. 22½^{cm}.

Prologue and five acts. Cast. Neither the author, Pierre Joseph Justin Bernard (called Gentil-Bernard) is mentioned, nor the composer, Jean Philippe **Rameau.**
                    ML 50.2.C29R2

— **Castor et Pollux,** tragedie, représentée par l'Académie royale de musique l'an 1737. Paroles de Mr Bernard. Musique de Mr Rameau. CXXIX. opera.

n.i., n.d. 479–538 p. 14½^{cm}. (Recueil général des opéra, Paris, 1745, t. xvi.)

Detached copy. Five acts and prologue. Cast.   ML 48.R4

Castor et Pollux—Continued.

— **Castor et Pollux,** tragédie représentée sur le Théatre de la Cour à Parme le six decembre MDCCLVIII.

[Parma], Borsi, n. d.   103 p.   24ᶜᵐ.

Five acts.   Bernard is not mentioned.   Argument, cast, and name of **Rameau** as the composer.   Italian title-page, "Castore e Polluce," and text face French.   The translation is said to be literal:
"Le traducteur . . . s'est attaché a rendre, presque vers pour vers le sens de l'original.   On sent ce qu'il y a d'épineux dans cet engagement.   On voudra bien passer sur quelques legeres changemens, que l'on a taché de ne point rendre étrangers au sujet: On scait que chacque langue a un tour, ou un caractere, qui lui est propre."
SCHATZ 8589

— **Castor et Pollux,** tragédie représentée, pour la première fois, par l'Academie royale de musique le 24 octobre 1737.   Reprise le 8 janvier 1754 et remise au Théâtre le mardi 24 janvier 1764.

Paris, De Lormel, 1764.   48 p.   24ᶜᵐ.

Five acts.   Cast and names of Bernard as author, of **Rameau** as the composer.
The *approbation* at end is dated Dec. 19, 1763.   SCHATZ 8590

— **Castor et Pollux,** tragédie.   Nouvelle édition.

Bordeaux, Pierre Phillippot, 1782.   31 p.   20ᶜᵐ.

Five acts.   Neither Gentil-Bernard is mentioned, nor **Rameau.**   ML 48.M2L

— **Castor et Pollux,** tragédie-lyrique, en cinq actes, représentée sur le Théâtre de la République et des Arts.   Le poëme est de Bernard. La musique est de Rameau.

Paris, Roullet, An V de la République françoise, [1796–97.]   31 p. 18½ᶜᵐ.

Cast.   SCHATZ 8586

— **Castor et Pollux,** tragédie-lyrique, en cinq actes, représentée sur le Théâtre de la République et des Arts.   Le poëme est de Bernard. La musique est de Rameau.

Paris, Roullet, An V de la République franç. [!] [1796–97].   29 p. 19ᶜᵐ.

Cast.   The text is the same as in the edition with "République françoise" in the imprint.   SCHATZ 11751

— **Castor et Pollux,** parodie nouvelle, représentée sur le Théatre de * * *, le lundi 14 janvier 1754.   Premiere et derniere édition.

Bruxelles, n. publ., 1754.   47, 4 p.   18½ᶜᵐ.

Three acts, *en vaudevilles.*   The 4 p. contain seven *airs notés.*   The author and musical arranger are not mentioned, and are unknown to Wotquenne.   ML 48.P2

Castore e Polluce.   Tragedia lirica in tre atti da rappresentarsi in Monaco nel Nuovo Teatro di Corte . . . nel carnovale dell' anno MDCCLXXXVIII.

n. i., 1788.   85 p.   15½ᶜᵐ.

Argument, cast, scenario, and name of Georg Joseph **Vogler** as the composer.
A note on p. [8] says:
"Questa tragedia lirica per comodo del Teatro, e servizio della musica da cinque, che era prima a Parigi è stata ridotta in tre atti."
The explanation of this somewhat misleading note is that Carlo Innocente Frugoni translated Pierre Joseph Justin Bernard's five-act "Castor et Pollux," as composed, for instance, by Rameau, into Italian.   Georg Joseph **Vogler,** who is mentioned as the composer, then reduced Frugoni's five-act Italian version to three acts, in which form the opera was first performed at Munich on January 12, 1787.
SCHATZ 10800

Castrini padre e figlio. Dramma giocoso per musica di Florimondo Ermionèo P. A. da rappresentarsi nel nobile Teatro di San Samuele il carnevale dell' anno MDCCLXXXVII.

Venezia, Modesto Fenzo, 1787. 83 p. 17½ᶜᵐ.

Two acts. By Giovanni Greppi. Cast, scenario, and name of Ferdinando **Robuschi** as the composer. On p. 47–49, argument and name of Antonio Capuzzi as composer of the music of Antonio Muzzarelli's "L'impostore punito, ballo tragico pantomimo." The other ballet, music by Santi, was called "Le baruffe chiozzote, ballo comico."

First performed December 26, 1786, as indicated.   SCHATZ 8840

— Li raggiri fortunati. Dramma giocoso per musica da rappresentarsi in Bologna nel nobile Teatro Marsigli Rossi la primavera dell' anno 1792 . . .

Bologna, Sassi, n. d. 4 p. l., 60 p. 17ᶜᵐ.

The imprimatur is dated April 18, 1792. Two acts. Impresario's dedication, cast, scenario and name of Ferdinando **Robuschi** as the composer. Giovanni Greppi whose "Castrini padre e figlio" this is, is not mentioned. With the opera were performed Carlo Fiorillo's ballets "L'equivoco ricompensato" and "Gl'uccellatori." The composers of the music are not mentioned.   SCHATZ 8846

Il Castruccio. *See* M. Curzio.

Les catastrophes liri-tragi-comiques.

Paris, Louis Denis Delatour, 1732. 12 p. 22½ᶜᵐ.

One act. It is really the third act of Riccoboni fils and Romagnesi's comedy "Le, amusemens à la mode," first performed at the Théâtre italien, Paris, April 21, 1732 and is said to be a kind of parody of "Jephte" and "Eriphile."   ML 52.2.C25

La catena d'Adone. Favola boschereccia d'Ottavio Tronsarelli.

[Roma], Francesco Corbelletti, 1626. 81 p. 14ᶜᵐ.

The curious ornamental t.-p. showing the title of the opera on a chain across the chest of Adonis is defective, but only in this that the place of publication has been torn off. On p. 3–4 the author's dedication, dated Rome, March 30, 1626, to Gio. Giorgio Aldobrandino, prince of Rossano, on p. 7 an avvertimento and the *imprimatur*, on p. 8 the characters, on p. 9–10 the argument, on p. 11–78 the prologue and five acts, on p. 79–81 the "Allegoria della favola," and on p. 5–6 this publisher's notice to the readers:

"Questa favola descritta nel poema del cavalier Marino à voi s'apresenta sparsa di pensieri, e ripiena d'affetti; alterato però con inventioni dal Signor Ottavio Tronsarelli e ristretta nel termine d'un giro di Sole; tra lo spatio di brevissimi giorni composta, e con non minore velocità di tempo d'alcune machine abbellita, e mirabilmente rappresentata nel palazzo dell' Illustrissimo Sig. Marchese Euandro Conti, non riempita da importuna lunghezza di vani intermedii, che, alienando le menti de gli uditori, non adornano, ma adombrano le attioni, ordinata con singolare accortezza dal Sig. Francesco de Cuppis, dalle note esquisite del Signor Domenico **Mazzochi** raddolcita, e da rare voci di famosissimi cantori sommamente honorata. Testimonio d'ogni pio detto sono i principi, e le principesse di Roma, che con lo splendore della loro presenza illustrarono il theatro di quella nobil favola, ove comparve l'Invidia & al favorevol suono dell' amico Plauso [?] se cadde, e tacque." SCHATZ 6222

Caterina e Blech, ballet. *See* Bernardini's Furberia e puntiglio.

Catherine, ou La belle fermière, comédie en trois actes et en prose, mêlée de chant. Paroles et musique de Julie Candeille. Représentée sur le Théâtre de la République, le 27 novembre 1792, sous le titre de la Belle fermière.

Paris, Maraden, 1793. 92 p. 19½ᶜᵐ.

Cast. According to a prefatory note the original title was "La fermière de qualité."
                                                        ML 50.2.C31C2

Cato in Utica.   Tr. of Graun's Catone in Utica.

Der Cato in Utica.   Tr. of Jommelli's Catone in Utica.

Cato in Utica.   Tr. of Piccinni's Catone in Utica.

Cato in Utika.   Tr. of Bach's Il Catone in Utica.

Il **Catone.**   *See* M. Curzio.

Il **Catone in Utica.**

[149]–241 p.   19ᶜᵐ.   (Pietro Metastasio, Opere drammatiche, Venezia, Giuseppe Bettinelli, 1733–37, v. 2.)

Three acts. Argument. No composer mentioned. On p. 229–241 "Mutazione dell' atto terzo" with Avviso:

"Conoscendo l'autore molto pericoloso l'avventurare in iscena il personaggio di Catone ferito: Cosi a riguardo del genio delicato del moderno teatro poco tollerante di quell' orrore, che facea l'ornamento dell' antico: come per la difficoltà d'incontrarsi in attore, che degnamente lo rappresenti: cambiò in gran parte l'atto terzo di questa tragedia . . ."

The two versions may be identified from the lines preceding the three last lines which are the same in both versions. In the original tragic version these lines are preceded by the dying Cato's words: "Spirar . . . con me . . . la libertà . . . latina"; in the later version by Fulvio's words: "Quando trionfi / Ogni perdita è lieve."   ML 49.A2M4

— **Catone in Utica.**

Metastasio, Poesie, Parigi, vedova Quillau, 1755, t. iii, [217]–356 p. 16ᶜᵐ.

Three acts. Argument. On p. [337]–356 the later version of the third act.
     ML 49.A2M42

— **Catone in Utica.**   Rappresentato, con musica del Vinci, la prima volta in Roma nel Teatro detto delle Dame, il carnevale dell' anno 1727.

pl., [3]–150 p.   26ᶜᵐ.   (Pietro Metastasio, Opere, t. 4, Parigi, vedova Herissant, 1780)

Three acts. On p. 129–150 the later version of the third act added. Argument.
     ML 49.A2M44

Catone in Utica.   Dramma per musica .da rappresentarsi nel Teatro di Livorno detto degli Armeni l' autunno dell' anno 1789 . . .

Livorno, Antonio Lami e comp., n. d.   56 p.   14½ᶜᵐ.

Two acts. By Metastasio. Argomento, cast, scenario, and name of composer, Gaetano **Andreozzi** ("musica tutta nuova"), but not of librettist.
First performed at Cremona, Teatro della Società, 1786.   Schatz 195

Catone in Utica.   Dramma per musica da rappresentarsi nel Real Teatro di S. Carlo nel dì 4 novembre 1784 per festeggiarsi i gloriosi nomi di Sua Maestà Cattolica . . .

Napoli, Vincenzo Flauto, 1784.   46 p.   15ᶜᵐ.

Three acts. By Metastasio. Dedication dated Naples, November 4, 1784, argument, cast, scenario, name of Francesco **Antonelli Torre** as composer, and note:

"I cambiamenti, che si veggono in questo dramma, sono gli stessi, che vi furono fatti nell' anno 1777 per uso di questo Regal Teatro."

With the opera were performed Domenico Lefevre's ballets, "La discesa d'Ercole all' inferno o sia Alceste ed Admeto. Ballo eroico in cinque atti" and "Gli amori di Mirtillo con Silvanzia." The music of the first was by Carlo Canobio.   Schatz 289

Il Catone in Utica. Dramma per musica da rappresentarsi nel Teatro Omodeo in Pavia nel carnovale dell' anno 1763 . . .

Pavia, Eredi Ghidini, n. d. 56 p. 15^{cm}.

Three acts. By Pietro Metastasio. Impresario's dedication, cast, scenario, and name of composer, Johann Christian **Bach**.

First performed at Milan, Regio Ducal Teatro, summer, 1762; at Naples, San Carlo, November 4, 1761. SCHATZ 526

— Il **Catone in Utica.** Drama per musica da rappresentarsi nel Gran ducal Teatro di Bronsevigo per festeggiare il glorioso giorno natalizio dell' Altezza Serenissima di Carlo, duca regnante di Bronsevigo-Luneburgo etc etc. il primo d' agosto MDCCLXVIII.

n. i., n. d. 130 p. 15$\frac{1}{2}$^{cm}.

Scenario, argument, cast, and name of Johann Christian **Bach** as composer. German title-page, "Cato in Utika," and text face Italian. SCHATZ 527

Catone in Utica. Dramma per musica da rappresentarsi nel nuovo Teatro Grimani di S. Benedetto il carnovale dell' anno MDCCLVII.

Venezia, Modesto Fenzo, 1757. 60 p. 14$\frac{1}{2}$^{cm}.

Three acts. By Metastasio. Argument, cast, scenario, and name of the composer, Vincenzo **Ciampi**.

First performed, as indicated, December 26, 1756. SCHATZ 1884

Il Catone in Utica del Signor abate Pietro Metastasio. Dramma per musica ra rappresentarsi nel Teatro di Lucca nell' autunno dell' anno MDCCXLIX.

Lucca, Filippo Maria Benedini, 1749. 88 p. 16$\frac{1}{2}$^{cm}.

Three acts. Argument, cast, scenario, and name of the composer, "Sig. Egidio **Duni**."

First performed at Florence, Teatro via della Pergola, carnival, 1740. SCHATZ 2835

Catone in Utica. Dramma per musica da rappresentarsi nel Teatro Grimani di S. Samuele per la solita fiera dell' Ascensione dell' anno MDCCLXI . . .

Venezia, Modesto Fenzo, 1761. 58 p. 15^{cm}.

Three acts. By Metastasio, who is not mentioned. Impresario's dedication, dated Venice, April 29, 1761, argument, cast, scenario, and name of Florian Leopold **Gassmann** as the composer. SCHATZ 3625

Catone in Utica. Dramma per musica da rappresentarsi nel Regio Teatro di Berlino . . .

Berlino, Ambrogio Haude, 1743. 159, [4] p. 16$\frac{1}{2}$^{cm}.

Three acts. Metastasio is mentioned as the author, Carl Heinrich **Graun** as the composer. Argument and scenario. German title-page, "Cato in Utica," and text face Italian.

First performed, as indicated, January 24, 1744. SCHATZ 4092

Catone in Utica. Drama per musica, da rappresentarsi nel Regio Teatro di Torino nel carnovale del 1732 . . .

Torino, Gio. Battista Valetta, 1731. 4 p. l., 72 p. 15$\frac{1}{2}$^{cm}.

Three acts. By Metastasio, who is not mentioned. Argument, cast, scenario, and name of Johann Adolph **Hasse** as composer.

First performed, as indicated, December 26, 1731. SCHATZ 4586

Il Catone in Utica. Dramma per musica da rappresentarsi nel Teatro Ducale di Stutgart festeggiandosi il felicissimo giorno natalizio di Sua Altezza Serenissima Elisabetta Sofia Federica duchessa di

Il **Catone in Utica**—Continued.

Wirtemberg e Tech . . . La poesia è del . . . Pietro Metastasio, . . . la musica è del celebre Sig. Nicolò Jommelli . . .

> *Stutgart, Giovanne Georgio Cotta, 1754. 99 p. 19^{cm}.*

Three acts. Argument, cast, scenario. German title-page, "Der Cato in Utica," and text face Italian.

Whether or not Jommelli used for his "Catone in Utica" of 1749 any of the music which he contributed to Leonardo Vinci's "Il Catone in Utica," Venice, 1747 (*see* Schatz 10754), I am unable to tell. Abert is silent on this Venice, 1747, opera by Vinci, Jommelli, and others.

First performed, as indicated, August 30, 1754; at Vienna, Burgtheater, 1749.

SCHATZ 4847

Catone in Utica. Dramma per musica da rappresentarsi nel carnovale dell' anno 1747 nel Teatro Capranica . . .

> *Roma, Genoroso Salomone, 1747. 72 p. 15½^{cm}.*

Three acts. Dedication with Metastasio's name as author, argument, scenario, cast, name of Gaetano **Latilla** as composer, and apologies "A'critici discreti" for the liberties taken with the text of the "dignissimo autore":

"Duo sono state le necessarie ragioni, che l'anno portato a ciò fare, la prima è la brevità, premendo a chi la fa rappresentare, che sia osservata; la seconda è la musica, la quale credendo non trovare il suo conto in alcune arie, benchè bellissime, ne à richiesta la mutazione. E cosa chiara, che è stata fatta in peggio; ma non v'era modo di evitarlo.

"Il terzetto aggiunto è forzato, e può dirsi, come di colui, che dipinse il Cipresso nel Mare, che non era quello il luogo, ma anche di ciò è cagione la musica, e la volontà altrui, come altresi d'ogn' altra cosa, che si troverà aggiunta . . . Si aggiunge a tuttociò il consentimento di persona a cui per lo stretto vincolo del sangue appartiene più che ad ogn' altro, in assenza dell' autore, aver cura de 'riguardi che si devono al medesimo."

SCHATZ 5456

Catone in Utica. Tragedia per musica di Artino Corasio Past. Arcade da rappresentarsi nel famosissimo Teatro Grimani di S. Gio. Grisostomo nel' carnevale del 1729.   Seconda editione.

> *Venezia, Carlo Buonarigo, n. d. front., 60 p. 15^{cm}.*

Three acts. By Metastasio, but with many alterations marked in the libretto. Dedication signed by Domenico Lalli, argument, scenario, cast and name of Leonardo **Leo** as the composer. According to Leo, Ricci dates the first performance, Rome, 1728, but Schatz records 1729 as above and Piovano more explicitly December 26, 1728 and shows at the same time that the Rome, 1728 opera was by Vinci.

SCHATZ 5557

Catone in Utica. Dramma per musica da rappresentarsi nel Regio Teatro di Torino nel carnevale del 1763 . . .

> *Torino, Gaspare Bayno, n. d. 78, [1] p. 16^{cm}.*

Three acts. By Metastasio, who is not mentioned. Argument, cast, scenario and name of Giovanni Francesco de **Majo** as composer. On p. 73–77 brief descriptions of Augusto Huss' ballets "L'amore vinto dall' amicizia," and "Il rapimento di Proserpina," music by Giuseppe Antonio Le-Messier.

First performed at Turin, December 26, 1762.

SCHATZ 5860

Catone in Utica. Dramma per musica da rappresentarsi alla corte elettorale Palatina in occasione del felicissimo giorno del nome del Serenissimo Elettore . . . il dì iv. novembre dell' anno MDCCLXX.

> *Mannheim, Stamperia dell' Accademia, n. d. 88 p. 16½^{cm}.*

Three acts. Argument, cast, scenario, and names of Metastasio as the author and of Niccolò **Piccinni** as the composer ("La musica è nuova composizione . . .")

According to Schatz this was the first performance of the opera. Cametti, following Florimo (second vol. *not* fourth) mentions "Napoli, San Carlo, 1770" which might, if correct, be later or earlier than the Mannheim performance.

SCHATZ 8078

Il **Catone in Utica**—Continued.

— **Cato in Utica,** ein musicalisches schauspiel, velches am churpfaelzischen Hof bei gelegenheit des hoechstbeglueckten nahmensfestes des durchlauchtigsten Churfuersten am 4. November 1770, aufgefuehrt worden.

Mannheim, Akademische buchdruckerey, n. d. 72 p. 15cm.

Argument, cast, scenario and names of Metastasio and **Piccinni.**
On p. 67–72 the description of Fabiani's ballets "Ariadne und Theseus" and "Die liebe und Psiche." The composers of the music are not mentioned. SCHATZ 8079

Catone in Utica. Tragedia per musica di Artino Corasio Pastore Arcade da rappresentarsi nel Teatro detto delle Dame nel carnovale dell' anno 1728 . . .

Roma, Bernabò, 1728. 84 p. 15½cm.

Three acts. By Metastasio. Dedication, argument, cast, scenario and name of Leonardo **Vinci** as the composer.
First performed December 27, 1727, as indicated. SCHATZ 10746

— Il **Catone in Utica.** Dramma per musica da rappresentarsi nel Teatro Tron di S. Cassiano il carnovale dell' anno MDCCXLVII.

n. i., n. d. 75 p. 16cm.

Three acts. By Metastasio, who is not mentioned. Argument, cast, scenario and note:
"La musica è del celebre fu Lunardo **Vinci,** eccettuate le arie segnate. Quelle che sono distinte con una stelletta sola sono del Signor Niccolò **Jomelli,** maestro del Pio Ospitale de Mendicanti."
The arias, not by Vinci and retaining an asterisk for those by Jommelli are: "Sperai vicino il lido" (I, 4. From Metastasio's Demofoonte), *"Sol mi basta, che talora" (I, 7), *"*O nel sen di qualche stella*" (I, 8), "Credi mi nel suo petto" (I, 13), *"Ritorna al tuo sovrano" (II, 2), *"*In che ti offende*" (II, 6), *"Grata sono al tuo bel core," *"*Se sciogliere non vuoi*" (II, 15), "Chi mai provò in amore" (II, 16), *"Per mancar a te di fede" (III, 1), "M'involi il mio tesoro" (III, 3), *"Per il mio bene" (III, 4), *"Deh placati al fine," *"Figlia, amico, io vado a morte" (III, 12).
The text of the arias in italics is from "Catone in Utica;" that of the other arias is not by Metastasio. SCHATZ 10754

Catone in Utica. Dramma per musica da rappresentarsi nel nobilissimo Teatro Venier in San Benedetto la fiera dell' Ascensione dell' anno 1791.

Venetia, Modesto Fenzo, 1791. 51 p. 18cm.

Three acts. By Metastasio, who is not mentioned. Argument, cast, scenario and name of Peter von **Winter** as the composer. On p. 20–30 argument and description without name of the composer of the music of Francesco Clerico's "Olimpia, ballo tragico in cinque atti." The title of the second ballet was "La donna bizzarra ossia L'amore politico." SCHATZ 11027

Catone Uticense. Drama per musica da recitarsi nel Teatro Grimani in S. Gio. Grisostomo, di Matteo Noris l'anno MDCCI . . .

Venetia, Niccolini, 1701. 54 p. (incl. front.) 14cm.

Three acts. Author's dedication, notice to the reader, and scenario. Carlo Francesco **Pollaroli,** the composer, is not mentioned. SCHATZ 8276

Catterina di Coluga. A. T. of the ballet Il sotteraneo.

Der **cavalier durch die liebe.** Tr. of Piccinni's Il cavaliere per amore.

Il **cavalier magnifico.** Dramma giocoso per musica da rappresentarsi nel Nuovo e nobilissimo Teatro dell' eccellentissima casa Balbi in Mestre nella presente primavera dell' anno 1779 . . .

Venezia, Modesto Fenzo, 1789 [!] *56 p. 16½ cm.*

Two acts. By Niccolò Tassi (not mentioned), whose text originally had the title "L'amante che spende." Impresario's dedication, cast, scenario and name of Carlo Caruso (*recte* Luigi **Caruso**) as the composer. On p. 31–37 detailed description of the "primo ballo. Il disertore francese" by Alessandro Guglielmi. The composer of the music is not mentioned.

First performed at Bologna, Teatro Formagliari, carnival 1777.   SCHATZ 1657

Il **cavalier Mignatta.** Intermezzi per musica a tre voci da rappresentarsi nel Pubblico Teatro di Lucca nel carnevale dell' anno MDCCLXIII. In occasione delle recite in prosa da farsi dall' Accademia de' Dilettanti della Comica.

Lucca, Francesco Antonio Berchielli, 1763. 22 p. 15 cm.

Two acts. Author unknown to Schatz. Cast and name of the composer, **Rinaldo di Capua.**

First performed at Rome, Teatro Capranica, carnival 1751.   SCHATZ 8800

Il **cavalier parigino.** L. T. of Monza's Il finto cavaliere parigino.

Il **cavalier per amore e la contadina dama.** A. T. of Piccinni's Il fumo villano.

Il **cavaliere errante.** Drama giocoso per musica da rappresentarsi nel Regio-ducal Teatro di Parma il carnovale dell' anno MDCCLXXX.

Parma, Reale stamperia, n. d. 54 p. 20 cm.

Two acts. Cast and name of Tommaso **Trajetta** as composer, but not of librettist, Giovanni Bertati. Two ballets were performed with the opera, "Gli amanti protetti da Amore" and "La festa da ballo disturbata dalla famiglia dei Covielli," both by Antonio Marliani, the composer of the music not being mentioned.

First performed, as indicated, December 26, 1779; at Venice, Teatro di San Moisè, spring, 1778.   SCHATZ 10389

— Il **cavaliero errante.** Dramma eroicomico per musica da rappresentarsi nel Piccolo Teatro Elettorale in Dresda l'anno 1780.

n. pl., Nella stamperia elettorale, n. d. 141 p. 16½ cm.

Two acts. German title-page, "Der irrende ritter," and text face Italian. Tommaso **Trajetta** is mentioned as composer.   SCHATZ 10390

Il **cavaliere per amore.** Azione comica da rappresentarsi ne' Teatri privilegiati di Vienna l'anno 1766.

Vienna, Ghelen, n. d. 44 p. 16 cm.

Two parts. Cast and names of "Pietro Sellini" (Giuseppe Petrosellini) as the author and of Niccolò **Piccinni** as the composer.

First performed at Rome, Teatro Valle, carnival, 1763 (Schatz); at Naples, Teatro Nuovo, winter, 1762 (Cametti, resp. Florimo).   SCHATZ 8080

— Il **cavaliere per amore.** Azzione comica per musica, da rappresentarsi nel Piccolo Teatro di S. A. E. di Sassonia.

Dresda, nel carnevale dell' anno 1766, n. publ. 107 p. 15 cm.

Two acts. Cast and names of **Piccinni** and of H. A. Busius, the translator. His German title-page, "Der cavalier durch die liebe," and text face Italian.

First performed, as indicated, February 22, 1766.   SCHATZ 8081

Il **cavaliere per amore**—Continued.

— Il **fumo villano.** Dramma giocoso da rappresentarsi nel Teatro Giustiniani di S. Moisè l'autunno dell' anno 1766.

Venezia, Modesto Fenzo, 1766. 60 p. 16ᶜᵐ.

Three acts. Cast, scenario, and note, "La musica è del Sig. maestro Niccolò **Piccinni**, ed alcune arie, ed il duetto ["'Se da voi non posso,' III, 4.] del Sig. maestro Bernardino **Ottani**, Accademico Filarmonico di Bologna."

The text is that of Giuseppe Petrosellini's "Il cavaliere per amore" expanded to three acts, and many alterations in the arias. For instance, the aria, "Una damina nobile" (I, 1), does not appear in this scene in "Il fumo villano." SCHATZ 8156

— Il **fumo villano** o sia Il cavalier per amore, e la contadina dama. Dramma giocoso per musica, da rappresentarsi nel Regio Teatro Danese.—Bondehovmod eller Kiøbmanden som Adelsmand, og bondepigen som frøken.

Kiøbenhavn, Lars Nielsen Svare, 1769. 167 p. 17ᶜᵐ.

Cast and name of **Piccinni** as the composer. Danish text faces Italian.

SCHATZ 8082

Li **cavalieri lunatici,** farsa per musica da rappresentarsi nel Teatro Tron di San Cassiano nell' autunno dell' anno 1774.

Venezia, n. publ., 1774. 52 p. 17ᶜᵐ.

Three acts. Author not mentioned, and unknown to Schatz. Scenario and name of Giacomo **Rust** as the composer. SCHATZ 9169

La **caverne,** drame lyrique en trois actes, représenté pour la premiere fois sur le Théâtre de la rue Feideau, le 16 février 1793, (v. st.) l'an Ier de la République; paroles de Dercis musique de Le Sueur; représenté à Liege par la Troupe d'artistes dramatiques. le 16 fructidor, an 3me. de la République Française, ou 27ᵇʳᵉ 1795, (v. st.)

Liège, Bollen, l'an quatrième de la République [1795–96]. 44 p. 21½ᶜᵐ.

Cast. Dercy's original title seems to have been "La caverne ou Les voleurs." ML 50.2.C34L2

Cécile, comédie en trois actes, en prose, mêlée d'ariettes; par M. M * * *, mise en musique par M. Dezedes. Corrigeé & imprimée suivant la représentation, au Théatre les Comédiens Italiens ordinaires du roi, le jeudi 4 janvier 1781.

Paris, Vente, 1781. 56 p. 19½ᶜᵐ.

By Mabille. The melody of the "Barcarole. Par un beau jour" (II, 3) is printed in the text.

Originally performed at Versailles, Théâtre de la cour, February 24, 1780; at Paris, Comédie italienne, February 26, 1780. SCHATZ 2516

Cefalo e Procri, ballet. *See* Sarti's Scipione.

Cefalo e Procri, ballet. *See* Tritto's L'Arminio.

La **ceinture de Venus.** Pièce en deux actes. Par M. le S * * *. Representée a la Foire de S. Germain 1715.

Le Théâtre de la foire, Paris, 1737, t. I, pl., [287]–349 p. 17ᶜᵐ.

By Alain René Le Sage. *En vaudevilles.* The melodies are printed in the "Table des airs," at the end of the volume. They were selected or composed and arranged by Jean Claude **Gillier**, the "compositeur" of the theatre. ML 48.L2I

Celio. Drama musicale del dottor Giacinto Andrea Cicognini Fiorentino . . .

Roma, Jacomo Dragondello, 1664.   104, [4] p.   14ᶜᵐ.

Three acts and Prologue. Scenario and dedication by the bookseller, Bartolomeo Lupardi, according to whom this is a new edition of "Il Celio." He does not mention the composers, nor does Schatz know them, though he records performances of Cicognini's text at Florence, 1646, and at Rome, Teatro di Tordinona. The [4] p. of the libretto contain the Protesta and a list of the "Comedie del Cicognini che ri ritrova nella sua botega Bartolomeo Lupardi . . ."   ML 50.2.C34

Cendrillon, opera comique de Mr. Anseaume; représenté pour la premiere fois sur le Théâtre de la foire S. Germain, le 20 février 1759.

Paris, N. B. Duchesne, 1759.   63, [1] p.   20ᶜᵐ.

One act. Cast. Composed, resp. arranged by Jean Louis **LaRuette** who is not mentioned. On p. 54 the air "Des rigueurs d'un cruel destin" and récitatif by "de la Ruette," "J'ai joui cette nuit" (I, 1), on p. 55–58 "Ah! dans quel état je vous voi" (I, 2), on p. 58–59 "Je le sçais bien" "air de M. La Ruette" (I, 2), on p. 59–61 "Les yeux vers moi tournés" (I, 2) by the same, as also on p. 61–63 "Amour, dont je ressens la flamme" (I, 7).   SCHATZ 5436

Cephal und Procris, ballet. *See* Holzbauer's Hadrian in Syrien.

Céphale, et Procris, ou L'amour conjugal, tragédie-lyrique, en trois actes, représentée, devant Sa Majesté, à Versailles, le 30 décembre 1773.

Paris, Pierre Robert Christophe Ballard, 1773.   1 p. l., 4, [6], 76 p. 19½ᶜᵐ.

Argument, cast, and names of Marmontel as the author, of **Grétry** as the composer.

First performed at Paris, May 2, 1775.   SCHATZ 4198

Cephale et Procris, tragedie representée par l'Academie royale de musique l'an 1694. Les paroles sont de M. Duché, & la musique de Mᶦˡᵉ de la Guerre. XXXII. Opera.

n. i., n. d.   front., 421–486 p.   (Recueil général des opéra, t. iv, Paris, 1703.)   14ᶜᵐ.

Detached copy. Five acts and prologue.
First performed, as indicated, March 15, 1694.   SCHATZ 5376
                                        Second copy.   ML 48.R4

Cephalus und Prokris. Ein melodrama von herrn professor Rammler. Die musik vom koenigl. preussischen kapellmeister herrn Reichardt.

p. 16–27.   18ᶜᵐ.   (Theater-Journal fuer Deutschland, fuenftes stueck Gotha, 1778.)

First performed at Hamburg, Theater b. Gänsemarkt, July 7, 1777.   SCHATZ 11754

— Procris et Cephale. Melodrame pour être représenté devant S. A. R. Monsieur le prince Henri de Prusse frère du roi. La musique du prologue e du melo-drame est composée par Mr. Reichard . . .

Berlin, G. J. Decker, 1777.   26 p.   19½ᶜᵐ.

One act. A french translation of Carl Wilhelm Ramler's text for Reichardt's "Cephalus und Prokris."
The French version was first performed at Rheinsberg in 1777, as indicated.   SCHATZ 8639

Ce qui plait aux dames. A. T. of Duni's La fée Urgèle.

Le cercle ou La soirée à la mode, comédie lyrique en un acte & en prose. Par M. Poinsinet de l'Académie des Arcades de Rome. Représentée pour la première fois par les Comédiens français ordinaires du roi le 7 septembre 1764.

Paris, Duchesne, 1764. 71 p. 19^{cm}.

Dedication and cast. The title "comédie lyrique" is misleading, since the play contains but one piece of music, the vaudeville "Serait-il vrai, jeune bergère," the air of which is printed on p. 70. Not recorded by Cl. & L. or Schatz.

ML 48.M2

La Cerere. Componimento per musica da cantarsi nel giorno natalizio della Sagra Real Maestà di Carlo Borbone rè delle due Sicilie & . . . Musica del Signor Domenico Terradellas detto lo Spagnolo [vignette]

Roma, Komarek, 1740. 16 p. 25^{cm}.

Two parts. Author not mentioned and unknown to me. Work not recorded by Schatz or Carreras i Bulbena. ML 50.2.C36T2

Cerere e Trittolemo, ballet. *See* Calderara's Ricimero.

Cerere placata. Festa teatrale data in occasione di celebrarsi la solenne funzione, in cui in nome di S. M. C. Carlo Terzo si tiene al sagro fonte la real principessa Maria Teresa Carolina . . . da S. E. il Signor duca d'Arcos . . . e rappresentata in Napoli il giorno 14 settembre 1772 in casa di detto eccmo Sig. duca.

n. i., n. d. 5 p. l., 54 p. 25^{cm}.

On verso of second p. l.: "Edizione fatta in Napoli nella Stamperia Simoniana." Two acts with ballets. Cast, argument, and names of Michele Sarcone as author, of Niccola **Jommelli** as composer. SCHATZ 4876

Cerere racconsolata. Dramma musicale.

Girolamo Bartolommei Smeducci, Drammi musicali morali, Firenze, 1656, v. i, p. [1]–58. 23^{cm}.

Prologue and five acts. Dedication, argument, allegoria. ML 49.A2B3

Ceres. Ein musikalisches vorspiel. Aufgefuehrt in Hannover, am geburtsfeste des koenigs, den 4 junius, 1773.

n. i., n. d. 31 p. 18^{cm}.

Prologue and one act. Neither the author, Friedrich Hildebrand von Einsiedel, nor the composer, Ernst Wilhelm **Wolf,** is mentioned. SCHATZ 11076

Cesare al Rubicone. Melodramma per musica . . . cantato in Cesena in casa Loccatelli in occasione di aver Sua Eminenza levato al sacro fonte il Sig. conte Giuseppe. Li 20 agosto 1725. Operetta del Sig. Co. Vincenzio Masini.

Faenza, Gioseffantonio Archi, 1725. 32 p. 18½^{cm}.

Dedication, dated Cesena, August, 1725, and signed Fabio Loccatelli, to whom Schatz attributes the libretto, argument and author's notice to the reader.

SCHATZ 6063

Il Cesare amante. Drama per musica di Ardio Rivarota [anagram] Accademico fra' Delfici Il Volonteroso. Da rappresentarsi nel Theatro Grimano.

Venetia, Giuliani, 1651. 99 p. 13½^{cm}.

Three acts with prologue. By Dario Varotari. Dedicatory ode, notice to the reader (p. 9–10 missing but supplied in ms.) with name of Marc' Antonio **Cesti** as

Il Cesare amante—Continued.

composer. The reader is informed that the "soggetto" and "il modo di sceneggiare" of this "operetta" are by the conte Maiolino Bisaccioni with convenient alterations.
First performed, as indicated, fall of 1651.   Schatz 1783

Cesare in Egitto. Dramma per musica da rappresentarsi nel Teatro Grimani a S. Samuelle per la fiera dell' Ascensione l'anno 1744 . . .

n. i., n. d. 1 p. l., 48 p. 15^{cm}.

Three acts. By Giacomo Francesco Bussani (not mentioned). Dedicatory sonnet, argument, scenario, cast, and name of the composer, Antonio **Colombo**.
First performed, as indicated, May 13, 1744.   Schatz 2115

Cesare in Egitto. Drama da rappresentarsi nel Regio-Ducal Teatro di Milano . . . nel carnevale dell' anno 1735.

Milano, Giuseppe Richino Malatesta, n. d. 52, [1] p. 14$\frac{1}{2}$^{cm}.

Three acts. By Giacomo Francesco Bussani, who is not mentioned. Cast, argument, scenario, and name of Geminiano **Giacomelli** as the composer. On the additional page, the substitute aria (II, 9) "Barbaro non pensar."   Schatz 3806

Cesare in Egitto. Dramma per musica da rappresentarsi in Argentina l'anno 1751 . . .

Argentina, Giovanni Henrico Heitz, 1751. 55 p. 15^{cm}.

Three acts. By Giacomo Francesco Bussani, who is not mentioned. Argument, cast, and name of Niccolò **Jommelli** as composer. (This opera mentioned by Abert?)
First performed at Strassburg, as indicated.   Schatz 4848

— Cesar en Egipte. Opera-tragique italien representé a Strasbourg l'an 1751. Sous les auspices de Son Excellence Monsieur le preteur roial. Traduit, par Mr. Adam, ancien senateur de la ville de Strasbourg.

Strasbourg, Jean Henri Heitz, 1751. 48, [2] p. 16^{cm}.

Three acts. Argument, cast, scenario, name of Niccolò **Jommelli** as composer, and "avis" that contrary to "la politesse de la langue françoise" the "Tu, Toi" has been retained partly to make the translation more literal, partly "parceque c'étoit assez le stile de s'énoncer des anciens."   Schatz 4902

Cesare in Egitto, dramma per musica da rappresentarsi nel Regio Ducal Teatro di Milano nel carnovale dell' anno 1770 . . .

Milano, Giovanni Montani, 1770. 5 p. l., 43 p. 14^{cm}.

Three acts. Dedication, argument, scenario, cast, and name of Niccolò **Piccinni** as the composer. The text is by Giacomo Francesco Bussani, retouched by Carlo Goldoni, neither of whom is mentioned.   Schatz 8083

Cesare in Egitto. Dramma per musica, da rappresentarsi sul Regio Teatro Danese, l'autunno dell' anno 1763.—Julius Caesar i Aegypten . . . oversadt paa dansk af R. Soelberg . . .

Kiøbenhavn, Lars Nielsen Svare, n. d. 93 p. 16^{cm}.

Three acts. By Giacomo Francesco Bussani, who is not mentioned. Argument, cast, and name of Giuseppe **Sarti** as the composer. ("La musica è tutta nuova.")
          Schatz 9427

Cesare nella Brettagna. *See* M. Curzio.

Cesare trionfante. *See* Freschi's Giulio Cesare trionfante.

Cha-Gian in Dely, ballet. *See* Cimarosa's Gli Orazi e i Curiazi.

The **chamber-maid.** A ballad opera of one act. As it is perform'd at the Theatre-Royal, by His Majesty's servants . . .

London, J. Watts, 1730. 2 p. l., 34 p. 21^{cm}.

By Edward Phillips, who is not mentioned. Cast and table of the 28 songs. The corresponding airs are printed in the text, with their titles.

First performed at Drury Lane February 10, 1730.   ML 50.5.C3

The **changelings.** A. T. of Court and country.

The **chaplet.** A musical entertainment. As it is perform'd by His Majesty's company of comedians at the Theatre-Royal in Drury-Lane. The music compos'd by Dr. Boyce.

London, M. Cowper, 1750. 22 p. 20½^{cm}.

Two acts. By Moses Mendez, who is not mentioned. Cast.

First performed December 2, 1749, as indicated (Genest).   AC 901.M5   v. 519

— The **chaplet.** A musical entertainment. As it is perform'd by His Majesty's company of comedians, at the Theatre-Royal in Covent-Garden. The music compos'd by Dr. Boyce.

London, T. Lowndes, T. Caslon [etc], 1767. front., 35, [1] p. 16^{cm}.

Two acts. By Moses Mendez, who is not mentioned. Covent-Garden cast of 1767.

LONGE 73

— The **chaplet.** A musical entertainment. In two parts. By Moses Mendez, Esq.

· *Edinburgh, Silvester Doig and William Anderson, 1792. (A collection of the most esteemed farces and entertainments, v. i, p. [329]–339.) 19^{cm}.*

Boyce is not mentioned.   SCHATZ 11753

La **chasse du cerf,** divertissement.

Jean Baptiste **Morin's** score, Paris, Christophe Ballard, 1709, contains also the libretto (on p. 3–7), the author of which I have not found.   M 1520.M8C4

The **chaste nimph.** A. T. of Butler's Calisto.

Le **château de Montenero.** A. T. of Dalayrac's Léon.

Che fingendo si prova un vero affetto. A. T. of Moratelli's I giochi olimpici.

The **Chelsea pensioner:** A comic opera. In two acts. As it is performed at the Theatre-Royal, Covent-Garden.

London, G. Kearsley, 1779. 2 p. l., 40 p. 21^{cm}.

Cast. The author-composer, Charles **Dibdin,** is not mentioned.

Tufts, quoting E. R. Dibdin, says: "Overture and six other items appeared in the Monthly Lyrist, etc., 1781."

First performed May 6, 1779, as indicated.   LONGE 164

La **chercheuse d'esprit,** opera comique de Monsieur Favart. Suivant la copie imprimée a Paris, MDCCXLIV.

n. i., n. d. 48 p. 16^{cm}.

One act. Text is in prose and vaudevilles. No music printed with the text.

Comp. next entry.   ML 50.2.C4

La chercheuse d'esprit—Continued.

—La chercheuse d'esprit, opera comique.   De Monsieur Favart.

Paris, Prault fils, 1756.   1 p. l., 59, 4 p.   19^cm.   (Theatre de M. Favart, Paris, Duchesne, 1763–77, t. vi.)

One act.   Text is in prose and vaudevilles.   The 4 p. contain 13 engraved airs only (with "Fin"), whereas Font says "suivi de tous les airs gravés (70 numéros)." This can apply only to a reissue of Veuve Allouel's ed. of 1741, not to the ed. of Prault fils.   Font does not mention Favart's musical collaborator.   Fétis attributes the music to **Duni** (before his arrival at Paris in 1757), but Duni can only have arranged the music anew.   Eitner lists a ms. score by Duni of this title as in the Brussels Conservatory library, but Wotquenne's catalogue shows no such score.

First performed at Paris, Foire St. Germain, February 20, 1741.   ML 49.A2F1

—La chercheuse d'esprit, opéra-comique, en un acte, de Monsieur Favart.

Paris, Prault, 1772.   47, [1] p.   19^cm.   ML 48.M2N

La chercheuse d'esprit, ballet-pantomime, par M. Gardel l'aîné. Représenté à Choisy pour la première fois et à Fontainebleau, en 1777.

Paris, les Marchands de pièces de Théâtre, 1777.   1 p. l., 8 p.   19^cm.

One act.   Cast and detailed synopsis of plot, which is clearly based on Favart. Composer not mentioned in libretto or by Lajarte who dates the first performance at Paris, Académie royale de musique as March 1, 1778.   ML 52.2.C28

The **Cherokee**, an opera, as performed at the Theatre-Royal, Drury-Lane.   By the author of the Haunted tower.

London, n. publ., 1795.   47, [1] p.   17½^cm.

Three acts.   Cast.   Neither the author, James Cobb, is mentioned, nor the composer, Stephen **Storace**.   Revived in 1802 with alterations and new music by Michael Kelly as "*Algonah.*"

First performed December 20, 1794, as indicated.   LONGE 233

La chevalerie.   Entrée in Michel's Les romans.

Chi dell' altrui si veste, presto si spoglia.   Commedia per musica di Giuseppe Palomba da rappresentarsi nel Teatro de' Fiorentini per terza opera di quest' anno 1783.

Napoli, n. publ., 1783.   55 p.   15^cm.

Three acts.   Argument, cast, and name of Domenico **Cimarosa** as composer.
                                                              ML 50.2.C42C3

—Chi dell' altrui si veste, presto si spoglia.   Commedia per musica di Giuseppe Palomba da rappresentarsi nel Teatro de' Fioren-tini per seconda opera del corrente anno 1787.

Napoli, n. publ., 1787.   52 p.   15^cm.

Three acts.   Argument, cast, name of the composer, **Cimarosa**, and this note by the author:

"Ritorna sulle scene questa mia commedia non diversa da quella rappresentata nel 1783 [at Naples, same theatre], se non se nelle sole parti di Martuffo, e Gabbamondo, con trasportale dal dialetto Toscano in Napolitano.   Se si è fatta mutazione in qualche aria, e finale è stata per maggiormente adattarla all' abilità di alcuni novelli attori, ma non si è uscito da musica, e parole tanto mie, quanto del rinomato maestro di capella, da cui fù scritta . . ."   SCHATZ 1913

Chi e cagion del suo mal, pianga se stesso. Dramma giocoso per musica da rappresentarsi nel Regio Teatro di via della Pergola la primavera del MDCCLXXXV . . .

Firenze, Giovanni Risaliti, 1785. 48 p. 16½ cm.

Two acts. Author not mentioned and unknown to Schatz. Cast and note: "La musica è di Dalindo Stinfalido Accademico Filarmonico." Real name unknown to Schatz and this academic name not recorded by Wotquenne. With the opera was performed, composer of the music not mentioned, Federigo Terrades' ballet "Gli sposi riuniti da Bacco." Schatz 11313

Chi e cagion del suo mal pianga se stesso. Dramma burlesco, poesia d'Ovidio, e musica d'Orfeo, rappresentato in Roma l'anno 1682.

Roma, (Francesco Tizzoni), 1682. 64, [1] p. 15 cm.

Three acts. Text and music, according to Schatz, by Filippo Acciajoli. First performed at the Palazzo Colonna, as indicated. ML 50.2.C43A2

Chi la dura la vince ossia La finta cantatrice. L. T. of P. Guglielmi's La virtuosa in Mergellina.

Chi la dura, la vince. Commedia per musica di Domenico Piccinni da rappresentarsi nel Teatro Nuovo sopra Toledo per second' opera di quest' anno 1798.

Napoli, n. publ., 1798. 48 p. 15 cm.

Two acts. Cast and name of Pietro Carlo Guglielmi as the composer. Schatz 4337

Chi la fa l'aspetta, ballet. *See* Astaritta's Il curioso accidente.

Chi la fa, l'aspetta. Dramma giocoso per musica da rappresentarsi nel Teatro alla Scala la primavera dell' anno 1788 . . .

Milano, Gio. Batista Bianchi, n. d. 60 p. 16½ cm.

Two acts. By Filippo Livigni, who is not mentioned. Impresario's dedication, cast, scenario, and name of the composer, Vincenzo Fabrizj. The first ballet was called "Il convitato di pietra," the second "Il finto giardiniere chinese." Both were by Luigi Dupen. The composer of the music is not mentioned. First performed at Bologna, Teatro Zagnoni, fall of 1786. Schatz 2968

Chi la fà, l'aspetta. Drama-comico da rappresentarsi in musica nel Teatro di San Fantino. Il carnovale dell' anno 1717.

Venezia, Antonio Bortoli, 1717. 36 p. 15 cm.

Three acts. Neither the author, Francesco Passarini, nor the composer, Girolamo Polani, is mentioned. Schatz 8249

Chi la fà l'aspetta, ballet. *See* Tarchi's Ifigenia in Aulide.

Chi la fa l'aspetta, ballet. *See* Zingarelli's La morte di Mitridate.

Chi la fa l'aspetti. A. T. of G. Giordani's L'impegno.

Chi la fà se l'aspetti, favola pastorale, per musica.

Viterbo, Girolamo Diotallevi, n. d. 1 p. l., 60 p. 14 cm.

Three acts. Publisher's dedication dated Viterbo, November 26, 1659. Neither author nor composer mentioned and both unknown to Allacci. Not recorded by Schatz, Wotquenne. ML 50.2.C44

Chi mal fa mal aspetti ovvero Lo scroccatore smascherato. Dramma tragicomico in musica da rappresentarsi nel nobilissimo Teatro Giustiniani in San Moisè l'autunno dell' anno 1792.

Venezia, Modesto Fenzo, 1792. 62 p. 17½cm.

Two acts. Author not mentioned, and unknown to Schatz. Cast and name of Silvestro di **Palma** as the composer. SCHATZ 7748

Chi ne fa ne aspetta, ballet. *See* Cimarosa's Volodomiro.

Chi non fà, non falla. Divertimento comico, per musica. Da rappresentarsi nel Teatro di Sant' Angelo per l'Assensa dell' anno 1732.

Venezia, Carlo Buonarrigo, n. d. 48 p. 15½cm.

Three acts. By the composer, Giuseppe Maria **Buini** (Schatz). Notice to the reader, without names of the librettist and the composer.
First performed at Bologna, Teatro Marsigli Rossi, carnival, 1729. SCHATZ 1391

Chi più sà manco l'intende, overo Gli amori di Clodio e Pompea. Dramma messo in musica da Antonio Draghi, vice maestro di cappella della Sac. Ces. Real Maestà dell' imperatrice Eleonora.

Vienna d'Austria, Matteo Cosmerovio, 1669. 8 p. l., 72 p. 15cm.

Three acts. By Cav. Ximenez, who does not sign the lengthy preface, "Ser.me Muse," a notice to the "Amico lettore," argument, and scenario. The author mentions Lodovico Brunacina [*recte* Burnacini] as the designer of the scenery, etc., and says that most of the ballet airs were composed by Santo Ventura, but some by Giov. Enrico Schmelzer.
First performed at Vienna, Theater der Kaiserl. Burg, 1669, with arias by emperor Leopold I. SCHATZ 2805

Argomento et allegoria della comedia musicale intitolata **Chi soffre speri.**

Roma, Stamperia della Rev. Camera Apostolica, 1639. 16 p. 20cm.

Three acts, with prologue. Neither the author, cardinal Giulio Rospigliosi, nor the composers, Virgilio **Mazzocchi** and Marco **Marazzoli**, are mentioned, nor the date of performance, Rome, Palazzo Barberini, February 27, 1639. SCHATZ 6223

Chi sta ben non si muova. Dramma giocoso per musica da rappresentarsi nel Regio Teatro di via della Pergola la primavera del MDCCLXXXVII . . .

Fienze, Stamperia già Albizziniana, 1787. 36 p. 16½cm.

Two acts. By Giovanni Bertati, who is not mentioned. Cast and name of Ferdinando **Robuschi** as the composer. SCHATZ 8843

Chi tutto abbraccia nulla stringe. Dramma giocoso per musica da rappresentarsi nel Teatro Giustiniani di San Moise l'autunno dell' anno 1573 [!].

Venezia, Modesto Fenzo, 1753. 47 p. 15cm.

Three acts. By Bartolomeo Vitturi, who is not mentioned. Argument, scenario, cast, and name of Giuseppe **Scolari** as the composer. SCHATZ 9791

Chi vuol non puole. Dramma giocoso per musica da rappresentarsi nel nuovo Teatro di Vicenza l'estate dell' anno 1795 . . .

Vicenza, Vendramini Mosca, n. d. 54 p. 17½cm.

Two acts. Impresario's dedication, cast, scenario, and name of Domenico **Della Maria** as composer. Author unknown to Schatz, who claims that the libretto originally was called "Il vecchio burlato." With the opera were performed the ballets, "La presa de Marochini" and "Le reclute per inganno," both by Innocenzo Parrodi, and a third ballet, the title of which is not given. The composers of the music are not mentioned. SCHATZ 2493

Le chiajese cantarine. Pazzia pe mmuseca de nota Pietro Trin-
chiera. Da rappresentarese a lo Teatro Nuovo a Monte Cravario
nchisto carnevale venturo de chisto corrente anno 1754.

*Nnapole, Se venneno a la porta de lo teatro, n. d. 2 p. l., 72 p.
15½*^{cm}.

Three acts. Cast and note that the arias "Doje note solamente" (I, 2), "Mo è no
tiempo de campare" (I, 10), "Io vorria, bellezza cara" (II, 4), etc., (the majority)
were composed by Nicola **Logroscino**, "Bene mio, ca già mme pare" (I, 1), "Si la
tempesta vide scetata" (I, 4), "Oh che gusto, che sente sto core" (I, 9), etc., by
Domenico **Fischietti**, "Sù le piume de' sospiri" (I, 5), "Io tradirti! e con qual
cuore?" (II, 2), etc., by Giacomo **Maraucci**. According to Schatz the title of the
text originally was "L'abate Collarone." ML 50.2.C45

Il chiamantesi filosofo. A. T. of Portugal's Non irritare le donne.

La Chiarina. Intermezzi in musica a tre voci da rappresentarsi nel
Teatro della Pace il carnevale dell' anno 1754 . . .

*Roma, nella libraria di S. Michele a Ripa Grande, 1754. 23 p.
15½*^{cm}.

Two parts. Author not mentioned and unknown to Schatz. Impresarios' dedication, cast and name of **Rinaldo di Capua** as composer. ML 50.2.C46R3

The children in the wood, an opera, in two acts, as performed at
the Royal Theatres of Drury-Lane and the Hay-market.

*London, Printed for the curious and not sold by the booksellers in
general, 1794. 36 p. 18*^{cm}.

Cast. Neither the author, Thomas Morton, is mentioned, nor the composer,
Samuel **Arnold**.
First performed at the Haymarket, October 1, 1793. LONGE 233

— The **children in the wood.** A musical piece, in two acts. With
the additions and alterations, as performed by the Old American
Company.

*New York, Printed at the Columbian Press for Benjamin Gomez,
1795. front., 57 p. 17*^{cm}.

The front. represents Mr. Hodgkinson as Walter, and Mr. Lee as Oliver.
Two acts. Cast. Neither the author is mentioned, nor the composer.
First performed at New York December 26, 1794; at Philadelphia, Southwark
Theatre, November 24, 1794, with the additional music by Benjamin **Carr**.
PR 1241.D7 v. 4

Chilonida. Dramma per musica da rappresentarsi il carnevale dell'
anno MDCCX. Posto in musica dal Sig. Marc' Antonio Ziani . . .

Vienna d'Austria, gli Heredi Cosmeroviani, n. d. 83 p. 14½^{cm}.

Three acts. Argument, scenario, and notice to the reader:
"Per un sovrano comando è stata forza il mutare diverse ariete nel presente dramma,
che fù composto molti anni sono dal conte Nicolò Minato. Volendo perciò chi hà
avuto la commissione di cambiarle, far conoscere di non aver posto mano nelle opere
degli altri, che per motivo d'ubbidienza, hà segnato con due virgolette al capo di ogni
verso le composte da lui, perche non siano attribuiti all' autore del drama gli altrui
difetti. Sappi dunque, che toltene le ariette sopraccennate, e qualche piccola mutazione, fattasi necessariamente nella scena X dell' atto secondo, tutto il restante si è
ristampato fedelmente secondo la prima Impressione, e vivi felice."
First performed at Vienna, Burgtheater, April 21, 1709. SCHATZ 11204

Chimene ou Le Cid. French version of Sacchini's Il Cidde.

Les **chimeres,** opéra-comique, en deux actes. Précédé d'un prologue, & suivi d'un divertissement. Joué à la Foire Saint-Germain
en 1726.

Alexis Piron, Oeuvres complettes, Liege, 1776, v. 4, [115]–253 p.
17½ᶜᵐ.

En vaudevilles. Parfaict, without mentioning the composer, enters this as "Les
chimeres ou Le bonheur de l'illusion . . . représentée le Samedi, 3 fevrier 1725.
non imp."   PQ 2019.P6

Il **chimico.** Commedia in musica da rappresentarsi nel Teatro
Grimani di S. Samuele nel carnovale 1757.

Venezia, Modesto Fenzo, 1757. 59 p. 14½ᶜᵐ.

Three acts. Cast, scenario, and name of the composer, Legrenzio Vincenzo **Ciampi.**
The author is unknown to Schatz. The text is not that by Antonio Palomba.
                                                               SCHATZ 1885

Il **chimico.** Commedia per musica di Antonio Palomba Napolitano
da rappresentarsi nel Teatro Nuovo sopra Toledo nell' inverno di
quest' anno 1742 . . .

Napoli, Nicolo de Biaso, 1742. 66 p. 15ᶜᵐ.

Three acts. Impresario's dedication, argument, cast, and name of Antonio **Palella**
as the composer.   SCHATZ 7711

Chinafarerne. Syngestykke i to acter, med en mellem-act.

n. i., n. d.   p. 287–374. 17½ᶜᵐ.

Detached copy. Neither the author, Peter Andreas Heiberg, nor the composer,
Claus **Schall,** is mentioned.
First performed at Copenhagen, Royal Theater, March 2, 1792.   SCHATZ 9583

Il **Chinese,** ballet. *See* Luigi Piccinni's L'amante statua.

Il **Chinese,** ballet. *See* Trento's La finta amalata.

Il **Chinese in Italia.** Dramma giocoso per musica di Alessandro
Pepoli da rappresentarsi nel nobile Teatro Giustiniani di San Moisè
l'autunno dell' anno 1793.

Venezia, Modesto Fenzo, 1793. 60 p. 8°.

Two acts. Cast, scenario, and name of Francesco **Bianchi** as composer. The
two ballets, by Urbano Garzia, composer not mentioned, were called "Giulia e
Blinval" and "Il matrimonio per astuzia."   SCHATZ 977

The **Chinese orphan:** An historical tragedy. Alter'd from a specimen of the Chinese tragedy in Du Halde's History of China.   Inter-
sper'd with songs, after the Chinese manner . . .

London, Charles Corbett, 1741. vii, [1], 75, [1] p. 20ᶜᵐ.

Five acts. Dedication signed by the author, William Hatchett.
Performance not recorded.   LONGE 125

Die **Chineser.** Ein musicalisches sing-gedicht, so auf dem Churfuerstl. Theatro aufgefuehret in Mannheim an 1756.

[Mannheim], Churfuerstl. buchdruckerey, n. d. 1 p. l., 53 p. 16ᶜᵐ.

One act. Dedicatory sonnet, cast, and name of Ignaz **Holtzbauer** as the composer ("eine neue composition"). Apparently the translation of Metastasio's "Le
Cinesi."   SCHATZ 4780

Der **chinesische held,** ein musicalisches schauspiel des herrn abt Peter Metastasio . . . welches an dem kaiserlichen hof von damen und cavaliers im jahre 1752. Waelsch gesungener vorgestellt, anjetzo aber in das teutsche uebersetzt worden von L. L. von C.

Wienn, zu finden in Krausens buchladen, 1755. 64 p. 17^{cm}.

Three acts. Argument. A translation of Metastasio's "L'Eroe cinese," which was first performed with music by Giuseppe Baptista (Josephus Johannes **Bonno**), who is not mentioned in the translation, at Schönbrunn, May 13, 1752. SCHATZ 1197

Der **chinesische held.** Tr. of Hasse's L'eroe cinese.

Der **chinesische held.** Tr. of Sacchini's L'eroe cinese.

Den **chinesiske helt.** Tr. of Sacchini's L'eroe cinese.

Les **Chinois.** *See* Il Cinese rimpatriato.

Le **Chinois poli en France.** *See* Il Cinese rimpatriato.

The **choice of Harlequin;** or, The Indian chief. A pantomimical entertainment; in two parts; as it is acted with the highest applause, at the Theatre Royal, Covent Garden.

London, Sold at No. 38, Clerkenwell Close, and by Mr. G. Riley, 1782. 32 p. 21^{cm}.

Cast, "Order of the procession," and editor's dedication to Thomas Harris, in which he claims:
"That the *Choice of Harlequin* has succeeded beyond any modern pantomime is not to be wondered at, when we consider the pomp of the scenes, and the marked originality with which they are displayed."
The composer, Michael **Arne,** is not mentioned. Biog. Dram. attributes the text to Messink.
First performed, as indicated, December 26, 1781. LONGE 102

— Songs, etc in the new pantomime called The **choice of Harlequin.**

n. i., n. d. 16 p. 20^{cm}.

Two parts. ML 52.2.C3

The **choleric fathers.** A comic opera. Performed at the Theatre-Royal in Covent-Garden. By Thomas Holcroft.

London, G. G. J. and J. Robinson, 1785. 2 p. l., 70, [1] p. 21^{cm}.

Three acts. Cast, and on the last (unnumb.) p. the note that "the third song in the third act ('Cupid, sure, of cunning knaves') is written by a friend of the author's, and two others have before appeared in print." The composer, William **Shield,** is not mentioned.
First performed November 10, 1785, as indicated. LONGE 96

Les **chouans de vitré,** fait historique, en un acte, en prose, par F. G. Desfontaines. Représenté pour la première fois sur le Théâtre du Vaudeville, le 24 Prairial de l'an second de la République une et indivisible. [June 12, 1794]

Paris, Au Théatre du Vaudeville, an deuxième [1793–94]. 47 p. 20^{cm}.

Cast. Interspersed with vaudevilles and airs, some of which are printed in the text. Not recorded by Cl. & L. or Schatz. ML 48.M2L

Gesaenge aus der **christlichen Judenbraut.** Eine komische oper in zwey aufzuegen. Die musik dazu ist von herrn Panek. Aufgefuehrt von der Mihuleschen gesellschaft.

Augsburg, n. publ., 1793. 48 p. 16^{cm}.

By Franz Xavier Girzik, who is not mentioned.
First performed at Augsburg, Stadtschauspielhaus; at Pressburg, Private theater of Count Erdödy, 1788. SCHATZ 7762

A new dramatic entertainment, called **A Christmas tale.** In five parts. As it is performed at the Theatre Royal in Drury-Lane. Embellished with an etching, by Mr. Loutherbourg.

London, T. Becket, 1774. 5 p. l., (incl. front.), 76 p. 20^{cm}.

Cast, prologue, prefatory note, and name of Charles **Dibdin** as composer. The text was imitated from "La fée Urgèle," by David Garrick, who is not mentioned.

First performed at London, Drury Lane, October 27, 1773.   LONGE 16

Chrononhotonthologos. *See* The tragedy of . . .

Ciana. L. T. of Latilla's Madama Ciana.

Il ciarlatano. Dramma per musica da rappresentarsi nel Teatro Giustiniani di S. Moisè nell' autunno dell' anno MDCCLIX.

Venezia, Modesto Fenzo, 1759. 70 p. 15½^{cm}.

Three acts. By Carlo Goldoni, who is not mentioned. Cast, scenario, and name of Giuseppe **Scolari** as composer.   SCHATZ 9793

Il ciarlone. L. T. of d'Avossa's La pupilla ed il ciarlone.

Il Ciclope.

Metastasio, Poesie, Parigi, vedova Quillau, 1755. t. vii, [391]– 398 p. 16^{cm}.

One act.   ML 49C.A2M42

— **Il Ciclope.** Breve cantata a due, scritta dall' autore in Vienna, ed eseguita privatamente in corte l'anno 1754, d'ordine dell' imperator Francesco I, desideroso di far prova della distinta voce di basso d'un suo confidente domestico.

[429]–434 p. 26^{cm}. (*Pietro Metastasio, Opere, t. ii, Parigi, vedova Herissant, 1780.*)

HL 49.82M44

Il Cid. L. T. of Sacchini's Il Cidde.

Le Cid. A. T. of Sacchini's Chimene.

Il Cidde. Dramma per musica da rappresentarsi in Lisbona nel Teatro della rua dos Condes nell' inverno dell' anno 1773.

[Lisbona], Stamperia reale, n. d. 76 p. 15½^{cm}.

Three acts. Argument, cast and names of Giovacchini Pizzi as the author, of Antonio **Sacchini** as the composer.

First performed at Rome, Teatro di Torre Argentina, carnival 1769. Wotquenne (Brussels catalogue) speaks of a "Chimena," first performed at Rome in 1762 but such a work is not recorded by Schatz.   SCHATZ 9223

— **Il Cid,** an opera; as performed at the King's Theatre in the Haymarket. The music by Signor Antonio Sacchini, a Neapolitan composer. The poetry by Giovan Gualberto Bottarelli. The translation by Botarelli, jun. . . .

London, W. Griffin, 1773. VIII, 47, [1] p. 19^{cm}.

Three acts. The VIII p. contain a dedication by the author, to the count de Lauraguais, dated London, January 14, 1773, just as flattering to the recipient as to Sacchini and the danseuse Heinel. This is followed by a rather self-adulatory letter sent by the count de Lauraguais to Bottarelli in response to one from this gentleman. It is dated Brompton, January 15, 1773, and in it the count says:

"car lorsque *Shakespear* etoit barbare et sublime, tout le reste l'étoit barbare et ridicule. J'ai bâti le théatre que les gens de goût desiroient depuis long-tems. Si c'est le motif du tribut que vous me rendez, il est raisonnable."

Il Cidde—Continued.

In his notice to the reader Bottarelli says "that no longer than five weeks were employed in the composing of this piece," meaning of course, his "composing" not the composition of Sacchini in which part of the original 1769 score was used. Not the same as Pizzi's text.

First performed as indicated in January 1773. SCHATZ 9246

— Chimene, ou Le Cid, tragédie en trois actes, représentée devant Leurs Majestés à Fontainebleau.

Paris, P. R. C. Ballard, 1783. 3 p. l., 47 p. 18ᶜᵐ.

Cast and names of Guillard as the author, of **Sacchini** as the composer. Several numbers of Sacchini's Italian version are known to have been retained.

First performed as indicated November 18, 1783, at the Académie royale de musique, February 9, 1784. SCHATZ 9224

Cidippe. Drama per musica da rappresentarsi nel Teatro di Canareggio. L'anno MDCLXXXIII.

Venetia, Francesco Nicolini, 1683. 57 p. 14ᶜᵐ.

Three acts. By conte Niccolò Minato, but with the addition of "alcune canzonette" printed with quotation marks, as for instance the very first "Giri pure la Fortuna." Argument, notice to the reader and scenario. Neither the author, nor the composer Antonio **Draghi** is mentioned.

In its original form first performed at Vienna, Hoftheater, November 18, 1671 with one aria by the emperor Leopold I. SCHATZ 2807

Il cieco d'acuta vista. A. T. of C. F. Pollaroli's Il Licurgo.

La Cifra. Dramma giocoso per musica da rappresentarsi nel Teatro Grande alla Scala l'autunno dell' anno 1790 . . .

Milano, Gio. Batista Bianchi, n. d. 76 p. 15½ᶜᵐ.

Two acts. Impresario's dedication dated Milan, October 16, 1790, cast, scenario and name of Antonio **Salieri** as the composer. The text was by Giuseppe Petrosellini, with alterations by Lorenzo da Ponte, neither of whom is mentioned. With the opera was performed Pietro Angiolini's ballo eroico "Rinaldo e Armida," the composer of the music not being mentioned.

First performed at Vienna, Hoftheater, December 11, 1789, as "La dama pastorella", at Rome, Teatro Valle, carnival 1780. SCHATZ 9281

— La cifra. Dramma giocoso per musica da rappresentarsi nel Reggio Teatro di S. Carlo, della Principessa la primavera dell' anno 1796.

Lisbona, Simone Taddeo Ferreira, 1796. 183 p. 15ᶜᵐ.

Two acts. Lorenzo Da Ponte is mentioned as author, Antonio **Salieri** as composer. Portuguese translation faces Italian. With the opera was performed, composer of the music not mentioned, Pietro Angiolini's ballet "Gli studi interotti."

ML 48.C6II

— Arien und gesaenge aus der komischen oper in zwey aufzuegen Das kaestchen mit der chiffer. Die composition ist von herrn capellmeister Salieri.

Berlin, n. publ., 1793. 55 p. 15ᶜᵐ.

Cast. The translator, Christian August Vulpius, is not mentioned.

First performed at Berlin, kgl. Nationaltheater, February 25, 1793. SCHATZ 9282

— Die entzifferung, eine komische oper in zwey aufzuegen. Die musik ist vom kapellmeister Salieri.

n. i., 1795. 55 p. 15½ᶜᵐ.

The translator, Heinrich Gottlieb Schmieder, is not mentioned.

First performed at Hannover, Schlosstheater, June 5, 1792. SCHATZ 9283

Cimene. Tragedia da cantarsi nel Teatro in S. Angelo nelle notte autunnali l'anno MDCCXXI.

Venezia, Marino Rossetti, 1721. 48 p. 15^{cm}.

Five acts. By Benedetto Pasqualigo. Argument, cast, scenario, but without names of composers Girolamo **Bassani,** and Marco **Zucchini,** or librettist.

Schatz 637

Il **Cinese rimpatriato.**

Intermezzo by Giuseppe **Sellitti,** first performed at Paris, June 19, 1753.
Libretto not in L. of C.
According to de La Laurencie in S. I. M. 1912, nos. 7/8, p. 14 "Il Cinese rimpa-triato" was given with an overture by Jommelli and contained among others the arias "Mi sta d'incanto," "Già colmo di piacere," "Io sono una donzella" and "Zerbi-notti d'oggidi."

— **Le chinois poli en France,** parodie du Chinois de retour, inter-mède italien. En un acte. Représentée pour la première fois sur le Théâtre de la Foire S. Laurent, le samedi 20 juillet 1754. Par M. Anseaume.

Paris, Duchesne, 1754. 48 p. 21^{cm}.

Parodied from **Sellitti's** "Il Cinese rimpatriato."
On p. 33–48, the melodies of the three "Ariettes" and the Duo, "L'amour d'un trait vainqueur." Of these "Petits maîtres sans cervelle" was the same as Sellitti's "Zerbinetti d'oggidi." The "Airs" are indicated by title or first words. Schatz 9828

— Les **Chinois,** comédie en un act, en vers, meslée d'ariettes; parodie del Cinese: représentée pour la premiere fois par les Comé-diens italiens ordinaires du roi, le 18 mars 1756. Nouvelle edition.

Paris, N. B. Duchesne, 1759. 80 p. 19^{cm}. (Theatre de M. Favart, Paris, Duchesne, 1763–77, t. iii.)

Cast. On p. [40], a "Catalogue de musiques nouvelles relatives aux pieces de théatres, & autres." On p. 41–80, eleven "Ariettes du Chinois, intermede."
The text was not wholly by Favart. He wrote it "avec M. Naigeon, 1756," as appears from p. xix of the preface of the first volume of his "Theatre." As the text gives the source of most of the ariettes, we know that the music of "Je vais, grace à ma fille" was the same as of "Già colmo di piacer," in **Sellitti's** "Cinese," likewise of "Que je baise cette main" (="Zerbinetti d'oggidi"), and of "Avec adresse, a ta maîtresse" (="Mi stà d'accanto") and that "Qu'une fête pour ce soir" (="Questo foglio"), and "Qu'il tombe qu'il meure" (="Lo voglio scannare") are from **Pergo-lesi's** Tracollo. "Ma fille, ma chere fille" has been identified by Wotquenne as "Ricerca il caro bene" in **Cocchi's** "La scaltra governatrice," and "Sous votre empire" as "Non son piccina" in the same opera. "Il m'a démis l'alouette" is a vaudeville. The final chorus "Epouse aimante" and the air "Son coeur d'abord palpite" (=Mh'a detto la mia mama) have not been identified by Wotquenne.

ML 49.A2F1

— Les **Chinois,** comedie en un acte, **en vers,** mêlée d'ariettes, parodie del Cinese, par Mr. Naigeon.

Amsterdam, la veuve de J. F. Jolly, 1760. 45, [3] p. 16^{cm}.

Cast, which is the same as in the preceding entry. The three additional pages con-tain "Divers pieces de théatre separé."
On p. [33]–45, the melodies of three "Airs choisis des Chinois."
First performed at Amsterdam, 1760.

Schatz 9825

Le Cinesi. Componimento drammatico che introduce ad un ballo.

Metastasio, Poesie, Parigi, vedova Quillau. 1755, t. iv, [441]–463 p. 16^{cm}.

One act. *See also* Un ballo cinese. ML 49.A2M42

Le **Cinesi**—Continued.

— Le **Cinesi.** Questa azione teatrale fu scritta in Vienna dall' autore per tre soli personaggi, l'anno 1735 . . . per servir d'introduzione ad un ballo cinese: e venne rappresentato con musica del Reütter, fra i trattenimenti del carnevale negl' interni appartamenti imperiali, dalle AA. RR. delle arciduchesse Maria Teresa (poi Imperatrice regina) e Marianna di lei sorella, e da una dama della corte Cesarea. Fu poi replicata da musici, e cantatrici, l'anno 1753, col quarto personaggio aggiuntovi dall' autore ad altrui istanza, in una signorile abitazione di campagna di S. A. S. il principe Giuseppe di Saxen-Hildburghausen, fra gli altri magnifici divertimenti dati dal medesimo alle Maestà imperiali di Francesco I e Maria Teresa, ne' giorni in cui piacque loro di far ivi dimora.

[379]–404 p. 26*cm*. (*Pietro Metastasio, Opere, t. ii, Parigi, vedova Herissant, 1780.*)

One act. I have seen it stated that **Caldara** was the composer. ML 49.A2M44

Cinna. Dramma per musica da rappresentarsi nel Teatro alla Scala il carnevale dell' anno 1793 . . .

Milano Gio. Batista Bianchi, n. d. 54 p. 8⁰.

Three acts. By Angelo Anelli, who is not mentioned. **Impresario's dedication,** dated Milan, December 26, 1792, argument, cast, scenario, and name of Bonifazio **Asioli** as composer. The libretto of the opera is followed (1 p. l., 8 unnumb. p.) by argument, cast, and detailed description of "Gli Sciti, ballo tragico pantomimo in cinque atti inventato, e diretto dal Sig. Filippo Beretti da eseguirsi nel Teatro alla Scala di Milano il carnevale dell' anno 1793." Composer of the music not mentioned

SCHATZ 348

Il **Cinna.** Dramma per musica da rappresentarsi nel nobilissimo Nuovo Teatro di Padova la fiera di Giugno an. 1795 . . .

Padova, li Fratelli Conzatti, n. d. 40, 15 p. 8°

Two acts. By Angelo Anelli, who is not mentioned. Dedication, argument, scenario, cast, and name of Ferdinando Pèr (**Paër**) as the composer. With the opera were performed Gaspare Ronzi's ballets, "La morte di Calisto" and "L'equivoco," of which the 15 additional p. contain argument, cast, description of the five acts, name of Vittorio Trento as composer of the music ("tutta nuova"), and Ronzi's dedication, dated Padova, June 13, 1795. SCHATZ 7560

Li **cinque pretendenti.** **L. T.** of Bernardini's La donna di spirito.

A new opera, call'd **Cinthia and Endimion:** or, The loves of the deities. As it was designed to be acted at court, before the late queen; and now acted at the Theatre Royal, by His Majesty's servants. Written by Mr. D'Urfey.

London, Sam. Briscoe and R. Wellington, 1697. 4 p. l., 48 p. 21½cm.

Errors in paging between p. 10 and 17.

Five acts. Prologue, epilogue, dedication. The composer, Daniel **Purcell**, is not mentioned. LONGE 224

Circe. A tragedy. As it is acted at His Royal Highness the duke of York's Theatre. By Charles D'Avenant . . . The third edition.

London, Jacob Touson, 1703. 2 p. l., 55, [1] p. 22cm.

Five acts. Entered because of the more than customary space given to songs and incidental music. The composer, John **Banister,** is not mentioned.

First performed 1677, as indicated. LONGE 128

La **Circe**.   Dramma per musica da rappresentarsi nel Teatro Grande alla Scala di Milano il carnevale dell' anno 1783 . . .

   Milano, Gio. Batista Bianchi, n. d.   64 p.   16ᶜᵐ.

Three acts.   By Domenico Perelli, duca di Monestarace (not mentioned).   Dedication, argument, cast, scenario, and name of the composer, **Cimarosa**.   With the opera were performed Domenico Rossi's ballets: "Alessandro nell' Indie," "Il giardino delle Tuillerie in Parigi," and "Ciacona."   The composer of the music is not mentioned.
First performed, as indicated, December 26, 1782.   SCHATZ 2005
                                          Second copy.   ML 48.A5 v. 8

Circe.   Tragedie en musique.   Representée par l'Academie royalle de musique.   Suivant la copie imprimée à Paris.

   Amsterdam, Antoine Schelte, 1695.   59 p. (incl. front.).   14ᶜᵐ.

Prologue and five acts.   Neither the author, Mᵐᵉ de Saintonge, nor the composer, **Desmarets,** is mentioned.
First performed, as indicated, October 1, 1694.   ML 50.2.C5D2

— **Circé**, tragedie représentée par l'Academie royale de musique l'an 1694.   Les paroles de Mad. Xaintonge, & la musique de M. Desmarets.   XXXIII. opera.   Torne V.

   n. i., n. d. v.   front., p. 1–66 (Recueil général des opéra, Paris, 1703). 14ᶜᵐ.

Detached copy.   Prologue and five acts.   SCHATZ 2530
                                          ML 48.R4   Second copy.

La **Circe**.   Drama per musica da rappresentarsi nel Teatro di Sant' Angelo l'anno MDCLXXIX . . .

   Venetia, Francesco Nicolini, 1679.   6 p. l., 46, [1] p.   14ᶜᵐ.

Three acts.   By Cristoforo Ivanovich, who dates his dedication, Venice, January 23, 1679.   Argument, scenario, and printer's notice to the reader, in which he says: ". . . per farti più delitioso il periodo carnovalesco, à Sant' Angelo, fà rappresentar questo scherzo di penna il Signor Francesco Santurini.   La riforma datali dal suo autore per conformarlo all' uso corrente, è stata causa di vestirlo di nuova musica, fatta dal Signor **Freschi** . . ."   SCHATZ 3347

Circe.   Dramma per musica da rappresentarsi nel nobilissimo Teatro di S. Benedetto la fiera dell' Ascensione dell' anno 1786.

   Venezia, Modesto Fenzo, 1786.   52 p.   17ᶜᵐ.

Two acts.   By Domenico Perelli, duca di Monestarace, who is not mentioned. Cast, argument, scenario, and name of the composer, Giuseppe **Gazzaniga**.   On p. 23–40 cast, preface, and minute description of Sebastiano Gallet's "Il Vologeso, ballo eroico pantomimo in cinque atti."   The composer of the music is not mentioned.
First performed, as indicated, May 20, 1786.   SCHATZ 3659

Circe oder des Ulisses erster theil, in einem singe-spiel vorgestellet, auf dem Hamburgischen Schau-platz.

   Hamburg, Nicolaus Spieringk, 1702.   Unpaged.   18½ᶜᵐ.

Three acts.   Neither the author, Friedrich Christian Bressand, is mentioned, nor the composer, Reinhard **Keiser**.
First performed at Brunswick, February, 1696.   SCHATZ 5082

Circe, in einem sing-spiele auf dem Hamburgischen Schau-platze fuergestellet.

   [Hamburg], mit Spieringischen schrifften, 1734.   Unpaged.   19ᶜᵐ.

Five acts.   The "Vorbericht" reads in part:
"Man hat in gegenwaertiger neuen opera *Circe* . . . welche mit der vor vielen jahren allhier ebenmaessig aufgefuehrten, keine verwandtschafft hat, sich gewisslich recht beflissen, denen zuschauern eine lust und vergnuegung zu verschaffen.   Eine

Circe—Continued.

auslaendische standes-person, (mehr von Ihm zu ruehmen verbeut uns seine bescheidenheit) [the Dutch minister Johann Mauricius] hat sich die muehe genommen, das gantze stueck von anfang biss zum ende, halb in frantzösischer, halb in einer andern frembden sprache, zu lieffern, und verschiedene schoene stellen aus den besten spanischen, frantzoesischen und hollaendischen schau-spielen, welche allesammt in ihrem lande beyfall gefunden, auszusuchen. Die uebersetzung ist von einem der besten dichter hiesiger gegenden [Johann Philipp Praetorius] . . . Die italiaenische arien sind auf unsrer schaubuehne noch alle neu, und von den besten meistern in Europa . . . Die anderen arien, choere und recitative sind die arbeit des ruhmbekannten herrn capellmeisters **Keisers** . . . Uebrigens hat man sein bestes gethan, durch und durch dasjenige, was dem zuschauer lange weile machen duerffte, sorgfaeltig zu vermeyden, und zu dem ende alle lange recitative eingezogen . . ."

First performed, as indicated, March 1, 1734.   SCHATZ 5081

Circe. Dramma per musica da rappresentarsi nel nobilissimo Teatro di San Samuele il carnovale dell' anno 1792.

Venezia, Modesto Fenzo, 1792. 45 p. 17½cm.

Three acts. By Domenico Perelli, duca di Monestarace, who is not mentioned. Argument, cast, scenario, and name of Ferdinando Per (**Paër**) as the composer. ("La musica tutta nuova.")   SCHATZ 7487

Circe abbandonata da Ulisse. Drama per musica di Aurelio Aureli da rappresentarsi nel famoso Teatro Grimano a SS. Gio. Paolo. Posto in musica dal Signor Carlo Francesco Polarolo . . .

Venetia, Nicolini, 1697. 48 p. 14½cm.

Three acts. Author's dedication dated Venice, November 12, 1697, argument, and scenario.

First performed at Piacenza, Nuovo Teatro Ducale della Cittadella, 1692.

                    SCHATZ 8324

Circe delusa. Drama per musica da rappresentarsi nel Teatro di Sant' Angelo nel carnovale dell' anno 1711 . . .

Venetia, Gio. Battista Tuccato, 1711. 48 p. 14cm.

Three acts. Dedication, "notizie, che si hanno in proposito di Circe," and scenario. Neither the composer, Giuseppe **Boniventi**, nor the librettist, Giorgio Antonio Falier, is mentioned.   SCHATZ 1186

Cirene. Dramma per musica da rappresentarsi nel Teatro di S. Angelo il carnovale 1742 . . .

Venezia, Marino Rossetti, n. d. 48 p. 15cm.

Three acts. By Silvio Stampiglia, who is not mentioned. Impresario's dedication dated Venice, January 30, 1742, argument, cast, scenario, and name of Pietro **Pellegrini** as the composer.   SCHATZ 7860

Ciro. Drama per musica da rappresentarsi nel Teatro Tron di San Cassano nel carnovale dell' anno 1709 . . .

Venezia, Marino Rossetti, n. d. 62 p. 15cm.

Three acts. Dedication signed by the author, P[ietro] P[ariati], argument, scenario, cast, and name of Tommaso **Albinoni** as composer.   SCHATZ 115

Il Ciro. Drama per musica del Signor Giulio Cesare Sorentino napoletano. Con prologo, aggiunte, mutationi & aggiustamenti all' uso di questa città fatte da altro soggetto con permissione dell' autore. Arrichite poi dalla sempre ammirabile musica del Sig. Francesco Cavalli. Dedicata . . . da Gio. Battista Balbi, direttore delle scene, machine, e balli.

Venetia, Gio. Pietro Pinelli, 1654. 96 p. 15cm.

Three acts, with prologue. Balbi's dedication, dated January 30, 1653 (*i. e.* 1654), argument, preface, and scenario.

Il Ciro—Continued.

The reader is told:

"Questo drama ha sortito i suoi natali in Napoli, sotto felice influsso di servire alle scene di Venetia: mà quando egli s'e ritrovato di quì s'avvide, che non haveva adobbi all' uso di questa città. La differenza del costume l'haveva, si nelle parole, come nel soggetto, allevato. con maniere differenti dal genio Veneto delicatissimo in ogni senti- mento: l'hà preveduto la virtù, e la prudenza dell' auttore, che gli fù padre, onde hà concessa facoltà di regolarlo, accrescerlo, e sminuirlo . . . Le mutationi, che egli hà fatte nel soggetto poco rileva, che si sappiano; basta che sono state approvate, e conos- ciute necessarie per seguire lo stile delle nostre scene. Molti sono li versi mutati, mà ritenuto il concetto, che vi era prima, e questi non importa il conoscerli. Li altri, che vedrai segnati nel margine con questo segno ,, sono quelli che intieramente sono stati aggionti, si come anco il prologo è d'inventione di questo sogetto già qualche tempo discorsa anco dà lui à qualche suo confidente: e hora gli hà fatta la poesia . . . Per ispiegarti la fretta, con che egli hà composto, basta che io ti giuri, che in due soli giorni hà aggiiustato il terzo atto, e fattivi li versi, che in quello vedi segnati ,, come ti hò già detto; havendo variato anco l'ordine del sogetto, ch'è molto differente dà quello che era prima. Egli però protesta, e si dichiara, che queste mutazioni, si come le hà fatte con permissione dell' auttore del drama, cosi ha mutato non per migliorare, mà per accommodarsi al costume. A tutti li versi aggiunti, ò mutati hà fatta la musica il Signor Francesco **Cavalli** Apollo dell' armonia: ti direi i luochi particolari dove la sentirai, mà basta, che l'ascolti, che senza altra notitia la riconoscerai, per l'esperienza della sua isquisitezza . . ."

This would imply that only the new text was composed by Cavalli. The original composer is not mentioned, and is unknown to Schatz.

First performed at Venice, Teatro Grimani a SS. Gio. e Paolo, carnival, 1654.

Schatz 1736

— Ciro. Drama per musica nel Teatro a SS. Gio. e Paolo l'anno 1665 . . .

Venetia, Giuliani, 1665. 84 p. 14^{cm}.

Three acts, with prologue. Scenario, argument, publisher's note to the reader, and his dedication, dated Venice, February 4, 1665.

The reader is informed:

"Torna di nuovo questo drama à ricalcar le scene del famosissimo Theatro Grimani, dove prima fece pompa de suoi splendori . . . lo troverai fecondato di nuove ariette, per meglio compiacerti. A queste hà fatta la musica il virtuosissimo Signor Andrea **Mattioli** mastro di capella dell' A. Sereniss. di Mantoa, che già famoso per molte com- positioni arrichite in altre città col freggio delle sue note, doppo l'haverti fatta ammirar nel *Perseo* la sua virtù, è stato anco pregato ad illustrar con queste gioie il presente drama per fartelo con nuove gemme comparir più pomposo . . ."

As the text is practically the same as in the 1654 ed., this can mean only that music by Mattioli was substituted for some of Cavalli's arias.   Schatz 1753

Ciro, musicalisches schau-spiel umb wegen der hohen gegenwarth S^r churfuerstl. Durchl. Clemens Augusts, hertzog in Bayern . . . im jahr 1733 vorgestellet zu werden. Aus dem welschen uebersetzet.

Muenchen, gedruckt bey Maria Magdalena Riedlin, wittib. 4 p. l., 95 p. 16^{cm}.

Three acts. Italian original by Leopoldo de Villati. Neither he nor the com- poser, Giovanni **Ferrandini**, is mentioned. With "Innhalt" and cast. The dia- logue is in German. The arias are in Italian with added German prose translation.

First performed at Munich, as indicated.   Schatz 3064

Ciro in Armenia, dramma per musica da rappresentarsi nel Regio- Ducal Teatro di Milano, nell carnovale dell' anno 1754 . . .

Milano, Giuseppe Richino Malatesta, 1753. 5 p. l., 59 p. 14½^{cm}.

Three acts. Dedication, argument, scenario, and cast. The composer, Maria Teresia **Agnesi**, is not mentioned, and the author is unknown to Schatz.

First performed, as indicated, Dec. 26, 1753.   Schatz 61

Ciro in Timbraja, ballet. *See* Guglielmi's Gli amanti della dote.

Ciro in Timbraja, ballet. *See* Guglielmi's Lo sciocco poeta di campagna.

Il **Ciro riconosciuto.**

72 p. 19ᶜᵐ. (Pietro Metastasio, Opere drammatiche, Venezia, Giuseppe Bettinelli, 1733–37, v. 4.)

Three acts and licenza.   Argument.   No composer mentioned.   ML 49.A2M4

— **Ciro riconosciuto.**

Metastasio, Poesie, Parigi, vedova Quillau, 1755, t. iv, [187]–300 p. 16ᶜᵐ.

Three acts and licenza.   Argument.   ML 49.A2M42

— **Ciro riconoscinto.** Rappresentato con musica del Caldara la prima volta nel giardino dell' Imperial Favorita . . . il dì 28 agosto 1736, per festeggiare il giorno dinascita dell' imperatrice Elisabetta . . .

pl., [111]–234 p. 26ᶜᵐ. (Pietro Metastasio, Opere, t. v, Parigi, vedova Herissant, 1780.)

Three acts, with licenza.   Argument.   ML 49.A2M44

— **Cyrus.**

Metastasio, Tragedies-opera, Vienne, 1751, v. I, 135 p.   14ᶜᵐ.

Three acts.   Richelet's translation of "Il Ciro riconosciuto."   ML 49.A2M47

Ciro riconosciuto. Del Signor Pietro Metastasio. Dramma per musica da rappresentarsi nel Teatro di S. Angelo il carnovale dell' anno 1737 . . . Seconda impressione.

Venezia, Marino Rossetti, 1737. 72 p. 16ᶜᵐ.

Three acts.   Impresario's dedication, cast, scenario, and notice to the reader in which is said:
"Come è indispensabile la brevità per il buon ordine di cotesto Teatro, cosi convenne, anche doppo che fu composto in musica cotesto dramma, per fatale necessità abbreviarlo di molto.   Vero è, che restano stampati tutti li recitativi, e postilati quelli, che non si dicono . . .   Si sono pur mutate le parole di molte arie, ma nell' incontro presente non si è potuto far à meno . . ."
The composer is not mentioned.   Wiel and Schatz attribute the music to Galuppi, Allacci and Groppo have "Musica da diversi."
Therefore Wotquenne and with him Piovano believes that at least part of the music was interpolated from *Caldara's* opera of the same title, Vienna, August 28, 1736.
First performed at Venice, January 5, 1737.   Schatz 3517

— **Ciro riconosciuto.** Dramma per musica da rappresentarsi nel Regio-Ducal Teatro di Milano nel carnovale dell' anno 1746 . . . in occasione del compimento degli anni di Sua Maestà Cattolica che Dio guardi.

Milano, Giuseppe Richino Malatesta, n. d. 4 p. l., 66 p. 14ᶜᵐ.

Three acts.   Argument, scenario, cast, and name of Galuppi as composer.
First performed, as indicated, December 26, 1745.   ML 50.2.C53G3

— **Ciro riconosciuto.** Dramma per musica da rappresentarsi nel carnovale dell' anno 1759. Nel nobil Teatro di Torre Argentina . . .

Roma, Gio. Zempel, n. d. 69 p. 15ᶜᵐ.

Three acts.   By Metastasio with alterations "per accomodarsi al genio presente."
Dedication, argument, *proteste*, scenario, cast, name of the author and the composer, Baldassare **Galuppi.**   Schatz 3445

72251°—vol 1—14——19

Il **Ciro riconosciuto.** Dramma per musica da rappresentarsi nel Teatro Ducale di Stutgart nel carnovale dell' anno 1752 . . . La poesia è del Signor abbate Pietro Metastasio . . . la musica è del Signor Gio. Adolfo Hasse . . .

Stutgart, Giovanne Georgio Cotta, n. d. 135 p. 18½cm.

Three acts. Argument, cast, scenario, German title page "Der erkennte Cyrus" and text face Italian.

First performed at Stuttgart, February 11, 1752; at Dresden, Hoftheater, January 20, 1751.　　　　　　　　　　　　　　　　　　SCHATZ 4525

Ciro riconosciuto. Dramma per musica da rappresentarsi nel Teatro Formagliari la primavera dell' anno MDCCXLIV.

(At end) Bologna, Maria Sassi, 1744. 1 p. l., 70, [2] p. 15cm.

Three acts. Impresario's dedication, dated Bologna, May 4, 1744, argument, cast, scenario, and names of Metastasio as author (with apologies for the cuts in his text) and of Niccolò **Jommelli** as composer.　　　　　　　SCHATZ 4879

Ciro riconosciuto. Dramma per musica da rappresentarsi nell' antico Teatro di Tordinona nel carnevale dell' anno 1737 . . .

Roma, Giovanni Zempel, 1737. 88 p. 15cm.

Three acts, with licenza. Dedicatory preface by the impresario Giuseppe Polvino Falliconti, argument, cast, scenario, names of Metastasio, the author, and of the composer, **Rinaldo di Capua.**

First performed at Rome, Teatro Tordinona, January 19, 1737.　SCHATZ 8795

Il **Ciro riconosciuto.** Drama per musica da rappresentarsi sul famosissimo Teatro di Brunsviga nella fiera d' inverno l' anno 1746.— Der wiedererkannte Cyrus . . .

Braunschweig, Friedrich Wilhelm Meyer, n. d. Unpaged. 18cm.

Three acts. By Metastasio, who is not mentioned. German text faces Italian. Note:

"Die sinfonie und arien dieser opera sind componirt von Sign. Giovanni **Verocai,** hochfuerstl. Braunschweig.-Lueneburgischen Concert-meister zu Wolffenbüttel."

The composer of the recitatives not known to Schatz.

First performed February, 1746, as indicated.　　　　　　SCHATZ 10718

La **citta felice.**　*See* M. Curzio.

La **città nuova.**　Commedia per musica da rappresentarsi nel Teatro alla Scala l' autunno dell' anno 1798, v. s. entrando l' anno VII. repubblicano.

Milano, Gio. Batista Bianchi, n. d. 47 p. 16½cm.

Two acts. Cast and name of the composer, Stefano **Cristiani** ("musica tutta nuova"). The author is unknown to Schatz. "Dopo alcune recite" were to be performed with the opera Filippo Beretti's ballets "La moglie virtuosa" and "Il calzolajo." The composer of the music is not mentioned.

First performed, as indicated, September, 1798.　　　　　SCHATZ 2292

Cittadini di Sinope festeggianti le nozze di Mitridate, ballet. *See* Piccinni's Tigrane.

Il **cittadino rinnobilito.**　A. T. of Pasque's L' albergia smascherata.

Der **civilisirte bauer.**　Tr. of Anfossi's Il zotico incivilito.

Le **Claperman,** opéra-comique, en deux actes, en prose & en vaudevilles, précédé d'un prologue, & suivi d'un divertissement.

Alexis Piron, Oeuvres complettes, Liege, 1776, v. 3, [149]–222 p. 17½cm.

First performed, according to Parfaict, who does not record the composer, February 3, 1724.　　　　　　　　　　　　　　　PQ 2019.P6

Clarisse, oder Das unbekannte dienstmaedgen. Eine komische operette in drey aufzuegen.

Leipzig, Christian Gottlob Hilschern, 1772. 136 p. 16^{cm}.

Neither the author, Johann Christoph Bock, nor the composer, Carl Leopold **Roellig,** is mentioned.

First performed at Hamburg, Theater beim Gaensemarkt, October 10, 1771.

Schatz 8856

Claudine ou Le petit commissionnaire, comedie en un acte, et en prose mêlée d'ariettes, par le C. Jacques Marie Deschamps. Musique du C. Bruni.

Paris, Huet, an deuxième, [1793–94]. 36 p. 21^{cm}.

Cast.

First performed at Paris, Théâtre Feydeau, March 6, 1794.   ML 50.2.C57B7

Claudine von Villa Bella. Ein singspiel. Von Goethe. Ächte ausgabe.

Leipzig, Georg Joachim Göschen, 1788. 1 p. l., 126 p. 17$\frac{1}{2}$^{cm}.

Three acts. Edition without "Göschen's Schriften," and with "Pedro von Rovero" in the list of characters instead of "Sebastian von Rovero."

PT 1915.C2 1788

Claudine von Villa Bella. Ein schauspiel mit gesang von J. W. Goethe. Aufgefuehrt im K. K. Nationaltheater.

Wien, zu finden beym Logenmeister, 1780. 71 p. 15$\frac{1}{2}$^{cm}.

The composer, Ignaz von **Be(e)cke,** is not mentioned.

First performed, as indicated, on June 13, 1780.   Schatz 677

Claudine af Villa Bella, et syngestykke i tre handlinger, af J. W. Goethe. Til brug for den Kongl. danske Skueplads, oversat af N. H. Weinwich. Musikken er af hr. C. Schall . . . Opført første gang paa Hs. Majestaet Kongens fødselsdag, d. 29 Jan. 1787.

Kiøbenhavn, Trykt paa S. Sønnichsens bekostning, n. d. 1 p. l., 125 p. 16^{cm}.   Schatz 9584

Arien und gesaenge aus dem singspiel **Claudine von Villa Bella.**

Berlin, n. publ., 1789. 40 p. 15^{cm}.

Three acts. Neither the author, Goethe, nor the composer, Johann Friedrich **Reichardt,** is mentioned.

First performed at Charlottenburg, Schlosstheater, July 29, 1789; at Berlin, Kgl. Nationaltheater, August 3, 1789.   Schatz 8640

Claudio Cesare. Dramma per musica. Nel Teatro Vendramino à San Salvatore. L'anno MDCLXXII di Aurelio Aureli, opera decima sesta ristampata . . .

Venezia, Francesco Nicolini, 1672. front., 69, [1] p. 13^{cm}.

Three acts. Author's dedication, dated Venice, December 27, 1672, and notice to the reader, mentioning Claudio Cesare **Boretti** as composer of this text, and also of Aureli's "Eliogabalo" and "Ercole in Tebe." Argument and scenario.

Schatz 1216

Claudius. *See* Keiser's Die verdammte staat-sucht.

Claudius, roemischer Kaeyser. L. T. of Keiser's Die verdammte staat-sucht.

Cleante. Dramma per musica da rappresentarsi in Roma nel nobil Teatro di Torre Argentina nel corrente carnevale dell' anno MDCCLII . . .

Roma, Fausto Amidei, n. d.   64 p.   15½ᶜᵐ.

Three acts. Author not mentioned, and unknown to Schatz. Dedication, argument, cast, scenario, and name of Niccolò **Sabatini** as the composer.   SCHATZ 9200

Clearco in Negroponte. Drama per musica da rappresentarsi nel Teatro Zane à San Moisè.   L'anno 1685 . . .

Venetia, Francesco Nicolini, 1685.   69 p.   13½ᶜᵐ.

Three acts. By Antonio Arcoleo, who signs the dedication with his initials. Argument, scenario, and notice to the reader, with name of Domenico **Gabrieli** as composer.
SCHATZ 3402

The **clemency of Titus.** An opera as perform'd at the Theatre Royal in the Hay-Market.   Composed by Frances Veracini . . .

London, J. Chrichley, 1737.   63 p.   17ᶜᵐ.

Three acts. Metastasio's "La clemenza di Tito," with an English translation, perhaps by Angelo Cori, who signs the dedication. Argument and cast.
First performed 1737, as indicated.   SCHATZ 10618

Clémentine, ou La belle-mère, comédie en un acte et en prose, mêlée d'ariettes: paroles de J. B. C. Vial; musique de Fay. Représentée, pour la première fois, au Théâtre Feydeau, le 2ᵉ jour complémentaire, an VII de la République française.

Paris, Huet, Charon, an VIII [1799–1800].   56 p.   18ᶜᵐ.

Cast.
First performed, as indicated, September 18, 1799.   SCHATZ 3037

La **clemenza di Scipione;** a new serious opera: as performed at the King's Theatre, in the Haymarket.   The music composed by Mr. Bach.   The translation by F. Bottarelli, A. M.

London, T. Cadell, 1778.   53, [1] p.   18½ᶜᵐ.

Three acts. Argument and cast. Librettist unknown to Schatz. English text faces Italian.
First performed, as indicated, in 1778; but previously in 1775 (Pohl).
SCHATZ 528

La **clemenza di Tito.**

72 p.   19ᶜᵐ. (Pietro Metastasio, Opere drammatiche, Venezia, Giuseppe Bettinelli, 1733–37, v. 4.)

Three acts and licenza. Argument. No composer mentioned.   ML 49.A2M4

— La **clemenza di Tito.**

Metastasio, Poesie, Parigi, vedova Quillau, 1755, t. iii, 109 p.   16ᶜᵐ.

Three acts and licenza. Argument.   ML 49.A2M42

— La **clemenza di Tito.** Dramma rappresentato con musica del Caldara la prima volta in Vienna nell' interno gran Teatro della Corte Cesarea, alla presenza degli augustissimi sovrani, il dì 4 novembre 1734, per festeggiare il nome dell' imperator Carlo VI . . .

pl., [109]–222 p.   26ᶜᵐ. (Pietro Metastasio, Opere, t. iii, Parigi, vedova Herissant, 1780.)

Three acts and licenza. Argument.   ML 49.A2M44

La **clemenza di Tito**—Continued.
— **Titus.**

> *Metastasio, Tragedies opera, Vienne, 1751, v. ii, p. [125]–237. 14^{cm}.*

Three acts.   Richelet's translation of "La clemenza di Tito."   ML 49.A2M47

La **clemenza di Tito**.   Dramma per musica, da rappresentarsi nel Real Teatro di S. Carlo, nel dì 30. di maggio 1772 . . .

> *Napoli, Francesco Morelli, 1772.   51 p.   16^{cm}.*

Three acts.   By Metastasio.   Impresario's dedication, with same date, argument, scenario, cast, and name of composer, Pasquale **Anfossi,** but not of librettist.

SCHATZ 273

La **clemenza di Tito**.   Drama per musica da rappresentarsi nel Regio Teatro di Torino nel carnovale del 1739 . . .

> *Torino, Pietro Giuseppe Zappata e figliuolo, n. d.   4 p. l., 71, [1] p. 16½^{cm}.*

Three acts.   By Metastasio.   Argument, scenario, cast, and name of the composer, Giuseppe **Arena,** but not of librettist.   Alessio Rasetti is mentioned as composer of the ballet music.

First performed, as indicated, December 26, 1738.   SCHATZ 309

La **clemenza di Tito**.   Dramma per musica da rappresentarsi nel Nuovo Teatro di Corte . . . nel carnevale dell' anno MDCCLXVIII. La poesia è dell' Sig. abbate Pietro Metastasio . . .   La musica è del sig. Andrea de Bernasconi . . .

> *Monaco, Mar. Magdal. Mayrin, n. d.   231, [21] p.   15½^{cm}.*

Three acts.   Argument, cast, scenario.   German title-page "Die guetigkeit des Titus" and text face Italian.   The unnumb. p. contain scenario, cast, and description in French and German of the two ballets "L'amour clairvoyant" ("Der sehende Cupido") and "La réconciliation généreuse."   Neither authors nor composers are mentioned.

First performed at Munich, January, 1768.   SCHATZ 856

La **clemenza di Tito**.   Dramma per musica, da rappresentarsi nella cesarea corte per il nome gloriosissimo della Sac. Ces. e Catt. Real Maestà di Carlo VI . . .   L'anno MDCCXXXIIII.   La poesia è del Sig. abbate Pietro Metastasio . . .   La musica è del Sig. Antonio Caldara . . .

> *Vienna d'Austria, Gio. Pietro Van Ghelen, n. d.   4 p. l., 72, [1] p. 16^{cm}.*

Three acts and licenza.   Argument and scenario.   Niccola Matteis is mentioned as composer of the ballet music.

First performed, as indicated, November 4, 1734.   SCHATZ 1498

La **clemenza di Tito**.   Dramma per musica da rappresentarsi per le felice nozze dell' Altezza Serenissima Elettorale di Massimiliano Giuseppe . . . con l'Altezza Serenissima Elettorale Maria Anna . . .   La poesia è del Sig. abbate Pietro Metastasio . . .   La musica è del Sig. Giuseppe Camerlocher . . .

> *[Monaco], Giov. Giac. Vötter, n. d.   6 p. l., 132 p.   20^{cm}.*

Three acts.   Argument, cast, and scenario.   German title page "Die guetigkeit des Titus" and text face Italian.   The anonymous German translator has added an "Unumgaengliche vorrede" about the difficulties of translation of Italian librettos into German and he says:

"Entschuldige, dass ich mich wenig oder garnicht an die worte der welschen feder gebunden, allein weil es fast eine unmoeglichkeit scheinen, solcher satzung mit aller

La **clemenza di Tito**—Continued.

schaerffe nachzukommen, indem einem jeden sprach-kuendigen nicht unbewust, wie
dass mancher unzuverbesseren seyender gedancken durch die ubersetzung (wenn
solche von wort zu worte zusammen gekuenstlet) seinen gantzen werth verliehre:
Jedoch suchte ich (wo es ohne zergliederung der wohlredenheit seyn koennen) meinen
woerter-schatz der welschen schreib-arth knapp an die seithe zu setzen . . ."
    First performed at Munich, Hoftheater, July, 1747.   SCHATZ 1523

La **clemenza di Tito**. Dramma per musica da rappresentarsi nel
Teatro dell' illustrissimo pubblico di Reggio per la fiera dell' anno
1759 . . .

  Reggio, Giuseppe Davolio, n. d.   4 p. l., 70, [2] p.   17½^{cm}.

    Three acts. By Metastasio. Impresario's dedication dated Reggio, April 28, 1759,
argument, cast, scenario, and name of the composer, Legrenzio Vincenzo **Ciampi**.
The first additional p. contains the substitute arias (I, 5) "Si spande al Sole in faccia"
and (I, 7) "Di questo core amante." The words of the first are from Metastasio's
"Il rè pastore," whereas those of the second are not listed by Wotquenne as from
Metastasio.
    First performed at Venice, Teatro di S. Moisè, carnival 1757.   SCHATZ 1880

La **clemenza di Tito**. Drama per musica del Sig. abbate Pietro
Metastasio da recitarsi nel Teatro del Falcone in Genova . . .

  Genova, Franchelli, 1736.   4 p. l., 72 p.   14½^{cm}.

    Three acts. By Metastasio. Impresario's dedication, argument, cast, scenario,
and name of the composer, Pietro Vincenzo **Ciochetti**. The *imprimatur* is dated
January 14, 1736.   SCHATZ 2011

La **clemenza di Tito**. Dramma per musica da rappresentarsi nel
Teatro di Camerino pel carnovale del 1757 . . .

  Camerino, Gabrielli, n. d.   71 p.   16½^{cm}.

    Three acts. By Metastasio. Impresario's dedication, argument, cast, and name
of the composer, Carlo Antonio **Cristiani**.   SCHATZ 2291

La **clemenza di Tito**. Dramma per musica da rappresentarsi nel
Regio Teatro di Torino nel carnevale del 1760 alla presenza di S. S.
R. M.

  Torino, Giacomo Giuseppe Avondo, n. d.   79, [1] p.   16^{cm}.

    Three acts. By Metastasio, who is not mentioned. Argument, cast, scenario,
and name of **Galuppi** as composer. With the opera were performed three ballets,
the first of which called "Orfeo e Euridice." The plot was by Giuseppe Salomoni,
detto di Portugallo," the music by Giuseppe Antonio Le Messier.
    First performed as indicated, as second opera of the season.   SCHATZ 3498

La **clemenza di Tito**. Drama per musica da cantarsi in Verona nel
Teatro dell' Accademia Filarmonica nella fiera d'Aprile dell' anno
1738 . . .

  Verona, Dionigi Ramanzini, n. d.   front., 59, [1] p.   18^{cm}.

    Three acts. By Metastasio, who is not mentioned. Dedication, argument, cast,
scenario, and name of Johann Adolph **Hasse** as composer. On the additional page
the aria "Da quelle luci amate" substituted for "Io sento, ch'in petto" for I, 3.
    First performed at Dresden, Hoftheater, January 17, 1738, but previously at
Pesaro, Teatro Pubblico, September 24, 1735, as "Tito Vespasiano ovvero La clemenza
di Tito."   SCHATZ 4526

— Die **guetigkeit des Titus Vespasianus** in einer opera vorgestellet
auf dem grossen Braunschweigischen Theatro in der Winter-messe
1744.

  Wolfenbuettel, Christian Bartsch, n. d.   Unpaged.   18½^{cm}.

La clemenza di Tito—Continued.

Three acts. Argument, scenario, and name of **Hasse** as the composer. Italian text of the arias added to the German translation.
First performed February 3, 1744, as indicated, but previously August, 1743.
SCHATZ 4527

— **La clemenza di Tito**, dramma da rappresentarsi in musica.— Die gnade des Titus . . .
Hamburg, Spiering, 1748. 87 p. 18ᶜᵐ.
Three acts. Argument, scenario, cast, and names of Metastasio as author, of Johann Adolph **Hasse** as composer. German text faces Italian.
Performed at Hamburg, Theater beim Gänsemarkt, October, 1748; previously there December 8, 1745. SCHATZ 4528

La clemenza di Tito. Dramma per musica da rappresentarsi nel Teatro Ducale di Stutgart, festeggiandosi il felicissimo giorno natalizio di Sua Altezza Serenissima Elisabetta Sofia Federica duchessa di Wirtemberg e Teck . . . La poesia è del . . . Metastasio . . . La musica è del . . . Nicolò Jommelli . . .
Stutgart, Giovanne Georgio Cotta, 1753. 117 p. 19ᶜᵐ.
Three acts. Argument, cast, scenario. German title page, "Die mildigkeit des Titues," and text face Italian.
First performed, as indicated, August 30, 1753. SCHATZ 4849

— **La clemenza di Tito.** Dramma per musica da rappresentarsi nel Real Teatro dell' Ajuda nel felicissimo giorno natalizio del fedelissimo monarca D. Giuseppe I . . . nel di 6 giugno 1771.
Lisbona, Stamperia reale, n. d. 75 p. 15ᶜᵐ.
Three acts. Argument, cast, scenario, and names of Metastasio as author, of Niccolò **Jommelli** as composer. Text seems to follow that of 1753 closely.
SCHATZ 4884

La clemenza di Tito. Dramma per music di Artimio Corasio, Pastore Arcade, da rappresentarsi nel famosissimo Teatro Grimani di S. Gio. Grisostomo il carnovale dell' anno 1735 . . .
Venezia, Marino, Rossetti, 1735. 72 p. 14½ᶜᵐ.
Three acts. Dedication by Domenico Lalli, argument, scenario, cast, name of Leonardo **Leo** as composer, and note that part of the text is not by Metastasio (by Lalli?). It applies to such arias as "Tremola qual la fronda" (I, 3), "Quando amore à servo un core" (I, 8), "Perfido amico ingrato" (II, 11).
First performed as above (Schatz); at Naples, 1735, Teatro S. Bartolomeo (Leo). Piovano fixed the date as Venice, January 29, 1735. SCHATZ 5553

La clemenza di Tito. Drama per musica da rappresentarsi nel Regio-Ducal Teatro di Milano nel carnovale dell' anno 1738 . . .
Milano, Giuseppe Richino Malatesta, 1738. 4 p. l., 60 p. 15½ᶜᵐ.
Three acts. By Metastasio, who is not mentioned. Dedication signed by the impresario, Gaetano Marizoli, argument, cast, scenario. Even the tailor is mentioned, but not the composer, Giovanni Maria **Marchi.**
First performed, as indicated, December 26, 1737. SCHATZ S5937

La clemenza di Tito, dramma per musica da rappresentarsi nell' estate dell' anno MDCCLV. Sul gran Teatro nuovamente eretto alla Real Corte di Lisbona, per festeggiare il felicissimo giorno natalizio di Sua Maestà Fedelissima D. Giuseppe Primo . . . La poesia del dramma è del celebre Sigr. abᵉ Pietro Metastasio . . . La licenza è

La clemenza di Tito—Continued.

del Sigr. Giuseppe Bonechy, Fiorentino, poeta di Sua Maestà Fedelissima . . . La musica è del Sigr. Antonio Mazzoni, Bolognese.

Lisbona, Stamperia Sylviana, 1755. front., 4 p. l., 52, [2] p. 21^cm.

Argument, cast, and scenario.
First performed, as indicated, June 6, 1755.　　　Schatz 6229

La clemenza di Tito. Dramma per musica da rappresentarsi nel Teatro Tron di S. Cassiano il carnovale dell' anno MDCCXLVIII.

n. i., n. d. 69 p. 17^cm.

Three acts. By Metastasio, who is not mentioned. Argument, cast, scenario, and name of Antonio Gaetano **Pampani** as the composer.　　　Schatz 7758

La clemenza di Tito. Dramma per musica da rappresentarsi nel famoso Teatro Grimani di S. Benedetto, il carnovale dell' anno MDCCLX.

Venezia, Antonio Comin, 1760. 48 p. 15^cm.

Three acts. By Metastasio, who is not mentioned. Cast, scenario, and name of Giuseppe **Scarlatti** as the composer.　　　Schatz 9542

La clemenza di Tito.

Four acts. Metastasio's text, altered by Caterino Mazzolà, music by **Mozart**.
First performed at Prague, Nationaltheater, September 6, 1791.
No 18th cent. ed. in L. of C.

— Titus. Eine ernsthafte oper in zwey aufzuegen; nach dem italienischen der Clemenza di Tito des Metastasio frey bearbeitet, und in musik gesetzt von W. A. Mozart. Zum erstenmal aufgefuehrt auf dem fuerstl. Operntheater zu Cassel im Maerz 1797.

Cassel, Hampesche Buchdruckerey, n. d. 71 p. 16^cm.

Cast.　　　ML 50.2.C58M77

La clemenza di Tito.　*See* Veracini's The clemency of Titus.

Cleofida, koenigin von Indien. A. T. of Händel's Triumph der grossmuth und treue.

Cleofide. Drama per musica da rappresentarsi nel Regio Teatro di Berlino per ordine di Sua Maestà nel carnovale dell' anno 1754.

Berlino, Haude e Spener, n. d. 115, [3] p. 17^cm.

Three acts. Same as Metastasio's "Alessandro nell' Indie." Argument, scenario, and name of the composer, Johann Friedrich **Agricola**. German title-page and text face Italian. Notes (in French) on the ballets follow the text.
First performed, as indicated, Berlin, January, 1754.　　　Schatz 67

Cleofide, dramma per musica da rappresentarsi nel Regio Teatro di Berlino per ordine di Sua Maestà nel carnovale dell' anno 1777.

Berlino, Haude e Spener, n. d. 125, [3] p. 15½^cm.

Three acts. Argument, cast, scenario, name of Johann Adolph **Hasse** as composer, and note to the effect that this is Metastasio's "L'Alessandro nell' Indie," but with "grandi cangiamenti già fatti da lungo tempo si nello sceneggiamento che nella poesia in un teatro forestiero, ' by Michel Angelo Boccardi, according to Schatz and Mennicke. German title page, "Cleofide," and text face Italian.
First performed, as indicated, January, 1777; at Dresden, Hoftheater, September 13, 1731.　　　Schatz 4573

Cleofile. Drama per musica d'Antonio Conte Zaniboni da rappresentarsi nel Teatro Giustiniano di S. Moisè il carnovale dell' anno 1721.

Venezia, Marino Rosetti, 1721. 44 p. 15ᶜᵐ.

Three acts. Argument, cast, scenario, and name of the composer, Giuseppe Maria **Buini.** Schatz 1381

Cleomene. Drama per musica da rappresentarsi nel Teatro di Sant' Angelo il carnovale dell' anno MDCCXVIII . . .

Venezia, Marino Rossetti, 1718. 58 p. 14½ᶜᵐ.

Three acts. Dedication signed by the author, Vincenzo Cassani, argument, notice to the reader, cast, scenario. The composer, Tommaso **Albinoni,** is not mentioned. Schatz 128

Il Cleomene. Drama per musica da recitarsi nel Teatro delle Dame nella primavera dell' anno MDCCXXXI . . .

Roma, Pasquino, n. d. 65 p. 16ᶜᵐ.

Three acts. Dedication by the impresario Francesco Cavanna, argument, scenario, cast, and name of Francesco **Ayara** as the composer.
Not recorded by Schatz. ML 50.2C59 A7

Cleomene. Dramma per musica da rappresentarsi in Bologna nel Teatro Zagnoni il carnevale dell' anno 1789 . . .

Bologna, Sassi, n. d. 46 p. 17ᶜᵐ.

Imprimatur dated December 9, 1788.
Three acts. By Giovanni de Gamerra, who is not mentioned. Impresario's dedication, argument, cast, and name of Giuseppe **Sarti** as the composer. With the opera were performed Urbano Garzia's ballets "Le Amazoni moderne, o sia Il ribello per amore" and "Il tuttor medico deluso," the composers of the music not being mentioned.
First performed, as indicated, December 27, 1788. Schatz 9428

— Cleomene. Dramma per musica da rappresentarsi in Perugia nel Teatro de' Signori nobili Accademici del Casino nel carnevale del anno 1791 . . .

Perugia, Constantini, 1791. 40 p. 16½ᶜᵐ.

Three acts. Impresario's dedication dated Perugia, January, 1791, argument, scenario, and name of Giuseppe **Sarti** as composer. Giovanni de Gamerra is not mentioned. With the opera were performed, composers of the music not mentioned, Giacomo Gentili's ballets "Esione liberata" and "Gl'amanti delusi."
ML 48.A5 v.7

Cleonice. Dramma per musica da rappresentarsi nel Teatro di Sant' Angelo il carnovale dell' anno 1740 . . .

Venezia, Marino Rossetti, 1740. 48 p. 25ᶜᵐ.

A neat 19th cent. page for page transcript.
Three acts. Dedication signed by Bartolomeo Vitturi, argument, cast, scenario, name of **Hasse** as the composer, and notice to the reader:
"La presente dramaticha composizione è del celebre Sig. abate Pietro Metastasio . . . ma poi ridotta all' uso de nostri teatri. Ora nuovamente si riproduce sovra le pubbliche scene, ma abbreviata di molto per adattarla, quanto fosse possibile, a chi la deve rappresentare; o se qualch' una delle arie non corrisponde totalmente alle scene, ciò nasce per esser stato in arbitrio dei musici di [?] a piacere, a cagione della ristrettezza del tempo . . ."
The alterations presumably were made by the librettist Vitturi. According to Schatz "Cleonice" is but a replica of Hasse's "Demetrio" of 1732 and was first performed at Vienna, Hoftheater, February, 1734. Mennicke says (p. 510):
"Diese erste fassung [of "Demetrio"] wurde auch unter dem titel "*Cleonice*" 1733 in Wien gegeben; dagegen wurde 1739 in Wien Hasses komposition mit eingelegten arien anderer komponisten wieder als *Il Demetrio* gegeben; auch Metastasios Textbuch dieser neuen gestalt des musikalischen teils hat "varianti." Diese neuere fassung gab man auch 1739 in Neapel."

Cleonice—Continued.

I prefer to let this *Cleonice* of Venice, 1740, stand under its own title, because the connection of the "Cleonice" text with that of "Demetrio" is so very slight. True, scenes I, 10, I, 11, I, 12, start out like I, 13, I, 14, and I 15, in Metastasio's "Demetrio," but they remain alike only for a few lines, and this is also true of a few other such scenes. Furthermore, the arias in such scenes have become different, "Amo te sola" (I, 11) having taken the place, for instance, of "Dal suo gentil sembiante" (I, 14). And this aria, "Amo te sola," is from Metastasio's "Clemenza di Tito," just as "È vero che oppresso" (III, 2) is not from his "Demetrio" but from his "Adriano in Siria." The fact is, that very little of the dialogue and very few more arias except "Ogni procella infida," will be found in "Demetrio." *Most of the arias, indeed, are not by Metastasio at all,* and the very few, that are, have been selected from his different works. Since it is known that Hasse was in Venice during the carnival of 1740, it stands to reason that he superintended the performance of the opera and composed anew whatever had to be composed for this decimated version of "Demetrio."

SCHATZ 4578

Cleonice regina di Siria. Drama. Da rappresentarsi sopra il Teatro di S. M. B.—Cleonice, queen of Syria. An opera. As it is represented at the King's Theatre in the Hay-Market.

London, G. Woodfall, 1763. 81 p. 20^{cm}.

Three acts. Text a pasticcio by author-compiler unknown to Schatz. English translation faces Italian. Argument, cast and note "The music by several celebrated masters." From Bremner's "Favourite songs" we know that the aria "Se più il mio core" (I, 10) was composed by Felice **Giardini** as also "Non so dir se pena sia" (II 9 words from Metastasio's "Isola disabitata") and "Quel labbro adorato" (III, 9, words from Metastasio's "Demetrio") was composed by **Galuppi**. "Io so qual pena" (words from Metastasio's "Demetrio") composed by **Giardini** and the duet "Tu parti mio," composed by **Bertoni,** do not figure in the libretto!

First performed as indicated, November 26, 1763.   ML 50.2.C6

Cleopatra. Dramma per musica da rappresentarsi nel nuovo Regio Ducal Teatro di Milano il carnovale dell' anno 1779 . . .

Milano, Gio. Batista Bianchi, n. d. 56 p. 16$\frac{1}{2}$^{cm}.

Three acts. By Mattia Verazj. Dedication, preface, argument, scenario, cast, and names of composer, Pasquale **Anfossi,** and librettist.

In the pref. Verazj speaks of his theories of libretto writing ("mi proposi pel mio primo drama un sistema") and criticizes prevailing methods at considerable length. He begins by stating that to have written in this one year [1778] four librettos for the same theatre and for the same actors was an unprecedented task.

First performed in January, 1779, as indicated.   SCHATZ 278
Second copy. ML 48.A5 v.7

Cleopatra, ballet. *See* Borghi's Eumene.

La Cleopatra. Drama per musica di Giacomo dall' Angelo da rappresentarsi nel noviss. Theatro di S. Salvatore . . .

Venetia, Giacomo Batti, 1662. 77 p. 14^{cm}.

Three acts with prologue. Author's dedication and argument. The composer, Daniele **Castrovillari,** is not mentioned.

First performed, as indicated, carnival, 1662.   SCHATZ 1691

Cleopatra. Dramma per musica da rappresentarsi nel Regio Teatro di Torino nel carnovale del 1776 . . .

Torino, Onorato Derossi, n. d. 64 p. 16$\frac{1}{2}$^{cm}.

Three acts. Cesare Oliveri is mentioned as the author, Carlo **Monza** as the composer of the opera, and Giuseppe Antonio Le Messier as the composer of the music for Giuseppe Canziani's ballets, "La disgrazia opportuna," "Alceste & Admeto" (described on p. 62–64), and "Il trionto di Cesare in Egitto."

Argument, cast, scenario. On p. viii the note: "Si sono variate alcune arie dall' originale."

First performed, as indicated, December 26, 1775.   SCHATZ 6613

Cleopatra, regina d'Egitto. Dramma per musica da rappresentarsi nel Teatro da S. Agostino il carnovale del 1795 . . .

Genova, Stamperia Gesiniana, n. d. 43 p. 14ᶜᵐ.

Two acts. By Antonio Simone Sografi, who is not mentioned. Cast, scenario, and name of Sebastiano **Nasolini** as the composer.

First performed under the original title "La morte di Cleopatra," at Verona, Teatro Nuovo, summer, 1791. Schatz 7023

La clochette, comédie en un acte et en vers, mêlée d'ariettes; représentée pour la première fois, par les Comédiens italiens ordinaires du roi, le jeudi 24 juillet 1766. Par M. Anseaume. La musique de M. Duny.

Paris, la veuve Duchesne, 1766. 38 p. 19ᶜᵐ.

Schatz and some opera dictionaries give the incorrect date of July 14.

Schatz 2836

— **La clochette,** comédie en un acte et en vers. Mêlée d'ariettes, par M. Anseaume. Représentée pour la première fois par les Comédiens italiens ordinaires du roi, le 24 juillet 1766. La musique de M. Duny.

Paris, Duchesne, 1771. 40 p. 19ᶜᵐ.

Cast. On p. 11–14, the ariette "Du printemps qui vient de renaître;" 15–16, "Vous n'me connoissez pas." Schatz 11692

— **La clochette,** comédie en un acte et en vers, mêlée d'ariettes, par M. Anseaume. Représentée pour la première fois par les Comédiens italiens ordinaires du roi, le 24 juillet 1766. La musique de M. Duny.

Paris, la veuve Duchesne, 1782. 40 p. 19ᶜᵐ.

Cast. Text the same as in the 1771 ed. Schatz 11693

Cloris und Tirsis in einem sing- und schaeffer-spiel fuergestellet aus dem Hamburgischen Schau-Platz im jahr 1719.

[Hamburg], Gedruckt bey Caspar Jakhel, n. d. Unpaged. 19ᶜᵐ.

German version, by D. Gazal of "Clori e Tirsi." The composer, Francesco Bartolomeo **Conti,** is not mentioned in the libretto, which contains German text throughout, the arias also being printed with Italian text. Argument.

First performed as "I satiri in Arcadia" (text by Pariati) at Vienna, Hoftheater, August 28, 1714. Schatz 2196

Clotilde. Dramma per musica da rappresentarsi nel Teatro Tron di San Cassiano l'autunno dell' anno 1748.

Venezia, Modesto Fenzo, 1748. 36 p. 14½ᶜᵐ.

Three acts. Argument, cast, and scenario. Neither the author, Francesco Passarini, nor the composer, Baldassare **Galuppi,** is mentioned. Possibly not all of the music was by him.

First performed, as indicated, November, 1748 (Pavan). Schatz 3516

La Clotilde. Drama per musica da recitarsi nel Teatro Tron à San Cassano. Nouamente riaperto à uso d'opere l'anno 1696 . . .

Venetia, Nicolini, 1696. 67 p. 15ᶜᵐ.

Three acts. Dedication by the author, Giovanni Battista Neri, notice to the reader, calling this "un parto di tre settimane," and giving the argument, scenario, and name of Giovanni Maria **Ruggeri** as the composer. Schatz 9135

La **Clotilde**—Continued.

— **Amar per vendetta.** Drama per musica da recitarsi nel Teatro di S. Moise. Nuouamente riaperto à uso d'opere l'autunno dell' anno 1702.

Venezia, Marino Rossetti, 1702.   59 p.   15½ᶜᵐ.

Three acts. Argument, scenario, and notice to the reader, informing him that for want of time it was necessary to fall back on a work previously performed.   This is, in fact, Neri's La Clotilde text (music by **Ruggeri**, neither of whom is mentioned), but with innumerable alterations, especially in the arias.   Schatz 9136

Le club des bons-gens, ou, La reconciliation, comédie en vers et en deux actes, mêlée de vaudevilles et d'airs nouveaux; représentée pour la première fois à Paris, au Théâtre de Monsieur, aujourd' hui de la rue Feydeau, les 24, 25 et 26 septembre 1791, interrompue en mars 1792 après 46 représentations; reprise au même théâtre le quintidi 25 messidor, l'an troisième de la république (lundi, 13 juillet 1795) avec les corrections et additions; pour la huitième fois le 17 thermidor, an 4. Paroles et airs du Cousin-Jacques.

Marseille, Mossy, cinquième année de la république, [1796–97]. *56 p.   21½ᶜᵐ.*   Schatz 704

The **coach drivers,** a political comic-opera. Adapted to the music of several eminent composers . . .

London, W. Flexney, 1766.   2 p. l., 26 p.   2 fold. pl.   20½ᶜᵐ.

Two acts. Ballad opera, the airs used in which are indicated by title. Author not recorded.   Longe 298

The **cobler:** or, A wife of ten thousand. A ballad opera. In two acts. As it is performed at the Theatre-Royal, Drury Lane.

London, T. Becket, 1774.   2 p. l., 36 p.   19½ᶜᵐ.

Two acts. Cast and prefatory note by the author and composer, Charles **Dibdin** who says:
"The hint of the subsequent trifle is taken from the *Blaise le savetier* of Sedan [Sedaine], as is the hint of the club-scene from an essay of Dr. Goldsmith . . . The pictures of low life I have in a manner considered myself obliged to draw as the proper subjects for ballads, which, unless they are familiar, and have something like character and contrast, 'tis next to impossibility but they must be dull and insipid."
The airs used by Dibdin are not indicated in the text.
First performed, as indicated, December 9, 1774.   Longe 32

The **cobler of Castlebury.** A musical entertainment, in two acts. As it is performed at the Theatre Royal, Covent-Garden.

London, G. Kearsley, n. d.   4 p. l., 35 p.   20ᶜᵐ.

Cast and dedication in which the author, Charles Stuart (not mentioned) calls this "my first dramatic essay." From the headings of the songs it appears that William **Shield** contributed the overture and all of the music except "Air I. There's nought can surpass," "Air VIII. A soldier is free from every care," both marked as by [Jean] **Gehot,** and "Air XIII. Tune, *I'll never leave thee.* My Nancy, I love you dear." "Air II. The blush of Aurora," words by Hartley, is marked as taken from Shield's collection of songs, and "Air IV. Duet. Farewell, my Lapstone" as by Shield and introduced at Dublin in "Love in a village."
First performed April 27, 1779, as indicated.   Longe 125

Le cocq de village, opera comique, par Monsieur Favart, représenté pour la premiere fois sur le Théâtre du Fauxbourg Saint Germain, le 31. Mars 1743. Nouvelle edition.

Paris, Prault fils, 1752.   44 p.   19½ᶜᵐ.

One act. No airs printed in the text, but all indicated by *timbres.* The text is the same as of the nouv. éd. below.   ML 50.2.C605

Le **cocq de village**—Continued.

—Le **cocq de village,** opera-comique, en un acte; par M. Favart: représenté pour la premiere fois sur le Théâtre du fauxbourg S. Germain, le 31 mars 1743. Nouvelle édition, augmentée de la musique.

n. i., n. d. 80 p. 19^{cm}. (Theatre de M. Favart, Paris, Duchesne, 1763–77, t. vi.)

One act. Prose, vaudevilles, and airs, many of the latter printed in the text. Font does not mention the composer. ML 49.A2F1

The **coffee-house.** A dramatick piece. As it is perform'd at the Theatre-Royal in Drury-Lane. By His Majesty's servants . . .

London, J. Watts, 1737. 6 p. l. (incl. front.), 38, [2] p. 19^{cm}.

One act. By James Miller, who is not mentioned. The [2] p. contain publisher's book-list, the p. l. contain prologue, cast, book list and preface, in which the author says that he has "printed the whole which was spoke in the representation," and that a comparison with Rousseau's "Le caffé" would prove that this was his source and would disprove the correctness of the general impression "that he hath represented the characters of a particular family who keep a considerable coffee-house in this town, and of several persons who frequent it."

In the text are printed the airs of the "Song. Set by Mr. Henry **Burgess**, jun": "What dire misfortune hath befel," "Song" [without name of composer]: "Love and drink, merry mortal," "Song. Set by Mr. **Carey**": "Yes, marriage sure must be divine," "Song. Set by Mr. **Carey**": "How brimful of nothing," "Song. Set by Mr. Henry **Burgess,** Esq.: "Learn all from me," "Song. Set by Mr. **Carey**": "What pleasures a coffee- house."

According to Genest, the piece was first performed January 26, 1738, which is obviously too late. Longe 59

Second copy, but lacking the [2] p. at end. Longe 190

Le **cognate in contesa.** Dramma giocoso per musica di Egesippo Argolide P. A. della Colonia Alfea. Da rappresentarsi nel Teatro Giustiniani in S. Moisè l'autunno dell' anno 1780.

Venezia, n. publ., n. d. 56 p. 17^{cm}.

Two acts. By Carlo Lanfranchi-Rossi. Cast, name of Francesco **Zanetti** as the composer. With the opera were performed Vincenzo Monari's ballets "Il Tartaro generoso" and "Il Svizzero ingannato," the composers of the music not being mentioned. Schatz 11137

Colinette à la cour. A. T. of Grétry's La double épreuve.

Colombine Arlequin, ou Arlequin Colombine. Pièce d'un acte. Par M. le S * * *. Représentée à la Foire de Saint Laurent 1715.

Le Théâtre de la foire, Paris, 1737, t. ii, pl., [45]–79 p. 17^{cm}.

By Alain René Le Sage. *En vaudevilles,* selected or composed and arranged by Jean Claude **Gillier,** the "compositeur" of the theatre and printed at the end of the volume in the "Table des airs." ML 48.L2 II

Colombine courtezan. A. T. of Cupid and Psyche.

Colombine-Nitétis. Parodie en un acte; mêlée de prose & de vaudevilles. Représentée par les marionnettes de la troupe de Francisque, à la Foire Saint-Laurant en 1722.

Alexis Piron, Oeuvres complettes, Liege, 1776, v. 5, [51]–98 p. 17½^{cm}.

A parody of Danchet's tragedy of this title, according to Parfaict, who does not record the composer and dates the parody March 7, 1723. PQ 2019.P6

Il **Colombo,** overo L'India scoperta. Dramma per musica . . .
Da rappresentarsi nel Teatro di Tor di Nona l'anno MDCXCI.

Roma, Gio: Francesco Buagni, 1690.   97 (incl. 3 pl.), [3] p.   13ᶜᵐ.

Three acts. Text and music by Cardinal Pietro **Ottoboni,** who signs the dedication to the princess Maria Otthoboni [! on t.-p.] with the Arcadian name "Crateo Pradelini." Argument and scenario, but not the cast. For further details *see* Wotquenne's catalogue or his source Ademollo.

The three additional, unnumbered pages contain *aggiunta*. Accordingly in I, 12, was added the aria "Quel povero core," in II, 3, dialogue and the aria "Madre non più languir," in II, 6, dialogue and the arias "Se t'invioli ò mia tiranna," "Quei lumi, quel labro," in II, 16, the duet "Se voi ch'io t'ami," and II, 12, was to be sung after II, 13.   SCHATZ 7371

Colombo nell' Indie, ballet. *See* Tritto's L'Artenice.

La **colonia.** Dramma giocoso per musica . . .

Parma, Stamperia reale, 1775.   56 p.   21ᶜᵐ.

Three acts. Dedication by the author, Gian-Antonio Riva, dated Colorno, October 9, 1775, where and when this "operetta" was first performed. Composer not mentioned and unknown to Schatz.   SCHATZ 11314

La **colonie.** French version of Sacchini's L'isola d'amore.

Die **colonie.** Tr. of Sacchini's La colonie.

Il **colonnello.** Drama giocoso per musica da rappresentarsi nel Teatro delle Dame nel carnevale dell' anno MDCCLXXVII . . .

Roma, Giovanni Bartolomicchi, n. d.   56 p.   15½ᶜᵐ.

Three acts. Author not mentioned and unknown to Schatz. Argument, scenario, cast and name of Giuseppe **Heiberger** as composer.   ML 50.2.C61H3

Il **colore fà la regina.** Drama per musica da rappresentarsi nel Teatro Grimani di San Gio. Grisostomo l'anno MDCC. Di Matteo Noris . . .

Venetia, Nicolini, 1700.   folded front., 72 p.   14½ᶜᵐ.

The title not on the t.-p., but on the frontispiece.

Three acts. Author's dedication, notice to the reader, and scenario. Carlo Francesco **Pollaroli,** the composer, is not mentioned.   SCHATZ 8277

Columbus: or, A world discovered. An historical play. As it is performed at the Theatre Royal, Covent-Garden. By Thomas Morton . . . The second edition.

London, W. Miller, 1792.   4 p. l., 66, [3] p.   21ᶜᵐ.

Five acts, prologue, and epilogue. Prefatory note and cast.   E 120.M88

— **Columbus:** or The discovery of America. An historical play as performed at the Theatre-Royal, Covent-Garden, London. By Thomas Morton . . .

Boston, William Spotswood, 1794.   2 p. l., 52, [3] p.   16½ᶜᵐ.

Five acts, prologue, and epilogue. London cast. Last page contains Spotswood's sales-list of "Plays, American editions."

First performed at London, as indicated, December 1, 1792. Entered here because performed with incidental music by Alexander **Reinagle,** Philadelphia, New Theatre, January 21, 1797.   E 120.M885

Il comando non inteso, et ubbidito. Drama per musica da rappresentarsi nel famosissimo Teatro Grimani di S. Gio. Grisostomo di Francesco Silvani . . .

Venezia, Marino Rossetti, 1709. 72 p. 14½ᶜᵐ.

Three acts. Author's dedication dated Venice, February 6, 1709, argument, notice to the reader, cast, scenario, and name of Antonio Lotti as composer.

SCHATZ 5716

Le combat nocturne, ou Les morts vivans. Opéra bouffon en un acte. Les paroles de M. Dancourt & la musique de M. Le Petit.

La Haye, Frédéric Staatman, 1770. 40 p. 18ᶜᵐ.

Cast.

SCHATZ 5489

La comédie. Entrée in Campra's Les Muses.

Les comédiens ambulans, opéra comique en deux actes et en prose; paroles de L. B. Picard; musique de F. Devienne; représenté pour la première fois sur le Théâtre de la rue Feydeau, le 8 nivose an 7.

Paris, Huet, an VII [1798–99]. 40 p. 20ᶜᵐ.

First performed December 28, 1798.

ML 50.2.C62D2

Les comediens corsaires. Prologue des deux pièces suivantes. Representé à la Foire S. Laurent 1726. & ensuite sur le Théâtre du Palais royal.

Below the title this Advertissement: "Ce prologue fut fait peu de temps après les *Comédiens esclaves*, comédie du théatre italien, & à l'occasion du goût qui règne depuis quelques années dans les pièces tant françoises qu'italiennes, dans la plûpart desquelles on voit le fond & la forme des divertissements forains."

— L'obstacle favorable. Piece d'un acte. Representée à la Foire S. Laurent 1726. & ensuite sur le Théâtre du Palais royal.

— Les amours déguisez. Piece d'un acte representée à la Foire S. Laurent 1726 & ensuite sur le Théâtre du Palais royal.

Le Théâtre de la foire, Paris, 1728, t. vi, 3 pl., [231]–372 p. 17ᶜᵐ.

By Le Sage, Fuzelier and d'Orneval. Largely *en vaudevilles*, a few of which indicated as composed by "M. l'Abbé." The airs, selected or composed and arranged by Jean Claude Gillier, the "compositeur" of the company, are printed at the end of the volume in the "Table des airs."

First performed September 20, 1726, as indicated.

ML 48.L2V1

The comical history of Don Quixote. As it was acted at the Queen's Theatre in Dorset Garden, by Their Majesties servants. Part I. Written by Mr. D'Urfey.

London, Printed for J. Darby, A. Bettesworth [etc], 1729. iv, 5–91 p. 17ᶜᵐ.

— The comical history of Don Quixote. As it is acted at both theatres, by Their Majesties servants. Part II. Written by Mr. D'Urfey.

London, Printed for Jacob Tonson and for John Darby [etc.], 1729. 93]–194 p. 17ᶜᵐ.

The comical history of Don Quixote—Continued.

— The **comical history of Don Quixote**. With the Marriage of Mary the Buxome. Part III . . . Written by Mr. D'Urfey.

London, Printed for John Darby, Arthur Bettesworth [etc], 1729. [195]–295, [5] p. 17^{cm}.

The [5] p. contain booklists by J. Tonson and J. Darby.

The three parts are paged consecutively.

First part: Five acts. Dedication, prologue, epilogue, cast.

Second part: Five acts. Dedication, preface, prologue, epilogue, and cast. In his preface Thomas Durfey takes issue with his critics, praises certain performers, and says:

"The rest of the characters in both the parts were likewise extremely well performed, in which I had as much justice done me as I could expect; nor was the musical part less commendable, the words everywhere being the best of mine in that kind: and if in the whole, they could draw such audiences for so long time, in such violent hot weather, I shall not despair, that when the season is more temperate, to see at their next representation, a great deal of good company. I have printed some scenes both in the first and second parts, which were left out in the acting—the play and the musick being too long; and I doubt not but they will divert in the reading, because very proper for the connexion . . ."

Third part: Dedication, prologue, epilogue, cast, and preface, in which Durfey defends himself against the critics of "some little distant obscenities and double entendres" in his piece, etc., tries to explain its "miscarriage" by the "accidents happening in the presentment," and says:

"The songish part which I used to succeed so well in, by the indifferent performance the first day, and the hurrying it on so soon, being straitned in time thro' ill management—(tho extremely well set to musick, and I'm sure the just critick will not say ill writ) yet being imperfectly performed, was consequently not pleasing, and the dances too, for want of some good performers, also disliked: all which, tho impossible for me to avoid, and not unreasonably to be attributed any way to a fault in me, yet the noisy party endeavoured to use me as ill as if it were, till the generous opposition of my friends gave me as much reason to thank them for their justice, as to despise the others malice . . ."

Whereas the score printed simultaneously with the performances in 1694 and 1696 (third part) says, "sett by the most eminent masters of the age" (parts I–II), and (part III) "being the last piece set to musick by the late famous Mr. Henry **Purcell**: and by Mr. Courtiville [Raphael **Courteville**], Mr. [Samuel] **Akeroyd**, and other eminent masters of the age [John **Eccles**, colonel **Pack**, **Morgan**]," the libretto does not even mention Purcell.								LONGE 68

I comici Italiani alla China, ballet. *See* Cimarosa's I due supposti conti.

La commedia in commedia. O. T. of Barlocci's libretto Il vecchio amante.

La commedia in commedia. Dramma giocoso per musica da rappresentarsi nel Teatro Bonacossi da S. Stefano in Ferrara nell' anno MDCCXLVII . . .

Ferrara, Bernardino Pomatelli, n. d. 72 p. 16^{cm}.

Three acts. Dedication by Eustacchio Bambini, who calls this his "secondo dramma musicale giocoso," cast, and name of Gaetano **Latilla** as composer. The text was really by Giovanni Barlocci.						SCHATZ 5457

La commedia in commedia. Dramma giocoso per musica da rappresentarsi nel Teatro Tron di S. Cassiano. Nel carnovale dell' anno 1749.

Venezia, Modesto Fenzo, 1749. 48 p. 14½^{cm}.

Three acts. By Giovanni Barlocci. With cast and name of **Rinaldo di Capua** as composer.

First performed at Rome, Teatro Valle, January 8, 1738.			SCHATZ 8803

La commedia in commedia—Continued.

— **L'ambizione delusa.** Drama giocoso per musica da rappresentarsi nel Teatro Tron di S. Cassano il carnovale dell' anno 1744.

Venezia, n. publ., n. d. 82 p. 17ᶜᵐ.

A much altered version of Giovanni Barlocci's "La commedia in commedia" as composed by **Rinaldo di Capua,** who is mentioned as composer in the 1744 version. This plays in Livorno, the original in Florence, and in the cast of the 1744 version appears "Fiorlindo, Parigino affettato amante di Lucinda," who is not in the original.

SCHATZ 8802

Commedianti fortunati. Commedia per musica di Pasquale Mililotti da rappresentarsi nel Teatro nuovo sopra Toledo per terza opera di quest' anno 1779.

Napoli, n. publ., 1779. 64 p. 15½ᶜᵐ.

Three acts. Cast and name of Antonio **Amicone** as composer. SCHATZ 174

Comment faire?, ou, Les épreuves de misanthropie et repentir, comédie en un acte, mêlée de vaudevilles, représentée pour la première fois sur le Théâtre du Vaudeville le 26 ventôse, an 7. par les CC. Dejouy et Longchamps.

Paris, Le Libraire au Théâtre du Vaudeville, an VII [1798–99]. 48 p. 20ᶜᵐ.

Cast. A few airs printed in the text, for instance, "No. 14. Air nouveau du C. **Jadin:** Dans nos bals" and "No. 38. Air nouveau du C. **Longchamps:** A tout le monde." Not recorded by either Cl. & L. or Schatz.

First performed, as indicated, March 16, 1799. ML 48.M2L

The **commodity excis'd:** or, The women in an uproar. A new ballad opera. As it will be privately acted, in the secret apartments of vintners and tobacconists . . . By Timothy Smoke.

London, Printed for the author, and sold by T. Bancks, 1733. 1 p. l., 32 p. 19ᶜᵐ.

Three acts and introduction. The airs are not even indicated by title.

LONGE 191

La compagnia d'opera a Nanchino. Drama giocoso da rappresentarsi nell' interno Piccolo Teatro del Palazzo reale di S. M. il rè di Prussia, il giorno 16. ottobre 1790. Composto da Antonio Filistri de' Caramondani poeta della Real corte, e messo in musica dal Sign. Felice Alessandri . . .

Berlino, Haude e Spener, 1790. 145 p. 15½°.

German title-page "Die operisten in Nanking" and text face Italian.

Two acts. Cast. SCHATZ 143

Il compimento di quattro desideri, ballet. *See* Anfossi's Ezio.

Compliment de la clôture de la Foire S. Laurent. *See* Jerosme et Fanchonette.

Le comte d'Albert, drame en deux actes, en prose et en vers. Représenté à Fontainebleau, le 13 novembre 1786, & à Paris, le 8 février 1787, par les Comédiens italiens ordinaires du roi. Les paroles, par Mr. Sedaine; la musique, par Mr. Grétry.

Paris, et se trouve à Bruxelles, chez Emmanuel Flon, 1787. 63 p. 22ᶜᵐ.

Cast and Avertissement, in which Sedaine narrates how he came to dramatize de la Fontaine's fable of the lion and the rat under the above title, and that he added

Le comte d'Albert—Continued.

a third act to the original two under the title of "suite" and, in fact, on p. 35–63 this third act is printed as:

"Suite du Comte d'Albert, opéra-comique en un acte, en prose et en vers, mis en musique. Composé par les mêmes auteurs, & représenté sur les mêmes théatres en même-tems que le Comte d'Albert."   ML 50.2.C64G7

— Le **comte d'Albert**, drame en deux actes, et en prose mêlé d'ariettes. Représenté à Fontainebleau, le 13 novembre 1786, & à Paris, le 8 février 1787, par les Comédiens italiens ordinaires du roi. Les paroles par Mr. Sedaine, la musique, par Mr. Gretry.

Amsterdam, César Noël Guerin, 1788. iv, [5]–52 p. 20½ cm.

No cast, otherwise the same contents as above.   ML 50.2.C64G8

— Arien und gesaenge aus dem singspiele **Graf Albert**, in drey akten. Musik von Gretry.

Berlin, n. publ., 1798. 37 p. 15½ cm.

Cast. Tr. by Heinrich Gottlieb Schmieder, who is not mentioned.
First performed at Berlin, Kgl. Nationaltheater, January 2, 1799; at Mayence, Nationaltheater, June 20, 1789.   SCHATZ 4142

Comus, a mask: (Now adapted to the stage) as alter'd from Milton's mask at Ludlow-Castle, which was never represented but on Michael-mas-Day, 1634; before the Right Hon[ble.] the earl of Bridgewater, Lord President of Wales. The principal performers were the Lord Brackly, Mr. Tho. Egerton, the lady Alice Egerton. The musick was composed by Mr. Henry Lawes, who also represented the Attendant spirit . . . The second edition.

London, R. Dodsley, 1738. 61, [2] p. 21 cm.

Three acts, prologue, and epilogue. Cast. The alterations of the text were by John Dalton. The composer of this version, Thomas Augustine **Arne**, is not mentioned.
First performed at London, Drury Lane, March 4, 1738.   ML 48.M2E

— **Comus**, a mask: . . . [same as in 2d ed.] The third edition.

London, R. Dodsley, 1738. 61, [2] p. 19 cm.

Contents same as of the 2d ed.   LCNGE 40

— **Comus**. A mask. By John Milton. Adapted for theatrical representation, as performed first at the Theatre-Royal, Covent-Garden, in the year 1744. Regulated from the prompt-book . . .

*London, John Bell, 1791. front., 1 p. l., xii, [3], 16–66, [2] p. 15 cm.
(J. Bell, British Theatre, London, 1791–97, v. 2.)*

The front. represents Miss Storace as Euphrosine in the opera, and is dated January 31, 1791. The 1 p. l. is an added engraved title page, with a scene from the opera, and is dated September 20, 1790.

Three acts, prologue, and epilogue. Biographical sketch of Milton, preface, editorial comment, reading, in part:

"*Comus*, as it is here given, is an adaptation to the modern stage—by the retrenchment of much dialogue, and the addition of many airs.—That the poetry of this beautiful piece suffers by a modern hand can be little doubted. Veneration for the author might wish it in the original state; but a dramatic exhibition must please to be repeated—the aim should be to venture as little innovation as possible. The music of **Arne**, in the modern Comus, is well known; it is as intelligent as modern music can be . . ."

In the preface we read:

"In the year 1774 [? 1772] it was abridged, and has ever since been performed as an afterpiece at the Theater-Royal in Covent-Garden . . ."

Though in parts a trifle shorter than in the 1738 ed., the text is *not* George Colman's abridged two-act version, but that of Dalton.   PR 1241.B4

Comus—Continued.

— **Comus:** a masque. Altered from Milton. In two acts.

[216]–230 p. 19^{cm}. (*Collection of the most esteemed farces and entertainments, t. iv, Edinburgh, 1792.*)

Covent-Garden and Edinburgh (1782) casts. George Colman's abridged version.

SCHATZ 11753 D

Il **conclave del MDCCLXXIV.** Dramma per musica. Da recitarsi nel Teatro delle Dame nel carnevale del MDCCLXXV . . .

Roma, Per il Cracas. All' insegna del silenzio. Con licenza ed approvazione, n. d. 155 p. 18^{cm}.

Three acts. This satirical drama is attributed by Schatz to abbate Sertori, though on p. 6 we read: "La poesia è in gran parte del celebre Sig. abate Pietro Metastasio." Below this: "La musica del Sig. Niccolò Piccini," though, of course, the satire was never composed or performed. Sertori simply used the two names then most in vogue. German title-page "Das conclave von MDCCLXXIV," argument and text face Italian.   SCHATZ 8084

— Das **conclave von MDCCLXXIV.** Ein drama fuer die musik. Welches im carneval des 1775 sten jahres auf dem Theater delle Dame aufgefuehret werden soll . . .

Rom. Bey Cracas. Im zeichen der verschwiegenheit, n. d. 78 p. 18^{cm}.

Merely a separate issue of the German translation in Schatz 8084. SCHATZ 8085

— Il **conclave del 1774.** Dramma giocoso per musica. 1797.

Venezia, Anno primo della Libertà italiana, n. publ. 72 p. 16½^{cm}.

Three acts. A later issue of the above, again with Metastasio's and Piccinni's names.   SCHATZ 8132

La **concordia della virtù, e della fortuna,** poemetto drammatico nel felicissimo giorno natalizio della Sac. Real Maestà di Amalia Willelmina regina de' Romani.

Pietro Antonio Bernardoni, Poemi drammatici, parte terza, Vienna, van Ghelen, 1707, p. 35–44. 16½^{cm}.

Argument. The composer, Carlo Agostino **Badia,** is not mentioned.
First performed, as indicated, April 21, 1702.   ML 49.A2B4

La **concordia fra il tempo e la gloria.** Componimento drammatico da cantarsi in occasione che Sua Altezza Reale l'arciduca Massimiliano di Austria onora della sua reale presenza la villa del cardinale Alessandro Albani.

Roma, Salomoni, 1775. xix p. 27^{cm}.

Two parts. Neither author nor composer mentioned and both unknown to me.

ML 50.2.C645

O **conde de bello humor.** Tr. of Bernardini's Il conte di bell' umore.

La **confederazione de i Sabini con Roma.** See M. Curzio.

Le **confident heureux,** opera-comique en un acte. Par M. Vadé. Représenté, pour la premiere fois, sur le Théâtre de l'Opéra-Comique le 31 juillet 1755.

La Haye, Pierre Gosse junior, 1759. 78 p. 16^{cm}. (Vadé, Oeuvres, La Haye, 1759, t. III.)

Le **confident heureux**—Continued.

En vaudevilles. Cast. On p. 72–78, the "Airs choisis du Confident heureux:" "Qu'importe à quel prix," "A l'amour tout est possible," "Loin de l'objet aimé," "Un bon Gaillard joyeux." The arranger of the music not mentioned by Schatz.

ML 49.A2V2

— Le **confident heureux**, opéra-comique, en un acte, représenté, pour la premiere fois, sur le Théatre de l'Opéra-comique, le 31 juillet 1755.

Paris, la veuve Duchesne, 1766. 60 p. 19^{cm}.

On p. 53–60, the "Airs:" "Qu'importe à quel prix," "A l'amour tout est possible," "Lors d'ici, et vous aussi," "Loin de l'objet aimé."   SCHATZ 11486

La **confusione della somiglianza** ossiano I due gobbi. O. T. of Portugal's La somiglianza ossiano I gobbi.

Le **confusioni per la somiglianza.** Dramma comico da rappresentarsi in musica nel Teatro di Monza l'autunno dell' anno 1792 . . .

Milano, Gaetano Motta, n. d.   4 p. l., 71, [2] p.   16½^{cm}.

The two add. p. contain the substitute duettino "Se più il matto non farete" (II, 1) and errata. Two acts, by Francesco Marconi, with impresario'sde dedication dated November 7, 1792, scenario, cast, names of the composer, Luigi **Crippa** ("musica tutta nuova") and of the author and author's preface. In this Marconi states that he has used with "pochissime variazioni" "una comedia in prosa di un ridicolo singolare, che ha per titolo *I due gobbi*, parto felice del Sig. Luigi Del-Buono Fiorentino."

With the opera were performed Gherardo Cavazza's ballets "La scoperta d'un isola nell' America del capitano Durson Inglese" and "L'uomo effeminato." The composer of the music is not mentioned.   SCHATZ 2290

La **congiura contro Galeazzo Maria Sforza Visconti.** A. T. of the ballet Il Bruto milanese.

La **congiura Pisoniana.** Dramma per musica da rappresentarsi nel Teatro Grande alla Scala il carnevale 1797 . . .

Milano, Gio. Batista Bianchi, n. d.   44 p.   16½^{cm}.

Three acts. Dedication by the author Francesco Salfi, cast, scenario, and name of Angelo **Tarchi** as the composer. With the opera were performed, the composers of the music not mentioned, Paolino Franchi's ballets "Lucio Giunio Bruto" and "L'Albagia in fumo."   SCHATZ 10215

Le **congiure del duca di Guisa,** ballet. *See* Bianchi's Demetrio.

The **conquest of Mexico.** Tr. of Vento's La conquista del Messico.

La **conquista del Messico.** A. T. of the ballet Guatimozin.

La **conquista del Messico**, drama per musica. Da rappresentarsi sopra il Teatro di S. M. B. Travagliato sopra un nuovo piano da Giovan Gualberto Bottarelli. La musica e' intieramente nuova del Signor Mattia Vento, maestro Napoletano . . . The conquest of Mexico . . .

London, W. Griffin, 1767.   39, [1] p.   19^{cm}.

Three acts. Argument, cast. Italian and English text.
First performed at London, Haymarket, 1767.   ML 50.2.C65V2

La **conquista del Perù.** A. T. of the ballet Il Pizarro nell' America.

La **conquista del Perù** ossia Amazile e Telesco, ballet. *See* Tarchi's Aldemira.

La **conquista del vello d'oro.** Drama per musica da rappresentarsi nel Teatro dell' illustrissimo pubblico di Reggio in occasione della fiera l'anno MDCCXVII.

> *Reggio, Ippolito Vedrotti, 1717. 74 p., [1] p. 16^{cm}.*

Three acts. Dedication dated Reggio, April 29, 1717, argument, cast, scenario, and name of the composer, Marc Antonio **Bononcini**, but not of the librettist, *conte* Niccolò Minato. SCHATZ 1207

La **conquista del vello d'oro.** A. T. of Gazzaniga's Gli Argonauti in Colco.

La **conquista del vello d'oro.** Dramma per musica da rappresentarsi nel Regio Teatro di Torino nel carnovale del 1791 . . .

> *Torino, Onorato Derossi, n. d. viii, 60 p. 15½^{cm}.*

Three acts. Argument, cast, scenario, and names of Giandomenico Boggio as author, of Gaetano **Isola** as composer. On p. 54–60 description of Domenico Ballon's ballets "L'incoronazione di Uladislao rè di Polonia in rè d'Ungheria," "Angelica e Wilton," and "I due cacciatori e la venditrice di latte," music of all three by Giuseppe Nucci.

First performed as indicated, December 26, 1790. SCHATZ 4905

La **conquista del vello d'oro,** ballet. *See* Nasolini's Tito e Berenice.

La **conquista del vello d'oro.** Drama per musica da rappresentarsi nel Regio Teatro di Torino nel carnovale del 1745 . . .

> *Torino, Pietro Giuseppe Zappata e figlio, n. d. 4 p. l., 56 p. 15^{cm}.*

Three acts. Author not mentioned and unknown to Schatz. Perhaps Angelo Cari's text, as previously (1738) composed by Pescetti?

Argument, scenario, cast and names of Giuseppe **Sordella** as composer of the opera, of Alessio Rasetti as composer of the three incidental ballets. SCHATZ 9961

La conquista di Granata. L. T. Curcio's La presa di Granata.

Il **consiglio fedele.** *See* M. Curzio.

Il **consiglio di Giove,** ballet. *See* Cimarosa's Le donne rivali.

Un **consiglio per li vecchj,** ballet. *See* Marinelli's Issipile.

The **conspirators.** A tragi-comic opera. As it was acted in England and Ireland, without applause . . .

> *Carrickfergus, n. publ., 1749. 59 p. 19½^{cm}.*

Neither author, composer, nor performance recorded by Clarence. LONGE 216

The **constant lady.** A. T. of The generous free-mason.

The **constant maid;** or, Poll of Plympton. A musical entertainment in two parts. As performed at the Royalty Theatre, Well-Close-Square. By the author of The Birth-day.

> *London, J. Jarvis, 1787. 2 p. l., 36 p. 21^{cm}.*

Cast. By O'Keeffe. The composer, Thomas **Carter,** is not mentioned. Schatz, though incorrectly, it would seem, dates first performance Jan. 16, 1788. LONGE 102

La **contadina.** O. T. of Hasse's Don Tabarrano.

La **contadina astuta,** ballet. *See* Paër's L'oro fa tutto.

La contadina astuta. A. T. and L. T. of Pergolesi's Livietta e Tracollo.

La contadina filosofa, ballet. *See* Alessandri's Il vecchio geloso.

La contadina impertinente. A. T. of the ballet La vindemmia.

La contadina in corte. A. T. of the ballet Il principe di Lago Nero.

La contadina in corte. Drama giocoso per musica da rappresentarsi nel Teatro chiamato da rua dos Condes l'anno 1765 . . .

Lisbona, Pietro Ferreira, n. d. 7 p. l., 133 p., [2] l. 16^{cm}.

Three acts. Author not mentioned and unknown to Schatz. Dedication, argument, and scenario. Portuguese title, "A Aldeana em corte," and text face Italian. On recto. of first p. l. and on first additional leaf, the aria, "Con la mia villanella," resp. "Com a minha Aldeana," transferred from II, 4 to II, 5. The composer, Giacomo **Rust,** is not mentioned.

First performed at Venice, Teatro di San Moisè, carnival, 1763.   SCHATZ 9180

La contadina in corte. Operetta giocosa per musica da rappresentarsi nei Teatri privilegiati di Vienna l'anno 1770.

Vienna, Giovanni Tomaso di Trattnern, n. d. 46 p. 16½^{cm}.

Two acts. Author not mentioned and unknown to Schatz. **Sacchini** is mentioned as the composer.

First performed at Rome, Teatro Valle, carnival, 1765; and at Vienna for the first time in 1767.   SCHATZ 9211

— **La contadina in corte.** Dramma giocoso per musica da rappresentarsi nel Ducal Teatro di Louisbourg . . .

Stuttgard, Erhard, 1771. 159 p. 16½^{cm}.

Three acts. Cast, scenario, and name of **Sacchini** as the composer. ("La musica sarà tutta nuova" [sic!]) German title-page, "Das bauren-maedgen am hofe," and text face Italian. Neither the translator nor the person who expanded the text from two to three acts is mentioned.

First performed, as indicated, in 1771.   SCHATZ 9213

— **Die baeurinn bey hofe,** ein kleines lustiges singspiel, aufgefuehret auf den privilegierten schaubuehnen in Wienn im Jahre 1767 und in das deutsche uebersetzet von J. A. E. v. G.

Wienn, gedruckt mit von Ghelischen schriften, n. d. Unpaged. 14½^{cm}.

Two acts. Translated by J. A. edler v. Ghelen. Scenario, cast, and name of **Sacchini** as the composer. Schatz calls this a "Separat-abdruck" of the German translation in the 1767 Italian libretto.   SCHATZ 9214

— **Die geadelte baeuerinn.** Ein komisches singspiel. Aufgefuehrt auf der Koenigl. Schaubuehne zu Prag in der fassnachtszeit 1774 unter der aufsicht des hr. Joseph Bustelli.

Prag, Johann Ferdinand Edl. v. Schoenfeld, n. d. 91 p. 15^{cm}.

Two acts. Scenario and name of **Sacchini** as the composer. Italian text faces German.

First performed at Prague in 1767.   SCHATZ 9212

La contadina in corte, ballet. *See* Sacchini's Armida.

La contadina incivilita. Dramma giocoso per musica da rappresentarsi nel Teatro di San Samuele nel carnovale dell' anno 1775.

Venezia, Antonio Graziosi, 1775. 63 p. 17ᶜᵐ.

Three acts. Cast, scenario, and name of composer, Pasquale **Anfossi**, but not of librettist, who is unknown to Schatz. The first ballet, "Venere e Adone," was by Giacomo Romoli. The composer of the music is not mentioned. A synopsis on p. 5–6.   SCHATZ 266

La contadina nel palazzo signorile. A. T. of the ballet Ninetta.

La contadina semplice. O. T. of I capricci in amore.

La contadina semplice. Commedia per musica da rappresentarsi nel Real Teatro del Fondo di Separazione nel carnovale dell' anno 1790.

Napoli, n. publ., 1790. 48 p.

Two acts. Author not mentioned and unknown to Schatz. Cast and name of Gaetano **Marinelli** as the composer.   SCHATZ 5954

La contadina spiritosa, ballet. *See* Zingarelli's Quinto Fabio.

La contadina superba ovvero Il giocatore burlato. Farsa per musica da rappresentarsi nel Real Teatro di Salvaterra nel carnovale dell' anno 1776.

[Lisbona], Stamperia reale, n. d. 75 p. 14½ᶜᵐ.

Two acts. Author not mentioned and unknown to Schatz. Scenario, cast, and name of Pietro **Guglielmi** as the composer.
First performed at Rome, Teatro Valle, carnival 1774.   SCHATZ 4295

Le contadine bizzarre. Dramma giocoso per musica da rappresentarsi ne' Teatri privilegiati di Vienna il carnovale dell' anno 1767.

Vienna, Ghelen, n. d. 80 p. 16ᶜᵐ.

Three acts. By Guiseppe Petrosellini, who is not mentioned. Cast, scenario, and name of Niccolò **Piccinni** as the composer.
First performed at Venice, Teatro di S. Samuele, fall 1763.   SCHATZ 8086

— La sciocchezza in amore. Dramma giocoso per musica di Ensildo Prosindio P. A. da rappresentarsi nel Teatro dell' Accademia vecchia [Verona] nell' autunno dell' anno MDCCLXIV . . .

Venezia, Modesto Fenzo, 1764. 70 p. 14½ᶜᵐ.

Three acts. Dedication, cast, and name of Niccolò **Piccinni** as the composer. This is Petrosellini's "Le contadine bizzarre" with many differences at least from the Vienna, 1767, edition. For instance, though the dialogue of the first four scenes is largely the same, the arias are different and Venezia, 1764, has in the first scene "Ah d'ascoltar già parmi" instead of "Destrier, che all' armi usato," etc. On p. 5–8 are enumerated seven "mutazioni di arie."   SCHATZ 8087

Le contadine furlane. Dramma giocoso per musica da rappresentarsi nel Teatro Giustiniani di S. Moisè il carnovale dell' anno 1771 dell' abbate Pietro Chiari.

Venezia, Antonio Grazioli, 1771. 54 p. 18ᶜᵐ.

Three acts. Cast, scenario, and name of the composer, Antonio **Boroni**. Pages 3–4, presumably containing dedication and argument, wanting.   SCHATZ 1252

Il conte Baccelone. Dramma giocoso per musica da rappresentarsi nel Teatro Giustiniani di San Moisè nell' autunno dell' anno 1774.

Venezia, Antonio Graziosi, 1774. 64 p. 17ᶜᵐ.

Il conte Baccellone—Continued.

Three acts. "La Contessina," by Marco Coltellini (not mentioned) with alterations. Cast, scenario, and name of Giacomo **Rust** as the composer. On p. 31–32 description without name of the composer of the music of Francesco Caselli's "Vertunno e Pomona." The other ballet, by Francesco Martini, was called "Diogene tentato, ma non vinto dall' amore."   SCHATZ 9178

Il conte Caramella.

[52]–106 p. 16½*cm*. (*Carlo Goldoni, Opere drammatiche giocose, t. iii, Torino, 1757.*)

Three acts.   ML 49.H2G6

— **Il conte Caramella.** Dramma di tre atti per musica. Rappresentato per la prima volta in Verona l'anno MDCCXLIX.

Carlo Goldoni, Opere-teatrali, Venezia, Zatta e figli, 1788–95, t. 40, [219]–274 p. 18*cm*.   PQ

Il conte Caramella. Opera. Dramma giocosa [!] in musica di Polesenno Tecio, Pastor Arcade. Da rappresentarsi nel Teatro di Piazza nella nobbile città di Vicenza nella fiera presente 1759 . . .

*Vicenza, n. pub., 1759. 50 p. 14½*cm*.*

Three acts. By Goldoni. Dedication, cast, scenario, and name of Baldassare **Galuppi** as composer.
First performed at Verona, Dec. 18, 1749.   SCHATZ 3446

— **Il conte Caramella,** dramma giocoso per musica, da rappresentarsi nel Nuovo Teatro in Dresda l'anno MDCCLV.—Der graf Caramella . . .

*[Dresden], Gedruckt bei der . . . Stoesselin und . . . Johann Carl Krausen, n. d. 143 p. 17*cm*.*

Three acts. Cast, scenario, and name of **Galuppi** as composer. German text faces Italian. The differences between this Dresden, 1755, and the Vicenza, 1759, libretti are few. For instance, in the latter the aria of I, 5, reads "Speranza è il più bel dono," at Dresden it was "Scherza il nocchier tallora." This was taken from Metastasio's Demetrio."   SCHATZ 3447

Lo co. de Scrignano. Commeddeja redicola pe mmuseca, de Tommaso Mariani, Romano. Da rappresentarese a lo Triato nuovo ncoppa Toleto nchisto carnevale de st'anno 1729 . . .

*Napoli, Agnolo Vocola, n. d. 76 p. 14½*cm*.*

Three acts. Impresario's dedication, argument, cast, and name of Costantino **Roberto** as composer of the second act only. The composers of the two other acts are not mentioned.   SCHATZ 8837

Il conte di Belfiore. Intermezzo per musica a tre voci da rappresentarsi nel Teatro Tron di S. Cassiano. Nel carnovale dell' anno 1749.

*Venezia, Modesto Fenzo, 1749. 17 p. 14½*cm*.*

Two parts. Cast. Author and composer not mentioned, and unknown to Schatz.
                                                                        SCHATZ 11315

Il conte di bell' umore. Intermezzi per musica a cinque voci da rappresentarsi nel Teatro della Palla Corda di Firenze [!] nel carnevale dell' anno 1783.

*Roma, Puccinelli, n. d. 56 p. 15½*cm*.*

Two acts. Cast and name of **Bernardini** (Marcello di Capua) as composer, who also wrote the libretto (Schatz).   SCHATZ 844

Il **conte di bell' umore**—Continued.

— Il **conte di bell' umore.** Azione comica per musica da rappresentarsi nel Teatro in parte piccola della Reggia città di Praga nella casa del conte Thun. Nell' autunno dell' anno 1783.

n. i., n. d. 167 p. 16½ᶜᵐ.

German title-page "Der graf bey guter Laune," and text face Italian. Marcello di Capua (**Bernardini**) is mentioned as composer. Schatz 831

— Il **conte di bell' umore:** Dramma giocoso per musica, da rappresentarsi nel Teatro della rua Dos Condes, nella primavera dell' anno 1791.

Lisbona, Antonio Rodrigo Galhardo, 1791. 161 p. 14½ᶜᵐ.

Two acts. Cast. Portuguese title, "O conde de bello humor," and text face Italian. **Bernardini** (Marcello di Capua) is mentioned as composer. Schatz 843

Il **conte di Cutro.** Drama civile fatto rappresentare da' Signori Accademici del Casino sotto la protezione del sereniss. principe Francesco Maria di Toscana.

n. i., n. d. p. [509]–616. 15½ᶜᵐ.

Three acts. By Giovanni Andrea Moniglia, and evidently detached from his "Poesie drammatiche," third part (1690) which is not in our set. Author's unsigned preface, argument, name of the composer, Lorenzo **Cattani**, and on p. 606–616 a "Dichiarazione de i proverbi e vocaboli propri degli abitatori del contado, e quella plebe Fiorentina adoprati nel presente drama.

First performed, as indicated, November 12, 1683, the birthday of Francesco Maria di Toscana, which the opera was to celebrate. Schatz 1712

Il **conte di Saldagna.** Tragedia per musica da rappresentarsi nel Teatro Grande alla Scala la primavera dell' anno 1787 . . .

Milano, Gio. Batista Bianchi, n. d. 68 p. 16½ᶜᵐ.

Three acts. By Ferdinando Moretti, who is not mentioned. Dedication, argument, cast, scenario, and name of Angelo **Tarchi** as the composer.

First performed, as indicated, June 10, 1787. Schatz 10216

Second copy. ML 48.A5 v. 7

Il **conte di Saldagna.** Tragedia per musica da rappresentarsi nel nobilissimo Teatro La Fenice il carnovale dell' anno 1795.

Venezia, Modesto Fenzo, 1795. 62 p. 18ᶜᵐ.

Three acts. By Ferdinando Moretti, who is not mentioned. Argument, cast, scenario, and name of Nicola Antonio **Zingarelli** as the composer. On p. [49]–62, argument, cast, and description of Onorato Viganò's "Le Amazzoni, ballo eroico pantomimo favoloso," music ("tutta nuova") by Antonio Holler. Schatz 11242

Il **conte immaginario.** Intermezzo per musica da rappresentarsi nel Teatro Tron di S. Cassiano, nell' autunno dell' anno 1748.

Venezia, Modesto Fenzo, 1748. 21 p. 14½ᶜᵐ.

Two acts. Cast and name of composer, Pietro **Auletta**, but not of librettist, who is unknown to Schatz. Schatz 501

Il **conte Nespola,** intermezzo. *See* Galuppi's Scipione nelle Spagne.

Il **conte Policronio** ovvero Le bugie hanno le gambe corte. Farsa in prosa con musica che si rappresenta per la prima volta nel Teatro della Real villa del Poggio a Cajano . . . dalla comica compagnia di Pietro Andolfati nell' autunno del 1791.

Firenze, Ant. Gius. Pagani e comp., 1791. 48 p. 16ᶜᵐ.

Two acts. "Il libretto è del sig. G. S. [Gaetano Sertor?] La musica è tutta nuova del Sig. Giuseppe **Moneta**." Impresario's dedication and cast. Schatz 6551

The **contention of the laurel.** A. T. of The battle of the poets.

La **contesa de' Numi.**

[429]–448 p. 19*cm*. (*Pietro Metastasio, Opere drammatiche, Venezia, Giuseppe Bettinelli, 1733–37, v. 2.*)

One act. No composer mentioned. Note on p. 431: "La seguente festa teatrale fu rappresentata in Roma in occasione della nascita del Real Delfino."

ML 49.A2M4·

— La **contesa de' Numi.**

*Metastasio, Poesie, Parigi, vedova Quillau, 1755, t. vi, [433]–459 p. 16*cm*.

One act.   ML 49.A2M42

— La **contesa de' Numi.** Festa teatrale scritta dell' autore in Roma l'anno 1729, ad istanza del cardinale di Polignac . . . e sontuosamente rappresentata la prima volta con musica del Vinci nell' ornatissimo cortile del palazzo di Sua Eminenza, per festeggiare la nascita del Real Delfino di Francia.

[395]–416 p. 26*cm*. (*Pietro Metastasio, Opere, t. 4, Parigi, vedova Herissant, 1780.*)

Two parts.   ML 49.A2M44

Le **contese di Pallade e Venere sopra il bando d'Amore.** Introdutione accademica rappresentata sù la sala dell' Ercole nel Palazzo publico. Poesia del Sig. dottor Bianchini.

*Bologna, per gl' HH. d' Evangelista Dozza, n. d. [23 p.] 19½*cm*.

In a prefatory note we are told that certain noblemen wished to honor "Cardinal Caraffa, dignissimo Legato di questa città" with an

"Accademia di belle lettere, accompagnandola con l'armonia della musica. E perche fù mai sempre opinione, che non possa darsi un vero seguace della virtù, che non habbia prima dal petto essigliato Amore, venne giudicato proporre ciò per problemma. Cosi sù la sera delli 29 del corrente doppo essersi radunati nella sala dell' Ercole del Palazzo publico li SS. Accademici Gelati, ed altri virtuosi, come ancora quantità di cavaglieri, e di dame, comparve l'Eminentissimo e Reverendissimo Sig. Cardinal Legato . . . ciascuno di quali dopo essersi posti ne proprij luoghi à sedere, al suono d'una bellissima sinfonia di varij stromenti musicali, si diede principio . . ."

This is followed by another note in which "Gio. Paolo **Colonna** organista in S. Petronio" is mentioned as the composer. As Colonna was appointed to this position in 1659 and became the choirmaster on Nov. 1, 1674, the date of this scenic "problemma" is at least approximately fixed. The *imprimatur* at end is not dated.

ML 50.2.C66C6

Le **contese domestiche.** Farza per musica a tre voci da cantarsi in Asinalunga nell' autunno dell' anno 1769 in occasione, che gli Accademici Smantellati recitano nel loro teatro la tragedia intitolata Il Temistocle . . .

*Siena, Francesco Rossi, n. d. 24 p. 16½*cm*.

Two parts. Author unknown to Schatz. Dedication dated Asinalunga, October 10, 1769, cast, and name of "Baldassare **Galuppi,** Napolitano," as composer.

Schatz 3448

Le **contese per amore.** O. T. of Deller's Eigensinn und launen der liebe.

La **contessa di Amalfi.** Dramma giocoso per musica, da rappresentarsi nel Teatro Elettorale.

*Dresda, n. publ., 1794. 141 p. 15½*cm*.

La **contessa di Amalfi**—Continued.

Two acts. By Giovanni Bertati, who is not mentioned. German title-page "Die graefinn von Amalfi" and text face Italien. Joseph **Weigl** is mentioned as the composer.

First performed at Dresden, December 13, 1794; at Vienna as "La principessa di Amalfi" at the Burgtheater, January 10, 1794. Schatz 10945

— La **principessa di Amalfi**. Dramma giocoso in due atti.

Berlino, Haude e Spener, n. d. 127 p. 15^cm.

Cast and names of Giovanni Bertati as author, of Joseph **Weigl** as the composer.
First performed at Charlottenburg, Schlosstheater, June 19, 1796. Schatz 10946

La **contessa di Bimbinpoli**. Dramma giocoso per musica da rappresentarsi nel Teatro della rua dos Condes in Lisbona nell' carnevale dell' anno 1773.

[Lisbona], nella stamperia reale, n. d. 83 p. 17^cm.

Three acts. By Giovanni Bertati. Cast, scenario, and names of composer, Gennaro **Astaritta**, and librettist.
First performed at Venice, carnival 1772. Schatz 368

— Il **divertimento in campagna**. Dramma giocoso per musica da rappresentarsi nel Teatro di S. A. E. di Sassonia.

Dresda, n. publ., 1783. 109 p. 15½^cm.

Two acts. Name of **Astaritta** as composer. German t. p. "Der zeitvertreib auf dem lande, ein scherzhaffes singspiel" and text face Italian, which is that of Bertati's "La contessa di Bimbinpoli." Schatz 369

La **contessa di Novaluna**. Dramma giocoso per musica di Giovanni Bertati da rappresentarsi nel nobilissimo Teatro Giustiniani di S. Moisè per la seconda opera dell' autunno 1786.

Venezia, Gio. Battista Casali, n. d. 68 p. 17½^cm.

Two acts. Composed by Vincenzo **Fabrizj** who is not mentioned. Impresario's dedication, cast and scenario. Schatz 2975

La **contessina**.

[45]–78 p. 16½^cm. (Carlo Goldini, Opere drammatiche giocose, t. iv, Torino, 1757.)

Three acts.
It is sometimes stated that Coltellini's "La contessina" is based on Goldoni's text. True, the characters are practically the same and so is the dialogue of II, 2 "La voglio far" (at least in Schatz 3613) but otherwise most, if not all, the recitatives and arias seem to be different. ML 49.A2G6

— La **contessina**. Dramma di tre atti per musica. Rappresentato per la prima volta in Venezia nell' anno MDCCXXXVI.

Carlo Goldoni, Opere teatrali, Venezia, Zatta e figli, 1788–95, v. 38, [127]–163 p. 18½^cm.

The earliest performance I find recorded is that in 1743 with Macari's music. PQ

La **contessina**. Dramma giocoso per musica da rappresentarsi nel Teatro delle Dame il carnevale dell' anno 1773 . . .

Roma, Lorenzo Corradi, n. d. 76 p. 15½^cm.

Three acts. By Marco Coltellini, who is not mentioned. Impresario's dedication, scenario, cast and name of Marcello di Capua (**Bernardini**) as composer.
First performed as indicated, February 1773. ML 50.2.C665B3

La contessina. Dramma giocoso per musica da rappresentarsi nel magnifico Teatro della Nobile Accademia degli Erranti in Brescia per la fiera d'Agosto 1774 . . .

Brescia, Fratelli Pasini, n. d. 75 p. 15½*cm*.

Three acts. By Marco Coltellini. Impresario's dedication and remark: "La musica parte è del Sig. Floriano Gusman [**Gassmann**], parte d'altri celebri maestri." Consequently a pasticcio.

First performed with Gassmann's music at Vienna, 1771. Schatz 3613

— **La contessina.** Drama giocoso per musica da rappresentarsi nel Regio Teatro.—Den unge grevinde. Et lystigt synge-spil . . .

Kiobenhavn, H. J. Grane, 1778. 133 p. 16½*cm*.

Three acts. By Marco Coltellini, who is not mentioned. Cast and name of **Gassmann** as the composer. Danish text faces Italian.

First performed, as indicated, March 26, 1778. Schatz 3614

— **Il superbo deluso.** Dramma giocoso per musica da rappresentarsi nel Real Teatro di Salvaterra nel carnovale dell' anno 1774.

[Lisboa], Nella stamperia reale, n. d. 75 p. 14*cm*.

Three acts. A somewhat condensed and altered version of Coltellini's "La contessina." Scenario, cast, and name of Florian Leopold **Gassmann** as the composer.

First performed under this later title at Turin, Teatro Carignano, fall, 1772.

Schatz 3621

La contessina. Comedia per musica da rappresentarsi nel Teatro Grimani di S. Samuele dalla Compagnia de' Comici il carnovale dell' anno 1743.

Venezia, Modesto Fenzo, n. d. 36 p. 15½*cm*.

Three acts. Neither the author, Carlo Goldini, is mentioned nor the composer Giacomo **Macari**, to whom a contemporary hand contributes the music.

Schatz 5809

La contessina. Dramma giocoso per musica da rappresentarsi nel magnif. Teatro Filarmonico di Verona l'autunno dell' anno 1775 . . .

Verona, Dionisio Ramanzani, 1775. 64 p. 16½*cm*.

Three acts. Impresario's dedication, cast, scenario and names of Marco Coltellini as the author, of Niccolò **Piccinni** as the composer. Schatz 8149

Les contrastes. A. T. of Beffroy de Reigny's Les deux charbonniers.

Il contrasto de fiumi Serchio di Lucca; Tebro di Roma; Ronco di Ravenna. Dramma musicale decantata alle glorie dell' illustriss. e Reverendiss. Monsig. Fabio Guinigi arcivescovo di Ravenna, in occasione delle Theologiche conclusioni dedicateli dal P. lettore Lorenzo Mario Bonatti Fiorentino Carmelitano, sotto l'assistenza del Rev. P. maestro Gio. Antonio Fioriti Lucchese . . .

Bologna, Gioseffo Longhi, 1674. 12 p. 20*cm*.

Four parts. Hardly a "dramma musicale." ML 48.A5 v.5

Il contratempo. A. T. of Gnecco's Auretta e Masulto.

I contrattempi. Commedia per musica da rappresentarsi nel Teatro di Monza l'autunno dell' anno 1781 . . .

Milano, Gio. Batista Bianchi, n. d. 72 p. 15*cm*.

Three acts. By Nunziato Porta, who is not mentioned. Dedication, cast, scenario, and name of Giuseppe **Sarti** as the composer. On p. 8, the note:

I **contratempo**—Continued.

"A compimento dell' azione, e del libro si è stampato il terzo atto, benchè per brevità non si reciti."

First performed at Venice, Teatro di S. Samuele, November, 1778.   SCHATZ 9429

— I **contratempi.** Dramma giocoso per musica da rappresentarsi nel Piccolo Teatro di S. A. E. di Sassonia.

Dresda, n. publ., 1781.   131 p.   16ᶜᵐ.

Two acts, Porta's third act having been dropped.   Other differences between the Milano ed. and this are noticeable.   For instance, I, 4 opens with the aria, "Non è sempre la femmina un male," instead of, as at Dresden, with "La mia Bella m'ha detto di nò."   German title-page, "Die zwischenfaelle," and text face Italian.   **Sarti** is mentioned as the composer.

First performed, as indicated, January 10, 1782.   SCHATZ 9430

— Gli **equivoci svelati.** Dramma giocoso per musica da rappresentarsi nel Nuovo Teatro in Vicenza . . .

Padova, Gio. Antonio Conzatti, 1786.   47 p.   17ᶜᵐ.

Two acts.   This is Porta's "I contratempi" text, with the usual alterations.   For instance, Padova ed. has I, 6 "Cerco invano in questo istante"; Milano has "Tortorella abbandonata," like Dresden.   Impresario's dedication, cast, and name of Giuseppe **Sarti** as the composer.

First performed, as indicated, December 26, 1786.   SCHATZ 9431

Il **contravveleno.**   A. T. of Andreozzi's La principessa filosofa.

Il **contravveleno.**   Farsa giocosa per musica.   Poesia di Giuseppe Foppa da rappresentarsi nel nobilissimo Teatro Venier in San Benedetto l'autunno dell' anno 1799.

Venezia, Fenzo, 1799.   40 p.   18ᶜᵐ.

One act.   Cast, scenario, and name of Francesco **Gardi** as the composer.   After the farce, Giovanni Monticini's ballet, "La pescatrice in Jassa," music by Vittorio Trento, was performed.

First performed November 7, 1799, as indicated.   SCHATZ 3547

La **contribuzione sforzata,** ballet.   *See* Galuppi's Sofonisba.

The **contrivances:** a ballad opera.

[183]–212 p.   22ᶜᵐ.   (Henry Carey, Dramatick works, London, 1743.)

One act.   The words of the air "Without affectation, gay, youthful and pretty" were "by another hand."   On p. 212 the statement: "All the songs in this opera were set to music by the author."   Consequently this is not a ballad opera in the usual sense.   ML 49.A2C2

First performed at London, Drury Lane, August 9, 1715.

— The **contrivances:** a ballad opera;   full of curious songs, by the facetious and witty Harry Carey.   As it is now acting at the Theatre-Royal in Covent-Garden, and at Dublin, with great applause . . . The seventh edition.

London, T. Lownds, 1765.   35 p. (incl. front.)   16½ᶜᵐ.

One act.   According to Tufts, the play was called a farce in the 1715 ed., in that of 1731 a comifarcical opera, and in that of 1743 ballad opera.   LONGE 69

— The **contrivances.**   By Mr. Henry Carey.

[282]–300 p.   19ᶜᵐ.   (Collection of the most esteemed farces and entertainments, t. iv, Edinburgh, 1792.)

Covent-Garden cast.   SCHATZ 11753

Il **convalescente innamorato**, ballet. *See* Martin y Soler's Le burle per amore.

Il **convalescente innamorato**, ballet. *See* Pio's Medonte.

La **conversazione**. Dramma di tre atti per musica.
Carlo Goldoni, Opere teatrali, Venezia, Zatta e figli, 1788–95, v. 42, [5]–46 p. *18ᶜᵐ.*   PQ
For first performance *see* entry below under Scolari.

La **conversazione**. By Jommelli. *See* his L'accademia.

La **conversazione**. Drama giocoso per musica di Polisseno Fegejo, Pastor Arcade. Da rappresentarsi nel Teatro Grimani di S. Samuele il carnovale dell' anno 1758.
Venezia, Modesto Fenzo, 1758. 46 p. 15ᶜᵐ.
Three acts. By Goldoni. Cast, scenario, and name of Giuseppe **Scolari** as the composer.   SCHATZ 9794

O **convidado de pedra**. A. T. of Gazzaniga's Dom João.

Il **convitato**, ballet: Gluck. *See* Calvi's Ezio.

Il **convitato di pietra**. *See also* Bernardini's L'ultima che si perde è la speranza.

Il **convitato di pietra**, ballet. *See* Bertoni's Tancredi.

Il **convitato di pietra**. Dramma giocoso per musica da rappresentarsi nel nobile Teatro Tron di San Cassiano nel carnovale dell' anno 1777.
Venezia, Gio. Battista Casali, 1777. 62 p. 18½ᶜᵐ.
Two acts. Author unknown to Schatz. Cast, scenario, and name of Giuseppe **Callegari** as composer.   SCHATZ 1511

Il **convitato di pietra**. A. T. of Fabrizj's opera "Don Giovanni Tenorio."

Il **convitato di pietra**. A. T. of Gazzaniga's Il Don Giovanni.

Il **convitato di pietra**, ballet. *See* Gazzaniga's Tullo Ostilio.

Il **convitato di pietra**, o sia Il dissoluto. Dramma tragicomico. Da rappresentarsi ne' Teatri privilegiati di Vienna l'anno 1777.
Vienna, Giuseppe nobile de Kurzbeck, n. d. 52 p. 17ᶜᵐ.
Three acts. Author not mentioned and unknown to Schatz. Scenario and name of Vincenzo **Righini** as the composer.
First performed at the Kaernthnerthor Theatre, as indicated, August 21, 1777.
    SCHATZ 8789

— Il **convitato di pietra**, o sia Il dissoluto. Dramma tragicomico.
Praga, n. publ, 1777. 111 p. 15½ᶜᵐ.
Three acts. Without names of the author and the composer, Vincenzo **Righini**. German t.-p. "Das steinerne gastmahl, oder Der ruchlose" and text face Italian, which is not exactly the same as in the Vienna, 1777, version. For instance, the latter does not have before the final scene with the "coro di furie" the farcical scene between "Corallino ed Arlechino." The text is, of course, neither that by Da Ponte nor that by Bertati.   SCHATZ 8781
First performed at Prague, Kgl. Theater i. d. Kotzen, 1777.

Il **convitato di pietra,** ballet. *See* Ferd. Rutini's Il matrimonio per industria.

Il **convito**; or, The banquet: a new comic opera. As performed at the King's Theatre in the Hay Market with alterations and additions, by Signor A. Andrei, the music entirely new, by Signor Bertoni.

London, H. Reynell, 1782. 77 p. 20^{cm}.

Two acts. Cast. English translation faces Italian text, which is an altered version of Filippo Livigni's libretto. Schatz 910

Il **convito.** Dramma giocoso per musica da rapprespentarsi nel Piccolo Teatro di S. A. E. di Sassonia.

Dresda, n. publ., 1783. 131 p. 15½^{cm}.

Two acts. By Filippo Livigne (not mentioned). **Cimarosa** is mentioned as the composer. German title-page "Das gastmahl" and text face Italian.
First performed at Dresden, as indicated, in 1783; at Venice, Teatro di S. Samuele, carnival, 1782. Schatz 1915

— Il **convito.** Dramma giocoso per musica da rappresentarsi nel Regio Teatro di S. Carlo della Principessa l'autunno dell' anno 1796.

Lisbona, Sim. Taddeo Ferreira, 1796. 151 p. 15^{cm}.

Two acts. By Filippo Livigni (not mentioned). Cast and name of the composer, **Cimarosa.** T.-p. and p. 149–151 supplied in ms. Portuguese text faces Italian. With the opera was performed Pietro Angiolini's "Il solitario reso sociabile per amore, ballo d'invenzione." The composer of the music is not mentioned.
Schatz 1914

Il **convito di Cesare,** ballet. *See* Bianchi's Morte di Cesare.

Le **convulsioni.** Seconda farsa.

26–48 p. 15^{cm}.

See "Amor non ha riguardi e Le convulsioni Farse in musica di Giuseppe Palomba da rappresentarsi nel Teatro de' Fiorentini per quart' opera dell' anno 1787," Napoli, n. publ., 1787. One act. Cast and name of Giuseppe **Curcio** as composer.
Schatz 2299

Cook, ossia Gl' Inglesi in Othaiti, ballet. *See* Mayr's Lodoiska.

The **cooper.** A musical entertainment. In two acts. By Dr. Arne.

[217]–237 p. 19^{cm}. *(Collection of the most esteemed farces and entertainments, t. vi, Edinburgh, 1792.)*

Hay-market cast, where the opera was first performed, June 12, 1772. Arne is also the reputed author of the text. Schatz 11753F

La **coquette de village,** ballet. *See* Bernasconi's Didone abbandonata.

La **coquette sans le sçavoir,** opera comique en un acte.

Paris, Prault fils, 1750. 44 p. 19^{cm}. *(Theatre de M. Favart, Paris, Duchesne, 1763–77, t. vii.)*

Cast. "M. Rousseau de Toulouse" is mentioned in the pref. of the first volume as Favart's collaborator. The piece is en vaudevilles.
First performed at Paris, Foire St. Germain, February 23, 1744. ML 49.A2F1

— La **coquette sans le savoir,** opera-comique, en un acte, de MM. Favart & Rousseau. Nouvelle édition.

Paris et se vend à Toulon, chez J. L. R. Mallard, 1772. 40 p. 19½^{cm}.

One act. En vaudevilles. ML 48.M2M

La coquette trompée, comédie lyrique; par M. Favart; représentée pour la premiere fois à Fontainebleau, sur le Théâtre de la cour, par ordre de Sa Majesté, le 13 nov. 1753.   Et à Paris, par l'Académie royale de musique, le mardi 8 août 1758.

n. i., n. d.   40 p.   19^{cm}.   (Theatre de M. Favart, Paris, Duchesne, 1763–77, t. i.)

Cast.   The composer, **Dauvergne,** is not mentioned.   Many of his airs are printed in the text.   "La coquette trompée" was the third act in a ballet called "Les fêtes d'Euterpe," the first of which, "La sibylle" (*see* "La sibille"), was written by Moncrif, the second, "Alphée et Aréthuse," by Danchet, music of both by Dauvergne.

ML 49.A2F1

Cora.   Ein singspiel [vignette].

Leipzig, Dykische buchhandlung, 1781.   5 p. l., 75 p. [1] p. errata. 19^{cm}.

On last p. l.:
"Nach schwedischem text: Der musik, welche herr **Naumann,** churfürstl. sächsischer wirklischer kapellmeister zu Dresden, in Schweden für das königliche Theater komponirt hat, untergelegt."
This note refers to Gudmund Göran Adlerbeth's text, "Cora och Alonzo" (based on Marmontel's "Les Incas ou La déstruction de l'empire du Pérou"), and its setting by Naumann for the inauguration of the Royal Operahouse, Stockholm, September 30, 1782.
The p. l. contain a preface signed by the author of the German text [Johann Leopold] N[eu]m[an]n and dated "Bl——[ase]witz, den 26 sten august 1780."   It is addressed to the composer, and is about as adulatory as possible.   Neumann says, for instance:
"Ueberall, wo sanfte herzen schlagen, segne man Ihren namen: wo die tonkunst tempel hat, stehe Ihr denkmal bey Händel und Marcello!"
The only remark historically important is this:
"Sie wissen, mein theurester freund, wie fest ich's beschlossen hatte, meinen deutschen text su Ihrer Cora schlechterdings nie von Ihren noten su trennen, und öffenlich einzeln abdrucken zu lassen, weil ich vollkommen überzuegt bin, dass dieser text alles, was er seyn kann, lediglich durch Ihre komposition, ohne Ihre musik aber, als ein auch zum lesen bestimmtes poetisches produkt, dem publikum nie interessant seyn könnte.   Die vorstellungen einiger freunde Ihrer Cora, dass der einzeln gedruckte text das singen aus dem klavierausuge, wenn zumal bey den chören mehrere personen aus einem exemplare singen sollten, nicht nur erleichtem, sondern auch sogar dabey unentbehrlich seyn würde, haben mich endlich überredet, meinen vorsatz su ändern . . ."
The German version was first performed at Schwedt (Brunswick), Hoftheater, Sept. 20, 1786; previously at a concert, Dresden, Hotel de Pologne, March 15, 1780.

SCHATZ 7042

— Cora.   Ein singspiel in drey akten.   Abdruck für die subscribenten zur aufführung dieser oper, im jahr 1781 zu Dresden, im Hessischen saal.

n. i., n. d.   6 p. l., 72 p.   16^{cm}.

The preface is identical with that in Schatz 7042, except that it is now signed "Neumann."   On the last p. l. an "Anmerkung:"
"Das im dritten akt auf der 65 seite befindliche Chor der priester und des volks ["Wie? heilig graues recht"], und die letzte arie der Cora, in eben diesem akte, ["Trübe tage stiller klage,"] stehen im schwedischen originale nicht.   Beyde stücke hat der verfasser des deutschen textes neu geschrieben, und herr Naumann componirt."

SCHATZ 7042a

— Cora.   Eine grosse heroische oper von Naumann.

Danzig, gedruckt in der Muellerschen officin, n. d.   32 p.   15^{cm}.

SCHATZ 7042b

Cora o La vergine del sole, ballet.   *See* Tarchi's Le Danaidi.

La **cordonnière allemande.** A. T. of Fridzeri's Les souliers morsdorés.

La **Corilda** overo L'amore trionfante della vendetta. Drama per musica da rappresentarsi nel Teatro Zane di S. Moisè l'anno MDCLXXXVIII . . .

Venetia, Francesco Nicolini, 1688. 52 p. 14½^{cm}.

Three acts. Dedication, argument, scenario, and printer's notice to the reader, referring to the unknown author as follows:

"Questo drama è parto d'un ingegno peregrino, che gode di essere conosciuto più dai versi, che dal nome."

For this reason alone Alacci's "Poesia di diversi" is incorrect, apart from the fact pointed out by Wotquenne that the anonymous dedication is signed "Humiliss^{mo} . . . servo." Wotquenne remarks that in the Brussels copy a contemporary hand has added, as author's name, that of Paolo Emilio Badi. Schatz 8887

Il **Corindo.** Favola boschereccia rappresentata in musica, nella villa di Pratolino.

Frenze, Vincenzio Vangelisti, 1680. 48 [1] p. 15^{cm}.

Three acts. Neither the author, Giuseppe Giacomini, is mentioned, nor the composer, who is unknown to Schatz.

First performed, as indicated, September, 1680. Schatz 11316

Il **Coriolano.** Dramma musicale fatto cantare da' signori convittori delle camere maggiori del nobil collegio Tolomei di Siena nel carnevale dell' anno MDCCVI.

Siena, Bonetti, 1706. 40 p. 14^{cm}.

Three acts. Argument. Not recorded by Allacci or Schatz. Perhaps composed by Giuseppe **Fabbrini,** if still music-master at the college in 1706.

ML 48.A5 v. 46

Coriolano. Tragedia per musica da rappresentarsi nel Regio Teatro di Berlino . . .

Berlino, Haude e Spener, 1782. 75, [3] p. 17^{cm}.

Three acts. Based on a prose sketch of Frederick the Great, by Leopoldo de Villati. He is mentioned as the author, and Carl Heinrich **Graun** as the composer. Cast, argument, and scenario. German title-page, "Coriolanus," and text face Italian.

Performed, as indicated, in January, 1782; first performed there December 3, 1749 (Schatz), December 19, 1749 (Mennicke). Schatz 4093

Coriolanus. Tr. of Graun's Coriolano.

Corisca e Satiro, intermezzi. *See* Spanò's Elisa.

La **corona.** Azione teatrale, scritta dall' autore in Vienna l'anno 1765 . . . e posta in musica dal Gluck; da rappresentarsi nell' interno dell' Imperial corte dalle Altezze Reali di quattro arciduchesse d'Austria . . . per festeggiare il giorno di nome dell' augustissimo loro genitore, del quale l'improvvisa perdita non permise la rappresentazione.

[119]–148 p. 26^{cm}. (Metastasio, Opere, t. xi, Parigi, vedova Herissant, 1782.)

One act. ML 49.A2M44

La corona d'Imeneo. Serenada cantata per le felicissime nozze di Sua Eccellenza Maxim. Clemente Giuseppe Maria Francesco de' conti del S. R. I. de Seinsheim . . . coll' illustrissima Signora Maria Anna, baronessa di Franckenstein etc. La musica è del Signor Guglielmo Küffner . . .

Wirzburgo, vedova di Gioseppo Antonio Nitribitt, 1772. 21 p. 16½cm.

The author is not mentioned, and is unknown to Schatz.   SCHATZ 5283

La coronatione d'Apollo per Dafne conversa in Lauro, intermezzi in musica del Sig. Silvestro Branchi, Academico Ravvivato, detto il Costante, per la sua opera intitolata, l'Amorosa innocenza, recitata nel Salone. A' gl'illustriss. Signori li Signori Fabio Gozadini confaloniero [etc, etc] dignissimi Antiani per il primo bimestre dell' anno 1623. Il compositore della musica è il Signor Ottavio Vernizzi.

Bologna, per gli eredi di Gio. Paolo Moscatelli, 1623. Unpaged. 14½cm.

Four intermezzi, preceded by the author's dedication to the gentlemen mentioned in the title, evidently his patrons. It is dated February 1, 1623.

In it Branchi calls his pastoral comedy "L'amorosa innocenza" and the present intermezzi:
"opere d'un vostro suddito, e divoto servidore, le quali per la stanchezza de' miei pensieri sepolte nell' oblio, non potevano più risorgere, se non col vostro benigno e potète favore, comparendo, come fanno, con tanta splendidezza sopra il Teatro solito del Salone . . ."
This somewhat mysterious statement is easily explained, since comparison proved the present text to be practically identical with that of his "*Coronatione d'Apollo. Per Dafne convertita in Lauro.* Balletto in musica," which formed part of his "*Trattenimento musicale d'Apollo con il Reno,*" Bologna. Moscatelli, 1621 (ML 52.2.T7), performed "nelle nozze sonttuose" of count Federico Rossi di S. Secondo and Donna Orsina Pepoli. The text was then simply in six scenes ("Uscita" 1–6) and in the sixth Apollo addressed about two pages to the bride and groom beginning with the line "Da te mi parto, o generoso heroe." In the 1623 edition the text is divided into four "intermizzi" with nine scenes, the first "uscita" of each intermezzo being preceded by a "sinfonia" as also the second "uscita" of the third and the third "uscita" of the fourth intermezzo. The text calls this last "Settima sinfonia. In cielo," but actually allusion is made only to six sinfonies. Apollo's compliments to the count and countess Rossi have been dropped (the line "Ogni parte miglior de la mia vita" being followed immediately by "Belle Naiadivezzose") but the 1623 version did not end with the line "E del bel lauro il pregio ogn'hor s'avviva." Instead, "La fama. Volando per aria in diversa maniera" sings after that "Felsina, tù vedesti," etc.   SCHATZ 10715

Coronazione d'Apollo e Dafne, ballet. *See* Bertoni's Sesostri.

Coronis, pastorale heroïque. Representée par l'Academie royale de musique. Suivant la copie imprimée à Paris.

[Amsterdam, Antoine Schelte], 1692. 36 p. (incl. front.) 13½cm.

Prologue and three acts. Neither the author, Chappuzeau de Beaugé, nor the composer, Teobaldo di **Gatti** (called Théobald) is mentioned.
First performed, as indicated, March 23, 1691.   ML 50.2.C 67 G2

— **Coronis,** pastorale heroique representée par l'Academie royale de musique l'an 1691. Les paroles sont de M. Baugé & la musique de M. Theobal. XXVII. opera.

n. i., n. d. front., p. 113–154. (Recueil général des opéra, v. iv, Paris, 1703.) 14½cm.

Detached copy. Three acts with prologue.
                                                        SCHATZ 3632.
                                             Second copy. ML 48.R4

Il **Corrivo.** Commedia per musica di G. M. D.[iodati] da rappresentarsi nel Teatro Nuovo sopra Toledo per prim' opera nella primavera di quest' anno 1787.

Napoli, n. publ., 1787. 52 p. 15ᶜᵐ.

Two acts. Cast and name of Giuseppe **Giordani** as the composer. Schatz 3839

Le **corsaire de Salé.** Piece d'un acte. Par Mʳˢ. le S * * & d'Or * *. Representé à la Foire Saint Laurent 1729.

Le Théâtre de la foire, Paris, 1731, t. vii, pl., [241]–294 p. 17ᶜᵐ.

By Le Sage and d'Orneval. *Largely en vaudevilles.* The airs, selected or composed and arranged by Jean Claude **Gillier,** the "compositeur" of the company, are printed at the end of the volume in the "Table des airs."
First performed August 20, 1729, as indicated. ML 48.L2VII

La **Corsala.** Commedia per musica di Giambatista Lorenzi, P. A. da rappresentarsi nel Teatro de' Fiorentini nell' autunno del corrente anno 1771.

Napoli, Vincenzo Flauto, 1771. 84 p. 15ᶜᵐ.

Three acts. Argument, scenario, cast and name of Niccolò **Piccinni** as composer. Schatz 8121

Il **corsaro algerino.** Comedia per musica da rappresentarsi nel Teatro de' Fiorentini nell' autunno di quest' anno 1765.

Napoli, Bernardo Lanciano, 1765. 4 p. l., 60 p. 14½ᶜᵐ.

Three acts. Argument, cast, name of Gennaro **Astaritta** as composer, and notice by the printer:
'La presente comedia, si rappresentò nel Teatro Nuovo nell' anno 1726, ora comparisce per seconda volta sù questo de' Fiorentini. . . . La troverai per altro vario dalla prima edizione ma ciò è addivenuto per moderarlo al buon gusto moderno; che per ciò si è dovuto cambiare l'idioma napoletano in toscano . . . Il tutto si è fatto accomodare dal Signor D. Giuseppe Palomba . . .
Florimo does not mention the 1726 performance, nor the original author, who is also unknown to Schatz. Schatz 377

La **corte.** Dramma morale di Francesco Sbarra, rappresentato in musica per intermezzi in Lucca nel Teatro de Borghi l'anno 1657.

n. i., n. d. [162]–192 p. 13½ᶜᵐ.

Detached copy. Four intermezzi, with argument, but without name of the composer, Marco **Bigongiari.** Schatz 1036

Una **cosa rara.** A. T. of the ballet Lilla e Lubino.

Una **cosa rara** o sia: Bellezza ed onestà. Dramma giocoso in due atti. Da rappresentarsi nei Teatri di Praga l'autunno dell' anno 1787.

Vienna, n. publ., n. d. 86 p. 15½ᶜᵐ.

Two acts. Lorenzo da Ponte is mentioned as the author, Vincenzio Martin (**Martin y Soler**) as the composer.
First performed at Vienna, November 17, 1786. Schatz 6015

— Una **cosa rara** o sia Bellezza ed onestà. Dramma giocoso per musica da rappresentarsi nel Teatro di S. A. E. di Sassonia.

Dresda, n. publ., 1787. 163 p. 16ᶜᵐ.

Two acts. **Martin y Soler** is mentioned, Da Ponte not. German title page "Die seltenheit, oder Schoenheit und tugend" and text face Italian.
First performed at Dresden, Churf. theater, April 12, 1788. Schatz 6017

Una **cosa rara**—Continued.

— **Bellezza ed onestà.** Dramma giocoso per musica da rappresentarsi nel nobilissimo Teatro Giustiniani in S. Moisè per la prima opera
del carnovale dell' anno 1788.

    Venezia, Gio. Battista Casali, n. d.   64 p.   18^{cm}.

Two acts. **Martin y Soler** is mentioned, but Da Ponte not. Cast added in
pencil.   SCHATZ 6030

— La **cosa rara**; a new comic opera, in two acts, as performed at the
King's Theatre, in the Hay-Market, the music entirely new by Signor
Martini; under the direction of Mr. Mazzinghi.

    London, C. Etherington, 1789.   2 p. l., 106 p.   19½^{cm}.

Cast.   English translation faces Italian text.   Added to the libretto, a [4] p. "List
of the subscribers to the boxes at the King's Theatre, 1789."   ML 48.M2M

— Una **cosa rara** o sia Bellezza ed onestà. Dramma giocoso per
musica da rappresentarsi nel Regio Teatro di via della Pergola la
primavera del MDCCXCI . . .

    Firenze, Stamperia Albizzinina, 1791.   67 p.   16½^{cm}.

Two acts.   Cast and names of "Vincenzo Martin" (**Martin y Soler**) and Da Ponte.
With the opera was performed (composer of the music not mentioned) the ballet, "Il
trionfo d'Ercole in Troia o sia Esione liberata."   ML 48.A5   v. 16

— Gesaenge aus dem singspiele: **Cosa rara,** oder Der seltne fall, in
zwey aufzuegen. Aus dem italienischen. In musik getzt von herrn
Martini.

    n i., 1797.   40 p.   15½^{cm}.

German version by Ferdinand Eberl, who is not mentioned.   SCHATZ 6019

— **Etwas seltsames** oder Schoenheit und ehrbarkeit. Ein lustiges
singspiel in zwey aufzuegen fuer das Kais. Koen. Hoftheater.

    Wien, Joseph Edler von Kurzek, 1787.   86 p.   16^{cm}.

Translator not mentioned, and unknown to Schatz.   Da Ponte and **Martin y Soler**
are mentioned.   SCHATZ 6016

— Arien aus der so grossen und beruehmten opera Una cosa rara osia
Bellezza ed onestà.   Die **seltne sache** oder Schoenheit und tugend
aus dem italiaenischen in zwey aufzuegen von abbate da Ponte.   Die
musik ist von hr. Vinzenz Martini . . .   Zum erstenmale in deutscher
sprache von der Wilhelmischen gesellschaft in Baaden aufgefuehret.

    Wien, mit Hraschanzkyschen schriften, 1787.   35 p.   15^{cm}.

Cast.   (Bound with Dittersdorf's "Betrug durch aberglauben," Schatz 2587.)

— The **siege of Belgrade.**   *See* Title.

La **cosa rara,** ballet.   *See* Tarchi's Lo spazzacamino principe.

Così fan tutte o sia La scuola degli amanti. Dramma giocoso in
due atti da rappresentarsi nel Teatro di corte l'anno 1790.

    Vienna, La società tipografica, n. d.   84 p.   16^{cm}.

Two acts.   Lorenzo da Ponte is mentioned as the author, "Wolfgango Mozart"
(**Mozart**) as the composer.

    First performed, as indicated, January 26, 1790.   SCHATZ 6762

Cosi fan tutte o—Continued.

— **Cosi fan tutte** o sia La scuola degli amanti. Dramma giocoso per musica, da rappresentarsi nel Teatro di S. A. E. di Sassonia.

Dresda, n. publ., 1791. 147 p. 15½ cm.

Two acts. Da Ponte is not mentioned; **Mozart** is. German title page, "Eine wie die andere oder Die schule der liebhaber," and text face Italian.
First performed, as indicated, October 5, 1791. Schatz 6763

— Cosi fan tutte.—**Eine machts wie die andere** oder Die schule der liebhaber. Ein komisches singspiel in zwey aufzuegen. Aus dem italienischen des abbate de la Ponte. Die music ist von Mozart.

Breslau, Grassische stadt-buchdruckerey, n. d. 47 p. 14½ cm.

Two acts. German text only.
First performed at Breslau, Wäser'sches Theater, January 16, 1795; at Berlin, National-theater, August 3, 1792. Schatz 6764

— Gesaenge aus der **Schule der liebhaber** oder Eine ist wie die andere. Eine komische oper aus dem italienischen von abate da Ponte, ins deutsche frei uebersetzt. Die musik dazu ist von Mozart. Aufgefuehrt von der Mihuleschen Gesellschaft.

Augsburg, n. publ., 1794. Unpaged. 15½ cm. Schatz 6765

— **Weibertreue,** oder Die maedchen sind von Flandern. Ein komisches singspiel in zwey akten, mit musik von Mozart. Nach Cosi fan tutte frey bearbeitet, von C. F. Bretzner.

Leipsig, Friedrich Gotthold Jacobaer, 1794. 4 p. l., 88 p. 15 cm.

In his "Vorbericht," Bretzner says:
"Bey der bearbeitung habe ich mir einige abweichungen und abkuerzungen erlaubt, die ich im deutschen gewande für nothwendig hielt"
and,
"Zwar erinnre ich mich gelesen su haben, dass sie [die oper] bereits an einigen orten deutsch, ohne grossen effekt gegeben worden: allein entweder war die uebersetzung gar zu elend, oder es lag die schuld an der ausfuehrung. Man lasse sich nicht abschrecken, wenn der effekt bey der ersten auffuehrung nicht ganz der erwartung entspraeche, die man sich davon gemacht hatte; man hoere sie nur mehreremal, und ich bin gewiss, man wird . . . sich nicht satt daran hoeren koennen."
First performed at Leipzig, Theater am Rannstädter Thore, 1794. Schatz 6766

— Gesaenge aus der oper: Die **wette,** oder Maedchenlist und liebe, in vier acten. Nach *Cosi fan tutte,* von C. F. Brezner. Die musik ist von Mozart.

Hamburg, Friedrich Hermann Nestler, n. d. 55 p. 16 cm.

First performed at Hamburg, Theater beim Gänsemarkt, July 6, 1796.
Schatz 6767

— **Veddemaalet** eller Elskernes skole. Et syngestykke af abbé da Ponte. Efter befaling forandret og oversat til Wolfgang Mozarts musik af Adam Gottlob Thoroup.

Kiøbenhavn, J. F. Morthorstes Enke, 1798. 96 p. 15 cm.

First performed at Copenhagen, October 19, 1798. Schatz 6768

Cosroe. Drama per musica da recitarsi nel Teatro Alibert pe'l carnevale dell' anno 1723. Presentato alla Maestà di Giacomo III. Rè della Gran Brettagna. [!!]

Roma, Bernabò, 1723. 72 p. 16 cm.

Three acts. Dedication, argument, scenario, cast, name of Antonio **Pollaroli** as the composer, and notice to the reader, which reads, in part:

Cosroe—Continued.

"Codesto componimento drammatico; uscito dalla famosa penna d'uno de' più eruditi poeti de nostri tempi. E ben però giusto, che a tua cognizione pervenga non essersi in conto a*l*cuno mutato il presente libro, ma essere tale, quale è stato recitato altre voltre, a riserva di pochi versi, e di alcune ariette, essendo convenuto il farlo per accomodarsi alla presente occasione."

This notice refers to Apostolo Zeno's "Ormisda."

"Cosroe" was first performed at Rome, as indicated, December 28, 1722.

SCHATZ 8267

Costantino.

Apostolo Zeno, Poesie drammatiche, Venezia, 1744, t. ix, p. [101]–199. 19^{cm}.

Five acts. Argument. Written in collaboration with Pietro Pariati. No composer is mentioned. In the "Catalogo" at end of t. x, date and place of first ed. are given as Venice, 1711.   ML 49.A2Z3

— Costantino. Pubblicato per la prima volta in Venezia 1711.

Apostolo Zeno, Poesie drammatiche, Orleans, 1785–86, t. xi, p. 100. 21^{cm}.

Five acts. Argument. No composer is mentioned. Written in collaboration with Pietro Pariati.   ML 49.A2Z4

Costantino. Drama da rappresentarsi per musica nel Teatro Tron di S. Cassano l'autunno dell' anno 1711 . . .

Venezia, Marino Rossetti, 1711. 72 p. 15^{cm}.

Five acts. By Apostolo Zeno and Pietro Pariati, who are not mentioned as authors, but Pariati signed the dedication. Argument, cast, scenario, and name of Carlo Francesco **Gasparini** as the composer.   SCHATZ 3589

Il Costantino Pio. Dramma posto in musica dal Signor Carlo Francesco Pollaroli, e rappresentato in Roma l'anno MDCCX.

Roma, Antonio de' Rossi, 1710. 90 p. 14^{cm}.

Three acts. Argument and scenario. The author not men*t*ioned, and unknown to Schatz.

First performed, as indicated, at the Sala de' Signori Capranica.   SCHATZ 8278

La costanza affricana soccorsa dall' arte magica, ballet. *See* Galuppi's Sofonisba.

La costanza combattuta in amore. Drama per musica da rappresentarsi nel Teatro Giustiniano à S. Moisè l'autunno dell' anno 1716 . . .

Venezia, Giacomo Valvasense, 1716. 60 p. 15½^{cm}.

Three acts. By Francesco Silvani, who is not mentioned. Dedication dated Venice, October 17, 1716, notice to the reader, with the name of Giovanni **Porta** as the composer, argument, scenario, and cast.   SCHATZ 8390

La costanza coniugale, ballet. *See* Andreozzi's Teodelinda.

La costanza d'Ulisse. Drama per musica nel felicissimo dì natalizio della S. C. R. M^{tà} dell' imperatore Leopoldo I . . . l'anno MDCC. posto in musica dal Sig^r Carlo Agostino Badia . . . con l'arie per li balletti del Sig^r Gio. Gioseffo Hoffer, violinista di S. M. C.

Vienna d'Austria, appresso Susanna Christina, vedova di Matteo Cosmerovio, n. d. [64] p. 17½^{cm}.

One act. The author, Giovanni Battista Ancioni, is not mentioned. Argument and description of Lodovico Burnacini's "Apparato nella peschiera del Cesareo giardino della Favorita" at Laxemburg, where the opera was first performed on June 9, 1700. Entirely different from "Gli amori di Circe."   SCHATZ 5442

Second copy, with two folded plates, lacking in the first copy.   ML 50.2.C69B2

La costanza di Rosmonda. Drama per musica di Aurelio Aureli, favola quinta. Rappresentata in Venetia nel Teatro Grimano l'anno 1659 . . .

> *Venetia, Valvasense, 1659. 92 p. 14^{cm}.*

Prologue and three acts. Author's dedication dated Venice, January 15, 1659, arguments, and scenario. The composer, **Rovettino,** is not mentioned. On p. 91–92, indication of the cuts, etc. SCHATZ 9108

— **La costanza di Rosmonda.** Drama in musica di Aurelio Aureli. Rappresentata nel Regio Teatro di Milano l'anno 1675 . . .

> *Milano, Marc' Antonio Pandolfo Malatesta, n. d. 7 p. l., 93 p. 14^{cm}.*

Prologue and three acts. Dedication by Antonio Lonati, argument, scenario. The composer, **Rovettino,** is not mentioned. SCHATZ 11744

Costanza e fortezza. Festa teatrale per musica, da rappresentarsi nel Reale castello di Praga per il felicissimo giorno natalizio della Sac.-Ces. e Catt. Reale Maestà di Elisabetta Cristina . . . l'anno MDCCXXIII. La poesia è del Sig. Pietro Pariati . . . La musica è del Sig. Gio. Gioseffo Fux . . . con le arie per li balli del Sig. Nicola Matheis . . .

> *Vienna d'Austria, Gio. Pietro Van Ghelen, n. d. 7 fold. pl., 4 p. l., 52 p. 23½^{cm}.*

The gorgeous plates, all designed by the court architect, Giuseppe Galli Bibiena, and engraved by different engravers, represent scenes from the opera, with exception of the second and last of the seven, which give an idea of the theatre erected for the occasion. The plates vary somewhat in size, pl. 2–6 being 63 x 48½^{cm}, pl. 1 being somewhat larger, pl. 7 somewhat smaller.

Three acts. Argument, and mutazioni.

First performed, as indicated, August 28, 1723. SCHATZ 3391

La costanza fortunata in amore. Drama per musica da rappresentarsi nel Teatro di San Fantino l'anno 1710. M. V. . . .

> *Venezia, Antonio Bortoli, 1710. 47 p. 15^{cm}.*

Three acts. By Francesco Maria Piccioli, who is not mentioned. Impresario's dedication, argument, scenario. Composer not mentioned and unknown to Schatz. SCHATZ 11317

La costanza guerriera, ballet. *See* Ottani's Fatima.

La costanza in amor rende felice. L. T. of Gazzaniga's L'amore costante.

La costanza in amore. A. T. of Anfossi's Isabella e Rodrigo.

La costanza in cimento con la crudelta. Dramma per musica da rappresentarsi nel Teatro di Sant' Angelo il carnevale del 1712 . . .

> *Venetia, Marino Rosetti, 1712. 60 p. 15^{cm}.*

Three acts. By Grazio Braccioli, cast, scenario, argument, and name of Floriano **Aresti** as composer. The dedication dated by the author December 26, 1711. SCHATZ 313

La costanza in trionfo. Drama per musica di Francesco Silvani. Da rappresentarsi nel Teatro di S. Angelo. Ristampato con nuove aggiunta . . .

> *Venezia, Nicolini, 1697. 63 p. 15^{cm}.*

La **costanza in trionfo**—Continued.

Three acts. Author's dedication, dated Venice, November 3, 16 6, argument, scenario, and notice to the reader with Marc' Antonio **Ziani's** name as composer, and statement:

"Eccomi ancor quest' anno in iscena con la quinta delle mie fatiche."

SCHATZ 11180

La **costanza negl' amori fra' pastori.** A. T. of Della Porta's L'Eurillo.

La **costanza nell' honore.** O. T. of Girolamo Polani's La vendetta disarmata dall' amore.

La **costanza premiata** o sia Il genio tutelare, ballet. *See* Andreozzi's Arsinoe.

La **costanza sforzata.** Die gezwungene bestaendigkeit oder Die listige rache des Sueno. An dem frohen geburths-tage des . . . Friderici IV. koenigs zu Dennemarck und Norwegen . . . auf dem Hamburgischen Schau-platz in einem sing-spiel aufgefuehret den 11. octobr. 1706.

n. d., n. i. Unpaged. 19^{cm}.

Three acts. The "Vorbericht" contains the argument and some curious remarks on the use of German in operas, including this: ". . . habe gemerckt, dass das dactylische und anacreontische metrum zu den musicalischen rejouissancen am geschicktesten und weil der musicus Reinhard Kaeyser [**Keiser**] sie zu recommandiren pfleget, so habe einige hineingeruecket, ob man sie wol bey den Italiaenern sehr sparsam antrifft." The author, resp. translator, Barthold Feind, is not mentioned. Some arias have Italian text added to the German. SCHATZ 5084

— La **costanza sforzata.** Die bezwungene bestaendigkeit. Oder: Die listige rache des Sueno. An dem frohen gebuhrts-tage des . . . Friderici IV. koenigs zu Dennemarck und Norwegen . . . auf dem Hamburgischen Schau-platz in einem sing-spiel aufgefuehret den 11 octobr. 1706.

Barth. Feind's Deutsche gedichte, Stade, 1708, pl., [321]–392 p. 17^{cm}.

Three acts. Contents as above.   ML 49.A2F2

La **costanza trionfante.** Drama per musica . . .

Venetia, li Bertani, 1673. 6 p. l., 59, [1] p. 14^{cm}.

Three acts. By Cristoforo Iwanovich, who is not mentioned. Dedication, argument "aggiustato alla presente riforma," cast name of Giovanni Domenico **Partenio** as the composer, scenario, and "avviso," which reads in part:

"Questo drammatico componimento fece la sua prima comparsa; ma con altra divisa in corte de' gran prencipi; hòra ch'è scelto per delicioso trattenimento de' geni virtuosi, che lo fanuo rappresentare generosamente nel Teatro Zane, è stato ritocato a momenti à compiacimēto de cavalieri protettori da una penna egualmente discreta, ed erudita, che ha saputo portare i suoi voli a teatri più famosi dell' Europa . . .

"Ritiene l'intreccio puro, è naturale; ma però con la riforma del titolo, dello scenegiare, e di più breve recitativo; viene, adorno di frequenti ariette, à farsi, vedere con qualche diferenza in ordine, all' uso corrente di Venetia, avvezza alla brevità & al diletto. Dagl' episodii si è cavata la sola inventione, d'salvar Hipermestra dal precipitio della torre sul volo d'un aquila, in che si scusi la necessità, che introduce il prodigio."   SCHATZ 7777

La **costanza trionfante degl' amori, e degl' odii.** Drama per musica da rappresentarsi nel Teatro Giustiniano di S. Moisè. Il carnoval dell' anno 1716 . . . Di Antonio Marchi.

Venezia, Carlo Bonarigo, 1716. 60 p. 14½^{cm}.

La costanza trionfante degl'amori, e degl'odii—Continued.

Three acts. Author's dedication dated January 18, 1715, M. V., notice to the reader with Antonio **Vivaldi**'s name as composer, argument, cast, scenario.

SCHATZ 10761

— **Artabano rè de Parti.** Drama per musica da rappresentarsi nel Teatro Giustiniano di San Moisè il carnovale dell' anno MDCCXVIII. Di Antonio Marchi . . .

Venezia, Marino Rossetti, 1718. 60 p. 15ᶜᵐ.

Three acts. Argument, cast, scenario, author's dedication, and notice to the reader, with name of Antonio **Vivaldi** as the composer, in both of which this is called the second appearance of the opera at S. Moisè. Comparison proves that this is the same as "La Costanza trionfante degl' amori e degl' odii," but with some alterations. For instance, the 1716 version has "Qual Pino errante" in I, 8, and "Tall' or il cacciator" in I, 10, whereas the 1718 ed. has "Tall' or il cacciator" in I, 8, and "Deh lasciami in pace" in I, 10.

SCHATZ 10762

— **L'odio vinto dalla costanza.** Dramma per musica da rappresentarsi nel Teatro di Sant' Angelo il carnovale dell' anno MDCCXXXI. Di Antonio Marchi.

Venezia, Carlo Buonarrigo, 1731. 48 p. 14½ᶜᵐ.

Three acts. Argument, cast, scenario. The same as the above, but partly rewritten by Bartolomeo Vitturi, with new music by Antonio **Galeazzi**, neither of whom is mentioned. In this version "Chi t'ama comprendi" is the aria in I, 8, and "Fremi, e pensa, o rio tiranno" in I, 10.

SCHATZ 10763

La costanza vince il destino. Dramma musicale da rappresentarsi nel famosissimo Teatro di SS. Gio. e Paolo, nell anno MDCLXXXXV . . . Composto in musica dal Sign. D. Pietro Romolo abbate Pignatta.

Venetia, Paulo Antonio Sanzonio, 1695. 72 p. 15ᶜᵐ.

Three acts. Composer's dedication as author of the text, dated Venice, October 15, 1695, argument, and scenario.

SCHATZ 8169

La costanza vince l'inganno. Drama pastorale da representarsi nel Theatro di Sua Altezza Serenissima del landgravio di Hassia à Darmstadio.

n. i., n. d. 111 p. 19ᶜᵐ.

Three acts. Author not mentioned, and unknown to Schatz, nor is Christoph **Graupner**, the composer, mentioned. German title-page, "Die bestaendigkeit besieget den betrug," and text face Italian. First performed, as indicated, 1719.

SCHATZ 4121

The cottage. An operatic farce. In two acts. By James Smith.

Tewkesbury, Printed by W. Dyde, n. d. 3 p. l., [1], 10–34 p. 21½ᶜᵐ.

Prologue and dedication "to the inhabitants of Tewkesbury." Dated 1796 by Biog. Dram.

LONGE 237

The cottagers, a musical entertainment: As it is performed at the Theatre Royal in Covent-Garden.

London, William Griffin, 1768. 2 p. l., 47 p. 21ᶜᵐ.

Two acts. Cast. Neither the author, Richard Joceline Goodenough, is mentioned, nor the composer. The opera was revived as:

LONGE 119

— **William and Nanny;** or, The cottagers, a musical entertainment: as it is performed at the Theatre-Royal in Covent-Garden.

London, W. Griffin, 1779. 2 p. l., 47 p. 20ᶜᵐ.

Two acts. Cast. First performed under this title November 12, 1779.

LONGE 214

The **cottagers,** an opera, in three acts. By George Saville Carey.

Printed (on p. 47–75) together with his "The inoculator," published at London, 1766. (Our copy lacks title page.)

No performance recorded.

LONGE 151

The **cottagers;** a comic opera. In two acts. By Miss A. Ross. (Aged fifteen years.) Daughter of Mrs. Brown, of the Theatre Royal, Covent-Garden . . . The second edition.

London, Printed for the author, 1788. 1 p. l., vii, [1], 61 p. 21ᶜᵐ.

A long list of subscribers, and a preface, signed by Anna Ross, and dated London, April 17, 1788, which, after apologies for "a crippled, puny, little bantling," ends:

"little can be dreaded from critical attacks, when fighting beneath the banners of a BILLINGTON, and well guarded by a *British* SHIELD."

This seems to point to William **Shield** as the composer.

Not performed.

LONGE 119

The **country burial.** A. T. of the ballad opera Silvia.

The **country wedding.** L. T. of Essex Hawker's The wedding.

The **coup de main,** or, The American adventurers; a musical entertainment. As it was acted at the new theatre in Dundee, by His Majesty's servants, from the Theatre-Royal, Edinburgh. Written by A. M'Laren . . .

Perth, Printed for the author, and sold by Mess. More, Nicol, and Miln, Dundee [etc.] 1784. 36 p. 17½ᶜᵐ.

One act. By Archibald Maclaren. Of the seventeen airs, nearly all were to be sung to popular ballad tunes.

ML 50.2.C74

Les **couplets en procès.** Prologue par Mʳˢ. le S * * & d'Or * * Representé à la Foire Saint Laurent 1730.

Le Théâtre de la foire, Paris, 1731, t. vii, pl., [323]–349 p. 17ᶜᵐ.

By Le Sage and d'Orneval. Largely *en vaudevilles.* The airs, selected or composed and arranged by Jean Claude **Gillier,** are printed at the end of the volume in the "Table des airs."

First performed February 18, 1730, as indicated.

ML 48.L2V11

La **cour.** Entrée in Boismortier's Les voyages de l'amour.

La **cour d'amour.** *See* Floquet's L'union de l'amour et des arts.

La **couronne de roses,** ou La fête de Salency, comedie en deux actes, mêlée d'ariettes, suivie d'un vaudeville. Par M. D. L. D. E. M. D. A. D. P. E. L. R. Et verbis & exemplis.

Paris, Merigot jeune, 1770. 36 p. 19ᶜᵐ.

On p. 29–36 the "Airs": "Se peut-il que l'on propose" (I, 1), "Je suis un officier nouveau" (I, 3), "La reine des fleurs" (I, 3), "L'autre jour à coups de pomme" (I, 6), and the vaudeville "Je suis le seigneur du village" (II, 4).

The text is preceded by an "Explication du sujet" with this remark:

"Il y a plus de trois ans que les paroles & la musique de la piece suivante sont faites. Trop éloigné de la Capitale pour en demander la réception au Théatre Italien, je me suis trouvé prévenu par M. Favart, qui a saisi ce sujet sous le même point de vue que moi, lorsque j'ai été à même de le faire; je sçais à combien de titres il mérite la préférence; mais comme les personnes mêmes qui la lui ont accordée m'ont dit que ma piece, à bien des égards, n'étoit pas inférieure à la sienne, j'ai cru pouvoir la mettre sous les yeux du public, non pour entrer en concurrence avec M. Favart, mais pour étendre davantage, s'il est possible, la renommée d'une institution qu'on ne sçauroit trop faire connoître.

SCHATZ 11488

Court and country: or, The changelings. A new ballad opera. As it was lately performed.

London, W. Webb, 1743. 2 p. l., 63 p. 19^{cm}.

Three acts and prologue. The 42 airs are merely indicated by title. The author is not recorded. Title contradicted by Genest's "not acted." LONGE 52

The court legacy. A new ballad opera. As it is acted at the Eutopean Palace. By the author of the New Atalantis . . .

London, J. Dormer, 1733. 55 p. 18½^{cm}.

Three acts and introduction. By Mary de la Rivière Manley. In the dedication "Atalia" calls this "a satire on the court of Eutopia." The 43 airs used (1, 10, 18, 14) are indicated by title. LONGE 275

The court medley: or, Marriage by proxy. An [!] new ballad opera. Of three acts.

London, J. Dickinson, 1733. 2 p. l., 59, [1] p. 19^{cm}.

Table of the 30 songs, the airs of which are indicated by title in the text. Neither author recorded nor performance. LONGE 49

— **The fortunate prince:** or Marriage at last. A new ballad opera. In three acts.

London, T. Webb, 1734. 2 p. l., 60 p. 19^{cm}.

On 2d p. l. "A table of airs in the opera," verso "Dramatis personae" printed by mistake between p. 2 and 3. This is identical with "The court medley," as comparison proved, except for the addition of three scenes after the words "with your Highness's kind offer" the rest of the sentence and song to air xxx, "My time, O ye Muses," being dropped. The additional scenes contain four songs to airs 30, "Since all the world's turn'd," 31 to 33 (airs not indicated). The "table of airs" however, lists the 30 airs as in "the Court medley" table! LONGE 49

Second copy (21cm.). LONGE 318.

The court of Alexander. An opera in two acts. As it is performed at the Theatre Royal in Covent-Garden . . .

London, T. Waller, n. d. vii, [8]–38 p. 19½^{cm}.

Two acts. By Alexander Stevens, who is not mentioned. Cast and argument. The composer, John Abraham **Fisher** (Squire) is not mentioned.

First performed January 5, 1770, as indicated. LONGE 37

La creatione del mondo.

p. 171–204. 15½^{cm}. (Ottavio Tronsarelli, Drammi musicali, Roma, Francesco Corbelletti, 1632.)

Five acts. Argument. No composer mentioned. ML 49.A2T7

Crédit est mort, opéra-comique, en un acte, mêlé de prose & de vaudevilles. Donné en 1726.

Alexis Piron, Oeuvres complettes, Liege, 1776, v. 5, [99]–146 p. 17½^{cm}.

Parfaict, etc., do not record the composer. PQ 2019.P6

Il credulo con farsa **La baronessa Stramba** da rappresentarsi nel Teatro Nuovo sopra Toledo per quart' opera in musica nel carnevale di quest' anno 1786.

Napoli, n. publ., 1786. 58 p. 15^{cm}.

Two acts. By Gius. Maria Diodati (not mentioned). Cast and name of the composer, **Cimarosa.** The second act consists of only one scene. Then follows with cast on p. 35–58 "La BARONESSA STRAMBA" in one act of 16 scenes. A prefatory note to this reads:

Il credulo—Continued.

"Si avverte, che la seguente farsa non è dell' autore del Credulo, ma di altro sog-getto, altra volta rappresentata con generale applauso, per cui si è dovuto risolvere l'argomento con una sola scena nell' atto II. per dar luogo alla farsa medesima. La musica è del medesimo egregio maestro **Cimarosa** con averci fatti de' nuovi pezzi, che sono distinti da questo segno * . . . Si è dovuto benanche trasportare litteral-mente il dialetto di D. Gironda e di D. Settimio in Toscano per i virtuosi, che ora ne rappresentano i caratteri . . ."

The *new pieces* begin:

"Fuggi . . . che fò . . . s'arresta," "Orsù sentimi bene," "Il punto tuo finale," "Comme! chisso che dice," "Crudel tiranno ingrato," "Vo girando qual Colomba," etc.

"La baronessa Stramba" is simply a somewhat altered version of Pasquale Mili-lotti's libretto "I matrimoni in ballo," first performed with Cimarosa's music at Naples, Teatro Nuovo sopra Toledo, carnival, 1776.

See the notes for next entry.   SCHATZ 1977 and 1985

— Il **credulo** con farsa L'**impresario in angustie** di G. M. D. da rappresentarsi nel Teatro Nuovo sopra Toledo per terz' opera in musica di quest' anno 1786.

Napoli, n. publ., 1786.   59, [3] p.   15^{cm}.

Two acts. By Giuseppe Maria Diodati. Cast and this notice by the author:

"La presente commedia era stata destinata per il venturo carnevale, per cui non si è proseguito l'argomento della medesima, e si è scritta la farsa; ma una indispensa-bile necessità del teatro ha fatto sì, che questa siegua per terza rappresentazione appresso all' altra mia *Le trame deluse*. Niente dissimile è *il Credulo* da quello dell' anno scorso, ch'il ragguardevole pubblico compatì generosamente, a riserba di una sola scena aggiunta, e due arie dell' istesso maestro **Cimarosa**, in grazia delle vir-tuose, che sono nuove per la recita del medesimo."

The three additional pages contain a substitute scene for scene XII of "Il credulo," which is practically, however, the same, except for the aria, "Voi vedrete in una sala."

The libretto (one act in thirteen scenes) of "L'impresario in angustie," with cast and name of composer, and designated as "atto II," begins on p. [37], after the first and only scene of act II of "Il credulo."

The "Il Credulo" libretto, with "La baronessa Stramba," must be earlier than the one with "L'impresario in angustie," because this (Schatz 1916) contains (as scene XIII) "Ora provate chiuso," in addition to the sixteen scenes common to both librettos. Furthermore, the remark about "due arie . . . in grazia delle virtuose, che sono nuove" applies to Marianna Santoro Limperani and Caterina Fiorentini, mentioned in the cast of *Schatz 1916*. But how should the librettos be dated, and when were they performed? *Schatz 1916* is called "terz' opera . . . di . . . 1786," *Schatz 1977* "quart' opera . . . nel carnevale di . . . 1786," and yet, as was seen, *Schatz 1916* must be later. Now, the author in *Schatz 1916* informs the public that this libretto, though intended for the coming carnival, which would be that of 1786/87, was, by some unavoidable necessity, made to follow his "Le trame deluse" as third opera of the season. Since we know (*see* Florimo) that Cimarosa's "Le trame deluse" was performed as second opera of the carnival season 1785/1786, it would again follow that "Il credulo" was the third opera of 1786, and also the fourth! Yet that might have been possible, except for the fact that Santoro-Limperani and Fiorentini and a few more singers in the cast of *Schatz 1916* are not listed by Florimo as having appeared at Naples at the Teatro Nuovo before 1787! The situation is still more puzzling in view of the statement in the preface of *Schatz 1916*, that it is "not different from Il credulo of last year." But *Schatz 1916* is written in the Napolitan dialect, and *Schatz 1977*, as the pref. note expressly states, had been translated from the Napolitan into Tuscan. Consequently, the latter version (Schatz 1977) would be later than *Schatz 1916*, which can not be, as was shown above. And, to make things still worse, the "last year" in the preface of a libretto dated 1786 surely can only mean 1785. No such performance of "Il credulo" has been traced by Florimo, and yet, here the author's own preface points to one. "Il credulo" was performed at Naples in the Napolitan dialect in 1785. This much may now be conceded, but beyond this the case of "Il credulo" is not clear.   SCHATZ 1916 and 1929

Il credulo deluso. Commedia per musica da rappresentarsi nel Teatro della città di Foggia nella primavera di quest' anno 1776 . . .

Napoli, n. publ., 1776. 70 p. 15½ᶜᵐ.

Three acts. Cast, name of **Paisiello** as the composer, and impresario's dedication, dated Foggia, May 8, 1776. This is an altered version of "Il mondo della luna," by Goldoni, who is not mentioned.

First performed at Naples, Teatro Nuovo, fall of 1774. Schatz 7666

— **Il mondo della luna.** Commedia per musica da rappresentarsi nel Teatro di S. Ferdinando a Ponte Nuovo. Per prima commedia di quest' anno 1792.

Napoli, Domenico Sangiacomo, n. d. 48 p. 16ᶜᵐ.

Three acts. Is "Il credulo deluso," with alterations. Cast and name of **Paisiello** as the composer.

First perfo med at St. Petersburg, Teatro di corte, Nov. 3–14, 1783. Schatz 7667

La creduta infedele. Commedia per musica da rappresentarsi nel Teatro de' Fiorentini per prim' opera in quest' anno 1783.

Napoli, n. publ., 1783. 58, [1] p. 15ᶜᵐ.

Three acts. Author not mentioned, and unknown to Schatz. Cast, scenario and name of Giuseppe **Gazzaniga** as the composer. Schatz 3677

La creduta selvaggia. Farsetta per musica da rappresentarsi nel Teatro alla Valle degl' illmi Sigg. Capranica. Nel carnevale dell' anno 1792 . . .

Roma, Puccinelli, n. d. 59 p. 16½ᶜᵐ.

Two acts. Author not mentioned and unknown to me. Cast and name of Giacomo **Tritto** as composer. ML 50.2.C76T7

La creduta vedova o sia La sposa costante. Farsetta per musica a cinque voci da rappresentarsi nel Teatro Valle degl' illustriss. Sigg. Capranica nell' estate dell' anno 1786 . . .

Roma, Michele Puccinelli, n. d. 62 p. 16ᶜᵐ.

Two acts. Author not mentioned and unknown to Schatz. Cast and name of Salvatore **Viganò** as composer. ML 50.2.C763V3

Li creduti spiriti. Dramma giocoso per musica da rappresentarsi nel nuovo Teatro Tron di S. Cassano il carnovale dell' anno 1764.

Venezia, Paolo Colombani, 1764. 58 p. 14½ᶜᵐ.

Three acts. "La musica de' Signori N. N.," of whom Johann Gottlieb **Naumann** is said by Schatz to have been one. Cast and notice to the reader, in which the impresario, Joseph Felix von Kurtz, is called "autore dell' intreccio, de' sentimenti, della condotta, e di tutta la macchina." Schatz 7064

Creonte. Dramma per musica da rappresentarsi nel nobilissimo Teatro di S. Benedetto nell' autunno dell' anno 1776.

Venezia, Modesto Fenzo, 1776. 46 p. 17ᶜᵐ.

Three acts. By unknown author. Argument, cast, scenario, and name of the composer, Dimitrij Stefanovitch **Bortniansky.**

First performed November 26, 1776, as indicated. Schatz 1255

Creonte. Drama per musica da rappresentarsi nel Teatro di S. Angelo l'anno 1691. Di Rinaldo Cialli. Nuovamente riformato . . .

Venetia, Nicolini, 1691. 64 p. 14½ᶜᵐ.

Three acts. Author's dedication, argument, scenario, and notice to the reader, with name of Marc' Antonio **Ziani** as the composer, and the usual apologies for the

Creonte—Continued.

defects of the text, forced, as he was, to "nel giro di pochi giorni . . . comporlo per gli accidenti della compagnia de signori musici" and to finish it "tra l'angustie d'un letto."   SCHATZ 11181

Creonte tiranno di Tebe.   L. T. of Pollaroli's La forza della virtù.

Cresfonte, rè di Scizia, ballet.   *See* Bianchi's Pizzarro.

Creso.   Dramma per musica da rappresentarsi nel Regio Teatro di Torino nel carnovale del 1768 . . .

   Torino, Stamperia reale, n. d.   viii, 43 p.   15½ cm.

   Three acts. By Giuseppe Giovacchino Pizzi (not mentioned). With argument, cast, scenario, and name of the composer, Pasquale **Cafaro.** Giuseppe Antonio Le Messier is mentioned as the composer of the ballet music.   SCHATZ 1452

Creso.   Drama per musica, nel felicissimo dì natalizio della S. C. R. Maestà dell' Imperatrice Eleonora Maddalena Teresa . . . l'anno MDCLXXVIII . . .

   Vienna d'Austria, Gio. Christoforo Cosmerovio, n. d.   7 p. l., 134 p. 15 cm.

   On p. 131–134 "Introduttione ad un balletto delli sette pianeti celesti. Per la licenza . . ." Three acts. Dedication by the author, conte Nicolò Minato, dated Vienna, January 6, 1678, argument, scenario, list of machines. The composer, Antonio **Draghi,** is not mentioned.   ML 50.2.C8D7

Il Creso.   Drama da rappresentarsi nel famosissimo Teatro Grimano di S. Gio. Grisostomo l'anno MDCLXXXI.   Di Giulio Cesare Corradi . . .

   Venetia, Francesco Nicolini, 1681.   80 p.   13 cm.

   Three acts. Corradi's dedication, argument, scenario, and notice to the reader with name of Giovanni **Legrenzi** as the composer of the music "la quale, ancorche nata nel maggior torbido dell' agitata sua mente è riuscita con tanta perfettione, che la confessarai un miracolo dell' arte."
   Further above it is said:
   "Eccoti il Creso, parto che non credeva quest' anno d'uscire alla luce . . . Sappi che pochi giorni furono destinati per fartelo comparire sù la scena . . ."
                                                                         SCHATZ 5542

Creso.   Dramma per musica da rappresentarsi nel nobilissimo Teatro di S. Benedetto il carnovale dell' anno 1770.

   Venezia, Modesto Fenzo, 1770.   46 p.   17 cm.

   Three acts. By Giovacchino Pizzi, who is not mentioned. Argument, cast, scenario, and name of Antonio **Sacchini** as the composer. On p. 9–10 brief description of Jean Baptiste Martin's ballet "La rete di Vulcano" without name of the composer of the music.
   First performed at Naples, Teatro di San Carlo, November 4, 1765. SCHATZ 9215

— Creso; a new serious opera: as performed at the King's Theatre in the Hay-Market.   The music entirely new, by Signor Antonio Sacchini.   The translation by F. Bottarelli, A. M.

   London, T. Cadell, 1767.   55, [1] p.   19 cm.

   Three acts. Argument, cast. Italian and English text. More than the customary liberties have been taken with Pizzi's text. They begin in the second scene of the first act, where the aria is "Se un' alma amante" instead of "Del mio tradito core." The number of scenes, too, has become different. The third act has now twelve instead of ten scenes.
   The last (unnumbered) page contains a list of "New music published in the course of last winter, by R. Bremner."   SCHATZ 9216

Creso. Dramma per musica da rappresentarsi nel nobilissimo Teatro di San Samuele la fiera dell' Ascensione dell' anno 1788.

Venezia, Modesto Fenzo, 1788. 46 p. 17^cm.

Three acts. By Giuseppe Giovacchino Pizzi, who is not mentioned. Argument, cast, scenario, and name of Pietro **Terziani** as the composer.

On p. 36–46 dedication, argument, and description of Onorato Viganò's "Orizia e Borea, ballo tragico pantomimo," music by Salvatore Viganò. The same were responsible for the second ballet "La donna incostante o sia Il festino de' teatri di Roma." SCHATZ 10289

Creso in Media. Dramma in musica da rappresentarsi nel Pubblico Teatro da S. Sebastiano in Livorno la primavera dell' anno 1780 . . .

[Livorno], Gio. V. Falorni, n. d. 48 p. 15½^cm.

Three acts. By Giuseppe Pagliuca, who is not mentioned. Impresario's dedication, argument, cast, scenario, and name of Joseph **Schuster** as composer.

First performed at Naples, Teatro di San Carlo, November 4, 1779. SCHATZ 9744

Creso rè di Lidia. Dramma per musica da rappresentarsi nel Teatro di via della Pergola nell' autunno del MDCCLXXVII . . .

Firenze, Gio. Risaliti, 1777. 37 p. 16^cm.

Three acts. By Giovacchino Pizzi. Argument, cast, scenario, and name of the composer, Giovanni Battista **Borghi** ("musica tutta nuova"), but not of the librettist. Paolo Franchi's ballets, "Il re pastore, ballo eroico pastorale" and "La tranquillità disturbata," were performed with the opera. The composers of the music are not mentioned. SCHATZ 1228

Creso tolto a le fiamme. Drama per musica. Da rappresentarsi nel Teatro a Sant Angelo. L'anno 1705. Di Aurelio Aureli.

Venezia, Marino Rossetti, 1705. 60 p. 15^cm.

Three acts. Argument and scenario. The composer, Girolamo **Polani**, is not mentioned. SCHATZ 8250

Creusa. Dramma per musica da rappresentarsi nel Teatro Grimani di San Samuele nella fiera dell' Ascensione l'anno 1739 . . .

Venezia, Marino Rossetti, 1739. 60 p. 15^cm.

Three acts. By Urbano Rizzi (Wiel and Schatz). The dedication is signed by Domenico Lalli. On p. 8 the foot-note: "le arie segnate colla stella sono di altro autore cangiate per commodo della musica, per la qual cagione si è anche cangiato il nome di Jone in quello di Gelone." Consequently, the libretto in its present form must have been the work of two authors. Argument, cast, scenario, and name of the composer, Pietro Lione **Cardena**.

First performed, as indicated, May, 1739. SCHATZ 1622

Creusa in Delfo. Dramma per musica in due atti misto di cori e danze da rappresentarsi nel Real Teatro di Salvaterra nel carnovale dell' anno 1774.

[Lisbona], Nella Stamperia reale, n. d. 69 p. 15^cm.

Three acts. Argument, scenario, cast, and names of Gaetano Martinelli as the author, of David **Perez** as the composer. SCHATZ 7880

Créuse l'Athenienne, tragedie représentée par l'Academie royale de musique l'an 1712. Les paroles de M. Roy & la musique de M. la Coste. LXXVIII. opera.

n. i., n. d. 14^cm. pl., 389–446 p. (Recueil général des opéra, t. x, Paris, 1714.)

Detached copy. Five acts and prologue. "Avertissement."

First performed, as indicated, April 5, 1712. SCHATZ 5354

Second copy. ML 48.R4

Les **crimes de la féodalite.** A. T. of Jadin's Alisbelle.

Crisippo. Drama per musica del dottor Grazio Braccioli Ferrarese da rappresentarsi in Ferrara nel Teatro a S. Stefano degl' illustris, simi Signori Co. Antonio Maria Paolo e fratelli Bonacossi, con l'occasione della solita Fiera di Maggio dell' anno MDCCX . . .

> *Ferrara, Bernardino Barbieri, n. d. 64 p. 15½ᶜᵐ.*

Three acts. Author's dedication dated Ferrara, May 10, 1710, argument, cast, scenario and name of Floriano **Aresti** as composer.   ML 50.2.C85A7

Crispo. Drama rappresentato nella sala dell' illustrissimo Sig. Federico Capranica nel carnevale dell' anno MDCCXXI.

> *Roma, Antonio de Rossi, 1721. 60 p. 15½ᶜᵐ.*

Three acts. Dedication by the author, Paolo Antonio Rolli (who is not mentioned), argument, cast, and name of the composer, Giov. Battista **Bononcini.** SCHATZ 1200

Il **Cristoforo Colombo nell' Indie,** ballet. *See* Brunetti's Bertoldo.

Critic upon critic; a dramatic medley, in three acts; as it is performed at the Theatre-Royal in Covent-Garden. By Leonard Mac Nally, Esq. Second edition.

> *London, J. Almon, 1792. 2 p. l., [1], 10–71 p. 20ᶜᵐ.*

Cast. In form of a ballad opera. Genest (v. 10, p. 197) claims that the play was printed in 1788, and that "from the plays and farces alluded to, or mentioned, it is almost certain that this piece was written in 1780—most or all of the characters are real persons under fictitious names . . . In 1792 critic upon Ccritic was reprinted . . . I am of the opinion that it was never acted . . from the nature of the piece it seems clear that it was never meant for representation . . . it seems not impossible that some bookseller in 1792 might affix a new title page and a cast of the play to the old copies of 1788, in order to sell them."   LONGE 232

La critica, opera by Jommelli. *See* Il giuoco de picchetto.

La critica teatrale. Dramma giocoso per musica da rappresentarsi nel Teatro Tron di San Cassiano nel carnovale dell' anno 1775.

> *Venezia, Gio. Battista Casali, 1775. 16½ᶜᵐ. 55 p.*

Three acts. Cast, scenario, and name of Gennaro **Astaritta** as composer, but not of librettist. According to Schatz, this is a later version of Raniero de' Calsabigi's "L'opera seria" libretto.
First performed at Turin, Teatro Carignano, fall of 1771.   SCHATZ 378

La critique a l'Opera-comique; petite piece en un acte: pour l'ouverture du Théâtre de la Foire Saint Germain, en 1742.

> *Charles François Pannard, Théâtre, Paris, Duchesne, 1763, v. 3, [259]–298 p. 17ᶜᵐ.*

In prose and vaudevilles. Composer not recorded by Parfaict, etc.   PQ 2019.P3

La critique des festes de Thalie. *See* Mouret's Les festes de Thalie.

Die critische nacht. Tr. of Boroni's La notte critica.

Croesus *See* Keiser's Der hochmuethige. . . .

La cuccagna, ballet. *See* Zingarelli's Annibale in Torino.

Cunegonda. Drama per musica da rappresentarsi nel Teatro di Sant' Angelo per il carnevale dell' anno MDCCXXVI.

Venezia, Marino Rossetti, 1726. 56 p. 15^{cm}.

Three acts. Neither the author, conte Agostino Piovene, is mentioned, nor Antonio **Vivaldi,** the composer. Argument, notice to the reader, cast, and scenario.

SCHATZ 10764

The **cunning man.** Tr. of Rousseau's Le devin du village.

Cupid and Psyche: or, Colombine-Courtezan. A dramatic panto-mime entertainment. Interspers'd with ballad tunes. As it is per-form'd at the Theatre-Royal in Drury-Lane, by His Majesty's servants.

London, J. Watts, 1734. 2 p. l., 18 p. 19½^{cm}.

One act. Author not recorded. Without music, and the titles of the ballad-tunes are not indicated.

First performed, as indicated, February 4, 1734. LONGE 33

Cupid's revenge: an Arcadian pastoral. As it is performed at the Theatre-Royal, Hay-Market. The music by Mr. Hook.

London, J. Bell, 1772. 3 p. l., 39, [1] p. 21^{cm}.

Two acts. Cast and dedication dated London, July, 1772. By Francis Gentleman. First performed June 12, 1772. LONGE 244

Cupido. *See* Keiser's Der sich raechende . . .

Cupido trionfatore o sia Apollo e Dafne, ballet. *See* Pio's Nettuno ed Egle.

A **cure for a scold.** A ballad farce of two acts. (Founded upon Shakespear's Taming of a shrew) As it is acted by his Majesty's Company of comedians at the Theatre Royal in Drury-Lane. By J. Worsdale, portrait-painter.

London, L. Gilliver, n. d. 5 p. l., 59, [1] p. 18½^{cm}.

Epilogue, cast, preface, in which this is called the author's first attempt, and James Worsdale's dedication. The 23 (8, 15) airs used are indicated by title.

First performed at Drury-Lane, February 25, 1735. LONGE 275

A **cure for dotage.** A musical entertainment; sung at Marybone-Gardens.

London, C. D. Piguenit, 1771. 1 p. l., 20 p. 21^{cm}.

Two parts. Neither author nor composer mentioned or recorded by Biog. Dram. and Genest. LONGE 204

Il **curioso accidente della caccia.** A. T. of the ballet Dove entrò cervo esce donna.

Il **curioso accidente.** Dramma giocoso per musica di Giovanni Bertati da rappresentarsi nel nobile Teatro Giustiniani in San Moisè per la prima opera dell' autunno 1789.

Venezia, Modesto Fenzo, 1789. 68 p. 18½^{cm}.

Three acts. Cast and name of Gennaro **Astaritta** as composer. On p. 65–66 text of the arias "Sento in gabbia innargentata" and "Quella fiamma, che v'accende," which were substituted for Signora Maria Caracci Caravoglia, who took the part of Gentilina instead of Signora Irene Tomeoni Dutillieu. On p. 67–68 "argomento del ballo primo intitolato Nina pazza per amore" and title of the second "Chi la fa l'aspetta," both invented by Eusebio Luzzi, the composer of the music not being mentioned. SCHATZ 385

Il curioso del suo proprio danno. Commedia per musica. Da rappresentarsi nel Teatro Nuovo sopra Toledo nel carnovale di quest' anno 1756.

Napoli, Girolamo Flauto, 1756. 72 p. 15^{cm}.

Three acts. By Antonio Palomba, who is not mentioned. Cast and name of Niccolò **Piccinni** as the composer.   SCHATZ 814

Il curioso indiscreto. Dramma giocoso per musica da rappresentarsi nel Teatro delle Dame il carnevale dell' anno 1777 . . . [vignette]

Roma, Si vendono da Giovanni Bartolomicchi, n. d. 67 p. 15½^{cm}.

Three acts. Author not mentioned and unknown to Schatz. Impresario's dedication, argument, scenario, cast and name of Pasquale **Anfossi** as composer.
                                                                          ML 50.2.C9A6

— **Il curioso indiscreto.** Dramma giocoso per musica da rappresentarsi in Firenze nel Teatro di via del Cocomero nell' autunno dell' anno 1777 . . .

Firenze, Anton Giuseppe Pagani, 1777. 62 p. 16½^{cm}.

Three acts. Cast and name of composer, Pasquale **Anfossi**, but not of librettist, who is unknown to Schatz. The ballets, by Onorato Viganò, composer of the music not mentioned, were called "La pastorella impertinente" and Il Giocatore."
                                                                          SCHATZ 232

— **Il curioso indiscreto.** Dramma giocoso per musica da rappresentarsi nel Teatro di Lucca l'autunno dell' anno 1779.

Lucca, Gio. della Valle, n. d. 87 p. 15^{cm}.

Three acts. Argument, cast, scenario, and name of Pasquale **Anfossi** as the composer. The author is unknown to Schatz. With the opera were performed Francesco Ricci's ballet "La sposa persiana" and Giuseppe Trafieri's "La vendemmia, ossia La contadina impertinente." The composers of the music are not mentioned.

The date of first performance is given as August 7, 1779.   SCHATZ 11670

Les Cyclopes. Intermède in Bourgeois' Les plaisirs de la paix.

Cymon. A dramatic romance. As it is performed at the Theatre-Royal, in Drury-Lane. The music by Mr. Arne . . . The third edition.

London, T. Becket and P. A. De Hondt, 1767. vi, [2], 86, [2] p. 19^{cm}.

Five acts, prologue and epilogue. Cast. By David Garrick, who is not mentioned. The composer was Michael **Arne,** not Thomas Aug. In the vocal scores the additional song "Be sure you regard" is headed as composed by **Dibdin.**

First performed January 2, 1767, as indicated.   LONGE 46

— **Cymon,** altered from David Garrick, Esq. In two acts.

[358]–403 p. 19^{cm}. (Collection of the most esteemed farces and entertainments, t. III, Edinburgh, 1792.)

Drury-Lane and Edinburgh (1783) casts.   SCHATZ 11753

— **Cymon.** A dramatick romance. The music by Mr. Arne. Adapted for theatrical representation, as performed at the Theatre-Royal, Covent-Garden. Regulated from the prompt-book, by permission of the manager . . .

London, John Bell, 1795. front., 1 p. l., iv, [2], 7–78 p. 15^{cm}. (J. Bell, British theatre, London, 1791–1797, v. 29.)

Cymon—Continued.

The front. represents Mr. Kelly as Cymon and is dated August 15, 1795. The p. l. is an added engraved title page with a scene from the play and is dated, July 30, 1795. Prologue and five acts. Covent-Garden cast. PR 1241.B4

Cyrillus der Kappadozier, ein junger martyrer, ein singspiel in zween aufzuegen, aufgefuehrt von der studirenden jugend des Katholischen schulhauses zu Augsburg bey St. Salvator den 2. 5. und 6. Herbstmondes [Sept.] 1785.

[*Augsburg*], *Joseph Simon Hueber, n. d. 16 p. 20*cm.

Author unknown to Schatz. Johann Evangelist **Drexel** is mentioned as the composer. With cast and "Vorbericht." At head of title: "Paulinus v. Rolla . . . ein trauerspiel . . . und." SCHATZ 2816

Cyrus. Tr. of Metastasio's text Il Ciro riconosciuto.

Cythere assiégée, opéra-comique en un acte; représenté à Bruxelles, pour la premiere fois, le 7 juillet 1748. Et à l'Opéra-comique le lundi 12 août 1754. Nouvelle édition.

*Paris, Duchesne, 1760. 48 p. 21*cm.

Cast and note:
"Cette piece fut d'abord faite en prose & couplets par M. Favart, en société avec M. Fagan, & représentée à Paris à l'ouverture de la Foire St. Laurent 1738 [as "Le pouvoir de l'amour, ou Le siège de Cythère"]; depuis entièrement refondue par M. Favart, pour la Troupe des Comédiens de Bruxelles; & donnée à Paris sur le Théâtre de l'Opéra-comique, selon l'ordre qui suit."
The text is best known as a vehicle for Gluck, whose "La Cythère assiégée" was first performed at Schwetzingen in 1759. A second version was performed at Paris, Académie royale de musique, August 11, 1775. ML 50.2.C95
Second copy (Theatre de M. Favart, Paris, Duchesne, 1763–77, t. vii). ML 49.A2F1

Airs, duets, trios, chorusses, etc in the **Czar:** a comic opera, in three acts. Performed at the Theatre-Royal, Covent-Garden.

*London, T. Cadell, 1790. 30 p. 21*cm.

Cast. The air, "The prince, unable to conceal his pain," according to a footnote, is not by the author, John O'Keefe (not mentioned). The opera was first called "The czar Peter," and finally, after being reduced to a farce, was called "The fugitive." The composer, William **Shield**, is not mentioned.
First performed, as indicated, March 8, 1790 LONGE 204

Da gratitudine amore. A. T. of Seydelmann's Il mostro.

Da ist nicht gut zu rathen, eine comische oper in zwey aufzuegen von Stephanie dem juengeren. Die musik dazu ist vom herrn Bartta. Aufgefuehrt im Kaiserl. Koengl. National theater.

*Wien, n. publ., 1778. 60 p. 16*cm.

Dedication, "An die kritik," in which author says, "Ich betrete heute eine neue laufbahn," and lengthy Vorrede, in which he denies having based this libretto on an older opera, called "Hulla."
First performed, as indicated, August 8, 1778. SCHATZ 615

La Dafne d'Ottavio Rìnuccini rappresentata alla Sereniss. Gran Duchessa di Toscana dal Signor Jacopo Corsi [coat of arms].

*Firenze, Giorgio Marescotti, MDC. 12 unnumb. l. 21*cm. SCHATZ 7918

La **Dafne**—Continued.

Printer's sign on recto of last leaf. No dedication, no preface. The two leaves preceding last l. contain a laudatory poem of eight stanzas, to Corsi, beginning:

"*Del S. Jacopo Corsi.*

Qual novo altero canto
O Musa, ò Dea mi detta, ond' io risuoni
Corsi tuo nobil vanto.
Corsi, che tutti sproni,
E tutti accendi alle virtù celesti,
Mentre primier le belle vie calpesti."

Strange to say, the chronological history of "Dafne" is still open to conjecture. At least, it has never been told in a manner as to silence criticism and I doubt very much that this can be done at present. Everything depends on a satisfactory interpretation of the strictly contemporary sources, which alone can establish the chronology of this, the first opera.

Before these sources are quoted for analysis, attention may well be called to the customary statement that Rinuccini's "Dafne" is based on his "Combattimento di Apollo col serpente Pitone," an intermedio performed in 1589 at Florence with Luca Marenzio's music. As a matter of fact, Rinuccini used only one number of this, the madrigal "Ebra di sangue in questo oscuro bosco" for his "Dafne" text.

The earliest document that calls for consideration is Rinuccini's dedicatory preface to his "L'Euridice" text, published in October 1600. In this he says, so far as the chronological history of "Dafne" is involved:

"È stata opinione di molti . . . che gli antichi Greci e Romani cantassero sulle scene le tragedie intere; ma si nobil maniera di recitare nonchè rinnovata, ma nè pur, che io sappia, fin qui era stata tentata da alcuno, e ciò mi credev'io per difetto della musica moderna, di gran lunga all'antica inferiore. Ma pensiero si fatto mi tolse interamente dall' animo M. Jacopo Peri: quando, udito l'intenzione del Signor Jacopo Corsi e mia, mise con tanta grazia sotto le note la favola di *Dafne* (composta da me, solo per fare una semplice prova di quello che potesse il canto dell' età nostra) che incredibilmente piacque a quei pochi che l'udirono.

"Onde, preso animo, e dato miglior forma alla stessa favola, e di nuovo rappresentandola in casa il Sig. Jacopo, fu ella, non solo dalla nobiltà di tutta questa patria favorita, ma dalla serenissima Gran Duchessa e gli illustrissimi Cardinali Dal Monte e Montaldo udita e commendata.

"Ma molto maggior favore e fortuna ha sortito l'*Euridice*, messa in musica dal medesimo Peri con arte mirabile e da altri non più usata . . ."

It will be noticed that Rinuccini does not mention Giulio Caccini at all, either in connection with "Euridice" or "Dafne." Caccini, in turn, neither in the dedicatory preface (dated December 20, 1600) of his "Euridice score" (dated 1600 but hardly published before our year 1601) nor in the dedication and preface of his "Le nuove musiche" (published at the earliest in July 1602, since the *imprimatur* is dated July 1, 1602. The title page is dated 1601 and the dedication February 1, 1601, both times 1601 being the same as 1602, new style) mentions his rival Peri. More singular still, he does not mention "Dafne," yet in his "Nuove Musiche e nuova maniera di scriverle" of 1614 he says:

"Molti anni avanti che io mettessi alcuna delle mie opere di musica per una voce sola alla stampa, se ne eran vedute fuora molte altre mie, fatte in diversi tempi et occasioni, delle quali furono più note la musica che io feci nella favola della *Dafne* del Sig. Ottavio Rinuccini, rappresentata in casa del Sig. Jacopo Corsi d'onorata memoria, a quest' Altezze Serenissime et altri Principi; ma le prime che io stampassi furon le musiche fatte l'anno 1600 nella favola dell' *Euridice*, opera del medesimo autore: e furon le prime che si vedesser date in luce in Italia da qualunque compositore di tale stile a una voce sola; diedi appresso fuore l'anno 1601 [!] quelle che io intitolai *Le nuove musiche* . . ." [for Peri's priority in the use of this famous term *see* Euridice].

In the preface of his "Euridice" score (dated 1600, but as the dedication is dated February 6, 1600, which is the same as February 6, 1601, new style, the score was published in 1601, new style) Jacopo Peri has this to say:

"Benchè dal Signor Emilio del Cavaliere, prima che da ogni altro ch'io sappia, con maravigliosa invenzione ci fusse fatta udire la nostra musica sulle scene; piacque nondimeno a' Signori Jacopo Corsi ed Ottavio Rinuccini (fin l'anno 1594), che io, adoperandola in altra guisa, mettessi sotto le note la favola di *Dafne*, dal Signor Ottavio composta, per fare una semplice pruova di quello che potesse il canto dell' età nostra . . .

La **Dafne**—Continued.

"Onde fatta udire a quei Signori la mia openione, dimostrai loro questo nuovo modo di cantare, e piacque sommamente, non pure al Signor Jacopo, il quale aveva di già composte arie bellissime per quella favola, ma al Signor Pietro Strozzi, al Signor Francesco Cini, et ad altri molti intendentissimi gentiluomini (chè nella nobiltà fiorisce oggi la muica), come anco a quella famosa, che si può chiamare Euterpe dell' età nostra, la Signora Vittoria Archilei . . . e per tre anni continui che nel carnovale si rappresentò, fu udita con sommo diletto e con applauso universale rice-vuta da chiunque vi si ritrovò. Ma ebbe miglior ventura la presente *Euridice* . . ."

Finally, Marco da Gagliano in the preface of his "Dafne" of 1608 writes:

"Ritrovandomi il carnoval passato in Mantova [carnival 1607–8] . . . volle [Vin-cenzo Gonzaga, duke of Mantova] fra l'altre che si rappresentasse la *Dafne* del Signor Ottavio Rinuccini da lui con tale occasione accresciuta e abbellita, fui impiegato a metterla in musica: il che io feci nella maniera che ora vi presento . . .

". . . credo che non sarà disutile, nè lontano dal nostro proposito il ridurvi in memoria come e quando ebbero origine si fatti spettacoli . . ."

"Dopo l'avere più e più volte discorso intorno alla maniera usata dagli antichi in rappresentare le lor tragedie . . . il Sig. Ottavio Rinuccini si diede a compor la favola di *Dafne*, il Sig. Jacopo Corsi, d'onorata memoria . . . compose alcune arie sopra parte di essa, delle quali invaghitosi, risoluto di vedere che effetto facessero su la scena, conferì insieme col Sig. Ottavio il suo pensiero al Sig. Jacopo Peri, peritis-simo nel contrapunto e cantore d'estrema esquisitezza: il quale, udita la loro inten-zione e approvato parte dell' arie già composte, si diede a comporre l'altre, che piacquero oltre modo al Sig. Corsi, e con l'occasione d'una veglia il carnovale dell' anno 1597 la fece rappresentare alla presenza dell' eccellentissimo Sig. Don Giovanni Medici e d'alcuni de' principali gentiluomini de la città nostra. Il piacere e lo stupore che partorì negli animi degl' uditori questo nuovo spettacolo non si può esprimere, basta solo che per molte volte ch'ella s'è recitata, ha generato la stessa ammirazione e lo stesso diletto. Per sì fatta prova venuto in cognizione il Sig. Rinuc-cini quanto fusse atto il canto a esprimere ogni sorta d'affetti, e che non solo (come per avventura per molti si sarebbe creduto) non recava tedio, ma diletto incredibile, compose l'*Euridice*, allargandosi alquanto più ne'ragionamenti. Uditala poi il Sig. Corsi, e piaciutole la favola e lo stile, stabilì di far la comparire in scena nelle nozze della Regina Cristianissima. [Florence, October 6, 1600] Allora ritrovò il Sig. Jacopo Peri quella artifiziosa maniera di recitare cantando, che tutta Italia am-mira . . ."

Not a word about Caccini's "Euridice," much less about his "Dafne," as if Marco da Gagliano, so liberal in his praise of Peri and Monteverdi, wished to rebuke Caccini for his undeniable tendency to appropriate the priority in all matters bearing on this new art of opera. To quote the later accounts of Vitali, Giustiniani, Bonini, Bardi, della Valle, Doni, would serve no useful purpose. They add either nothing new or by combining hear-say with deductions from earlier printed accounts, they partake of the character of secondary sources and merely help to confuse matters.

All these accounts have been made conveniently accessible by Solerti in his book "Le origini del melodramma." My arguments are based on this and on that in Solerti's more historical book "Gli albori del melodramma." Also his book "Musica, ballo e drammatica alla corte Medicea dal 1600 al 1640" was helpful, but I regret that Solerti was not always at his best in dissecting for reconstructive purposes the mass of contemporary data so patiently unearthed by him, since he utilized them for some rather loose and contradictory statements in his second work mentioned above.

The only definite date of performance is given by Marco da Gagliano. He says that Jacopo Corsi during carnival of 1597 had Peri's "Dafne" performed in the pres-ence of Giovanni Medici and some of the principal gentlemen of Florence. He does not specifically state that the performance took place at Corsi's palace nor that it was the first performance but it is only reasonable to interpret his remarks to that effect. Marco da Gagliano does not say, as one sometimes find stated, that he was present. Being in Florence at the time as a rising student of composition under Bati, he either based his account on personal experience or on contemporary local reports. At any rate, his account carries with it considerable weight.

Rinuccini does not mention a date of performance. He merely says that Peri's "Dafne" was performed before a few enthusiastic listeners and later in an improved form of the text at Corsi's palace before a large audience of Florentine noblemen, the Grand Duchess and the cardinals Del Monte and Montalto.

The presence of *both* these cardinals furnishes the pivotal clue. We know from the "Storia d'Etichetta" (a record of events at court by the master of ceremonies) that they actually attended on January 21, 1599, a performance of "Daf' thoughne,'

La **Dafne**—Continued.

not at Corsi's palace but at court, at the Palazzo Pitti "nella sala delle statue," the same hall in which "Euridice" was first produced one year later, on October 6, 1600. This apparent contradiction between Rinuccini and the "Storia d'Etichetta" would be a barrier to further deductions, but fortunately the household accounts of Corsi's wife are preserved and therein we find under date of January 18, 1599, the entry of a certain sum "a Romolo [spenditore] per ispese fatte nei giorni che s'è fatto la comedia" and under April 23 a similar entry. This last entry *may* refer to expenditures of the Corsis for the Palazzo Pitti performance of "Dafne" but this inference is not at all obligatory. Also Signora Corsi may have made her entry for January 18 several days later but, in the absence of proof, we are justified in following the lines of least resistance and in assuming that she made her entry of January 18 for expenses incurred by a performance of "Dafne" at the latest on January 18, 1599. Since such a performance is not recorded in the "Storia d'Etichetta" it would follow that it took place at Corsi's palace, if at all, and not at court. Therewith we have a loophole for reading into Rinuccini's account that "Dafne" was performed at Corsi's palace not later than January 18, 1599, in the presence of the two cardinals who were in the city as early as January 5, 1599.*

Peri's account, at first reading, appears to be clear and definite, but, on the contrary, it is misleading. In first place, he either meant that Corsi and Rinuccini "fin l'anno 1594" *requested* him to compose "Dafne" or that at the request of these two gentlemen he *composed* "Dafne" "fin l'anno 1594." *At any rate, he does not say, though that is now commonly taught, that "Dafne" was performed in 1594.* Even if the second interpretation of his ambiguous statement is accepted, it is clear that after "Dafne" was composed "fin l'anno 1594," it must have consumed time to prepare and rehearse the work for performance. This necessarily narrows the margin of the year 1594 still more. Now, according to modern Gregorian chronology, the last months of the old Julian Florentine year 1594 coincide with the first months of our year 1595. *Consequently we are practically obliged* to look to the first months of our year 1595 as the earliest possible date of performance of "Dafne," even if Peri with his words "fin l'anno 1594" intended a reference to the first performance of his "Dafne."

Peri does not say *where* "Dafne" was performed. On the other hand *his* words, too, leave no doubt that the first performance was witnessed by only comparatively few music lovers. He then explicitly states that the work delighted the hearers "per tre anni continui che nel carnovale si rappresentò." By what turn of reasoning Solerti could interpret this clear-cut statement to mean that "Dafne" was first performed during carnival of 1594/5 and *then* during the three successive carnivals 1595/6, 1596/7, 1597/8, I am utterly unable to understand. It seems to me that Peri's words bind us to the interpretation that "Dafne" was performed during three successive carnivals *inclusive* of the first (apparently more or less tentative) performance.

Pietro Bardi, conte di Vernio, who was an eye and ear witness, said in 1634 of this performance:

---

* The question suggests itself: Were perhaps these cardinals in each other's company in Florence at some earlier date, which would help to establish the correct chronology of "Dafne"? Alessandro Guidotti says in his dedication of the score of Emilio de' Cavalieri's "Rappresentatione di anima et di corpo" (Roma, Nicolò Mutii MDC): ". . . nel 1595 il *Giuoco della cieca* alla presenza de gl'illustrissimi cardinali Monte, e Mont' Alto, e del Sereniss. arciduca Ferdinando." This is corroborated by a letter written on November 14, 1595, from Florence by Piermaria Cecchini to Giov. Battista Laderchi, secretary of the duke of Ferrara. These two documents offset any argument that may be derived from the fact that neither the "Storia d'Etichetta" nor Settimani in his diary mention the presence of the cardinal del Monte when speaking of the performance of Cavalieri's "Il Giuoco della cieca" at the Palazzo Pitti on October 29, 1595. On the other hand, in none of the various sources is any allusion whatsoever made to a performance of "Dafne" in October 1595 at the Corsi palace in the presence of these two cardinals. Nor is this surprising, since the first performance of "Dafne," according to both Peri and Marco da Gagliano, took place during *carnival*, whatever the year of first performance may have been. There appears to be no record of both cardinals mentioned being in Florence at the same time except in October 1595 and during carnival 1599.

Of course, there always remains the possibility of a misprint in either Peri's 1594 or Marco da Gagliano's 1597. However, we are not justified in assuming a misprint— which, by the way, so far as I can see, would not simplify matters—until circumstantial or direct evidence obliges us to do so.

La **Dafne**—Continued.

"La prima poesia, che in istile rappresentativo fosse cantata in palco, fu la *Favola di Dafne* del Signor Ottavio Rinuccini, messa in musica dal Peri con poco numero di suoni, con brevità di scene, e in piccola stanza recitata, e privatamente cantata, e io restai stupido per la meraviglia."

Of a "Dafne" by Caccini not a word is said, though Bardi's hereditary interest in Caccini was pronounced.

Carnival began in Florence like in other Italian cities end of December. This would imply that Peri's "Dafne" was first performed in 1595 during carnival, repeated during carnival 1595/6 and again repeated during carnival 1596/7 *or*, if we adhere to Marco da Gagliano's date of carnival 1597 as that of the first performance, that "Dafne" was first performed during carnival 1597, repeated during carnival 1597/8 and again repeated during carnival 1598/99.

If we accept the first alternative, then neither Solerti's nor my interpretation of the meaning of "tre anni continui" could possibly carry us down to the performance or performances in January, *i. e.* carnival, 1599, at which the two cardinals undoubtedly were present. It would imply that Peri observed silence on the most conspicuous performance of his "Dafne" recorded. That is hardly credible.

If we accept Marco da Gagliano's carnival 1597 as the date of the first performance and further accept my conjecture that the Palazzo Pitti performance of January 21, 1599, was preceded by a performance at Corsi's palace not later than January 18, 1599, before the same two cardinals, then the contradictions between the contemporary reports would seem to vanish.

This theory that "Dafne" was first performed in carnival 1597 seems to be weakened by the long interval between "fin l'anno 1594" the earliest possible date of composition and carnival 1597, the deducted date of first performance. True, but we have seen that it is not at all necessary to argue that Peri composed "Dafne" "fin l'anno 1594" (which may mean January, February, even March of our 1595). If "fin l'anno 1594" he merely was requested by Corsi and Rinuccini to try his hand at an operatic setting of "Dafne," then it stands to reason, as this was a venture into a virgin field of composition, that Peri did not go about his task in a hurry. Indeed his words "onde fatta udire a quei Signori la mia openione" would seem to imply preliminary deliberation and tests before he demonstrated to them "questo nuovo modo di cantare" and the actual composition of such "nuove musiche," as Peri—prior to Caccini—called them in the dedication of his "Euridice" score, with such a *raffinement* of careful attention to the setting of the verses as Riemann has revealed to us lately, presumably at that statge of the operatic game was not a matter of just a few days. Furthermore, if the work was first performed during carnival 1597, rehearsals, etc., must have preceded the performance so that after all the interval between "fin l'anno 1594" and carnival 1597 is narrowed perceptibly.

Finally, the acceptance of carnival 1597 as the date of first performance would explain readily why Peri, who certainly was not a seeker after priority, while insisting on his own different manner of procedure, in his "Euridice" preface, should so unreservedly have credited Emilio de' Cavalieri with the priority of making heard "la nostra musica sulle scene." If Peri's "Dafne" had been composed "fin l'anno 1594" and performed early in 1595, this tribute to Emilio de' Cavalieri would be just a trifle too liberal. On the other hand, if Peri's "Dafne" was not performed until carnival 1597, then Peri's tribute would be entirely plausible and justified, since Emilio de' Cavalieri created somewhat of a sensation with his scenic musical pastoral "Il Giuoco della cieca," performed on October 29, 1595, at the Palazzo Pitti in continuation of his pastoral experiments "Il satiro" and "Disperazione di Fileno," both of the year 1590 and the texts of all three by Laura Guidiccioni.

Without claiming to have unravelled the knotty problem, I believe the chronological history of "Dafne" to be about about as follows:

Not later than "fin l'anno 1594" Rinuccini's "Dafne" text was ready in its original form for a composer. Not earlier than "fin l'anno 1594" **Peri** began to compose it. The first performance took place before a small audience of connoisseurs at Corsi's palace during carnival 1597. The work was repeated during carnival 1597/8 at Corsi's palace in the original or in the improved version of which Rinuccini speaks. The work was again repeated, this time surely in the improved version, at Corsi's palace before the two cardinals Del Monte and Montalto not later than January 18 (carnival) 1599 and again, but at the Palazzo Pitti before the same cardinals and a large audience of Florentine nobility, on January 21, 1599.

From the household accounts of Signora Corsi we further know that "Dafne" must again have been performed at the Corsi palace late in August, 1600, and it is perhaps for this performance that the libretto (of course the improved version; the

La **Dafne**—Continued.

original version is not extant) was printed. It should be noted that Signora Corsi does not mention Peri.

Again "Dafne" was revived on October 26, 1604, at the Palazzo Pitti (not at the Corsi palace, as Gandolfi incorrectly stated) in honor of the duke of Parma. The libretto for this performance (a reissue of the 1600 ed. with new title page and negligible differences. For the differences between the texts of 1600, 1604 and 1608 *see* 2d vol. of Solerti's "Gli albori del melodrama") exists, whereas no copy of the libretto used for the performance at Mantova in 1608 of Marco da Gagliano's "Dafne" in a further revision of the text by Rinuccini, has been traced. Possibly no such libretto was published. The performance of 1604 is recorded in Tinghi's diary, which forms the substance of Solerti's fascinating book "Musica, ballo e drammatica alla corte Medicea dal 1600 al 1640." It should be noted that Tinghi does not mention a composer.

Whose score was used for these performances of August 1600 and October 26, 1604? Giulio Caccini started on his voyage to France in September 1604. Consequently this fact together with his own statement that his "Dafne" music was performed at Corsi's palace, whereas the 1604 performance occurred at the Palazzo Pitti, excludes Caccini. The probabilities are that Peri's score was used.

That Caccini's "Dafne" music was not used for performance during Peri's "tre anni continui," I think, is a fairly safe hypothesis, especially as Peri does not mention interpolations from a score by Caccini, whereas he did not hesitate to state that some of Caccini's "Euridice" music was used in the first performance of his own "Euridice" on October 6, 1600. That Caccini's "Dafne" music was not drawn upon for the performance on January 21, 1599, is certain, since it did not take place at the Corsi palace but at the Palazzo Pitti.

There remains the performance late in August 1600. To this Peri laid no claim and as no composer is mentioned by Signora Corsi, it is permissible to argue that at least for this performance music by Caccini was used. Permissible but not obligatory, because Caccini's words "la musica che io feci nella favola della Dafne del Sig. Ottavio Rinuccini, rappresentata in casa del Sig. Jacopo Corsi" do not necessarily imply either that he composed the whole text or even that the music composed by him was used in a stage performance of Rinuccini's "Dafne" favola. What makes the use of music by Caccini even in August 1600 doubtful is, that Caccini forgot—and he was not given to forgetting such things—to mention his share in the history of "Dafne" in his "Euridice" preface, though he had ample time to incorporate pertinent remarks therein! For the same psychological reason it is doubtful that "Dafne" music by Caccini was performed at all up to the time that he sent his "Nuove musiche" to the press in 1602, since they, too, fail to mention any music composed by him for Rinuccini's "Dafne"!

On purpose so far nothing has been said about Corsi's "Dafne" music. This much Peri makes perfectly clear, that Jacopo **Corsi** was the first to compose "Dafne" music and that Corsi had already composed "arie bellissime per quella favola" before he, Peri, undertook to set the "Dafne" text according to his own ideas. Peri's account does not permit us to argue that these arias by Corsi were interpolated for the performances of Peri's score. In view of Peri's silence on this point, the correctness of Marco da Gagliano's statement that Peri "approvato parte dell' arie già composte, si diede a comporre *l'altre*" which would seem to imply that in carnival 1597 a score was used, largely by Peri, but partly by Corsi, becomes rather doubtful.

A disturbing element is thrown into the chronology of "Dafne" as outlined above by the entry of the "Storia d'Etichetta" for the performance of "Dafne" on January 21, 1599. The "Storia d'etichetta" does not mention Peri, but says "si fece nella sala delle statue la pastorella in musica *del* Sig. Jacopo Corsi." It is of course possible that Corsi had composed the entire "Dafne" text in the meantime and a literal interpretation of the entry in the "Storia d'etichetta" would therefore mean that a "Dafne" score by Corsi was performed on January 21, 1599. While conceding this possibility, something else must be taken into consideration which weakens this possibility very much.

The courtier diarists do not seem to have taken the trouble to inform themselves about the composers who furnished the music for these court entertainments. Thus the ambassador of Parma wrote to his duke about "Euridice": "si rappresentò in casa del Granduca da un gentiluomo della città la favola di Orfeo et Euridice in versi e sempre in musica, che durò un ora e mezza." Furthermore Tinghi attributed the score of "Euridice" to Emilio de' Cavalieri and just as hazy were Giovanni del Maestro's notions about the composer of "Euridice" when he said in his "Memorie": "dopo desinare si fece una commedia nel Palazzo de' Pitti sul salone di sopra, tutta in musica *opera del Signor Jacomo Corsi* e materia del Signor Ottavio Rinuccini." The correct state of affairs was, however, recorded by Michelangnolo Buonarotti in

La **Dafne**—Continued.

his official "Descrizione" (1600) of the festivities. Without mentioning Peri or Caccini, he wrote: "la onde avendo il Signor Jacopo Corsi, *fatta messere in musica* con grande studio la Euridice, affettuosa e gentilissima favola del Signor Ottavio Rinuccini."

Thus, quite in keeping with the ideas of the time, Jacopo Corsi, Maecenas and "Padre" of music (as Marco da Gagliano calls him), was considered to have had a kind of proprietory right as author in the entertainments planned and financed by him for court. It was of no particular interest to courtiers to know the names of professionals engaged to provide the music for entertainments under the auspices of a gentleman like Corsi. Other librettos of the time have come to my notice which bear out this impression. In such cases, as in the case of "Dafne," words like "la pastorella in musica del Sig. Jacopo Corsi" would therefore by no means always signify *composed* by Corsi, but the "pastorella in musica" which Corsi engaged some musician to compose for entertainments planned by him.

Notwithstanding the plain historical fact of priority—Rinuccini's "primier le belle vie calpesti" is more than a mere poet's compliment—very little interest was taken in Corsi's share in the first opera until, quite accidentally, Miss Hortense Panum, while collecting material for her and Mr. Behrend's history of music, discovered, at the Brussels Conservatory library in 1888, two excerpts from "Dafne" in a collection of (late 16th and early 17th century) monodies, and these excerpts bore the heading, "del Sr Jacopo Corsi." Miss Panum then published these two excerpts (the one Apollo's "Non curi la mia pianta," the other the final chorus, "Bella ninfa fugitiva") in the Musikalisches Wochenblatt, 1888 (y. 19, p. 346–347). This fact was not mentioned by Mr. Wotquenne when he, in 1901, with not quite correct historical notes, published the two Corsi *torsi* in photographic facsimile on two fly-leaves between p. 46–47 of his "Annexe I" of the "Catalogue de la Bibliothèque du Conservatoire Royal de musique. "Bella ninfa" was also published by Hortense Panum and W. Behrend in their "Illustreret Musikhistorie," 1905 (p. 218–219), and both pieces by Solerti in his "Gli albori del melodramma" (I, Suppl.).

It is one of the caprices of fate, indeed, that the "Dafne" scores of both **Peri** and **Caccini** should have been lost, but that music by Jacopo **Corsi**, who was the first to compose at least parts of Rinuccini's text of this, the first opera, should have been preserved!

Dafni. Favola boschereccia per musica. Da rappresentarsi nel Teatro Malvezzi l'anno MDCXCVI . . .

Bologna, gli eredi del Sarti, n. d. 72 p. 13^{cm}.

Prologue and three acts. Dedication by "Gli Uniti" and notice by the anonymous author, Eustacchio Manfredi, to the reader, beginning:

"Tu leggi in questo piccol volume il drama stesso, che vedrai rappresētare sù queste scene; ne per altro si è dato alle stampe, che per aiutar il tuo orecchio mentre l'udirai à cantare. Voglio dire, che egli non è fatto per leggerlo fuori di questa occasione, e che quando quest' opera sia udita con diletto hà attenuto il suo intento. Siasi ella tragedia, o pastorale, o tragicomedia, o qualsivoglia altro poema, che importa? ella è un divertimento per musica addattato al gusto presente, ed al genio della maggior parte, e però dispensato dalle leggi rigorose della Poetica . . ."

The composer, Giuseppe Antonio Vincenzo **Aldrovandini**, is not mentioned.
First performed, as indicated, August 18, 1696.   ML 50.2.D2

Il Dafni. Tragedia satirica. Da rappresentarsi in musica nel famosissimo Teatro Grimano di S. Gio. Grisostomo l'anno 1705.

Venezia, Marino Rossetti, 1705. 82 p. 14½^{cm}.

Five acts. By conte Girolamo Frigimelica Roberti, who does not sign his lengthy "Proemio" (p. 3–11) giving his theories of a proper "tragedia satirica." Argument and scenario. Carlo Francesco **Pollaroli**, the composer, is not mentioned.
                                                              SCHATZ 8279

Dal finto il vero. Commedia per musica di Saverio Zini da rappresentarsi nel Teatro Nuovo nella primavera di quest' anno 1776 . . .

Napoli, n. publ., 1776. 60 p. 15^{cm}.

Three acts. Cast, scenario, and name of **Paisiello** as the composer. SCHATZ 7604

Dal finto il vero—Continued.

— **Dal finto il vero.**   Dramma giocoso per musica da rappresentarsi nel Piccolo Teatro di S. A. E. di Sassonia.

Dresda, n. publ., 1782.   119 p.   15½^{cm}.

Two acts.   Without Zini's name, but with that of **Paisiello**.   German title page "Das ist er ja selbst" and text face Italian.
First performed, as indicated, 1782.   SCHATZ 7605

Dalisa.   Dramma per musica da rappresentarsi nel Teatro Grimani di S. Samuele nella fiera dell' Ascensione dell' anno MDCCXXX.

Venezia, Carlo Buonarigo, n. d.   45, [1] p.   15^{cm}.

Three acts.   By conte Niccolò Minato, with alterations by Domenico Lalli, who signs the dedication.   Argument, scenario, cast, and name of Johann Adolph **Hasse** as the composer.   SCHATZ 4577

Daliso e Delmita.   Dramma per musica da rappresentarsi nel nobilissimo nuovo Teatro di Padova nella fiera del Santo l'anno 1789 . . .

Padova, Conzatti, n. d.   52 p.   17½^{cm}.

Two acts.   Dedication, argument, cast, scenario, and name of the composer, Francesco **Bianchi**.   The text is, according to Schatz, a later version of Giovanni di Gamerra's "Delmita e Daliso." On p. 46–52 argument, cast, and full description of "Ercole e Dejanira, ballo tragico in cinque atti," by Francesco Clerico, the composer not being mentioned.   SCHATZ 997

Daliso, e Delmita.   Dramma per musica rappresentato nell' Imperial Teatro di Vienna per l'arrivo de' Reali Sovrani di Toscana nell' estate dell' anno 1776.

n. i., n. d.   40 p.   19½^{cm}.

Two acts.   Argument and on p. 4 "Il tenente De Gamerra poeta dell' Imperial Teatro al pubblico di Vienna" with the opening remark:
"I primi passi che avanzo sull' orme gloriose del mio immortal maestro dovrebbero farmi temere una caduta, se non mi vedessi da lui incoraggito e sostenuto."
First performed on July 29, 1776, with music by Antiono **Salieri** (not mentioned) as indicated, but with title "Delmita e Daliso."   ML 48.A5   v.45

La dama avventuriera.   Commedia per musica di Giuseppe Palomba da rappresentarsi nel Nuovo Teatro de' Fiorentini per prim' opera di quest' anno 1780.

Napoli, n. publ., 1780.   67 p.   15^{cm}.

Three acts.   Cast and name of Pietro **Guglielmi** as the composer.   SCHATZ 4240

La dama immaginaria.   Azione teatrale da rappresentarsi nel Teatro Giustiniani di San Moisè il carnovale dell' anno 1777.

[Venezia], n. publ., n. d.   54 p.   17½^{cm}.

Two parts.   Cast and name of Gennaro **Astaritta** as composer.   The author, Pietro Antonio Bagliacca, is not mentioned.   SCHATZ 370

La dama pastorella.   O. T. of Salieri's La cifra.

La dama soldato.   Dramma giocoso per musica da rappresentarsi nel nobilissimo Teatro Giustiniani in San Moisè l'autunno dell' anno 1792.

Venezia, Modesto Fenzo, 1792.   17½^{cm}.

Incomplete after p. 54.   Two acts.   By Caterino Mazzolà, who is not mentioned. Cast, scenario, and name of Giuseppe **Gazzaniga** as the composer.   SCHATZ 3660

La dama soldato. Dramma giocoso per musica, da rappresentarsi nel Teatro elettorale, di Caterino Mazzolà . . .

Dresda, n. publ., 1791. 147 p. 15½ᶜᵐ.

Two acts. Johann Gottlieb **Naumann** is mentioned. German title page "Die dame als soldat" and text face Italian.

First performed, as indicated, May 7, 1791. Schatz 7043

— Was thut die liebe nicht! Eine nach der oper: La dama soldato des Signore Mazzola frei bearbeitete operette in zwei aufzuegen. Die musik ist von herrn kapellmeister Naumann.

Leipzig, Wilhelm Heinsius der juengere, 1793. 87 p. 16ᶜᵐ.

Translator not mentioned and unknown to Schatz, but comparison shows that the text is practically the same as in our Hamburg, 1804, libretto, attributed by Schatz to Christian August Vulpius.

First performed at Königsberg, Ackermannsches theater, January 31, 1796. Schatz 7044

Die dame als soldat. Tr. of Naumann's La dama soldato.

Damira placata. Drama da rappresentarsi nel loco ov' era il Teatro Zane à S. Moisè. Posto in musica dal Signor Marc' Antonio Ziani. Consacrato al genio de' curiosi.

Venetia, Francesco Nicolini, 1680. 48 p. 14ᶜᵐ.

Three acts. By Filippo Acciajuoli, who is not mentioned. Prefatory poem to the "signori curiosi," argument, and scenario.

First performed, as indicated, carnival, 1680. Schatz 11200

Damon and Phillida. A ballad opera in one act. As it is perform'd at the Theatre-Royal, Drury-Lane, by His Majesty's servants. With the musick prefix'd to each song.

London, Printed for J. and R. Tonson, in the Strand, 1765. 31 p. 19½ᶜᵐ.

Lacks front. On p. [5], a publisher's list.

The 15 airs are mostly printed with their titles.

Schatz says, under "Damon and Phillida:" "Words by Colley Cibber, altered from his pastoral, 'Love in a riddle.' The music partly composed, partly selected out of various ballads and dance tunes, and adapted to the words of the songs by Henry **Carey.** First acted at the Theatre Royal in Drury Lane, London, 1729." The date of performance and Carey's connection with "Damon and Phillida" may be open to discussion, but it is a fact, as comparison proved, that "Damon and Phillida," both as to characters, words, and the airs used, is kin to Cibber's "Love in a riddle." If Clarence says "*entirely* taken" therefrom, he seems to be mistaken, but certain parts have been lifted verbatim from "Love in a riddle," for instance, from the air III, "Tell me, Philly, tell me roundly," to air VII, "I'll range around the shady bow'rs." The modus operandi seems to have been to lift the desired scenes out of "Love in a riddle," and to connect them with new dialogue. Whether this condensed version under a new title is due to Cibber himself, I am unable to tell.

Genest says, under Drury Lane, January 7, 1729, when writing of the first performance of Cibber's "new pastoral," "Love in a riddle," on that day: "not long after, formed the best scenes of 'Love in a riddle' into a musical entertainment—they have been frequently acted as 'Damon and Phillida.'"

The British Museum has the work in the London 1729 edition.

ML 50.5.D17
Second copy (perfect, with front.). Longe 26

— Damon and Phillida. A ballad opera. In one act. By Colley Cibber, Esq.

[241]–256 p. 19ᶜᵐ. (Collection of the most esteemed farces and entertainments, t. v, Edinburgh, 1792.)

Drury-Lane cast. Schatz 11753E

Damon and Phillida. Altered from Cibber into a comic opera. With the addition of new songs and chorusses. As it is performed at the Theatre Royal in Drury-Lane.

London, T. Lowndes, T. Caslon [etc] 1768. 1 p. l., 34 p. 18½ᶜᵐ.

One act. Cast, in which Cymon was played by Charles **Dibdin,** who is not mentioned as the author resp. composer responsible for this new version of "Damon and Phillida." Genest's date of first performance, February 23, 1769, is contradicted by the title page, it would seem.   LONGE 322

The **Danaides;** or, The daughters of Danaus. A tragi-pantomime ballet.

Noverre, Jean George, Works, Tr. from the French, London, 1783, v. 3, p. 1–28. 21½ᶜᵐ.

Argument and detailed description of the nine scenes.   GV 1787.N8

Les **Danaides,** tragedie-lyrique, en cinq actes, représentée pour la premiere fois, sur le Théatre de l'Académie-royale de musique, le lundi 19 avril 1784 . . .

Paris, P. de Lormel, 1784. viii, 56 p. 23ᶜᵐ.

Five acts. By Du Roullet and baron von Tschudi, who are not mentioned. On p. iv, the note: "La musique est de MM. le chevalier **Gluck & Salieri.**" Cast and avertissement, which reads, in part:

"On nous a communiqué un manuscrit de M. de Calzabiggi, auteur de l'Orphée & de l'Alceste italiens, dont nous nous sommes beaucoup aidés. Nous avons emprunté quelques idées du ballet des Danaides du célèbre M. Noverre, ce moderne rival des Batilles & des Pilades; nons y avons joint les nôtres, & du tout nous avons composé notre plan.

"Un de nos amis, que sa famille nous a défendu de nommer, a bien voulu, pour accélérer l'ouvrage, mettre en vers une partie de notre composition, & ce n'est pas certainement celle dont le style paraîtra le plus négligé. La mort vient de nous enlever cet excellent homme connu par plusieurs ouvrages en prose & en vers, également estimés."

The work by Calsabigi alluded to is supposed to have been his "Ipermnestra o Le Danaidi." Gluck's name as joint-composer was merely used to help the opera to a success. After twelve performances Gluck notified the public that his collaboration had consisted merely in giving his former pupil, Salieri, expert advice.

Clément and Larousse give April 26, 1784, as the date of first performance. So does Schatz, stating that the date of April 19 in the libretto and in the score is an error.
                                                                                    SCHATZ 9285

Le **Danaidi.** A. T. of the ballet L'Ipermestra.

Le **Danaidi,** ballet. *See* Borghi's La morte di Semiramide.

Le **Danaidi.** Dramma per musica da rappresentarsi nel Teatro alla Scala il carnevale dell' anno 1795 . . .

Milano, Gio. Batista Bianchi, n. d. 56 p. 16ᶜᵐ.

Three acts. By Gaetano Sertor, who is not mentioned. Impresario's dedication, dated Milan, December 26, 1794, argument, cast, scenario, and name of Angelo **Tarchi** as the composer. On p. [47]–56, prefatory note, cast, description, but not name of the composer of the music of Gaetano Gioja's "Cora, o La vergine del sole, ballo eroico pantomimo diviso in cinque atti." His other (comic) ballet was "La vindemmia o La contadina impertinente."   SCHATZ 10217

Die **dankbare tochter.** A. T. of Kuerzinger's Julie.

La **danse.** *See* Fragments, composés . . . de l'acte . . . de La danse.

Il Danubio consolato. Poemetto drammatico nel giorno del glo-riosissimo nome della Sac. Ces. R. Maestà di Giuseppe I. augustissimo imperador de' Romani.

Pietro Antonio Bernardoni, Poemi drammatici, parte terza, Vienna, van Ghelen, 1707, p. 123–136. 16½ᶜᵐ.

The composer, Attilio **Ariosti,** is not mentioned.
First performed, as indicated, March 19, 1707.   ML 49.A2B4

La danza.

Metastasio, Poesie, Parigi, vedova Quillau, 1755, t. ii, [455]–464 p. 16ᶜᵐ.

One act.   ML 49.A2M42

—**La danza.** Cantata a due voci, eseguita la prima volte alla presenza de' sovrani da una dama, e da un cavaliere l'anno 1744, con musica del Bonno.

[385]–392 p. 26ᶜᵐ. (Pietro Metastasio, Opere, t. i, Parigi, vedova Herissant, 1780.)

ML 49.A2M44

La danza di Diana.

p. 105–141. 15½ᶜᵐ. (Ottavio Tronsarelli, Drammi musicali, Roma, Francesco Corbelletti, 1632.)

Ballet. One act. No composer mentioned.   ML 49.A2T7

Daphne oder Die fruhlingsfeier in Arkadien. *See* Hensel's Die geisterbeschwoerung.

Daphne and Amintor. A comic opera, as it is performed at the Theatre Royal in Drury-Lane. A new edition.

London, J. Newbery, W. Griffin [etc.], 1766. front., 1 p. l., iii, [4]–30 p. 19½ᶜᵐ.

One act with prologue. Cast and preface, in which the author, Isaac Bickerstaff (not mentioned), says that instead of utilizing the two existing English translations of St. Foix' "Oracle," he thought it "juster to give a more faulty paraphrase of my own.

"With regard to the music, I apprehend it must please; as it has been selected with the greatest attention, both to the beauty of the airs, and its effect upon the theatre. There are, indeed, some people, who may possibly be of opinion, that I ought to have chosen old English and Scotch ballads; or got music composed in the same taste. But, in fact, such sort of compositions scarce deserve the name of music at all; at least they can have little or no merit on the stage, where everything ought to be supported by a degree of action and character."

A pasticcio made up from music by **Shalon, Vento, Cocchi, Piccinni, Mon-signy.** Tuft's statement that James Hook "wrote some of the music" is not borne out by Squire's Brit. Mus. catalogue, which merely shows that later on interpola-tions by Hook were used.

First performed, as indicated, October 8, 1765.   Longe 26

—**Daphne and Amintor.** A comic opera. Altered from the Oracle of Monsieur St. Foix and Mrs. Cibber. By Isaac Bickerstaff, Esq.

[367]–380 p. 19ᶜᵐ. (Collection of the most esteemed farces and entertainments, t. v, Edinburgh, 1792.)

Drury-Lane cast.   Schatz 11753E

Daphnis and Amaryllis: a pastoral. The music by Mr. Handel, and other eminent masters . . .

Exon, Printed by Andrew Brice, 1766. 16 p. 19^{cm}.

Two acts. The text is the same as of James Harris' "The spring."   LONGE 293

Daphnis et Alcimaduro, pastouralo toulouzeno de M. de Mondonvillo, accoumoudadou à noste patois de Mountpellié, per estre executado dins nostro Academio de musiquo lou 25 dou mès d'Aous d'aquesto annado. Nouvelle édition.

Paris, Didot, 1778. 27, [1] p. 20^{cm}.

Dedicatory poem and Avis, in which it is said that in order to render the performance at the "Concert de cette Ville" easier it became necessary to alter the text somewhat on account of the great difficulty of translating the patois of Toulouse into that of Montpellier. Where the translation was impossible without interfering with Mondonville's music, it was deemed best to retain the words in the patois of Toulouse. Text and music by **Mondonville.**

First performed at Fontainebleau, October 29, 1754.   ML 50.2.D25M6

Daphnis et Chloé.

Libretto of first act and outline of second of this unfinished opera by Jean Jaques **Rousseau,** text by Olivier de Corancez, precedes on 2 p. l. the score of the "Fragmens de Daphnis et Chloé," Paris, Espru, 1779. The text of the duo "Dans un nouveau parentage" was by Rousseau, who has told us that he composed these fragments 1775.   M 1500.R89

Plan, for the first act of **Daraxes.** An opera: of two acts only.

[186]–198 p. 21^{cm}. (Aaron Hill, Dramatic works, London, T. Lownds, 1760, vol. ii.)

The plan for *both* acts is followed by the complete text of first act of "Daraxes, a pastoral opera."   LONGE 326

Darby's return.—A comic sketch. As performed at the theatre in this city, with universal applause   (Written in 1789, by Mr. William Dunlap). Characters [follows cast].

For this one-act libretto *see* the New York magazine, January, 1790, p. 47–51. Dunlap prescribes that as an introduction "some airs from the Pcor Soldier" be played. I do not know who arranged the music for this potpourris overture and of the few ballad airs used in the sketch.

First performed, as indicated, November 24, 1789.   AP 2.A2N5

Dardanus, tragédie de Mr Rameau, représentée par l'Académie royale de musique, avec les changemens faits par l'auteur en 1760.

Paris, Aux dépéns de l'Academie, 1761. 27 p. 21^{cm}.

The author, Charles Antoine Le Clerc de La Bruère, is not mentioned.

First performed at Paris, Académie royale de musique, November 19, 1739.

     ML 50.2.D27R2

Dardanus, tragédie en quatre actes; représentée pour la premiere fois, par l'Academie royale de musique, le mardi 30 novembre 1784.

Paris, P. de Lormel, 1784. x, 46 p. 23^{cm}.

Four acts. Cast, name of **Sacchini** as the composer and long "avertissement" (p. iii–vi) in which Guillard gives at length his reasons for the changes he made in de La Bruyère's "Dardanus" of 1739 resp. of 1744. The verses which he added are printed throughout with quotation marks. This preface is decidedly of interest from a dramaturgic standpoint.

First performed at Trianon, before the King on September 18, 1784.

     SCHATZ 9217

Dardanus—Continued.

— **Dardanus**, tragedie en trois actes, représentée devant Leurs Majestés à Fontainebleau, le 20 octobre 1785; et à Paris, sur le Théatre de l'Académie royale de musique, le vendredi 13 janvier 1786.

Paris, P. de Lormel, 1786. 40 p. 24ᶜᵐ.

Cast. On p. [2] the note: "Le poëme est de la Bruere remis au théatre avec les changemens, par M. Guillard. La musique est de M. Sacchini."

In his 3-act version, too, Guillard's added verses are printed in quotation. The reduction resulted from a condensation of the second and third acts into one act.

SCHATZ 9248

Il **Dario**, dramma per musica da rappresentarsi nel Nuovo Teatro alla Cavallerizza nella fiera di Pascha dell' anno MDCCLIII in Lipsia.

n. i., 1753. 115 p. 17ᶜᵐ.

Three acts. Author not mentioned and unknown to me. German text faces Italian. Argument, cast, scenario and note: "La musica è di diversi celebri compositori."

ML 50.2.D29

Dario. Dramma da rappresentarsi nel Regio Teatro di Berlino con musica del Sign. Felice Alessandri . . . il carnovale dell' anno 1791. Composto con balli, pantomimi e insieme analoghi da Antonio de' Filistri.

Berlino, Haude e Spener, n. d. 167 p. 15½ᶜᵐ.

German title-page "Darius" and text face Italian. Three acts. Argument, cast, and scenario.

SCHATZ 144

Dario. L. T. of Freschi's L'incoronazione di Dario.

Dario in Babilonia. Dramma per musica di Francesco Beverini, da rappresentarsi nel Teatro Vendramino à S. Salvatore l'anno 1671 . . .

Venetia, Francesco Nicolini, 1671. 76 p. 14ᶜᵐ.

Three acts. Author's dedication dated Venice, January 24, 1671, argument, notice to reader, and scenario, but without the name of the composer, Giovanni Antonio **Boretti.**

SCHATZ 1217

Il **Dario ravivato.** Drama del Sonnolento Tassista. Da rappresentarsi in musica . . .

Venetia, Francesco Batti, 1675. front., 72 p. 13½ᶜᵐ.

Three acts. By Giovanni Antonio Bonis. Author's dedication dated Venice, January 6, 1675, notice to the reader, argument, scenario. Composers not mentioned, and unknown to Schatz, who records this as a pasticcio.

SCHATZ 11318

Darius. Tr. of Alessandri's Dario.

Das ist er ja selbst. Tr. of Paisiello's Dal finto il vero.

Dasius ein junger blutzeug Jesu Christi. Ein singspiel in zween choeren [!] Die musikalischen toene zum singspiele hat verfertigt herr Michael Demler, componist und claviermeister in Augsburg.

On p. [3–12] of "Trebellius koenig der Bulgarer . . . ein trauerspiel . . . aufgefuehrt von der studirenden jugend des katholischen schulhauses zu Augsburg bei St. Salvator den 2. 3. und 6 ten herbstmondes [Sept.] 1774. Gedruckt . . . bey Joseph Simon Hueber . . ."

With cast. On p. [5] "in zween aufzuegen." The author is not mentioned and is unknown to Schatz.

SCHATZ 2504

The **daughters of Danaus.** A. T. of Noverre's ballet The Danaides.

A day at Rome: a musical entertainment, in two acts. As it was damned at the Theatre Royal, Covent-Garden, on Thursday, October 11, 1798.

*London, H. D. Symonds and G. Cawthorne, 1798. vii, [1], 32 p. 21*cm.

Cast and preface by the author, Charles Smith, of date James Street, Adelphi, October 20, 1798, in which he denies that Caleb Whitefoord wrote any of the text, and asserts that the text is correctly printed from the prompter's book, except the first song in the second act,

"Where the original is restored, in lieu of a substitute written at the request of one of the performers, on such short notice, that she had not sufficient time to commit it to her memory."

He continues by saying:

"It was not till towards the middle of the piece that the aukward dress, and a deficiency in the recitation of one of the actors, occasioned marks of disapprobation; which increased so as to preclude the possibility of hearing even the elegant and scientific music of [Thomas] **Attwood.**" LONGE 254

De gustibus non est disputandum. Dramma di tre atti per musica. Rappresentato in Venezia il carnovale dell' anno MDCCLIV.

*Carlo Goldoni, Opere teatrali, Venezia, Zatta e figli, 1788–95, v. 38, [67]–125 p. 18½*cm.

PQ

De gustibus non est disputandum. Dramma giocoso per musica. Da rappresentarsi nel Teatro Tron di S. Cassiano il carnovale dell' anno 1754.

*Venezia, Modesto Fenzo, 1754. 59 p. 15½*cm.

Three acts. Cast, scenario, and one of Carlo Goldoni's (not mentioned) charming prefaces, which reads in part:

"Lettor carissimo, se uno tu sei di quegli, a' quali abbia io protestato di non volere quest' anno, e forse mai più comporre de' simili drammi buffi, voglio anche communicarti la ragione, che ad astenermene mi obbligava, ed i motivi, che mi hanno fatto dal mio proponimento discendere. Il dramma serio per musica, come tu saprai, è un genere di teatrale componimento di sua natura imperfetto, non potendosi osservare in esso veruna di quelle regole, che sono alla tragedia prescritte. Molto più imperfetto il dramma buffo esser dee perchè cercandosi dagli scrittori di tai barzellette servire più alla musica, che a sè medesimi e fondando, o nel ridicolo o nello spettacolo la speranza della riuscita, non badano seriamente alla condotta, ai caratteri, all' intreccio, alla verità, come in una commedia buona dovrebbe farsi. Questa è poi la ragione per cui cotai libretti, che si dicono *buffi*, rarissime volte incontrano. Io ne ho fatti parecchi, che il Tevernini librajo in Merceria alla Providenza ha potuto stamparne quattro tometti in 12. Di questi alcuni hanno avuto fortuna grande, altri mediocre, ed alcuni altri l' hanno sofferta pessima, e questi forse saranno i men cattivi, e più regolati de' primi. L' esito dipende tal' ora dalla musica, per lo più dagli attori, e sovente ancora dalle decorazioni. Il popolo decide a seconda dell' esito, se l' opera è a terra, il libro è pessimo. Se è un poco serio, è cattivo perchè non fa ridere; se è troppo ridicolo è cattivo perchè non vi è nobiltà . . ."

Goldoni does not mention Giuseppe **Scarlatti** as the composer of this "operetta" as he calls it. SCHATZ 9543

The **dead alive:** A comic opera. In two acts. As it is performed at the theatres in London and Dublin. By John O'Keefe, Esq.

*Dublin, Sold by the booksellers, 1783. 45 p. 16½*cm.

Cast. The composer, Samuel **Arnold,** is not mentioned.

First performed June 16, 1781, as indicated. LONGE 148

— The **dead alive:** or, The double funeral. A comic opera. In two acts. With additions and alterations. As performed by the

The **dead alive**—Continued.

Old American company in New-York: with universal applause. By John O'Keefe . . . with an account of the author.

New-York, Printed by Hodge, Allen, and Campbell, 1789. 1 p. l., iv, [7]–46 p. 18½^{cm}.

Cast. Composed by Samuel **Arnold**, who is not mentioned.
First performed June 16, 1781, at the Haymarket, London; in America, as indicated, September 24, 1789.   ML 50.6.D3

The **death of captain Faulknor**; or, British heroism. An opera' (in one act.) As performed at the theatre Royal, Covent-Garden.

London, Glindon and co., 1795. 19 p. 20¼^{cm}.

Cast. According to the prefatory note of date London, May 6, 1795: "The dialogue of this little production, first brought forward at Mrs. Martyr's benefit, was purposely written to introduce songs, for the most part selected on the occasion. And as the words of such selected songs have not long been published in the operas to which they immediately belong, the writer of the present trifle does not think himself at liberty here to insert them. The words of the new songs, therefore, are only introduced."
Author not known to Biog. Dram., which says "not printed"! Composer unknown to me. First performed May 6, 1795 (Genest).   ML 50.2.D31

Debora e Sisara. Azione sacra per musica di Carlo Sernicola, P. A. Da rappresentarsi nel Real Teatro di S. Carlo nella quaresima dell' anno 1788 . . .

Napoli, Vincenzo Flauto, 1788. 43 p. 19^{cm}.

Two acts. Impresario's dedication dated Naples, February 10, 1788, argument, scenario, cast, and name of Pietro **Guglielmi** as the composer.   SCHATZ 4241

— **Arsinoe e Breno.** Dramma serio per musica da rappresentarsi nel Nuovo Teatro della nobiliss. Accademia Intronata di Siena l' estate dell' anno 1790.

Siena, Pazzini Carli, n. d. 40 p. 17½^{cm}.

Two acts. Argument and cast. Comparison proves that Sernicola's text of "Debora e Sisara, azione sacra" was simply, more or less, secularized into a "dramma serio" by an unknown author. For instance, whereas the words of the finale quartett of the first act "Rabbia, furor, dispetto" were retained, the original finale tutti of the second act "Tolse il ciel le nostre pene" has become "Con noi cantino le sfere." Both operas begin "Ah! qual viltade è questa," but after that their texts disagree very much oftener than not. The composer, Pietro **Guglielmi**, is not mentioned.
A footnote on p. 6 says that the title of the first ballet by Giacomo Gentili would be "La felicità nata dalle sventure" and of the second "Il bottaro." The composers of the music are not mentioned.   SCHATZ 4315

Decio sacrificato alla patria. *See* M. Curzio.

Decius and Paulina, masque. *See* The lady's triumph.

La **Deidamia.** Poema drammatico di Scipione Herrico. Da rappresentarsi nel Teatro Novissimo nell' anno 1644 . . .

Venetia, Matteo Leni e Giovanni Vecellio, 1644. 106 p. 14^{cm}.

Three acts with prologue. The author's dedication is dated January 5, 1644. The composer, Pietro Francesco **Cavalli**, is not mentioned.   SCHATZ 1745

La **Delia** o sia La sera sposa del sole. Poema dramatico di Giulio Strozzi.

Venetia, Gio. Pietro Pinelli, 1639. 80 p. 13^{cm}.

Three acts. Author's dedication dated Venice, January 20, 1639, argument, allegoria, and notice to the reader which reads in part:

La Delia—Continued.

"La musica è sorella di quella poesia, che vuole assorellarsi seco, ma, quando non s' intendono bene tra di loro, non sono ne attenenti, ne amiche.

"Il canto, che raddolcisce gli animi, riesce in due maniere un' abborita cantilena, ò quãdo s' hà da gir dietro alle chimere del poeta, ò quando dileguandosi la parola, ò la finale d' al cuna voce nell' ampiezza de' teatri, smarriscono gli uditori il filo de gli ammassati concetti. . . . Per questo io son ricorso alla stampa, acciò ch' ella sia la contracifra di que' musici, che cantano talhora più volontieri à loro medesimi, ch' agli ascoltanti . . ."

At the end of the libretto a note informs us that more than three hundred verses were dropped in the performances of the opera. The composer, Francesco Paolo Sacrati, is not mentioned. SCHATZ 9256

Le délire ou Les suites d'une erreur, comedie en un acte, en prose mêlée d'ariettes, représentée pour la premiere fois le 16 frimaire, sur le Théâtre de l'Opéra comique national, an 8. Paroles du citoyen R. St.-Cir, musique du citoyen Berton.

Paris, Du Pont, an VII. [1798–99] 1 p. l., 45 p. (incl. front.) 20^{cm}.

Text followed by 4 unnumb. pages of a book-list by Martinet, which originally can not have been issued in this form with the libretto, since one of the books is dated 1806.
First performed December 6, 1799, as indicated. ML 50.2.D35B2

Il delirio comune, per la incostanza de' genii. Drama per musica da recitarsi nel Teatro Grimani in S. Gio. Grisostomo, di Matteo Noris l'anno MDCCI . . .

Venezia, Niccolini, 1701. 70, [1] p. (incl. front.) 14^{cm}.

The additional p. contains lines omitted by the printer in II, 10. Three acts. Notice to the reader and scenario. Carlo Francesco Pollaroli, the composer, is not mentioned.
First performed fall of 1700, at the theatre mentioned, according to Schatz.
SCHATZ 8280

Delmita e Daliso. O. T. of Salieri's Daliso e Delmita.

Il Demetrio.

[149]–225 p. 19^{cm}. (Pietro Metastasio, Opere drammatiche, Venezia, Giuseppe Bettinelli, 1733–37, t. i.)

Three acts and licenza. Argument. No composer is mentioned. ML 49.A2M4

— Demetrio.

Metastasio, Poesie, Parigi, vedova Quillau, 1755, t. I, [205]–319 p. 16^{cm}.

Three acts and licenza. Argument. ML 49.A2M42

— Demetrio. Rappresentato con musica del Caldara la prima volta in Vienna, nell' interno gran teatro della Cesarea corte alla presenza de' sovrani, il dì 4 novembre 1731, per festeggiare il nome dell' imperator Carlo VI . . .

pl., [213]–334. 26^{cm}. (Pietro Metastasio, Opere, t. I, Parigi vedova Herissant, 1780.)

Three acts and licenza. Argument. ML 49.A2M44

Il Demetrio. Dramma per musica del Sig. Pietro Metastasio da rappresentarsi in Livorno nel Nuovo Teatro dagli Armeni. L'autunno dell' anno 1785 . . .

Livorno, Antonio Lami e comp., n. d. 62 p. 14½^{cm}.

Il **Demetrio**—Continued.

Two acts. Argument, cast, scenario, and impresario's prefatory note, in which he says:

"si è dovuto mutilare forse troppo quest' opera, e defraudarla di gran parte delle sue bellezze. Il togliere tutti a un tratto gl'inconvenienti, e gli abusi introdotti nelli spettacoli teatrali sarebbe cosa troppo pericolosa ad un impresario. Dal canto mio vorrei veder tornare quei tempi in cui il buon senso, il buon gusto, e la proprietà prevalevano al *gran spettacolo:* vorrei che un drama di celebre autore facesse gustare tutt' i meriti suoi, e che una rappresentazione non si riducesse ad una *Accademia di canto*, come pare che ammano ammano vada a ridursi: vorrei che la dansa si limitasse nella dansa medesima. Ma spetta ad un pubblico, non a me, a correggere gli abusi, col dar moto ad una riforma degna d'un secolo illuminato."

Composer not mentioned, and unknown to Schatz. As third ballet was given, composer of the music not mentioned, Domenico Ricciardi's "Il barbier di Siviglia."

SCHATZ 11319

Demetrio. Dramma per musica da rappresentarsi nel Nuovo Teatro di Corte . . . nel carnevale dell' anno MDCCLXXII. La poesia è dell' Sig. abbate Pietro Metastasio . . . La musica e dell' Sig. Andrea de Bernasconi . . .

Monaco, Francesco Gioseppe Thuille, n. d. 147, [39] p. 15cm.

Three acts. Argument, cast, and scenario. German title-page "Demetrio," and text face Italian. The unnumb. p. contain cast and description of the ballets, "Medée et Jason, ballet tragique . . . par le Sieur Trancart" ("Medea und Jason") and "Les fêtes ou Jalousies du sérial, ballet tragi-comique . . . par le Sieur. Trancart . . ." ("Das Festin, oder Die eifersucht der frauenzimmer des tuerkischen kaisers"). The composer of the music is not mentioned.

First performed at Munich in January, 1772. SCHATZ 857

Il Demetrio, dramma per musica da rappresentarsi nel nobilissimo Teatro di S. Benedetto il carnovale dell' anno 1780.

Venezia, Modesto Fenzo, 1780. 45 p. 17cm.

Two acts. By Metastasio. Argument, cast, scenario, and name of the composer, Francesco **Bianchi.** On p. [21]–30, cast and full description of "Le congiure del duca di Guisa, ballo eroi-tragico in quattro atti," by Domenico Ricciardi, the composer of the music not being mentioned.

First performed in January, 1780, as indicated. SCHATZ 1008

Demetrio. Drama per musica di Pietro Metastasio . . . Da rappresentarsi nel Teatro delle Dame nel carnevale dell' anno MDCCXXXII . . .

[Roma], Pasquino, n. d. 81 p. 15cm.

Three acts. Impresario's dedication, argument, scenario, cast, and name of Giovanni Antonio **Giai** as the composer. SCHATZ 3816

Demetrio. Dramma per musica da rappresentarsi nel Teatro Grimani di San Samuele per la fiera dell' Ascensione dell' anno 1742 . . .

Venezia, Marino Rossetti, n. d. 48 p. 14½cm.

Three acts. By Metastasio, who is not mentioned. Dedication dated May 1, 1742, argument, cast, scenario, and name of **Gluck** as the composer.

First performed, as indicated, May, 1742. SCHATZ 3929

Il Demetrio. Dramma per musica da rappresentarsi nel nobilissimo Teatro di S. Benedetto nella fiera dell' Ascensione dell' anno MDCCLXXV.

Venezia, Modesto Fenzo, n. d. 66 p. 17cm.

Three acts. By Metastasio, who is not mentioned. Argument, cast, scenario and name of Pietro **Guglielmi** as the composer. On p. [25]–42 cast, argument and description of Giuseppe Canziani's "Ines di Castro, ballo tragico in cinque atti." The composer of the music is not mentioned.

First performed, as indicated, May 24, 1775. SCHATZ 4310

Il **Demetrio.** Dramma per musica da rappresentarsi nel famosissimo Teatro Grimani di S. Gio. Grisostomo nel carnevale dell' anno MDCCXXXII . . .

Venezia, Marino Rossetti, 1732.   72 p.   14½ᶜᵐ·

Attached to this copy are 5 p. of arias in ms. which possibly were intended as substitutes. Three acts. By Metastasio. Dedication, argument, cast, scenario, and name of Johann Adolph **Hasse** as the composer.   Schatz 4532

— Il **Demetrio,** dramma per musica rappresentato alla regia elettoral corte di Dresda il carnovale dell' anno MDCCXL.

n. i., n. d.   (double) 111 p.   16ᶜᵐ.

Three acts.   Argument, cast and names of Metastasio as author, of Joh. Ad. **Hasse** as composer.   German title page, "Demetrius . . . Dresden, gedruckt . . . bey der verw. . . . Stoesselin" and text face the Italian, which is not quite the same as in the Venice, 1732, edition.   For instance, in I, 7, the chorus, "Ogni Nume, ed ogni Diva" precedes the dialogue, "Dal tuo labbro o Regina," with which the 1732 ed. begins, and the aria in I, 8, is now "Se libera non sono" instead of "Se non posso su quel trono."   Schatz and Mennicke call this Hasse's second version.
First performed, as indicated, February 8, 1740.   Schatz 4533

— **Demetrio.**   Drama per musica da rappresentarsi nel Regio Teatro di Torino nel carnovale del 1748 . . .

Torino, Pietro Giuseppe Zappata e figliuolo, n. d.   4 p. l., 66 p. 16ᶜᵐ.

Three acts.   Argument, scenario, cast and names of Jon. Ad. **Hasse** as composer of the opera, of Alessio Rasetti as composer of the ballets.   The text is not quite the same as in the original Dresden, 1740, edition for Hasse's second "Demetrio" version.   For instance, the aria, "Frà tanti pensieri Di regno, e d'amore" (I, 3) has become "Fra il tumulto de' pensieri Dell' impero e del mio affetto;" "Ogni procella infida" (I, 5) has been replaced by "Chi non sa, che gran conforto," and the aria, "Pensa, che sei crudele" has been dropped from III, 2, and "Quel labbro adorato" from III, 4.   Schatz 4585

Il **Demetrio.**   Dramma per musica da rappresentarsi alla Corte elettorale Palatina il giorno del nome del Serenissimo elettore . . . l'anno MDCCLIII.

Mannheim, Niccolò Pierron, n. d.   3 p. l., 103 p.   15½ᶜᵐ.

Three acts.   Argument, cast and names of Metastasio as author, of Niccolò **Jommelli** as composer.
First performed, as indicated, November 4, 1753; at Parma, Teatro Ducale, carnival, 1750, as "Demetrio, re di Siria."   Schatz 4850

— **Demetrius.**   Ein musicalisches schau-spiel welches an dem glorreichen nahmens-tag Ihro Churfuerstl. Durchleucht zu Pfaltz . . . aufgefuehret worden, im jahr 1753.

Mannheim, Nicolaus Pierron, n. d.   3 p. l., 111 p.   16ᶜᵐ.

Three acts.   Argument, cast, and names of Metastasio and **Jommelli**.   German translation for the above performances.   Schatz 4851

Il **Demetrio.**   Drama per musica.   Di Giacomo dall' Angelo.   Da rappresentarsi nel Teatro di S. Moisè l'anno 1666 . . .

Venetia, Francesco Nicolini, 1666.   7 p. l. (incl. front.), 94 p.   14½ᶜᵐ.

Three acts.   Author's dedication dated, Venice, January 1, 1666, notice to the reader with name of Carlo **Pallavicino** as the composer, argument and scenario.
                    Schatz 7735

Il Demetrio. Dramma per musica da rappresentarsi nel nobilissimo Teatro di S. Benedetto nella Fiera dell' Ascensione dell' anno 1768.

Venezia, Modesto Fenzo, 1768. 46 p. 17ᶜᵐ.

Three acts. By Metastasio, who is not mentioned. Argument, cast, scenario and name of Antonio Gaetano **Pampani** as the composer. SCHATZ 7761

Demetrio. Dramma per musica da rappresentarsi nel Teatro di S. Samuelle per la fiera dell' Ascensione dell' anno MDCCLI.

Venezia, In Merceria, 1751. 48, [1] p. 15ᶜᵐ.

Three acts. By Metastasio, who is not mentioned. Argument, cast, scenario and name of David **Perez** as the composer. On the additional p. the additional arias: "Già della morte il gelo" and "Crude stelle più serene." SCHATZ 7876

Demetrio. *See* Pescetti's Demetrius.

Demetrio. Dramma per musica da rappresentarsi nel Regio Teatro di Torino nel carnevale del 1762 . . .

Torino, Gaspare Bayno, n. d. viii, 67 p. 16½ᶜᵐ.

Three acts. By Metastasio, who is not mentioned. Argument, cast, scenario and names of Giuseppe **Ponzo** (on a printed slip) as composer of the opera, of Giuseppe Antonio Le-Messier of the three ballets which have only general titles like "Di pastori, giardinieri e pastorelle."

First performed December 26, 1761, as indicated. SCHATZ 8354

Demetrio. Drama per musica.—Demetrius . . .

Hamburg, Spiering, 1744. 111 p. 19ᶜᵐ.

Three acts. By Metastasio, who is not mentioned. Scenario, cast, argument, and name of Paolo **Scalabrini** as composer "a risserva di alcune arie di diversi autori." German text faces Italian.

First performed at Hamburg, Theater b. Gänsemarkt, November 4, 1744.

SCHATZ 9516

Demetrio. Dramma per musica da rappresentarsi nel Nuovo Teatro in Padova per la solita fiera di giugno 1752 . . .

Padova, Stamperia Conzatti, 1752. 69 p. 17½ᶜᵐ.

Three acts. By Metastasio, who is not mentioned. Dedication, argument, cast, scenario, and name of Giuseppe **Scarlatti** as the composer. SCHATZ 9544

Demetrio. Drama per musica, del Signor abb. Pietro Metastasio . . . da rappresentarsi in Lisbona nel Teatro Novo alla rua dos Condes l'anno 1739 . . .

Bologna, Giuseppe le Longi, 1739. 4 p. l., 151 p. 16½ᶜᵐ.

Three acts. Portuguese t.-p. and text face Italian. Argument, cast, scenario. Gaetano Maria **Schiassi**, the composer is not mentioned.

First performed at Milan, Regio Ducal Teatro, August 28, 1732. ML 50.2.D37S3

Il Demetrio. Dramma per musica del Sigʳ abbate Metastasio. Da rappresentarsi nel Teatro dell' illustrissima città di Lodi il carnevale dell' anno 1764 . . .

Lodi, Gli eredi di Nicola Trabatti, n. d. 6 p. l., 48 p. 15ᶜᵐ.

Three acts. Dedication, cast, scenario, and name of "maestro Vagenzail," Georg Christoph **Wagenseil**, as composer.

First performed, according to Schatz, at Florence, Teatro via della Pergola, December 26, 1746. ML 48.A5 v.10

Demetrio a Rodi. Festa per musica da rappresentarsi nel Regio Teatro di Torino per le nozze delle LL. AA. RR. Vittorio Emanuele . . . e Maria Teresa . . . l'anno MDCCLXXXIX.

    Torino, Onorato Derossi, n. d.   viii, 48 p.   16ᶜᵐ.

Two acts. Argument, cast, and names of Giandomenico Boggio as the author, of Gaetano **Pugnani** as the composer of the opera, and of Vittorio Amedeo Canavasso as the composer of the music of Giuseppe Banti's four act "Il trionfo improvviso, ballo pantomimo," which is described, with cast, on p. 44–48.   SCHATZ 8503

Demetrio e Tolomeo. Drama per musica. Da rappresentarsi nel Teatro di S. Angelo l'autunno dell' anno 1702 . . .

    Venezia, Marino Rossetti, 1702.   60 p.   15ᶜᵐ.

Three acts. Dedication dated Venice, November 16, 1702, and signed by the author, Antonio Marchi, argument, scenario, and notice to the reader, with name of Antonio **Polaroli** (Pollaroli) as the composer.   SCHATZ 8258

Demetrio in Athene. A. T. of Wilderer's Il giorno di salute.

Il Demetrio rè della Siria. Drama per musica . . . Demetrius, Koenig in Syrien in einer opera vorgestellet auf dem grossen Braunschweigigen Theatro in der winter-messe anno 1734.

    Wolfenbuettel C. Bartsch, n. d.   Unpaged.   18ᶜᵐ.

By Metastasio (not mentioned). Three acts. Argument, scenario, and name of the composer, Antonio **Caldara.** German text faces Italian.
    First performed at Vienna, Hoftheater, November 4, 1731.   SCHATZ 1480

Demetrio, rè di Siria. O. T. of Jommelli's Demetrio.

Demetrio tiranno. Drama rappresentato nel nuovo Teatro di Piacenza . . . Poesia d'Aurelio Aureli . . . e musica di D. Bernardo Sabadini . . .

    Parma, Stampa di corte, 1694.   71 p.   15½ᶜᵐ.

Three acts. Dedication, argument, cast, scenario.   SCHATZ 9193

Demetrius. Tr. of Bernasconi's Demetrio.

Demetrius. Tr. of Hasse's Demetrio.

Demetrius. An opera. As perform'd at the Theatre Royal in the Hay-Market. Composed by John Baptist Pescetti.

    London, J. Chrichley, 1737.   61 p.   17ᶜᵐ.

Three acts. English text faces Italian. By Metastasio, who is not mentioned. Dedication signed by Angelo Cori, argument, and cast.
    First performed, as indicated, February 12/23, 1737.   SCHATZ 7964

Demetrius. Tr. of Scalabrini's Demetrio.

Demetrius in Athen. A. T. of Wilderer's Der tag des heyls.

Democrit der zweyte. Tr. of Dittersdorf's Democrito corretto.

Democrito. Drama per musica da rappresentarsi nel Teatro di S. A. S. di Carignano.

    Torino, Francesco Antonio Gattinara, 1718.   2 p. l., 75 p.   14½ᶜᵐ.

Three acts. Author not mentioned, and unknown to Schatz. Argument, scenario, and name of Carlo Francesco **Gasparini** as the composer.   SCHATZ 3563

Democrito corretto.   Opera giocosa in due atti.

Composed by **Dittersdorf,** and first performed at Vienna Jan. 27, 1787.
Not in L. of C.

— Gesaenge aus dem singspiele: **Democrit der zweyte**, in zwey
aufzuegen, nach dem italienischen.   Die musik ist von Ditters von
Dittersdorf.

Hamburg, Johann Matthias Michaelsen, 1791.   40 p.   17ᶜᵐ.

Translator unknown to Schatz; not identical with Schmieder's version.
First performed at Hamburg, Theater beim Gaensemarkt, July 27, 1791.

SCHATZ 2588

Il **Demofonte.**   Drama per musica di Francesco Beverini Lucchese . . .

Roma, Moneta, 1669.   5 p. l., 96 p.   13ᶜᵐ.

Three acts.   Author's dedication, dated Rome, June 23, 1669, and Antefatto.   Composer not mentioned.   ML 50.2.D38

Demofonte.   Dramma per musica da rappresentarsi nel Teatro
Vendramin di San Salvatore la prossima fiera dell' Ascensione dell'
anno 1754.

Venezia, Modesto Fenzo, 1754.   47 p.   15ᶜᵐ.

Three acts.   By Metastasio.   Cast, scenario, and name of the composer, Giovachino
Cocchi.   SCHATZ 2042

Il **Demofoonte.**

[323]–392 p.   19ᶜᵐ.   (*Pietro Metastasio, Opere drammatiche, Venezia, Giuseppe Bettinelli, 1733–37, v. 2.*)

Three acts and licenza.   Argument.   No composer mentioned.   ML 49.A2M4

— **Demofoonte.**

*Metastasio, Poesie, Parigi, vedova Quillau, 1755, t. iii, [357]–463 p.
16ᶜᵐ.*

Three acts and licenza.   Argument.   ML 49.A2M42

— **Demofoonte.**   Rappresentato con musica del Caldara la prima
volta in Vienna nell' interno gran Teatro della Cesarea Corte, . . .
il dì 4 novembre 1733, per festeggiare il nome dell' imperator Carlo
VI . . .

*pl., [151]–262 p.   26ᶜᵐ.   (Pietro Metastasio, Opere, t. 4, Parigi,
vedova Herissant, 1780.)*

Three acts and licenza.   Argument.   ML 49.A2M44

— **Démophon.**

Metastasio, Tragedies-opera, Vienne, 1751, t. iv, p. [21]–144.   14ᶜᵐ.

Three acts.   Richelet's translation of "Demofoonte."   ML 49.A2M47

Demofoonte.   Dramma per musica da rappresentarsi nel Teatro da
S. Agostino la primavera dell' anno 1774 . . .

Genova, Stamperia Gesiniana, n. d.   6 p. l., 56 p.   14½ᶜᵐ.

Three acts.   By Metastasio.   Impresario's dedication, argument, cast, and scenario.   "La musica è in parte del celebre maestro Sig. Pasquale **Anfossi,** e parte di
varj. altri celebri autori."

The ballets, by Vincenzo Galleotti, composer of the music not mentioned, were
entitled: "La dolce vendetta" and "La caccia d'Enrico Quarto."   SCHATZ 274

Demofoonte. Dramma per musica da rappresentarsi nel Nuovo teatro di corte . . . nel carnevale dell' anno MDCCLXVI. La poesia è dell' Sig. abbate Pietro Metastasio . . . La musica è del Sig. Andrea de Bernasconi . . .

> *Monaco, Francesco Gioseppe Thuille, n. d. 12 p. l., 167, [19] p. 14^{cm}.*

Three acts. Argument, cast, and scenario. German title-page "Demophoon," and text face Italian. The unnumb. p. contain cast and description of the anonymous ballets "Les amours d'Arion & de Léucosie" ("Die lieb des Arion gegen die Leucosie") and "L'assembleé des dieux pour le mariage d'Alcide & d'Hebé."

Schatz 864

Demofoonte, a serious opera; as performed at the King's Theatre, in the Hay-Market. The poetry by Metastasio, the most part of the music by Signor Ferdinando Bertoni.

> *London, G. Bigg, 1778. 51 p. 20½^{cm}.*

Three acts. Argument, cast, Italian and English text.   Schatz 911

Demofoonte. *See* Duni's Demophontes, king of Thrace.

Demofoonte, dramma per musica da rappresentarsi nel Regio Ducal Teatro di Milano, nel carnovale dell' anno 1759 . . .

> *Milano, Giuseppe Richino Malatesto, n. d. 45 p. 14½^{cm}.*

Three acts. By Metastasio. Dedication, argument, scenario, cast, and name of the composer, Antonio **Ferradini**.
First performed, as indicated, December 26, 1758.   Schatz 3063

Il Demofoonte. Dramma per musica da rappresentarsi nel Nuovo Teatro in Padova per la solita fiera di giugno 1758 . . .

> *Padova, Conzatti, 1758. 62 p. 18^{cm}.*

Three acts. By Metastasio, who is not mentioned. Impresario's dedication, argument, cast, scenario, and name of **Galuppi** as composer.
First performed at Madrid, R. Colisco del Buen Retiro, December 18, 1749.

Schatz 3484

Demofoonte. *See* Graun's Demofoonte, rè di Tracia.

Demofoonte. Dramma per musica, da rappresentarsi nel Regio Teatro alla corte di Dresda nel carnevale dell' anno MDCCXLVIII. La poesìa è del celebre Sigr. abbate Pietro Metastasio . . . Fu posto in musica dal Sigr. Gio. Adolfo Hasse . . .

> *n. i., n. d. 7 p. l., 203 p. 16½^{cm}.*

Three acts. Argument, scenario, cast. German title page, "Demophoon," and text face Italian.
First performed, as indicated, February 9, 1748.   Schatz 4534

— Demofoonte. Dramma per musica da rappresentarsi nel famosissimo Teatro di Grimani di S. Gio. Grisostomo, il carnovale dell' anno 1749 . . .

> *Venezia, All' insegna della scienza, 1749. 60 p. 16^{cm}.*

Three acts. By Metastasio, who is not mentioned. Argument, cast, scenario, and name of Johann Adolph **Hasse** as the composer. A leaf inserted between p. 8–9 contains the aria (I, 12) "Padre perdona, oh pene," changed from "Deh perdona, o padre amato." The text is not quite the same as in the original Dresden, 1748, edition. For instance, the aria "Del cielo sdegnato" (I, 4) has replaced "Sperai vicino il lido" and "Ah che ne mal verace" (III, 3) has been replaced by "Non si dà fra l'umane vicende." "T'intendo ingrata" (I, 5) has been retained.   Schatz 4582

Demofoonte—Continued.

— Il **Demofoonte.** Dramma per musica del Signor abbate Pietro Metastasio . . . da rappresentarsi nel Teatro della città Valletta in Malta nell' autunno di quest' anno MDCCLXV.

Malta, Capaci, n. d. 48 p. 14½ᶜᵐ.

Three acts. Impresario's dedication dated Malta, July 15, 1765, and name of Johann Adolph **Hasse** as the composer. The text is somewhat different from the Dresda, 1748, edition. For instance, the aria "T'intendo, ingrata" has been dropped from I, 5, and "Ah che nel mal verace" from III, 3. This second version of the opera (Schatz and Mennicke) was first performed at Naples, Teatro di San Carlo, November 4, 1758. SCHATZ 4574

Demofoonte. Dramma per musica da rappresentarsi nel Teatro Obizzi in Padova in occasione della Fiera [June] dell' anno MDCCXLIII.

Padova, Giovambatista Conzatti, n. d. 72 p. 17½ᶜᵐ.

Three acts. Argument, scenario, cast, name of Niccolò **Jommelli** as composer ("La musica sarà") and notice to the reader which begins:

"Questo è il quinto anno che s'apre di primavera, con qualche grido, questo teatro, ed altretanti sono i drammi in musica che vi si sono fatti rappresentare del celebre Sig. abate Metastasio con solo dispiacere di doverli per comodo della stagione abbreviare, che però in questo, come negl' altri, nel dichiararsi chi vi ha mesto mano che lo ha fatto senza pregiudizio alla somma stima che nutre per un tanto virtuoso, rimette il lettore a leggerne, e ammirarne il vero originale nelle opere stampate del medesimo . . ."

This was done, and it was found that indeed Metastasio's text was slightly shortened. For instance, in the dialogue of I, 5 (with aria "T'intendo ingrata") in Creusa's monologue the lines "Dove andò quel sereno," etc., were dropped, as were the arias "Tu sai chi son" (II, 1), "E'soccorso d'incognita mano" (II, 4), "Ah che nè mal verace" (III, 3) and the entire scene III, 9 "Dove, crudel, dove mi guidi."

Otherwise Metastasio was not tampered with, since only the aria in I, 13 "Se ardire, e speranza" was replaced by "Temo in un punto." ML 50.2.D39J5

— **Demofoonte**, dramma per musica da rappresentarsi nel Regio-Ducal Teatro di Milano, nel carnovale dell' anno 1753 . . .

Milano, Giuseppe Richino Malatesta, n. d. 6 p. l., 51, [1] p. 14½ᶜᵐ.

Three acts. By Metastasio, who is not mentioned. Dedication ("il secondo dramma") dated Milan, January 27, 1753, argument, cast, scenario and name of Niccolò **Jommelli** as composer. The unnumb. p. contains the aria "Solo effetto era d'amore" substituted for "Il suo leggiadro viso" in I, 8. The text in this libretto does not coincide fully with that in the Padova, 1743, edition. For instance, I, 5 of the Milan ed. has become much different in the dialogue and has no aria. Scene I, 13 has now the aria "Di pena si forte" (from Metastasio's "Ipermestra") instead of "Temo in un punto" and II, 3 has now the aria "Benchè innocente sia" instead of "Se tronca in ramo." ML 50.2.D39J6

— **Demofoonte.** Dramma per musica da rappresentarsi nel Teatro Ducale di Stutgart festeggiandosi il felicissimo giorno natalizio di Sua Altezza Serenissima Carlo, duca regnante di Wirtemberg e Teck . . . La poesia e del . . . Pietro Metastasio . . . La musica è nuovamente composta dal Signor Nicolò Jommelli . . . I balli sono inventati dal Signor Giovanni Giorgio Noverre . . .

Stutgart, Cotta, 1764. 231, [2] p. 21½ᶜᵐ.

Three acts. Argument, cast, scenario. German title page, "Demophon," and text, by Caj. Neusinger (Abert), face Italian. Schatz and Abert call this Jommelli's second version.

The text of the Stutgart version differs somewhat from that of the Padova version. For instance, Stutgart starts out with an added scene "Adrasto! Ah dunque" with aria "Per lei fra l'armi" which originally belonged to I, 4. The original I, 1 scene "Credimi, o padre" has now become I, 2. In I, 5 the dialogue is again different (also from Milan, 1753) and there is no aria. The scene I, 13, "Consigliatemi, o Dei"

Demofoonte—Continued.

has been dropped entirely. Instead, the former I, 12 "O là ministri" in a much longer form is used as last scene of the first act and now with a duet instead of with a solo aria.

On p. 82–109 cast and description of the ballet "La morte di Licomede—La mort de Licomède . . . La musica di nuova composizione del Signor Teller" [Florian Deller], on p. 160–187 cast and description of the ballet "Ipermestra-Hipermenestre," "musica . . . "novamente composta dal Signor Rodolfo." [Rudolph. This settles Abert's query on p. 80 of his Jommelli biography]. The third ballet, without name of the composer, was called "Atalanta ed Ippomene—Atalante et Hippomene."

First performed, as indicated, February 11, 1764.   SCHATZ 4852

— **Demofoonte.** Dramma per musica da rappresentarsi nel Real Teatro dell' Ajuda nel felicissimo giorno natalizio del fedelissimo monarca D. Giuseppe I . . . nel di 6. giugno 1775.

Lisbona, Stamperia reale, n. d.   88 p.   15ᶜᵐ.

Three acts. Argument, cast, scenario and names of Metastasio as author, of Niccolò **Jommelli** as composer. Text only very slightly different from the Stuttgart ed. For instance, the whole first act is the same, also the third, except that III, 7 (which is in the other librettos) with aria "Che mai risponderti" has been dropped.

SCHATZ 4853

Demofoonte. Dramma per musica da rappresentarsi nel famosissimo Teatri Grimani di S. Gio. Grisostomo nel carnevale dell' anno 1738.

Venezia, Marino Rossetti, n. d.   72 p.   15ᶜᵐ.

Three acts. By Metastasio who is not mentioned. Argument, cast, scenario and name of Gaetano **Latilla** as composer.   SCHATZ 5458

Demofoonte. Dramma per musica da rappresentarsi nel Regio Teatro di Torino nel carnovale del 1754 . . .

Torino, Zappata ed Avondo, n. d.   5 p. l., 63 p.   15½ᶜᵐ.

Three acts. By Metastasio who is not mentioned. Argument, scenario, cast and names of Gennaro **Manna** as composer of the opera, of Rocco Gioanetti as composer of the dances.   SCHATZ 5903

Il Demofoonte. Dramma per musica da rappresentarsi nel nobilissimo Teatro di S. Benedetto il carnovale dell' anno 1769 . . .

Venezia, Modesto Fenzo, 1769.   56 p.   17ᶜᵐ.

Three acts. By Metastasio who is not mentioned. Impresario's dedicatory sonnet, argument, cast, scenario and name of the composer, Joseph **Misliweczek.**

First performed in January, 1769, as indicated.   SCHATZ 6529

Il Demofoonte. Drama per musica da rappresentarsi nel nobilissimo Teatro di S. Benedetto il carnovale dell' anno MDCCLXXV.

Venezia, Modesto Fenzo, 1775.   1 p. l., 56 p.   17ᶜᵐ.

Three acts. By Metastasio who is not mentioned. Argument, cast, scenario and name of **Paisiello** as the composer.

On p. 23–32 cast and description of Jean Favier's "Iffigenia in Tauride, ballo eroico pantomimo." The composer of the music is not mentioned.   SCHATZ 7698

Demofoonte. Dramma per musica da rappresentarsi nel nuovo Teatro Tron in S. Cassano il carnovale dell' anno 1764.

Venezia, Paolo Colombani, 1764.   62 p.   17ᶜᵐ.

Three acts. By Metastasio who is not mentioned. Argument, cast, scenario an name of Gaetano **Pampani** as the composer.

With the opera were performed Giuseppe Salamoni's ballets, "La isola incantata di Circe la maga" and "Il matematico." The composers of the music are not mentioned.

First performed at Rome, Teatro Alibert, 1757.   SCHATZ 7752

Demofoonte. Dramma per musica da rappresentarsi nel Teatro Rangone il carnevale dell' anno 1783 . . .

Modena, Eredi di Bartolomeo Solani, n. d. 46 p. 18^{cm}.

Three acts. By Metastasio who is not mentioned. Impresario's dedication, argument, cast and name of Antonio **Pio** as composer ("La musica è tutta nuova"). First performed as indicated, Dec. 26, 1782. ML 48.A5 v. 30

Demofoonte. Dramma per musica da rappresentarsi nel Teatro alla Scala il carnevale dell' anno 1794 . . .

Milano, Gio. Batista Bianchi, n. d. 58, [6] p. 16^{cm}.

Three acts. By Metastasio who is not mentioned. Impresario's dedication dated Milan, February 8, 1794, argument, cast, scenario and name of "Marco Portogalli di **Portogallo**" as the composer. The unnumb. p. contain argument and description of a four-act ballet by Gaetano Gioja, the composer of the music not being mentioned. SCHATZ 8403

Demofoonte. Dramma per musica da rappresentarsi nel nobilissimo Teatro di S. Benedetto il carnovale dell' anno MDCCLXXXVII.

Venezia, Modesto Fenzo, 1787. 56 p. 17^{cm}.

Three acts. By Metastasio who is not mentioned. Argument, cast, scenario and name of Alessio **Prati** as the composer. On p. 53–56, argument, cast, scenario, but not the name of the composer of the music of Filippo Beretti's "Li due sposi sfortunati, ballo tragico pantomimo." First performed December 26, 1786, as indicated. SCHATZ 8454

Demofoonte. Dramma per musica da rappresentarsi nel Regio Teatro di Torino nel carnovale del 1788 . . .

Torino, Onorato Derossi, n. d. viii, 72 p. 15½^{cm}.

Three acts. By Metastasio who is not mentioned. Argument, cast, scenario and names of Gaetano **Pugnani** as composer of the opera, and of Vittorio Amedeo Canavasso as composer of Giuseppe Trafieri's ballets "Adone e Venere," "I viaggiatori areostatici" and "Di popoli di Frigia," of which the first is described with cast on p. 65–71. First performed as indicated, December 26, 1787. SCHATZ 8504

Demofoonte. Drama per musica di Artimio Corasio Pastore Arcade. Da representarsi nel famosissimo Teatro Grimani di S. Gio Grisostomo il carnovale dell' anno 1735 . . .

Venezia, Marine [!] Rossetti, n. d. 72 p. 15½^{cm}.

Three acts. By Metastasio. Dedication by Domenico Lalli, argument, scenario, cast, and name of Gaetano Maria **Schiassi** as the composer. SCHATZ 9600

Demofoonte. Dramma per musica da rappresentarsi nel Nuovo Teatro delli quattro Signori associati cavalieri, e patrizj de la Regioinclita città di Pavia il carnevale dell' anno 1777 . . .

Pavia, Giuseppe Bolzani, n. d. 65 p., 1 l. 15^{cm}.

Three acts. By Metastasio who is not mentioned. Impresario's dedication, argument, cast, scenario and name of Joseph **Schuster** as the composer. First performed at Forli, Nuovo Teatro della Città, spring of 1776. SCHATZ 9760

Demofoonte. Dramma per musica da rappresentarsi nel Nuovo Teatro dell' ill^{ma} città di Crema in occasione del solenne suo primo aprimento il giorno 24 settembre dell' anno 1786 . . .

Milano, Gio. Batista Bianchi, n. d. 68 p. 16½^{cm}.

Three acts. By Metastasio, who is not mentioned. Impresario's dedication, argument, cast, scenario, and name of Angelo **Tarchi** as the composer. With the opera was performed, composer of the music not mentioned, Sebastiano Gallet's "ballo serio Il Pizarro nell' America, ossia La conquista del Perù." SCHATZ 10218

Demofoonte. Dramma per musica del Signor abate Pietro Metastasio, Poeta Cesareo. Da rappresentarsi nel Regio Ducal Teatro Vecchio
di Mantova il carnovale dell' anno 1770 . . .

*Mantova, L'erede di Alberto Pazzoni, n. d. 61 p. 17*ᶜᵐ.

Three acts. Dedication, dated Feb. 3, 1770, argument, cast, scenario, and name
of Tommaso **Trajetta** as composer. Sᴄʜᴀᴛᴢ 10408

Demofoonte. Drama per musica da rappresentarsi sul famosissimo
Teatro di Brunsviga nella fiera d' inverno l'anno 1742.—Demophoon . . .

*Wolffenbuttel, Christian Bartsch, n. d. Unpaged. 17½*ᶜᵐ.

Three acts. By Metastasio, who is not mentioned. German text faces Italian.
Argument, scenario, and name of Giovanni **Verocai** as the composer.
First performed, as indicated, February, 1742. Sᴄʜᴀᴛᴢ 10719

Demofoonte, dramma per musica del Signore abatt. Pietro Metastasio da rappresentarsi nel Teatro di Lucca nel carnovale dell' anno
MDCCXLI.

Lucca, Francesco Marescandoli, n. d. 80 p. 14 ᶜᵐ.

Three acts. Argument, cast, scenario and name of Leonardo **Vinci** as the composer. Sᴄʜᴀᴛᴢ 10745

Demofoonte e Fillide. Cantata a due voci da rappresentarsi in
beneficio di Irene Tomeoni e di Vicenzo Maffoli nel Teatro presso la
Corte.

*Vienna, Antonio Patzowsky, 1794. 24 p. 17½*ᶜᵐ.

Two parts. Argument and "protesta":
"Con idea ben diversa da quella di rappresentarla in teatro fu composta, senza
apparato d'intreccio, e di spettacolo, la seguente cantata, che dipinge semplicemente
il contrasto di due amanti nell' atto di una violenta separazione . . . L'introduzione di alcuni pezzi di musica, e il cambiamento di qualche verso debbonsi attri-
buire alla necessità."
Author and composer unknown to Schatz.
First performed 1794, as indicated. Sᴄʜᴀᴛᴢ 11320

Demofoonte, rè di Tracia. Dramma per musica da rappresentarsi
nel Regio Teatro di Berlino . . .

*Berlino, A. Haude, 1745. 141, [3] p. 16*ᶜᵐ.

Three acts. By Metastasio, who is not mentioned. Argument, scenario, and
name of Carl Heinrich **Graun** as the composer. German title-page "Demophontes,
koenig in Thracien," and text face Italian. Frederick the Great composed two or
three arias for the opera.
First performed at Berlin, Kgl. Operntheater, January 17, 1746. Sᴄʜᴀᴛᴢ 4113

— **Demofoonte,** opera per musica da rappresentarsi nel Regio Teatro
di Berlino . . . nel carnovale del MDCCLXXIV.

*Berlino, Haude e Spener, 1774. 97, [3] p. 18*ᶜᵐ.

Three acts. Argument, cast, scenario, and names of Metastasio as author of the
text ("Si è dovuto abbreviarla e farvi qualche cangiamento") and of Carl Heinrich
Graun as composer of the music ("Vi sono molti cangiamenti"). German title page,
"Demophontes," and text face Italian. Sᴄʜᴀᴛᴢ 4094

Demokrit. Eine komische oper in drei akten vom verfasser der
Grossen toilette. In musik gesetzt von C. Kalkbrenner, kapellmeister
Sr. K. H. des prinzen Heinrich von Preussen . . .

*Berlin, Friedrich Maurer, 1791. 72 p. 17*ᶜᵐ.

Author unknown to Schatz.
First performed at Rheinsberg, Theatre of Prince Henry of Prussia. Sᴄʜᴀᴛᴢ 4997

Il **demone amante,** overo Giugurta. Drama per musica da rappresentarsi nel Teatro di Sant' Angelo, l'anno 1686 . . .

Venetia, Francesco Nicolini, 1686. 84 p. 14ᶜᵐ.

Three acts. Publisher's dedication, notice to the reader (calling this "un' allegro capriccio della dramatica fantasia"), and scenario. Neither the author, Matteo Noris, nor the composer, Carlo Francesco **Pollaroli,** is mentioned. Schatz 8281

Démophon. Tr. of Metastasio's text Demofoonte.

Demophon. Tr. of Jommelli's Demofoonte.

Démophon, opéra lyrique en trois actes, représenté pour la premiere fois, par l'Academie royale de musique le mardi 15 septembre 1789.

Paris, P. de Lormel, 1789. vi, 7–54 p. 23ᶜᵐ.

Cast and names of Desriaux as author, of [Johann Christoph] **Vogel** as composer. Cl. & L. and Schatz give Sept. 22 as the date, the printed score as above.

ML 50.2.D4V6

— **Démophon,** opera lyrique en trois actes. Représenté pour la premiere fois, par l'académie[!]-royale de musique, le mardy 15 septembre 1789. Les paroles sont de M. Deriaux. Musique de Vogel.

Paris, Ruault, 1789. 26 p. 22ᶜᵐ.

ML 50.2.D4V62

Demophontes. Tr. of Graun's Demofoonte.

Demophontes, king of Thrace. An opera. As perform'd at the Theatre Royal in the Hay-Market. Composed by Egidio Duni Napolilano.

London, J. Chrichley, 1737. 63, [1] p. 17ᶜᵐ.

Three acts. Metastasio's "Demofoonte" with English translation facing the Italian. Dedication by Angelo Cori, argument, cast. On the add. p. the aria, "Mi fai gioire" (II, 1), substituted for "Nel tuo dono."
First performed, as indicated, May 24, 1737. Schatz 2837

Demophontes, koenig in Thracien. Tr. of Graun's Demofoonte, rè di Tracia.

Demophoon. Tr. of Bernasconi's Demofoonte.

Demophoon. Tr. of Hasse's Demofoonte.

Demophoon. Tr. of Verocai's Demofoonte.

Le **depart de l'opera-comique;** compliment, en un acte. Représenté à la clôture de la Foire S. Laurent 1759.

Paris, Duchesne, 1759. 22, [2] p. 19ᶜᵐ. (Theatre de M. Favart, Paris, Duchesne, 1763–77, t. viii.)

Cast. Prose and vaudevilles. No airs printed in the text, nor following the text. The [2] p. contain catalogues of plays. Font does not mention Favart's musical collaborator.
First performed on October 9, 1759. ML 49.A2F1

— Le **depart de l'Opéra comique,** compliment en un acte. Représenté à la clôture de la Foire St. Laurent 1759.

Paris, la veuve Duchesne, 1766. 28 p. 19ᶜᵐ.

On p. 22–28, "Airs:" "Aux spectateurs indulgens," "J'avois un petit oiseau," "Viens calmer ma douleur." Favart is not mentioned. Schatz 11489

Le **dereiglement des passions,** etc.   *See* Ballet du dereiglement.

Descrizione dell' apparato della comedia et intermedii d'essa recitata in Firenze il giorno di S. Stefano l'anno 1565. nella gran Sala del palazzo di sua Ecc. illust. nelle reali nozze. Dell illustriss. & eccell. S. il S. Don Francesco Medici principe di Fiorenza. & di Siena, & della regina Giouanna d'Austria sua consorte.   Ristampata, con nuoua aggiunta.

Fiorenza, i Giunti, 1566.   26, [2] p.   16½ᶜᵐ.

The last [2] p. contain colophon and printer's mark.

On p. [3]–10 a most minute and fascinating description of the *apparatus* (*i. e.* auditorium, seating arrangements, etc.) with name of Giovanni Battista Cini as author of the intermedii "Psiche ed Amore" performed with Francesco d'Ambra's comedy "La Cofanaria."   From Il Lasca's edition of the "Descrizione" (*see* below) we know that it was originally written by Cini.

On p. 10–23 description and text of the six intermedia.   The text of these is exactly the same as in the edition below, but the description is shorter.   Also this difference appears that the musical data (substantially the same as in the edition below) follow each intermedio, instead of being grouped together at the end.   Alessandro **Striggio** is mentioned as the composer of the first, second, fifth intermedio, Francesco **Corteccia** of the third, fourth and sixth.

On p. 24–26 description of the banquet, etc., following the performance.

ML 52.2.D3

— **Descrizione de gl'intermedii** rappresentati con la commedia nelle nozze dell' illustrissimo, ed eccellentissimo Signor principe di Firenze e di Siena.

Firenze, Filippo Giunti, 1593.   22 p.   15ᶜᵐ.

Forms part of "La COFANARIA.   Commedia di Francesco d'Ambra.   Con gl'intermedii di Giovambattista Cini.   Recitata nelle nozze del . . .   Don Francesco de Medici, & della Sereniss. regina Giovanna d'Austria.   Di nuovo ristampata," same publisher, same date.

The description of the six "intermedii . . . tratti dalla novella di *Psiche,* e d'*Amore* descritta molto piacevolmente da Apuleio nel suo Asin d'oro" is preceded by a dedication signed "Il Lasca" (*pseud.* of the poet, Antonio Francesco Grazzini).   It is undated, but is obviously of about the same date as the dedication of the comedy by the editor, Alessandro Ceccherelli, "Firenze il di 15. di gennaio 1565."   Il Lasca says:

"Essendo da altri con fretta & per ciò con poca cura stati mandati in luce gl'intermedij che con la commedia si fecero nelle Lor Realissime Nozze cavati da una semplice descrittione fatta dall' autor loro innanzi a la loro rappresentatione ad instanzia di Sua Altezza accioche ella potesse più agevolmente intenderli, mosso di lui, & di loro à compassione che pareva che poca cura se ne prendesse mi son messo ad allargargli alquanto, e ridurli nella forma che le vedranno . . ."

With these remarks, Il Lasca refers to the publication of the "Descrizione dell' apparato della commedia ed intermedia d'essa, fatta in Firenze il giorno di S. Stefano l'anno 1565."

The description of the intermedii proper Il Lasca follows up, "a soddisfazione de' curiosi musici," with a description of the orchestra employed and other musical features, and then says:

"L'invenzione, & le parole de gl'intermedij furono di M. Gio. Battista Cini, & sotto la sua cura furno condotti si come la commedia, e tutto il restante ad essa appartemente . . .

"Messer Alessandro **Strig[g]io** fece le musiche del primo del secondo, & del quinto, intermedio.   Quelle del terzo, del quarto, & dell' ultimo furno fatte dal Maestro della cappella di Lor Eccellenze illustrissime: Messer Francesco **Corteccia.**"

The music is generally considered lost, but a remark on p. 18 of Il Lasca's description makes it clear that it was in the press in 1565 ("stampandosi la musica").   Il Lasca issued an edition of his "Descrizione de gl'intermedii" in 1566, with a "rather better" text and a different dedication, as Mr. G. E. P. Arkwright, the editor of the Musical Antiquary, added to a footnote of mine in my reprint (with introductory remarks) of the 1593 "Descrizione" in his journal, October, 1911.   The "Descrizione" had previously been reprinted in the fifth volume of the "Teatro Comico Fiorentino," Firenze, 1750 (copy in L. of C.).

The **deserter.**   Tr. of Pietro Guglielmi's Il disertore.

The **deserter.**   Tr. of Monsigny's Le déserteur.

Songs, etc in the **Deserter of Naples;** or, Royal clemency: To which is added, An ode to friendship . . . and other favorite pieces performed at the Royalty Theatre.

[London], Printed for A. Cleugh, C. Stalker, [etc.], n. d.   16 p.   21cm.

The text of "The Deserter of Naples," on p. [1]–8. Of the last song, "Anacreon" ("To banish life's troubles") [Richard John Samuel] **Stevens** is mentioned as the composer. A note on p, [3] says:

"This beautiful and by far most interesting piece ever performed on the boards of the Royalty Theatre, is the production of Mr. Delphini, and executed under his direction."

He undoubtedly utilized Dibdin's "The deserter," but does not seem to have used any of the songs in Dibdin's version of Monsigny's "Le déserteur."

Performed 1788, as indicated.   LONGE 102

Le **déserteur,** drame en trois actes, en prose, mêlée de musique; par M. Sedaine. La musique par M. * * * Représentée pour la premiere fois per les Comédiens italiens ordinaires du Roi, le lundi 6 mars 1769.

Paris, Claude Herissant, 1769.   68 p.   19cm.

Composed by **Monsigny,** who is not mentioned.   SCHATZ 6569

— Le **deserteur.**   Drame en trois actes, en prose, mêlé de musique. Par M. Sedaine. La musique par M. * * * Représenté à Paris, pour la première fois, par les Comédiens italiens ordinaires du roi, le lundi 6 mars 1769. Et à Fontainebleau, le 8 octobre 1769, en présence de Sa Majesté. Seconde edition, revue par l'auteur.

Paris, Claude Herissant, 1770.   viii, 84, [4] p.   18½cm.

Cast and preface, in which Sedaine comments on the troubles of a librettist in general and on his in particular. He says in part:

"Dans ce genre d'ouvrage, l'interêt doit soutenir la musique pendant les premières représentations, dût-elle y nuire; mais lorsqu'en suite la piéce est sçue, lorsqu'on peut l'entendre sans l'inquiétude de ce qui doit arriver, la musique fait écouter le poëme sans dégoût, cinquante représentations dans la même année, avantage que n'ont pas des ouvrages de littérature beaucoup plus estimables . . ."

The text is the same as in the 1769 edition.   ML 50.2.D45

— The **deserter;** a new musical drama, as it is performed at the Theatre-Royal in Drury Lane.

London, T. Becket, 1773.   vi, [2], 36 p.   20cm.

Two acts. Cast and preface signed by Charles **Dibdin,** who says:

"Le Deserteur [text by Sedaine, music by Monsigny], is well known to have been these five years the most favourite musical piece on the French stage: . . .

"It was thought, therefore, that if the unnecessary incidents were expunged, and those retained were rendered more probable; if, by making an uniform partition between the dialogue and the songs, it could be brought more to wear the complexion of an Opera, The Deserter might be entitled to a favourable reception on the English stage: how far these suggestions were reasonable, the public (who are the best judges, and by whose arbitration I shall always be proud to abide) will determine.

"With regard to the music, as I found it a work of great invention, I should have kept it in its original state, had it been possible; but, besides the excessive length of the songs, the continual breaks into recitative, the frequent sudden alterations of the stile, and above all, that sameness which so particularly characterizes the French music, I found it much too grave to stand the least chance of success in an afterpiece: I, therefore, selected what I thought the beauties, and what I could not effect by having recourse to the original, I have endeavoured to supply myself.

"In justice to the French composer, I think it absolutely necessary to declare, that the songs, beginning 'One conduct's for both love and war,' 'The nymph who in

Le **deserteur**—Continued.

my bosom reigns,' and 'The whims of folks in love'; are wholly my own; and that
the first air in the piece ["I can't for my life"], and that beginning, 'My life's three
parts diminish'd' are by **Philidor**, a name of no inconsiderable note in the musical
world."

In Broderip & Wilkinson's vocal score also "I'd have you to know" and "I'll
fly these groves" are headed as composed by **Dibdin**.

First performed, as indicated, November 2, 1773.   LONGE 13

— The **deserter**. in two acts. By C. Dibdin.

[22]–48 p. 19^{cm}. (Collection of the most esteemed farces and entertainments, t. iv, Edinburgh, 1792.)

Drury-Lane and Edinburgh (1782) casts.   SCHATZ 11753D

— The **deserter**, a comic-opera; in two acts, as performed at the
theatre, New-York, with universal applause. By Mr. C. Dibdin.

New-York, Samuel Campbell, 1787. 31, [1] p. 17^{cm}.

New York cast.

First performed in America, as indicated, June 8, 1787.   ML 50.6.D36

— Der **deserteur**, ein singspiel in drey aufzuegen aus dem franzoesischen uebersetzt mit musik.

Frankfurt am Mayn, mit Andreäischen schriften, n. d. 103 p., 11
p. (folded music, dated 1773)

Cast. Johann Joachim Eschenburg's version, who is not mentioned. The music
contains (voice and bass) "Ein solches herz zu kränken," "Mein schäferstab war
fort," "Aller Welt blut," "Ach! vergesset alle schmerzen."   SCHATZ 6570

Les **desesperés**, prologue des deux pièces suivantes. Par M^{rs}. Le
S * *, & d'Or * * *. Représentée à la Foire S. Laurent.
1732.

— **Sophie et Sigismond**. Pièce d'un acte. Par M^{rs}. Le S * *.
& d'Or * * *. Représentée à la Foire S. Laurent. 1732.

— La **sauvagesse**. Piece d'un acte. Par M^{rs}. Le S * *. &
d'Or * * * Représentée à la Foire S. Laurent. 1732.

Le Théâtre de la foire, Paris, 1737, t. ix, [117]–274 p. 17^{cm}.

By Le Sage and d'Orneval. Largely en vaudevilles. The airs, selected or composed and arranged by Jean Claude **Gillier**, are printed at the end of the volume in
the "Table des airs."

First performed July 7, 1732.   ML 48.L2IX

Desiderius, koenig der Longobarden, musicalisches schauspiel,
an dem frohen gebuhrts-tage des Allerdurchlauchtigsten . . . Joseph
I, erwehlten roemischen kaeysers . . . zu allerunterthaenigster freu-
denbezeugung auf dem Hamburgischen Schau-platz vorgestellet, im
Jahr 1709, den 26 Julii.

n. i., n. d. Unpaged. 19^{cm}.

Five acts. Towards the end of his astrological, historical, and what not "Vorbericht" the author, Barthold Feind (not mentioned), says that the part of Flori-
ana is:

"einigermassen eine imitation des Silvani, in seinem Duello d'amore e di vendetta,
die ich bloss darum erwehlt, weil sie gelegenheit zu allerhand actiones auf dem
theatro giebt, und ich nicht gerne schauspiele verfertige, worinnen die acteurs viel
zeit zu traeumen haben . . ."

The composer, Reinhard **Keiser**, is not mentioned. To some arias the Italian
text has been added.   SCHATZ 5085

Despina e Niso. Intermezzi da rappresentarsi nel Teatro Tron di San Cassano l'anno 1724.

Venezia, Marino Rossetti, n. d. 10 p. 15^{cm}.

Two parts. Neither the author (unknown to Schatz) nor the composer, Alessandro Scarlatti, is mentioned. Mentioned by Dent? According to Schatz, the intermezzi were performed 1724, with Orlandini's "L'Antigona," but originally with Scarlatti's own "L'amor generoso" at Naples, Teatro del R. Palazzo, October 1, 1714.

SCHATZ 9534

The **destruction of the world.** A. T. of Noah's flood.

Les **dettes,** comédie en deux actes et en prose, mêlée d'ariettes, paroles de M. Forgeot, musique de M. Champein. Représenté, pour la première fois, à Paris, par les Comédiens Italiens ordinaires du Roi, le 8 janvier 1787; & à Versailles, devant Leurs Majestés, le 23 février suivant.

Paris, Prault, 1787. 46 p. 21½^{cm}.

Cast.

SCHATZ 1794

— De **schulden,** zangspel gevolgd naar het fransche. Door Hendrik Ogelwight, junior.

Amsterdam, J. Helders en A. Mars, 1791. 53 p. 16½^{cm}.

First performed at Amsterdam, Stads Schouwburg, July, 1791. SCHATZ 1795

Deukalion und Pyrrha. Ein musikalisches drama mit gesaengen.

Breslau und Leipzig, Christian Friedrich Gutsch, 1779. 40 p. 15^{cm}.

Neither the author, Karl Emil Schubert, nor the composer, Franz Andreas Holly, is mentioned.

First performed at Breslau, Schuch'sches Theater, December 18, 1780.

SCHATZ 4769

Les **deux avares,** comédie en deux actes en prose, mêlée d'ariettes; représentée pour la premiere fois à Fontainebleau, devant Sa Majesté, le samedi 27 octobre 1770. Les paroles sont de M. Fenouillot de Falbaire. La musique est de M. Gretry.

[Paris], Pierre Robert Christophe Ballard, 1770. 2 p. l., 58 p. 19½^{cm}.

Cast and "Description du lieu de la scéne." ML 50.2.D48G7

First performed, as indicated, at Paris, Comédie italienne, December 6, 1770.

— Les **deux avares,** comedie en deux actes en prose, mêlée d'ariettes; représentée pour la première fois à Fontainebleau, devant Sa Majesté, le samedi 27 octobre 1770. Les paroles sont de M. Fenouillot de Falbaire. La musique est de M. Gretry.

Paris, Pierre Robert Christophe Ballard, 1771. 64 p. 18^{cm}.

Cast, "Description du lieu de la scène" and on p. 31–34 (I, 15), the air of the "*Duo. La garde passe, il est minuit.*"

SCHATZ 4143

— Les **deux avares,** comédie en deux actes en prose, meslee d'ariettes; représentée pour la premiere & la seconde fois à Fontainebleau, devant Sa Majesté, le 27 octobre & le 7 novembre 1770. Et pour la premiere fois, à la Comedie italienne, le 6 dicembre de la même année. Par Monsieur de Falbaire. La musique est de M. Grétri.

Paris, Delalain, 1771. 47, [4] p. 18^{cm}.

Cast, prefatory note, and description of the place of action. The last 4 p. contain the air of the vaudeville, "De tous nos projets" (II, 6). SCHATZ 11704

Les deux avares—Continued.

— Das **grab des Mufti** oder Die zwey geitzigen. eine komische oper in zwey akten nach dem franzoesischen des herrn Feuvillet de Felbaire und Gretris composition. (zum erstenmal aufgefuehrt auf des Markgrafen Heinrichs Koenigl. Hoheit Hoftheater zu Schwedt.

*Stettin, Johann Franz Struck, 1778.   103 p.   15½*ᶜᵐ.

SCHATZ 4144

— Die **beiden geizigen**, ein singspiel in zween aufzuegen aus dem franzoesischen uebersetzt, mit musik.

*Frankfurt am Mayn, mit Andreaeischen schrifften, 1772.   80 p., 12 p. (folded music)   17*ᶜᵐ.

German version, by Johann Heinrich Faber.   The music (voice and bass) consists of "Nur meinem schatze bin ich hold" ("Sans cesse auprès de mon trésor"), I, 4; "Lass Dich nicht mehr vom kummer plagen" ("Plus de dépit, plus de tristesse"), I, 7; and "Die Wache ziehet schon vorbey" ("La garde passe, il est minuit"), I, XV.

SCHATZ 4146

Les deux baillis.   A. T. of Les vendangeurs.

Les deux charbonniers, ou, Les contrastes, comédie en prose et en deux actes.   Mêlée d'ariettes.   Représentée, pour les premières fois, les 7, 9, 13, 15, 17, 19, 21, 23, 27 et 30 fructidor an VII, par les Comédiens du Théâtre du palais Egalité, *dit* Montansier.   Paroles et musique du Cousin-Jacques.

*Paris, Moutardier, an VIII [1799–1800]   74 p.   21½*ᶜᵐ.

Cast and Avant-propos according to which Cousin Jacques (Beffroy de Reigny) first offered his piece to the Théâtre Faydeau, Nov. 16, 1798.   He then practically rewrote it in accordance with suggestions of the actor Juliet.   Then the Théâtre Faydeau was closed for five months, and the author decided to transfer his work to the Théâtre Montansier.   He concludes his remarks with observations on the cast.

First performed, as indicated, August 24, 1799.   SCHATZ 705

Les deux chasseurs, et la laitière, comédie en un acte, meslée d'ariettes; représentée pour la première fois sur le Théatre des Comédiens italiens ordinaires du Roi, le 21 juillet 1763.

*Paris, la veuve Duchesne, 1771.   32 p.   18*ᶜᵐ.

By Anseaume.   Neither he nor the composer, **Duni** mentioned.   With the melodies of the ariettes, "Je suis percé jusq'aux os," "Le briquet frape la pierre," "Voilà la petite laitière," "Hélas, j'ai répandu mon lait," and the vaudeville "J'étois gissant à cette place."   Schatz, Clément & Larousse, and others give, incorrectly, July 23 as the date.   SCHATZ 2838

— Les **deux chasseurs et la laitiere,** comédie en un acte, mêlée d'ariettes, représentée pour la premiere fois sur le Théatre des Comédiens italiens ordinaires du roi, le 21 juillet 1763.

*Paris, la veuve Duchesne, 1780.   32 p.   19*ᶜᵐ.

On p. 3–5 the air of "Je suis percé jusqu'aux os," 12–13 "Le briquet frappe la pierre," 25–27 "Helas! hélas! j'ai répandu mon lait," and on p. 30–31 the vaudeville "J'étois gissant à cette place."   Neither Anseaume is mentioned, nor **Duni**.

SCHATZ 11694

— Das **milch maedchen und die beiden jaeger,** ein singspiel in einem aufzuge aus dem franzoesischen uebersetzt.   Mit musik.

*Frankfurt am Mayn, mit Andreaeischen schriften, 1772.   46 p., 11 p. (folded dated music).   17*ᶜᵐ.

Les deux chasseurs, et la laitière—Continued.

German version by Christian Friedrich Schwan. With cast. The musical supplement (voice and bass) contains: "Wenn der stein den stahl berührt" ["Le briquet frappe la pierre]", p. 1–4; "Hier ist das kleine milchmädchen" ["Voilà la petite laitière"], p. 4–5; "Sag, wie dir das gefällt" ["Voici tout mon projet"], p. 6–10; "Ich lag in lauter angst und beben" ["J'etois gissant à cette place"], p. 10–11.

First performed at Mannheim, Theater a. d. Fruchtmarkt, 1771.   SCHATZ 2839

— **Das milchmaedgen und die zween jaeger.** Eine operette, aus dem franzoesischen des herrn Anseaume. 1773.

n. i., n. d. 15 p. 17ᶜᵐ.

Lyrics only. The composer is not mentioned. Not Schwan's version.
First performed at Berlin, Theater i. d. Behrenstrasse, August 5, 1772.

SCHATZ 2840

Les deux coffrets. A. T. of the pasticcio Le génie Asouf.

Les deux cousines, ou La bonne amie; comédie en un acte, meslée d'ariettes; par M. Delaribadière; la musique, de M. Desbrosses: Représentée pour la premiere fois far les Comédiens italiens ordinaires du roi, le 21 may 1763.

Bruxelles, Jean Joseph Boucherie, 1764. 38, [2] p. 16ᶜᵐ.

With author's dedication and cast. The two additional pages contain the "Approbation" of Mai 1, 1763, and the "Extrait du privilège."   SCHATZ 2528

Les deux miliciens, ou L'Orpheline villageoise, comédie en un acte et en prose, meslée d'ariettes; par M. d'Azemar . . . La musique est de M. Fridzeri. Représentée pour la premiere fois par les Comédiens italiens ordinaires du roi, le 24 août 1771 . . .

Paris, la veuve Duchesne, 1772. 40 p. 18ᶜᵐ.

Cast. On p. 36–40 the melody of the "*Pastorale.* Colin un jour sur la fougere."
SCHATZ 3370
Second copy.   YUIN PQ

— **Die beiden militzen,** ein singspiel in einem aufzuge aus dem franzoesischen uebersetzt, mit musik.

Frankfurt am Mayn, mit Andreaeischen schriften, 1773. 67 p., 16 p. (obl. folded music). 16½ᶜᵐ.

Cast. By Johann Heinrich Faber. The 8 p. of music incorrectly bound in with this copy belong to "Der Holzhauer," by Philidor, whereas the 16 p. that belong with "Die beiden militzen" are incorrectly bound in with Philidor's "Der holzhauer." They consist of "O! wie quälet doch die liebe" (I, 1), "Sobald es tagt" (I, 5), "Letzthin erzählte auf den wiesen" (I, 6).   SCHATZ 3371

Les deux morts, ou La ruse de carnaval, opéra-comique. Par J. Patrat. Representé sur le Théatre des Comédiens italiens ordinaires du roi, le mardi 27 février 1781.

Paris, Vente, 1781. 43 p. 20ᶜᵐ.

One act. *En vaudevilles.* Cast. Arranger of the music not mentioned and unknown to me.   ML 50.2.D487

Les deux pages. *See* Dezède's Auguste et Théodore.

Les deux petits Savoyards, comédie en un acte, mêlée d'ariettes par M. Mars. . . . des V . . . Musique de M. Dal . . . Représentée, pour la premiere fois, par les Comédiens italiens ordinaires du

Les deux petits Savoyards—Continued.

roi, le mercredi, 14 janvier 1789 et à Versailles, devant Leurs Majestés, le vendredi suivant.

Paris, Brunet, 1789. 70 p. 18ᶜᵐ.

Cast. By Marsollier. Music by **Dalayrac**.   SCHATZ 2336
                                                    Second copy.   ML 48.C6I

— Les **deux petits Savoyards**, opera en un acte. Musique de Mr. d'Alayrac.

Hambourg, P. F. Fauche, 1795. 15 p. 14½ᶜᵐ.

The author, Marsollier, is not mentioned.   ML 50.2.D49D2

— Les **deux petits Savoyards**, opera en un acte, musique de Mr. d'Alayrac.

Hamburg, Mees père et comp., n. d.

The author, Marsollier, is not mentioned.
First performed at Hamburg, Théâtre de la Societé française dramatique et lyrique,
March 4, 1795.   SCHATZ 11688

— Die **beyden kleinen Savoyarden**, ein singspiel in einem aufzuge. Nach dem französischen.

Leipzig, C. G. Martini, 1795. 41 p. 16ᶜᵐ.

Translation revised by Heinrich Gottlieb Schmieder according to Schatz.
Dalayrac is not mentioned as composer.   SCHATZ 2338

— Die **zween Savoyarden**, ein singspiel in einem aufzuge. Aus dem franzoesischen auf die musik des herrn Dallayrac uebersetzt. Von J. Perinet. Aufgefuehrt auf dem k. k. privilegierten Marinellischen theater in der Leopoldstadt.

Wien, Matthias Andreas Schmidt, 1792. 47 p. 16½ᶜᵐ.

                                                            SCHATZ 2340

— Os **dois rapazes Saboyanos**: Comedia com musica em hum so' acto, para se representar no Real Theatro de S. Carlos, no dia 11 de janeiro de 1796 em beneficio de Miguel Cavana.

Lisboa, Simao Thaddeo Ferreira, 1796. 142 p. 14ᶜᵐ.

Dalayrac is mentioned as composer. Portuguese text faces Italian, by Giuseppe
Carpani (Schatz), first used at Monza, Teatro Arciducale, fall of 1791. SCHATZ 2339

Les deux prisonniers. A. T. of Dalayrac's Adolphe et Clara.

Les deux soeurs. A. T. of Belle et bonne.

Les deux soeurs rivales, comédie en un acte; meslée d'ariettes. Représentée pour la premiere fois par les Comédiens italiens ordinaires du roi le jeudi 22 juillet 1762. Les paroles sont de M. de Laribadiere. La musique de M. Desbrosses.

Paris, Ballard, 1762. 48 p. 19ᶜᵐ.

Author's dedication and cast. The text interspersed throughout with the airs of
the ariettes.   ML 50.2.D495D2

Les deux Suisses. O. T. of Gaveaux' L'amour filial.

Les **deux suivantes,** opera-comique en trois actes; représenté pour la premiere fois sur le Théâtre de la Foire S. Laurent en 1730.

Charles François Pannard, Théâtre. Paris, Duchesne, 1763, v. 2, 128 p. 17ᶜᵐ.

Prose and vaudevilles. According to Parfaict, the text was written jointly by Pannard and Pontau, composed by **Gilliers,** and first performed July 20, 1730.

PQ 2019.P3

Les **deux sylphes,** comédie en un acte et en vers, mêlée d'ariettes, par M. Imbert. Représentée pour la premiere fois par les Comédiens italiens ordinaires du roi le 18 octobre 1781.

Paris, Jean François Bastien, 1781. 46, [1] p. 22ᶜᵐ.

Cast. The composer, **Désaugiers,** is not mentioned. ML 50.2.D5D2

Les **deux tuteurs,** comédie en deux actes, en prose, mêlée d'ariettes. Representée, pour la premiere fois, à Fontainebleau, devant Leurs Majestés, le 11 octobre 1783, & à Paris, au Théâtre italien, le 8 mai 1784.

Paris, Brunet, 1784. 2 p. l., 56 p. 20ᶜᵐ.

Cast. ML 50.2.D51D2

— Les **deux tuteurs,** comédie en deux actes, en prose, mêlée d'ariettes. Représentée pour la première fois à Fontainebleau devant Leurs Majestés le 11 octobre 1783 & à Paris, au Théâtre italien, le 8 mai 1784. Par M. de la Chabeaussière. Musique de M. le chevalier d'Aleyrac.

Toulouse, J. B. Broulhiet, 1785. 39 p. 19ᶜᵐ.

Cast. ML 50.2.D51D22

— Gesaenge aus dem singspiele: Die **zwey vormuender,** in zwey aufzuegen, nach dem franzoesischen von d'Arien. In Musik gesetzt von Dalayrac.

Hamburg, J. M. Michaelsen, 1788. 24 p. 16½ᶜᵐ.

First performed at Hamburg, Theater beim Gänsemarkt, August 4, 1788.

Schatz 2341

The **devil of a duke:** or, Trapolin's vagaries. A (farcical ballad) opera, as it is acted at the Theatre-Royal in Drury-Lane. To which is prefix'd the musick to each song, set for the spinnet, harpsichord, German flute, violin, and hautboy, with the thorough base to each tune. The second edition.

London, Charles Corbett and John Torbuck, 1732. 1 p. l., 43, [1] p. 19ᶜᵐ.

One act. Cast, and on last (unnumb. page) the table of the 21 songs, the airs of which are indicated in the text by title. The musick is *not* prefixed to any of the songs in this edition of Robert Drury's text, nor is Mr. **Seedo** mentioned as the composer of any of them, his airs in the first ed. (1732) having been engraved separately. (Squire). In this second ed.:

"the first ["Se guacci—Do not ask me if I love you"] and eighteenth ["Fly, Cupid, fly, and give." Title of air not mentioned] were wrote by another hand and inserted at the desire of the performers."

First performed Sept. 23, 1732, as indicated. Longe 120

The **devil to pay**; or, The wives metamorphos'd.   An opera.   As it is perform'd at the Theatre-Royal in Drury-Lane, by His Majesty's servants.   Written by the author of The beggars wedding.   With the musick prefix'd to each song.

London, J. Watts, 1732.   4 p. l., 31 p.   19ᶜᵐ.

One act. Cast, table of the 16 songs, prologue, and dedication, signed by the author, Cha. Coffey, though John Mottley is said by some to have collaborated and Theophilus Cibber to have been responsible for this reduction of the original three acts to one. Ballad opera, in which air IV, "Ye Gods! you gave to me a wife," is marked as "set by Mr. **Seedo**." The airs are printed in the text with their titles.

First performed August 6, 1731, (in three acts according to Squire, reduced to one act in 1732).   ML 50.5.D37

— The **devil to pay**: or, The wives metamorphos'd.   An opera.   As it is perform'd at the Theatre-Royal in Drury-Lane, by His Majesty's servants . . .   With the musick prefix'd to each song.

London, J. Watts, 1748.   front., 4 p. l., 30 p.   21½ᶜᵐ.

One act. Same dedication, prologue, table of songs, but a different cast.
ML 50.5.D39

— The **devil to pay**: or The wives metamorphos'd.   An opera.   As it is performed at the Theatres-Royal, by His Majesty's servants . . .

London, T. Lowndes, 1771.   37 p. (incl. front.), 10 p.   16½ᶜᵐ.

The 10 p. contain catalogue of "Books printed for T. Lowndes."
One act. Dedication, prologue, cast, table of the 16 songs, their airs being indicated in the text by title.   Longe 69

— The **devil to pay**: or, The wives metamorphos'd.   By Charles Coffey, Esq.

[64]–88 p.   19ᶜᵐ.   (Collection of the most esteemed farces and entertainments, t. II, Edinburgh, 1792.)

Drury-Lane and Edinburgh (1782) casts. Ballad opera. The air IV, "Ye Gods! you gave to me a wife," was "set by Mr. **Seedo**."   Schatz 11753B

Le **devin du village**, intermede; par J. J. Rousseau; représenté pour la premiere fois à Fontainebleau, sur le Théâtre de la Cour, devant Leurs Majestés, les 18 & 24 oct. 1752.   Et à Paris, par l'Académie royale de musique le 1 mars, 1753.

Geneve, Pierre Gosse, 1760.   59 p.   18½ᶜᵐ.

One act. Text by Rousseau, with exception of that of the ariette "Avec l'objet de mes amours," which was by Cahusac. Cast, Rousseau's "première & unique dédicace" to Duclos, his "Avertissement" and (printed in the text) the airs as in the score published by Mᵈᵉ Boivin, Le Clerc, etc. The Avertissement reads: "Quoique j'aie approuvé les changemens que mes amis jugèrent à propos de faire à cet intermède, quand il fut joué à la cour et que son succés leur soit dû en grande partie, je n'ai pas jugé à propos de les adopter aujourd'hui, & cela par plusieurs raisons. La première est, que puisque cet ouvrage porte mon nom il faut que ce soit le mien, dût-il en être plus mauvais. La seconde, que ces changemens pouvoient être fort bien en eux mêmes, & ôter pourtant à la pièce cette unité si peu connue, qui seroit le chef-d'oeuvre de l'art, si l'on pouvoit la conserver sans répétitions & sans monotonie. Ma troisième raison est, que n'ayant fait cet ouvrage que pour mon amusement, son vrai succés est de me plaire; or personne ne sait mieux que moi comment il doit être pour me plaire le plus."

First performed at Fontainebleau October 18, 1752, with recitatives by Yeliotte and Francoeur instead of those by Rousseau and with an overture and a final Divertissement made up from music by Rameau, Dauvergne and others. First performed at Paris, Académie royale de musique together with Michel Blavet's one act opera-bouffon "Le jaloux corrigé" on March 1, 1753, with an overture and a final Diver-

Le devin du village—Continued.

tissement-Pantomime composed by Rousseau in the meantime. Either at this or the second Paris performance Rousseau's own recitatives were restored.

ML 50.2.D515R6

— **Le devin du village,** intermède; représenté, à Fontainebleau, le mercredi 14 novembre 1770. Les paroles et la musique sont de J. J. Rousseau. Les ballets sont de la composition de Laval.

Genève, n. publ., 1796. 13 p. 21ᶜᵐ.

Cast. One act. Of the first seven scenes the text in this edition is practically the same as in the score published by Mᵐᵉ· Boivin (175-) and Le Clerc (176-) but that of the eighth (last) scene differs considerably. Nor I do not find it in the Le Duc (178-) or Dufant et Dubois scores (181-). The most striking difference is this that the *Choeur avec le Devin* "Colin revient à sa bergère" does not appear in this Geneva edition of the text and that Colin's *Romance* "Dans ma cabane obscure" is preceded by the chorus "Chantons, chantons le dieu qui règne en nos hameaux."

ML 50.2.D5515R7

— The **cunning-man,** a musical entertainment, in two acts. As it is performed at the Theatre Royal in Drury-Lane. Originally written and composed by M. J. J. Rousseau. Imitated, and adapted to his original music, by Charles Burney . . .

London, T. Becket and P. A. de Hondt, 1766. 4 p. l., 30, [1] p. 20ᶜᵐ.

Two acts. Cast and preface, in which Burney apologizes for defects in his translation:

"The native simplicity and beauty of the original poetry, he could not flatter himself with the hopes of preserving in the translation . . . However, the airs have been scrupulously preserved from change or mutilation . . ."

In a foot-note he adds:

"Upon rehearsing the music, it has been thought necessary to retrench the second act, for fear of satiety."

These cuts are printed in the text with inverted commas.

First performed, as indicated, November 21, 1766.   LONGE 257

— The **cunning-man** . . . The second edition.

Same title, imprint, date, text, cast, and preface.   LONGE 26

— The **cunning man.** A musical entertainment. In two acts. From the Devin du village of Rousseau. By Dr. Charles Burney.

p. [196]-207. 19ᶜᵐ. (Collection of the most esteemed farces, performed on the British stage, Edinburgh, 1792, vol. ii.)

Cast.   SCHATZ 11753B

— Les **amours de Bastien et Bastienne,** parodie du Devin de village. Par Madame Favart, & Monsieur Harny. Representée pour la première fois, par les Comédiens italiens ordinaires du roi, le samedi 4 août 1753.

La Haye, Jean Neaulme, 1755. 32 p. 19ᶜᵐ.   ML 48.A4

— Les **amours de Bastien et Bastienne,** parodie du Devin de village, par Madame Favart, & Monsieur Harny; représentée pour la première fois par les Comédiens italiens ordinaires du roi, le mercredi 26 septembre 1753. Nouvelle édition.

Paris, N. B. Duchesne, 1759. 47, [1] p. 19ᶜᵐ. (Theatre de M. Favart, Paris, Duchesne, 1763-77, t. v.)

One act. *En vaudevilles.* Cast. Written in collaboration with Favart, who is not mentioned. The arranger of the music not known to Font.   ML 49.A2F1

Le **devin du village**—Continued.

— Les **amours de Bastien et Bastiene** parodié du Devin du Village par Madame Favart et Mr. Harny. Représentée pour la première fois par les Comédiens ordinaires du roi le mercredi 26 Septembre 1753 & augmentée depuis d'une Ronde qui se trouve après la Parodie.

*Avignon, Jacques Garrigan, 1768. 24 p. 19½*cm.   ML 48.M2M

— Les **amours de Bastien et Bastienne,** parodie du Devin de village, par Madame Favart & monsieur Harny; représentée pour la première fois par les Comédiens italiens ordinaires du roi, le mercredi 26 septembre 1753. Nouvelle édition.

*Paris, la veuve Duchesne, 1770. 43 p. 18½*cm.

One act. Printed in the text are the airs of "J'ons pardu mon ami," "Hélas'! Tu t'en vas!" "Plus matin que l'aurore," "Quand un tendron viant," "Autrefois à sa maîtresse," "De ce volage Colas répond," "La voici . . . tôt décampons," "On n'a dans l'mariage," "Ma peine vous rend fiere," "Non, infidele, cours à ta Belle," "Va, je te rens la pareille," "Mes enfants, après la pluie," "A présent J'nons pus rian," "Autrefois la jeune Thérèse."   SCHATZ 11481

Les **devins de la Place Saint-Marc.** Entrée in Campra's Les festes venitiennes.

Di rado l'uom sa giudicar se stesso, ballet. *See* P. Guglielmi's Alessandro nell' Indie.

Le **diable a quatre,** ou La double métamorphose, opera-comique en trois actes. Par M. S. . . . Représenté pour la première fois sur le Théâtre de la Foire S. Laurent, le 19 août 1756. Et repris le 12 février 1757, à la Foire S. Germain.

*La Haye, Jean Neaulme, 1757. 56 p. 19½*cm.
See next entry.   ML 50.2.D52P4

— Le **diable a quatre,** ou La double métamorphose, opera-comique en trois actes, par M. S . . . . .

*Paris, Duchesne, 1762. 51 p. 19*cm.

By Sedaine. The music consisted of popular airs. It is therefore a mistake if sometimes **Philidor** is recorded as the composer instead of as the arranger of the score.   SCHATZ 11490

— Le **diable a quatre,** ou La double métamorphose, opera comique, en trois actes, représenté pour la premiere fois sur le Théatre de la Foire Saint Laurent, le 19 août 1756; & repris le 12 février 1757 à la Foire Saint Germain. Par M. S . . . .

*Paris, Duchesne, 1770. 60 p. 19*cm.

Cast. On p. 4–6 the ariette "Oui, oui, je veux en sortir" (I, 3), 22–24 "En grand silence, avec prudence" (II, 1), 37–40 "Ah! quel plaisir hors de moi" (III, 1).   SCHATZ 11691

Le **diable d'argent.** Prologue. Représenté par la Troupe du Sieur Francisque à la Foire S. Germain 1720. Pendant laquelle le chant ayant été défendu, ou joüa par tolerance ce prologue & les deux pièces suivantes en prose.

— **Arlequin, roi des Ogres,** ou Les bottes de sept lieues. Pièce d'un acte. Représentée par la troupe du Sieur Francisque à la Foire de S. Germain 1720.

Le **diable d'argent**—Continued.

— La **queuë de verité.** Pièce d'un acte. Représentée par la troupe du Sieur Francisque à la Foire de Saint Germain. 1720.

Le Théâtre de la foire, Paris, 1724, t. iv, 3 pl., [95]–211 p. *17ᶜᵐ.*

According to a note on 2d p. l. the plays in t. iv were by Le Sage, Fuzelier, and D'Orneval. The title-page of "Le diable d'argent" explains the absence of operatic features in these three plays.   ML 48.L2IV

Diana. *See* Keiser's Die entdeckte verstellung.

Diana al bagno, ballet. *See* Gazzaniga's Amor per oro.

Diana e Endimione, ballet. *See* Bertoni's L'anello incantato.

Diana ed Endimione. A. T. of the ballet L'amor vincitore.

Diana ed Endimione, ballet. *See* P. Guglielmi's Il disertore.

Diana sorpresa, ballet. *See* Marescalchi's Il tutore ingannato.

Diana su l'Elba, introduzione musicale alla gran caccia fatta sull' acqua nelle vicinanze di Dresda per ordine di S. M. in occasione delle nozze di L.L. A.A. R.R.—Diane sur l'Elbe . . .

Dresde, J. C. Stössel, n. d. Upaged. 18½ᶜᵐ.

Author not mentioned, and unknown to Schatz. Italian and French (prose) text. Johann David **Heinichen** is mentioned as composer.

First performed, as indicated, September 18, 1719.   SCHATZ 4704

Diana und Endymion. Ein singspiel von Friedrich Karl von Strombeck. Nach Metastasio.

Braunschweig, Joh. Christoph Meyer, 1795. 47 p. 18ᶜᵐ.

Two acts. No composer or performance recorded by Schatz.   SCHATZ 11604

Diana's mask.

See p. 59–62 (4th act) of Sir Robert Stapylton's tragi-comedy, "The stepmother . . . acted with great applause at the Theatre in Little Lincolns-Inn-fields," London, J. Straeter, 1664.

— **Apollo's mask.**

Ibidem, p. 42–44 (3d act).   LONGE 122

Diane, divertissement pour le roi.

[351]–358 p. *17½ᶜᵐ.* (*Antoine Danchet, Théâtre, Paris, 1751, t. iii.*)

One act. Apparently identical with the entrée, "Diane & Endimion," in the condensed version of Quinault-Lully's ballet, "Le triomphe de l'amour," which Danchet and **Campra** edited for its revival on Sept. 11, 1705.   PQ 1972.D2

Diane et Endimion. Entrée in Quinault's Les amours des Déesses.

Diane et Endimion. A. T. of de Bury's La vengeance de l'amour.

Diane sur l'Elbe. Tr. of Heinichen's Diana su l'Elba.

La **diavolessa.** Dramma di tre atti per musica. Rappresentato per la prima volta in Venezia l'autunno dell' anno MDCCLV con musica del Buranello.

Carlo Goldoni, Opere Teatrali, Venezia, Zatta e figli, 1788–95, v. 43, [179]–239 p. *18ᶜᵐ.*   PQ

La **diavolessa**. Dramma giocoso per musica di Polisseno Fegejo, P. A. Da rappresentarsi nel Teatro di S. Samuele l'autunno dell' anno MDCCLV.

> *Venezia, Angiolo Geremia, n. d. 52 p. 16^{cm}.*
>
> Three acts. By Goldoni. Cast and name of Baldassare **Galuppi** as composer.
>
> SCHATZ 3449

— Li **vaghi accidenti fra amore, e gelosia**. Dramma giocoso per musica, da rappresentarsi nel Nuovo Teatro alla Cavallerizza nella fiera di Giubilate dell' anno MDCCLVI. In Lipsia. — Die artigen zufaelle zwischen liebe und eifersucht . . . Auf dem neuerrichteten Theater im allhiesigen Reuthause . . . in Leipzig aufgefuehret . . .

> *n. i., n. d. 159 p. 16$\frac{1}{2}$^{cm}.*
>
> Three acts. By Goldoni. Scenario and name of **Galuppi** as composer. German text faces Italian text, which is practically identical with that of "La Diavolessa."
>
> SCHATZ 3450

Il **diavolo a quattro**, ballet. *See* Calvi's Ezio.

Il **diavolo a quattro** ossia La doppia metamorfosi, ballet. *See* Calegari's Artemisia.

Il **diavolo a quattro** ossia La doppia metamorfosi, ballet. *See* Caruso's Il matrimonio in commedia.

Il **diavolo a quattro** ossia La doppia metamorfosi, ballet. *See* Gassmann's L'amore artigiano.

Didio Giuliano. Drama rappresentato nel nuovo Teatro Ducale in Piacenza . . . Poesia del dottor Lotto Lotti, e musica di Don Bernardo Sabadini . . .

> *Parma, Stamparia Ducale, 1687. 20 p. 14^{cm}.*
>
> Three acts. Impresario's dedication, argument, scenario, and curious notice to the reader which reads in part:
> "ciò che si rende oscuro nel verso, non riesce poi chiaro a gl'idioti, massime fra le consonanze della musica; essendo hoggidì un gran precetto il sodisfare l'udito commune; abbenche però se ne servissero anche i primi maestri; di questa verità te ne fà fede Tacito parlando di Seneca à cui bisognava *esse auribus saeculi accomodatus*. Legiolo dunque solo in teatro, contemplando, chi lo rappresenta unito all' ingegnosa armonia del Sig. D. Bernardo **Sabadini** eroico compositore de nostri tempi; mà non applicare a trascorrerlo con occhio curioso fuori di teatro, perche non ne caverai alcuna allettazione, cosa che pure da sudetti antichi era considerata . . ."
>
> SCHATZ 9199

Dido; a comic opera. As it is performed at the Theatre Royal in the Hay-Market.

> *London, T. Davies, 1771. 2 p. l., 34 p. 19$\frac{1}{2}$^{cm}.*
>
> Two acts with prologue. Neither Thomas Bridges, the author, nor the composer is mentioned. Towers is presumably mistaken, if he attributes the music to Dr. **Arne**. He probably confused this with Arne's masque with harlequinade "Dido and Aeneas," composed 1733. (*See* Cummings.)
> First performed, as indicated, July 24, 1771.   LONGE 32

Dido. Tr. of Albinoni's Didone abbandonata.

Dido. Tr. of Piccinni's Didon.

Dido, koenigin von Carthago in einem singe-spiel auf dem Hamburgischen Theatro vorgestellet.

[*Hamburg*], *Gedruckt im jahr 1707.* `Unpaged.` *18½ᶜᵐ*.

Three acts. Neither the author, Hinsch, nor the composer, Christoph **Graupner,** is mentioned in the "Vorrede." SCHATZ 4122

Didon, tragedie representée par l'Academie royale de musique l'an 1693. Les paroles de Mad. Xaintonge, & La musique de M. Desmarets. XXX opera.

n. i., n. d. front , p. 281–344 (Recueil général des opéra, t. iv, Paris, 1703). 14ᶜᵐ.

Detached copy. Prologue and five acts.
First performed, as indicated, September 11, 1693. SCHATZ 2531
Second copy. ML 48.R4

Didon, tragédie lyrique en trois actes; représentée à Fontainebleau devant Leurs Majestés, le 16 octobre 1783 et pour la premiere fois sur le Théatre de l'Academie-royale de musique le lundi 1ᵉʳ décembre 1783.

Paris, P. de Lormel, 1783. viii, 51, [1] p. 23ᶜᵐ.

Three acts. Cast and names of Marmontel as author, of Niccolò **Piccinni** as composer. SCHATZ 8088

— Dido, heroische oper in drey akten; zur musik von Piccini, nach dem franzoesischen von C. Herklots.

Berlin, n. publ., 1799. 48 p. 15ᶜᵐ.

Three acts. Cast.
First performed at Berlin, Kgl. Nationaltheater, March 18, 1799. SCHATZ 8089

Didon abandonnée. Tr. of Jommelli's Didone abbandonata.

La **Didone** di Gio. Francesco Busenello. Opera rappresentata in musica nel Teatro di San Casciano nell' anno 1641.

Venetia, Andrea Giuliani, 1656. 80 p. 15ᶜᵐ.

Three acts with prologue. Argument. Without name of the composer, Pietro Francesco **Cavalli.** SCHATZ 1718

Didone. Dramma per musica da rappresentarsi nel Regio Teatro di Torino nel carnovale del 1773 alla presenza di S. S. R. M.

Torino, Onorato Derossi, n. d. viii, 64 p. 15½ᶜᵐ.

Three acts. By Metastasio. Argument, cast, scenario, and name of the composer, Giuseppe **Colla.** One of Bartolommeo Lany's ballets performed with the opera was called "Piramo e Tisbe" and is described on p. vii–viii; the music was by Paolo Ghebard. SCHATZ 2107

Didone. Dramma per musica da rappresentarsi nel Regio Teatro di S. Carlo. In benefizio di Marianna Albani la sera dei 16 ottobre 1799.

Lisbona, Simone Taddeo Ferreira, 1799. 99 p. 15ᶜᵐ.

Incorrectly dated: MDCCLXXXXVIX. Three acts. By Metastasio (who is not mentioned) with alterations by the theatre poet Giuseppe Caravita. Argument. cast, scenario and name of Settiminio **Marino** as the composer. Portuguese text faces Italian. SCHATZ 5968

La **Didone.** Dramma di Paolo Moscardini colla musica del Sig. D. Andrea Mattioli mastro di capella del' Altezza Sereniss. di Mantoua.

Bologna, Giacomo Monti, 1656. 119 p. 13½ᶜᵐ.

Three acts with prologue. Author's dedication dated Bologna, April 25, 1656, brief scenario, and notice to the reader in which the author pays his compliments to Mattioli, to the "nuoua, e bizzarra inuentione delle machine del Sig. Gio. Battista Barbieri Ferrarese" and the "nobilissima maestria e magnificenza delle scene de' Sig. Angelo Michele Colonna, Agostino Metelli, e Domenico Santi."   SCHATZ 6102

La **Didone.** Dramma in musica da rappresentarsi nel pubblico Teatro di Forli nella primavera dell' anno 1779 . . .

Forlì, Achille Marozzi, n. d. 66 p. 17½ᶜᵐ.

Three acts. By Metastasio, who is not mentioned. Impresario's dedication, dated Forlì, May 8, 1779, cast, scenario, and name of Bernard(in)o **Ottani** as the composer.
SCHATZ 7364

La **Didone.** Dramma serio in musica. Da rappresentarsi in Firenze nel R. Teatro dei Risoluti posto in via S. Maria nell' estate dell' anno 1795 . . .

Firenze, Anton Giuseppe Pagani e comp., 1795. 39 p. 16½ᶜᵐ.

Three acts. Cast and names of Metastasio as the author, of **Paisiello** as the composer.

First performed as indicated, August 1, 1795; as "Didone abbandonata," at Naples, Teatro di S. Carlo, November 4, 1794.   SCHATZ 7699

Didone. Drama per musica da rappresentarsi nel Regio Teatro di Torino nel carnovale del 1750 . . .

Torino, Pietro Giuseppe Zappata e figliuolo, n. d. 4 p. l., 63 p. 16ᶜᵐ.

Three acts. By Metastasio, who is not mentioned. Argument, cast, scenario, and name of Domingo **Terradellas** as composer.   SCHATZ 10285

Second copy.   ML 48.A5   v. 4

La **Didone,** ballet. *See* Tritto's Apelle e Campaspe.

La **Didone abbandonata.**

[435]–506 p. 19ᶜᵐ. (Pietro Metastasio, Opere drammatiche, Venezia, Giuseppe Betinelli, 1733–37, t. i.)

Three acts. Argument. No composer is mentioned. This is one of his texts which Metastasio later on revised. Here are a few telling differences between the original and the later version: The original version has in I, 11 the aria "Ogni amator suppone; the later version has no aria. In the original version I, 14 begins "Lo so, quel cor feroce" and has the aria "Infelice e sventurato." This scene was suppressed in the later version, so that the later I, 14 is the same as the original I, 15 "Come! Da' labbri tuoi." In the original version II, 1 begins "Signor ove te'n vai," in the later version "Chi fu che all inumano."   ML 49.A2M4

— **Didone abbandonata.**

Metastasio, Poesie, Parigi, vedova Quillau, 1755, t. ii, [307]–403 p. 16ᶜᵐ.

Three acts and licenza. Argument. "Nella forma in cui sono stati ridotti dall' autore." (*See* note on p. 169 of t. vi.)

—Same, t. vi, [281]–390 p. 16ᵐ.
"Come . . . nell' altre edizioni."   ML 49.A2M42

— **Didone abbandonata.** Primo drama dell' autore, rappresentato la prima volta con musica del Sarro in Napoli, nel carnevale dell' anno 1724.

pl., [3]–108 p. 26ᶜᵐ. (Pietro Metastasio, Opere, t. iii, Parigi, vedova Herissant, 1780.)

Three acts and licenza. Argument.   ML 49.A2M44

Didone abbandonata. Tragedia di Pietro Metastasio . . . Da rappresentarsi in musica nel Teatro delle Dame nel carnevale dell' anno MDCCXXXII . . .

[Roma], Pasquino, n. d. 83, [1] p. 15^cm.

Three acts. Last unnumb. p. contains the aria, "M'offendi; e pur conviene," as substitute for "Tacerò se tu lo brami" (II, 12). Impresario's dedication, argument, scenario, cast. Composer not mentioned, and unknown to Schatz. SCHATZ 11380

Didone abbandonata. Tragedia per musica ridotta ad uso del nuovo famosissimo Teatro di S. Girolamo. Da rappresentarsi nel carnovale dell' anno 1747.

Venezia, Luigi Pavini, 1747. 69 p. 11^cm.

Three acts. Cast, scenario, and name of composer, Andrea **Adolfati**. Based on Metastasio's libretto of the same title. SCHATZ 57

Didone abbandonata. Tragedia di Artino Corasio, pastore Arcade, da rappresentarsi in musica nel Teatro Tron di S. Cassano il carnevale dell' anno MDCCXXV . . .

Venezia, Marino Rossetti, n. d. 67 p. 15½^cm.

Three acts. By Metastasio. Dedicatory sonnet, argument, scenario, cast, and name of Tommaso **Albinoni** as composer. SCHATZ 89

— **Dido,** musiclische [!] opera, welche auff dem Theatro zu Bresslau in Novembr. anno 1726 vorgestellet . . .

n. i., n. d. Unpaged. 8^cm.

Three acts, with Italian and German text, name of **Albinoni** as composer, and argument. Closely-trimmed copy. Pagination possibly cut off in trimming. SCHATZ 90

Didone abbandonata. Dramma per musica del Signore abate Pietro Metastasio Poeta Cesareo da rappresentarsi nel Teatro di Lucca nell' autunno dell' anno 1775.

Lucca, Filippo Maria Benedini, 1775. 60 p. 14^cm.

Three acts. Argument, cast, scenario, and name of Pasquale **Anfossi** as composer. First performed at Venice, Teatro di S. Moisè, in May, 1775; at Lucca on August 23, 1775. SCHATZ 233

La **Didone abbandonata.** Da rappresentarsi in musica nel Teatro nuovo di corte . . . nel carnovale 1760. La poesia è del Signor abbate Pietro Metastasio . . . La musica è del Sig. Andrea di Bernasconi . . .

Monaco, Giov. Giac. Vötter, n. d. 89, [8] p. 15^cm.

Three acts. Argument, cast, and scenario. The unnumb. p. contain description in French, of the ballets, "Le prie del' oiseau ou du Papegai, ballet pantomime de demi-caractère" and "La coquette de village, pantomime comique." The ballets were invented by Du Buisson de Chalandray. The composer of the music is not mentioned.

Previously performed at Munich, carnival of 1756, and at Venice, Teatro di S. Giov. Grisostomo, carnival, 1741. SCHATZ 858

Didone abbandonata, ballet. *See* Cherubini's Ifigenia in Aulide.

La **Didone abbandonata.** Dramma per musica da rappresentarsi sopra il famoso Ducal Teatro di Bronsevigo nella fiera d'Inverno dell' anno 1751.

Bronsevigo, gli heredi Keitel, n. d. 131 p. 18½^cm.

Three acts. By Metastasio. German text and title-page, "Die verlassene Didone," face Italian. Argument, scenario, and names of the author and the composer, "Ignatio **Fiorillo**, maestro di capella di corte."

First performed, as indicated, February, 1751. SCHATZ 3200

La **Didone abbandonata,** dramma per musica da rappresentarsi nel Regio-ducal Teatro di Milano, nel carnovale dell' anno 1755 . . .

　　Milano, Giuseppe Richino Malatesta, 1755.　5 p. l., 60 p.　14½cm.

Three acts.　By Metastasio.　Dedication, argument, scenario, cast, and name of the composer, Giovanni Andrea **Fioroni.**　　　　　　　　　　　　SCHATZ 3206

Didone abbandonata.　Dramma per musica da rappresentarsi nel Teatro di S. Benedetto il carnevale dell' anno MDCCLXIV.

　　Venezia, Giorgio Fossati, n. d.　71 p.　17cm.

Three acts.　By Metastasio. Reprint of the author's sonnet from the first edition of his drama, now used as a dedication to the most excellent ladies of Venice, argument, scenario, cast, and name of **Galuppi** as composer.

First performed at Modena, Teatro Molzo, carnival, 1741 (Piovano).　SCHATZ 3503

[La **Didone abbandonata**].—Die verlassene Dido, ein musicalisches drama, welches auf dem koeniglichen schlosse zu Hubertusburg an dem hoechstbeglueckten geburthstage Ihro Majestaet Augusti III . . . aufgefuehret worden.

　　Dresden, bey der verw. Stoesselin, 1742.　(double) 102, [2] p.　16cm.

The Italian title-page apparently missing.

Three acts and licenza.　By Metastasio, who is not mentioned.　Argument and name of Johann Adolph **Hasse** as composer.

First performed, as indicated, October 7, 1742.　　　　　　SCHATZ 4535

— **Didone abbandonata.**　Tragedia da rappresentarsi nel Regio Teatro di Berlino per ordine di Sua Maestà.

　　Berlino, Haude e Spenez, 1769.　131, [3] p.　15½cm.

Three acts.　Argument, scenario, and names of Metastasio as author, of Johann Adolph **Hasse** as the composer.　German title-page, "Die verlassene Dido," and text face Italian, which is not quite the same as in the Dresden version.　For instance, the eleventh scene, "Non partirò se pria," has been dropped and "Non è più tempo, Araspe," originally the twelfth, has become the eleventh scene.

Performed December, 1769, as indicated; previously, December 29, 1752.

　　　　　　　　　　　　　　　　　　　　　　　　SCHATZ 4536

La **Didone abbandonata.**　Dramma per musica da rappresentarsi nel Teatro Ducale di Stutgart festeggiandosi il felicissimo giorno natalizio di Sua Altezza Serenissima Elisabetta Sofia Federica duchessa di Wurtemberg et Teck . . .　La poesia è del . . .　Pietro Metastasio . . .　La musica è del Sig. Nicolo Jommelli . . .

　　Stutgart, Giovanne Georgio Cotta, 1751.　117 p.　18cm.

Three acts.　Argument, cast, scenario.　German title page, "Die verlassene Dido," and text face Italian.　Schatz calls this Jommelli's second version.

First performed, as indicated, August 30, 1751.　At Vienna this "Neuschöpfung" (Abert) was first performed on December 8, 1749.　According to Abert, the first version of the opera was first performed at Rome, Teatro di Torre Argentina in 1746, according to Schatz on Saturday, January 28, 1747.　　　SCHATZ 4854

La **Didone abbandonata.**　Dramma per musica da rappresentarsi nel Teatro Ducale di Stuttgart festeggiandosi il felicissimo giorno natalizio di Sua Altezza Serenissima Carlo, duca regnante di Wirtemberg e Teck etc.　La poesia è del Signor abbate Pietro Metastasio . . . La musica è nuovamente composta dal Signor Nicolò Jommelli . . . I balli sono inventati dal Signor Giovanni Giorgio Noverre . . .

　　Stuttgart, Cotta, 1763.　207 p.　21cm.

Three acts.　Argument, scenario, cast.　French title-page, "Didon abandonnée," and text face Italian.　On p. [74]–89 cast and description of the ballet "Medea e Giasone-Medee et Jason," music by Rudolph (Abert); on p. [138]–157 of "Orfeo ed

La **Didone abbandonata**—Continued.

Euridice, ballo eroico-Orphée & Euridice," music by Deller (Abert). Schatz and Abert call this Jommelli's third setting. The text is strikingly different from that of the 1751 edition. For instance, Adrasto has been dropped from the list of characters, the opera begins "No principessa, amico" instead of "Non più. Fedel Adrasto." The aria "D'aversa sorte" has been dropped from the first scene, in fact the text of the three first scenes has been condensed into one, so that the aria "Dirò che fida sei" in I, 5, now comes in I, 3, the aria "Fra lo splendor nel trono" has been dropped from I, 9 (resp. I, 7), the scene (I, 10) "De gli nomini ornamento" with the aria "Vorrei pria esanime" has been replaced by (I, 8) "Empio! L'orror, che porta" with the aria "Se dalle stelle tu non sei guida," etc., etc.

First performed, as indicated, February 11, 1763. SCHATZ 4855

Didone abbandonata. Dramma per musica da rappresentarsi hel nobilissimo Teatro di S. Benedetto il carnovale dell' anno 1770.

Venezia, Modesto Fenzo, 1770. 61 p. 17ᶜᵐ.

Three acts. By Metastasio, who is not mentioned. "Sonetto dell' autore, premesso alla prima edizione di questo suo dramma," argument, cast, scenario, and name of Francesco de **Majo** as composer.

First performed December 26, 1769, as indicated. SCHATZ 5855

Didone abbandonata, dramma per musica da rappresentarsi nel famosissimo Teatro Grimani di S. Gio. Grisostomo nel carnovale dell' anno MDCCLI.

Venezia, In merceria all' insegna della scienza, n. d. 68 p. 15ᶜᵐ.

Three acts. By Metastasio, who is not mentioned. Argument, scenario, cast, and name of Gennaro **Manna** as composer. SCHATZ 5901

Didone abbandonata. A serious opera. Written by Metastasio. As performed at the King's Theatre in the Hay-Market. The music by the most celebrated composers under the direction of Signor Sacchini.

London, T. Cadell, n. d. 55, [1] p. 18ᶜᵐ.

Three acts. Cast. English translation faces Metastasio's much altered text-The unnumb. page contains a list of R. Bremner's "New music." Probably a libretto for the performances at London, 1775–76, of which Burney (IV, 504) says "chiefly by **Sacchini.**" SCHATZ 11321

Didone abandonata. Drama per musica da rappresentarsi nel Teatro di S. Bartolomeo nel carnevale dell' anno 1724 . . .

Napoli, Francesco Ricciard, 1724. 72 p. 15ᶜᵐ.

Three acts. By Metastasio who is not mentioned. Impresario's dedication, argument, scenario, cast and name of Domenico **Sarro** as the composer. ML 50.2.D55S2

— **Didone abbandonata.** Tragedia di Artino Corasio, pastore Arcade da rappresentarsi nel famosissimo Teatro di S. Gio. Grisostomo nell' autunno dell' anno 1730 . . .

Venetia, Carlo Buonarigo, n. d. 1 p. l., 72 p. 15ᶜᵐ.

Three acts. By Metastasio. Domenico Lalli's dedication, argument, cast, scenario, and name of Domenico **Sarro** as the composer. SCHATZ 9422

Didone abbandonata. Dramma per musica da rappresentarsi sul Regio Teatro Danese, l'inverno dell' anno 1762. — Den forladte Dido . . .

Kiøbenhavn, Lars Nielsen Svare, n. d. 127 p. 15½ᶜᵐ.

Three acts. Argument, cast, and names of Metastasio as author, of Giuseppe **Sarti** as composer. ("La musica è tutta nuova.") SCHATZ 9432

La **Didone abbandonata.** Dramma per musica da rappresentarsi in Ferrara nel Teatro Bonacossa da San Steffano il carnevale dell' anno 1763 . . .

Ferrara, Fornari, n. d.   59 p.   15ᶜᵐ.

Three acts. By Metastasio. Impresario's dedication, argument, cast, scenario, and name of Giuseppe **Scolari** as composer. ("La musica tutta nova sarà composta.")

SCHATZ 9806

Didone abbandonata, dramma per musica del Sig. abate Pietro Metastasio da rappresentarsi nel Teatro Giustiniani di S. Moisè. L'autunno dell' anno 1757.

Venezia, Modesto Fenzo, 1757.   58 p.   15ᶜᵐ.

Three acts.   Cast, argument, scenario, and name of Tommaso **Trajetta** as composer.

SCHATZ 10402

Didone abbandonata. Drama di Artino Corasio Pastore Arcade. Da rappresentarsi in musica nel Teatro delle Dame nel carnevale dell' anno 1726 . . .

Roma, Bernabò, n. d.   78 p.   14½ᶜᵐ.

Three acts. By Metastasio. Dedication, argument, scenario, cast and name of Leonardo **Vinci** as composer.   ML 50.2.D55V4

La **Didone abbandonata.** Dramma per musica da rappresentarsi in Perugia nell' apertura del Nuovo Teatro Civico del Verzaro l'autunno dell' anno MDCCLXXXI . . .

Perugia, Mario Riginaldi, n. d.   xii, 68 p.   18½ᶜᵐ.

Three acts. By Metastasio. Cast, argument, scenario, name of Francesco **Zanetti** as composer, and (on xii p.) description and historical sketch of the new theatre, the erection of which was begun on June 12, 1778, and which was to be opened in September, 1781.

On p. [25]–31, argument and description of "Il trionfo di Alessandro o sia La prigionia di Dario, ballo eroico in quattro atti, composto e diretto dal signor Domenico Ricciardi." Music ("tutta nuova") by Mattia Stabingher.

First performed at Livorno, Teatro di San Sebastiano, carnival, 1766.

ML 48.A5 v. 5.

La **Didone delirante.** Drama da rappresentarsi in musica nel famoso Teatro Grimano di SS. Gio. e Paolo l'anno MDCLXXXVI. Di Antonio Franceschi . . .

Venetia, Francesco Nicolini, 1686.   72 p.   14½ᶜᵐ.

Three acts. Author's dedication, notice to the reader, in which the author calls this "primo parto del mio debole ingegno," and names Carlo **Pallavicino** as the composer, argument, and scenario.   SCHATZ 7736

Diesmal hat der mann den willen! Ein originalsingspiel in einem aufzuge. Aufgeführt auf der K. K. Nationalschaubühne. Die musik ist vom herrn Ordonez.

Wien, bey dem logen meister, 1778.   28 p.   16½ᶜᵐ.

By Johann Friedrich Schmidt, who is not mentioned.

First performed, as indicated, April 22, 1778.   SCHATZ 7291

Les **Dieux acteurs.** Entrée in Brassac's L'empire de l'amour.

Les **dieux d'Égipte.** A. T. of the ballet Les fêtes de l'Himen.

Il **difficile per inganno facile,** ballet. *See* Andreozzi's Il disprezzo vinto.

Il **dilettante.** A petit burletta, in two parts. As performed at Marybone-Gardens. The music composed by Mr. Hook.

London, W. Woodfall, 1772. 19 p. 23ᶜᵐ.

Author not recorded. Cast and author's dedication, dated August 1772:
"This piece being merely thrown together for the purpose of giving excellent talents an opportunity of exertion, is inscribed to that delicate composer, Mr. Hook; and those able, very approved performers . . ." ML 50.2.D56H6

Dioclesian. *See* H. Purcell's The prophetess or The history of Dioclesian.

Il **Dioclete.** Drama per musica da rappresentàrsi nel Teatro di S. Angelo l'anno MDCLXXXVII . . .

Venetia, Francesco Nicolini, 1687. 70, [1] p. 14½ᶜᵐ.

Three acts. By Andrea Rossini, who is not mentioned. Impresario's dedication, argument, scenario, and notice to the reader, in which the author calls this "la mia terza fatica," and Teofilo **Orgiani** the composer of the opera. The imprimatur at the end is dated January 15, 1687.
First performed, as indicated, January 18, 1687. SCHATZ 7297

Diocletiano. Drama per musica da rappresentarsi nel sempre famoso Teatro Grimano à SS. Gio. e Paolo. L'anno MDCLXXV. Di Matteo Noris . . .

Venetia, Francesco Nicolini, 1685. front., 72 p. 13½ᶜᵐ.

Three acts. Author's dedication, dated Venice, December 10, 1674, argument, and scenario. The composer, Carlo **Pallavicino,** is not mentioned. SCHATZ 7721

Diogene tentato ma non vinto dall' amore, ballet. *See* Rust's Il conte Baccelone.

Dioméde, tragedie représentée par l'Academie royale de musique l'an 1710. Les paroles de M. de la Serre. La musique de M. Bertin. LXXIV. opera.

n. i., n. d. pl., 63–128 p. 14ᶜᵐ. (Recueil général des opéra, Paris, 1714, t. x.)

Detached copy. Prologue and five acts.
First perlormed, as indicated, April 28, 1710. SCHATZ 879
Second copy. ML 48.R4

Diomede punito da Alcide. Drama di Aurelio Aureli posto in musica dal Signor Tomaso Albinoni da rappresentarsi nel Teatro à Sant' Angelo . . .

Venezia, Nicolini, 1701. 48 p. 14ᶜᵐ.

Three acts. Author's dedication, argument, scenario, and cast. SCHATZ 107

Diomede punito da Alcide. Drama rappresentato nel nuovo Teatro Ducale di Piacenza . . . Poesia d'Aurelio Aureli . . . e musica singolare di D. Bernardo Sabadini . . .

Parma, Stampa ducale, 1691. 80 p. 15ᶜᵐ.

Three acts. Dedication, argument, cast, scenario, and brief description of the ballets. SCHATZ 9194

Dionisio overo La virtù trionfante del vizio. Drama per musica da rappresentarsi nel sempre famoso Teatro Grimano di S. Gio. e Paolo l'anno MDCLXXXI . . .

Venetia, Francesco Nicolini, 1681. 67 p. 13½ᶜᵐ.

Dionisio—Continued.

Three acts. By Matteo Noris, who dates his dedication, Venice, January 12, 1681. Argument, scenario, and notice to the reader informing him that Petronio **Franceschini** having died after the composition of the first act, the other two acts and the overture were composed by [Giovanni Domenico] "Dottor **Partenio**."

SCHATZ 3319

Dionisio re di Portogallo. Drama per musica rappresentato nella Villa di Pratolino.

Firenze, Anton Maria Albizzini, 1707. 4 p. l., 61 p. 17^{cm}.

Three acts. Argument and scenario. Neither the author, Antonio Salvi, is mentioned, nor the composer, Giacomo Antonio **Perti**.

First performed, as indicated, September, 1707. ML 50.2.D57P3

Dionisio Siracusano. Drama per musica da rappresentarsi nel nuovo Teatro Ducale di Parma il carnevale dell' anno 1689 . . .

Parma, Stamperia ducale, n. d. 88 p. 15^{cm}.

Three acts. By Antonio Salvi, who is not mentioned. Impresario's dedication, argument, cast, scenario, and notice to the reader which reads in part:

"Se . . . vedrai il suddetto drama cangiato, diminuito, ò accresciuto, sappi che essendo trabalzati simili componimenti da un teatro a l'altro, cangiando rappresentanti, è necessario il dar nuova forma alle parti secondo le abilità appoiche un' abito fabbricato per la vita d'un' uomo di rado s'acconcia a quella d'un altro."

Bibiena, the scene painter, is mentioned, also Torelli, the "inventore degli abiti," but not the composer, Giacomo Antonio **Perti**. SCHATZ 7955

Le directeur dans l'embarras. Tr. of Cimarosa's L'impresario in angustie.

La direttrice prudente. Commedia per musica da rappresentarsi nel Teatro de' Fiorentini nell' autunno di quest 'anno 1767.

Napoli, Vincenzo Flauto, 1767. 72 p. 15^{cm}.

Three acts. Pages 3–4, presumably containing the cast and name of Niccolò **Piccinni** as composer and possibly the name of the author are wanting. SCHATZ 8122

The disappointed virgin. A. T. of The marriage promise.

The disappointment: or, The force of credulity. A new American comic-opera, of two acts. By Andrew Barton, esq. . . .

New-York, Printed in the year, 1767. v, [7]–58 p. 16½^{cm}.

Epilogue and prologue which begins:
> " Tho' distant far, from fam'd Britania's isle,
> Where comic-scenes, call cynics forth to smile;
> Our artless muse, hath made her first essay
> T'instruct and please you with a modern play "

and preface, signed by Andrew Barton, which reads in part:

"The following local piece, intitled, (The Disappointment, or the Force of Credulity) was originally wrote for my own, and the amusement of a few particular friends, who (unknown to me) were pleased to signify their approbation of it, in such a manner, that it soon engrossed the chief part of the conversation of all ranks of people; who expressed their desire to hear it, and have it published. Under these circumstances, I was greatly at a loss how to proceed, I did not choose (as I saw no merit in it) to expose it to the criticisms of criticks, to put it in the power of gentlemen skill'd in scholastick knowledge, to ridicule my ignorance, or condescend to the intreaties of those, who I thought had no more sense than myself, and who might (perhaps) have made it better than it really is. Conscious therefore of my own inability, I determined to excuse myself to all; and in this determination I persisted for some time, but at last, for my own safety, was obliged to capitulate and surrender on the following stipulations; First, the infrequency of dramatic compositions in America: Secondly, the torrent of solicitations from all quarters: Thirdly, the necessity of contributing to the entertainment of the city: Fourthly and lastly, to put a stop (if

The disappointment—Continued.

possible) to the foolish and pernicious practice of searching after supposed hidden treasure. These terms, hard as they are, I have with reluctance been forced to submit to, I am therefore obliged in vindication of my conduct, to assure the public that the story is founded on matter of fact, transacted near this city, not long since, and recent in memory of thousands; for the truth of which assertion I appeal to numbers of my fellow citizens."

This first American ballad opera (with 18 airs indicated by title. "Air IV. Yankee Doodle") was to have been first performed by the American Company at Philadelphia on April 20, 1767, but it was withdrawn, "personal reflections" rendering it "unfit for the stage." "The disappointment" is sometimes attributed to Thomas Forrest or to John Leacock, but the evidence is not sound (Sonneck).

ML 50.6.D52

— The **disappointment**; or, The force of credulity. A new comic-opera, in three acts. By Andrew Barton, esq. Second edition, revised and corrected with large additions by the author . . .

Philadelphia, Francis Shallus, 1796. iv, [5]–94 p., 1 l. 18½ᶜᵐ.

The piece now has 20 songs, none of which with indication of the air. The preface is the same, but prologue and epilogue are different. Not performed. ML 50.6.D54

La **discesa d'Ercole all' inferno** o sia Alceste ed Admeto, ballet. *See* Antonelli's Catone in Utica.

La **discesa d'Ercole all' inferno,** ballet. *See* Cherubini's Hgenia in Aulide.

La **discordia fortunata**. Dramma giocoso per musica da rappresentarsi nel Teatro di S. Samuele nel carnovale dell' anno 1775.

Venezia, Antonio Graziosi, 1775. 71 p. 17ᶜᵐ.

Three acts. Cast, scenario, and name of **Paisiello** as the composer. The author not mentioned, and unknown to Schatz. SCHATZ 7607

— L'**avaro deluso**. Dramma giocoso per musica da rappresentarsi nel Piccolo Theatro di S. A. S. E. di Sassonia.

Dresda, n. publ., 1776. 151 p. 15½ᶜᵐ.

Three acts. Is "La discordia fortunata," with alterations, for instance I, 3, "Oh! Oh!" and I, 5 "Se state alla sua cura" having been dropped. German title page, "Der verspottete geitzige," and text face the Italien. **Paisiello** is mentioned as the composer.

First performed November 20, 1776, as indicated. SCHATZ 7608

— L'**avaro deluso**. Dramma giocoso per musica da rappresentarsi nel Theatro in Parte Piccola della regia città di Praga, nella casa del Signor conte di Thun.

[Praga], n. publ., nell' autunno dell' anno 1784. 147 p. 16ᶜᵐ.

Three acts. **Paisiello** is mentioned as the composer. German title page "Der betrogene geizhalz," and text face Italian.

First performed as indicated. SCHATZ 7609

— Der **betrogene geizige**; oder: Wer das glueck hat, fuehrt die braut heim! Eine nach dem italienischen freibearbeitetete komische oper in drei aufzuegen von C. A. Vulpius. Die musik ist von Paisiello.

Leipzig, Johann Samuel Heinsius, 1794. 15ᶜᵐ.

First performed at Weimar, Herzogl. Theater, April 26, 1786. SCHATZ 7610

The **discovery of America**. A. T. of Columbus.

Il **disertor francese**: Dramma giocoso per musica da rappresentarsi nel Reggio Teatro di S. Carlo, della Principessa la primavera dell' anno 1796.

Lisbona, Simone Taddeo Ferreira, 1796.   157 p.   14½ cm.

Two acts.   The author not mentioned, and unknown to Schatz.   Cast, scenario, and name of Giuseppe **Gazzaniga** as the composer.   Portuguese text faces Italian. With the opera was performed "Il disprezzo vendicato dal disprezzo.   Ballo di caratere russo d'invenzione e direzione del Sig. Pietro Angiolini."   The composer of the music is not mentioned.

First performed at Bologna, Teatro Lagnoni, fall of 1789.   SCHATZ 3681
Second copy.   ML 48.C6II

Il **disertore**.   A. T. of the ballet Alessio ed Eloisa.

Il **disertore**.   Drama serio per musica da rappresentarsi nel nobilissimo Teatro di S. Benedetto il carnovale dell' anno 1785.

Venezia, Modesto Fenzo, 1784.   front., 79 p.   18 cm.

Three acts.   Cast, scenario, name of composer, Francesco **Bianchi,** and that of the librettist, Bartolomeo Benincasa, who (p. 3–11) addresses an interesting esthetic preface, "Agli amatori del melodrama italiano," in which he explains at length his reasons for attempting "un nuovo genere di dramma"—indeed, a kind of reform of libretto writing.   One of his reasons is that Metastasio and his predecessors "non hanno mai scritto, che drammi eroicamente erotici," and that "avendo egli quel sommo uomo esaurito il suo genere" he had become somewhat tedious to the Italian nation.   Benincasa pleads for "un dramma in musica, che sia tra la grand' opera eroica e la comica operetta."   He finally remarks that the present opera was sketched, put in verses, composed, and staged in 35 days.

On p. [37]–44, argument, cast, scenario, and detailed description of the five-act "I baccanali, ballo tragico pantomimo d'Innocenzio Gambuzzi."   Neither of this nor the second ballet, "Le vendemmie fiamminghe" is the composer mentioned.

First performed, as indicated, December 26, 1784.   SCHATZ 978

Il **disertore**; a new comic opera; as acted at the King's Theatre in the Hay- Market.   Written by Mr. Badini.   The music entirely new, by Signor Guglielmi.

London, T. Baldwin, 1770.   viii, [2], 95 p.   17½ cm.

Three acts.   Author's dedication, dated May 10, 1770, cast, and author's preface, in which he says:

". . . I shall be blamed in having written it [the drama] rather for singers than for actors . . .   This piece was written merely to replace another, the representation of which had been forbidden.   The spectacle exhibited at present by France in the island of Corsica, appearing to me well calculated for the stage, I wrote an opera intitled—I Francesi in Corsica—the business and the characters of which were a striking portraiture of the odd manners of our age.   Political cautions however quashed my design, and I was then obliged to take "The Deserter" in hand.   Though the ground of this drama be taken from the French, yet a comparison of the two pieces will shew, that the French dramatist only furnished me with the block for making the work . . .   In writing the songs, as on them generally depends the success of our operas, I have carefully endeavoured to suit them to the capital object of vocal music: which is, to heighten the energy of sentiments inspired by the accents of tenderness, pity, joy and love in general.   Every accompaniment deficient in this view, fails of its proper effect: and a good reason of so few operas taking is, that when the music has no affinity with the words, it becomes purely a futile clutter of instruments; an unmeaning harmony, which, not affecting the heart, soon tires the ear, and causes the spectator to repeat that *bon mot* of Fontenelle: *Sonate que me veux-tu?*"

On an inserted leaf he adds that, "rather than to jar with any body, and chiefly with musicians," he has replaced Lovatini's "Se quel ciglio ancor ti miro" (II, 6) by "Tergi'l bel ciglio, o cara."   English translation, with caption title, "The deserter," faces the Italian text.   SCHATZ 4242

Il **disertore**—Continued.

— Il **disertore.**   Dramma giocoso per musica da rappresentarsi nel Teatro della rua dos Condes in Lisbona nell' estate dell' anno 1772.

[Lisbona], Nella stamperia reale, n. d.   4 p. l., 52 p.   17ᶜᵐ.

Three acts. Cast, scenario, and name of Pietro **Guglielmi** as composer. Badini's text is considerably altered.   For instance, the aria "Se quel ciglio ancor rimiro" is now at the end of II, 4, instead of II, 6, and the very first aria, "Ogni amante che si sposa," has been replaced by "All' amoroso ardore." With the opera was performed, composer of the music not mentioned, Vinceslao de Rossi's "Diana ed Endimione, picciolo ballo."   SCHATZ 4243

Il **disertore,** ballet.   *See* P. Guglielmi's L'impostore punito.

Il **disertore.**   Dramma serio per musica da rappresentarsi nel Teatro da S. Agostino il carnovale dell' anno 1799.   Dedicato ai cittadini liberi.

Genova, Stamperia della Libertà, Anno II. della Repubblica Liguria. 45 p.   13½ᶜᵐ.

Two acts. By Bartolomeo Benincasa, who is not mentioned. Cast and name of Angelo **Tarchi** as the composer.
First performed at London, Haymarket, spring of 1789.   SCHATZ 10235

Il **disertore francese,** ballet.   *See* Anfossi's Antigono.

Il **disertore francese,** ballet.   *See* Caruso's Il cavalier magnifico.

Il **disertore francese,** ballet.   *See* G. Giordani's Ariarate.

Il **disertore francese,** ballet.   *See* Jommelli's Armida abbandonata.

La **diserzione per equivoco,** ballet.   *See* Curcio's La conquista di Granata.

La **disfatta de' Mori.**   Dramma per musica da rappresentarsi nel Regio Teatro di Torino nel carnovale del 1791 alla presenza di S. S. R. M.

Torino, Onorato Derossi, n. d.   viii, 54 p.   16ᶜᵐ.

Three acts. Cast, argument, scenario, and names of the author, Giandomenico Boggio, and of the composer, Giuseppe **Gazzaniga.**   On p. 49–53 a description of the ballets designed by Domenico Ballon, "L'Americana in Europa" and "Orfeo ed Euridice."   According to a footnote Gluck's music was used for this ballet. The necessary alterations and the additional music were composed by Gaetano Pugnani.
                                                        SCHATZ 3662

La **disfatta di Abdurahamel, tiranno di Trabacca,** ballet.   *See* Andreozzi's Argea.

La **disfatta di Dario.**   A. T. of the ballet Il trionfo di Alessandro.

La **disfatta di Dario.**   Dramma per musica da rappresentarsi nel Teatro della città d'Alessandria in occasione della solita fiera d'Ottobre MDCCLXXIX sotto la protezione di S. R. M.

Alessandria, Ignazio Vimercati, n. d.   59, xx p.   18ᶜᵐ.

Three acts. Argument, cast, scenario, and notice:
"Il presente dramma composto molti anni sono in diversa forma dal duca Morbelli [S. Angelo Morbilli] Napoletano, e ridotto poi ad uso teatrale dall' abate Giuseppe Casali Romano, si è ora variato, anche notabilmente, per adattarlo al maggior comodo della musica e alle circostanze di questo Teatro. È la musica di nuova composizione del Sig. maestro Giuseppe **Ferrero.**"

La disfatta di Dario—Continued.

On p. i–xvi, "Proemio per il primo ballo," cast, argument, and Felice Alessandri's name as composer of the music of "L'enlevement des Sabines. Ballet heroique du sieur Sebastien Gallet, executé pour la première fois . . ." The second ballet, "Il feudatario ingannato," by Daniele Curtz; the third, "La festa Strasburghese," by Gallet. The composers are not mentioned. On p. xvii–xx, a list of the box-holders.   SCHATZ 3081

La disfatta di Dario.   Dramma per musica da rappresentarsi nel Teatro Grande alla Scala il carnevale dell' anno 1789 . . .

Milano, Gio. Batista Bianchi, n. d.   56 p.   16^{cm}.

Three acts. Author not mentioned and unknown to Schatz, though this may be called a barely recognizable version of Morbilli's text of the same title. Dedication, argument, cast, scenario, and name of Giuseppe **Giordani** as the composer. With the opera were performed the ballets "Le nozze de' Sanniti" and "Dorina, e l'uomo selvatico," by Gaspero Angiolini, who also composed the music.

First performed at Milan, as indicated, February 7, 1789.   SCHATZ 3836

Second copy. ML 48.A5 v.8

La disfatta di Dario.   Dramma per musica da rappresentarsi nel Regio Teatro di Torino nel carnovale del 1774 . . .

Torino, Onorato Derossi, n. d.   viii, 52 p.   19^{cm}.

Three acts. By the duca Sant' Angelo Morbilli, who is not mentioned. Argument, cast, scenario, and name of Giovanni **Masi** as the composer of the opera, of the dance music, Paolo Ghebard.   SCHATZ 6062

La disfatta di Dario.   Dramma per musica da rappresentarsi in Firenze nel Teatro di via del Cocomero nell' autunno dell' anno 1776 . . .

Firenze, Anton-Giuseppe Pagani, 1776.   50 p.   16½^{cm}.

Three acts. By the duca Sant' Angelo Morbilli, who is not mentioned. Argument, cast, and name of **Paisiello** as the composer.

First performed at Rome, Teatro Argentina, carnival, 1776.   SCHATZ 7664

— La disfatta di Dario.   Dramma per musica da rappresentarsi nel Teatro da S. Agostino il carnovale dell' anno 1782 . . .

Genova, Stamperia Gesiniana, n. d.   62, [1] p.   13½^{cm}.

Three acts. The author is not mentioned. Argument, cast, and name of **Paisiello** as the composer. On p. [55]–62, cast and description of Domenico Ricciardi's "Orfeo ballo . . . in cinque atti," music by "maestro Suster" (Josef Schuster, 1748–1812).

SCHATZ 7664a

La disfatta di Dario.   Dramma per musica da rappresentarsi nel nobilissimo Teatro di S. Benedetto il carnovale dell' anno 1778.

Venezia, Modesto Fenzo, 1778.   48 p.   16½^{cm}.

Three acts. Argument, cast, scenario, name of Tommaso **Trajetta** as composer, but not of librettist, duca Sant' Angelo Morbilli.   SCHATZ 10409

La disfatta di Vario.   A. T. of the ballet La Tusneida.

La disgrazia opportuna, ballet.   *See* Monza's Cleopatra.

Il disinganno.   *See* La verità raminga.

La disperata speranza ravvivata ne' successi di Giacopo Quinto di Scozia e Maddalena di Francia.   *See* Bazzani's L'inganno trionfato.

Li disprezzatori delle donne, osia Le vicende amorose. Dramma giocoso per musica, da rappresentarsi nel Teatro Elettorale.

Dresda, n. publ., 1793. 137 p. 15½^{cm}.

Two acts. Author not mentioned, and unknown to Schatz. Giacomo **Tritto** is mentioned as the composer. German title-page "Die veraechter der schoenen oder Der wechsel in der liebe," and text face Italian.

First performed, as indicated, November 6, 1793; at Rome, Teatro Capranica, April, 1787, as "Le vicende amorose." Schatz 10458

— **Le avventure galanti.** Dramma per musica da rappresentarsi in Genova nel Teatro da S. Agostino la primavera del 1789 . . .

Genova, Stamperia Gesiniana, n. d. 88 p. 14^{cm}.

Two acts. The same text as "Le vicende amorose." Cast, scenario, and name of Giacomo **Tritto** as the composer.

On p. 81–88, cast, argument, and description, without name of the composer of the music of Urbano Garzia's "Emirena e Sigismondo, ballo eroico pantomimo." His other ballet was called "Gli amanti ridicoli ossia La capricciosa umiliata." Schatz 10482

— **I raggiri d'amore.** Dramma giocoso per musica da rappresentarsi nel Ces. Reg. Teatro di Trieste nell' estate dell' anno 1793.

Trieste, Stamperia governiale, n. d. 59 p. 18^{cm}.

Two acts. Author not mentioned, and unknown to Schatz. Impresario's dedication, dated Trieste, August 13, 1793, cast, scenario, and name of Giacomo Tritta (**Tritto**) as composer.

First performed at Padova, Teatro Obizzi, June, 1792, with the above title. Schatz 10480

— **Le vicende amorose.** Dramma giocoso per musica da rappresentarsi nel Regio Teatro di S. Carlo, della Principessa il carnevale dell' anno 1797.

Lisbona, Simone Taddeo Ferreira, n. d. 111 p. 14½^{cm}.

One act. Cast and name of Giacomo **Tritto** as the composer. Portuguese text faces Italian. Schatz 10483

Il disprezzo. Azione drammatica giocosa per musica da rappresentarsi nel nobile Teatro di San Samuele il carnovale dell' anno 1782.

Venezia, Modesto Fenzo, 1782. 82 p. 16^{cm}.

One act only, followed by second act of Anfossi's "Amanti canuti," both with cast, scenario, and name of composer, Pasquale **Anfossi,** but not of librettist of "Il disprezzo," who is unknown to Schatz. On p. 36 the impresario gives his reasons for substituting the second act of "Gli Amanti canuti" for the second act of "Il disprezzo." Even this substitution was an afterthought, because at first the sketched second act was to be dropped for the first act of Anfossi's "La forza delle donne." Schatz 279

Il disprezzo vendicato dal disprezzo, ballet. *See* Gazzaniga's Il disertor francese.

Il disprezzo vinto dal disprezzo. Commedia per musica da rappresentarsi nel Real Teatro del Fondo di Separazione per second' opera del corrente anno 1795 . . .

Napoli, n. publ. 1795. 42 p. 15½^{cm}.

Two acts. Author not identified by Schatz. Cast, argument, and name of composer, Gaetano **Andreozzi.** Contains also the plot of "Il difficile per inganno facile, ballo favoloso composto e diretto dal Sig. Gio. Battista Giannini," p. 5–7.

First performed, as indicated in the impresario's dedication, dated August 2, 1795, as "seconda opera." Schatz 207

Le **dissensioni d'amore nel campo,** ballet. *See* G. M. Rutini's Sicotencal.

Il **dissoluto.**   A. T. of Righini's Il convitato di pietra.

Il **dissoluto punito** o sia Il D. Giovanni.   Dramma giocoso in due atti.   Da rappresentarsi nel Teatro di Praga l'anno 1787.

  Praga, Schoenfeld, n. d.   85 p.   16ᶜᵐ.

  Two acts.   Da Ponte is mentioned as the author, Wolfgango Mozzart (**Mozart**) as the composer.
  First performed at Prague, Altstaedtisches Theater des grafen F. A. von Nostitz, October 29, 1787.   SCHATZ 6788

— Arien und gesaenge aus der oper: **Don Juan.**   In zwei aufzuegen, aus dem italiaenischen.   Die musik ist von Mozart.

  Frankfurt, n. publ., 1789.   31 p.   15ᶜᵐ.

  Two acts.   German version by Heinrich Gottlieb Schmieder.
  First performed at Mayence, Churfürstl. Nationaltheater, May 23, 1789 (first perf. in German of Mozart's opera).   SCHATZ 6789

— **Don Juan** oder Die redende statue.   Ein singspiel in vier aufzuegen nach dem italiaenischen Il Don Giovanni.   Die musik ist von herrn Wolfgang Mozart, kayserl. koenigl. kapellmeister.

  n. i., 1793.   30 p.   15½ᶜᵐ.

  Lyrics only.   SCHATZ 6859

— Gesaenge zu der oper: **Don Juan,** oder Der steinerne gast.   In zwey aufzuegen, nach dem italiaenischen.   Die musik ist von Mozart.

  n. i., 1795.   39 p.   17ᶜᵐ.   SCHATZ 6790

La **distruzione d'Aquileja** fatta da Attila rè degli Unni, ballet.
See Guglielmi's Enea e Lavinia.

La **distruzione del Perù.**   A. T. of G. Giordani's Pizzarro nell' Indie.

La **distruzione di Cartagine,** ballet.   *See* Andreozzi's Amleto.

I **divertimenti dei Calabresi,** ballet.   *See* Gagni's I matti gloriosi.

Il **divertimento de' Quaqueri nella China,** ballet.   *See* Gagni's I matti gloriosi.

Il **divertimento in campagna.**   L. T. of Astaritta's La contessa Bimbinpoli.

La **divisione del mondo.**   Drama per musica nel famoso Teatro Vendramino di S. Salvatore, di Giulio Cesare Corradi l'anno MDCLXXV . . .

  Venetia, Francesco Nicolini, 1675.   front., 72 p.   14ᶜᵐ.

  Three acts.   Author's dedication, dated Venice, February 4, 1675, argument, scenario, and notice to the reader, with name of Giovanni **Legrenzi** as the composer.
                       SCHATZ 5534

The **divorce.**   A musical entertainment.   As sung at Marybone-Gardens.   The music composed by Mr. Hook.

  London, J. Wheble, 1771.   1 p. l., 18 p.   21ᶜᵐ.

  Two parts.   Cast.   By Lady Dorothea Dubois, who is not mentioned.
  Not to be confused, as does Grove's Dict., with Jackman's farce of 1781.
                       LONGE 184

Le docteur Sangrado. Opera-comique en un acte par Mrs. Anseaume & * * * Représenté pour la premiere fois sur le Théâtre de la Foire S. Germain, le 13 février 1758.

Paris, N. B. Duchesne, 1758. 64 p. 20½^{cm}.

With cast. **Duni** is named as the composer of the "ariettes" "Pour guérir toute maladie," "Au fond d'ma poitreine," "Si tant de mes confrères;" Jean Louis **La Ruette** of the chorus "Honneur, au docteur Sangrado," the trio "Rentrez chez nous." On p. 47–64, "*Airs* du Docteur Sangrado." No. 1, "Avec moi viens, mignone;" No. 2 (duet), "Le vin est un mortel venin—On ne peut trop chérir;" No. 3, "Fille à mon âge;" No. 4, "A ma soeur, en douceur" (this with basse-continue); No. 5, "Oui je crois cela;" No. 6, "Avec soin j'ai sçu." SCHATZ 2859.

Der docktor, eine komische oper in drey aufzuegen, nach dem italiaenischen. Die musik ist von Joseph Chudy ganz neu dazu verfertigt worden. Aufgefuehrt in dem neuerbauten Schauspielhause von der Schmallöggerischen gesellschaft.

Pressburg, Johann Michael Landerer, n. d. [4 p. l., 52 p.] 16^{cm}.

Pagination cut off by binder. Chudy's dedication and cast. Evidently based on Goldoni's "Il signor dottore."

First performed, as indicated, in 1779. SCHATZ 1872

The doctor and the apothecary. By Dittersdorf, with additions by Storace. *See* Der apotheker und der doctor.

Doctor und apotheker. O. T. of Dittersdorf's Der apotheker und der doktor.

Os dois rapazes Saboyanos. Tr. of Dalayrac's Les deux petits Savoyards.

Doktor Faust: ein komisches duodrama, von Schink.

18–43 p. 18^{cm}. (Theater journal fuer Deutschland, Sechstes stueck, Gotha, 1778.)

Excerpts only from the two acts. SCHATZ 11754

Doktor Faust. Eine original-oper in vier aufzuegen von D. Schmieder. In musik gesezt von Ignatz Walter.

Bremen, Friedrich Meiers erben, n. d. 38 p. 16½^{cm}.

On a fly leaf, the cast in ms., also the date of first performance, Bremen, December 28, 1797. SCHATZ 10859

La dolce vendetta, ballet. *See* Anfossi's Demofoonte.

La dolce vendetta, ballet. *See* Cherubini's Quinto Fabio.

Dom João, ou O convidado de pedra. Tr. of Gazzaniga's Il Don Giovanni.

Domitiano. Drama da rappresentarsi nel famoso Teatro Grimano à S. Gio. Paolo . . .

Venezia, Francesco Nicolini, 1673. front., 72 p. 14½^{cm}.

Three acts. Dedication by the author, Matteo Noris, dated Venice, December 27, 1672, "historia," and scenario. The composer, Giovanni Antonio **Boretti,** is not mentioned. ML 48.M2O

Domitiano—Continued.

— **Domitiano.** Drama da rappresentarsi nel famoso Teatro Grimano à SS. Gio. Paolo l'anno MDCLXXIII. Seconda impressione . . .

Venetia, Francesco Nicolini, 1673. front., 70 p. 13½^{cm}.

Three acts. Matteo Noris' dedication, dated Venice, December 27, 1672, notice to the reader, argument, and scenario. Giovanni Antonio **Boretti**, the composer, is not mentioned.   SCHATZ 1218

Il **Domizio.** Drama per musica da rappresentarsi nel Teatro di Sant' Angelo. L'anno MDCXCVI. Di Giulio Cesare Corradi . . .

Venetia, Nicolini, 1696. 70 p. 14^{cm}.

Three acts. Author's dedication, argument, scenario, and name of Marc' Antonio **Ziani** as the composer.   SCHATZ 11182

Don Anchise Campanone. A. T. of Paisiello's Gli amanti comici.

Il **Don Calandrano.** L. T. of Sacchini's L'avaro deluso.

Don Chisciotte, ballet. *See* Zingarelli's Il mercato di Monfregoso.

Don Chisciotte alle nozze di Gamace. Divertimento teatrale. Da rappresentarsi ne' Teatri privilegiati di Vienna.

Vienna, Giovanni Tomaso di Trattnern, 1770. 28 p. 16^{cm}.

One act. Giovanni [Antonio] Gastone Boccherini is mentioned as the author, Antonio **Salieri** as the composer.   SCHATZ 9286

D. Chisciotte della Mancia. Commedia per musica di Gianibattista Lorenzi, P. A. Da rappresentarsi nel Teatro de' Fiorentini nell' està di quest' anno 1769.

Napoli, Stamperia Avelliniana, 1769. 82 p. 15½^{cm}.

Three acts. Notice to the reader, cast, and name of **Paisiello** as the composer.
SCHATZ 7611

— **Don Quischott von Mancia.** Ein lustiges singspiel aufgefuehret auf den kaiserl. koenigl. schaubuehnen in Wien im jahre 1771.

Wien, v. Ghelen, n. d. 74 p. 16½^{cm}.

Three acts. **Paisiello** is mentioned as the composer of acts I–II, Florian **Gassmann** of act III and of the arias, etc., "Spring nur, spring du Lumpenhund" (I, 4), "Mein bester Sancio" (I, 5), "So lang die jugend" (II, 4), "Sie schlaeft die schoene" (II, 9), "Ihr herren, ihr verlangt" (II, 10), "Hoert, wenn ihr wollt" (II, 11).
SCHATZ 7612

Don Chisciotte in corte della duchessa.

Apostolo Zeno, Poesie drammatiche, Venezia, 1744, t. ix, p. [417]–538. 19^{cm}.

Five acts. Argument. Written in collaboration with Pietro Pariati. No composer is mentioned. In the "Catalogo" at end of vol. x, date and place of first ed. are given as Vienna, 1719. Fehr does not know why Gozzi, the editor, changed the original title "Don Chisciotte in Sierra Morena."   ML 49.A2Z3

— **Don Chisciotte in corte della duchessa.** Pubblicato per la prima volta in Vienna 1719.

Apostolo Zeno, Poesie drammatiche, Orleans, 1785–86, t. xi, p. 101–222. 21^{cm}.

Five acts. Argument. No composer is mentioned. Written in collaboration with Pietro Pariati.   ML 49.A2Z4

Don Chisciotte in corte della duchessa. Opera serioridicola per musica da rappresentarsi nella Cesarea Corte . . . nel carnevale dell' anno MDCCXXVII. La poesia è del Sig. abate Giovan Claudio Pasquini . . . La musica è del Sig. Antonio Caldara . . .

Vienna d'Austria, Gio. Pietro Van Ghelen, n. d. 4 p. l., 98 p. 17^{cm}.

Five acts. Argument and scenario. Nicola Matteis is mentioned as the composer of the ballet music.

First performed at Vienna, as indicated, February 6, 1727.   SCHATZ 1502

— Don Chisciotte in corte della duchessa. Opera serioridicola per musica del Signore abate Gio. Claudio Pasquini.

n. i., n. d. front., p. [317]–421. 19^{cm}.

Detached copy. Five acts. Argument and scenario, but without name of the composer. Pages 422–424 contain "Argomento della farsa intitolata l'Epouse suivante o sia la Sposa cameriera del Signor Chevrier per farsi abraccio," Indice and errata.   SCHATZ 1481

Don Chisciotte in Sierra Morena. Tragicommedia per musica, da rappresentarsi nella Cesarea Corte . . . nel carnevale dell' anno MDCCXIX. La musica è del Sig. Francesco Conti.

Vienna d'Austria, Gio. Van Ghelen, n. d. 8, 92 p.

Five acts. By Apostolo Zeno and Pietro Pariati (not mentioned). O. T of the above. Scenario. Niccola Matteis is mentioned as the composer of the ballet music.

First performed, as indicated, February 11, 1719.   SCHATZ 2194

— Don Quixotte in dem Mohrengebuerge, auf dem beruehmten Hamburgischen Schau-Platze in einer opera vorgestellet.

Hamburg, Caspar Jakhel, 1722. Unpaged. 18½^{cm}.

Five acts. Translated by Johann Samuel Müller (not mentioned). Cast, scenario, and "Vorbericht," in which appears this characteristic information:

"Die historie vom Don Quixott ist der welt so bekannt, dass es sehr ueberfluessig seyn wuerde, etwas davon zu beruehren. Wer aber ein meister-stueck von possirlicher und doch dabey in ihrer art haupt-schoener music zu hoeren verlanget, der mag die von dem hochberuehmten kaiserl. vice-capellmeister **Conti** auf gegenwaertige opera verfertigte composition nur gewisslich dafuer halten. Er hat darin so kuenstlich zu scherzen und so scherzhaft zu kuensteln gewust, dass sich auch ein kenner bloss bey dem anblick gewisser saetze des lachens kaum enthalten und doch dabey nicht umhin kann, die grosse geschicklichkeit des verfassers an ende ganz ernsthaft zu bewundern. Von den arien werden einige italiänisch andere aber teutsch gesungen, damit ein jeder etwas nach seinem sinne finde; doch stehet bey dem italiaenischen auch das teutsche und bei dem teutschen das italiaenische in einerley reim-gebaende um beydes gebrauchen zu können. Der Recitativ hingegen ist ganz teutsch gelassen so wie man ihn samt dem übrigen von Braunschweig bekommen hat: ausgenommen, dass der Cardenio, als dessen partie allhier ein Italiaener [Signore Valentini] macht, in der vorstellung, alles italiaenisch recitiren wird, ob es gleich im buche teutsch stehet."   SCHATZ 2195

Il Don Chissiot della Mancia. Dramma per musica da rappresentarsi nel Teatro di Canal Regio. L'anno MDCLXXX . . .

Venetia, Francesco Nicolini, 1680. 56 p. 13½^{cm}.

Three acts. Publisher's dedication, argument, scenario, and notice to the reader, which reads:

"Perche giornalmente ti vengono a presentate opere mascherate, e perche s'avvicina anco il tempo delle maschere mascherato col nome di Chissiot t'apresento anch'io questo drama, che di Chissiot non contiene altro che la pretesa bravura, ricevilo per opera, per comedia, per quello che ti piace ch'io in ogni forma m'aqueto alle tue sodisfationi, sappi che è stato composto nel ristretto termine di soli giorni quattro."

By Marco Morosini, music by Carlo **Sajon**, neither of whom is mentioned.

          SCHATZ 9264

Don Colascione. L. T. of Latilla's La finta cameriera.

Il D. Gastone overo La più costante tra le maritate. Opera tragi-comica. Di Giacinto Andrea Cicognini . . .

> *Roma, Giuseppe Corvo e Bartolomeo Lupardi, 1675. 136 p. 13½cm.*

Three acts and prologue. Publisher's dedication, in which Lupardi says that the general applause given to Cicognini's dramas induced him to publish anew this one. The composer unknown to Schatz. ML 50.2.D59

Don Giovanni o sia Il convitato di pietra.

Composed by Giuseppe **Gazzaniga.** Forms second act of Il capriccio dramma-tico, Venezia (1787). Schatz 10580

—Il **Don Giovanni,** ossia Il convitato di pietra. Dramma per musica in un sol' atto da rappresentarsi nel Teatro della rua dos Condes nel carnovale dell' anno 1792 . . .

> *Lisbonna, Simone Taddeo Ferreira, 1792. 117 p. 15cm.*

Impresario's dedication, scenario, and name of Giuseppe **Gazzaniga** as the com-poser. Portuguese title page "Dom João, ou O convidado de pedra" and text face the Italien by Bertati, who is not mentioned. Schatz 3682

Il Don Giovanni. A. T. of Mozart's Il dissoluto punito.

Don Giovanni Tenorio ossia Il convitato di pietra. Melodramma per musica da rappresentarsi in Bologna nel nobile Teatro Zagnoni il carnevale dell' anno 1791.

> *Bologna, Sassi, n. d. 43 p. 17cm.*

Imprimatur dated Feb. 8, 1790. Cast and scenario. Neither the author, Giam-battista Lorenzi, nor the composer, Vincenzo **Fabrizj,** is mentioned. Under the title "Il convitato di pietra," Fabrizi's opera was performed, 1796, at Lisbon, together with Cimarosa's "La finta amalata." (*See* this—ML 48.C6 III.) Schatz 2973

Don Juan. Tr. of Mozart's Il dissoluto punito.

Don Juan oder Die redende statue. Tr. of Mozart's Il dissoluto punito.

Don Micco e Lesbina. Intermede. Par les Srs. Dominique & Romagnesi . . . Representée à la suite du Joüeur, le 17 août 1729.

> *Les parodies du Nouveau Théâtre italien, Nouv. éd., Paris, 1738, t. iv, [203]–220 p. 16½cm.*

One act. The airs and vaudeville used are printed at the end of the volume in the "Table des airs" (*see* Le Joueur). This is a parody of the intermezzo of the same title which had been imported from Italy *via* Brussels (1728). ML 48.P3

Don Mirtillo contrastato. Dramma giocoso per musica da rap-presentarsi nel nobilissimo Teatro della nobil Donna Tron Veronese in San Cassiano l'autunno dell' anno 1791 . . .

> *Venezia, Modesto Fenzo, 1791. 56 p. 17½cm.*

Two acts. Author not mentioned, and unknown to Schatz. Impresario's dedica-tion, cast, scenario, and name of Giuseppe **Giordani** as the composer. ("La musica è tutta nuova.") With the opera was performed Antonio Terrades's ballet, "L'ospedale de' pazzi." The composer of the music is not mentioned. Schatz 3837

Don Paduano. Mmenzeone pe' museca de nota' Pietro Trinchera. Da rappresentarese a lo Tiatro de la Pace nchesta nvernata prence-peata a lo 1745 . . .

> *Napoli, Dommineco Ascione, 1745. 2 p. l., 52 p. 15cm.*

Three acts. Dedication, cast, and name of Nicola **Logroscino** as composer. Schatz 5672

D. Pedro, infante di Portogallo, ballet. *See* Sacchini's Lucio Vero.

Don Pietro, rè di Castiglia, ballet. *See* Anfossi's Zemira.

D. Procopio in corte del Pretejanni. Commedia per musica da rappresentarsi nel Teatro Nuovo sopra Toledo per second' opera di quest' anno 1782.

Napoli, n. publ., 1782. 66 p. 15½ᶜᵐ.

Three acts. Author not mentioned, and unknown to Schatz. Argument, cast, and name of Giacomo **Tritto** as the composer. SCHATZ 10468

Don Quichote chez la duchesse, ballet comique en trois actes; représenté pour la premiere fois par l'Académie royale de musique, le 12 février 1743. Nouvelle édition.

Paris, N. B. Duchesne, 1760. 47, [1] p. 19ᶜᵐ. (Theatre de M. Favart, Paris, Duchesne, 1763–77, t. vi.)

Prose and ariettes, composed by **Boismortier** (not mentioned) and printed in the text. ML 49.A2F1

Don Quischott von Mancia. Tr. of Paisiello's D. Chisciotte della Mancia, with third act, etc by Gassmann.

Don Quixote. An entertainment for music, sung at Marybone-Gardens. The music composed by Dr. Arnold.

London, C. D. Piguenit, 1774. 2 p. l., 33 p. 18ᶜᵐ.

Two parts. Prefatory note, in which the author "is well aware of the dangerous ground on which he stands" with his attempt at bringing Don Quixote and Sancho before the public, and particularly at Marybone Gardens. Attributed to D. J. Piguenit by Biog. Dram. but with Covent Garden as place of performance. "This was acted only one night for the benefit of Mr. Reinhold." LONGE 291

Don Quixote in England. A comedy. As it is acted at the New Theatre in the Hay-Market. By Henry Fielding, Esq. . . .

London, J. Watts, 1754 [!]. 8 p. l., 64 p. 19ᶜᵐ.

Three acts, with introduction. Cast, table of the 15 songs, the airs of which (ballad airs) are printed in the text, and mostly with their titles, author's dedication, and preface, in which Fielding says that

"this comedy was begun at Leyden in the year 1728, and after it had been sketched out into a few loose scenes, was thrown by, and for a long while no more thought of. It was originally writ for my private amusement . . . Mr. Booth and Mr. Cibber . . . upon seeing the aforesaid sketch, both dissuaded me from suffering it to be represented on the stage; and accordingly it was remanded back to my shelf, where, probably, it would have perished in oblivion, had not the solicitations of the distrest actors in Drury-Lane prevail'd on me to revise it, at the same time that it came into my head to add those scenes concerning our elections. Being thus altered, it was often rehearsed on that theatre, and a particular day appointed for its action; but the Giant Cajanus, of a race who were always enemies to our poor Don, deferred his appearance so long, that the intervention of the actor's benefits would have put it off till the next season, had I not brought it on where now it appears . . ."

The date on title-page is 1754, not 1734, yet the cast is exactly the same as that given by Genest under Haymarket, 1734, "about April." LONGE 53

Don Quixote. For Purcell's opera, *see* The comical history of Don Quixote.

Don Quixotte. Operette in drey akten.

n. i., n. d. [101]–156 p. ("Schauspiele von J. von Soden," Berlin, 1788, v. 1, no. 2.) 16ᶜᵐ.

Detached copy. Presumably not performed. The composer, Ignaz von **Becke,** is not mentioned. SCHATZ 678

Don Quixotte der zweite. Ein komisches singspiel aus dem italienischen, in zwey aufzuegen. Die musik ist vom herrn von Dittersdorf.

　　Oels, Samuel Gottlieb Ludwig, n. d.　80 p.　16^{cm}.

　By the composer.
　First performed at Oels, Hoftheater, February 4, 1795.　　　　Schatz 2589

Don Quixotte in dem Mohrengebuerge. Tr. of Conti's Don Chisciotte in Sierra Morena.

Don Salterio Civetta. Dramma giocoso per musica da rappresentarsi nel nobile Teatro di San Samuele il carnovale dell' anno 1776.

　　Venezia, Gio. Battista Casali, 1776.　62 p.　17^{cm}.

　Three acts. Author not mentioned and unknown to Schatz. Cast and name of Michele **Mortellari** as the composer.　　　　Schatz 6690

Don Sancho: or, The students whim.

　　5 p. l., 20 p.　19^{cm}.

　Title page wanting of this farce, printed 1739. Two acts with epilogue, prologue, and a masque, "Minerva's triumph." Clarence lists this as a "ballad opera," though no airs are indicated in the text to which the 12 songs of the piece were to be sung. Still, the second player's words in the prologue, "meer ballad farce," may mean that the piece was intended as such. The dedication is signed by Elizabeth Boyd as author, as also a prefatory note in which she says that Mr. Chetwood, the prompter of Drury-Lane, secured a hearing for "Don Sancho" in the Green-room, that the piece was "acknowledged worthy of the town's applause," but that the lateness of the season, etc., prevented a performance."　　　　Longe 59

Don Saverio. A musical drama. As it is perform'd at the Theater-Royal in Drury-Lane. The musick by Mr. Arne.

　　London, J. Watts, 1750.　2 p. l., 16 p.　21^{cm}.

　Two acts. Cast, argument, and footnote:
　"The intention of this piece is to display different kinds of expression in music; florid epithets or forc'd conceits are avoided, and the songs and recitative are endeavour'd to be written (as near as possible) in such a dialect as the character concern'd would naturally make use of on such an occasion, it being a standing rule in musical productions, that, where the meaning of the poet is in the least intricate, the song is unattended to, and the music lost."
　Text presumably by the composer.
　First performed 1749, as indicated.　　　　Longe 241

Don Saverio. Comedia per musica da rappresentarsi nel Teatro di S. Moisè l'autunno dell' anno 1744.

　　Venezia, Valvassense, 1744.　48 p.　15½^{cm}.

　Three acts. By Antonio Palomba, with argument, cast, and name of composer, Giuseppe d'**Avossa** ("d'Anossa"), but not of librettist. Original title of Palomba's text was "La Violante."　　　　Schatz 513

Don Sylvio von Rosalva oder Der sieg der natur ueber die schwaermerey.

　　n. i., n. d.　164 p.　17^{cm}.

　Five acts. Neither the author, Samuel Gottlieb Bürde, nor the composer, **Phanty,** is mentioned.
　First performed at Schleswig, Herzogl. Hoftheater, March 7, 1796.　Schatz 8004

Don Sylvio von Rosalva oder Der sieg der natur ueber die schwaermerey. Eine komische oper in fuenf aufzeugen von S. G. Buerde.

　　Koenigsberg, Friedrich Nicolovius, 1795.　164 p.　17^{cm}.

　Five acts. The composer, F. Sigismund **Sander,** is not mentioned.
　First performed at Oels, Hoftheater, June 17, 1797.　　　　Schatz 9371

Don Tabarrano.

n. i., n. d. [*22 p.*] *17cm.*

Probably belongs to the text of some opera. The two intermezzi, text by Andrea Belmuro, music by Johann Adolph **Hasse,** were first performed at Dresden, Hoftheater, July 26, 1737, as intermezzi to Hasse's "Atalante."

First performed as "La Contadina" in the fall of 1728 at Naples, Teatro di San Bartolomeo, as intermezzi to the opera "Clitarco." Schatz 4529

— **Don Tabarrano,** intermezzi. Da rappresentarsi nel nuovo Real Teatro Privilegiato in Dresda. L'anno MDCCXLVII.

n. i., n. d. (*double*) *24 p.* *15cm.*

Two parts. Cast. Neither Belmuro, the author, nor **Hasse,** the composer, is mentioned. German text and title page, "Don Tabarrano," face Italian. The text is not quite the same as in Schatz 4529. For instance, in the first intermezzo the aria "Collà sul praticello" has been added, and in the second the aria "Se non credi alle parole" replaces "Strappami il core, o barbaro," and the final duet is "O che gioja, o che contento" instead of "Pace si, si, dolce mia vita."

First performed, as indicated, February 13, 1747. Schatz 4530

— **Il Tabarano.** Intermezzo in musica da rappresentarsi sopra il Nuovo Teatro dell' opera pantomima del Nicolini in Bronseviga.— Der Tabaran . . .

Braunsweig, Keitel, n. d. *Unpaged.* *18cm.*

Two parts. German text faces Italian. Neither Belmuro nor **Hasse** is mentioned. The text follows Schatz 4529 fairly closely except toward the end, and the final duet now begins "Deh ti plachi"!

First performed, as indicated, 1749. Schatz 4531

D. Taddeo in Barcellona. Commedia di un atto per musica di Giambattista Lorenzi P. A. da rappresentarsi nel Teatro Nuovo sopra Toledo nella primavera del corrente anno 1774.

Napoli, n. publ., 1774. *38 p.* *14½cm.*

Notice to the reader, cast, and name of Antonio **Pio** as the composer.

Schatz 8185

Il D. Tifone. Farsetta per musica a tre' voci del Signor abate F. P. P. A. Da rappresentarsi nel Teatro alla Pallacorda di Firenze nel carnevale dell' anno 1752 . . .

Roma, Ottavio Puccinelli, 1751. *24 p.* *15½cm.*

Two parts. Impresario's dedication, cast and name of Giacinto **Quagliattini** as composer. *F. P.* does not seem to apply to any of the Arcadian names listed by Wotquenne. Not recorded by Schatz or Allacci. ML 50.2.D595Q2

Il Don Trastullo. L. T. of Jommelli's La cantata e disfida di D. Trastullo.

La donna amante di tutti, e fedele a nessuno. Commedia per musica di Giuseppe Palomba da rappresentarsi nel Real Teatro del Fondo di Separazione per terza opera di quest' anno 1783.

Napoli, n. publ., 1783. *60 p.* *15½cm.*

Three acts. Argument, cast, and name of Pietro **Guglielmi** as the composer.

Schatz 4288

La donna ancora è fedele. Dramma per musica, rappresentato in Roma nel MDCLXXVI . . .

Roma, il success. del Mascardi, 1676. *72 p.* *13cm.*

Prologue and three acts. By Domenico Filippo Contini, who is not mentioned. In his dedication the publisher, Francesco Leone, speaks of this drama as "rapresentato in Roma il presente anno," and mentions Bernardo **Pasquini** as the composer.

ML 50.2.D6P2

La donna astuta. Dramma giocoso per musica da rappresentarsi nel nobilissimo Teatro Giustiniani in San Moisè il carnovale dell' anno 1793.

Venezia, Modesto Fenzo, 1793. 46 p. 17½^{cm}.

Two acts. The author is not mentioned, and is unknown to Schatz. Cast, scenario, and name of Giuseppe **Gazzaniga** as the composer, except for a few designated substitute arias.   SCHATZ 3691

La donna bizarra. L. T. of Bernardini's La donna di spirito.

La donna bizzarra ossia L'amore politico, ballet. *See* Winter's Catone in Utica.

La donna di genio volubile. Dramma giocoso per musica di Giovanni Bertati . . . da rappresentarsi nel nobilissimo Teatro Giustiniani in San Moisè l'autunno dell' anno 1796.

Venezia, Modesto Fenzo, 1796. 64 p. 18^{cm}.

Two acts. Cast, scenario, and name of Marco **Portugal** as the composer. On p. 31–38, argument and description of Carlo Taglioni's four-act "La sposa rapita, ballo tragicomico." His second ballet was called "La scuola olandese ossia L'amante in statua." The composers of the music are not mentioned.

First performed, as indicated, October 5, 1796 (Carvalhaes).   SCHATZ 8404

— **La donna di genio volubile.** Dramma giocoso per musica in due atti da rappresentarsi nel Teatro Elettorale di Sassonia.

Dresda, n. publ., 1798. 111 p. 15^{cm}.

Two acts. Cast (in pencil) and name of Marcos **Portugal** as the composer. German title-page "Die wankelmuethige," and text face Italian.

First performed, as indicated, December 8, 1798.   SCHATZ 8405·

— **La donna di genio volubile:** dramma giocoso per musica di Giovanni Bertati . . . da rappresentarsi nel Regio Teatro di S. Carlo della Principessa in benefizio di Domenico Caporalini. Ai 23 di gennaio dell' anno 1799.

Lisbona, Simone Taddeo Ferreira, 1798. 163 p. 15^{cm}.

Two acts. Prefatory note, scenario, and name of Marco **Portogallo** as composer. Portuguese translation faces Italian. On p. [127]–163, Italian text, with Portuguese translation, argument, cast of the pasticcio ("La musica di diversi auttori i più celebri"): "L'ESILIO D'APOLLO. Cantata per musica a quatri voci di Giuseppe Caravita . . ." [as in title of the opera].   ML 48.C6 IV

La donna di governo. Dramma di tre atti per musica.

Carlo Goldoni, Opere teatrali, Venezia, Zatta e figli, 1788–95, v. 44, [63]–122 p. 18^{cm}.

According to Schatz, first performed at Prague, Theater in der Kotzen, with music by Domenico **Fischietti**.   PQ

La donna di governo. Dramma giocoso per musica di Polisseno Fegejo da rappresentarsi nel Teatro Giustiniani di San Moisè. Nel presente autuno 1764.

Venezia, Modesto Fenzo, 1764. 70 p. 14½^{cm}.

Three acts. By Goldoni. Cast, scenario, and name of Baldassare **Galuppi** as composer.   SCHATZ 3451

La donna di spirito. Dramma giocoso per musica da rappresentarsi nel Teatro alla Scala l'autunno dell' anno 1791 . . .

Milano, Gio. Batista Bianchi, n. d. 4 p. l., 67 p. 16½^{cm}.

Two acts. Impresario's dedication, dated Milan, September 20, 1791, cast, scenario, and name of Marcello di Capua (**Bernardini**) as composer. The libretto was written by the composer (Schatz), and it was based on Goldoni's comedy, "La vedova scaltra." The first ballet, performed in 1791, together with the opera, was called "Lo spazzacamino principe," and was by Antonio Muzzarelli, the composer of the music not being mentioned.

First performed at Rome, Teatro Valle, in the spring of 1787. SCHATZ 842

— Le quattro nazioni. Dramma giocoso per musica da rappresentarsi in Firenze nel Régio Teatro di via Santa Maria nell' estate dell' anno MDCCXCIII . . .

Firenze, Stamp. Albizziniana, 1793. 60 p. 16½^{cm}.

Two acts. Cast, name of Marcello di Capua (**Bernardini**) as composer and note that the text has "per suo originale" Goldoni's "La vedova scaltra." Schatz lists "Le quattro nazioni" as a later version of "La donna bizzarra" (*see* below) but, though a few lines are the same in both, they are really two entirely different librettos. Not even the number of scenes is the same and the characters are named differently. For instance, whereas "Armellina, locandiera" and "Monsieur Tremo'" appear in both, "Donna Aurora, donna di spirito" does not appear at all in "La donna bizzarra," where "D. Elvira, donna spiritosa e bizarra" is a combination of both "Donna Aurora" and "Donna Elvira, sorella di Donna Aurora" of the other libretto. As a matter of comparison, the text and the characters of "Le quattro nazioni" are identical with those of "La donna di spirito," the four nations being represented in both by "Don Mauro, Spagnuolo," "Monsieur Tremo," "Francese," "Baron Zuffre', Tedesco," "M. Birif, Olandese," and "Don Ruggiero, cavaliere italiano." Consequently, "Le quattro nazioni" is simply a later title of "La donna di spirito," and the text of both, to repeat it, has very little in common with that of "La donna bizzarra," though possibly the same music was used as for "La donna di spirito." Much more related is the text of: SCHATZ 833

— Li cinque pretendenti. Dramma giocoso per musica da rappresentarsi nel Ces. Reg. Teatro di Trieste il carnovale dell' anno 1794

Trieste, Stamperia governiale, n. d. 58 p. 16^{cm}.

Two acts. Cast and name of Marcello di Capua (**Bernardini**) as composer. The characters in this libretto are the same as of "La donna di spirito." The first act has seventeen scenes, and of these fourteen appear in the first act of "La donna di spirito." The alterations in the second act are more pronounced and only a few scenes have been retained, yet unmistakably "La donna di spirito" is the original.

SCHATZ 849

— La donna bizarra. Commedia per musica da rappresentarsi nel Real Teatro del Fondo di Separazione nel carnevale di questo corrente anno 1791.

Napoli, Vincenzo Flauto, n. d. 45 p. 15½^{cm}.

Two acts. Cast and name of Marcello di Capua (Marcello **Bernardini**) as composer. Schatz considers this a later version of "La donna di spirito," but *see above* the note under "Le quattro nazioni." On p. 5–9 argument, cast, and detailed description of "Il trionfo de' Spagnoli, o sia La disfatta de' Marrocchini. Ballo composto e diretto dal Sig. Gio. Battista Giannini." Pietro Dutilieu is mentioned as the composer of the music. SCHATZ 832

La donna di spirito, ballet. *See* Tritto's L'Arminio.

La donna di tutti i caratteri. Commedia per musica di Antonio Palomba Napolitano da rappresentarsi nel Teatro de' Fiorentini nell' inverno di quest' anno 1763.

Napoli, Vincenzio Mazzola-Vocola, 1763. 64 p. 15ᶜᵐ.

Pages 39–62 missing.
Three acts. Cast and name of Pietro **Guglielmi** as the composer.
First performed at the same theatre, fall of 1762.   SCHATZ 4289

La donna difficile, ballet. *See* Rust's L'idolo cinese.

La donna dottoressa. Intermezzo.

Cremona, Ferrari, 1754. 24 p. 18½ᶜᵐ.

Three parts, with name of the composer, Pietro **Chiarini.** The author is unknown to Schatz.   SCHATZ 1855

La donna Girandola. Farsa giocosa in due atti per musica dell' ab. Pietro Chiari Bresciano . . . da rappresentarsi nel Teatro Grimani di S. Samuele nel carnovale dell' anno 1763.

Venezia, Modesto Fenzo, 1763. 34 p. 15½ᶜᵐ.

Two acts. Cast and name of Salvatore **Perillo** as the composer.   SCHATZ 7924

La donna giudice, e parte. Intermezzo a due voci da rappresentarsi nel Teatro di S. Angelo l'autunno dell' anno 1746.

Venezia, Modesto Fenzo, 1746. 16 p. 14½ᶜᵐ.

Two parts. Cast and name of Giovanni **Cingoni** as composer. Author unknown to Schatz.   SCHATZ 2009

La donna giudice e parte, intermezzo. *See* Galuppi's Scipione nelle Spagne.

La donna innamorata. Dramma giocoso per musica di Giovanni Bertati . . . da rappresentarsi nel nobilissimo Teatro Giustiniani in San Moisè il carnovale dell' anno 1796.

Venezia, Modesto Fenzo, 1796. 56 p. 17½ᶜᵐ.

Two acts. Cast, scenario, and name of Giuseppe **Nicolini** as the composer.
First performed, as indicated, January 28, 1796.   SCHATZ 7142

La donna instabile. Dramma giocoso per musica di Giovanni Bertati da rappresentarsi nel Teatro Giustiniani in S. Moisè il carnovale dell anno 1776.

Venezia, Gio. Battista Casali, n. d. 62 p. 16½ᶜᵐ.

Three acts. Cast, scenario, and name of the composer, Giovanni Battista **Borghi.**
Pages 3–4, presumably containing the argument, are wanting. Pages 61–62 contain an additional scene for act II, which begins (Signor Valerio), "Ma signore, vi prego."
Pages 31–32 contain the argument of "Il naufragio felice, ballo eroico pantomimo," by Giov. Battista Marten. The title of the second ballet, by Francesco Rasetti, was "L'incostanza del militare in amore." The composers of the music are not mentioned.
First performed in January, 1776.   SCHATZ 1229

Letra de la tonadilla a siete, intitulada: **Doña Maria la tarbernera.**

Barcelona, Pablo Campins, n. d. 16 p. 16ᶜᵐ.

Imprimatur at end dated: Barcelona, July 23, 1774.
Not recorded by Schatz.   ML 50.2.D607

Donna Marzia. O. T. of Barlocci's libretto Madama Ciana.

La **donna militaire**. A. T. of the ballet Il seguito tra l'armi.

La **donna ne sa più del diavolo** ovvero Il matrimonio non è per i vecchi. Dramma giocoso per musica in un solo atto da rappresentarsi nel Regio Teatro di S. Carlo della Principessa l'estate dell' anno 1797.

> *Lisbona, Simone Taddeo Ferreira, 1797. 95 p. 14^{cm}.*

Cast and name of Giovanni Battista **Longarini** as composer. The text appears to be an altered version of Gaetano Sertor's "Il divorzio sepra matrimonio ossia La donna che non parla." Portuguese translation faces Italian. SCHATZ 5683

La **donna nobile**. Intermezzi in musica da rappresentarsi il carnovale del 1730. nel Teatro Tron a S. Cassano.

> *Venezia, Carlo Buonarrigo, 1730. 21 p. 15^{cm}.*

At end, one p. advertising matter, by the publisher.
Three parts. The author not mentioned, and unknown to Schatz. Cast and name of Giuseppe Maria **Orlandini** as the composer.
First performed under the title of "Melinda e Tiburzio" at Venice, Teatro di San Angelo, carnival, 1721. SCHATZ 7340

La **donna sempre al suo peggior s'appiglia**. Commedia per musica di Giuseppe Palomba da rappresentarsi nel Teatro Nuovo per terz' opera in quest' anno 1785.

> *Napoli, n. publ., 1785. 60 p. 15^{cm}.*

Three acts. Cast and name of the composer, **Cimarosa**. SCHATZ 1981

La **donna sensibile** o sia Gli amanti riuniti. Commedia per musica di Domenico Piccinni da rappresentarsi nel Teatro del Real Fondo di Separazione per second' opera del corrente anno 1798.

> *Napoli, n. publ., 1798. 52 p. 15^{cm}.*

Two acts. Argument, cast, and name of Giacomo **Tritto** as the composer. SCHATZ 10469

La **donna vana**. Commedia da rappresentarsi in musica nel Teatro de' Fiorentini nell' inverno dell' anno 1764 . . .

> *Napoli, Vincenzo Mazzola-Vocola, 1764. 72 p. 14½^{cm}.*

Three acts. By Antonio Palomba, who is not mentioned. Impresario's dedication, dated November, 1764, cast, and name of Niccolò **Piccinni** as the composer. SCHATZ 8123

Le **donne Ateniesi e i loro compagni**, ballet. *See* Pasque's Arianna e Teseo.

Le **donne bisbetiche** o sia L'antiquario fanatico. L. T. of Bernardini's La finta Galatea o sia L'antiquario fanatico.

Le **donne cambiate**. Dramma giocoso per musica in due atti da rappresentarsi nel Teatro Elettorale di Sassonia.

> *Dresda, n. publ., 1799. 115 p. 15½^{cm}.*

Two acts. By Giuseppe Foppa, who is not mentioned. German title-page, "Die verwandelten weiber," and text face Italian. Marcos **Portugal** is mentioned as the composer.
First performed, as indicated, October 2, 1799; at Venice, San Moisè, October 22, 1797 (Carvalhaes). SCHATZ 8406

Le **donne che comandono**. A. T. of Goldoni's text Il mondo al rovescio.

Le donne che comandono. A. T. of Galuppi's Il mondo alla roversa.

Le donne dispettose. Commedia per musica di notar' Antonio Palomba da rappresentarsi nel Teatro de' Fiorentini nell' autunno di quest' anno 1754.

Napoli, Ricciardi, 1754.   96 p.   15^{cm}.

Three acts.   Cast and name of Niccolò **Piccinni** as the composer.   SCHATZ 8124

Le donne dispettose. Commedia per musica di Giuseppe Palomba da rappresentarsi nel Real Teatro del Fondo di Separazione per prim' opera in questo corrente anno 1793 . . .

Napoli, n. publ., 1793.   43, [1] p.   15^{cm}.

Two acts.   Dedication, cast, and name of Gabriele **Prota** as the composer.   On the unnumb. p., the substitute aria "Arma di gloria il core" (II, 4).   SCHATZ 8473

Le donne invidiose ossia L'onestà trionfante, ballet.   *See* Bianchi's La sposa in equivoco.

Le donne letterate. Commedia per musica di Gio. Gastone Boccherini . . . da rappresentarsi ne' Teatri privilegiati di Vienna.

[Vienna], Ghelen, 1770.   Unpaged.   16^{cm}.

Three acts.   Scenario and name of Antonio **Salieri** as the composer.
First performed at Vienna, Burgtheater, January, 1770.   SCHATZ 9335

Le donne rivali. Intermezzo in musica a cinque voci da rappresentarsi nel Teatro Valle dell' illm̃i Signori Capranica.   Nel carnevale dell' anno 1780 . . .

Roma, Agostino Palombini, 1780.   48 p.   16^{cm}.

Two acts.   Author not mentioned and unknown to Schatz.   Cast and name of **Cimarosa** as composer.   ML 50.2.D616C3

— **Le donne rivali.** Intermezzo in musica da rappresentarsi nel nobil Teatro Tron di San Cassiano nell' autunno dell' anno MDCCLXXX.

Venezia, Pietro Sola, n. d.   54 p.   17^{cm}.

Two acts.   Cast, scenario, and name of the composer, **Cimarosa**.   The author is unknown to Schatz.   With the intermezzo were performed the ballets, "Il consiglio di Giove" and "Il sargente burlato."   The composer of the music is not mentioned.
                                                                    SCHATZ 2004

Le donne sempre donne. Dramma giocoso per musica del Signor abate Pietro Chiari da rappresentarsi nel Teatro Giustiniani di S. Moisè l'autunno dell' anno 1767.

Venezia, Modesto Fenzo, 1767.   82 p.   16^{cm}.

Three acts.   Cast, scenario, and name of Andrea **Luchesi** as the composer.
                                                                    SCHATZ 5741

Le donne vendicate.

[53]–102 p.   16½^{cm}.   (Carlo Goldoni, Opere drammatiche giocose, t. i, Torino, 1757.)

Three acts.   ML 49.A2G6

— **Le donne vendicate.** Dramma di tre atti per musica.

Carlo Goldoni, Opere teatrali, Venezia, Zatta e figli, 1788–95, v. 43, [341]–393 p.   18^{cm}.

First performed with **Cocchi's** music, as in next entry.   PQ

Le donne vendicate. Dramma giocoso per musica di Polisseno Fegejo, Pastor Arcade. Da rappresentarsi nel Teatro Tron di S. Cassiano. Il carnevale dell' anno 1751.

Venezia, Modesto Fenzo, 1751. 58 p. 15½ᶜᵐ.

Three acts. By Goldoni. Cast. The composer, Gioacchino **Cocchi,** is not mentioned. SCHATZ 2043

Le donne vendicate. Commedia per musica di Giuseppe Palomba da rappresentarsi nel Teatro Nuovo sopra Toledo per prim' opera nel corrente anno 1796.

Napoli, n. publ., 1796. 43 p. 15ᶜᵐ.

Two acts. Cast. Gaetano **Monti** is mentioned as the composer except for the arias marked with an asterisk. It is not said by whom these were composed.
First performed at Naples, Teatro Nuovo sopra Toledo, October 17, 1781. SCHATZ 6601

Le donne vendicate. Intermezzi per musica a quattro voci da rappresentarsi nel Teatro alla Valle nel carnevale dell' anno 1763 . .

Roma, S. Michele a Ripa, 1763. 36 p. 15ᶜᵐ.

Three acts. The author, Goldoni, is not mentioned. Dedication by the impresario, Angolfino Palombini, cast, and name of Niccolò **Piccinni** as "maestro di capella." SCHATZ 8090

— **Le donne vendicate.** Dramma giocoso per musica da rappresentarsi nel Teatro Grimani di S. Samuele il carnovale dell' anno 1764.

Venezia, Modesto Fenzo, 1764. 48 p. 15½ᶜᵐ.

Three acts. Cast, scenario, and name of Niccolò **Piccinni** as the composer. The text is somewhat different from the Rome, 1763, edition. For instance, act I, scenes 4 and 5, "T'hò pur trovato alfine" and "Non mi conosce! A me corpo di Bacco," have been added. SCHATZ 8091

Das donnerwetter. A. T. of Winter's Der bettelstudent.

Die doppelte verwandlung, eine freye nachahmung von der bekannten und beliebten komischen oper: Le diable à quatre; Aufgefuehret auf der kaiserl. koenigl. privil. deutschen Schaubuehne.

Wien, im Krausischen Buchladen, 1767. 80 p. 16ᶜᵐ.

Three acts. On p. 2 the note: "Die worte der arien sind nach den melodeyen lauter lustiger, und meistens bekannter liedchen und taenze verfasset."
Unlike in French librettos, the tunes are not indicated. Author unknown to Schatz. SCHATZ 11450

Il doppio equivoco. Dramma giocoso per musica da rappresentarsi in Parma nel R. D. Teatro di corte il carnevale dell' anno MDCCXCIV . . .

Parma, Stamperia Carmignani, n. d. viii, 60 p. 18ᶜᵐ.

Two acts. Scenario, name of Gaspare **Rugali** as the composer and impresario's dedication which begins:
"Il dramma . . . non vanta altro merito che quello della novità. Il compositore della musica si espone al giudizio del pubblico con questa prima sua produzione."
The author is unknown to Schatz. With the opera was performed Giovanni Monticini's ballet (composer of the music not mentioned) "Il trionfo di Gustavo re di Svezia." SCHATZ 9128

La Doralba. Dramma civile del Signor dottore Bernardino Moscheni. Da recitarsi in musica nel Teatro di Pescia da gl'Accademici Cheti . . .

Lucca, li Marescandoli, 1683. 4 p. l. (incl. front.), 76 p. 16ᶜᵐ.

Three acts. Scenario and dedication ("la prima volta in publico sul nostro teatro"). Apparently not recorded by Nerici. Composer unknown to Wotquenne.
ML 50.2.D618

Dorcis e Cleobisa, ballet. *See* G. Giordani's Caio Ostilio.

Das **dorf im gebuerge.** Ein schauspiel mit gesang in zwey akten von August von Kotzebue. Zum erstenmale aufgefuehrt auf dem k. k. National-Theater, am jahresfest der braven Wiener-Freywilligen, den 17. april 1798. Die musik ist vom hrn. kapellmeister Weigl dem aeltern.

> *Wien, Carl Schaumburg und compagnie, n. d.* *2 p. l., 84 p.* *16½*^{cm}.
> Cast and dedicatory poem to Maria Theresa.   SCHATZ 10932

Der **dorfbader.** Von H. B.

> *Muenchen, Johann Nepomuck Fritz, 1783.* *56 p.* *16*^{cm}.
> Last p. incorrectly numbered 24. By Heinrich Braun. Composer unknown to Schatz.   SCHATZ 11605

Der **dorfbalbier.** Eine komische oper in zwey aufzuegen.

> *Leipzig, in der Dyckischen buchhandlung, 1772.* *88 p.* *15*^{cm}.
> Note on p. [4]: "Das stueck ist eine nachahmung des *Blaise le savetier* von Mr. Sedaine" and prefatory note on p. [2] by the author, Christian Felix Weisse, who is not mentioned:
> "Diese kleine komische oper war eine von den ersten versuchen des verfassers in dieser gattung. Ein beduerfniss auf dem Kochischen Theater an etwas neuem, zu einer zeit, wo man dergleichen zu haben wuenschte, hat sie erst vor kurzem dem staube entrissen, worinnen sie seit vielen jahren gelegen und immerdar haette liegen sollen. Herr [Johann Adam] **Hiller,** dieser vortreffliche tonkuenstler, beschenkte die kleinen lieder, so wie die uebrigen komischen opern, mit einer artigen musik, die ebenfalls im drucke erscheinen wird. Der verfasser sieht nach diesen umstaenden vorher, dass sie mit den vorhergehenden stuecken dieses zweyten bandes ein gleiches schicksal haben wuerde: man wuerde bald auf anderen theatern zu der musik text machen, den er noch weniger, als den gegenwaertigen, auf seine rechnung moechte geschrieben haben . . ."
> First performed at Leipzig, Theater am Rannstaedter Thore, 1771. SCHATZ 4719

— Der **dorfbalbier.** Eine komische oper in zwey aufzuegen.

> *C. F. Weisse, Komische opern, Carlsruhe, 1778, t. ii. [195]–252.* *18½*^{cm}.
> On p. [196], the note: "Das stueck ist eine nachahmung des *Blaise le savetier* von M. Sedaine." The composer, Johann Adam **Hiller,** is not mentioned.
>   ML 49.A2W2

Gesaenge aus der oper Der **dorfbarbier,** in zwey aufzuegen. Die musik ist von Schenk.

> *Hamburg, Peter Christian Heinrich Rabe, 1799.* *23 p.* *15*^{cm}.
> By Joseph and Paul Weidmann, who are not mentioned.
> First performed at Hamburg, Theater beim Gaensemarkt, January 4, 1799; at Vienna, Burgtheater, October 30, 1796.   SCHATZ 9592

Arien und gesaenge aus dem komischen singspiele in drei aufzuegen: Die **dorfdeputirten.** Musik von Schuhbauer.

> *Berlin, n. publ., 1796.* *38 p.* *16*^{cm}.
> By Gottlob Ephraim Heermann, who is not mentioned. Cast.
> First performed at Berlin, Nationaltheater, September 23, 1796; at Munich, Churfuerstl. Schaubühne bei St. Salvator, May 8, 1783.   SCHATZ 9710

Die **dorfdeputierten,** eine komische oper in drey aufzuegen. Die musik dazu ist neu von hrn. Teuber [Teyber] verfertiget.

> *n. i., 1792.* *p. [225]–312, xii. bd.* *16½*^{cm}.
> Apparently detached from a collection containing works of the author, Gottlob Ephraim Heermann.
> First performed at Vienna, Kärntnerthor Theater, January 8, 1785. SCHATZ 10295

Die **dorfdeputirten**, eine komische oper in drey aufzuegen aus dem
italiaenischen nach dem lustspiele des hr. Goldoni il Feudatorio, der
Lehnserbe. von H.

Weimar, Carl Ludolf Hoffmann, 1773. 180 p. 16^cm.

By Gottlob Ephraim Heermann. Composed by Ernst Wilhelm **Wolf,** who is not
mentioned.

First performed at Weimar, Schlosstheater in der Wilhelmsburg, July 21, 1772; at
Berlin, Theater in der Behrenstr., Juni 15, 1772. Schatz 11077

— Arien und gesaenge aus den **Dorfdeputirten,** einer komischen
oper in drey aufzuegen, aus dem italiaenischen nach dem lustspiele
des hrn. Goldoni il Feudatorio, der Lehnserbe. von H.

Riga, Gottlob Christian Froelich, n. d. 19 p. 16½^cm.

By Gottlob Ephraim Heermann. The composer, Ernst Wilhelm **Wolf,** is not
mentioned. Schatz 11077a

Die **dorffeyer.** Ein schauspiel mit gesang in einem akte. Zum pro-
log auf das hoechste geburtsfest unsers gnaedigsten landesvaters.
Von der Secondaischen Schauspieler gesellschaft aufgefuehrt in
Leipzig, den 22. und 23. december, 1790.

n. i., n. d. 42 p. 16^cm.

Neither the author, Heinrich Blümner, is mentioned, nor the composer (unknown
to Schatz). Schatz 11451

Die **dorfgala.** Ein lustspiel in drey aufzuegen mit arien und
gesaengen. Fuer das Hoftheater zu Weimar. Die musik ist von
herrn Schweitzer.

Gotha, Carl Wilhelm Ettinger, 1774. 136 p. 15½^cm.

Dedicatory poem signed by the author, Friedrich Wilhelm Gotter.

First performed at Weimar, Kleines Schlosstheater, June 30, 1772. Schatz 9770

— Arien und gesaenge aus der komischen oper: Die **dorfgalla.** In
zwey aufzuegen. Von Gotter und Schweizer.

Hamburg, J. M. Michaelsen, 1778. 16 p. 18^cm.

First performed at Hamburg, Theater beim Gänsemarkt, January 21, 1779.
Schatz 9771

Die **dorfhaendel,** oder Bund ueber eck. Ein komisches original-
singspiel in zwey aufzuegen. In musik gesetzt von herrn Ruprecht,
mitglied des K. K. Nat. Hof-Theaters. Aufgefuehrt im K. K. Hoftheater naechst dem Kaerntnerthor.

Wien, beym logenmeister, 1785. 55 p. 17½^cm.

Author not mentioned, and unknown to Schatz.

First performed, as indicated, November 15, 1785. Schatz 9163

Der **dorfjahrmarkt.** *See* G. Benda's Der jahrmarkt.

Die **dorfschule.** Von H. B.

n. i., 1783. 56 p. 16½^cm.

By Heinrich Braun. Composer not recorded by Schatz. Schatz 11606

La **Dori.** Drama per musica da rappresentarsi nel Teatro novissimo
di S. Salvatore . . .

Venetia, Si vende in Frezzaria e Spadaria, 1663. 5 p. l., 72 p. 14^cm.

Three acts and prologue. Dedication signed *A. B.* and dated Venice, January 1,
1663, argument, scenario. Neither the author, Apollonio Apolloni, is mentioned, nor
the composer, Marc' Antonio **Cesti.**

La **Dori**—Continued.

The date of first performance is generally given as indicated by this edition of the libretto, but Schatz dates it Florence, Teatro dei Sorgenti, carnival, 1661, with the title, "La Dori ovvero La schiava fedele."   SCHATZ 1778

— La **Dori.** Drama per musica da rappresentarsi nel Teatro novissimo di S. Salvatore . . .

Venetia, Francesco Nicolini, 1666. 6 p. l., 72 p. 13^{cm}.

Prologue and three acts. Dedication signed *F. N.* and dated Venice, January 1, 1663, argument, scenario. The composer, Marc' Antonio **Cesti,** and the author, Apollonio Apolloni, are not mentioned   SCHATZ 11683

— La **Dori** overo Lo schiavo reggio. Drama per musica da rappresentarsi nel nobilissimo Teatro Grimano di SS. Gio. e Paolo l'anno 1667 . . .

Venetia, Francesco Nicolini & Steffano Curti, 1667. 7 p. l. (incl. front.), 64 p. 13$\frac{1}{2}$^{cm}.

Three acts, with prologue, publisher's dedication, dated January 16, 1667, argument, scenario, and preface, with **Cesti**'s name as composer, and this remark:
"Si è incontrato molte difficoltà, così nel ritrovare l'originale della musica, come nell' agguistarlo, & nel trasportare le parti . . . si sono aggionte alcune ariette per maggiormente adornare il drama."
The modifications were very slight; for instance, in Act I the third scene, "Astro d'Amore gradito," with the aria "E gran felicità goder," was dropped and the second scene, "Viverò, viverò, Ma s'il Fato," added. In Act II the aria in scene 9, "Chi non prova d'Amor ignudo," was added, but the scene 14, "Ahi qual fiero timore," dropped. In the third act, scene 12, "De l'insigne reali," was dropped; also the final quartet, "Amori volate," for which was substituted "Pur cangia i suoi rigori."   SCHATZ 1785

— La **Dori.** Drama per musica ristampato, e rappresentato . . . agli augusti sponsali della Reale Altezza di Mariana Christina, delfina di Francia, nata principessa elettorale di Baviera. Alla med.^{ma} R. A. consecrato con l'aggiunta di nuovo prologo posto in musica dal S. D. Giuseppe Antonio Bernabei . .

Monaco, Giovanni Jeclino, 1680. 7 p. l., 104 p. 15^{cm}.

Three acts. Argument. The dedication is signed by Ventura Terzago, who wrote the poetry of the new prologue and probably was also responsible for considerable modifications of the original libretto. For instance, it may be noted for purposes of identification that in the second act the fourteenth scene, "Ahi qual fiero timore," and the third scene, "O destino, destino," have been dropped; that the scene "Sotto vario altro pianetta" has been added, and the second scene, "Erasto, Erasto," considerably enlarged beyond the original seventeen lines.
First performed, as indicated, at Munich, Churfürstl. Hoftheater, in March, 1680.   SCHATZ 1779

— Il **regio schiavo,** o sia La Dori: Drama per musica da recitarsi da diversi cavalieri nel Teatro di castello: che serve per introduttione ad un' essercitio d'arme rappresentato da otto altri cavalieri.

Mantova, gli Osanna, 1672. 91 p. 15^{cm}.

Three acts. Argument. Neither Apolloni nor **Cesti** mentioned. On p. 87–91 introductory remarks and text of marchese Annibale Lanzoni's "Introduttione al ballo di otto guerrieri. *Bellona in macchina.*"   ML 50.2.D62C3

La **Doriclea.** Dramma musicale di Giovanni Faustini.

Venetia, Francesco Miloco, 1645. 89, [5] p. 13$\frac{1}{2}$^{cm}.

Three acts, with prologue, author's dedication, and argument. Pietro Francesco **Cavalli,** the composer, is not mentioned. The five additional pages contain what appears from this notice to the reader:

La **Doriclea**—Continued.

"Questa scena [Sfortunata quella hora] cantata dopo la terza dell' atto primo di questa favola, & le due seguenti, ["Povere innamorate," after Act II, sc. 6, and "Cittadina de' monti," after Act III, sc. 4] poste in quella del Titone, sono state composte per dilettare gl'uditori, & per aggradire à rappresentanti."

First performed at Venice, Teatro di S. Cassiano, carnival, 1645.   SCHATZ 1737

Doriclea ripudiata da Creso. Drama per musica di G. B. C. Da rappresentarsi nel Teatro Giustiniano di S. Mosè il carnovale dell' anno 1729 . . .

Venezia, Alvise Valvasense, 1729. 2 p. l., 48 p. 14½ cm*.

Three acts. By Giovanni Battista Corte, who dates his dedication of "un mio drama, primo parto della mia debolissima penna," Venice, December 29, 1728. Argument, notice to the reader, scenario, and cast. The name of the composer, Giovanni **Porta,** is not mentioned.   SCHATZ 8378

Dorilla e Nesso. Intermezzi by N. A. Porpora. *See his* Eumene.
SCHATZ 8366

Dorilla in Tempe. Melodramma eroico pastorale da rappresentarsi nel Teatro di Sant' Angelo nell' autunno 1726 . . .

Venezia, Marino Rossetti, 1726. 48 p. 15½ cm*.

Three acts. Dedication by the author, Antonio Maria Luchini, dated Venice, November 9, 1726, notice to the reader, cast, scenario, and name of Antonio **Vivaldi** as composer.   SCHATZ 10765

Dorina e Grullo, intermezzi. *See* Caldara's L'Anagilda.

Dorina e l'uomo selvatico, ballet. *See* G. Giordani's La disfatta di Dario.

La **Dorinda.** Favola pastorale . .

Roma, Antonio de' Rossi, 1723. 47 p. 15½ cm*.

Three acts. Author not mentioned and unknown to Schatz. Dedication, signed by the composer, Carlo Francesco **Gasparini,** and notice to the reader. Possibly the text is the same as that "by many attributed to Benedetto Marcello" (Allacci).
SCHATZ 3592

Dorinda. Pastorale da rappresentarsi per musica nel Teatro Grimani di S. Samuel. Nella fiera dell' Ascensione l'anno 1729 . . .

Venezia, Carlo Buonarrigo, n. d. 24 p. 15 cm*.

Three acts. Domenico Lalli says in his dedication "da ignoto autore composta, ed accomodata per il presente divertimento." If the text had been by Benedetto Marcello or by Benedetto Pasqualigo, as some authorities contend, Lalli surely would have known the author. Argument, cast, and names of Giovanni Battista **Pescetti** and Baldassare **Galuppi** as composers.   SCHATZ 7967

Doris, ein musikalisches schaeferspiel, welches auf dem neuen Koeniglichen Theater, im Zwinger, in Dresden aufgefuehret worden. Im jahr 1747.

n. i., n. d. 59 p. 15½ cm*.

Two acts. Cast and name of Johann Georg **Schürer** as the composer. Author not mentioned and unknown to Schatz.

First performed, as indicated, February 13, 1747.   SCHATZ 9731

La **Dorisbe** overo L'amor volubile e tiranno, drama per musica di Gio. Domenico Pioli da recitarsi nella Sala de' Sig. Capranica nel carnevale dell' anno 1711 . . .

Roma, Rocco Bernabò, 1711.   front., 81 p.   14ᶜᵐ.

Three acts.   Dedication, argument, cast.   The composer, Alessandro **Scarlatti**, is not mentioned.

Dent does not mention the opera under this title, only under the alternative title, which would seem to have been, according to Dent, the original title.   If he mentions (p. 117) a libretto with date 1707, this is probably an error for 1709, when the opera was first performed, in May, at the Teatro di S. Bartolomeo, Schatz giving the exact date of May 25.   SCHATZ 9531

Dorothée, pantomime à spectacle; précédée des Preux chevaliers, prologue-pantomime.   Par M. Audinot.   Représentée, pour la première fois, sur le Théâtre de l'Ambigu-comique, à la Foire Saint-Germain, en l'année 1782.

Paris, Cailleau, 1782.   16 p.   18½ᶜᵐ.

The prologue is in one act, "Dorothée" in three.   Synopsis of the plot.   The composer of the music is not mentioned.   The approbation is dated January 26, 1782.

Probably not identical with the "Dorothée," music by Jean Baptiste de Rochefort, mentioned by Fétis.   ML 48.B2

Dorval e Virginia, dramma per prosa, e musica da rappresentarsi nel Reggio Teatro di S. Carlo, della Principessa per celebrare il felicissimo giorno natalizio di Sua Altezza Reale il serenissimo Signore D. Giovanni principe del Brasile . . . li 13 di maggio, 1795.

Lisbona, Simone Taddeo Ferreira, 1795.   151 p.   14½ᶜᵐ.

Four acts.   By Giuseppe Foppa, who is not mentioned.   Cast, scenario, and name of Pietro [Carlo] **Guglielmi** as the composer.   Portuguese text faces Italian.   With the opera was performed (composer of the music not mentioned) Pietro Angiolini's "ballo di carattere pollacco, Zeboschi ed Esing, ossia Il vero amico."   SCHATZ 4344

Dorval e Virginia.   Dramma prosa, e musica di Giuseppe Foppa da rappresentarsi nel nobilissimo Teatro Venier in San Benedetto il carnovale dell' anno 1793.

Venezia, Modesto Fenzo, 1792.   72 p.   17½ᶜᵐ.

Three acts.   Prefatory note, cast, scenario, and name of Angelo **Tarchi** as the composer.   On p. 63–72, argument, cast, description, and name of Vittorio Trento as composer ("La musica e tutta nuova") of Giuseppe Traffieri's "Bianca de' Rossi, ballo tragico pantomimo."   His second ballet was called "Le nemiche degli nomini."

SCHATZ 10219

La **dot,** comédie en trois actes et en prose, mêlée d'ariettes; représentée, pour la premiere fois, par les Comédiens italiens ordinaires du roi, devant Leurs Majestés, à Fontainebleau, le 8 novembre 1785; & à Paris le lundi 21 du même mois.

Paris, Brunet, 1784.   62, [1] p.   19ᶜᵐ.

Cast.   Neither author nor composer mentioned.   ML 50.2.D63D2

— La **dot,** comédie en trois actes et en prose, mêlée d'ariettes, paroles de M. Desfontaines, musique de M. d'Alairac, représentée . . . [same dates as in 1784 ed.]   Édition conforme à la partition gravée.

Paris, Brunet, 1786.   64 p.   22ᶜᵐ.

Cast.   Text practically the same as in the 1784 ed.   ML 50.2.D63D22

La **dot de Suzette**, comédie en un acte et en prose, mêlée de musique; représentée pour la première fois sur le Théâtre de l'Opéra-comique-national, rue Favart, le 19 fructidor, an 6 de la République. Par le C^en Dejaure, musique du C^en Boieldieu.

Paris, Vente, an VI. [1797–98] 31 p. 21^cm.

Cast.
First performed, as indicated, Sept. 5, 1798. ML 50.2.D64B6

The **double disappointment**; a farce. As it is acted at the Theatre Royal in Covent-Garden. By the late Moses Mendez, esq.

London, F. Noble [etc.] 1760. 40 p. 19½^cm.

One act. The songs, partly to be sung to indicated popular airs, are so few that the piece can hardly be considered an operatic entertainment.
First performed at Covent Garden, 1747 (Biog. Dram.), but not performed there until March 22, 1759, says Genest, who dates first performance, Drury Lane, March 18, 1746. ML 50.5.D79
Second copy. LONGE 17

The **double disguise**, a comic opera in two acts: As performed at the Theatre-Royal in Drury-Lane. The songs set to music by Mr. Hook.

London, J. Bell, 1784. 28 p. (incl. port.) 21^cm.

The port. is that of Miss Phillips in the character of Emily.
Cast. Probably by Mrs. James [Harriet Horncastle] Hook.
First performed March 8, 1784, as indicated. LONGE 95

The **double elopement**. A. T. of Linley's The duenna.

La **double épreuve**, ou Colinette à la cour, comédie lyrique en trois actes, représentée pour la première fois par l'Académie royale de musique, le mardi 1er janvier 1782. Les paroles de M * * *. La musique de M. Grétry.

Paris, P. de Lormel, 1784. 62 p. 19^cm.

Cast. By Jean Baptiste Lourdet de Santerre, who based the text on Favart's "Ninette à la cour." In the avertissement he says:
"Il a cru trouver tout ce qu'il désiroit dans le sujet très connu de Ninette à la cour; & peu jaloux de la gloire de l'invention, il ne s'est fait aucun scrupule de s'en emparer: les théâtres étrangers, comme les théâtres anciens, sont un fonds commun où il est permis à tout le monde de pinser. Et pourquoi plusieurs poëtes n'auroient-ils pas la liberté de faire d'un opéra bouffon italien ce qu'on fait des tragédies de Sophocle & d'Euripide?"
On p. 39–40, the air of "On trouve un objet charmant" (II, 11), and on p. 60–61, "L'amitié vive & pure" (III, 10). SCHATZ 4147

La **doublefête**. A. T. of Martini's L'amoureux de quinze ans.

The **double funeral**. A. T. of Arnold's The dead alive.

La **double métamorphose**. A. T. of Le diable à quatre.

Dove entrò cervo, esce donna, o sia Il curioso accidente della caccia, ballet. *See* Rust's La caccia d'Enrico IV.

The **downfall of bribery**: or, The honest men of Taunton. A new ballad-opera of three acts. As it was lately perform'd by a company of players at a certain noted inn at Taunton in Somersetshire.

The downfall of bribery—Continued.

By Mark Freeman, of the said town, freeholder and grocer. . . .   To which is added, A new ballad by way of epilogue. Spoken by the person who acted in the character of *Freeman*.

   London, Sam. Pike, n. d.   3 p. l., 36 p.   19^{cm}.

   Three acts. Table of the 16 airs, the titles of which are indicated in the text. This quotation of a quotation from the Craftsman, No. 385, Nov. 24, 1733, on the title page gives a clue to the origin of the piece:
   "A few persons at Taunton, who had it in their power to turn the election of a mayor, lately refused a sum of two thousand pounds for their votes upon that occasion."   Longe 168

The dragon of Wantley. A burlesque opera. The musick by Mr. John Frederick Lampe, and performed at the Theatre-Royal in Covent-Garden. Moderniz'd from the old ballad after the Italian manner, by Sig. Carini [*pseud.*] The 12th ed., with additions. To which is prefix'd, the original ballad (cum notis variorum) by way of argument, &c. &c. &c. . . .

   London, J. Shuckburgh, 1738.   32 p.   19½^{cm}.

   Title vignette.
   Three acts. By Henry Carey. Cast. The text is preceded on p. 13 by "Puff" signed "P. Anderson. Westminster, Jan. 1, 1738"; p. 7–13, "An excellent ballad"; p. 6, "A critical remark on the old ballad, call'd The Dragon of Wantley . . ."; and p. [iii]–v, Carey's dedication of date Pall-mall, Jan. 3, 1738, to the composer, in which he says:
   "Many joyous hours have we shared during its composition, chopping and changing, looping, eking out, and coining of words, syllables, and jingle, to display in English the beauty of nonsense, so prevailing in the Italian operas. . . . Lowness (figuratively speaking) is the sublimity of burlesque: if so, this opera is, consequently, the tip-top sublime of its kind. Your musick, on the other hand, is as grand and pompous as possible, by which means the contrast is the stronger, and has succeeded accordingly."
   After complimentary remarks about the performers, Carey says:
   "in a more singular sense we stand indebted to Mr. Rich, who received our poor disconsolate *Dragon* with pleasure, after it had lain several years dormant in the repository, and under the inspection, of the most wise, most learned, and judicious, 'Squire *What-d'ye-call-him*, Master of Drury-Lane play-house."
   First performed at London, Covent Garden, October 26, 1737.   ML 50.2.D67L2

—— The **dragon of Wantley**, a burlesque opera. Set to musick by Mr. John Frederick Lampe.

   [89]–114 p.   22^{cm}.   (Henry Carey, Dramatick works, London, 1743.)
   Three acts. Argument.   .   ML 49.A2C2

—— The **dragon of Wantley**, a burlesque opera. Set to musick by Mr. John Frederick Lampe.

   London, T. Lowndes, T. Caslon, W. Nicoll, and S. Bladon, 1770. front., 36 p.   17^{cm}.
   Three acts. Same dedication.   ML 50.2.D67L3

—— The **dragon of Wantley**. A burlesque opera. As perform'd at the theatres with universal applause. Set to musick by Mr. John Frederick Lampe. To which is added the old ballad, from whence this opera was taken.

   London, Printed for the proprietors, n. d.   24 p.   16½^{cm}.
   Three acts.   Longe 69

The dragoness. L. T. of Lampe's Margery.

Drei heirathen an einem tage.　A. T. of Mühle's Die singschule.

Arien und gesaenge aus der komischen oper: Die **drei pucklichen.**
In zwey aufzuegen.
>*Hamburg, J. M. Michaelsen, 1780.　16 p.　18^{cm}.*

First performed at Hamburg, Theater b. Gänsemarkt, Juni 7, 1779, previously at Lübeck, December 11, 1772.
Schatz attributes this to **Paisiello,** as a German version of his "I tre gobbi" (Goldoni). However, he lists no such opera in his "Chronologisches Verzeichnis" of Paisiello's works. Possibly it is a German version of Paisiello's "La somiglianza dei nomi," first performed at Naples, Teatro Nuovo sopra Toledo, spring, 1771.

Schatz 7663

Die **drei sultaninnen.**　A. T. of Süssmayer's Soliman der Zweite.

Die **drey liebhaber.**　Tr. of Cimarosa's I tre amanti.

Die **drey paechter.**　*See* Dezède's Les trois fermiers.

Die **drey ringe,** oder Kaspar der mundkoch.　Eine komische oper
in drey aufzuegen.　Von Emanuel Schikaneder.　Die musik dazu ist
von herrn Schak, deutscher saenger.
>*n. i., 1796.　23 p.　15½^{cm}.*

First performed at Regensburg, Thurn u. Taxische Schaubühne im Ball-Hause, March 25, 1788.
Schatz 9568

Die **drey wuensche.**　A. T. of Der kluge mann.

Die **drey wünsche.**　A. T. of Georg Benda's Der holzhauer.

Die **drey wuensche.**　A. T. of Philidor's Der holzhauer.

Le **droit du seigneur,** comédie en trois actes, en prose, mêlée
d'ariettes; par M. Desfontaines: représentée devant Leurs Majestés
à Fontainebleau, le 17 octobre 1783, et à Paris, par le [!] Comédiens
italiens ordinaires du Roi, le 29 décembre de la même année.
>*Amsterdam, Cesar Noël Guerin, 1784.　48 p.　18^{cm}.*

Schatz 6036

— Gesaenge aus dem singspiele: Das **herrnrecht,** in drey aufzuegen
nach dem franzoesischen, von D'Arien.　In musick gesetzt von
Martini.
>*Hamburg, J. M. Michaelsen, 1789.　38 p.　15^{cm}.*

By Bernhard Christian d'Arien.
First performed at Hamburg, Theater b. Gänsemarkt, March 13, 1789.
Schatz 6037

— Das **recht des lehnsherrn.**　Ein singspiel in 3 aufzuegen, nach
dem franzoesischen, frey bearbeitet zu einer musik von Martini.
>*Oels, Ludwig, n. d.　84 p.　16^{cm}.*

Translator not mentioned and unknown to Schatz.
First performed at Oels, Hoftheater, February 13, 1796.　　Schatz 6038

Le **drole de corps.**　A. T. of Le mauvais plaisant.

Airs, duets, chorusses, etc., in the new masque called The **Druids.** As performed at the Theatre Royal, Covent-Garden. The words chiefly taken from Ben Johnson; the music composed by Mr. Fisher. The second edition.

London, T. Evans, 1775.   19, [1] p.   19^{cm}.

Cast.   Text by Woodward (Clarence: "The Stage").   The first ed. was published 1774.   Composed by John Abraham **Fisher.**   Not recorded by Genest.

ML 52.2.D72

Drusilla, vedova ingegnosa e D Strabone, dottore in medicina. O. T. of Mariani's text La vedova ingegnosa.

Il **duca d'Atene,** a new comic opera, as performed at the King's Theatre in the Hay Market.   Written by C. F. Badini.   The music entirely new by Signor Bertoni.

London, E. Cox, 1780.   1 p. l., 97 p.   19½^{cm}.

Prefatory note and cast.   English translation faces Italian text.   ML 48.M2K

Li due amanti in inganno.   Dramma giocoso per musica da rappresentarsi nel Teatro Tron di San Cassiano nel carnovale dell' anno 1775.

Venezia, Gio. Battista Casali, 1775.   70 p.   17½^{cm}.

Three acts.   Author not mentioned, and unknown to Schatz.   Cast, scenario, and names of Giacomo **Rust** as the composer of acts I and III, of Matteo **Rauzzini** as composer of act II.   SCHATZ 9181

Li due amanti rivali.   L. T. of Caruso's La virtuosa alla moda.

Li due avari, ballet.   See Anfossi's Gengis-Kan.

I due avari, ballet.   See Zingarelli's Ifigenia in Aulide.

I due baroni.   L. T. of Cimarosa's I due baroni di Rocca Azura.

I due baroni di Rocca Azzurra.   Farsetta da rappresentarsi nel Teatro della Vittoria di Montalboddo l'autunno dell' anno 1787.

Sinigaglia, Domenico Lazzarini, 1787.   48 p.   16½^{cm}.

Two acts.   By Giuseppe Palomba, who is not mentioned.   Cast and name of **Cimarosa** as composer.

First performed at Rome, Teatro Valle, February, 1783.   ML 50.2.D75C3

— Li **due baroni di Rocca Azurra.**   Dramma giocoso per musica da rappresentarsi nel Real Teatro di Salvaterra nel carnovale dell' anno 1791.

[Lisboa], Stamperia reale, n. d.   77 p.   16½^{cm}.

Two acts.   By Giuseppe Palomba (not mentioned).   Scenario, cast and name of the composer, **Cimarosa.**   SCHATZ 1918

— I **due baroni di Rocca Azura.**   Dramma giocoso per musica da rappresentarsi nel Teatro di S. A. E. di Sassonia.

Dresda, n. publ., 1790.   111 p.   15^{cm}.

Two acts.   With name of the composer, **Cimarosa.**   German title, "Die beyden barons von Rocca Azura" and text face Italian.

First performed at Dresden as indicated in 1790.   SCHATZ 1919

I due baroni di Rocca Azzurra—Continued.

— **I due baroni.** Commedia per musica di Giuseppe Palomba da rappresentarsi nel Real Teatro del Fondo di Separazione per second' opera del corrente anno 1793.

Napoli, n. publ., 1793. 48 p. 15^{cm}.

Two acts. Cast, name of **Cimarosa** as composer, and author's pref., in which he says:

"Eccoti ridotti in commedia gl'intermezzi de *Due Baroni* da me composti, son già più anni per il Teatro di Roma. Mi è convenuto adornarla di alcune nuove scene per adattare al buffo napoletano il carattere del Baroncino; come ancora mi è stato necessario di variare alcune arie per comodo dei presenti attori . . . senza partirmi dall . . . Cimarosa . . ." SCHATZ 1978

I due cacciatori e la venditrice di latte, ballet. *See* Isola's La conquista del vello d'oro.

Li due castellani burlati. L. T. of Fabrizi's I castellani burlati.

I due Cesari. Drama per musica da rappresentarsi nel Teatro Vendramino di S. Salvatore. L'anno MDCLXXXIII. Di Giulio Cesare Corradi . . .

Venetia, Francesco Nicolini, 1683. 72 p. 14½^{cm}.

Three acts. Corradi's dedication, argument, scenario, cast, and name of Giovanni **Legrenzi** as the composer. SCHATZ 5543

Le due contesse. Intermezzi per musica a cinque voci da rappresentarsi nel Teatro Valle nel carnevale dell' anno 1776 . . . [woodcut]

Roma, Ottavio Puccinelli, 1776. 62 p. 15½^{cm}.

Two parts. By Giuseppe Petrosellini, who is not mentioned. Publisher's dedicatory poem, cast and name of Giuseppe **Paisiello** as composer. ML 50.2.D76P2

— **Le due contesse,** intermezzo per musica a cinque voci da rappresentarsi nel Real Teatro di Colorno l'autunno dell' anno MDCCLXXVII.

Parma, Stamperia reale, n. d. 67 p. 20½^{cm}.

Two parts. By Giuseppe Petrosellini, who is not mentioned. Cast and name of **Paisiello** as the composer. SCHATZ 7613

— **Le due contesse.** Azzione comica per musica da rappresentarsi nel Piccolo Teatro di S. A. S. E. di Sassonia.

Dresda, n. publ., 1781. 147 p. 15½^{cm}.

Two acts. Without name of Petrosellini, but with name of **Paisiello.** German title page, "Die zwey comtessinnen," and text face Italian.
First performed 1781, as indicated. SCHATZ 7614

I due dittatori.

Apostolo Zeno, Poesie drammatiche, Venezia, 1744, t. ii, 87–182 p. 19^{cm}.

Three acts and licenza. Argument. No composer is mentioned. In the "Catalogo" at the end of t. x, date and place of first ed. are given as Vienna, 1726. (First performed November 4, music by *Caldara*.) ML 49.A2Z3

— **I due dittatori.** Pubblicati per la prima volta in Vienna 1726.

Apostolo Zeno, Poesie drammatiche, Orleans, 1785–86, t. vi, p. 311–398. 21^{cm}.

Five acts and licenza. Argument. No composer is mentioned. ML 49.A2Z4

Le due finte gemelle.   L. T. of Piccinni's Le finte gemelle.

Li due fratelli ridicoli.   A. T. of Alessandri's La finta baronessa.

Le due gemelle.   L. T. of P. Guglielmi's L'inganno amoroso, and A. T. of his L'equivoco amoroso, another L. T. of the same opera.

I due gemelli.   A. T. of the ballet Mysis ed Eufrasia.

Li due gemelli e La scuffiara.   Drammi giocosi per musica ciascun di un atto di Giambattista Lorenzi **P. A.** da rappresentarli [!] nel Nuovo Teatro de' Fiorentini nel carnevale del corrente anno 1784.

   Napoli, n. publ., 1784. 78 p.   15ᶜᵐ.

   Cast, name of Giacomo **Tritto** as the composer, and notice to the public:
   "La prima di queste due farse è l'istessa, che nel carnevale dell' anno scorso fu rappresentata in questo medesimo teatro.   Il carattere di Ortensio, che allora si sosteneva da un tenore, adesso viene disimpegnato dalla Sig. Caterina Fiorentini, avendo impreso a far tal parte per esservi riavuta dalla sua infermità, per la quale con reciproco consenso si suo che dell' impresario fù scritturata altra cantante col carattere di seconda Buffa.   Allora quando fu data la parte di Ortensio alla prefata Sig. Caterina Fiorentini, era di già scritta si la poesia, che la musica della seconda farsa denominata La Scuffiara, per la quale a sua istanza si è aggiunto un personaggio di più col nome di Giulietta, e l'aria, che canta ["Fin a tanto che userete"] non è del maestro Tritto per essere il medesimo assente.   Si è ben' anche aggiunto il carattere di Cecchino per concatenare meglio le idee, e la sua aria ["Parce per carità"] e del maestro [Gaetano] **Monti,** come anche quella di Pippa, ["Or che ballar degg'io"].
   On p. [43]–78 "La scuffiara."   SCHATZ 10456

I due gobbi.   A. T. and L. T. of Portugal's Le confusioni della somiglianza.

Li due gobbi rivali.   Farsetta per musica a trè voci che serve per intermezzo nel Teatro della Pallacorda di Firenze in Roma, nel carnevale dell' anno 1752 . . .

   Roma, Ottavio Puccinelli, 1752.   24 p.   15½ᶜᵐ.

   Two parts.   Author not mentioned and unknown to me.   Dedication by the impresario Alessandro Abinante, cast and name of "Engelberto Rendeut Liegere" (Engelbert **Rendeux**) as composer.   ML 50.2.D77R2

I due litiganti.   L. T. of Sarti's Fra i due litiganti il terzo gode.

Le due orfane e i due tutori innamorati.   Dramma giocoso per musica da rappresentarsi in Firenze nel R. Teatro de' Risoluti posto in via Santa Maria nella estate dell' anno 1792 . . .

   Firenze, Ant. Gius. Pagani e comp., 1792.   63, [1] p.   16½ᶜᵐ.

   Two acts.   The author is not mentioned and unknown to Schatz.   Cast and name of the composer: "La musica tutta nuova del Sig. Giuseppe **Moneta** maestro onorario, e compositore della R. Corte di Toscana."
   First performed at Rome, Teatro Valle, fall of 1790.   SCHATZ 6552

Le due pastorelle smarrite, ballet.   *See* Baini's Il finto Parigino.

Le due rivali in amore.   Dramma per musica da rappresentarsi nel Teatro Giustiniano di S. Moise nell' autuño dell' anno 1728.

   Venezia, Carlo Buonarigo, n. d.   48 p.   14ᶜᵐ.

   Three acts.   By Aurelio Aureli, who is not mentioned.   Argument, scenario, cast, and name of Tommaso **Albinoni** as composer.   SCHATZ 108

Le due rivali o sia La prova del vero amore, ballet.   *See* Astaritta's Ipermestra.

I due sciocchi delusi. A. T. of Portugal's La vedova raggiratrice.

I due sindaci. A. T. of Rutini's I vendemmiatori.

Li due sindaci ossia La vendemmia, ballet. *See* P. Guglielmi's Le due gemelle.

I due sordi. L. A. T. of Paër's Il matrimonio improviso.

Le due sorelle incognite. Dramma giocoso per musica da rappresentarsi nel nobile Teatro dell' eccell.^{ma} casa Giustiniani in S. Moisè il carnevale 1783.

> *Venezia, n. publ., n. d. 56 p. 17^{cm}.*

Two acts. Author unknown to Schatz. Cast, name of the composer, Antonio **Calegari,** and scenario. On p. 5–6, the argument of "L'ircana in Julfa ballo pantomimo regolato e diretto da Gasparo Ronzi . . ." The composer of the music is not mentioned. SCHATZ 1509

Li due sposi sfortunati, ballet. *See* Prati's Demofoonte.

Le due sultane rivali, ballet. *See* Sarti's La giardiniera brillante.

I due supposti conti ossia Lo sposo senza moglie. Dramma giocoso per musica da rappresentarsi nel Teatro Grande alla Scala l'autunno dell' anno 1784 . . .

> *Milano, Gio. Batista Bianchi, n. d. 72 p. 16^{cm}.*

Two acts. By Angelo Anelli (not mentioned), with dedication, scenario, cast, and name of the composer, **Cimarosa** ("La musica è nuova"). With the opera were performed Filippo Beretti's ballets, "I comici Italiani alla China" and "L'innocenza scoperta." The composer of the ballet music is not mentioned.
First performed at Milan, La Scala, October 10, 1784. SCHATZ 1920

— **I due supposti conti** ossia Lo sposo senza moglie. Dramma giocoso per musica da rappresentarsi nel Teatro di S. A. E. di Sassonia.

> *Dresda, n. publ., 1787. 135 p. 15^{cm}.*

Two acts, with name of the composer, **Cimarosa.** German t.-p. "Die vorgeblichen grafen oder Der braeutigam ohne braut," and text face Italian. SCHATZ 1921

— **Lo sposo senza moglie.** Dramma giocoso per musica da rappresentarsi nel nobilissimo Teatro Onigo in Treviso la fiera dell' anno 1792 . . .

> *Treviso, Giulio Trento, 1792. 36 p. 18^{cm}.*

Two acts. By Angelo Anelli (not mentioned). Impresario's dedication, cast, scenario, and name of the composer, **Cimarosa.** A later version of his "I due supposti conti." With the opera were performed Giuseppe Bartolomei's ballets, "Il generoso perdono" and "La scuola di scultura." SCHATZ 2006

I due vedovi, ballet. *See* Tarchi's Alessandro nell' Indie.

I due vedovi. Commedia per musica da rappresentarsi nel Teatro Elettorale di Sassonia.

> *Dresda, n. publ., 1798. 159 p. 15^{cm}.*

Three acts. By Giovanni de Gamerra, who is not mentioned. German title-page "Der wittwer und die wittwe," and text face Italian. Peter von **Winter** is mentioned as the composer.
First performed, as indicated, January 13, 1798; at Vienna, Burgtheater, January 12, 1796. SCHATZ 11029

I due vergognesi da nozze, ballet. *See* Galuppi's L'Ipermestra.

Le duel comique. Tr. of Paisiello's Il duello.

Il duello. Commedia di un atto per musica di Giambatista Lorenzi
P. A. da rappresentarsi nel Teatro Nuovo sopra Toledo nella primavera del corrente anno 1774.
> *Napoli, n. publ., 1774. 72 p. 14½ᶜᵐ.*
> Cast and name of **Paisiello** as the composer.   SCHATZ 7676

— Le duel comique, opera bouffon, en deux actes. Imité de l'Italien, sur la musique du Signor Paesiello, par M. Moline. Représenté
pour la premiere fois, par les Comédiens italiens, ordinaires du roi,
le lundi 16 septembre, 1776.
> *Paris, la veuve Duchesne, 1776. 2 p. l., 67 p. 20ᶜᵐ.*
> **Méreaux** is not mentioned. (*See* next entry.)   ML 50.2.D8P19

— Le duel comique, opera bouffon. En deux actes, et en prose;
mêlé d'ariettes. Representé devant Leurs Majestés, à Fontainebleau, le 10 octobre 1777.
> *[Paris], P. Robert Christophe Ballard, 1777. 2 p. l., 56 p. 20½ᶜᵐ.*
> Cast and note: "Les paroles sont de M. Moline. La musique du Sieur **Paesiello**,
> redigée & augmentée par M. [Jean Nicolas Le Froid] de **Méreaux**."
>   ML 50.2.D8P2

Il duello d'amore e di vendetta. O. T. of Silvani's text Li sdegni
cangiati in amore.

Il duello d'amore e di vendetta. Drama per musica. Da recitarsi nel famoso Teatro Vendramino di S. Salvatore. L'anno 1700.
Poesia di Francesco Silvani . . . Ristampato . . .
> *Venezia, Nicolini, 1700. 68 p. 14½ᶜᵐ.*
> Three acts. Author's dedication, dated Venice, December 26, 1699, argument,
> cast, and scenario. The composer, Marc' Antonio **Ziani**, is not mentioned.
>   SCHATZ 11183

Il duello per complimento. A. T. and L. T. of Cimarosa's I
nemici generosi.

Songs, duets, trios, &c. in The duenna; or, The double elopement.
As performed at the Theatre-Royal in Covent-Garden.
> *London, J. Wilkie [etc.] 1775. 2 p. l., 20 p. 19½ᶜᵐ.*
> Three acts. By Richard Brinsley Sheridan, who is not mentioned. Cast. The
> music was composed and compiled by Thomas **Linley** in conjunction with his son
> Thomas. *See also* "The governess."
> First performed, as indicated, October 21, 1775 (Schatz); November 21, 1775
> (Genest).   ML 50.2.D85

— The duenna; or, The double elopement. A comic opera.
> *[79]–115 p. 16ᶜᵐ. (A volume of plays, Dublin, 1791.)*
> Without name of author or composer.   PR 1269.v6

— The duenna: a comic opera, in three acts: as it is performed, by
His Majesty's servants . . .
> *London, E. Johnson, 1776. 1 p. l., ii, 43 p. 20½ᶜᵐ.*
> Three-act parody by Israel Pottinger (not mentioned) of Sheridan's "Duenna."
> The ironical dedication to David Garrick is dated June 18, 1776. The tunes are indi-
> cated by quoting first lines from the original piece. The **Linleys** are not mentioned.
>   LONGE 310

The **duenna**—Continued.

— The **duenna**, a comic opera, in three acts: as it is performed by His Majesty's servants . . . A new edition. [vignette]

London, E. Johnson, n. d. 1 p. l., ii, 43 p. $20\frac{1}{2}$ cm.

Same parody. ML 50.2.D852

Duglas ed Ernestina, ballet. *See* Spontini's Adelina Senese.

The **dumb lady cur'd**. A. T. of The mock doctor.

Der **dumme gaertner**. L. T. of Schack's Anton der dumme gaertner.

I **duo** [!] **tiranni al soglio**. Drama per musica. Nel Teatro Vendramino di San Salvatore. L'anno 1679. Di Matteo Noris . . .

Venetia, Francesco Nicolini, 1679. 80 p. $13\frac{1}{2}$ cm.

Three acts. Author's dedication dated January 15, 1679, argument, scenario. The composer, Antonio **Sartorio**, is not mentioned. SCHATZ 9481

Die **durch blut und mord erlangete liebe**, oder Nero. In einem sing-spiel auf dem Hamburgischen Schau-Platz vorgestellet anno 1705.

n. i., n. d. *Unpaged.* 19 cm.

Three acts. Neither the author, Friedrich Christian Feustking, nor the composer, Georg Friedrich **Händel**, is mentioned. Argument and scenario.

First performed, as indicated, Theater beim Gänsemarkt, February 25, 1705.

SCHATZ 4475

Der **durch den fall des grossen Pompejus erhoehete Julius Caesar**. In einem sing-spiel auf dem grossen Hamburgischen Schau-platz aufgefuehret. Im jahr 1710 im monaht novembr.

[Hamburg], mit Spieringischen schrifften, n. d. *Unpaged.* 19 cm.

Five acts. "Historischer vorbericht." Neither the author, resp. translator, Barthold Feind, nor the composer, Reinhard **Keiser**, is mentioned. The Italian text is added to some of the arias. SCHATZ 5086

Der **durch den tod Helenen versoehnte Achilles**. A. T. of Keiser's Das zerstoerte Troja.

Die **durch die tugend gestuerzte wueterey**. Tr. T. of Draghi's La tirannide abbattuta dalla virtù.

Die **durch verstellung und grossmuth uber die grausamkeit siegende liebe** oder Julia [vignette], wurde in einem sing-spiel auf dem Hamburgischen Schau-platz vorgestellet im monath februar. 1717.

Hamburg, Friderich Conrad Greflinger, n. d. *Unpaged.* $18\frac{1}{2}$ cm.

Five acts. Historical "Vorbericht," scenario, and note that this is the sixty-seventh opera by Reinhard **Keiser**. The author, resp. translator, Johann Joachim Hoë, is not mentioned. The Italian text is added to some of the arias. Based on Giacomo Francesco Bussani's text, "Antonio e Pompeiano." SCHATZ 5087

Der durchlauchtige secretarius, oder Almira, Koenigin in Castilien, in einem sing-spiel auf dem grossen Hamburgischen Schauplatz auffgefuehret und in die music gesetzt durch Reinhard Keisern . . . im jahr 1706.

[Hamburg], n. publ., Gedruckt in obgemeldten jahr. Unpaged. 18½ᶜᵐ.

Three acts. Scenario and argument. The author, resp. translator, Barthold Feind, is not mentioned. To some of the arias the Italian text has been added. The text is a revision by Feind of Friedrich Christian Feustking's text, which, in turn, was taken from Giulio Pancieri's "L'Almira."   SCHATZ 5122

The **Dutchman,** a musical entertainment, as performed at the Theatre-Royal in the Hay-Market. By Thomas Bridges, Esq. . . .

London, T. Lowndes, 1775. 35 p. 20ᶜᵐ.

Two acts. Cast. The composer not recorded by Clarence or Schatz.
First performed, September 8, 1775 (Genest), August 21, 1775 (Schatz).
                                        LONGE 116

Les **eaux de Merlin.** Pièce d'un acte, précédée d'un prologue. Par M. le S * * *. Representée à la Foire de Saint Laurent 1715.

Le Théâtre de la foire, Paris, 1737, t. ii, 2 p. l., [81]–131 p. 17ᶜᵐ.

By Alain René Le Sage. *En vaudevilles,* selected or composed and arranged by Jean Claude **Gillier,** the compositeur of the theatre, and printed at the end of the volume in the "Table des airs."
First performed July 25, 1715.   ML 48.L2 II

Gl'eccessi della gelosia. Drama per musica di Domenico Lalli da rappresentarsi nel Teatro di S. Angiolo nel carnevale dell' anno 1722 . . .

Venezia, Marino Rossetti, 1722. 56 [1] p. 15ᶜᵐ.

Three acts. Author's dedication, argument, cast, scenario, and name of Tommaso **Albinoni** as composer. The supplementary page contains the aria, "Chiama l'amante fido," as substitute for "Il mio core ingelosito" (III, 13).   SCHATZ 116

— La **Mariane.** Dramma per musica di Domenico Lalli da rappresentarsi nel Teatro di S. Angelo l'autunno dell' anno MDCCXXIV . . .

Venezia, Marino Rossetti, n. d. 59, [1] p. 14½ᶜᵐ.

Three acts. Argument, scenario, cast, and Lalli's dedication, dated November 15, 1724. The supplementary page contains the arias "Al cader di ria tempesta," as substitute for "A un sleale un traditore" (Act II, sc. 1), and "S'ha pietà delle mie pene" for "Un certo non sò che" (Act III, sc. 3). The same page contains this note: "La musica delle arie è del Signor Giovanni **Porta,** à riserva di quelle signate con stelletta, che sono del primo lor compositore." Accordingly, only four arias were retained from "Gl'eccessi della gelosia." These are: "Quanto è grave il mio dolore" (I, 1), "Lieto parto amato bene" (I, 11), "Escimi tutto in lagrime" (II, 12), "Basta dir che la mia pena" (III, 9). The dialogue is largely the same as in Albinoni's opera.
                                        SCHATZ 117

— La **Mariane.** Drama per musica da rappresentarsi in Firenze nel Teatro di via del Cocomero. Nel carnevale dell' anno MDCCXXVI . . .

Firenze, Domenico Ambrogio Verdi, n. d. 60, [1] p. 15ᶜᵐ.

The additional page contains the substitute aria "Maggior pena di tutte le pene," for I, 12.
Three acts. Antefatto, cast, scenario. No author or composer is mentioned, but comparison proved most of the dialogue to be the same as in Domenico Lalli's libretto,

Gl'eccessi della gelosia—Continued.

"Gl'eccessi della gelosia," Venice, 1722, as composed by **Albinoni,** and in 1724 repeated there as "La Mariane," with a few arias retained from Albinoni's opera, but most of them composed by Giov. **Porta.** As to the arias in this 1726 ed., most of them are not contained in the Venetian librettos. The few that are, either belong to those expressly in the 1724 ed., stated to be by **Albinoni,** as, for instance, "Lieto parto amato bene," or by **Porta,** as "Farò (voglio) vendetta sì." ML 48.A5 v. 18

Echo und Narcissus in einem singe-spiel vorgestellet im jahr 1694. *n. i., n. d. [60] p. 18*cm.

Three acts. By Friedrich Christian Bressand. Neither he is mentioned, nor the composer, Georg **Bronner.**

First performed at Hamburg, as indicated; at Brunswick, Hochfürstl. grosses Theater, in 1693. SCHATZ 1334

L'éclipse totale, comédie en un acte et en vers, mêlée d'ariettes; représentée, pour la premiere fois, par les Comédiens italiens ordinaires du Roi, le jeudi 7 mars 1782. Les paroles sont de M. de la Chabeaussiere. La musique de M. Dalayrac.

*Paris, Brunet, 1782. 24 p. 19½*cm.

Cast. SCHATZ 2342

L'école de la jeunesse, ou Le Barnevelt françois; comédie, en trois actes et en vers; meslée d'ariettes: par M. Anseaume. La musique est de M. Duny. Représentée pour la premiere fois par les Comédiens italiens ordinaires du roi, le 24 janvier 1765.

*Paris, Duchesne, 1765. 96 p. 19½*cm.

Cast. On p. 93–96 the same music as below. ML 50.2.E2D9

— **L'école de la jeunesse,** ou Le Barnevelt françois, comédie en trois actes et en vers, meslée d'ariettes, par M. Anseaume. La musique est de M. Duny. Représentée pour la première fois par Les Comédiens italiens ordinaires du Roi, le 24 janvier 1765.

*Paris, la veuve Duchesne, 1770. 79 p. 18*cm.

On p. 74–75, the melody of the *Vaudeville.* "Le grand philosophe Panglose," p. 77–79 of the *"Ariette.* On scait bien qu'il faut qu'un marchand." SCHATZ 2841

— **Die schule der jugend,** ein sing-spiel in drey aufzuegen aus dem franzoesischen uebersetzt, mit musik.

*Frankfurt am Mayn, mit Andreâischen schriften, 1774. 112 p., 10 p. (folded music). 16*cm.

German version by Johann Heinrich Faber. **Duni** is not mentioned. The musical supplement contains: "Wenn des wilden krieges plagen" ["Quand le feu de la guerre"] (p. 1–5), "Stets geliebt und verfolgt" ["Adoré, poursuivi des belles"] (p. 5–10).

First performed at Frankfurt a/M., Theater im Junghofe, 1774. SCHATZ 2842

L'école des amans. Pièce d'un acte. Par Messieurs le S * * * e F * * *. Representée à la Foire de Saint Germain 1716.

*Le Théâtre de la foire, Paris, 1737, t. ii, pl. [317]–351 p. 17*cm.

By Alain René Le Sage and Fuzelier. The airs, selected or composed and arranged by Jean Claude **Gillier,** are printed at the end of the volume in the "Table des airs." ML 48.L2 II

L'ecole des amours grivois. O. T. of Favart's Les amours grivois.

L'école des tuteurs. Opera-comique. Par M. Rochon de la Valette. Représenté le 4. février 1754 sur le Théâtre de l'Opera-comique.

   Paris, Duchesne, 1754. 44, [1], [3] p. 18½ᶜᵐ.

One act. Largely *En vaudevilles.* Cast. On the [3] p. the airs of "Ah lisons de tant d'allarmes," "Mais ce deguisement" and "Tuteurs insensés." Composer, resp. arranger, of the music unknown to me.   ML 50.2.E23

Ecuba. Dramma per musica da rappresen ars nel Regio Teatro di Torino nel carnovale del 1769 alla presenza di S. S. R. M.

   Torino, Stamperia Mairesse, a spese di Onorato Derossi, n. d. viii, 59, [1] p. 16ᶜᵐ.

Three acts. By Jacopo Durandi, who is not mentioned. Cast, argument, scenario, and names of Ignazio **Celoniat** as composer of the opera, of Giuseppe Antonio Le Messier and Paolo Ghebart of the ballet music.   SCHATZ 1771

Edalide e Cambise. Dramma per musica per celebrare il felicissimo giorno natalizio di Sua Maestà . . . Donna Maria I . . . li 17 dec. 1780.

   [Lisboa], Stamperia Reale, n. d. 37 p. 16ᶜᵐ.

One act. Argument, cast, and names of Gaetano Martinelli as author, of João Cordeiro da **Silva** as composer.   SCHATZ 9886

Das edelgestein. Ceraunia von Ulissipone jetzo Lisbona. Tr. of La gemma Ceraunia . . .

Die edelmuethige Octavia. A. T. of Keiser's Die roemische unruhe.

Edgar and Emmeline. In two acts. By Dr. Hawkesworth.

   [97]–129 p. 19ᶜᵐ. (Collection of the most esteemed farces and entertainments, t. iv, Edinburgh, 1792.)

Drury-Lane, Edinburgh (1790) and Glasgow (1782) casts. Music by Michael **Arne** (Squire).
First performed, as indicated, January 31, 1761.   SCHATZ 11753

Edipo, ballet. *See* Zingarelli's La morte di Cesare.

Gesaenge zu der oper: Die **edle rache** in zwei aufzuegen von Franz Xaver Huber. Die musik hierzu ist von herrn Franz Xaver Suessmayer . . .

   n. i., n. d. 48 p. 16½ᶜᵐ.

First performed at Vienna, Kärntnerthor Theater, August 27, 1795.   SCHATZ 10177

Der edle wettstreit. Tr. of Paisiello's Le gare generose.

Egilina. Dramma per musica da rappresentarsi nel Teatro alla Scala il carnevale dell' anno 1793 . . .

   Milano, Gio. Batista Bianchi, n. d. 60 p. 16ᶜᵐ.

Three acts. Impresario's dedication dated Milan, January 26, 1793, argument, cast, scenario, and name of the composer, Giovanni Battista **Borghi**, but not of Angelo Anelli, the librettist. Pages 49–60 contain argument, cast, and detailed description of Filippo Beretti's "Andronico e Ramira, ballo eroico pantomimo" and of his ballet, "Il giudice, e padre." The composers of the music are not mentoined.   SCHATZ 1231

Egeria. Festa teatrale, scritta . . . dall' autore in Vienna, e rappresentata la prima volta con musica dell' Hasse nella Cesarea corte . . . per l'incoronazione della S. R. M. di Giuseppe II . . . l'anno 1764.

323–344 p. 26ᶜᵐ. (Metastasio, Opere, t. viii, Parigi, vedova Herissant, 1781.)   ML 49.A2M44

Egeria. Del Sig. ab. Metastasio P. Ces.

n. i., n. d. Unpaged. 21ᶜᵐ.

On p. [7]: "In Vienna, Nella stamperia di Ghelen." Vignettes by Anton Tischler. One act. Cast and name of Johann Adolph **Hasse** as the composer. First performed at Vienna, Burgtheater, April 24, 1764.   Schatz 4537

L'Egeste. Melodrama da rappresentarsi nel Teatro Giustiniano di San Moisè nel fine del carnovale, dell' anno, MDCCXXVII.

Venezia, Marin Rossetti, n. d. 60 p. 15½ᶜᵐ.

Three acts. By Carlo Paganicesa. Argument. Neither the author is mentioned nor the composer, Antonio **Cortona**. In a notice "Fingesi" it is said: "Le convenienze del teatro, e del tempo anno ricercata alcuna alterazione del drama. S' è studiato d' intrecciar all' eroico dell' azione qualche tratto comico per renderla più vivace, onde possa meglio adattarsi anche agl' occhi de spettatori."   Schatz 2265

L'Egisto. Favola dramatica musicale di Giovanni Faustini.

Venetia, Pietro Miloco, 1643. 93, [1] p. 13½ᶜᵐ.

The additional p. contains list of errata. Prologue and three acts, notice to the reader without name of the composer, Pietro Francesco **Cavalli**. First performed at Venice, Teatro S. Cassano, fall of 1643. According to von Weilen an opera "L'Egisto rè di Cipro," text by Faustini, music by Cavalli, was performed at Vienna, "1642 oder 1643."   Schatz 1719

— **L'Egisto.** Favola dramatica musicale di Giovanni Faustini.

Firenze, Franceschini e Logi, 1646. 84 p. 13ᶜᵐ.

Prologue and three acts. Dedication by Curtio Mannari dated Florence, May 27, 1646, brief notice to the reader. **Cavalli** is not mentioned. The text seems to be the same as in the Venice, 1643, edition.   Schatz 1719a

L'Egisto rè di Cipro. Drama per musica da rappresentarsi nel Teatro di San Casciano. L'anno 1698. Di Giulio Cesare Corradi . . .

Venetia, Nicolini, 1698. 68 p. 14ᶜᵐ.

Three acts. Author's dedication, argument, scenario. The composer, Marc' Antonio **Ziani**, is not mentioned.   Schatz 11184

L'Egiziana. Dramma comico per musica da rappresentarsi nel Teatro Giustiniani di S. Moisè il presente carnovale MDCCLXIII.

Venezia, Francesco Valvasense, n. d. 60 p. 15ᶜᵐ.

Three acts. Author not mentioned and unknown to Schatz. Argument, cast, scenario, and name of Mattia **Vento** as the composer.   Schatz 10610

— **L'Egiziana.** Dramma giocoso per musica da rappresentarsi nel Regio Ducal Teatro di Milano l'autunno dell' anno 1763 . . .

Milano, Giovanni Montano, n. d. 60 p. 14½ᶜᵐ.

Three acts. Impresario's dedication, argument, cast, and name of Mattia **Vento** as composer. The author is unknown to Schatz.   ML 48.A5 v.3

L'Egiziana—Continued.

— La **Zingara**.　Dramma giocoso per musica da rappresentarsi ne' Teatri privilegiati di Vienna l'estate dell' anno MDCCLXIX.

Vienna, Gio. Tom. de Trattnern, n. d.　67 p.　15½^{cm}.

Three acts.　Scenario and note: "La musica è del Signor Mattia **Vento** . . . ma molta parte ancora del Signor Floriano **Gassmann** . . ." The text has been changed in many scenes.　For instance, II, 8 has now the aria "Quando il cuor non si contenta" instead of "Di galanti cicisbei," and act III begins "Favorisca, padrone, e poi mi dica," instead of "I ladri scellerati."　　　　　　　　　　　SCHATZ 10611

— La **Zingara**.　Dramma giocoso per musica da rappresentarsi in Firenze nel Teatro di via del Cocomero, nella primavera dell' anno 1771 . . .

[Firenze], Ant. Giuseppe Pagani, n. d.　front., 56 p.　16½^{cm}.

The portrait is that of "Pietro Leopoldo I., arciduca d'Austria, Gran duca di Toscana," under whose protection the opera was performed.　The engraved title page has an exquisite design.

Three acts.　Cast, scenario, arguments of the incidental ballets, and same note of authorship (**Vento** and **Gassmann**) as in the Vienna (1769) ed.　This means, of course, that the Vienna version was used; but, again, differences in the text are noticeable.　For instance, II, 8 now has the aria, "Noi sole semplicette" instead of, as at Vienna, "Quando il cuor non si contenta."　　　　　　　SCHATZ 10612

Programme du ballet d'Églé, comédie en vers, de M. Vallier . . . représentée devant Leurs Majestés, à Fontainebleau, le 29 october 1765.

[Paris], Christophe Ballard, 1765.　35 p.　20½^{cm}.　(Journal des spectacles, t. ii, Paris, 1766.)

Cast, program, text of the few incidental songs, and names of Antoine **d'Auvergne** as composer of the music, of Laval, père et fils, as "composers" of the ballets.　According to the Journal (t. I, p. 15), this ballet preceded the comedy as a prologue.　After the comedy came another one-act ballet, the text of which, with a prefatory note and names of the same authors, is printed on p. [11]–35 of the present publication as:

　　　　　　　　　　　　　　　　　　　　　ML 48.J7

— Le **triomphe de Flore**, ballet, représenté devant Leurs Majestés, à Fontainebleau, le 29 octobre 1765.

[Paris], Christophe Ballard, 1765.

Églé.

One-act ballet, by Laujon.　Music by **Lagarde**.　The published score has the title as "Aiglé."

First performed at Versailles, January 13, 1748.　Revived on February 25, 1750, and first performed at the Académie royale de musique on February 18, 1751.

Not in L. of C.

— La **fortune au village**, parodie de l'acte d'Églé; par Madame Favart & M.B.　Représentée pour la premiere fois par les Comédiens italiens ordinaires du roi, le 8 octobre 1760 . . .　La musique de M. Gibert.

Paris, Duchesne, 1761.　56 p.　19^{cm}.　(Theatre de M. Favart, Paris, Duchesne, 1763–77, t. v.)

One act.　Without vaudevilles.　Cast.　Paul César **Gilbert's** ariettes printed in the text, which Font attributes to Favart, his wife, and Bertrand.　The parody followed the revival of "Églé," on June 24, 1760.　　　　　ML 49.A2F1

Egle.　*See* Traetta's Le feste d'Imeneo.

Egle e Cloco, o siano I satiri puniti, ballet. *See* Tritto's La fedeltà tra le selve.

Egle e Dafni, ballet. *See* Misliweczek's Il trionfo di Clelia.

L'eglogue de Versailles. *See* Lully's L'idylle sur la paix.

Die **eheverbindung in der maske.** Tr. of G. M. Rutini's Il matrimonio in maschera.

Der **ehrliche raeuber.** Ein schauspiel mit gesang in 2 aufzuegen von C. G. Korb. In musik gesetzt von dem herzogl. Meckl. Strel. kapelldirektor herrn Zeller.

Neubrandenburg, gedruckt in der officin des verfassers, 1785. 84 p. 16cm.

Dedication and author's "Vorbericht," dated Neubrandenburg, June, 1785, in which he says:

"Eine anekdote aus der zeit der grossen theuerung im saechsischen Erzgebirge, im jahre 1772, welche in den oeffentlichen zeitungen damaliger zeit als wahr berichtet wurde, hat mir den stoff zu gegenwaertigem stuecke geliefert. Sie ist meines wissens noch nicht fuers Theater benutzt worden . . . Mein erster dramatischer versuch, "Johanna oder Unschuld und liebe" in drey aufzuegen, den ich ohne namen und druckort unter der jahrzahl 1781 herausgab, ward auf hiesigem herzoglichem Hoftheater dreymal kurz hintereinander vorgestellt, und in einigen gelehrten zeitungen sehr guetig beurtheilt . . ."

The rest is taken up with his defense of the "zu hohe Schwung" of the language of his miners, but "bey operetten aber, glaubt' ich, wuerde diese freyheit zu entschuldigen seyn."

First performed at Neubrandenburg, Herzogl. Schauspielhaus, July 2, 1787.

SCHATZ 11164

Ehrlichkeit und liebe. Ein laendliches schauspiel mit gesang. Von herrn Wagenseil. Die musik dazu ist von . . . herrn Wolf. Hierauf folgt: Ertappt! ertappt! Ein lustspiel in einem aufzug von herrn Wezel.

Kaufbeuren, Neth, 1781. Unpaged. 15½cm.

By Christian Jacob Wagenseil. Music by Ernst Wilhelm **Wolf.** At head of title: "Von der buergerlichen Agenten Gesellschaft A. C. wird den 16 april und ersten may 1781 auf dem gewoehnlichen Theater aufgefuehrt."

Cast and "Poetische vorerimerung" and prose prefatory note.

First performed at Gotha, Hoftheater, July 21, 1779.   SCHATZ 11078

Der **ehrsuechtige Arsaces.** In einer opera auf dem Hamburgischen Schau-platz vorgestellet im jahr MDCCXXII.

n. pl., n. d., Gedruckt bey Caspar Jakhel.

Three acts. Based, according to Schatz, by Johann Mattheson on Antonio Salvi's "Amore e maestà." The Italian text of the arias is added to the German. The "Vorbericht" states that by Statira is meant Queen Elizabeth of England and by Arsaces the Count of Essex. Cast, scenario, and note:

"Die arien hat theils **Orlandini** [Giuseppe Maria], theils **Amadei** [Filippo] gesetzet."   SCHATZ 7354

Eifersucht auf dem lande. Tr. of Sarti's Le gelosie vilane.

Die **eifersucht auf der probe.** Tr. of Anfossi's Il geloso in cimento.

Die **eifersuechtige faunen,** ballet. *See* Piccinni's Das gute maegdchen.

Der eifersuechtige liebhaber. Tr. of Grétry's Les fausses apparences.

Der eifersuechtige mann. Eine haeusliche scene, als zwischenspiel in zwey auftritten, nach einem italiaenischen text, und Piccini's komposition, von Bock.

    n. i., n. d.   p. [78]–110.   16^{cm}.

Detached from his "Komische opern der Italiener," Leipzig, 1782.
Schatz does not give the title of the Italian original, perhaps "Gelosia per gelosia."
First performed at Leipzig, Koch'sches Theater, October 12, 1779. SCHATZ 8119

Der eigensinn der liebe. Tr. of Seydelmann's Il capriccio corretto.

Eigensinn und launen der liebe. Ein komisches singspiel in drey aufzuegen. Aus dem italienischen frei uebersetzt von G. F. W. Grossmann.

    Frankfurt und Leipzig, Herrmannische buchhandlung, 1783.   112 p. 16^{cm}.

Florian **Deller**, the composer, is not mentioned.
First performed at Bonn, Churf. Köln. Hoftheater, April 28, 1782, in this German version, but according to Schatz first performed at Ludwigsburg about 1770 as "Le contese per amore."   SCHATZ 2495

Die eigensinnige. Tr. of Piccinni's La capricciosa.

Die eigensinnige ehefrau. Tr. of Gazzaniga's La moglie capricciosa.

Eine ist wie die andere. Tr. of Mozart's Così fan tutte.

Eine machts wie die andere. Tr. of Mozart's Così fan tutte.

Eine wie die andere oder Die schule der liebhaber. Tr. of Mozart's Così fan tutte o sia La scuola degli amanti.

Das einfaeltige maedgen. A. T. of von Schacht's Der betrogene vormund.

Der eingebildete Sokrates. Tr. of Paisiello's Socrate immaginario.

Die eingebildeten philosophen. Tr. of Paisiello's I filosofi immaginari.

Der einsiedler. Ein schauspiel mit gesang von L.

    Leipzig, Christian Gottlob Hilscher, 1780.   48 p.   15^{cm}.

Neither author nor composer nor performance recorded by Schatz. Not found in "Deutsches-Anonymen Lexikon."   SCHATZ 11452

Der einspruch. Eine operette in einem aufzuge von J. B. Michaelis.

    Leipzig, Dyckische buchhandlung, 1772.   1 p. l., 108 p.   16½^{cm}.

The composer, Christian Gottlob **Neefe**, is not mentioned in the author's "Vorrede," which is dated Halberstadt, May 10, 1772, and appears to be intended for a collection of his librettos. The Vorrede reads in part:
"Mich däuchte immer, wenn wir nun ja operetten haben sollen und muessen; so waeren solche kleine stuecke von einem akte noch das beste mittel, die liebhaberey der menge mit dem geschmacke des ernsten kenners zu vereinigen . . . *Amors Gukkasten* . . . Ich verfertigte diese operette meisten vor laenger als jahr und tag

Der **einspruch**—Continued.

in Osnabrueck, waehrend meines aufenthalts bey dem hannoeverischen theater. Wegen meiner Psyche muss ich um verzeihung bitten. Sie ist nicht die Psyche der fabel; sondern ein laendliches, naives ding . . .

"*Den Einspruch* fieng ich bereits 1770 in Leipzig an: als ich zum Theater kam, suchte ich ihn wieder hervor; und hier in Halberstadt legte ich die letzte hand daran . . .

"Einige freunde wuenschten meinen *Herkules auf dem Oeta* dieser sammlung beygefuegt. Er ward voriges jahr in Hannover fuer den geburtstag des koenigs in England, binnen weniger als acht tagen verfertigt, komponirt und aufgefuehrt . . . Er steht bereits, durchgaengig verbessert, in dem diesjaerigen Leipziger Musenalmanach. In diesem gegenwaertigen Abdrucke sind noch einige kleine veraenderungen dazu gekommen."

First performed at Berlin, Koch'sches Theater in der Behrenstrasse, October 16, 1773. SCHATZ 7071

Der **Eiserne mann.** A. T. of Dittersdorf's Gott Mars.

Elektra, eine musikalische declamation. Von hrn. direktor Cannabich in musik gesetzt.

Mannheim, C. F. Schwan, 1780. 14 p. 19½^{cm}.

One act. By Wolfgang Heribert, freiherr von Dalberg.
First performed at Mannheim, Nationaltheater, September 4, 1781. SCHATZ 1574

Les **elemens,** troisième ballet dansé par le roy dans son Palais des Tuilleries, l'an 1721. Representé par l'Academie royale de musique, l'an 1725. Musique de Messieurs Lalande & Destouches. Paroles de M. Roy. CIV. opera.

n. i., n. d. pl., 393–452 p. 14^{cm}. (Recueil général des opéra, t. xiii, Paris, 1734.)

Detached copy. Four entrées and prologue. Dedicatory poem and "avertissement."

The four entrées are called "L'air," "L'eau," "Le feu," and "La terre."
First performed at the Académie royale de musique, May 29, 1725, and at court on December 22, 1721. Revised 1725, 1754, etc. SCHATZ 5379
Second copy. ML 48.R4

— Les **élémens,** ballet, par Roy, dansé par Louis XV, dans son palais des Tuileries, l'an 1721; et représenté à l'Académie royale de musique en 1725.

n. i., n. d. [243]–285 p. 18^{cm}.

Detached copy. The composers, **Lalande** and **Destouches,** are not mentioned. ML 52.2.E4

— **Momus exilé.** Critique du Ballet des elémens. Par M. Fusillier. Représentée pour la premiere fois, par les Comédiens italiens ordinaires du roi, le 25 juin 1725.

Les parodies du Nouveau théâtre italien, Nouv. éd., Paris, Briasson, 1738, t. iii, [53]–98 p. 16½^{cm}.

One act. By Fuzelier. Airs and vaudeville printed at the end of the volume in the "Table des airs" (84 p.). ML 48.P3

— Le **cahos,** ambigu comique. Représenté pour la premiere fois par les Comédiens italiens ordinaires du roi, le 27 juillet 1725.

Les parodies du Nouveau théâtre italien, Nouv. éd., Paris, 1738, t. iii, [99]–162 p. 16½^{cm}.

Prologue and four acts, representing the four elements, L'air, L'eau, etc. Parody by Le Grand (*see* t. I) of the "Ballet des élémens." The airs and vaudeville used are printed at the end of the volume in the "Table des airs" (84 p.). ML 48.P3

Les **elemens**—Continued.

— **Il etoit tems,** parodie de l'acte d'Ixion dans le ballet des Elemens. Représentée pour la premiere fois sur le Théatre de la Foire St. Laurens, le 28 juin 1754.　Par Mr. Vadé.

　La Haye, Pierre Gosse, 1760.　30 p.　16ᶜᵐ.　(Vadé, Oeuvres, t. ii, La Haye, 1760.)

One act, *en vaudevilles.* On p. 25–30 the *airs .notés* "Maris qui croyez," "Au milieu du cours trainant," "Eh Madame qu'attendez-vous," "Un amant doit-il se taire." "Ixion" is the same as the entrée "L'air."　　　　ML 49.A2V2

Elena. Drama per musica nel Teatro à S. Cassano, per l'anno 1659 . . .

　Venetia, Andrea Giuliani, 1659.　9 p. l. (incl. front.), 63, [1] p 13½ᶜᵐ.

Three acts. By conte Niccolò Minato. Prologue, author's dedication dated Venice December 26, 1659, argument, scenario, and notice to the reader, in which Minato informs us that "il soggetto di questo drama uscì dal felicissimo ingegno del già Sign. Giovanni Faustini di famosa memoria."　　　　Sᴄʜᴀᴛᴢ 1746

Elena e Paride. Dramma per musica da rappresentarsi nel Regio Teatro di via della Pergola l'autunno del MDCCXCV . . .

　Firenze, Stamperia Albizziniana, 1795.　31 p.　16½ᶜᵐ.

Three acts. Cast, note on p. 3, "Poesia tutta nuova con musica di varj autori," and on p. 2 this Avviso:

"Per render meno vistosa la seduzione di Elena, si è finto, sull' esempio ancora di altri drammatici, che Elena sia promessa sposa, ma non già consorte, di Menelao.

"La ristrettezza del tempo, e la necessità di adattare le arie ed i pezzi concertati alla musica, già fatta, può servire di qualche scusa ai molti difetti del dramma e della poesia."

With the opera were performed (composer of the music not mentioned) Giuseppe Trafieri's ballet, "La vendetta di Nino."

First performed, as indicated, October, 1795.　　　　ML 48.A5　v.14

Elena rapita da Paride.　*See also* Freschi's Helena rapita da Paride.

L'Elenia. Dramma per musica da recitarsi nel Teatro di S. Angelo l'anno 1730 . . .

　Venezia, Valvasense, 1730.　47 p.　15ᶜᵐ.

Three acts. By Luisa Bergalli, who is not mentioned. Dedication, argument, scenario, cast and name of Tommaso **Albinoni** as composer.　　　　Sᴄʜᴀᴛᴢ 105

L'élève de l'amour.　A. T. of Dalayrac's Sargines.

Elfrida, a dramatic poem. Written on the model of the ancient Greek tragedy. By Mr. Mason. The second edition.

　London, J. and P. Knapton, 1752.　1 p. l., xix, [1], 80 p.　19ᶜᵐ.

The xix p. contain five "Letters concerning the following drama, dated 'Pemb. Hall, 1751.'" Not this but a dramatized version by Colman was used with Thomas Aug. **Arne**'s music at Covent Garden, November 21, 1772.　　　　Lᴏɴɢᴇ 44

— **Elfrida,** a dramatic poem. Written on the model of the ancient Greek tragedy. By William Mason . . . Adapted for theatrical representation, as performed at the Theatre-Royal, Covent-Garden, in the year 1773 . . .

　London, George Cawthorn, 1796.　front., 1 p. l., 68 p.　15ᶜᵐ.　(J. Bell, British Theatre, London, 1791–1797, v. 35.)

The front represents Mrs. Hartley as Elfrida and is dated November 12, 1796. The p. l. is an added engraved title page of same date.

Elfrida—Continued.

Five acts. Argument, cast and prefatory note. The date 1773 in the title would indicate that this is George Colman's dramatization (first performed November 21, 1772) of the dramatic poem "Elfrida" (1752) and not William Mason's own, performed February 22, 1779. Thomas Augustine **Arne**, the composer of the incidental music, is not mentioned. PR 1441.B4

L'Elfrida. Dramma tragico per musica da rappresentarsi in Firenze nel R. Teatro dei Risoluti posto in via S. Maria nell' estate dell' anno 1795 . . .

Firenze, Anton Giuseppe Pagani e comp., 1795. 40 p. 16½ cm.

Three acts. Argument, cast and name of Giovanni **Paisiello** as composer. The author, Ranieri de' Calsabigi, is not mentioned.
First performed at Naples, Teatro di S. Carlo, Nov. 4, 1792. ML 48.A5 v. 14

— **Elfrida.** Tragedia per musica da rappresentarsi nel nobilissimo Teatro La Fenice per la fiera dell' Ascensione dell' anno 1796.

Venezia, Stamperia Valvasense, n. d. 54, [1] p. 18½ cm.

Two acts. By Ranieri de' Calsabigi, who is not mentioned. Argument, cast, scenario and name of **Paisiello** as the composer. On p. [29]–37 cast and description of Michiele Fabiani's "Il trionfo di Alessandro ossia La prigionia di Dario, ballo eroico in quattro atti . . . La musica tutta nuova del Sign. Valentino Bertoja."
First performed at Naples, Teatro di S. Carlo, November 4, 1792. Schatz 7615

— **L'Elfrida.** Dramma serio per musica da rappresentarsi in Parma nel R. D. Teatro di Corte l'autunno dell' anno MDCCXCVIII . . .

Parma, Stamperia Carmignani, n. d. 40 p. 17½ cm.

Two acts. By Ranieri de' Calsabigi who is not mentioned and whose text has been considerably altered. The chief alteration consists in a joyful instead of a tragic end of the drama. Schatz says that **Paisiello** set the text totally anew which does not appear quite probable. At any rate, however, he is mentioned as the composer. Argument, cast and scenario. Schatz 7703

Elfrida, ballet. *See* Zingarelli's Artaserse.

Eliogabalo. Drama per musica nel famoso Teatro Grimano l'anno MDCLXVIII di Aurelio Aureli. Opera decimaquarta. Seconda edittione . . .

Venetia, Francesco Nicolini, 1668. 76 p. 14 cm.

Three acts. Author's dedication, dated Venice, January 10, 1667, notice to the reader mentioning Giovanni Antonio **Boretti** as the composer, argument and scenario. Schatz 1219

L'Elisa. Commedia per musica di Antonio Palomba Napoletano da rappresentarsi nel Teatro de' Fiorentini nell' autunno di quest' anno 1744 . . .

Napoli, Domenico Langiano e Domenico Vivenzio, n. d. 80 p. 16½ cm.

Three acts. Impresario's dedication, cast and name of the composer, Gioacchino **Cocchi.** Schatz 2038

Elisa, ou Le voyage au Mont-Bernard, opera en deux actes. Paroles du citoyen R. S. C. Musique du citoyen Chérubini.

Paris, Huet, n. d. 44 p. 19 cm.

By baron, J. A., Révéroni Saint-Cyr.
First performed at the Théâtre Feydeau, December 13, 1794. ML 50.2.E3C3

Elisa. Dramma per musica da rappresentarsi nel Piccolo Teatro Elettorale. Composto da Caterino Mazzolà . . .

> *Dresda, Stamperia elettorale, 1781. 133 p. 15½ᶜᵐ.*

Two acts. Johann Gottlieb **Naumann** is mentioned as the composer. German title-page "Elise" and text face Italian.
First performed as indicated, April 21, 1781.   Schatz 7047

Elisa. Comedia da rappresentarsi per musica nel Teatro di Sant' Angelo l'autuno dell' anno 1711 . . .

> *Venetia, Marino Rossetti, 1711. 58 p. 15½ᶜᵐ.*

Three acts. Dedication by Domenico Lalli as the author, who in a somewhat lengthy notice to the reader comments on his conception of a musical comedy, argument and scenario. The composer, Giovanni Maria **Ruggeri**, is not mentioned.
                                                         Schatz 9129

Elisa. Drama pastorale per musica da recitarsi nell' antico Teatro della Pace nel carnevale dell' anno 1738 . . .

> *Roma, Giovanni Zempel, n. d. 64 p. 16ᶜᵐ.*

Three acts. Author not mentioned and unknown to me (*not* Palomba's text). Dedication by the impresario Giuseppe Polvini Faliconti ("Lo scarso tempo, nel quale è stato questo drama scelto a 'comici adattato, e di musica rivestito . . ."), argument, cast, scenario and name of "Gasparo **Spanò,** maestro di capella Napolitano" as composer. On p. 25–27, 44–46 the text of two intermezzi with characters **Corisca e Satiro** (not recorded by Schatz or Allacci). Music composed perhaps by **Spanò.**   ML 50.2.E3S7

Elisa regina di Tiro. Dramma per musica da rappresentarsi nel Teatro di S. Angelo nel carnovale dell' anno 1736 . . .

> *Venezia, Domenico Tabacco, 1736. 59 p. 14½ᶜᵐ.*

Three acts. Altered version of "L'Astarto" by Apostolo Zeno and Pietro Pariati who are not mentioned. Impresario's dedication, argument, cast, scenario and name of **Galuppi** as composer.
First performed as indicated, January 27, 1736 (Pavan).   Schatz 3485

Elisabetta e Blech, ballet. *See* Curzio's Le nozze a dispetto.

Élisca ou L'amour maternel, drame lyrique en trois actes en prose, mêlé d'ariettes. Paroles d'Ed. Favières. Musique de Grétry. Représenté pour la première fois, sur le Theâtré de l'Opéra-comique national le 12, nivôse de l'an 7 de la République.

> *Paris, Au bureau général du mercure de France, chez Cailleau, an VII. [1798–99]. 88 p. 21ᶜᵐ.*

On p. [1], Cailleau's (signed) warning against reprints of the piece; on p. [2], a dedicatory poem by Favières.
First performed January 1, 1799, as indicated.   ML 50.2.E33G7

Elise. Tr. of Naumann's Elisa.

Elisinde. Eine original-operette in drei aufzuegen von C. A. Vulpius.

> *[177]–272 p. 15ᶜᵐ. (Vulpius, Operetten, Bd. I, Baireuth & Leipzig, 1790.)*

Detached copy. Composed by Christian Ludwig **Dieter,** who is not mentioned.
First performed at Stuttgart, Kleines Theater a. d. Planie, 1794.   Schatz 2577

Eliza; a new musical entertainment; as performed at the New Theatre in the Hay-Market. Written by Mr. Rolt. The music composed by Mr. Arne.

[London], To be had at the theatre, 1754. 2 p. l., 35 p. 20^{cm}.

Three acts. Cast. On p. 35, note stating that "some parts" of the piece had been altered on account of the music.

First performed at Dublin, Theatre Royal, 1743 (Grove); but, according to Cummings, Dublin, November 29, 1756; at London, Drury Lane, January 20, 1757 (Genest). Longe 116

— **Eliza;** an English opera, as perform'd at the Theatre Royal in Drury-Lane. The music composed by Mr. Arne.

[London], R. Francklin, 1757. 2 p. l., 28 p. 20^{cm}.

Three acts. Cast. Longe 183

Elmine, ein schauspiel mit gesang in drey aufzügen von dem freyherrn von Drais in Carlsruh. [vignette]

Nürnberg, George Peter Monath, 1781. 78 p. (incl. engr. front.) 15^{cm}.

The composer, Johann **André**, is not mentioned.
First performed at Berlin, Döbbelinssches Theater, February 14, 1782.
Schatz 185

L'Elmira generosa. Commeddea pe musica de nota' Pietro Trinchera da rappresentarese a lo Teatro Nuovo a Mmonte Cravario nchisto carnevale dell' anno 1753.

Napoli, Stamperia de' Muzj, 1753. 75 p. 15^{cm}.

Three acts. Cast and prefatory note, naming as composers "Don Nicola loscroscino [**Logroscino**] tutte l'arie, finale, e duetto segnate co lo signo § e lo riesto da lo Sio Don Manuele **Barbella** celebre vertoluso de violino." To Logroscino's music, therefore, belonged, for instance, "M'ha sturbata Ciommetella" (I, 5), "Frabuttiello fortantiello" (I, 7), "Al mon do quì conto" (I, 9), and other arias. Schatz 5675

Elmiro, rè di Corinto. Melodrama da rappresentarsi in musica nel . . . Teatro Grimani di S. Gio. Grisostomo l'anno MDCLXXXVII . . .

Venetia, Antonio Bosio, 1686. 60 p. 14^{cm}.

Three acts. Publisher's dedication, dated Venice, December 26, 1686, argument and scenario. Neither Vincenzo Grimani, the author, nor Carlo **Pallavicino**, the composer, is mentioned. Schatz 7722

Elpinice. L. T. of G. Giordani's L'Acomate.

Elkernes skole. A. T. of Mozart's Veddemaalet.

Elskoos magt. Tr. of Naumann's Tutto per amore.

[Elvira. Dramma per musica in tre atti.]

68 p. 15½^{cm}.

Lacks title page and p. 7–18, which apparently included the description of a ballet. Three acts. By Raniero de' Calsabigi, who is not mentioned. Impresario's dedication, dated Naples, January 12. 1794, argument, cast, and name of **Paisiello** as the composer. Schatz 7695

Elysium, ein vorspiel mit arien, an dem geburtsfeste Ihro Maiestät der königinn aufgeführt von der Gesellschaft Koeniglicher schauspieler zu Hannover den 18ten Januar 1770.

n. i., n. d. 44 p. 14½^{cm}.

Neither Johann Georg Jacoby, the author, nor Anton **Schweitzer**, the composer, is mentioned.
First performed at Hanover, Schlosstheater, January 18, 1770. Schatz 9772

L'embarras des richesses, comédie-lyrique en trois actes, représentée pour la première fois, par l'Académie-royale de musique, le mardi 26 novembre 1782.

> *Paris, P. de Lormel, 1782.   95 p.   23ᶜᵐ.*

Cast. **Grétry** is mentioned as the composer, but not the author, Jean Baptiste Lourdet de Santerre.   SCHATZ 4148

L'Emilio.   *See* Title catalogue.

Emira.   Opera bernesca da rappresentarsi nel Teatro di S. Moisè il carnovale dell' anno MDCCXLV.

> *Venezia, Domenico Lovisa, n. d.   44 p.   15ᶜᵐ.*

Three acts.   Notice to the reader, cast, and note: "La musica è d'autori diversi." Author not mentioned, and unknown to Schatz.   SCHATZ 11332

Emira.   Dramma per musica da rappresentarsi nel Teatro Vendramin di S. Salvatore nella prossima fiera dell' Ascensione l'anno 1756.

> *Venezia, Modesto Fenzo, 1756.   36 p.   14ᶜᵐ.*

Three acts.   Dedication, cast, scenario, and name of the composer Gioacchino **Cocchi.**   The author is unknown to Schatz.
First performed at Milan, Regio Ducal Teatro, January, 1756.   SCHATZ 2032

Emira e Zopiro.   Dramma tragico per musica da rappresentarsi nel Regio Teatro di via della Pergola l'autunno del MDCCXCV . . .

> *Firenze, Stamperia Albizziniana, 1795.   32, [2] p.   17ᶜᵐ.*

The [2] p. contain "Variazioni occorse per comodo della musica."   Three acts. Argument, cast, and name of Giuseppe Maria **Curcio** as composer ("La musica è tutta nuova").   The author is unknown to Schatz.   With the opera was performed Giuseppe Trafieri's "La vendetta di Nino (argument on p. 4), ballo eroico tragico pantomimo" and his "L'avaro, ballo comico pantomimo."   The composers of the music are not mentioned.
First performed, as indicated, September 8, 1795.   SCHATZ 2308
Second copy.   ML 48.A5   v.14

Emirena e Sigismondo, ballet.   *See* Tritto's Le avventure galanti.

Emma und Edgar, ein duodrama.   Von Ignaz Reichert . . . Die musik ist von herrn Joseph Lacher . . .

> *Menmmingen* [!] *Andreas Seyler, 1788.   15 p.   16½ᶜᵐ.*

Schatz records no performance.   SCHATZ 5362

Emma und Eginhard.   A. T. of Telemann's Die last-tragende liebe.

L'empire de l'amour, ballet heroique, représenté par l'Académie royale de musique, l'an 1733.   Paroles de M. de Montcrif.   Musique de M. Le ch. de Br.   CXVIII. opera.

> *n. i., n. d.   front., p. 265–310.   14ᶜᵐ.   (Recueil général des opéra, Paris, 1739, t. xv.)*

Detached copy.   Prologue and three entrées called "Les mortels," "Les Dieux acteurs," "Les genies du feu."   Music by the Marquis de **Brassac.**
First performed at Paris, Académie royale de musique, April 14, 1733.   SCHATZ 1308
Second copy.   ML 48.R4

L'émulation parmy les divinitez.   Tr. of Heinichen's La gara degli dei.

The **enchanted castle.** A. T. of the mock-tempest.

The **enchanted wood,** a legendary drama, in three acts, as performed at the Theatre Royal, Hay-Market.

London, J. Debrett, 1792. 2 p. l., 56, [4] p. 20½^{cm}.

The [4] p. contain last page of the text and publisher's book lists. Cast and prefatory note that this is an accommodation to the prevailing taste by the introduction of "the lighter parts" for theatrical representation of a "legendary poem in dialogue" written at the age of fifteen by the author. Neither he, Mr. Frances, nor the composer of the dozen songs is mentioned.

First performed, as indicated, July 25, 1792.   LONGE 220

The **enchanter;** or, Love and magic. A musical drama. As it is performed at the Theatre-Royal in Drury-Lane. The music composed by Mr. Smith.

London, J. and R. Tonson, 1760. 18 p. 19^{cm}.

Two acts. Cast and advertisement:
"As the recitative commonly appears the most tedious part of a musical entertainment, the writer of the following little piece has avoided it as much as possible; and has endeavour'd to carry on what fable there is, chiefly by the songs."
By David Garrick, who is not mentioned.
First performed December 13, 1760.   LONGE 306

L'**enchanteur Mirliton.** Prologue representé à la Foire de S. Laurent 1725.

Le Théâtre de la foire, Paris, 1728, t. vi, pl., 18 p. 17^{cm}.

One act. The plays in t. vi. were written by Le Sage, Fuzelier, and d'Orneval, according to a note on 3d p. l. Largely *en vaudevilles*. The airs, selected or composed and arranged by Jean Claude **Gillier,** the "compositeur" of the theatre, are printed at the end of the volume in the "Table des airs."
First performed July 21, 1725, followed by "Le temple du Mémoire" and "Les enragez."   ML 48.L2VI

Das **ende der babylonischen monarchie,** oder Belsazer, in einem singe-spiele auf dem Hamburgischen Schau-platze aufgefuehret 1723. Erster theil.

Hamburg, Caspar Jakhel, n. d. Unpaged. 17½^{cm}.

Three acts. Neither the author, Joachim Beckau, nor Georg Philipp **Telemann,** the composer, is mentioned. The reader is informed in a prefatory note:
"Da der poetische verfasser der opera, Belsazer, so viel materie gefunden, dieselbe weitlaeuftiger auszufuehren, als hat man fuer gut gehalten solche in zweyen besonderen theilen vorzustellen, wovon gegenwaertiger den ersten ausmachet und der zweyte diesen in kurzem begleitenwird. Die 5te scene im ersten act ist aus gewissen absichten hinein geruecket, aber auch bezeichnet, dass sie nicht hauptsaechlich zum wercke gehoere und also bey fuerfallendem umstande weggelassen werden koenne."
This scene is put in quotation marks and to the German text of the aria "Ja, meine Schoene und geliebte" is added the Italian "Si mia bella, si mia cara."
                    SCHATZ 10258

— Das **ende der babylonischen monarchie,** oder Belsazer, in einem singe-vorspiele auf dem Hamburgischen Schau-platze aufgefuehret 1723. Zweyter theil.

Hamburg, Caspar Jakhel, n. d. Unpaged. 18^{cm}.

Three acts.   SCHATZ 10259

Endimion, musicalische pastoral: welche auf dem Theatro zu Breslau in der fassnacht anno 1727 vorgestellet . . .

n. i., n. d.   Unpaged. $17\frac{1}{2}^{cm}$.

"Endimione." Three acts. Dedicatory poem by Ludwig Wussin, dated Breslau, January 7, 1727, and name of composer, Antonio **Bioni,** but not of the librettist, Francesco Mazzari. German text faces Italian.   SCHATZ 1043

Endimion, the man in the moon, masque. *See* Imposture defeated.

L'Endimione. Serenata.

[277–317] p. 19^{cm}. (Pietro Metastasio, Opere drammatiche, Venezia, Giuseppe Bettinelli, 1733–37, v. 3.)

Two parts. No composer mentioned.   ML 49.A2M4

— L'Endimione.

Metastasio, Poesie, Parigi, vedova Quillau, 1755, t. ix, [49]–99 p. 16^{cm}.

Two parts.   ML 49.A2M42

—. L'Endimione.

pl., [111]–158 p. 26^{cm}. (Metastasio, Opere, t. x, Parigi, vedova Herissant, 1782.)

Written for the marriage of D. Antonio Pignatelli, principe di Belmonte and D. Anna Francesco Pinelli di Sangro, Naples, 1720. Composer not known to Schatz.
                          ML 49.A2M44

Endimione. Serenata a quattro voci, musica del Signor Andrea Bernasconi, dilettante. Da rappresentarsi nel famosissimo Teatro Grimani di San Gio. Crisostomo l'ultima sera di carnovale dell' anno MDCCXLII.

Venezia, n. publ., n. d.   30 p. 17^{cm}.

Two parts. By Metastasio. Cast.
First performed at Venice, as indicated, February 6, 1742.   SCHATZ 869

L'Endimione tragicomedia da rappresentarsi in musica nel Teatro di S. Angelo l'autunno dell' anno 1709 . . .

Venetia, Gio. Battista Zuccato, 1709.   57 p. 15^{cm}.

Three acts. Author's dedication, with his initials, preface, argument, and scenario. The composer, Giuseppe **Boniventi,** is not mentioned. The author was Francesco Mazzari.   SCHATZ 1190

L'Endimione ovvero Il trionfo d'amore. Pastorale per musica ornata di balli, trasformationi, e machine: da rappresentarsi . . . nel Ducal Teatro di Stutgart la primavera dell' anno 1759. Con la musica tutta nuova, espressamente composta dal Signor Nicolò Jommelli . . .

Stutgart, Cristofero Frederico Cotta, n. d.   71 p. $18\frac{1}{2}^{cm}$.

Two acts. By Metastasio (not mentioned), with alterations. German title-page, "Endymion oder Der triumph des Amors," and text face Italian.
First performed without the alternative title at Genua, Teatro del Falcone, spring of 1756.   SCHATZ 4856

L'Endimione—Continued.

— L'Endimione. Serenata per musica da cantarsi nella Real Villa di Queluz per celebrare l'augusto nome di Sua Maestà Fedelissima D. Pietro III. . . . li 29 giugno 1780.

[Lisbona], Stamperia Reale, n. d. 32 p. 14ᶜⁿ.

Two acts. Cast and names of Metastasio as author, of Niccolò **Jommelli** as composer. Text seems to be practically the same as that of 1759. SCHATZ 4895

Endlich fand er sie. A. T. of Dieter's Der irrwisch.

Endlich fand er sie. A. T. of von Kospoth's Der irrwisch.

Endlich fand er sie. A. T. of Preu's Der irrwisch.

Endlich fand er sie. A. T. of Umlauf's Das irrlicht, also of the L. T. of this, Der irrwisch.

L'Endriague, opéra-comique, en trois actes. Mêlé de danses, de divertissemens, & de grands airs de musique du célèbre Rameau. Représenté par la troupe de Dolet, à la Foire Saint-Germain, en 1723.

Alexis Piron, Oeuvres complettes, Liege, 1776, t. 3, [99]–148 p. 17½ᶜᵐ.

Composer not mentioned by Parfaict, who dates the first performance February 3, 1723. PQ 2019.P6

Endymion, pastorale heroïque; representée par l'Academie royale de musique, l'an 1731. Paroles de M. de Fontenelle. Musique de M. Collin de Blamont. CXIV. opera.

n. i., n. d. front., 50 p. 14ᶜᵐ. (Recueil général des opéra, Paris, 1739, t. xv.)

Detached copy. Five acts. The "avertissement" (p. 2) informs the reader that considerable differences were necessitated in the interest of the music between the piece as here printed and as it appears in de Fontenelle's works.

First performed at Paris, as indicated in the score, on June 15, 1731, but according to Schatz, May 17, 1731. SCHATZ 1066

Second copy. ML 48.R4

Endymion oder Der triumph des Amors. **Tr.** of Jommelli's L'Endimione ovvero Il trionfo d'amore.

Enea e Lavinia, ballet. *See* Caruso's L'Artaserse.

Enea e Lavinia, ballet. *See* P. Guglielmi's La morte di Cleopatra.

Enea e Lavinia. Dramma per musica da rappresentarsi nel Real Teatro di S. Carlo nel di 4 novembre 1785 per festeggiarsi i gloriosi nomi . . . di Ferdinando IV . . .

Napoli, Vincenzo Flauto, 1785. 58 p. 15ᶜᵐ.

Three acts. By Gaetano Sertor or Vincenzo de Stefano (not mentioned). Dedication, cast, scenario, and name of Pietro **Guglielmi** as the composer. On p. 9–22 argument, cast, and description of Domenico Lefèvre's "Alessandro nell' Indie, ballo eroico in tre atti," music principally by Mathias Stabingher. On p. 23 argument of Lefèvre's comic ballet "Le figlie astute." SCHATZ 4285

— Enea e Lavinia. Dramma per musica da rappresentarsi nel Teatro da S. Agostino il carnovale dell' anno 1796 . . .

Genova, Stamperia Gesiniana, n. d. 43 p. 14ᶜᵐ.

Two acts. Argument, cast, scenario, and name of Pietro **Guglielmi** as composer. The author, Gaetano Sertor (or Vincenzo de Stefano) is not mentioned. With the opera were performed, music by Giovanni Scannavino, Luigi Dupen's ballets "La distruzione d'Aquileja, fatta da Attila re degli Unni" and "La Nina pazza per amorea." SCHATZ 11711

Enea e Lavinia, a new serious opera; as performed at the King's Theatre, in the Hay-market. The music entirely new by Signor Antonio Sacchini.

London, G. Bigg, 1779. 1 p. l., 57 p. 19ᶜᵐ.

Three acts. Author not mentioned and unknown to Schatz (G. G. Bottarelli?). Argument and cast. English translation faces the Italian. The ballets "Hippomenes and Atalanta" and "The forge of Vulcan" were performed with the opera.

SCHATZ 9218

Enea e Lavinia. Dramma per musica da rappresentarsi in Firenze nel Teatro di via della Pergola, nel carnevale dell' anno 1768 . . .

n. i., n. d. Unpaged. 21ᶜᵐ.

Title within engraved ornamental border, text in ornamental borders, and vignettes at the head of each of the three acts. Impresario's dedication, argument, cast, scenario, and name of Tommaso **Traietta** as the composer. The dedication informs the reader that the libretto is an Italian translation by conte Jacopo Antonio San-Vitale of Bernard Le Bouvier de Fontenelle's drama. The impresario, Giuseppe Compstoff, has also this to say:

"Nuda ella viene, e priva di quegli aiuti teatrali, che alla illuminata mente di V. A. R. ed agli occhi d'un pubblico giustamente critico potrebbero renderla e luminosa, e bizzarra. Un solo uomo privato giugner non può a quel segno, a cui tender possono le mire di personaggi illustri, che si fan gloria di istradare i dipendenti loro per la via d'un onesto lusinghiero piacere alle vere massime d'una più soda, e perfetta morale. L'*Ifigenia in Tauride*, e l'*Olimpiade* sul nostro teatro tra innumerabili evviva poco fa rappresentate, rendono abbastanza testimonianza del vero. Vide il Fiorentino teatro sotto gli augusti auspici felicissimi della R. A. V. ciò, che a lui sembrava quasi impossibile; lo vide, e grandemente lo applaudi . . ."

First performed at Parma, Teatro Ducale, April 1761. SCHATZ 10399

Enea e Turno, ballet. *See* Bianchi's Briseide.

Enea in Cartagine, dramma per musica da rappresentarsi nel Regio Teatro di Torino nel carnovale del 1770 alla presenza di S. S. R. M.

Torino, Onorato Derossi, n. d. xii, 56 p. 16ᶜᵐ.

Three acts. By Giuseppe Maria d'Orengo. Argument, cast, scenario, and names of the composer, Giuseppe **Colla,** and of the author. The ballets were designed by Augusto Huss, their music composed by Giuseppe Antonio Le Messier.

First performed, as indicated, December 26, 1769. SCHATZ 2109

Enea in Cartagine. Dramma per musica da rappresentarsi nel Teatro della Città d'Alessandria in occasione della solita fiera d'ottobre 1784 . . .

Alessandria, Ignazio Vimercati, n. d. 47, xvi p. 16ᶜᵐ.

Two acts. By G. M. d'Orengo, who is not mentioned. Argument, cast, scenario, and name of Carlo Monsa (**Monza**) as the composer. With the opera were performed Paolino Franchi's ballets, "Il finto giardiniere" and "Padmani e Mirda," the latter (in 5 acts) described with argument, cast, and scenario on the xvi p. at end of the libretto. The composers of the music are not mentioned. SCHATZ 6618

Enea in Italia. Drama per musica presentato li 26. luglio 1678 all' Altezza Serenissima Elettorale di Ferdinando Maria, duca dell' una, e l'altra Baviera . . . da Ventura Terzago . . . posto in musica da D. Giuseppe Antonio Bernabei . . . recitato a Gennaro 1679.

Monaco, Giovanni Jecklino, n. d. 7 p. l., 118 p. 14½ᶜᵐ.

Author's dedication, argument, and scenario. SCHATZ 825

Enea in Italia. Drama musicale rappresentato in Pisa nel palazzo del granduca di Toscana per festeggiare il giorno natalizio della serenissima granduchessa Vittoria.

G. A. Moniglia, Poesie drammatiche, parte prima, Firenze, Vincenzio Vangelisti, 1689, p. [595]–628. 24^{cm}.

Three acts. Argument with remarks:
"Questo piccolo drama fu composto dall' autore in Pisa nel tempo, che vi dimorava la corte serenissima; ove fu ancora rappresentato colla più vaga e ricca pompa . . . Fu l'intento primiero il dare con questo componimento una leggiadra, e non mendicata Introduzione a sontuosissimi balletti tra dame, e cavalieri della medesima corte. La pose in musica il famoso Jacopo **Melani**, e lo cantarono i più celebri professori di Toscana."
First performed at Pisa as indicated in 1670.   ML 49.A2M7

Enea in Italia. Drama per musica nel famoso Teatro Grimani. Del Bussani . . .
Venetia, Nicolini, 1675. 6 p. l. (incl. front.), 69 p. 14^{cm}.

Three acts. Author's dedication, argument, and scenario. The composer, Carlo **Pallavicino**, is not mentioned.   SCHATZ 7723
Second copy without the front. and list of characters. ML 48.A5 v.10

Enea ne gli Elisi. Poemetto drammatico nel felicissimo giorno natalizio della Sac. Ces. Real Maestà di Leopoldo I. augustissimo imperador de' Romani.
Pietro Antonio Bernardoni, Poemi drammatici, parte terza, Vienna, van Ghelen, 1707, p. 65–78. 16½^{cm}.

Argument. The composer is not mentioned. Von Weilen lists a work of the same title, music by **Badia** (overture by **Fux**) under July 26, 1702 (instead of June 9, the correct date of the birthday of Joseph I) as from Bernardoni's Poemi drammatici, vol. I.   ML 49.A2B4

L'Enea negli Elisi ovvero Il tempio dell' eternità.
[393]–427 p. 19^{cm}. (Pietro Metastasio, Opere drammatiche, Venezia, Giuseppe Bettinelli, 1733–37, v. 2.)

One act. Argument. No composer mentioned, but composed by **Fux** and first performed under this title at Vienna, August 28, 1731. In subsequent editions of Metastasio's works published under the A. T., which *see*.   ML 49.A2M4

Enea nel Lazio, ballet. *See* Giordani's Tito Manlio.

Enea nel Lazio. Dramma per musica da rappresentarsi nel Real Teatro di Salvaterra nel carnevale dell' anno 1767.
Lisbona, Michele Manescal da Costa, n. d. 57 p. 16^{cm}.

Three acts. Argument, scenario, cast, and name of Niccolò **Jommelli** as the composer. The author, Mattia Verazi, is not mentioned.
First performed at Stuttgart, Schauplatz im Lusthause, Aug. 30, 1755.
                      SCHATZ 4893

Enea nel Lazio.
[335]–362 p. 17^{cm}. (Rolli, Componimenti poetici, Nuova edizione, Verona, G. Tumermani, 1744.

Three acts. Argument. The composer, Nicolò **Porpora**, is not mentioned.
First performed at London, Lincoln's Inn Fields, June 1734.   ML 49.A2R7

Enea nel Lazio. Dramma eroitragico composto con cori, e balli analoghi da Antonio de' Filistri . . . Da rappresentarsi con musica del Signor Vincenzo Righini . . . nel gran Teatro Reale di Berlino il carnovale dell' anno 1793.

>   *Berlino, Haude & Spener, n. d.   127 p.   15½^{cm}.*

> Three acts.   Argument and cast.   German title-page, "Aeneas in Latium," and text face Italian.
> First performed at Berlin, January, 1793, as indicated.   SCHATZ 8782

Enea nel Lazio, ballet.   *See* Sarti's Il trionfo della pace.

Enea nel Lazio. Dramma per musica da rappresentarsi nel Regio Teatro di Torino nel carnevale del 1760 alla presenza di S. S. R. M.

>   *Torino, Giacomo Giuseppe Avondo, n. d.   viii, 56 p.   16^{cm}.*

> Three acts.   Argument, cast, scenario, and names of composer, Tommaso **Trajetta**, and librettist, Vittorio Amedeo Cigna [-Santi].   The ballet-airs were composed by Giuseppe Antonio Le Messier.   SCHATZ 10391

Enée et Lavinie, tragedie en musique, representée par l'Academie royalle de musique.   Suivant la copie imprimée à Paris.

>   *[Amsterdam, Antoine Schelte], 1696.   57 p. (incl. front.)   13½^{cm}.*

> Five acts and prologue.   Neither the author, De Fontenelle, is mentioned, nor the composer, Pascal **Colasse**.
> First performed, as indicated, December 16, 1690.   ML 50.2.E4C6

— **Enée et Lavinie,** tragedie representée par l'Academie royale de musique l'an 1691.   Les paroles de M. de Fontenelle & la musique de M. Collasse.   XXVI.   opera.

>   *n. i., n. d.   front., 51–112 p.   14^{cm}.   (Recueil général des opéra, Paris, 1703, t. 4.)*

> Detached copy.   Five acts, with prologue.
> First performed, as indicated, Dec. 16, 1690.   SCHATZ 2099
>   Second copy.   ML 48.R4

Enée et Lavinie, tragédie representée pour la premiere fois par l'Académie royale de musique, le mardi 14 février 1758.

>   *Paris, Aux dépens de l'Académie, chez la V. Delormel & fils, 1758.   48 p.   22½^{cm}.*

> Five acts.   Cast.   De Fontenelle is mentioned as the author, **Dauvergne** as the composer.   ML 50.2.E4D2

L'enfance de Jean Jacques Rousseau, comédie en un acte, mêlée de musique, représentée, pour la première fois, sur le Théâtre de l'Opéra-comique national, le 4 prairial l'an second de la République [May 23, 1794].   Les paroles sont d'Andrieux, la musique est de D'Alayrac.

>   *Paris, Maradan, Seconde année de la République [1793–94].   47 p.   17½^{cm}.*

> Cast.   SCHATZ 2343

L'enfant gâté ou Folette et Roger-Bontems.   *See* Le carnaval et la folie.

L'enfant trouvé.   A. T. of Monsigny's **Félix.**

Engelberta.

Apostolo Zeno, Poesie drammatiche, Venezia, 1744, t. iv, p. [191]–
280. 19ᶜᵐ.

Five acts. Argument. No composer is mentioned. In the "Catalogo" at end of
t. x, date and place of first ed. are given as: "in Milano. 1708. E in Ven. 1709.
ma tronco." Fehr says: "Benche lavoro scritto in comune, questo dramma si trova
fra quegli scriti dal solo Zeno (Ediz. Gozzi, vol. lv)." ML 49.A2Z3

— **Engelberta.** Pubblicata per la prima volta in Milano 1708.

Apostolo Zeno, Poesie drammatiche, Orleans, 1785–86, t. iii, p. 349–
435. 21ᶜᵐ.

Three acts. Argument. No composer is mentioned. ML 49.A2Z4

Engelberta. Drama per musica da rappresentarsi nel Teatro Tron
di San Cassano il carnovale dell' anno MDCCVIII . . .

Venezia, Marino Rossetti, 1708. 58 p. 15ᶜᵐ.

Five acts. By Apostolo Zeno (*see above*), who is not mentioned. Dedication,
argument, cast, and scenario. The composer, Carlo Francesco **Gasparini**, is not mentioned.

SCHATZ 3564

Engelberta. Dramma per musica da rappresentarsi nel famoso
Teatro Tron a S. Cassano il carnovale dell' anno 1742. M. V.

Venezia, Giovanni Milli, 1743. 48 p. 15ᶜᵐ.

Three acts. Zeno (*see above*) is mentioned as the author, Giuseppe Antonio **Pag-**
anelli as the composer. Argument, scenario, and cast. SCHATZ 7354

Engelberta o sia La forza dell' innocenza. Drama per musica da
rappresentarsi in Bologna nel Teatro Malvezzi l'anno MDCCIX . . .

Bologna, Costantino Pisarri, n. d. 16ᶜᵐ.

Incomplete, p. 79, etc., missing. Five acts. By Apostolo Zeno (*see above*), who is
not mentioned. Dedication, argument, cast, scenario. Composer not mentioned, and
unknown to Schatz, who records this as a pasticcio.
First performed, as indicated, June 8, 1709. SCHATZ 11323

L'Engelberta, o sia La forza dell' innocenza, drama per musica da
rappresentarsi nel Regio Palazzo, in occasione di festeggiare il glorioso
nome di Carlo III, monarca delle Spagne, etc . . .

Napoli, Ant. Parrino e Michele Luigi Mutio, n. d. 72 p. 16½ᶜᵐ.

Three acts. By Zeno (*see above*), who is not mentioned. Publisher's dedication
dated Naples, October 30, 1709, argument, scenario, cast, and note:
"La musica è del Sig. Antonio **Orefici** fino al segno *. Il rimanente è del Signor
Francesco **Mancini** vice-maestro della Real Cappella."
The sign appears at the end of act II, scene 11. Between the acts and after the
third act was performed "MELISSA SCHERNITA. Intermezzo. Primo [—Terzo]. It
is printed on p. 61–72, but it is not said by whom it was composed, possibly by Orefici,
since at the end of the first act the reader is referred to the intermezzo as printed at
the end. Schatz, however, attributes all three to Francesco Mancini.
First performed, as indicated, November 4, 1709. SCHATZ 7294

The Englishman out of Paris. A. T. of The reapers.

L'enigma del fato, sciolto da Giove. Scherzo musicale, nel giorno
del gloriosissimo nome della Sac. Real Maestà di Giuseppe I. re de'
Romani.

Pietro Antonio Bernardoni, Poemi drammatici, parte terza, Vienna,
van Ghelen, 1707, p. 17–33. 16½ᶜᵐ.

Argument. The composer is not mentioned by von Weilen.
First performed at Vienna, March 19, 1707, as indicated. ML 49.A2B4

L'enigma disciolto. Favola pastorale in musica da rappresentarsi nel Teatro dell' illustrissima Accademia degli Erranti di Brescia l'anno 1708.

> *Brescia, Gio. Maria Rizzardi, n. d. 36 p. 15ᶜᵐ.*

Three acts. Argument and brief notice to the reader. Neither the author, Giovanni Battista Neri, nor the composer, Carlo Francesco **Pollaroli**, is mentioned.

First performed at Reggio Teatro della Comunità, 1698. SCHATZ 8282

— Gl'amici rivali. Favola pastorale in musica. Da rappresentarsi nel Teatro di S. Fantin. Questo carnevale 1714 . . .

> *Venezia, n. publ., n. d. 58 p. 14½ᶜᵐ.*

Three acts. Impresario's dedication dated December, 1714, argument, cast.

This "operetta musicale" as the impresario calls it, is but a somewhat altered version of "L'enigma disciolto," text by Giovanni Battista Neri, music by Carlo Francesco **Pollaroli**, neither of whom is mentioned in the libretto. In the original version, for instance, the first act ends with the aria, "Amor vien sù gli occhi," whereas "Gli amici rivali" has "Orinda mia crudel." SCHATZ 8283

L'enjouée. Entrée in Mouret's Les Graces.

L'enlevement des Sabines, ballet heroique. *See* Ferrero's La disfatta di Dario.

Enone.

> *Apostolo Zeno, Poesie drammatiche, Venezia, 1744, t. iii, p. [169]–247 p. 19ᶜᵐ.*

Five acts and licenza. Argument. No composer is mentioned, but first composed by **Caldara**. In the "Catalogo" at end of t. x, date and place of first ed. are given as Vienna, 1734. (First performed August 28.)

ML 49.A2Z3

— Enone. Pubblicata per la prima volta in Vienna 1734.

> *Apostolo Zeno, Poesie drammatiche, Orleans, 1785–86, t. vii, p. 343–415. 21ᶜᵐ.*

Five acts and licenza. Argument. No composer is mentioned (but *see* above).

ML 49.A2Z4

Les enragez. Pièce d'un acte, representée à la Foire Saint Laurent 1725.

> *Le Théâtre de la foire, Paris, 1728, t. vi, pl., [71]–122 p. 17ᶜᵐ.*

Le Sage, Fuzelier, and d'Orneval are mentioned as the authors. Largely *en vaudevilles*. The airs, selected or composed and arranged by Jean Claude **Gillier**, the "compositeur" of the company, are printed at the end of the volume in the "Table des airs."

First performed July 21, 1725, preceded by "L'enchanteur Mirliton" and "Le temple du Mémoire." ML 48.L2VI

Enrichetta, ballet. *See* Bianchi's La sposa in equivoco.

L'Enrico. Dramma per musica da rappresentarsi in Firenze nel Teatro di via del Cocomero, nel carnevale dell' anno 1732 . . .

> *Firenze, Giuseppe Pagani e Melchiorre Alberighi, 1732. 78 p. 15ᶜᵐ.*

Three acts. By Francesco Vanneschi. Impresario's dedication, argument, case, scenario, and name of the author. Composer not recorded by Allacci or Schatz.

ML 48.A5 v.18

Enrico IV, ballet. *See* Mugnes' Fernandez Cortes.

L'enrolement d'Arlequin, opéra-comique en un acte. Mêlé de prose & de vaudevilles. Joué en 1726.

Alexis Piron, Oeuvres complettes, Liege, 1776, v. 5, [147]–202 p. 17½ cm.

Composer not recorded by Parfaict, etc.   PQ 2019.P6

Les ensorcelés ou Jeannot et Jeannette. Parody of Rameau's Les surprises de l'amour.

Die entdeckte Semiramis. Tr. of Hasse's La Semiramide riconosciuta.

Die entdeckte verstellung, oder Die geheime liebe der Diana [vignette]. In einem pastoral auf dem Hamburgischen Schau-platz, vorgestellt im april des 1712ten jahrs.

Hamburg, Friedrich Conrad Greflinger, n. d. Unpaged. 19^{cm}.

Three acts. By Johann Ulrich Koenig, who says in his "Vorbericht" that he selected this sujet, though of the more than 130 operas performed at Hamburg during the last 40 years, more than 30 had been taken from the "Historia fabulosa, oder Mythologie der Alten." He further says:
"In der hauptverwirrung folgte einem Italiaener, von welchem auch die hin und wieder eingemengte italiaenischen arien, den liebhaber zu gefallen, beybehalten."
He means Francesco de Lemene's "Endimione." The composer, Reinhard Keiser, is not mentioned.   SCHATZ 5088

— **Der sich raechende Cupido,** [vignette] in einem musicalischen schau-spiele auf dem Hamburgischen Theatro aufgefuehret im jahr 1724.

Hamburg, Caspar Jakhel, n. d. Unpaged. 18^{cm}.

Three acts. Cast and "vorbericht," according to which this is an altered, partly condensed, partly augmented version of "Diana." It is further stated that all the music was composed by Reinhard Keiser, except the Italian arias, "Giove vieni," "Lontan da tuoi bei rai," "Bendato arcier," "Qual solinga tortorella," "Cantan lieti," "Più cori, più vite," and "Pensa che fost' e sei," which were interpolated. The author, Johann Ulrich König, is not mentioned.   SCHATZ 5129

Das entfuehrte bauernmaedchen. Tr. of Bianchi's La villanella rapita.

Die entfuehrung aus dem serail. A. T. of André's Belmont und Constanze.

Die entfuehrung aus dem serail. A. T. of Dieter's Belmont und Constanze.

Arien und gesaenge zum singspiel: **Die entfuehrung aus dem serail.** In musik gesezt von herrn musikdirektor Knecht, in Biberach.

Kaufbeuren, Dorn, n. d. Unpaged. 16^{cm}.

Three acts. By Christoph Friedrich Bretzner, who is not mentioned. Cast added in contemporary hand.
First performed at Kaufbeuren, Theater der bürgerlichen Agenten Gesellschaft A. C., September, 1790; at Biberach, Theater der evangelischen Meister-Saenger Gesellschaft im Schlachthause, February 2, 1787.   SCHATZ 5197

Die **entfuehrung aus dem serail**. Ein singspiel in drey aufzuegen, nach Bretznern frey bearbeitet, und fuer das K. K. Nationaltheater eingerichtet. In musik gesetzt vom herrn Mozart. Aufgefuehrt im K. K. Nationalhoftheater.

> *Wien, beym logenmeister, 1782. 67 p. 16*^{em}.

Text retouched by Gottlieb Stephanie d. jüng.
First performed, as indicated, July 16, 1782. Schatz 6811

— Die **entführung aus dem serail**. Ein singspiel in drey aufzügen, nach Bretznern frey bearbeitet. In musik gesetzt vom herrn Mozart. Zum erstenmale gegeben bey abermaliger eröfnung der Deutschen Schaubühne unter der general-unternehmung Sr. Durchlaucht fürst Georg Martin Lubomirski etc etc. den 8 may 1783.

> *Warschau, Gedruckt in der Königlichen und der Republik privil. Gröllischen buchdruckerey, n. d. 70 p. 16½*^{cm}.

Cast and dedication. Stephanie's version of Bretzner's text. Schatz 6856

— Arien und gesaenge aus dem singspiel: **Belmonte und Konstanze** in drei aufzuegen. Frei bearbeitet nach Bretzner. Die musik ist vom herrn Mozart.

> *Berlin, n. publ., 1788. 32 p. 16*^{cm}.

First performed at Berlin, Nationaltheater, October 16, 1788. ML 50.2.E5M8

— Arien und gesaenge aus dem singspiel: **Belmonte und Konstanze** in drei aufzuegen. Die musik ist vom herrn Mozart.

> *Berlin, n. publ., 1798. 26 p. 16*^{cm}.

The same version as above. Schatz 6812

Entrepreneuren i Knibe. Tr. of Cimarosa's L'impresario in angustie.

Die **entzifferung.** Tr. of Salieri's La cifra.

Epaminonda. Dramma per musica da rappresentarsi nel famosissimo Teatro Grimani di S. Gio. Grisostomo nel carnovale dell' anno 1732 . . .

> *Venezia, Carlo Buonarigo, n. d. 1 p. l., 72 p. 15*^{cm}.

Three acts. Author not mentioned, but text by Domenico Lalli, according to Schatz. Dedication, argument, scenario, cast, and name of Geminiano **Giacomelli** as the composer. Schatz 3811

The **Ephesian matron.** A comic serenata, after the manner of the Italian. As it is performed at Ranelagh House. The music by Mr. Dibdin.

> *London, W. Griffin, 1769. 6, [2]–24 p. 19*^{cm}.

One act. Cast and advertisement, according to which this piece, "at a short warning . . . in great haste put together," was a deliberate experiment of the managers of Ranelagh House in "improvement upon the detached songs and ballads usually sung in their orchestra" by attempting to imitate the Italian intermezzi, such as La serva padrona, Baiocco e Serpilla, etc. The author, Isaac Bickerstaffe, is not mentioned. Longe 306

— The **Ephesian matron,** a comic serenata, after the manner of the Italian. By Isaac Bickerstaffe, Esq. The music by Mr. Dibdin.

> *[45]–55 p. 19*^{cm}. *(Collection of the most esteemed farces and entertainments, t. vi, Edinburgh, 1792.)*

Ranelagh House cast, where the work was first performed, 1769. Schatz 11753F

Les **époux réunis,** opera-comique en deux actes; représenté pour la premiere fois sur le Théâtre de la Foire, en 1736.

Charles François Pannard, Théatre, Paris, Duchesne, 1763, v. 3, 68 p. 17^{cm}.

Prose and vaudevilles. Composer not recorded by Parfaict, etc., who dates the first performance Feb. 3, 1736. **PQ 2019.P3**

Epponina. O. T. of Giovannini's text Giulio Sabino.

L'épreuve. A. T. of La ruse d'amour.

L'épreuve villageoise, opéra bouffon en deux actes et en vers, représenté pour la première fois par les Comédiens italiens ordinaires du roi, le jeudi 24 juin 1784, après avoir été joué devant Leurs Majestés à Versailles sous le titre de Théodore & Paulin, le vendredi 5 mars, & sur le Théatre italien, le jeudi 18 du même mois. Par D. Desforges. Musique de M. Grétry.

Paris, Prault, 1784. 70 p. 19½^{cm}.
Cast. Same dedication and "Lettre" as below. **ML 50.2.E55G7**

— **L'épreuve villageoise,** opéra bouffon, en deux actes, en vers, représenté pour la première fois par les Comédiens italiens ordinaires du roi, le jeudi 24 juin 1784, après avoir été joué devant Leurs Majestés à Versailles, sous le titre de Théodore & Paulin, le vendredi 5 mars, & sur le Théatre italien, le jeudi 18 du même mois. Par Mr Desforges. Musique de M. Grétry.

Paris, Prault, 1785. 53 p. 18^{cm}.
Cast, author's dedication, and a "Lettre à Monsieur de Corancé" dated June 23, 1784, in which Desforges says:
"Malgré l'indulgence qui dicta le jugement porté sur Theodore & Paulin dans le Journal de Paris, je sentis que l'ouvrage, trop sérieux peut-être, & conséquemment peu susceptible d'un vrai succès sur un théâtre consacré à la gaîté, devoit subir une métamorphose; je m'en occupai. M. Grétry me donna des idées qui fixèrent & égayèrent les miennes." SCHATZ 4149

Les **épreuves de misanthropie et repentir.** A. T. of Comment faire.

L'Epulone. Opera melo-dramatica esposta, con le prose moralicritiche, dal P. Francesco Fulvio Frugoni . . .

Venetia, Combi & La Noù, 1675. 16 p. l. (incl. front. and port.), 652, [54] p. 22½^{cm}.
The text of the allegorical, didactic, morality play "L'Epulone" (five acts and prologue) on p. 1–160 of this most curious volume. No composer or performance recorded. **PQ**

Gli equivoci. Dramma buffo in due atti. Ad imitazione della comedia inglese di Shakespeare, che ha per titolo: Les meprises. Da rappresentarsi nel Teatro di Corte l'anno 1787.

Vienna, Giuseppe nob. de Kurzbek, n. d. 84 p. 16½^{cm}.
Lorenzo da Ponte is mentioned as the author, Stephen **Storace** as the composer. First performed December 27, 1786, as indicated. SCHATZ 10079

Gli equivoci—Continued.

— Gli **equivoci.**   Dramma buffo in due atti.   Da rappresentarsi nel Teatro Elettorale di Sassonia.

Dresda, n. publ., 1797, 173 p.   15ᶜᵐ.

Stephen **Storace** is mentioned as the composer. German title-page, "Die irrthuemer," and text face Italian, which follows the original Vienna ed. with very few differences' the "Ah il flebil suono" (I, 11) for instance, having become "La meschina nel mio seno" (I, 10).

First performed at Dresden, November 18, 1797.   SCHATZ 10080

Gl'equivoci d'amore, e d'innocenza.   Dramma per musica da rappresentarsi nel famosissimo Teatro Grimani di San Gio. Grisostomo. Nell' autunno 1723 . . .

Venezia, Marino Rossetti, 1723.   48 p.   15ᶜᵐ.

Three acts. By Antonio Salvi, who is not mentioned. Printer's dedication, argument, cast, scenario, and name of Carlo Francesco **Gasparini** as the composer.

SCHATZ 3565

Gli **equivoci del sembiante.**   Drama per musica da rappresentarsi nel Teatro novo di Casale l'anno 1703.

Milano, Carlo Giuseppe Quinto, n. d.   83, [1] p.   14½ᶜᵐ.

Three acts. Scenario and argument with name of Antonio **Caldara** as composer and this clue as to the author:

"Ti sarà comparso, o lettore, sotto de gli occhi un' altro drama intitolato la Statira lavorato sù questo stesso argomento; mà perche fù questo fatica di brevissimo tempo, mi venne capriccio di riformarlo à mio comodo; cominciata l'idea, mi è convenuto novamente rinovarla per l'aggionta di due personaggi, e terminar l'opera con tutta celerità . . ."

Schatz attributes the text to Domenico Filippo Contini, at the same time attributing the music to Alessandro Scarlatti, which is obviously incorrect. ML 48.A5 v.12

Gli **equivoci in amore** overo La Rosaura, drama per musica.   Da rappresentarsi nelle felicissime nozze dell' eccellentissima Signora la Signora Donna Tarquinia Colonna, con l'eccellentissimo Sig. D. Marco Ottoboni, duca di Fiano . . . e dell' eccellentissima Signora donna Cornelia Ottoboni, con l'eccellentissimo Signor D. Urbano Barberini . . .

Roma, Gio. Francesco Buagni, 1690.   57, [1] p.   14½ᶜᵐ.

Three acts. By Giovanni Battista Lucini, who is not mentioned. Dedication with name of Alessandro **Scarlatti** as the composer, argument, and cast.

First performed December, 1690, in Rome, at the French Embassy. SCHATZ 9535

Gl'equivoci nel sembiante.   Dramma per musica . . .

Roma, Francesco Tizzoni, 1679.   front., 52 p.   13ᶜᵐ.

Three acts. Dedication by the impresario Pietro Giov. Leone, which begins:

"Comparisce nel Theatro del Mondo il presente dramma spogliato di quella vaga melodia [by Alessandro **Scarlatti**, who is not mentioned] di cui si leggiadramente vestito passeggiò non ha molto pe Theatri di Roma non per altro che per isvelare ad ogni uno Gl'equivoci nel sembiante."

The "discreto lettore" is informed

"Questi è parto di quella penna, dalla quale già nacque il dramma famoso intitolato 'La donna ancora è fedele' . . ." [by Domenico Filippo Contini].

First performed at Rome, Teatro Capranica, carnival 1679. Dent gives the alternative title "L'errore innocente," but this must have been added later on.

SCHATZ 9527

Gli **equivoci svelati.**   L. T. of Sarti's I contratempi.

L'equivoco, ballet.   *See* Paër's Cinna.

L'equivoco. Commedia per musica di Liviano Lantino da rappresentarsi nel Teatro de' Fiorentini nell' està di quest' anno 1764.

Napoli, Vincenzo Mazzola-Vocola, 1764. 52 p. 15^{cm}.

Three acts. Cast and name of Niccolò **Piccinni** as the composer. Text by Antonio Villano, called as above. Schatz 8125

L'equivoco. Commedia per musica da rappresentarsi nel Real Teatro del Fondo di Separazione per prim' opera di questo corrente anno 1791.

Napoli, Vincenzo Flauto, n. d. 47 p. 15½^{cm}.

Two acts. Author not mentioned, and unknown to Schatz. Cast and name of Giacomo **Tritto** as the composer. With the opera was performed Giovanni Battista Giannini's "La morte di Meleagro, ballo tragico in cinque atti," of which argument, cast, and name of Giuseppe Ercolano as composer of the music ("tutta nuova") on p. 5–7. Schatz 10462

L'equivoco curioso. Commedia per musica di Giuseppe Palomba da rappresentarsi nel Teatro de' Fiorentini per quart' opera di quest' anno 1790.

Napoli, n. publ., 1790. 43 p. 15^{cm}.

Two acts. Cast and name of Domenico **Cercià** as composer. Schatz 1774

L'equivoco dei due molinari, ballet. *See* **Paër's Tegene e Laodicea.**

L'equivoco delli due amanti molinari, ballet. *See* **Nasolini's Gl'Indiani.**

L'equivoco fortunato, ballet. *See* **Gnecco's L'indolente.**

L'equivoco ricompensato, ballet. *See* **Robuschi's Li raggiri fortunati.**

Er soll und muss ein narr seyn. Tr. of **Schuster's Il pazzo per forza.**

Er war nicht ganz barbar. A. T. of **Ebers'** opera **Inkle und Yariko.**

Eraclea. Tragicomedia per musica da rappresentarsi nel Teatro Vendramino di San Salvatore. L'anno MDCXCVI . . .

Venetia, Nicolini, 1696. front., 60 p. 14^{cm}.

Five acts. Dedication by the author, Giovanni Cesare Godi, dated Venice, February 5, 1696, notice to the reader, argument, and scenario. The composer, Bernardo **Sabadini**, is not mentioned. Schatz 9195

Eraclito e Democrito. Commedia per musica. Da rappresentarsi nei Piccoli Teatri di S. M. il rè di Prussia.

Berlino, Haude e Spener, n. d. 99 p. 17^{cm}.

Two acts. Cast. Neither the author, Giovanni de Gamerra, nor the composer, Antonio **Salieri**, is mentioned. German title-page, "Heraclit und Democrit," and text face Italian.

First performed at Charlottenburg, Schlosstheater, July 3, 1796; at Vienna, Hoftheater, n. d. Burg, August 13, 1795. Schatz 9287

Erano. Ein schauspiel mit gesaengen aus den zeiten der kreuzzuege. Drey akte von A. J. G. C. Batsch.

n. i., 1779.   56 p.   16⅓ᶜᵐ.

One act.   No composer mentioned.   Not recorded by Schatz.   ML 50.2.E58

Erast und Lucinde.   Tr. of Grétry's Silvain.

Ercole al Termedonte.   Dramma per musica da rappresentarsi nel Real Teatro di S. Carlo nel dì 12 di gennaio 1793.   Festeggiandosi la nascita di Ferdinando IV . . .

Napoli, Vincenzo Flauto, 1793.   20, 24 p.   15½ᶜᵐ.

Two acts.   The author is not mentioned, and not known to Schatz.   Impresario's dedication, cast, scenario, and name of Niccolò **Piccinni** as the composer.

On the first p. 11–19, argument and cast of Giambattista Giannini's ballet in five acts, "L'amanti schiavi," and argument of his other ballet, "Gli Europei nell' isola de' canibali."   The composers of the music are not mentioned.   Schatz 8126

Ercole e Dejanira, ballet.   *See* Bianchi's Daliso e Delmita.

Ercole e Dejanira, ballet.   *See* Paër's La virtù al cimento.

Ercole in cielo.   Tragedia per musica da rappresentarsi nel Teatro Grimani di San Gio. Grisostomo.   L'anno MDCXCVI . . .

Venetia, Nicolini, 1696.   82 p.   16ᶜᵐ.

Four acts.   Dedication signed by the author, conte Girolamo Frigimelica Roberti, long dramaturgic notice to the reader, argument, and scenario.   The composer, Carlo Francesco **Pollaroli**, is not mentioned.   Schatz 8284

Ercole in Lidia.   Dramma del Signor conte Maiolino Bisaccioni, gentil' huomo della camera del rè Christianissimo.   Rappresentato nel Teatro Novissimo nell' anno 1645.

Venetia, Giovanni Vecellio e Matteo Leni, 1645.   144 p.   14ᶜᵐ.

Three acts and prologue.   Giovanni **Rovetta** is mentioned as the composer.
                                    Schatz 9105

L'Ercole in Tebe.   Drama per musica del dottor Gio. Andrea Moniglia fiorentino riformato all' uso di Venetia da Aurelio Aureli per il Teatro Vendramino à S. Salvatore.   L'anno MDCLXXI . . .

Venetia, Curti and Nicolini, 1671.   front., 72 p.   15ᶜᵐ.

Three acts.   Author's dedication dated Venice, December 12, 1670, argument, and scenario.   No composer is mentioned, but Aureli, in his libretto of "Claudio Cesare," distinctly mentions Giovanni Antonio **Boretti** as composer of his "L'Ercole in Tebe."   Schatz 1222

Ercole in Tebe.   Festa teatrale rappresentata in Firenze per le reali nozze de' Serenissimi sposi Cosimo Terzo, principe di Toscana, e Margherita Luisa, principessa d'Orleans.

Fiorenza, Nella nuova Stamperia all' insegna della stella, 1661.   4 p. l., 152 p.   23ᶜᵐ.

The thirteen magnificent plates engraved by Valerio Spada, which were published with the volume, are wanting in our copy.   (*Compare* Wotquenne and below.)

Prologue and five acts.   Dedication by the author, Giovanni Andrea Moneglia (Moniglia), dated Florence, June 25, 1661, and argument.   On p. [109]–152 a minute and very interesting "Descrizione dell' Ercole in Tebe.   Festa Teatrale," by Alessandro Segni (*see* below), which mentions the participants in the ballets and in the abbattimento, and on p. 150 reads:

"il tutto condotto a fine sotto l'accorta direzione del Sig. Lionardo Martellini, che alle machine, ed al Teatro era sopr' intendente.   Si come i cori che sopra vi s'udivano insieme con tutte le musiche della presente festa, fur regolate dalli SS. Filippo

Ercole in Tebe—Continued.

Franceschi, e Pietro Strozzi, avendole composte il Sig. Jacopo **Melani,** soggetto cosi esquisito in tal professione, che ben hà mostrato in questo, ed altri simili componimenti non dovere la presente età invidiare nella perfezione dell' armonia a' piu antichi secoli tanto millitanti dai Greci, e ferono spiccare maggiormente la squisitezza di tal composizione le perfettisime voci, e acconcie maniere de' professori che nella festa ebber parte i quali tutti essendo de' migliori che oggi vivan nell' Europa, eran pur o per nascita, o per altra cagione dependenti da questa corte . . .

For further details consult Ademollo's "I primi fasti del Teatro di Via della Pergola in Firenze," who, however, is conspicuously silent about the date of performance, July 8, 1661, according to Schatz. ML 50.2.E6M2

— **Ercole in Tebe.** Festa teatrale representata in Firenze per le reali nozze de' serenissimi sposi Cosimo Terzo principe di Toscana e Margherita Aloisa principessa d'Orleans.

Fiorenza, nuova Stamperia all' insegna della stella, 1661. 120 p. 16½ᶜᵐ.

Five acts and prologue. Dedication signed by the author, Giovanni Andrea Moneglia (Moniglia), and dated "Firenze 25. giug. 1661," and argument. Jacopo **Melani,** the composer, is not mentioned. In this edition the "Descrizione" was omitted. SCHATZ 6290

— **Ercole in Tebe.** Festa teatrale rappresentata in Firenze per le reali nozze de' serenissimi sposi Cosimo Terzo principe di Toscana, e Margherita Luisa principessa d'Orleans.

G. A. Moniglia, Poesie drammatiche, parte prima, Firenze, Vincenzio Vangelisti, 1689, v. 1, [119]–256 p., 13 pl. 24ᶜᵐ.

Five acts and prologue, each preceded by a "Descrizione," written, so Moniglia informs us in the preface of the volume, by Alessandro Segni. He does not mention the composer, Jacopo **Melani,** until the last. Argument. ML 49.A2M7

Ercole sul Tago. Dramma per musica da cantarsi nella Real Villa di Queluz per celebrare il felicissimo giorno natalizio della Serenissima Signora Donna Maria Francesca Benedetta principessa del Brasile li 25 luglio 1785. L'autore della poesia Vittorio Amadeo Cigna Torinese, della musica Luciano Xavier di Santi . . .

[Lisbona], Stamperia Reale, n. d. 23 p. 14½ᶜᵐ.

One act. Cast and argument. SCHATZ 9395

Ercole su'l Termodonte. Drama per musica nel famoso Teatro Vendramino di S. Salvatore l'anno 1678. Del Bussani . . .

Venetia, Francesco Nicolini, 1678. front., 72 p. 15ᶜᵐ.

Three acts. Author's dedication, argument, and scenario. Antonio **Sartorio,** the composer, is not mentioned. SCHATZ 9493

Ercole sul Termodonte. Dramma per musica, da rappresentarsi nel Teatro Reale Privilegiato di Dresda l'anno 1747.

n. i., n. d. (double) 86 p. 15½ᶜᵐ.
Three acts. Argument, cast, and scenario. Neither Giacomo Francesco Bussani, the author, nor Johann Georg **Schürer,** the composer, is mentioned. German title-page, "Hercules am Thermodon," and text face Italian.
First performed, as indicated, July 19, 1747. SCHATZ 9732

Ercole su'l Termodonte. Drama per musica da recitarsi nella Sala dell' illᵐᵒ Sig. Federico Capranica l'anno 1723.

Roma, Stamperia del Bernabò, 1723. 71 p. 14½ᶜᵐ.
Three acts. By Giacomo Francesco Bussani, who is not mentioned. Argument, scenario, cast and name of Antonio **Vivaldi** as composer. ML 50.2.E61V4

L'Ercole trionfante. Drama rappresentato nel nuovo Teatro Ducale di Piacenza . . . Riformato all' uso corrente da Aurelio Aureli . . .

Parma, Stamperia ducale, 1688.   *87 p.*   *15½*^{cm}.

Three acts. Impresario's dedication, argument, cast, scenario, and prefatory note by Aureli, which reads, in part:

"Nel 1661 fù questo drama cõ titolo d'Ercole in Tebe [music by Jacopo Melani] composto dalla penna erudita del Sig. dottor Gio. Andrea Moneglia di Firenze per le nozze reali degli Serenissimi sposi Cosimo Terzo prencipe di Toscana e Margherita Luisa prencipessa d'Orleans. Nel 1671 per comando di soggetto auttorevole mio gran patrone in Venetia fui costretto à riformarlo in molte parti, e nelle ariette all' uso di quella città, dove rapprestato nel Teatro Vendramino à S. Salvatore con la musica del già Sig. Antonio **Boretti** V. Mastro all' ora di capela di questa A. S. incontrò non ordinario aggradimento, & applauso. Ora non sò per qual forza di stella venga à comparirti nel Teatro Ducale famosissimo di Piacenza con quella magnificenza, ch'è propria di chi lo fà rappresentare. Averti però che lo vedrai in moltissime scene riformato dall' altro che feci, e con la maggior parte dell' arie per non dir quasitutte rinovate quali poste in musica dalla virtù ammirabile del Sig. D. Bernardo **Sabadini** servitore attuale di questa A. S. . . ."   SCHATZ 9196

Die erdichtete luft-geister. A. T. of Blaise's Isabella und Gertraude.

Die erdichteten lehnserben. Tr. of Sarti's I finti eredi.

L'erede riconosciuta. A. T. and L. T. of Piccinni's La pescatrice.

Der eremit auf Formentara. Ein schauspiel mit gesang in zwey aufzuegen von Kozebue.

n. i., 1790.   *76 p.*   *17*^{cm}.

Peter **Ritter**, the composer, is not mentioned.
First performed at Mannheim, Nationaltheater, December 14, 1788.   SCHATZ 8822

Arien zum Eremit auf Formentara. Eine oper in zween aufzuegen. Die musik ist von hrn. Wolf, kapellmeister zu Weimar . . . Aufgefuehrt von der Rechenmacherischen gesellschaft. 1790.

n. i., n. d.   *Unpaged.*   *16*^{cm}.

By August von Kotzebue, who is not mentioned.
First performed, as indicated, at Regensburg, Theater im Ballhause, 1790; at Weimar, Hoftheater, November 26, 1789.   SCHATZ 11081

— Eremiten paa Formentara. Et skuespil med sang i to acter af August v. Kotzebue. Til kapelmester Wolfs musik. Oversat af P. D. Faber.

Kiøbenhavn, Nicolaus Moller og søn, 1791.   *94 p.*   *15*^{cm}.

Preface signed by the translator, giving details concerning his engagement for the work of translating Kotzebue's text.   SCHATZ 11082

Die erfinderische liebe. Tr. of Paisiello's L'amore ingegnoso.

Ergasto ed Eurilla, vinti dall' amore, ballet. *See* Mayr's Lodoiska.

Ergilda. Dramma per musica di Bartolomeo Vitturi da rappresentarsi nel Teatro di S. Angelo l'autunno dell' anno 1736 . . .

Venezia, Marino Rossetti, 1736.   *48 p.*   *15½*^{cm}.

Three acts. Impresario's dedication, argument, scenario, cast, and name of **Galuppi** as composer.
First performed, as indicated, November 12, 1736.   SCHATZ 3486

L'Erginda. Favola per musica di Aurelio Aurelii. Accademico frà gl'Imperfetti L'indifferente.

Venetia, Giuliani, 1652. 75 p. (incl. front.). 15ᶜᵐ.

Prologue and three acts. Author's dedication, notice to the reader, and scenario. The composer, Gasparo **Sartorio,** is not mentioned.

First performed at Venice, Teatro de' S. S. Apostoli, carnival, 1652. SCHATZ 9496

L'Erginia imascherata. Dramma da rappresentarsi in musica. Nel Teatro di S. Fantino l'anno 1710.

Venezia, Andrea Mercurio, 1710. 45 p. 14½ᶜᵐ.

Three acts. Cast and scenario. Author (Antonio Marchi) and composer (unknown to Schatz) not mentioned. SCHATZ 11324

Erifile. Drama per musica da rappresentarsi in Roma nel Tratro delle Dame nel corrente carnevale dell' anno MDCCLII . . .

Roma, Fausto Amidei, n. d. 63 p. 15ᶜᵐ.

Three acts. Author not mentioned and unknown to Schatz. Dedicatory poem, argument, scenario, cast and name of Girolamo **Abos** as composer. ML 50.2.E63A2

L'Erifile. Drama per musica da rappresentarsi nel famoso Teatro Vendramino à S. Salvatore, l'anno 1697 . . .

Venezia, Nicolini, 1697. 60 p. 14½ᶜᵐ.

Three acts. Dedication signed by the author, Giovanni Battista Neri, argument, scenario, notice to the reader, with name of Attilio **Ariosti** as composer.

SCHATZ 319

Erifile. Dramma per musica da rappresentarsi nel Ducale Teatro il carnovale dell' anno 1781 . . .

Modena, per gli eredi di Bartolomeo Soliani, n. d. 45 p. 16ᶜᵐ.

Three acts. Impresario's dedication, argument, scenario, cast, and name of the composer, Francesco **Bianchi,** but not of the author, Giovanni di Gamerra.

First performed, as indicated, February 3, 1781; at Florence, Teatro della Pergola, January. 1779. SCHATZ 989

Erifile. Dramma per musica da rappresentarsi nel Teatro da S. Agostino il carnovale dell' anno 1783 . . .

Genova, Stamperia Gesiniana, n. d. 54, [1] p. 13½ᶜᵐ.

Three acts. By Giovanni di Gamerra, who is not mentioned. Argument, cast, scenario, and name of Giuseppe **Giordani** as the composer. On p. 49–54, cast and description of "Zorei e Ozai ballo pantomimo in quattro atti composto . . . da Francesco Clerico," who was also responsible for the music. SCHATZ 3844

Erifile. Dramma per musica da rappresentarsi nel Regio Teatro di Torino nel carnovale del 1786 . . .

Torino, Onorato Derossi, n. d. viii, 43 p. 15½ᶜᵐ.

Three acts. By Giovanni de Gamerra (with alterations), who is not mentioned. Argument, cast, scenario, and the names of Carlo **Monza** as composer of the opera, of Vittorio Amedeo Canavasso as composer of the music for Francesco Clerico's ballets, of which the two first had the titles "La vanità corretta dal disprezzo" and "La caduta di Troia." Cast, argument, scenario.

First performed at Turin, as indicated, December 26, 1785. SCHATZ 6614

Erifile regina di Lacinto. Dramma per musica del Sig. de Gamerra. Rappresentato per la prima volta nel Regio Teatro di Londra l'anno MDCCLXXVIII.

[Sassari, Giuseppe Piattoli, 1784]. 6 p. l., 64 p. 19ᶜᵐ.

The imprint on the first p. l., bearing the engraved coat of arms of and inscription to cavaliere Rovero di Piea. The other p. l. contain a lengthy dedication by the

Erifile regina di Lacinto—Continued.

publisher and a prefatory note dated Sassari, July 11, 1784, and addressed by him to the author. According to this the agreement was that several of Gamerra's works, including such that were not yet published, were to be published. Nothing came of it because "un ragguardevole personaggio di questa città," to whose care they had been entrusted, kept them and they were not found again until after his death. On the basis of his privilege of 1778 Piattoli now first publishes "Erifile" and, as he justly remarks, in view of the paper, press work, and a few exquisite vignettes, in a better make up than was customary. He finally wishes to know the author's pleasure with respect to the other dramas.

    The opera was first performed at London, Haymarket, February, 1778.

Schatz 9244

Erigone.   O. T. of Mondonville's Bacchus et Erigone.

Erik Eiegod.   Eine oper af J. Baggesen.

    Kiøbenhavn, J. F. Morthorstes enke, 1798.   64 p.   16½^{cm}.

    Three acts. The composer, Friedrich Ludwig Aemilius **Kunzen,** is not mentioned. First performed at Copenhagen, Royal Theatre, January 30, 1798.   Schatz 5316

L'Erinto, drama regio musicale comparso tra le festive accoglienze fatte dalla Serenissima casa elettorale alla venuta del reverendissimo, et eminentissimo principe Massimiliano Gandolfo, arcivescovo di Saltzburgo . . .

    Monaco, Giovanni Jecklino, 1671.   8 p. l., 99 p.   18½^{cm}.

    Three acts and prologue. Argument and dedicatory sonnet signed:
    "Il Gisberti consacrando le fatiche de due grandi autori, dell' illm̃o Signor conte Bissari poeta, e del S. Gio. Gasparo **Kerl** M. di capella elet."
    Performed, as indicated, at Munich, Hoftheater, 1671; previously there, 1661.

Schatz 5141

L'Erismena.   Drama per musica di Aurelio Aureli, favola seconda dedicata all' illustriss. Signor Giacomo Cavalli.

    Venetia, Andrea Giuliani, 1655.   89, 23 p.   13½^{cm}.

    Three acts with prologue, followed by the 23 p. of the "Scenario dell' Erismena di Aurelio Aureli." Author's dedication, preface mentioning Pietro Francesco **Cavalli** as the composer, and argument.
    First performed at Venice, Teatro di S. Apollinare, carnival 1655.   Schatz 1720

L'Eritrea.   Drama undecima posthumo di Giovanni Faustini. Da rappresentarsi nel noviss. Teatro di S. Apponale l'anno 1652. Posta in musica dal Sig. Francesco Cavalli dignissimo organista di San Marco . . .

    Venetia, Giuliani, 1652.   84 p.   14^{cm}.

    Three acts with prologue. Dedication by Giacomo Batti and Delucidatione della favola.

Schatz 1721

Der erkennte Cyrus.   Tr. of Hasse's Il Ciro riconosciuto.

L'Ermelinda.   Drama per musica da rappresentarsi nel Teatro di Canaregio l'anno 1679 del nobil huomo Sier Marco Morosini . . .

    Venetia, Francesco Nicolini, 1679.   57 p., 1 l.   14^{cm}.

    Three acts. Publisher's dedication, argument, scenario, list of errata (1 fly leaf) and notice to the reader, in which the author says:
    "dopo haver composte dieci opere comiche, che non poco t'hanno sodisfatto, ti presento in drama per musica una regina, giovinetta, semplice e nuda; coprila tu col manto del tuo compatimento, ch'io m'accingo alla fatica. Vivi felice."
    The composer, Carlo **Sajon,** is not mentioned.   Schatz 9263

L'Ermengarda. Dramma per musica da rappresentarsi nell' autunno MDCCXXIII. Nel Teatro Giustiniano di San Moise.

Venezia, Carlo Buonarrigo, n. d. 48 p. 14½ᶜᵐ.

Three acts. Argument and scenario. Neither the author Antonio Maria Luchini, is mentioned, nor the composer, Tommaso **Albinoni**. Schatz 91

L'Ermengarda regina de' Longobardi. Drama per musica da rappresentarsi nel famoso Teatro Grimano a S. S. Giovanni, e Paolo, l'anno 1670 . . .

Venetia, Francesco Nicolini, 1670. front., 81 p. 14ᶜᵐ.

Three acts. Publisher's notice, in which he says:

". . . *Ermengarda*, (che doveva esser rappresentata per seconda, mà, che per la perdita del Sig. cav. Cesti è stato necessatiamente alterato dall' ordine . . .

"Spera [l'autore] perciò se non in altro di sodisfarti nella quantità dell' ariette quanto nemiche delle buone regole del filo del drama, e della brevità, altretanto però grate al moderno secolo per l'harmonia della musica (composta dalla virtù impareggiabile del Sig. Antonio **Sartorio**, mastro di capella del Sereniss. duca di Bronsuich . . ."

The author, Pietro Dolfino, is not mentioned. Argument and scenario. Schatz 9482

L'Ermione. Drama per musica nel giorno natalizio, e primo di maggiorità dell' Altezza Serenissima Elettorale di Massimiliano Emanuele, duca dell' una, e l'altra Baviera . . . l'anno M.DCLXXX. Posto in musica dal S. D. Giuseppe Antonio Bernabei . . .

Monaco, Giovanni Jecklino, n. d. 7 p. l., 80, [1] p. 14½ᶜᵐ.

Argument, scenario, and dedication signed by the author, Ventura Terzago, and dated "Monaco 11. Luglio 1680." Both in acts first and second ballets were introduced, and at the end of the opera one was performed, called "Ganimede." The ballets were invented by Mons. Rodier. The composer of the music is not mentioned. Schatz 826

Das **erndte-fest.** Tr. of Schulz' Høst-gildet.

Ernelinda. Dramma per musica da rappresentarsi nel Teatro Tron di S. Cassiano. Il carnovale dell' anno 1750.

Venezia, Modesto Fenzo, 1750. 36 p. 14½ᶜᵐ.

Three acts. Cast, scenario, and notice to the reader, who is told:

"La prima volta, che fù dato alla luce il presente dramma parto di celebre autore [Francesco Silvani] si recitò in questo teatro col titolo la *Fede tradita, e vendicata*, e ne trasse un sommo universale applauso. In altri teatri con diversi titoli ma sempre fortunamente replicossi, ed ora su queste scene comparisce di bel nuovo, benchè abbreviato di molto quando non volessimo dire stroppiato . . ."

According to Wiel, "La fede tradita, e vendicata" was performed at Venice, 1704 and 1715, with music by Francesco Gasparini, and 1726, with music by Antonio Vivaldi. Now, one of the later titles of the libretto was, "Ricimero," and an opera of this title (music by **Galuppi**) was first performed at Milan, Regio Ducal Teatro, December 26, 1744 (Piovano). Neither Galuppi nor any other composer is mentioned in the Ernelinda (Venice, 1750) libretto, which points to a pasticcio, and indeed, Allacci says, "musica da diversi." Wiel simply has, "Musica;?" Schatz attributes the music to "Galuppi & andere componisten," evidently on the strength of Galuppi's "Ricimero," of Milan, 1744. Piovano does not commit himself, but says that if Ernelinda was by Galuppi, it could have been but a replica of his "Ricimero." The quotation from the notice to the reader does not permit such an interpretation. The probabilities are that "Ernelinda" was a pasticcio, with ingredients from **Gasparini, Vivaldi,** and **Galuppi**. Schatz 3522

Ernelinde, princesse de Norvege, tragédie lyrique en trois actes, représentée, pour la premiere fois, par l'Academie-royale de musique, le mardi 24 novembre 1767.

Paris, Aux dépens de l'Académie, chez de Lormel, 1767. 75 p. 22½ cm.

Three acts.   Dedication signed by the author, Poinsinet, argument, cast, name of **Philidor** as composer, and this prefatory note:

"J'ai imité de l'italien ce poeme, compôsé par Mathieu Noris, Vénitien, & représenté, pour la premiere fois, à Venise en 1684, sur le théâtre de saint Chrisostôme, qui étoit alors un des plus fameux de l'Europe.   Cet auteur a joui long-tems, même après sa mort, d'une grande réputation; nous avons de lui 40 opera, mais celui-ci est le seul qui se soit conservé sur les théâtres d'Italie, malgré la vicissitude des goûts & des tems.   Je l'ai vu représenter à Parme, mis en musique par le sieur Ferardini, professeur à Naples.   Le grand intérêt qui me parut résulter de ce drame, me détermina d'abord à le traduire, & de retour en France, cherchant à tenter un nouveau genre sur le théâtre de notre Académie-Royale, j'ai cru ne pouvoir mieux faire que de l'imiter.   Le fameux abbé Metastasio m'avoit prévenu; il en a copié des scênes entieres, & notamment la septieme du second acte, dans son Adrien: il ne m'en falloit pas davantage pour me convaincre du mérite réel de ce poeme.   Mais quels changemens n'ai-je pas été contraint d'y faire?   Un opera dure cinq heures en Italie, il n'en doit pas durer trois en France, encore est-il nécessaire d'y insérer au moins un Ballet par acte, chôse absolument inconnue dans l'opera Italien.   A Paris tout se chante; à Rome, à Londres, à Vienne, les scènes se débitent.   A ces corrections, que la durée horaire & le goût national m'ont rendu indispensables, j'en ai joint, que mon goût particulier m'a dictées.   Le troisieme acte n'a aucune ressemblance avec l'original."

ML 50.2.E65P3

Ernesto ed Elisa, ballet.   *See* Prota's I studenti.

Ero e Leandro.   Dramma per musica da rappresentarsi nel Real Teatro di S. Carlo nel dì 13. di agosto 1794.   Per festeggiarsi la nascita di S. M. la regina . . .

Napoli, Vincenzo Flauto, 1794.   47 p.   14½ cm.

Two acts.   Author not mentioned, and unknown to Schatz.   Impresario's dedication dated Naples, August 13, 1794, argument, scenario, cast, and name of Ferdinando Pér (**Paër**) as the composer.   On p. 9–15, cast and description of Domenico Le Fevre's "Venere con Adone ossia Le gelosie di Diana e di Marte, ballo allusivo al dramma di Ero e Leandro."   The composer of the music is not mentioned.   SCHATZ 7551

Die eroberung des gueldenen fluesses.   A. T. of Keiser's Jason.

L'eroe castigliano, ballet.   *See* Zingarelli's Apelle.

L'eroe cinese.

Metastasio, Poesie, Parigi, vedova Quillau, 1755, t. vi, 76 p.   16 cm.

Three acts.   Argument.   ML 49.A2M42

— **L'eroe cinese.**   Dramma scritto dall' autore in Vienna . . . rappresentato la prima volta con musica del Bonno da giovani distinte dame, e cavalieri nel Teatro dell' Imperial giardino di Schönbrunn . . . nella primavera dell' anno 1752.

pl., [181]–258 p.   26 cm.   (Metastasio, Opere, t. vii, Parigi, vedova Herissant, 1780.)

Three acts.   Argument.   ML 49.A2M44

L'eroe cinese del Sig. abate Pietro Metastasio.   Dramma per musica da rappresentarsi nel Teatro Giustinian di San Moisè.   Nella prossima fiera dell' Ascensione l'anno MDCCLIII.

Venezia, Modesto Fenzo, n. d.   47 p.   14½ cm.

Three acts.   Argument, cast, scenario.   Composer not mentioned and unknown to Schatz.   SCHATZ 11325

L'eroe cinese, dramma per musica da rappresentarsi nel Reggio Teatro di Sans-Souci . . .

Berlino, Haude e Spener, 1773. 4 p. l., 109 p. 17ᶜᵐ.

Three acts. Argument, cast, scenario, and names of Metastasio as author, of Johann Adolph **Hasse** as composer. German title page, "Der chinesische held," and text face Italian.

First performed, as indicated, at Potsdam, July 18, 1773; at Hubertusburg, Neues Hofopernhaus, October 7, 1753. Schatz 4538

L'eroe cinese. Dramma per musica da rappresentarsi nel nuovo Teatro di Corte . . . nel carnovale dell' anno MDCCLXXI.

Monaco, Francesco Gioseppe Thuille, n. d. 145, [1] p. 16ᶜᵐ.

Three acts. Argument, cast, scenario, and names of Metastasio as the author, of **Sacchini** as the composer. German title-page, "Der chinesische held," and text face Italian.

First performed at Munich, April 27, 1770. Schatz 9219

— **L'eroe cinese,** azione drammatica, da rappresentarsi nel Regio Teatro Danese—Den chinesiske helt . . .

Kiøbenhavn, H. J. Graae, 1773. 51 p. 17ᶜᵐ.

Metastasio's three acts reduced to one! Argument, cast, and name of **Sacchini** as the composer. Danish text faces Italian.

First performed, as indicated, February 5, 1773. Schatz 9220

L'eroe coronato. Serenata per musica da cantarsi in occasione delle publiche feste per la inaugurazione della statua equestre di S. M. Fedelissima D. Giuseppe I . . . celebrate dal senato della Camera di Lisbona il di vii. giugno MDCCLXXV.

[Lisbona], Nella Stamperia reale, n. d. 22 p. 19ᶜᵐ.

Gaetano Martinelli is mentioned as the author, but David **Perez**, the composer, is not mentioned. Schatz 7881

Gli eroi spartani. Dramma per musica per celebrare il felicissimo giorno natalizio del serenissimo Signore Don Giuseppe principe del Brasile li 21 agosto 1788.

[Lisbona], n. d., Nella stamperia reale. 31 p. 16½ᶜᵐ.

One act. Gaetano Martinelli is mentioned as the author, Antonio Leal **Moreira** as the composer. Argument and cast.

First performed at Lisbon, as indicated. Schatz 6630

L'eroica gratitudine. A. T. of Hasse's Il Ruggiero.

L'eroica gratitudine. A. T. of Metastasio's drama Il Ruggiero.

L'eroico amore. A. T. of Gasparini, Polaroli and Ballarotti's L'Alciade.

L'Eroina lusitana. Dramma per musica da rappresentarsi nel Regio Teatro di S. Carlo detto della Principessa alla presenza di Sue Altezze Reali li serenissimi principi del Brasile nostri signori la prima volta, che onorano il teatro medesimo in occasione delle pubbliche feste per lo felicissimo nascimento di . . . D. Antonio principe della Beira . . . l'autunno del l'anno 1795.

Lisbona, Simoni Taddeo Ferreira, 1795. 143 p. 14ᶜᵐ.

Two acts. Gaetano Martinelli is mentioned as the author, Antonio Leal **Moreira** as the composer. ("La musica è tutta nuova.") Argument and cast. Portuguese text faces Italian. Moreira is called "compositore di musica della Real camera di S. M. F. e maestro del Real Seminario di Lisbona." Schatz 6635

Erosine, pastorale héroïque; représenté devant Leurs Majestés, à Fontainebleau, le 9 novembre 1765.

[Paris], Christophe Ballard, 1765. 24 p. 20½^{cm}. (Journal des spectacles, t. ii, Paris, 1766.)

One act. Cast and names of de Moncrif as author of the text, of Pierre Montan **Berton** as composer of the music, and of Laval, père et fils as "composers" of the ballet. Printed also as entrée in "Les fêtes liriques." ML 48.J7

Die errettete unschuld, oder Germanicus, roemischer general. In einem singe-spiel auff dem Grossen Hamburgischen schau-platz vorgestellet. Im jahr 1706.

n. i., n. d. Unpaged. 18½^{cm}.

Three acts. Argument and scenario. Neither the author (unknown to Schatz) nor the composer, Carl Heinrich **Grünewald,** is mentioned. SCHATZ 4226

L'erreur d'un bon père. A. T. of Dalayrac's Alexis.

L'erreur d'un moment, ou La suite de Julie; comédie mêlée d'ariettes et en un acte, par M. Monvel; représentée pour la première fois le 14 juin 1773. La musique est de M. Des Aides.

Paris, veuve Duchesne, 1773. viii, [9]–63 p. 19^{cm}.

Monvel's dedication and cast. On p. 62–63, the "Air: Guillot un jour" (I, 7).
YUDIN PQ

— **L'erreur d'un moment,** ou La suite de Julie; comédie, mêlée d'ariettes, et en un acte. Par M. Monvel; représentée pour la première fois le 14 juin 1773. La musique est de M. Des Aides.

Paris, veuve Duchesne, 1773. 39 p. 18½^{cm}.

Cast. On p. 38–39, the "Air. Guillot un jour" (I, 7). SCHATZ 2517

— Arien und gesaenge aus dem singspiel in einem aufzuge: **Der kurze irrthum** nach dem franzoesischen des herrn Monvel von Grossmann, aufgefuehrt von der Tillyschen gessellschaft.

n. i., 1790. 8 p. 16½^{cm}.

First performed at Rostock, Stadt-theater, 1790. SCHATZ 2518

— Die **reue vor der that.** Ein singspiel in einem aufzuge von Monvell. Aus dem franzoesischen uebersetzt von G. F. W. Grossmann.

Frankfurt und Leipzig, Hermannische buchhandlung, 1783. 52 p. 14½^{cm}.

First performed at Frankfurt a. M., Neues Schauspielhaus im Junghofe, 1783.
SCHATZ 2519

L'errore innocente. A. T. of A. Scarlatti's Gl'equivoci nel sembiante.

L'Ersilla. Drama per musica di Giovanni Faustini. Favola sesta.

Venetia, Francesco Valvasense, 1648. 83 p. 13½^{cm}.

Three acts and prologue. Argument. Composer not mentioned, and unknown to Schatz.

First performed at Venice, Teatro di San Moisè, carnival, 1648. SCHATZ 11326

Erwin und Elmire, ein schauspiel mit gesang [verses]
Frankfurt und Leipsig, 1775.   64 p.   16ᶜᵐ.
One act.   By Johann Wolfgang von Goethe, who is not mentioned.   First edition
in book-form, originally published in "Iris," 1775.
First performed with music by Johann **André** at Berlin, Dobbelinsches Theater,
July 17, 1775.   Schatz 186

Erwin und Elmire.   Ein singspiel.   Von Goethe.   Ächte ausgabe.
Leipzig, Georg Joachim Göschen, 1788.   1 p. l., 64 p.   17½ᶜᵐ.
Two acts.   In verse.   PT 1915.E8   1788

Erwin und Elmire, ein schauspiel mit gesang in zwey aufzuegen,
von J. W. Goethe [verses].   Aufgefuehrt auf der hochfuerstlich.—
Thurn und Taxischen Hof-schaubuehne.
Regensburg, mit Breitfeldischen schriften, n. d.   47 p.   17ᶜᵐ.
Nothing further recorded by Schatz.   Schatz 11453

Die **erzwungene ehe.**   Tr. of Il matrimonio per forza.

An **escape from France.**   A. T. of Reeve's British fortitude.

Eschila e Timoleone ossia La caduta di Timofane, tiranno di
Corinto, ballet.   *See* Cimarosa's Traci amanti.

L'esclave ou Le marin généreux.   Tr. of Piccinni's Gli stravaganti.

A escola dos ciosos.   Tr. of Salieri's La scola de gelosi.

L'esiglio d'Amore.   Drama del Signor Francesco Berni.   Cantato
in Ferrara, nel Teatro di Cortile, con machine ordinate dal Signor
Carlo Pasetti.   E musica de' Signori D. Andrea Mattioli, e Filiberto
Laurenzi . . .
Ferrara, Gioseppe Gironi, 1651.   4 p. l., 75, [1] p.   15ᶜᵐ.
Three acts, with prologue.   Dedication dated Ferrara, February 20, 1651, **and**
notice to the reader, informing him of the more than customary haste in writing **and**
preparing the libretto.   Schatz 6106

L'esilio d'Apollo, pasticcio.   *See* Portugal's La donna di gen**io**
volubile, Lisbona, 1798.

L'esilio di M. T. Cicerone.   *See* M. Curzio.

L'esilio di Tarquinio il Superbo, VII. rè di Roma, ballet.   *See*
Zingarelli's La morte di Mitridata.

Esione.   Drama per musica da recitarsi nel Regio Teatro a la presenza de le Loro A. A. R. R. l'anno 1699 . . .
Torino, Gio. Battista Fontana, n. d.   4 p. l., 88 p.   16ᶜᵐ.
Three acts.   Cast, argument, and name of composer, Francesco **Ballarotti.**   The
librettist, Pietro d'Averara, is indicated by initial in the dedication.   Schatz 592

Esione liberata, ballet.   *See* Sarti's Cleomene.

L'Esopo.   Tragicomedia per musica da rappresentarsi alle Sac.
Cesaree e Reali Maestà nel carnovale dell' anno MDCCIII.   Posta in
musica dal Sigr Marc' Antonio Ziani . . . con l'arie per li balletti del
Sigr Gio. Gioseffo Hoffer . . .

L'Esopo—Continued.

Vienna d'Austria, gli heredi Cosmeroviani della Stamperia di S. M. C., n. d.   80 p.   14½ᶜᵐ.

Three acts. Author not mentioned, and unknown to Schatz. In the notice to the reader the anonymous author calls his text a "drama burlesco, ti dirò, che hò voluto conformarlo alla piacevole stagione del carnevale, in cui deve rappresentarsi."

SCHATZ 11185

L'Espagnol genereux—Der grossmuethige Spanier, ballet. *See* Tozzi's Zenobia.

L'esperance. *See* L'indifférence.

L'età dell' oro.

p. 259–286.   15½ᶜᵐ.   (Ottavio Tronsarelli, Drammi musicali, Roma, Francesco Corbelletti, 1632.)

Three acts. Argument. No composer mentioned.   ML 49.A2T7

Eteocle e Polinice. Drama per musica da rappresentarsi nel Teatro à S. Salvatore, l'anno MDCLXXV . . .

Venetia, Francesco Nicolini, 1675.   front., 72 p.   14ᶜᵐ.

Three acts. By Tebaldo Fattorini who is not mentioned. Dedication, argument, scenario and notice to the reader with name of Giovanni **Legrenzi** as composer.

SCHATZ 5535

Etio. A. T. of P. A. Ziani's L'innocenza risorta.

Il étoit temps. *See* Destouches and Lalande's ballet Les élémens.

Les étrennes de l'amour, comédie-ballet; en un acte. Représentée, pour la premiere fois par les Comédiens françois ordinaires du roi, le 1 janvier 1769. Les paroles sont de M. Cailhava. La musique de M. Boyer.

Paris, Le Jay, 1769.   39, [1] p.   19½ᶜᵐ.

Printed in the text the airs "Qui mieux que moi," "Que votre dessein," "Un militaire semillant," "De Phaeton la fin," "De tes froideurs," "Tendres amants si vous voulez" (vaudeville).   ML 50.2.E75

Etwas seltsames oder Schoenheit und ehrbarkeit. **Tr.** of Martin y Soler's Una cosa rara.

L'Eudamia. Drama pastorale per musica . . . da rappresentarsi in essa città [Parma] nel nuovo Ducal Teatro nel carnovale del 1718.

Roma & in Parma, Paolo Monti, 1718.   4 p. l., 48 p.   17½ᶜᵐ.

Three acts. By conte Vincenzo Piazza di S. Stefano. In the impresario's dedication we are told that the present "drama" had been previously heard and published in Rome. This dedication is dated Parma, February 6, 1718, and the *reimprimatur* February 3, 1718. On p. 47–48 it is stated that Giovanni Maria **Capello** was the composer and that "per secondare le singolari idee delle di lui incomparabili modulazioni si sono variati alcuni versi, e specialmente si è posta qualche aria nella forma seguente." These are "Quel core altero" (I, 6), "Ahi che non son sicuri" (II, 4), "Su quest' Olmo" (III, 8), "La tua nemica e mia" (III, 9), "Or son tutto contento" (III, 12), "Che siate maledette" (III, 12).   SCHATZ 1589

L'Eudossia. Dramma per musica recitato per le vacanze del carnevale dell' anno 1696. Nel nobile collegio Tolomei di Siena.

Siena, Stamp. del Publ., n. d.   64 p.   14ᶜᵐ.

Three acts and prologue. Argument. Not recorded by Allacci, Wotquenne or Schatz. Presumably composed by Giuseppe **Fabbrini**, if he still was in charge of the music at the college in 1696.   ML 48.A5   v.46

Eufrosine. Tr. of Méhul's Euphrosine et le tyran corrigé.

Eugenia. Dramma del Signor Beaumarchais ridotto a prosa, e musica da Giuseppe Foppa per rappresentarsi nel nobilissimo Teatro Venier in San Benedetto l'autunno dell' anno 1792.

Venezia, Modesto Fenzo, 1792. 63 p. 17½cm.

Three acts. Cast and name of Sebastiano **Nasolini** as the composer. With the opera was performed Giuseppe Traffieri's ballet "L'Americana in Scozia." The composer of the music is not mentioned. Schatz 7000

— **Eugenia.** Dramma per musica, da rappresentarsi nel Teatro Elettorale.

Dresda, n. publ., 1794. 151 p. 16cm.

Three acts. **Nasolini,** the composer, is mentioned, but not Foppa, the author. German title page, "Eugenie," and text face Italian, which has been versified and otherwise shows differences from the original.

First performed 1794, as indicated. Schatz 7001

Eugenie. Tr. of Nasolini's Eugenia.

Eumene.

Apostolo Zeno, Poesie drammatiche, Venezia, 1744, t. v, p. [353]–447 p. 19cm.

Three acts. Prefatory note and argument. No composer is mentioned. In the "Catalogo" at end of t. x, date and place of first ed. are given as Venice, 1698. (*See* below.) ML 49.A2Z3

— **Eumene,** pubblicato per la prima volta in Venezia 1698.

Apostolo Zeno, Poesie drammatiche, Orleans, 1785–86, t. i, p. 235–318. 21cm.

Three acts. Argument. No composer is mentioned. ML 49.A2Z4

Eumene. Drama per musica da rappresentarsi nel famosissimo Teatro Grimani di San Gio. Grisstomo l'autunno dell' anno MDCCXVII . . .

Venezia, Marino Rosetti, 1717, n. d. 72 p. 15cm.

Three acts. Publisher's dedication, argument, scenario, cast, name of Tommaso **Albinoni** as composer, and notice to the reader. The libretto is by Antonio Salvi (not mentioned), but in an altered version as appears from the notice to the reader: "In questa nuova edizione si è, per degni rispetti, cambiato il luogo, e in consequenza alcuno de' nomi degli attori . . ." Schatz 92

Eumene. Drama per musica da rappresentarsi nel Teatro Giustiniano di S. Mosè il carnovale dell' anno MDCCXXIII.

Venezia, Carlo Buonarrigo, 1723. 49 p. 15cm.

Three acts. By Apostolo Zeno, who is not mentioned, and whose text is not to be confused with Salvi's. Argument, notice to the reader, cast, scenario, and name of Tommaso **Albinoni** as composer. Schatz 118

Eumene. Dramma per musica da rappresentarsi in Roma nel nobil Teatro di Torre Argentina nel corrente carnevale dell' anno MDCCLIV . . .

Roma, Fausto Amidei, n. d. 59 p. 15cm.

Three acts. Argument, cast, scenario, name of Antonio **Aurisicchio** as composer, and dedicatory poem of the librettist, "Gioacchino Pizzi fra gli Arcadi Nivildo Amarinzio." Schatz 503

Eumene. Dramma per musica da rappresentarsi nel nobilissimo Teatro di S. Benedetto il carnovale dell' anno 1784.

Venezia, Modesto Fenzo, 1784.   53 p.   16½^{cm}.

Three acts.   Argument, cast, scenario, and name of composer, Ferdinando Giuseppe **Bertoni,** but not of librettist, Apostolo Zeno.   On p. 23–30, description, with cast, of the first ballet, "Adriano in Siria, ballo eroico," by Domenico Leflevre [! Le Fèvre].   The composer of the music is not mentioned.

First performed, as indicated, December 26, 1783.   SCHATZ 938.

Eumene. Dramma per musica da rappresentarsi nel nobilissimo Teatro di S. Benedetto il carnovalle dell' anno 1778.

Venezia, Modesto Fenzo, 1778.   55 p.   17^{cm}.

Three acts.   By Apostolo Zeno.   Argument, cast, scenario, and name of the composer, Giovanni Battista **Borghi.**   On p. 21–28, cast, preface, and detailed description of "Cleopatra, ballo tragico pantomimo . . . del Giuseppe Canziani."   The composer is not mentioned.

First performed, as indicated, December 26, 1777.   SCHATZ 1233

Eumene. Dramma per musica da rappresentarsi nel Real Teatro dell' Ajuda nel felicissimo giorno natalizio del fedelissimo monarca D. Giuseppe I . . .

[Lisboa], Nella stamperia reale, n. d.   72 p.   16^{cm}.

Three acts.   By Apostolo Zeno.   Argument, scenario, cast, and names of the composer, João de Sousa **Carvalho,** and the librettist.

First performed, as indicated, June 6, 1773.   SCHATZ 1668

Eumene. Dramma per musica da rappresentarsi nel Regio Teatro di Torino, nel carnovale del 1778 . . .

Torino, Onorato Derossi, n. d.   viii, 52 p.   16½^{cm}.

Three acts.   By Apostolo Zeno, who is not mentioned.   Argument, cast, scenario, and name of Giacomo **Insanguine** as composer.   Vittorio Amedeo Canavasso composed the music for the ballets, which had titles not specific enough to be quoted.

                    SCHATZ 4838

Eumene. Drama per musica da rappresentarsi nella Sala dell' illustriss. Sig. conte d'Alibert nel carnevale dell' anno 1721 . . .

Roma, Tinassi, 1721.   81 p.   15^{cm}.

Three acts.   By Apostolo Zeno, who is not mentioned.   Antonio d'Alibert's dedication, argument, cast, name of Nicolà Antonio **Porpora** as the composer.   On p. 71–81, the text of the two intermezzi, "Dorilla e Nesso."   Schatz gives Porpora as the composer of these, too, but it should be noted that Porpora's name appears at the end of the opera text on p. 69, with no reference to these intermezzi.   The author of their text is not mentioned, and is unknown to Schatz.   On p. 81, the substitute aria for III, 15, "Resta superbo cor."   SCHATZ 8366

Eumene. Drama per musica da rappresentarsi nel nobil Teatro a Torre Argentina il carnevale dell' anno 1765 . . .

Roma, Ottavio Puccinelli, n. d.   56 p.   15^{cm}.

Three acts.   By Apostolo Zeno, who is not mentioned.   Dedicatory sonnet, argument, scenario, cast and name of Antonio **Sacchini** as composer.

First performed in January 1765, as indicated.   ML 50.2.E85S2

Eumene. Drama per musica da rappresentarsi nel giorno natalizio dell' Altezza Serenissima Elettorale Massimisliano Emanuele . . . in Monaco il dì 11 luglio dell' anno 1720.

Monaco, Enrigo Teodoro di Cöllen, n. d.   3 p. l., 70, [20] p.   15^{cm}.

Three acts.   By Antonio Salvi, who is not mentioned.   Cast, scenario, and notice to the reader.   The composer, Pietro **Torri,** is not mentioned.   The unnumb. 20 p. contain a scene-by-scene synopsis of the text in German.   SCHATZ 10364

Eumene. Drama per musica da rappresentarsi nel Teatro di S. Angelo l'autunno dell' anno MDCXCVII. Di A. Z.

Venezia, Girolamo Albrizzi, 1697. 6 p. l., 58 p. 15ᶜᵐ.

Three acts. By Apostolo Zeno. Argument, dramaturgic prefatory note, and scenario. The composer, Marc' Antonio **Ziani**, is not mentioned SCHATZ 11201
Second copy. ML 48.A5 v.10

L'Eupatra. Drama per musica. Di Giovanni Faustini. Favola duodecima.

Venetia, li Ginammi, 1655. 118 p. 14ᶜᵐ.

Prologue and three acts. Argument, scenario, publisher's dedication and notice to the reader, in which he says:
"Ecco finalmente l'Eupatra già anni quattro promessa. Duodecima fatica drammatica del Sig. Gio. Faustini di felice memoria. Se le sue opere hanno in questa città, & nell' Italia tutta, dove frequentemente vengono rappresentate ottenuti gl'applausi universali, non si deve temere, che anco questa Principessa non habbia a cõseguire i dovuti li allori . . . L'autore quasi presago di sua intempestiva morte lasciò di suo pugno ne' fogli alcune notarelle, onde andavano poste certe canzonette, che sono poi state fatte da virtuosissimo soggetto. A gl'idioti paiono oscure quelle favole, che solo si svelano nell' ultime scene, ma gl'intendenti, e studiosi l'amirano, poiche in simili compositioni devono tenersi sospesi anco gl'ingegni più curiosi, che così hà sempre professato l'autore, non solo nelle dodeci opere sin' hora stampate, mà in altre ancora, che si riserbano gl'anni venturi, havendo egli sempre applicato tutto l'animo all' inventione, da che, per la continua, & incessante applicatione, ne derivò l'origine di sua infermità, che troppo acerbamente in età di trentadue anni gli levò la vita . . . Alcune cose per capo di brevità, tutto che stampate, non si cantano; si potranno però scorrere, essendo li versi segnati nel margine con due virgole."
The composer, Pietro Andrea **Ziani**, is not mentioned.
First performed at Venice, Teatro di Sant' Apolinare, carnival, 1655.
SCHATZ 11214

Euphrosine et Le tyran corrigé, ou Le pouvoir de l'amour; comédie en trois actes & en vers, par F. Hoffman, mise en musique par E. Méhul, représentée pour la premiere fois par les Comédiens italiens ordinaires du Roi, le samedi 4 sept. 1790, avec l'ancien & nouveau troisième acte, pour l'agrément des lecteurs & la facilité de l'exécution théâtrale.

Liege, Bollen, Troisième année républicaine, [1794–95]. 88 p. 19½ᶜᵐ. SCHATZ 6242

— **Eufrosine,** zangspel, met balletten. Door P. C. Witsen Geysbeek.

Amsteldam, Abraham Mars, 1798. [x], 123 p. 16½ᶜᵐ.

Five acts. Dedicatory poem by Geysbeek dated November 1, 1798, and "voorbericht." SCHATZ 6274

Eurene. Drama per musica da rappresentarsi nel Regio Ducal Teatro di Milano nel carnovale dell' anno 1729 . . .

Milano, Giuseppe Richino Malatesta, 1729. 5 p. l., 59 p. 14½ᶜᵐ.

Three acts. Impresario's dedication, argument, cast, scenario, and name of Luca Antonio **Predieri** as composer. The author, Claudio Nicola Stampa, is not mentioned.
First performed in January, 1729, as indicated ML 48.A5 v.3

L'Euridamente. Drama regio di Giacomo dall' Angelo, L'Assicurato frà gl'Imperfetti. Da rappresentarsi nel Teatro di S. Moisè . . .

Venetia, Gio. Pietro Pinelli, 1654. 84 p. 14ᶜᵐ.

Three acts and prologue. Author's dedication dated Venice, January 20, 1654; and his notice to the reader with the name of Francesco **Luccio** as composer and with apologies for the defects of his drama, due partly to his inexperience as librettist and due also "perche nell' istesso tempo, che io componevo era posto alle note musicali." SCHATZ 5746

L'**Euridice** d'Ottavio Rinuccini, rapresentata nello sponsalitio della Christianiss. regina di Francia, e di Navarra.   [coat of arms]
Fiorenza, Cosimo Giunti, 1600.   4 p. l., 16 l.   20½ᶜᵐ.

On verso of last leaf printer's mark, a wood-cut.

The preliminary matter consists of the title page (verso blank), Ottavio Rinuccini's dedication to Maria Medici dated "Di Firenze il dì [blank] d'Ottobre 1600" (p. l. 2–3, verso of 3 blank) and the list of Interlocutori (p. l. 4, verso blank). Though easily accessible by quotation elsewhere, the famous dedication follows here in full:

"È stata openione di molti, Christianiss. Regina, che gl'antichi Greci, e Romani cantassero su le scene le tragedie intere, ma sì nobil maniera di recitare non che rinnouata, ma ne pur che io sappia fin quì era stata tentata da alcuno, & ciò mi credeu'io per difetto della musica moderna di gran lunga all' antica inferiore, ma pensiero sì fatto mi tolse interamente dell' animo M. Iacopo Peri, quando vdito l'intentione del Sig. Iacopo Corsi, e mia mise con tanta gratia sotto le note la fauola di Dafne composta da me solo per far vna semplice proua di quello, che potesse il canto dell' età nostra che incredibilmente piacque a que pochi, che l'vdirono, onde preso animo, e dato miglior forma alla stessa fauola, e di nuovo rappresentandola in casa il Sig. Iacopo, fu ella non solo dalla nobiltà di tutta questa Patria fauorita, ma dalla Serenissima Gran Duchessa, e gl'illustrissimi Cardinali Dal Monte, & Montalto vdita, e commendata, ma molto maggior fauore, e fortuna ha sortito l'Euridice messa in musica dal medesimo **Peri**, con arte mirabile, e da altri non più vsata hauendo meritato dalla benignità, e magnificenza del Sereniss. Gran Duca d'essere rappresentata in nobilissima scena alla presenza di V. M. del Cardinale Legato, e di tanti principi, e signori d'Italia, e di Francia, la onde cominciando io a conoscere, quanto simili rappresentationi in musica siano gradite, ho voluto recar in luce queste due, perche altri di me più intendenti si ingegnino di accrescere, e migliorare si fatte poesie, di maniera, che non habbiano inuidia a quelle antiche tanto celebrate da i nobili scrittori. Potrà parere ad alcuno, che troppo ardire sia stato il mio in alterare il fine della fauola d'Orfeo, ma cosi mi è parso conueneuole in tempo di tanta allegrezza, hauendo per mia giustificatione esempio di poeti Greci, in altre fauole, & il nostro Dante ardì di affermare essersi sommerso Vlisse nella sua nauigitione, tutto che Omero, e gl'altri poeti hauessero cantato il contrario. Cosi parimente ho seguito l'autorità di Sofocle nel L'Aiace in far riuolger la scena non potendosi rappresentar altrimenti le preghiere, & i lamenti d'Orfeo. Riconosca V. M. in queste mie ben che piccole fatiche l'humil deuotione dell' animo verso di lei, & viua lungamente felice per riceuer da Iddio ogni giorno maggior grazie, e maggior fauori."

It will be noticed that Rinuccini mentions only Jacopo **Peri** as composer of his "L'Euridice," yet we know from Peri himself, that part of the music used on October 6, 1600, the date of first performance of "L'Euridice" was by Giulio **Caccini**. He informed the public in his score of "L'Euridice," dated 1600, but actually published in February, 1601, at the earliest, since the dedication[1] is dated February 6, 1600 (old style; new style=February 6, 1601):

"E benchè fin allora l'avessi fatta nel modo appunto che ora viene in luce, nondimeno Giulio Caccini (detto *Romano*) il cui sommo valore è noto al mondo, fece l'arie d'Euridice et alcune del *Pastore e Ninfe del coro*; e de' cori "Al canto, al ballo," "Sospirate" e "Poi che gli eterni imperi": e questo perchè dovevano essere cantate da persone dependenti da lui, le quali arie si leggono nella sua, composta e stampata pur dopo che questa mia fu rappresentata a S. M. Cristianissima . . ."

In other words, Peri would give us to understand that the interpolation of music by his rival, Caccini, was wholly unnecessary; that it was forced on him; that Caccini had composed, by October 6, 1600, only a small part of Rinuccini's text; and that he completed the score not until after the performances. Convinced of his own priority, Peri seems to have felt especially disappointed because Caccini succeeded in getting his own, later score sooner published than he, Peri.

If Peri's statements are correct, then Caccini must have composed the larger part of his score in a hurry, since he dates the dedication of his score December 20, 1600, which permits the inference that the score was not on the market until early in 1601, *i. e.*, dated by the publisher, Giorgio Marescoti 1600, but published during that part of the old-style year 1600, which according to the new would be 1601. Peri's statements are indirectly corroborated by the fact that Caccini is singularly silent on the whole question of priority, and has nothing whatsoever to say about the history of his score in the performances of 1600. He simply writes:

---

[1] In this dedication Peri speaks of his "Euridice" as "*le nuove musiche* [!!] fatte da me nello sponsalizio della Maestà Vostra." In other words, Peri used this famous term, at least in print, prior to Caccini, whose "Le Nuove musiche" have as date of dedication February 1, 1601, *id est* 1602, and as date of the Licenza July 1, 1602. The old-style date of the title page (1601) is misleading. The modern date, of course, is 1602.

L'**Euridice**—Continued.

"Avendo io composto in musica in stile rappresentativo la favola d'Euridice e fatta la stampare."

Caccini did not have the satisfaction of seeing his entire score performed at Florence until December 5, 1602, when his "L'Euridice" was given in honor of cardinals Montalto and Del Monte and marchese Peretti. The performance lasted two hours, and it would seem that Caccini had at least this satisfaction, that no interpolations from Peri's "L'Euridice" were forced upon him.

Solerti, who discovered this performance of 1602, describes the 1600 libretto in his "Albori" (vol. 2) exactly as above, i. e., with a blank date in Rinuccini's dedication, but in his "Gli origini del melodramma" he reprints the dedication, with the date of October 4, and so did Guidi in his reprint of Peri's "Euridice" score. It seems that two issues of the libretto exist differing from each other in that particular only.

SCHATZ 7919

Euridice di Tessaglia. Pastorale regia di recita musicale del. Co Pietro Paolo Bissari K.

Vicenza, gl'heredi Amadij, 1658. 78, [2] p. 13½^{cm}.

Prologue and three acts. Argument. The two p. at end contain a notice to the reader. Composer not mentioned, and unknown to Schatz. SCHATZ 11327

L'**Eurillo** overo La costanza negl' amori fra' pastori. Dramma pastorale da recitarsi nel carnevale del presente anno 1697 in casa del Signor conte Centini. Posto in musica dal Signor Gioseppe della Porta.

Roma, Gioseppe Vannacci, 1697. 48 p. 13½^{cm}.

Three acts. Author unknown to Schatz. The notice to the reader says:
"L'Eurillo dramma pastorale altre volte si è visto ne' teatri, e si fa vedere il presente anno in Roma, mutato però nella maggior parte per l'arie aggiunte, e per alcune scene, e parte de' recitativi levati, ed accresciuti da Pintace de Trosis: Ciò si è fatto per conformarsi al gusto moderno; se ritroverai qualche errore, compatiscilo, attribuendo alla fretta si è havuta, essendo in meno d'un mese mutata, posta in musica, ed imparata da recitanti." SCHATZ 2477

Eurimedonte e Timocleone, ovvero I rivali delusi. Drama per musica da rappresentarsi nel nuovo famosissimo Teatro di S. Girolamo per la fiera delle Bagatelle l'anno 1746 . . .

Venezia, Luigi Pavini, 1746. 60 p. 11^{cm}.

Three acts. By Girolamo Zanetti, who is not mentioned. Impresario's dedication, argument, cast, scenario, and name of Johann Ad. **Hasse** as the composer. Schatz says that the performance took place in the house of Sig. Angelo Maria Labia, with wax figures on the stage and the singers behind the scenes, (as was done so frequently at Venice in the latter part of the 17th cent.). Also, Schatz says, the names in the cast were all fictitious. SCHATZ 4579

Eurione. Dramma per musica da rappresentarsi nel Nuovo Teatro delli quattro signori Associati Cavalieri e patrizj della Regio-inclita città di Pavia. Nella primavera dell' anno 1775 . . .

Pavia, Porro, Bianchi e compagni, n. d. 48 p. 16^{cm}.

Three acts. Dedication, argument, cast, scenario, and names of Francesco **Bianchi** as composer; of "Cleofante Doriano P. A.," (conte Antonio Papi) as author. The imprimatur is dated May 25, 1775. With the opera were performed (composers of the music not mentioned) Gaspare Angiolini's ballets, "L'orfano nella China" and "Sidney e Silly." ML 48.A5 v. 12

Eurione. Dramma per musica da rappresentarsi nel Nuovo Teatro di Padova per la solita fiera di giugno dell' anno 1754 . . .

Venezia, Modesto Fenzo, 1754. 46 p. 17^{cm}.

Three acts. Impresario's dedication, argument, cast, scenario, name of Antonio Gaetano **Pampani** as the composer. The author, Cleofonte Doriano, P. A. (=conte Antonio Papi), is not mentioned.

First performed at Rome, Sala dei Sig^{ri} Capranica, carnival, 1754. SCHATZ 7760

L'Euripo. Drama per musica di Giovanni Faustini, favola settima . . .

Venetia, Francesco Miloco, 1649. 90 p. 14^{cm}.

Three acts, with prologue. Argument. The composer, Pietro Francesco **Cavalli,** is not mentioned.
First performed at Venice, Teatro di S. Moisè, carnival, 1649.   SCHATZ 1738

Euristeo.

Apostolo Zeno, Poesie drammatiche, Venezia, 1744, t. v, p. [197]–265. 19^{cm}.

Three acts and licenza. Argument. No composer is mentioned. In the ".Catalogo" at end of t. x, date and place of first ed. are given as Vienna, 1724. (First performed May 17, music by *Caldara.*)   ML 49.A2Z3

— **Euristeo.** Pubblicato per la prima volta in Vienna 1724.

Apostolo Zeno, Poesie drammatiche, Orleans, 1785–86, t. vi, p. 169–232. 21^{cm}.

Three acts and Licenza. Argument. No composer is mentioned.   ML 49.A2Z4

Euristeo. Dramma per musica da rappresentarsi nel Teatro Grimani di S. Samuele nella fiera dell' Ascensione dell' anno MDCCXXXII.

Venezia, Carlo Buonarigo, 1732. 1 p. l., 48 p. 14^{cm}.

Three acts. By Apostolo Zeno, modernized by Domenico Lalli, neither of whom is mentioned. Dedication, argument, scenario, cast, and name of Johann Adolph **Hasse** as composer. On p. 48, the aria, "Non mi chiamar crudele," substituted for "Torna al padre" (I, 7).   SCHATZ 4580

L'Europa galante. Festa teatrale per musica da rappresentarsi nel Regio Teatro di Berlino per il felicissimo giorno natalizio della Sacra Real Maestà di Sofia Dorotea, regina madre . . .

Berlino, A. Haude e J. C. Spener, 1748. 77, [3] p. 16½^{cm}.

Three acts. Based on Houdart de la Motte's "L'Europe galante" by Leopoldo de Villati, who is not mentioned. Carl Heinrich **Graun** is mentioned as the composer. German title-page, "Das galante Europa," and text face Italian.
First performed, as indicated, March 27, 1748.   SCHATZ 4095

Europa riconosciuta. Dramma per musica da rappresentarsi nel nuovo Regio Ducal Teatro di Milano nella solenne occasione del suo primo aprimento nel mese d'Agosto dell' anno 1778 . . .

Milano, Gio. Batista Bianchi, n. d. 80 p. 16^{cm}.

Two acts. Mattia Verazi's name as author (in half-title preceding the title page), that of Antonio **Salieri** ("La musica è nuova composizione") as the composer. Dedication, argument, scenario, and cast. This opera was followed by Verazi's "Apollo placato, azione teatrale pantomimica," of which is printed on p. [69]–80 cast, argument, and description with the name of Luigi de Baillou as the composer of the ballet music and of Antonio Salieri of "la musica del recitativo istrumentato, dell' aria e del coro, con cu termina il ballo."
First performed at La Scala, as indicated, August 3, 1778.   SCHATZ 9288
     Second copy. ML 48.A5 v.12

L'Europe galante, ballet. Representé par l'Academie royale de musique, l'an 1697. Les paroles de M. de la Mothe & la musique de M. Campra. XLIII. opera.

n. i., n. d. front., 123–270 p. 14^{cm}. (Recueil général des opéra, Paris, 1703. t. vi.)

Detached copy. Five entrées.
First performed, as indicated, October 24, 1697.   SCHATZ 1548
     Second copy. ML 48.R4

Gli **Europei nell' isola de'canibali,** ballet. *See* Piccinni's Ercole al Termedonte.

Evelina. Score title of Sacchini's Arvire et Evelina.

Les **événements imprévus,** comédie en trois actes, mêlée d'ariettes; représentée devant Leurs Majestés, à Versailles, le 11 novembre 1779, et à Paris, par les Comédiens italiens ordinaires du roi, le samedi 13 du même mois. Les paroles sont de M. d'Hèle. La musique de M. Grétry.

> *Paris, la veuve Duchesne, 1780. 48 p. 19^cm.*

Cast. On p. 3–5 the air of "Qu'il est cruel d'aimer" (I, 1) and on p. 19–21 of "Ah! dans le siècle" (II, 1). SCHATZ 4151

— Die **unvermutheten zufaelle.** Ein singspiel in drey aufzuegen. Aus dem franzoesischen auf die musik des herrn Grétry übersetzt von herrn Stephanie dem juengern. Aufgeführt auf dem k. k. National-hoftheater.

> *Wien, zu finden beym logenmeister, 1781. 61 p. 16½^cm.*

First performed, as indicated, September 1, 1781. SCHATZ 4152

Gl'**evenimenti di Rugero.** L. T. of Albinoni's Alcina delusa da Rugero.

Evergete. Dramma per musica da rappresentarsi nel famosissimo Teatro Grimani di S. Gio. Grisostomo, l'autunno dell' anno 1748.

> *Venezia, All' insegna della Scienza, 1748. 58 p. 15½^cm.*

Three acts. By Francesco Silvani and Domenico Lalli, who are not mentioned. Argument, scenario, cast, and name of Lorenzo **Gibelli** as the composer.

SCHATZ 3828.

The **exploits of Harlequin.** A. T. of the British stage.

Die **eyfersucht der bauern.** Tr. of Sarti's Le gelosie villane.

Der **eyfersuechtige bauer.** Tr. of Naumann's Il villano geloso.

L'**Ezio.**

> [359]–434 p. 19^cm. (*Pietro Metastasio, Opere drammatiche, Venezia, Giuseppe Bettinelli, 1733–37, t. 1.*)

Three acts. Argument. No composer is mentioned. ML 49.A2M4

— **Ezio.**

> *Metastasio, Poesie, Parigi, vedova Quillau, t. ii, 1755, [193]–306 p. 16^cm.*

Three acts. Argument. ML 49.A2M42

— **Ezio.** Rappresentato la prima volta in Roma con musica dell' Auleta, nel Teatro detto delle Dame, il dì 26 decembre 1728.

> *pl., [219]–340 p. 26^cm. (Pietro Metastasio, Opere, t. ii, Parigi, vedova Herissant, 1780.)*

Three acts. Argument. ML 49.A2M44

— **Aetius.**

> *Metastasio, Tragedies-opera, Vienne, 1751, t. iii, p. [129–261] 14^cm.*

Three acts. Richelet's translation of "Ezio."

Ezio. Opera del Signor abbate Metastasio. Dramma per musica da rappresentarsi nel Teatro di Brescia il carnovale 1743 . . .

Brescia, Giuseppe Pasini, 1742. 70 p. 17^{cm}.

Three acts. Cast, dedication, argument, and note, "La musica è di diversi autori."   ML 50.2.E9

Ezio. Dramma per musica del Signore abate Pietro Metastasio . . . da rappresentarsi nel Pubblico teatro di Lucca nell' autunno dell' anno MDCCLXXXII.

Lucca, Francesco Bonsignori n. d. 64 p. 15^{cm}.

Three acts. Argument, cast, scenario, and name of Felice **Alessandri** as composer.

First performed at Verona in 1767 at the Teatro Filarmonico.   SCHATZ 145

Ezio. Dramma per musica da rappresentarsi nel Teatro Giustiniani di San Moisè nella prossima fiera dell' Ascensione dell' anno 1778 . . .

Venezia, n. publ., n. d. 17$\frac{1}{2}$^{cm}. 56 p.

Three acts. By Metastasio. Impresario's dedication, cast, scenario, argument, and names of composer, Pasquale **Anfossi** ("La musica sarà tutta nuova"), and librettist. On p. 21–24, description, with cast, signed by Marc Antonio Missoli as author of "L'origine degli amori di Marc Antonio nell' arrivo di Cleopatra in Tarso." As second ballet, by the same author, was performed "Il compimento di quattro desiderj." Composers of the music not mentioned.   SCHATZ 275

Ezio. Drama per musica di Pietro Metastasio frà gli Arcadi Artino Corasio. Da rappresentarsi nel Teatro detto delle Dame nel carnovale dell' anno 1729 . . .

Roma, Zempel, e de Meij, n. d. 80 p. 15$\frac{1}{2}$^{cm}.

Three acts. Dedication, argument, cast, scenario, and name of Pietro **Auletta** as composer.

First performed, as indicated, on December 26, 1728.   SCHATZ 498

Ezio: drama musica. Da rappresentarsi sopra il Teatro di S. M. B. Seconda edizione.—Ezio, an opera. Set to music. As it is represented at the King's Theatre in the Hay-Market . . .

London, G. Woodfall, 1764–5. 47 p. 19^{cm}.

Cast and argument. English translation faces the considerably altered Italian by Metastasio. Neither he is mentioned nor the composer. Burney (IV, 485) calls this a pasticcio, mentioning the arias, "Recagli quell' arciero," "Caro mio bene addio," and "Mi dona, mi renda," as composed by Giovanni Battista **Pescetti**. Other composers were J. Chr. **Bach, Galuppi,** G. F. de **Majo,** and **Vento.**

First performed, as indicated, November 24, 1764.   ML 48.M2N

Ezio. Dramma per musica da rappresentarsi nel nobilissimo Teatro di S. Benedetto il carnovale dell' anno MDCCLXVII . . .

Venezia, Modesto Fenzo, 1767. 72 p. 17$\frac{1}{2}$^{cm}.

Three acts. Impresario's dedication, argument, cast, and name of composer, Fernando Giuseppe **Bertoni,** but not of Metastasio.

First performed January, 1767.   SCHATZ 912

Ezio. Drama per musica, da rappresentarsi nel Regio Teatro di Torino nel carnovale del 1731. Alla presenza delle Reali Maestà del re, e della regina di Sardegna, etc.

Torino, Gio. Battista Valetta, n. d. 4 p. l., 64 p. 15$\frac{1}{2}$^{cm}.

Three acts. By Metastasio. Argument, scenario, cast, and name of the composer, Riccardo **Broschi.**

First performed, as indicated, December 26, 1730.   SCHATZ 1340

Ezio. Dramma per musica da rappresentarsi nel Nuovo Teatro delli quattro Signori Associati Cavalieri e patrizj della Regio inclita città di Pavia nel carnovale dell' anno 1784 . . .

Pavia, Pietro Galeazzi, n. d. 1 p. l., 50 p. 14½^{cm}.

Three acts. By Metastasio. Dedication, argument, scenario, cast, and name of the composer, Giovanni Battista **Calvi.** Of the three ballets by Eusebio Luzzi, the first was called "Il diavolo a quattro" (music by Gaspare Angiolini), and the second "Il convitato," music by "Sig. cavaliere Gluch" [!]. No such ballet is mentioned by Wotquenne or Liebeskind. Probably the music of Gluck's ballet Don Juan (Vienna, 1761) was used. SCHATZ 1518

Ezio. Drama per musica da rappresentarsi in Verona nel Teatro dell' Accademia Filarmonica nel carnovale 1740 . . .

Verona, Dionigi Ramanzini, n. d. 70 p. 18½^{cm}.

Pages 49–50 (act II, sc. XIV) have been supplied in ms., so a note informs at end, from the Padova 1765 ed. of Trajetta's "Ezio." Pages 20–21 also in ms.

Three acts. By Metastasio. Argument, cast, scenario, and statement: "La musica è del Sign. Antonio **Cortona** e di altri." SCHATZ 2264

Ezio, dramma per musica da rappresentarsi nel nobilissimo Teatro di S. Benedetto nel carnovale dell' anno MDCCLXXII.

Venezia, Modesto Fenzo, 1772. 48 p. 18^{cm}.

Three acts. By Metastasio, who is not mentioned. Cast, argument, scenario, and name of Giuseppe **Gazzaniga** as the composer.

First performed in February, 1772. SCHATZ 3687

Ezio. Drama per musica da rappresentarsi nel Regio Teatro di Berlino per il felicissimo giorno natalazio della Sacra Real Maestà di Sofia Dorotea regina madre . . .

Berlino, Haude e Spener, 1755. 16½^{cm}.

Imperfect; ends with p. 152.

Three acts. Altered from Metastasio by Giampietro Tagliazucchi, who is not mentioned. Argument, scenario, and name of Carl Heinrich **Graun** as the composer. German title page, "Aetius," and text face Italian.

First performed, as indicated, April 1, 1755. SCHATZ 4096

Ezio. Dramma per musica, da rappresentarsi nel Teatro della Regia Elettoral corte di Dresda, nel carnevale dell' anno MDCCLV. La musica è del Sig^r Gio. Adolfo Hasse . . .

Dresda, la vedova Stössel e Giovanni Carlo Krause, n. d. 4 p. l., 72 p. 21½^{cm}.

Three acts. By Metastasio, who is not mentioned. Argument, cast, scenario. Schatz and Mennicke call this Hasse's second version.

First performed, as indicated, January 20, 1755. The so-called first version was first performed at Naples, carnival, 1730 (Mennicke); Naples, fall of 1730 (Schatz, who gives the cast). SCHATZ 4539

Ezio. Dramma per musica da rappresentarsi nel Teatro Malvezzi la primavera dell' anno MDCCXLI.

Bologna, Bartolomeo Borghi, n. d. 76, [1] p. 17½^{cm}.

Three acts. Argument, cast, scenario, and names of Metastasio as author, of Nicolò **Jommelli** as composer.

First performed, as indicated, April 29, 1741. SCHATZ 4857

Ezio—Continued.

— **Ezio.** Dramma per musica da rappresentarsi nel Teatro Ducale di Stutgart festeggiandosi il felicissimo giorno natalizio di Sua Altezza Serenissima Carlo duca regnante di Wirtemberg e Teck, etc. La poesia è del Signor abbate Pietro Metastasio . . . La musica è nuovamente composta dal Signor Nicolò Jommelli . . .

Stutgart, Cristofero Frederico Cotta, 1758. 135 p. 18^{cm}.

Three acts. Argument, cast, scenario. German title page, "Aetius," and text face Italian, which is not quite the same as in the first version of 1741. For instance, scene I, 6, has been much condensed and lacks the aria, "Se un bell' ardire," as also in the much altered scene I, 8, the aria, "Se povero il ruscello," and II, 3, the aria, "Cara, se un core amante." The last two scenes of the first act are totally different, etc., etc. The Stuttgart version, unless a fourth version exists, would then belong to the third version (Vienna, October 4, 1749) and was first performed, as indicated, February 11, 1758. The second version was first performed at Naples, Teatro di San Carlo, November 4, 1748.   SCHATZ 4858

— **Ezio.** Dramma per musica da rappresentarsi nel Real Teatro dell' Ajuda in occasione di festeggiarsi il felicissimo giorno natalizio di Sua Reale Maestà l'augustissima Signora D. Marianna Vittoria . . . nella primavera dell' anno 1772.

Lisbona, Stamperia reale, n. d. 74 p. 16^{cm}.

Three acts. Argument, cast, scenario, and names of Metastasio as author, of Niccolò **Jommelli** as composer ("nuova composizione"). The text is somewhat different from that of the third (resp. fourth) version of 1758. For instance, the scene I, 8, "Ezio sappia, ch'io bramo," has a different dialogue; I, 9, "Vedrem, se ardisce ancora," has become I, 10; the scene, "Eccomi al cenno tuo," with the aria, "So chi t'accese," has been added as I, 9, and the two last scenes in act I are again different, the act closing with the line, "Quando si sa morir," instead of "Io qui torno a palpitar." Schatz calls this the third setting of "Ezio" by Jommelli.

First performed, as indicated, March 31, 1772.   SCHATZ 4894

Ezio. Dramma per musica da rappresentarsi nel Teatro di S. Angelo l'autunno dell' anno 1737 . . .

Venezia, Marino Rossetti, n. d. 70 p. 15^{cm}.

Three acts. By Metastasio, who is not mentioned. Impresario's dedication, argument, cast, scenario, and name of Giovanni Battista **Lampugnani** as composer.   SCHATZ 5388

Ezio. Dramma per musica da rappresentarsi nel Teatro Grimani à San Samuele per la fiera dell' Ascensione l'anno 1743.

Venetia, Steffano Monti, n. d. 1 p. l., 54 p. 15½^{cm}.

Three acts. Argument, cast, scenario, and name of Giovanni Battista **Lampugnani** as the composer. Metastasio is not mentioned.

First performed at Venice, Teatro di S. Angelo, fall of 1737.   SCHATZ 11719

Ezio. Drama per musica da rappresentarsi nel famosissimo Teatro Grimani di S. Gio. Grisostomo nel carnevale MDCCXLVII.

[Venezia], n. publ., n. d. 2 p. l., 50 p. 15^{cm}.

Three acts. By Metastasio, who is not mentioned. Impresario's dedication, argument, cast, scenario, and name of Giovanni Battista **Pescetti** as the composer.   SCHATZ 7965

Ezio. Dramma per musica di Artino Corasio, Pastor Arcade, da rappresentarsi nel famosissimo Teatro Grimani di S. Gio. Grisostomo nell' autunno dell' MDCCXXVIII . . .

Venezia, Carlo Buonarigo, n. d. 1 p. l., 72 p. 14½^{cm}.

Three acts. By Metastasio, who is not mentioned. Dedication dated Venice, Nov. 20, 1728, and signed by Domenico Lalli as impresario, argument, cast, scenario, and name of Nicolà Antonio **Porpora** as the composer.   SCHATZ 8370

Ezio. Dramma per musica da rappresentarsi nel Teatro di San Samuelle per la fiera dell' Ascensione l'anno MDCCLIV.

Venezia, Angiolo Geremia, n. d. 48 p. 15½cm.

Three acts. By Metastasio, who is not mentioned. Argument, cast, scenario, and name of Giuseppe **Scarlatti** as the composer. SCHATZ 9545

Ezio. Dramma serio per musica da rappresentarsi nel Nuovo Teatro di Vicenza la state dell' anno 1792 . . .

Vicenza, Giusto, n. d. 55 p. 17cm.

Two acts. Dedication by the impresario, Angelo Recaldini, cast, and names of Metastasio as author, of Angelo **Tarchi** as composer ("La musica è tutta nuova"). With the opera was performed, composer of the music not mentioned, Filippo Beretti's ballet, "La caccia d'Isabella regina di Spagna." SCHATZ 10239

Ezio. Dramma per musica da rappresentarsi nel Nuovo Teatro in Padova la fiera dell' anno 1765 . . .

Padova, Fratelli Conzatti, n. d. 66 p. (incl. port.) 18cm.

The engraved port. is that of "Petrus Metastasius ex numismate anni 1750." Three acts. Impressario's dedication, argument, cast, scenario, and names of composer, Tomasso **Trajetta**, and author, Metastasio.

First performed at Padova in June, 1765; at Rome, Teatro delle Dame, carnival, 1757. SCHATZ 10410

Ezio, ballet. *See* Zingarelli's Quinto Fabio.

Fabio vincitor di se stesso. *See* M. Curzio.

The fable of the pantomime dances explained.

n. i., n. d. 16 p. 20½cm.

Casts. Contains short explanation of the three dances, "Annette and Lubin," "The Dutch wedding," and "The nymphs of Diana: or Cupid turned Faun." The first is preceded by an introductory note to the effect that this is Noverre's pantomime version of Adolphe Blaise's opera, "Annette et Lubin" (1762). ML 52.2.F2

La facendiera. Dramma giocoso per musica da rappresentarsi in Torino nel Teatro di S. A. S. il Signor principe di Carignano nell' autunno dell' anno 1751.

Torino, Ignazio Cafasso, n. d. 48 p. 14½cm.

Three acts. Cast. Author and composer not mentioned, and unknown to Schatz, who calls this a pasticcio.

First performed at Venice, Teatro di S. Moisè, 1746. SCHATZ 11328

Le facheux veuvage, opéra-comique, en trois actes. Donné à la Foire Saint-Laurent en 1725.

Alexis Piron, Oeuvres complettes, Liege, 1776, v. 4, 113 p. 17½cm.

En vaudevilles. Composer not recorded by Parfaict, etc. PQ 2019.P6

Der fagottist, oder Die zauberzither. Ein singspiel in drey aufzuegen von Joachim Perinet. Die musik ist von hrn. Wenzel Mueller . . .

Wien, Mathias Andreas Schmidt, 1791. 70 p. 16½cm.

Cast.

First performed at Vienna, Marinellische schaubühne in der Leopoldstadt, June 8, 1791. Krone gives the title as, "Kaspar der Fagottist oder die Zauberzitter." SCHATZ 6920

Der **fagottist**—Continued.

— Die **zauberzither.** Eine komische oper in drey aufzuegen. Neubearbeitet. Die musik ist von herrn Wenzel Müller in Wien. Aufgefuehrt auf dem kurfuerstl. Hoftheater in Muenchen.

[*Wien*], *Franz Seraph Huebschmann, 1795.   4 p. l.   83 p.   15½*cm*.

The second and third p. l. contain a preface signed *C.*, which reads, in part:

"Herr Perinet in Wien, bey dem Marinellischen Theater, nahm die fabel zu dieser komischen oper aus dem vierten band des von Wieland herausgegebenen vortreflichen Dschinnistan, die aber dort *Lulu*, oder die Zauberfloete ueberschrieben ist und gab ihr den titel: *Die zauberzither und der Fagottist.*   Man geizt jetzt nach spektakelstuecken, (ich will nicht untersuchen, ob die gute sache der komischen oper dadurch gewinnen wird) und so wurde denn die Zauberzither in Wien, in Prag aufgenommen, und sehr oft gegeben.   Auch wuenschte man sie auf andern theatern zu schen; allein, der dialog und die verse, eins wie das andere, wimmelte von abgeschmacktheiten, wohl sogar von unanständigen zweydeutigkeiten, dass man bedenken tragen musste, diese oper in ihrer originalgestalt zu geben.   Die oekonomie des stueckes musste bleiben, weil sie zu genau mit der musik vereinigt war; selbst in einigen gesaengen durften gewisse ungereimtheiten nur gedaempft und geschwaecht werden, weil man sonst verse—ohne musik gehabt haben wuerde . . .   Wenigstens habe ich alles versucht, herrn Muellers musik keinen eintrag zu thun . . ."

First performed at Munich, churfuerstl. National Schaubühne, February 27, 1795.

SCHATZ 6921

— Gesaenge aus dem singspiele: Die **zauberzither,** oder Der fagottist in drey aufzuegen von Joachim Perinet.   Musik von Wenzel Mueller in Wien.

*Rostock, n. publ., 1796.   16 p.   16*cm*.

First performed at Rostock, Stadttheater, 1796.   SCHATZ 6922

— Die **zauberzither.** Eine komische oper in drey aufzuegen. Neubearbeitet. Die musik ist von herrn Wenzel Mueller in Wien. Zweyte auflage.

*Prag, Calve, 1796.   front., vi, [2], 124 p.   15*cm*.

Contains the same preface as the Vienna ed. of 1795.   SCHATZ 11714

The **fair American:** a comic opera, in three acts; as it is performed, with universal applause, at the Theatre-Royal, Drury-Lane.   Written by F. Pilon . . .

*London, J. Almon, 1785.   2 p. l., 9–68 p.   20*cm*.

The music was composed by Thomas **Carter,** who is not mentioned.   Cast and author's dedication.

First performed, as indicated, May 18, 1782.   ML 50.2.F13C2

Second copy.   LONGE 95

The **fair Caledonian.**   A. T. of Love and money.

The **fair foundling.**   A. T. of Patie and Peggy.

The **fair maid of Kent.**   A. T. of Windsor castle.

The **fairies.**   An opera.   Taken from A midsummer night's dream, written by Shakespear.   As it is perform'd at the Theatre-Royal in Drury-Lane.   The songs from Shakespear, Milton, Waller, Dryden, Lansdown, Hammond, etc.   The music composed by Mr. Smith.

*London, J. and R. Tonson and S. Draper, 1755.   48 p.   18*cm*.

Three acts and prologue.   Cast and argument.   "Generally attributed to Garrick, but is repudiated by him," says the Dict. of Nat. biog.   The Advertisement on p. [6] would seem to imply that John Christopher Smith himself wrote, *i. e.* compiled, the text:

The **fairies**—Continued.

"Many passages of the first merit, and some whole scenes in the *Midsummer Night's Dream*, are necessarily omitted in this opera, to reduce the performance to a proper length; it was feared that even the best poetry would appear tedious when only supported by recitative. Where Shakespear has not supplied the composer with songs, he has taken them from Milton, Waller, Dryden, Lansdown, Hammond, etc., and it is hoped they will not seem to be unnaturally introduced."

On the other hand, these two lines in the "Prologue, written and spoken by Mr. Garrick" (which, by the way, is a plea for English opera), would lead us to suspect Garrick's authorship, after all:

"I dare not say, who wrote it—I could tell ye,
To soften matters—Signor Shakespearelli."

First performed, as indicated, February 3, 1755. ML 50.2.F14
Second copy. LONGE 50
Third copy. LONGE 298

— The **fairies**. An opera. Taken from A midsummer night's dream, written by Shakespear. As it is perform'd at the Theatre-Royal in Drury-Lane. The songs from Shakespear, Milton, Waller, Dryden, Lansdown, Hammond, &c. The music composed by Mr. Smith. The second edition.

London, J. and R. Tonson and S. Draper, 1755. 48 p. 19½ cm.

Three acts and prologue. Cast and argument. Same as the first edition.
ML 50.2.F142

The **fairy Favour**. A masque . . .

London, Joseph Cooper, 1766. 4 p. l., 19 p. 20 cm.

One act. By Thomas Hull. The composer not recorded by Clarence.
Performed at Covent Garden, 1766. LONGE 109

The songs and description, of the pantomime; called, The **fairy Favour:** or, Harlequin animated. First performed at the Theatre Royal, Drury Lane. Monday, December 27, 1790.

London, J. Wrighten, n. d. 11 p. 20 cm.

One act. Cast. By the publisher? No composer recorded by Clarence.
LONGE 207

The **fairy prince:** a masque. As it is performed at the Theatre-Royal in Covent-Garden.

London, T. Becket, 1771. 4 p. l., 25 p. 19 cm.

Two parts. Cast and Advertisement in which the author, George Colman (not mentioned), says:

"The greater part of this masque is borrowed, with some variation, from Ben Jonson. The same liberty has been taken with a few passages of Shakespeare, and a chorus of the late Gilbert West, Esq. The final chorus is from Dryden . . ."

Thomas Aug. **Arne** is mentioned as the composer.
First performed November 12, 1771. LONGE 52

The **fairy-queen:** an opera. Represented at the Queen's theatre by Their Majesties servants.

London, Jacob Tonson, 1692. 3 p. l., 52 p. 21½ cm.

Five acts. Prologue and preface. According to Barclay Squire "an anonymous adaptation of Shakespeare's "Midsummer night's dream," in which, curiously enough, not a single line by Shakespeare appears with [Henry] **Purcell's** music. It was produced at the Dorset Garden Theatre in the spring of 1692."

The curious preface reads in part: "And many of the English gentry are sensible what advantage Paris receives, by the great number of strangers which frequent the opera's three days in a week, throughout the year. If therefore an opera were established here, by the favour of the nobility and gentry of England; I may modestly conclude it would be some advantage to London, considering what a sum we must yearly lay out among tradesmen for the fitting out so great a work. That Sir William

The **fairy-queen**—Continued.

Davenant's Siege of Rhodes was the first opera we ever had in England, no man can
deny . . . 'Tis true, the Siege of Rhodes wanted the ornament of machines, which
they value themselves so much upon in Italy.   And the dancing which they have in
such perfection in France. . . .   That a few private persons should venture on so
expensive a work as an opera, when none but princes or states exhibit 'em abroad,
I hope is no dishonour to our nation.   And I dare affirm, if we had half the encouragement in England, that they have in other countries, you might in a short time have
as good dancers in England as they have in France, though I despair of ever having
as good voices among us, as they have in Italy.   These are the two great things which
travellers say we are most deficient in . . ."   ML 50.2.F145

A **fairy tale.**   In two acts.   Taken from Shakespeare.   As it is
performed at the Theatre-Royal in the Hay-Market.

  London, G. Kearsly, 1777.   24 p.   21^{cm}.

  Two acts.   Cast.   In the text are mentioned as composers (principally) Michael
Arne and **Dibdin, Burney, Hook, Smith.**   Text adapted by George Colman (not
mentioned) from "A midsummer night's dream."
  First performed at Drury Lane, November 26, 1763 (Genest).   LONGE 243

The **faithful country maid.**   A. T. of The village wedding.

Falaride, tiranno d'Agrigento.   Drama per musica da rappresentarsi nel Teatro di Sant' Angelo l'anno MDCLXXXIV . . .

  Venetia, Francesco Nicolini, 1684.   57 p.   14½^{cm}.

  Three acts.   By Adriano Morselli.   Dedication, argument, and name of Giovanni
Battista **Bassani** as composer, but not of librettist.
  First performed at same theatre, fall of 1683.   SCHATZ 634

Il **falegname.**   Commedia per musica da rappresentarsi nel Regio-
Ducal Teatro di Mantova la primavera dell' anno 1782 . . .

  Mantova, Alberto Pazzoni, n. d.   72 p.   17½^{cm}.

  Three acts.   By Giuseppe Palomba, who is not mentioned.   Dedication dated
Mantova, May 8, 1782 (the opening of the operatic season), cast, scenario and name
of Domenico **Cimarosa** as composer.
  First performed at Naples, Teatro de' Fiorentini, 1780.   ML 50.2.F147C4

— Il **falegname.**   Dramma giocoso per musica da rappresentarsi nel
Teatro Giustiniani in San Moisè per prima opera dell' autunno 1784.

  Venezia, Modesto Fenzo, 1784.   52 p.   16½^{cm}.

  Two acts.   By Giuseppe Palomba.   Cast, name of the composer, **Cimarosa,**
scenario, and prefatory note, in which appears this statement:
  "Quest' opera certamente non è delle più regolate, nè delle più adattate al gusto
d'un publico intelligente com' è quello di questa città, essendo il presente dramma
di un poeta Napolitano, e scritto per il Teatro di Napoli dove non viene osservata nè
aggiustatezza di caratteri, nè condotta di rappresentazione."
                                                              SCHATZ 1922

— Il **falegname.**   Dramma giocoso per musica da rappresentarsi nel
Teatro di S. A. E. di Sassonia.

  Dresda, n. publ., 1787.   135 p.   15½^{cm}.

  Two acts, with name of the composer, **Cimarosa,** and cast added in ms.   German
title-page, "Der tischler" and text face Italian.
  First performed at Dresden in 1787.   SCHATZ 1923

Der **fall ist noch viel seltener** oder Die geplagten ehemaenner.
O. T. of Schack's Die geplagten ehemaenner.

The **fall of Phaeton.** As it is perform'd at the Theatre-Royal in Drury-Lane. Invented by Mr. Pritchard. The musick compos'd by Mr. Arne. And the scenes painted by Mr. Hayman.

London, R. Turbut, 1736. 23 p. 19^{cm}.

Argument and cast. "The fall of Phaeton" on p. [5]–15 is followed on p. [17]–23 by "the songs in HARLEQUIN RESTOR'D, or Taste alamode."
First performed 1736, as indicated.

ML 50.2.F15A7

Le **fallaci apparenze.** Dramma giocoso per musica in due atti. Poesia di Gio. Battista Lorenzi, accomodata dal tenente Antonio Valli da recitarsi nell' autunno 1793 nel nobilissimo Teatro di San Samuele.

Venezia, Modesto Fenzo, 1793. 62 p. 18½^{cm}.

Scenario and name of Gennaro **Astaritta** as composer. Lorenzi's text originally was called "Gelosia per gelosia."

SCHATZ 386

Fallaride, tiranno d'Agricento, ballet. *See* Andreozzi's La principessa filosofa.

Die **falschen verdachte.** Ein singspiel in zween aufzuegen. Dem publikum der stadt Botzen von den hiesigen tonkuenstlern gewiedmet. Aufgefuehrt im fasching des jahrs 1796.

n. pl., Karl Jos. Weiss, n. d. 88 p. 15½^{cm}.

With name of the composer, Franz Peter Gregorius **Bihler,** but not of the librettist, who is unknown to Schatz.
First performed, as indicated, February 5, 1796.

SCHATZ 1037

False and true, a play in three acts, now performing at the Theatre Royal, Hay-market.

London, J. Bell, 1798. 2 p. l., 57, 5 p. 20½^{cm}.

Cast. Interspersed with songs, etc. By Rev. Moultrie. Neither he nor the composer, Samuel **Arnold,** is mentioned.
First performed August 11, 1798.

LONGE 249

Le **false apparenze.** Commedia per musica di Giuseppe Palomba da rappresentarsi nel Teatro de' Fiorentini per prim' opera del corrente anno 1791.

Napoli, n. publ., 1791. 42 p. 15^{cm}.

Two acts. Cast and name of Pietro **Guglielmi** as the composer.

SCHATZ 4244

Le **false magie per amore.** Commedia per musica di Giuseppe Palomba da rappresentarsi nel Teatro Nuovo sopra Toledo per quart' opera di quest' anno 1791.

Napoli, Vincenzo Flauto, 1791. 46 p. 15½^{cm}.

Two acts. Cast and name of the composer, Domenico **Cercià.**

SCHATZ 1775

La **Falsirena.** Drama per musica. Da rappresentarsi nel Teatro di S. Angelo l'anno 1690. Di D. Rinaldo Cialli . . .

Venetia, Nicolini, 1690. 72 p. 14^{cm}.

Three acts. Argument, scenario, notice to the reader, with name of Marc' Antonio **Ziani** as composer, and Tomaso Bezzi for the "sceniche rappresentanze," who also signed the dedication.
First performed, as indicated, carnival, 1690.

SCHATZ 11196

La **Falsirena**—Continued.

— **Marte deluso.** Drama per musica da rappresentarsi nel Teatro di S. Angelo l'anno 1691. Di D. Rinaldo Cialli . . .

Venetia, Nicolini, 1691. 58 p. 14^{cm}.

Three acts. Author's dedication, "motivi del drama," scenario, and notice to the reader, with Marc' Antonio **Ziani**'s name as composer, beginning: "Eccoti un poetico innesto tronco vecchio, gambo nuovo." This refers to the fact that this is "La Falsirena," with a new title and considerably altered. For instance, I, 1 has now the aria, "Speranze gradite," instead of "Speranza dolce e cara"; the second scene begins with the aria, "Si, si rapide correte," instead of "Perche mai luci adorate"; and the aria, "Il dardo di Cupido," has been dropped from the third scene.

First performed, as indicated, carnival, 1691. SCHATZ 11197

Il **falso amico,** ballet. *See* La villeggiatura in scompiglio.

Il **falso Tiberino.** Drama per musica da rappresentarsi nel Teatro Tron di San Cassano il carnovale dell' anno MDCCVIII . . .

Venezia, Marino Rossetti, 1708. 7 p. l., 58 p. 15^{cm}.

Three acts. Attributed by Allacci and Schatz to Zeno (and Pariati), but no such text appears in his collected works. Impresario's dedication, argument, cast, and name of Carlo Francesco **Pollaroli** as the composer. SCHATZ 8285

Falstaff osia Le tre burle. Dramma giocoso per musica in due atti da rappresentarsi nel Teatro Ellettorale di Sassonia.

Dresda, n. publ., 1799. 183 p. 15½^{cm}.

Two acts. By Carlo Prospero Defranceschi, who is not mentioned. Antonio **Salieri** is mentioned as the composer. German title-page, "Falstaff oder Dreymahl angefuehrt," and text face Italian.

First performed at Dresden, as indicated, October 26, 1799; at Vienna, Burgtheater, January 6, 1799; Kärnthnerthortheater, January 3, 1799. SCHATZ 9289

— Arien und gesaenge zu dem komischen singspiel: **Falstaff** in zwey aufzuegen. Nach dem italiaenischen von C. Herklots. Die musik von Salieri.

Berlin, n. publ., 1799. 70 p. 16^{cm}.

First performed at Berlin, Kgl. Nationaltheater, December 16, 1799. SCHATZ 9290

La **fama dell' onore, della virtù, dell' innocenza** in carro trionfante. Dramma per musica da rappresentarsi nel Teatro Grimani di S. Samuele nel carnovale dell' anno 1727 . . .

Venezia, Alvise Valvasense, n. d. 22 p. 14½^{cm}.

Three acts. Dedication by Montebaldo Vovi, apparently as author, prefatory note, cast, and name of Salvatore **Apolloni** as composer. Schatz attributes the text incorrectly to several authors, since the author speaks of himself in the prefatory note in the first person and says, of course exaggerating, that the text "fù composta in trè minuti e mezzo d'ora." SCHATZ 300

La **famiglia in scompiglio.** A. T. of Cimarosa's Li amanti comici.

La **famiglia in scompiglio.** Dramma giocoso per musica, da rappresentarsi nel Piccolo Teatro di S. A. E. di Sassonia. Dresda, il carnevale 1766.

n. i., n. d. 141 p. 15½^{cm}.

Three acts. Author not mentioned, and unknown to Schatz. Cast, scenario, and names of Giuseppe **Scolari** as the composer, of H. A. Bussius as translator. His German title, "Die in verwirrung lebende familie," and text face Italian.

First performed at Dresden, January 16, 1766, as indicated; at Parma, Teatro Ducale, October 26, 1762. SCHATZ 9795

La **famiglia riunita.**   A. T. of the ballet Orlina.

La **famiglia riunita.**   A. T. of the ballo pantomimo Zulima.

La **famiglia stravagante.**   Dramma giocoso per musica da rappresentarsi in Parma nel R. D. Teatro di Corte il carnevale dell' anno MDCCXCIII . . .

Parma, Stamperia Carmignani, n. d.   viii, 56 p.   17½ᶜᵐ.

Two acts.   The author is not mentioned, and is unknown to Schatz.   Impresario's dedicatory poem, cast, and name of Giuseppe **Nicolini** as the composer.

First performed, as indicated, January, 1793; at Piacenza, Teatro della Cittadella, carnival, 1793. SCHATZ 7151

Die **familien-heirath,** oder Der rekruten-aushub.   Eine operette in zwey aufzuegen.

Weimar, Hoffmanische buchhandlung, 1780.   135 p.   14½ᶜᵐ.

Composed by Christian Ludwig **Dieter,** who is not mentioned.   Author unknown to Schatz, and also date of first performance at Stuttgart. SCHATZ 2578

La **famille américaine,** comédie en un acte et en prose mêlée de chants.   Paroles du citoyen Bouilly.   Musique du citoyen Dalayrac. Représentée pour la première fois sur le Théâtre de l'Opéra-comique national, le 1ᵉʳ ventôse de l'an 4ᵐᵉ de la République française.

Blois, Jean François Billault, an IVᵉ de la République [1795–96]. 63 p.   21½ᶜᵐ.

Cast and dedicatory poem "A la citoyenne Dugazon," who played "Madame Daranville, veuve américaine."

First performed, as indicated, February 20, 1796. ML 50.2.F17D2

La **famille indigente,** fait historique en un acte, mélé de chant. Représenté pour la première fois, à Paris, sur le Théâtre de la rue Feydeau, le 4 germinal, an 2ᵉ de la République, 24 mars 1795. Paroles du C. Planterre, musique du C. Gavaux.

Paris, Huet, 1797, an V.   31 p.   21½ᶜᵐ.

Cast.

Schatz and Cl. & L. give March 24, 1794, as date of first performance. ML 50.2.F172G2

La **famille réunie,** comédie en deux actes, en prose, mêlée d'ariettes, représentée pour la premiere fois par les Comédiens italiens ordinaires du roi, le [*blank*] novembre 1790.   Les paroles sont de M. Favart; la musique de M. Chapelle.

Paris, Brunet, 1790.   1 p. l., 43 p.   21ᶜᵐ.

Cast and dedicatory poem by "Favart fils." First performed Nov. 30, 1790. ML 50.2.F174C3

La **famille suisse,** opéra en un acte.   Représenté sur le Théâtre de la rue Feydeau, le 23 pluviôse de l'an cinquième.   Paroles de C. Saint-Just.   Musique de A. Boieldieu.

Paris, Fauvelle et Sagnier, n. d.   51 p.   21ᶜᵐ.

Cast and prefatory note by the author thanking for the "l'accueil favorable" of his piece.

First performed, as indicated, Feb. 11, 1797. ML 50.2.F176B6

Il fanatico burlato. Commedia per musica di Saverio Zini da rappresentarsi nel Real Teatro del Fondo di Separazione per prim' opera di quest' anno 1787 . . .

Napoli, n. publ., 1787. 48 p. 15ᶜᵐ.

Two acts. Impresario's dedication, prefatory note, and name of the composer, **Cimarosa.** The dedication by the impresario, Giuseppe Lucchesi, reads in part:

"Di diversa natura saranno, S. R. M., li spettacoli che in quest' anno si rappresenteranno nel vostro Real Teatro del Fondo di quelli dell' anno scorso. Non vi si reciteranno delle tragedie in musica, ma saranno delle commediole toscane con balleti, avendo procurato di conservar tutta quella decenza tanto necessaria nei teatri. Par che questo genere di rappresentazione incontri più il genio del paese, e la M. V. che con tanto calore promove gli onesti divertimenti, spero che voglia proteggere questo mio spettacolo per potere in tal guisa meritare il pubblico compatimento . . ."

With the opera were performed Giambattista Giannini's "Aci e Galatea, ballo pastorale" and "Il maestro di cappella, o sia Il tutore deluso, ballo di mezzo carattere." The composer of the music is not mentioned.   Schatz 1924

Il fanatico in berlina. L. T. of Paisiello's La locanda.

Il fanatico per gli antichi Romani. Commedia per musica di Giuseppe Palomba da rappresentarsi nel Teatro de' Fiorentini nella primavera di quest' anno 1777.

Napoli, n. publ., 1777. 60 p. 15ᶜᵐ.

Three acts. Cast and name of the composer, Domenico **Cimarosa.**
Schatz 1982

Il fanatico per la musica. Dramma giocoso in musica da rappresentarsi nel Teatro Zagnoni in Bologna la primavera dell' anno 1782 . . .

Bologna, Sassi, n. d. 51 p. 15ᶜᵐ.

Two acts. Author unknown to Schatz. Impresario's dedication, cast, scenario, and names of the composers, Luigi **Caruso** and Carlo **Spontoni.**
First performed at Reggio, Teatro Pubblico, carnival, 1782; at Rome, Teatro delle Dame, February 10, 1781.   Schatz 1667

La fanciulla mal custodita, ballet. *See* Anfossi's Gli artigiani.

La fanciulla mal custodita, ballet. *See* Sarti's Fra i due litiganti il terzo gode, Milano, (1795).

The fancy'd queen. An opera. As it is acted at the Theatre-Royal in Covent-Garden.

London, Charles Corbett, 1733. 2 p. l., 43, [1] p. 19ᶜᵐ.

One act and prologue. Cast. Ballad opera, the airs of the 25 songs of which are indicated by title. By Robert Drury, who is not mentioned.
First performed during the summer of 1733.   Longe 189

Fanfale. Parody of Destouches' Omphale.

Il fantastico, commedia per musica.

Three acts. By Gennaro Antonio Federico, music by Leonardo **Leo,** first performed at Naples, Teatro Nuovo sopra Toledo, carnival 1743.
Not in L. of C.

— Il nuovo D. Chisciotte. Commedia per musica ra rappresitarsi nel Teatro de' Fiorentini nell' autunno di quest' anno 1748 . . .

Napoli, Domenico Langiano, 1748. 4 p. l., 56 p. 15ᶜᵐ.

Three acts. Dedication by the impresario Tomaso Garzia ("nella stagion presente nel mio teatro comparir deve"), cast, prefatory note and remark:

Fanfale—Continued.

"La musica di tutte l'arie segnate col segno § è del fu maestro di cappella D. Leonardo **Leo**, e quella della sinfonia, recitativi, finali, duetto, e dell' altre arie senza alcun segno, è del Signor D. Pietro Gomens (**Gomes**), maestro di capella dell' Ecc. Sig. duca di Castropignano."

Accordingly, only the arias "Quanto Amore è tristarello" (I, 3) "Aure amene, che spirate" (I, 7), "A me tu chiami bestia" (I, 11), "Si signore, io lo farò" (I, 12), "Cor mio inzuccherato" (I, 14), "Capace di più amarti" (I, 17) were by Leo. In other words, only the first act seems to have contained arias by him. The prefatory note sheds further light on this curious replica:

"Essendoci stato addossato il carico di dirigere la presente commedia, ultimo parto del lepidissimo ingegno del fu Gennaro Antonio Federici, assai rinomato in sì fatti componimenti teatrali, e che col nome del *Fantastico* [music by Leo] fu rappresentata sul Teatro Nuovo nel carnovale del 43.; noi, per mancanza del dilei autore, abbiamo accettato l'impegno; avendo avuto però il riguardo di non alterarla punto, se non se in quello, a cui siamo stati astretti dalla pura necessità. Quindi è, che se la trovi abbreviata di molto, e varia ancora in qualche parte di essa, come nel principio, ne' finali, ed in molte arie, ciò non è seguito, perchè forse siasi stimato superfluo, o non proprio quello ch'è stato tolto, o variato, nè per inferir alcun biasmo alla memoria dell' autore, il quale come quello, ch'era molto apposto [mutilated] tiche composizioni, non fu mai capace di simili mende. Ma ciò si è dovuto fare per incontrare il genio del publico, cui tanto alletta nelle sceniche rappresentazioni non meno la novità degli avvenimenti, che la brevità dell' azzione: ed anco per esserci stato d'uopo adattarla all' abilità de' presenti cantanti totalmente diversi da quelli, che la prima volta la rappresentarono, a qual effetto dovè per necessità seguirne il divisato cambiamento . . ." ML 50.2.F178L3

La fantesca. O. T. of Hasse's Il capitano Galoppo.

Faramondo.

Apostolo Zeno, Poesie drammatiche, Venezia, 1744, t. vi, 104 p. 19^cm.

Three acts. Argument. No composer is mentioned. In the "Catalogo" at end of t. x., date and place of first ed. are given as Venice, 1699. (*See* below.) ML 49.A2Z3

— Faramondo, pubblicato per la prima volta in Venezia, 1699.

Apostolo Zeno, Poesie drammatiche, Orleans, 1785–86, t. i, p. 319–413.

Three acts. Argument. No composer is mentioned. ML 49.A2Z4

Il Faramondo. Drama per musica da rappresentarsi nella Sala dell' illmo Sig. conte d'Alibert nel carnovale dell' anno 1720 . . .

Roma, Stamperia del Bernabò, 1720. 72 p. 15^cm.

Three acts. So unlike Zeno's "Faramondo" as to be practically a new text by unknown author. Dedication by conte d'Alibert ("nel mio nuovo teatro . . . questo secondo drama"), argument, scenario, cast and name of Francesco Gasperini (**Gasparini**) as composer. ML 50.2.F2G3

Faramondo. Drama per musica da rappresentarsi nel Teatro Grimani di San Gio. Grisostomo l'anno MDCXCIX . . .

Venetia, Nicolini, 1699. 72 p. (incl. front.) 15^cm.

Three acts. Dedication signed with Apostolo Zeno's initials, argument, scenario The composer, Carlo Francesco **Pollaroli**, is not mentioned.

First performed, carnival, 1699, as indicated. SCHATZ 8286

— Faramondo. Drama per musica rappresentato nella Villa di Pratolino.

Firenze, Gio. Filippo Cecchi, 1699. 4 p. l., 70 p. 17^cm.

Three acts. Neither Zeno, the author, nor Carlo Francesco **Pollaroli**, the composer, is mentioned. Scenario and argument, which reads in part:

"il drama, parto in principio d'una famosa penna; ma cui è convenuto patire qualche alterazione, per essersi voluto adattare alla brevità del tempo, e alla comodità del Teatro."

Faramondo—Continued.

The alterations are very much more numerous than these words would permit to infer. The Florence replica, for instance, begins, "Più che mai fiere, oh Dio" instead of "Sveno, Germano; O Dio!" and the scenes VII, "Del Tasso infausto," VIII, "Mio rè, pronta qui veggo," have been replaced by "Tardi giungemmo, amici" and "Signore, a tanta pompa."   Schatz 8325

The **farmer**: A comic opera. In two acts. As it is performed at the Theatres Royal in London and Dublin. By John O'Keefe, Esq.

Dublin, T. M'Donnell, 1788.   55 p.   17½^{cm}.

London and Dublin casts. The composer, William **Shield**, is not mentioned.
First performed at Covent Garden, October 31, 1787.   Longe 149

— The songs, duets, choruses, etc in the musical entertainment of the **Farmer**. Performed at the Theatre-Royal, Covent-Garden. The musick composed and selected by Mr. Shield. Seventh edition.

London, T. Cadell, 1789.   23 p.   21^{cm}.

Cast. John O'Keefe, the author, is not mentioned.   ML 50.2.F18 S3

— The songs, duets, choruses, etc in the musical entertainment of the **Farmer**. Performed at the Theatre-Royal, Covent-Garden. The musick composed and selected by Mr. Shield. Eighth edition.

London, T. Cadell, 1791.   19 p.   19^{cm}.

Two acts. By John O'Keefe, who is not mentioned. (Bound in at the end of the libretto of Paisiello's "La locanda," London, 1792.)   Schatz 7672

— The **farmer**: A comic opera in two acts as it is performed at the Theatres Royal in London and Dublin. By John O'Keefe, Esq.

Dublin, T. McDonnell, 1792.   36 p.   17^{cm}.

London and Dublin (1792) casts. William **Shield**, the composer, is not mentioned.   Schatz 9866

Farnace. Dramma per musica da rappresentarsi sopra il famoso Ducal Teatro di Bronsevico nella fiera estiva dell' anno 1754.

[Bronsevico], Keitel, n. d.   111 p.   15^{cm}.

Three acts. German title page, "Farnaces," and text face Italian. Argument, cast, scenario. Author (Antonio Maria Lucchini) and composer (unknown to Schatz) not mentioned.
First performed August, 1754, as indicated.   Schatz 11329

Farnace. Drama per musica da rappresentarsi nel Teatro di Sant' Angelo l'autunno dell' anno 1703 . . .

Venezia, Marino Rossetti, 1703.   71 p.   15^{cm}.

Three acts. By Lorenzo Morani (not mentioned). Publisher's dedication, dated Venice, November 15, argument, notice to the reader, cast, scenario, and name of Antonio **Caldara** as composer.   Schatz 1493

Farnace. Dramma per musica da rappresentarsi nel Teatro di Brusselles nel carnovale dell' anno 1729 . . .

Brusselle, n. publ., n. d.   4 p. l., 53, [11] p.   18½^{cm}.

Dedication by the impresario Gio. Sebastiano Brillandi ("dovendo esser l'ultimo [drama] della presente stagione"), scenario, argument, cast and name of Antonio **Cortona** as the composer. This preliminary matter (except the dedication) and the text both in Italian and French.
A curious libretto. It is clearly by Luchini (not mentioned) but with noticeable, even if not very numerous differences. For instance, the scene I, 8 in the Venice 1726 version (*see* Vivaldi) "A sorprendermi il cor" is not in the Brussels version and the former scene I, 9 "Qual sembianza improvisa" is now I, 8 but with the aria

Farnace—Continued.

"Fia quel semplice augelletto" instead of "Al vezzeggiar d'un volto." The second act begins with the former scene II, 3 "Di Farnace e del figlio" and III, 12 (with which the unpaged matter begins) is the same (though much condensed) as the former scene III, 13 and last "Berenice morrà, morrà Pompeo." Now, the text of acts I and II is given complete with added French prose translation, whereas of the third act only the Italian text of the just mentioned (last) scene was printed, but to this was added the complete French prose translation of the third act.　　ML 50.2.F21C6

Farnace. Drama per musica da rappresentarsi nel Regio Teatro di Torino nel carnevale del 1751 . . .

　　Torino, Pietro Giuseppe Zappata e figliuoli, n. d.　4 p. l., 56, [1] p. 15½ᶜᵐ.

Three acts. Author not mentioned, and unknown to Schatz. Argument, cast, scenario, and name of David **Perez** as the composer. On the add. p., the substitute aria, "Quell' alma feroce" (I, 9). Comparison with Ant. M. Lucchini's "Farnace" text, as, for instance, set by Rinaldo da Capua (1739), proves that these two texts, notwithstanding the many differences, are identical. Rinaldo da Capua's opera begins: "Benche vinto, e sconfitto;" that of Perez: "Del nemico Farnace," which are the opening words of scene 3, act I, in Rinaldo da Capua's "Farnace."

　　　　　　　　　　　　　　　　　　　　　　　　　SCHATZ 7878

Farnace. Dramma per musica da rappresentarsi in Firenze nel Teatro di via della Pergola nel carnevale dell' anno 1749 . . .

　　Firenze, Cosimo Maria, Pier, n. d.　55 p.　15ᶜᵐ.

Three acts. Author not mentioned, and unknown to Schatz, but unmistakably, and notwithstanding many differences, the text is identical with Lucchini's "Farnace" text, as comparison proves. Lucchini's text, at least in Rinaldo da Capua's setting (1739), begins: "Benche vinto, e sconfitto;" in the Pescetti setting: "Del nemico Farnace," which are the opening words of scene 3, act I, in Rinaldo da Capua's opera.

　　Argument, cast, scenario, and name of Giovanni Battista **Pescetti** as the composer.

　　　　　　　　　　　　　　　　　　　　　　　　　SCHATZ 7966

Farnace. Drama per musica da rappresentarsi nel Teatro Tron di San Cassiano il carnovale dell' anno MDCCXVIII. Di Domenico Lalli . . .

　　Venezia, Marino Rossetti, 1718.　60 p.　15ᶜᵐ.

Three acts. Author's dedication, argument, cast, scenario, and name of Carlo Francesco **Pollaroli** as the composer.　　　　　　　　SCHATZ 8287

Farnace. Dramma per musica da rappresentarsi nel Teatro di S. A. S. E. di Baviera nel carnevale del' anno 1740.

　　Monaco, Giv. Giac. Vötter, n. d.　61 p.　15ᶜᵐ.

Three acts. By Antonio Maria Lucchini, who is not mentioned. Argument, cast, scenario, and name of Giovanni **Porta** as the composer. At the end of the argument we read:

"Il dramma non comparisce come nuovo . . . Ognun sà quanta sempre, benchè in varie guise mutato, incontrasse lode, e applauso. Pur questa volta ancora diverso dalle passate in alcune parti apparisce, ma tanto solo, quanto è convenuto adattarlo agli egregi attori, che il rappresentano, e cantano, a cui per comodo della musica è costretti la poesia a servire, più che a se stessa."

First performed at Bologna, Teatro Malvezzi, spring of 1731.　　SCHATZ 8379

Farnace. Dramma per musica da rappresentarsi nel famosissimo Teatro Grimani di S. Gio. Grisostomo l'autunno dell' anno 1739 . . .

　　Venezia, Marino Rossetti, 1739.　47 p.　14½ᶜᵐ.

Three acts. By Ant. M. Lucchini. Composed by **Rinaldo di Capua**. Dedicatory preface by the impresario, Domenico Lalli, argument, cast, scenario, and name of the composer.　　　　　　　　　　　　　　　　　　SCHATZ 8796

Farnace. Dramma per musica da rappresentarsi nel nobile **Teatro** di San Samuele la fiera dell' Ascensione dell' anno 1776.

Venezia, Gio. Battista Casali, 1776.   56 p.   17^{cm}.

Three acts. By Antonio Maria Lucchini, who is not mentioned. Argument, cast, scenario, and name of Giuseppe **Sarti** as the composer ("La musica sarà tutta nuova"). On p. [23]–34, argument, name of Carlo Canobbio as composer of the music, and description of Onorato Viganò's "Andromaca in Epiro, ballo eroico, tragico pantomimo."   SCHATZ 9473

Farnace. Drama per musica da rappresentarsi nel Teatro di Sant' Angelo nel carnovale dell' anno 1726.

Venezia, Marino Rossetti, 1726.   57 p.   14$\frac{1}{2}$^{cm}.

Three acts. By Antonio Maria Luchini, who is not mentioned. Argument, cast, scenario, and name of Antonio **Vivaldi** as the composer.   SCHATZ 10766

Farsa per musica nelle nozze de' nobili sposi Niccolò Panciatichi e marchesa Vittoria Ximenes d'Aragona.

Firenze, Stamperia Moückiana, 1762.   xxiii p.   20^{cm}.

Vignettes, etc. Dedicatory poem by "L'autore G. S. G." Carl' Ambrogio **Meli** is mentioned as the composer. The piece has no title, but may be called "Imene ed Armonia" from the only two characters in the play.   ML 48.M2F

Farsetta per musica da rappresentarsi nel Teatro alla Valle nel carnevale dell' anno 1751 . . .

Roma, Ottavio Puccinelli, 1751.   27 p.   15$\frac{1}{2}$^{cm}.

Two parts. Author not mentioned. Dedication by the publisher and Angelo Lungi, cast and note "La musica è del Sig. Gioacchino **Cocchi** diretta dal Sig. Antonio Colli." The four characters of the farsetta are S. Niccolò Tagliaciocchi, Agnolella, Calandra, Trappola.   ML 50.2.F22C7

— **Farsetta in musica** da rappresentarsi nel Teatro della città di Spolti nel carnevale dell' anno 1758 . . .

Spoleti, Domenico Giannini, n. d.   30, [1] p.   16$\frac{1}{2}$^{cm}.

Two parts. Dedication, cast with same characters as above and name of Gioacchino **Cocchi** as the composer.   ML 50.2.F22C72

Der **faschingsschmaus,** ein singspiel in zween aufzuegen, von der studierenden jugend des katholischen schulhauses in Augsburg bey St. Salvator aufgefuehrt den 20. 21. und 22ten Hornunge [Feb.] 1797.

[Augsburg], Joseph Anton Hueber, n. d.   [15] p.   18$\frac{1}{2}$^{cm}.

Cast and "Vorbericht," in which "Matthäus **Fischer,** regulierter chorherr des heiligen Augustus zum heiligen Kreuze in Augsburg" as composer. At head of title: "Strafe der ungerechten rachbegierde, ein bürgerliches trauerspiel . . . und"   SCHATZ 3220

The **fashionable lady;** or, Harlequin's opera.   In the manner of a rehearsal.   As it is perform'd at the Theatre in Goodman's-Fields. Written by Mr. Ralph.

London, J. Watts, 1730.   4 p. l.; 94, [2] p.   18$\frac{1}{2}$^{cm}.

The [2] p. contain advertisement by Watts.

Ballad opera. Three acts. Cast. James Ralph's dedication and table of the 68 songs, the airs for which are printed in the text with their titles.

First performed April 2, 1730.   LONGE 276

Der **fassbinder.**   Tr. of Audinot and Gossec's Le tonnelier.

La **fata Alcione** ossia Amore ed innocenza, ballet.   *See* Mayr's Avviso ai maritati.

La **fata benefica,** ballet. *See* Cimarosa's I nemici generosi.

La **fata benefica,** ballet. *See* P. Guglielmi's Admeto.

La **fata benefica.** Dramma giocoso per musica da rappresentarsi nel nobile Teatro dell' eccell^{ma} casa Giustiniani in S. Moisè il carnevale 1783.

> *Venezia, n. publ., n. d. 55 p.*
> Two acts. Author not mentioned and unknown to Schatz. Cast and name of Michele **Mortellari** as the composer. Schatz 6680

La **fata capricciosa.** Dramma giocoso per musica di Giovanni Bertati da rappresentarsi nel nobile Teatro Giustiniani in San Moisè il carnovale dell' anno 1789.

> *Venezia, Modesto Fenzo, 1789. 58 p. 18^{cm}.*
> Two acts. Scenario and name of Francesco **Gardi** as the composer. Schatz 3548

La **fata meravigliosa.** Dramma giocoso per musica da rappresentarsi nel Teatro di S. Cassano nel carnevale 1745 . . .

> *Venezia, Modesto Fenzo, 1746 [!]. 59 p. 15½^{cm}.*
> Three acts. Author not mentioned and unknown to Schatz. Impresario's dedication, cast, scenario, and name of Giuseppe **Scolari** as the composer.
> Schatz 9796

La **fata Urgella,** ballet. *See* Gnecco's Lo sposo di tre.

Le **fate.** Dramma per musica.

> *Dresda, la vedova Stössel, n. d. Unpaged. 18½^{cm}.*
> One act. Argument. Neither the author, Stefano Benedetto Pallavicini, is mentioned nor the composer, Giovanni Alberto **Ristori**.
> First performed August 10, 1736, at Dresden, Hoftheater. Schatz 8817

The **father and the son rivals.** Tr. of T. Giordani's Il padre e il figlio rivali.

Le **fatiche d'Ercole per Deianira.** Drama per musica di Aurelio Aureli, favola decima. Rappresentata nel famosiss. Teatro Grimani . . .

> *Venetia, Francesco Nicolini, 1662. front., 82 p. 14^{cm}.*
> Prologue and three acts. Author's dedication, argument, and notice to the reader, in which he says:
> "Sono hoggidi le persone della città di Venetia divenute così suogliate ne i gusti de i drami, che non sanno più, che desiderar di vedere, ne l'intelletto di chi compone sà più, che inventare per acquistarsi gl'applausi de' spettatori, ò per incontrare la sodisfattione della maggior parte (che di tutti è impossibile) . . . Confesso d'essermi in queste affaticato più che negl' altri miei drami per incontrar il tuo genio."
> The composer, Pietro Andrea **Ziani**, is not mentioned.
> First performed, as indicated, carnival, 1662. Schatz 11221

Fatima. Dramma per musica da rappresentarsi nel Regio Teatro di Torino nel carnovale del 1779 . . .

> *Torino, Onorato Derossi, n. d. viii, 54 p. 17^{cm}.*
> Three acts. Author not mentioned, and not known to Schatz. Argument, cast, scenario, and name of Bernard(in)o **Ottani** as the composer. On p. 55 was to follow a description of Alessandro Guglielmi's ballet "La costanza guerriera," music by Vittorio Amedeo Canavasso. Schatz 7361

Le **faucon,** opéra comique, en un acte, en prose, mêlé d'ariettes par M. Sedaine, la musique de M * * * Représenté devant Sa Majesté à Fontainebleau, le 2 novembre 1771, et à Paris, par les Comédiens italiens, ordinaires du roi, le 19 mars 1772.

Paris, Claude Herissant, 1772. 47, [1] p. 21½^{cm}.

Composed by **Monsigny.** Prettily illustrated by Huault. Schatz 6573

— Le **faucon,** opera-comique, en un acte, en prose mêlée d'ariettes' par M. Sedaine. La musique de M . . . Représenté devant Sa Majesté, à Fontainebleau, le 2 novembre 1771; & à Paris par les Comédiens italiens ordinaires du roi, le 19 mars 1772.

Paris, Claude Herissant, 1772. 32 p. 19^{cm}.

Cast. No music printed in the text. Schatz 11726
Second copy. Yudin PQ

La **fausse aventuriere,** opera-comique, en deux actes, mêlé d'ariettes. Par Mrs. Anseaume & de Marcouville. Représenté pour la première fois sur le Théâtre de la Foire Saint Germain, le mardi 22 mars 1757.

Paris, Duchesne, 1757. 64 p. 20^{cm}.

Cast. Composed resp. arranged by Jean Louis **Laruette.** On p. 56–64, the airs, "Cours à ta belle" (I, 1), "Sexe dangereux, trompeur" (I, 6), "Quelle folie extrême" (I, 8). Schatz 5437

La **fausse-foire.** Prologue des deux pièces suivantes. Représenté par la troupe du Sieur Francisque à la Foire de Saint Laurent 1721 . . .

Below the title, this Avertissement:
Le privilège de l'Opéra comique ayant été accordé à d'autres qu'au Sieur Hamoche & à la Dlle de Lisle, (les deux aresboutans de ce spectacle, sous les noms de Pierrot & d'Olivette) ces deux acteurs se joignirent à la troupe du Sr. Francisque, & joüèrent ce prologue avec les deux pièces qui le suivent. Comme les Comédiens italiens s'établirent à la Foire, le secret dépit qu'en eûrent les Comédiens françois, fut favorable à la troupe de Francisque. Ils la laissèrent paisiblement représenter des pièces en prose; mais les privilégiez ses voisins lui firent interdire par l'Opéra, non seulement le chant & la danse, mais jusqu'aux machines & changemens de décoration."

— La **boîte de Pandore.** Pièce d'un acte. Representée par la troupe du sieur Francisque à la Foire de Saint Laurent. 1721.

— La **tête-noire.** Pièce d'un acte représentée par la troupe du Sr Francisque à la Foire de Saint Laurent 1721.

Le Théâtre de la foire, Paris, 1724, t. iv, 3 pl., [353]–502 p. 17^{cm}.

According to a note on 2d p. l., the plays in t. iv were written by Le Sage, Fuzelier, and d'Orneval. These three are practically without music. Below the title of the last play, this Avertissement:
"Cette pièce fut faite à l'occasion d'un faux-bruit qui courut à Paris, qu'il y avoit dans certaine communauté une jeune demoiselle, dont le visage ressembloit à une tête de mort. On offroit, disoit-on, une somme considérable au premier garçon qui voudroit l'épouser. Il se présenta effectivement, pour la voir, un grand nombre de jeunes-gens, qui étoient assez crédules pour ajoûter foi a cette fable, & qui vouloient même entrer par force dans cette communauté. On fut obligé, pour les repousser, de mettre pendant plusieurs jours des gardes à la porte."

First performed July 31, 1721. ML 48.L2IV

La **fausse magie.** Comédie en vers, et en deux actes mêlée de chant, représenté pour la première fois sur le Théâtre de la Comédie italienne, le mercredi premier février 1775. Par M. Marmontel . . .

Paris, la veuve Duchesne, 1775. 72 p. 18^{cm}.

Cast. The composer, **Grétry,** is not mentioned. On p. 72 the couplet air of "Veut-on que la bonne aventure." ML 50.2.F23G7

La **fausse magie**—Continued.

— La **fausse magie**, comédie en vers et en deux actes, mêlée de chant, représentée pour la première fois sur le Théatre de la Comédie italienne, le mercredi 1er février 1775. Par M. Marmontel . . . La musique est de M. Grétry.

> *Paris, la veuve Duchesne, 1775. 48 p. 18ᶜᵐ.*
>
> Cast. On p. 47–48, the couplet air of "Veut-on-que la bonne aventure."
>
> SCHATZ 4153

— Die **abgeredete zauberey**. Eine komische oper in einem aufzuge, aus dem franzoesischen des herrn Marmontel uebersetzt von Stephanie dem juengern. Die musik dazu ist vom herrn Gretry. aufgefuehrt auf dem K. K. Nationaltheater.

> *Wien, zufinden beym logen meister, 1778. 50 p. 16ᶜᵐ.*
>
> First performed, as indicated, October 27, 1778. SCHATZ 4154

— Das **blendwerk**. Eine komische oper in einem aufzuge. Nach dem franzoesischen des Marmontel und beybehaltener Gretryscher musik . . .

> *Gotha, Carl Wilhelm Ettinger, 1781. 64 p. 15½ᶜᵐ.*
>
> By Wilhelm Christian Dietrich Meyer, who is not mentioned, and who, oddly enough, selected this motto for his title page:
> "Was nicht der muehe verlohnt gesprochen zu werden, das laesst man heutzutage singen. *Beaumarchais.*"
> First performed at Mannheim, Churf. deutsche Schaubühne, February 25, 1779.
>
> SCHATZ 4155

— Der **zauberspiegel**. Eine komische oper, in zwei aufzeugen. Nach dem franzoesischen. Mit beibehaltung der Gretryschen musik von Ch. F. v. B——n.

> *n. i., n. d. 54 p. 15½ᶜᵐ.*
>
> By Christian Friedrich, freiherr v. Bonin.
> First performed at Berlin, Döbbelinsches Theater, January 18, 1781.
>
> SCHATZ 4156

La **fausse peur**, comédie en un'acte, mêlée d'ariettes, représentée pour la premiere fois par les Comédiens italiens, le lundi 18 juillet 1774. Par M. N * * *. La musique est de M. d'Arcis, elève de M. Gretry, âgé de 14 ans & demi.

> *Paris, Valade, 1775. 48 p. 17½ᶜᵐ.*
>
> Cast. The prodigy's dedication to his mother is followed by an Avant-propos, in which the anonymous author says:
> "En donnant cette bagatelle, je n'ai pas prétendu a voir fait une bonne pièce: je me suis trouvé très-heureux de n'en a voir pas fait une détestable. Mon but étoit de procurer à un enfant interessant l'occasion de faire briller son génie naissant . . .
> "On a trouvé que les scenes étoient décousues: je le crois bien. On en a retranché plusieurs: on a ôté deux *duo* presque à l'instant de représenter . . . Cependant, j'ose espérer qu'à la lecture on reviendra de ce préjugé défavorable . . ."
> He thanks the public for the kind reception of his "enfant." This might lead to the inference that the composer's father was the author, but we know from the revised edition of the text, composed by Dalayrac as "La leçon," that it was written by Marsollier. On p. 43–48 the airs of "Il faut cesser d'être sévere," "Quel éclat brille dans sesyeux" and the vaudeville "Allons, cette heureuse journée." SCHATZ 2411
>
> Second copy. SCHATZ 11671

Les **fausses apparences** ou L'amant jaloux, comédie, en trois actes, mêlée d'ariettes; représentée devant Leurs Majestés, à Versailles en novembre [Nov. 20] 1778.

Paris, la veuve Duchesne, 1779.   2 p. l., 80 p.   20^{cm}.

Cast.   **Grétry** is mentioned as composer, d'Hèle as author.   No music printed with the text.   ML 50.2.F235G6

— Les **fausses apparences,** ou L'amant jaloux, en trois actes, mêlée d'ariettes.   Les paroles sont de M. d'Hèle.   La musique de M. Grètry.   Représentée devant Leurs Majestés, à Versailles, en novembre [Nov. 20] 1778.

Paris, la veuve Duchesne, 1780.   64 p.   19^{cm}.

Cast.   On p. 35–37 the voice and bass of the ariette "Le mariage est une envie" (II, 3) and on p. 52–54 of "Tandis que tout sommeille" (II, 14).

First performed at Paris, Comédie-italienne, Dec. 23, 1778.   Schatz 4157

— **L'amant jaloux,** ou Les fausses apparences, comédie en trois actes, melée d'ariettes; représentée devant Leurs Majestés, à Versailles en Novembre 1778.   Les paroles sont de M. d'Hele.   La musique de M. Grétry.

Toulouse, Broulhiet, 1780.   46 p.   18½^{cm}.

Cast.   ML 50.2.F235G7

— Der **eifersuechtige liebhaber.**   Ein singspiel in drey aufzuegen. Aus dem franzoesischen; auf die musik des herrn Gretry uebersetzt, von hrn. Stephanie dem juengern.   Aufgefuehrt im k. k. National Theater.

Wien, zu finden beym logenmeister, 1780.   60, [1] p.   17^{cm}.

First performed, as indicated, October 12, 1780.   Schatz 4158

Les **fausses infidélités.**   A. T. of Philidor's Zémire et Mélide.

Fausta restituita all' impero.   Dramma per musica da rappresentarsi nel nuovo Teatro di Tor di Nona dell' illustriss. Signor conte d'Alibert l'anno 1697 . . .

Roma, Domenico Ant. Ercole, 1697.   59 p.   13½^{cm}.

Three acts.   Dedication by Pietro Leone, the book dealer, who hardly was responsible for the alterations of Novello de Bonis "Odoacro" text.   Neither he is mentioned, nor Giacomo Antonio **Perti,** the composer.   Argument and scenario.

    Schatz 7959

Das **faustrecht in Thueringen.**   Erster theil.   Ein schauspiel mit gesang in vier aufzügen nach Halper a Spada für die schaubühne bearbeitet von Karl Friedrich Hensler.   Die musik von Ferdinand Kauer . . .

Wien, Schmidt, 1797.   94 p.   17^{cm}.

First performed at Vienna, Marinellische Schaubühne in der Leopoldstadt, April 7, 1796.   Schatz 5027

— Das **faustrecht in Thueringen.**   Zweyter theil . . . [same as above].

Wien, Schmidt, 1797.   96 p.   17^{cm}.

First performed at the same theatre, January 17, 1797, or already in 1796.

    Schatz 5028

Das **faustrecht in Thueringen**—Continued.

— Das **faustrecht in Thueringen**. Dritter und letzter theil . . . [same as above]

Wien, Schmidt, 1797. 100 p. 17cm.

On p. [2]: "Aufgefuehrt auf der k. k. privil. Marinellischen Schaubühne in Wien." Schatz does not record the date.   SCHATZ 5029

Le **faux lord**, comédie en deux actes, en prose, mêlée d'ariettes, représentée devant Leurs Majestés, et à Paris, par les Comédiens italiens ordinaires du Roi, le 6 décembre 1783.

Paris, Brunet, 1783. 4 p. l., 86 p. 19cm.

The dedication is addressed to "A mon père" and signed "Votre tendre fils, Piccinni l'aîné." In it he calls this piece "mon premier essai." Cast and names of [Giuseppe Maria] "Piccinni fils" as author, of Niccolò **"Piccinni** père" as composer.   SCHATZ 8092

Les **faux monnoyeurs**, ou La vengeance, drame en trois actes, mêlés de chants. Paroles de J. G. A. Cuvelier; musique de Gresnich; décorations de Moench. Représenté pour la première fois le 12 floréal, an 5, [May 1, 1797] sur le Théatre Montansier au Palais-Egalité. *Paris, Barba, an cinquième de la République, [1797–98]. 42 p. 20cm.* Cast.   SCHATZ 4131

Le **faux-prodige**. A. T. of Piron's text La robe de dissention.

La **favola d' Apollo e Dafne**, ballet. *See* Rispoli's Nitteti.

La **favola de' tre gobbi**. Intermezzo.

[153]–175 p. 16½cm. Carlo Goldoni, Opere drammatiche giocose, t. iv, Torino, 1757.

Two parts. First performed with music by Vincenzo Legrenzio **Ciampi** at Venice, Teatro di San Moise, carnival 1749.   ML 49.A2G6

— La **favola de' tre gobbi**. Intermezzo di due parti per musica.

Carlo Goldoni, Opere teatrali, Venezia, Zatta e figli, 1788–95, v. 35, [181]–205 p. 18½cm.   PQ

Il **favore de gli Dei**. Drama fantastico musicale fatto rappresentare dal Serenissimo Sig. duca di Parma nel suo Gran Teatro per le felicissime nozze del Serenissimo Sig. principe Odoardo suo primo genito con la Serenissima Signora principessa Dorotea Sofia di Neoburgo . . . Poesia d'Aurelio Aurelj . . . e musica di D. Bernardo Sabadini . . .

Parma, Stampa ducale, 1690. xvi, 88 p. 21½cm.

Three acts. Aureli's dedication, "Dilucidatione," cast, scenario, list of the "Machine in aria e in terra" and Aureli's interesting and instructive prefatory note which reads:

"Non persuaderti di leggere in questo drama altezza di frase. La mia penna avuezza à radere il suolo non sà spiegare voli di Dedalo. Scrissi più per la musica, che per la lettura. Dove fù dalla magnanimità di questa A. S. fatta una scielta dei più canori Cigni, e delle più dolci sirene d'Italia, m' auria parso commettere un grand' errore à non procurar di ponere ogni studio nella facilità dei versi, e nei metri dell' arie per dar materia al compositore della musica di farti godere delle lor soavissime voci à quel segno maggiore, ch'hà potuto per mettermi con adeguata misura il gran numero d'essi. Ne credere di compassare la recita di questo drama col solito spazio di tempo, che si pratica ne gl' altri ordinarj. Perche si come il Gran Teatro di Parma è il più maestoso di quanti n'abbia l'Europa, anzi il mondo tutto, nulla cedendo in

Il **favore de gli Dei**—Continued.

pregio à gl' antichi più famosi di Roma già dal tempo distrutti, ne questi s'apre giamai, che solo in occasione di nozze di serenissimi principi Farnesi; Così in esso rappresentandosi qualche drama non mai scompagnato da moltiplicità di musici, da varietà di scene, e da quantità di machine, fù, e sarà sempre chi hà scritto, e scriverà per il medesimo in simile occorrenze costretto à passar la misura dell' ore limitate all' altre dramatiche compositioni. Due cose in questo drama hò studiate. Inventione parte necessaria ad ogni poeta, e dispositione delle cose inventate. Nella prima hò procurato con la varietà dell' apparenze di recar diletto, e non tedio alla grandezza, e nobiltà de' spettatori nel corso di sett'ore, che può forse durare la recita dell' opera, in cui mi dichiaro d'essermi scapricciato à mia voglia mercè alla generosità senza pari di S. A. S. mio clementissimo patrone, che mi hà concesso ampio campo di poter farlo. Nell' altra hò impiegato ogni studio per trovare quella facilità più propria al drameggiare. L'onore (di cui me ne dichiaro incapace) del pregiato commando di S. A., che m'obligò in breve tempo à due si gloriose fatiche, l'una per il Giardino, l'altra per il Gran Teatro, animò e invigeri la mia debolezza à una pronta obedienza. Se avrò in qualche parte mancato à quanto si richiederebbe ad un pondo si grave; Spero che l'armonia della musica del virtuosissimo Sig. D. Bernado **Sabadini** mastro di capella di S. A. S. sia per rapirti à tal segno la mente, che ò non vedrai, ò vedendole non sdegnerai di leggere, e compatire le mie debolezze. Vivi felice."

Our copy lacks the unnumb. page after p. 88 with reference to "Girolamo Pajani, suonatore d'arpa" as also the fifteen magnificent plates in the Brussels Conservatory copy, partly reproduced in fac-simile by Wotquenne in his catalogue.

First performed, as indicated, May 25, 1690.   ML 50.2.F237S2

Favourite songs, written and composed by Mr. Dibdin. As they are performed in a divertissement, prepared purposely for their introduction at the Theatre-Royal Covent-Garden.

London, Printed for the author, n. d.   xxx, [2] p.   20^{cm}.

Two acts. Cast. A prefatory note says:
"From the popularity of the following songs, it was conceived that they might be brought on the stage with effect. Mr. Harris adopted the suggestion, and procured a vehicle to be prepared for their introduction:—not however before he had consulted their author and composer . . ."

The [2] contain "songs and other publications," to be had at "Mr. Dibdin's warehouse," "songs in the Oddities," etc.

Must have been published 1789 or later.   Longe 214

La **fede in cimento**. L. T. of M. A. Bononcini's Il trionfo di Camilla, regina de' Volsci.

La **fede in cimento**. L. T. of Gasparini's L'amor generoso.

La **fede ne' tradimenti**. Drama per musica che si rappresenta nel Teatro dell' Illⁱᵐᵃ Accademia de' Remoti in Faenza l'estate dell' año 1723 . . .

Faenza, Stamperia dell' archi impressor camerale, n. d.   61, [1] p. 15½^{cm}.

Three acts. Impresario's dedication, dated Faenza, June 10, 1723, scenario, argument, protesta, with name of Girolamo Gigli as author, cast, and name of Giuseppe Maria **Buini** as composer.   ML 48.A5   v. 4

La **fede ne' tradimenti**. Dramma per musica . . . fatto cantare da SS. convittori del nobil collegio Tolomei di Siena. Per il carnovale di quest' anno.

Siena, nella Stamper. del publ., 1689.   5 p. l., 49 p.   13½^{cm}.

Three acts. The dedication to prince Domenico Rospigliosi is dated "Siena li 12. febbraio 1689" and signed by Girolamo Gigli as author. Then comes notice, "Lettore amico," "Ristretto dell' opera," characters, scenario, cast of the dances (mostly noblemen), and name of the composer, Giuseppe **Fabbrini**, "maestro di capella della Metropolitana e del Collegio."   Schatz 2962

Second copy.   ML 48.A5   v. 46

La **fede ne' tradimenti**—Continued.

— La **fede ne' tradimenti**. Dramma per musica fatto cantare da' SS. Convittori del nobil Collegio Tolomei di Siena. Per il carnivale di quest' anno 1689.

Siena, Stamper. del Publ., 1689. 3 p. l., 48 p. 14^{cm}.

Three acts. The same text as in the preceding entry. Neither Gigli nor **Fabbrini** mentioned. Argument and note:
"Quest' operetta medesima si trova con l'aggionta di due ridicoli fatta dal Sig. Franco de Lemene." ML 50.2.F24F2

La **fede ne' tradimenti**. Drama per musica da recitarsi nel Teatro di S. Angelo l'autunno dell' anno 1721 . . .

Venezia, Marino Rossetti, 1721. 48 p. 14½^{cm}.

Three acts. Argument, cast, and dedication, with name of Girolamo Gigli, the author. Carlo Luigi **Pietragrua**, the composer, is not mentioned. Schatz 8165

La **fede ne tradimenti**. Drama per musica da recitarsi nel Teatro di San Fantino l'anno 1705 . . .

Venezia, Marino Rossetti, 1705. 60 p. 15^{cm}.

Three acts. By Girolamo Gigli, with alterations by Giuseppe Beretta. Neither they nor the composer, Carlo Francesco **Pollaroli**, are mentioned. Impresario's dedication, dated Venice, October 30, 1705, and argument. Schatz 8288

La **fede ne' tradimenti**. Drama per musica da rappresentarsi nel Teatro di S. Bartolomeo nella state dell' anno 1718 . . .

Napoli, Michele Luigi Muzio, 1718. 58 p. 13½^{cm}.

Three acts. By Girolamo Gigli, who is not mentioned. Impresario's dedication, dated Naples, May 15, 1718, argument, scenario, cast, and name of Domenico **Sarro** as the composer. Schatz 9415

La **fede tra gl'inganni**. Drama per musica. Da rappresentarsi nel Teatro di Sant' Angelo. Il carnovale MDCCVII . . .

Venezia, Marino Rossetti, 1707. 48 p. 14½^{cm}.

Three acts. Publisher's dedication, argument, scenario, and Rossetti's notice to the reader, in which he says that this text was written by the author "ne' primi anni della sua applicazione al teatro," and that "trè anni sono lo concesse à chi desiderò esporlo sovra le scene in Rovigo." Neither the author, Francesco Silvani, is mentioned, nor the composer, Tommaso **Albinoni**. Schatz 119

La **fede tradita e vendicata**. O. T. of Silvani's text Ricimero.

La **fede tradita e vendicata**. *See* Galuppi's Ernelinda.

La **fede tradita e vendicata**. Drama per musica da rappresentarsi nel Teatro Tron di S. Casciano l'anno 1704. Poesia di Francesco Silvani . . .

Venezia, Gio. Battista Zuccato, 1704. 72 p. 14½^{cm}.

Three acts. Author's dedication, dated Venice, January 5, 1704, argument, notice to the reader, in which the author calls this his second drama, cast, and name of Carlo Francesco **Gasparini** as the composer. Schatz 3566

— La **fede tradita e vendicata**. Drama per musica da rappresentarsi nel famoso Teatro di S. Bartolomeo in questo presente anno . . .

Napoli, Salvatore Votto, 1707. 70 p. 14^{cm}.

Three acts. Dedication, notice to the reader, argument, cast, and scenario. The "amico lettore" is informed by Carlo de Pretis that the drama being "sempre lontano dal costume Napoletano; stato è d'uopo a me Carlo de Petris di ridurlo all' uso di questa città . . . La musica è dell' ammirabilissimo Signor Francesco **Gasparini**,

La **fede tradita e vendicata**—Continued.

con qualche cosa di più de Signor Gioseppe **Vignola** . . ." The alterations are considerable, but more in the arias than in the dialogue. For instance, the very first aria is now "Sovvengati che sei," instead of "Se l'amor mio t'è caro;" scene sixth, act III, now begins, "Ah che disgratia, udite," instead of "L'infelice Ernelinda, o principessa," etc., etc.　　　　　　　　SCHATZ 3567

La **fede tradita e vendicata.** Dramma per musica da rappresentarsi nel Teatro di Sant' Angelo il carnovale dell' anno 1726 . . .

　　Venezia, Marino Rossetti, 1726. 48 p. 14½ᶜᵐ.

　　Three acts. By Francesco Silvani, who is not mentioned. Impresario's dedication, argument, cast, scenario, and name of Antonio **Vivaldi** as the composer.
　　　　　　　　SCHATZ 10767

La **fedeltà coronata,** oder Die gekroente treue, in einem singspiel auff dem grossen Hamburgischen Schau-platz vorgestellet. Im jahr 1706.

　　n. i., n. d. Unpaged. 18½ᶜᵐ.

　　Three acts. Argument by the author, Hinsch (not mentioned), and "avertissement" signed by the composer, Reinhard **Keiser,** in which he says in part:

　　"Soweit erstrecket sich der inhalt, so der herr autor zum vorbericht gesetzet: wobey ich dieses hinzu zu fuegen, dass mein wunsch dahin ziele, dieser opera mit so lustigem humeur zuzusehen, als mein gemueht bisher verdruss bey meinem zustande empfunden. Da nun dieses meine drey und dreissigste composition der schauspiele, so moechten vielleicht die inventiones zu vielen 100. arien einem connosseur einiges nachsinnen erwecken. Jedoch kan ich nicht in abrede seyn, dass zu deren verfertigung mich nichts als die liebe zu diesem theatro, fürnemlich aber die hoefligkeit eines vornehmen hauses encouragirt . . . Und da die meisten widrige raisonnements von denen gefaellet worden, welche etwass ihre passiones verleitet, oder sich flattiren, dass sie unter die zahl der musickenner gehoeren, wenn sie etwan ein menuet auff der hautbois oder violine spielen, so kann ich gegentheils versichern, dass ich niemals auff dergleichen jugements reflectirt, noch um den mauvait gout du par-terre mich bekuemmert, weil ich weiss, wie weit der menschen urtheil, so oeffters so unzeitig als irraisonnabel zu aestimiren. Einige arien aus meiner *Almira* habe desswegen hinein geruecket, weil dieselbe vereits vor 2. jahren, ehe allhier Almira auffgefuehrt, componirt, und damit sie nicht eben gar versteckt blieben, so habe darinnen einigen liebhabern leicht favorisiren koennen, obgleich dieselbe meistens gedruckt, und mit naechsten zusammt der *Octavia* zum vorschein kommen werden. Die italiaenische, so mit cursiv-lettern gezeichnet, sind mir von einem autore, dessen poësie mir bissher viel plaisir gemacht, communicirt . . ."　　　　　　　　SCHATZ 5089

La **fedeltà coronata.** L. T. of Orlandini's Antigona.

La **fedeltà nelle selve.** Dramma giocoso per musica dell' ab. Michelangelo Prunetti, romano, Accademico Quirino. Da rappresentarsi nel nobilissimo Teatro Giustiniani in San Moisè il carnovale dell' anno 1793 . . .

　　Venetia, Modesto Fenzo, 1792. 56 p. 17½ᶜᵐ.

　　Two acts. Cast and name of Giacomo **Tritto** as the composer.　　SCHATZ 10484

— La **fedeltà tra le selve.** Commedia per musica da rappresentarsi nel Real Teatro del Fondo di Separazione per second' opera del corrente anno 1796 . . .

　　Napoli, n. publ., 1796. 48 p. 15ᶜᵐ.

　　Two acts. By Michelangelo Prunetti, who is not mentioned. Impresario's dedication dated Naples, August 2, 1796, cast, and name of Giacomo Tritta (**Tritto**) as the composer. With the opera was performed Lauchelin Duquesney's "Egle, e Cloco o siano I satiri puniti, ballo favoloso pantomimo . . . La musica è tutta nuova scritta dal sig. Hayden." Cast and description of the ballet on p. 7–11.

　　First performed at Venice, Teatro di San Moisè, carnival 1793 as "La fedeltà nelle selve."
　　　　　　　　SCHATZ 10470

La fedeltà riconosciuta. Dramma giocoso posto in musica da Sua Eccellenza nobil uomo Francesco Moro Lin da cantarsi nel suo casino.

Venezia, Modesto Fenzo, 1798. 48 p. 17½^{cm}.

Two acts. Author not mentioned and unknown to Schatz. who says that the text is a later version of "La finta giardiniera." SCHATZ 6674

La fedeltà riconosciuta. A. T. of P. v. Winter's Belisa.

La fedeltà tra le selve. L. T. of Bianchi's La villanella rapita.

Federico II rè di Prussia, ballet. *See* Salieri's Axur rè d'Ormus.

Fedra, ballet. *See* Campobasso's Antigona.

Fedra. Dramma per musica da rappresentarsi nel Real Teatro di S. Carlo nel dì I. gennaro 1788 . . .

Napoli, Vincenzo Flauto, 1788. 54 p. 15½^{cm}.

Two acts. Impresario's dedication, cast, name of **Paisiello** as the composer, and author's preface with this footnote by the impresario:

"Non s'intende per qual ragione il Sig. abate Salvioni autore di questo dramma, da noi in qualche parte cangiato per comodo delle nostre scene, abbia tralasciato di rammentare fra loro, che trattarono questo argomento, l'immortale [Carlo Innocente] Frugoni."

As a matter of fact, Salvioni did not write a new libretto, but simply modified Frugoni's "Ippolito ed Aricia." SCHATZ 7668

La fée Urgele. Comédie en quatre actes, meslée d'ariettes, représentée devant Leurs Majestés, à Fontainebleau, le 26 octobre 1765.

[Paris], Christophe Ballard, 1765. 52 p. 20½^{cm}. (Journal des spectacles, t. ii, Paris, 1766.)

Cast and name of Egidio Romualdo **Duni** as composer. The Journal on p. 14, t. I, attributes the text to Charles Simon "Favart & compagnie." Font says: "Voisenon a retouché des détails." ML 48.J7

— **La fée Urgele,** ou Ce qui plait aux dames, comédie en quatre actes, meslée d'ariettes; représentée devant Leurs Majestés, par les Comédiens italiens ordinaires du roi, à Fontainebleau, le 26 octobre 1765. Et à Paris le 4 décembre suivant.

Paris, la veuve Duchesne, 1765. 68, 8 p. 19^{cm}. (Theatre de M. Favart, Paris, Duchesne, 1763–77, t. ix.)

The 8 p. contain three "Airs de la Fée Urgele": "C'est une misere" (II, 4), "Nous allons ici" (IV, 2), "L'avez-vous vu mon bien aimé" (III, 5). Cast. "Epitre aux dames," name of **Duni** as composer, and remark: "Les paroles sont de MM. * * *" ML 49.A2F1

— **La fée Urgèle,** ou Ce qui plait aux dames, comédie en quatre actes melée d'ariettes. La musique est de M. Duni . . .

Paris, Par la compagnie des librairès, 1768. 48 p. 19^{cm}.

Without "Epitre" or music. SCHATZ 2843

— **La fée Urgele,** ou Ce qui plait aux dames, comedie en quatres actes, mêlée d'ariettes; représentée sur le Théâtre de la cour, par les Comédiens françois ordinaires du roi, le [*blank*] 1770.

Copenhague, Cl. Philibert, 1770. 68 p. 19^{cm}.

"Epitre aux dames," cast, and name of **Duni**. The authors are not mentioned. YUDIN PQ

La fée Urgele—Continued.

— La **fée Urgèle,** ou Ce qui plaît aux dames, comédie en quatre actes, mêlée d'ariettes; représentée devant Leurs Majestés, par les Comédiens italiens ordinaires du roi, à Fontainebleau, le 26 octobre 1765 & à Paris le 4 décembre suivant.

Paris, la veuve Duchesne, 1781. 56 p. 19^{cm}.

Cast. On p. 29–31, the ariette, "C'est une misère" (II, 4); 41–43, the romance, "L'avez-vous vu, mon bien aimé" (III, 6); 46–48, the ariette, "Nous allons ici souper" (IV, 2). SCHATZ 11695

— Die **fee Urgele** oder Was den damen gefaellt, ein singspiel in vier aufzuegen aus dem franzoesischen uebersetzt mit musik.

Frankfurt am Mayn, mit Andreäischen schriften, [1776]. 84 p., 14 p. (folded dated music). 16½^{cm}.

German version by Johann Heinrich Faber. Cast. The musical supplement contains the arias (voice and bass): "Recht schöne blumen verkauf ich" ["Je vends des bouquets"], p. 1–5; "Wenn man liebt, ist man vergnüget" ["Ahí que l'amour Est chose jolie"], p. 5–9; "Unsern jungen leuten fehlt" ["C'est une misère Que nos jeunes gens"], p. 10–14.

First performed at Mannheim, Theater auf dem Fruchtmarkt, 1772.
SCHATZ 2844

La féerie. Entrée in Niel's Les romans.

Het feest der Brahminen. Tr. T. of Wenzel Mueller's Das sonnenfest der Braminen.

Les feintes infidélités. A. T. of Philidor's Les femmes vengées.

La felicità della terra. A. T. of Sarti's Astrea placata.

La felicità della terra. A. T. of Schürer's Astrea placata.

La felicità di Partenope. Componimento drammatico da cantarsi in Roma per festeggiare la nascita di S. A. R. il Serenissimo principe delle Due Sicilie D. Filippo di Borbone . . .

Roma, Ottavio Puccinelli, 1747. 20 p. 23½^{cm}.

Two parts. Dedication signed by Gaetano Pescatori, and note: "La poesia è di N. N. Pastore Arcade. La musica è del Sig. Giovanni **Cordicelli**." Not recorded by Schatz. ML 48.M2A

La felicità nata dalle sventure, ballet. *See* P. Guglielmi's Arsinoe e Breno.

Félix, ou L'enfant trouvé, comédie en trois actes; en prose & en vers mis en musique. Représentée devant Leurs Majesté's à Fontainebleau le 10 novembre, & par les Comédiens italiens ordinaires du roi, le 24 novembre 1777.

Paris, la veuve Ballard & fils, 1777. 2 p. l., 90 p. 20^{cm}.

Cast. Sedaine, the author, is mentioned, but not the composer, **Monsigny.** On p. 85–90 the ariettes "Courir les bois" and "Ah! qu'une fillette est à plaindre."
ML 50.2.F25M7

— **Félix,** ou L'enfant trouvé, comédie en trois actes, en prose et en vers mis en musique. Représentée devant Leurs Majestés, à Fontainebleau, le 10 novembre & par les Comédiens italiens ordinaires du roi, le 24 novembre 1777. Le drame est de M. Sedaine. La musique est de M * * *

Paris, la veuve Ballard & fils, 1784. 62 p. 18^{cm}.

Cast. SCHATZ 6574

Félix—Continued.

— Gesaenge aus **Felix**, oder Der findling, ein schauspiel mit gesang, in drey aufzuegen. Aus dem franzoesischen von Sedaine, uebersetzt von Johann André. Die musik ist von Monsigni.

Riga, Julius Conrad Daniel Müller, 1790. 23 p. 17ᶜᵐ.

First performed at Riga, Theater i. d. grossen Koenigstrasse, 3/14 May, 1790.

Schatz 6575

Female curiosity. A. T. Kelly's Blue-beard.

The **female duellist**: an after piece. With songs set to music by Mr. Suett. As it was performed at the King's Theatre, in the Haymarket, by His Majesty's company from the Theatre Royal, Drury Lane.

London, J. Owen, 1793. 2 p. l., 52 p. 20ᶜᵐ.

Two acts. Cast, and note that the piece was based partly on Beaumont and Fletcher's "Love's cure." The author is not recorded by Genest.

Genest dates the first performance, Drury Lane, May 22, 1793. Longe 225

The **female parson**: or, Beau in the sudds. An opera. As it is acted at the New theatre in the Hay-Market . . . By Mr. Charles Coffey . . .

London, Lawton Gilliver and Fran. Cogan, 1730. 4 p. l., 53 p. 19ᶜᵐ.

Three acts with prologue. Dedication. Ballad opera. The 27 airs (8, 8, 11) are printed in the text with their titles.

First performed 1730, as indicated. Longe 47

The **female rake**: or, Modern fine lady. A ballad comedy. As it is acted at the New theatre in the Hay-Market . . .

London, J. Dormer, 1736. 51 p. (incl. front.) 18½ᶜᵐ.

Two acts. Two prologues, epilogue, and cast. The airs of the 16 songs (8, 8) are indicated by title. Author not recorded by Clarence, but Tufts gives Joseph Dorman.

Longe 150

La **femme.** Entrée in Mouret's Les festes de Thalie.

La **femme repudiée.** A. T. of Arlequin Hulla.

Les **femmes et le secret**; comédie en un acte, mêlée d'ariettes. Par Monsieur Quétant. Représentée pour la premiere fois par les Comédiens italiens ordinaires du roi, le 9 novembre 1767.

Avignon, Louis Chambeau, 1768. 39 p. 19½ᶜᵐ.

The composer, Pierre **Vachon**, is not mentioned. ML 50.2.F25V22

— Les **femmes et le secret**, comédie en un acte, meslée d'ariettes, représentée pour la premiere fois par les Comédiens italiens ordinaires du roi, le 9 novembre 1767. Par M. Quétant.

Paris, Cailleau, 1770. 51 p. 18½ᶜᵐ.

Ariettes printed in the text: "Quand je reviens du cabaret" (scene 1), "Je vois Lucas tous les jours" (scene 11), "Cher Lubin, si tu m'aimes bien" (scene 24). The composer, Pierre **Vachon**, not mentioned. Schatz 10570

— Les **femmes et le secret**, comédie en un acte, mêlée d'ariettes. Représentée pour la premiere fois par les Comédiens italiens ordinaires du roi, le 9 novembre 1767. Par M. Quétant.

Paris, Cailleau, 1779. 48 p. 18ᶜᵐ.

On p. 3–5 the ariette en vaudeville, "Quand je reviens du cabaret," on p. 46–47 the vaudeville, "Cher Lubin, si tu m'aimes." The composer, Pierre **Vachon**, is not mentioned. Schatz 11750

Les **femmes vengées,** ou Les feintes infidélités, opera-comique en un acte et en vers; par M. Sedaine. La musique de M. Philidor. Représenté pour la premiere fois, le lundi 20 mars, par les Comédiens italiens ordinaires du roi.

Paris, Musier, 1775. 56 p. 18ᶜᵐ.

Cast. On p. 50–56 the airs of the *vaudeville,* "Ne donnons jamais à nos femmes," the *ariette,* "Quand Paris, sur le mont Ida," and the *romance,* "Si jamais je fais un ami." Schatz 8014

— Les **femmes vengées,** ou Les feintes infidélités, opéra-comique en un acte et en vers; par M. Sédaine. La musique de M. Philidor. Représenté pour la première fois, le lundi 20 mars [1775] par les Comédiens italiens ordinaires du roi.

Paris, Musier fils, 1782. 56 p. 19ᶜᵐ.

Cast. On p. 50–51 the vaudeville, "Ne donnons jamais," on p. 53–55 the ariette, "Quand Paris sur le mont Ida," and p. 55–56 the romance, "Si jamais je fais." Schatz 11738

Le **fenzeune abbentorate.** Commeddea pe mmuseca de nota' Pietro Trinchera da rappresentarese a lo Teatro de la Pace nchesta corrente nnvernata de lo 1745 . . .

Napoli, Domenico Langiano e Domenico Vivenzio compagni, n. d. 60 p. 15ᶜᵐ.

Three acts. Impresario's dedication, cast and name of Pietro **Gomes** as composer. ML 50.2.F26G6

Feraspe. Dramma per musica da rappresentarsi nel Teatro di S. Angelo l'autunno dell' anno 1739 . . .

Venezia, Marino Rossetti, 1739. 48 p. 15ᶜᵐ.

Three acts. By Francesco Silvani, partly rewritten by Bartolomeo Vitturi, neither of whom is mentioned. Impresario's dedication, argument, cast, scenario, and name of Antonio **Vivaldi** as the composer. Schatz 10768

Ferdinand und Nicolette, oder Liebe erhaelt den sieg. Tr. of Grétry's Aucassin et Nicolette.

La **fermière de qualité.** O. T. of Candeille's Catherine.

La **fermière écossaise.** A. T. of Vachon's Sara.

Fernando Cortes conquistator del Messico. Dramma per musica da rappresentarsi nel Regio Teatro di via della Pergola il carnevale del MDCCLXXXIX . . .

Firenze, Stamp. Albizziniana, 1789. 32, [1] p. 17ᶜᵐ.

Two acts. Author not mentioned and unknown to Schatz. Cast and name of Giuseppe **Mugnes** as the composer. On p. 4–9 introductory remarks, cast, and detailed scenario of Onorato Viganò's "Enrico IV. Ballo semi-comico pantomimo, tratto dalla commedia intitolata; La partita a caccia d'Enrico IV. di Monsieur Collè." The composer of the music is not mentioned. Schatz 6864

Fernando nel Messico. Dramma per musica da rappresentarsi nel nobil Teatro di Torre Argentina nel carnevale dell' anno 1787 . . .

Roma, Arcangelo Casaletti, 1787. 60 p. 16ᶜᵐ.

Three acts. By Filippo Tarducci with the interpolation of "versi di Metastasio che caduti opportunamente sotto la penna dell' autore, si fa egli un pregio di servirsene." This in naive contrast with his dedication in which he deplores the stagnation of dramatic poetry and the uniformity of ideas for which the music "sembra già stanca."

Fernando nel Messico—Continued.

Hence his present experiment as librettist, etc. Argument, scenario, cast, and name of Giuseppe **Giordani** as the composer. With the opera were performed Onorato Vigano's ballets, "Oreste o sia La morte di Clitennestra" and "Gelosia per gelosia," music by Luigi Marascalchi. SCHATZ 3838

Fernando nel Messico. Dramma per musica da rappresentarsi nel Teatro Venier in San Benedetto il carnovale dell' anno 1798.

Venezia, Modesto Fenzo, 1798. 45 p. 17^{cm}.

Three acts. By Filippo Tarducci (not mentioned), with alterations. Argument, cast, scenario, and name of Marco **Portogallo** as the composer. With the opera were performed Onorato Vigano's ballets, "Adelaide" and "Amore e magia." The composers of the music are not mentioned.

First performed, as indicated, January 16, 1798. SCHATZ 8409

Fernando und Yariko, ein singspiel in drey aufzuegen von dem hofrath v. Eckhartshausen.

Muenchen, Joseph von Cratz, 1784. 95 p. 15½^{cm}.

The composer, Franz Christian **Neubauer,** is not mentioned. SCHATZ 7092

Das fest der freundschaft. A. T. of P. v. Winter's Das lindenfest.

Arien aus dem vorspiele: Das fest der Thalie, bey eroeffnung des Herzoglich Gothaischen Hof-Theaters den 2ten october, 1775.

n. i., n. d. 7 p. 17^{cm}.

Neither Heinrich August Ottokar Reichard, the author, is mentioned, nor Anton **Schweitzer,** the composer. SCHATZ 9773

— Das fest der Thalie, ein vorspiel von R * * *, die musik vom herrn Schweizer. Bey eröffnung des ehemaligen Gothaischen Hoftheaters 1776.

p. 353–359. 18½^{cm}. (Litteratur und Theater Zeitung, Berlin, 1783.)

Cast. SCHATZ 4772

Das fest der weiblichen tugend. A. T. of Blaise, Duni, and Philidor's Das rosenmaedchen.

Das fest der winzer. L. T. of Kunzen's Die weinlese.

Das fest Germaniens. Vorspiel mit gesang und tanz zur feier des hohen beilagers der Durchlauchtigsten prinzessin von Mecklenburg-Strelitz Therese Mathilde Amalia mit des erbprinzen von Thurn und Taxis Karl Alexander, Durchlaucht. Die musik ist von dem herzogl. kapell-director herrn Zeller . . .

Neustrelitz, Hofbuchhandlung, 1789. 12 p. 16^{cm}.

One act. Cast. By Christian Friedrich von Bonin, who is not mentioned. First performed at Neustrelitz, Hoftheater, May 27, 1789. SCHATZ 11165

La festa di ballo disturbata dalla famiglia dei Covielli, ballet. *See* Traetta's Cavaliere errante.

La festa di Flora, ballet. *See* Sacchini's Lucio Vero.

La festa interotta, o sia Il trionfo della virtù, composizione serio comica da rappresentarsi nel Teatro di Ratisbona . . .

Regensburg, Gedruckt mit Zunkelischen schriften, n. d.   97 p.   16ᶜᵐ.

"Prologo contadinesco" (p. 14–41) and one act.   Cast, names of Domenico Friggieri as author and of Theodor freiherr von **Schacht** as composer, with exception of some arias by others in the prologue, and "avvertimento," by the author:

"avendo io acconsentito a vedere di nuovo compatir sulla scena quest' operetta da me composta in occasione di un giorno di vera allegrezza . . . mi è convenuto per rendere la rapresentazione di questa convenevole ad ogni tempo (lasciando tuttavia intatta la prima musica) cambiare in molti luoghi il senso, le parole, i versi, e sostituire al venerato nome di veri personaggi, enti e nomi immaginati . . .''

To fill out the evening, the prologue was added by him.   German title-page, "Das unterbrochene fest oder Der triumph der tugend,'' and text face Italian.

Must have been performed after 1780.   Schatz 9563

Una festa villereccia, ballet.   *See* Tarchi's L'Arminio.

Le feste o Le gelosie del seraglio, ballet.   *See* Borghi's Ricimero.

Le feste d'Apollo, celebrate sul Teatro di Corte nell' augosto del MDCCLXIX.   Per le auguste seguite nozze tra il reale infante Don Ferdinando e la R. arciduchessa infanta Maria Amalia.

Parma, Nella Stamperia reale, n. d.   15, 20, 27, 28 p., and 5 pl. (incl. front.).   24½ᶜᵐ.

The plates are by P. A. Martini, and the first (dated "Parigiis 1769") and the fifth were also engraved by him.   The others were engraved by Helman and C. Bagnoy. The artist of the exquisite vignettes, etc., is not mentioned.

Prologue and three acts, respectively entitled "Bauci e Filemone," "Aristeo," and "Orfeo."   Each is preceded by the argument and cast, Avvertimento, scenario, and name of **Gluck** as the composer ("Tutta la musica").   The avvertimento reads, in part:

"Al prologo succedono pertanto tre atti diversi, due de' quali nuovamente composti. Altri ne erano già in pronto, che, alternati coi primi, potevano contribuire alla desiderata varietà.   Si seppe appena che l'atto d'Orfeo, applaudito, anni sono sul Teatro Imperiale di Vienna, avrebbe incontrato sul nostro l'aggradimento dell' Augusta Persona, a cui queste feste sono sacre in gran parte, che si determinò di preferirlo.''

"Orfeo" was Ranieri de' Calsabigi's complete text compressed into one act of seven scenes; the two others, and probably the prologue, by Carlo Innocente Frugoni, though neither of them is mentioned.

Performed, as indicated, August 24, 1769.   Schatz 3897
                                                Second copy.   ML 48.M2B

Le feste d'Imeneo nell' augustissimo sposalizio delle Altezze Reali di Giuseppe, arciduca d'Austria, ec. ec. ec. e della Reale infanta Donna Isabella di Borbone, ec. ec. ec. celebrate sul Reale Teatro di Parma nel settembre dell' anno MDCCLX.   Composizione del Signor abate Frugoni.

n. i., n. d.   front., p. [99]–176.   16½ᶜᵐ.

Evidently a detached copy.   In his esthetic preface, "Ai leggitori,'' Carlo Innocente Frugoni says:

"Questo spettacolo teatrale è composto di tre suggetti disgiunti, ciascun de' quali si rinchiude in un' atto; ed è precedute da un prologo.''

The prologue is entitled "Il trionfo d'amore,'' the single acts "Atto d'Iride,'' "Atto di Saffo," and "Atto di Egle."   Each act is preceded by the characters (not the cast) and by the argument.   The opera is followed by "Aci e Galatea, balletto pantomimo,'' with argument and description of the twelve scenes.   Tommaso **Traetta** is not mentioned in the libretto either as composer of the ballet or of the opera. The ballet, according to the preface, was already "conosciuto sulle' nostre scene, ma universalmente desiderato'' and the act "Egle'' was "espressamente addottato'' for its introduction.   Schatz 10392

Le feste d'Iside. Dramma per musica da rappresentarsi nel nobilissimo Teatro La Fenice l'autunno 1799.

Venezia, Stamperia Valvasense, 1799. 61 p. 16½^{cm}.

Two acts. Gaetano Rossi's retouched version of Zeno and Pariati's "Sesostri rè d'Egitto," who are not mentioned. Argument, cast, and name of Sebastiano **Naso-lini** also as composer of the "pezzi postillati . . . di nuova poesia del Sig. Gaetano Rossi." On p. [31]–37 preface, argument, cast, and description of Lorenzo Panzieri's "Il sotteraneo ossia Catterina di Coluga, ballo eroicomico, in quattro atti," music by Catterino Cavos.

First performed at Florence, Teatro di via della Pergola, carnival, 1794.

SCHATZ 7002

Feste de buveurs. Entrée in Bourgeois' Les plaisirs de la paix.

La feste des barqueroles. Entrée in Campra's Les festes venitiennes.

La feste des Druides. A. T. of Laruette's Le Guy de Chesne.

Le feste di Flora, ballet. *See* Cherubini's Ifigenia in Aulide.

Le feste di Flora, ballet. *See* Jommelli's Bajazet.

Le feste galanti. Festa teatrale per musica da rappresentarsi nel Regio Teatro di Berlino per il giorno natalizio della Sacra Real Maestà di Sofia Dorotea, regina madre . . .

Berlino, A. Haude, 1747. 77, [3] p. 20^{cm}.

Three acts. Leopoldo de Villati is mentioned as the author ("L'invenzione . . . è trata dal francese [Duché's "Les festes galantes"] e composta ad uso di musica") and Carl Heinrich **Graun** as the composer. Argument and scenario. German title-page, "Die galanten feste," and text face Italian.

First performed at Berlin, Kgl. Operntheater, March 27, 1747 (Schatz); April 6, 1747 (Mennicke). SCHATZ 4114

— **Le feste galanti.** Festa teatrale per musica da rappresentarsi nel Regio Teatro di Berlino . . .

Berlino, Haude et Spener, 1767. 67, [4] p. 16^{cm}.

Three acts. Leopoldo de Villati is mentioned as author and Carl Heinrich **Graun** as the composer. German title-page, "Die galanten feste," and text face Italian.

Performed, as indicated, April 6, 1767. SCHATZ 4097

La feste marine. Entrée in Campra's Les festes venitiennes.

Le feste persiane, ballet. *See* Jommelli's Semiramide.

Les festes de l'Amour et de Bacchus. Pastorale representée par l'Academie royale de musique. Suivant la copie imprimée à Paris.

[Amsterdam, Antoine Schelte], 1686. 45 p. (incl. front.) 13½^{cm}.

Prologue and three acts. Neither the author, Quinault (*see* next entry), is mentioned nor **Lully**, the composer. ML50.2.F3L9

— **Les festes de l'Amour et de Bacchus,** pastorale representée par l'Academie royale de musique l'an 1672. Les paroles sont de M. Quinault, & la musique de M. de Lully. III. opera.

n. i., n. d. pl., 101–142 p. 14^{cm}. (Recueil général des opéra, t. I, 1703.)

Detached copy. Three acts and prologue. The text is said to have been really a joint-product of Molière, Benserade, and Quinault.

First performed, as indicated, November 15, 1672 (Schatz); December, 1672 (Prunières). SCHATZ 5766

Second copy. ML 48.R4

Les festes de l'Amour et de Bacchus—Continued.

— Les **festes de l'Amour et de Bacchus.** Pastorale representée par l'Academie royale de musique, au Jeu de Paulme del Bel-Air, en 1672.

Quinault, Théatre, Paris, 1739, t. iv, pl., 51 p.   *17ᶜᵐ.*

Prologue and three acts. **Lully** is not mentioned.   PQ 1881.A1   1739

Les festes de l'été, ballet, représenté par l'Academie royale de musique, l'an 1716. Paroles de M. Pellegrin. Musique de M. Monteclair. XC. opera.

n. i., n. d.   *pl., p. 1–75.*   *14ᶜᵐ.*   (*Recueil général des opéra, Paris, 1734, t. xii.*)

Detached copy. Prologue and four entrées. By Simon Joseph de Pellegrin and Marie Anne Barbier.

First performed, as indicated, June 12, 1716.   Sᴄʜᴀᴛᴢ 6589
                                        Second copy.   ML 48.R4

Les festes de l'Hymen.   A. T. of La roze.

Les festes de Paphos.   Ballet heroïque mis en musique par Monsieur Mondonville . . . Representé pour l'Académie royale de musique le 9ᵉ may 1758.

This is the title of the full score published "chez l'auteur," etc. It consists of an overture and three acts, called: "Venus et Adonis," "Bacchus et Erigone" and "L'Amour et Psyché."

This work, of which the L. of C. does not possess the libretto, was but the combination of three one act ballets of the above titles into one. "Venus et Adonis," text by Collé, had first been performed at Verseilles, Théâtre des Petit-Cabinets, April 27, 1752, and "Bacchus et Erigone" was first performed—Schatz claims under the title of "Erigone"—as after-piece to Dancourt's comedy "Les trois cousines" at Versailles, March 13, 1747. As to "L'Amour et Psyche," Hellouin does not know the circumstances under which it was written and performed, but "Je sais seulement"—he says—"que le sempiternel abbé de Voisenon en avait fait les paroles, que son collaborateur prétendit toujours être de lui . . . En 1769, il servit de rentrée à Sophie Arnould qui fut reçue avec transport."

Chouquet and Schatz date this performance December 1, 1769, and enter it under "Psyché," under which title this ballet had already figured separately in 1762 and 1766, it would seem. Lajarte says: "Mondonville et Voisenon reprirent le sujet de la 3ᵉ entrée [exactly this "L'Amour et Psyché"], pour en faire un acte séparé" and Chouquet says under "Psyche" (1769): "C'est le sujet du 3ᵉ acte des *Fêtes de Paphos* remanié." The impression seems to be that the text and incidentally the music of "L'Amour et Psyché" were changed after 1758. I doubt this, since the text of the score and the text in the following publication agree absolutely.

— **Bacchus et Erigone,** ballet-heroïque en un acte. Le poeme est de de la Bruere. La musique est de M. de Mondonville.

n. i., n. d.   *14 p.*   *22½ᶜᵐ.*

This is followed on p. [15–33] by:

— **L'Amour et Psyché,** ballet-héroïque en un acte. Le poeme & la musique sont de M. de Mondonville.

Casts. On p. 33 the Approbation of date: Paris, September 26, 1769! In the cast of "L'Amour et Psyché" Mˡˡᵉ Arnould appears as "Psyché." Hence, if Chouquet's date of December 1, 1769, for the reappearance of Sophie Arnould in a revival of Mondonville's act is correct, the actual publication of the two librettos in this edition probably occurred about that time. As was stated above, the text of "L'Amour et Psyché" agrees absolutely with that of the third act in the score of "Les festes de Paphos" (1758). That of "Bacchus et Erigone" is only slightly different, Comus' air "Cher Bacchus, c'est assez" (I, 3) and Bacchus' air "Mon sort rendoit" (I, 5) not being in the libretto of 1769.   ML 52.2.B105M6

Les festes de la paix, divertissement en un acte; a l'occasion de l'inauguration de la statue du roi, & de la publication de la paix; représenté pour la premiere fois par les Comédiens italiens ordinaires du roi le 4 juillet 1763. Nouvelle édition, augmentée de plusieurs scenes nouvelles.

Paris, Duchesne, 1763. 72 p. 19cm. (Theatre de M. Favart, Paris, Duchesne, 1763–77, t. ix.)

Cast and names of Favart as author and of **Philidor** as composer. Many of his ariettes printed in the text. ML 49.A2F1

Les festes de Thalie, balet représenté pour la premiere fois, par l'Académie royale de musique, le dimanche 19 août 1714. Les paroles de M. de la Font & la musique de M. Mouret. LXXXV. opera.

n. i., n. d. pl., p. [177]–232. (Recueil général des opéra, t. xi, Paris, 1720.) 14cm.

Detached copy. Three acts, with prologue. The single acts are called "La fille," "La veuve," "La femme." This was followed by a kind of epilogue, called "La critique des Festes de Thalie," by the same author and composer. The "Avertissement" is so interesting as to deserve a quotation in full:

"Voilà je croi, le premier opera où l'on ait vû des femmes habillées à la françoise, & des confidentes du ton des soubrettes de la comédie; c'est aussi la premiere fois que l'on a hazardé de certaines expressions convenables au comique, mais nouvelles jusqu'alors & même inconnües sur la scène lyrique; le public en fut d'abord allarmé, cependant le théatre qui règne du commencement jusqu'à la fin de ce Balet se trouva si amusant & si enjoüé, qu'on y venoit en foule presque à contre-coeur. Je me fis conscience de divertir ainsi le public malgré lui, & pour rendre son plaisir pur & tranquile je me dépêchai de faire moi-même la Critique de mon ouvrage où je donnai tout le merite du succès à la musique & à la danse. Le public me sçut si bon gré d'avoir eu cette attention pour lui, & devint si fort de mes amis que pendant quatre-vingt representations il ne pouvoit se resoudre à me quitter, & même encore aujourd' hui il parle de ce Balet avec plaisir."

The score of 1714 has the title, "Les festes ou Le triomphe de Thalie." "La critique des Festes de Thalie" was first performed on October 9, 1714, and the score was published in the same year. The entrée, "La veuve," was replaced on March 12,, 1715, by "La veuve coquette," and the entrée, "La Provençale," was added on September 17, 1722. This was parodied by Duni at the Théatre-Italien on March 4, 1758, as "La fille mal gardée;" "La veuve coquette," at the Opéra-comique à la Foire Saint-Laurent, on September 22, 1759, as "La veuve indécise;" and Laujon and Parvi gave a parody of "Les festes de Thalie" at the Théâtre-Italien on August 21, 1745, as "La fille, la femme et la veuve." SCHATZ 6741–6742
Second copy. ML 48.R4

— La **Provençale,** entrée, remise au Théatre le mardi 31 janvier 1758.

n. i., n. d. 16 p. 22½cm.

In the "Approbation" at end (dated January 29, 1755 [!]) this is called, "Acte détaché du Ballet des Fêtes de Thalie." Cast and names of De Lafonds as author, of "feu M. **Mouret**" as composer. ML 52.2.F3
Second copy. ML 48.R4

— La **fille mal gardée,** ou Le pedant amoureux, parodie de la Provençale. Représentée pour la premiere fois par les Comédiens italiens ordinaires du roi le 4 mars 1758.

Paris, N. B. Duchesne, 1758. 44, [45–48], 49–80 p. 19cm. (Théatre de M. Favart, Paris, Duchesne, 1763–77, t. v.)

One act. Cast. The [45–48] p. contain catalogues of plays; p. 49–80, twelve "Ariettes du Pedant amoureux, ou La fille mal gardée. Par M. **Duny.**" None of the vaudeville airs printed in the text, which was written by Madame Favart in collaboration with her husband and Lourdet de Santerre. ML 49.A2F1

Les **festes de Thalie**—Continued.

— La **fille mal gardée,** ou Le pédant amoureux, parodie de La Provençale, représentée, pour la première fois, par les Comédiens italiens ordinaires du roi, le 4 mars 1758.

> *Paris, N. B. Duchesne, 1759.　28 p.　19^{cm}.*
> No music in the text.　　　　　　　　　　　　　　　Schatz 2845

— La **veuve indécise,** opéra-comique, parodie de La veuve coquette. Représentée pour la première fois sur le Théatre de l'Opéra-comique, à la Foire S. Laurent, le lundi 24 septembre 1759.

> *Paris, la veuve Duchesne, 1767.　40 p.　19^{cm}.*
> Neither Vadé, the author, nor **Duni,** the composer, mentioned in the libretto.　On p. 31–40, the melodies of the "*Airs de la Veuve indécise.*" No. 1, "Dans le mariage;" No. 2, "Eh! pour-quoi tant attendre;" No. 3, "Un aveu mérité;" No. 4, "Non pas, ma Mie" and the "*Vaudeville,*" "Une fille à dix-huit." "La veuve coquette" is the title of the "nouvelle entrée" of 1715 for Mouret's ballet, "Les festes de Thalie."
> 　　　　　　　　　　　　　　　　　　　　　　　Schatz 2858

— La **veuve indécise,** opéra comique; parodie de La veuve coquette; représentée pour la première fois, sur le Théâtre de l'Opéra comique, à la Foire Saint Laurent, le 24 septembre 1759.

> *[105]–136 p.　15½^{cm}.　(Jean Joseph Vadé, Oeuvres complettes, t. iv, Nouv. éd., Troyes, an VI, [1798])*
> One act.　**Duni** is not mentioned.　　　　　　　　PQ 2068.V2

Les **festes galantes,** ballet.　Representé par l'Academie royale de musique l'an 1698.　Les paroles sont de M. Duché, & la musique de M. Desmarets.　XLV. opera.

> *n. i., n. d.　front., p. 229–290　(Recueil général des opéra, t. vi, Paris, 1703).　14^{cm}.*
> Detached copy.　Prologue and three acts with "Avis," in which we read:
> "J'ay balancé long-temps, si je laisserois à ce ballet, le titre, que l'on sçait qu'il avoit deux ans, avant que l'on eût pensé à faire l'Europe Galante."
> First performed, as indicated, May 10, 1698.　　　　Schatz 2532
> 　　　　　　　　　　　　　　　　Second copy.　ML 48.R4

Les **festes greques et romaines,** ballet heroique, representé par l'Academie royale de musique, l'an 1723.　Paroles de M. Fuselier. Musique de M. Colin de Blamont.　CII. opera.

> *n. i., n. d.　pl., 263–318 p.　14^{cm}.　(Recueil général des opéra, Paris, 1734, t. xiii.)*
> Detached copy.　Prologue and three entrées called "Les jeux olympiques," "Les bacchanales," "Les saturnales."　The long preface (p. 265–270) reads in part:
> "Les Festes grecques et romaines forment un ballet d'une espece toute nouvelle. La Muse lyrique n'avoit jusqu'à présent tiré ses poëmes que de la chroniques des Amadis, de l'Ariosto, des Métamorphoses d'Ovide, du Tasse & d'autres semblables auteurs.　La France n'a encore soûmis que la fable à la musique; l'Italie plus hazardeuse a placé dans ses opera les événemens de l'histoire.　Les Scarlatti & les Buononcini ont fait chanter des Heros que Corneille & Racine auroient fait parler.　Enhardy par ces examples, on s'est dispensé de glaner dans les champs trop souvent moissonnez de la mythologie & du romain: Heureux si on est aprouvé en ouvrant aux poètes du théâtre chantant, une carriere digne d'occuper les Génies amateurs du vray-semblable.
> "On a rassemblé dans ce ballet, les fêtes de l'antiquité les plus connuës, & qui ont semblé les plus favorables au théâtre & à la musique.　On les confond toutes sous le nom de Festes grecques & romaines, parce qu'effectivement Rome adopta tous les Dieux d'Athenes.　On a pris soin d'assortir à ces Fêtes célebres des avantures & des noms illustres . . ."
> First performed, as indicated, July 13, 1723.　　　　Schatz 1067
> 　　　　　　　　　　　　　　　　Second copy.　ML 48.R4

Les festes nouvelles, ballet. Représenté par l'Académie royale de musique, l'an 1734. Paroles de M. Massip. Musique de M. Plessis-C. CXX. opera.

*n. i., n. d. front., p. 381–430 (Recueil général des opéra, Paris, 1739, t. xv). 14*cm

Detached copy. Prologue and three *entrées*, composed by Duplessis, Le jeune, and called "Ulysse et Circe," "Le bal champêtre," "Le triomphe de l'Amour sur Bacchus."

First performed, as indicated, July 22, 1734. Schatz 2861

Second copy. ML 48.R4

Les festes venitiennes, ballet, représentée par l'Academie royale de musique l'an 1710. Les paroles de M. Danchet & la musique de M. Campra. LXXV. opera.

*n. i., n. d. front., 129–180 p. 14*cm *. (Recueil général des opéra, Paris, 1714, t. x.)*

Detached copy. Three *entrées* with prologue and *avertissement* with statement that the libretto is printed according to the original version of June 17, 1710, not with the additions introduced later on. On p. 131 then follows this:

"Ordre des Festes Venitiennes. Premiere représentation le 17 Juin 1710. *Prologue,* sous le titre du Triomphe de la folie sur la raison, dans le temps du carnaval. *Premiere entrée.* La feste des barqueroles. *Deuxième entrée.* Les serenades & les joüeurs. *Troisième entrée.* L'amour saltinbanque.

"Dixième représentation le 8. juillet. *Première entrée,* substituée à celle des *Barqueroles,* La *feste marine.*

"XXIIIme représentation le 8. aoust. Le prologue a été supprimé & l'on a ajouté le *Bal,* nouvelle entrée, que l'on a placée entre la premiere & la deuxieme.

"XXXIVme représentation le 5 septembre. L'on a substitué à la place de *la Serenade,* une nouvelle entrée sous le titre *des Devins de la Place Saint Marc.*

"LIme représentation le 14. octobre. L'on a supprimé *La feste marine,* & l'on a donné une nouvelle entrée sous le titre de *l'Opera.* En même temps on a donné un nouvel ordre aux Entrées, en remettant le Prologue. *Les Devins* pour premiere entrée. *L'amour saltinbanque,* seconde. *L'Opera,* troisième. *Le bal,* quatrième. On a depuis ajoutée *La Comedie,* qui se trouve à la suite de toutes ces entrées."

Schatz 1549

These additions, etc., follow: Second copy. ML 48.R4

— Premiere entrée ajoutée. **Feste marine.** *(181–192 p.)*

Schatz 1550

— Deuxième entrée ajoutée. **Le Bal.** *(193–208 p.)*

Schatz 1551

— Troisième entrée ajoutée **Les Devins de la place Saint Marc.** *(209–220 p.)*

Schatz 1552

— Quatrième entrée ajoutée **L'Opéra** *(221–236 p.)*

Schatz 1553

— Cinquième entrée ajoutée **Le triomphe de la folie,** comedie *(237–252 p.)*

Schatz 1554

— Les **fêtes vénitiennes:** Le triomphe de la folie sur la raison—La fête des barqueroles—Les serenades et les joueurs—Les saltinbanques de la place Saint Marc.

*50 p. 17½*cm *. (Antoine Danchet, Théâtre, Paris, 1751, t. iii.)*

"Les saltinbanques" ("la troisième et dernière entrée") is called in caption "L'amour saltinbanque." These entrées are followed by: PQ 1972.D2

— — **Fête marine**—Les devins de la Place Saint Marc—L'opera [incl. " Le ballet de Flore "].

[51]–90 p. ibidem.

These three are called Première-troisième entrée. They are followed by:

Les festes venitiennes—Continued.

— — Le **triomphe de la folie,** comédie—Le bal.

[91]–120 p.   ibidem.

At the end of "Le bal": "Fin des Festes venitiennes"! For an explanation of this otherwise unintelligible matter, *see* main entry for "Les festes vénitiennes."

Das festin oder Die eifersucht der frauenzimmer des tuerkischen kaisers.   Tr. T. of the ballet Les fêtes ou Jalousies du sérail.

Il festino.   Dramma di tre atti per musica.   Rappresentato per la prima volta in Parma nel Teatro Regio-ducale il carnovale dell' anno MDCCLVII [Dec. 26, 1756] con musica del Ferradini.

*Carlo Goldoni, Opere teatrali, Venezia, Zatta e figli, 1788–95, v. 38, [5]–66 p.   18½**cm.*

PQ

The festivall of light.   A. T. of the masque Luminalia.

La fête d'amour, ou Lucas et Colonette, piece en vers et en un acte. Par Madame Favart.   Représentée pour la première fois par les Comédiens italiens ordinaires du roi, le 5 décembre 1754.   Nouvelle édition, augmentée de la musique.

n. i., n. d.   64 p.   (Theatre de M. Favart, Paris, Duchesne, 1763–77, t. v.)

Prologue (with cast) and one act (without cast).   The ariettes are printed in the text.   Their composer is unknown to Font, who mentions as authors of the text, besides Mad. Favart, her husband and Chevalier.   ML 49.A2F1

La fête de l'égalite.   Comédie en un acte, par J. B. Radet et F. G. Desfontaines; représentée pour la première fois à Paris sur le Théâtre du Vaudeville, le 7 ventose de l'an deux de la République française. Nouvelle edition.

*Paris, Au Théâtre du Vaudeville, Prairial, an IIIᵉ [May–June 1795]. 44 p.   20**cm.*

Cast.   Interspersed with airs and vaudevilles, a few of which are printed in the text.   Not recorded by Cl. & L. or Schatz.

First performed, as indicated, February 25, 1794.   ML 48.M2L

La fête de La cinquantaine, opéra en deux actes.   Paroles du C. Faur, musique du C. Dézède.

*Paris, Huet, 1796.   61 p.   20**cm.*

With cast and "Avertissement de l'auteur."   In this he says that "cette bagatelle y [at the 'Théâtre ci-devant Italien'] fut recue en 1781.   Lue une seconde fois en 1784," but not performed.   After fifteen years of waiting, further promises of performance, which does not materialize.   At end, compliments to the "artistes du Théâtre de la rue de Louvois," who first performed the opera January 9, 1796.   SCHATZ 2527

La fête de Saint Cloud.   O. T. of Les bateliers de Saint Cloud.

La fête de Salency.   A. T. of La couronne de roses.

La fête du château, divertissement mêlé de vaudevilles & de petits airs; par M. * * *   Représenté pour la première fois par les Comédiens italiens ordinaires du roi, le 25 septembre 1766.

*Paris, la veuve Duchesne, 1766.   76, [3] p.   19**cm.*

One act.   By Charles Simon Favart, who is not mentioned.   On p. 74–76, the airs, "Belle rose, que j'arrose" and "Pour Colette, que j'adore."   The first of the couplets, "Oui, je l'ai dit," was to be sung to "Air de **Rameau:** *Dans ce convent.*"   Favart's

La fête du château—Continued.

musical collaborator unknown to Schatz and Font, who says that the play was "d'abord joué chez la marquise de Mauconseil." The [3] p. contain the approbation and privilèdge du roi. Towers has an opera of the above title under Duni, but Fètis, Eitner, Schatz have not. Eitner and Towers also have an opera of the same title under de Saint-Pierre. ML 50.2.F33.

— Second copy (forms part of "Theatre de M. Favart," Paris, Duchesne, 1763–77, t. ix.) ML 49.A2.F1

— **La fête du chateau,** divertissement mêlé de vaudevilles & de petits airs, par M * * *. Représenté pour la première fois par les Comédiens italiens ordinaires du roi, le 25 septembre 1766.

Paris, la veuve Duchesne, 1766. 52 p. 19^{cm}.

Text the same (incl. music of the two airs) as in the 76 p. ed. of 1766.

ML 50.2.F331

—**La fête du château,** divertissement mêlé de vaudevilles & de petits airs; par M. * * * ' Représenté pour la première fois par les Comédiens italiens ordinaires du roi, le 25 septembre, 1766.

Paris, la veuve Duchesne, 1767. 60 p. 19 ^{cm}.

Schatz 11491

La fête du serail, pantomime-ballet; donné au Panthéon, pour la première fois, le dimanche 9 mars 1788.

Paris, P. de Lormel, 1788. 14 p. 18½^{cm}.

One act. Cast and scene by scene description of the action. The imprimatur is dated March 8, 1788. Neither the author nor the composer is known to Schatz.

ML 48.B2

Les fêtes ou Jalousies du sérail—Das festin oder Die eifersucht der frauenzimmer des tuerkischen kaisers, ballet. *See* Bernasconi's Demetrio.

Les fêtes d'Hébé, ou Les talens lyriques. Ballet représenté pour la premiere fois, par l'Academie royale de musique, le jeudy vingt-un may 1739.

[Paris], Jean Baptiste Christophe Ballard, 1739. 57, [1] p. 24^{cm}.

Prologue and three entrées: "La poësie," "La musique," "La danse." Cast, and on p. [3]: "Extrait d'une lettre, écrite à M. **Rameau**," the composer, by the author, Gaultier de Mondorge, who is not mentioned. He says: "Vous me fachés beaucoup, monsieur, quoi? il faut absolument que le poëme d'un ballet soit imprimé avant la représentation; je me flattois qu'on pourroit se soustraire à l'usage, & qu'il nous suffiroit d'exposer simplement le sujet de chaque entrée. Songés donc que je n'ai jamais compté vous envoyer qu'un enchaînement de scenes qui prêtassent à la musique & au spectacle; & en verité, des scenes ainsi sacrifiées ne prétendent point à la lecture." ML 52.2.F4R1

— **Les fêtes d'Hebé,** ou Les talens lyriques, ballet, représenté pour la premiere fois par l'Académie royale de musique, le jeudi 21 may 1739. Repris le mardi 25 juillet 1747. Et remis au Théâtre le mardi 18 may 1756.

Paris, Aux dépens de l'Académie, chez la V. Delormel & fils, 1756. 52 p. 23^{cm}.

Prologue and three entrées called: "La poésie," "La musique," "La danse." Cast and name of Jean Philippe **Rameau** as composer. The author, Gaultier de Mondorge, is not mentioned. ML 52.2.F4R2

Les **fêtes d'Hébé**—Continued.

— **L'amour impromptu,** parodie de l'acte d'Eglé dans les Talens lyriques. Représentée sur le Théâtre de l'Opera-comique, le 10. juillet 1756.

Paris, Duchesne, 1756. 31, [1] p. 19ᶜᵐ. (Theatre de M. Favart, Paris, Duchesne, 1763–77, t. viii.)

Cast. One act. En vaudevilles. On p. 26–31 four of the airs. Compare next entry.   ML 49.A2F1

— **L'amour impromptu,** parodie de l'acte d'Eglé dans les Talens lyriques. Représentée sur le Théâtre de l'Opera-comique le 10 juillet 1756.

Paris, Veuve Duchesne, 1767. 32 p. 18½ᶜᵐ.

One act. On p. 23–32 the "Airs de L'amour impromptu": "O Dieux! qu'elle est belle," "Quitte la plaine," "Répondez, Je respire," "Chantez, sautez, jeunes beautez," "Prenez au village une maitresse." The "acte d'Eglé" is the same as the third entrée, "La danse," though none of the entrées of Rameau's "Les fêtes d'Hébé ou Les talens lyriques" are called "Eglé." ("Eglé, bergere" is one of the characters in "La danse.) The text of the parody was by Favart. According to Font it is the same as his unpublished parody, "Sansonnet et Tonton" of 1739, which had been forbidden by the police. This, however, he mentions (p. 339) as a parody of the *second* entrée, "La musique"! Malherbe's preface to the reprint of Rameau's "Les fêtes d'Hébé" score does not face this contradiction and his remarks on the parody are not felicitous.   Schatz 11479

Les **fêtes de l'automne.** *See* Floquet's Le seigneur bienfaisant.

Les **fêtes de l'Himen et de l'Amour;** ou Les dieux d'Egipte, ballet-héroïque, donné à Versailles le quinze mars 1747, représenté, pour la premiere fois, par l'Academie-royale de musique, le mardi 5 novembre 1748, remis au théâtre en juillet 1754, & le mardi 4 juin 1765.

Paris, Aux dépens de l'Académie, chés de Lormel, 1765. 46 p. 22½ᶜᵐ.

Three entrées called "Osiris," "Canope," "Arnéris ou Les Isies," and each preceded by prefatory remarks. Cast and names of de Cahusac as author, of Jean Philippe **Rameau** as composer.   ML 52.2.F42R2

— Les **fêtes de l'Hymen et de l'Amour,** ballet héroique, en trois actes et en vers. Représenté par l'Académie royale de musique de Bordeaux. Nouvelle édition.

Paris, Ruault, 1778. 16 p. 21ᶜᵐ.

Cast. Neither Cahusac nor **Rameau** is mentioned. The prologue has been dropped.   ML 52.2.F42R3

Les **fêtes liriques.** Nouveau ballet-héroïque, en trois entrées, de différents auteurs: représentées, par l'Académie-royale de musique, le vendredi 29 août 1766.

Paris, Aux dépens de l'Académie, chés de Lormel, 1766. 56 p. 23ᶜᵐ.

Cast. Written by different authors, the three entrées were also set to music by different composers. The libretto mentions "**Francoeur** neveu" (Louis Joseph) as composer of the first "Lindor et Ismene;" Jean Philippe **Rameau** as composer of the second "Anacréon;" de Moncrif as author and Pierre **Berton** as composer of the third "Erosine, pastorale-héroïque, en un acte, représentée, devant Leurs Majestés, à Fontainebleau, le 9 novembre 1765." (*See* also Erosine.) "Lindor et Ismene" was written by Michel de Bonneval and, according to Schatz, the text is the same as that of "Le Roman merveilleux," fourth entrée in his ballet "Les Romans"(1736). The text of "Anacréon" was by Louis de Cahusac, and this one-act opéra-ballet had first been performed on October 23, 1754. It is not to be confused with Rameau's Anacréon, text by Gentil-Bernard, first performed May 31, 1757, as third act in his "Les surprises de l'amour."   ML 52.2.F46

Les **fêtes vénitiennes.** *See* Campra's Les festes venitiennes.

Il **Fetonte.** *See* M. Curzio.

Fetonte.

p. 71–103. 15½ᶜᵐ. (Ottavio Tronsarelli, Drammi musicali, Roma, Francesco Corbelletti, 1632.)

Five acts. Argument. No composer mentioned. ML 49.A2T7

Fetonte. Dramma per musica da rappresentarsi nel Regio Teatro di Berlino . . .

Berlino, Haude e Spener, 1770. 83, [3] p. 16½ᶜᵐ.

Three acts. Leopoldo de Villati is mentioned as the author ("La poesia tratta dall' originale francese" [Quinault's Phaeton] . . . Vi sono stati fatti diversi cangiamenti) and Carl Heinrich **Graun** as composer. Count Algarotti is known to have assisted Villati and possibly Frederick the Great collaborated. Argument and scenario. German title-page, "Phaeton," and text face Italian.

Performed, as indicated, January, 1770; originally March 29, 1750. SCHATZ 4098

Fetonte. Dramma per musica da rappresentarsi nel Gran Teatro Ducale di Luisburgo festeggiand osi il felicissimo giorno natalizio di Sua Altezza Serenissima Carlo duca regnante di Wirtemberg et Teck, etc. La musica è nuova composizione del Signor Nicolò Jommelli . . . I balli nascon tutti dal tronco del soggetto e sono stati immaginati dall' autore del drama . . .

[Stutgart], Cotta, 1768. 159 p. 17ᶜᵐ.

Three acts. By Mattia Verazi, who is not mentioned. Scenario and cast. French title-page, "Phaeton," and text face Italian.

First performed, as indicated, February 11, 1768. Not to be confused with his "Fetonte," text by Leopoldo de Villati, with alterations and interpolations, first performed at Stuttgart, Schauplatz im Lusthause, February 11, 1753. SCHATZ 4860

— **Fetonte.** Dramma per musica da rappresentarsi nel Real Teatro dell' Ajuda nel felicissimo giorno natalizio del fedelissimo monarca D. Giuseppe I . . . nel di 6 giugno 1769.

Lisbona, Stamperia reale, n. d. 72 p. 16ᶜᵐ.

Three acts. Scenario, cast, and names of Mattia Verazi as author, of Niccolò **Jommelli** as composer ("nuova composizione"). The text seems to follow the 1768 edition closely, though, for instance, the chorus "Della gran buccina," at end of I, 5 has been dropped. SCHATZ 4859

Fetonte sulle rive del Po. Componimento drammatico per le nozze delle A. A. R. R. di Vittorio Amedeo duca di Savoja, e di Maria Antonia Ferdinanda infanta di Spagna, da cantarsi nel palazzo di Sua Eccellenza Fra' D. Emanuello De Sada e Antillon . . .

[At end] Torino, Pietro Giuseppe Zappata, e figlio, 1750. 4 p. l., 27 p. 23ᶜᵐ.

One act. Argument, cast, and names of Giuseppe Baretti as author, and of Giovanni Antonio **Giai** as the composer.

First performed, as indicated, June, 1750. SCHATZ 3818

Feudal times; or, The banquet-gallery: a drama, in two acts. First represented at the Theatre-Royal, Drury-Lane, on Saturday, Jan. 19th, 1799. Written by George Colman, the younger . . .

London, Cadell and Davies, n. d. vi, [2], 55 p. 21ᶜᵐ.

Cast, preface dated Piccadilly, February 13, 1799, and name of Michael **Kelly** as composer. In Corri, Dussek & co's vocal score the overture is headed as composed by **Dussek.** LONGE 249

Il **feudatorio,** ballet.   *See* Monza's Ifigenia in Tauride.

Il **feudatorio ingannato,** ballet.   *See* Ferrero's La disfatta di Dario.

Il **feudatorio pentito,** ballet.   *See* Zingarelli's Artaserse.

La **Fiammetta.**   Opera bernesca in musica da rappresentarsi in Venezia nel Teatro Giustiniano di San Moisè nel carnevale nell' anno 1743.   M. V.

> *Venezia, Girolamo Bortoli, 1744.*   *58 p.*   *15ᶜᵐ.*

Three ac s.   Cast and scenario.   Author and composer not mentioned, and unknown to Schatz.   Schatz 11330

La **fida ninfa.**   Dramma per musica da rappresentarsi in Verona nella dedicazione del nuovo Teatro Filarmonico.   [vignette]

> *n. i., n. d.*   *[191]–256 p.*   *18ᶜᵐ.*

Evidently detached copy.   Three acts.   The text is preceded by Giulio Cesare Becelli's very interesting preface on p. [193]–202, in which he says that the text was written by the author [marchese Scipione Maffei] when eighteen years of age. Later on he altered and used the text for a special musical purpose and forgot all about it, until the refusal of "alcuni valenti poeti" to furnish a new drama for the opening festivities of the new Teatro Filarmonico in Verona, in 1730 induced him to use his own text instead.   Becelli then tells us how Giuseppe Maria **Orlandini,** the composer, came from Bologna to Verona to confer with Maffei on further changes in the text and how he came as Maffei's guest "per levar arie, o aggiungere, e per adattarle al di lui piacere nel modo, e nel sito, e in altre circostanze della scena, secondando anche il genio dei cantanti: anzi in alcuni luoghi vi erano due arie invece di una, perchè il maestro prendesse la più geniale, di qualcuna ancora essendosi servito, che avea con applauso usata in cantate . . ."   Hence Maffei's hostile views on this kind of cooperation between dramatist and composer.   Finally, Becelli makes some noteworthy remarks on the same subject.   Schatz records, but evidently incorrectly, Antonio Vivaldi as the composer.   ML 50.2.F4O7

— La **fida ninfa.**   Drama per musica.

> *[241]–293 p.*   *17½ᶜᵐ.*   (*Marchese Scipione Maffei, Poesie, Verona, 1752, t. ii*).

Three acts.   **Orlandini** is not mentioned.   PQ

Fidarsi è bene, ma non fidarsi è meglio.   Divertimento comico per musica da rappresentarsi nel Teatro Giustiniani à San Moisè.   In occasione della fiera dell' Ascensione.   L'anno MDCCXXXI.

> *Venezia, Carlo Buonarrigo, n. d.*   *47, [1] p.*   *15ᶜᵐ.*

Three acts.   Attributed by Schatz and Wiel to the composer Giuseppe Maria **Buini,** who is not mentioned.   Schatz 1396

Il **fido amante,** ballet.   *See* Sarti's Medonte.

Il **fido amico,** oder: Der getreue freund Hercules und Theseus. Auf dem grossen Hamburgischen Schau-platz in einem singe-spiel auffgefuehret im jahr 1708.

> *n. i., n. d.*   *Unpaged.*   *18½ᶜᵐ.*

Three acts.   Neither the author, Breymann (who based his text on Moniglia's "Ercole in Tebe"), nor the composer, Christoph **Graupner,** is mentioned in the notice to the "Geehrter leser."   Some arias have Italian and German text, which is on the whole German.   Schatz 4123

La **fiera di Batavia,** ballet.   *See* Curcio's Solimano.

La fiera di Sinigaglia, ballet. *See* Andreozzi's Teodelinda.

La fiera di Sinigaglia. Dramma di tre atti per musica. Rappresentato per la prima volta in Bologna l'estate dell' anno MDCCLXI.

Carlo Goldoni, Opere teatrali, Venezia, Zatta e figli, 1788–95, t. 41, [115]–180 p. 18ᶜᵐ.

For correct date of first performance *see* next entry. **PQ**

La fiera di Sinigaglia. Dramma giocoso per musica di Polisseno Fegejo Pastore Arcade [Goldoni] Da rappresentarsi nel Teatro delle Dame per le prime recite del carnevale 1760 . . .

Roma, Giuseppe e Nicolò Grossi, 1760. 72 p. 15ᶜᵐ.

Three acts. Impresario's dedication, cast, scenario, and name of the composer, Domenico **Fischietti**. **SCHATZ 3239**

La fiera di Venezia. Dramma giocoso per musica di Giov. Gastone Bocherini da rappresentarsi nel Piccolo Teatro di S. A. E. di Sassonia.

Dresda, n. publ., 1775. 167 p. 16ᶜᵐ.

Three acts. Antonio **Salieri** is mentioned as the composer. German title-page, "Der markt von Venedig," and text face Italian.

First performed at Dresden, 1775, as indicated; at Vienna, Burgtheater, January 29, 1772. **SCHATZ 9293**

— La **fiera di Venezia,** comedia per musica in tre atti, di Gio. Gastone Boccherini, Lucchese, poeta Arcade; da rappresentarsi nel Regio Teatro.—Markedet i Venedig . . . Oversat paa dansk af R. Soelberg.

Kiøbenhavn, H. J. Graae, n. d. 127 p. 16½ᶜᵐ.

Cast and name of Antonio **Salieri** as the composer.
First performed, as indicated, April 10, 1777. **SCHATZ 9295**

— La **fiera di Venezia.** Commedia per musica da rappresentarsi in Milano per la solenne occasione della sua prima apertura in agosto dell' anno 1779 . . .

Milano, Gio. Batista Bianchi, n. d. 84 p. 16ᶜᵐ.

Three acts. Dedication, cast, scenario, and names of Boccherini as the author, of Antonio **Salieri** as the composer. With the opera were performed, music by Mattia Staubingher, Antonio Muzzarelli's ballets "La sconfitta delle Amazoni" and "Le avventure d'Ircana."
First performed August 21, 1779, as indicated. **SCHATZ 9291**

— Die **messe zu Venedig,** eine operette aufgefuehret am Churpfaelzischen hofe 1772.

Mannheim, Hof u. Akademie buchdruckerei, n. d. 82 p. 16ᶜᵐ.

Three acts. Cast and name of Antonio **Salieri** as the composer. A separate edition of the German translation for the Italian performances at Mannheim, Hoftheater, November 22, 1772. On p. 76–82, cast and description of Lauchery's ballet "Der tod des Hercules," "die musick bestehet aus verschiedenen schoenen stuecken mehrern beruehmten meistern." **SCHATZ 9292**

— Arien und gesaenge aus dem singspiele Der **jahrmarkt zu Venedig,** in drey akten. Die musik ist vom herrn Salieri.

Berlin, n. publ., 1799. 54 p. 16ᶜᵐ.

Three acts. The translator, Heinrich Christian Pleissner, is not mentioned. Cast.
First performed at Berlin, Kgl. National Theater, February 25, 1799. **SCHATZ 9294**

A fig for invasion. A. T. of The times.

Figaro als barbier zu Sevilla. Tr. of Paisiello's Il barbiere di Seviglia.

Figaro's heyrath. Tr. of Mozart's Le nozze di Figaro.

Figaros hochzeit. Tr. of Mozart's Le nozze di Figaro.

Figaros hochzeit oder List über list. Tr. of Mozart's Le nozze di Figaro.

Figaro's hochzeit oder Der tolle tag. Tr. of Mozart's Le nozze di Figaro.

La **figlia dell' aria** o sia L'innalzamento di Semiramide, ballet. *See* Righini's Armida.

La **figlia obbediente.** Dramma giocoso per musica da rappresentarsi nel Teatro di Monza l'autunno dell' anno 1780 . . .

> *Milano, Giovanni Battista Bianchi, n. d. 60 p. 16^{cm}.*
> Two acts. By unknown author. Dedication, cast, scenario, and name of the composer, Carlo **Bosi.** With the opera were performed Innocente Parodi's ballets "Le gelosie d'Annetta e Fiorillo" and "Accampamento di Micheletti." The composers of the music are not mentioned.   SCHATZ 1256

Le **figlie astute,** ballet. *See* Brunetti's Bertoldo.

Le **figlie astute,** ballet. *See* P. Guglielmi's Enea e Lavinia.

Il **figlio delle selve.** Dramma per musica da rappresentarsi nel Teatro Fontanelli in Modona [!] l'anno MDCCI . . .

> *Modona [!], Antonio Capponi, n. d. 1 p. l., 60 p. 13½^{cm}.*
> Three acts. Impresario's dedication ("La prima opera, ch'io pongo su'l mio teatro"), argument, and cast. Neither the composer, Gaetano **Boni,** nor the librettist, Carlo Sigismondo Capece, is mentioned.
> First performed, as indicated, December 27, 1700.   SCHATZ 1181

Il **figlio delle selve.** Favola pastorale per musica da rappresentarsi per comando del Serenissimo Elettore Palatino. L'anno MDCCLIII.

> *Mannheim, Nicola Pierron, n. d. 3 p. l., 77 p. 16^{cm}.*
> Three acts. By Carlo Sigismondo Capece, and partly rewritten by Francesco Bardella, who are not mentioned. Argument, cast, and name of Ignaz **Holzbauer** as the composer.
> First performed at Schwetzingen, Neues Churfuerstl. Theater, 1753.
>   SCHATZ 4781

Il **figlio delle selve.** Dramma pastorale per musica da rappresentarsi nel Teatro del Falcone la primavera dell' anno 1755 . . .

> *Genova, Franchelli, n. d. 5 p. l., 48 p. 14½^{cm}.*
> Three acts. Dedication signed by Francesco Bardella (who, according to Schatz, based this text on that of Carlo Sigismondo Capece), argument, and remark:
> "La musica de' recitativi, e dell' arie segnate con una stella è del Signor Felice **Mazzinghi,** & l'altre arie sono di vari autori."   SCHATZ 6217

Il figlio delle selve. Dramma per musica da recitarsi nel Reggio Teatro di Torino . . .

Torino, Gio. Battista Fontana, 1699. 94 p. 14½cm.

Three acts. On p. 91–92, "Scena aggiunta. O Frulla se m'ami;" on p. 93–94, additions for I, 11, "Col nome di Sergesto—Mentre mi fingo amante" and, at end of I, 11, "Doppo rigide tempeste." Neither Carlo Sigismondo Capece, the author, is mentioned, nor Alessandro **Scarlatti**, the composer.

First performed, as indicated, 1699; at Rome, at the poet's home, 1687, the dedication of the original ed. of the libretto being dated January 18, 1687. SCHATZ 9530

Li figliuoli rivali del padre. A. T of Caldara's Camaide, imperatore della China.

Filandro. L. T. of Albinoni's L'incostanza schernita.

Filandro, dramma comico pastorale per musica rappresentato alla corte di Dresda, il giorno natalizio di Sua Altezza Reale ed Elettorale la principessa Maria Antonia Valpurga . . . il dì 18. luglio 1747.

n. i., n. d. 143 p. 16½cm.

Three acts. By Vincenzo Cassani, who is not mentioned. Argument, cast, scenario, and name of Nicolà Antonio **Porpora** as the composer. German title-page, "Philander," and text face Italian. The text is the same as Cassani's "L'incostanza schernita." SCHATZ 8357

La fileuse; Parody of Destouches' Omphale.

Il Filindo. Pastorale eroica per musica da rappresentarsi nel Teatro Giustiniano di S. Moisè. L'autunno dell' anno MDCCXX . . .

Venezia, Marino Rossetti, 1720. 48 p. 14½cm.

Three acts. By Pietro d'Averara. Impresario's dedication, notice to the reader, cast, scenario, and name of the composer, Giuseppe Maria **Buini**, but not of the author. SCHATZ 1382

Filippo rè della Grecia. Drama per musica da recitarsi nell' impareggiabile Teatro Grimani di S. Gio. Grisostomo l'anno MDCCVI . . .

Venezia, Marino Rossetti, 1706. 76 p. 15cm.

Five acts. Impresario's dedication, argument, notice to the reader, with name of Carlo Francesco **Pollaroli** as the composer, cast, and scenario. The author, conte Pietro Giorgio Barziza, is not mentioned. SCHATZ 8289

Filippo rè di Macedonia. Drama per musica di Domenico Lalli. Da recitarsi nel Teatro di S. Angelo il carnevale dell' anno 1721 . . .

Venezia, Marino Rossetti, 1721. 48 p. 14cm.

Three acts. Dedication by Lalli, argument, cast, scenario, and names of Giuseppe **Boniventi** as composer of the first and second acts, of Antonio **Vivaldi** of the third. SCHATZ 1196

La fille. Entrée in Mouret's Les festes de Thalie.

La fille mal gardée. *See* Mouret's Les festes de Thalie.

La filli di Tracia. Drama da rappresentarsi in musica nel Teatro à S. Stefano in Ferrara l'anno 1664. Con la musica del Sig. D. Andrea Matioli mastro di capella del Sereniss. di Mantoua . . .

Ferrara, gl'heredi dei Suzzi, n. d. 134 p., [3] l. 13½cm.

Three acts with prologue. Conte Ercole Pinamonte Bonacossi is mentioned as author in the impresario's dedication, which is dated Ferrara, February 17, 1664. Argument. The three additional leaves contain a list of errata and the imprimatur. SCHATZ 6105

La **Filo** overo Giunone repacificata con Ercole per le nozze de' Serenissimi Ranuccio II duca di Parma, e Margarita, principessa di Savoia: da cantarsi nel Teatro maggiore di S. A. col motivo ad un torneo, che dovrà seguire un' altra sera.   Drama del conte Francesco Berni.

Parma, Erasmo Viotti, n. d.   4 p. l., 159, [1] p.   14ᶜᵐ.

On last page repetition of the imprint with date 1660.
Three acts, prologue, three intramezzi and congratulatory epilogue.   In a prefatory note Francesco **Manelli** is mentioned as composer.
First performed 1660, as indicated.   SCHATZ 5889

— I **sei gigli.**   Torneo per le nozze de' Serenissimi Ranuccio II, duca di Parma, e Margarita, principessa di Savoia: intimato nella Filo, e da combattersi nel Teatro maggiore di S. A.   Componimento del conte Francesco Berni.

Parma, Marco Vigna, 1660.   31 p.   14½ᶜᵐ.

Prologue and five comparse.   Francesco **Manelli** is mentioned as the composer.
                                          SCHATZ 5891

La **filosofa olandese,** ballet.   *See* Anfossi's La maga Circe.

I **filosofi immaginarj.**   L. T. of Astaritta's I visionari.

I **filosofi immaginari.**   Dramma per musica da rappresentarsi nel nuovo Teatro de' Fiorentini.

Napoli, n. publ., 1784.   34 p.   15ᶜᵐ.

Two acts.   By Giovanni Bertati, who is not mentioned.   Cast and name of **Paisiello** as the composer.
First performed at St. Petersburg, Eremitage, February 7/18, 1779, as "Gli astrologi imaginarj," and this in turn was an alteration of Bertati's original title, "I visionarj."   SCHATZ 7616

— I **filosofi immaginarii.**   Dramma giocoso per musica da rappresentarsi nel Teatro de la rua dos Condes nel anno de 1790.—Os filosofos imaginarios . . .   Traduzido do idioma italiano para o portuguez.

Lisboa, Simão Thaddeo Ferreira, 1790.   95 p.   15ᶜᵐ.

Two acts.   Dedication, cast, and name of Giov. **Paisiello** as composer.   Bertati is not mentioned.   ML 48.C6II

— I **visionari.**   Dramma giocoso per musica, da rappresentarsi nel Teatro Elettorale.

Dresda, n. publ., 1793.   93 p.   15½ᶜᵐ.

Two acts.   **Paisiello** is mentioned as the composer.   German title-page, "Die phantasten," and text face Italian.
First performed 1793, as indicated.   SCHATZ 7619

— Die **eingebildeten philosophen.**   Ein singspiel in zwey aufzuegen, aus dem italiaenischen auf die musik des herrn Paesello uebersetzt.   Von Stephanie dem juengern.   Aufgefuehrt auf dem kais. kön. Nat. Hoftheater.

[Wien], Zu finden beym logenmeister, 1781.   44 p.   16ᶜᵐ.

First performed, as indicated, May 22, 1781.   SCHATZ 7617

— Arien aus den **Philosophen.**   Ein singspiel in zwey aufzuegen.

n. i., n. d.   24 p.   16½ᶜᵐ.

Same version as the foregoing.
First performed at Pressburg, private theater of Graf Erdödy, 1788.   SCHATZ 7618

Filosofia ed amore. Dramma di tre atti per musica. Rappresentato per la prima volta in Venezia il carnovale dell' anno MDCCLX.

Carlo Goldoni, Opere teatrali, Venezia. Zatta e figli, 1788–95, v. 38, [271]–334 p. 18½^{cm}.

PQ

Filosofia ed amore, dramma giocoso per musica di Polisseno Fegejo, P. A. Da rappresentarsi nel Teatro Giustinian di S. Moisè, il carnovale dell' anno MDCCLX.

Venezia, Modesto Fenzo, 1760. 68 p. 15^{cm}.

Three acts. By Goldoni. Cast, scenario, and name of Florian Leopold **Gassmann** as the composer. SCHATZ 3615

Il filosofo. Intermezzo.

[193]–209 p. 16½^{cm}. (Carlo Goldoni, Opere drammatiche giocose, t. iv, Torino, 1757.)

Two parts. First composer unknown to Schatz. ML 49.A2G6

— **Il filosofo.** Intermezzo di due parti per musica.

Carlo Goldoni, Opere teatrali, Venezia, Zatta e figli, 1788–95, v. 35, [251]–270 p. 18½^{cm}.

PQ

Il filosofo amante. Farsa per musica da rappresentarsi nel real Teatro di Salvaterra nel carnovale dell' anno 1776.

[Lisbona], Nella Stamperia reale, n. d. 77 p. 16½^{cm}.

Two acts. By unknown author. Cast, scenario, and name of the composer, Giovanni Battista **Borghi.** SCHATZ 1232

Il filosofo deriso, ballet. *See* P. Guglielmi's Rinaldo.

Il filosofo di campagna. Dramma di tre atti per musica. Rappresentato a Madrid l'anno MDCCLX.

Carlo Goldoni, Opere teatrali, Venezia, Zatta e figli, 1788–95, v. 43, [63]–122 p. 18^{cm}.

For first performance *see* next entry. PQ

Il filosofo di campagna. Dramma giocoso per musica di Polisseno Fegejo, Pastor Arcade. Da rappresentarsi nel Teatro Grimani di S. Samuel l'autunno dell' anno 1754 . . .

Venezia, Modesto Fenzo, 1754. 60 p. 15½^{cm}.

Three acts. By Goldoni. Impresario's dedication, cast, scenario, and name of Baldassare **Galuppi** as composer.

First performed at Milan, Regio-Ducal Teatro, summer 1750. SCHATZ 3452

— **Il filosofo di campagna.** Dramma giocoso per musica, da rappresentarsi in Dresda l'anno MDCCLV.—Der land-mann ein philosoph . . .

Dresden, gedruckt bey der verwitt. . . . Stoesselin, und . . . Johann Carl Krausen, n. d. 158 p. 17^{cm}.

Three acts. Cast, scenario, and name of **Galuppi** as composer. German text faces the Italian, which follows closely that of the original ed. of 1754, though some differences are noticeable. For instance (I, 4), "Taci, amor, nel seno mio" has been replaced by "Agitato gelo, e tremo," words which do not appear to be by Goldoni at all. SCHATZ 3453

Il **filosofo di campagna**—Continued.

— La **serva astuta** o sia Il filosofo in campagna, intermezzo in due parti a cinque voci da rappresentarsi nel Teatro di Sant' Angelo l'autunno dell' anno MDCCLXI.

Venezia, Valvasense, n. d.   24 p.   15½ᶜᵐ.

Cast. Goldoni is mentioned as the author, and **Galuppi** as the composer. A thoroughly-altered condensation in two acts. The characters of Eugenia and Rinaldo have been dropped, Lena has become Fiorillo, and the intermezzo begins, "Povera padroncina," instead of "Candidetto Gelsomino."   Schatz 3513

Il **filosofo di campagna.** Dramma giocoso per musica da rappresentarsi alla Corte elettorale Palatina . . . l'anno 1756.

Mannheim, Stamperia elettorale, n. d.   173 p.   16ᶜᵐ.

Three acts. Neither Goldoni, the author, nor Ignaz **Holzbauer**, the composer, is mentioned.   Schatz 4782

Il **filosofo in campagna.** A. T. of Galuppi's La serva astuta.

Os **filosofos imaginarios.** Tr. of Paisiello's I filosofi immaginarii.

Der **findling.** A. T. of Monsigny's Felix.

La **finta amalata:** Farsa per musica in un solo atto. Da rappresentarsi nel Regio Teatro di S. Carlo, della Principessa.

Lisbona, Simone Taddeo Ferreira, 1796.   167 p.   15½ᶜᵐ.

Cast. Portuguese translation faces Italian. Neither the author (unknown to Schatz) is mentioned, nor Domenico **Cimarosa**, the composer. The text is a condensation (with alterations) of the two-act text of the same title composed, for instance, by Vittorio Trento for Florence, 1793.
First performed 1796, as indicated.
On p. [69]–167:

— Il **convitato di Pietra.**

One act ("farsa II" of the evening). Cast, scenario, and name of Vincenzo **Fabrizi** as composer. The author, Giambattista Lorenzi, is not mentioned. The above is the A. T. of their "Don Giovanni Tenorio," Bologna, 1791.   ML 48.C6 III

La **finta amalata.** Dramma giocoso per musica da rappresentarsi nel nobile Teatro Veronese in San Cassano il carnovale dell' anno 1794. Posto in musica dal Signor maestro Vittorio Trento.

Venezia, Casali, 1794.   55 p.   18ᶜᵐ.

Two acts. Author not mentioned, and unknown to Schatz. With the opera were performed the ballets, "I Veneziani a Costantinopoli" and "Il Chinese."
First performed at Florence, Teatro La Palla a Corda, spring of 1793.
                                                        Schatz 10432

La **finta amante.** Opera comica di due atti per musica da rappresentarsi nel Teatro de' Fiorentini.

Napoli, n. publ., 1788.   34 p.   15ᶜᵐ.

Two acts. Author not mentioned, and unknown to Schatz. Cast and name of **Paisiello** as the composer.
First performed at St. Petersburg, Teatro di corte, 1780, and previously, in June, 1780, for the meeting of Catherine II with Joseph II of Austria   Schatz 7669

La **finta Astrea.** Farsetta in musica a tre voci da recitarsi nel Teatro alla Valle il carnevale dell' anno 1755 . . .

Roma, Ottavio Puccinelli, 1754.   24 p.   15½ᶜᵐ.

Two parts. Author unknown to me. Dedication by Angelo Lungi, cast and name of Giacinto **Quagliattini** as composer.   ML 50.2.F43Q2

La finta baronessa o Li due fratelli ridicoli. L. T. of Alessandri's La finta principessa.

La finta cameriera. Drama giocoso da rappresentarsi sopra il Nuovo Teatro dell' Opera pantomima del Nicolini in Bronseviga.

Bronseviga, heredi Keitel, n. d. Unpaged. 19ᶜᵐ.

Three acts. By Giovanni Barlocci, who is not mentioned. Argument, scenario, and name of Bald. **Galuppi** as composer. German title page, "Das verstellte Kammermaedgen," and text face the Italian.
First performed, as indicated, 1751.
"La finta cameriera" is generally attributed to Latilla. Piovano suspects that this Brunswick version, though bearing Galuppi's name, either was by Latilla or else that it was a pasticcio, partly from Galuppi.   SCHATZ 3454

La finta cameriera. Divertimento giocoso per musica da rappresentarsi nel Teatro di Sant' Angelo la primavera dell' anno 1743. Nella fiera dell' Ascensione.

Venezia, Modesto Fenzo, 1743. 60 p. (incl. front.). 13½ᶜᵐ.

Three acts. By Giovanni Barlocci, who is not mentioned. Cast and name of Gaetano **Latilla** as composer. Became known also as "La giardiniera contessa" and "Don Colascione."
First performed at Rome, Teatro Valle, spring of 1738.   SCHATZ 5445

La finta cantatrice. A. T. of P. Guglielmi's Chi la dura la vince.

La finta cecità di Antioco il Grande. Drama per musica nel felicissimo dì natalizio . . . Leopoldo I . . . l'anno MDCXCV. Posto in musica dal Sr. Antonio Draghi maestro di Cap. di S. M. C. con l'arie per li balletti del Sr. Gio. Gioseffo Hoffer, violinista di S. M. C.

Vienna d'Austria, Susanna Cristina, vedova di Matteo Cosmerovio, n. d. 106 p. 15ᶜᵐ.

Three acts, with ballets and Licenza by Donato Cupeda, by whom the dedication is signed and dated "Vienna, 9. di Giugno, 1695." Followed by "Benigno lettore" and argument and scenario.
First performed at Vienna, Hoftheater, June 9, 1695.   SCHATZ 2797

La finta Cingara per amore. Farsa per musica ·in due atti, a cinque voci da rappresentarsi nel nobil Teatro Grimani di S. Gio. Grisostomo il carnovale dell' anno 1780 . . .

Venezia, Pietro Sola, 1780. 51 p. 17ᶜᵐ.

Impresario's dedication, cast, scenario, name of Carlo **Franchi** as composer of the first and of Pasquale **Anfossi** of the second act. The author is unknown to Schatz.
First performed at Rome, Teatro di Tor di Nona, carnival, 1774.   SCHATZ 3331

La finta contessina. Farsetta per musica da rappresentarsi nel Teatro alla Valle nel carnevale dell' anno 1751 . . .

Roma, Ottavio Puccinelli, 1751. 26 p. 15½ᶜᵐ.

Two parts. Author not mentioned and unknown to me. Dedication by the publisher and Angelo Lungi ("ponendosi sulle scene il terzo scherzo musicale"), cast and name of Antonio **Colli** as composer.   ML 50.2.F433C7

La finta Galatea o sia L'antiquario fanatico.

Two acts. Text and music by Marcello di Capua (**Bernardini**). First performed at Rome, Teatro della Pace, carnival 1785.
L. of C. has no 18th cent. ed. under this, the original title

La **finta Galatea**—Continued.

— Le **donne bisbetiche** o sia L'antiquario fanatico.   Farsetta in musica a cinque voci da rappresentarsi nel Pubblico Teatro della nobil città di Orvieto nel carnevale dell' anno 1791 . . .

Orvieto, Luigi Carlucci, n. d.   47 p.   16½ᶜᵐ.

Two acts.   Cast, name of Marcello di Capua (**Bernardini**) as author and composer and impresario's dedication to the ladies of Orvieto, in which he says:

"Non v' à più dubbio, che il Teatro fu instituito per la riforma de' costumi.   Questo deve sempre essere l'unico suo fine, cioè dilettare, e nell' istesso tempo dolcemente ammaestrare lo spettatore con ispirargli orrore al vizio, che nelle sceniche rappresentazioni o si riprende, o si dileggia, ed animarlo alla virtù, che si commenda, e di cui se ne presentano dei modelli . . .

"Consequiamo alla vostra protezione la presente farsetta, che serve per interrompere colla musica le altre teatriche rappresentanze . . ."   ML 50.2.D61B2

La **finta giardiniera.**   Dramma giocoso per musica da rappresentarsi in Prato nel carnevale dell' anno 1775 nel Teatro pubblico dei Nobili Accademici Semplici . . .

Firenze, Gio. Bat. Stecchi e Anton Giuseppe Pagani, 1775.   74 p. 16ᶜᵐ.

Three acts.   Impresario's dedication, cast, and name of the composer, Pasquale **Anfossi**, but not of librettist, who is unknown to Schatz.

First performed at Rome, Teatro delle Dame, carnival, 1774.   Schatz 234

— La **finta giardiniera.**   Dramma giocoso per musica da rappresentarsi nel Piccolo teatro di S. A. S. E. di Sassonia.

Dresda, n. publ., 1775.   175 p.   16½ᶜᵐ.

Three acts.   Scenario and name of **Anfossi** as composer.   German title-page "Die verstellte gaertnerin," and text face Italian.

First performed, as indicated, February 7, 1775.   Schatz 235

La **finta matta.**   Commedia per musica di Domenico Piccinni da rappresentarsi nel Teatro de' Fiorentini per terz' opera di quest' anno 1789.

Napoli, n. publ., 1789.   59 p.   15½ᶜᵐ.

Two acts.   Cast and name of Silvestro di **Palma** as the composer.   Schatz 7741

La **finta pazza.**   Dramma giocoso per musica da rappresentarsi nel Teatro Giustiniano di S. Moisè.   Nella fiera della Ascensione dell' anno 1747.

Venezia, Modesto Fenzo, 1747.   front., 48 p.   15ᶜᵐ.

Three acts.   Cast and scenario.   Author and composer not mentioned and unknown to Schatz.   Schatz 11331

La **finta pazza.**   Drama di Giulio Strozzi.   Seconda impressione.

Venetia, Gio. Battista Surian, 1641.   96 p.   13½ᶜᵐ.

Three acts with prologue.   Author's dedication dated Venice, January 14, 1641, and his notice to the reader, which begins:

"Questa è l'ottava fatica rapresentativa, che mi trovo haver fatta; cinque delle quali hanno di già più volte passeggiate le scene, e'in questa m'e riuscito assai felicemente lo sciorre più d'un nodo di lei senza magia, e senza ricorrere a gli aiuti sopranaturali, e divini."

At the end he mentions Francesco **Sacrati** as the composer.   Then follows "Sonetti del Sig. Francesco Melosi alla Signora Anna Renzi, celebre cantatrice di Roma, rappresentante in Venetia La finta pazza" and "Pianto di Deidamia nella Finta pazza. Espresso mirabilmente in musica dalla Sig. Anna Renzi Romana."   At end this note by "Gio. Battista Surian libraio al frequente compratore":

"Sono stato sforzato dall' avidità de' lettori di quest' opera à metterla due volte in un mese sotto il torchio; tanto applauso hà ricevuto dalle lingue universali La finta pazza nel Teatro Novissimo della città di Venetia, ov' ella con regale apparato è stata in 17 giorni dodici volte rappresentata."   Schatz 9253

La finta pazzia d'Ulisse. Drama per musica da recitarsi nel Teatro Vendramino di S. Salvatore l'anno 1696. Di Matteo Noris . . .

Venetia, Francesco Nicolini, 1696. 83 p. 14^{cm}.

Three acts. Author's dedication, notice to the reader with scenario and name of Marc Antonio **Ziani** as the composer and scenario.

First performed, as indicated, carnival, 1696. SCHATZ 11186

La finta pazzia di Diana. Pastorale giocosa per musica da rappresentarsi nel Teatro Giustinian di S. Moisè nel carnovale dell' anno 1748.

Venezia, Modesto Fenzo, 1748. 36 p. (incl. front.). 15^{cm}.

Three acts. Cast. Author and composer not mentioned and unknown to Schatz.

SCHATZ 11332

La finta Polacca. L. T. of Pergolesi's Livietta e Tracollo o sia La contadina astuta.

La finta principessa. Dramma giocoso per musica da rappresentarsi nel Teatro del Falcone l'autunno dell' anno 1783 . . .

Genova, Giovanni Franchelli, n. d. 68 p. 14$\frac{1}{2}$^{cm}.

Two acts. By Filippo Livigni, who is not mentioned. Cast and name of Felice **Alessandri** as composer.

First performed at Venice, Teatro di S. Moisè, 1782. SCHATZ 146

— La finta baronessa, o Li due fratelli ridicoli, dramma giocoso per musica da rappresentarsi nel Reggio teatro di S. Carlo, della Principessa, l'estate dell' anno 1795.

Lisbona, Simone Taddeo Ferpeira, 1795. 195 p. 14$\frac{1}{2}$^{cm}.

Two acts. By Filippo Livigni. With cast, scenario, and name of Felice **Alessandri** as composer. The Portuguese faces the Italian text, which is practically the same as that of "La finta principessa." SCHATZ 150

La finta principessa. Dramma giocoso per musica da rappresentarsi nel nobile Teatro di San Samuele il carnovale dell' anno 1796.

Venezia, Casali, 1796. 69 p. 18^{cm}.

Two acts. By Filippo Livigni, who is not mentioned. Scenario, cast, and name of Gaetano **Marinelli** as the composer. ("La musica del tutto nuova.")

SCHATZ 5967

La finta Savia. Drama di Giulio Strozzi. [vignette]

Venetia, Matteo Leni e Giovanni Vecellio, 1643. 190, 1 (errata) p. 14$\frac{1}{2}$^{cm}.

Three acts, with prologue and two "canzonetta cantata per intermezzo." Strozzi's dedication, dated Venice, January 1, 1643, "argumento historico," argument preceding each scene, and this note after the list of characters:

"Molti versi si tralascieranno per la lunghezza dell' opera fabricata dall' autore per poterla anco rappresentare senza canto)."

Following the text of the opera: (p. 182–183) "breve ristretto dell' argomento;" (p. 186–190) "Osservationi;" and this statement on p. 184–185:

"La musica di questo drama è per la maggior parte compositione esquisita del Signor Filiberto **Laurenzi** da Bertinoro, il quale con la sua virtù hà saputo dalla buona scuola di Roma, e dalla degna di Venetia far un misto ottimo, e molto adeguato così al recitativo, come all' arioso per questa opera.

"Il Signor [Arcangelo] **Crivelli** hà maestrevolmente favorite alcune delle mie scene, ed alcun' altre sono state honorate dal Signor [Tarquinio] **Merula**, ed altre finalmente nobilitate dal Signor Benedetto **Ferrari**: e perche l'operatione lodi i facitori, habbiamo ad ogni scena posto il nome dell' autor della musica.

La finta savia—Continued.

"Le macchine, e le scene con numerose mutationi sono state inventate dal vivacissimo Sig. Gio. Burnacini da Jesena, il quale fù gli anni adietro il primo, che ravvivò i teatri di Venetia con queste maestrose apparenze . . .

"La sig. Anna Renzi romana stupor de' teatri, che illustrò la mia Finta pazza, hora si compiacerà con l'armonica sua maravigliosa espressione di far apparire la Finta savia molto migliore di quello, ch'io l'habbia composta. Lo stesso operanno con la dolcezza della lor voce, e con la gentilissima maniera di rappresentare tanti altri illustri musici, e principalmente la Signora Anna di Valerio romana similmente, che col celeste suo canto sà condire tutte le terrene amarezze, non potendo in lei l'occhio, e l'orecchio desiderar di vantaggio, ond' ella sarà quest' anno il sigillo di tutte le musicali meraviglie."

First performed January 1, 1643, at Venice, Teatro di S. S. Gio. e Paolo.

SCHATZ 5474

La finta schiava. Intermezzi in musica a tre voci da rappresentarsi nel Teatro della Pace il carnevale dell' anno 1754 . . .

Roma, Si vendono nella libraria di S. Michele Ripa Grande, 1754. 24 p. 15ᶜᵐ.

Two parts. Neither author nor composer mentioned and both unknown to me. Cast and dedication by Angelo Lungi and Gioacchino Puccinelli, the publisher.

ML 50.2.F438

La finta semplice. Dramma di tre atti per musica. Rappresentato per la prima volta in Venezia il carnovale dell' anno MDCCLXIV con musica del Perillo.

Carlo Goldoni, Opere teatrali, Venezia, Zatta e figli, 1788–95, t. 41, [239]–298 p. 18ᶜᵐ.

PQ

La finta semplice. Dramma giocoso per musica da rappresentarsi nel Teatro Giustiniani di S. Moisè il carnovale dell' anno 1764.

Venezia, Modesto Fenzo, 1764. 60 p. 15ᶜᵐ.

Three acts. By Goldoni, who is not mentioned. Schatz attributes the text incorrectly to Luigi Coltellini. Cast, scenario, and name of Salvatore **Perillo** as the composer.

SCHATZ 7926

La finta semplice o sia Il tutore burlato. Dramma giocoso da rappresentarsi in Lisbona nel Teatro della rua dos Condes nella primavera dell' anno 1773.

[Lisbona], Stamperia reale, n. d. 78 p. 15½ᶜᵐ.

Three acts. By Pasquale Mililotti, who is not mentioned. Cast, scenario, and name of "Giacomo Monopoli detto **Insanguine**."

First performed at Naples, Teatro Nuovo sopra Toledo, 1769.   SCHATZ 4837

La finta sposa olandese. Farsetta in musica a cinque voci da rappresentarsi nel Teatro Capranica nel carnevale dell' anno 1777 . . .

Roma, Ottavio Puccinelli, 1776. 60 p. 15ᶜᵐ.

Two acts. Impresario's dedication of this "farsetta," cast, and name of Marcello di Capua (Marcello **Bernardini**) as composer. Author not mentioned, and unknown ₜo Schatz.   SCHATZ 846

La finta Tedesca. Intermezzi per musica a quattro voci da rappresentarsi nel Teatro di Tordinona, nel carnivale dell' anno 1753 . . .

Roma, Giuseppe Agazzi, 1753. 22, [1] p. 15½ᶜᵐ.

Two parts. Cast, publisher's dedication, and name of Giovanni Battista Casale (**Casali**) as composer. The author is unknown to Schatz.   ML 50.2.F44C2

La finta Tedesca. Intermezzo per musica, da rappresentarsi nel Nuovo Real Teatro di Potsdam . . .

Potsdam, C. F. Voss, 1749. 45 p. 17½cm.

Three parts. Author not mentioned, and unknown to Schatz. Cast. The composer, Johann Adolph **Hasse**, is not mentioned. German title page, "Die verstellte Teutsche," and text face Italian.

First performed, as indicated, summer of 1749; previously at Hamburg, Theater beim Gänsemarkt, November 16, 1746; and originally, as "Pantaleone e Carlotta," as intermezzi in his "Attalo, rè di Bitinia," at Naples, Teatro di San Bartolomeo, spring of 1728.   SCHATZ 4540

La finta zingana ossia Il solachianello. L. T. of Pietro Guglielmi's La finta zingara.

La finta zingara. Farsa per musica di Giambattista Lorenzi, P. A. da rappresentarsi nel Teatro de' Fiorentini nel carnevale di quest' anno 1785.

One act. Cast and name of Pietro **Guglielmi** as composer. Forms p. 33–71 of his "Le sventurate fortunate, Napoli, 1785."

First performed, as indicated, Jan. 10, 1785.   SCHATZ 4274

— **La finta zingana** ossia Il solachianello. Commedia in musica da rappresentarsi per terz' opera nel Teatro di questa città di Salerno nell' inverno del 1791 . . .

Napoli, Vincenzo Mazzola-Vocola, 1791. 34 p. 15cm.

One act, with running title "atto secondo"! Impresario's dedication dated Salerno, December 1791, with name of Pietro **Guglielmi** as the composer, and cast. Lorenzi's text has been noticeably altered. For instance, the second scene, "E ben? se astretti siamo," has become the third and "Dico avete finito di gracchiare?" has been added as the second. The differences become more numerous towards the end.

SCHATZ 4245

Le finte gemelle. Farsa per musica a quattro voci.

Firenze, Stecchi e Pagani, 1771. 1 p. l., 56 p. 16cm.

Two acts. At end: "Farsa in musica fatta rappresentare nell' estate del MDCCLXXI nella villa Palmieri de Tre-Visi da S. E. Milord Co. di Cowper." Niccolò **Piccinni** is mentioned as the composer. Giuseppe Petrosellini, the author, is not mentioned.

First performed at Rome, Teatro alla Valle, January 2, 1771, but Cametti claims under the title of "Le due finte gemelle."   SCHATZ 8094

— **Le finte gemelle.** Dramma giocoso per musica da rappresentarsi in Lisbona nel Teatro della rua dos Condes nell' estate dell' anno 1773.

[Lisbona], Stamperia reale, n. d. 94 p. 17cm.

Three acts. Cast, scenario, and names of Giuseppe Petrosellini as author, of Niccolò **Piccinni** as composer. Obviously an expansion of the two-act version. The dialogue is otherwise fairly the same (with the customary changes of arias, of course) up to and including II, 12. Then the Florence two-act version ends with the "ultima: Dice bene il proverbio," which closes with the final *tutti* of the three-act version, "Deh scendi Amore dal carro adorno."   SCHATZ 8093

— **Le due finte gemelle.** Intermezzo in musica a quattro voci da rappresentarsi nel Nobil Teatro Tron di San Cassiano il carnovale dell' anno MDCCLXXXIII . . .

Venezia, Modesto Fenzo, 1783. 51 p. 17½cm.

Two acts. Impresario's dedication, cast, scenario, and name of Niccolò **Piccinni** as the composer. Though the impresario, Giuseppe Pratini speaks of this as "questo nuovo intermezzo" and though we read "La musica sarà," the text (with the customary alterations) is that of Giuseppe Petrosellini's "Le finte gemelle." SCHATZ 8157

I finti amori. Commedia per musica da rappresentarsi nel Teatro de' Fiorentini nell' està del corrente anno 1784.

Napoli, n. publ., 1784. 74 p. 15^{cm}.

Three acts. Author not mentioned and unknown to Schatz. Cast and name of Pietro **Guglielmi** as the composer.   SCHATZ 4246

— **I finti amori.** Dramma giocoso per musica da rappresentarsi nel Teatro di S. A. E. di Sassionia.

Dresda, n. publ., 1790. 151 p. 15^{cm}.

Two acts! Pietro **Guglielmi** is mentioned as the composer. German title-page ' Liebe zum schein," and text face Italian.
First performed, as indicated, January 9, 1790.   SCHATZ 4247

— **L'impostore punito.** Dramma giocoso per musica da rappresentarsi nel Teatro alla Scala l'autunno dell' anno 1785 . . .

Milano, Gio. Batista Bianchi, n. d. 70, 22, 19 p. 16^{cm}.

Two acts. Dedication, cast, scenario, and name of Pietro **Guglielmi** as the composer. The text is that of "I finti amori," but with many alterations. For instance, I, 4, "Caro sposo, sposo amato," has become I, 5, and II, 1, has the aria, "Sa lei Signor marchese," instead of "Sta in quell' abito celata." The additional pages contain argument and description of Sebastiano Gallet's "Le rapt des Sabines, ballet heroique" in five acts and of his "Le maréchal." This is followed by the descriptions of his "Il disertore, ballo tragi-comico" and "Le pazzie amorose." The title of "Il disertore" has the date of performance of 1785, whereas the two French ballets have not. On p. 7 of the libretto the titles of the two ballets to be performed are "L'amor vincitore ossia Diana ed Endimione" and "Le pazzie amorose." Apparently there was either confusion in the plans of the management or confusion in binding.
First performed, as indicated, October 22, 1785.   SCHATZ 4300

I finti eredi, opera comica, da rappresentarsi nel Teatro Imperiale di Pietroburgo, l'anno 1785, composta nuovamente dal Sigr. Giuseppe Sarti . . .

Pietroburgo, Breitkopf, n. d. 7 p. l., 197 p. 18½^{cm}.

Two acts. By Giovanni Bertati, who is not mentioned and whose "Il villano geloso" this is. Scenario, cast, and dedication by Sarti which reads in part:
"C'est le premier fruit de mes travaux, qui paroit au jour, depuis que j'ai le bonheur, tant désiré, de me trouver au service de Vôtre Majesté Impériale."
French title-page "Les héritiers supposés," and text face Italian. SCHATZ 9433

— **I finti eredi.** Dramma giocoso per musica da rappresentarsi nel Teatro di S. A. E. di Sassonia.

Dresda, n. publ., 1787. 147 p. 15^{cm}.

Two acts. Cast added in pencil and name of **Sarti** as the composer. This ed. of Bertati's text shows differences from the St. Petersburg ed. For instance, "Se la bella per via troverò" of the latter (I, 4) has become "La mia cara, la mia bella" and "Staremo allegramente" (II, 10) has become "Nel mirar la bella dama." German title-page "Die erdichteten lehnserben," and text face Italian.   SCHATZ 9434

— **I finti eredi:** Dramma giocoso per musica da rappresentarsi nel Regio Teatro di S. Carlo, della Principessa, l'estate dell' anno 1794.

Lisbona, Simone Taddeo Ferreira, 1794. 171 p. 15^{cm}.

Two acts. Cast, scenario, and name of Giuseppe **Sarti** as the composer. Portuguese text faces Italian.   SCHATZ 9467

I finti filosofi, ballet. *See* Curcio's Le nozze a dispetto.

Gli finti filosofi, ballet. *See* P. Guglielmi's Gli amanti della dote.

Li **finti filosofi,** ballet. *See* Guglielmi's Lo sciocco poeta di campagna.

Il **finto astrologo.** Dramma giocoso per musica da rappresentarsi nel Real Teatro di Salvaterra nel carnovale dell' anno 1792.

[*Lisbona*], *Nella stamperia reale, n. d. 70 p. 16½ cm.*

Two acts. Cast, scenario, and name of the composer, Francesco **Bianchi.** The librettist is not mentioned, and is unknown to Schatz.
First performed at Rome, Teatro Valle, carnival, 1790. SCHATZ 998

Il **finto cavaliere.** O. T. of Accorimboni's Das herbstabentheuer oder Wer wagt, gewinnt.

Il **finto cavaliere parigino.**

Two acts. Author unknown to Schatz. Music by Carlo **Monza.**
First performed at Rome, Teatro Capranica, carnival, 1770.
Not in L. of C.

— Il **cavalier parigino.** Operetta per musica da rappresentarsi nel Regio Ducal Teatro di Milano l'autunno dell' anno 1774 . . .

Milano, Giovanni Montani, n. d. 48 p. 15½ cm.

Two acts. The author is not mentioned. Dedication, scenario, and name of Carlo **Monza** as the composer. SCHATZ 6619

Il **finto chimico.** Drama per la musica rappresentato nella Villa di Pratolino.

Firenze, Vincenzo Vangelisti, 1686. 52 p. 15½ cm.

Three acts. Author and composer unknown to Wotquenne and Schatz.
ML 48.A5 v. 30

Il **finto Esaù,** overo Gli odii fraterni. Drama da recitarsi nel presente carnevale 1698. Da scolari di D. Giuseppe Fianello, alunno di Santi Apostoli . . .

Venetia, Domenico Lovisa, 1698. 79 (incl. front.), [1] p. 14 cm.

Three acts. Dedication signed by the author, Giuseppe Fianello, notice to the reader, including the argument, scenario, and name of Antonio **Pacelli** as the composer. The opera was performed "in una casa privata in contrada di Santa Marina," as Schatz says. SCHATZ 7377

Il **finto giardiniere,** ballet. *See* Monza's Enea in Cartagine.

Il **finto giardiniere,** ballet. *See* Zingarelli's Annibale in Torino.

Il **finto Parigino.** Intermezzo in musica da rappresentarsi nel nobil Teatro Tron di S. Cassiano l'autunno dell' anno 1784 . . .

Venezia, n. publ., n. d. 45 p. 17½ cm.

Two acts. Impresario's dedication, argument, cast, and name of Lorenzo **Baini** as the composer. Author unknown to Schatz. The ballet, by Giovanni Graziolli, *detto* Schizza (composer of the music not mentioned), was called, "Le due pastorelle smarrite, o sia La generosità." The intermezzo not to be confused with Baini's "Il Parigino in Italia." SCHATZ 552

Il **finto pazzo.** L. T. of Pergolesi's Livietta e Tracollo o sia La contadina astuta.

Il finto pazzo per amore. Opera buffa a sette voci da rappresentarsi nel Teatro dell' eccellentissima casa Grimani a S. Gio. Grisostomo il carnevale dell' anno 1779.

Venezia, Modesto Fenzo, 1779. 63 p. 17^{cm}.

Two acts. Author not mentioned, and unknown to Schatz. Cast, scenario, and name of Michele **Mortellari** as the composer. SCHATZ 6681

Il finto pazzo per amore. O. T. of Sacchini's Il soldato per forza impazzito per amore.

Lo finto Perziano. O. T. of Trinchera's text Li nnamorate correvate.

Il finto Policare. Tragicommedia per musica, da rappresentarsi nella Cesarea Corte . . . nel carnevale dell' anno MDCCXVI.

Vienna d'Austria, Gio Van Ghelen, n. d. 72 p. 14½^{cm}.

Three acts. By Pietro Pariati. Argument, scenario, and names of the composer, Francesco Bartolomeo **Conti,** and the author. Nicola Matteis is named as the composer of the ballet music.

First performed in February, 1716. SCHATZ 2200

— **Der verstellte Policare,** musicalische opera, welche auff dem Theatro zu Bresslau in Aprili 1726 vorgestellet . . .

n. i., n. d. Unpaged. 18^{cm}.

Three acts. Impresario's dedication, argument, scenario, and name of the composer, Francesco **Conti.** German text faces Italian. SCHATZ 2201

Il finto principe.

16½^{cm}. [63]–116 p. (Carlo Goldoni, Opere drammatiche giocose, t. iii, Torino, 1757.)

Three acts. Below the list of characters, the note:

"Le arie marcate con questo segno * sono messe dagli attori a loro piacimento; l'altre sono del libro."

Consequently, such arias as "Se col labbro vi dicon gl'amanti" (I, 3), "Pien d'ardir, costante, e forte" (I, 5), "La speranza di quest' alma" (I, 6), and others were interpolated.

According to Schatz, this pasticcio by unknown composers was performed as early as fall 1749 at Venice, Teatro Tron di San Cassiano. ML 49.A2G6

— **Il finto principe.** Dramma di tre atti per musica. Rappresentato per la prima volta in Venezia l'anno MDCCLV.

Carlo Goldoni, Opere teatrali, Venezia, Zatta e figli, 1788–95, t. 39, [249]–302 p. 18^{cm}.

PQ

Il finto Stregone. Farsa giocosa per musica di un atto solo di Giuseppe Foppa da rappresentarsi nel Teatro Giustiniani in San Moisè l'autunno dell' anno 1798.

Venezia, Modesto Fenzo, 1798. 40 p. 18^{cm}.

Cast, scenario, and name of Francesco **Gardi** as the composer. After the farce, was performed Giuseppe Cajani's ballet, "Nicola e Cirilla," the composer of the music not being mentioned. SCHATZ 3549

Fire and water! A comic opera: In two acts. Performed at the Theatre-Royal in the Hay-Market. By Miles Peter Andrews.

London, T. Cadell, 1780. 4 p. l., 40 p. 20^{cm}.

Cast and prefatory note that the piece was in the hands of the manager "long before any of the late disturbances." The composer, Samuel **Arnold,** is not mentioned.

First performed July 8, 1780, as indicated. LONGE 135

The **first of August.** A. T. of Dibdin's The waterman.

Der **fischer im trueben.** Tr. of Sarti's Fra i due litiganti il terzo gode.

Die **fischerinn,** ein singspiel. Auf dem natuerlichen schauplatz zu Tiefurth vorgestellt.

n. i., 1782. Unpaged. 16^cm.

One act. Neither the author, Goethe, nor the composer, Corona Elisabeth Wilhelmine **Schröter,** is mentioned. The singspiel begins with the Erlkönig ballad. First performed, as indicated, July 22, 1782. SCHATZ 9696

Das **fischermaedchen.** Tr. of Pietro Guglielmi's La bella pescatrice.

Das **fischermaedchen.** Tr. of Piccinni's La pescatrice.

Fiskerne. Et syngespil i tre handlinger af Johannes Ewald.

n. i., n. d. 128 p. 19^cm.

On p. [3-5], the story of the event on which the plot is based. The composer, Johann Ernst **Hartmann,** is not mentioned. First performed at Copenhagen, Royal Theater, January 31, 1780. SCHATZ 4465

Den **flanevurne kone.** Tr. of Galuppi's La moglie bizzarra.

Il **flauto magico.** Tr. of Mozart's Die zauberflöte.

Flavio Anicio Olibrio.

Apostolo Zeno, Poesie drammatiche, Venezia, 1744, t. x, p. [383]-476. 19^cm.

Three acts. Argument. Written in collaboration with Pietro Pariati. No composer is mentioned. In the "Catalogo" at end of the volume the date and place of first ed. is given as Venice, 1708 (but *see* below). ML 49.A2Z3

— **Flavio Anicio Olibrio.** Pubblicato per la prima volta in Venezia 1708.

Apostolo Zeno, Poesie drammatiche, Orleans, 1785-86, t. x, p. 96. 21^cm.

Three acts. Argument. No composer is mentioned. Written in collaboration with Pietro Pariati. ML 49.A2Z4

Flavio Anicio Olibrio. For later version *see* La Tirannide debellata

Flavio Anicio Olibrio. Drama per musica da rappresentarsi nel. Teatro di via della Pergola nella presente estate dell' anno 1723 . . .

Firenze, Domen. Ambrogio Verdi, n. d. 70 p. 14½^cm.

Three acts. Neither the authors, Zeno and Pariati, nor the composer, Carlo Francesco **Gasparini,** are mentioned. Dedication, cast, scenario, and argument. First performed at Venice, Teatro Tron di San Cassiano, carnival 1707.
SCHATZ 3568
Second copy. ML 48.A5 v. 18

Flavio Bertarido rè de Longobardi. Drama per musica di Stefano Ghisi [Ghigi], patritio veneto. Da rapresentarsi nell' impareggiabile Teatro Grimani di S. Gio. Grisostomo l'anno MDCCVI . . .

Venezia, Francesco Pongini, 1706. 84 p. 14^cm.

Three acts. Author's dedication in which he calls this "una primitia del mio debole talento," notice to the reader in which he says "questa è la prima compositione, che in simil genere, sia uscita dalla mia penna," argument, cast, and scenario. The composer, Carlo Francesco **Pollaroli,** is not mentioned. SCHATZ 8290

Flavio Cuniberto. Drama per musica da rappresentarsi nel famo-sissimo Teatro Grimano in S. Gio. Grisostomo. L'anno MDCLXXXII di Matteo Noris . . .

Venetia, Francesco Nicolini, 1682.   84 p.   13ᶜᵐ.

Three acts. Author's dedication, argument, and scenario. Giovanni Domenico **Partenio**, the composer, is not mentioned.   SCHATZ 7778

— **Flavio Cuniberto.** Drama per musica rappresentato nella villa di Pratolino.

Firenze, Pietro Antonio Brigonci, 1702.   4 p. l., 64 p.   16½ᶜᵐ.

Three acts. Scenario and argument with this remark:
"è parto della già nota penna del Signor Matteo Noris, che avrà la discretezza di soffrire la mutazione fattasi quivi nell' arie, le quali non si sono rinnovate per riprovare in conto alcuno quelle, che si gentilmente vi stavano, ma per recare qualche sorte di varietà ad un' opera, che viene in iscena dopo essere stata già veduta comparire su più famosi teatri."
The alterations are quite numerous. For instance in I, 14 the aria "Amor, tu reggimi" has replaced "Perch'io veggo se son tradito," "Su, miei spirti che s'aspetta" in I, 18 "Spirti fieri a la vendetta," "Parlar potesse il cuore" in I, 20 "Deggio credesti o gelosia." Neither **Partenio** is mentioned, nor the composer of the interpolations.   ML 50.2.F6P2

Flavius Bertaridus, koenig der Longobarden, in einer opera auf dem Hamburgischen Schau-platze vorgestellet. Im jahr 1729.

[Hamburg], Gedruckt mit Stromerschen schriften, n. d.   Unpaged. 18½ᶜᵐ.

Three acts. Neither the author, Stefano Ghigi ("Flavio Bertarido, rè de' Longobardi") nor the translators, Christoph Gottlieb Wendt and Georg Philipp Telemann, are mentioned. Argument, cast, scenario, and note:
"Annoch ist zu gedenken, dass mit der uebersetzung dieses schauspieles zwo federn beschaefftiget gewesen sind, deren die eine im zweyten actu, nach dem duetto: Care pene etc anfaenget; die music aber ist vom herrn capellmeister **Telemann.**"
To some of the arias the original text has been added.
First performed November 23, 1729.   SCHATZ 10260

Fleur d'épine, comédie. En deux actes et en prose, melée d'ariettes; tirée d'Hamilton, par Monsieur de V * * *. Représentée pour la premiere fois par les Comédiens italiens ordinaires du roi, le 22 août 1776.

Paris, Ruault, 1776.   28 p.   19ᶜᵐ.

The composer, Mme. **Louis,** née Bajon, is not mentioned.   ML 50.2.F65L7

— **Fleur d'épine,** comédie en deux actes, mêlée d'ariettes, tirée d'Hamilton, par M. de V * * *. Représentée pour la premiere fois par les Comédiens italiens ordinaires du roi le 22 août 1776.

Paris, la veuve Duchesne, 1777.   40 p.   18ᶜᵐ.

Cast. On p. 37–40 the air of "Quand on est tendre." By de Voisenon. The composer, Mme. **Louis,** née Bajon, is not mentioned.   SCHATZ 11721

Les fleurs. Entrée in Rameau's Les Indes galantes.

A flight from Lapland. A. T. of Lord Mayor's day.

The flight of Harlequin. A. T. of Reeve's Blue Beard.

The **flitch of bacon**; a comic opera, in two acts: As it is performed at the Theatre-Royal in the Hay-Market. By the Rev. Hen. Bate . . .

Dublin, Printed for the Company of booksellers, 1779. 2 p. l., 32 p. 17ᶜᵐ.

Cast and dedication dated Buckingham-street, June 1, 1779. The compiler-composer, William **Shield**, is not mentioned.

First performed August 19, 1778 (Schatz), August 17, 1778 (Genest), as indicated.

LONGE 118

La **Flora**. Melodrama da rappresentarsi nel Theatro di Sant' Angelo l'anno 1681. Di Novello Bonis . . .

Venetia, Francesco Nicolini, 1681. 60 p. 14ᶜᵐ.

Three acts. Author's dedication, argument, scenario, and notice to the reader with the names of Antonio **Sartorio** and Marc' Antonio **Ziani** as the composers and the statement "Questa è la mia terza fatica." SCHATZ 9495

Flora: or, Hob in the well. An opera. Being Mr. Dogget's farce of the Country wake, alter'd after the manner of the Beggar's opera.

[77]–109 p. 18ᶜᵐ. (Colley Cibber, Dramatic works, London, J. Rivington and sons [etc.], 1777.)

Two acts. 1768 cast! As will be seen from a comparison of this entry with the following, there is a contradiction of authorship, on which confused data will be found in the reference books. As a matter of fact, the text in *all* the following entries is identical! Consequently "Flora" (later on called Flora, or, Hob in the well) is either by Hippisley *or* by Cibber. If some authorities seek a way out of the difficulty by saying that Hippesley altered a farce by Cibber, "Hob, or, The country wake" (1715) into a ballad opera (1729), Cibber's farce itself being an alteration of Thomas Dogget's farce "The country-wake" (1696), they forget that Cibber never wrote a farce of the title, "Hob, or, The country wake." The probabilities are that "Flora" has been attributed incorrectly to Hippisley and that Cibber was indeed its author. PR 3347.A1

— **Flora**; an opera. As it is now acting at the Theatre Royal in Lincoln's-inn-Fields. Being Mr. Dogget's farce of the Country-wake, alter'd after the manner of the Beggar's opera. To which is added, the musick engrav'd on copper-plates. Written by a gentleman . . . The third edition.

London, Printed by T. Wood, 1729. 32 p, 8 p. (music) 20ᶜᵐ.

Two acts. Ballad-opera. John Hippisley appears in the cast as Sir Thomas Testy. The airs of the 24 songs are indicated by title in the text. They are engraved without their titles in the musical supplement.

First performed, as indicated, 1729. LONGE 197

— **Flora**; or Hob in the well. An opera. As it is now acting at the Theatre Royal in Drury-Lane. Being Mr. Dogget's farce of the Country wake, alter'd after the manner of the Beggar's opera. By Mr. Hippisley . . . The seventh edition.

London, T. Lowndes, 1768. 36 p. (incl. front.) 16ᶜᵐ.

Two acts. Cast. Ballad opera, most of the airs of the 24 songs being indicated by title. William **Bates**, who is not mentioned, is the reputed arranger of the music, but Longman, Lukey & Co's vocal score says: "as now performed at Covent Garden the overture, duet, and principal songs composed by Mr. Bates. LONGE 73

— **Flora**; or, Hob in the well. In two acts. By Colley Cibber [!] Esq.

[301]–328 p. 19ᶜᵐ. (Collection of the most esteemed farces and entertainments, t. iv, Edinburgh, 1792.)

SCHATZ 11753D

Floridante.

[101]–141 p. 17^{cm}. (Rolli, Componimenti poetici, Nuova edizione, Verona, G. Tumermani, 1744.)

Three acts. Argument and dedication. The composer, **Händel**, is not mentioned.

First performed at London, Haymarket, December 9, 1721. ML 49.A2R7

— Der **thrazische printz Floridantes** in einem singe-spiele auf dem Hamburgischen Schau-Platze vorgestellet.

Hamburg, Caspar Jakhel, 1723. Unpaged. 18^{cm}.

Three acts. German version by Joachim Beckau of Rolli's "Floridante." Neither they nor the composer, Georg Friedrich **Händel**, are mentioned. Italian text of the arias added to the German. Argument and scenario.

First performed at the Theater beim Gänsemarkt, as indicated, 1723.

Schatz 4477

Floridea. Dramma per musica da recitarsi in Venetia l'anno MDCLXXXVIII . . .

Venetia, Francesco Nicolini, 1688. 52 p. 14^{cm}.

Three acts. Dedication by the impresario Luigio Rincepa, dated Venice, November 22, 1687, notice to the reader, with apologies for the additional "canzonette," the alterations and the cuts in the "recitativi troppo lunghi." Author (Giulio Pancieri) and composer (unknown to Schatz) not mentioned. Argument, scenario.

Schatz 11333

Florizel and Perdita. See Arne's The sheep-shearing.

Die flucht des Aeneas nach Latien. A. T. of Porpora-Telemann's Der streit der kindlichen pflicht und der liebe.

The **flying lovers.** A. T. of The rape of Colombine.

Foca Superbo. Drama per musica di A. Luchini da rappresentarsi nel famoso Teatro Grimani di S. Gio. Grisostomo. Il carnoval dell' anno 1716 . . .

Venezia, Marino Rossetti, 1716. 60 p. 15^{cm}.

Three acts. Argument, notice to the reader, cast, scenario, and author's dedication dated Venice, December, 1716, in which he says:

"Che una primizia della mia debole penna si faccia vedere per la prima volta in uno de più famosi teatri può non esser considerabile . . ."

The composer, Antonio **Lotti**, is not mentioned. Schatz 5717

La foire de Guibray. See Arlequin Mahomet.

Folette ou L'enfant gâté. Parody of Destouches' Carnaval & la folie.

Folette et Roger-Bontems. A. T. of L'enfant gâté.

La folle giornata. L. A. T. of Mozart's Le nozze di Figaro.

La folle par amour. A. T. of Dalayrac's Nina.

La follia e la saggiezza, ballet. See Bianchi's Alessandro nell' Indie.

La fondation de Marseille. A. T. of Massilie.

La fondazion di Venezia.

[265]–284 p. 16½^cm. (Carlo Goldoni, Opere drammatiche giocose, t. iii, Torino, 1757.)

Divertimento in seven actions. Argument. ML 49.A2G6

— **La fondazione di Venezia.** Dramma di un atto solo per musica. Rappresentato per la prima volta in Venezia l'autunno dell' anno MDCCXXXIV.

Carlo Goldoni, Opere teatrali, Venezia, Zatta e figli 1788–95, v. 36, [13]–25 p. 18½^cm.

According to Schatz, **Macari**'s setting of 1736 was the first. PQ

La fondazion di Venezia. Divertimento per musica da cantarsi dalla Compagnia de Comici nel Teatro Grimani a S. Samuele la prima sera delle recite autunnali in Venezia in quest' anno 1736.

Venezia, Alvise Valvasense, n. d. 23 p. 14½^cm.

Prologue and seven azioni. Prefatory note. Neither the author, Carlo Goldoni, is mentioned, nor Giacomo **Macari**, the composer. SCHATZ 5810

La fontaine de Jouvence. *See* La nouvelle Bastienne.

Fontainebleau; or, Our way in France. A comic opera in three acts. As performed at the Theatres-Royal in Covent-Garden, and Smock-Alley. Written by J. O'Keefe, Esq. The music selected and composed by William Shield [!]

Dublin, G. Perrin, 1787. 75, [1] p. 16½^cm.

Cast. In Longman & Broderip's vocal score "Love does so run" is headed as composed by Dr. **Arne**, "How sweet! how fresh!" as by Stephen **Paxton** and "Brooks to your sources" as by Domenico **Corri**.

First performed at London, Covent-Garden, November 16, 1784. LONGE 148

Le fontane incantate, ballet. *See* Gluck's Il trionfo di Clelia.

Le fontane incantate, ballet. *See* Pasque's Arianna e Teseo.

Il fonte d'acqua gialla, o sia Il trionfo della pazzia. Farsetta per musica da rappresentarsi nel Teatro Valle degl' illustriss. Sigg. Capranica. Nell' autunno dell' anno 1786 . . .

Roma, Michele Puccinelli, n. d. 75 p. 16^cm.

Two acts. Cast, name of Marcello di Capua (**Bernardini**) as author and composer and his dedication. ML 50.2.F7B2

The **fool turn'd critick:** A comedy: As it was acted at the Theatre Royall. By His Majesties servants. By T. D. Gent.

London, James Magnes and Richard Bentley, 1678. 2 p. l., 59, [1] p. 21½^cm.

In this five-act play by Thomas Durfey there is a fair amount of singing, but, what is quite unusual, three of the airs (presumably by Durfey) are printed in the text, with their words. They are: "The age is refin'd," "I found my Caelia one night undrest," "To ramble from taverns." LONGE 112

Second copy. LONGE 160

The **fool's opera;** or, The taste of the age. Written by Mat. Medley. And performed by his company in Oxford . . . To which is prefix'd A sketch of the author's life, written by himself.

London, T. Payne [ca. 1730]. 4 p. l. (incl. front.), 22, [2] p. 18^{cm}.

The front., a scene from the play, shows, in upper left hand corner, what appears to be the portrait of the author, whose real name was Anthony Aston, for the title of the biographical sketch (p. 15–22) is: "A sketch of the life, etc. of Mr. Anthony Aston, commonly call'd Tony Aston. Written by himself:—Now all alive." (The importance of this autobiographical sketch for the history of the American theatre was pointed out by me in the New Music Review, June, 1907.) The sketch is preceded, on p. 12–14, by "A ballad, call'd A dissertation on the Beggar's opera." The 17 airs used are indicated by title. Text preceded by cast (Aston, sen., playing the poet) and prefatory note to the reader. The [2] p. at end contain book advertisements by J. Applebee and T. Payne.   Longe 291

A **fool's preferment,** or, The three dukes of Dunstable. A comedy. As it was acted at the Queens Theatre in Dorset-Garden, by Their Majesties servants. Written by Mr. D'urfey. Together, with all the songs and notes to 'em, excellently compos'd by Mr. Henry Purcell. 1688. Licensed, May 21. 1688 . . .

[London] Printed for Jos. Knight and Fra. Saunders, 1688. 4 p. l., 85, [3 p.], 16 p. (music). 21½^{cm}.

Five acts, prologue, and epilogue. Durfey's dedication, cast. After the epilogue, a list of "plays printed for Henry Herringman." The songs, voice and bass, have a special title page:

NEW SONGS sung in The fool's preferment, or, The three dukes of Dunstable.

In the Savoy. Printed by E. Jones, for Jos. Knight and Fran. Saunders, 1688.

Of the eight songs, all but two have the name of Henry Purcell as composer at end. The two are: "I'le sail upon the dog-star" and "A Scotch song . . . A dialogue by Jockey and Jenny." Mr. Squire has pointed out that neither the words of these nor of "Fled is my love; 'Tis Death alone" and "If thou wilt give me back" appear in the play, and that, on the other hand, the play contains two songs—"In yonder cowslip" and "I'll lay me down"—for which no music is given.

First performed before May, 1688, as indicated.   M 3.3.P9 II.11
— Second copy, without the music.   Longe 132

The **footman:** an opera. As it is acted at the New-Theatre in Goodman's-Fields.

London, Henry Lintot, 1732. iv, [4], 76 p. 19^{cm}.

Three acts, introduction, and epilogue. Cast and dedication. Ballad opera, most of the 68 airs being indicated by title. Author not recorded by Clarence.

First performed March 7, 1732, as indicated.   Longe 52

The **force of credulity.** A. T. of The disappointment, ballad opera.

De **forelskte haandverksfolk.** Tr. of Latilla's L'amore artigiano.

La **forest enchantée,** représentation tirée du poëme italien de la Jérusalem délivrée Spectacle orné de machines, animé d'acteurs pantomimes & accompagné d'une musique (de la composition de M. Geminiani) qui en exprime les différentes actions; exécuté sur le grand Théâtre du palais des Thuilleries pour la premiere fois le dimanche 31 mars 1754.

[Paris], Ballard, 1754. 16 p. 18½^{cm}.

Five acts. Description of "ce spectacle . . . de l'invention du Sieur Servandoni" and this interesting prefatory note:

"La décoration théâtrale est un des genres de la peinture qui produit le plus ces illusions agréables qui font appeller cet art le rival de la nature. Ce genre de peindre

La forest enchantée—Continued.

exige des connoissances approfondies de l'architecture, et de la perspective; et elles doivent être jointes à toutes les parties de la peinture qui sont communes aux autres genres. La méchanique doit aussi fournir au decorateur des moyens ingénieux de faire valoir, par des changemens et des oppositions, ses différents tableaux. Il seroit à souhaiter, sans doute, que le genre de spectacle auquel l'art des decorations théâtrales est particulierement adapté dans toute l'Europe, et qui intéresse à ses jeux trois Muses qui gagnent à être bien unies, pût toujours rassembler tous les secours que chacune d'elles doit lui offrir; mais si cette réunion difficile se voit rarement, des beautés particulieres suppléent au moins trés-souvent à cette perfection générale. Un poëme rempli d'action et d'intérêt semble en effet avoir moins besoin du charme de la musique et de l'illusion de la peinture. Une musique saillante et pleine de génie paroît aussi quelquefois distraire entierement de l'attention qu'on croiroit nécessaire aux poëmes. Pourquoi la peinture ne s'efforceroit-elle pas d'avoir l'avantage d'occuper seule toute l'attention des spectateurs? Pourquoi n'aspireroit-elle pas à la gloire de faire oublier quelques instans ses soeurs, et de recueillir, sans les partager, les applaudissemens flateurs d'une nation éclairée sur les arts qui contribuent tous à sa gloire et à ses plaisirs? C'est le but qu'ose se proposer le Sieur Servandoni.''
ML 52.2.F6G3

La forêt de Dordone. *See* Prologue des deux pièces . . .

The **forge of Vulcan,** ballet. *See* Sacchini's Enea e Lavinia.

Den **forladte Dido.** Tr. of Sarti's Didone abbandonata.

De **forsonede medbeylere.** Tr. of P. Guglielmi's I rivali placati.

Den **forstilte tvistighed.** Tr. of Monsigny's Rose et Colas.

La fortezza al cimento. Drama per musica di Francesco Silvani da rappresentarsi nel famoso Teatro Vendramino di S. Salvatore . . . MDCIC.

(*At end*) *In Venetia 1699. Per il Nicolini. 2 p. l. (incl. front.), 66, [1] p. 13½ᶜᵐ.*

Three acts. Author's dedication dated Venice, February 14, 1699, scenario, notice to the reader with argument, name of Giuseppe [Antonio Vincenzo] **Aldrovandini** as composer and remark that this is the author's "seconda fatica" during the present carnival season.
SCHATZ 134

Den **fortraengte ubekiendte.** A. T. of Anfossi's Jeannette.

La fortuna incatenata. *See* M. Curzio.

La fortuna per dote. Tragicomedia da rappresentarsi in musica, nel famosissimo Teatro Grimano di S. Gio. Grisostomo. L'anno 1704.

Venezia, Marino Rossetti, 1704. 83, [1] p. 14½ᶜᵐ.

The unnumb. p. contains "errori." Five acts. Neither the composer, Carlo Francesco **Pollaroli,** nor the author, conte Girolamo Frigimelica Roberti is mentioned. The latter, as was his custom (on p. 2–8), gives a "Notizia poetica," with his views of what constitutes a *tragicomedia.* He says in part:

"Propone alla fantasia un' immagine di poema mescolato di tragedia e di comedia" but "da tutto questo si comprende quanto sia diversa la tragicomedia, dalla tragedia di lieto fine.''

(Count Roberti may not have been a great poet, but his dramaturgic esthetic prefaces are well worth studying for a history of opera-libretto.) The "notizia poetica" is followed by a "notizia istorica" and a detailed description of "Le scene, ed i cori d'intermezzo.''
SCHATZ 8291

La **fortuna tra le disgratie.** Dramma per musica da rappresentarsi nel Teatro di Sant' Angelo, l'anno 1688. Di D. Rinaldo Ciali [!] . . .

Venetia, Francesco Nicolini, 1688. 59 p. 14ᶜᵐ.

Three acts. Publisher's dedication, scenario, and notice to the reader with name of Paolo **Biego** as composer. SCHATZ 1014

The **fortunate prince,** or, Marriage at last. L. T. of The court medley.

La **fortune au village.** Parody of Lagarde's Eglé.

Le **fortune di Rodope e Damira.** Drama per musica di Aurelio Aureli, favola terza.

Bologna, Giacomo Monti, 1658. 96 p. 14ᶜᵐ.

Prologue and three acts. Argument and notice to the reader with cast [!!] and name of the composer as follows:

"Agradisci le mie debolezze, honorate di musica dalla somma virtù del Signor padre **Ziani** . . . Per sodisfare in parte à la tua curiosità, sono stati qui sotto stampati li nomi di quelli virtuosi, che rappresentano le parti del drama . . ."

First performed at Bologna, Teatro Guastavillani, carnival 1658; at Venezia, Teatro di Sant' Apolinare, carnivale, 1657. SCHATZ 11215

The **fortune hunter.** A. T. of Barthelemon's The noble pedlar.

La **forza d'amore.** Dramma per musica.

Siena, Stamparia del Pubblico, n. d. 4 p. l., 24 p. 14ᶜᵐ.

Prologue and three acts. Unsigned dedication. Written ca. 1690, perhaps by Girolamo Gigli and composed by Giuseppe **Fabbrini**, both of Siena.

ML 48.A5 v.46

La **forza d'amore.** Dramma giocoso per musica da rappresentarsi nel Teatro Tron di S. Cassiano il carnovale dell' anno 1745.

Venezia, n. publ., n. d. 79 p. 17ᶜᵐ.

Three acts. By Panicelli, who is not mentioned. Cast, scenario, name of composer, **Galuppi,** and note that for briefness' sake scene 8, act II, scenes 10–12, act III and other verses are omitted in performance. Also that the following substitute arias are not by the author of the libretto: "Figlia presto monta in barca" (I, 4), "Voi la spada, o mia signora" (II, 4), "In mezzo a mille straggi" (II, 7), "Bel visino graziosino" (III, 8), "Se per dispetto io piango" (III, 9), "Il cor mi sento" (III, 13), "Son stordita via tacete" (III, last scene).

First performed, as indicated, January 30, 1745. SCHATZ 3478

La **forza d'amore.** Drama per musica da rappresentarsi nel Teatro di SS. Gio. e Paulo l'anno 1697 . . .

Venetia, Nicolini, 1697. 55, [1] p. 14½ᶜᵐ.

The unnumb. p. contains "errori di stampa."

Three acts. Neither Lorenzo Burlini, the author, nor Carlo Francesco **Pollaroli,** the composer, is mentioned. Dedication, argument, scenario, and notice to the reader, in which we read:

"Il drama poi per malignità d'alcune stelle contrarie, prima che comparirti sù la scena ha incontrato tali, e tante opposizioni, che se non s'è trattenuto, s'è però si cangiato di forma, che appena lo potrebbe riconoscere chi nel suo primo stato conosciuto l'havesse." SCHATZ 8292

La **forza del sanguine.** O. T. of Silvani's libretto Zoe.

La forza del sangue. Drama per musica da rappresentarsi nel famoso Teatro Grimani di San Gio. Grisostomo l'autunno dell' anno 1711 . . .

Venezia, Marino Rossetti, 1711. 82 p. 14$\frac{1}{2}$cm.

Three acts. Dedication signed by the author, Francesco Silvani, and dated Venice, November 14, 1711, argument, cast, scenario. The composer, Antonio **Lotti**, is not mentioned. SCHATZ 5718

La forza del sangue, e della pietà. Drama per musica . . . Cantato per le vacanze del carnevale l'anno 1686 da' Signori convittori del nobil collegio Tolomei di Siena.

Siena, nella stamp. del publ. 1686. 6 p. l., 71, [1] p. 13$\frac{1}{2}$cm.

The dedication is dated, "Siena li 15 febbraio 1686," and signed by Girolamo Gigli as author. Then, "L'autore al cortese lettore," from which it apnears that this was Gigli's second libretto, and that it was composed by Giuseppe **Fabrini** (Fabbrini). This followed by "Argomento istorico," scenario, casts of opera and *balli* and note calling attention to the unnumb, l. between p. 20–21. From the dedication it appears that Gigli's *Geneviéfa* is to be dated 1685. SCHATZ 2963

La forza dell' amicizia. Dramma per musica da rappresentarsi in Mantova l'anno 1700 . . .

[Mantova], Gio. Batt. Grana, n. d. 81 p. 15$\frac{1}{2}$cm.

Three acts. Dedication, argument, cast, scenario. Author (Adriano Morselli, whose "Pirro e Demetrio" this is) and composer (unknown to Schatz) not mentioned. SCHATZ 11334

La forza dell' amore, Die macht der liebe oder Die von Paris entfuehrte Helena, in einem singe-spiel, auf den grossen Hamburgischen Schau-platze fuergestellet und in die music gebracht durch Reinhard Keisern . . .

Hamburg, n. publ., 1709. Unpaged. 18$\frac{1}{2}$cm.

Three acts. Scenario and "vorbericht," which reads, in part:
"Den anlass zu gegenwaertigem schau-spiele, hat eine italiaenische opera, dieses nahmens gegeben, welche ehemahls von Sigr. [Pietro Antonio] Fiocco [text by Giovanni Filippo Appoloni?] in Amsterdam, hernach auf den beruehmten Braunschweigischen Theatro [as Helena rapita da Paride], nicht ohne geringe approbation, aufgefuehret worden. Wie weit man aber selbigem sujet gefolget, wird der geneigte leser am besten beurtheilen koennen, wenn er beyde erfindungen gegen einander haelt . . . Von der musique ist nur dieses zu erinnern: Dass die meisten arien nach dem goûst, theils fuerstlicher, theils anderer vornehmẽ standes-persohnen lange vorher, ehe man die Helena gefangen, eingerichtet gewesen . . . Die italiaenische aria "Sta in quel vago," etc im 5ten auftritt der 3ten handlung ist von der ausarbeitung und invention eines jungen cavalliers . . ."
To many of the arias the Italian text has been added to the German. SCHATZ 5090

La forza dell' amore e dell' amicizia, ballet. *See* P. Guglielmi's Tamerlano.

La forza dell' innocenza. A. T. of Zeno and Pariati's text Engelberta.

La forza dell' innocenza. A. T. of Orefici and Mancini's L'Engelberta.

La forza della pace. Intermezzi per musica a trè voci da rappresentarsi nell' antico Teatro della Pace nel carnevale dell' anno 1752 . . .

Roma, Ottavio Puccinelli, 1751. 24 p. 15$\frac{1}{2}$cm.

On p. 23–24 a poem "La pace." Two parts. Author not mentioned and unknown to Schatz. Possibly Girolamo Aureli wrote the text. Publisher's dedication, cast and name of **Rinaldo di Capua** as composer. ML 50.2.F75R3

La **forza della virtù**.   A. T. of Orlandini's Ataulfo rè de' Goti.

La **forza della virtù**.   Drama per musica da rappresentarsi nel Teatro Malvezzi l'anno MDCXCIV.   Di Domenico David . . .

Bologna, gl' Eredi d' Antonio Pisarri, 1694.   8½ p.   19cm.

Three acts.   Dedication dated Bologna, May 23, 1694, argument, cast, scenario, and notice to the reader, which reads, in part:

"Ecoti ricomparire in Teatro la Forza della virtù—Se la troverai in parte mutata dal suo primo originale, resta accertato, che la sola necessità di portarla alle nostre scene, il desiderio di compiacere a'signori musici, & il genio di sodisfare a noi stessi, è stata la cagione di tale alterazione . . ."

The composer, Giacomo Antonio **Perti**, is not mentioned.   SCHATZ 7948

La **forza della virtù**.   Drama per musica da rappresentarsi nel Teatro di S. Gio. Grisostomo.   L'anno MDCXCIII.   Di Domenico David.   Seconda impressione . . .

Venetia, Nicolini, 1693.   72 p. (incl. front.).   14cm.

Three acts.   Author's dedication, argument, "allegoria del drama," notice to the reader, and scenario.   Carlo Francesco **Pollaroli**, the composer, is not mentioned.   SCHATZ 8293

— **Creonte tiranno di Tebe**.   Drama per musica da rappresentarsi nel Theatro di S. Bartolomeo di Napoli in quest' anno 1699 . . .

Napoli, Dom. Ant. Parrino e Michele Luigi Mutio, 1699.   57 p.   13½cm.

Three acts.   Scenario, cast, and publisher's dedication, according to which "questo drama . . . fù veduto con sommo piacimento ne' primi teatri d'Italia intitolato *la Forza della virtù* . . ." This refers to Domenico David's text, composed by Carlo Francesco **Pollaroli**, but at Naples the text was somewhat altered, and music by Alessandro **Scarlatti** and others was interpolated.   ML 50:2.C78P7

La **forza delle donne**.   O. T. of Bertati's text Ogus o sia Il trionfo del bel sesso.

La **forza delle donne**.   Dramma giocoso per musica di Giovanni Bertati da rappresentarsi nel Teatro Giustiniani in S. Moisè l'autunno dell' anno 1778.

n. i., n. d.   [3]–62 p.   17½cm.

Two acts.   Cast and name of composer, Pasquale **Anfossi**.   Interpolated between p. 32–33 are 4 p. describing "Vertunno e Pomona, ballo pastorale," invented by Filippo Beretti.   The composer of the music is not mentioned.   SCHATZ 267

La **forza delle donne**, ballet.   *See* Stabinger's L'astuzie di Bettina.

La **forza delle prime impressioni**.   A. T. of Capuzzi's I bagni d'Abano.

La **forza vinta dall' onore**.   Drama musicale da rappresentarsi nel Teatro di S. Moisè in Venezia l'anno 1703 . . .

Venezia, Zuccato, 1703.   48 p.   16cm.

Three acts.   Dedication, with the initials of the author, Andrea Minelli, argument, scenario.   The composer, Niccolò **Le Mixte**, is not mentioned   SCHATZ 5486

Le **fossé du scrupule**, opera-comique en un acte; avec un prologue, un épilogue & un divertissement; représenté pour la premiere fois sur le Théâtre de la Foire, en 1738.

Charles François Pannard, Théâtre, Paris, Duchesne, 1763, v. 3, [69]–138 p.   17cm.

In prose and vaudevilles.   Composer not recorded by Parfaict, who dates first performance July 26, 1738.   PQ2019.P3

The **four seasons** or Love in every age. Interlude in The island princess.

The **fox trap't.** A. T. of The raree show.

Fra i due litiganti il terzo gode. O. T. of Sarti's I pretendenti delusi.

The original Milan, 1782 libretto of Sarti's opera not in L. of C.

— **I pretendenti delusi.** Dramma giocoso per musica da rappresentarsi nel nobile Teatro dell' Eccell.^{ma} casa Giustiniani in S. Moisè l' autunno 1782.

Venezia, n. publ., n. d.   58 p.   17^{cm}.

Two acts. Cast, scenario, and name of Giuseppe **Sarti** as composer. Text by Goldoni (not mentioned), originally with the title, "Le nozze."

Sarti's opera was first performed at Milan, Teatro alla Scala, September 14, 1782, as "Fra i due litiganti il terzo gode," its best known title.   SCHATZ 9453

— **Fra i due litiganti il terzo gode.** Dramma giocoso per musica in trè atti, da rappresentarsi nel Teatro Elettorale.

Dresda, n. publ., 1784.   117 p.   16^{cm}.

Sarti is mentioned as the composer. German title-page "Unter zwey streitenden siegt der dritte," and text face the Italian, which is the same as "I pretendenti delusi," but with some differences. For instance, the aria, "E destin troppo infelice," has been dropped at the beginning of I, 11, and of course the original two acts have become three.   SCHATZ 9457

— **Fra i due litiganti il terzo gode:** Dramma giocoso per musica da rappresentarsi nel Reggio Teatro di S. Carlo, della Principessa l' autunno dell' anno 1793.

Lisbona, Simone Taddeo Ferreira, 1793.   151 p.   15^{cm}.

Two acts. Cast, scenario, and name of Giuseppe **Sarti** as the composer. Portuguese text faces Italian. With the opera was performed (composer of the music not mentioned) Gaetano Ghelardini's ballet, "Le vendemmie, o sia La villanella rapita."   SCHATZ 9468

— **Fra i due litiganti il terzo gode.** Dramma giocoso per musica da rappresentarsi nel Teatro alla Scala l' autunno dell' anno 1795 . . .

Milano, Gio. Batista Bianchi, n. d.   60 p.   15½^{cm}.

Two acts. Impresario's dedication, cast, scenario, and name of Giuseppe **Sarti** as the composer. The text is the same as "I pretendenti delusi," but with many alterations. With the opera were performed Gaspare Ronzi's ballets, "Il rè pastore" and "La fanciulla mal custodita," the composer of the music not being mentioned.   SCHATZ 9454

— **I due litiganti.** Dramma giocoso per musica da rappresentarsi nel nobilissimo Nuovo Teatro di Padova il carnovale dell' anno 1792 . . .

Padova, per li Conzatti, n. d.   52 p.   17^{cm}.

Two acts. Impresario's dedication, cast, scenario, and name of Giuseppe **Sarti** as the composer. The text is the same as "I pretendenti delusi," but with considerable alterations. On p. 29, argument, without name of the composer of the music of Giuseppe Bartolomei's ballet, "Bacco e Arianna."   SCHATZ 9456

Fra i due litiganti il terzo gode—Continued.

— Le **nozze di Dorina,** a new comic opera, in two acts, as performed at the King's Theatre in the Haymarket. The music by the celebrated Signor Sarti, under the direction of Mr. Storace.

London, J. Hammond, n. d.   55 p.   20ᶜᵐ.

Cast.   English translation faces the Italian, which takes the usual unlimited liberties with Goldoni's text.

First performed at London, same theatre, January 6, 1784, as "I rivali delusi;" under the above title, it would seem, shortly after Storace's return to England, in 1787.

ML 48.M2K

— Le **nozze di Dorina.**   Dramma giocoso per musica da rappresentarsi nel Teatro di S. A. S. il Signor principe di Carignano nel carnovale dell' anno 1796.

Torino, Onorato Derossi, n. d.   2 p. l., 60 p.   14½ᶜᵐ.

Two acts.   Cast, scenario, and name of Giuseppe **Sarti** as the composer.   The text is the same as "I pretendenti delusi," but, of course, with many alterations.   On p. [53]–60, cast, argument, and description (without name of the composer of the music) of Filippo Beretti's "Andronico e Ramira, ballo eroico pantomimo."

First performed under this title at Naples, Reale Teatro del Fondo, December 10, 1784.   Schatz 9455

— Der **fischer im trueben.**   Ein singspiel.   Die musik ist von herrn Joseph Sarti . . .

Stuttgardt, Drukkerey der herzoglichen Hohen Karls-Schule, 1785. 139 p.   16ᶜᵐ.

Three acts.   German text and Italian text, with running title, "Fra due litiganti il terzo gode."   The version retains the "E destin troppo infelice," at I, 11, but shows other differences.   For instance, "Vuò soffrire a un certo segno" (I, 1) has become "La donna è sempre istabile."   Schatz 9458

— Gesaenge aus dem singspiele: **Im trueben ist gut fischen,** in zwey abtheilungen.   Neu bearbeitet von Schink.   In musik gesetzt von Sarti.

Hamburg, Friedrich Hermann Nestler, n. d.   48 p.   15ᶜᵐ.

First performed at Hamburg, Theater beim Gänsemarkt, September 21, 1785.

Schatz 9459

— **Im trueben ist gut fischen.**   Ein singspiel in drey aufzuegen. Nach dem italiaenischen frey bearbeitet von Johann Andre.   Die musik ist vom herrn Joseph Sarti.

Koeln am Rhein, Joh. Godschalk Langen, 1786.   64 p.   16ᶜᵐ.

First performed at Mannheim, National Theater, December 29, 1785.

Schatz 9460

— **Unter zwey streitenden zieht der dritte den nutzen.**   Ein singspiel in drey aufzuegen.   Aufgefuehrt auf dem hochfuerstlichen Hoftheater in Salzburg.

Salzburg, Waisenhaus buchdruckerei, 1787.   79 p.   15ᶜᵐ.

Cast and name of Giuseppe **Sarti** as the composer.   Translated by Ludwig Zehnmark.

First performed 1787, as indicated.   Schatz 9461

— **I oprørt vand er godt at fiske.**   Et syngespil i tre acter, hvortil musiken er komponeret af Sarti.   Oversat af Lars Knudsen.

Kiøbenhavn, S. Poulsens forlag, 1795.   88 p.   16ᶜᵐ.

First performed at Copenhagen, Theater paa Kongens Nytorv, April 7, 1795.

Schatz 9462

Die frage und die antwort. A. T. of Hiller's Lisuart und Dariolette.

Fragments, composés du Prologue des Amours des dieux, de l'acte de L'amour enjoué et de celui de La danse; représentés devant Leurs Majestés à Versailles le mercredi 6 mars 1765.

[Paris], Christophe Ballard, 1765. 3 v. in 1. 11, 1 p. l., 16, 2 p. l., 20 p. 20½ᶜᵐ.

Casts and names of Louis Fuzelier as the author, and of Jean Joseph **Mouret** as the composer of the Prologue, of Antoine **Dauvergne** as composer of "L'amour enjoué, ballet en un acte," of Jean Philippe **Rameau** as composer of "La danse, troisième entrée du ballet des Talents lyriques." Laval, père et fils, are mentioned in each case as the "composers" of the ballets. ML 48.J7

Fragments de Mʳ de Lully, ballet, mis au théâtre par Mʳˢ· Danchet & Campra. Representé par l'Academie royale de musique l'an 1702. LVI. opera.

n. i., n. d. 14ᶜᵐ. front., 391–437 p. (Recueil général des opéra, t. vii, Paris, 1703.)

Detached copy. Prologue and the entrées, "Feste marine," "Les guerriers," "La bergerie," "Les Bohémiens," and the additional "divertissement comique *Cariselli.*" The words were selected and partly translated from different sources by Danchet, and the music was arranged by Campra. An "avertissement" (p. 392) reads:

"Comme ce ballet a été varié dans l'espace de huit mois, qu'il a été representé; on a crû devoir y joindre les trois nouvelles entrées qui y ont été ajoûtées successivement. On y a encore ajoûté les noms des acteurs & actrices, pour faire connoître ceux qui occupent presentement le théâtre."

First performed, as indicated, September 10, 1702. Schatz 5767
Second copy. ML 48.R4

— Trois nouvelles entrées ajoutées aux Fragments en differents temps. Les paroles de M. Danchet & la musique de M. Campra.

n. i., n. d. 439–486 p. 14ᶜᵐ. (Recueil général des opera, Paris, 1703, t. vii.)

Detached copy. Casts. The individual titles are: "Le triomphe de Vénus," "La sérénade venitienne," and "Le bal interrompu." Schatz 1563

— Le bal interrompu. Cette entrée & la suivante ont été ajoutées aux Fragments de Lulli; & représentées en 1703, dans la reprise qui se fit de ces Fragmens.

— Le jaloux trompé. Divertissement. Représenté pour la premiere fois en 1703. sous le titre de la Serenade venitienne, dans le ballet des Fragmens de M. de Lully. Remis au Théâtre à la suite du Carnaval & La folie. Le jeudi 18 janvier 1731.

[265]–290 p. 17½ᶜᵐ. (Antoine Danchet, Théâtre, t. ii, Paris, 1751.)
PQ 1972.D2

Le Franc Breton, ou Le négociant de Nantes, comédie en un acte et en vers libres, par M. de Jaure. Représentée pour la première fois à Paris, par les Comédiens italiens ordinaires du roi, le 15 février 1791.

Paris, Cailleau & fils, 1791. 35 p. 21ᶜᵐ.

Cast. The composers, Rodolphe **Kreutzer** and **Solié,** are not mentioned. ML 50.2.F8K7

La **Francese a Malghera.** Dramma giocoso per musica da rappresentarsi nel Teatro Tron di S. Cassano nell' autunno dell' anno 1764. Dell' abbate Pietro Chiari, Bresciano.

Venezia, Modesto Fenzo, 1764.   72 p.   16½ cm.

Three acts. Cast, scenario, and name of composer, Tommaso **Trajetta** ("La musica tutta nuova ").   SCHATZ 10411

Il **Francese bizarro.** Opera buffa a sette voci da rappresentarsi nel Teatro dell' eccellentisima casa Grimani S. Gio. Grisostomo il carnevale dell' anno 1779.

Venezia, Modesto Fenzo, 1779.   62 p.   16½ cm.

Two acts. Cast, scenario, and name of composer, Gennaro **Astaritta**, but not of librettist, who is unknown to Schatz.   SCHATZ 371

— Il **Francese bizzarro.** Opera buffa da rappresentarsi nel Teatro di S. A. E. di Sassonia.

Dresda, n. publ., 1786.   131 p.   15½ cm.

Two acts. Name of **Astaritta** as composer. German title-page, "Der wunderliche Franzos. Ein komisches singstück," and text face Italian.
First performed at Dresden in 1786.   SCHATZ 372

La **Francese brillante.** Dramma giocoso per musica da rappresentarsi nel Pubblico Teatro di Lucca l'autunno dell' anno 1767.

Lucca, Giuseppe Simoni, 1767.   84, [1] p.   14½ cm.

Three acts. By Pasquale Mililotti, who is not mentioned. Cast and name of Pietro **Guglielmi** as the composer.
First performed, as indicated, August 22, 1767; at Naples, Teatro de' Fiorentini, summer of 1763.   SCHATZ 4284

La **Francese di spirito.** Commedia per musica di Giuseppe Maria Mililotti da rappresentarsi nel Teatro Nuovo sopra Toledo per prima opera di quest' anno 1781.

Napoli, n. publ., 1781.   55 p.   15 cm.

Two acts. Cast and name of Giacomo **Tritto** as the composer. At end this characteristic foot-note:
"Si è dovuto togliere dalla commedia il personaggio di Smeraldina, che stando indisposta, si è licenziata da se medesima dal teatro per tutto l'anno. Ed essendosi dovuto in parte ristampare il libretto, in quello, che è rimasto, se mai si trova il nome di Smeraldina, il savio lettore non ne faccia caso."   SCHATZ 10471

Il **Francese in Londra,** ballet. *See* Anfossi's Le gelosie villane.

I **Francesi brillanti.** Dramma giocoso per musica da rappresentarsi nel Real Teatro dell' Ajuda nell' autunno dell' anno 1765.

Lisbona, Michele Maneschal da Costa, n. d.   78 p.   16 cm.

Three acts. Pasquale Mililotti, the author, not mentioned. Cast, scenario, and name of **Paisiello** as the composer. Mililotti's title originally was "La Francese brillante."
First performed at Bologna, Teatro Marsigli Rossi, June, 1764.   SCHATZ 7687

La **Frascatana.** Dramma giocoso per musica da rappresentarsi nel Teatro Grande della nobilissima Accademia Intronata di Siena, nel carnevale dell' anno bisestile 1776 . . .

Siena, Vincenzo Pazzini Carli e figli, n. d.   76 p.   16½ cm.

Three acts. By Filippo Livigni who is not mentioned. Impresario's dedication, cast, and name of **Paisiello** as the composer.
First performed at Venice, Teatro S. Samuele, 1774.   SCHATZ 7620

La **Frascatana**—Continued.

— La **Frascatana**. Dramma giocoso per musica del Signore Filippo Livigni da rappresentarsi nel Piccolo Teatro di S. A. S. E. di Sassonia.

Dresda, n. publ., 1776. 181 p. 16^{cm}.

Three acts. **Paisiello** is mentioned as the composer. German title page, "Die Frascatanerin," and text face Italian.
First performed, as indicated, 1776. SCHATZ 7621

— La **Fraschetana;** a new comic opera: as performed at the King's Theatre in the Hay-Market. The music by Signor Paisiello, under the direction of Mr. Giardini.

London, T. Cadell, 1776. 75 p. 18^{cm}.

On verso of last p. a catalogue of Bremner's latest publications. Three acts. Livigni's text with numerous alterations and interpolations. English translation faces Italian.
First performed 1776 as indicated. SCHATZ 7622

— La **Frascatana**. Dramma giocoso per musica, da rappresentarsi nel Regio Teatro.—Landsbye-pigen fra Frascati . . . Oversadt paa dansk af R. Soelberg.

Kiøbenhavn, H. J. Graae, 1776. 143 p. 16½^{cm}.

Three acts. Text by Livigni, who is not mentioned. Cast and name of **Paisiello** as the composer.
First performed at Copenhagen, October 31, 1776. SCHATZ 7623

— La **Frascatana** oder Das maedchen von Fraskati, ein singspiel in drey aufzuegen. Die musik von Paisello.

n. i., 1782. 102 p. 17½^{cm}.

German version by Johann Friedrich Schmidt. SCHATZ 7624

— La **Frascatana**. Ein singspiel in drey aufzuegen. Die musick von Paisello.

n. i., 1782. 128 p. 16½^{cm}.

The translator is not mentioned, but it is practically the same version as Schatz 7624, as comparison proves. ML 50.2.F84P2

— Arien und Gesaenge aus der grossen komischen oper: Das **maedchen von Fraskati,** in drey aufzuegen. So wie sie auf der Tillyschen schaubuehne aufgefuehret wird. Die musik ist von Paisiello.

Luebeck, n. publ., 1785. 24 p. 16½^{cm}.

Schmidt's version.
First performed at Lübeck, Theater i. d. Bäckergrube, 1785; at Weimar, Herzogl. Comödienhaus, January 15, 1784. SCHATZ 7625

— L'**infante de Zamora,** comédie en trois actes, mêlées d'ariettes, parodiées sur la musique de la Frascatana, del Signor Paesielo, par M. Framery. Cette édition est la seule qui soit conforme à la partition gravée, à laquelle on a fait beaucoup de changemens.

La Haye, les Libraires associés, 1783. 55, [1] p. 19½^{cm}.

First performed at Versailles, 1781; at Paris, Théâtre de Monsieur, not until June 22, 1789. ML 50.2.F84P22

La **Frascatana nobile**. Commedia per musica di Pasquale Mililotti da rappresentarsi nel Teatro Nuovo sopra Toledo nell' inverno del corrente anno 1776.

Napoli, n. publ., 1776. 60 p. 15^{cm}.

Three acts. Cast and name of the composer, Domenico **Cimarosa**. SCHATZ 1995

Die **Frascatanerin.** Tr. of Paisiello's La Frascatana.

La **Fraschetana.** L. T. of Paisiello's La Frascatana.

Lo **frate nnammorato.** Commeddeja pe mmusica de Jennarantonio Federico Napolitano da rappresentarese a lo Triato de li Shiorentine lo carnevale de chist' anno 1734 . . .

Napole, Nicola de Bejase, n. d. 80 p. 14½^{cm}.

Three acts. Impresario's dedication, cast, name of Giammattista Pergolese (**Pergolesi**) as the composer, and notice to the reader, which reads, in part:

"Sta commedeja se rappresentaje ll'anno 1732. [September] nne lo stisso triato . . . Te s'avisa, ca non se ll'e cagnato autro, se non che cierte poch' arie, che bedarraje segnate con cchisto signo §, co l'accaseone, che l'è parzo de buono a lo masto de cappella de cagnarence la museca, secunno l'abbeletà de chi l'ha da cantare; & ppe ffarela non poco cchiù breve, s'è accortata no poco all' atto terzo." Schatz 7903

I **fratelli nemici.** Tragedia per musica da rappresentarsi nel Regio Teatro di Berlino . . . MDCCLVI.

Berlino, Haude e Spener, n. d. 115, [4] p. 16½^{cm}.

Three acts. By G. P. de Tagliazucchi, who begins his prefatory note:

"La traduzione italiana di una eccellente tragedia francese, che ò l'onore di presentare al publico m'obbliga a pregarlo del suo compatimento, s'ei troverà, che l'osservanza di un metro regolare, la rima determinatamente obbligata, e la scelta delle parole alla musica confacenti m'anno forzato nelle arie a prendermi qualche libertà senza però gran torto al sentimento. Sia in una, sia in altra maniera decentemente vestita leggiadra giovane sarà sempre leggiadra. Ne' recitativi, dove il metro non mi legava, e la rima, servendo di solo ornamento alla poesia, s'è venuta naturalmente a intromettere dove luogo à trovato, mi lusingo, che il lettore m'incontrerà fedele, ed esatto; non senza aver avuto però tutto il riguardo di conformarmi al genio particolare di nostra favella da quello della Francese cosè diferente . . ."

Tagliazucchi herewith alludes to the fact that his text was merely the Italian version of an "excellent French tragedy," written by Frederick the Great and based on Racine's "Les frères ennemis." Scenario and name of Carl Heinrich **Graun** as composer. German text (by Francesco Grugnanelli, according to Mennicke) and title-page, "Die uneinigen brueder," face Italian.

First performed, as indicated, January 9, 1756. Schatz 4100

— I **fratelli nemici.** Tragedia per musica da rappresentarsi nel Regio Teatro di Berlino . . . MDCCLVI.

Berlino, Haude & Spener, n. d. 115, [4] p. 16½^{cm}.

Exactly like Schatz 4100, except that instead of the German translation a French version, "Les frères ennemis, opéra tragique," faces the Italian Schatz 4101

Li **fratelli Pappamosca.** L. T. of F. Guglielmi's La villanella ingentilita.

I **fratelli riconosciuti.** Dramma per musica da rappresentarsi in Parma nella primavera dell' anno 1726 . . .

Parma, Eredi di Paolo Monti, 1726. xii, 46, [1] p. 15½^{cm}.

Three acts. By Francesco Silvani, whose original title was "La verità nell' inganno." The Protesta reads, in part:

"Se quest' opera, che nell' anno 1717 fù rappresentata in Vienna, ora viene notabilmente variata, ciò si è per aderire in parte al genio de signori interessati, in parte per incontrare la soddisfazione del compositore della musica, ed in parte ancora per uniformarsi al gusto de cantanti."

Giovanni Maria **Capello** is mentioned as the composer of the music ("di nuova, studiosa composizione"). The alterations of the text were by Carlo Innocenzio Frugoni (Schatz). Dedication, argument, cast, scenario. Schatz 1590

I fratelli rivali. Dramma per musica da rappresentarsi nel nobilissimo Teatro Venier di San Benedetto l'autunno 1793.

*Venezia, Casali, 1793. 78 p. 18½*cm.

Two acts. Author not mentioned, and unknown to Schatz. Cast and name of Peter von **Winter** as the composer. On p. [33]–43, argument, cast, description, without name of the composer of the music of Filippo Beretti's "Andronico e Ramira, ballo eroico pantomimo." SCHATZ 11032

— **I fratelli rivali.** Dramma giocoso per musica da rappresentarsi nel Teatro Elettorale.

*Dresda, n. publ., 1795. 127 p. 16*cm.

Two acts. Cast added in pencil. Peter von **Winter** is mentioned as the composer. German title-page, "Die brueder als nebenbuhler," and text face Italian. First performed, as indicated, October, 1795. SCHATZ 11033

— Arien und gesaenge aus der oper Die **brueder als nebenbuhler,** in zwey aufzuegen. Die musik ist von Winter.

*Frankfurt am Main, n. publ., 1798. 24 p. 17*cm.

Translated by Matthäus Stegmayer, who is not mentioned. First performed at Frankfurt a/M., National theater, 1798. SCHATZ 11034

Il fratricida innocente. Drama eroico per musica da rappresentarsi in Bologna nel Teatro Malvezzi l'anno MDCCVIII.

*Bologna, Costantino Pisarri, n. d. 71, [1] p. 16*cm.

Three acts. By Apostola Zeno (not mentioned). Earlier and better-known title of the text is "Venceslao." Argument, scenario, cast. The composer, Giacomo Antonio **Perti,** is not mentioned. Fehr attributes the music to **Predieri,** by whom Schatz records no such opera. First performed, as indicated, May 19, 1708. SCHATZ 7949

La Fredegonda. Drama per musica da rappresentarsi nel Teatro Tron in S. Casciano l'anno 1705 . . . Poesia di Francesco Silvani . . .

*Venezia, Marino Rossetti, 1705. 72 p. 14½*cm.

Three acts. Author's dedication dated Venezia, December 26, 1704, notice to the reader as argument, cast, scenario, and name of Carlo Francesco **Gasparini** as the composer. SCHATZ 3569

Fredegunda. [vignette] In einem musicalischen schau-spiele auf dem Hamburgischen Schau-platze vorgestellt im mertz monath 1715.

*Hamburg, Fridrich Conrad Greflinger, 1716. Unpaged. 18*cm.

Five acts. In his "vorbericht" the author, Johann Ulrich König, says: "Die generale approbation, mit welcher meine letzte opera: L'inganno fedele angenommen worden, hat mich aufgemuntert, abermahl ein solches schau-spiel auszuarbeiten, welches um so viel weniger fuerchten darf zu missfallen, weil es schon in italiaenischer sprache, worinn es zuerst geschrieben worden, bereits den beyfall aller verstaendigen erworben. Wer inzwischen glaubt, dass gegenwaertige bogen nichts als eine blosse ubersetzung, wird sich vielleicht zu meinem vortheil betrogen finden, wann er die muehe nehmen will, das italiaenische nachzusehen . . ." To some of the arias the Italian text has been added. Reinhard **Keiser,** the composer, is not mentioned. Koenig took his text from Francesco Silvani's "La Fredegonda." SCHATZ 5123

— **Fredegunda,** in einem musicalischen schau-spiele auf dem Hamburgischen Schau-platze vorgestellt im jahr 1736.

*Hamburg, Georg Diedrich Spieringks wittwe, n. d. Unpaged. 18½*cm.

Five acts. Neither the author, Johann Ulrich Koenig, nor the composer, Reinhard **Keiser,** is mentioned. The Italian text has been added to some of the arias. The text seems to the same as in the edition of 1715. SCHATZ 5091

Fremore und Melime. Ein schauspiel mit gesang in drey akten von einem jungen kavalier, die musik von dem kurbayerschen kammerkompositeur Michl.

Frankfurt am Mayn, mit Andreaeischen schriften, 1778. 77 p. 15½ cm.

Text by H., graf von Spaur.
First performed at Mayence, Theater a. d. gr. Bleiche, January, 1778.
SCHATZ 6484

Le frenesie d'amore. L. T. of Buini's Il Savio delirante.

Les frères ennemis. Tr. of Graun's I fratelli nemici.

Freud- und liebes-streitt in einer operette vorgestellt auf dem Oettingischen Schau-Platz.

Oettingen, Stephan Rolck, 1699. 4 p. l., 35 p. 19 cm.

Three acts with prologue. By the composer, **Conradi**, who signs his dedication "Johann Melchior Counradi." He informs the reader:

"Dieses ist das erste mahl das auf dem allhiesigen Schau-Platz etwas aufgefuehret wird so den nahmen einer operette verdienen moechte. Zwar ist dieses unser absehen nimmer mehr gewesen dass diese geringe arbeit noch auf eine solche weise sollte an das licht gegeben werden: Allein ein gnaediger befehl hat verursachet, dass dieses werck'gen noch den schein einer operette bekommen. Du darfst dir aber, geneigter leser, nicht einbilden dass du viel galantes hierinnen antreffen werdest, sondern man ueberreicht dir nichts als ein *pastoral*, da zu vor die Musen sich ueber die abwesenheit unserer Durchleuchtigsten fuerstin hoechstens betrueben; welche aber von dem Apollo getroestet und endlich benachrichtiget werden, dass dieses theure fuerstenhaupt wieder gesund und gluecklich angekommen, vorueber sich die Musen, schaeffer und schaefferinnen, sehr erfreuen. Sonsten, wann unsere verse dir auch nicht das geringste contentement geben koennen: So wisse, das selbige, wie auch die musique nimmermehr vor einen oeffentlichen schau-platz, sondern nur die muessige stunden durch ein anmuthiges exercitium zu vertreiben, seyn verfertiget worden. Im uebrigen wirst du, geneigter leser, dich selbsten erinnern, dass wir alle, und also auch du den fehlern unterworffen." SCHATZ 2181

Die freundschaft auf der probe. Tr. of Grétry's L'amitié à l'épreuve.

Der freybrief. Eine posse mit gesang in einem akt.

Berlin, n. publ., 1788. 55 p. 16½ cm.

By Georg Ernst Lüderwald, who is not mentioned.
1) The music was partly selected from Joseph **Haydn**'s "La fedeltà premiata," partly from **Mozart**, with additional music by the arranger, Frido. Stephan Johann Maria Andreas freiherr von **Weber**, none of whom mentioned in the libretto.
First performed in a *two*-act version at Nürnberg, Nationaltheater, December 22, 1796; in its original *one*-act version at Meiningen, 1789.
2) With music composed by the author under the pseudonym Georg Ernst **Lange** in one act at Riga, 2/13 July, 1792.
3) With music composed by Julius **Miller**, in one act at Flensburg, 1802.
SCHATZ 4610a

— **Der freybrief.** Ein singspiel in zwey aufzuegen. Die musik ist von Haiden.

n. i., [Nuernberg?] 1797. 14 p. 16 cm.

SCHATZ 4610

Das freyschiessen oder Das gluekliche bauernmaedchen, eine operette in zween aufzuegen von J. A. W.

Goettingen, F. A. Rosenbusch, 1786. 86 p. 15 cm.

By Johann August Weppen. The composer, Christian Ludwig **Dieter**, is not mentioned.
First performed at Stuttgart, Herzogl. Kl. Theater, August 31, 1787. SCHATZ 2575

Der fried zwischen Romulo und Tatzio. Tr. of the ballet L'alliance de Romulus et de Tatius.

Frigga, opera i en act. I deras kongl. majestäters och det konql. husets närvero första gången upförd af Konql. musicaliska academien i Stockholm, den 31 Maji 1787.

> *Stockholm, Konql. Tryckeriet, 1787. 4 p. l., 31 p. 23ᶜᵐ.*

Cast, scenario, and names of the author, Carl Gustav af Leopold, and the Composer, Olof **Ahlström.**   Schatz 69

The **frolics of fancy.**   A. T. of A match for a widow.

Den **fromme pige.**   Tr. of Piccinni's La buona figluola.

Die **fruehlingsfeier in Arkadien.**   A. T. of Hensel's Die geisterbeschwoerung.

Die **fruehlingsnacht,** eine operette in einem akte. Von J. W. A. Schoepfel.

> *Frankfurt und Leipzig, Christian Gottlieb Hertel, 1773. 86 p. 17ᶜᵐ.*

In the "Vorrede," dated Leipzig, June 15, 1773, the author calls this the "erstling meiner Muse," hopes for a favorable reception of it, and says:

"Die operetten machen seit einigen jahren, wie in Italien und Frankreich, also auch in Deutschland, den hauptgegenstand des theaters aus, und der geschmack an komoedien und trauerspielen ist dadurch um ein merkliches gefallen. Das weiche gefuehl, welches die mit gesaengen untermischte musik der oper in uns hervorbringt, gab vermuthlich zu dieser veraenderung anlass . . . Weise [!] und Hiller sind solche namen [as against the foreigners] die das teutsche publicum, wenigstens das feinere und gesittete publicum, nie ohne achtung ausprechen wird . . ." Schatz 11612

Das fruehstueck auf der jagd, oder Der neue richter, ein laendliches lustspiel mit gesang in zween aufzuegen. Hauptsaechlich fuers Schultheater von C. W.

> *Sorau und Leipzig, Erdmann Gotthelf Deinzer, 1785. 63 p. 16ᶜᵐ.*

By Christian Gotthilf **Weissflog,** who also composed the music and who says, in his "Vorerrinerung:"

"Gegenwaertige kleine komische operette ist urspruenglich nur fuer schultheater bestimmt gewesen. Ich muss indessen gestehen, dass mir seit etlichen jahren zwar viele schauspiele bekannt geworden, die sich noch weit besser fuer schultheater schicken, als dieses; aber sehr wenig komische opern, die der Kleinen aehrenleserin und der Friedensfeier des herrn Weiss gleich kaeme. Aber auch in diesen fallen die gesaenge zu unvermutend ein; ein fehler, der fast in allen komischen opern bemerkt wird.

"Es laesst allerdings sehr sonderbar, und ist oft wider alle erwartung des zuschauers, wenn der akteur oder die aktrise ganz unvermuthet zu singen anfaengt, und noch dazu das singt, was eigentlich haette sollen gesprochen werden. Ich habe diesen fast allgemeinen fehler in dieser operette zu vermeiden gesucht, und die gesaenge niemals so unvermuthet anheben, sondern gleichsam vorher erst ankuendigen lassen. So verlangt es die natur, und so haben es sachverstaendige auch sehr lange gewuenscht . . . Sollte sie beifall finden, so ist der verleger gesonnen, auch die musik dazu in einem vollkommenen clavierauszug auf praenumeration herauszugeben . . ."

Schatz 10983

Fuenf und zwanzig tausend gulden. A. T. of Walter's Im dunkeln ist nicht gut munkeln.

Der fuerst und sein hofnarr.   A. T. of von Seyfried's Orion.

Der **fuerst und sein volk.** Ein teutsches nationaldrama mit gesaengen in einem aufzuge. Nach einer wahren begebenheit. Aufgefuehrt auf der Joseph Secondaischen Schaubuehne in Leipzig.

Leipzig, Kindel, n. d. 56 p. 14^{cm}.

One act. Cast and notice to the reader, which is dated Leipzig, March 5, 1791, and reads in part:

"Die musick ist zu den arien und choeren vom herrn von **Dittersdorf** und **Bertoni.** Die texte sind zwar untergelegt; man glaubt aber, dass wahre kenner diese wahl nicht misbilligen, und oefters angemessener, als die worte des originals selbst, finden werden. Das duett aber in der vierten scene, und das sextett nebst dem chor in der neunten scene ist vom herrn **Pitterlin,** Musickdirecktor der Jos. Secondaischen Schaubuehne, wie wenigstens dem verfasser duenkt, sehr brav gearbeitet worden."

For author *see* next entry. SCHATZ 8204

— Der **fuerst und sein volk.** Ein deutsches nationaldrama mit gesaengen in einem aufzuge. Nach einer wahren begebenheit.

n. i., 1794. 48 p. 16^{cm}.

Neither the author, Georg Carl Claudius, *called* Franz Ehrenberg, is mentioned, nor the composers, Friedrich August **Pitrerlin, Dittersdorf,** and **Bertoni.** First performed at Leipzig, Theater am Rannstaedter Thore, March 5, 1791.

SCHATZ 11613

Der **fuerst von Taranto.** Tr. of Paer's Il principe di Taranto.

La **fuga.** Commedia per musica di Giambatista Lorenzi P. A. Da rappresentarsi nel Teatro Nuovo sopra Toledo nella està del 1777.

Napoli, Vincenzo Mazzola-Vocola, 1777. 82 p. 15^{cm}.

Three acts. Scenario, cast, name of Gaetano **Monti** as the composer, and notice to the reader, who is informed that Lorenzi had written the text in two acts only, but that "al rispettabile comando di personnagio assai lumino" he rewrote it in three acts.

SCHATZ 6603

La **fuga dell' invidia.** Poemetto dramatico nel giorno del gloriosissimo nome . . . dell' imperatore Leopoldo I . . . L'anno MDCCI. Posto in musica dal Sigr Marc' Antonio Ziani . . .

[Vienna], Susanna Cristina, vedova di Matteo Cosmerovio, n. d. Unpaged. 16½^{cm}.

One act. Author not mentioned and unknown to Schatz. Argument. First performed, as indicated, Nov. 15, 1701. SCHATZ 11187

The **fugitive.** L. T. of Shield's The czar.

The **fugitive;** or, Happy recess. A dramatic pastoral, in two acts, as written for the Royalty Theatre: By Thomas Shapter . . .

London, Printed for the author, by John Abraham, n. d. 4, 30 p. 20^{cm}.

In his preface the author tells us that the piece was hastily written for the Royalty Theatre in the spring of 1790, accepted and turned over to "Mr. [John] **Moulds,** composer, to adapt to music," but owing to illness the latter did not finish the muic until about the close of the season. He then "repossessed" the music, by permission of the managers for private purposes. The score "fell into some other hands which rendered a fresh copy of the scores necessary to be taken." The piece was to reopen the new season, but the copyist was exasperatingly slow: "the whole was finally delivered about the beginning of September, just before the theatre opened anew, and was getting forward for rehearsal, when, suddenly, the second season came to a close . . ." LONGE 207

Il **fumo villano.** L. T. of Piccinni's Il cavaliere per amore.

Les **funerailles de la Foire.** Pièce d'un acte. Par Mrs. le S * *. & D'Or * *. Représentée sur le Théâtre du Palais Royal, par ordre de S. A. Royale Madame, le jeudy 6. octobre 1718.

Le Théâtre de la foire, Paris, 1737, t. iii, pl., [377]–410 p. 17cm.

By Le Sage and d'Orneval. Largely *en vaudevilles.* The airs, selected or composed and arranged by Jean Claude **Gillier,** "compositeur" of the theatre, are printed at the end of the volume in the "Table des airs." A note on the title page reads: "Cette pièce fut faite sur le bruit qui courut à la fin de la Foire de S. Laurent 1718, qu'il n'y auroit plus d'Opéra comique. Et comme S. A. R. Madame la voulut voir représenter, ou la fit jouer devant Elle au Palais royal." ML 48.L2 III

Il **fuoco eterno custodito dalle Vestali.** Drama musicale per la felicissima nascita della sereniss. arciduchessa Anna Maria, Figlia. Delle S.S. C.C. R.R. M.M. dell' imperatore Leopoldo, e della imperatrice Claudia Felice. Et alle medesime M. M. consacrato. Posto in musica dal S͡r Antonio Draghi . . . Con l'arie per li balletti del S͡r Gio. Erico Smelzer . . .

Vienna d'Austria, Gio. Christoforo Cosmerovio, 1674. 11 p. l. (incl. front.), 83 p., 12 fold. pl. 34cm.

The extraordinary pl. (size of the vol., except the first, which is 78 x 51cm.) were designed by Lodovico Burnacini, the court-theatre engineer, and engraved by Matthaeus Küsel.

Three acts. Dedication by the author, conte Nicolò Minato, dated Vienna, October 23, 1674, argument, allegoria, scenario, list of the "machine" and "attioni et apparenze," etc., and notice to the reader in which Minato commenting on his difficulties says "è stato un impossibile solo possibile à Cesare."

First performed at Vienna, Hoftheater, as indicated, September 1674.

ML 50.2.F89D7

La **furba burlata.** Commedia per musica da rappresentarsi nel Teatro Nuovo nell' està dell' anno 1762.

Napoli, Vincenzo Mazzola-Vocola, 1762. 68 p. 14½cm.

Three acts. By Pietro di Napoli, according to a ms. note on the title page. Cast and notice:

"La musica per la maggior parte è del Signor D. Niccola **Piccinni** . . . L'aria di Cannetella ed il terzetto nel primo atto, sono del Signor D. Niccola **Logroscino;** e tutte l'arie segnate con questo segno * sono del Signor D. Giacomo **In Sanguine** detto Monopoli . . ."

These starred arias, or parts of arias or dialogue are: "Birbante cò creanza" (I, 1), "Ma chesto soccede" (I, 1), "Che sia cortese e placido" (I, 3), "Mme sapisse a ddi perchè" (I, 9), "Ch'v'à schiaffato ncanna" (II, 3), "Sospira, si lamenta" (II, 4), "E tu malantrino" (II, 7), "L'esempio de chesta vedè" (II, 8), "E se dippiù ti chiede" (II, 9), "Te fa i buono ogne designo" (II, 11), "No Don Framinio non truove cchiù" (III, 1), "Io cchiù nesciuno" (III, 2), "Perchè e sicuro pegno" (III, 4), "Ave trovato sto bello coreí" (III, 7).

First performed at Naples, Teatro de' Fiorentini, fall of 1760. SCHATZ 8159

Furberia e puntiglio. Farsa giocoso per musica di Giuseppe Foppa da rappresentarsi nel Teatro Giustiniani in San Moisè l'autunno dell' anno 1798.

Venezia, Modesto Fenzo, 1798. 48 p. 18cm.

One act. Cast, scenario, and name of Marcello di Capua (Marcello **Bernardini**) as composer. On p. 43–48, argument of "Caterina e Blech. Ballo eroico pantomimo in quattro atti d'invenzione ed esecuzione di Giuseppe Cajani da rappresentarsi nel Teatro Giustiniani in San Moisè l'anno 1798." Cajani also composed the music.

First performed at Venice, as indicated, September 18, 1798. SCHATZ 834

Le **furberie deluse**. Commedia per musica di Giuseppe Palomba. Da rappresentarsi nel Teatro Nuovo sopra Toledo, per quart' opera di questo corrente anno 1793.

Napoli, Vincenzo Flauto, 1793. 43 p. 15ᶜᵐ.

Two acts. Cast and name of Gabriele **Prota** as the composer.   SCHATZ 8474

I **furbi burlati**. Commedia per musica da rappresentarsi nel Teatro de' Fiorentini la primavera di quest' anno 1773.

Napoli, 1773, n. publ. 70 p. 15½ᶜᵐ.

Three acts. Author not mentioned. Cast and name of Niccolò **Piccinni** as the composer. The text is but a revamped version of Pietro di Napoli's "La furba burlata," composed by Niccolò Piccinni, with exception of two pieces in the first act, by Nicola Logroscino, and several arias by Giacomo Insanguine, and first performed at Naples, Teatro de' Fiorentini, fall of 1760. According to Schatz, and at least the libretto with Piccinni's name as only composer would appear to corroborate his claim, the music of "I furbi burlati" was entirely by Piccinni, though perhaps Schatz goes too far if he says "vollständig neu bearbeitet." Cametti is of no assistance in this matter.   SCHATZ 8127

Il **furbo contro al furbo**. Commedia per musica da rappresentarsi nel nobilissimo Teatro in S. Samuele il carnovale dell' anno 1797.

Venezia, Stamperia Valvasense, n. d. 79 p. 17ᶜᵐ.

Two acts. Cast and name of the composer, Valentino **Fioravanti** ("musica del tutta nuova"), to whom Schatz also attributes the text, though the libretto simply says: "La poesia del tutto nuova del Sig. N. N." Schatz based his information, probably, on a somewhat altered version of the libretto "Chi la fa, chi la disfa, e chi l'imbroglia," Trieste, 1802, in which Fioravanti figures both as author and composer.   SCHATZ 3131

Il **furbo malaccorto**.   L. T. of Fioravanti's L'astuta in amore.

Il **furbo malaccorto**.   Opera in musica da rappresentarsi nel Teatro della città di Cosenza . . .

Napoli, Amati Cons., 1782. 72 p. 15ᶜᵐ.

Three acts. Impresario's dedication (dated 1782) and cast. Neither the author, Giambattista Lorenzi, nor the composer, **Paisiello**, is mentioned.

First performed at Naples, Teatro Nuovo, winter, 1767.   SCHATZ 7677

Furcht und hoffnung, vorspiel mit gesang.   In musik gesezt von C. D. Stegmann.

Hamburg, Rabe und Freystatzky wittwe, 1798. 16 p. 16ᶜᵐ.

Author not mentioned, and unknown to Schatz.

First performed at Hamburg, Theater beim Gänsemarkt, April 11, 1798.

    SCHATZ 10038

Le **furie d'Oreste**.   A. T. of Marescalchi's ballet La morte d'Egisto.

Il **furio Camillo**. Drama del Sig. Matteo Noris da recitarsi nel Teatro Malvezzi l'anno 1693.

Bologna, Giulio Borzaghi, 1693. 83 p. 14ᶜᵐ.

Three acts. Argument, scenario, and notice to the reader, referring to the first performance at Venice and mentioning Giacomo Antonio **Perti** as the composer.

First performed, as indicated, January 17, 1693; at Venice, Teatro di San Salvatore, carnival, 1692.   SCHATZ 7950

Il furio Camillo—Continued.

— **Il furio Camillo.** Dramma per music di Mateo Noris, da rappresentarsi in Mantova l'anno MDCC . . .

 Mantova, Alberto Pazzoni, n. d. 6 p. l., 60 p. 15^{cm}.

Three acts. Dedication by Giacomo Sironi, argument, cast, scenario and substitute aria "Trionfi Giuliva" in II, 1, for "De cori, e del' alme." **Perti** is not mentioned. ML 50.2.F9P3

I furori di Orlando. Dramma semi-giocoso per musica, da rappresentarsi nel Teatro di Ratisbona per ordine di Sua Altezza Serenissima il principe regnante della Torre e Tassis . . .

 [Ratisbona], Stamperia Zunckeliana, n. d. 8 p. l., 167 p. 15^{cm}.

Three acts. German title-page, "Die rasereyen des Rolands," and text face Italian. **"Touchemolin,** primo violino e direttore de concerti di S^a A^{sa} S^{ma} il principe della Torre e Tassis," is mentioned as the composer. A long, pretentious, but noteworthy, "Avertissement aux amateurs du spectacle," by the author, Domenico Friggieri, precedes the text, which is a scathing arraignment of the average Italian opera libretto. He says:

"Je n'ignore point ce que les Gens d'Esprit et de bon sens pensent du mérite prétendu des Operas Comiques Italiens. Je conviens sincerement avec eux, qu'on n'y trouve ni conduite, ni intéret, ni sens commun &c.

"Cependant on ne doit point supposer, comme a fait quel q'un, que ce genre de Composition soit l'ouvrage des Poëtes. L'Italie, qui a toujours produit des Hommes savants en toutes sciences, abonde encore aujourd'hui en grands Poëtes capables par leur génie de donner à cette partie de l'Art drammatique la perfection, dont elle seroit susceptible. Mais ceux ci n'oseroient employer leurs talents a composer des Operas Comiques, par des raisons assez solides, qu'on trouvera dans mon Histoire du Theatre de Musique Italien que je donnerai d'ici a quelque tems au Public. Histoire, qui ne sera pas peu divertissante, ni peu instructive pour bien des Gens.

"Il est sur que ces Farçes, qu'on represente en Musique, depuis un certain nombre d'années, et surtout après le depart de Mr. Goldoni pour la France, sont des productions de certains Rimailleurs mércenaires, qui n'ont presque aucune connoissance ni de la Poësie, ni du Theatre, ni du Monde. Il arrive cependant a quelques uns de ces pauvres Versificateurs a gages, d'enfanter quelque fois, ou de choisir un sujet assez bon et d'imaginer un Plan, sur le quel ils pourroient travailler de façon, a ne point mériter tout a fait le mépris des Gens de Esprit; Mais, malheureusement gênés dans leur travail, et contraints par des Entrepreneurs presque tous ignorants, avâres, et souvent paillards à contenter le gout des Acteurs, et des charmantes Actrices, qui doivent jouer pour la premiere fois leur piece, (gout, qui comme on peut aisement se le persuader n'est jamais des plus fins, et delicats) ils defigurent le sujet heureusement trouvé, et le Plan bien conçu, surchargeant l'un, et l'autre d'un amâs de plattes bouffoneries, de Scenes pastiches, de Dialogues impertinents, et mille autres sottises; de façon, qu'ils produisent un monstre, qui sortant ensuit improprement paré de tous les charmes possibles d'une exéllente Musique, n'en est que plus meprisable, et cents fois plus hideux, et extravagant, que celui, imaginé par Horace dans son Epitre sur l'Art Poëtique.

"Une preuve de ce que je dis ici, c'est que ce même Dramme lyrique, que je presente au Public, sous le titre des Fureurs de Rolland, a été donné il y a quelques années par un de ces Compositeurs, dont je viens de parler, farci de mille défauts, comme on peut le voir dans un Exemplaire, que je conserve. On ne pouvoit pourtant pas appeller sa piece tout a fait mauvaise, ni même mediocre; et la parcourant plus d'une fois pour voir si on pourroit la produire sur ce Theatre, elle m'a fait naitre la resolution de la refaire, plus tot que de la rejetter, conservant les mëmes Personnages, une grande partie du Plan imaginé par son premier Auteur, beaucoup des ses idées, et de ses Vers tres bons, jusqu' au nombre de 235 a peu prés.

"J'ai ajouté de mon invention tout le Spectacle, comme aussi tout le 3me Acte, et la Catastrophe, et plusieurs Scenes. J'ai corrigé, et refait les Caracteres des Personnages. J'ai rejetté avec dédain une mauvaise plaisanterie, qui devenoit une Satire peu honette contre la Musique Française: de telles sottises n'etant propres, qu'a fomenter, et maintenir cette haïne déraisonable, et ce mépris réciproque d'une Nation a une autre; Effet détestable des prejugés enfantés par la vanité, et la bêtise. Enfin j'ai tant refondu cette piece, qu'il seroit bien difficile a son ancien Compositeur d'y reconnoitre une partie de son Plan, et des ses idées. Je me flatte hardiment de

I furori di Orlando—Continued.

la'voir rendue beaucoup meilleure. Du moins on y verra Rolland, pas seulement
Fou, mais furieux: et l'on n'y rencontrera point mille bouffoneries indecentes, et
outrées, qui ne peuvent que faire rire les sots. Il est vrai que, justement par cette
raison ma piece sera trouvée mauvaise par les soidisants Acteurs Italiens; mais je me
soucie fort peu des·leurs suffrages, aussi bien que de la critique de quelques uns de
leurs partisans.''

First performed as indicated, carnival, 1777.   SCHATZ 10383

Gabriella di Vergy, ballet. *See* Anfossi's La Nitteti.

Das gaertner-maedchen. Eine komische oper, in drey aufzuegen,
herausgegeben von dem verfasser.

Weimar, Karl Rudolf Hoffmann, 1771. 6 p. l., 124 p. 16^{cm}.

Three acts. Neither the composer, Ernst Wilhelm **Wolf,** is mentioned, nor the
author, Johann Carl August Musaeus, whose long preface occupies the p. l. and which
reads, in part:

"Ein eigennütziger Akteur von der Kochischen Gesellschaft und ein vorlauter
Kunstrichter, vertreten bey dieser kleinen thearalischen Arbeit die Stelle drin-
gender Freunde und Gönner, denen man nichts abschlagen kann: sie nöthigen mir
beyde, durch ihren Eifer dieses Stück der Vergessenheit zu entreissen, die öffent-
liche Bekanntmachung desselben ab, so wenig dieses jemals meine Absicht war.
Der erste, der aller Vermuthung nach entweder dem Herrn Koch das Manuskript
des Gärtnermädchens unter irgend einem Vorwand abzuschwatzen gemusst, oder aus
den ausgeschriebenen Rolen das Stück zusammen gestoppelt haben mag, wie dieses
einige abgeschmackte Zusätze und Abänderungen wahrscheinlich machen, ist so
unverschämt, um einen kleinen Gewinnst zu erhaschen, diese Operette an einen
Buchdrucker in Berlin zu vertrödeln, der sie ohne mein Vorwissen, mit allen Fehlern
der unkorrekten Abschrift abgedruckt hat. Der andere versucht seit drey Jahren
an mir bey aller Gelegenheit seine kritischen Kräfte, ohne dass er mich bisher aus
meinem Ruhepunkte hätte bewegen können, und ohne den unbefugten Herausgeber
dieser Operette, hätte er noch drey Jahr schwatzen mögen, ich hätte kein Wort
darüber verlohren. Ich war versichert, dass das Publikum bey der Menge parthei-
ischer Richter in ein unbescheidenes Urtheil eines einzigen zu viel Misstrauen setzt,
als dass es sich, ehe es selbst meine Arbeit mit der Kritik darüber vergleichen konnte,
von ihm sollte übertäuben lassen. Aber nun da durch die Gewinnsucht eines Nieder-
trächtigen, den ich in der Kochischen Gesellschaft nicht vermuthet hätte, diese
Operette in der nachtheiligsten Gestalt öffentlich erscheinet, dürfen die Fehler des
Berliner Drucks leicht auf meine Rechnung kommen, und dadurch würde das Urtheil
des Kunstrichters allerdings einiges Gericht erhalten. Es bleibt mir daher kein
andrer Weg übrig, als solche selbst abdrucken zu lassen, und sie dem Publico vor-
zulegen. Ich habe nichts hauptsächliches daran verändert, und nur dem Dialog an
einigen Stellen wo er mir zu weitschichtig und geschwätzig schien, etwas abge-
nommen. Eigentlich hatte ich diese Stellen schon nach der ersten Aufführung
weggestrichen, sie sind aber, wie ich sehe all beybehalten worden, vermuthlich um
den Druck mehr anzuschwellen. Andere Veränderungen habe ich um deswillen
nicht unternommen, weil das Ganze dadurch leicht eine neue Gestalt würde bekommen haben, und die Leser ausser Stande seyn würden, das Stück mit den darüber
gefällten Kritiken zusammen zuhalten, und über beydes selbst zu urtheilen. In
Ansehung dieser leztern ist für die Leser eine Erläuterung nöthig. Es scheinet, als
wenn ganz verschiedene Kunstrichter ihr Urtheil wider mich vereinigt hätten, in
der That ist es aber nur der einzige Christian Heinrich Schmid, der sein hölzernes
Schwerdt gegen mich gezückt hat. Alles was er in der Nachricht von den theatralischen Vorstellungen auf der Leipziger Bühne, in der Klotzischen Bibliothek wider
das Gärtnermädchen deklamiret, das hat er in den Zusätzen zur Theorie der Poesie,
in seinem Almanach der deutschen Musen und in dem Parterre wiedergekäuet.

"Ueber eine solche theatralische Kleinigkeit als eine Operette ist, würde es
unschicklich seyn, sich weitläuftig vertheidigen zu wollen; indessen glaube ich, dass
einige Anmerkung über die voreiligen Urtheile des Herrn Schmid hier nicht ganz
überflüssig sind. Was er eigentlich bisher gegen das Gärtnermädchen erinnert hat,
ist dieses, dass das Süjet aus einem schlechten französischen Roman genommen, dass
das ganze Stück Weissische Nachahmung sey, dass dem Herrn Weisse viele Verse
abgestohlen wärem, und dass ich keine Situation zu nutzen verstünde. Alles übrige
ist Petulanz in dem Modeton der Klotzischen Schule.

Das **gaertner-maedchen**—Continued.

"Es ist wahr, die Idee zum Gärtnermädchen ist aus dem Französischen Roman La Jardiniere de Vincennes, aber mag doch dieser gut oder schlecht seyn, was liegt daran?

". . . Die Weissische Nachahmung bezieht sich hauptsächlich auf die Person des Martins, dieser soll bis auf die kleinsten Einfälle von dem Schösser in der Liebe auf dem Lande kopirt seyn. Wer sollte denken, dass eine Perucke einen Kunstrichter täuschen und zu einem falschen Urtheile verführen könnte? . . .

"Worinne übrigens die Weissische Nachahmung liegen soll, das weiss ich nicht, so viel weiss ich, dass ich bey der Ausarbeitung des Gärtnermädchens kein besonderes Muster vor Augen gehabt habe, und nur der Idee überhaupt gefolgt bin, zwischen dem Grotesken der Opera Buffa und dem leeren der französischen Operette das Mittel zu halten, welches dem deutschen Geschmack angemessen scheint. Dass mich aber die komischen Opern des Herrn Weise auf diese Idee gebracht haben, das räume ich ganz gerne ein . . .

"Weil ich aber doch überhaupt Herr Weisen soll geplündert haben, so versteht sich, dass ihm auch viele Verse im Gärtnermädchen ganz zugehören, dieser Vorwurf ist in der That für mich ein Kompliment. Herr Schmid hält also viel von meinen Versen für Weisische? Sie müssen doch so schlecht nicht seyn als er sie ausschreyet."

First performed at Weimar, Schlosstheater in der Wilhelmsburg, 1769.

SCHATZ 11079

Der **gaertner von Sidon.** Tr. of Philidor's Le jardinier de Sidon.

Das **galante Europa.** Tr. of Graun's L'Europa galante.

Die **galanten feste.** Tr. of Graun's Le feste galanti.

La **Galatea.**

[241]–275 p. 19*cm*. (*Pietro Metastasio, Opere drammatiche, Venezia, Giuseppe Bettinelli, 1733–37, v. 3.*)

Two parts. No composer mentioned. Text written 1722 at Naples for the Duke of Monteleone. First composer unknown to Schatz. ML 49.A2M4

— La **Galatea.**

*Metastasio, Poesie, Parigi, vedova Quillau, 1755, t. ix, 48 p. 16*cm*.*

Two parts. ML 49.A2M42

— La **Galatea.**

pl., [9]–46 p. 26*cm*. (*Metastasio, Opere, t. x, Parigi, vedova Herissant, 1782.*)

Two parts. ML 49.A2M44

Galatea ed Acide. Pastorale, da rappresentarsi nel Nuovo Real Teatro di Potsdam . . .

*Posdamo, C. F. Voss, 1748. 31 p. 16½*cm*.*

Three acts. By Leopoldo di Villati, who is not mentioned. The music is known to have been selected principally from Joh. Ad. **Hasse's** works. The Argomento simply says:

". . . Le altre parti della presente pastorale sono episodiche, & ordite solo ad effetto di potervi applicare, come si ha fatto per comando sovrano, l'arie de' migliori compositori di musica."

It is not certain whether or not music by Graun, Quantz, Nichelmann, and Frederick the Great was used. German title page, "Galathee und Alcides," and text face Italian.

First performed, as indicated, July 11, 1748. SCHATZ 4541

Galathee und Alcides. Tr. of Hasse's Galatea ed Acide.

Galieno. Drama da rappresentarsi nel famosissimo Teatro Grimano di SS. Gio. e Paolo. L'anno MDCLXXVI. Di Matteo Noris . . .

Venetia, Francesco Nicolini, 1676. front., 72 p. 14ᶜᵐ.

Three acts. Author's dedication, dated Venice, December 23, 1675, argument, and scenario. The composer, Carlo **Pallavicino,** is not mentioned.   SCHATZ 7724

An English musical entertainment, called **Galligantus.**

London, n. publ., 1758. iv, 5–24 p. 21ᶜᵐ.

Preface "From the author of Jack and the giant." Supposed to be taken from Henry Brooke's "Jack the giant queller." Composer not recorded by Schatz.
First performed at London, Hay-market, 1758 or 1759 and at Drury-Lane, April 14, 1760, according to Genest.   LONGE 318

La **Galzeuco** ossia Golconda liberata dalla tirannide di Scour-Malou, ballet. *See* Pugnani's Achille in Sciro.

The **gamester.** Tr. of Il marito giocatore e la moglie bacchettona.

Ganimede, ballet. *See* Bernabei's L'Ermione.

Ganymed in Vulkans schmiede, ein singspiel in zwey aufzuegen, vom sel. herren Demler in musik gesetzt, aufgefuehrt von den schülern der dritten klasse am Katholischen schulhause bey St. Salvator den 30 May, 1 und 2 Brachmonat 1797.

Augsburg, Joseph Anton Hueber, n. d. [9] p. 18½ᶜᵐ.

At head of this title: "Myrtil oder Der gedemuetigte stolz, ein lustspiel in drey aufzuegen. Und." Cast and "Vorbericht," in which we read:
"Die fabel von Ganymed soll zum beweise dienen, wie schaendlich sich die jugend verirrt, wenn sie sich dem heiligen joche des gehorsams entzieht, sich ihrem leichtsinne ueberlaesst und ihren blinden trieben folget . . ."
The author is not mentioned, and is unknown to Schatz.   SCHATZ 2505

La **gara.** Opera dramatica rappresentata in musica, per introduttione di torneo fatto in Vienna per la nascita della Serenissima infanta di Spagna Donna Margarita Maria d'Austria, dedicata a . . . marchese di Castel Rodri . . . da Alberto Vimina.

Vienna d'Austria, Matteo Riccio, 1652. 4 pl. (folded, 52 by 38ᶜᵐ), 61 p. 30½ᶜᵐ.

The plates bear the legend "Joa-ˢ Burnacinus pichtor et architectus. Invenchtor. Seb.ᵃⁿ Ienet. Sculpt." Prologue and three acts, with an "intermedio" before act second, an intermedio and the Torneo before act third. Brief descriptions precede each act, etc., and to that of the Torneo the names of the participating nobility are added. From the tone of the descriptions, which record also the impression of the spectacle made, it appears that this volume was issued *after* the performances. The text is preceded by the argument and Alberto Vimina's dedication as author, dated Vienna, January 7, 1652. The composer is not mentioned by von Weilen. The work is not recorded by Schatz.   ML 50.2.G2

La **gara.** Componimento drammatico, scritto dall' autore in Vienna, e posto in musica dal Reutter, l'anno 1755 . . . ed eseguito negl' interni appartamenti della Regia imperial corte . . . in occasione del felicissimo parto dell' imperatrice regina, in cui diede alla luce l'Altezza Reale dell' arciduchessa Maria-Antonia, poi Delfina, indi regina di Francia.

[179]–188 p. 26ᶜᵐ. (Metastasio, Opere, t. xi, Parigi, vedova Herissant, 1782.)

ML 49.A2M44

La **gara degli atleti.** *See* Cafaro's Il natal d'Apollo.

La gara degli dei, festa musicale rappresentata in uno de' Reali giardini di Dresda per servire d'introduzione agli spettacoli destinati da S. M. a solennizare le nozze de' Serenissime principi Federigo Augusto . . . e Maria, Gioseffa, arciduchessa d'Austria. Musica del Sig. Gio. Davvide Heinichen . . .

Dresda, G. C. Stössel, n. d. Unpaged. 18½^{cm}.

Author unknown to Schatz. French title page, "L'émulation parmy les divinitez," and text (in prose) face Italian.

First performed, as indicated, September 10, 1719. SCHATZ 4705

La gara de gli elementi, per riverir le nozze de' serenissimi Ranuccio II. duca di Parma e Margarita, principessa di Savoia. Introduzione al combattimento a cavallo in Piazza intimatosi nello Scherzo del Giardino. Componimento del conte Francesco Berni.

Parma, Mario Vigna, 1660. 23 p. 15^{cm}.

On p. 4, "Il Signor Carlo Pasetti inventò la struttura del monte, e de carri, e'l Signor Benedetto **Ferrari** compose la musica." SCHATZ 3070

La gara per la gloria. Divertimento teatrale per musica da rappresentarsi nel Teatro di S. Mosè gl'ultimi giorni del carnovale 1744.

Venezia, n. publ., 1744. 23 p. 15½^{cm}.

Three parts. Neither the author, Bartolomeo Vitturi, is mentioned, nor the composer, Gaetano **Latilla**

First performed in February, 1744, as indicated. SCHATZ 5459

La gara tra la commedia e la musica. Introduzione.

Carlo Goldini, Opere teatrali, Venezia, Zatta e figli, 1788–95, [5]– 11 p. 18½^{cm}.

Not recorded by Schatz. PQ

Le gare degli amanti. Dramma giocoso per musica ad uso del Real Teatro di Colorno nell' autunno dell' anno MDCCLXXIII.

Parma, Dalla Reale Stamperia, n. d. 58 p. 21^{cm}.

Three acts. Luigi Bernardo Salvoni is mentioned as author, and Gian-Francesco **Fortunati** as composer. ("La musica tutta nuova.")

First performed at Parma, Teatro Ducale, Dec. 26, 1772. SCHATZ 3310

Le gare dell' inganno e dell' amore, drama da recitarsi nel nobilissimo Theatro Zane di S. Moisè, l'anno 1689 . . .

Venetia, Zamaria Rossi, 1689. 5 p. l., 48 p. 15^{cm}.

Three acts. By Paolo Emilio Badi, who is not mentioned. Scenario, argument, impresario's dedication, and notice to the reader, which evidently refers to some local event involving the Teatro di S. Moisè and the reputation of Venice's fair treatment of strangers. He says that it fell to his lot to sustain this theatre "sbattuto non dalla disgratia, ma dalla malignità," and that he selected this "*operina*," "composta in due giri di sole e posta in musica in tre notti," by Teofilo **Orgiani,** who has united "la maestria romana con le bizzarie teatrali di Venetia." SCHATZ 7298

Le gare di politica e d'amore. Drama per musica da rappresentarsi nel nuovo famoso Teatro Grimani a San Samuele l'anno MDCCXI . . .

Venezia, Marino Rossetti, 1711. 60 p. 14½^{cm}.

Three acts. Publisher's dedication, dated Venice, January 28, 1711, argument, scenario, and notice to the reader, in which we read:

"Hò scelto il drama presente, che per esser stato, sol l'anno scorso, degno divertimento d'un gran principe d'Italia, giova crederlo eguale anche esposto al tuo benigno aggradimento sù le Venete scene."

While this refers to the text by Antonio Salvi (not mentioned), with its original title, "Berenice," it does not mean that the music of Giovanni Maria **Ruggeri** (not mentioned) had been previously performed. SCHATZ 9137

Le gare generose. Drama per musica. Da rappresentarsi nel Teatro Tron di S. Cassiano. L'autunno dell' anno 1712 . . .

Venezia, Marino Rossetti, 1702 [!]. 60 p. 15ᶜᵐ.

Three acts. Dedication, argument, name of the composer, Tommaso **Albinoni,** and cast. In the dedication count Antonio Zaniboni calls this "la mia prima poetica fatica."

The date of publication is a misprint for 1712.   SCHATZ 94

Le gare generose. Commedia per musica da rappresentarsi nel Teatro de' Fiorentini per prim' opera in quest' anno 1786.

Napoli, n. publ., 1786. 58 p. 15ᶜᵐ.

Two acts. By Giuseppe Palomba, who is not mentioned. Cast, argument, and name of **Paisiello** as the composer.   SCHATZ 7679

— Gli **schiavi per amore.** Dramma giocoso per musica da rappresentarsi nel Teatro di S. A. S. il Signor principe di Carignano nell' autunno dell' anno 1791.

Torino, Onorato Derossi, n. d. iv, 73 p. 15ᶜᵐ.

Two acts. Palomba's "Le gare generose," text with modifications. Cast, scenario, and name of **Paisiello** as the composer. On p. 70–73, incorrectly numbered as 60–63, cast and argument of Paolino Franchi's "Inkle e Iariko, ballo tragico-pantomimo in tre atti." Neither of this nor of his "Il calzettaro ossia Tanto va la gatta al lardo che ci lascia lo zampino, ballo comico pantomimo" is the composer of the music mentioned.   SCHATZ 7700

— **Le gare generose** ossia Gli schiavi per amore. Dramma giocoso per musica da rappresentarsi in Parma nel R. D. Teatro di Corte il carnevale dell' anno MDCCXCVI . . .

Parma, Stamperia Carmignani, n. d. [viii], 48 p. 17½ᶜᵐ.

Two acts. By Giuseppe Palomba, who is not mentioned. Impresario's dedication, cast, scenario, and name of **Paisiello** as the composer. With the opera were performed Paolino Franchi's ballets, "Il bottaro di Svezia" and "La pianella perduta."
SCHATZ 7626

— **Le gare generose.** Dramma giocoso per musica, da rappresentarsi nel Teatro Elettorale.

Dresda, n. publ., 1792. 141 p. 15½ᶜᵐ.

Two acts. Text by Palomba, who is not mentioned. German title page, "Der edle wettstreit," and text face Italian. **Paisiello** is mentioned as the composer.

First performed, as indicated, October 3, 1793.   SCHATZ 7627

— Gesaenge aus dem singspiele: Die **beyden fluechtlinge,** in zwey aufzuegen, nach dem italiaenischen. Die musik von Paisiello.

Hamburg, Johann Matthias Michaelsen, 1791. 36 p. 16ᶜᵐ.

By Heinrich Gottlieb Schmieder.

First performed at Hamburg, Theater b. Gänsemarkt, June 30, 1791; at Mayence; Nationaltheater, 1789.   SCHATZ 7628

Il **Gastaldo burlato,** ballet. *See* Andreozzi's Teodelinda.

Gastfreiheit und armut. A. T. of Kaffka's Philemon und Baucis.

Das **gastmahl.** Tr. of Cimarosa's Il convito.

Die **gastwirthinn.** Tr. of Salieri's La locandiera.

Das **gaukelspiel.** A. T. of Dittersdorf's Hokus Pokus.

Die **geadelte baeuerinn.** Tr. of Sacchini's La contadina in corte.

Der **geadelte landmann.** A. T. of Paisiello's Das witzige land-maedchen.

Die **gecroente tapferkeit des Heraclius.** A. T. of Keiser's Die wiederhergestellte ruh.

Der **gedemüthigte Phaeton.** O. T. of Keiser's Der siegende Phaeton.

Der **gedemuethigte stolz.** A. T. of Ditterdorf's Terno secco.

Der **gedultige Socrates,** in einem musicalischen lust-spiele auf dem Hamburgischen Schau-platze vorgestellet, 1721.

Hamburg, Caspar Jakhel, n. d. Unpaged. 18ᶜᵐ.

Three acts. Neither the author of the Italian original, nor the translator, Joh. Ulrich Koenig, nor the composer, Georg Philipp **Telemann,** is mentioned. To many of the arias the Italian text has been added to the German, which is based on Christian Flemmer's comedy "Die zwei weiber oder Die geduld des Socrates," performed 1680 at Brunswick, after conte Niccolò Minato's "La patienza di Socrate con due mogli." SCHATZ 10261

Die **gefangene.** Tr. of Piccinni's La schiava.

Der **gefoppte braeutigam,** eine komische oper in zwey aufzuegen. Die musik ist vom herrn Ditters, edlen von Dittersdorf.

Hall am Kocher, Schmeisser, n. d. 16 p. 16½ᶜᵐ.

Originally in Italian as "Lo sposo burlato." At least the German version by the composer himself.

First performed in Italian at the castle Johannesberg in Silesia, 1773; in German; at Vienna, Kärnthnerthor Theater, September, 1783, or at Breslau, Wäsersches Theater, in the same year. SCHATZ 2590

— Gesaenge aus dem **Gefoppten braeutigam,** komischen sing-spiele in zwey aufzuegen von Ditterodorf [!]

n. i., n. d. 23 p. 16ᶜᵐ.

SCHATZ 2590A

Die **geheime liebe der Diana.** A. T. of Keiser's Die entdeckte verstellung.

Die **geheimen begebenheiten Henrico IV, koenigs von Casti-lien und Leon,** oder: Die getheilte liebe. In einer opera auff dem grossen Hamburgischen Schau-platz vorgestellet im jahr 1711. im monath Februarius.

Hamburg, Friderich Conrad Greflinger, n. d. Unpaged. 18½ᶜᵐ.

Five acts by Johann Joachim Hoe, who is not mentioned. "Vor-Bericht" and dedication, the latter signed by Johann **Mattheson,** who composed the opera. Many of the arias have both Italian and German text. SCHATZ 6100

Der **geist des widerspruchs.** Tr. of Schuster's Lo spirito di con-tradizione.

. . . Die **geisterbeschwoerung,** eine operette.—**Daphne** oder Die fruehlingsfeier in Arkadien, eine oper.

Hirschberg, Wolfgang Pittschiller und komp., 1799. (Singspiele von Johann Daniel Hensel, Erstes baendchen) 76, 77–116 p. 17ᶜᵐ.

Both are in three acts. Hensel says in prefatory note dated Hirschberg, February, 1799:

"Die haeufigen, und nach meiner ueberzeugung gegruendeten klagen, dass meistens an den texten unsrer neuern operetten gar nichts sey, bewogen mich, einen

Die geisterbeschwoerung—Continued.

versuch zu machen, ob ich nicht eine operette verfertigen koennte, die, ohne fade zu seyn, scherzhaft unterhielte, einen moralischen zweck ausfuehrte, und, wenn gleich keine meisterstuecke von poesien, (die in der operette in der regel zu wenig geschaetzt werden) doch verse enthielte, die sich musikalisch gut bearbeiten liessen.

"Dies geschah zu einer zeit, da das geisterzitiren in einer gewissen gegend mode war, und ich verfertigte die *Geisterbeschwoerung*, wo jenes unwesen hier persiflirt werden sollte. Da sich aber bis jetzt die zeiten geaendert haben: so aenderte ich auch mein stueck. Die anspielungen fielen weg, und es blieb blos die posse . . . Die komposition dazu, auch von mir selbst, giebt den saengern hinlaenglich gelegenheit sich zu zeigen . . .

"Daphne entstand auf folgende weise schon früher. Herr steuerrath Weisse hatte am ende seines Kinderfreundes den hauptgegenstand des gegenwaertigen stuecks, als operette fuer die heranwachsende jugend ausgefuehrt. Ich fand nun, dass derselbe gegenstand, mit einiger abaenderung und den noethigen zusaetzen, zu einem grossen singspiele (oper) anzuwenden sey, wenn man nur nicht praechtige operndekorationen forderte, sondern sich einmal wieder in die laendlich griechische schaeferwelt versetzen wollte. Ich versuchte also die umaenderung, und da ich laengst schon den dichter und komponisten, die sich so selten recht in die haende arbeiten, einmal in einer person zu vereinigen gewuenscht hatte, setzte ich es auch in musik. Das stueck ward als konzert aufgefuehrt und hatte das glueck in beider ruecksicht von kennern und liebhabern allen beifall zu erhalten. Ich feilte nachher gelegentlich an text und musik . . ."

Schatz records no stage performances. 　　　　SCHATZ 4635

　　　　　　　　　　Second copy. ML 49.A2H3

Die geister-burg. Ein singspiel in 2 aufzuegen von F. Hochkirch. Die musik ist von Ritter.

n. i., 1799. 24 p. 16^{cm}.

First performed at Aurich, 1799. 　　　　SCHATZ 8823

Die geisterinsel. Ein singspiel in vier handlungen, nach Shakespear, Gotter und J. W. D. [Joh. Wilh. Döring], umgearbeitet von Johann Daniel Hensel.

Hirschberg, Wolfgang Pittschiller und Komp., 1799. 6 p. l., 135 p. 17^{cm}.

In his intelligent preface, dated Hirschberg, January, 1799, Hensel gives his reasons for having made an effort to improve on Gotter's "Geisterinsel." After characterizing Gotter's talents, characteristics, and methods, he makes this remark:

"Ueberhaupt scheint Gotter so wenig als die meisten singdichter gehoerige kenntniss der musik und komposition gehabt zu haben; wenn er auch vielleicht ein guter musikus geheissen haben mag. Es fehlt auch noch ein eignes werk ueber die musikalische dichtkunst, welches aber niemand als ein dichter und komponist zugleich schreiben koennte, in welchem dann unsere dichter so manches paradoxon finden moechten."

After a few more remarks on this subject and on his version of the Geisterinsel in particular, he says:

"Sobald ich musse haben werde, denke ich diese oper auch zu komponiren, und villeicht ist schon ein theil davon fertig wenn der text gedruckt erscheint. Was ich machen werde, kann ich freilich nicht im voraus sagen; aber die erfahrung hat mich gelehrt, dass eine edle simplicitaet mit etwas arbeit, in gehoeriger abwechslung mit harmonischer fuelle, so viel und eigentlich mehr wirkt, als alle kuensteleien und jetzt so sehr gesuchten ueberladungen, zu denen das publikum durch Mozart und dessen nachahmer so sehr verwoehnt ist, dass es nur immer die ohren voll haben will . . ."

Schatz records no performances. 　　　　SCHATZ 4637

　　　　　　　　　　Second copy. ML 49.A2H3

Arien und gesaenge aus dem singspiele Die **geisterinsel** in drey akten. Komponirt vom herrn kapellmeister Reichardt.

Berlin, n. publ., 1798. 64 p. 15½^{cm}.

Three acts. By Friedrich Wilhelm Gotter, who is not mentioned. Cast.
First performed at Berlin, Kgl. Nationaltheater, July 6, 1798. 　　SCHATZ 8641

Gesaenge aus der oper: Die **geisterinsel** in drei aufzuegen von Gotter. In musik gesetzt von J. R. Zumsteeg.

Altona, Eckstorff junior, n. d. 32 p. 15½ᶜᵐ.
First performed at Stuttgart, Hoftheater, November 7, 1798. SCHATZ 11294

Der **geizige**. Tr. of Anfossi's L'avaro.

Die **geizigen in der falle**. Tr. of Schuster's Gli avari in trappola.

Die **gekroente treue**. A. T. of Keiser's La fedeltà coronata.

Das **gelaechter des Democritus**. Tr. of Pistocchi's Le risa di Democrito.

Geld ist die loosung. Tr. of Paër's L'oro fa tutto.

La **Gelidaura**. Drama per musica da rappresentarsi nel famosissimo Teatro Grimani di S. Giovanni e Paolo, l'anno 1692 . . .

Venetia, Girolamo Albizzi, 1692. 67 p. 15½ᶜᵐ.
Three acts. Dedication by Lovigi Carenpi, dated Venice, January 12, 1692, argument, scenario, and notice to the reader, in which "Francesco **Quesnda**, maestro della Capella Reale di Sicilia" is mentioned as the composer, and the text attributed to the pen "di un cavalier" since deceased, but reduced "all' uso di questa città." The name of the author is unknown to Schatz. SCHATZ 8525

La **gelosa di se stessa**. A. T. of Rust's L'amor bizzaro.

La **gelosia**. Dramma giocoso per musica da rappresentarsi nel Teatro Grimani di S. Samuele l'autunno dell' anno 1765.

Venezia, Giorgio Fossati, n. d. 48 p. 17ᶜᵐ.
Three acts. Impresario's dedication, cast, name of Nicola **Logroscino** as composer ("musica nuova"), and note, "La poesia è nuova di un' autore bolognese," whose name is not known to Schatz. SCHATZ 5671

La **gelosia**, ballet. *See* Mortellari's Troja distrutta.

Gelosia e pazzia sono sorelle. Dramma giocoso per musica da rappresentarsi in Firenze l'autunno dell' anno 1784. Nel Nuovo Regio Teatro degl' Intrepidi detto La Palla a Corda . . .

Firenze, Stamperia Bonducciana, 1784. 56 p. 16ᶜᵐ.
Two acts. Cast and note: "La musica è di diversi celebri autori." Author not mentioned, and unknown to Schatz. With the opera was performed the ballet, "Le tuteur trompé o sia Il maestro di musica." SCHATZ 11335

Gelosia per gelosia, ballet. *See* Giordani's Fernando nel Messico.

Gelosia per gelosia. O. T. of Lorenzi's text Le fallaci apparenze.

Gelosia per gelosia, ballet. *See* Paisiello's Il re Teodoro in Venezia.

Le **gelosie d'Annetta e Fiorillo**, ballet. *See* Bosi's La figlia obbediente.

Le **gelosie di Diana e di Marte**. A. T. of Venere con Adone.

Le **gelosie di Pippo**. L. A. T. of Bianchi's La villanella rapita.

Le gelosie fortunate. Dramma giocoso per musica di Filippo Livigni da rappresentarsi nel nobile Teatro di San Samuele l'autunno dell' anno 1786.

Venezia, Modesto Fenzo, 1786. 80 p. 18ᶜᵐ.

Two acts. Cast, scenario, and name of Pasquale **Anfossi,** as composer. On p. 45 the argument of the "ballo primo Il Gonzalvo, ballo tragico pantomimo . . . [by] Antonio Muzzarelli," who was also responsible for the second ballet, "La cappriciosa umiliata." The composers of the music are not mentioned. SCHATZ 269

Le gelosie villane. Dramma giocoso per musica da rappresentarsi in Casale nel Teatro Sacchi nell' autunno dell' anno 1779 . . .

Casale, Giovanni Meardi, n. d. 4 p. l., 61 p. 14½ᶜᵐ.

Two acts. By Tommaso Grandi. Impresario's dedication dated Casale, Oct. 10, 1779, cast, scenario, and name of composer, Pasquale **Anfossi,** but not of librettist. The titles of the ballets were "Il Francese in Londra" and "Le serenate noturne," both by Regina. Composer of the music not mentioned. SCHATZ 280

Le gelosie villane. Dramma giocoso per musica del Signore Tommaso Grandi da rappresentarsi nel Piccolo Teatro di S. A. E. di Sassonia l'anno 1778.

Dresda, Stamperia elettorale, n. d. 133 p. 16ᶜᵐ.

Three acts. Scenario and name of Giuseppe **Sarti** as the composer. The text is somewhat different from the Naples version, where I, 3, opens with "A chi tocca di noi?" instead of "Tardi è pur, nè ho ancor trovato." German title-page, "Die eyfersucht der bauern," and text face Italian.

First performed, as indicated, January 14, 1778; at Venice, Teatro di S. Samuele, November, 1776. SCHATZ 9436

— **Le gelosie villane.** Cantata da rappresentarsi nel Teatro Nuovo in quest' anno 1784.

Napoli, n. publ., 1784. 52 p. 15ᶜᵐ.

Three acts. By Tommaso Grandi, who is not mentioned. Cast and name of Giuseppe **Sarti** as the composer. SCHATZ 9435

— **Le gelosie vilane.** Dramma giocoso per musica da rappresentarsi ne' Piccoli Teatri di S. M. il rè di Prussia. Messo in musica dal Sign. Sarti.

Berlino, Haude e Spener, 1791. 103 p. 15ᶜᵐ.

Three acts. Noticeably different from both Naples and Dresden, I, 3, beginning, for instance, in Berlin, "Misera condizion del nostro sesso." German title-page, "Eifersucht auf dem lande," and text face Italian.

First performed, as indicated, October 5, 1791; at Potsdam, Schloss theater, March 29, 1783. SCHATZ 9437

Le gelosie villane in Montefosco, ballet. *See* Martin y Soler's Vologeso.

Il geloso. Dramma giocoso per musica da rappresentarsi in Lisbona nel Teatro della rua dos Condes il carnovale dell' anno 1775.

[Lisbona], Stamperia reale, n. d. 94 p. 16ᶜᵐ.

Three acts. Dedicatory sonnet, cast, scenario, and names of Girolamo Tonioli as author, of Alberto Giuseppe Gomes da **Silva** as composer. SCHATZ 9880

Il geloso in cimento. Dramma giocoso per musica di Giovanni Bertati da rappresentarsi nel Teatro di San Samuele nell' autunno dell anno 1774. [vignette]

Venezia, Antonio Graziosi, 1774. 64 p. 17ᶜᵐ.

Three acts. Cast, scenario, and name of Pasquale **Anfossi** as composer.
First performed at Vienna, Burgtheater, May 25, 1774. SCHATZ 236

Il geloso in cimento—Continued.

— Die eifersucht auf der probe. Eine operette in drey aufzügen.
Nach dem Geloso in cimento von Pasqual Anfossi.

Gera, Heinrich Gottlieb Rothe, 1791. 80 p. 16½ᶜᵐ.

Three acts. By Johann Joachim Eschenburg, who is not mentioned.
First performed at Hamburg, Theater beim Gänsemarkt, January 12, 1781.

Schatz 237

Il geloso in cimento, ballet. *See* Bianchi's Le villanelle astute.

Il geloso in cimento, ballet. *See* Ferd. Rutini's Il matrimonio per
industria.

Il geloso schernito. Intermezzo per musica da rappresentarsi nel
Teatro Giustinian di S. Moisè. L'autunno dell' anno 1746.

Venezia, Modesto Fenzo, 1746. 16 p. 15ᶜᵐ.

Three parts. Neither **Pergolesi,** the composer, nor the author is mentioned. The
latter is unknown to Schatz.
First performed at Naples, Teatro di S. Bartolomeo, 1731 (Schatz). Schatz 7905

Il geloso senza rivale, ballet. *See* P. Guglielmi's L'impresa d'opera.

La gemma Ceraunia d'Ulissipone hora Lisbona. Drama
musicale per li felicissimi sponsali della S. R. Maesta di D. Pietro re
di Portogallo, con la Serenissima Maria Sophia prencipessa elettorale
palatina. Eshibito, per commando del Serenissimo Filippo Guglielmo
elettore palatino. Nella sua elettorale residenza di Heidelberga . . .

Heydelberga, Michaele Franz, 1687. 9 p. l., 161 p. 30ᶜᵐ.

Three acts. Dedication by the author, conte Nicolò Minato, argument, scenario.
The composer, Sebastiano **Moratelli,** is not mentioned. German half-title, "Das
edelgestein Ceraunia von Ulissipone jetzo Lisbona," title-page, "Das kleinod Ceraunia
von Ulissipone jetzo genannt Lisbona . . ." and text face Italian.
First performed, as indicated, July 1, 1687. ML 50.2.G25

Le generose gare tra Cesare e Pompeo. Drama per musica da
rappresentarsi nel famoso rinovato Teatro Vendramino di S. Salvatore l'anno 1686 . . .

Venetia, Francesco Nicolini, 1686. 71, [1] p. 13½ᶜᵐ.

Three acts. By Rinaldo Cialli, who signs the dedication. Notice to the reader,
with name of Domenico **Gabrieli** as the composer, argument, and scenario.

Schatz 3403

La generosità d'Alessandro ossia Apelle e Campaspe, ballet. *See*
Zingarelli's Il Pirro.

La generosità di Tiberio. Dramma per musica da rappresentarsi
nel Teatro Tron di S. Cassiano l'autuno dell' anno 1729 . . .

Venezia, Carlo Buonarrigo, 1729. 58, [1] p. 15ᶜᵐ.

Three acts. By conte Niccolò Minato, who is not mentioned. Publisher's dedica-
tion, argument, cast, scenario, and names of Santo **Lapis** as composer of acts I–II, of
Bortolo **Cordans** of act III. Minato's text was originally called "La prosperità di
Elio Sejano." Schatz 5431

La generosità politica. Dramma per musica da rappresentarsi nel
Teatro Grimani di San Samuele nella fiera dell' Ascensione dell'
anno 1736 . . .

Venezia, Marino Rossetti, 1736. 46 p. 15ᶜᵐ.

Three acts. By Domenico Lalli & Carlo Goldoni, according to Schatz, but by Goldoni alone according to Wiel. The text is the same as that of Goldoni's "Pisistrato"

La generosità politica—Continued.

but with arias like the substitute for I, 9 "Chi mai saper desia" which are not by Goldini. Domenico Lalli's dedication, argument, cast, scenario, and name of Giovanni Maria **Marchi** as the composer.   Schatz 5936

Il generoso perdono, ballet.   *See* Anfossi's La maga Circe.

Il generoso perdono, ballet.   *See* Cimarosa's I due supposti conti.

The **generous Free-mason:** or, The constant lady. With the humours of Squire Noodle, and his man Doodle. A tragi-comifarcical ballad opera. In three acts. With the musick prefix'd to each song. By the author of the Lover's opera.

London, J. Roberts, 1731.   2 p. l., 51, [1] p.   19½^{cm}.

Three acts. Dedication signed by "the author A Free Mason." He is known to have been William Rufus Chetwood. Largely a ballad opera, but some of the 25 airs have indication of their composer. Thus, airs 9 ("Tho' danger's allarm me"), 12 ("Oh! come to my arms"), and 25 ("By Masons art") are marked as composed, resp. set by Henry **Carey**; 14 ("Great Amurath all hearts obey") as by Mr. **Charke**; and 23 ("Be still, you monsters") and 24 ("Neptune from all ills") as by J. **Sheeles**. The last (unnumb.) p. contains publisher's proposals.

"Said to have been acted at Bartholomew Fair, 1731" (Squire); "acted for the third time at the Haymarket, January 1, 1731" (Genest).   ML 50.5.C4

Second copy. Longe 49

The **generous Portuguese.**   A. T. of The island princess.

La Geneviefa. Drama per musica cantato nelle vacanze del carnevale l'anno 1685. Da' Signori Convittori del Nobil Collegio Tolomei di Siena nell' aprimento del loro nuovo teatro . . .

Siena, Stăp. del Publ., n. d.   5 p. l., 62 p.   14^{cm}.

Three acts. Dedication by the convittori, dated Siena, February 1, 1685, argument, cast and note by "Gli attori del drama a chi legge" in which they say:

"Fù composto adattato alla musica perche dovendosi quest' anno la prima volta aprire il teatro di questo Nobil Convitto, ebbemo genio di onorarlo con qualche cosa di singolare, & ambimmo la gloria, che il Collegio Tolomei di Siena fosse il primo frà tanti che ne se conta l'Italia à dar trattenimento di musica sù le scene. Perciò frà gli attori, niuno ammettemmo che non fosse del numero de' convittori. L'aver potuto eseguire pensier sì nobile e un debito che ci corre col Sig. Girolamo Gigli che alle nostre richieste cōpose il drama . . . Il Sigr. Giuseppe Fabrini (**Fabbrini**), che ha data l'anima al verso con l'armonia della musica, e da cui apprìdiamo questo nobile divertimento vi dira, che solamente poche ore delle nostre ricreazioni abbiamo impiegata in esercitarci nel canto . . ."   ML 50.2.G29

Gengis-Kan. Dramma per musica da rappresentarsi nel Regio Teatro di Torino nel carnovale del 1777 . . .

Torino, Onorato Derossi, n. d.   viii, 56 p.   19^{cm}.

Three acts. Argument, cast, scenario, and name of Pasquale **Anfossi** as composer, but not of librettist, who is unknown to Schatz. On p. 49–55, description, with cast and argument, of the ballet, "Il rè pastore;" on p. 56, titles of the two other ballets, "Li due avari" and "Il matrimonio cinese." These ballets were (*see* p. vi) by Paolo Franchi, and the music was composed by Vittorio Amedeo Canavasso. Schatz 260

I geni riuniti, ballet.   *See* Caruso's Il matrimonio in commedia.

I geni riuniti, ballet.   *See* Gassmann's L'amore artigiano.

Le **génie Asouf,** ou Les deux coffrets, féerie mélo-dramatique, en prose et en deux actes, mêlée de pantomime, chants et danses; par le c^en Cuvelier; représentée, pour la première fois, à Paris, le 4 nivôse an 4, sur le Théâtre de la Cité; et remise en vendémiaire an 8, sur celui de l'Ambigu-comique. Deuxième édition.

Paris, A l'imprimerie a prix-fixe, an VIII. [1799–1800]. *23 p. 20^cm.*

Cast and dedication. A pasticcio, made up as indicated in the libretto from **Pleyel, Cherubini,** Othon Joseph **Vanderbroeck, Paisiello, Grétry, Monsigny, Kreutzer, Le Sueur.**

First performed, as indicated, December 25, 1795. SCHATZ 10591

Les **genies,** ballet représenté pour la premiere fois, par l'Academie royale de musique; le jeudy dix-huit octobre 1736.

[Paris], Jean Baptiste Christophe Ballard, 1736. xii, 38, [1] p. 24^cm.

Prologue and four entrées: "Les nymphes," "Les gnomes," "Les salamandres," "Les sylphes." Cast and Avis in which the author, Fleury (not mentioned), says: "Pour mieux meriter la curiosité du public, je fais paroître sur la scene une nouvelle Muse qui a mis cet opera en musique."

He means Mlle **Duval.** ML 52.2.G3

— Les **genies,** ballet représenté par l'Académie royale de musique l'an 1736. Paroles de Mr Fleuri, musique de Melle Duval. CXXVII opera.

n. i., n. d. 371–428 p. 14½^cm. (Recueil général des opéra, Paris, 1745, t. xvi.)

Detached copy. Prologue and entrées "Les nymphes," "Les gnomes ou L'amour ambitieux," "Les salamandres ou L'amour violent," "Les sylphes ou L'amour leger." Text preceded by same Avis. ML 48.R4

Les **genies du feu.** Entrée in Brassac's L'empire de l'amour.

Il **genio tutelare.** A. T. of the ballet La costanza premiata.

Il **Genserico.** Melodrama da rappresentarsi nel famoso Theatro Grimano à SS. Gio. e Paolo, l'anno 1669 . . .

Venetia, Francesco Nicolini, 1669. front., 80 p. 14^cm.

Three acts. By conte Niccolò Beregani, with publisher's dedication dated Venice, January 31, 1669, argument, and scenario. Neither the author nor the composer, Marc' Antonio **Cesti,** is mentioned. SCHATZ 1780

Gensericus. *See* Conradi's Der grosse koenig der afrikanischen Wenden . . .

Le **gentilhomme de campagne,** bouffonnerie dansée durant les Vendanges.

n. i., n. d. 7 p. 21½^cm.

Eight entrées, preceded by récit. Title page apparently wanting. Possibly danced in "Les Vendanges," comedy by Dancourt, September 30, 1694. Not recorded by Parfaict or De La Vallière. ML 52.2.G33

The **gentle shepherd,** a Scots pastoral comedy. By Allan Ramsay . . .

London, A. Miller, 1763. iv, 63, [5] p. 17^cm.

The [5] p. contain a glossary. Five acts. Dedication dated Edinburgh, June, 1725. Ballad comedy, the airs of the 21 songs being indicated by title.

First performed 1729 at Edinburgh. LONGE 69

The **gentle shepherd**—Continued.

— The **gentle shepherd**. A Scots pastoral comedy, As written by
Allan Ramsay. To which is added, a complete glossary . . .

London, George Cawthorn, 1796. front., 1 p. l., xi, [2], 14–120 p.
15ᶜᵐ. (J. Bell, British Theatre, London, 1791–1797, v. 25.)

At end the note: "This play was originally published June, 1725." The front.
represents Miss Leaks as Peggy and the 1 p. l. is an added engraved title page with a
scene from the play. It is dated January 9, 1795.

Ramsay's dedication of this ballad comedy to Susanna, countess of Eglinton,
dedicatory poem to her, signed *H. W.*, Ramsay's poem to Josiah Burchet.

PR 1241.B4

The **genuine Grub-street opera**. *See* The Welsh opera.

Georget et Georgette, opéra-comique en un acte. Répresenté pour
la premiere fois sur le Théâtre de l'Opéra comique de la foire Saint
Laurent, le 28 juillet 1761.

Avignon, Louis Chambeau, 1768. 28 p. 19ᶜᵐ.

Neither the author, Harney de Guerville, is mentioned, nor the composer, Charles
Guillaume **Alexandre**. YUDIN PQ

Gesaenge aus dem singspiele: Die **geplagten ehemaenner,** in zwey
aufzuegen, eine fortsetzung des singspiels Lilla. In musik gesezt von
Schak.

Hamburg, Joh. Matthias Michaelsen, 1792. 48 p. 15½ᶜᵐ.

By Schikaneder.

First performed at Hamburg, Theater beim Gänsemarkt, October 1, 1792; at
Vienna, Theater auf der Wieden, 1789, as "Der fall ist noch viel seltener oder Die
geplagten ehemänner." SCHATZ 9569

Der **geraubte eimer**. Tr. of Zingarelli's La secchia rapita.

Der **geraubte eymer**. Tr. of Salieri's La secchia rapita.

Die **gerechtfertigte liebe**. Tr. of Naumann's Amore giustificato.

Das **gerettete Troja**. A. T. of Joh. Ad. Hiller's Poltis.

Germanico. Drama per musica da rappresentarsi nel Regio Teatro
di Torino nel carnovale del 1744 alla presenza di Sua Maestà.

Torino, Pietro Giuseppe Zappata e figliuolo, n. d. 4 p. l., 63 p.
15½ᶜᵐ.

Three acts. By Niccolò Coluzzi. Argument, cast, scenario and name of composer, Andrea **Bernasconi,** but not of librettist. Alessio Rasetti is mentioned as
composer of the ballet music. SCHATZ 865

Germanico. Dramma per musica da rappresentarsi nel nobilissimo Teatro Venier in San Benedetto il carnovale dell' anno 1797.

Venezia, Modesto Fenzo, 1797. 45 p. 17½ᶜᵐ.

Two acts. Author not mentioned, and unknown to Schatz. Argument, cast,
scenario, and name of Gaetano **Marinelli** as the composer.

First performed on February 4, 1797, as indicated. SCHATZ 3955

Il **Germanico.** Drama per musica da rappresentarsi nel famosimo Teatro Grimani di S. Gio. Grisostomo. Nel carnevale dell' anno MDCCXVI . . .

> *Venezia, Marino Rossetti, MDCCXI.* [!] *2 front., 60 p. 15ᶜᵐ.*

The title is not on the title page, but on the second front. Three acts. By conte Pietro Giorgio Barziza, who is not mentioned. Impresario's dedication dated Venice, January 24, 1716, argument, notice to the reader, with name of Carlo Francesco **Pol-laroli** as the composer, cast, and scenario. SCHATZ 8294

Il **Germanico al Reno.**   Festa teatrale.

> *G. A. Moniglia, Poesie drammatiche, seconda parte, Firenze, Cesare e Francesco Bindi, 1690, p. [217]–293. 24ᶜᵐ.*

Three acts. Scenario, argument. No composer or performance mentioned. Not recorded by Schatz. ML 49.A2M7

Germanico in Germania.   O. T. of Coluzzi's text Arminio.

Germanico in Germania. Dramma per musica da rappresentarsi nel nobilissimo Teatro delle Dame il carnevale dell' anno 1770 . . .

> *Roma, Lorenzo Corradi, 1770. 60 p. 16ᶜᵐ.*

Three acts. By Nicola Coluzzi, who is not mentioned. Dedication, argument, scenario, cast, and name of Carlo **Monza** as the composer. According to the argument, this is a retouched version of the text written originally for Rome, 1732. SCHATZ 6609

Germanico in Germania. Drama per musica di Niccolò Coluzzi. Da rappresentarsi nella Sala degl' illustrissimi Signori Capranica nel carnevale dell' anno 1732 . . .

> *Roma, Antonio de' Rossi, n. d. 64, [1] p. 15½ᶜᵐ.*

Three acts. Impresario's dedication, argument, cast, scenario, and name of Nicolà Antonio **Porpora** as composer. At end, the substitute scene, II, 11, "O del mio caro ben voci gradite." SCHATZ 8358

Germanico in Germania, ballet. *See* Rossetti's Olimpiade.

Il **Germanico Marte.** Drama per musica, da rappresentarsi nel Teatro di corte . . . Per ordine di S. A. R. Monsignor Francesco Antonio, arcivescovo e prencipe di Salisburgo . . . Musica del Sig. Antonio Caldara . . .

> *Salisburgo, Giovanni Gioseppe Mayr, n. d. 100, [3] p. 15ᶜᵐ.*

Three acts and licenza. By unknown author (Schatz). Argument and scenario. On p. 38–43, 69–72, the intermezzo, in two parts, of "Grespilla e Fanfarone," by unknown author. SCHATZ 1482

Germanico sul Reno. Drama per musica da rappresentarsi nel famosissimo Teatro Vendramino di San Salvatore l'anno MDCLXXVI. Di Giulio Cesare Corradi . . .

> *Venetia, Francesco Nicolini, 1676. front., 68 p. 15½ᶜᵐ.*

Three acts. Author's dedication, dated Venice, January 27, 1676, argument, scenario, and name of Giovanni **Legrenzi** as the composer.   SCHATZ 5536
Second copy. ML 48.M2 O

Germanicus, roemischer general. A. T. of Grünewald's Die errettete unschuld.

Germondo. Dramma di tre atti per musica. Rappresentato per la prima volta in Venezia il carnovale dell' anno MDCCXXXIX.

Carlo Goldoni, Opere teatrali, Venezia, Zatta e figli, 1788–95, v. 36, [67]–101 p. 18½^{cm}.

Not recorded by Schatz, Wiel, or Allacci. Traetta's opera was later.   PQ

Gerone tiranno di Siracusa. Drama per musica da rappresentarsi nel Teatro del Falcone di Genova nell' autunno 1700 . . .

Genova, Gio. Batt. Scionico, n. d.   4 p. l., 88 p.   14½^{cm}.

Three acts. By Aurelio Aurelj, who is not mentioned. Publisher's dedication, dated Genova, November 3, 1700, argument, cast, scenario, and name of Carlo Francesco **Gasparini** as the "maestro di capella," or composer.   SCHATZ 3588

Gerone tiranno di Siracusa. Drama per musica da rappresentarsi nel Teatro di S. Bartolomeo il dì 19. novembre di questo corrente anno 1727. Festeggiandosi il nome glorioso di S. M. C., e C. Elisabetta Cristina imperatrice regnante . . .

Napoli, Francesco Ricciardo, 1727.   60 p.   14½^{cm}.

Three acts. According to Schatz an altered version of Aurelio Aureli's "Hierone, tiranno di Siracusa." Dedication, argument, scenario, casts of the opera and of the three intermezzi "Porsugnacco e Grilletta (p. 22–26, 41–45, 54–58) and name of Joh. Ad. **Hasse** as composer of opera and intermezzi.   ML 50.2.G3H2

Gerusalemme distrutta. Dramma sacro per musica da rappresentarsi nel Regio Teatro di via della Pergola la quadragesima del MDCCXCIV . . .

Firenze, Stamperia Albizziniana, 1794.   39 p.   16^{cm}.

Two acts. Brief argument, cast, and names of Antonio Simone Sografi as author, of Nicola Antonio **Zingarelli** as composer.   SCHATZ 11244

Das gespenst, eine operette in zwey aufzuegen von Ludwig Ysenburg von Buri.

Neuwied, Gehra und Haupt, 1789.   56 p.   17^{cm}.

Dedicatory poem. Text and music by the above.
First performed at Neuwied, Hoftheater, 1789.   SCHATZ 1421

Das gespenst mit der trommel. Ein deutsches komisches singspiel in zwey aufzuegen, nach Goldoni's Conte Caramella frey bearbeitet. Die musik ist vom herrn von Dittersdorf.

Oels, Samuel Gottlieb Ludwig, n. d.   79 p.   15½^{cm}.

Author unknown to Schatz.
First performed at Oels, Hoftheater, August 16, 1794.   SCHATZ 2591

Der gestuerzte und wieder erhoehte Nebucadnezar, koenig zu Babylon, unter dem grossen propheten Daniel in einem singe-spiel auf dem grossen Hamburgischen Schau-platze vorgestellet im jahr 1704.

Theatralische, galante und geistliche gedichte von Menantes [Christ. Fr. Hunold], Hamburg, 1706, p. [137]–196.   16½^{cm}.

Three acts. In prefatory remarks Menantes says (on p. 136):
Zwar gestehe gern, dass die music des herrn capell-meisters Mons. Kaeysers [Reinhard **Keiser**] ein ungemeines zu ihrer approbation gethan; allein ohne der composition eines solchen vortreflichen virtuosen wuerde auch schwerlich eine zeile von meiner arbeit auf dem hiesigen theatro habe absingen lassen. In dem es zuweilen ein guter verfasser mit einem ungeschichten componisten, wie ein geschickter musicus mit einem unverstaendigen verss-macher entgelten muss."   ML49.A2H9

Die **getheilte liebe.** A. T. of Mattheson's Die geheimen begebenheiten Henrico IV, Koenigs von Castilien und Leon.

Die **getreue braut.** Tr. of P. Guglielmi's La sposa fedele.

Der **getreue freund Hercules und Theseus.** A. T. of Graupner's
Il fido amico.

Die **getreuen Oesterreicher,** oder Das aufgeboth. Ein volks-
stueck mit gesang in drey aufzuegen, fuer die K. K. priv. Marinellische
schaubühne bearbeitet von Karl Friedrich Hensler. Nebst einem
mit dem stueck verbundenen militaerischen kontratanz von Johann
Sartory. Die musik ist von Wenzel Mueller, kapellmeister.
  Wien, Joseph Kamesina, 1797. 92 p. 16ᶜᵐ.
  Dedication by the author to Prince Ferdinand, herzog zu Wuertemberg und Teck.
  First performed, as indicated, October 4, 1797.   SCHATZ 6929

Die **gezwungene bestaendigkeit** oder Die listige rache des Sueno.
See Keiser's La costanza sforzata.

La **ghinghetta,** ballet. *See* Fabrizj's opera L'amore per interesse.

La **ghinghetta,** ballet. *See* Tarchi's L'impostura poco dura.

Giaccona, ballet. *See* Rossetti's Olimpiade.

Den **giaerrige.** Tr. of Anfossi's L'avaro.

Gianguir.
  *Apostolo Zeno, Poesie drammatiche, Venezia, 1744, t. ii, p. [183]–
  280. 19ᶜᵐ.*
  Five acts and licenza. Argument. No composer is mentioned. In the "Catalogo," at end of t. x, date and place of first ed. are given as Vienna, 1724. (First performed November 4, music by *Caldara.*)   ML49.A2Z3

— **Gianguir.** Pubblicato per la prima volta in Vienna 1724.
  *Apostolo Zeno, Poesie drammatiche, Orleans, 1785–86, t. vi, p. 79–168.
  21ᶜᵐ.*
  Five acts and licenza. Argument. No composer is mentioned.   ML49.A2Z4

Gianguir. Dramma per musica da rappresentarsi in Copenhagen
il carnevale dell' anno 1755.—Janguir . . .
  Kiφbenhavn, Andreas Hartvig Godiche, n. d. 129 p. 15½ᶜᵐ.
  Three acts. Cast, argument, name of Apostolo Zeno as author, and note: "La
  musica è di diversi autori." Danish text faces Italian.   SCHATZ 11337

Gianguir. O. T. of Caldara's Pharao und Joseph.

Gianguir. Dramma per musica da rappresentarsi nel famoso Teatro
di Grimani di S. Benedetto, il carnovale dell' anno MDCCLX.
  Venezia, Antonio Comino, 1760. 57 p. 14½ᶜᵐ.
  Five acts. By Apostolo Zeno (not mentioned). Argument, cast, scenario, and
  name of the composer, Vincenzo Legrenzio **Ciampi.**
  First performed Dec. 26, 1759, as indicated.   SCHATZ 1881

Gianguir. Dramma per musica da rappresentarsi nel Teatro Tron di S. Cassano l'anno MDCCXXIX . . .

Venezia, Marino Rossetti, n. d. 59 p. 14½^cm.

Three acts. By Apostolo Zeno, who is not mentioned. Impresario's dedication, dated Venice, September 26, 1728, argument, scenario, cast, and name of the composer, Geminiano **Giacomelli**.　　　　　　　　　　　　　　　　SCHATZ 3812

Gianguir. Dramma per musica da rappresentarsi nel famosissimo Teatro Grimani in San Gio. Grisostomo nel carnovale dell' anno 1738 . . .

Venezia, Marino Rossetti, n. d. 60 p. 14½^cm.

Three acts. By Apostolo Zeno, who is not mentioned. Impresario's dedication, argument, cast, scenario, and name of Giovanni Antonio **Giai** as the composer.
　　　　　　　　　　　　　　　　　　　　　　　　　　SCHATZ 3814

La **Giannetta** o sia L'incognita perseguitata. L. T. of Anfossi's L'incognita perseguitata.

Giannina e Bernadone. Dramma giocoso per musica da rappresentarsi nel Teatro di S. A. E. di Sassonia.

Dresda, n. publ., 1785. 135 p. 16½^cm.

Two acts, with name of the composer, Domenico **Cimarosa**. German title-page "Hannchen und Bernardon," and text face Italian. The author, Filippo Livigni, is not mentioned.

First performed at Dresden, January 4, 1785; at Venice, Teatro di S. Samuele, fall of 1781.　　　　　　　　　　　　　　　　　　　SCHATZ 1926

— **Giannina, e Bernadone.** Commedia per musica da rappresentarsi nel Teatro de' Fiorentini in quest' anno 1795.

Napoli, n. publ., 1795. 48 p. 15^cm.

Two acts. By Filippo Livigni, who is not mentioned. Cast and name of Domenico **Cimarosa** as the composer.　　　　　　　　　　　ML 50.2.G33C3

Giannina e Bernadone ossia Il geloso sincerato, ballet. *See* Cimarosa's Artemisia.

The **giant's causeway.** A. T. of Arnold's Harlequin Teague.

La **giardiniera brillante.** Intermezzo per musica a quattro voci. Da rappresentarsi in Lisbona nel Teatro della rua dos Condes nell' estate dell' anno 1773.

[Lisbona], Stamperia reale, n. d. 72 p. 16^cm.

Two parts. Author not mentioned, and unknown to Schatz. Cast, scenario, and name of Giuseppe **Sarti** as the composer. With the opera were performed (composers of the music not mentioned) Vincislao de Rossi's ballet, "Le due sultane rivali" and Alessandro Guglielmi's "Li pescatori."

First performed at Rome, January 3, 1768, Teatro Valle.　　SCHATZ 9469

La **giardiniera contessa.** L. T. of Latilla's La finta cameriera

Il **giardiniere convinto da Amore,** ballet. *See* Galuppi's L'amante di tutte.

Il **giardino delle Tuillerie in Parigi,** ballet. *See* Cimarosa's Circe.

Giasone. Drama musicale, del D. Hiacinto Andrea Cicognini, Academico Instancabile. Da rappresentarsi in Venetia nel Theatro di San Cassano nell' anno 1649 . . .

Venetia, Giacomo Batti, 1649. 118 p. (incl. front.). 14½ cm.

Three acts, with prologue. Scenario, a notice to the reader, the argument, an "Applauso poetico . . . *Ode* di Aurelio Aureli, Ac. Ins.," a "Sonetto" by Bort. Castore, and the author's dedication, dated January 5, 1648 (1649 *n. st.*). Pietro Francesco **Cavalli,** the composer, is not mentioned. II, 4 begins, "Per qual nuovo vigore." SCHATZ 1751

— Il **Giasone.** Dramma musicale del dottor Giacinto Andrea Cicognini Fiorentino.

Venetia, Niccolò Pezzana, 1664. 108 p. 14 cm.

Three acts, with prologue. Argument, notice to the reader, and scenario, but without name of the composer, **Cavalli.** The text seems to be the same as in the 1649 ed.

Replica first performed at Venice, Teatro di S. Cassiano, February 23, 1666. SCHATZ 1722

— Il **Giasone.** Drama per musica di D. Hiacinto Andrea Cicognini . . . da rappresentarsi nel Teatro di San Cassano l'anno 1666 . . .

Venetia, Camillo Bortoli, 1666. 90 p. 14 cm.

Prologue and three acts. Publisher's dedication, dated Venice, February 23, 1666, argument, scenario, and notice to the reader, from which it appears that "Il Giasone" was revived and substituted in a hurry for an opera called "La Semiramide," text by Moniglia, and which was actually in preparation. **Cavalli** is not mentioned. II, 4 begins, "Per qual nuovo vigore," and the third act has only nineteen scenes. "Sotto il tremulo ciel" is III, 1, as in the "Novello Giasone," instead of III, 2, and, as in that version, the character of "Rosmira giardiniera" is absent. ML 50.2.G36 C1

— Il **Giasone.** Drama musicale di D. Giacinto Andrea Cicognini Academico Instancabile. Di nuovo riveduto, e con aggiunte ristampato . . .

Milano, Gioseffo Marelli, n. d. 96 p. 14 cm.

Prologue and three acts. Text preceded by the Argument; a sonnet, "In lode del Sig. dottor Giacinto Andrea Cicognini. Nuovo auttore del bellissimo Giasone l'anno 1650," by Giulio Strozzi; and dedication, by Emanuel di Meschita, in which he says:

"Se mai alcuna dramma ha havuto credito, ed applauso pel suo utilizzante costume, uno n'è il Giasone del Sig. Cicognini, il quale, dovendo di nuovo, uscir dalle stampe, e scena fare di se stesso . . ."

The composer, **Cavalli,** is not mentioned. II, 4 begins, "Effetti singolari," and there are other striking differences between this ed. and that of 1649. For instance, the last act now has twenty scenes instead of twenty-two. "Sotto il tremulo ciel," as in the "Novello Giasone," is III, 1 instead of III, 2, and, as there, the character of "Rosmira giardiniera" has been dropped. I conjecture that this Milan edition is even later than the Rome "Il novello Giasone." ML 50.2.G36C2

— Il **novello Giasone.** Dramma per musica recitato nel Teatro Novo di Roma in Tordinona l'anno 1671 . . .

Roma, il success. al Mascardi, 1671. 6 p. l., 80 p. 13½ cm.

According to Schatz, the opera was actually revived at Rome during the carnival of 1671; but Wotquenne, in the Brussels catalogue, says that, according to Ademollo, the revival did not take place. A later issue (in three acts, with prologue and argument) of Cicognini's "Giasone," published by Bartolomeo Lupardi, who says in his dedication, dated January 17, 1671, of this libretto:

"Esce presentemente da miei torchi, e ch'havrà à recitarsi ne' giorni correnti nel nuovo theatro."

The Rome version is considerably altered from the original. For purposes of identification, it may be noted that the character of "Rosmina giardiniera" does not appear in the "Novello Giasone." Its third act has nineteen instead of twenty-two scenes, the first of which beginning, "Sotto'l tremulo ciel," which had been III, 2. II, 4 begins, "Qual 'ardir, qual valore." On p. 53–54 of the Rome version there is an "Intermedio. SATIRO & AMORE." SCHATZ 1750

Giasone e Medea, ballet. *See* Andreozzi's L'Arbace.

Giasone e Medea, ballet. *See* Borghi's L'Olimpiade.

Giasone e Medea, ballet. *See* Giordani's Osmane.

Giasone e Medea, ballet. *See* Martin y Soler's L'arbore di Diana.

La Gierusalemme liberata. Drama da rappresentarsi in musica nel famosissimo Teatro Grimano di SS. Gio. e Paulo l'anno 1687.   Di Giulio Cesare Corradi . . .

> *Venetia, Francesco Nicolini, 1687.   71, [1] p.   14^{cm}.*

Three acts. Author's dedication, notice to the reader with name of Carlo **Pallavicino** as the composer, and scenario.
First performed in January, 1687, as indicated.   SCHATZ 7725

I giganti abbattuti.   *See* M. Curzio.

La gigantomachie.   A. T. of Piron's text Le mariage de Momus.

Il Gige in Lidia. Drama per musica del dottore Giovambattista Neri da recitarsi nel Teatro Formagliari l'anno 1683 . . .

> *Bologna, per l'erede del Barbieri, n. d.   60 p.   13^{cm}.*

Three acts. Author's dedication and notice to the reader with the name of Domenico **Gabrieli** as composer, imprimatur, argument, and scenario.   SCHATZ 3398

Gilles, garçon peintre z'amoureux-t-et rival. Parade, représentée pour la premiere fois sur le Théâtre de la Foire S. Germain, le 2 mars 1758.

> *Paris, N. B. Duchesne, 1758.   48 p.   16½^{cm}.*

One act. Cast and dedicatory poem by the author, Poinsinet le jeune. The composer, Jean Benjamin de **La Borde**, is not mentioned.   SCHATZ 5348

Ginevra. Dramma per musica da rappresentarsi nel Teatro di San Samuelle [!] l'autunno dell' anno MDCCLIII.

> *Venezia, Angiolo Geremia, n. d.   43 p.   15^{cm}.*

Three acts. Argument, cast, scenario, and name of composer, Ferdinando Giuseppe **Bertoni,** but not of librettist, Antonio Salvi.   SCHATZ 913

Ginevra. Dramma per musica da rappresentarsi nel Teatro di San Samuele nella Fiera dell' Ascensione l'anno 1733 . . .

> *Venezia, Marino Rossetti, n. d.   59 p.   15½^{cm}.*

Three acts by Antonio Salvi with modifications (marked with an asterisk), dedicatory preface by the impresario, Domenico Lalli, notice to the reader, cast, name of the composer, Giuseppe **Sellitti,** and scenario.
First performed on May 13, 1733, as indicated.   SCHATZ 9826

La Ginevra degli Almieri, ballet. *See* Cimarosa's L'apprensivo raggirato.

Ginevra di Scozia, ballet. *See* Gnecco's L'indolente.

Ginevra di Scozia, ballet. *See* Mayr's Lodoiska.

La Ginevra infanta di Scozia. Dramma per musica da rappresentarsi in Ferrara l'anno 1690 nel Teatro del Sig. Co. Pinamonte Bonacossi . . .

> *Ferrara, Bernardino Pomatelli, n. d.   72 p.   14^{cm}.*

Three acts. Dedication signed by the author, Giulio Cesare Grazzini, argument, scenario, and notice to the reader about "questo nuovo dramma," and with name of Giovanni Battista **Bassani** as composer.   SCHATZ 632

La **Giocasta.** Drama musicale.

G. A. Moniglia, Poesie drammatiche, seconda parte, Firenze, Cesare e Francesco Bindi, 1690, p. [81]–148. 24ᶜᵐ.

Three acts. Argument with remark:

"Questo componimento fu chiesto dal Sig. cavaliere Antonio [Marc' Antonio] **Cesti** al serenissimo principe Mattias di Toscana, e l'A. S. mostrò all' autore desiderio di gratificare il Sig. cavaliere Cesti, laonde ne venne servita; ma partendosi poi il Sig. cavaliere dal servizio di S. M. C. e trattenendosi in Firenze alla corte di Toscana, si stmarrì l'occasione di farlo comparire sù le scene, la quale (mancando la vita del Sig. Cesti) non s'è mai ritrovata, riserbatasegli non di meno tra le sue disavventure la gran fortuna di comparire presentemente alle stampe . . ."

Accordingly, Cesti cannot have composed this opera, which is not mentioned as extant by Eitner, after 1669, nor before 1666, the years of his activity at Vienna.

ML 49.A2M7

Giocasta. Drama musicale da rappresentarsi nel Nuovo Teatro del serenissimo elettor Palatino nel carnovale dell' anno MDCXCVI.

Dusseldorf, Gio. Christiano Schleuter, n. d. Unpaged. 18½ᶜᵐ.

Three acts. Argument and scenario. German title-page, "Giocasta," and text face Italian. At the end of the libretto is a notice to the reader, in which he is informed that the text is by Gio. Andrea Moniglia with alterations and substitute verses, that it was composed "mit kuenstlich einstimmender music des hr. Joh. Ugo Vilderer [Johann Hugo **Wilderer**], geistreichen ubereinstimmungen ["spiritose sinfonie"!] des hr. Georgio **Krafft,**" and that the text "damit auch ermelte Giocasta denen so in der italianischen sprache nicht erfahren ihre anmuth nicht gaentzlich vorenthalten moege" was translated by the "raht und referendarius Godfrid Rulant . . . ins teutsche." Schatz 11014

Giocasta, regina d'Armenia. Drama per musica del Signor dottor Gio. Andrea Moniglia Fiorentino riformata all' uso di Venetia per il Teatro Zane à S. Moisè l'anno MDCLXXVII . . .

Venetia, Frencesco Nicolini, 1677. 60 p. 13½ᶜᵐ.

Three acts. Publisher's dedication dated Venice, December 16, 1676, argument, scenario, and notice to the effect that after Moniglia's death the text

"pervenne in mano ad amico suo parzialissimo, che lo destinò à far pompa di se medesimo in loco più riguardevole, col fine di non renderlo disuguale agl' altri parti di sua felicissima penna, che in più tēpi, & in molto numero hanno saputo acquistarsi gl'applausi e l'ammiratione de theatri più cospicui d'Europa. La congiontura non lo permise . . . Sappi che per addattarlo al genio & all' uso di questo cielo, non meno che alla ristrettezza del loco, è stato necessario abbreviarlo in modo, che si sono tralasciati non solo molti versi, e forse de più belli, mà le scene intiere, & le parti istesse, col riguardo però dovuto fatto osservare à tutto potere dall' amico suo sudetto di sempre valersi di versi dello stesso autore, oltre alcuni poche per la necessità d'unirne il sentimento aggiustato ne luochi concisi. Alcune arie però che vi restano aggiùte per maggiore abbellimento come parti per sè stesse disgiunte dall' essenza del drama si sono fatte scrivere dalla peña non men vaga che erudita del Sig. Giacomo Castoreo . . . e le vedrai nella stampa contrasegnate con li versi ancora con questo segno ,,."

Accordingly, for instance, the entire sixth scene, first act, "Ogni bravo / Sen vadi alle mura," was added by Castoreo. The composer, Carlo **Grossi,** is not mentioned. Schatz 4217

Il **giocator fortunato.** A. T. of Piccinni's L'astratto.

Il **giocatore.** L. T. of Il marito giogatore e la moglie bacchettona.

Il **giocatore,** ballet. *See* Anfossi's Il curioso indiscreto.

Il **giocatore,** ballet. *See* Mortellari's Le astuzie amorose.

Il **giocatore burlato.** A. T. of Pietro Guglielmi's La contadina superba.

I **giochi olimpici** overo Che fingendo si prova un vero affetto. Drama destinato per lo giorno del nome della serenissima Anna elettrice Palatina . . . Posto in musica dal Sig. D. Sebastiano Moratelli . . . Dusseldorf li 26. luglio 1694.

n. pl., Per Gio. Christiano Schleuter, stampatore, n. d. Unpaged. 19cm.

Three acts with an "Intermedio allusivo al giorno del nome . . ." between second and third act. Dedication signed by the author, Giorgio Maria Raparini.

SCHATZ 6628

Il **gioco del pichetto.** *See* Il giuoco di picchetto.

Gioconda, ballet. *See* Cimarosa's Artaserse.

Giorgio principe della Servia, ballet. *See* Portugal's Gli Orazi e I Curiazi.

Il **giorno di notte.** Drama per musica. Da rappresentarsi nel famosissimo Teatro Grimani in S. Gio. Grisostomo l'anno 1704. Di Matteo Noris.

Venezia, Marino Rossetti, 1704. 70 p. 14cm.

Three acts. Notice to the reader and scenario. The composer, Carlo Francesco **Pollaroli,** is not mentioned. SCHATZ 8295

Il **giorno di salute** ovvero Demetrio in Athene. Dramma per musica da rappresentarsi nei giorni del carnovale dell' anno 1697. Per comando del serenissimo elettore Palatino.

Dusseldorf, Gio. Christiano Schleuter, n. d. Unpaged. 18½cm.

Three acts. German title-page, "Der tag des heyls oder Demetrius in Athen," and text face Italian. Argument, scenario, and notice to the reader, which reads:
"Fu questo componimento poetico destinato dalla Regia Magnificenza del serenissimo elettor Palatino mio signore per solennizzare il giorno natale della serenissima elettrice consorte . . . Ma perchè cade questo felicissimo giorno nei giorni più caldi d'Agosto, tempo mal a proposito per i chiusi teatri, fù perciò stimato molto più proprio di aprirne, ò per dir meglio, farne nascere uno in campagna sù le rive del Reno, e nel Reno medesimo, con tanta prestezza fù fabbricato; dove comparve a meraviglia bene la grandezza del animo di chi l'ordinò, e l'arte meravigliosa di chi l'eseguì, riuscendo sopra d'ogni credenza la festa vaga, e magnifica. Fù egli per cio riserbato a comparir sù la scena in questo tempo del carnevale. Dove se fà pompa di qualche vaghezza, sappi o lettore, che tutta la gloria si deve all' indefessa applicazione, e buon gusto dell' illustriss. Signore baron di Demanstein, cameriere e gran falconiere de S. A. E. P. . . . Parte ancor, se ne deve al Sign. Gio. Hugo **Wilderer** organista di questo Serenissimo Elettore, il quale se ben di lingua e di nazione tedescha possiede non di meno tutta l'arte di far comparir sù le scene con tutta la loro forza, e gentilezza le nostre muse toscane. L'ariette per i balli furono invenzione del Signore Giorgio Crafft [Krafft]: e fù studio di Mons. Rodier l'intreccio, e la vaghezza di essi; che anno tanto di parte nell' adornamento dell' opera. E la bella, e capricciosa disposizione delle scene è tutta gloria del pennello del Sign. Antonio Bernardi . . ."
It follows from this preface that Schatz is entirely mistaken if he attributes the text to baron Demanstein, who was merely the manager. SCHATZ 11015

La **giovane scaltra.** A. T. of Paisiello's Amore ingegnoso.

Giovanna d'Arco o sia La pulcella d'Orleans. Dramma serio per musica del cittadino Sografi da rappresentarsi nel Teatro La Fenice l'estate dell' anno 1797.

Venezia, Stamperia Valvaseniz, n. d. 46 p. 17cm.

Three acts. Cast and name of the composer, Gaetano **Andreozzi.** The opera was followed by Zemira e Azor, ballo pantomimo in quattro atti, composto dal cittadino Francesco Clerico. La musica sarà del sudetto autore" (p. 43–46 of libretto, with argument).
First performed at Vicenza, Teatro Eretenio, summer of 1789. SCHATZ 196

Il **Giove di Creta.** Dramma giocoso per musica da rappresentarsi nel nobile Teatro Tron di San Cassiano nell' autunno dell' anno 1776 . . .

Venezia, Gio. Battista Casali, 1776. 62 p. 17½ᶜᵐ.

Three acts. Author not mentioned, and unknown to Schatz. Dedication, cast, scenario, and name of Giacomo **Rust** as the composer.   Schatz 9171

Giove in Argo. Melodrama pastorale . . . da representarsi in musica nella Sala del Ridotto in Dresda, l'autunno del 1717.

Dresda, Giovan Riedel, n. d. Unpaged. 19ᶜᵐ.

Three acts. Dedication signed by the author, Antonio Maria Luchini, and dated Dresda, novembre, 1717, argument, cast (with changes after libretto had been printed on slip pasted over the original cast), and name of Antonio **Lotti** as composer. French title page, "Jupiter en Argos," and text face Italian. The text of the opera is followed, also in Italian and French, by the text of "Vespetta e Milo," the three "Intermedi cantati . . . Dresde, che'z Jean Riedel, 1717," and this notice to the reader:

"La musica del primo e del secondo intermezzo e composizione del Signore cavaliere Alessandro **Scarlati.** La musica del terzo intermezzo e composizione del Signore Francesco **Conti** o Contino, maestro di capella di Sua Maestà Cesarea.

"Li versi del primo e secondo intermezzo sono fatti intieramente dall' illustre penna del Signore Silvio Stampiglia, poeta di Sua Maestà Cesarea, tutte le opere di questo celebre poeta sono come li quadri di Tiziano, e di Vandec [!] . . . Il terzo intermezzo e composizione del Signore baron Francesco Ballerini . . . Le arie che sono tradote in francese, di Vespetta e di Milo, si possono cantare come le italiane. Adio."

These intermezzi do not seem to be mentioned in Dent's Scarlatti biography. For a separate ed. of the libretto, *see* under title (Schatz 9522). The date of first performance is given by Schatz for these intermezzi and the opera as October 25, 1717. This would seem to contradict the inference from the date of the dedication.
          Schatz 5719

The **gipsies.** A comick opera, in two acts. As it is performed at the Theatre-Royal in the Hay-Market.

London, T. Cadell, 1778. 2 p. l., 30, [2] p. 21ᶜᵐ.

The [2] p. contain book-lists of the publisher.

Cast. Neither the author, Charles Dibdin, is mentioned, nor Samuel **Arnold,** the composer. The piece is based on Favart's "La Bohémienne."

First performed August 3, 1778, as indicated.   Longe 102

Il **giramondo.** Intermezzi da rappresentarsi in Venezia nel carnovale 1749 nel Teatro di S. Cassiano.

Venezia, Modesto Fenzo, 1749. front., 18 p. 15ᶜᵐ.

Two parts. Cast. Neither the author (unknown to Schatz) is mentioned, nor Leonardo **Leo,** the composer. (Leo does not list this opera.)   Schatz 5561

Il **Girello.** Drama per musica da rappresentarsi nel loco ove era il Theatro à San Moise l'anno MDCLXXXII.

Venetia, Gio. Francesco Valvasense, 1682. 59 p. 14ᶜᵐ.

Pages 3–4, with the dedication are missing.

Three acts. Argument, scenario, and notice to the reader, which reads in part:

"Hora ti presento una bizzaria dramatica, dico una bizzaria, perche, ell'è una terza entità partecipante del Comico e de Drammatico. Quest' è il Girello parto d'ingegnosissima penna, altre volte veduto campeggiare con indicibile applauso sù le scene d'Italia. Vi troverai in esso qualche alterazione nella nova tessitura del verso, mà non però variera il suo essere sostantiale. Il tutto hò fatto per conformarmi allo stile corrente, che sempre inclina alla novità. Sò, che il genio di Venetià è tutto capricio; ama assaissimo le bizzarie . . ."

Neither the original author, Filippo Acciajuoli, is mentioned, nor Francesco Antonio **Pistocchi,** who according to Schatz was the composer. The opera was performed by wax figures on the stage with the singers behind the scenes. Schatz 8198

La **Gismonda.**   Commedia per musica di Antonio Palomba Napoletano da rappresentarsi nel Teatro de' Fiorentini nella primavera di
quest' anno 1750.

Napoli, Domenico Langiano, 1750.   72 p.   15ᶜᵐ.

Three acts.   Cast and name of the composer, Gioacchino **Cocchi.**   SCHATZ 2039

Gismondo rè di Polonia.   Dramma per musica da rappresentarsi
nel Teatro detto delle Dame nel carnevale dell' anno 1727 . . .

Roma, Bernabò, n. d.   76 p.   15ᶜᵐ.

Three acts.   Author not mentioned and unknown to Schatz.   Argument, cast,
scenario, and name of Leonardo **Vinci** as the composer.   SCHATZ 10747

Il **giudice, e padre,** ballet.   *See* Borghi's Egilina.

Il **giudicio di Paride.**   Pastorale per musica in un atto da rappre-
sentarsi . . . per le felicissime nozze di Sua Altezza Reale Federico
Enrico, principe di Prussia . . . e . . . la principessa Wilhelmina di
Hassia Cassel . . .

Berlino, Haude e Spener, n. d.   39 p.   17ᶜᵐ.

One act.   Carl Heinrich **Graun** is mentioned as the composer and Leopoldo di
Villati as the author, though it is known that Frederick the Great and count Algarotti
collaborated with him.   Argument.   German title page, "Das urtheil des Paris,"
and text face Italian.
First performed at Charlottenburg, Theater der Orangerie, June 25, 1752.
                                                        SCHATZ 4099

Giudizio di Paride, ballet.   *See* Calderara's Ricimero.

Il **giudizio di Paride,** ballet.   *See* Galuppi's Cajo Mario.

Il **giudizio di Paride,** ballet.   *See* Monza's Sesostri.

Giugurta.   A. T. of C. F. Pollaroli's Il demone amante.

Giuletta e Romeo, fatto patrio veronese ballet.   *See* Tarchi's
L'Arminio.

Giulia e Blinval, ballet.   *See* Bianchi's Il chinese in Italia.

Giulietta e Pierotto.   Dramma giocoso per musica.   Da rappresentarsi negl' Imperiali Regj Teatri di Corte.   L'anno 1794.

Vienna, Mattia Andrea Schmidt, n. d.   135 p.   16ᶜᵐ.

Two acts.   Giovanni de Gamerra is mentioned as author, Giuseppe **Weigl** as
composer in the "protesta."   German title-page, "Giulietta e Pierotto," and text
face Italian.
First performed October 16, 1794, as indicated.   SCHATZ 10934

— **Giulietta e Pierotto.**   Dramma giocoso per musica da rappresentarsi nel Teatro di S. A. E. di Sassonia.

Dresda, n. publ., 1796.   151 p.   15½ᶜᵐ.

Two acts.   Joseph **Weigl** is mentioned as the composer.   German title-page, "Jul-
chen und Peter," and text face Italian, which seems to follow de Gamerra's original
Vienna version closely.
First performed, as indicated, October 8, 1796.   SCHATZ 10955

Giulietta e Romeo, ballet.   *See* Bianchi's Le villanelle astute.

Giulietta e Romeo, ballet.   *See* Tarchi's Antioco.

Giulietta e Romeo, ballet. *See* Tritto's Nicaboro in Jucatan.

Giulietta e Romeo. Tragedia per musica da rappresentarsi nel Teatro alla Scala il carnevale dell' anno 1796 . . .

Milano, Batista Bianchi, n. d. 68 p. 15½ᶜᵐ.

Three acts. By Giuseppe Foppa, who is not mentioned. Impresario's dedication dated Milan, January 30, 1796, argument, cast, scenario, and name of Nicola Antonio **Zingarelli** as the composer. On p. [55]–68 prefatory note, argument, description of Gaspare Ronzi's "Astarbea, ballo eroico-tragico-pantomimo," the composer of the music not being mentioned. SCHATZ 11247

Second copy. ML 48.A5 v.9

— **Giulietta, e Romeo.** Tragedia per musica da rappresentarsi nel Regio Teatro di S. Carlo della Principessa l'estate dell' anno 1798. *Lisboa, Simone Taddeo Ferreira, 1798. 111 p. 15ᶜᵐ.*

Three acts. By Giuseppe Foppa, who is not mentioned. Cast, scenario, and name of Nicola **Zingarelli** as the composer. Portuguese text faces Italian.

ML 50.2.G43Z3

— **Julie und Romeo.** Ein singspiel in drey aufzuegen. Dem geehrtesten publikum der stadt Botzen von den hierortigen ton-kuenstlern gewiedmet im fasching des jahres 1798 . . .

Botzen, Zu haben bey dem eingange des saals, n. d. 50 p. 16ᶜᵐ.

With name of **Zingarelli** as the composer. The translator is not mentioned.

SCHATZ 11248

Giulietta ed Armidoro. L. T. of Cimarosa's L'amor costante.

Giulio Cesare. L. T. of Bianchi's La morte di Cesare.

Giulio Cesare in Egitto.

Opera in three acts. Text by Nicola Francesco Haym, music by Georg Friedrich **Händel.**

First performed at London, Haymarket, February 20, 1724.
Not in L. of C.

— **Julius Caesar in Aegypten.** In einem sing-spiele auf dem Hamburgischen Schau-Platze vorgestellet im jahr 1725.

[Hamburg], Gedruckt mit Stromerschen schrifften, n. d. Unpaged. 17½ᶜᵐ.

Three acts. Dedication, dated Hamburg, November 12, 1725, by the translator, Thomas Lediard, cast, scenario, and "Vorbericht," which reads, in part:
"Endlich kommt die so lang versprochene praechtige opera, "Julius Caesar in Aegypten," zum vorschein . . . Diese opera ist anfaenglich von dem beruehmten italiaenischen poeten Haym, zum behuef des Koenigl. theatri auf dem Hay-Market in London, in italiaenischer sprache geschrieben, und daselbst gegen ende des 1724, jahres . . . aufgefuehrt worden . . . Der hiesige uebersetzer, der sowohl das italiaenische *originel*, als the englische *translation* davon, vor sich gehabt, hat sich weder an das eine, noch an die andere, sclavisch gebunden . . . auch vielleicht zuweilen von allen beyden abgewichen; jedoch hat er allezeit das hauptwesen und den verstand dieses geschickten autoris zum grund geleget. Die von dem welt-beruehmten . . . George Friedrich Hendel (**Händel**) componirte music ist in allen arien und italiaenischen accompagnements unveraendert geblieben. Die compo-sition des teutschen recitativ, und der teutschen accompagnements, wie auch der simphonien, ist von dem hertzogl. Weissenfelschen concert-meister hr. J. G. **Linike** . . . die uebersetzung . . . ist (ausser dem teutschen chor, so von einer weit geschick-terer hand hergegeben und an einen dazu bequemen ort eingerneckt worden) ein versuch von T. Lediard."

The Italian text of the arias is added to the German
First performed, as indicated, Theater beim Gaensemarkt, November, 1725.

SCHATZ 4478

Giulio Cesare in Egitto—Continued.

— **Julius Caesar in Aegypten,** in einem Sing-spiele auf dem Hamburgischen Schau-platze vorgestellet im jahr 1733.

[*Hamburg*], *mit Spieringischen schriften, n. d.   Unpaged.   18^{cm}*.

Three acts. Cast, scenario. The Italian text added to many of the arias. A later edition of the above.   SCHATZ 11690

Giulio Cesare in Egitto. Drama per musica nel famoso Teatro Vendramino di S. Salvatore. L'anno MDCLXXVII. Del Bussani . . .

Venetia, Francesco Nicolini, 1677.   69 p. (incl. front.)   13½^{cm}.

Three acts. Author's dedication, argument, scenario, and notice to the reader, with the name of Antonio **Sartorio** as the composer.   SCHATZ 9489

Giulio Cesare trionfante. Drama per musica da rappresentarsi nel Teatro di S. Angelo l'anno MDCLXXXII . . .

Venetia, Francesco Nicolini, 1682.   front., 60 p.   14^{cm}.

Three acts. By Luigi Orlandi, who dates his dedication Venice, January 10, 1682. Scenario and notice to the reader, mentioning Giovanni Domenico **Freschi** as composer.   SCHATZ 3349

— **Cesare trionfante.** Dramma per musica da rappresentarsi in Bologna nel Teatro Malvezzi l'anno 1694.

Bologna, Giulio Borzaghi, n. d.   65 p.   13½^{cm}.

Three acts. Scenario and notice to the reader:
"Eccoti il Giulio Cesare Trionfante, che duoi lustri, e più fù rapresentato in Venetia con quel applauso che sino al giorno d'oggi di lui risuona. Non ti spiaccia vederlo cangiato in molti luoghi dal suo primiero intreccio, poiche fù necessario l'uniformarsi al costume di dove ora si rapresenta, come ancora la diversità delle voci de' virtuosi cantanti obligò chi lo diregge à variarne molte ariette per vietarne gl' incomodi, che nella musica sariano insorti, e maggiormente fù fatto ciò col pensiere di renderlo più dilettevole con la novità di quelle . . ."
Author and composer unknown to Schatz, but the note quoted above furnished a clue. Comparison showed that this is merely a somewhat altered version of Luigi Orlandi's text. For instance, I, 6 is now "Che d'impudica fiamma—*Nobil fiamma del mio Sole*" instead of "Sicuro di mia fede—*E gran pena amar*" and to I, 9 an aria "Sveglia in sen" has been added. Presumably in 1694 **Freschi's** music was largely used.   ML 50.2 C 37

Giul. Flavio Crispo. Tragedia da cantarsi nel celebre Teatro Grimani in S. Gio. Grisostomo nelle notti carnovalesche MDCCXXII . . .

Venezia, Marino Rossetti, 1722.   5 p. l., 62 p.   17^{cm}.

Five acts. By Benedetto Pasqualigo, who signs the dedicatory sonnet with his Arcadian name Merindo Fesanio. Argument, cast, scenario, and name of the composer, Giovanni Maria **Capello.**   SCHATZ 1591

Giulio Sabino, ballet. *See* Bianchi's Alessandro nell' Indie.

Giulio Sabino. Dramma per musica da rappresentarsi nel nobilissimo Teatro di San Benedetto il carnovale dell' anno 1781.

Venezia, Modesto Fenzo, 1781.   56 p.   17^{cm}.

Three acts. Pietro Giovannini, the author, is not mentioned. The title of his text originally was "Epponina." Argument, cast, scenario, and name of Giuseppe **Sarti** as the composer. On p. [21]–36, argument, cast, description, without name of the composer of the music of Sebastiano Gallet's "Il rè pastore, ballo eroico pantomimo in cinque atti." His second ballet was called "Il trionfo dell' Amore fra i dastori."   SCHATZ 9438

Giulio Sabino—Continued.

— **Giulio Sabino.** Dramma per musica in tre atti da rappresentarsi nel Teatro Imp. presso la porta d'Italia.

Vienna, Giuseppe nob. de Kurzbek, 1785. 58 p. 16½^{cm}.

Three acts. Argument and name of Giuseppe **Sarti** as the composer. German title-page, "Julius Sabrinus," and text face Italian, which is not quite the same as in the original Venice 1781 edition. For instance, "Un dolce contento" (I, 10) has become "Frema pur avverso il fato." Schatz 9439

— **Giulio Sabino.** Dramma per musica da rappresentarsi nel Teatro da S. Agostino la primavera dell' anno 1781 . . .

Genova, Stamperia Gesiniana, n. d. 68 p. 14^{cm}.

Three acts. Impresario's dedication, argument, cast, scenario, and name, of Giuseppe **Sarti** as the composer. The text is practically the same as in the original Venice, 1781 edition, but "Pensieri funesti" has been dropped from I, 1. On p. [55]–68 cast, prefatory note, and description without name of the composer of the music of Luigi Bardotti's ballet, "Carolina e Mexicow." Schatz 9440

— **Giulio Sabino.** Dramma per musica da rappresentarsi nel Regio Teatro di via della Pergola la primavera del MDCCLXXXV . . .

Firenze, Stamperia già Albizziniana, 1785. 28 p. 16^{cm}.

Two acts. Argument, cast, and name of Giuseppe **Sarti** as the composer. With the opera was performed, composer of the music not mentioned, Federigo Terrades' ballet, "Il trionfo di Rodrigo." Schatz 11747

— **Giulio Sabino.** A new serious opera, in two acts. As performed at the King's Theatre in the Hay-Market. The music entirely new, by the celebrated Signor Giuseppe Sarti, under the direction of Mr. Mazzinghi.

London, J. Stevenson, 1788. 1 p. l., 51, [6] p. 20^{cm}.

The 6 p. at the end contain "A list of the subscribers to the boxes at the King's Theatre, 1788." Argument, cast, and English prose translation. Though "Pensieri funesti" has been dropped from I, 1, and "Lungi del caro bene" has been added to the first scene, the text of the first act is practically the same as in the original Venice edition, of which the second and third act with omissions make up the second act of the London version.

First performed, as indicated, April 5, 1788. Schatz 9441

— **Giulio Sabino.** Dramma per musica da rappresentarsi nel Regio Teatro di S. Carlo della Principessa in occasione di solennizzare il felicissimo giorno natalizio di Sua Altezza Reale il Serenissimo Signore Don Giovanni, principe del Brasile, etc. li 13 maggio dell' anno 1798.

Lisbona, Simone Taddeo Ferreira, 1798. 103, [2] p. 15^{cm}.

Two acts and licenza. The author, Pietro Giovannini is not mentioned. Prefatory note, argument, cast, scenario, and name of Giuseppe **Sarti** as composer. Portuguese translation faces Italian. ML 48.C6xxii

— **Julius Sabinus.** Eine ernsthafte oper in drei aufzügen. Nebst einem anhange das hochgraefl. Erdoedische Operntheater betreffend; fuer welches diese oper uebersetzt, und zum drucke befoerdert ist von Johann Nepomuck Schueller, mitglied der graeflichen Operngesellschaft in Pressburg.

Pressburg, gedruckt mit Weberischen schriften, 1785. 52 p. 17^{cm}.

The "Anhang" does not appear in this copy.

Three acts. Cast, name of Giuseppe **Sarti** as the composer and "Vorrede," in which the opera is promised "unter der führung des herrn Kumpf den zweiten Jänner, als anfangsoper der 1786sten jahres." Schatz 9442

Giulio Sabino—Continued.

— **Julius Sabinus.** Ein ernsthaftes singspiel in drey akten. Nach dem italienischen frey bearbeitet.

Nuernberg, im Verlag der aeltern Christoph Weigel'schen kunst und buchhandlung, 1791. xii, 68 p. 15½^{cm}.

The "Vorrede" is dated Nuernberg, February 1, 1791, and initialed N[ikolaus] A[dam] H[eiden]. Heiden first comments on the success of Sarti's "Meisterwerk," then on the typically Italian make-up of the original text showing "wenig aufmerksamkeit fuer die poesie, sondern ganz allein fuer composition," on the impossibility of remedying certain defects without altering the music, adds an argument, and then makes these interesting remarks:

"nach einem Neumann, Eschenburg und Cramer die produkte der auslaendischen dichtkunst und musik fuer unsere landsleute, durch zweckmaesige bearbeitung geniessbar zu machen, heisst in der that nicht wenig gewagt. Wem die hartnaeckigen schwierigkeiten, die sich einem uebersetzer italienischer opern; die nicht im geschmacke eines Pleissners oder anderer aehnlicher uebersetzer arbeiten will, haufenweise entgegen stellen, nur einigermassen bekannt sind, der wird mir sehr gerne zugestehen, dass es nicht leicht ein muehsameres und nicht selten undankbareres geschaefte giebt, als die unterlegung des deutschen textes unter fremde, besonders italienische musik." SCHATZ 9479

Giulio Sabino. Dramma per musica da rappresentarsi nel Regio Teatro di Torino nel carnovale del 1790 . . .

Torino, Onorato Derossi, n. d. viii, 48 p. 15½^{cm}.

Three acts. By Pietro Giovannini, who is not mentioned and whose title originally was "Epponina." Argument, cast, scenario, and name of Angelo **Tarchi** as the composer. On p. 44–48 brief descriptions of Gaspare Angiolini's (who also composed the music) ballets, "L'orfano," "Il rè alla caccia," and "Il tutore sorpreso."
SCHATZ 10220

Giulio Villenvelt, o sia L'assassino di Scozia, ballet. *See* G. Giordani's Aspasia.

Giunio Bruto. Dramma per musica da rappresentarsi nel Teatro da S. Agostino l'estate dell' anno 1782 . . .

Genova, Stamperia Gesiniana, n. d. 60 p. 13½^{cm}.

Two acts. Argument, cast, scenario, and name of composer, **Cimarosa.** The author is unknown to Schatz. On p. [51]–60, description of Onorato Viganò's "Armida e Rinaldo, ballo eroico pantomimo." Neither of this nor of Viganò's other ballet, "Il misantropo o sia Il poter delle donne," is the composer of the music mentioned. SCHATZ 1992

Giunone placata. Componimento dramatico da cantarsi per le felicissime nozze dell' Eccellenze Loro il Signor D. Filippo Bernualdo Orsini . . . e la Signora D. Teresa Caracciolo . . . [vignette]

Roma, Generoso Salomoni, 1762. 28 p. 27^{cm}.

Vignettes. Two parts. "Nidastio Pegeate, P. A." [real name not given by Wotquenne] is mentioned as the author, Antonio **Aurisicchio** as the composer.
ML 50.2.G44A8

Giunone repacificata. A. T. of Manelli's La Filo.

Il **giuocatore fortunato.** A. T. of Piccinni's L'astratto.

I **giuochi d'Agrigento.** Dramma per musica del conte Alessandro Pepoli da rappresentarsi nell' apertura del nuovo Teatro detto La Fenice.

Venezia, Curti, 1792. 1 p. l., 86 p., front. and 4 ports. 18½^{cm}.

The front. represents the façade of La Fenice; the portrait (between p. [6]–7), Giovanni **Paisiello,** who is mentioned as composer. The other ports. represent Brigida Banti (at p. 19), Giacomo David (at p. 54), and Gasparo Pachiarotti (at p. 68). Prefatory note, argument, scenario, and cast.

First performed at Venice, as indicated, May 16, 1792. SCHATZ 7629
Second copy. Lacks the ports. of Paisiello and Banti. ML 48.M2N

I giuochi d'Agrigento—Continued.

— **Giuochi d'Agrigento.** Dramma per musica da rappresentarsi nel Regio Teatro di S. Carlo della Principessa nel 4 novembre 1799.

Lisbona, Simone Taddeo Ferreira, MDCCLXXXXVIX [!] *109 p. 14½cm.*

Three acts. By conte Alessandro Pepoli, who is not mentioned. Argument, cast, scenario, and name of Giovanni **Paisiello** as composer Portuguese text faces Italian.

ML 50.2.G45P2

Second copy. ML 48.C6 III

Il giuoco de' matti. Dramma scherzoso per musica. Da rappresentarsi nel Teatro di Malta nell' autunno di quest' anno 1755 . . .

Napoli, Domenico Lanciano, 1755. 4 p. l., 65 p. 15½cm.

Three acts. Impresario's dedication and cast. Neither the author, Antonio Palomba, is mentioned, nor Gaetano **Latilla**, the composer.

First performed at Naples, Teatro Nuovo, summer of 1754. SCHATZ 5453

Il giuoco dell' arco, ballet. *See* Pasque's Arianna e Teseo.

Il giuoco di picchetto. Divertimento per musica da rappresentarsi alla Corte Elettorale palatina.

Mannheim, Stamperia elettorale ed accademica, n. d. 23 p. 15½cm.

Our copy is interleaved, contains ms. corrections and other indications that it was used for preparation of a performance. The pagination is faulty, as 13–14 are repeated. The real p. 13 begins with a repetition of the first four lines of the aria "Heureuse paix, tranquille indifférence" (from Destouches' "Issé" of 1708, I, 3) and p. 14 contains the aria "Del destin non vi lagnate" (from Metastasio's "Olimpiade" text). The second p. 13, which should have been p. 15, begins with the aria "Lorsque l'amour dans ses noeuds," and the second p. 14 contains the aria "D'un infelice amante." Other arias are: "No: non dicsti il vero," "Ah Teseo! Ah del mio cor," "Già fucina è questo petto," "Io sono stata in Ascoli." A German *lied*, "Ich bin ein musikant," is not in this libretto. The characters are, "Gioconda," "Placido," "Severino." Neither the author is mentioned, nor the composer.

As "Il gioco del pichetto, scherzo giocoso per **musica**," this one-act opera was performed at Coblenz, Hoftheater, 1772, and an Italian-French libretto, without composer's or author's name, was published at Confluenza, 1772. In May, 1773, the opera was then performed at Schwetzingen, Hoftheater. It is apparently for this performance that our libretto was printed. Pichler attributed, without stating his reasons, the music to Pietro **Guglielmi** but Schatz, and later Piovano, ascribe the music to **Jommelli** on the ground that the text is the same as that of Jommelli's "La conversazione," Lisbona 1775. Furthermore, Schatz refers to a score of the opera (advertised by Bertling in his catalogue no. 28), in which there is a note to the effect that Jommelli composed the music.

In his Jommelli biography (p. 426–428) Abert deals with a score by Jommelli called "La critica," which, he says, was performed at Stuttgart in 1766 and which has been preserved at the Conservatory, Naples, as a "Cantata." In his analysis of the plot Abert mentions as characters: Placido, Severino, Lesbia, Gioconda, Siface, Acamante, Palmira. In his ms., "Chronologische Folge der . . . Jommelli . . . Werke," Schatz has an entry, while referring to the score at Naples, under "La critica. Anfang des Jahres 1767" (first he had the date 1766), with this cast:

Placido	Arcangelo Cortoni.
Severino	Francesco Guerrieri.
Lesbia	Maria Masi-Giura *detta* la Morsarina.
Gioconda	Monaca Buonani.
Siface	Giuseppe Aprile.
Acamante	Giovanni Maria Rubinelli.
Palmira	Anna Cesari-Seemann.

In other words, Schatz adds a sixth character, yet he plainly gives the cast of the Stuttgart production of "La critica," since the artists mentioned (*comp.* Sittard) belonged to the Stuttgart opera "Etat" of 1767.

The text of "La critica" Abert is inclined to ascribe to Gaetano Martinelli, who supplied Jommelli at Stuttgart with other texts. It is plainly to a large extent the same as that of Jommelli's "La conversazione" and of "Il giuoco di picchetto." Under all these circumstances it is fairly safe to assume that "Il giuoco di picchetto," as performed at Coblenz and Schwetzingen, was Jommelli's "La critica" reduced to three characters. ML 50.2G47

Il giuramento alla vendetta. Dramma per musica da rappresentarsi nel tempo della fiera in Treviso l'anno 1744 nel Teatro di S. E. Dolfino . . .

Venezia, Modesto Fenzo, 1744. 44 p. 15^{cm}.

Three acts. Dedication, argument, cast, and name of Girolamo **Micheli** as the composer. Text by conte Angelo Schietti (who is not mentioned), originally under the title "La pace per amore." SCHATZ 6482

Il Giustino. Tragedia.

[449]–520 p. 19^{cm}. (Pietro Metastasio, Opere drammatiche, Venezia, Giuseppe Bettinelli, 1733–37, v. 3.)

Five acts. Argument. No composer mentioned and none recorded by Schatz.
ML 49.A2M4

— **Giustino.**

Metastasio, Poesie, Parigi, vedova Quillau, 1755, t. ix, [289]–419 p. 16^{cm}.

Five acts. Argument. ML 49.A2M42

— **Giustino.**

[251]–360 p. 26^{cm}. (Metastasio, Opere, t. x, Parigi, vedova Herissant, 1782.)

Five acts. ML 49.A2M44

Il Giustino. Drama per musica da recitarsi nel Teatro Formagliari la primavera dell' anno MDCCXI . . .

Bologna, Costantino Pisarri, n. d. 76, [1] p. 16½^{cm}.

Five acts. By conte Nicolò Beregani, who is not mentioned. Dedication by Giuseppe Filippo Calderini, dated Bologna, April 19, 1711, argument, cast, scenario, name of Tommaso **Albinoni** as composer, and notice to the reader to the effect that this is a version of Beregani's text, as modernized by Pietro Pariati SCHATZ 129

Giustino. Melodrama da rappresentarsi nel celebre Teatro Vendramino di San Salvatore. L'anno MDCLXXXIII . . .

Venetia, Francesco Nicolini, 1683. front., 69, [2] p. 14^{cm}.

Three acts. Publisher's dedication, alluding to conte Nicolò Beregani as the author, argument, brief notice to the reader, and scenario. The composer, Giovanni **Legrenzi**, is not mentioned. SCHATZ 5544

Giustino. Dramma per musica da recitarsi nel Teatro dell' illm̃o Sig. Federico Capranica nel carnevale dell' anno 1724 . . .

Roma, Bernabò, 1724. 68 p. 14½^{cm}.

Three acts. By Nicolò Beregani (not mentioned), with alterations. Federico Capranica's dedication, argument, cast, scenario, and name of Antonio **Vivaldi** as the composer. SCHATZ 10769

Der gleichgueltige ehemann. Tr. of Schuster's Il marito indolente.

La gloria d'Amore. Spettacolo festivo fatto rappresentare dal serenissimo Sig. duca di Parma sopra l'acque dell gran peschiera novamente fatta nel suo giardino per gl'acclamati sponsali del serenissimo Sig. principe Odoardo suo primo genito con la serenissima

La **gloria d'Amore**—Continued.

Signora principessa Dorotea Sofia di Neoburgo . . . Poesia d'Aurelio Aureli . . . e musica di D. Bernardo Sabadini, mastro di capella della medesima A. S.

Parma, Stampa ducale, 1690. viii, 30 p. 20^{cm}.

Three acts. Dedication by the author, his prefatory note, cast, and scenario. This copy lacks the 15 plates which accompany the copy in the Royal Conservatory Library at Brussels showing "les appareils théatraux, d'une hardiesse et d'une magnificence incroyables" (Wotquenne) as invented by the brothers Gasparo, Pietro, and Domenico Mauro, of Venice, whose merits are extolled in the notice to the reader mentioned above.

First performed May 24, 1690, as indicated. SCHATZ 9198

La **gloria d'Orfeo.** Dramma musicale.

Girolamo Bartolommei Smeducci, Drammi musicali morali, Firenze, 1656, v. i, p. [233]–288. 23^{cm}.

Prologue and three acts. Argument, allegoria and dedication to Francesco d'Este, duca di Modona e Reggio, in which Bartolomei says:

"Ritorna il mio Orfeo dalla stampa riformato a rinnovare a V. A. S. la divota offerta, nella quale Egli per prima s'affrettò per giungere opportuno nel tempo delle felicissime nozze di V. A. con auguri di desiderata prosperità . . ." ML 49.A2B3

La **gloria trionfante d'amore.** Drama per musica. Da rappresentarsi nel Teatro di Sant' Angelo l'autunno dell' anno 1712. Del dottor Grazio Braccioli . . .

Venezia, Marino Rossetti, 1712. front., 60 p. 15^{cm}.

Three acts. Author's dedication dated Venice, November 16, 1712, argument cast, scenario, and name of Giacomo **Rampini** as the composer. SCHATZ 8596

The **glorious first of August.** A. T. of Attwood's The mouth of the Nile.

Der **glueckliche betrug.** A. T. of Keiser's Der Hamburger jahrmarckt.

Der **glueckliche schatzgraeber,** ein komisches singspiel von einem aufzuge.

Wien, Joh. Thom. edler v. Trattnern, 1773. 20 p. 16½^{cm}.

Neither the author, Paul Weidmann, mentioned, nor the composer (unknown to Schatz). SCHATZ 11455

Die **glueckliche unschuldige.** Tr. of Paisiello's L'innocente fortunata.

Der **glueckliche zufall.** A. T. of Lange's List und ungefaehr.

Die **gluecklichen jaeger.** Ein singspiel in drey aufzuegen. In musik gesetzt von hrn. Umlauf.

n. i., n. d. p. [69]–132. 16½^{cm}. (Gottlieb Stephanie d. jüng., Singspiele, Liegnitz, 1792, no. 2.)

Detached copy. First performed at Vienna, Kärnthnerthor Theater, February 17, 1786 (Schatz); February 17, 1785 (Haas). SCHATZ 10525

Die **gluecklichen reisenden.** Tr. of Anfossi's I viaggiatori felici.

Der **gluecks wechsel** oder Mutter Natur in ihren kindern. Tr. of Piccinni's Le vicende della sorte.

Das **gluekliche bauern maedchen.** A. T. of Dieter's Das frey-schiessen.

Die **gnade des Titus.** Tr. of Hasse's La clemenza di Tito.

Gneo Marzio Coriolano. Drama musicale fatto rappresentare da' Signori Accademici del Casino sotto la protezione del sereniss. principe cardinale Francesco Maria di Toscana.

> *G. A. Moniglia, Poesie drammatiche, parte prima, Firenze, Vincenzio Vangelisti, 1689, p. [299]–378. 24ᶜᵐ.*

Three acts. Argument and prefatory note, which reads in part:
"Fu questo drama composto dall' autore per servirne la sereniss. granduchessa Vittoria sua signora, la quale dopo un' anno ne fece regalo al serenissimo principe Francesco Maria oggi cardinale de' Medici, e l'A. S. sotto l'autorevole sua protezione lo espose alle scene de' Sig. Accademici del Casino, posto in musica dal padre Lorenzo **Cattani** Agostiniano, maestro di cappella dell' illustriss. e sacra religione de' cavalieri di S. Stefano in Pisa . . . Ben dodici volte fu recitata, e l'istesso numerosissimo concorso v'intervenne la prima, che l'ultima volta, adoprando ciascheduno industria nel ritrovar mezzi per essere ammesso all' udienza . . ."
First performed as indicated, summer 1686.   ML 49.A2M7

Les **gnomes** ou L'amour ambitieux. Entrée in Duval's Les génies.

I **gobbi.** A. T. of Portugal's La somiglianza.

Golconda liberata dalla tirannide di Scour-Malou. A. T. of the ballet La Galzeuca.

The **golden pippin:** an English burletta, in three acts. As it is performed at the Theatre Royal, Covent Garden. By the author of Midas.

> *London, T. Becket, 1773. 2 p. l., 51 p. 20ᶜᵐ.*

By Kane O'Hara. The music is a pasticcio made up partly of ballad airs, partly from **Francesco** [di Majo?], **Galuppi, Giordani, Duni, Philidor, Fischietti, Fisher, Monsigny, Hændel, Bryan, Bates, Vivaldi,** and especially Thomas Augustin **Arne,** who selected and arranged the music.
First performed, as indicated, February 6, 1773.   LONGE 26

— The **golden pippin.** In two acts. By Kane O'Hara, Esq.

> *19ᶜᵐ. [57]–79 p. (Collection of the most esteemed farces and entertainments, t. iii, Edinburgh, 1792.)*

Covent-Garden and Edinburgh (1776) casts. Names of the composers.
     SCHATZ 11753C

Das **goldene gefaess.** A. T. of Kauer's Ritter Willibald.

Golpone e Birina, intermezzi. *See* Giacomelli's Achille in Aulide.

Il **gondoliere** ossia Gli sdegni amorosi. Intermezzo di due parti per musica. Rappresentato per la prima volta in Milano nell' anno MDCCXXXII.

> *Carlo Goldoni, Opere teatrali, Venezia, Zatta e figli, 1788–95, v. 35, [39]–50 p. 18½ᶜᵐ.*

Two parts.
First performed at Milan in January, 1733, according to Schatz, who does not know the composer.   PQ

Il **gondoliere**—Continued.

— Gli **sdegni amorosi.** Intermezzo.

[247]–256 p. 16½*cm*. (*Carlo Goldoni, Opere drammatiche giocose, t. iv, Torino, 1757.*)

Two parts.

Il **Gonzalvo,** ballet. *See* Anfossi's Le gelosie fortunate.

Gonzalvo in America, ballet. *See* Nicolini's Gli Sciti.

Il **Gordiano.** Drama per musica da rappresentarsi nel famoso Teatro Vendramino di San Salvatore l'anno 1688 . . .

Venetia, Francesco Nicolini, 1688. 60 p. 14½cm.

Three acts. By Adriano Morselli, who is not mentioned. Publisher's dedication, notice to the reader with name of Domenico **Gabrieli** as composer, argument, and scenario. SCHATZ 3404

Il **Gordiano Pio.** Drama per musica nel felicissimo giorno natalizio della S. R. M^tà di Giuseppe I. rè de' Romani . . . Rappresentata nella città di Neustatt l'anno MDCC. Posto in musica dal Sig. Marc' Antonio Ziani . . . con l'arie per li balletti del Sig^r Gio. Gioseffo Hoffer . . .

Vienna d'Austria, Susanna Cristina, vedova di Matteo Cosmerovio, n. d. 6 p. l., 101 p. 14½cm.

Three acts and licenza. Dedication by the author, Donato Cupeda, dated Vienna, July 26, 1700, argument, scenario, and notice to the reader, in which Cupeda says:
"Questo drama composto nella convalenza da una lunga infirmità, nõ poteva riuscire che un' aggregato di debolezze . . . La sua lunghezza, che nella rappresentazione avrebbe portato assai più di tempo, che'l prescritto da sovrano comando, m'hà obbligato a seguire il costume, che corre ne' teatri d'Italia, cioè d'abbreviarlo per la musica, con lasciarlo intero alla stampa. I versi che in quella si tralascieranno, sono segnati con le due virgolette "; mà perchè tal volta accade, ch'alcuno nõ si toglia interamente, si è aggiunto un picciolo asterismo *, che dinoterà quella parte di esso, che resterà ancora nella musica . . ."
Accordingly, for instance, the whole scene I, 6, "Se di Roma per l'impero," was dropped and in I, 12, the aria, "Per le svele erra, e si lagna," was followed by the words "Amata Oronta," etc. SCHATZ 11188

Gott Mars oder Der eiserne mann. Ein komisches singspiel in zwey aufzuegen. Text und musik ist vom herrn von Dittersdorf.

Oels, Ludwig, n. d. 96 p. 16cm.

First performed at Oels, Hoftheater, May 30, 1795. SCHATZ 2592

Der **gouverneur der canarischen inseln.** Tr. of Ghinassi's Il governatore dell' isole canarie.

Il **governadore.** Commedia per musica di Domenico Canicà. Da rappresentarsi nel Teatro Nuovo sopra Toledo, nel carnevale di quest' anno 1747.

Napoli, Domenico Langiano, e Domenico Vivenzio, 1747. 80 p. 15cm.

Three acts. Cast, name of "Niccolò Croscino" (Nicola **Logroscino**) as composer, and "protesta" reading in part:
"Comparisce in istampa, e sulle scene la presente commedia molto diversa da quella, che già da prima l'autore ideata, e scritta l'avea." SCHATZ 5673

La governante.   Intermezzo in musica a cinque voci da rappresentarsi nel Teatro Valle dell' illm̃i Signori Capranica nel carnevale dell'
anno 1777 . . .

   *Roma, Arcangelo Casaletti, 1777.   55 p.   15*cm*.*

   Two parts.   Author not mentioned and unknown to Schatz.   Dedication, imprimatur, cast, and name of Michele **Mortellari** as the composer.   SCHATZ 6686

Il governatore dell' isole Canarie.   Intermezzo in musica a cinque
voci da rappresentarsi nel Teatro Valle degl' illustriss. Sigg. Capranica nel carnevale dell' anno 1785 . . .

   *Roma, Agostino Palombini, n. d.   54 p.   15*cm*.*

   Two acts.   By Catterino Mazzolà, who is not mentioned.   Cast and name of
Agostino **Accorimboni** as composer.   ML 50.2.G6A2

Il governatore dell' isole Canarie.   Intermezzo in musica da rappresentarsi nel Teatro di S. A. E. di Sassonia.

   *Dresda, n. publ., 1785, n. d.   143 p.   16*cm*.*

   Two acts.   By Caterino Mazzolà, who is not mentioned.   Stefano **Ghinassi** is
named as the composer.   German title page, "Der gouverneur der canarischen
inseln," and text face Italian.   SCHATZ 3802

The governess, a comic opera: As it is performed at the Theatre-
Royal in Crow-street.

   *Dublin, n. publ., 1777.   2 p. l., 40 p.   16½*cm*.*

   Three acts.   Cast.   A pirated version by Ryder who took the part of Enoch Issachar
of "The duenna," text by Sheridan, music by Thomas **Linley,** father, and Thomas
Linley, son.   According to Tufts, a 1793 Dublin ed. calls Sheridan the author.
                                        LONGE 148
                     Second copy.   LONGE 323

Das grab des Mufti oder Die zwey (zwei) geizigen.   Tr. of Grétry's
Les deux avares.

Das grab des Mufti, oder Die zwey geizigen.   Eine komische oper
in zwey akten von A. G. Meissner.

   *Leipzig, Dykische buchhandlung, 1776.   4 p. l., 95, [1] p.   16*cm*.*

   Dedication by the author, dated Leipzig, March 8, 1776, and his "Vorbericht," in
which he concedes the impossibility of avoiding all the defects of the French original
["Les deux avares"] by Falbaire, and says:
   "Ob es mir im gegentheil gelungen sey, durch ganz neue gesaenge, durch ein
drittheil neuer scenen, durch mehrern dialog, anstatt des beynah immer fortdauern-
den singens, und durch gaenzliche umarbeitung von Karls und Wilhelminens charakter das stueck selbst zu verbessern, das mag das urtheil der kenner entscheiden;
wenn sie anders diese kleinigkeit der muehe werth schaetzen, sie mit dem urbilde,
oder wenigstens mit der woertlichen uebersetzung des herrn Andre zu vergleichen.
Der beyfall einiger meiner freunde . . . und beynahe noch mehr als dies, das versprechen eines unsrer groessten tonkuenstler, des herrn [Johann Adam] **Hiller,** der
diese arbeit in der handschrift sah, und ihr naechstens durch seine komposition
vorzuege zu geben versprach, die sie jetzt noch nicht besitzt, haben mich zu diesen [!]
schritt ermuntert . . ."
   First performed at Leipzig, Theater am Rannstädter Thore, January 17, 1779.
                                        SCHATZ 4720

— **Das grab des Mufti,** oder Die zwey geizigen.   In zwey akten.
Nach Falbaire.

   *A. G. Meissner, Operetten, Leipzig, 1778.   5 p. l., 95, [1] p.   17*cm*.*

   Same as the 1776 edition, the first p. l., with the title page for the collection, having
been added.   ML 49.A2M3

Ein **grab in Arkadien.** L. T. of Schmittbauer's Lindor und Ismene.

Les **Graces,** ballet en action, tiré de la piece de M. de Sainte-Foix; de la composition de M. Gardel l'aîné . . . Représenté devan Leurs Majestés à Versailles le 4 février 1779.

[Paris], P. R. C. Ballard, 1779. 16 p. 20ᶜᵐ.

One act. Cast. Not recorded by Lajarte. Composer of the music unknown to me. ML 52.2.G7

The **Graces:** an Anacreontic ballet.

Jean George Noverre Works. Tr. from the French, London, 1783, v. 3, p. [93]–144. 21½ᶜᵐ.

One act. Preface, argument, and detailed description of the eleven scenes.

GV 1787.N8

The **Graces.** An intermezzo; in one act. As it is performed at the Royal Circus in St. George's Fields.

London, G. Kearsly, 1782. 24 p. 21ᶜᵐ.

One act. Text and music by Charles **Dibdin,** who is not mentioned.

Longe 256

Les **Graces,** ballet-heroique, représenté par l'Académie royale de musique, l'an 1735. Paroles de Mʳ. Roy. Musique de Mʳ Mouret. CXXII. opera.

n. i., n. d. 75 p. 14½ᶜᵐ. (Recueil général des opera, Paris, t. xvi, 1745).

Prologue and the entrées, "L'ingenue," "La melancholique," "L'enjouée." Avertissement.

First performed, as indicated, May 5, 1735. ML 48.R4

Les **Graces vengées.** Tr. of Metastasio's libretto Le Grazie vendicate.

Die **graefinn von Amalfi.** Tr. of Weigl's La contessa di Amalfi.

Graf Albert. Tr. of Grétry's Le comte d'Albert.

Graf Balbarone oder Die maskerade. O. T. of Gerl's Der bestrafte hochmuth.

Der **graf bey guterlaune.** Tr. of Bernardini's Il conte di bell' umore.

Der **graf Caramella.** Tr. of Galuppi's Il conte Caramella.

Gesaenge aus dem singspiele: **Graf von Waltron** oder Die subordination, in vier aufzuegen. In musik gesezt von Ignaz Walter.

Hamburg, Joh. Matthias Michaelsen, 1792. 31 p. 16ᶜᵐ.

The author, Johann Baptist Bergobzoomer, is not mentioned.
First performed at Riga, Vietinghoff'sches Theater, Dec. 31/Jan. 11, 1785/1786.

Schatz 10860

Il **gran Cidde.** Dramma per musica da rappresentarsi nel Regio Teatro di Torino nel carnovale del 1769 alla presenza di S. S. R. M.

Torino, Onorato Derossi, n. d. xii, 50 p. 16ᶜᵐ.

Three acts. Argument, cast, scenario, name of the author, Giovacchino Pizzi, and of the composer, "Carlo Defranchi" (**Franchi**). The ballet airs were composed by Giuseppe Antonio Le Messier and "Paolo Ghebart."
First performed, as indicated, December 26, 1768. Schatz 3328

Il gran conte di Cordanova.   Farsetta in musica a tre voci da rappresentarsi nel Teatro a' Saponari nel carnevale dell' anno 1754 . . .

Roma, Puccinelli, 1754.   24 p.   15½^{cm}.

Two parts.   Author not mentioned and unknown to me.   Possibly Girolamo Aureli wrote the text.   Cast, name of Giovanni **Massi** as composer and impresario's dedication which begins:

"La mira principale di quest' intermezzi, che vi offeriamo, è stata, come bene apparisce di notare e pungere la ridicola ambizione di taluni; che quantunque da bassi natali traggan l'origin loro, vogliono tuttavia spacciarsi par nobili e generosi."   ML 50.2.G68M2

Il Gran Costanzo . . . da rappresentarsi nel Teatro di Mantova.

Mantova, Gio. Batt. Grana, 1706.   72 p.   15^{cm}.

Three acts.   Dedication and argument.   Neither author nor composer mentioned. Work unknown to Schatz, Allacci, etc.   ML 50.2.G7

Il gran Macedone.   Drama per musica da rappresentarsi nel Teatro di San Casciano l'anno 1690 . . .

Venetia, Girolamo Albrizzi, 1690.   69 p.   12º.

Three acts.   Impresario's dedication, dated [blank] November, 1690, scenario, argument, notice to the reader, with name of the composer, Giuseppe **Boniventi**, but not of the librettist, Giulio Pancieri.   On p. 69, this notice to the reader:

"Se nell' opera scorgerai, che in una medesima scena, come quella delle Loggie dirupate vengono personaggi più d'una volta, compatisci, perche non vi e stato commodo di raddoppiar le mutazioni di scene."   SCHATZ 1191

Il gran Mogol.   O. T. of Lalli's text L'Argippo.

Il gran Mogol.   Drama per musica di Domenico Lalli.   Da rappresentarsi nel Teatro di S. Bartolomeo nel giorno 26. di decembre 1713 . . .

Napoli, Michele Luigi Muzio, 1713.   6 p. l., 56 p.   14^{cm}.

Three acts.   Dedication by the impresario, Nicola Serino, argument, scenario, cast, names of Francesco **Mancini** as composer and of Angiolo Birini as author of the buffo scenes and of certain designated arias.   SCHATZ 5879

Il gran Tamerlano.   Dramma per musica da rappresentarsi nel Regio-Ducal Teatro di Milano nel carnovale dell' anno 1772 . . .

Milano, Gio. Batista Bianchi, n. d.   76 p.   14½^{cm}.

Three acts.   By conte Agostino Piovene, who is not mentioned.   Dedication, argument, cast, name of Joseph **Misliweczck** as the composer, and avvertimento:

"Le scene, le arie ec. contrassegnate col seguente asterisco (*) sono aggiunte, o cambiate.   Un tale arbitrio non recherà maraviglia a chi sà, che il Tamerlano, o sia il Bajazet è stato sformato tante volte, quante è comparso sopra le scene.   Qualunque però egli siasi al presente, non si toglierà da esso il merito della buona volontà a chi ha stimati necessari simili cambiamenti."

First performed, as indicated, December 26, 1771.   SCHATZ 6530

Il gran Tamerlano.   Tragedia per musica, da rappresentarsi sul Regio Teatro Danese, nel principio dell' anno 1764.—Den store Tamerlan . . . oversadt paa dansk, af R. Soelberg . . .

Kiφbenhavn, Lars Nielsen Svare, n. d.   103 p.   16^{cm}.

Three acts.   By conte Agostino Piovene, who is not mentioned.   Argument, cast, and name of Giuseppe **Sarti** as the composer.   ("La musica è tutta nuova.")   SCHATZ 9445

Il gran Tamerlano. Drama per musica da rappresentarsi nel famosissimo Teatro Grimano di SS. Gio. e Paulo l'anno 1689 di Giulio Cesare Corradi . . .

Venetia, Nicolini, 1689. 80 p. 14½^{cm}.

Three acts. Author's dedication, scenario, and argument, with name of Marc' Antonio **Ziani** as the composer.

First performed, as indicated, carnival, 1689.   SCHATZ 11189

Il gran Tamerlano vincitore di Bajazet. Da rappresentarsi nel Teatro Vendramin à San Salvatore. L'autunno del 1746.

Venezia, Alvise Valvasense, 1746. 15 p. 17½^{cm}.

One act. By "Sig. Verdacchio Predamosche, fra Disperati il Satirico." Cast, argument, and name of Daniel **Barba** as composer.   SCHATZ 598

La grand-mère amoureuse, parody. *See* Lully's Atys.

La grandezza d'animo oder Arsinoe [vignette]. In einem singe-spiel auf dem grossen Hamburgischen Schau-platze vorgestellet. Im jahr 1710.

n. i., n. d. Unpaged. 19^{cm}.

Five acts. Scenario and "vorbericht," with name of Reinhard **Keiser** as the composer. The author, resp. translator, Breymann, is not mentioned. The Italian text has been added to some of the arias.   SCHATZ 5093

Le Grazie vendicate. Componimento drammatico rappresentato in musica nell' Imperial Favorita il dì 28. agosto 1735 per festeggiare il felicissimo giorno natalizio della augustissima imperadrice.

11 p. 19^{cm}. (Pietro Metastasio, Opere drammatiche, Venezia, Giuseppe Bettinelli, 1733–37, v. 4.)

One act. No composer mentioned.   ML 49.A2M4

— Le **Grazie vendicate.**

Metastasio, Poesie, Parigi, vedova Quillau, 1755, t. vii, [241]–257 p. 16^{cm}.

One act.   ML 49.A2M42

— Le **Grazie vendicate.** Azione teatrale, scritta dall' autore in Vienna, l'anno 1735, . . . rappresentata la prima volta con musica del Caldara negl' interni privati appartamenti dell' Imperial Favorita dalle reali arciduchesse Maria Teresa (poi imperatrice regina) e Marianna di lei sorella, e da una dama della Cesare corte, per festeggiare il dì 28 agosto, giorno di nascita dell' imperatrice Elisabetta.

[393]–406 p. 26^{cm}. (Pietro Metastasio, Opere, t. iii, Parigi, vedova Herissant, 1780.)

One act.   ML 49.A2M44

— Les **Graces vengées.** Drame en musique, exécuté au Palais de la Favorite, pour célébrer le jour de la naissance de l'impératrice, epouse de Charles VI.

Metastasio, Tragedies-opera, Vienne, 1751, t. iv, 19 p. 14^{cm}.

One act. Richelet's translation.   ML 49.A2M47

Die **Grazien,** ein prolog. Zur hoechsten geburtsfeyer des prinzen Heinrichs Koeniglicher Hoheit, von C. L. Hempeln, geb. Karschin.

9–18 p. 18^{cm}. (Theater Journal fuer Deutschland, Sechstes stueck, Gotha, 1778.)

The composer, Johann **André**, is not mentioned.
First performed at Berlin, Döbbelinsches Theater, January 18, 1778.   SCHATZ 187
Second copy.   SCHATZ 11754

Di **Greci festeggianti la riconciliazione** d'Achille e d'Agamennone, ballet.   *See* Bianchi's Briseide.

I **Greci in Tauride,** dramma per musica in tre atti da rappresentarsi nel Regio Teatro di Berlino per ordine di Sua Maestà nel carnovale del MDCCLXXIII.

Berlino, Haude e Spener, 1772.   91 p.   16^{cm}.

By Antonio Landi, who is not mentioned.   Argument, scenario, and name of the composer, Johann Friedrich **Agricola**.   German title-page, "Die Griechen in Taurica," and text face Italian.   A footnote on p. [8] informs the reader that certain arias were taken from the same composer and author's "Oreste e Pilade" of the previous season.   The facts are these, according to Schneider's history of opera in Berlin: The second opera of the carniveval season of 1772 was this "Oreste e Pylade," which displeased Frederick the Great so much that he ordered a revision of the work. This revision was first performed on March 24, 1772, under the title of "I Greci in Tauride," at Potsdam.   SCHATZ 68

Il **Greco in Troia.**   Festa teatrale rappresentata in Firenze per le nozze de' serenissimi sposi Ferdinando Terzo, principe di Toscana, e Violante Beatrice, principessa di Baviera.

Firenze, Stamperia di S. A. S., 1688.   7 p. l., 96 p.   16^{cm}.

Three acts.   Dedication by the author, Matteo Noris, dated December, 1688, scenario, and notice to the reader.   Composer not mentioned, and unknown to Schatz.
SCHATZ 11339

The **green-room controversy.**   A. T. of The rivals.

The **Greshamite.**   A. T. of Harlequin-Hydaspes.

Grespilla e Fanfarone, intermezzi.   *See* Caldara's Il Germanico Marte.

Gretna Green, a comic opera, in two acts.   As performed at the Theatre Royal, Smoke-Alley.

[Dublin], Printed for the booksellers, n. d.   22 p.   17½^{cm}.

Neither the author, Charles Stuart, is mentioned, nor the composer, Samuel **Arnold.**
No ballad airs indicated in the text, though the opera consisted mostly of "Italian, French, Irish, English & Scotch music" as the title page of Preston's vocal score tell us.   The airs used are indicated in the vocal score, which contains two numbers headed as by **Giordani** and only one number "September the thirteenth" besides the overture as composed by Arnold.
First performed at London, Haymarket, August 28, 1783.   LONGE 233

The **grey mare the better horse.**   A. T. of The Welsh opera.

Die **Griechen in Taurica.**   Tr. of Agricola's I Greci in Tauride.

Grilletta e Pimpinone.   Intermezzi by Conti in his opera Sesostri rè di Egitto, Vienna, 1717.

SCHATZ 2198

Griselda.

Apostolo Zeno, Poesie drammatiche, Venezia, 1744, t. iii, p. 86. 19ᶜᵐ.

Three acts. Prefatory note and argument. No composer is mentioned. In the "Catalogo," at end of t. x, date and place of first ed. are given as "in Venezia 1701. E in Vienna 1725." ML 49.A2Z3

— Griselda. Pubblicata per la prima volta in Venezia 1701.

Apostolo Zeno, Poesie drammatiche, Orleans, 1785–86, t. II, p. 137– 216. 21ᶜᵐ.

Three acts. Argument. No composer is mentioned. ML 49.A2Z4

Griselda. Drama per musica da rappresentarsi nel Teatro Tron di S. Cassiano nel carnovale 1728 . . .

Venezia, Andrea Rumieri, 1708 [!] 55 p. 14½ᶜᵐ.

Three acts. Publisher's dedication dated Venice, January 26, 1728, argument, scenario, cast, name of Tommaso **Albinoni** as composer, and notice to the reader, in which this is called an altered version of Zeno's "Griselda." SCHATZ 120

Griselda.

[142]–186 p. 17ᶜᵐ. (Rolli, Componimenti poetici, Nuova edizione, Verona, G. Tumermani, 1744.)

Three acts, based on Zeno. Argument and dedication. The composer, Giov. Batt. **Bononcini,** is not mentioned.

First performed at London, Haymarket, February 22, 1722. ML 49.A2R7

Griselda. Drama per musica da rappresentarsi nel Teatro Tron di S. Cassiano l'autunno dell' anno MDCCLI.

n. i., n. d. 66 p. 14½ᶜᵐ.

Three acts. Argument, scenario, cast, name of Gaetano **Latilla** as the composer, and note that this drama by Apostolo Zeno has been kept intact "a scena per scena," except "di qualche arietta, e di qualche parola, per maggior comodo della musica." First performed at Venice, 1751, as indicated. SCHATZ 5460

Griselda, ballet. *See* Martin y Soler's Ifigenia in Aulide.

Griselda. Drama per musica da rappresentarsi nel Teatro Grimani di S. Samuele nel mese di maggio dell' anno 1720 . . .

Venezia, Marin Rossetti, 1720. 60 p. 14½ᶜᵐ.

Three acts. Impresario's dedication, argument, cast, scenario, name of Gioseppe Maria **Orlandini** as the composer, and notice to the reader, which is characteristic: "Il presente dramma rappresentato in Venezia nel 1701 nel Teatro Tron di S. Cassano . . . composto dall' incomparabile penna del celeberrimo letterato, Sig. Apostolo Zeno . . . questo adunque se in qualche parte adulterato si vede, per il cambiamento dell' arie, nomi di personaggi, ed altre picciole mutazioni, ad altro attribuir non si deve, che alla pura necessità di averlo dovuto stampare, come per l'apunto è stato ultimamente recitato in Mantova nel 1718 dopo l'applauso, che per quasi tutti li teatri d'Italia ha riportato . . ."

First performed with Orlandini's music at Brescia, Teatro dell' Accademia degli Erranti, 1716? SCHATZ 7330

— La virtù nel cimento. Dramma per musica da rappresentarsi nel Teatro arciducale di Mantova nel carnovale dell' anno MDCCXVII . . .

Mantova, Alberto Pazzoni, n. d. 63 p. 15ᶜᵐ.

Three acts. By Apostolo Zeno who is not mentioned. Impresario's dedication dated Mantova, January 16, 1717, argument, cast, scenario, and name of Giuseppe Maria **Orlandini** as the composer. Most of the dialogue and a number of arias are identical with Schatz 7330, but many arias are different. For instance, that of I, 5, in the Mantova version reads "Nella crudel mia sorte," in the Venice version, "Non è colpa del cor." SCHATZ 7331

La Griselda. Dramma eroicomico per musica da rappresentarsi nel nobilissimo Teatro di San Samuele per la prima opera dell' autunno 1793 . . .

Venezia, Modesto Fenzo, 1793. 2 pl., 83 p. 20^cm.

The plates are designed by F. Galimberti, engraved by G. Zatta. **Two** acts. Dedication by the author, Angelo Anelli, who is not mentioned, argument, cast, scenario, and name of Niccolò **Piccinni** as the composer. With the opera were performed Guiseppe Canciani's ballets, "Piramo e Tisbe" and "Il tradimento punito." The composers of the music are not mentioned.

First performed, as indicated, October 8, 1793.   SCHATZ 8095

— **La Griselda.** Dramma eroicomico per musica da rappresentarsi negl' Imperiali regi teatri di corte. Vienna 1794.

[Vienna], Mattia Andrea Schmidt, n. d. 119 p. 16½^cm.

Two acts. Niccolò **Piccinni** is mentioned as composer. German title-page, "Griselda," and text face Italian.

First performed, as indicated, August 30, 1794.   SCHATZ 8096

Griselda. Drama per musica, da rappresentarsi nel Teatro di S. Casciano. L'anno MDCCI . . .

Venezia, Niccolini, 1701. 72 p. 15^cm.

Three acts. Dedication by A[postolo] Z[eno] as the author ("questo mio drama"), argument, scenario, and notice to the reader, in which Zeno points out the differences between his plot and the sources. The composer, Antonio **Pollaroli,** is not mentioned.   SCHATZ 8266

Griselda. Dramma per musica da rappresentarsi nel Teatro di S. A. S. E. di Baviera. Nel carnevale dell' anno 1735.

Monaco, Giovanni Giacomo Vötter, n. d. 85 p. 15^cm.

Three acts. By Apostolo Zeno, who is not mentioned. Argument, scenario, cast. Pietro **Torri,** the composer, is not mentioned.

First performed at the same theater, October 12, 1723.   SCHATZ 10365

Griselda. Drama per musica da rappresentarsi nel Teatro Grimani di S. Samuel nella fiera dell' Ascenssione l'anno 1735 . . .

Venezia, Marino Rossetti, 1735. 47 p. 15½^cm.

Three acts. By Apostolo Zeno, who is not mentioned. Dedication, argument, cast, scenario, and name of Antonio **Vivaldi** as the composer.   SCHATZ 10770

Der grosse könig der afrikanischen Wenden Gensericus als Roms und Karthagos ueberwinder. O. T. of Conradi's Sieg der schoenheit.

Das grosse loos. Eine komische oper in zwey aufzuegen. Fuer das herzogl. Weimarische Hof-Theater. Die musik ist vom herrn capellmeister Wolf.

Weimar, Carl Ludolf Hofmann, 1774. 112 p. 15^cm.

By Friedrich Just Bertuch (not mentioned) after Favart's Le cocq de village. First performed at Gotha, Schloss-Theater im Ballhause, September 2, 1774.   SCHATZ 11080

Der grossmuethige bassa. Tr. of Bernardini's Il bassa generoso.

Der **grossmuethige Roland** in einem singe-spiel auff dem Hamburgischen Theatro vorgestellet. Im jahr 1695.

n. i., n. d. Unpaged. 18cm.

Three acts. Gottlieb Fiedler (not mentioned or Ludwig Postel, according to Neisser), the translator says in the prefatory note, which contains also the argument:

"Dieses schau-spiel, wie imgleichen *La superbia d'Alessandro* sind vormahls auff den praechtigen theatro zu Hannover mit so grossen vergnuegen der Durchlauchtigsten Herrschaft als auch aller hohen anwesenden auffgefuehret worden, dass man sich endlich erkuehnet sie nunmehr in teutscher sprache vorzustellen. Es hat aber die unvergleichliche musique, die zu beyden von einem der beruehmtesten virtuosen dieser zeit gesetzt worden, verursacht, dass die gantze version durchgehends nach selbiger eingerichtet und so viel moeglich auch nicht die geringste expression uebergangen ist."

These remarks refer to Agostino **Steffani,** whose "Orlando generoso," text by Ortensio Mauro, had first been performed at Hanover, 1691, in December.

First performed at Hamburg, Opernhaus beim Gänsemarkt, January, 1696.

SCHATZ 10034

Der **grossmuethige Scipio Africanus,** in einem singe-spiel auf dem Hamburgischen schau-platz vorgestellet 1694.

n. i., n. d. Unpaged. 18cm.

Three acts. Argument. Neither Gottlieb Fiedler, the author, is mentioned, nor Johann Sigismund **Kusser,** the composer. Text based, according to Schatz, on conte Niccolò Minato's "Scipione Affricano." SCHATZ 2285

Der **grossmuethige seefahrer.** Tr. of Piccinni's Gli stravaganti.

Der **grossmuethige Spanier.** Tr. T. of the ballet L'Espagnol généreux.

Die **grossmuethige Spartanerin** oder Archidamia. Tr. of Hasse's La Spartana generosa.

Die **grossmuethige Tomyris.** [vignette] In einem sing-spiel auf dem Hamburgischen schau-platz fuergestellet in monath Julius, 1717.

Hamburg, Friedrich Conrad Greflinger, n. d. Unpaged. 19cm.

Three acts. Scenario, dedication signed with the initials of the author, Johann Joachim Hoë, historical "vorbericht" with statement that the text is based on one by Domenico Lalli ["L'amor di figlio non conosciuto"], and note that this is the sixty-eighth opera by Reinhard **Keiser.** To some of the arias the Italian text has been added. SCHATZ 5094

Die **grossmuethigen feinde.** Tr. of Cimarosa's I nemici generosi.

La **grotta del mago Merlino.** Farsetta per musica a cinque voci da rappresentarsi nel Teatro Valle dell' illustrissimi Signori Capranica nel carnevale dell' anno 1786 . . .

Roma, Gioacchino Puccinelli, 1786. 51 p. 15½cm.

Two acts. Cast and name of Antonio Amiconi (**Amicone**) as composer. Author unknown to Schatz. SCHATZ 175

La **grotta di Trofonio.** Commedia per musica da rappresentarsi nel Teatro de' Fiorentini per terza opera del corrente anno 1785.

Napoli, n. publ., 1785. 57 p. 15cm.

Two acts. Argument, cast, name of **Paisiello** as the composer, and notice by the author Giuseppe **Palomba,** in which he admits his indebtedness to Casti's libretto of the same title (music by Salieri), though protesting that, on the whole, his text is a different treatment of the subject. The "eruditi versi" of Casti, with which he has enriched his own "debole verseggiatura," are designated by asterisks, and are: "Orsù

La **grotta di Trofonio**—Continued.

già compresi il vostro desio" (I, 1), "Spirti invisibili" (I, 5), "Ma non avreste appetito di noi" (II, 12), "Trofonio, Trofonio, filosofo Greco" (II, 17), "In questo minuto" (II, 18), "L'umore e il cervello" (II, 18).   SCHATZ 7680

— Die **Trofonius-hoehle.**   Ein komisches singspiel in zwey aufzuegen.   Aus dem italiänischen auf die musik des herrn Paesello übersetzt, von Stephanie dem juengem.

[Wien, n. d.], bey dem logenmeister.   109 p.   17ᶜᵐ.

First performed, with Palomba's Italian text, at Vienna, Burgtheater, July 15, 1787.   SCHATZ 7704

La **grotta di Trofonio.**   Opera comica da rappresentarsi nel Teatro di S. A. E. di Sassonia.

Dresda, n. publ., 1786.   157 p.   15ᶜᵐ.

Two acts. The author, Giambattista Casti, is not mentioned. The composer, Antonio **Salieri**, is mentioned. German title-page, "Die hoehle des Trophonius," and text face Italian.

First performed at Vienna, Burgtheater, October 12, 1785; at Dresden in 1786, as indicated.   SCHATZ 9297

— La **grotta di Trofonio.**   Dramma giocoso per musica da rappresentarsi in Parma nel R. D. Teatro di corte il carnevale dell' anno MDCCXCI . . .

Parma, Stamperia Carmignani, n. d.   viii, 60 p.   18ᶜᵐ.

Two acts. By Giambattista Casti, who is not mentioned. Scenario and name of Antonio **Salieri** as the composer.   SCHATZ 9296

— Die **zauberhoele des Trofonius,** eine komische oper in zwei akten nach der italienischen oper La grotta di Trofonio. Die musik ist von herrn Salieri . . . Frei uebersetzt von Johann August Halbe, schauspieler. Aufgefuehrt auf der K. K. priv. Leopoldstädter Schaubuehne.

[Wien], Mathias Andreas Schmidt, 1789.   79 p.   17½ᶜᵐ.

First performed 1789, as indicated.   SCHATZ 9298

— Arien und gesaenge aus **Trofons zauberhoele.**   Ein komisches singspiel in zwey aufzuegen. Aus dem italienischen uebersetzt. Die musik ist von Salieri.

Riga, Julius Conrad Daniel Mueller, 1794.   20 p.   17ᶜᵐ.

Two acts. The translator, Christian Gottlob Neefe, is not mentioned.

First performed at Riga, Theater i. d. Königsstrasse (Sept. 22) October 3, 1794.
                                                            SCHATZ 9299

La **grotte de Versailles.**   *See* Lully's L'eglogue de Versailles.

Grotte di Vulcano.   *See* Scipione Affricano.

The **grove,** or Love's paradice.   An opera, represented at the Theatre Royal in Drury-Lane . . . By Mr. Oldmixon.

London, Richard Parker, 1700.   4 p. l., 46, [2] p.   21½ᶜᵐ.

Five acts, with prologue and epilogue. Cast, dedication, and preface, in which the author says:

"As for those persons who . . . thought the catastrophe was not enough prepar'd, and that the discovery in the last act was huddled and in confusion, they will now see if what he had writ had been spoken, every thing wou'd have appear'd clear and natural, which, to shorten the entertainment, had been before broken and disor-

The **grove**—Continued.

der'd . . . 't was at first intended for a pastoral, tho in the three last acts, the dignity of the characters rais'd it into the form of a tragedy . . . As to what relates to the composition, no man ever consulted the meaning of words more than Mr. [Daniel] **Purcel** has done . . ."

First performed 1700, as indicated.   LONGE 79

Second copy.   LONGE 178

Grub-street opera. *See* The Welsh opera.

Grullo e Dorina, intermezzi. *See* Caldara's L'Anagilda.

Grullo, e Moschetta. Intermezzi in musica da rappresentarsi nel Teatro di S. Angelo nel carnovale 1732.

Venezia, Carlo Buonarigo, n. d. 16 p. 15½ᶜᵐ.

Three parts. Author not mentioned, and unknown to Schatz. **The composer,** Giuseppe Maria **Orlandini,** is not mentioned.   SCHATZ 7332

— **Grullo and Moschetta.** An interlude. Performed by Sig. Anna Maria Faini, and Signor Antonio Lottini, at the King's Theatre in the Hay-Market. The musick is composed by Sig. Giuseppe Maria Orlandini, chapel master to his Royal Highness the Great Duke of Tuscany.

London, J. Chrichley, 1737. 15 p. 16½ᶜᵐ.

Not only condensed to two instead of three parts, but so altered as to be largely a different text. The English translation is added.

First performed 1737, as indicated.   SCHATZ 7333

The **guardian out-witted.** A comic opera. As it is performed at the Theatre Royal in Covent Garden. The musick composed by Tho. Aug. Arne . . .

London, J. and R. Touson and T. Lownds, 1764. vii, [1], 66 p. 19½ᶜᵐ.

Three acts. Cast and preface, in which Arne, who is also known as the author, though he, "with all possible caution, endeavoured to conceal" his name, calls this, "the fifth dramatic piece I have written," but "the first I ever presumed to offer as a candidate for public approbation," and continues by saying:

"Should I have failed in the execution, let no unjust imputation fall on the system, which (if properly treated) is, by a mutual display of the sister arts, more various and entertaining than mere speech, unrelieved and unassisted by the power of harmony; for, in this species of drama, the dillettanti in music are drawn to coincide with the lovers of plays, having every charm of an opera, except the recitative, which (though it raises the dignity of the tragic Muse) is not so proper in common conversation . . ."

He then gives his ideas on "recitative in serious operas."

First performed, as indicated, December 12, 1764.   LONGE 36

Guatimozin ossia La conquista del Messico, ballet. *See* Zingarelli's Ifigenia in Aulide.

Der **guck kasten,** oder Das beste komt zulezt. Eine komische operette in zwei aufzuegen, nach einem italienischen text.

n. i., n. d. p. [73]–126. (J. C. Kaffka, Sammlung auserlesener theaterstücke, Breslau, 1784.)

Detached copy. Composed by the author.

First performed at Breslau, Neues Wäsersches Theater, 1782.   SCHATZ 4984

Günther von Schwarzburg, ein singspiel in drei aufzügen für die kurpfälzische Hofsingbühne.

Mannheim, Kuhrfuerstl. Hofbuchdruckerei, n. d.   6 p. l. (incl. port.), 83, [1] p.   16^{cm}.

The portrait is that of Günther von Schwarzburg.

Three acts.   Cast, names of Anton Klein as the author, of Ignaz **Holzbauer** as the composer of the opera, of Cannabich as composer of Lauchery's ballet and biographical sketch of the hero of the opera, which begins with these remarks, revealing the tendency of the author and composer:

"Deutsche helden, die verdienten, dass ihr bild mitten unter dem menschlichen geschlechte aufgestellet würde, sollten die in ihrem vaterlande vergessen werden? Ist nur die asche Roms und Athens allein kostbar und verehrungswürdig? Und sind dies auch noch Römer und Griechen, die auf unseren schaubühnen erscheinen, oder hören wir nur ihren namen nennen? Wir werfen unsere augen auf fremde tugendmuster, die vielleicht niemals gewesen sind, und sehen nicht, was in unserm schose ist. Ist vielleicht liebe zum fremden der hang unserer nation? Nein; ich bemerke, dass es vielmehr eine unrühmliche, ich könte sagen, eine sklavische gewohnheit vieler deutschen schriftsteller ist, die, indem sie alle zeiten und alle völker kennen, ihre eigenen schätze zu übersehen scheinen. Wie fruchtbar ist unser boden! wie reich ist das gebiet unserer geschichte! Ich habe mir aus derselben einen der vornehmsten helden gewählet."

First performed at Mannheim Churfuerstl. Hoftheater, January 5, 1777.

SCHATZ 4783

La guerra aperta. A. T. of Della Maria's **Il** matrimonio per scomessa.

La guerra aperta. Commedia per musica da rappresentarsi nel Real Teatro del Fondo di Separazione per quart' opera del corrente anno 1796 . . .

Napoli, n. publ., 1795.   47 p.   15^{cm}.

Two acts.   Author not mentioned and unknown to Schatz.   Impresario's dedication dated Naples, January 18, 1796, cast, and name of Francesco **Ruggi** as the composer.   With the opera was performed (composer of the music not mentioned) Giovanni Battista Giannini's "Inganno ed amor van sempre insieme, ballo di mezzo carattere."

SCHATZ 9144

La guerra del MDCLXXXIII fra i Turchi e gli Austriaci, ballet. *See* Rust's Artaserse.

Il guerrier generoso, ballet.   *See* Insanguine's Motezuma.

La guerriera Spartana. Drama di Giacomo Castoreo.   Per rappresentarsi in musica nel Theatro Novissimo di Sant' Apolinare . . .

Venetia, Giacomo Batti, 1654.   95 p. (incl. front.)   14^{cm}.

Prologue and three acts.   Author's dedication dated Venice, January 6, 1654, argument, and notice to the reader with name of Pietro [Andrea] **Ziani** as composer, and this remark:

"La mia povera Guerriera è stata accusata in giuditio come rea di non haver à bastanza lussingato il tuo genio; e per castigo (oltre l'haverli in più d'un loco amutilato le membra) si trattava di disperderli il proprio nome. Vi fù anco chi l'accusava di furto . . . Mà di questo non se ne parli, perchè potrò io bene difenderla quando occorresse."

SCHATZ 11216

Die guetigkeit des Titus. Tr. of Bernasconi's La clemenza di Tito.

Die guetigkeit des Titus. Tr. of Camerlocher's La clemenza di Tito.

Die **guetigkeit des Titus.** Tr. of Hasse's La clemenza di Tito.

Guilt makes a coward. A. T. of Lord Blunder's confession.

The **Guinea outfit.** A. T. of The sailor's farewell.

La **guirlande.** Opera-comique, representé pour la première fois sur le Théâtre de Roüen, le jeudi 24 mars 1757.

> *Rouen, De l'imprimerie de Machuel, 1757. 32 p. 19½ᶜᵐ.*

One act. Cast added by contemporary hand. This is a *comédie en vaudevilles* and should not be confused with Rameau's one act opéra-ballet, with which it has nothing to do. Unknown to the lexicographers. ML 50.2.G9

Gustaf Adolph och Ebba Brahe, lyrisk drame i tre acter. Första gången upförd den 24 januarii 1788.

> *n. i., n. d. [81]–159 p. 17ᶜᵐ. Kellgrens Saml. Skrift. Band. I.)*

Detached copy. Dedication signed by the author, Johan Henric Kellgren. The composer, Georg Joseph **Vogler,** is not mentioned. SCHATZ 10795

Gustavo Primo, rè di Svezia. Dramma per musica da rappresentarsi nel Teatro Grimani di S. Samuele in tempo della Ascensione nell' anno 1740 . . .

> *Venezia, Marino Rossetti, n. d. 48 p. 14½ᶜᵐ.*

Three acts. Impresario's dedication, cast, scenario, and names of "il Sig. dottor Carlo Goldoni Veneto" as author, and of Baldassare **Galuppi** as composer. O. T. of the following.

First performed May 25, 1740, as indicated. SCHATZ 3474

Gustavo Vasa. Dramma di tre atti per musica. Rappresentato per la prima volta in Venezia in tempo dell' Ascensione l'anno MDCCXL.

> *Carlo Goldoni, Opere teatrali, Venezia, Zatta e figli, 1788–95, v. 36, [103]–144 p. 18½ᶜᵐ.*

Same as "Gustavo Primo, rè di Svezia." PQ

Gustavo Vasa, ballet. *See* Rust's L'isola capricciosa.

Gustavo Vasa, ballet. *See* Sarti's Adriano in Siria.

Das **gute maedchen.** Tr. of Piccinni's La buona figliuola.

Das **gute maedel.** Tr. of Piccinni's La buona figliuola.

Das **gute maegdchen.** Tr. of Piccinni's La buona figliuola.

Gute menschen lieben ihren fuersten, oder Die Jakobiner in Deutschland. Ein zeitstueck in drey aufzeugen, fuer die Marinellische schaubuehne bearbeitet von Karl Friedrich Hensler. Die militärische symphonie und die musik zwischen den akten ist ganz neu verfasst, von herrn Ferdinand Kauer . . .

> *Wien, Mathias Andreas Schmidt, 1799. 84 p. 17ᶜᵐ.*

First performed, as indicated, July 18, 1799. SCHATZ 5032

Die gute mutter. Eine comische oper in zwey aufzuegen . . . aufgefuehrt auf den K. K. Hof-theatern in Wien.

[Wien], Kurtzbek, 1795. 2 p. l., 100 p. 15½ᶜᵐ.

By Johann Baptist von Alzinger, who is not mentioned.   Name of Paul **Wranitzky** as composer, and dedication to Maria Theresia, which reads, in part:
"Eure Majestaet geben bey allen gelegenheiten huldreichst zu erkennen, wie sehr Allerhoechst Dieselbe deutschen fleiss, deutsche kunst, deutsche verdienste hervorgezogen, ermuntert, belohnt wissen wollen. Auch das deutsche singspiel verdankt dem patriotischen winke Eurer Majestaet sein daseyn; denn dieser wink war fuer die Hofdirection ein befehl . . . so wagt es die Hofdirection . . . dieses erste opernbuch . . . zu den fuessen ihrer monarchinn zu legen."
First performed at Vienna, Hoftheater naechst dem Kaernthnerthore, May 11, 1795.
SCHATZ 11110

Ein gutes herz ziert jeden stand.   A. T. of Weigl's Der lumpensammler.

Der gutherzige polterer.   Tr. of **Martin** y Soler's - Il burbero di buon cuore.

Der gutsherr.   A. T. of Dittersdorf's Der schiffspatron.

Le Guy de Chesne, ou La feste des Druides, comedie en un acte et en vers libres, meslée d'ariettes.   Représentée pour la premiere fois par les Comédiens italiens ordinaires du roi, le mercredi 26 janvier 1763.   Avec la musique.

Paris, Duchesne, 1763. 37, [1] p. 17ᶜᵐ.

Neither the author, Jean Baptiste de Janquières, is mentioned, nor the composer, resp. arranger, Jean Louis **Laruette.**   On p. 34, the vaudeville, "Avant d'obtenir ma bergère," and on p. 36–37, the air, "Amour, entends ma voix" (I, 8).
SCHATZ 5439

Hadrian in Syrien.   Tr. of Holzbauer's Adriano in Siria.

Die haeuslichen zwistigkeiten.   A T. of Salieri's Die mode.

La haine vaincue par la force du sang.   Tr. of Lotti's Gl'odj delusi dal sangue.

The hall of Fingal.   A. T. of Oscar and Malvina.

Das Hallorenfest.   Ein singeschauspiel in drei akten.   Von F. G. Schlicht.

Magdeburg, Scheidhauerscher verlag, 1783. xvi, 124 p. 16½ᶜᵐ.

The text is preceded by a "Vorerrinnerung," in which the author describes the "Halloren" of Halle a/S, their habits, customs, organisation, etc., and their festivals called "Hallorenstechen" and "Pfingstbier."   No composer recorded.
ML 50.2.H16

Der Hamburger jahr-marckt oder Der gluechliche betrug.   In einem schertzhafften sing-spiele auf dem Hamburgischen Schauplatze vorgestellet im jahr 1725.

[Hamburg], mit Stromerischen schrifften, n. d.   Unpaged. 19ᶜᵐ.

Five acts.   Cast and prefatory note stating that his text had to be written in a hurry; that it is not meant to cast reflections on any particular persons:
"Das gantze werck gruendet sich auf einen erlaubten schertz, der doch allemahl die laster, durch vorstellung ihrer hesslichkeit, stillschweigend bestrafet. Der verfasser, so zwar ein Nieder-Sachse, aber der Hamburgischen mund-arth nicht recht kundig ist [Johann Philipp Praetorius], verspricht sich ein geneigtes nachsehen derer

Der **Hamburger jahr-marckt**—Continued.

in dem niederteutschen und sonst mit eingeschlichenen fehler; den dritten auftritt der vierten handlung hat eine fremde hand verfertiget und mit eingeruecket. Die . . . music haben wir dem . . . herrn capellmeister **Keiser** zu dancken."
Italian text has been added to some of the arias. SCHATZ 5095

Der **handwercks-mann ein edel-mann.** Tr. of Hasse's "L'artigiano gentiluomo."

Hannchen Robert, eine operette in drey aufzuegen von M * * * s.
Gotha, Carl Wilhelm Ettinger, 1779. 102 p. 15ᶜᵐ.
By Jacob Matthesius. No composer mentioned by Schatz. SCHATZ 11615

Hannchen und Bernardon. Tr. of Cimarosa's Giannina e Bernardone.

Hannibal in Capua, in einem sing-spiele, auf dem Hamburgischen Schau-platze vorgestellet.
[Hamburg], Gedruckt mit Spieringischen schrifften, 1735. 1 v. Unpaged. 19ᶜᵐ.
Three acts. Author unknown to Schatz. Some Italian arias were interpolated with addition of German translations and changes in the recitative. The composer, Johann Wolfgang **Franck,** is not mentioned. "Vorbericht" (argument) and scenario.
First performed at Hamburg, Opernhaus am Gänsemarkt, February 21, 1735, and in the original version 1681. SCHATZ 3335

Hanns der schuhflicker. Tr. of Philidor's Blaise le savetier.

Hanns Klachl, oder Das rendezvous in der neuen alee. Ein komisches singspiel in zwei aufzuegen. Die musik ist vom hrn. Tuczek.
n. i., 1797. 88 p. 15½ᶜᵐ.
By F. G. Quolfinger, ritter von Steinsberg, who is not mentioned.
First performed at Teplitz, Schlosstheater, 1797. SCHATZ 10500

— **Hanns Klachls** zweyter theil. Eine komische oper in zwey aufzuegen.
n. i., 1797. 91 p. 15½ᶜᵐ.
Composed by **Tuczek.** Neither he nor the author (Quolfinger?) is mentioned. SCHATZ 10501

Happiness at last. A. T. of The rover.

The **happy captive,** an English opera. With an interlude, in two comick scenes, betwixt Signor Capoccio, a director from the Canary Islands; and Signora Dorinna, a virtuosa.
London, printed for the author and sold by J. Brindley, 1741. vi, [2], 40 p. 19ᶜᵐ.
Three acts. Dedication by the author, Lewis Theobald, and Advertisement stating that the subject of the opera is "shadow'd out from a novel in Cervantes's *Don Quixote,* (book IV, of the first part) call'd, *The history of the slave* . . . The interlude, which is added in two comick scenes, is entirely new to our climate: and the success of it is submitted to experiment, and the taste of an audience."
The interlude (intermezzo), "CAPOCCHIO AND DORINA," is ascribed by Clarence to Colley Cibber, who is said to have abridged it from "The temple of dulness." (*See* this.) The composer is not mentioned, and no performance is recorded. LONGE 191

The **happy lovers:** or, The beau metamorphos'd.   A ballad farce.

2 p. l. (incl. front.), 28 p.   18½^{cm}.

Lacks title page.   Published 1736.   One act.   Cast.   By Henry Ward, who is not mentioned.   Ballad opera, the 16 airs of which are indicated by title.

According to the t.-p., acted at Lincoln's Inn-Fields in 1736 and Genest does not deny it in his vol. X.   LONGE 159

Happy recess.   A. T. of The fugitive.

Die **harfe.**   Operette von Wilhelm Schreiber.

Offenbach, Weiss und Brede, 1793.   62 p.   16½^{cm}.

Two acts.   Prefatory poem and "Vorrede" dated "Baaden, im Dezember 1792," in which Aloys Wilhelm Schreiber mentions Ignatz **Walter** as the composer, and says:
"Ich entwarf die gegenwaertige operette, weil mir das sujet gefiel, und weil wir so wenige ertraegliche deutsche singspiele besizzen, ohngeachtet diese gattung immer mehr einheimisch auf unsern buehnen wird.   Man deute mir diese aeusserung nicht als eigenliebig, denn es gehoert in der that wenig dazu, etwas besseres in diesem fache zu liefern, als die herren Eberl und konsorten."
Schatz records no performance.   SCHATZ 10861

— Die **zauberharfe.**   Ein singspiel nach August La Fontaine bearbeitet, vom verfasser des Waldbruders im Eichthale.

Offenbach, C. L. Brede, 1798.   62 p.   15^{cm}.

Same as "Die harfe," as comparison showed.   SCHATZ 11664

Harlequin animated.   A. T. of The fairy Favour.

Harlequin everywhere.   A. T. of Dibdin's The mirror.

Harlequin forrester.   A. T. of Reeve's Merry Sherwood.

Harlequin-Hydaspes: or, The Greshamite.   A mock-opera.   As it is perform'd at the Theatre in Lincoln's-Inn-Fields.

London, J. Roberts, 1719.   vii, [1], 55 p.   18^{cm}.

Three acts.   Cast and preface in which the reader is informed that the piece is "principally intended as a burlesque upon the famous opera of *Hydaspes:* and whoever shall think it worth his while to compare 'em, will find it work'd up accordingly.   But the inventor being a foreigner, and not having English enough to put his plan in execution himself, he was forc'd to call in another gentleman to his assistance; who having in his eye the present humorous dispute between some members of the faculty, could not but think it an excellent incident to enliven and diversify the design.   And hence it is that the performance is of such a mixt nature, as 'tis hard to give it a name, being half opera and half comedy . . ."
Most of the arias are simply parodies of such in Francesco Mancini's "L'Idaspe fedele" (London, Hay-market, May 23, 1710) and in every such case the Italian text, mostly by Giovanni Pietro Candi, is added in a footnote.   The parody is ascribed to a Mrs. Aubert, whose musical assistant (perhaps **Pepusch**?) is not recorded.
First performed May 22, 1719, as indicated.   LONGE 200

Harlequin Mungo; or, A peep into the tower: A new pantomimical entertainment, in two acts: as performing at the Royalty Theatre, Well-street, Goodman's-Fields.   The pantomime by Mr. Bates.   The music composed by Mr. Reeve . . .

London, Printed by J. Skirven for J. Griffith, n. d.   1 p. l., 6–32 p. 21^{cm}.

Cast.
First performed 1789, as indicated.   LONGE 102

Harlequin restor'd, or Taste a la mode.   *See* Arne's The fall of Phaeton.

Songs, airs, etc. in the entertainment of **Harlequin Teague**; or, The giant's causeway. As it is now performing at the Theatre-Royal, Hay-Market.

*London, T. Cadell, 1782.   21, [1] p.   20*cm*.*

One act.   Cast and name of Samuel **Arnold** as the composer.   The author, George Colman, is not mentioned.
First performed August 18, 1782. ML 52.2.H2A7

Harlequin traveller.   A. T. of Dibdin's The touchstone.

Songs, chorusses, etc.   As they are performed in the new entertainment of **Harlequin's Jubilee,** at the Theatre Royal in Covent-Garden.

*London, W. Griffin, 1770.   3 p. l., 13 p.   19½*cm*.*

Pantomime.   The singers mentioned at head of the songs.   The Advertisement dated Clement's Inn, January 29, 1770, begins:
"Mr. Woodward claims no merit in this trifling production, but the thought, which arose from the prologue to the *Jubilee*"
of which this a burlesque parody.   The composer is not mentioned (**Dibdin** composed the *Jubilee*). LONGE 32

Harlequin's opera.   A. T. of The fashionable lady.

Harlequin's wedding.   A. T. of Linley's The triumph of mirth.

Hartford-Bridge: or, The skirts of the camp.   An operatic farce in two acts.   Performed at the Theatre-Royal, Covent-Garden.   Written by Mr. Pearce.

*London, T. N. Longman, 1793.   3 p. l., 41 p.   20½*cm*.*

Cast, William Pearce's dedication, dated April 18, 1793, and his prefatory note with name of William **Shield**, who partly compiled, partly composed the music. Of his "Heaving of the lead" he says:
"The ballad in question was written on ship-board a few years since, and given to Mr. Shield previous to his late visit to Italy . . ."
First performed November 3, 1792. LONGE 222

Harvest-home.   A comic opera, in two acts.   As performed, with universal applause, at the Theatre-Royal, in the Hay-Market.   By Mr. Dibdin.

*London, Harrison & co., 1787.   27 p.   20½*cm*.*

Cast.   Text and music by Charles **Dibdin.**
First performed May 16, 1787, as indicated. LONGE 99

Hass und aussoehnung, oder Die verfolgte und triumphirende liebe.   Ein schauspiel mit gesang in vier aufzuegen.

*Glatz, Ernst Ferdinand Rordorf, 1797.   139, [1] p.   16*cm*.*

Dedicatory poem, "vorbericht" by the publisher, who was also the author.   The composer, Joseph **Grueger,** is not mentioned.   The clavierauszug was published according to advertisements on the last page. SCHATZ 4223

Songs, duets, trios and chorusses, in The **haunted tower.**   A comic opera, in three acts, as performed at the Theatre-Royal, Drury-Lane.

*London, J. Jarvis, 1789.   2 p. l., 24 p.   21*cm*.*

Cast.   Neither the author, James Cobb, nor Stephen **Storace** is mentioned, who, according to Longman and Broderip's vocal score "selected, adapted and composed" the music.   "Tho' pity I cannot deny" is there headed as by **Pleyel,** "Whither my love" as by **Paisiello,** "What blest hours" as by **Linley,** "Love

The **haunted tower**—Continued.

from the heart" as by **Martini**, "Dangers unknown impending" and "Dread parent of despair" as by **Sarti**.

First performed November 24, 1789, as indicated.   Longe 203

Second copy.   Longe 223

— Songs, duets, trios and chorusses, in The **haunted tower**. A comic opera in three acts, as performed at the Theatre royal, Drury-Lane.

London, J. Jarvis, 1791.   24 p.   20½ᶜᵐ.

Cast.   Without names of Cobb or **Storace**.   ML 50.2.M2S8

Second (closely trimmed) copy.   Longe 218

— The **haunted tower**, a comic opera in three acts.   As performed at the Theatre-Royal, Drury Lane.   Written by Mr. Cobb.

Dublin, P. Burne and J. Jones, n. d.   56 p.   17ᶜᵐ.

Cast.   Stephen **Storace**, the composer, is not mentioned.   Schatz 10081

Der **hausfreund**.   Tr. of Grétry's L'ami de la maison.

Der **haushahn**, ein faschingsstueck in zween aufzuegen.   Aufgefuehrt im K. K. Schauspielhause am Kaerntnerthore.   Die musik zu den gesaengen ist von herrn kapellmeister Hofmeister.

Wien, beym Logenmeister, 1783.   46 p.   16ᶜᵐ.

In his "Vorrede" the author, Johann Rautenstrauch (not mentioned) says: "Das publikum wird ersucht, dieses stueck fuer nichts anderes anzusehen, als was es ist—fuer eine kinderey . . ."

Composed by Franz Anton **Hoffmeister,** and first performed 1783, as indicated.

Schatz 4749

He **wou'd if he cou'd;** or, An old fool worse than any: a burletta. As it is performed at the Theatre Royal in Drury-Lane.   The music by Mr. Dibdin.

London, W. Griffin, 1771.   2 p. l., 27 p.   21ᶜᵐ.

.Cast.   By Isaac Bickerstaffe, who is not mentioned.

First performed as indicated, April 12, 1771.   Longe 251

— **He would if he cou'd**: or, An old fool worse than any.   A burletta.   In two acts.   By Isaac Bickerstaff, Esq.

[289]–306 p.   19ᶜᵐ.   (Collection of the most esteemed farces and entertainments, t. v, Edinburgh, 1792.)

Drury-Lane cast.   Schatz 11753E

Die **heimlich geschlossene ehe**.   Tr. of Cimarosa's Il matrimonio segreto.

Heinrich der Loewe, herzog von Braunschweig.   Ein historisches schauspiel mit gesang in fuenf aufzuegen, fuer die buehne bearbeitet von B. H. C. Reinhard, Schauspieler.

Braunschweig, Carl August Schroeder, 1793.   133 p.   15½ᶜᵐ.

2 unnumb. p. of advertisements bound with the text.   No composer recorded by Schatz.   Schatz 11618

Heinrich der Löwe.   Ein allegorisches singspiel in zwei aufzuegen von D. Schmieder.   Nach einer geschichte Heinrich des Löwen.   Die

Heinrich der Löwe—Continued.

musik von C. D. Stegmann, Operndirektor des kurfuerstl. Mainzischen Nationaltheaters.

n. i., 1792. 2 p. l., 74 p. 13^{cm}.

"Der kroenungsfeier Sr. Majestaet des deutschen kaisers Franz des Zweiten geweiht."

First performed at Frankfurt a/M, Nationaltheater, July 15, 1792. SCHATZ 10039

Heinrich und Lyda, eine scene aus dem menschlichen leben.

Leipzig, Christian Gottlob Hilscher, 1776. 32 p. 15^{cm}.

Neither the author, Bernhard Christian d'Arien, nor the composer, Christian Gottlob **Neefe**, is mentioned.

First performed at Berlin, Döbbelin'sches Theater, March 26, 1776. SCHATZ 7073

Die helden-muethige schaefer Romulus und Remus auf dem Hamburgischen Schau-platze in einer opera vorgestellet im jahr MDCCXXIV.

[Hamburg], Gedruckt bey Casper Jakhel, n. d. Unpaged. 18½^{cm}.

Three acts. Cast, scenario, and "Vorbericht," which reads, in part:

"Diese geschichte auf unserm Hamburgischen theatro in einem sing-spiel anitzo aufzufuehren, ist man durch die vortrefl. music dieser von dem sehr beruehmten componisten Sign. Giovanni **Porta** hierueber in Italien verfertigten und nachgehends in London und Braunschweig unter dem nahmen *Rhea Silvia*, mit dem groesten applausu aufgefuehrten opera, veranlasst. . . . So hat man bey diesem stuecke nicht allein einen gantzen recitativ, sondern auch eine neue lustige partie des Coridons nebst vielen andern embellissements der angenehmen music des Sign. Porta beylegen wollen.

"Die mit einem sternchen bezeichneten italiaenischen arien, sind vom erstbenannten Signore Porta, die uebrige, so wohl teutsch als italiaenische arien aber, wie auch der gantze Recitativ, die choere, simphonien und entréen, der composition des hrn. Johann Paul **Kuntz** wie die auffuehrung dieser opera gaentzlich anvertrauet worden."

All the Italian arias, by far the most of them starred (and therefore by Porta), have added German text. The original text is by Paolo Antonio Rolli.

The opera was first performed as "Numitore" at London, Haymarket, on April 13, (Schatz), April 2 (Fassini) 1720, and then, as "Rhea Sylvia," at Brunswick in 1723.

SCHATZ 8381

Helena. *See* Keiser's La forza dell' amore.

Helena rapita da Paride. Drama per musica nel Teatro Novissimo di S. Angelo. L'anno MDCLXXVII . . .

Venetia, Francesco Nicolini, 1677. 64 p. 14½^{cm}.

Three acts and prologue. By Aurelio Aureli, who is not mentioned. Publisher's dedication, argument, scenario and notice to the reader with name of Domenico **Freschi** as composer. This original edition has in act I nineteen scenes, in act II twenty-six and in act III seventeen, whereas the second ed. of 1677 (*see* below) has twenty, twenty-eight and twenty. In this I, 14 has aria "Voglio, che mora," whereas the first ed. has "Con la scorta de la vendetta." In this the prologue begins "Da le rotanti sfere," in the second ed. "Nubi mie tempestose." I, 20 of this second ed. begins "Ho vinto Amori" and has aria "Arcieri alati / Sù brillate." ML 50.2.H3F7

— **Helena rapita da Paride.** Drama per musica nel Teatro Novissimo di S. Angelo. L'anno MDCLXXVII. Seconda impressione. Con nove aggionte . . .

Venetia, Francesco Nicolini, 1677. 68 p. 14^{cm}.

Three acts, with prologue. By Aurelio Aureli, who is not mentioned. Publisher's dedication, author's notice to the reader, with name of Giovanni Domenico **Freschi** as composer, and scenario. SCHATZ 3351

Helena rapita da Paride—Continued.

— **Elena rapita da Paride.** Drama per musica nel Teatro Zane à S. Moisè di Aurelio Aureli. Seconda impressione . . .

   Venetia, Francesco Nicolini, 1687. 71 p. 14^{cm}.

Three acts. Author's dedication, dated Venice, January 18, 1687, argument, scenario, notice to the reader, who is informed that Francesco **Navarra** not only composed several additional arias for this revival of **Freschi**'s opera, but also changed some of the latter's arias "per aggiustarsi all' abilità de musici che le cantano." This is putting it very mildly, as the new version differs considerably from the old. For instance, the prologue has been dropped entirely, and not many scenes have been left intact. Thus in I, 4 (in the original ed. incorrectly numbered as fifth scene), Enone sang, 1677, "Gelosia, non tormentarmi / Non ti voglio nel mio core," but, 1687, "Gelosia, non posso più. / Tu mi laceri quest' alma."   Schatz 3358

L'Helena rapita da Theseo. Dramma musicale da recitarsi nel Teatro di S. Gio. e Paolo.

   Venetia, Michiel Miloco, 1653. 94 p. 13^{cm}.

By Giacomo Badoaro after suggestions of Giovanni Faustini. Three acts with prologue. Argument and minute "Scenario" on p. [77]–94. The composer, Pietro Francesco **Cavalli**, is not mentioned.

First performed, as indicated, carnival 1653.   Schatz 1735

Helena und Paris, ein musikalisches schauspiel in drei aufzeugen, nach dem italienischen frei bearbeitet. Die musik ist von herrn Winter. Aufgefuehrt zu Muenchen, 1782.

   n. i., n. d. 64 p. 15^{cm}.

Three acts. By Carl J. Förg, who signs the "Vorerrinerung" (argument) with his initials. Scenario, cast, and prefatory dedication by Winter, dated Munich, 1782, in which he says:

"Schon verschiedene meiner deutschen landsleute, und kunstverwandten unternamen es, auch in dem erhabnen fache von theatermusik ihre faehigkeiten zu zeigen, und sich zu dem verdienste der in dieser gattung beruehmt gewordenen auslaender hinauzuschwingen. Ich will hier nicht untersuchen, in weit sie hierinn ihren entzweck erreichet, oder nicht erreichet haben. Soviel kann ich aber zur ehre der Deutschen bezeugen, dass herr Holzbauer einer der ersten diese bahn mit ruhme betrat. Ich fuehlte ebenfalls den trieb in mir, dem beispiele dieser maenner zu folgen. Ich war anfangs misstrauisch auf mich selbst, und wollte diese neigung in mir ohne weiters unterdruecken. Allein ich war zu schwach, und so enstund unter schwankender unentschlossenheit gegenwaertiges werk . . ."

First performed at Munich, National Schaubuehne, February 5, 1782.

    Schatz 11035

— **Helena und Paris.** Ein heroisches singspiel in drei aufzeugen. Die musik ist vom herrn Kapellmeister Winter.

   Berlin, n. publ., 1797. 23 p. 16^{cm}.

First performed at Berlin, Nationaltheater, February 6, 1797.   Schatz 11036

Heliates und Olympia. A. T. of Keiser's Die blut-durstige rache.

Helvetic liberty; or, The lass of the lakes. An opera. In three acts. Dedicated to all the archers of Great Britain. By a Kentish bowman . . .

   London, L. Wayland, 1792. 1 p. l., vii, [2], 4–64 p. 18½^{cm}.

The text is preceded by the unknown author's dedication (in form of an address), "To the toxophilites for Kent." No composer or performance recorded by Clarence.

    Longe 276

Hemmeligheden, et comisk syngestykke i en handling, efter Mr. Quetant's original. Omarbeidet til det Kongelige Theaters Burg af Adam Gottlob Thoroup, sadt i musik af hr. Kuntzen.

Kiøbenhavn, P. M. Liunges vorlag, 1796. 79 p. 16½ᶜᵐ.

First performed, as indicated, November 22, 1796. SCHATZ 5320

Henri IV, drame lyrique, en trois actes et en prose. Par M. de Rozoy, citoyen de Toulouse, etc., etc. Représenté pour la première fois sur le Théatre des Comédiens italiens ordinaires du roi, le 14 novembre 1774.

Paris, Vente, 1775. 54, [1] p. 18½ᶜᵐ.

On p. [3], "Vers au Roi, en lui présentant le premier exemplaire imprimé de Henri IV, drame lyrique." SCHATZ 6039

L'Heraclio. Melodrama da rappresentarsi nel Theatro Grimano di SS. Gio. e Paolo l'anno 1671 . . .

Venetia, Francesco Nicolini, 1671. front., 66, [1] p. 14ᶜᵐ.

Three acts. By conte Nicolò Beregani, who is not mentioned. Publisher's dedication, dated Venice, January 17, 1671, argument, scenario. The composer, Pietro Andrea **Ziani,** is not mentioned. SCHATZ 11217

Heraclit und Democrit. Tr. of Salieri's Eraclito e Democrito.

Texte von den arien und gesaengen aus dem **Herbstabentheuer,** oder: Wer wagt, gewinnt. Ein komisches singspiel in zwey aufzuegen.

n. i., 1790. 24 p. 16ᶜᵐ. SCHATZ 11678

— Das **herbstabendtheuer.** Oder: Wer wagt, gewinnt. Ein komisches singspiel. in zwei aufzügen, nach der ersten idee des Finto cavaliere und Ackorimboni's komposition, von [Johann Christoph] Bock.

147–219 p. (Komische Opern der Italiener, Th. II, no. 3.)

Detached copy.

First performed at Dresden, Hoftheater, 1779. "Il Finto cavaliere" was first performed at Rome, Teatro della Pace, 1777. SCHATZ 15

Hercole perseguitato. *See* M. Curzio.

Hercule filant, parody. *See* Omphale.

Hercules. A masque. Set to musick by Mr. John Eccles.

Forms (with cast) the third act (p. 26–30) of "THE NOVELTY. Every act a play. As it is acted at the New-Theatre in Little Lincolns Inn-fields, by His Majesty's servants. Written by Mr. Motteux, and other hands," London, Richard Parker and Peter Buck, 1697. From Peter Motteaux's interesting preface it appears that the masque was finished by him and Eccles first and the other "acts" were later on built around it, as it were. He also says:

"The foregoing lines were published as a preface to that masque, some few copies of which were printed for the use of the audience, the first day of the novelty's being acted. I have nothing to add, but that altogether it has met with better success than I cou'd expect, since (thanks to my friends) it was not only beneficial to me on the third, but also on the sixth day, and that in a season when the town is most empty . . ." LONGE 127

Hercules. A musical drama. As it is perform'd at the Kings' Theatre in the Hay-Market. The musick by Mr. Handel.

London, J. and R. Tonson and S. Draper, 1745. 40 p. 19^{cm}.

Three acts. This is, of course, Händel's secular "oratorio" "Hercules," text by Thomas Broughton.

First performed January 5, 1745.   LONGE 306

Hercules. *See* Keiser's Die verbindung des grossen . . .

Hercules am Thermodon. Tr. of Schürer's Ercole sul Termodonte.

Hercules unter denen Amazonen, in einer opera vorgestellt, im jahr 1694.

Hamburg, Conrad Neumann, n. d. 2 p. l., 44 p. 18½^{cm}.

Three acts. Argument and scenario.   SCHATZ 5272

— **Hercules.** Anderer theil.

Hamburg, Conrad Neumann, n. d. 1 p. l., 45–90 p. 18½^{cm}.

Three acts.

This opera, text by Friedrich Christian Bressand, music by Johann Philipp **Krieger** (neither of whom mentioned), was first performed, as above, on two evenings at Hamburg, Opernhaus beim Gänsemarkt; as one opera of five acts; at Brunswick, Courttheatre, 1693.   SCHATZ 5273

Les **héritiers supposés.** Tr. of Sarti's I finti eredi.

Herkules auf dem Oeta. In einem aufzuge. Komponirt vom herrn musikdirektor Graefe zu Hannover.

n. i., n. d. 22 p. 16^{cm}.

By Johann Benjamin Michaelis, who is not mentioned.
No performance recorded by Schatz.   SCHATZ 4061

Herkules auf dem Oeta. Eine operette in einem aufzuge, von J. B. Michaelis.

Leipzig, in der Dyckischen Buchhandlung, 1772. 22, [1] p. 15^{cm}.

The composer, Joseph Aloysius **Schmittbauer,** is not mentioned.
First performed at Hanover, Schlosstheater, June 4, 1771.   SCHATZ 9656

Héro et Léandre, ballet pantomime, en un acte, représenté, pour la premiere fois, à Paris, sur le Théâtre de la République et des Arts, le 6 frimaire an 8 [November 27, 1799]; par L. J. Milon, artiste de ce théâtre.

Paris, A l'Imprimerie à prix-fixe, an VIII. [1799–1800.] 28 p. 20^{cm}.

One act. Cast, detailed description and "Avertissement," in which the author defends himself principally against the charge of a plagiarism on Gardel's "Ballet de Paris." The composer is not mentioned.   ML 52.2.H3

Second copy.   ML 48.B2

Der **herr als bedienter.** Tr. of Schuster's Il servo padrone.

Der **herr doctor.** Tr. of Fischietti's Il signor dottore.

Das **herrnrecht.** Tr. of Martini's Le droit du seigneur.

Hesione, tragedie représentée par l'Academie royale de musique l'an 1700: Les paroles de M. Danchet & la musique de M. Campra. LI. opera.

n. i., n. d. front., 109–166 p. 14ᶜᵐ. (Recueil général des opera, Paris, 1703, t. vii.)

Detached copy. Five acts, with prologue.
First performed, as indicated, Dec. 21, 1700. SCHATZ 1555
Second copy. ML 48.R4

— **Hesione,** tragédie, représentée par l'Académie royale de musique, pour la premiere fois le 21 décembre 1700.

[27]–*82 p. 17½ᶜᵐ. (Antoine Danchet, Théâtre, t. ii, Paris, 1751.)*
Prologue and five acts. The composer, André **Campra,** is not mentioned.

PQ 1972.D2

— **Hesione,** parodie. Représentée pour la premiere fois par les Comédiens italiens ordinaires du roi, le 28 octobre 1729.

Les parodies du Nouveau Théâtre italien, Nouv. éd., Paris, 1738, t. iv, [221]–269 p. 16½ᶜᵐ.
One act. By Dominique and Romagnesi (*see* t. I). The airs and vaudeville used are printed at end of the volume in the "Table des airs" (92 p.). ML 48.P3

L'heureuse nouvelle, comédie en un acte, mêlée de vaudevilles, représentée sur le Théatre de Liège, à l'occasion des fêtes données pour la naissance de Mᵍʳ le Dauphin . . . Par M. de * * * Valbray.

Liége, F. J. Desoer, 1782. 38 p. 19ᶜᵐ.
Cast and dedication by Valbray, the author. The arranger of the music not recorded by Schatz.
First performed, as indicated, January 2, 1782. SCHATZ 11494

Heyrath aus liebe. Ein nachspiel mit arien und gesaengen.
Gotha, Carl Wilhelm Ettinger, 1781. 80 p. 16½ᶜᵐ.
Two acts. Neither the author, Schack Hermann Ewald, nor the composer, Johann Friedrich **Hönicke,** is mentioned.
First performed at Gotha, Hoftheater, July 9, 1777. SCHATZ 4787

Die heyrath durch betrug. Tr. of Anfossi's Il matrimonio per inganno.

Hier gehen die maedchen auf die freierei aus. A. T. of Spindler's Die liebe in der Ukräne.

Hierone tiranno di Siracusa. Drama rappresentato nel nuovo Teatro Ducale in Piacenza . . . Poesia di Aurelio Aureli, e musica singolare di D. Bernardo Sabadini, organista della sudetta A. S.

Parma, Stamperia Ducale, 1688. 92 p. 15½ᶜᵐ.
Three acts. Impresario's dedication, argument, cast, scenario, and notice to the reader, in which Aureli speaks of
"gli applausi, che benignamente donasti questo carnevale passato in Parma alla mia Olimpia, ed al Teseo in Atene." SCHATZ 9197

Gesaenge aus dem singspiele: Hieronimus Knicker, in zwey aufzuegen. In musik gesezt von Dittersdorf.

Hamburg, Joh. Matthias Michaelsen, 1792. 32 p. 17ᶜᵐ.
The text differs from Vulpius' version and may be approximately the original text as written by Dittersdorf. For instance, Vulpius has (as No. 5) "Herr! Sie

Hieronimus Knicker—Continued.

werden übel fahren," the Hamburg text "Ey, Sie müssen sich ja schaemen"; Vulpius has (as no. 6) "Liebe fraegt nach keinem stande," Hamburg "Bin ich gleich vom Bauernstande"; Vulpius has (as no. 7) "Mein Onkel ist ein halber narr," Hamburg "Mein onkel ist ein harter mann."

First performed at Vienna, Marinellische schaubuchne in der Leopoldstadt, July 1789.　　　　　　　　　　　　　　　　　　　　　　　　　ML 50.2.H35D4

— **Hieronymus Kniker** [!].　Eine komische operet+ɛ in 2. aufzuegen. Nach Dittersdorfs musik neubearbeitet.

   Passau, Niklas Ambrosi, 1793.　72 p.　16½^{cm}.

   Originally by the composer, altered by Vulpius.　-　　　　　Schatz 2593

— **Hieronimus Knicker.**　Eine komische operette in zwey aufzuegen.　Nach Ditterdorfs musik neubearbeitet.

   n. i., 1793.　78 p.　16½^{cm}.

   Practically the same version as Schatz 2593.　　　　　　Schatz 2594

The Highland fair; or, Union of the clans.　An opera.　As it is perform'd at the Theatre-Royal, in Drury Lane, by His Majesty's servants.　Written by Mr. Mitchell.　With the musick, which wholly consists of select Scots tunes, prefix'd to each song.

   London J. Watts, 1731.　7 p. l., 78 p.　19½^{cm}.

   Lacks the front., designed by W. Hogarth, "A Scots opera."　Three acts and introduction.　On p. [vii–x], "Books printed for J. Watts," preceded by a table of the tunes and dedication.and followed by the cast.　The 51 tunes are printed in the text with their titles.

   First performed, as indicated, March 20, 1731.　　　　　ML 50.5.H43

   Second copy, with Hogarth's front., making 8 p. l.　　　　Longe 50

Songs, duetts, etc in the **Highland reel.**　Comic romance.　In three acts; performed at the Theatre-Royal, Covent-Garden.　The musick composed and compiled by Mr. Shields [!]　Fifth edition.

   London, T. Cadell, 1789.　23 p.　21^{cm}.

   Cast.　John O'Keefe, the author, is not mentioned.

   First performed, as indicated, November 6, 1788; at Dublin, Theatre, Smock Alley, 1786.　　　　　　　　　　　　　　　　　　　　　　PR 1241.D7

— The **highland reel,** a comic opera.　In three acts.　As it is performed at the Theatres-Royal in London and Dublin.　By John O'Keefe, Esq.

   Dublin, Sold by the booksellers, 1790.　72 p.　17^{cm}.

   London and Dublin (1790) casts.　William **Shield,** the composer is not mentioned.

   　　　　　　　　　　　　　　　　　　　　　　Schatz 9869

   Second copy.　Longe 205

Hilft's nicht, so schadt's nicht.　A. T. of Dittersdorf's Das rote kaeppchen.

L'Himen et l'Amour.　*See* Mondonville's Les projets de l'Amour.

Hipermenestre.　Tr. of the ballet Ipermestra.

L'Hipermestra. Festa teatrale rappresentata dal Sereniss. principe cardinale Gio. Carlo di Toscana per celebrare il giorno natalizio del real principe di Spagna.

Firenze, Stamperia di S. A. S., 1658. 9 p. l. (incl. front.), 78 p. 21ᶜᵐ. 13 fold. pl. (50 to 58 by 38ᶜᵐ.).

The plates are unsigned in our copy. Wotquenne says "gravées par Silvio degli Alli." Twelve represent scenes from the opera, the thirteenth represents an interior view of the Teatro de la Pergola, seen from the stage.

Three acts and prologue, preceded by the Antefatto and the author Moniglia's dedication of date Florence, June 12, 1658. The text is followed by: DESCRIZIONE DELLA PRESA D'ARGO E DE GLI AMORI DI LINCEO CON HIPERMESTRA; festa teatrale . . . per celebrare il natale del Sereniss. principe di Spagna. In Firenze, Nella stamperia di S. A. S. MDCLVIII" (32 p. 21cm.). According to Moniglia's preface to his "Poesie drammatiche" this description of "Hipermestra" was written by Orazio Ricasoli Rucellai. He gives a minute synopsis of the action, mentions the noblemen who participated in the ballets and in the Abbattimento, narrates the preparations for performance, the beginning of which he dates June 18, 1658 "verso le 24 ore" [!], with a display of extraordinary hospitality towards his guests by the cardinal, gives a brief description of the new "Teatro dell' Accademia de gl'Immobili" (Teatro de la Pergola) and says:

"Terminata che fu la composizione di questo dramma, speditamente si trasmise al Sig. Francesco Cavallo (**Cavalli**) a Venezia, acciò che con l'artifizio di suo armonioso contrappunto traesse altrui di mezo al cuore i più teneri, e compassionenoli affetti, che all' espressione delle parole, e de gli avvenimenti poetici fussero più confacevoli, ed egli che viene oggi reputato il primo compositore d'Italia, particolarmente sopra lo stile drammatico, con prestezza incredibile ne rimandò il componimento di tanta dolcezza, e soavità di stile, che avendo a detta d'ognumo nell' altre sue opere acquistata la palma sopra i maestri più esimij, in questa può dirsi che abbia superato sè stesso. Il pensiero poi di fare la scelta de' musici, e delle voci più adattate alle parti degl' interlocutori, & assister loro con ogni maggiore studio, e diligenza, fu dato da S. A. alli SS. marchese Filippo Niccolini suo Maestro di camera, e march. Gio: batista del Monte suo Cavellerizzo maggiore, ed alli SS. Pietro Strozzi, e Filippo Franceschi, che hanno somma diletazione nella musica, & ottimo gusto al pari de professori medesimi . . ." ML 50.2.H38C2

— L'Ipermestra. Festa teatrale rappresentata dal sereniss. principe cardinale Gio. Carlo di Toscana per celebrare il giorno natalizio del Real principe di Spagna.

Firenze, Vincenzio Vangelisti, 1689 (Giovanni Andrea Moniglia, *Poesie drammatiche, parte prima, Firenze, Vincenzio Vangelisti, 1689, v. 1, 1 p. l., 118 p., 12 pl. 24ᶜᵐ.*

The plates are the same as in the 1658 ed. but on a smaller scale (34 x 24cm.) of poorer workmanship and less ornate. The thirteenth pl. (inside view of the Teatro della Pergola) is not in this ed.

Three acts and prologue. Antefatto and after the list of Interlocutori the first, introductory, part of Rucellai's "Descrizione," with name of **Cavalli**, date of first performance, etc., and the description of the prologue. That of the single acts precedes them. ML 49.A2M7

Hippodamie, tragedie représentée par l'Academie royale de musique l'an 1708. Les paroles de M. Roy & la musique de M. Campra. LXX. opera.

n. i., n. d. 279–332 p. 14ᶜᵐ. (Recueil général des opera, Paris, 1710, t. ix.)

Detached copy. Five acts, with prologue and Avertissement.
First performed, as indicated, March 6, 1708. SCHATZ 1556
Second copy. ML 48.R4

Hippolyte et Aricie, tragedie, représentée pour la premiere fois, par l'Academie royale de musique; le jeudy premier octobre 1733.

[Paris], Jean Baptiste Christophe Ballard, 1733. xx, 56 p. 23ᶜᵐ.

Prologue and five acts. Cast. Neither the composer Jean Philippe **Rameau,** is mentioned, nor the author, Pellegrin, who, in a preface, defends himself against his critics. ML 50.2.H4R2

— Hipolyte et Aricie, tragedie représentée par l'Academie royale de musique, l'an 1733. Paroles de M. Pellegrin. Musique de M. Rameau. CXIX. Opera.

n. i., n. d. pl., 311–380 p. 14ᶜᵐ. (Recueil général dés opera, t. xv, Paris, 1739.)

Detached copy. Five acts and prologue. Préface (p. 313–318), giving the historical basis of the plot, etc. SCHATZ 8587
Second copy. ML 48.R4

— Hippolyte et Aricie, tragedie, représentée par l'Académie royale de musique de Paris, en octobre 1733. en septembre 1742. Et par l'Academie royale de musique de Lyon, en février 1743.

Lyon, Aimé Delaroche, 1743. iv, 54 p. 23ᶜᵐ.

Five acts and prologue. Cast. SCHATZ 8587a

— Hippolite et Aricie, parodie; représentée pour la premiere fois par les Comédiens italiens ordinaires du roi, le 11 octobre 1742. Nouvelle édition.

Paris, N. B. Duchesne, 1759. 56 p. 19ᶜᵐ. (Theatre de M. Favart, Paris, 1763–77, t. i.)

One act. *En vaudevilles.* Cast. Several of the airs are printed in the text. On p. 51–56, "Ariette chantée par Mlle Victoire" with remark, "A la reprise de cette parodie en 1757, Mlle. Victoire chantoit cette ariette ["Dans mon coeur s'élève"] à la scene IV après le couplet: Enfin j'ai découvert leur feu." The arranger of the music is not mentioned by Font. ML 49.A2F1

Hippomenes and Atalanta, ballet. *See* Sacchini's Enea e Lavinia.

Das hirten maegdchen. Ein sing-spiel in neun komischen idyllen. Die musik ist von herrn Winter.

Muenchen, Joseph von Craetz, 1784. 46, [2] p. 16ᶜᵐ.

By Heinrich Braun, who is not mentioned. Cast.
First performed at Munich, National Schaubuehne, March 26, 1784.

SCHATZ 11037

The **history of Dioclesian.** A. T. of H Purcell's The prophetess.

The **history of Sʳ Francis Drake.** Exprest by instrumentall and vocall musick, and by art of perspective in scenes, etc. The first part. Represented daily at the Cockpit in Drury-Lane at three afternoon punctually.

London, Henry Herringman, 1659. 1 p. l., 37 p. 20½ᶜᵐ.

"The description of the frontispiece" (on p. 1) ends with this allusion to "the Cruelty of the Spaniards in Peru," performed 1658 and by the same author, Sir William Davenant, who is not mentioned:
"This frontispiece was the same which belong'd to the late representation; and it was convenient to continue it, our argument being in the same country."
While the scenery of the first to sixth "entry" is lovingly described and while there are such remarks as "the curtain rises [in the first entry] by degrees to an ascending ayre," the libretto is silent on the question of who composed the music,

The history of Sr Francis Drake—Continued.

but presumably one or more of Davenant's previous collaborators were responsible for it: Dr. Charles Coleman, Captain Henry Cook, Henry Lawes, and George Hudson.

On May 5, 1659, Evelyn wrote in his diary with rather unfavorable (and also unfair) comment of "a new opera after the Italian way in recitative, music and sceanes." For chronological reasons it stands to argue that he had "the history of Sr Francis Drake" in mind rather than (as is usually claimed) "The cruelty of the Spaniards in Peru." It is also noteworthy that Davenant incorporated "The History, etc." as the third and "The cruelty, etc." as the fourth act of his medley, "The playhouse to be let," 1673. ML 50.2.H5

Hob in the well. L. A. T. of Flora.

Der hochmuethige Alexander. Tr. of Händel's Alessandro.

Der hochmuethige, gestuerzte und wieder erhabne Croesus. [vignette] In einem singe-spiele vor vielen jahren auff dem grossen Hamburger schau-platze vorgestellet, jetzo von neuem wieder aufgefuehret im jahr 1711.

Hamburg, Friedrich Conrad Greflinger, n. d. Unpaged. 19^{cm}.

Three acts. The "Inhalt und Vorbericht" reads, in part:

" . . . ein italiaenischer poet [he refers to conte Nicolò Minato's "Creso"] . . . hat aus diesen theils wahrhafftigen, theils wahrscheinlichen begebenheiten, mit einmischung sinnreicher zufaelle und verwirrungen, ein auf zwo repraesentationes eingetheiltes sing-spiel in seiner sprache verfertigt, woraus vor vielen jahren ein hiesiger liebhaber der music und poesie, auff ansuchen vornehmer freunde, bey seltenen muessigen stunden, dieses gegenwaertige sing-spiel in die teutsche sprache gebracht, und theils nach der aus der erfahrung verspuehrten neigung hiesiger zuschauer, mit untermischung einiger lustbarkeiten, noch mehr auff den endzweck eingerichtet, dass nebst schicklichen staats- und sitten-lehren, die tugend zur liebe und nachfolge, die laster zur vermeidung vorgestellet, am allermeisten aber aus dem verlauff der an sich im hauptwercke warhafftigen geschichte die unbestaendigkeit weltlicher ehre und reichthums anerkanndt werde; wodurch, weil es der zeit einigen applausum gefunden, und nur, dass es in der auffuehrung etwas zu weitlaeufftig und langwaehrend waere, bemerckt worden, man es jetzo mit einiger mehrern einschraenkung und verkuertzung von neuem aufflegen lassen, und wieder auf hiesige schaubuehne bringen wollen."

Neither the author, Lucas von Bostel, is mentioned, nor the composer, Reinhard **Keiser.**

Originally performed at Hamburg in 1684. SCHATZ 5124

— **Der hochmuethige, gestuerzte und wieder erhabene Croesus,** in einem musicalischen schau-spiele auf dem Hamburgischen Schau-platze vorgestellet im jahr 1730.

[Hamburg], mit Stromerischen schrifften, n. d. Unpaged. 19^{cm}.

Three acts. "Vorbericht" and name of Reinhard **Keiser** as the composer. The author, Lucas von Bostel, is not mentioned. The text is slightly different from that in the edition of 1711. For instance, the opening aria of I, 2, "Ungluecks-triebe," has been replaced by "Hoffe noch, gekraencktes herz" and the aria in I, 13, "Geneigtes geschicke," has been dropped.

First performed, as indicated, December 4 or 6, 1730. SCHATZ 5096

Die hochzeit des Figaro. Ein komisches singspiel in zwey aufzuegen. Aus dem franzoesischen frei bearbeitet.

Bruenn, Johann Sylv. Siedler, 1789. 130 p. 16½^{cm}.

Author unknown to Schatz. Composed by **Dittersdorf,** who is mentioned as composer.

First performed at Brünn, Kgl. Staedtisches Theater, 1789; at Graz, Ständ. Theater, June 15, 1801. SCHATZ 2596

Die hochzeit des Figaro. Tr. of Mozart's Le nozze di Figaro.

Das **hochzeitfest des Amors und der Norizia.** Theatralisches singgedicht bey der hoechstbeglueckten vermaehlung Sr. Koeniglichen Majestaet Joseph, roemischen koenigs etc etc etc und der Kaiserlich Koeniglichen Hohheit Josepha Antonia . . . im jahr 1765.

Muenchen, Johann Friedrich Ott, n. d.   Unpaged.   20 p.

Two acts. Cast and names of Eugenio Giunti as author, of Pietro Pompeo **Sales** as composer. Italian text faces German, which was by Antonio Giunti. The Italian title was "Le nozze di Amore e di Norizia."

First performed January 12, 1765, as indicated.   Schatz 9268

Die **hoeflichen bauern,**   A. T. of Der neue herr.

Die **hoehle des Trophonius.**   Tr. of Salieri's La grotta di Trofonio.

Hokus Pokus! Eine komische oper in zwei aufzuegen **von** C. A. Vulpius. Die musik ist von Dittersdorf.

Leipzig, Johann Samuel Heinsius, 1794.   88 p.   15ᶜᵐ.

According to Schatz, Vulpius's version is not the original one.

First performed at Leipzig, Theater b. Rannstädter Thore, October 25, 1793; at Breslau, Wäsersches Theater, November 4, 1791.   Schatz 2597

— **Hokus Pokus** oder Das gaukelspiel. Eine komische oper in zwey aufzuegen. Mit der musik des edlen v. Dittersdorf.

n. i., 1795.   56 p.   15½ᶜᵐ.

Lyrics only, slightly different from Schatz 2597. For instance (I, 8), the aria, "Was thut man nicht um's liebe geld?" has become "Bey meiner schwarzen Seele! Ha! das ding ist ja zum lachen." The list of characters is also different. For instance "Arnolph, ein pferdehändler," has become "Graf Goldbraun, ein pferdehaendler," and "Zachaeus Mantelbret" is now called Mathes.   Schatz 2598

Holger Danske, eine oper in drey acten.

p. 7–110.   16ᶜᵐ.   (Cramer's Musik, Copenhagen, 1789).

German translation by Carl Friedrich Cramer of Jens Emanuel Baggesen's Danish original as composed by Friedrich Ludwig Aemilius **Kunzen.** Cramer's interesting and important preface (p. 7–31), addressed to Wieland, under date of December 19, 1788, comments on Baggesen's use of Wieland's "Oberon" for his "Holger Danske" text, on the Danish language as a vehicle for musical expression and on Kunzen's setting of Baggesen's text.

First performed at Copenhagen, Royal Theatre, March 31, 1789.

ML 4.M3 and Schatz 5321

Die **Hollandgaenger.**   A. T. of Wilhelm und Roeschen.

Der **holzhauer,** oder Die drey wuensche. Eine komische oper in einem aufzuge. Eine freye uebersetzung.

Berlin, Christian Friedrich Himburg, 1772.   78 p.   14ᶜᵐ.

Based on the libretto by de Guichard and Castet for Philidor's opera, "Le bûcheron, ou Les trois souhaits," Paris, 1763. This, in turn, was based on Perrault's tale, "Les souhaits ridicules." As the lyrics in this translation are practically identical with those in the "Gesaenge" of the next entry, with exception of the "Schlusschor," it stands to reason that the librettist of the "Gesaenge" was also responsible for the "free translation" of 1772. This he then merely modified for Benda's *singspiel* purposes.   Schatz 770a

— Gesaenge aus dem **Holzhauer,** einer komischen operette in einem akt. Die musik von herrn Georg Benda.

Riga, Gottlob Christian Froelich, n. d.   13 p.   15ᶜᵐ.

The author, Friedrich Wilhelm Gotter, not mentioned.

First performed at Riga on June 27 (July 8), 1785; at Gotha, Hoftheater, January 2, 1778.   Schatz 770b

Der holzhauer oder Die drey wuensche. Tr. of Philidor's Le bucheron.

L'homme à deux femmes. A. T. of Deshayes' Zelia.

The **honest men of Taunton.** A. T. of the downfall of bribery.

The honest Yorkshire-man. A ballad farce. Refus'd to be acted at Drury-lane playhouse: but now perform'd at the New theatre in Goodman's Fields, with great applause. Written by Mr. Carey . . .
 London, L. Gilliver, 1736. 6 p. l., 3–32 p. 20½ cm.

Title-page mutilated. One act with prologue and two epilogues, one spoken by Mrs. Cantrell the three first nights," the other "spoken after the third night, in the summer season, at the Haymarket." Haymarket and Goodman's Fields casts and preface.

The 20 numbered airs are not printed in the text, but their tunes are indicated by title except air I., which is simply marked as by **Porpora**, air 17 as by **Haendel**, and airs 7 ("Come hither my country 'Squire"), 8 ("In vain you mention pleasure") 9 ("Love's a gentle generous passion"), 11 ("I am in truth"), 12 ("That man who best"), 15 ("Thou only darling"), 19 ("Now Fortune is past"), and 20 ("Come learn by this ye batchelors") as "set by the author," consequently composed by **Carey** himself. In the Musical Antiquary, Mr. Tufts, under 1736, says, "Ten airs by Carey, two by Dr. Green, one by Handel, one by Signor Porpora, six named." In our edition ten numbered airs are named and Dr. Greene is not mentioned. Our edition furthermore has an unnumbered song, "Tune, *When the bright God of Day*—Whoe'er to a wife," which was interpolated from the ballad opera, "Cure for a scold." The airs in our copy not mentioned so far are: Air 2 "In vain, dear Cloe," 3 "Hark! away, 'tis the merry ton'd horn," 4 "The charms of Florimel," 5 "To the same tune" (meaning the unnumbered "When the bright God of Day"), 6 "London is a fine town," 10 "Gilly-flow'r, gentle Rosemary," 13 "I had a pretty lass a tenant of my own," ¯4 "Bartholomew-Fair," 16 "The nymph that undoes me," 18 "A beggar got a beadle." (*Note the differences in the next entry!*).

The preface reads, in part:
"The very generous Reception this FARCE has met with from the Publick during its Representation in the Haymarket last Summer, and Goodman's Fields this Winter, is a Manifestation of the bad Taste and monstrous Partiality of the Great Mogul of the Hundreds of Drury, who, after having had the Copy Nine Months in his Hands, continually feeding me with fresh Promises of bringing it on the Stage, return'd it at last in a very ungenerous Manner, at the End of the Season, when it was too late to carry it to any other House; but the Young Actors having, as usual, formed themselves into a Summer Company, Mr. Cibber, Jun. sent to me in a very respectful Manner, requesting the Farce, which accordingly was put in Rehearsal; but to our great Disappointment and Surprize, the Company, after one Night's Acting, was suddenly interdicted, and the House shut up . . .

"My next and last Complaint is against Pyrate Printers . . .
"The Produce of a Man's Brain is as much his Property as the Grain or Produce of his Field, or any other Part of his real or Personal Estate, and it is equally criminal to rob him of one as of the other. . .
"We have Laws in Force against Street-Robbers, House-breakers, &c. and yet at the same Time Pyrate-Printers daringly and openly rob Authors and Proprietors of Copies of their just Rights; and though the Labour of the Brain supports so many and such great Branches of Trade, such as Paper-makers, Stationers, Letter-founders, Printers, Booksellers, Bookbinders, &c. &c. &c. to the Maintenance of above 100,000 Families, and tho' Books pay so many and such large Duties, to wit, on Paper, Pasteboard, Leather, Stamps, Advertisements and Entries, to very near, if not more than One Fourth of the Net Produce, yet Authors and their Assigns are the only Persons unshelter'd by the Government from the Robberies and Pyracies of Printers, who to the Shame and Scandal of our most excellent Constitution, commit such Ravages as are tolerated in no other Country.
"I hope to be excus'd in speaking thus warmly, having, for my own Part, suffer'd very largely in this Particular; nor do I live a Week, but I see myself injur'd of more than would support me a Month in a handsome Affluence. But of all Pyracies, that of this FARCE was the most flagrant and impudent, for impatient to stay till I had publish'd my own Copy, they villainously and surreptitiously anticipated me,

The honest Yorkshire-man—Continued.

thereby robbing me of a considerable Sum, and imposing on the Publick, not only a false and spurious Edition, but at double the Price I ever intended it."

First performed at Lincoln Inn's Fields (*not* at Covent Garden) July 11, 1735, as "The Wonder! An honest Yorkshireman;" at The Haymarket August 1, 1735 ("last time" Genest); at Goodman's Fields November 12, 1735. (Genest v. 3 contradicts the data in his index in v. 1). ML 50.5.H65

— The **honest Yorkshire-man**. A ballad opera.

[213]–244 p. 22^{cm}. (Henry Carey, Dramatick works, London, 1743.)

One act. Same preface. Of the 21 airs, ten are indicated as by **Carey**, one by **Porpora**, one by **Haendel**, two by Dr. **Green**, and six as ballad airs with their titles, but note the striking difference between this ed. and that of the Dramatick works. In the latter the arrangement is as follows. Airs: 1 by Porpora; *2 and 3 by Carey; 4 by Dr. Green*, but with same text "My charming Arabell"; 5 is the same (the unnumb. song of 1736 having disappeared); 6—*there is no air numbered 6;* 7, 8, 9, 10, 11, 12, 13 are the same; 14 is "O London is a fine town" with the same text as the former 6 "O London is a dainty place"; 15 is "*London-Bridge is broken down*"; 16 is the same as the former 15; 17 is *by Dr. Green* but with same text "Let prudes and coquets" as of former 16; 18, 19, 20, 21 are the same as the former 17, 18, 19, 20. ML 49.A2C2

— The **honest Yorkshire-man**, a ballet farce, acted with great applause at the Theatres Royal in Drury-Lane and Covent Garden. Written by Mr. Harry Carey . . .

London, T. Lownds, 1763. 36 p. (incl. front.) 16^{cm}.

One act. Preface, prologue, epilogues, casts (Drury-Lane and Covent-Garden). LONGE 73

L'honor al cimento. L. T. of Orgiani's Gli amori di Rinaldo con Armida.

Les **Horaces**, tragédie-lyrique, en trois actes, mêlée d'intermèdes. Représenté devant Leurs Majestés, à Fontainebleau, le 2 novembre 1786.

[Paris], P. R. C. Ballard, 1786. 4 p. l., 53 p. 19½^{cm}.

Cast. Guillard is mentioned as the author, Antonio **Salieri** as the composer. First performed at Paris, Académie royale de musique, December 7, 1786. ML 50.2.H6S2

Les **Horaces et les Curiaces**, ballet. *See* P. Guglielmi's Vologeso.

The **Horatii and Curiatii**. A tragic ballet.

Noverre, Jean George, Works, Tr. from the French, London, 1783; v. 3, p. 145–181. 21½^{cm}.

Five parts. Detailed scene by scene description. GV 1787.N8

Horatio. *See* M. Curzio.

Horatius Coclès, acte lyrique, representé pour la première fois sur le Théâtre national de l'Opéra, le décadi 30 pluviose, l'an deuxième [February 18, 1794]. Paroles du C. Arnault. Musique du C. Méhul.

n. i., n. d. [51]–66 p. 19½^{cm}.

Before 1800? Not detached from his Oeuvres, 1818 (3 v.) or 1824–27 (8 v.)? ML 50.2.H63M2

An **hospital for fools.** A dramatic fable. As it is acted at the Theatre-Royal, by His Majesty's servants. To which is added the songs with their basses and symphonies, and transposed for the flute. The musick by Mr. Arne. Sung by Mrs. Clive . . .

London, J. Watts, 1739. 6 p. l., [5]–28, [1] p., [7] p. (music) 20ᶜᵐ.

One act and introduction. By James Miller, who is not mentioned. The first p. l. contains publisher's advertisement dated November 19, 1739, the p. l. 4–6 contain "An additional song. The musick by Mr. [Thomas Augustine] Arne. Sung by Mrs. Clive: "How smoothly glides the fool," air and bass. The [7] p. contain "Songs with their basses and symphonies, and transpos'd for the flute. The musick by Mr. Arne. Sung by Mrs. Clive": "A fool enjoys the sweets of life," "Our folly is our neighbour's gains," and "If life can yield."

First performed, as indicated, November 15, 1739. ML 50.2.H7
Second copy, lacking first p. l. (half-title). LONGE 40

Høst-gildet. Et syngespil i een act, ved Thomas Thaarup.

Kiøbenhavn, P. M. Høpffner, 1790. 48 p. 19ᶜᵐ.

Cast. The composer, Johann Abraham Peter **Schulz**, is not mentioned.
First performed at Copenhagen, Royal Theatre, September 16, 1790.
SCHATZ 9721

— Das **erndte-fest.** Ein singspiel in einem aufzuge vom herrn Thaarup. In musik gesetzt vom herrn kapellmeister Schulz. Aus dem daenischen nach der dritten veraenderten auflage.

Altona, J. F. Hammerich, 1795. 68 p. 16ᶜᵐ.

The "Vorrede des uebersetzers" is signed by F. H. W. Froelich and dated "Rundhoff, bey Schleswig, im Juny 1794." In it he says:
"Dass die arien der uebersetzung mit der musik in der vollkommensten uebereinstimmung stehen, ist allein das werk des herrn kapellmeisters Schulz, dessen guete meine arbeit einer wiederhohlten durchsicht wuerdigte." SCHATZ 9722

Der **hufschmied.** Tr. of Philidor's Le maréchal ferrant.

Les **huit Mariannes,** parodie en un acte. Représentée, pour la première fois, à l'Hôtel de Bourgogne, par les Comédiens italiens, en Mai 1725.

Alexis Piron, Oeuvres complettes, Liege, 1776, v. 5, [203]–255 p. 17½ᶜᵐ.

In prose and vaudevilles. A parody of the tragedy, "Hérode & Mariamne" according to Parfaict, who dates it, without mentioning the composer, April 28, 1725.
PQ 2019.P6

L'huitre et les plaideurs, ou Le tribunal de la chicane. Opera-comique, en un acte, en prose, mêlé de morceaux de musique & vaudeville, représenté sur le Théatre de la Foire Saint-Laurent en 1759 & 1761. Par M. Sedaine. La musique de M. Philidor. La musique, les ariettes & le vaudeville s'y trouvent gravés.

Paris, Claude Herissant, 1761. 34, [1] p. 20½ᶜᵐ.

No music. Cast. In his *avertissement* the author says:
"Cette petite pièce, ou plutôt cette farce a été représentée pour la première fois à la Foire Saint-Laurent de l'année 1760 [! comp. title]; proposée, faite, mise en musique, apprise & représentée en moins de dix-sept jours. Elle avoit tous les défauts d'un ouvrage indigeste & précipitée; cependant le reproche le plus unanime fut son peu de durée. C'est ce qui m'a excité à l'étendre en y joignant des couplets, des scènes & des morceaux de musique qui couvrissent du moins l'irrégularité de l'ouvrage. Et de fait, un opera-comique qui n'est point composé de scènes à tiroirs, & qui n'a ni amour, ni intrigue, ni mariage, ne peut guéres tenir son succès que des charmes de la musique & du mérite de l'exécution."
First performed, as indicated, (but without music?), September 17, 1759.
SCHATZ 8036

L'humanità nelle fere, overo Il Lucullo. Drama per musica da rappresentarsi nel famoso Teatro di S. Bartolomeo in quest' anno 1708 . . .

Napoli, Salvatore Votto, n. d.   5 p. l., 62 p.   14^{cm}.

Three acts. Dedication by the impresario, Andrea del Pò, argument, cast, scenario, and printer's notice, which reads, in part:

"Se nelle commedie già rappresentate, per cagione della lunghezza, e del nuovo costume c'hoggi corre, più volte ti supplicai di compatire il Sign. Carlo de Petris, che fù soverchiamente ardito in togliere, ed aggiungere qualche cosa di più alle scene degli altri; questa volta te ne priego d'avvantaggio, e se in luogo di Prezia Dama, dalla quale par che nasca la mossa di Lucullo contro Mitridate in questa commedia vi troverai Tilla, Prezia stimela in tutto supposta, e Tilla un semplice personaggio introdotto per ornamento della commedia, e non necessario, non usandosi più simile personaggio.

"La musica è del Signor Alessandro **Scarlatti,** con qualche cosa di più del Signor Giuseppe **Vignola.**"

Dent says, "Probably produced before elsewhere, since the libretto mentions additions by Vignola," whereas Schatz calls this the original ed. of the libretto.

SCHATZ 9538

The **humours of Covent-Garden.**   A. T. of The rival milliners.

The **humours of John Bull:** an operatical farce, in two acts.

n. i., n. d.   [75]–130 p.   17^{cm}.

Detached copy.   A short prefatory note tells us that

"several political allusions to events of the period at which it was written, would have effectually prevented the appearance of this performance on our chaste stage, even if the author's stomach had not been too squeamish to digest the various disgusts of theatric solicitation."

By Sylvester Otway (*pseud.* of James Oswald), and first printed 1789 in his volume of poems.

LONGE 323

The **humours of Punch's resignation.**   A. T. of Politicks in miniature.

The **humours of the court:** or, Modern gallantry.   A new ballad opera.   As it was intended to have been perform'd at one of the theatres.

London, W. James, 1732.   vii, [1], 9–72 p.   20½^{cm}.

Three acts and introduction.   Neither author nor performance recorded by Clarence.   The 24 airs used are indicated by title.   The text is preceded by a short preface, in which the author trusts that his piece will meet with as much success as many others not any better than his.

ML 50.5.H9

Second copy LONGE 49

The **humours of the times;** or, What news now?   A comic opera, in two acts, written by Archibald M'Laren . . .   To which is annexed a copy of a letter from the manager of the Dublin Theatre to the author, containing his approbation of the piece.

London, Printed for the author, 1799.   24 p.   17^{cm}.

The "letter" is not in this copy.   List of subscribers, and note that, owing to "Mr. Daly's resignation of the theatre, and the insurrection that followed," the play was not brought out.   Of the eight songs, two were to be sung to the tunes, "This is no me" and "Duncan Davison."   "God save the King" evidently furnished the melody for the finale.   The other songs have no indication of air.

LONGE 323

The musical farce of **Hunt the slipper.** In two acts. As performed at the Theatre-Royal, Smoke-Alley.

[Dublin], Printed for the booksellers, 1792. 34 p. 15½^{cm}.

Cast. Only the air, "For fortune's like a tight or slip-shoe," is headed as composed by Samuel **Arnold,** though he is recorded as having composed all the music. The author, Henry Knapp, is not mentioned.

First performed July 21 (Schatz), August 21 (Genest), 1784, at London, Haymarket.

LONGE 223

Le **Huron,** comédie en deux actes et en vers, mêlée d'ariettes; représentée pour la premiere fois par les Comédiens italiens ordinaires du roi, le 20 août 1768.

Paris, Merlin, 1768. 47 p. 19½^{cm}.

Neither Marmontel, the author, is mentioned, nor **Grétry,** the composer.

ML 50.2.H8G6

— Le **Huron,** comédie en deux actes et en vers, meslée d'ariettes' représentée pour la première fois par les Comédiens italiens ordinaires du Roi, le 20 août 1768.

Paris, Merlin, 1770. 48 p. 18^{cm}.

Neither Marmontel, the author, nor **Grétry,** the composer, is mentioned. On p. 13–16 the air of "Vous me charmez" (I, 4); on p. 23–26, of "L'amour naissant n'a pas encore" (I, 7). SCHATZ 4159

— Le **Huron,** comédie en deux actes et en vers, mêlée d'ariettes. Représentée, pour la premiere fois, par les Comédiens italiens ordinaires du roi, le 20 août 1768.

Paris, Merlin, 1772. 48 p. 19^{cm}.

On p. 45–48, "Air du Huron" ("Vous me charmez"). Neither **Grétry** is mentioned, nor Marmontel. ML 50.2.H8G7

— Le **Huron,** comédie en deux actes et en vers, mêlée d'ariettes; représentée pour la premiere fois par les Comédiens italiens ordinaires du roi, le 20 août 1768.

Paris, Merlin, 1779. 48 p. 19^{cm}.

On p. 13–16 the air of "Vous me charmez, vous enflammez" (I, 4), 23–26 "L'amour naissant n'a pas encore" (I, 7). Neither Marmontel is mentioned, nor **Grétry.**

SCHATZ 11705

Hurtado e Miranda, ballet. *See* Luchesi's Ademira.

Hurtado e Miranda, ballet. *See* Monza's Ifigenia in Tauride

Hylas. Entrée in Grenet's Le triomphe de l'harmonie.

Hypermenestra. Tr. of Fiorillo's Ipermestra.

Hypermenestra. Tr. of Hasse's Ipermestra.

Hypermnestre, tragedie, representée par l'Academie royale de musique, l'an 1716. Paroles de M. De Lafonds. Musique de M. Gervais. XLI. opera.

n. i., n. d. pl., p. 77–129 (Recueil général des opéra, t. xii, Paris, 1734). 14^{cm}.

Detached copy. Five acts and prologue.

First performed, as indicated, November 3, 1716. SCHATZ 3791a

Second copy. ML 48.R4

Hypermnestre—Continued.

— **Hypermnestre,** tragedie, mise au Theatre de l'Academie royale de musique de Lyon, pour la prémière fois en 1742.

*Lyon, Aimé Delaroche, 1742.　63 p.　23½*cm.

Five acts and prologue.　Cast.　Neither the author, Joseph de Lafont, nor the composer, Charles Hubert **Gervais,** is mentioned.　　　　　　　　SCHATZ 3791b

— La **bonne femme,** parodie de l'opéra d'Hipermnestre.　Par les Srs. Dominique & Romagnesi . . .　Représentée pour la premiere fois, par les Comédiens italiens ordinaires du roi, le 28 juin 1728.

*Les parodies du Nouveau Théâtre italien, Nouv. éd., Paris, Briasson, 1738, t. iv, [37]–72 p.　16½*cm.

One act.　The airs and vaudeville printed at end in the "Table des airs" (92 p.).
　　　　　　　　　　　　　　　　　　　　ML 48.P3

Der **hypochondriste.**　Tr. of Naumann's L'ipocondriaco.

Hypsipile.　Tr. of Metastasio's text Issipile.

Hysipile.　Ein musicalisches schauspiel, welches an dem glorreichen nahmens-tag Ihro Churfuerstl. Durchleucht zu Pfaltz . . . aufgefuehret worden im jahr 1754.

*Mannheim, Nicolaus von Pierron, n. d.　6 p. l., 131 p.　15½*cm.

Three acts.　Argument, cast, scenario, and name of Ignaz **Holzbauer** as the composer ("eine neue composition").　Apparently a translation of Metastasio's "Issipile."
First performed at Mannheim, Hoftheater, November 4, 1754.　　　SCHATZ 4785

L'Ibraim sultano.　Drama postumo del Sig. dottor Adriano Morselli.　Da rappresentarsi in musica nel famoso Teatro Grimano di San Gio. Grisostomo l'anno 1692 . . .

*Venetia, Nicolini, 1692.　front., 46, [2] p.　14*cm.

Three acts.　Publisher's dedication, argument, and scenario.　The composer, Carlo Francesco **Pollaroli,** is not mentioned.　The 2 unnumb. p. contain the substitute arias: "Fortunati miei pensieri" (I, 2), "Ti lascierò se vuoi" (I, 11), "Non nieghi la sorte" (III, 8), and "O guerriero" (III, 15).　　　　　SCHATZ 8296

Ich heisse Theiss, oder Der aepfeldieb.　Eine operette in einem aufzuge.　Verfasst von Ludwig Erdmann.

*Regensburg, im Montagischen verlag, 1778.　30 p.　17*cm.

The composer, Johann **Gaertner,** is not mentioned.
First performed at Fulda, Liebhabertheater, ca. 1781.　　　　　SCHATZ 3553

Idalide.　Dramma per musica da rappresentarsi nel Regio Teatro di Torino nel carnovale del 1786 . . .

*Torino, Onorato Derossi, n. d.　viii, 64 p.　16*cm.

Three acts.　By Ferdinando Moretti, who is not mentioned.　Argument, cast, and names of Salvatore **Rispoli** as composer of the opera, of Vittorio Amedeo Canavasso of Francesco Clerico's ballets, "I barbari sacrifizi distrutti, ballo serio pantomimo in cinque atti," "Le avventure del carnovale, ballo comico," and "Li montanari nel Perù," the first two of which are described on p. 59–64.　　　　　SCHATZ 8814

L'**Idalide** o sia La vergine del sole. Dramma per musica da rappresentarsi in Firenze nel Regio Teatro degl' Intrepidi detto della Palla a Corda . . .

> *Firenze, Ant. Gius. Pagani e comp., 1788. 34 p. 16½ᶜᵐ.*

Two acts. By Ferdinando Moretti, who is not mentioned. Argument, cast, and name of Giuseppe **Sarti** as the composer. With the opera was performed the ballet, "Il nottambulo."

First performed at Milan, Teatro alla Scala, January 8, 1783. Schatz 9444

Idaspe. Dramma per musica da rappresentarsi nel famosissimo Teatro Grimani di S. Gio. Grisostomo nell carnevale dell' anno MCCXXX . . .

> *Venezia, Carlo Buonarigo, n. d. 1 p. l., 47 p. 15½ᶜᵐ.*

Three acts. By Giovanni Pietro Candi (not mentioned). Dedication by Dom. Lalli, argument, cast, scenario, and name of the composer, Riccardo **Broschi**.

Schatz 1339

L'idea del comando nel cuore di Germanico invincibile. *See* M. Curzio.

L'idea di tutte le perfezioni. Introduzione al balletto de' serenissimi principi Francesco & Antonio Farnesi, fatto rappresentare dal sereniss. Sig. duca di Parma nel suo Nuovo Teatrino, in occasione de' felicissimi sponsali del serenissimo Sig. principe Odoardo suo primogenito, con la serenissima Signora principessa Dorotea Sofia di Neoburgo. Poesia del dottore Lotto Lotti . . . e musica di Giuseppe Tosi.

> *Piacenza, Bazachi, 1690. 32 p. 19ᶜᵐ.*

Casts for both the introduzione and the ballet, the latter danced by twelve princes and cavaliers.

First performed, as indicated, May 5, 1690. L. of C. does not have the five plates mentioned by Wotquenne. Schatz 10379

L'idolo cinese. Commedia per musica di Giambattista Lorenzi P. A. da rappresentarsi nel Real Teatro del Fondo di Separazione per seconda opera del corrente anno 1783.

> *Napoli, n. publ., 1783. 64 p. 15ᶜᵐ.*

Three acts. Argument, cast, name of **Paisiello** as the composer, and note that "per brevità si tralasciano molte scene dell' atto terzo," also that "per comodo delle cantanti," the aria, "Da tanti affanni oppressa," would be substituted in I, 9 for "Sapessi almen se barbaro," and "Agitato dallo sdegno," in II, 13, for "L'ussignol col mesto canto."

First performed at Naples, Teatro Nuovo, spring, 1767. Schatz 7670

L'idolo cinese. Dramma giocoso per musica da rappresentarsi nel Teatro di San Samuelle il carnovale dell' anno 1774.

> *Venezia, Modesto Fenzo, 1773. 61 p. 17ᶜᵐ.*

Three acts. By Giambattista Lorenzi, who is not mentioned. Cast, scenario, and name of Giacomo **Rust** as the composer. On p. 29–32, description, without name of the composer of the music of Onorato Vigano's "Arianna abbandonata da Teseo e soccorsa da Bacco, ballo eroico pantomimo." His second ballet was called "La donna difficile." Schatz 9179

Idomenée, tragedie représentée par l'Academie royale de musique l'an 1712. Les paroles de M. Danchet & la musique de M. Campra. LXXVII. opera.

n. i., n. d. 315–388 p. 14ᶜᵐ. (Recueil général des opéra, Paris, 1714, t. x.)

Detached copy. Five acts, with prologue.
First performed, as indicated, January 12, 1712.   SCHATZ 1557
                                             Second copy. ML 48.R4

— **Idoménée**, tragedie.

[121]–182 p. 17½ᶜᵐ. (Antoine Danchet, Théâtre, Paris, 1751, t. iii.)

Prologue and five acts. The composer, André **Campra**, is not mentioned.
                                                      PQ 1972.D2

Idomeneo. Drama per musica da rappresentarsi in Roma nel Teatro di Torre Argentina nel carnevale dell' anno 1756 . . .

Roma, Fausto Amidei, n. d. 63 p. 15ᶜᵐ.

Three acts. Author not mentioned and not known to Schatz. Dedication, argument, scenario, cast and name of Baldassare **Galuppi** as composer.
First performed as indicated, January 7, 1756.   ML 50.2.I3G2

Idomeneo. Dramma per musica da rappresentarsi nel Teatro Nuovo di Corte per comando di S. A. S. E. Carlo Teodoro . . . nel carnovale 1781. La poesia è del Signor abate Gianbattista Varesco . . . La musica è del Signor maestro Wolfgango Amadeo Mozart . . . La traduzione è del Signor Andrea Schachtner . . .

Monaco, Francesco Giuseppe Thuille, n. d. 121 p. 15½ᶜᵐ.

Argument, scenario, and cast. German title page, "Idomeneus," and text face Italian.
First performed, as indicated, January 29, 1781.   SCHATZ 6818

Idomeneus. Tr. of Mozart's Idomeneo.

L'idylle sur la paix, et L'Eglogue de Versailles. Divertissements representez en differents temps par l'Academie royalle de musique. Les paroles de differents auteurs, & la musique de M. de Lully. XVIII. opera.

n. i., n. d. front., 73–80, 81–90 p. 14ᶜᵐ. (Recueil général des opéra, t. iii, Paris, 1703.)

Detached copy. One act. A note on p. 74 says of the "Idylle:"
"Ce divertissement a quelques fois précedé à l'Opera celuy des Fêtes de l'Amour & de Bachus. Il est icy imprimé comme il l'a été en musique dans l'année 1685. Les paroles de l'Idyle sont de Mr Racine."
First performed at Sceaux, Orangerie of the marquis de Seigneley, 1685. (The plate has the title, "L'idile de Sceaux," and shows the château in the background.)
                                                      SCHATZ 5776
                                             Second copy. ML 48.R4

— **L'eglogue de Versailles.**

On p. 89–90, the "Augmentation tireé du dernier intermede de la comedie de Porceugnac, dont on s'est servi pour preceder l'Eglogue lorsqu' elle a été jouée ensuite de la Mascarade" [scil. "Le carnaval"]. Molière is named as author of this augmentation. As author of the "Eglogue de Versailles" ["Grotte de Versailles," according to Prunières] proper, Philippe Quinault is mentioned on p. 80.
First performed at Versailles, 1668, and at Paris, Academie royale de musique, **1685.**   SCHATZ 5775a
                                             Second copy. ML 48.R4

L'Iffide greca. Drama per musica da rappresentarsi nel Teatro Giustiano di S. Moisè. Nel carnovale dell' anno 1722.

Venezia, Marino Rossetti, 1722. 48 p. 15ᶜᵐ.

Three acts. By conte Niccolò Minato, who is not mentioned. Argument, cast, scenario. The composer, Pietro **Scarpari,** is not mentioned. SCHATZ 9561

Iffigenia in Tauride, ballet. *See* Paisiello's Il Demofoonte.

Ifianassa, e Melampo. Drama musicale rappresentato nella Villa di Pratolino.

G. A. Moniglia, Poesie drammatiche, parte prima, Firenze, Vincenzio Vangelisti, 1689, p. [379]–433 p. 24ᶜᵐ.

Three acts. Argument with name of Giovanni **Legrenzi** as composer. First performed as indicated, fall of 1685. ML 49.A2M7

L' Ifigenia. Dramma per musica da rappresentarsi nel Teatro di Sant' Angelo il carnevale dell' anno 1707.

Venezia, Marino Rossetti, 1707. 59 p. 14½ᶜᵐ.

Three acts. Argument, scenario, and notice to the reader signed with the initials of Aurelio Aureli:

"Quest' opera da molto tempo sepolta con le ceneri del poeta [Pietro Riva] hà havuto quest' anno l'onore di passare in mano de Cavalieri prottetori del Teatro, e d'esser posta sù le scene. Il Sig. Agostino Bonaventura **Colletti,** che hà fatto spiccare la virtù sua nelle arie nuove del Parida già recitato, l'hà adornata colla musica; ed à me doppo d'avermi intrecciato qualche mio verso è rimasta la fortuna di presentarla al vostro aggradimente . . ." SCHATZ 2112

Ifigenia. Drama per musica da rappresentarsi nel nobil Teatro a Torre Argentina il carnevale dell' anno 1766 . . .

Roma, Ottavio Puccinelli, n. d. 56 p. 15½ᶜᵐ.

Three acts. Argument, scenario, cast, name of Carlo **Franchi** as composer and dedication with this allusion to the author: "opera d'insigne letterato vivente, celebre ancora per altre sue felici produzioni." Comparison proved this to be Vittorio Amedeo Cigna-Santi's "Ifigenia in Aulide." ML 50.2.I4F7

L' Ifigenia. O. T. of Jommelli's Ifigenia in Aulide.

Ifigenia in Aulide.

Apostolo Zeno, Poesie drammatiche, Venezia, 1744, t. I, 80 p. 19ᶜᵐ.

Three acts and licenza. Argument and publisher's prefatory note for the entire collection.

No composer is mentioned.

In the "Catalogo," at end of t. x, date and place of first ed. of "Ifigenia in Aulide" are given as Vienna, 1714. (November 4, music by *Caldara.)* ML 49.A2Z3

— **Ifigenia in Aulide.** Pubblicata per la prima volta in Vienna 1714.

Apostolo Zeno, Poesie drammatiche, Orleans, 1785–86, t. iv, p. 185–266. 21ᶜᵐ.

Three acts. Argument. No composer is mentioned. ML 49.A2Z4

Ifigenia in Aulide. Dramma per musica da rappresentarsi nel regio Teatro di Torino nel carnevale del 1762 alla presenza di S. S. R. M.

Torino, Gaspare Bayno, n. d. viii, 63 p. 15½ᶜᵐ.

Three acts. Argument, cast, scenario, and names of composer, Ferdinando Giuseppe **Bertoni,** and librettist, Vittorio Amedeo Cigna [-Santi]. The second of the ballets, all three by Eligio Devisse and composed by Giuseppe Antonio Le Messier, was called "L'arrivo d'Europa nell' isola di Creta." SCHATZ 914

Ifigenia in Aulide. Dramma per musica, da rappresentarsi nella Cesarea corte per il nome gloriossimo della Sac, Ces, e Catt. Maestà Carlo VI . . . L'anno MDCCXVIII. La poesia è del Sig. Apostolo Zeno . . . La musica è del Sig. Antonio Caldara . . .

Venezia, Domenico Lovisa, n. d. 60 p. 15^{cm}.

Three acts and licenza. Argument and scenario. The ballet music was composed by Niccola Matteis.

First performed at Vienna, Hoftheater, November 4, 1718.   SCHATZ 1484

Ifigenia in Aulide. Dramma per musica da rappresentarsi nel Regio Teatro di Torino nel carnovale del 1788 alla presenza di S. S. R. M.

Torino, Onorato Derossi, n. d. 68 p. 16^{cm}.

Three acts. By Ferdinando Moretti. Argument, cast, scenario, and names of the author and the composer, **Cherubini.** On p. 62–67 description with cast of Giuseppe Traffieri's ballets, music by Vittorio Amedeo Canavasso, "Mercato fiammengo," "Didone abbandonata," and "La nuova della pace."   SCHATZ 1838

— **Ifigenia in Aulide.** Dramma per musica da rappresentarsi nel Teatro Grande alla Scala l'autunno dell' anno 1788 . . .

Milano, Gio. Batista Bianchi, n. d. 4 p. l., 60 p. 16½^{cm}.

Three acts. Dedication, argument, cast, scenario, and name of Luigi **Cherubini** as composer. The author, Ferdinando Moretti, is not mentioned. The text of the opera is preceded by prefatory note, argument, and cast, without name of the composer of the music, of Domenico Le Fevre's "La discesa d'Ercole all' inferno, ballo eroico in cinque atti." His second ballet was called "Le feste di Flora."

      SCHATZ 11684

Ifigenia in Aulide. Dramma per musica da rappresentarsi nel Regio Teatro di Berlino . . .

Berlino, Haude e Spener, 1768. 93 p. 16^{cm}.

Three acts. Carl Heinrich **Graun** is mentioned as the composer and Leopoldo di Villati as the author, though Frederick the Great probably was a joint author. A note on p. [4] says:

"Questa è un' imitazione dell' Ifigenia di Racine; il fine però ne è diverso, essendosi qui seguito Euripide . . ."

Argument and scenario. German title page, "Iphigenia in Aulis," and text face Italian.

Performed in January, 1768, as indicated; originally December 13, 1748.

      SCHATZ 4102

Ifigenia in Aulide. Drama per musica da rappresentarsi nel Real Teatro di S. Carlo a dì 18 decembre 1753 in cui si commemora l'augusto nome della regina regnante . . .

Napoli, Domenico Lanciano, n. d. 5 p. l., 48 p. 14^{cm}.

Three acts. Mattia Verazi, the author, is not mentioned. Dedication stating that this is the first performance of the opera at San Carlo, argument, cast, scenario, and note that the music is by Niccolò **Jommelli,** except certain indicated arias by Tommaso **Traetta.** These arias were: "La tua diletta figlia" (I, 1), "Fra i dolci affetti miei" (I, 3), "M'ama il bell' idol mio" (II, 10), "Già la vittima fatale" (II, 13).

First performed at Rome, Teatro di Torre Argentina, February 9, 1751, as 'L'Ifigenia."   SCHATZ 4861

— **L'Ifigenia,** dramma per musica da rappresentarsi nel Teatro in Cassel.

Cassel, D. Estienne, 1766. 153 p. 16^{cm}.

Three acts. Neither Verazi nor **Jommelli** mentioned. Argument, scenario, cast. German title, "Iphigenia," and text face Italian, which is noticeably different from the Naples edition of 1753. For instance, the opera now begins, "Sorgi Euribate:

Ifigenia in Aulide—Continued.

Olà," instead of "Signor, perche si mesto?" the arias, "La tua diletta figlia" (I, 1) and "Fra i dolci affetti miei" (I, 2), are not in the Cassel version, which has "Sperai vicino il Lido" in I, 2, etc., etc.

SCHATZ 4862

Ifigenia in Aulide. Dramma per musica di Luigi Serio poeta di corte. Da rappresentarsi nel Real Teatro di S. Carlo nel dì 12 gennaio 1779 . . .

Napoli, Vincenzo Flauto, 1779. 61 p. 15½^{cm}.

Three acts. Impresario's dedication, dated January 12, 1779, argument, scenario, cast, and name of Vincenzo Martin (**Martin y Soler**) as the composer. With the opera was performed Lepicq's ballet, "Griselda," of which argument and description appears on p. [7]–16, and Domenico Rossi's ballet, "Il servo di due padroni." The composers of the music are not mentioned.

SCHATZ 6028

Ifigenia in Aulide. Drama per musica da rappresentarsi in Firenze nel Teatro di via della Pergola nel carnevale dell' anno 1732 . . .

Firenze, Verdi, n. d. 67 p. 14½^{cm}.

Three acts, with licenza. By Apostolo Zeno, who is not mentioned. Impresario's dedication, argument, cast, scenario, and name of Giuseppe Maria **Orlandini** as the composer.

SCHATZ 7334

Ifigenia in Aulide.

[395]–423 p. 17^{cm}. (Rolli, Componimenti poetici, Nuova edizione, Verona, G. Tumermani, 1744.)

Three acts. Argument. The composer, Niccolò **Porpora**, is not mentioned. First performed at London, Haymarket, June 7 (Burney), May 3 (Schatz), 1735.

ML 49.A2R7

Ifigenia in Aulide. Dramma per musica, da rappresentarsi nel Teatro di S. A. S. E. di Baviera nel carnevale del' anno 1738. La musica è del Sig. Giovanni Porta . . .

Monaco, Giov. Giac. Vötter, n. d. 86 p. 15^{cm}.

Three acts. By Apostolo Zeno, who is not mentioned. Argument, cast, and scenario.

First performed in January, 1738, as indicated.

SCHATZ 8380

L'Ifigenia in Aulide. Dramma per musica da rappresentarsi nel Regio Teatro di via della Pergola l'autunno del MDCCLXXXIV . . .

Firenze, Giovanni Risaliti, 1784. 39 p. 16^{cm}.

Three acts. By Luigi Serio, who is not mentioned. Argument, cast, and name of Alessio **Prati** as the composer ("La musica è tutta nuova"). On p. 5, argument, cast, description, and name of Antonio Capuzzi as the composer of the music of Domenico Ricciardi's ballet, "La Vergine del sole o sia Alonzo e Cora, ballo eroico."

SCHATZ 8451

Ifigenia in Aulide. Dramma per musica da rappresentarsi nel Teatro da S. Agostino il carnovale dell' anno 1784 . . .

Genova, Stamperia Gesiniana, n. d. 59 p. 14½^{cm}.

Three acts. By Luigi Serio, who is not mentioned, but with alterations. Argument, cast, scenario, and name of Lorenzo **Rossi** as the composer. SCHATZ 8918

Ifigenia in Aulide. Dramma serio per musica da rappresentarsi nel nobiliss. Nuovo Teatro di Padova per la fiera del Santo 1785 . . .

Padova, Penada, n. d. 36 p. 17^{cm}.

Two acts. Author not mentioned, and unknown to Schatz. Antonio Zardon's dedication as impresario, argument, cast, scenario, and name of Angelo **Tarchi** as the

Ifigenia in Aulide—Continued.

composer. With the opera were performed Domenico Rossi's ballets, "Il primo giorno dell' anno nella China" (music by Luigi Marescalchi) and "Chi la fà l'aspetta."
Schatz 10231

Ifigenia in Aulide. Dramma per musica da rappresentarsi nel Teatro Grande alla Scala il carnevale dell' anno 1787 . . .

    Milano, Gio. Batista Bianchi, n. d. 70 p. 16½^{cm}.

Three acts. Dedication ("cotesto secondo spettacolo . . . della corrente stagione"), argument, cast, scenario, and names of Nicola **Zingarelli** as composer, of Ferdinando Moretti as author ("Il dramma composizione nuova"). With the opera were performed (composers of the music perhaps mentioned in the separate libretto published) Paolino Franchi's ballets, "Guatimozin ossia La conquista del Messico," "I due avari," and "Il matrimonio per concorso."

First performed, as indicated, January 27, 1787.   Schatz 11250
Second copy.   ML 48.A5 v. 8
Third copy.   ML 48.A5 v. 7

— Ifigenia in Aulide. Dramma per musica da rappresentarsi nel Teatro della molto Ile. città di Barcellona, l'anno 1799.

    Barcellona, Francesco Genéras, n. d. 54 p. 15^{cm}.

Three acts. Argument, cast, and name of Nicola **Zingarelli** as composer. The author, Ferdinando Moretti, is not mentioned.   ML 48.A5 v. 16

L'Ifigenia in Tauride. Tr. of Gluck's Iphigénie en Tauride.

Ifigenia in Tauride. Dramma per musica da rappresentarsi nel Real Teatro di Salvaterra nel carnovale dell' anno 1776.

    [Lisbona], Stamperia reale, n. d. 67 p. 15^{cm}.

Three acts. Argument, cast, scenario, and names of Mattia Verazi as author, of Niccolò **Jommelli** as composer.

First performed at Naples, Teatro di San Carlo, May 30, 1771.   Schatz 4890

Ifigenia in Tauride. Dramma per musica da rappresentarsi alla Corte elettorale Palatina in occasione del felicissimo giorno del nome del serenissimo elettore . . . l'anno MDCCLXIV.

    Mannheim, Stamperia elettorale, n. d. 1 p. l., 134 p. 15^{cm}.

Three acts. Argument, cast, scenario, name of Mattia Verazi as author (on p. 1.) and of Giovanni Francesco de **Majo** as composer. ("La musica è nuova composizione.")

First performed, as indicated, November 4, 1764.   Schatz 5856

— Iphigenia in Tauris. Ein musikalisches schauspiel welches auf hoechst begluecktem hohen nahmens-tag Ihro Churfuerstl. Durchleucht zu Pfaltz . . . an dem Chur-Pfaeltzischen hoffe aufgefuehret worden, im jahr 1764.

    Mannheim, Churfuerstl. Buchdruckerey, n. d. 208 p. 15½^{cm}.

Three acts. Argument, cast, scenario, and names of Mattia Verazi as author and of Giovanni Francesco de **Maio** as composer. German translation issued for the performances under Schatz 5856.   Schatz 5857

Ifigenia in Tauride. Dramma per musica da rappresentarsi nel Teatro alla Scala il carnevale dell' anno 1784 . . .

    Milano, Gio. Batista Bianchi, n. d. 59 p. 16½^{cm}.

Three acts. By Benedetto Pasqualigo, who is not mentioned. Dedication, argument, cast, and name of Carlo **Monza** as the composer. With the opera were performed Paolino Franchi's ballets, "Hurtado e Miranda," "Il feudatorio," and "Pulcinella, cavaliere d'industria." The composer of the music is not mentioned.
Schatz 6610
Second copy. ML 48.A5 v.8

Ifigenia in Tauride. Tragedia da cantarsi nel celebre Teatro Grimani nella via di San Gio. Grisosostomo nelle notti carnevalesche dell' anno MDCCXIX. Offerita . . . da Merindo Fesanio Past. Arc. della colonia de SS. Animosi di Venezia.

Venezia, Marino Rossetti, 1719. front., 80 p. 18½ cm.

Five acts. By Benedetto Pasqualigo. Dedicatory poem by the author under his Arcadian name, notice to the reader by way of argument, Italian translation of Ovide's third elegy, cast, scenario, and name of Giuseppe Maria **Orlandini** as the composer. Pasqualigo says in the notice to the reader:

"L'argomento in Tauride fù ridotto con novità di ritmo nel di lui teatro, dal Sig. Pier Jacopo Martelli, & io per la prima volta, ho osato di maneggiarlo in poche giornate degli ozj autunnali, in gratia del canto, sulle Venete scene, con invenzione di doppia peripezia, e riconoscimento per discorso, e per segni, e con qualche disperata difficoltà avvenutami nel framischiare la dignità della mitologia, la puntualità della poetica, e l'eccellenza dell' esemplare, con la delicatezza dell' armonia, con le ripugnanze del teatro, dell' uso, e del carnovale senza una mostruosa deformità."

SCHATZ 7335

Ifigenia in Tauride. Dramma per musica da rappresentarsi nel nobilissimo Teatro di S. Benedetto il carnovale dell' anno 1786.

Venezia, Modesto Tenzo, 1786. 56 p. 17 cm.

Three acts. By Benedetto Pasqualigo. Argument, cast, scenario, and name of Angelo **Tarchi** as the composer. On p. [23]–34 argument and description of Antonio Muzzarelli's "Gli amori d'Igor, primo Zar di Moscovia, ballo eroico pantomimo," music ("tutta nuova") by Vittorio Trento. SCHATZ 10221

Ifigenia in Tauride. Dramma per musica da rappresentarsi in Schönbrunn festeggiandosi li felicissimi nomi delle loro maestà imperiali e reali l'anno 1763.

Vienna, Stamperia di Ghelen, n. d. Unpaged. 16 cm.

Three acts. Argument, cast, scenario, and name of Tommaso **Traetta** as composer, but not of librettist, Marco Coltellini.

According to Schatz, this opera was performed at Schönbrunn on October 4, 1763, but previously at Vienna, Burgtheater, carnival of 1758. This conflicts with the note on the last page of the libretto:

"Sebbene il presente dramma sia stato composto espressamente dall' autore per questa occasione; pure è convenuto farvi alcuni cambiamenti, che potranno vedersi dalla nuova ristampa che se ne farà in appresso." SCHATZ 10393

— **Ifigenia in Tauride** di Marco Coltellini. Dramma per musica rappresentato nel Teatro di Vienna l'autunno dell' anno 1763.

Livorno, Marco Coltellini, 1763. 69 p. 18 cm.

Three acts. **Traetta**, the composer, is not mentioned. From the dedication to the English consul at Livorno, Giovanni (John) Dick, it appears that this gentleman practically started Coltellini on his public career as a poet and incidentally, that this Livorno edition was published after the performances at Vienna. As it is decidedly different, not only verbally but in the number of scenes, etc., beginning, for instance, with a chorus not in the Vienna edition, presumably we have in this Livorno edition the corrected one, promised by Coltellini in the footnote at the end of the Vienna edition. SCHATZ 10393a

Second copy. ML 48.A5 v.32

— **Ifigenia in Tauride.** Dramma per musica da rappresentarsi nel Regio-Ducal Teatro Vecchio di Mantova il carnovale dell' anno 1777 . . .

Mantova, L'erede di Alberto Pazzoni, n. d. 48 p. 17½ cm.

Three acts. Dedication dated Mantova, December 26, 1776, argument, cast, name of the composer, Tommaso **Traetta**, and scenario. The author, Marco Coltellini, is not mentioned.

First performed, as indicated in the dedication, "nel corso del prossimo carnovale" between December 26, 1776, and February 10, 1777, the dates given in the calendar of performances on p. 9. ML 48.A5 v.24

Ifigenia in Tauride. Tragedia di Merindo Fesanio Past. Arc. Variata ad uso di cantarsi la seconda volta nel Teatro celebre Grimani in S. Gio. Grisostomo nel carnovale MDCCXXV.

Venezia, Marino Rossetti, n. d.   front., 59 p.   16½^{cm}.

Five acts. By Benedetto Pasqualigo. Argument, cast, scenario, and name of Leonardo **Vinci** as composer.   SCHATZ 10750

Die illumination. Ein komisches original-singspiel in zwey aufzeugen.   Fuer das K. K. National Hoftheater.

[Wien], beim Logen-meister, 1787.   104 p.   16^{cm}.

Neither the author (unknown to Schatz; J. Gross, according to Haas) is mentioned, nor the composer, Paul Ignaz **Kürzinger**.
First performed at Vienna, Kärnthnerthor Theater, November 25, 1787.

SCHATZ 5338

Die im betruge vertheidigte unschuld. Tr. of L'innocenza difesa nell' inganno.

Im dunkeln ist nicht gut munkeln, oder Fuenf und zwanzig tausend gulden.   Ein singspiel in drei aufzuegen.   Musik von Walter.

n. i., n. d.   Unpaged.   16^{cm}.

By Christian Heinrich Spiess, who is not mentioned.
First performed at Dresden, Theater b. d. schwarzen Thore, August 15, 1792; at Prague, Graefl. Nostiz'sches Theater i. d. Altstadt, January 16, 1783.   SCHATZ 10862

Im finstern ist nicht gut tappen. Eine posse zum singen in zween aufzuegen.   Von Hiesberger.   In musik gesetzt von Schenk. Aufgefuehrt auf dem K. K. Theater am Kaerntnerthor.

[Wien], 1787, Ist beim logenmeister zu haben.   72 p.   15^{cm}.

First performed, as indicated, October 9, 1787.   SCHATZ 9596

Der im schaefer verborgene koenig. Tr. of Hasse's Il re pastore.

Im trueben ist gut fischen. Tr. of his Fra i due litiganti il terzo gode.

[Imene ed Armonia]. *See* Farsa per musica.

L'imenei di Delfo. Serenata per musica da cantarsi nel Real Palazzo dell' Ajuda per celebrare gli augustissimi sposalizi de' serenissimi Signori infanti di Portogallo, e di Spagna Don Giovanni con Donna Carlotta Giovacchina, e Donna Marianna Victoria con Don Gabriele Antonio li 28. marzo, 1785.

[Lisbona], n. publ., n. d., Nella stamperia reale.   31 p.   15^{cm}.

Argument and cast.   Gaetano Martinelli is mentioned as the author, Antonio Leal **Moreira** as the composer.   SCHATZ 6631

Gli imenei stabiliti dal caso. Drama per musica da rappresentarsi nell' antichissimo Teatro Tron di S. Casciano.   L'anno 1703 . . .

Venezia, li beredi Nicolini, 1703.   front., 72 p.   14½^{cm}.

Three acts. By Francesco Silvani, who is not mentioned. Dedication dated Venezia, December 23, 1702, argument, notice to the reader, scenario, and name of Carlo Francesco **Gasparini** as the composer.   SCHATZ 3570

Imeneo.

Apostolo Zeno, Poesie drammatiche, Venezia, 1744, t. iv, p. [281]–354. 19ᶜᵐ.

Three acts and licenza. Argument. No composer is mentioned. In the "Catalogo" at end of t. **x**, date and place of first ed. are given as Vienna, 1727. (First performed August 28 at Laxenburg, music by **Caldara**.) ML 49.A2Z3

— **Imeneo.** Pubblicato per la prima volta in Vienna 1727.

Apostolo Zeno, Poesie drammatiche, Orleans, 1785–86, t. vii, p. 83–152. 21ᶜᵐ.

Three acts and licenza. Argument. No composer is mentioned. ML 49.A2Z4

Imeneo in Atene. Componimento dramatico di Silvio Stampiglia da rappresentarsi in musica nel Teatro Grimani a San Samuel.

Venezia, Marino Rossetti, 1726. 45 p. 15ᶜᵐ.

Three acts. Argument, cast, and name of Nicolà Antonio **Porpora** as the composer. Schatz 8359

Imeneo in Atene, componimento drammatico di Silvio Stampiglia, da rappresentarsi in musica nel Teatro di S. Samuele nella Fiera dell' Ascensione dell' anno MDCCL.

Venezia, All' insegna della Scienza, n. d. 34 p. 15½ᶜᵐ.

Three acts. Argument, scenario, cast, and name of Domingo **Terradellas** as the composer. Schatz 10284

L'impazzito. Intermezzi à tre voci da recitarsi nel Teatro alla Valle il carnevale dell' anno 1748 . . .

Roma, Giuseppe Vaccari, 1748. 23 p. 15ᶜᵐ.

Two parts. Cast, names of "Girolamo Aureli Romano Accademico Occulto" as author, of Giovanni Battista **Casali** as composer and dedication by the impresario Angelo Lungi in which he says "li presenti intermezzi delle commedie che si recitano al pubblico ogni sera differenti" and later on calls them "operette." ML 50.2.I45C2

L'impegno. Commedia per musica di Saverio Zini da rappresentarsi nel Teatro Nuovo per prim' opera di quest' anno 1783.

Napoli, n. publ., 1783. 48 p.

Two acts. Cast and name of the composer, Giovanni **Furno**. Schatz 3389

L'impegno o sia Chi la fa l'aspetti. Farsetta per musica a cinque voci da rappresentarsi nel Teatro Capranica nel carnevale dell' anno 1786 . . .

Roma, Gioacchino Puccinelli, 1786. 48 p. 15ᶜᵐ.

Two parts. Author not mentioned, and unknown to Schatz. Cast and name of Giuseppe **Giordani** as the composer. Schatz 3845

L'impegno superato. Commedia per musica di G. M. D. da rappresentarsi nel Real Teatro del Fondo di Separazione per terz' opera del corrente anno 1795 . . .

Napoli, n. publ., 1795. 54 p. 15½ᶜᵐ.

Two acts. By Giuseppe Maria Diodati. Dedication dated Naples, November 21, 1795, scenario, cast, and name of the composer, Domenico **Cimarosa**. On p. 7–15, argument, cast, and description of Gio. Battista Giannini's "Zorilan, ballo chinese" in five acts. "La musica del ballo, la sua maggior parte è presa dalle composizioni del celebre Signor D. Giovanni Paesiello." Schatz 1996

Les importuns. A. T. of Ziste et Zeste.

Les importuns.   A. T. of Bacelli's Le nouveau marié.

L'impossibile fatto possibile.   A. T. of Castrovillari's La Pasife.

L'impostore punito.   L. T. of P. Guglielmi's I finti amori.

L'impostore punito, ballet.   *See* Robuschi's Castrini, padre e figlio.

L'impostore scoverto.   A. T. of Ruggi's L'ombra di Nino.

L'impostore smascherato.   Commedia per musica di G. M. D.
Da rappresentarsi nel Teatro Nuovo sopra Toledo per prima commedia del corrente anno 1794.

> *Napoli, n. publ., 1794.   42 p.   15^{cm}.*

Two acts. By Giuseppe Maria Diodati. Cast and name of Giacomo **Tritto** as
the composer.   SCHATZ 10472

Gl'impostori.   Drama per musica da rappresentarsi nel Teatro
Giustiniani di San Moisè l'autunno 1751.

> *Venezia, n. publ., n. d.   81 p.   14½^{cm}.*

Three acts. Scenario and cast. Neither the author (*not* Goldoni) is mentioned,
nor the composer, Gaetano **Latilla**. On p. 81 the added aira, "Il polso non batte"
(II, 3).   SCHATZ 5446

L'impostura.   Commedia per musica da rappresentarsi nel Teatro
de' Fiorentini per quart' opera del corrente anno 1796.

> *Napoli, n. publ., 1796.   46 p.   15^{cm}.*

Two acts. Author not mentioned and unknown to Schatz. Cast and name of
"Giuseppe **Mugnes,** maestro di capella Napoletano" as the composer.
                                                              SCHATZ 6863

L'impostura poco dura.   Dramma giocoso per musica da rappresentarsi nel Teatro alla Scala, l'autunno dell' anno 1795 . . .

> *Milano, Gio. Batista Bianchi, n. d.   59, [1] p.   16½^{cm}.*

Two acts. Author not mentioned and unknown to Schatz. Gaetano Maldonati,
the impresario's dedication dated Milan, October 10, 1795, cast, scenario, and name
of Angelo **Tarchi** as the composer. According to Schatz this libretto with seven
characters was an altered version of "Le vicende d'amore" with five characters.
With the opera were performed, composers of the music not mentioned, Gaspare
Ronzi's ballets, "Lauso e Lidia" and "La ghinghetta."   SCHATZ 10236

Imposture defeated: or, A trick to cheat the devil.   A comedy as
it was acted by His Majetsies [!] servants, at the Theatre in Drury-
lane.

> *London, Richard Wellington, 1698.   4 p. l., 47, [1] p.   20^{cm}.*

Five acts with prologue and epilogue. In the fifth act, "*Endimion,* the man in
the moon. A masque." The other acts, too, contain more than the customary
number of songs, etc. On verso of title page and on last (unnumb.) page publisher's
booklists. Cast and notice to the reader, in which the author (not mentioned),
George Powell, denies the charge of a partial plagiarism and says:
". . . This triffle of a comedy, was only a slight piece of scribble, purely design'd
for the introduction of a little musick, being no more than a short weeks work, to
serve the wants of a thin play-house and long vacation . . ."
The composer is not mentioned.
First performed 1698, as indicated.   LONGE 195

L'impresa d'opera. Dramma giocoso da rappresentarsi nel Teatro Giustiniani di S. Moisè il carnovale dell' anno MDCCLXIX. Di Bortolomio Cavalieri. A. F.

*Venezia, Modesto Fenzo, 1769. 72, [2] p. 14*cm.

Three acts. Cast, scenario, and name of Pietro **Guglielmi** as the composer. With the opera were performed, composers of the music not mentioned, Giuseppe Anelli's ballets, "Il geloso senza rivale" and "Il matrimonio per concorso." SCHATZ 4282

L'impresario. Intermezzo da rappresentarsi dalla Signora Anna Faini et il Sig. Antonio Lottini nel Regio Teatro d'Hay-Market. Musica del Sig. Domenico Sarri.

*Londra, J. Chrichley, 1737. 1 p. l., 29 p. 17*cm.

Two acts. By Metastasio, who is not mentioned. English title-page, "The master of the opera," and text face Italian, which formed originally (though with certain differences) the intermezzi in Metstasio's "Didone abbandonata."

First performed, as indicated, 1737; at Naples, Teatro di San Bartolomeo, carnival 1724. SCHATZ 9411

L'impresario burlato. Dramma giocoso per musica di Francescantonio Signoretti da rappresentarsi nel Teatro Nuovo sopra Toledo per prim' opera in questo corrente anno 1797.

*Napoli, Stamperia Flautina, 1797. 42 p. 15*cm.

Two acts. Cast and name of Luigi **Mosca** as composer. ML 50.2.I49M6

L'impresario dell' Isole Canarie. Intermezzo per musica da rappresentarsi nel Teatro dell' opera pantomima de Piccoli Hollandesi sopra la Piazza de Cappuccini. A Vienna, la primavera dell' anno MDCCXLVII.

*n. i., n. d. Unpaged. 22*cm.

Two parts. Cast and name of Metastasio as author. The composer, Leonardo **Leo,** is not mentioned.

First performed at Venice, Teatro di S. Angelo, 1741 (Schatz), 1742 (Wiel). SCHATZ 5558

— L'impresario dell' Isole Canarie. Intermezzo per musica, da rappresentarsi nel Nuovo Real Teatro di Potsdam . . .

*Potsdam, C. F. Voss, 1748. 31 p. 18*cm.

Two parts. Cast. Neither Metastasio nor **Leo** is mentioned. German title page "Der impressarius, oder Opern verwalter von den Canarischen Inseln," face Italian. which is, especially in the second intermezzo, different from the Vienna text of 1747. SCHATZ 5559

L'impresario di Smirne. Dramma giocoso per musica da rappresentarsi nel Ces. Reg. Teatro di Trieste nel carnovale 1798.

*[Trieste], Stamperia governiale, n. d. 63 p. 17½*cm.

Two acts. Cast and impresario's dedication, dated February 3, 1798, and beginning: "Un lepidissimo drama di nuova ed espressamente composta poesia, vestita da una brillante ed adattata musica del Signor maestro Domenico **Rampini,** sorte per la prima volta su queste illustri scene . . ."

The author was Giuseppe Foppa. SCHATZ 8592

L'impresario in angustie.

One act. By Giuseppe Maria Diodati; music by Domenico **Cimarosa.** For the original edition *see* his "Il credulo deluso," Napoli, 1786. (Schatz 1929)

First performed at Naples, Teatro sopra Toledo, carnival, 1786.

L'impresario in angustie—Continued.

— **L'impresario in angustie** ed Il convitato di pietra. Farse per musica da rappresentarsi nel Teatro alla Scala l'autunno 1789 . . .

　　Milano, Gio. Batista Bianchi, n. d.　8, 28 p.　16ᶜᵐ.

　　One act, containing "L'impresario in angustie" only. Dedication, in which this is called the second opera of the season, cast, name of Domenico **Cimarosa** as composer. With the opera were performed Antonio Muzzarelli's ballets (composers of the music not mentioned), "Gli amori d'Igor primo Czar di Moscovia," (alternately performed with) "Il Capitano Cook all' isola Ottaiti," and "La letteraria fanatica."

　　　　　　　　　　　　　　　　　　　　　Schatz 11755

— **L'impresario in angustie.** Farsa per musica da rappresentarsi nel Teatro della rua dos Condes nel carnovale dell' anno 1792 . . .

　　Lisbona, Simone Taddeo Ferreira, 1792.　99 p.　15ᶜᵐ.

　　One act. Impresario's dedication, scenario, cast, and name of Domenico **Cimarosa** as composer. The author, Diodati, is not mentioned. Portuguese title page, "O impresario em angustia," and text face Italian.　　ML 48.C6 II

— **L'impresario in angustie,** ou Le directeur dans l'embarras, opéra bouffon, en deux actes, représenté sur le Théâtre de Monsieur. Musique del Signor Cimarosa, paroles françaises de M. Du Buisson.

　　Paris, et se trouve à Bruxelles, chez J. L. de Boubers, 1792.　35 p. 23ᶜᵐ.

　　First performed, as indicated, May 6 or 7, 1789.　　ML 50.2.I5C3

— **L'impresario in angustie** con farsa Il **convitato di pietra.** Da rappresentarsi nel Teatro di Capua per ultima opera in musica in questo carnevale . . .

　　Napoli, n. publ., 1793.　60 p.　14½ᶜᵐ.

　　Each in one act. The second farce on p. [32]–60. Impresario's dedication dated Capua, January 6, 1793, casts, and names of Domenico **Cimarosa** as composer of the first, and of Giacomo **Tritto** of the second farce, which was written by Giambattista Lorenzi and was first performed, together with Tritto's "Li due gemelli," at Naples, Teatro de' Fiorentini, carnival, 1783.　　Schatz 10466

— **L'impresario in angustie.** Dramma giocoso per musica, da rappresentarsi nel Teatro elettorale.

　　Dresda, n. publ., 1794.　87 p.　16½ᶜᵐ.

　　One act, with name of the composer, **Cimarosa.** German title-page, "Der schauspiel direktor in der klemme," and text face Italian.
　　First performed at Dresden in 1794.　　Schatz 1930

— **Entrepreneuren i knibe.** Et syngestykke i to acter. Oversat af det italienske. Musiken af Domenico Cimarosa.

　　Kjøbenhavn, Johan Frederik Schultz, 1795.　46, [1] p.　16½ᶜᵐ.

　　With pref. by the translator, Frederik Gottlob Sporon.
　　First performed at Copenhagen December 15, 1795.　　Schatz 1933

Der impresarius oder Opernverwalter von den Canarischen inseln. Tr. of Leo's L'impresario dell' Isole Canarie.

L'impromptu du coeur, opera-comique. De M. Vadé. Représenté pour la première fois sur le Théâtre de la Foire Saint Germain, le mardi 8 février 1757.

La Haye, Pierre Gosse junior, 1759. 45 p. 16^{cm}. (Vadé, Oeuvres, La Haye, 1759, t. iv.)

One act. Largely *en vaudevilles.* Cast. On p. 42–45, the *airs notés,* "Par un beau soir m'y promenant," "Louis que le Ciel," "Qu'on est heureux de faire."

ML 49.A2V2

L'impromptu du Pont-Neuf. Piece d'un acte. Faite par Monsieur P * * pour la naissance de Monseigneur le Dauphin. Representée pour la premiere fois gratis par l'Opera-comique, à la Foire Saint Laurent le 9. septembre 1729.

Le Théâtre de la foire, Paris, 1731, t. vii, pl., [295]–322 p. 17^{cm}.

By Panard. Largely *en vaudevilles.* The airs, selected or composed and arranged by Jean Claude **Gillier,** are printed at the end of the volume in the "Table des airs."

First performed September 9, 1729, preceded by "Le corsaire de Salé" and "Les spectacles malades" and the ballet-pantomime, "La nôce angloise." ML 48.L2VII

An **improved edition** of . . . Midas. *See* Midas.

In amor ci vuol destrezza. Opera buffa del nobile Signor Carlo Lanfranchi Rossi . . . fra gli Arcadi Egesippo Argolide. Da rappresentarsi nel nobile Teatro in San Samuele l'autunno dell' anno 1782.

Venezia, Modesto Fenzo, 1782. 58 p. 18^{cm}.

Two acts. Cast, scenario, and name of Vincenzo Martini (**Martin y Soler**) as the composer. On p. [35]–38, "Descrizione del ballo, Minosse rè di Creta o sia La fuga d'Arianna e di Fedra," with cast, by Onorato Viganò; music by Luigi Marescalchi.

SCHATZ 6010

— **L'accorta cameriera.** Dramma giocoso per musica da rappresentarsi nel Regio Teatro di Torino nell' autunno dell' anno 1783.

Torino, Onorato Derossi, n. d. 51, [1] p. 15^{cm}.

Two acts. By Carlo Giuseppe Lanfranchi Rossi, who is not mentioned. Cast and name of Vincenzo Martini (**Martin y Soler**) as the composer. Giuseppe Herdlitzka's ballets, "Il ritorno opportuno" and "Le reclute del villaggio," were performed with the opera. The composers of the music are not mentioned.

SCHATZ 6031

Das in die preussische krone verwandelte wagengestirn. A. T. of Graupner's Bellerophon.

Der in krohnen erlangte gluckswechsel oder Almira, koenigin von Castilien. In einem sing-spiel auff dem grossen Hamburgischen Schau-Platz vorgestellet im jahr 1704.

[Hamburg], Gedruckt im selben jahr, n. d. Unpaged. 18½^{cm}.

Three acts. Argument and scenario. Neither Friedrich Christian Feustking, the author resp. translator of Giulio Pancieri's "L'Almira," nor Georg Friedrich **Händel,** the composer, is mentioned. Some arias have Italian text added to the German.

First performed, as indicated, Theater beim Gänsemarkt, January 8, 1705.

SCHATZ 4479

— **Der in cronen erlangte gluckswechsel,** oder Almira, koenigin von Castilien, in einem singe-spiel auf dem Hamburgischen Schauplatz vorgestellet.

[Hamburg], Philip Ludwig Stromer, 1732. Unpaged. 18^{cm}.

Three acts. Scenario and cast. Neither Feustking, the author, nor **Händel,** the composer, is mentioned. This version is considerably different from the edition of

Der in krohnen erlangte glueckswechsel—Continued.

1704. For instance, I, 4, has now the aria, "Se lento ancora un fulmine," instead of "Proverai di che fiere saette," and the aria, "Zuerne was hin," has been dropped altogether from this scene.   SCHATZ 4500

Der in Syrien triumphirende kayser Hadrianus. Tr of Broschi's Adriano in Siria.

Die in verwirrung lebende familie. Tr. of Scolari's La famiglia in scompiglio.

L'inaspettata consolazione nelle sventure, ballet. *See* Bianchi's Trionfo della pace.

Gl'Inca del Perù. Tr. of part of Rameau's Les Indes Galantes.

Inca il tiranno, ballet. *See* Bertoni's Andromaca.

L'incanti per amore. Comedia per musica di Terentio Chirrap Napoletano [Pietro Trinchera]. Da rappresentarsi nel Teatro Nuovo nell' autunno di quest' anno 1741 . . .

    Napoli, Nicola di Biase, 1741. 60 p. 14½^{cm}.

Three acts. Impresario's dedication dated October 2, 1741, cast, and name of the composer, Antonio **Palella.**   SCHATZ 7712

L'incanto superato. Favola romanzesca per musica, da rappresentarsi nel Teatro Elettorale.

    Dresda, n. publ., 1795. 95 p. 16^{cm}.

Two acts. Author not mentioned and unknown to Schatz. Franz Xaver **Süssmayer** is mentioned as the composer. German title-page, "Der besiegte zauber," and text face Italian.

First performed at Dresden, 1795, as indicated; at Vienna, Burgtheater, July 8, 1793.   SCHATZ 10179

Les Incas du Pérou. Entrée in Rameau's Les Indes galantes.

L'incendie. *See* Floquet's Le seigneur bienfaisant.

Les incidents, ballet. *See* P. Guglielmi's Vologeso.

L'incognita fortunata. Farsa per musica di Epitide Corebio, P. A. da rappresentarsi nel Real Teatro del Fondo di Separazione nell' està del presente anno 1782.

    Napoli, n. publ., 1782. 36 p. 15^{cm}.

One act. By Gaetano Ciliberti. Cast and name of Giacomo **Rust** as the composer.   SCHATZ 9172

L'incognita perseguitata. O. T. of Petrosellini's text La nuova Giannetta.

L'incognita perseguitata. Dramma giocoso da rappresentarsi nel Regio-ducal Teatro di Milano l'estate dell' anno 1773 . . .

    Milano, Gio. Batista Bianchi, n. d. 80 p. 14½^{cm}.

Three acts. By Giuseppe Petrosellini. Cast, scenario, and name of composer, Pasquale **Anfossi,** but not of librettist.

First performed at Rome, Teatro delle Dame, 1773.   SCHATZ 238

L'incognita perseguitata—Continued.

— **Metilda ritrovata.** Dramma giocoso per musica da rappresentarsi ne' Teatri privilegiati di Vienna.

Vienna, Giuseppe Kurtzboeck, 1773. 71 p. 16ᶜᵐ.

Three acts. Scenario and name of composer. Somewhat altered version of **Anfossi's** "L'incognita perseguitata." The cast is added in ink in this copy.
First performed as indicated in the title on August 31, 1773.   SCHATZ 239

— La **Giannetta** o sia L'incognita perseguitata; dramma giocoso per musica, da rappresentarsi nel Regio Teatro. Jeannette, eller Den fortraengte ubekiendte; et lystigt synge-spil . . . Oversadt paa dansk af R. Soelberg.

Kiøbenhavn, H. J. Graae, 1775. 128 p. 17ᶜᵐ.

Three acts. Cast and name of **Anfossi** as composer.
First performed, as indicated, on November 1, 1775.   SCHATZ 240

— **L'inconnue persécutée.** Comédie en deux actes et en prose, mêlée d'ariettes, imitées de l'italien, sur la musique du Sieur Anfossi. Par M. Moline. Représenté devant Sa Majesté, à Fontainebleau, le 25 octobre 1776.

Paris, Pierre Robert Christophe Ballard, 1776. 2 p. l., 63 p. 20½ᶜᵐ.

Cast. Jean Baptiste **Rochefort,** who arranged the score and inserted music of his own, is not mentioned.
First performed as above at Paris, Comédie italienne, November 12, 1776. Not to be confused with de Rosoy's version of Petrosellini's text, first performed, with Anfossi's music, at Paris, Académie royale de musique, September 21, 1781.
        ML 50.2.I55A6

L'incognita perseguitata. Dramma giocoso per musica d'Ensildo Prosindio, P. A. da rappresentarsi nel Teatro Grimani di S. Samuele il carnovale dell' anno MDCCLXIV.

Venezia, Modesto Fenzo, 1764. 55 p. 16ᶜᵐ.

Three acts. By Giuseppe Petrosellini. Cast, scenario, and name of Niccolò **Piccinni** as the composer.   SCHATZ 8097

— **L'incognita perseguitata.** Dramma giocoso per musica d'Ensildo Prosindio P. A. Da rappresentarsi nel Real Teatro dell' Ajuda in occasione di festeggiarsi il felicissimo giorno natalizio di Sua Reale Maestà l'augustissima Signora D. Marianna Vittoria . . . nella primavera dell' anno MDCCLXVI.

Lisbona, Michele Manescal da Costa, n. d. 69 p. 15ᶜᵐ.

Three acts. Cast, scenario, and name of Niccolò **Piccinni** as composer. Text by Giuseppe Petrosellini.
First performed at Lisbon, as indicated, March 31, 1766.   ML 48.C6 I

— **L'incognita perseguitata.** Dramma giocoso per musica da rappresentarsi nel Piccolo Teatro di S. A. E. di Sassonia.

Dresda, n. publ., 1768. 117 p. 15½ᶜᵐ.

Three acts. Cast, scenario, and name of Niccolò **Piccinni** as the composer. Petrosellini's text, with only very few alterations. German title-page, "Die verfolgte unbekannte," and text face Italian.
First performed December 3, 1768, as indicated.   SCHATZ 8098

Gl'incontri stravaganti. Commedia per musica da rappresentarsi nel Teatro Nuovo sopra Toledo nel carnevale di questo corrente anno 1790.

Napoli, n. publ., 1790. 52 p. 15ᶜᵐ.

Two acts. Cast and name of **Bernardini**(Marcello di Capua) as composer. Librettist not mentioned, and unknown to Schatz. SCHATZ 840

L'incoronatione di Dario. Drama per musica da rappresentarsi nel Teatro di S. Angelo, l'anno MDCLXXXIV . . .

Venetia, Francesco Nicolini, 1684. front., 60 p. 14ᶜᵐ.

Three acts. Dedication, argument, and scenario. Neither the author, Adriano Morselli, nor the composer, Giovanni Domenico **Freschi,** is mentioned. Act first has sixteen scenes only, though the libretto counts seventeen. SCHATZ 3350

— Dario. Drama per musica da recitarsi nel Teatro di Sant' Angelo l'anno MDCLXXXV . . .

Venetia, Francesco Nicolini, 1685. 56 p. 14ᶜᵐ.

Three acts. Publisher's dedication, argument, and scenario. Nicolini calls this a reprint in his dedication, but it really is not, being a considerably-altered version.

For instance, the character of "Niceno" has been dropped, whereas that of "Dalisa" has been added. Accordingly, for instance, Niceno's aria (I, 13), "Torbida notte, e fosca," does not appear in the 1685 version and all the arias for Dalisa in this do not appear in the original version. SCHATZ 3357

L'incoronatione di Poppea di Gio. Francesco Busenello. Opera musicale rappresentata nel Teatro Grimano l'anno 1642.

Venetia, Andrea Giuliani, 1656. 61 p. 15ᶜᵐ.

The title page (verso blank) is followed immediately in this copy by the "*argomento*" on p. 5, the first of the signature A 3, the signatures being in twos. **Monteverdi,** the composer, is not mentioned. Three acts and prologue. SCHATZ 6593

L'incoronazione di Dario. Drama per musica, da rappresentarsi nel Teatro di S. Angelo per opera terzo nel carnevale dell' anno 1716 . . .

Venezia, Marino Rossetti, 1717. 57 p. 15ᶜᵐ.

Three acts. Dedication, argument, cast, scenario, name of Antonio **Vivaldi** as the composer, and note:

"Eccoti l'Incoronazione di Dario, opera del Sig. Adriano Morselli già da molti anni defonto. Se la retrovi in qualche parte mutata, e per le arie, e per gli caratteri de rappresentanti, non si è fatto ad altro fine, che per accomodarla all' uso moderno del teatro, & alla compagnia che deve rappresentarla . . ." SCHATZ 10771

L'incoronazione di Serse. Drama per musica da rappresentarsi nel famoso Teatro Grimano di San Gio. Grisostomo l'anno 1691 . . .

Venetia, Nicolini, 1691. front., 60 p. 15ᶜᵐ.

Three acts. Dedication dated Venice, December 26, 1690, and signed with the initials of the author, Adriano Morselli, argument, scenario, and notice to the reader, with name of Giuseppe Felice **Tosi** as the composer. SCHATZ 10376

Second copy. ML 48.M2O

L'incoronazione di Siroe, ballet. *See* Sarti's Siroe.

L'incoronazione di Uladislao rè di Polonia in rè d'Ungheria, ballet. *See* Isola's La conquista del vello d'oro.

L'incostante. Intermezzo per musica da rappresentarsi nel Real Teatro di Salvaterra nel carnovale dell' anno 1775.

[Lisbona], Stamperia reale, n. d. 48 p. 14^{cm}.

Two acts. Author not mentioned and unknown to Schatz. Cast, scenario, and name of Niccolò **Piccinni** as the composer.

First performed at Rome, Teatro Capranica, February, 1766. SCHATZ 8138

— Il volubile. Intermezzi per musica a quattro voci da rappresentarsi nell' antico rinovato Teatro della Pace nel corrente carnevale 1769 . . .

Roma, Angelo Maria Ansillioni, 1768. 35 p. 16^{cm}.

Two parts. Text identical with that of his "L'incostante," Lisbon, 1775, containing arias like: "Signorina mia carina" (I, 1), "Tutta ricci, tutta nei" (I, 3), "Poverina, innocentina" (II, 4), "Il Signor conte, che venga presto" (II, 5), etc.

ML 50.2.V75P3

L'incostanza degli amanti, ballet. *See* Insanguine's Medonte.

L'incostanza del militare in amore, ballet. *See* Borghi's La donna instabile.

L'incostanza schernita. O. T. of Cassani's libretto Filandro.

L'incostanza schernita, Dramma comico-pastorale di Vincenzo Cassani, da rappresentarsi nel Teatro Grimani a S. Samuele nell' fiera dell' Ascensione . . .

Venezio, Marino Rossetti, 1727. 48 p. 14½^{cm}.

Three acts. Author's dedication, argument, notice to the reader, cast, scenario, and name of Tommaso **Albinoni** as composer.

First performed at Venice in 1727, as indicated above. SCHATZ 95

— Filandro. Dramma comico-pastorale da rappresentarsi nel Teatro Giustiniano di San Moisè l'anno MDCCXXIX. Di Vicenzo Cassani. Edizione seconda.

Venezia, Marino Rossetti, n. d. 42 p. 14½^{cm}.

Three acts. Arguments, name of **Albinoni** as composer, and cast. "Filandro" is merely a slightly modified version of "L'incostanza schernita," as a comparison proves. Hence, "Edizione seconda." In the later version the part of "Ergasto" has been added, of which the author says "è aggiunto solo per accomodarsi al numero de' personaggi di già obbligati, conoscendo benissimo essere una parte inutile, e superflua, senza però, che guasti l'ordine, e l'orditura del dramma." SCHATZ 109

L'incostanza trionfante overo Il Theseo. Drama per musica nel Teatro di San Cassano . . .

Venetia, Andrea Giuliani, 1658. 14 p. l. (incl. front.), 66 p. 14^{cm}.

Prologue and three acts. Publisher's dedication dated Venice, January 16, 1658, argument, quotations from Plutarch, cast [!], scenario, and notice to the reader:

"Trionfa in questo drama l'Incostanza di Theseo, e molto più l'incostanza dell' auttore di essa, mentre che altri l'hà inventato, altri l'hà regulato, uno l'hà disposto, e molti l'hanno ordinato; che dirò poi di coloro, che l'hanno illustrato & abbellito con la poesia? L'inventore, che allo splendor della nascita hà sposato la vivacità dell' ingegno, pensò di confidare questo suo eruditissimo parto, per esser ben vestito, alla penna dovitiosa del Signor Francesco Piccoli . . . Ma su'l meglio del lavoro gli convenne da Venetia far passaggio a' paesi lontani; onde non potendo egli assistere alla perfettione dell' opera, nè alle alterationi, anzi diversificando necessitate dalla prattica della scena, accioche questo drappo facesse un vago vedere, come sotto la virtù singolare del M. R. P **Ziani** farà un bel sentire; si è fatto ricorso à penna sublime, che hoggi per suo solo diporto vola per questo nostro cielo italiano."

Piccoli, he continues, to distinguish his own verses from those of the other collaborators, adopted the expedient of putting his own in quotation marks, but in the hurry of publication many were not so printed, and so Piccoli's caution was largely in vain.

SCHATZ 11222

Les **Indes dansantes.**   Parody of Rameau's Les Indes galantes.

Les **Indes galantes,** ballet heroique, représenté par L'Académie royale de musique, pour la premiere fois, le mardi 23 août 1735; repris avec la nouvelle entrée des Sauvages, le samedi dixième mars 1736.   Remis au théâtre le mardi 28 mai 1743.

[*Paris*], *Jean Baptiste Christophe Ballard, 1743. viii, 60 p. 24*^{cm}.

Prologue and four entrées: "Le turc généreux," "Les Incas du Pérou," "Les fleurs," "Les sauvages." "Avertissement" (p. iii–vii). Neither the author, Louis Fuzelier, is mentioned, nor the composer, Jean Philippe **Rameau.**   ML 52.2.I4R2

— **Prologue des Indes galantes.** Représenté devant Leurs Majestés à Versailles le samedi 16 février 1765.

[*Paris*], *Christophe Ballard, 1765. 12 p. 20½*^{cm}. (*Journal des spectacles, t. 1, Paris, 1766.*)

Cast and names of Louis Fuzelier as author of the text, of Jean Philippe **Rameau** as composer, and of Laval père et fils as "composers" of the ballets.   ML 48.J7

— Les **Incas du Perou,** acte de ballet. Représenté devant Leurs Majestés à Versailles le mercredi 30 janvier 1765.

[*Paris*], *Christophe Ballard, 1765. 23 p. 21*^{cm}.

Cast and names of Louis Fuzelier as author, of Jean Philippe **Rameau** as composer, and "Laval, père & fils" as "composers" of the ballets.   ML 52.2 I5
Second copy (Journal des spectacles, t. I, Paris, 1766).   ML 48.J7

— Les **sauvages,** entrée ajoutée aux Indes galantes. Représentée devant Leurs Majestés à Versailles le samedi 16 février 1765.

[*Paris*], *Christophe Ballard, 1765. 23 p. 20½*^{cm}. (*Journal des spectacles, t. 1, Paris, 1766.*)

Cast and names of Louis Fuzelier as author of the text, of Jean Philippe **Rameau** as composer of the music, and of Laval, père et fils as "composers" of the ballets.
ML 48.J7

— Les **Indes galantes,** ballet-heroique, représenté par l'Académie royale de musique, l'an 1735. Paroles de Mr Fuselier. Musique de Mr Rameau. CXXIII. opera.

n. i., n. d. 77–144 p. 14½^{cm}. (*Recueil général des opera, Paris, 1745, t. xvi.*)

Prologue and the entrées "Les Incas du Perou," "Le Turc généreux," "Les fleurs," "Les sauvages, nouvelle entrée ajoutée." Text preceded by an Avertissement and followed by this note:
"On avertit encore, que Les Incas du Perou, sont devenus la seconde entrée, et Le Turc généreux la première, l'Académie les ayant rangées ainsi, dans la Remise du 28 mai, 1743."   ML 48.R4

— **Gl'Incâ del Perù.** Seconda entrata dell' opera delle Indie galanti rappresentata in Parma sul Teatro della Corte nel giorno XVIII di dicembre l'anno MDCCLVII. Tradotta dal franzese dal Signor abate Frugoni . . .

Parma, Monti, n. d. 23 p. 19^{cm}.

Neither Louis Fuzelier, the author of "Les Indes Galantes," nor **Rameau,** the composer, is mentioned.   SCHATZ 8588

Les **Indes galantes**—Continued.

— Les **Indes dansantes,** parodie des Indes galantes. Représentée pour la première fois, par les Comédiens italiens ordinaires du roi, le lundi 26 juillet, 1751.

Paris, La V. Delormel & fils, [etc.], 1751. 67, [1], 6 p. 18½^{cm}.

Casts. On the 6 p. twelve "Airs de la parodie des Indes galantes." *Comp.* next entry.
ML 50.2.I56

— Les **Indes dansantes,** parodie des Indes galantes. Représentée pour la premiere fois, par les Comédiens italiens ordinaire [!] du roi, le lundi 26 juillet 1751. Troisième edition.

Paris, la veuve Delormel & fils et Prault fils, 1752. 71, [1], 8 p. 18½^{cm}.

Casts. Three entrées called "Le Turc généreux," "Les Incas du Perou," "Les fleurs" after which "La feste des fleurs." On the [8] p. nineteen "Airs de la parodie des Indes galantes." (*See* next entry.)
ML 50.2.I57

— Les **Indes dansantes,** parodie des Indes galantes; représentée pour la premiere fois par les Comédiens italiens ordinaires du roi, le lundi 26 juillet 1751. Quatrième édition.

Paris, N. B. Duchesne, 1759. 86 p. 19^{cm}. (Theatre de M. Favart, Paris, 1763–77, t. I.)

Cast. Three entrées, called "Le turc généreux," "Les Incas du Pérou," and "Les fleurs," after which, "La fête de fleurs." *En vaudevilles.* Quite a few of the airs are printed in the text, and on p. 73–86 are printed seven "Airs et vaudevilles, des Divertissements de la parodie des Indes dansantes avec le duo et le trio." The arranger of the music is not mentioned by Font. This text is not that of the parody in its original form. Originally it had four entrées, and as "L'ambigue de la folie, ou Le ballet des dindons" it was first performed in 1743, after Rameau's ballet-opera had been revived on August 31, 1743.
ML 49.A2F1

L'**India scoperta.** A. T. of Ottoboni's Il Colombo.

The **Indian chief.** A. T. of The choice of Harlequin.

L'**Indiana a Londra,** ballet. *See* Santi's Il marito indolente.

Gl'**Indiani.** Dramma nuovo per musica da rappresentarsi nel nobilissimo Teatro Venier in San Benedetto l'autunno dell' anno 1796.

Venezia, Modesto Fenzo, 1796. 41, [1] p. 18^{cm}.

Two acts. By Mattia Botturini who is not mentioned. Argument, cast, scenario, and name of Sebastiano **Nasolini** as the composer. With the opera was performed Onorato Viganò's ballet, "La morte d'Ettore" musie, ("tutta nuova,") by Alessandro La Motte) and Giuseppe Domenico de Rossy's ballet, "L'equivoco delli due amanti molinari" (composer not mentioned).
First performed December 9, 1796.
SCHATZ 7004

L'**Indienne,** comédie en un acte, mêlée d'ariettes, représentée pour la première fois par les Comédiens Italiens ordinaires du roi, le mercredi 31 octobre 1770. La musique est de M. Cifolelli, maître de chant & de mandoline.

Paris, la veuve Duchesne, 1771. 28, [2] p. 19^{cm}.

The 2 unnumb. p. contain a "Catalogue des pièces de théatre qui se vendent séparement chez F. J. Desoer . . . à Liege." The author, Nicolas Etienne Framery, is not mentioned.
SCHATZ 1897
Second copy. SCHATZ 11685

L'indifférence. Prologue des deux pièces suivantes. Par M^rs le S * *. F * *. & d'Or * *. Representé à la Foire de S. Laurent 1730.

— **L'amour marin.** Pièce d'un acte. Par M^rs le S * *. F * *. & d'Or * *. Representé à la Foire de S. Laurent. 1730.

— **L'esperance.** Piece d'un acte. Par M^rs le S * *. F * *. & d'Or * *. Representée à la Foire de S. Laurent. 1730.

Le Théâtre de la foire, Paris, 1731, t. viii, 3 pl., [239]–367 p. 17^cm.

By Le Sage, Fuzelier, and d'Orneval. *Largely en vaudevilles.* The airs, selected or composed and arranged by Jean Claude **Gillier**, are printed at the end of the volume in the "Table des airs."
First performed September 5, 1730.   ML 48.L2VIII

L'indolente. Dramma giocoso per musica da rappresentarsi in Parma nel R. D. Teatro di Corte il carnevale dell' anno MDCCXCVII . . .

Parma, Stamperia Carmignani, n. d. viii, 54, [10] p. 17½^cm.

Two acts. By Giuseppe Palomba, who is not mentioned. Impresario's dedication, scenario, and name of Francesco **Gnecco** as the composer. ("La musica è tutta nuova espressamente composta.") The additional pages contain the title of the second ballet, "L'equivoco fortunato," and preface, cast, and description of Urbano Garzia's "Ginevra di Scozia, ballo tragico-pantomimico in cinque atti." The composers of the music are not mentioned.   SCHATZ 3962

Indtoget. Syngestykke i to akter. Musiken af kapelmester Schultz. Førstegang opført paa den Kongelige Danske Skueplads den 26 februar, 1793.

n. i., n. d. 17^cm. p. [111]–208. (Peter Andreas Heiberg, Skuespil. 3 bind.)

On p. [113]–131, "Fortale til det første oplag" and "Fortale til denne an den udgave," the latter dated, "Kiøbenhavn d. 16 Julii 1794," and both of considerable historical importance.   SCHATZ 9723

L'industrie. Prologue des deux pièces suivantes. Par M^rs le S * * F * * & d'Or * * Representée à la Foire Saint Laurent 1730.

— **Zemine et Almanzor.** Piece d'un acte. Par Mrs. le S * * F * * & d'Or * * Representée à la Foire Saint Laurent 1730.

— Les **routes du monde.** Piece d'un acte. Par M^rs le S * * F * * & d'Or * * Representée à la Foire Saint Laurent 1730.

Le Théâtre de la foire, Paris, 1731, t. viii, 3 pl., [67]–183 p. 17^cm.

By Le Sage, Fuzelier, and d'Orneval. *Largely en vaudevilles.* The airs, selected or composed and arranged by Jean Claude **Gillier**, are printed at the end of the volume in the "Table des airs."
First performed March 27, 1730.   ML 48.L2VIII

Le industrie amorose. O. T. of Bertati's text Il matrimonio per inganno.

Le industrie amorose. Dramma giocoso per musica di Giovanni Bertati da rappresentarsi nel Teatro Giustiniani in S. Moisè l'autunno dell' anno 1778.

n. i., n. d. 2 p. l., 64 p. 17½^cm.

Two acts. Impresario's dedication, cast, and name of Bernard(in)o **Ottani** as the composer. On p. 33 is printed the argument of a ballet by Filippo Beretti, but neither the title nor the composer of the music is mentioned.   SCHATZ 7365

Ines de Castro. Dramma per musica da rappresentarsi nel Regio Teatro di via della Pergola l'autunno del 1793 . . .

Firenze, Pietro Pantosini, 1793. 46 p. 16½ᶜᵐ.

Two acts. By Cosimo Giotti. Argument, cast, and names of composer, Gaetano **Andreozzi,** and librettist. The text of the opera preceded, on p. 6–12, by Argomento, cast, and detailed description of "La morte d'Agamemnone, ballo tragico in cinque atti," by Francesco Clerico (composer of music not mentioned).

First performed, as indicated, September 8, 1793. Sᴄʜᴀᴛᴢ 213

Ines de Castro. Dramma per musica da rappresentarsi nel nobilissimo Teatro Venier in San Benedetto l'autunno dell' anno 1795.

Venezia, Modesto Fenzo, 1795. 53 p. 18ᶜᵐ.

Three acts. Cast, argument, scenario, and names of Francesco **Bianchi,** Sebastiano **Nasolini,** Ignazio **Gerace,** Giuseppe **Cervellini** as composers. The author, Luigi De Sanctis, is not mentioned. On p. [23]–31 argument, cast, and full description of "Mario e Felice, ballo tragico pantomimo" by Eusebio Luzzi, music ("tutta nuova") by Vittorio Trento. The second ballet, "Lo spazza camino," was also by Luzzi, but the composer is not mentioned.

Bianchi's "Ines de Castro" first performed at Naples, May 30, 1794, Teatro di San Carlo. Sᴄʜᴀᴛᴢ 1012

Ines de Castro. Dramma per musica da rappresentarsi nel nuovo e nobilissimo Teatro detto La Fenice il carnovale dell' anno 1793.

Venezia, Modesto Fenzo, 1793. 61 p. 17½ᶜᵐ.

Three acts. Author not mentioned and unknown to Schatz. Argument, cast, scenario, and name of Giuseppe **Giordani** as the composer. With the opera were performed Onoràto Viganò's ballets "Le avventure di Milord Wilver e di Miledi sua sposa" and "La fiera d'Amsterdam." The composers of the music are not mentioned.

Sᴄʜᴀᴛᴢ 3846

Ines de Castro, ballet. *See* P. Guglielmi's Il Demetrio.

Ines de Castro, ballet. *See* Zingarelli's Antigono.

L'infante de Zamora. *See* Paisiello's La Frascatana.

L'infausto matrimonio, ballet. *See* Portugal's La pazzagiornata.

L'infedeltà fedele. Commedia per musica di Giambattista Lorenzi P. A. Da rappresentarsi nell' apertura del Real Teatro del Fondo di Separazione. Nella està del corrente anno 1779.

Napoli, n. publ., 1779. 71 p. 15ᶜᵐ.

Three acts. Scenario, cast, name of the composer, Domenico **Cimarosa,** and notice to the reader, in which Lorenzi says:

"Eccoti un libro per l'apertura di questo nuovo Real Teatro. In esso ho studiata la maniera di slontanarmi da quelle solite buffonerie popolesche e volgari, che ne' nostri piccoli teatri si costumano, contentandomi di usar nella favola moderati sali, che bastassero a dare un convenevole risalto a quel tragico, che in essa ho introdotto, e che finora non fu nelle farse musicali praticato. Fu mio pensiero, che tra quel tutto serio de Real Teatro di Sarr Carlo, e quel tutto giocoso de' suddetti teatrini, servisse questo di un mezzano spettacolo, che discretamente partecipasse cosi dell' uno, che dell' altro fare, onde ciascuno avesse nella Capitale un teatro corrispondente al suo genio."

First performed, as indicated, July 20, 1779. Sᴄʜᴀᴛᴢ 1936

— **L'infedeltà fedele.** Operetta per musica da rappresentarsi nel Piccolo Teatro di S. A. E. di Sassonia.

Dresda, n. publ., 1782. 125 p. 16ᶜᵐ.

Three acts, with name of the composer, **Cimarosa.** German title-page, "Treu in der Untreue," and text face Italian.

First performed, as indicated, October 5, 1782. Sᴄʜᴀᴛᴢ 1937

L'infedeltà punita. Drama per musica. Da rappresentarsi nel famoso Teatro Grimani di S. Gio. Grisostomo. L'autunno dell' anno 1712 . . .

Venezia, Marino Rossetti, 1712. 72 p. 15^{cm}.

Three acts. Dedication dated Venice, November 12, 1712, and signed with the initials of Francesco Silvani, the author, argument, cast, and scenario. The composers, Carlo Francesco **Pollaroli** and Antonio **Lotti**, are not mentioned.

SCHATZ 8326

L'infedeltà sorpresa, ballet. *See* Tritto's La vergine del sole.

Gl'ingannati. Commedia per musica di Gennarantonio Federico, Napoletano. Da rappresentarsi nel Teatro de' Fiorentini nell' autunno di questo anno 1734 . . .

Napoli, Nicola di Biase, 1734. 78 p. 14^{cm}.

Three acts. Impresario's dedication, cast, and name of Gaetano **Latilla** as the composer. SCHATZ 5454

L'ingannator ingannato. Drama per musica da rappresentarsi nel Teatro Grimani di S. Samuel l'autunno dell' anno 1710.

Venezia, Marino Rossetti, 1710. 60 p. 14½^{cm}.

Three acts. By Antonio Marchi, who is not mentioned. Argument, notice to the reader, and scenario. The composer, Giovanni Maria **Ruggeri**, is not mentioned. Pages 3–6, presumably with the dedication, are wanting. SCHATZ 9138

L'ingannatore ingannato. Dramma giocoso per musica da rappresentarsi nel Teatro di S. Cassano nell' autunno dell' anno 1764 dell' abbate Pietro Chiari . . .

Venezia, Modesto Fenzo, 1764. 56 p. 16½^{cm}.

Three acts. Cast, scenario, and name of composer, Ferdinando Giuseppe **Bertoni.** (Music called "tutta nuova.") SCHATZ 939

Gl'inganni amorosi scoperti in villa, scherzo giocoso di Lelio Maria Landi, da rappresentarsi nel Teatro Formagliari l'anno MDCXCVI. Musica del Signor Giuseppe Aldrovandini . . .

Bologna, gli eredi del Sarti, n. d. 95 p. 13^{cm}.

Three acts. Author's dedication dated Bologna, January 28, 1695 [=1696, new style], notice to the reader, scenario. The composer, Giuseppe Antonio Vincenzo **Aldrovandini,** is not mentioned. SCHATZ 135

Gl'inganni delusi. Commedia per musica di Giuseppe Palomba. Da rappresentarsi nel Real Teatro del Fondo di Separazione per prim' opera di quest' anno 1789 . . .

Napoli, n. publ., 1789. 48 p. 15^{cm}.

Two acts. Impresario's dedication dated Napoli, June 13, 1789, cast, and name of Pietro **Guglielmi** as the composer. SCHATZ 4290

Gl'inganni delusi, ballet. *See* Zingarelli's Il ratto delle Sabine.

Gl'inganni felici.

Apostolo Zeno, Poesie drammatiche, Venezia, 1744, t. vii, 92 p. 19^{cm}.

Three acts. Argument. No composer is mentioned. In the "Catalogo" at end of t. x, date and place of first ed. are given as Venice, 1695.

(First composed by *Pollaroli.*)

ML 49.A2Z3

Gl'inganni felici—Continued.

—Gl'**inganni felici,** pubblicati per la prima volta in Venezia 1695. *Apostolo Zeno, Poesie drammatiche, Orleans, 1785–86, t. I, 102 p. 21ᶜᵐ.*

Three acts. Argument. No composer is mentioned. ML49.A2Z4

Gl'**inganni felici.** Drama per musica da rappresentarsi nel nuovo Teatro Giustiniano in San Moisè l'autunno dell' anno 1722. *Venezia, Marino Rossetti, 1722. 60 p. 14½ᶜᵐ.*

Three acts. By Apostolo Zeno. Argument, cast, scenario, and name of the composer ("Gioseppe Boini") Giuseppe Maria **Buini.** Schatz 1392

Gl'**inganni felici.** Drama per musica. Da recitarsi nel Teatro di S. Angelo. L'anno MDCXCVI . . . *Venezia, Nicolini, 1696. 68 p. 14ᶜᵐ.*

Three acts. Dedication, with the initials of the author, Apostolo Zeno, argument, and scenario. The composer, Carlo Francesco **Pollaroli,** is not mentioned Schatz claims that the opera was first performed as above during fall of 1695. Schatz 8297

Gl'**inganni fortunati.** Pastorale per musica da recitarsi in Venezia nel Teatro Giustiniano a S. Moisè nel mese di Maggio dell' anno 1720 . . . *Venezia, Marin [!] Rossetti, 1720. 42 p. 15ᶜᵐ.*

Three acts. By Belisario Valeriani. Impresario's dedication, argument, scenario. Neither the author (whose "La caccia in Etolia" this is) is mentioned, nor the composer, Giuseppe Maria **Buini.** Schatz 1393

Gl'**inganni fortunati.** Commedia per musica da rappresentarsi nel Real Teatro del Fondo di Separazione per quart' opera di quest' anno 1788 . . . *Napoli, n. publ., 1788. 45 p. 15½ᶜᵐ.*

Two acts. Author not mentioned, and unknown to Schatz. Dedication signed "Giuseppe Lucchesi," cast, and name of the composer, Valentino **Fioravanti.** On p. 42–45, cast, and argument of "Orbecch, ballo eroico favoloso composto, e diretto del Sig. Giambattista Giannini," music ("tutta nuova") by Pietro Dutillieu. The second ballet, also by Giannini (composer not mentioned), was merely a "mascherata pantomima." Schatz 3157

Gl'**inganni innocenti** overo L'Adalinda, favola drammatica musicale composta, e fatta rappresentare da gl'Accademici Sfaccendati nell' Ariccia per la villeggiatura dell' autunno l'anno 1673 . . . *Ronciglione, n. publ., 1673. 6 pl., 96 p. 13ᶜᵐ.*

Three acts. Dedication, argument, scenario. Author and composer not mentioned, and unknown to Schatz. Eitner dates Agostini's opera of the above title as Milan, 1679. Schatz 11340

L'**inganno.** Commedia per musica di Gaetano Ciliberti tra gli Arcadi Epitide Corebio da rappresentarsi nel Real Teatro del Fondo di Separazione per prima opera di quest anno 1782. *Napoli, n. publ., 1782. 66 p. 15ᶜᵐ.*

Three acts. Cast and name of the composer, Luigi **Caruso.** Schatz 1652

L'inganno amoroso.   Commedia per musica da rappresentarsi nel Teatro Nuovo sopra Toledo per prima opera del corrente anno 1786.

> *Napoli, n. publ., 1786.   64 p.   15^{cm}.*

Two acts.   By Giuseppe Palomba, who is not mentioned.   Cast and name of Pietro **Guglielmi** as the composer.

First performed, as indicated, June 12, 1786.   SCHATZ 4248

— **Le due gemelle.**   Dramma giocoso per musica da rappresentarsi nel Pubblico Teatro di Lucca nell' estate dell' anno MDCCXC.

> *Lucca, Francesco Bonsignori, 1790.   67 p.   15^{cm}.*

Two acts.   Cast and name of Pietro **Guglielmi** as the composer.   This is his "L'inganno amoroso" (text by Palomba), but with many alterations.   For instance, the aria, "Non dubiti, signora" has been dropped from I, 1; I, 2 begins, "Sei un ridicolo, sei un villano," instead of "Costei, per quanto scorgo," which now opens I, 3. With the opera were performed (composers of the music not mentioned) Pietro Giudice's "La caccia d'Enrico IV," Carlo Taglioni's "Li due sindaci, ossia La vendemmia," and Gaetano Ghelardini's "L'inverno ossia La pianella perduta."

First performed, as indicated, July 17, 1790; at Monza, Teatro Arciducale, fall of 1788.   SCHATZ 4249

— **L'equivoco amoroso** ossia Le due gemelle.   Dramma giocoso per musica da rappresentarsi in Parma nel R. D. Teatro di Corte il carnevale dell' anno MDCCXCII . . .

> *Parma, Carmignani, n. d.   4 p. l., 52, [2], 13 p.   17^{cm}.*

Two acts.   Impresario's dedication, with remark that this drama "è oramai conosciuto in tutta l'Italia," cast, scenario, and name of Pietro **Guglielmi** as the composer. The text is Giuseppe Palomba's "L'inganno amoroso," but with many differences. For instance, I, 8 has become "Voi qui, bella tiranna," instead of "Cari ochietti vezzosetti."

First performed, as indicated, December 24, 1791.   SCHATZ 4311

L'inganno d'amore.   Drama di Benedetto Ferrari dedicato alla S. C. M. dell' imperatore Ferdinando III.   Rappresentato in musica nell' anno dell' imperiale dieta 1653 in Ratispona.

> *n. i., n. d.   42 unnumb. p., 7 folded pl.   31^{cm}.*

The t.-p. and plates were designed by "Joan⁸ Burnacinius" and engraved by "Jacobo Sandrart."   The t.-p. is followed by a dedication, signed and dated by the author, "Ratispona, 20 febraro 1653," by the argument, the description of the theatre, etc., Antonio **Bertali's** name as composer of the music, prologue, and three acts. The Italian libretto is followed by: "Innhalt und verfassung der comoedi von Liebs betrug, ersinnet von Benedicto Ferrari . . . auff den Kays: Reichs Tag zu Regenspurg in music vorzuhalten in dem jahre 1653.   Von hoechstgedachter roem. Kays. may. capelmaister Antonio Bertali in die music gesetzt.   Gezieret mit denen *scenen* und verstellungen des *theatri* durch Johan Burnaccini Roem. Kays. Mayest. ingenier. Gedruckt in der Kays. freyen Reichs Statt Regenspurg bey Christoff Fischer im 1653. jahr."   SCHATZ 874

L'inganno del ritratto.   Dramma giocoso per musica da rappresentarsi in Firenze nel R. Teatro dei Risoluti posto in via S. Maria nella estate dell' anno 1791 . . .

> *Firenze, Anton Giuseppe Pagani e comp., 1791.   52 p.   16½^{cm}.*

Two acts.   By author unknown to Schatz.   Cast and name of Gennaro **Astaritta** as composer.   ML 48.A5v.15

Inganno ed amor van sempre insieme, ballet.   *See* Ruggi's La guerra aperta.

L'inganno felice. Pastorale da rappresentarsi in musica nel Teatro di Santa Margerita l'autunno 1730.

Venezia, Carlo Buonarrigo, 1730. 40 p. 15^{cm}.

Three acts. Argument, scenario, and notice to the reader:
"Ecco un famosissimo parto di celebre penna [Francesco de Lemene's "La Ninfa Apollo" (Schatz)] mà non già lo stesso, quale usci dalle mani del suo proprio autore. 'l cangiamento del titolo, l'aggiunta d'un personaggio, la mutazione delle ariette, e la variazione, e traspozione di qualche scena lo rendono in buona parte da quello diverso. Sappia però chi legge, che un tale cambiamento non è già effetto di poca stima verso un così illustre poeta, ne presunzione di migliorar la poesia, mà pura necessità di accomodarla al numero, ed alla abilità di chi deve rappresentarla, ed all' uso, e gusto della musica del moderno teatro."

Composer not mentioned and unknown to Schatz, who lists Logroscino's "L' inganno felice," text by Tommaso Mariani (originally "Fingere per godere") as first performed at Naples, Teatro Nuovo sopra Toledo, winter of 1739. SCHATZ 11341

L'inganno fortunato. Drama da rappresentarsi in musica nel Teatro Giustiniano di S. Moisè—nell' autunno dell' anno 1721.

Venezia, Marino Rossetti, 1721. 45 p. 14½^{cm}.

Three acts. Author's dedication, argument, cast, and scenario. According to the dedication signed by Bortolamio Pavieri, the libretto was originally by Sig. Gio. Battista Sara, "who then consigned it to Pavieri's pen "per ridurlo nello stato presente." The composer, Giuseppe **Boniventi**, is not mentioned. SCHATZ 1192

L'inganno innocente. Drama per musica da rappresentarsi nel Teatro di Sant' Angelo l'anno 1701. Poesia di Francesco Silvani, servitore di S. A. Sereniss. di Mantoua . . .

Venezia, Per il Nicolini, 1701. 60 p. 14½^{cm}.

Three acts. Author's dedication dated Venice, January 16, 1701, argument, scenario, and notice to the reader to the effect that this text, now performed for the first time, was written six years previously. The composer, Tommaso **Albinoni**, is not mentioned. SCHATZ 121

L'inganno poco dura. Commedia per musica di Saverio Zini da rappresentarsi nel Teatro de' Fiorentini per second' opera del corrente anno 1796.

Napoli, n. publ., 1796. 46 p. 15^{cm}.

Two acts. Cast and name of Marco **Portugal** as composer. SCHATZ 8426

L'inganno regnante overo L'Atanagilda regina di Gottia, drama per musica da rappresentarsi nel famosissimo Teatro Grimano di SS. Gio. e Paulo l'anno 1688. Di Giulio Cesare Corradi . . .

Venetia, Francesco Nicolini, 1688. 72 p. 14^{cm}.

Three acts. Argument, scenario, notice to the reader with the name of Marc' Antonio **Ziani** as composer, and dedication, in which Corradi says:
"La maggior fortuna, che possano havere quest' anno le dramatiche mie rime, si è l'acquisto del Signor Nicola Paris, cigno famoso di V. A. S. [Ernst August, duke of Brunswick] per bocca di cui devono esser publicate sulle scene dell' Adria."
First performed, as indicated, carnival, 1688. SCHATZ 11205

L'inganno scoperto per vendetta. Drama per musica da rappresentarsi nel Teatro Vendramino di S. Salvatore l'anno 1691. Di Francesco Silvani . . .

Venetia, Nicolini, 1691. 60 p. 14^{cm}.

Three acts. Author's dedication, argument, scenario, notice to the reader with name of Giacomo Antonio **Perti** as the composer, and remark, "eccoti il primo parto dramatico della mia penna smascherato."

Consequently, this can not have been the original version of Silvani's text, the less so as in 1683 he called "Martio Coriolano" his second drama. SCHATZ 7956

L'inganno tradito dall' amore. Drama per musica, da rappresentarsi nel Teatro di corte . . . di Salisburgo . . . Poesia del Sig. Antonio Maria Luchini. Musica del Sig. Antonio Caldara . . .

Salisburgo, Giovanni Gioseppe Mayr, n. d. 68 p. 15½^{cm}.

Three acts and licenza. Argument and scenario. Pages 26–29, 54–57 contain the intermezzo in two parts "Atamo huomo vecchio e Palancha giovine" by an unknown author.

First performed at Vienna, Hoftheater, October 1, 1721.   SCHATZ 1485

L'inganno trionfante in amore. Drama per musica da rappresentarsi nel Teatro di S. Angelo l'autunno dell' anno MDCCXXV . . .

Venezia, Marino Rossetti, 1725. 60 p. 15½^{cm}.

Three acts. Dedication, argument, cast, scenario, and note to the effect that this is the modernized version of a text heard many years ago. Neither the original author, Matteo Noris, nor Giovanni Maria Ruggeri, who modernized the text, nor Antonio **Vivaldi**, the composer, is mentioned.   SCHATZ 10772

L'inganno trionfato, overo La disperata speranza ravvivata ne' successi di Giacopo Quinto di Scozia, e Maddalena di Francia. Drama del dottor Oratio Francesco Ruberti parmiggiano . . . recitato nella rocca del Signor conte di Sissa in un suo teatrino per le nozze del Sig. Mario Terzi, suo figlio, e Signora contessa Lucretia Scoffona l'anno M.DC.LXXIII e posto in musica dal Sig. Franc. Maria Bazzani.

Parma, Pietro del Frate e Galeazzo Rosati, n. d. 5 p. l., 131, [1] p. 15^{un}.

Three acts with prologue and licenza. Cast, argument, dedication, and scenario. On p. 116–131 a description of the theatre. The author calls this his "primo scenico intreccio."   SCHATZ 670

L'inganno vinto dalla ragione. *See* Lotti's Teuzzone.

L'ingenue. Entrée in Mouret's Les Graces.

L'Inglese in Italia. Dramma giocoso per musica da rappresentarsi in Bologna nel Teatro Formagliari il carnevale dell' anno 1769.

Bologna, Sassi, n. d. 54 p. 15^{cm}.

Cast, scenario, and name of Antonio [Maria] **Mazzoni** as the composer. Author not mentioned and unknown to Schatz.

First performed, as indicated, January, 1769.   SCHATZ 6230

Gl'Inglesi in America, ballet. *See* Bianchi's Il ritratto.

Gl'Inglesi in Othaiti. A. T. of the ballet Cook.

L'ingratitudine gastigata. Drama per musica da rappresentarsi nel Teatro Tron di San Casciano l'anno 1698. Di Francesco Silvani . . .

Venezia, Per il Nicolini, 1698. 59 p. 14^{cm}.

Three acts. Dedication signed by the author and dated "Venetia li 17 genaro 1697. M. V." (=Jan. 17, 1698), argument, notice to the reader, scenario. The composer, Tommaso **Albinoni**, is not mentioned.   SCHATZ 96

L'inimico delle donne. Dramma giocoso per musica di Giovanni Bertati da rappresentarsi nel Teatro di San Samuel l'autunno dell' anno 1771.

Venezia, Modesto Fenzo, n. d. 54 p. 17½^{cm}

Three acts. Cast, scenario, and name of **Galuppi** as composer.   SCHATZ 3455

L'inimico delle donne—Continued.

— **Il nemico delle donne.** Dramma giocoso per musica. Da representarsi ne' Teatri privilegiati di Vienna l'anno 1775.

[*Vienna*], *Giuseppe Kurzbök, n. d. 69 p. 16^cm.*

Three acts. Scenario and names of Giovanni Bertati as author and of **Galuppi** as composer. While the first act follows closely the original ed. of "L'inimico delle donne," beginning with the second act the two librettos become somewhat different. That of Vienna drops several scenes and, for instance, substitutes the aria (II, 3) "Qui non si dice: cara" for "Se fossi in Italia." Also, the second act now begins "Quanto siete sollecita" instead of "Cugina mia, vitrovo."
First performed, as indicated, January 17, 1775.   Schatz 3456

Inkle and Jarico: An opera, in three acts. As performed at the Theatre-Royal in the Hay-Market, on Saturday, August 11th, 1787. Written by George Colman, junior.

London, G. G. J. and J. Robinson, n. d. 75 p. 20½^cm.

Cast. The composer, Samuel **Arnold**, is not mentioned. He utilized, as Longman & Broderip's vocal score shows, some ballad airs.
Genest gives August 4, 1787, as date of first performance.   Longe 99

Inkle e Iariko, ballet. *See* Paisiello's Gli schiavi per amore.

Inkle e Jariko, ballet. *See* Prati's La morte di Semiramide.

Inkle und Jariko, oder Er war nicht ganz Barbar. Ein singspiel in einem aufzuge, von J. W. D.[öring].

Cassel, Griesbach, 1798. 56 p. 15^cm.

The composer, Carl Friedrich **Ebers,** is not mentioned.
First performed at Rostock, Stadttheater, December 28, 1801.   Schatz 2890

Das inkognito. Singspiel in einem aufzuge, nach Saintfoix.

n. i., n. d. 56 p. 15^cm. (Herklots operetten, No. 1, Berlin, 1793.)

Detached copy. The name of the composer, Joseph Augustin **Gürrlich,** is not mentioned.
First performed at Berlin, Kgl. Nationaltheater, November 9, 1797.
Schatz 4372a

L'innalzamento di Semiramide. A. T. of the ballet La figlia dell' aria.

Gli innamorati. Dramma per musica di Giuseppe Foppa da rappresentarsi nel nobilissimo Teatro Venier di San Benedetto l'autunno dell' anno 1793.

Venezia, Casali, 1793. 64 p. 17½^cm.

Two acts. According to note on p. 3, based on Goldoni's "Gli innamorati," and "riprodotto in quest' anno con alcuni cangiamenti proprj della circostanza." Cast and name of Sebastiano **Nasolini** as composer of the first and Vittorio **Trento** of the second act. On p. [33]–43, argument, cast, and description of Filippo Beretti's "Andronico e Ramira, ballo eroico pantomimo," in five acts. The composer of the music is not mentioned.
First performed at the same theatre, February 4, 1793.   Schatz 7031

Innocence seduced. A. T. of The wanton Jesuit.

L'innocente fortunata. Dramma per musica da rappresentarsi nel Teatro di Siena la prossima estate dell' anno 1774.

Firenze, Anton Giuseppe Pagani, 1774. 55 p. 16½^cm.

Three acts. By Filippo Livigni, who is not mentioned. Cast and name of **Paisiello** as the composer.
First performed at Venice, Teatro di S. Moisè, carnival, 1773.   Schatz 7631

L'innocente fortunata—Continued.

— **La semplice fortunata.** Commedia per musica da rappresentarsi nel Teatro Nuovo nell' està di questo anno 1773.

Napoli, Vincenzo Flauto, 1773. 72 p. 15½ᶜᵐ.

Three acts. Of Livigni's "L'innocente fortunata" very little of the dialogue, but a number of arias, have been retained, as, for instance, "Donna son, ma non m'inganno," but instead of being sung in I, 2, it now stands in I, 13. Scenario, cast, and name of **Paisiello** as the composer.   SCHATZ 7632

— **L'innocente fortunata.** Dramma giocoso per musica, da rappresentarsi nel Piccolo Teatro Elettorale. L'anno 1780.

Dresda, Stamperia elettorale, n. d. 151 p. 16ᶜᵐ.

Three acts. Livigni's text. German title page, "Die glueckliche unschuldige," and text face Italian. **Paisiello** is mentioned as the composer.   SCHATZ 7633

L'innocenza difesa. Drama per musica da rappresentarsi nel Teatro di S. Angelo nel carnovale dell' anno 1722 . . .

Venezia, Marino Rossetti, 1722. 57 p. 15ᶜᵐ.

Three acts. By Francesco Silvani (not mentioned). Publisher's dedication, argument, east, scenario, and name of Fortunato **Chelleri** as composer.

First performed, as "L'innocenza giustificata," at Milan, Regio Ducal Teatro, 1711.
          SCHATZ 1814

L'innocenza difesa. Drama per musica da rappresentarsi nell' antico Teatro della Pace nel carnevale dell' anno 1720 . . .

Roma, Antonio de' Rossi, 1720. 67 p. 14½ᶜᵐ.

Three acts. Neither Francesco Silvani (a later version of whose "L'innocenza giustificata" this is) nor Giuseppe Maria **Orlandini**, the composer, is mentioned. Argument, cast, and scenario.

First performed at Verona, Teatro della Città, fall, 1714.   SCHATZ 7336

L'innocenza difesa nell' inganno. Dramma da rappresentarsi in musica.—Die im betruge vertheidigte unschuld . . .

Copenhagen, Andreas Hartwig Godiche, 1753. 79 p. 15ᶜᵐ.

Three acts. Scenario, argument, cast. Author (Domenico Lalli, whose altered "Il gran Mogol" this is) and composer (unknown to Schatz) not mentioned.
          SCHATZ 11342

L'innocenza giustificata. O. T. of Chelleri's L'innocenza difesa.

L'innocenza giustificata. Drama per musica di Francesco Silvani. Da rappresentarsi nel famoso Teatro Vendramino di S. Salvatore . . .

Venezia, Nicolini, 1699. front., 72 p. 14½ᶜᵐ.

Three acts. Argument, scenario, Silvani's dedication, dated Venice, December 24, 1698, and his important notice to the reader:

"Hò io ancora à tacere doppo gl'attentati, contro la mia riputazione, ad ogni parto dramatico, che mi esca dalla penna? Il generoso compatimento con cui ricevesti l'anno passato nel Teatro Tron di S. Casciano l'opera mia intitolata l'Ingratitudine gastigata, svegliò nel cuore non sò di chi, un bel pensiero di rapirmi quel poco di fama, che mi risultava dalla tua sola bōta, col publicare essere quella, fatica d'altro ingegno, variando però nel nominare l'auttore, e portando l'invidia à ricercarlo sino dentro a i sepolori. Quest' anno sù la medesima buona opinione della tua somma generosità, si hà voluto prevenirne l'evento, ed all' uscire di questo dramma, si è fatta precorrere una voce egualmente impropria, che questo pure sia frutto d'un' altra mente .

" . . . questa volta per sempre io devo assicurare la mia riputazione, con una publica protesta solennizata dall' auttorità della stampa, che tutte le dramatiche composizioni, & altre, che siano uscite, o siano per uscire da torchi col mio nome in fronte, sono, e saranno tutte fatiche del mio povero, e debolissimo ingegno . . . e così

L'innocenza giustificata—Continued.

interamente mie, che nel comporle, nè le hò communicate con chi si sia, ne da chi si sia hò ricevuto un minimo consiglio, se non nel comporre il drama intitolato il Principe Selvaggio recitatosi nel Teatro di S. Angelo l'anno 1695, il quale fù da me composto cō l'altrui assistenza e consiglio, e che perciò corre senza nome, cosi grāde è la giustizia della mia gelosia di non farmi auttore d'un' opera, di cui io non habbia tutto il debito alla mia fattica, come deve fare ogni uomo d'onore . . . ti prego onorare del tuo benigno compatimento queste povere mie rime, che ritroverai animate dalla virtù singolare del Sig. K.ᵉ Benedetto **Vinacese**, che in questa sua prima uscita sovra le Venete scene con le sue note, ti dà un gran saggio del suo profondo intendimento, e della fertile bizarria delle sue idee . . ."

This preface gives the key to the frontispiece, which shows a shepherd pointing out to his dog a house with the inscription, "Modica sed mea." Schatz 10740

— **L'innocenza giustificata.** Drama per musica di Francesco Silvani, da rappresentarsi in Mantova l'anno MDCC . . .

Mantova, Alberto Pazzoni, n. d. 6 p. l., 52 p. 15ᶜᵐ.

Three acts. Dedication by Giacomo Sironi, argument, cast, scenario. Benedetto **Vinacese** is not mentioned as the composer. The text shows slight differences from the original edition. For instance, in I, 5 the aria "Se si potesse amar" has been replaced by "Se non scocasse Amor." ML 50.2.I58

L'innocenza protetta. A. T. of Valentini's Rosina consolata.

L'innocenza protetta dal Cielo, o siano Li portentosi effetti della gran madre Natura, intermezzo in tre atti da rappresentarsi nel Teatro di Sant' Angelo il carnovale dell' anno 1762.

Venezia, Valvasense, n. d. 44 p. 15½ᶜᵐ.

Cast, scenario, name of Carlo Goldoni (*see* A. T. of the above) as author and note: "Musica del sig. N. N. dilettante." His name unknown to Wiel. Schatz 11358

L'innocenza riconosciuta. Drama per musica da rappresentarsi nel Teatro di Sant' Angelo l'autunno dell' anno MDCCXVII.

Venezia, Marino Rossetti, 1717. 48, [1] p. 14½ᶜᵐ.

Three acts. By Francesco Malipiero, who is not mentioned. "Quello si ha dall' istoria," cast, and scenario. The composer, Carlo Francesco **Pollaroli**, is not mentioned. Schatz 8298

L'innocenza risorta, overo Etio. Drama per musica da rappresentarsi nel famoso Teatro di S. Casciano. L'anno MDCLXXXIII . . .

Venetia, Francesco Nicolini, 1683. 58 p. 13½ᶜᵐ.

Three acts. By Adriano Morselli, who is not mentioned. Dedication, scenario, argument, and notice to the reader with name of Pietro Andrea **Ziani** as the composer.

First performed, as indicated, carnival, 1683. Schatz 11224

L'innocenza scoperta, ballet. *See* Cimarosa's I due supposti conti.

L'innocenza vendicata, overo La Santa Eugenia. Dramma per la musica da rappresentarsi nella solenne celebratione della festa della Gloriosa Santa Rosa di Viterbo nel Teatro della medesima città nel corrente anno 1686.

Viterbo, Pietro Martinelli, n. d. 67 p. 13½ᶜᵐ.

Notitia istorica, avertimenti. Author and composer not mentioned and unknown to Schatz. Schatz 11343

L'innocenza vendicata. A. T. of Tozzi's La morte di Dimone.

Ino. Ein melodrama in einem aufzuge von Joh. Christian Brandes.
Leipzig, Dykische buchhandlung, 1790. 1 p. l., 22 p. 18½^{cm}.
Note on p. [1]: "Verfertigt im jahr 1777."
First performed with music by Johann Friedrich **Reichardt,** who is not mentioned, at Leipzig, Theater am Rannstaedter Thore, October 7, 1779. ML 52.2.I5

— **Ino.** Ein melodrama von herrn Brandes. Die musik ist von herrn Reichard . . .
n.i.,n.d. p.[75]–107. 14½^{cm}. (*"Melodramen," no.iv,Pilsen,1791.*)
One act. Argument. SCHATZ 8643

Ino e Temisto, ballet. *See* Nasolini's La Calliroe.

Arien und gesaenge aus dem singspiel **Die insel der Alcina** in zwey aufzuegen, aus dem italiänischen uebersetzt von C. Herklots. Die musik ist von dem saenger des koenigl. Nationaltheaters, Herrn Bianchi.
Berlin, n. publ., 1794. 32 p. 16^{cm}.
Cast. Translation of Bertati's libretto, "L'isola d'Alcina," composed by Antonio **Bianchi.**
First performed at Berlin, Nationaltheater, February 16, 1794. SCHATZ 972

Die insel der Alcina. Tr. of Gazzaniga's L'isola di Alcina.

Die insel der liebe. Tr. of Sacchini's L'isola d'amore.

L'interesse gabba tutti. Dramma giocoso per musica da rappresentarsi nel Regio Teatro di via della Pergola la primavera del MDCCXCV . . .
Firenze, Pietro Fantosini, 1795. 39, [1] p. 16½^{cm}.
Two acts. By Cosimo Mazzini, who is not mentioned. Cast and name of Gaetano **Marinelli** as the composer. ("La musica è nuova.") With the opera was performed Charles Auguste Favier's ballet, "Il matrimonio per gratitudine." The composer of the music is not mentioned. SCHATZ 5961

Intermezzi in derisione della setta Maomettana, coll' espressione d'alcuni riti de' Turchi nel porgere preghiere al falso loro profeta. Da recitarsi in Seminario Romano nella commedia de' Signori Convittori delle Camere Piccole per le vacanze del carnevale del 1717. La musica è del Sig. Francesco Gasparini . . .
Napoli, Felice Mosca, n. d. 16 p. 20½^{cm}.
Three parts. Author not mentioned and unknown to me. The characters are Ali, Balocco, Despino, Osmino. Cast and brief prefatory note. ML 50.2.I59G2

Intramezzi da rappresentarsi nella Filli di Sciro in Ancona quest' anno 1639. Stampati per facilitarne l'intelligenza a gli spettatori . . .
Ancona, Marco Salvioni, 1639. 15 p. 19^{cm}.
Prologue and four intermedii. Salvioni's dedication, dated Ancona, February 23, 1639, contains this information:
"Dovendosi però trà pochi giorni rappresentare da questa nobiltà la Filli di Sciro, pastorale della felice memoria del Sig. conte Guid' Ubaldo Bonarelli onore, e gloria di questa patria, & havendole aggiunti alcuni intramezzi il Sig. conte Prospero fratello di lui, hò risoluto per commodo degl' ascoltanti, stamparli . . ."
The composer is not mentioned. ML 50.2.I6

Gl'intrichi di Don Facilone. Dramma giocoso per musica da rappresentarsi nel Real Teatro di Salvaterra nel carnovale dell' anno 1786.

[Lisbona], Stamperia reale, n. d. 67 p. 16^{cm}.

Two acts. Author not mentioned and unknown to Schatz. Scenario, cast, and name of Pietro **Guglielmi** as the composer.
First performed as "Gl'intrighi di D. Facilone," at Rome, Teatro Valle, carnival, 1776. Schatz 4296

Gl'intrighi amorosi. Dramma giocoso per musica del Sig. abbate Giuseppe Petrosellini P. A. Da rappresentarsi nel Teatro di San Samuel il carnovale dell' anno 1772.

Venezia, Modesto Fenzo, 1772. 69 p. 18^{cm}.

Three acts. Cast, scenario, and name of **Galuppi** as composer. Schatz 3504

L'intrigo amoroso. Dramma giocoso per musica di Giovanni Bertati . . . Da rappresentarsi nel nobilissimo Teatro Giustiniani in San Moisè l'autunno dell' anno 1795.

Venezia, Modesto Fenzo, 1795. 62 p. 18$\frac{1}{2}^{cm}$.

Two acts. Cast, scenario, and name of Francesco Ferdinando **Paër** as the composer. On p. 57–62 cast, prefatory note, and argument of Pasquale Brunetti's "La selvaggia ovvero Adelia e Roberto, ballo di mezzo carattere." The composer of the music is not mentioned.
First performed, as indicated, December 26, 1795 (Schatz), "autunno" (Wiel). Schatz 7505

— **L'intrigo amoroso.** Dramma giocoso per musica da rappresentarsi nel Regio Teatro di S. Carlo della Principessa l'estate dell' anno 1798.

Lisboa, Simone Taddeo Ferreira, 1798. 142 p. 14$\frac{1}{2}^{cm}$.

Two acts. Cast and name of Ferdinando Per (**Paër**) as the composer. Bertati is not mentioned. Portuguese text faces the Italian. Schatz 7559

— **L'intrigo amoroso.** Dramma giocoso per musica in due atti da rappresentarsi nel Teatro elettorale di Sassonia.

Dresda, n. publ., 1799. 127 p. 15$\frac{1}{2}^{cm}$.

Two acts. By Bertati, who is not mentioned. Ferdinando Pär (**Paër**) is mentioned as composer. German title page, "Die liebesintrigue," and text face Italian.
First performed April 17, 1799, as indicated. Schatz 7506

— **Saed** ossia Il serraglio. Dramma giocoso per musica da rappresentarsi nel Teatro di S. A. S. il Signor principe di Carignano nella primavera dell' anno 1798.

Torino, Onorato Derossi, n. d. 54 p. 14$\frac{1}{2}^{cm}$.

Two acts. Cast, scenario, and name of Ferdinando Për (**Paër**) as the composer. Follows closely the original text by Bertati, who is not mentioned. Schatz 7507

L'intrigo della lettera. Farsa giocosa per musica d'un atto solo da rappresentarsi nel Teatro Giustiniani in San Moisè del cittadino Giuseppe Foppa.

Venezia, Modesto Fenzo, Anno primo della Libertà italiana [1797]. 38 p. 18^{cm}.

Cast, scenario, and name of Simon **Mayr** as the composer. Schatz 6154

— **L'intrigo della lettera,** farsa giocosa per musica d'un atto solo da rappresentarsi nel Regio Teatro di S. Carlo della Principessa.

Lisboa, Simone Taddeo Ferreira, 1798. 91 p. 14^{cm}.

The author, Giuseppe Foppa, is not mentioned. Cast and name of Simon **Mayr** as composer. Portuguese text faces Italian. ML 50.2.I65M2

L'intrigo delle mogli. Commedia per musica di Giuseppe Palomba da rappresentarsi nel Real Teatro del Fondo di Separazione per quart' opera del corrente anno 1783.

> *Napoli, n. publ., 1783. 57 p. 15ᶜᵐ.*
>
> Three acts.   Cast and name of Giuseppe **Gazzaniga** as the composer.
>
> Schatz 3679

L'intrigue portugaise. A. T. of Gaveaux' Sophie et Moncars

The intriguing chambermaid. A comedy of two acts. As it is acted at the Theatre-Royal in Drury-Lane, by His Majesty's servants. Taken from the French of Regnard, by Henry Fielding, Esq. . . .

> *London, J. Watts, 1750.   6 p. l., 40 p.   20ᶜᵐ.*
>
> Ballad opera.   Cast, poem "sent to the author by an unknown hand," prologue, epilogue and a very complimentary "Epistle to Mrs. Clive," who played "Lettice" in this ballad farce.   Fielding says, among other things:
>
> "It is your misfortune to bring the greatest genius for acting on the stage, at a time when the factions and divisions among the players have conspired with the folly, injustice, and barbarity of the town, to finish the ruin of the stage, and sacrifice our native entertainments to a wanton affected fondness for foreign musick; and when our nobility seem eagerly to rival each other, in distinguishing themselves in favour of Italian theatres, and in neglect of our own . . ."
>
> On last p. l. a "table of the songs" (12), the airs of which are printed in the text.
> First performed at London, Drury Lane, January 15, 1734.   ML 50.5.I5

— **The intriguing chambermaid.** In two acts. By Henry Fielding, Esq.

> *[138]–168 p.   19ᶜᵐ.   (Collection of the most esteemed farces and entertainments, t. iii, Edinburgh, 1792.)*
>
> Drury-Lane and Edinburgh (1781) casts.   Ballad opera.   Schatz 11753C

The intriguing courtiers; or, The modish gallants. A comedy, (after the manner of Shakespear). Wherein the secret histories of several persons are faithfully represented. In which is introduced, An interlude, (after the manner of a rehearsal). Call'd, The marriage promise; or, The disappointed virgin. Consisting of variety of new songs, set to several English, Irish, and Scots ballad-tunes and country-dances.

> *London, W. James, 1732.   60 p.   20ᶜᵐ.*
>
> The interlude (four characters) is introduced in the final, sixth scene of the fifth act. The tunes are indicated in the headings of the eight songs.   The comedy otherwise contained no music.   Neither author nor performance recorded by Clarence.   Longe 197

L'inutile precauzione, ballet. *See* Mayr's Lauso e Lidia.

L'inutile precauzione. L. T. of Paisiello's Il barbiere di Seviglia.

L'inutile precauzione, ballet. *See* Tritto's Il barone in angustie.

Der invalide. Ein militaerisches original-lustspiel in drey aufzeugen. Von C. F. Hensler. Die mit dem stueck verbundene musik ist vom hrn. Wenzel Mueller, kapellmeister der Marinellischen schaubuehne.

> *n. i., n. d.   p. [121]–224.   17ᶜᵐ.*
>
> Detached copy.   First performed, as indicated, June 22, 1786.   Schatz 6934

L'inverno ossia La pianella perduta, ballet. *See* Guglielmi's Le due gemelle.

L'inverno o sia La pianella persa. Farsa in prosa con musica alla francese che si rappresenta dalla Compagnia accademica toscana di Pietro Andolfati addetta al Regio Teatro degli Infuocati di Firenze . . .

Firenze, Stamperia Albizziniana, 1790. 30 p. 16½ᶜᵐ.

Two parts. Author and composer not mentioned, and unknown to Schatz.

SCHATZ 11344

Iole, regina di Napoli. Drama per musica da rappresentarsi nel famosissimo Teatro Grimani di Ss. Gio. e Paolo, l'anno MDCXCII. Di Giulio Cesare Corradi . . .

Venetia, Nicolini, 1692. 58 p. 14½ᶜᵐ.

Three acts. Author's dedication, argument, scenario, and notice to the reader, in which Corradi says: "la virtù del Sign. Carlo Polarolo **[Pollaroli]** hà questa volta oltrepassato il credibile." SCHATZ 8323

Ipermestra.

Metastasio, Poesie, Parigi, vedova Quillau, 1755, t. v, [95]–171 p. 16ᶜᵐ.

Three acts and licenza. Argument. ML 49.A2M42

— **Ipermestra.** Dramma, scritto in gran fretta dall' autore in Vienna d'ordine sovrano, per essere eseguito nell' interno della Corte con musica dell' Hasse da grandi, e distinti personaggi a loro privatissimo trattenimento: ma pubblicamente poi rappresentato la prima volta da musici, e cantatrici nel gran Teatro di Corte . . . in occasione delle nozze delle AA. RR. di Marianna, arciduchessa d'Austria, e del principe Carlo di Lorena, l'anno 1744.

pl., [97]–180 p. 26ᶜᵐ. (Metastasio, Opere, t. vi, Parigi, vedova Herissant, 1780.)

Three acts and licenza. Argument. ML 49.A2M44

Ipermestra. Dramma per musica da rappresentarsi nel nobilissimo Teatro Venier in San Benedetto la fiera dell' Ascensione dell' anno 1789.

Venezia, Modesto Fenzo, 1789. 48 p. 18½ᶜᵐ.

Two acts. By Metastasio. Argument, cast, scenario, and name of Gennaro **Astaritta** as composer, but not of librettist.. On p. 23–33, argument, cast, and detailed description of the first ballet, "Alessio ed Eloisa o sia Il disertore, ballo eroicomico," by Douberral, and originally performed in London (p. 24); and on p. 48, the title of the second ballet, "Le due rivali o sia La prova del vero amore, ballo campestre." The composers of the music are not mentioned. SCHATZ 387

Ipermestra. Drama per musica da rappresentarsi nel Teatro novissimo a S. Samuele per la fiera dell' Ascensⁿᵉ l'anno 1748.

[Venezia], n. publ., n. d. 1 p. l., 44 p. 15½ᶜᵐ.

Three acts, with argument, cast, scenario, and name of composer, Ferdinando Giuseppe **Bertoni**, but not of librettist, Metastasio. SCHATZ 926

Ipermestra. Drama per musica da rappresentarsi nel Regio ducal Teatro di Milano nel carnovale dell' anno 1728 . . .

Milano, Giuseppe Richino Malatesta, 1727. 59 p. 13½ᶜᵐ.

Three acts. By Antonio Salvi (not mentioned). Dedication dated Milan, December 24, 1727, and signed by the composer, "Giuseppe Ferdinando **Brivio** e compagni" ("la nostra prima opera"), argument, cast, and scenario. According to the argument, several arias were interpolated "a piacimento de' signori attori," which would explain "nelle arie qualche sentimento non troppo addattato alla scena." SCHATZ 1327

L'Ipermestra.   L. T. of Cavalli's L'Hipermestra.

Ipermestra, dramma per musica, da rappresentarsi nel Ducal Teatro di Bronsevico, nella fiera estiva MDCCLIX.

n. i., n. d.   131 p.   19^{cm}.

Three acts.   Argument, scenario, and names of the author, Metastasio, and the composer, "Ignazio **Fiorillo**, maestro di capella in attual servizio di corte."   German title-page, "Hypermenestra," and text face Italian.

First performed, as indicated, August 13, 1759.   SCHATZ 3201

L'Ipermestra.   Dramma per musica da rappresentarsi nel Teatro Vendramin di S. Salvadore nella fiera dell' Ascensione dell' anno MDCCLXI.

Venezia, Modesto Fenzo, 1761.   48, [8] p.   14½^{cm}.

Three acts.   By Metastasio, who is not mentioned.   Argument, cast, scenario, and name of the composer, Baldassare **Galuppi** ("La musica sarà nuova").   The additional pages contain the plot of the ballets, "L'Asiatico generoso" and "I due vergognesi da nozze," by Pierre Granget, the composers of the music not being mentioned.

An opera by Galuppi, of the same title, was performed at Milano, Regio Ducal Teatro, 1758.   SCHATZ 3457

Ipermestra.   Drama per musica da rappresentarsi nel famosissimo Teatro Grimani di San Gio. Grisostomo il carnovale dell' anno 1724.

Venezia, Marino Rossetti, 1724.   48 p.   15½^{cm}.

Three acts.   By Ant. Salvi, who is not mentioned.   Argument, cast, scenario, and name of Geminiano **Giacomelli** as the composer.   SCHATZ 3813

Ipermestra.   Dramma per musica da rappresentarsi nel famosissimo Teatro Grimani di S^a Giõ Grisostomo nell' autunno 1744.

n. i., n. d.   50 p.   15½^{cm}.

Three acts.   By Metastasio, who is not mentioned.   Argument, cast, scenario, and name of **Gluck** as the composer.

First performed, as indicated, at Venice, November 21, 1744.   SCHATZ 3930

L'Ipermestra.   Dramma per musica da rappresentarsi nel Real Teatro in occasione delle felicissime nozze della serenissima arciduchessa Maria Anna d'Austria . . . e . . . Carlo Alessandro di Lorena . . . l'anno 1744.   La poesia è del Sig. abb. Pietro Metastasio . . .   La musica è del Sig. Giovanni Adolfo Hasse . . .   La musica della licenza e dell' ultimo coro, è del Sig. Luca Predieri . . .

Vienna, Gio. Pietro v. Ghelen, n. d.   4 p. l., 51, [1] p.   15½^{cm}.

Three acts.   Argument, scenario, and name of Ignaz Holzbauer as composer of the ballet music.

First performed at the Burg, January 8, 1744, and at the Hoftheater January 25, 1744.   SCHATZ 4542

— Ipermestra, dramma per musica da rappresentarsi nella villa di Sant' Uberto festeggiandosi il felicissimo giorno natalizio di S. R. M. Augusto III . . . l'anno MLCCLI.

n. i., n. d.   5 p. l. (double), 72, [4] p.   19^{cm}.

At end: "Friedrichsstadt, appresso la vedova Harpeter."   Three acts and licenza. Argument, scenario, and names of Metastasio as author, of Johann Adolph **Hasse** as composer.   German title page, "Hypermenestra," and text face Italian, which is not quite the same as in the Vienna (1744) edition.   For instance, the aria in I, 1, "Abbiam penato, è ver," has become "Tornerai nel fido amante," and that in III, 6, "Perdono al crudo acciaro," has become "L'amato, bene."   Schatz and Mennicke call this Hasse's second version.

First performed, as indicated, October 7, 1751.   SCHATZ 4543

Ipermestra—Hipermenestre, ballet. *See* Jommelli's Demofoonte.

Ipermestra. Drama per musica da rappresentarsi nel nobilissimo Teatro di S. Benedetto il carnovale dell' anno MDCCLXXIV.

Venezia, Modesto Fenzo, 1774. 1 p. l., 52 p. 17^{cm}.

Three acts. By Metastasio, who is not mentioned. Argument, cast, scenario, and name of Johann Gottlieb **Naumann** as the composer. On p. 20–25 description of Antoine Trancard's "Il ratto di Proserpina, ballo eroico." The composer of the music is not mentioned.

First performed, as indicated, February 1, 1774. SCHATZ 7049

Ipermestra. Dramma per musica da rappresentarsi nel nobilissimo Nuovo Teatro di Padova la fiera di Giugno dell' anno 1791 . . .

Padova, Conzatti, n. d. 40 p. 17$\frac{1}{2}$^{cm}.

Three acts. By Metastasio, who is not mentioned. Impresario's dedication, argument, cast, scenario, and name of **Paisiello** as the composer. With the opera was performed Filippo Beretti's ballet, "Gli Sciti." The composer of the music is not mentioned. SCHATZ 7702

Ipermestra. Dramma per musica da rappresentarsi in Alessandria nel Teatro Solerio coll' occasione della solita fiera d'autunno nell' anno MDCCLV.

Alessandria, Ignazio Vimercati, n. d. 56 p. 16^{cm}.

Three acts. By Metastasio, who is not mentioned. Cast, argument, scenario, and name of "Guiseppe **Re**, dilettante" as the composer. SCHATZ 8618

Ipermestra. Dramma per musica da rappresentarsi nel Teatro alla Scala il carnevale dell' anno 1786 . . .

Milano, Gio. Batista Bianchi, n. d. 6 p. l., 44 p. 16^{cm}.

Three acts. Dedication, argument, cast, name of Salvatore **Rispoli** as the composer, and allusion to Metastasio, the author, with—

"rincrescimento di aver tolti tanti eccellenti pezzi, per sostituirne degli altri infinitamente inferiori, onde uniformarsi al costume, o per dir meglio all' abuso che si è introdotto negli spettacoli musicali in Italia."

With the opera were performed Sebastiano Gallet's ballets, "Ludovico il Moro," "L'amore maestro di scuola," and "Popolo d'Argo." The composer of the music is not mentioned.

First performed, as indicated, December 26, 1785. SCHATZ 8815

Second copy. ML 48.A5 v.1

L'Ipermestra o Le Danaidi, ballet. *See* Anfossi's L'Olimpiade.

Ipermestra ossia La morte di Danao, ballet. *See* Giordani's Nicomede.

Iphide Greca, drama per musica.

By Conte Nicolò Minato, composed by Antonio **Draghi** for the birthday of Empress Margherita July 12, 1670.

Not in L. of C. Compare Wotquenne.

— Iphis auss Griechen-Land. Gesungene vorstellung an dem geburths-tag Ihrer Kaiserlichen Mayestät frawen Margariten geborner infantin auss Hispanien . . . In sing-kunst gerichtet durch herrn Antoni Draghi . . . Aus dem welschen ins teutsch uebersetzt.

Wienn, Mattheo Cosmerovio, 1670. 46 p. 14$\frac{1}{2}$^{cm}.

Three acts, the original Italian "von herrn Nicola Minato." With "Inhalt," "Wahrscheinende erfindung hierueber," "Under-redner" (characters), "Veraenderungen des schaw-platzes" ("Erfindungen herrn Ludwigen Burnacini"), and "Taentz" (designed by the imperial balletmaster Ventura Santo. SCHATZ 2801

Iphide Greca. Drama per musica del conte Nicolo Minato.

Venetia, li Bertani, 1671.   66, [5] p.   13½^{cm}.

Three acts. Argument, scenario, and notice to the reader, which reads in part:
"Questo nobilissimo drama, se ne passa dal soglio de Cesari à dilettar il genio de gli Adriatici eroi . . . E vero, che per la disparità del loco, e di chi fà rappresentarla, egli è un colosso rimesso fra l'angustie d'un nichio non suo; i saloni di Venetia, non sono la regia di Cesare . . . Per questo capo, si tralasciano il più bello degli apparati . . .
"La musica del primo atto sarà parto delle virtù dell' ecc. dottor Gio. Domenico **Partenio**; nel secondo del Sig. D. Domenico **Freschi** e nel terzo del Sig. Gasparo **Sartorio** . . .
"Si sono aggionte alcune seconde stroffe, & altre nove ariette . . . Queste saranno stampate nel fine del libro cole sue annotationi havendo cosi voluto chi le scrisse, confessando non pater aggiungersi perfettioni al perfetto . . ."
First performed at Venice, by the Accademici Soliti, spring, 1671.
                                                                SCHATZ 7779

Iphigenia in einem sing-spiel auf dem Hamburgischen Schau-platze vorgestellet.   Im jahr 1731.

[Hamburg], Gedruckt mit Stromerschen schrifften, n. d.   Unpaged. 18½^{cm}.

Three acts. Argument and scenario. Neither Christian Heinrich Postel, by whom this libretto originally was written, nor the composer, Carl Heinrich **Graun**, is mentioned. Christian Heinrich Postel's "Die wunderbahr errettete Iphigenia" had been composed 1699 by Keiser for Hamburg. Retouched by Georg Caspar Schürmann, as "Iphigenia in Aulis," the libretto with Graun's music was first performed at Brunswick on August 16, 1728 (compare Uffenbach's Reisebeschreibung of this year). The opera was revived there on February 5, 1731. Further retouched, the opera was then first performed at Hamburg on December 3, 1731.
                                                                SCHATZ 4103

Iphigenia, ein singspiel in zween aufzuegen.

p. [5–12] of "Thoas, Koenig und feldherr der Lemnier.   Ein trauerspiel . . . aufgefuehrt von der studierenden jugend des Katholischen Schulhauses zu Augsburg bey St. Salvator. den 2, 3 und 6ten herbstmondes 1779.   [Augsburg], Joseph Simon Hueber."

Cast and name of Ludwig Bartholomaeus **Pündter** as the composer.
                                                                SCHATZ 8514

Iphigenia in Aulis.   An opera.

English translation of conte Francesco Algarotti's five-act libretto, "Iphigenie en Aulide."   *See* [125]–177 p. of his "An essay on the opera," Glasgow, 1768.
                                                                ML 3858.A39

Iphigenia in Aulis.   Tr. of Graun's Ifigenia in Aulide.

Iphigenia in Tauris.   Tr. of Gluck's Iphigénie en Tauride.

Iphigenie en Aulide, opera.

A five-act opera text, written by conte Francesco Algarotti and included to illustrate his esthetic theories on librettos (p. 97–157) in his "Saggio sopra l'opera in musica," of which the L. of C. has the Livorno (1763) ed.   ML 3858.A37

— **Iphigenia in Aulis.**   An opera.

The above in English translation (p. [125]–177) of "An essay on the opera."   Glasgow, 1768.   ML 3858.A39

Iphigénie en Aulide, tragédie-opera, en trois actes; représentée, pour la première fois, par l'Académie-royale de musique, le mardi 12 avril 1774.

Paris, Delormel, 1774. 63 p. 23ᶜᵐ.

Three acts. By Du Roullet, who is not mentioned by name but who wrote the "Avertissement" according to which the verses retained from Racine are so marked in the text. Cast and name of **Gluck** as the composer.
The first performance took place on April 19, not 12. SCHATZ 3898

— Iphigénie en Aulide, tragédie opéra, en trois actes, dont la musique est de M. le chevalier Gluck, représentée, pour la première fois, par l'Académie royale de musique le mardi 12 avril 1774. Nouvelle edition.

Bordeaux, Pierre Philippot, 1783. 38 p. 20ᶜᵐ.

Three acts. ML 48.M2L

Iphigénie en Tauride, tragedie représentée par l'Academie royale de musique l'an 1704. Les paroles de M. Duché & la musique de M. Desmarets. Mise au Théâtre par MMrs. Danchet & Campra. LXI. Opera.

n. i., n. d. front., p. 233–290. (Recueil général des opéra, t. viii, Paris, 1706.) 14ᶜᵐ.

Detached copy. Prologue and five acts, with "Avertissement:"
"Il y a huit ans que cet opera est fait, & que Mr. Desmarests l'a mis en musique à la reserve de la plus grande partie du cinquième acte qui est de Mr. Campra, aussi bien que quelques endroits qui étoient demeurez imparfaits, & le Prologue, dont les paroles ne sont point de celuy qui a fait la piece, mais de Mr. Danchet qui a bien voulu s'en charger."
First performed, as indicated, May 6, 1704. SCHATZ 2537
Second copy. ML 48.R4

— Prologue de la tragédie d'Iphigenie, représenté par l'Académie royale de musique, en 1704.

[125]–131 p. 17½ ᶜᵐ. (Antoine Danchet, Théâtre, t. II, Paris, 1751.)

The avertissement on p. 127 says that Danchet wrote this prologue for and finished Duché's text, written in 1697, and composed by **Desmarets** with exception of most of the fifth act, which was composed by **Campra**. PQ 1972.D2

Iphigénie en Tauride, tragédie en quatre actes, représentée pour la premiere fois, par l'Académie royale de musique le mardi 11 mai 1779.

[Paris], P. de Lormel, 1779. vi, 50 p. 25ᶜᵐ.

Four acts. Cast and names of Guillard as the author and of **Gluck** as the composer. Owing to the indisposition of Mlle. Levasseur, the first performance was deferred to May 18, the date printed on the full score. SCHATZ 3903

— Iphigenia in Tauris. Ein tragisches singspiel in vier aufzuegen. Aus dem franzoesischen des herrn Guillard. Die musik ist vom herrn ritter Gluck. Aufgeführt auf dem K. K. Nationalhoftheater.

Wien, beym logenmeister, 1781. 46 p. 17ᶜᵐ.

German version, by Johann von Alzinger, who is not mentioned, but who, in a preface, challenges his critics to furnish a better translation.
First performed, as indicated, Oct. 23, 1781. SCHATZ 3904

Iphigénie en Tauride—Continued.

— **L'Ifigenia in Tauride.** Tragedia in quattro atti. Tradotta dal francese in Italiano, dall' abate Lorenzo da Ponte poeta de' Teatrali imperiali. La musica è del Signor cavalier Gluck.

Vienna, Giuseppe nob. de Kurzbeck, 1783. 91 p. 16cm.

German text (by v. Alzinger) and t.-p. "Iphigenia in Tauris," face Italian.
First performed at Vienna, Nationaltheater n. d. Burg, December, 1783.

SCHATZ 3905

Iphigénie en Tauride, tragédie-lyrique en quatre actes, représentée, pour la première fois, par l'Académie royale de musique, le mardi 23 janvier 1781. Les paroles sont de M. Dubreuil. La musique de M. Piccini.

Paris, P. de Lormel, 1783. 28 p. 19½cm.

Cast.   ML 50.2.I65P3

Iphis aus Griechen-Land. Tr. of Draghi's Iphide Greca.

L'ipocondriaco. Intermezzo.

[231]–246 p. 16½cm. (Carlo Goldoni, Opere drammatiche giocose, t. iv, Torino, 1757.)

Two parts. First composer unknown to Schatz.   ML 49.A2G6

— **L'ippocondriaco.** Intermezzo di due parti per musica.

Carlo Goldoni, Opere teatrali, Venezia, Zatta e figli, 1788–95, v. 35, [231]–249 p. 18½cm.

L'ipocondriaco. Drama per musica rappresentato nella villa di Pratolino.

Firenze, Gio. Filippo Cecchi, 1695. 4 p. l., 77 p. 17cm.

Three acts, without the names of the composer or the author of the libretto, which Schatz attributes to Giovanni Cosimo Villafranchi. According to the author's preface, he intended to call "Quest' operetta . . ." "Heautontimerumenos." Composer unknown to Schatz. Giuseppe Maria **Buini** too young to have been the composer, though somewhere so stated.   SCHATZ 1395

L'ipocondriaco. Dramma giocoso per musica del Signore Giovanni Bertati da rappresentarsi nel Piccolo Teatro di S. A. S. E. di Sassonia.

Dresda, n. publ., 1776. 143 p. 16½cm.

Three acts. Johann Gottlieb **Naumann** is mentioned as the composer. German title page, "Der hypochondriste," and text face Bertati's Italian text, originally called "Il principe ipocondriaco."
First performed, as indicated, March 16, 1776.   SCHATZ 7050

L'ipocondrico risanato. Intermezzi per musica a cinque voci, da cantarsi nel Teatro alla Valle l'anno 1746 . . .

Roma, Komarek, 1746. 40 p. 15cm.

Two parts. Dedication by the impresario Angiolo Lungi, cast and name of Gioacchino **Cocchi** as composer. The characters are Pandolfo, Drusilla, Purgone, Rosalba, Lesbino. Author not mentioned and unknown to me.   ML 50.2.I67C6

L'Ipolito [!], dramma per musica da rappresentarsi nel Regio-Ducal Teatro di Milano nel carnovale dell' anno 1745 . . .

Milano, Giuseppe Richino Malatesta, 1745. 5 p. l., 63 [1] p. 14½cm.

Three acts. By marchese Gioseffo Gorini Corio, who is not mentioned. Dedication dated Milan, January 31, 1745, argument, cast, scenario, and name of Cristoforo Kluck (**Gluck**) as the composer. The additional page contains the substitute arias (I, 13) "Sovra la preda esangue" and (III, 1) "Dirai all' idol mio." SCHATZ 3931

L'Ippolita. Commedia per musica di Gennarantonio Federico, Napoletano da rappresentarsi nel Teatro de' Fiorentini, nella primavera di questo anno 1733 . . .

Napoli, Nicola di Biase, n. d. 79 p. 14½ cm.

Three acts. Dedication, cast, and name of the composer, Niccolò **Conti.**

SCHATZ 2207

Ippolito ed Aricia. Dramma per musica da rappresentarsi alla Corte elettorale Palatina in giorno del nome del serenissimo elettore . . . l'anno MDCCLIX.

Mannheim, Stamperia elettorale, n. d. 8 p. l., 96 p. 16 cm.

Five acts. By Carlo Innocenzio Frugoni, who is not mentioned. Argument, cast, scenario, and names of Ignaz **Holzbauer** as composer of the opera ("nuova composizione") and of Christian Cannabich as composer of the "arie dei balli, che non si cantano."

First performed at Mannheim, Hoftheater, November 4, 1759. SCHATZ 4784

L'ircana in Julfa, ballet. *See* Calegari's Le due sorelle incognite.

Ircano inamorato. Intermezzi per musica da rappresentarsi nel Nuovo Teatro di S. Margerita l'autunno 1729.

Venezia, Carlo Buonarrigo, 1729. 11 p. 15 cm.

Two parts. Neither the author, Belisario Valeriani, is mentioned, nor Fortunato **Chelleri,** the composer.

First performed at Ferrara, Teatro Bonacossi à S. Stefano, May, 1715, with his "La caccia in Etolia." SCHATZ 1816

Irene, dramma per musica, rappresentato alla Regia elettoral corte di Dresda.

n. i., n. d. 149 p. 16 cm.

Three acts. By Stefano Benedetto Pallavicini, who is not mentioned. Argument and name of Johann Adolph **Hasse** as the composer. German title page, "Irene . . . Dresden . . . bey der verwittibten Hof-buchdr. Stoesselin, 1738," and text face Italian.

First performed, as indicated, February 8, 1738. SCHATZ 4544

Irene. Tragedia per musica da rappresentarsi nel Teatro Grimano di San Gio. Grisostomo l'anno MDCXCV . . .

Venetia, Nicolini, 1695. front., 69 p. 15 cm.

Five acts. Dedication by the author, conte Girolamo Frigimelica Roberti, and one of his lengthy esthetic-dramaturgic prefaces, argument, scenario, and on p. 11 the substitute arias, "De la gloria, e de l'amor" (III, 1), "Ne l'amante son gran nimici" (III, 8) and "A morire, a morir" (IV, 9). Music attributed by Allacci and Schatz to Carlo Francesco **Pollaroli,** who is not mentioned. Schatz records, but incorrectly, fall 1694 as the date of first performance. Allacci has 1695, as above.

SCHATZ 8299
Second copy. ML 48.M2O

L'Irene. Drama per musica da rappresentarsi nel Teatro di S. Bartolomeo di Napoli . . .

Napoli, Parrino & Mutio, 1704. 4 p. l., 51 p. 14 cm.

Three acts. By conte Girolamo Frigimelica Roberti (who is not mentioned), but condensed to permit the insertion of buffo scenes, supposedly by Nicola Barbapiccola, who signs the dedication. Argument, scenario, cast, and notice to the reader:

"Questo drama dovendosi rappresentare in questo teatro di Napoli, per ridurlo in sì breve tempo a luce, hà ricevuto qualche alteratione dalla sua prima forma . . . Sappi in tanto, che per non defraudare alla lode (che degnamente è dovuta al Sig. Gio. Battista **Pullaroli** [Carlo Francesco Pollaroli?] primo compositore della musica) si segneranno l'arie del medesimo col segno §. Tutte l'altre sono del Sig. Domenico **Scarlatti.**"

L'Irene—Continued.

The marked arias are "Sento una forza in petto" (I, 2), "Guerra, guerra, voglio guerra" (I, 4), "Non hà pena l'amor più crudele" (I, 5), "Belle catene" (I, 6), "La speranza d'un core ardente" (I, 6) etc., etc., in fact, at least one half of the arias in the opera.   SCHATZ 9539

Irene augusta. Drama per musica da rappresentarsi nel famoso Teatro Griman¹ di S. Gio. Grisosostomo. L'autunno dell' anno 1713.

Venezia, Marino Rossetti, 1713. 70 p. 14½ᶜᵐ.

Three acts. By Francesco Silvani, who is not mentioned. Argument, cast, scenario, and name of Antonio **Lotti** as composer.   SCHATZ 5720

Irene e Costantino drama per musica nel Theatro Vendramino di S. Salvatore l'anno 1681 . . .

Venetia, Francesco Nicolini, 1681.

Three acts. By Andrea Rossini, who is not mentioned. Publisher's dedication, argument, scenario, and notice to the reader, in which Nicolini says:

"L'anno passato doveva rappresentarsi in quest' istesso teatro, ma accidenti non ordinarii & insidiosi furono i contradestini, che ne lo divertirono . . . Le corde della musica sono torture della penna, e la circonferenza delle scene è un carcere dell' ingegno."

The composer, Antonio **Zannettini** is not mentioned.   SCHATZ 11142

Iride. *See* Traetta's Le feste d'Imeneo.

The **Irish mimic**; or Blunders at Brighton: A musical entertainment in two acts. As performed at the Theatre-Royal, Covent-Garden. With universal applause. Written by John O'Keeffe.

London, T. N. Longman, 1795. 1 p. l., 54 p. 20ᶜᵐ.

Cast. The composer, William **Shield** (Squire), is not mentioned.
First performed April 23, 1795.   LONGE 229

The **iron chest**: a play; in three acts. Written by George Colman, the younger. With a preface. First represented at the Theatre-Royal, in Drury-Lane, on Saturday, 12th March, 1796 . . .

London, Cadell and Davies, 1796. 1 p. l., xxiii, [1], 127 p. 21ᶜᵐ.

Cast, notice to the reader dated Picadilly, July 20, 1796, and preface. The latter, in which Stephen **Storace** is appreciatively mentioned as the composer, gives a narrative of the incidents and accidents leading up to the first performance, at which the piece was saved from a fiasco by Storace's music (his last work), but principally the preface assails Kemble, the acting manager and principal performer, whom Colman held responsible for the near fiasco. (The piece became eminently popular afterwards and by 1798 three editions had appeared.) In the notice to the reader, Colman states his indebtedness for the ground work of the play to William Godwin's novel, "Things as they are," and that "the songs, duets, and chorusses, are intended merely as vehicles for musical effect."   LONGE 236

Der **irrende ritter.** Tr. of Traetta's Il cavaliero errante.

Das **irrlicht,** oder Endlich fand er sie. Ein singspiel in drey aufzuegen, nach herrn Bretzner frey bearbeitet, und fuer das k. k. Nationalhoftheater zugerichtet. Die musik neu vom herrn Umlauf. Aufgefuehrt auf dem k. k. Hoftheater naechst dem Kaernthuer thor.

Wien, beym Logenmeister, 1785. 71 p. 15ᶜᵐ.

First performed, as indicated, October 21, 1785; at Vienna, Burgtheater, January 17, 1782.   SCHATZ 10526

Das **irrlicht**—Continued.

— Arien und gesaenge aus dem **Irrwisch,** oder Endlich fand er sie, einer komischen oper, in drey aufzuegen. Von herrn Bretzner. Die musik ist von herrn Umlauf.

Riga, Gottlob Christian Froelich, n. d. 19 p. 15½ᶜᵐ.

First performed at Riga, Vietinghof'sches Theater, 14/25 May, 1786; at Mannheim, Nationaltheater, February 5, 1786. Schatz 10527

Die **irrthuemer.** Tr. of Storace's Gli **equivoci.**

Der **irrwisch,** oder Endlich fand er sie. Eine operette in drey akten.

Stuttgart, Christoph Gottfried Maentler, 1782. 91 p. 14½ᶜᵐ.

By Christoph Friedrich Bretzner. Composed by Christian Ludwig **Dieter.** Neither author nor composer is mentioned.

First performed at Stuttgart, Kl. Schauspielhaus a. d. Planie, September 23, 1782. Schatz 2579

Arien und gesaenge aus dem **Irrwisch.** Ein singspiel in drey aufzuegen von C. F. Bretzner. Die musik ist vom freyherrn von Kosboth.

n. i., 1784. 20 p. 16ᶜᵐ.

First performed at Berlin, Döbbelinsches Theater, October 2, 1780.

ML 50.2.I68K6

— Arien aus der operette: Der **irrwisch,** oder Endlich fand er sie; in drey acten, von herrn C. F. Bretzner. Die musik ist vom herrn baron von Kospoth.

n. i., 1787. 22 p. 16ᶜᵐ.

Schatz 5218

Der **irrwisch,** oder Endlich fand er sie. Eine operette in drey akten [silhouette] Componirt vom herrn Preu in Leipzig.

98 p. 16ᶜᵐ. (*C. F. Bretzner, Operetten, 1. band, Leipzig, 1779.*)

The silhouette is a portrait of the actress F. R. Koch.
First performed at Leipzig, Theater am Rannstädter Thore, 1779. Schatz 11680

— Der **irrwisch,** oder Endlich fand er sie. Eine operette in drey akten. Von C. F. Bretzner. Componirt vom herrn Preu in Leipzig.

Leipzig, Carl Friedrich Schneidern, 1788. 84 p. 15ᶜᵐ.

Schatz 8464

Der **irrwisch** oder Endlich fand er sie. **L. T.** of Umlauf's Das irrlicht oder Endlich fand er sie.

Isabella, e Rodrigo o sia La costanza in amore. Dramma giocoso per musica di Giovanni Bertati da rappresentarsi nel nobilissimo Teatro in S. Samuele nell' autunno dell' anno 1776.

Venezia, Gio. Battista Casali, 1776. 71 p. 17ᶜᵐ.

Two acts. Cast, scenario, and name of Pasquale **Anfossi** as composer.

Schatz 241

— **Isabella e Rodrigo,** o sia La costanza in amore. Dramma per musica da rappresentarsi nel Teatro Elettorale di Dresda.

Dresda, n. p., 1784. 117 p. 16ᶜᵐ.

Two acts. Cast (added in pencil), with name of **Anfossi** as composer. German title-page, "Isabella und Rodrigo, oder die Beständigkeit in der liebe," and text face Italian. Schatz 242

Isabella und Rodrigo oder Die beständigkeit in der liebe.   Tr. of Anfossi's Isabella e Rodrigo.

Isabelle et Gertrude, ou Les sylphes supposés, comédie en un acte meslée d'ariettes, par M. Favart.   Représentée pour la première fois par les Comédiens italiens ordinaires du roi, le 14 août 1765.

 Paris, la veuve Duchesne, 1765.   43, [5] p.   19ᶜᵐ.

  The additional unnumbered p. contain: "Poëme, qui a donné lieu à la comédie d'Isabelle & Gertrude, par Monsieur de Voltaire."   The composer and arranger of the score, Adolphe **Blaise,** is not mentioned.   SCHATZ 1064

— **Isabelle et Gertrude** ou Les sylphes supposés; comédie en un acte, meslée d'ariettes; par Mr. Tavart [!]   La musique est de M. Blaise.   Représentée pour la première fois par les Comédiens italiens, ordinaires du roy, le 14 août 1765.

 Mannheim, Charles Fontaine, 1767.   139 p.   16½ᶜᵐ.

  German title page: "Isabella und Gertraude oder Die erdichtete luft-geister," and text face the French.   In a note Favart acknowledges his indebtedness to Voltaire and Marmontel.   SCHATZ 1065

— **Isabelle et Gertrude,** ou Les sylphes supposés; comédie en un acte, meslée d'ariettes; par M. Favart.   La musique est de M. Blaise.

 n. i., n. d.   63 p.   19ᶜᵐ.   (Theatre de M. Favart, Paris, Duchesne, 1763–77, t. ix.)

  On p. 53–63, seven "Airs d'Isabelle et Gertrude."   Text preceded by Favart's dedication to Voisenon, and the same avertissement as in Schatz 1065.

                                                          ML 49.A2F1

— **Isabelle et Gertrude** ou Les sylphes supposés.   Comédie en un acte, mêlée d'ariettes, par M. Favart.   La musique est de M. Blaise.   Representée pour la première fois par les Comédiens italiens ordinaires du roi, le 14 août 1765.

 Paris, la veuve Duchesne, 1784.   46 p.   19ᶜᵐ.

  On p. 41–42, the vaudeville, "Pour nous est fait le plaisir," and on p. 44–46 the air of "O nuit! charmante nuit!"   SCHATZ 11677

Isacio tiranno.   Drama per musica da rappresentarsi nel famosissimo Teatro Grimani di San Gio. Grisostomo l'autunno dell' anno 1710 . . .

 Venezia, Marino Rossetti, 1710.   72 p.   14ᶜᵐ.

  Three acts.   Dedication, cast, argument, scenario, and notice to the reader, which begins:
  "Ecco la presente seconda mia fatica, qual' prende coraggio dal tuo generoso compatimento donato alla prima mia del Vincitor generoso l'anno 1708 . . ."
  This points to Francesco Briani as author.   The composer, Antonio **Lotti,** is not mentioned.   SCHATZ 5721

Les Isies.   A. T. of Arnéris, entrée in Rameau's Les fêtes de l'Himen et de l'Amour.

Isis, tragedie en musique, ornée d'entrées de ballet, de machines, & de changements de theatre, representée devant Sa Majesté à Saint Germain en Laye.   Suivant la copie imprimée à Paris.

 [Amsterdam, Antoine Schelte], 1682.   69 p. (incl. front.)   13½ᶜᵐ.

  Prologue and five acts.   Without name of composer and author, but with names of the dancers in the prologue and in the ballets.   (See below.)   ML 50.2.I69L9

Isis—Continued.

— **Isis,** tragedie en musique, ornée d'entrées de ballet, de machines, & de changemens de theatre.   Representée devant Sa Majesté à Saint Germain en Laye.   Suivant la copie imprimée à Paris.

[Amsterdam, Antoine Schelte], 1686.   69 p. (incl. front.).   13½ᶜᵐ.

Prologue and five acts.   Without name of composer and author, but with names of the dancers in the prologue and the ballets.   ML 49.A2L9

— **Isis,** tragedie représentée par l'Academie royale de musique l'an 1677.   Les paroles de M. Quinault, & la musique de M. de Lully. IX. opera.

n. i., n. d.   14ᶜᵐ.   front., 1–68 p.   (Recueil général des opéra, t. ii, Paris, 1703.)

Detached copy.   Five acts and prologue.

First performed, as indicated, August, 1677 (Schatz), April, 1677 (Prunières); previously, at Saint Germain en Laye, January 5, 1677.   SCHATZ 5768
                                    Second copy.   ML 48.R4

— **Isis,** tragedie en musique, ornée d'entrées de ballets, de machines & de changemens de théatre.   Représentée devant Sa Majesté, à Saint Germain en Laye le 5. janvier 1677.

Quinault, Théatre, Paris, 1739, t. iv, pl., p. [337]–407.   17ᶜᵐ.

Prologue and five acts.   **Lully** is not mentioned.   PQ 1881.A1   **1739**

The **island of St. Marguerite,** an opera, in two acts, and first performed at the Theatre Royal, Drury Lane, on Friday, November 13, 1789.

London, J. Debrett, 1789.   vi, [7]–32 p.   21ᶜᵐ.

Prologue, cast, and editor's Advertisement, dated Piccadilly, November 30, 1789, in which he says that the piece is founded on Voltaire's story of the Man in the Iron mask, and that—

"The author [John St. John], as appears from his prologue, knows the value of liberty, and, consequently, could not withhold his applause from a people struggling for a free constitution: but delicacy required that even the appearance of anything that might be construed into an insult to a foreign country should be avoided . . ."

The composer, Thomas **Shaw,** is not mentioned.   The music was partly selected by the author.   LONGE 203

The **island princess;** or, The generous Portuguese: Made into an opera: as it is performed at the Theatre Royal.   All the musical entertainments, and the greatest part of the play new, and written by Mr. Motteux.

London, Printed by John Darby for Mary Poulson, 1724.   72 p. 16ᶜᵐ.

Five acts, with prologue and epilogue.   Cast, Peter [Anthony] Motteux's dedication and preface, in which he says that this piece is based on Fletcher's Island princess:

"As I found it not unfit to be made what we here call an opera, I undertook to revise it, but not as I wou'd have done, had I design'd a correct play . . .   The success has answer'd my intent, far beyond expectation.   However, I am not willing to attribute it to myself, but chiefly to the excellency of the musical part.   What Mr. **Daniel Purcel** has set is so fine, that as he seems inspir'd with his brother's wonderful genius, it cannot but be equally admir'd.   The notes of the interlude set by Mr. [Jeremiah] **Clarke** have air and humour that crown them with applause: and the dialogue and Enthusiastic song, which Mr. **Leveridge** set, are too particularly lik'd not to engage me to thank him for gracing my words with his composition, as much as for his celebrated singing . . ."

The piece is not an opera in our sense—merely a play with some incidental music. The composers are again mentioned in the text, Daniel Purcell being the chief contributor.   The text of Clarke's interlude is printed on p. 63–70, under the title: "The

The island princess—Continued.

FOUR SEASONS, or Love in every age. A musical interlude. Set to musick by Mr. Jeremy Clarke," and a note reads:
"This entertainment is perform'd at the end of the last act, but was design'd for another season, and another occasion . . ."
The "opera" was first performed at London, Drury Lane, 1699.   LONGE 75

L'isle des Amazones. Pièce d'un acte. Par Mrs le S * *. & D'Or * *. Qui devoit être représentée à la Foire de Saint Laurent 1718. mais dont on n'eut pas besoin, & que la suppression de l'Opéra comique a empêché d'être jouée depuis.
Le Théâtre de la foire, Paris, 1737, t. iii, pl., [331]–376 p.   17ᶜᵐ.

By Le Sage and d'Orneval. Largely *en vaudevilles*. The airs, selected or composed and arranged by Jean Claude **Gillier**, the "compositeur" of the theatre, are printed at the end of the volume in the "Table des airs."
Parfaict says that the piece was first performed at the Foire Saint Laurent in 1720.
ML 48.L2 III

L'isle des foux, comédie en deux actes mêlée d'ariettes, parodie de l'Arcifanfano de Goldoni, par Messieurs * * * & Anseaume. Représentée par les Comédiens italiens ordinaires du roi. La musique est de M. Duny.
Paris, Claude Herissant, 1762.   46 p.   19ᶜᵐ.

By Anseaume, Lefèbure de Marcouville, and L. A. Bertin d'Antilly.
First performed at Paris, as indicated, December 29, 1760.   SCHATZ 2846

L'isle du mariage. Opera-comique en un acte. Representée pour la premiere fois sur le Théatre de la Foire S. Laurent le 20ᵉ jour d'août 1733.
Le Théâtre de la foire, Paris, 1737, t. ix, 2, pl., [223]–279 p.   17ᶜᵐ.

By Carolet. Largely *en vaudevilles*. The airs, a few of which by **Cor(r)ette**, are printed at the end of the volume in the "Table des airs."
Parfaict gives July 20, 1733, as date of first performance.   ML 48.L48X

L'isle sonnante, opéra-comique, en trois actes. Réprésentée par les Comédiens italiens ordinaires du roi, le lundi 4 janvier 1768.
Paris, Cluade [!] Herissant, 1768.   43 p.   19ᶜᵐ.

Neither the author, Charles Collé, nor the composer, **Monsigny**, is mentioned.
First performed 1767 at Villers-Cotterets, private theatre of the duke of Orléans.
SCHATZ 6576

— L'isle sonnante, opera comique en trois actes, représenté par les Comédiens italiens ordinaires du roi, le lundi 4 janvier 1768. La musique de M * * *.
Paris, la veuve Duchesne, 1771.   40 p.   19ᶜᵐ.

Cast. Composed by **Monsigny**. Neither he is mentioned, nor Charles Collé, the author.
SCHATZ 11727

Ismène, pastorale héroïque, donnée à Versailles, en 1747 & 1748. Représentée pour la première fois par l'Académie royale de musique, le vendredi 28 août 1750. Reprise le jeudi 18 février, 1751. Et remise au Théâtre, le vendredi 3 août 1759.
n. i., n. d.   18 p.   24ᶜᵐ.

One act. Cast and names of de Moncrif as author, of **Rebel** and **Francoeur** as composers.
ML 50.2.I7R22

Ismène—Continued.

— Ismène, pastorale héroïque. Représentée devant Sa Majesté, à Fontainebleau, le 12 octobre 1769.

[*Paris*], *Pierre Robert Christophe Ballard, 1769. 24 p. 20^{cm}.*

One act. Cast and names of de Moncrif as author, of **Rebel** and **Francoeur** as composers. ML 50.2.I7R24

Ismene et Ismenias; tragedie en trois actes, représentée devant Leurs Majestés, à Choisy, le lundi 13 juni 1763, et pour la premiere fois par l'Academie-royale de musique, le mardi 11 décembre 1770.

Paris, de Lormel, 1770. 54 p. 22½^{cm}.

Cast and Avertissement (argument). By Laujon, who is mentioned as author. **J. B. de La Borde,** the composer, is not mentioned. ML 50.2.I7L2

L'isola capricciosa. Dramma giocoso per musica da rappresentarsi nel nobile Teatro di San Samuele il carnovale dell' anno 1780.

Venezia, Modesto Fenzo, 1780. 64 p. 16^{cm}.

Two acts. By Caterino Mazzolà, who is not mentioned. Cast, scenario, and name of Giacomo **Rust** as the composer. On p. [33]–39, cast and description of Francesco Clerico's "Gustavo Vasa, ballo eroico pantomimo in cinque atti," without name of the composer ot the music. Schatz 9174

L'isola d'Alcina. O. T. of Broschi's Bradamante nell' isola d'Alcina.

L'isola d'Alcina. *See* Gazzaniga's L'isola di Alcina.

L'isola d'Alcina. Tragedia del Sig. Co. Fulvio Testi posta in musica da Francesco Sacrati . . .

Bologna, gli eredi del Dozza, 1648. 57 p. 16½^{cm}.

Five acts, with prologue. Dedication by Sacrati and notice to the reader, in which he says:

"Se rozza ti parerà la musica dell' Alcina, scusala, ti suplico, ò lettore, che nata fra le rozezze della villa, non può esser che tale. Per ingannar l'otio, mi diedi a comporla, mentre à Panzano, delitie vilereccia, dell' illustriss. Sig. Cornelio Malvasia, attendevo il di lui ritorno dal campo; non con pensiero, che giamai ella havesse à rendersi ardita di comparire ne publici teatri di Bologna . . .

"Averti in oltre, che se la vedrai introdotta sù la scena da un prologo diverso da quello che ne suoi primi natali la condusse sotto gl'occhi de'principi Estensi, è opportunità ricercata dal tempo, e dal loco dove hà da rapresentarsi."

First performed at Bologna, 1648, as indicated. Schatz 9250

L'isola d'amore. Commedia in musica da rappresentarsi nel Teatro Giustiniani di S. Moisè nel carnovale dell' anno MDCCLII.

Venezia, n. publ., 1752. front., 72, 3 p. 15^{cm}.

Three acts. By Antonio Rigo, called Gori, who is not mentioned. Argument, cast, scenario, and name of Gaetano **Latilla** as composer. Page 72 and the 3 add. p. contain substitute arias, "Alla guerra, che questo mio core" for "Or con l'immagine d'un bel Torello" (I, 6), "Nel mio core poverino" for "Non so se m'intendete" (I, 4), "Lavorando Nina mia" for "Mamma mia" (II, 2), "Non dubitate o cara" for "Soccorso bramate." Schatz 5461

L'isola d'amore, azione comica per musica da rappresentarsi alla Corte ellettorale palatina . . .

Mannheim, Stamperia elettorale ed academ., n. d. 71 p. 16½^{cm}.

Two acts. Cast, scenario and name of Antonio **Sacchini** as composer. Author not mentioned and unknown to Schatz.

First performed at Mannheim, Hoftheater, January 1772; at Rome, Teatro alla Valle, carnival 1766. ML 50.2.I73S3

L'isola d'amore—Continued.

— **L'isola d'amore.** Intermezzo per musica a quattro voci da rappresentarsi in Lisbona nel Teatro della rua dos Condes nella primavera dell' anno 1774.

[Lisbona], Stamperia reale, n. d.   62 p.   16ᶜᵐ.

Two acts. Author not mentioned and unknown to Schatz. Cast and name of Antonio **Sacchini** as the composer.
First performed at Lisbon, as indicated, April 20, 1774.   SCHATZ 9225

— **L'isola d'amore.** Dramma giocoso da rappresentarsi nel Theatro di Ratisbona . . .

Ratisbona, n. publ., 1775.   139 p.   17ᶜᵐ.

Two acts. Cast and name of Antonio **Sacchini** as the composer. German titlepage, "Die insel der liebe," and text face Italian.
First performed 1775, as indicated.   SCHATZ 9227

— **La colonie,** comédie en deux actes, imitée de l'italien, et parodiée sur la musique du Sig. Sacchini.   Représentée pour la premiere fois par les Comédiens italiens, le 16 août 1775.

Paris, la veuve Duchesne, 1776.   47 p.   18ᶜᵐ.

Two acts. By Nicolas Etienne Framery. Cast and prefatory note, in which Framery gives the "canevas italien" of L'isola d'amore" to show the differences between this and his *parodie* and to ask the public's indulgence for his irregularities, etc., caused by the difficulty to "conserver tous les morceaux de musique" and yet to turn the text of the "auteur inconnu de l'intermède italien" into acceptable French.   In the text are printed the airs of "Dès ce soir l'hymen m'engage" (I, 1), "Ah, ma honte en est extrême" (I, 2), "Qu'est-ce donc vous arrête" (II, 2), "Quel sort t'amène" (II, 3).   SCHATZ 9228

— **Die kolonie,** ein singspiel in zween aufzuegen. Aus dem franzoesischen.   Mit musik.

Frankfurt am Mayn, mit Andreaeischen schriften, 1778.   60 p.   15½ᶜᵐ.

The music is wanting in this copy. Two acts. German version by Johann André. Neither Framery nor **Sacchini** is mentioned.
First performed at Mannheim, Churf. deutsche Schaubühne im Schütthause, February 21, 1779.   SCHATZ 9229

— Arien aus dem singspiele: **Die colonie.** In zwey aufzuegen. Die musik ist von Sacchini.

Hamburg, J. M. Michaelsen, 1780.   23 p.   16½ᶜᵐ.

Two acts. Joh. André's version.
First performed at Hamburg, Theater beim Gänsemarkt, February 8, 1780.
          SCHATZ 9230

— **Die insel der liebe,** ein singspiel in zween aufzuegen, aufgefuehret an dem Churpfaelzischen hofe im jahr 1772.

Mannheim, Hof u. Akademie-buchdruckerei, n. d.   52 p.   16ᶜᵐ.

Cast and name of Antonio **Sacchini** as the composer. German Tr. of the Italian Mannheim ed. of 1772.   SCHATZ 9226

— **Die insel der liebe.** Ein singspiel in zwey aufzuegen. Theils aus der franzoesischen, theils aus der italienischen gleichen namens opera, neu bearbeitet fuer die Hochfuerstlich Thurn und Taxische Schaubuehne.

Regensburg, gedruckt mit Breitfeldischen schriften, 1781.   55 p.   16½ᶜᵐ.

L'isola d'amore—Continued.

Cast and names of **Sacchini** as composer of the opera, of baron [Theodor] von **Schacht** as composer of the choruses and dances, who says in the dedication:

"Cet opera vous fit autre fois, grand plaisir, & vous admiriés a juste titres les talens du çelebre Saçchini. Empressée de contribuer à vos plaisirs, la troupe allemande qui jouit du bonheur de se voir appuyée par vous, voulut redonner cette piece, se vit arretée par plusieurs morçeaux omis dans la traduction. Encouragé par le succès de Lausus & Lydie, j'entrepris de remettre la piece, avec toute la musique, laissant soigneusement les belles scenes que nous devons a l'auteur de la Colonie, & pour en faire un spectacle nouveau, j'y aioutais les choeurs, vaudevilles, duos & danses."

SCHATZ 9231

L'isola de' cannibali, ballet. *See* Tritto's La molinara spiritosa.

L'isola della fortuna. Dramma giocoso per musica da rappresentarsi nel Real Teatro dell' Ajuda nell' autunno dell' anno MDCCLXVII.

Lisbona, Michele Manescal Da Costa, n. d. 79 p. 16^{cm}.

Three acts. Cast, scenario, and names of Giovanni Bertati as author, of Andrea **Luchesi** as composer.

First performed at Venice, Teatro di S. Samuele, fall of 1765. SCHATZ 5742

L'isola della luna. Dramma giocoso per musica in due atti di Antonio Piazza Venetiano da rappresentarsi nel nobile Teatro di San Samuele l'autunno dell' anno 1780 . . .

Venezia, Modesto Fenzo, 1780. 64 p. 16½^{cm}.

Two acts. Impresario's dedication, cast, and name of Giovanni **Valentini** as the composer. SCHATZ 10585

L'isola di Alcina. Dramma giocoso per musica da rappresentarsi nel Teatro Giustiniani di S. Moisè il carnevale dell anno 1772 di Giovanni Bertati.

Venezia, Antonio Graziosi, 1772. 64 p. 16½^{cm}.

Three acts. Cast, scenario, and name of Giuseppe **Gazzaniga** as the composer. SCHATZ 3665

— **L'isola di Alcina.** Dramma giocoso per musica da rappresentarsi nel Piccolo Teatro di S. A. E. di Sassonia.

Dresda, n. publ., 1773. 139 p. 15½^{cm}.

Three acts. With the names of Bertati and **Gazzaniga**. German title page, "Die insel der Alcina," and text face Italian, which follows fairly closely the original. SCHATZ 3666

— **L'isola d'Alcina;** dramma giocoso per musica da rappresentarsi nel Regio Teatro.—Alcines øe, et lystigt synge-spil . . . Oversat paa dansk af R. Soelberg.

Kiøbenhavn, H. J. Graae, 1777. 103 p. 16½^{cm}.

Three acts. Cast and name of Giuseppe **Gazzaniga** as the composer.
First performed, as indicated, March 6, 1777. SCHATZ 3667

— **L'isola d'Alcina.** Dramma giocoso per musica da rappresentarsi nel Teatro Zagnoni in Bologna il carnevale dell' anno 1779.

Bologna, Sassi, n. d. 57 p. 15½^{cm}.

Three acts. Cast, scenario, and name of Giuseppe **Gazzaniga** as composer. Bertati is not mentioned. ML 48.A5 v.30

L'isola di Bellamarina.   Dramma giocoso per musica di Domenico
Mantile da rappresentarsi nel Teatro Nuovo sopra Toledo per terz'
opera di quest' anno 1791.

Napoli, Vincenzo Mazzola-Vocola, 1792.   48 p.   15ᶜᵐ.

Two acts. Argument, cast, and name of the composer, Francesco Antonio De
Blasis.   Schatz 2420

L'isola di Bengodi.   Dramma giocoso per musica da rappresentarsi
nel Teatro Giustiniani di S. Moisè l'autunno dell' anno 1777.

n. i., n. d.   51 p.   18ᶜᵐ.

Two acts. Cast, name of Gennaro **Astaritta** as composer ("la musica sarà tutta
nuova"), and Avvertiments:
   "Riconoscerà il leggitore in questo dramma, sotto altro titolo, la Cuccagna del
celebre Sig. Goldoni . . . Il gusto de' finali introdottosi nelle opere buffe posterior-
mente alla rappresentazione del dramma suddetto, ha fatto, che per necessità si
dovesse cambiar l'ordine del libretto, riducendolo a due soli atti, per essersi trasportata nel primo finale una parte dell' argomento dell' atto secondo, e nel finale secondo
la catastrofe del dramma. Qualche altro cambiamento, che vi s'incontra si nella
introduzione, che nelle arie, non è stato eseguito che per adattarsi in parte al gusto
corrente de' signori compositori di musica, ed in parte ai personaggi, che le devono
cantare, non intendendo mai con simili cambiamenti di volersi correggere l'opera
d'un autore troppo cognito e rispettato."
   With the opera were performed, composer of the music not mentioned, Riccardo
Blèck's ballets, "Il pentimento amoroso" and "Lo sposo deluso."   Schatz 382

L'isola disabitata.   Dramma di tre atti per musica.   Rappresentato per la prima volta in Bologna nell' estate dell' anno MDCCLII.

*Carlo Goldoni, Opere teatrali, Venezia, Zatta e figli, 1788–95, v. 42,
[327]–375 p.   18ᶜᵐ.*   PQ

First composer unknown to Schatz.

L'isola disabitata.

*Metastasio, Poesie, Parigi, vedova Quillau, 1755, t. iv, [405]–439 p.
16ᶜᵐ.*

One act. Argument.   ML 49.A2M42

— **L'isola disabitata.**   Questa azione teatrale fu scritta dall' autore
in Vienna l'anno 1752, per la Real Corte Cattolica, dove venne mag-
nificamente rappresentata la prima volta con musica del Bonno, sotto
la direzione del celebre cavalier Broschi.

*[341]–378 p.   26ᶜᵐ.   (Pietro Metastasio, Opere, t. II, Parigi, vedova
Herissant, 1780.)*

One act. Argument.   ML 49.A2M44

L'isola disabitata.   Azione per musica da rappresentarsi nel Ducal
Teatro di Louisbourg . . . il dì 4. novembre 1761. Giorno di S.
Carlo, festa dell' insigne suo ordine ducale. La poesia è del Signor
abbate Pietro Metastasio . . . La musica è nuovamente composta
dal Signor Nicolò Jommelli . . . I balli sono inventati e diretti dal
Signor Giovanni Giorgio Noverre . . .

[Stutgart], Cotta, n. d.   65, [6] p.   18ᶜᵐ.

Two acts. Argument and cast. German title page, "Die unbewohnte insel,"
and text face Italian. On p. [32]–[33] brief description of the ballet, "Amore vincitore dell' indifferenza," on the six add. p. of "Il riconoscimento inaspettato."   Of
these ballets the music probably was composed by either Deller or Rudolph.
   First version first performed at Genoa, Teatro del Falcone, spring of 1756.

                                                              Schatz 4863

L'isola disabitata. Azione per musica del Sig. abbate Pietro Metastasio . . .

Venezia, Aloise Valvasense, 1775. 40 p. 17½ᶜᵐ.

Two parts. Argument and name of Johann Gottlieb **Naumann** as the composer. First performed at Venice, Teatro particolare (Schatz), February, 1773.

SCHATZ 7061

L'isola disabitata: cantata seria per musica da rappresentarsi nel Regio Teatro di S. Carlo della Principessa l'estate dell' anno 1799.

Lisbona, Simone Taddeo Ferreira, 1799. 59 p. 14ᶜᵐ.

One act. Metastasio is mentioned as author, **Paisiello** as composer. First performed, as indicated, July 3, 1799.

SCHATZ 7693

L'isola disabitata. Dramma giocoso per musica di Polisseno Fegejo, pastor Arcade. Da rappresentarsi nel Teatro Grimani di S. Samuel l'autunno dell' anno 1757.

Venezia, Modesto Fenzo, 1757. 58 p. 15ᶜᵐ.

Three acts. By Goldoni. Cast, scenario, and name of Giuseppe **Scarlatti** as the composer.

SCHATZ 9546

— L'isola disabitata. Dramma giocoso per musica di Polisseno Fegeio P. A. Da rappresentarsi nel Piccolo Teatro di S. A. E. di Sassonia . . . Dresda l'autunno del 1767.

n. i., n. d. 2 p. l., 157 p. 16½ᶜᵐ.

Three acts. By Goldoni. Cast, scenario, and name of Giuseppe **Scarlatti** as the composer. German title page, "Die unbewohnte insel," with date, "Dresden. Im fruehlinge des 1767 sten jahres," and text face the Italian, which seems to follow the Venice, 1757, ed. closely, though differences are noticeable. For instance, "Povere donne; che s'ha da far?" has become "Ah meschinella, che deggo far?"

SCHATZ 9547

L'isola disabitata. Azione drammatica per musica da rappresentarsi nel Nuovo Teatro del pubblico di Bologna in occasione del faustissimo passaggio per detta città della Maestà di Maria Carolina arciduchessa d'Austria, real sposo di sua Maestà siciliana . . .l'anno MDCCLXVIII.

Bologna, Lelio dalla Volpe, n. d. xii (incl. front.: coat of arms), 28 p. 23½ᶜᵐ.

The imprimatur is dated April 8, 1768; count Giov. Luca Pallavicino's dedication, Bologna, April 26, 1768. The libretto, with argument, cast, and name of Tommaso **Trajetta** as composer, is by Pietro Metastasio, but "si sono aggiunte, e cambiate alcune arie, e recitativi a fine di ridurla in due parti e d'introdurvi dei balli coerenti alla azione medesima." All such changes are marked with an asterisk.

SCHATZ 10394

— L'isola disabitata, azione per musica del Signor abate Pietro Metastasio; da rappresentarsi nel Regio Teatro danese. —Den ubeboede øe . . .

Kiøbenhavn, H. J. Graae, 1772. 55 p. 17ᶜᵐ.

Two acts. Cast, argument, and name of Tommaso **Trajetta** as composer. Danish text faces Italian. First performed, as indicated, January 8, 1773 (Schatz).

SCHATZ 10395

La isola incantata di Circe la maga, ballet. *See* Pampani's Demofoonte.

L'isola piacevole, ballet. *See* Gardi's La semplice.

L'isola piacevole. Dramma giocoso per musica da rappresentarsi nel nobilissimo Teatro Giustiniani in San Moisè il carnovale dell' anno 1797.

Venezia, Modesto Fenzo, 1797. 59 p. 18ᶜᵐ.

Two acts. By Lorenzo da Ponte, who is not mentioned. Argument, cast, scenario, and name of Vicenzo Martini (**Martin y Soler**) as the composer. A note on p. 7 says: "La sinfonia esprime una gran burrasca di mare, che a poco a poco và abbonazzando."

On p. 34, short description of "Li sposi contenti ballo analago all' opera . . . La musica è tutta nuova del Signor Antonio Cappuci." This, like the second ballet (title on an inserted slip), "La piazza di Pusilipo in Napoli," by Carlo Taglioni.

First performed at London, Haymarket, 1795.   SCHATZ 6011

— **L'isola piacevole.** Dramma giocoso per musica da rappresentarsi nel Regio Teatro di via S. Maria nell' estate dell' anno 1797 . . .

Firenze, Stamperia Albizziniana, 1797. 48 p. 16½ᶜᵐ.

Two acts. Argument, cast, and name of Vincenzo Martini (**Martin y Soler**) as composer. Da Ponte is not mentioned.   ML 48.A5 v. 15

Issé, pastorale heroique. Representée par l'Academie royale de musique l'an 1697. Les paroles de M. de la Mothe, & la musique de M. Destouches. XLIV. opera.

n. i., n. d. pl., p. 171–228. (Recueil général des opéra, Paris, 1703, t. vi.) 14ᶜᵐ.

Detached copy. Three acts and prologue, with "Epistre" addressed to the duke of Burgundy, and a sort of argument.

First performed, as indicated, December 30, 1697; at Trianon before the King, December 17, 1697.   SCHATZ 2546
Second copy. ML 48.R4

— **Issé,** pastorale heroïque, représentée pour la première fois devant Sa Majesté, en trois actes, à Trianon, le 17. decembre 1697 par l'Academie royale de musique. Et remise au théatre le 14 octobre 1708 en cinq actes. Les paroles de M. de la Mothe, & la musique de M. Destouches. LXXI. Opera.

n. i., n. d. front., p. 333–386. (Recueil général des opéra, t. ix, Paris, 1710.) 14ᶜᵐ.

Detached copy. With Prologue. The "Epistre" has not been reprinted.
                    SCHATZ 2547
Second copy. ML 48.R4

— **Issé,** pastorale héroïque, en cinq actes, représentée, devant Sa Majesté, à Versailles, le 18 décembre 1773.

[Paris], P. Robert Christophe Ballard, 1773. 54 p. 19ᶜᵐ.

Five acts. Cast and note:
"Les paroles sont de feu M. Lamothe. La musique de feu M. **Destouches**, avec des changements dans les Fêtes, par M. [Pierre Montan] **Berton**, Maître de la Musique du roi, Directeur de l'Opera."   ML 50.2.I75D2

Issea. Favola pastorale per musica da rappresentarsi nel Regio Teatro di Torino per le auguste nozze della real principessa Maria Giuseppa Luisa Benedetta di Savoja col real principe Luigi Stanislao Saverio . . . l'anno MDCCLXXI.

Torino, Onorato Derossi, n. d. viii, 42 p. 16ᶜᵐ.

Two acts. Cast, scenario, and names of Vittorio Amedeo Cigna-Santi as the author, of Gaetano **Pugnani** as the composer of the opera, and of Giuseppe Antonio Le Messier of the ballet music.   SCHATZ 8507

L'Issipile.

[299]–358 p. 19*cm*. (*Pietro Metastasio, Opere drammatiche, Venezia, Giuseppe Bettinelli, 1733–37, t. i.*)

Three acts. Argument. No composer is mentioned. ML 49.A2M4

— Issipile.

Metastasio, Poesie, Parigi, vedova Quillau, 1755, t. ii, [105]–192 p. 16cm.

Three acts. Argument. ML 49.A2M42

— Issipile. Dramma rappresentato la prima volta con musica del Conti nel picciolo interno Teatro della Corte Cesarea, alla presenza degli augustissimi sovrani, nel carnevale del 1732.

pl., [121]–218 p. 26cm. (Pietro Metastasio, Opere, t. ii, Parigi, vedova Herissant, 1780.)

Three acts. Argument. ML 49.A2M44

— Hypsipile.

Metastasio, Tragedies opera, Vienne, 1751, t. v., 103 p. 14cm.

Three acts. Richelet's translation of "Issipile." ML 49.A2M47

L'Issipile. Drama per musica da rappresentarsi nel Teatro delle Dame nella primavera dell' anno 1732 . . .

Roma, Si vendono a Pasquino, 1732. 72 p. 15cm.

Three acts. By Metastasio, who is mentioned as author. Argument, scenario and dedication by Francesco Cavanna from which it would appear that this "nuova fatica" of Metastasio's was sent to Cavanna "che si esponga al giudizio di Roma." No composer is mentioned and no cast is given. These points combined with the fact that Metastasio himself recorded as first performance that at Vienna, carnival 1732 in Conti's setting would lead to the conclusion that the planned performance at Rome in 1732 did not materialize. ML 50.2.I78

L'Issipile. Drama per musica da rappresentarsi nella Cesarea Corte . . . nel carnevale dell' anno MDCCXXXII. La poesia è del Sig. abbate Pietro Metastasio . . . La musica è del Sig. Francesco Conti . . .

Vienna d'Austria, Gio. Pietro Van Ghelen, n. d. 68 p. 16½cm.

Three acts. Argument, scenario. The ballet music was by Nicola Matteis. SCHATZ 2205

Issipile. Drama per musica da rappresentarsi nel Regio Teatro di Torino, nel carnovale del 1738 alla presenza delle Maestà Loro.

Torino, Gio. Battista Scotto, 1738. 4 p. l., 71, [1] p. 15cm.

Three acts. By Metastasio, but the reader is informed that the first scene of the third act, and the two substitute arias printed at the end—"Svenasti il padre intanto" (I, 14) and "No, non vedrete mai" (II, 1)—are not by him. Argument, scenario, cast, and names of **Galuppi** as composer of the opera; of the ballet music, Alessio Basetti. Schatz calls this Galuppi's first setting of the text.

First performed, as indicated, December 26, 1737. SCHATZ 3499

— Issipile. Dramma per musica da rappresentarsi nel Regio-Ducal Teatro di Parma nel carnovale dell' anno MDCCLVI

Parma, Monti, n. d. 76 p. 18cm.

Three acts. By Metastasio, with indicated alterations. Argument, cast, scenario, and name of **Galuppi** as the composer, whose second setting of the text this was, according to Schatz. SCHATZ 3514

L'Issipile. Dramma per musica da rappresentarsi nel Teatro Giustinian di S. Moisè nel carnovale dell' anno 1758.

Venezia, Modesto Fenzo, 1758. 78 p. 15½cm.

Three acts. By Metastasio. Cast and name of Florian Leopold **Gassmann** as the composer.   SCHATZ 3622

Issipile. Dramma per musica del Sig. abbate Pietro Metastasio da rappresentarsi nel nobilissimo Teatro La Fenice l'autunno dell' anno 1796.

Venezia, Stamperia Valvasense, n. d. 61, [1] p. 18cm.

Three acts. Cast and name of Gaetano **Marinelli** as the composer. On p. [29]–42, argument, cast, and description of Lorenzo Panzieri's "Odervik, ballo eroico in cinque atti;" music "tutta nuova, ed espressamente scritta" by Vittorio Trento. A second ballet (author and composer not mentioned) had the title, "Un consiglio per li vecchj."

First performed, as indicated, November 12, 1796.   SCHATZ 5956

L'Issipile. Dramma per musica da rappresentarsi nel Teatro di Macerata nel carnevale dell' anno 1748 . . .

Macerata, gli eredi del Pannelli, 1748. 70, [1] p. 13cm.

Three acts. Metastasio is mentioned as the author in the impresario's dedication, dated, "Macerata 15. [!] del 1748." Argument, cast, scenario, and name of Antonio Maria **Mazzoni** as the composer. The additional page contains a substitute aria: 'Parti, deh! fuggi" for "Perchè l'altrui misura."   SCHATZ 6226

L'Issipile. Dramma per musica di Pietro Metastasio trà gli Arcadi Artino Corasio. Da rappresentarsi nel Teatro Grimani di S. Gio. Grisostomo l'autunno dell' anno MDCCXXXII.

Venezia, Carlo Buonarrigo, n. d. 60 p. 15cm.

Three acts. Dedication signed by Domenico Lalli, argument, scenario, cast, name of Giovanni **Porta** as the composer, and notice that the recitatives not by Metastasio are marked in quotation, and the arias not by Metastasio are marked with an asterisk. To the latter belong, for instance, "Non è terribile" (I, 8), "Chi da un bel volto amato" (I, 10), "Leon ne la foresta" (II, 15). Such substitute arias, etc., were probably by Domenico Lalli.   SCHATZ 8391

L'Issipile. Dramma da rappresentarsi in musica nel Teatro privilegiato vicino alla corte nell' autunno dell' anno 1760.

Vienna d'Austria, Stamperia di Ghelen, n. d. Unpaged. 16cm.

Three acts. By Metastasio, who is not mentioned. Argument, cast, and name of Giuseppe **Scarlatti**, who is mentioned as composer.   SCHATZ 9548

— Hypsipile. Ein musicalisch-theatralisches schau-spiel, so in Wien auf der privilegirten Schaubuehne naechst der Burg sur herbstzeit aufgefuehret worden, im jahr 1760. Verfasset von herrn abbate Metastasio . . . und in das teutsche uebersetzt von J. A. E. v. G.

[Wien], mit von Ghelischen schriften, n. d. Unpaged. 15½cm.

Three acts. Translated by Johann Anton, edler von Ghelen. Argument, cast, and name of Giuseppe **Scarlatti** as the composer.   SCHATZ 9549

Ist's nicht die eine, so ist's die andere. A. T. of Lorazi's Der kapellmeister.

L'Italia rigenerata, ballet. *See* Cristiani's L'amante democratico.

L'Italia rigenerata, ballet. *See* Zingarelli's Meleagro.

L'Italiana in Londra. Intermezzo in musica a cinque voci da rappresentarsi nel Teatro Valle dell' illm̃i Signori Capranica. Nel carnevale dell' anno 1779 . . .

Roma, Agostino Palombini, 1779. 48 p. 15½ᶜᵐ.

Two acts. Author not mentioned and unknown to Schatz. Cast and name of Domenico **Cimarosa** as composer. ML 50.2.I8C2

— **L'Italiana in Londra.** Opera in musica da rappresentarsi nel Picolo Teatro di S. A. S. di Brunsuic-Luneburg.

Brunsuic, n. publ., 1781. 151 p. 16ᶜᵐ.

Two acts, with name of the composer, **Cimarosa.** Author unknown to Schatz. German title-page, "Die Italienerin zu London," and text face Italian.
First performed, as indicated, in 1781; at Rome, Teatro Valle, 1779.

SCHATZ 1939

— **L'Italiana in Londra.** Commedia per musica da rappresentarsi nel Teatro Nuovo sopra Toledo per quart' opera di questo corrente anno 1794.

Napoli, n. publ., 1794. 43 p. 15ᶜᵐ.

Two acts. Author unknown to Schatz. Cast and notice to the public that this opera, by **Cimarosa**, has never before been performed at Naples, and that
"vi si è aggiunto un quartetto nel primo atto, che prima non vi era, e due arie nuove dell' istesso maestro. Tutto il dippiù della musica non si è punto alterato giacchè la medesima ha sempre sortito un' esito felice in tutti que' luoghi ove si è rappresentata." SCHATZ 1938

— Die **Italienerin zu London.** Eine komische oper in 2. aufzuegen. Nach dem italiaenischen frey bearbeitet von H. C. Pleissner . . . [vignette].

Frankfurt am Mayn, Johann Georg Fleischer, 1783. 91, [1] p. 16ᶜᵐ.

Two acts, with Heinrich Christian Pleissner's dedication to Grossmann, the director of the "Chur-Coellnische Hof-Schauspielergesellschaft," to which Pleissner appears to have belonged "seit . . . drei jahren."
First performed at Bonn, Hoftheater, 1783. SCHATZ 1941

— Gesaenge aus dem singspiele: Die **Italienerin zu London,** in zwey aufzuegen, nach dem italienischen. In musik gesezt von Cimarosa.

Hamburg, J. M. Michaelsen, 1789. 36 p. 14½ᶜᵐ.

German version in two acts by Johann Christoph Bock.
First performed at Hamburg, Theater beim Gänsemarkt, July 3, 1789; at Weimar, Hoftheater, Oct. 7, 1786. SCHATZ 1940

L'Italiano maritato a Parigi, ballet. *See* Bianchi's Pizzarro.

Die **Italienerin zu London.** Tr. of Cimarosa's L'Italiana in London.

L'ivrogne corrigé ou Le mariage du diable.

In 1759 at the Foire St. Laurent this was performed (text by Anseaume) with music adapted by **Laruette** to popular airs and vaudevilles. (*See* Schatz 5434, "L'yvrogne corrigé.") For Vienna, 1760, **Gluck** then arranged and partly composed this anew.
The Vienna, 1760, libretto not in L. of C.

L'ivrogne corrigé—Continued.

— Der **letzte rausch**, ein singspiel in zwei aufzuegen nach dem franzoesischen l'yrogne [!] corrigé des herrn Anseaume. Die musik ist von hrn. ritter Gluck.

Mannheim, C. F. Schwan, 1780.   56 p.   15½ᶜᵐ.

Translator not mentioned and unknown to Schatz. The "Anmerkung" on p. 2 reads:

"Zu der musik des hrn. de la Ruette ist diese uebersetzung nicht zu brauchen. Diejenignen also, welche die Gluckische musik nicht haben, und das stueck nach der franzoesischen composition geben wollen, müssen solche nach der am ende angehaengten uebersetzung einrichten." [p. 49–56]

This refers to the first act, scenes 3, 4, and 5, including the Vaudeville.

First performed at Vienna, Nationaltheater, 1781, by the pupils of I. H. F. Müller's Theaterpflanzschule   SCHATZ 3909

Ixion.   *See* Destouches and Lalande's ballet Les élémens.

Jack the gyant queller.   O. T. of Little John and the giants.

Die **jagd,** eine komische oper in zween aufzuegen.   Auf der kais. koenigl. privil. deutschen Schaubuehne aufgefuehret im jahre 1766.

Wien, Johann Paul Krauss, n. d.   48 p.   15ᶜᵐ.

The dedication begins: "So soll ich es denn wagen meine komische oper drucken zu lassen" and renders it clear that the author was a "junger theatralischer dichter." Composer not mentioned.   SCHATZ 11456

Die **jagd.**   Eine komische oper in drey aufzuegen.

Leipzig, Dyckische buchhandlung, 1770.   5 p. l., 220 p.   15½ᶜᵐ.

Neither the author, Christian Felix Weisse, nor the composer, Johann Adam **Hiller,** is mentioned.   On verso of t.-p. the note: "Dieses stueck ist zum theil aus dem lustspiele *La partie de chasse de Henri IV.* [by Collé] genommen." The other p. l. contain Weisse's dedicatory poem to Anna Amalia von Sachsen-Weimar und Eisenach, praising her for her protection of German histrionic art.

First performed at Weimar, Kleines Schlosstheater, January 29, 1770.

SCHATZ 4721

— Die **jagd.**   Eine komische oper in drey aufzuegen.

C. F. Weisse, Komische opern, Carlsruhe, 1778, t. iii, 134 p.   18½ᶜᵐ.

On p. [2] the note: "Dieses stueck ist zum theil aus dem lustspiele: *La partie de chasse de Henri IV* genommen." The composer, **Hiller,** is not mentioned.

ML 49.A2W2

Die **jagd.**   Eine komische oper in zwey aufzuegen nach Colle und Weise.   Fuer das kaiserl. koenigl. Hoftheater.   Die musik ist von hrn. Schenk.

Wien, Christoph Peter Rehm, 1799.   80 p.   15½ᶜᵐ.

By Karl Friedrich Hensler, who is not mentioned.

First performed at the Kaerntnerthor Theater, May 7, 1799.   SCHATZ 9597

Der **jahrmarkt.**   Eine komische oper in zwei aufzuegen.

Leipzig, Verlag der Dykischen buchhandlung, 1778.   102 p.   16½ᶜᵐ.

By Friedrich Wilhelm Gotter, who says in his "Nachricht" (p. [3]), dated Gotha, February, 1778:

"Das gegenwaertige stueck wird schon, seit eingien jahren, auf verschiedenen theatern im manuskript aufgefuehrt.   Auch ist der klavierauszug von der dazu gehoerigen [Georg] **Benda** ischen musik, unter der benennung von *Dorfjahrmarkt,* im naemlichen verlag erschienen.   Diese verschiedenheit des titels wird hoffentlich niemanden irre machen, und so wenig, als eine oder die andere abweichung im text, einer besonderer eroerterung beduerfen."

Der jahrmarkt—Continued.

The "Vorbericht" of the vocal score as published by Dyk at Leipzig in 1776 helps to give precision to Gotter's rather vague "Nachricht." The Vorbericht reads in translation:

"This comic opera by herr Gotter originally had but one act. Afterwards the opera was divided into two acts and herr [Joh. Adam] Hiller, at the request of his friend, herr Benda, composed the song at the end of the first act and the introductory chorus of the second. Some time afterwards a new actor in Seyler's Theater, for which the piece originally had been written, took the part of the colonel, and in order to recommend him also as a vocalist to the public, the herren Engel and Hiller wrote the arias p. 22 and p. 68 [of the vocal score], Engel the text and Hiller the music. With permission of the herren Benda and Gotter, these additional numbers are included in the vocal score, made by Hiller out of friendship for me and the author of the opera . . ."

The text of the 1778 publication is practically identical with that of the vocal score of 1776 (including Engel's contributions), and therefore does not represent the opera as it was first performed at Gotha, Schlosstheater, February 10, 1775, in one act. The first performance at Leipzig took place at the Koch'sches Theater am Rannstaedter Thor, April 25, 1775, and at Hamburg, Theater auf dem Gänsemarkt, May 8, 1776. The opera also became known under the title of "Lukas (Lucas) und Bärbchen." ML 50.2.J2B2

Second copy. Schatz 772

— Arien und gesaenge zum **Dorfjahrmarkt.**
n. i., 1790. 16 p. 16½ cm.
First performed at Mannheim, Nationaltheater, February 13, 1780. Schatz 773

Der **jahrmarkt zu Gruenwald.** A. T. of Th. Weigl's Die mario-nettenbude.

Der **jahrmarkt zu Magerndorf.** Tr. of Fischietti's Il mercato di Malmantile.

Der **jahrmarkt zu Malmantile.** Tr. of Fischietti's Il mercato di Malmantile.

Der **jahrmarkt zu Venedig.** Tr. of Salieri's La fiera di Venezia.

Jakob und Benjamin, aufgefuehrt von den schuelern der zweyten classe an dem Katholischen schulhause bey St. Salvator im monate May 1784.
Augsburg, Joseph Simon Hueber, n. d. [15] p. 19½ cm.
"Singspiel" in two acts. "Die musik ist vom herren Michael **Demmler**" (p. 2). With cast. The author is not mentioned, and is unknown to Schatz. At head of this title: "Die sieben heil. schlaefer, ein geistliches schauspiel in dreyen aufzuegen-und." Schatz 2506

Die **Jakobiner in Deutschland.** A. T. of Kauer's Gute menschen lieben ihren fuersten.

Le **jaloux dupé.** A. T. of Apell's L'amour peintre.

Le **jaloux puni** ou La serenade. Entrée in Bourgeois's Les plaisirs de la paix.

Le **jaloux puni.**
Le Nouveau théatre italien, Paris, 1753, t. iii, 61–75 p.
"Divertissement" at the end of the first act of the comedy, "Le jaloux," performed by the Comédiens italiens ordinaires du roi, December 23, 1723. The text of "Le jaloux puni" is by de Beauchamp; the music (*en vaudevilles*) composed or arranged by **Mouret.**

Le jaloux trompé. Entrée in Fragments de Monsieur Lully.

Jamie and Bess, or, The laird in disguise; a Scots pastoral comedy, in imitation of the Gentle shepherd. Second edition.

1 p. l., xv–xxvii, [2], 30–185 p. 22cm. (Poems, chiefly in the Scotish dialect, by Andrew Shirrefs, Edinburgh, Printed for the author, 1790.)

Five acts, prologue, and epilogue. Cast, address to the critics, and "An address in Scotch . . . spoken by Mr. Briarly, previous to the representation of Jamie and Bess, January 12, 1788." After the epilogue, an "Address to his crutch" was sung, the music from "forty pieces of original music inscribed to the Right Honourable David, Earl of Buchan." The whole was in the nature of a ballad opera, the 12 airs used all being Scotch tunes.   LONGE 283

Janguir. Tr. of Zeno's text Gianguir.

Janus. *See* Keiser's Der bey dem allgemeinen welt-friede . . . geschlossene tempel des . . .

Le jardinier de Sidon, tire des Oeuvres de M. de Fontenelle, comédie en deux actes, mêlée d'ariettes, représentée pour la premiere fois, par les Comédiens italiens ordinaires du roi, le lundi 18 juillet 1768.

Paris, Claude Herissant, 1768. 34 p. 19cm.

In the *avertissement* the anonymous editor of the piece says that the "véritable auteur" is de Fontenelle, that the piece is now performed thirteen years after his death, and that a comparison with de Fontenelle's "Abdolonime" will show just how he, the editor, modified his model in deference to the exigencies of theatrical action.

Schatz attributes the text to R. T. Regnard de Pleinchêne. The composer, François André Danican **Philidor,** is not mentioned.   SCHATZ 8015

— Le jardinier de Sidon, tiré des Oeuvres de M. de Fontenelle. Comédie en deux actes, meslée d'ariettes. Représentée pour la premiere fois par les Comédiens italiens ordinaires du roi, le lundi 18 juillet 1768.

Paris, Claude Herissant, 1770. 32 p. 19cm.

Neither author nor **Philidor,** the composer, mentioned.   SCHATZ 11739

— Der gaertner von Sidon, ein singspiel in zween aufzuegen aus dem franzoesischen uebersetzt mit musik.

Frankfurt am Mayn, mit Andreaeischen schriften 1773. 56 p., 13 p. (folded music).

Cast. Version used by Theob. Marchand's company; by Johann Heinrich Faber. Neither he nor **Philidor** is mentioned. The music consists of "Meinen garten will das Geschick" (I, 2, "Laisser là mon jardin"), "Glaubt, die meisten freunde" (II, 6, "Je compare les amis"), "Glücklich ist der, den die sorgen" (II, 7, "Trop heureux qui peut").   SCHATZ 8016

Le jardinier et son seigneur, opéra comique, en un acte et en prose, par M. Sedaine.

Paris, par la Compagnie des libraires, 1769. 35 p. 19cm.

The composer, **Philidor,** is not mentioned.   SCHATZ 11740

— Le jardinier et son seigneur, opéra comique, en un acte, en prose, mêlé de morceaux de musique: représenté sur le Théâtre de la Foire Saint-Germain, le mercredi 18 février 1761. Par M. Sedaine. La musique de M. Philidor.

Paris, Claude Hérissant, 1785. 38 p. 18cm.

On p. 36–38 the airs of "Laissez la grandeur qui brille" and "La beauté dans vos yeux." Cast.   SCHATZ 8017

La **jardinier supposé.** A. T. of Philidor's L'amant déguisé.

Les **jardiniers,** comédie en deux actes et en prose, meslée d'ariettes; par M. Davesne: Représentée pour la premiere fois par les Comédiens italiens ordinaires du Roi, le 15 juillet 1771 . . .

> *Paris, la veuve Duchesne, 1772. 52 p. 19ᶜᵐ.*

> Cast. The composer, **Prudent,** is not mentioned. On p. 50–52 the air of the "Romance. Lorsque j'avois du chagrin," (II, 8). Schatz 8475
> Second copy. Yudin PQ

Les **jardins de l'Hymen.** A. T. of La rose.

Jason, oder Die eroberung des gueldenen fluesses, in einem musicalischen schau-spiele auf dem Hamburgischen Theatro vorgestellet im jahr 1720.

> *[Hamburg], Caspar Jakhel, n. d. Unpaged. 19ᶜᵐ.*

> Three acts. Neither the author, resp. translator, Friedrich Christian Bressand, is mentioned, nor Reinhard **Keiser,** the composer. Several Italian arias by others were interpolated. Their text has been added to the German. The text was based partly on the opera, "Giasone overo La conquista del velo d'oro," partly on Bressand's "Die unglückliche liebe des tapferen Jasons." Schatz 5097

Jason, ou La toison d'or, tragedie representée par l'Academie royale de musique l'an 1696. Les paroles sont de M. Rousseau, & la musique de M. Collasse. XXXVII. opera.

> *n. i., n. d. front., 233–290 p. 14ᶜᵐ. (Recueil général des opéra, Paris, 1703, t. 5.)*

> Detached copy. Five acts with prologue.
> First performed, as indicated, Jan. 6, 1696. Schatz 2100
> Second copy. ML 48.R4

The **jealous clown:** or, The lucky mistake. An opera (of one act) as perform'd at the New theatre in Goodman's-Fields. By Thomas Gataker, Gent. To which is annex'd the musick.

> *London, Henry Parker, 1730. 24 p. 19ᶜᵐ.*

> Cast and dedicatory poem to the author on his "maiden works," by T. Keen, dated Doctors Commons, December 14, 1730. Ballad-opera, the airs to the 13 songs of which are indicated by title. The music is not annexed to this copy.
> Longe 136

Jean Jacques Rousseau dans son hermitage. A. T. of the pasticcio La vallée de Montmorency.

Jeannette, eller Den fortraengte ubekiendte. Tr. of Anfossi's L'incognita perseguitata.

Jeannot et Jeannette. A. T. of Les ensorcelés.

Jephté. Tragedie tirée de l'Ecriture Sainte; représentée pour la premiere fois par l'Academie royale de musique, le quatrième mars 1732. Remise le vingt-sixième fevrier 1733.

> *Paris, Jean Baptiste Christophe Ballard, 1738. xvi, 57 p. 22½ᶜᵐ.*

> Prologue and five acts. Cast. Neither the author, Simon Joseph de Pellegrin, is mentioned, nor the composer, Michel **Montéclair.** On p. iii–v a preface in which the author says:
> "Ce n'a pas été sans trembler, que j'ay entrepris de mettre sur le Théâtre de l'Académie royale de musique, un sujet tiré de l'Ecriture-Sainte: Des amis judicieux avoient beau me représenter que ce genre de tragédie n'étoit nouveau que par rap-

Jephté—Continued.

port au lieu, où j'allois l'introduire, & que ces matières respectables étoient encore plus propres au chant qu'à la simple déclamation; j'avois la prévention à combattre: et la prévention ne se donne pas la peine de raisonner.''

He then continues to answer the objections of his critics in detail.

"Pour ce qui regarde le ballet dont on faisoit un obstacle insurmontable, je ne comprens pas surquoy on pouvoit se fonder, pour l'exclure de ma tragedie. L'art de danser n'est-il pas de tous les temps, & ne convient-il pas à tous les peuples? La nation juive ne s'y adonnoit-elle pas autant que toutes les autres . . . La fille de Jephté n'alla-t-elle pas audevant de son père, vainqueur des Ammonites, avec des tambourins & des danses? . . .''

The printed score has as date of first performance (followed by the reference books), February 28, 1732.   ML 50.2.J3M6

— **Jephté**, tragedie, tirée de l'Ecriture Sainte; representée par l'Academie royale de musique, l'an 1732. Paroles de M. Pellegrin. Musique de M. Monteclair. CXV. opera.

n. i., n. d. pl., 51–120 p. 14ᶜᵐ. (Recueil général des opéra, Paris, 1739, t. xv.)

Detached copy. Prologue and five acts. On p. 53–57 the same preface as in the 1738 ed.   SCHATZ 6590

Second copy. ML 48.R4

Jerosme et Fanchonnette, pastorale de la Grenouillere, en un acte. Par M. Vadé. Représentée pour la premiere fois sur le Théâtre de l'Opera-comique le 18 février 1755. Nouvelle édition.

Paris, Duchesne, 1757. 42, [6] p. 19½ᶜᵐ.

On the [6] p. "Catalogue de théatres."

En vaudevilles. Cast. On p. 39–40 the airs of the duo "Quand l'amour fait d'l' ouvrage" and of the rondo "L'amour a sur la riviere." The arranger of the music unknown to me.   ML 50.2.J4

— **Jerosme et Fanchonette**, pastorale de la Grenouillere, en un acte. Par M. Vadé. Representée, pour la premiere fois, sur le Théatre de l'Opéra-comique le 18 février 1755.

La Haye, Pierre Gosse junior, 1760. 45, [1] p. 16ᶜᵐ. (Vadé, Oeuvres, La Haye, 1759, t. iii.)

En vaudevilles. Cast. On the unnumbered p. the *air noté* of the duo, "Quand l'Amour fait d'louvrage."   ML 49.A2V2

— **Compliment de la clôture** de la Foire S. Laurent, 1755. Suivi de celui de la Foire S. Germain de la même année. Tous deux chantés à la fin de *Jerôme et Fanchonette* le 6 octobre 1755.

La Haye, Pierre Gosse, junior, 1759. 16 p. 16ᶜᵐ. (Vadi, Oeuvres La Haye, 1759, t. III.)

Cast. On p. 14–16, "Autre compliment chanté à l'Opera comique à la clôture de la Foire S. Laurent."

Jery und Bätely. Ein singspiel. Von Goethe. Ächte ausgabe.

Leipzig, Georg Joachim Göschen, 1790. 1 p. l., 56 p. 17½ᶜᵐ.

One act. Edition without "Göschen's Schriften," and with "zurück tretend" on p. 52 in two words.   PT 1958.J5 1790

— **Jery und Bätely.** Ein singspiel. Von Goethe. Ächte ausgabe.

Leipzig, Georg Joachim Göschen, 1790. 1 p. l., 56 p. 17½ᶜᵐ.

One act. Edition without "Göschen's Schriften," and with "zurücktretend" on p. 52 in one word. Goethe's singspiel had been first performed with music by Carl Siegmund, freiherr von Seckendorff at Weimar, July 12, 1780. PT 1958.J5 1790a

Le jeune-vieillard. Pièce en trois actes, tirée des *Contes Persans*. Representée à la Foire de S. Laurent 1722. par les Comediens italiens de S. A. R. Monseigneur le duc d'Orleans régent.

Le Théâtre de la foire, Paris, 1724, t. v, pl., [141]–268 p. 17^{cm}.

Prose play by Le Sage, Fuzelier, and d'Orneval. The few incidental musical numbers were composed by Jean Joseph **Mouret**. The airs are printed in the "Table des airs" at the end of the volume. ML 48.L2V

Les jeunes mariés. Opera comique en un acte. Par Mr. Parmentier.

La Haye, Pierre Gosse junior, 1751. 72, [7] p. 16½^{cm}.

Prose and vaudevilles. The [7] p. contain the airs of the "Menuet de L'esprit folet—Qu'il est charmant," "Musette nouvelle de Mr. de **Blaise**—Qu'il m'est doux d'être votre époux," "Musette de Monsieur **Rochar**—Tout suit dans l'univers," and the vaudeville—"A trente ans jadis une fille." Both Parfaict and Font (also Schatz) attribute the text, not to Parmentier, but to Favart, and claim that it was first performed at the Foire St. Laurent August, 1740 (Font), July 1, 1740 (Parfaict). Font says that the next entry is a "reprise avec remaniements" of the 1740 play. At any rate, the differences between the 1755 version and that of 1751 are so slight as to be hardly noticeable. SCHATZ 11715

— **Les jeunes mariés,** opera-comique en un acte. Représenté sur le Théatre de la Foire S. Germain, le 15 mars 1755. Nouvelle édition.

Paris, Duchesne, 1757. 56 p. 19^{cm}. (Theatre de M. Favart, Paris, Duchesne, 1763–77, t. vii.)

Several of the airs are printed in the text. ML 49.A2F1

— **Les jeunes mariés,** opera-comique en un acte. Représenté sur le Théatre de la Foire S. Germain, le 15 mars 1755.

Paris, la veuve Duchesne, 1767. 64 p. 19^{cm}.

On p. 49–62, seventeen unaccompanied "Airs des jeunes mariés." SCHATZ 11495

La jeunesse ou L'amour ingenu. Entrée in Campra's Les ages, ballet.

Les jeux olympiques. Entrées in Colin de Blamont's Les festes grecques et romaines.

The jew decoy'd; or The progress of a harlot. A new ballad opera of three acts. The airs set to old ballad tunes.

London, E. Rayner, E. Nutt [etc], 1733. 53 p. (incl. front.) 16^{cm}.

Three acts and introduction. Table of the 17 songs, the airs of which are indicated by title in the text. Of this ballad opera, founded on Hogarth's prints, no author and no performance recorded by Clarence. LONGE 73

Joas, ein koenig der Juden. Tr. of Michl's Gioas rè di Giuda.

Le jockei, comédie en un acte et en prose, mêlée d'ariettes; représentée sur le Théâtre de l'Opéra-comique, ci-devant Théâtre italien, le 16 nivôse, l'an IV, (6 janvier 1796, vieux style.). Paroles du citoyen **Hoffman.** Musique du citoyen **Solié.**

Paris, Vente, an IVe (1796 vieux style.) 29 p. 19½^{cm}.

ML 50.2.J6S6

Johann, der muntere seifensieder. Ein deutsches singspiel in drey aufzuegen von Wilhelm Rothammer.

Wien, Franz Anton Hoffmeister, 1791. 71 p. 16^{cm}.

Not recorded by Schatz, Riemann, Towers.   SCHATZ 11626

Jordens lyksalighed. A. T. of Sarti's Astrea tilfredsstillet.

Joseph, der unterkoenig in Aegypten, von seinen bruedern erkannt, ein singspiel in zween aufzuegen, aufgefuehrt von der studirenden jugend des katholischen schulhauses zu Augsburg bey St. Salvator. den 4, 5, und 6 ten Herbsmondes [Sept.] 1785.

[Augsburg], Joseph Simon Hueber, n. d. 18 p. 20^{cm}.

With cast, "Vorbericht," and name of the composer, Johann Evangelist **Drexel.** The author is unknown to Schatz. The singspiel was preceded by "Georgius, der grosse heilige martyrer, ein trauerspiel."   SCHATZ 2817

Le joueur. Parody of Orlandini's Il giocatore.

The jovial crew. A comic opera. As it is acted at the Theatre-Royal, by His Majesty's servants . . . With the music prefix'd to each song.

London, J. Watts, 1731. 4 p. l., 68 p. 20^{cm}.

Three acts. Author unknown. The p. l. contain a 2 p. list of "Books printed for J. Watts." Cast, table of the fifty-three songs, and "advertisement," which reads in part:

"It may be perhaps necessary to inform the world, that the groundwork of this piece is an old comedy of Richard Brome's; the prose part of it consisting chiefly of fragments, collected from the *Merry beggars*, and so disposed as to introduce the songs with propriety. The songs, (except about half a dozen) were written about three years ago, by a gentleman who is since dead. This circumstance is mentioned here only to obviate some idle rumours which have been spread about relating to the author . . ."

The "idle rumours" perhaps refer to the statement, recorded also by Baker and Schatz, that the interpolations were written by Edward Roome, Matthew Concanen, and Sir William Yonge.

Ballad opera, the airs being printed in the text with their titles.

Performed at Drury Lane February 8, 1731.   ML 50.5.J6

— **The jovial crew:** or, The merry beggars. A comic opera. As it is performed at the Theatre-Royal in Covent-Garden. A new edition, with additional songs, and alterations.

London, J. and R. Tonson, 1767.

Three acts. Cast. This edition has only 43 "airs," without music and without even the titles of the airs. Schatz enters under "The jovial crew or The merry beggars" an opera by William **Bates,** London, Covent Garden, February 14, 1760." The present libretto may be a later edition of this (according to Schatz) revised text of "The jovial crew." Grove records under Bates: "The ladies' frolic, an alteration of The jovial crew (jointly with Dr. **Arne**) 1770." Cummings lists under Arne both "The jovial crew" (1769) and "The ladies' frolic" (1770). The vocal score mentions as composers Bates *and* Arne.   LONGE 27

Die jubelhochzeit. Eine komische oper in drey aufzuegen.

Leipzig, Dyckische buchhandlung, 1773. 208 p. 15½^{cm}.

Neither the author, Christian Felix Weisse, nor the composer, Johann Adam **Hiller,** is mentioned.

First performed at Hamburg, Theater beim Gänsemarkt, November 2, 1774, as "Das jubelfest;" April 5, 1773, at Berlin, Theater in der Behrenstrasse.   SCHATZ 4722

The **judgment of Paris.** An English burletta. In two acts. As it is performed at the Theatre-Royal in the Hay-Market. The music composed by Mr. Barthelemon . . .

London, T. Becket and P. A. De Hondt, 1768. 34 p. 19^{cm}*.*

Two acts. By Ralph Schomberg, who is not mentioned. Cast and dedication. First performed 1768, as indicated.　　　　　　　　　　　　　LONGE 52

The **judgment of Paris;** or, The triumph of beauty. A pastoral ballad opera of one act. As it is perform'd at the Theatre-Royal in Lincoln's-Inn-Fields . . .

London, Printed and sold by J. Roberts, 1731. 2 p. l., 15 p. 18^{cm}*.*

The 19 airs used are indicated by title. Author not recorded by Clarence. First performed May 6, 1731.　　　　　　　　　　　　　　　LONGE 290

Judith, oder Der entsatz Bethuliens. Ein singspiel in zweyen choeren nach dem herrn abte Metastasio.

Page [3–14] (20^{cm}.) of "Die niederlage der Hunnen vor Augsburg. Ein trauerspiel in dreyen aufzuegen, aufgefuehrt von der studirenden jugend des katholischen schulhauses zu Augsburg bey St. Salvator den 4. 5. und 6. herbstmondes [Sept. 4–6], 1780. Gedruckt bei Joseph Simon Hueber . . ."
Two acts with cast. Johann Michael **Demler** is mentioned as the composer. The translator is not mentioned and is unknown to Schatz. Translated from Metastasio's "La Betulia liberata."　　　　　　　　　　　SCHATZ 2507

Le **jugement de Midas,** comédie. En trois actes et prose: melée d'ariettes, représentée pour la premiere fois par les Comédiens italiens, ordinaires du roi, le samedi 27 juin 1778. Par Monsieur d'Hele. Musique de M. Gretry.

Paris, Ruault, 1778. 52 p. 19^{cm}*.*

Cast.　　　　　　　　　　　　　　　　　　　　　　ML 50.2.J9G7

— Le **jugement de Midas,** comédie en trois actes, en prose, mêlée d'ariettes, par M. d'Hèle; représentée pour la première fois par les Comédiens italiens ordinaires du Roi, le samedi 27 juin 1778. Musique de M. Grétry.

Paris, la veuve Duchesne, 1779. 64 p. 18½^{cm}*.*

Cast.　　　　　　　　　　　　　　　　　　　　　　SCHATZ 4161

— Das **urtheil der Midas,** eine operette in drey aufzuegen. Aus dem franzoesischen des hrn. d'Hèle. Die musik ist von hrn. Gretry.

Muenster, Philipp Heinrich Perrenon, 1781. 72 p. 16½^{cm}*.*

By Rothmann, who is not mentioned.　　　　　　　　　　　SCHATZ 4162

— Das **urtheil des Midas.** Komische oper, in drei aufzuegen. Nach dem franzoesischen. Mit beibehaltung der Gretryschen musik von Ch. F. v. B——n [Bonin], und von J. André. Zum erstenmal in Berlin aufgefuehrt den 9ten julius 1781.

n. i., n. d.　p. [148]–230. 15½^{cm}*.*

Detached copy.
First performed at Berlin, Döbbelinsches Theater, July 9, 1781.　SCHATZ 4163

— Gesaenge aus dem **Urtheile des Midas,** einer komischen oper **in** drey akten. In die musik gesetzt von Gretry.

Mitau, Johann Friedrich Steffenhagen, 1783. 39 p. 16^{cm}*.*

German translation by Christian Gottlob Neefe.
First performed at Bonn, Churf. Köln. Hoftheater, February 21, 1781.
　　　　　　　　　　　　　　　　　　　　　SCHATZ **4164**

Le jugement de Paris.   Pastorale héroique, représentée par l'Academie royale de musique, l'an 1718.   Paroles de Monsieur Pellegrin-
Barbier.   Musique de M. Bertin.   XLIV. opera.

*n. i., n. d.   pl., 259–316 p.   14ᶜᵐ.   (Recueil genéral des opéra,
Paris, 1734, t. xii.)*

Detached copy. Prologue and three acts. The text was by Simon Joseph de
Pellegrin and Marie Anne Barbier.
First performed according to Schatz on June 14, 1718, but the score gives June 21,
1718.   · SCHATZ 880
                                      Second copy. ML 48.R4

— Le **jugement de Paris.**   Pièce d'un acte.   Par Monsieur
D'Or * *.   Représentée à la Foire de Saint Laurent 1718.

Le Théâtre de la foire, Paris, 1737, t. iii, pl., [61]–93 p.   17ᶜᵐ.

By d'Orneval. The airs, selected or composed and arranged by Jean Claude
Gillier, the "compositeur" of the theatre, are printed at the end of the volume in the
"Table des airs." The piece was a parody of the pastorale héroïque of the same
title, by abbé Pellegrin, music by Bertin.   ML 48.L2III

Le jugement de Paris, ballet-pantomime en trois actes, par le
citoyen Gardel.   Musique d'Haydn, Plesyel [! Pleyel], et du citoyen
Méhul.   Donné pour la première fois sur le Théâtre de l'Academie
de musique, le 5 mars 1793, an II de la République.

Paris, la veuve Delormel, an VI [1797–98].   x, 21 p.   19ᶜᵐ.

Cast, detailed scene-by-scene synopsis, and avant-propos, in which Gardel says:
"J'ai toujours remarqué dans les ballets d'action que les effets de décorations, et
les divertissements variés et agréables, étoient ce qui attiriot le plus la foule des
spectateurs, et les vifs applaudissements; d'après cette remarque, j'ai cherché un
sujet qui pût se plier à faire valoir les grands talens que l'Opéra, de Paris seul, possède
en danse, et qui me permit d'étendre les idées que le hasard pourroit m'offrir: l'histoire
poétique est le terrein inépuisable que le maître de ballet doit cultiver . . ."
                                                              ML 52.2.J9

Le jugement de Paris—Das urtheil des Paris, ballet.   *See* Tozzi's
Zenobia.

Julchen und Peter.   Tr. of Weigl's Giulietta e Pierotto.

Julia.   A. T. of Keiser's Die durch verstellung . . . siegende liebe
oder . . .

Julie, comédie en trois actes, mêlée d'ariettes; par Mr. Monvel.   La
musique est de Mr. Des Aides.   Représentée pour la première fois
par les Comédiens italiens ordinaires du roi, le 22 septembre 1772.

Paris, La veuve Duchesne, 1773.   59 p.   19½ᶜᵐ.

At end, list of contents (3 p.) of F. J. Desoeur's "Recueil général des Opéra
bouffons," in seven volumes. On p. 58–59 (incorrectly numbered 69) the melody
of the final "Choeur. Le plaisir succède aux larmes."   SCHATZ 2520

— **Julie,** comédie en trois actes, mêlée d'ariettes; par Mr. Monvel,
la musique est de Mr. Des Aides.   Représentée pour la premiere fois
par les Comédiens italiens ordinaires du roi, le 22 septembre 1772.

Paris, la veuve Duchesne, 1775.   69 p.   17½ᶜᵐ.

Cast. On p. 68–69, the air of the final "Choeur": "Le plaisir succède aux larmes."
                                                              YUDIN PQ

Julie—Continued.

— **Julie,** ein singspiel in drey aufzuegen aus dem franzoesischen uebersetzt mit musik.

*Frankfurt am Mayn, mit Andreaeischen schriften, 1774. 128, 12 p. 15½*cm.

The 12 p. of music (folded. obl. engraved) contain melody and bass of the *"Arie.* Sanft schlief einst Lieschen in dem grase" (II, 1) and *"Arie* Ay, ay, ay, ay, **ay"** (III, 3). The translator, Johann Heinrich Faber, is not mentioned.

First performed at Frankfort o/M, Theater im Junghof, 1774.   SCHATZ 2521

— **Was einem recht, ist dem andern billig.** Ein singspiel in drey aufzuegen von Monvell. Nach einer freyen uebersetzung, **von** G. F. W. Grossmann. Die musik ist von Desaides.

*Frankfurt und Leipzig, Hermannische buchhandlung, 1783. 116 p. 16*cm.

First performed at Frankfort, Neues Schauspielhaus im Junghof, 1783.
     SCHATZ 2522

Julie oder Die dankbare tochter, ein lustspiel mit gesang. Von F. G. von Nesselrode. Die musik ist vom fuerstl. Taxischen operndirecteur hrn. Kirzinger.

*Regensburg, Montagische buchhandlung, 1780. 102 p. 16½*cm.

First performed 1780, as indicated.   SCHATZ 5339

Julie und Armidor. Tr. of Cimarosa's Giuletta ed Armidoro.

Julie und Romeo. L. T. of Benda's Romeo und Julie.

Julie und Romeo. Tr. of Zingarelli's Giulietta e Romeo.

Julius Caesar. *See* Keiser's Der durch den fall . . . erhoehete . . .

Julius Caesar i Aegypten. Tr. of Sarti's Cesare in Egitto.

Julius Caesar in Aegypten. *See* Händel's Giulio Cesare in Egitto.

Julius Sabinus. Tr. of Sarti's Giulio Sabino.

Dem **Jupiter abgelegte huldigung.**

*Unpaged. 19*cm.

At end: "Muenchen, gedruckt bey Maria Magdalena Riedlin, wittib, 1727." One act. Argument. Not recorded by Schatz.   SCHATZ 11628

Jupiter en Argos. Tr. of Lotti's Giove in Argo.

Jupiter et Calisto. *See* Mondonville's Les projets de l'amour.

Jupiter et Niobe. *See* Les amours des dieux.

Just in time. A comic opera, in three acts. As performed at the Theatre-Royal, Covent-Garden with the greatest applause. **Written** by Thomas Hurlstone.

*London, J. Debrett, n. d. 2 p. l., 67, [1] p. 20½*cm.

Publisher's book-list on last page. Cast, dedication dated November 27, 1792, and preface, in which the author calls this "his first dramatic bantling." Originally, he says, it was a two-act comedy, written at a very early age, for private perform-ance by a party of friends. The manuscript fell into Mr. Colman, sen.'s hands,

Just in time—Continued.

who agreed to produce it, if songs were added. This was done, but Colman's death prevented the performance. The piece was finally brought out for the benefit of Mr. Munden, May 10, 1792, at Covent Garden. The composer, Thomas **Carter**, is not mentioned. In Longman and Broderip's vocal score "When the lads and the lasses" is headed as "written and composed by Mr. **Johnstone**" and text of "Fell war" as written by Carter. LONGE 220

Justinus.   *See* Schieferdecker's Der von dem ackers-pflug zu den thron erhabene kaeyser Justinus.

Das kaestchen mit der chiffer.   Tr. of Salieri's La cifra.

Die kantons-revision.   Eine komische oper in drei aufzuegen von Ludwig v. Baczko.

>   *Koenigsberg, Hartung, 1794.   96 p.   15½ᶜᵐ.*

Wilhelm Ferdinand **Halter** is mentioned as the composer.
First performed at Koenigsberg, Ackermann'sches Schauspielhaus, 1794.

SCHATZ 4449

Der kapellmeister; oder Ist's nicht die eine, so ist's die andre. Ein komisches singspiel in zwey aufzuegen nach einem italiaenischen texte, und Lorazi's Komposition, von Bock.

>   *n. i., n. d.   p. [111]–196.   17ᶜᵐ.   (Komische opern der Italiener, Leipzig, 1781, Bd. I.)*

Detached copy.   Added to text, a 2 p. book list of the publisher.
First performed at Leipzig, Theater beim Rannstaedter Thore, October 14, 1779, and at Dresden, Churfuerstl. Kleines Theater, in the same year. This is a German version of Girolamo Lorazi's "Il maestro di cappella burlato," Rome, Teatro della Pace, carnival, 1777.   SCHATZ 5684

Der kapellmeister.   Tr. of Pergolesi's Il maestro di cappella.

Karoline oder Die parforcejagd, eine operette in vier aufzuegen.

>   *n. i., 1781.   84 p.   16½ᶜᵐ.*

Dedication to Friedrich, fuert zu Waldeck by Carl August Seidel.   Not recorded by Schatz, Riemann, Towers.   ML 50.2.K2

Kaspar der mundkoch.   A. T. of Schack's Die drey ringe.

Kaspars zoegling, oder Der sieg der bescheidenheit auf der insel des vergnuegens.   Ein original-singspiel in zween aufzuegen, für das kinderinstitut dieses theaters verfertiget von J. Perinet.   Die musik ist vom hrn. Ferdinand Kauer, lehrer der Marinellischen Singschule.

>   *Wien, Mathias Andreas Schmidt, 1791.   50 p.   17ᶜᵐ.*

Cast.
First performed, as indicated, February 1, 1791.   SCHATZ 5035

Der kaufmann von Smyrna, eine operette in einem aufzuge.   Die musik ist von herrn Holly in Prag.

>   *Frankfurth und Leipzig, n. publ., 1774.   36 p.   18ᶜᵐ.*

The author, Christian Friedrich Schwan, is not mentioned.
First performed at Berlin, Kochsches Theater in der Behrenstrasse, November 13, 1773.   SCHATZ 4770

Gesaenge aus dem singspiele: Der kaufmann von Smirna, in einem aufzuge, nach dem franzoesischen des herrn von Champfort, von Schwan.   In musik gesezt von Stegmann.

>   *Hamburg, Joh. Matthias Michaelsen, 1792.   15 p.   16½ᶜᵐ.*

First performed at Königsberg, Ackermann'sches Theater, 1773.   SCHATZ 10040

Der **kaufmann von Smyrna,** eine operette in einem aufzuge. Die musik ist von herrn G. Vogler.

Mannheim, C. F. Schwan, 1771. 75, [4] p. 15^{cm}.

The unnumbered pages contain a sale's catalogue of the publisher.

In a prefatory note dated Mannheim, July 22, 1771, C. F. Schwan, who was also the author of the piece, says:

"Das lustspiel, 'der Kaufmann von Smyrna,' so wie ich es vor einem jahre aus dem franzoesischen des hn. von Champfort uebersetzt, hat zwar gefallen; allein man setzte mit recht daran aus, dass es zu kurz sey. Ich habe diesem fehler dadurch abzuhelfen geglaubt, wenn ich es in eine operette verwandelte . . . Wegen den veraenderungen, die ich hie und da gemacht, werde ich mich wohl nicht entschuldigen duerfen. Es waere unschicklich gewesen, wenn Dornal und Amalie keine arien bekommen haetten, und wenn dieses seyn sollte, so musste ich sie allein auf das theater bringen und also eine scene einschalten. Den rechtsgelehrten habe ich mit vielem vorbedacht weggelassen. Ich finde es sehr unnatuerlich, wenn jemand sich selbst veraechtlich macht . . ."

First performed at Mannheim, Schauspielhaus auf dem Fruchtmarkt, 1771.

Schatz 10797

Kayser Hadrianus. *See* Broschi's Der in Syrien triumphirende . . .

The **Kentish barons:** a play in three acts. Interspersed with songs. By the Honourable Francis North. First performed at the Theatre-Royal, Hay-Market, Saturday, June 25th, 1791.

London, J. Ridgway, 1791. 2 p. l., 44 p. 19½^{cm}.

Cast. The composer is not mentioned, and is unknown to Schatz. Longe 216

Kierligheds-brevene. Et syngespil i tre acter af Charlotta Dorothea Biehl.

Kiøbenhavn, Nicolaus Møller, 1774. 72 p. 16^{cm}.

Cast. **Sarti,** the composer, is not mentioned.

First performed at Copenhagen, Courttheatre in Christiansborg Slot, March 22, 1775. Schatz 9446

Kildar, ballet. *See* Zingarelli's Il ratto delle Sabine.

Die **kinder der natur,** ein singspiel in zween aufzuegen nach dem französischen des Marivaux. Aufgeführt auf der K. K. National-schaubühne. Die musik ist von herrn Aspelmayer.

Wien, zu finden bey dem logenmeister, 1778. 47 p. 16^{cm}.

Author unknown to Schatz.

First performed on July 15, 1778, as indicated. Schatz 364

Kindliche liebe. Tr. of Gaveaux's L'amour filial.

King Arthur: or, The British worthy. A dramatick opera. Perform'd at the Qveens theatre by Their Majesties servants. Written by Mr. Dryden.

London, J. Tonson, 1691. 6 p. l., 51, [1] p. 22½^{cm}.

Five acts, prologue and epilogue. Cast and dedication to the marquis of Hallifax, largely an eulogy of Charles II. It reads, in part:

"This Poem was the last Piece of Service, which I had the Honour to do, for my Gracious Master, King Charles the Second: And though he liv'd not to see the Performance of it, on the Stage; yet the Prologue to it, which was the Opera of Albion and Albanius, was often practis'd before Him at Whitehal, and encourag'd by His Royal Approbation . . .

"In the mean time, while the Nation is secur'd from Foreign Attempts, by so powerful a Fleet, and we enjoy not only the Happiness, but even the Ornaments of Peace, in the Divertisement of the Town, I humbly offer you this Trifle, which if it succeed upon the Stage, is like to be the chiefest Entertainment of our Ladies and

King Arthur—Continued.

Gentlemen this Summer.   When I wrote it, seven Years ago, I employ'd some reading about it, to inform my self out of Beda, Bochartus, and other Authors, concerning the Rites and Customs of the Heathen Saxons; as I also us'd the little Skill I have in Poetry to adorn it.   But not to offend the present Times, nor a Government which has hitherto protected me, I have been oblig'd so much to alter the first Design, and take away so many Beauties from the Writing, that it is now no more what it was formerly, than the present Ship of the Royal Sovereign, after so often taking down, and altering, to the Vessel it was at the first Building.   There is nothing better, than what I intended, but the Musick; which has since arriv'd to a greater Perfection in England, than ever formerly; especially passing through the Artful Hands of Mr. [Henry] **Purcel,** who has Compos'd it with so great a Genius, that he has nothing to fear but an ignorant, ill-judging Audience.   But the Numbers of Poetry and Vocal Musick, are sometimes so contrary, that in many places I have been oblig'd to cramp my Verses, and make them rugged to the Reader, that they may be harmonious to the Hearer: Of which I have no Reason to repent me, because these sorts of Enter- tainment are principally design'd for the Ear and Eye; and therefore in Reason my Art on this occasion, ought to be subservient to his.   And besides, I flatter my self with an Imagination, that a Judicious Audience will easily distinguish betwixt the Songs, wherein I have comply'd with him, and those in which I have followed the Rules of Poetry, in the Sound and Cadence of the Words.   Notwithstanding all these Disadvantages, there is somewhat still remaining of the first Spirit with which I wrote it: . . ."

First performed 1691, as indicated.   ML 50.2.K54

— **King Arthur:** or, The British worthy. A masque. Altered from Dryden, by David Garrick, Esq. And now performed at the Theatre-Royal in Drury-Lane. The music by Purcell and Dr. Arne. The scenes by French and Carver.

London, W. Strahan, T. Lowndes, [etc.], 1781. 55 p. 21^{cm}.

Cast of 1781 and prefatory note:
"The names of Dryden and **Purcell** have made the following performance hitherto regarded as one of the best calculated to shew the effects of poetry, action and music . . .   The success of this, as well as of all other theatrical exhibitions, will wholly depend upon the present taste; but it is hoped, and believed, that two of our greatest geniuses in poetry and music, if they have justice done them upon the stage, bid fair for public approbation.—There are some slight alterations made, for the greater convenience of representation; and some few songs added, where it was thought such additions would be of service to the whole."

Detailed information on Arne's share in this new version will be found in Cum- mings' book on Arne.

First performed, as indicated, December 13, 1770.   Longe 251

King Pepin's campaign.   A burlesque opera, of two acts.   Acted at the Theatre Royal in Drury-Lane in the year 1745 [!]

London, W. Reeve, 1755. [!] 24 p: 19^{cm}.

Two acts. Cast. Neither William Shirley, the author, is mentioned, nor Thomas Augustine **Arne,** the composer.

First performed April 15, 1745, as indicated.   Longe 59
                                       Second copy.   Longe 204

The kingdom of the birds.   A. T. of Wonders in the sun.

Kiøbmanden som adelsmand, og bondepigen som frøken.   A. T of Piccinni's Bondehovmod.

Arien aus der operette Die kleine aehrenleserin.   Aus Weissens Kinder-freund.   In musick gesetzet von herrn Wittrock.   Nebst einem prolog von herrn Goedicke.

Luebeck, den 31 maerz 1785, n. publ. 16 p. 16^{cm}.

The operetta was followed by Gellert's comedy, "Die kranke frau."   Casts for both.   The "Prolog fuer Bernh. Aug. v. Wickede" consumes five pages of the sixteen.   Schatz 11068

Die **kleinen wagehaelse,** ein singspiel in zween aufzuegen, **von** den schuelern der dritten classe an dem katholischen schulhause bey St. Salvator aufgefuehrt im Maymonate 1785 zu Augsburg.

[Augsburg], Joseph Simon Hueber, n. d. 14 p. 19ᶜᵐ.

With "Vorbericht," cast, and name of the composer, Johann Evangelist **Drexel.** Preceded by "Die kinderzucht, ein lustspiel." Schatz 2818

Die **kleinmuehtige selbst-moerderin Lucretia** oder Die staatsthorheit des Brutus. Musicalisches trauer-spiel auf dem Hamburgischen Schau-platz aufgefuehret. Im jahr 1705.

n. i., n. d. Unpaged. 19ᶜᵐ.

Five acts. Lengthy historical "vorbericht," which reads, in part:

"Die fehler, so in den italiaenischen arien moechten angemercket werden, sind niemanden als dem verfasser dieser opera beyzumessen [Barthold Feind], denn er hat dem zuschauer lieber seine eigne gedancken in dieser sprache verkauffen, als die arbeit mit fremden federn schmuecken wollen, so viel wie moeglich hat er sich nach dem deutschen metro gerichtet, weil die caesur der ital. verse insgemein etwas hart klinget. Des Corneille *Lucrece* haben wir nicht gelesen, und die italiaenische comedie des Sigre dottore Bonnicelli hat uns eben so wenig als des cardinals Delfino *Lucrezia Romana*, so nur eine tragoedia Msta . . . dienen koennen . . . Wir koennen nicht erachten, was die Deutschen bissher abgeschreckt, ein schauspiel in ihrer muttersprache von dieser beruehmten liebes-geschichte zu verfertigen . . . Die aria im 4. auftritt der 4. handlung 'Hab ich ja zuviel verbrochen' ist des verfassers nicht, doch war von des hn. capellmeisters Kaeysers [Reinhard **Keiser**] composition, wie das gantze schauspiel."

First performed, as indicated, November 23, 1705. Schatz 5099

— Die **kleinmuehtige selbst-moerderin Lucretia.** Oder: Die staatsthorheit des Brutus. Musicalisches trauer-spiel.

Barth. Feind's Deutsche gedichte, Stade, 1708, pl., p. [175]–250. 17ᶜᵐ.

Five acts. Date for first performance as Hamburg, November 29, 1705, and same "Vorbericht."

The composer, Reinhard **Keiser,** is not mentioned. ML 49.A2F2

Das **kleinod Ceraunia von Ulissipone jetzo genannt Lisbona.** Tr. of La gemma Ceraunia . . .

Der **kluge Jakob.** Eine komische oper in drey akten von J. K. Wezel.

Leipzig, Dykische buchhandlung, 1787. 143 p. 15½ᶜᵐ.

The composer, freiherr von **Kospoth,** is not mentioned.

First performed at Berlin, National Theater, February 26, 1788. Schatz 5219

Arien und gesaenge aus dem singspiele: Der **kluge mann,** oder: Die drey wuensche, in einem aufzuge.

Hamburg, Friedrich Hermann Nestler, n. d. 15½ᶜᵐ.

Schatz enters this under Georg **Benda**'s "Der holzhauer," but "Der kluge mann" and "Der holzhauer" have nothing in common except a few of the characters, the sub-title, and the idea of the piece. In Benda's opera the main characters are called, "Valentin, der holzhauer; Brigitte, Valentins frau; Wilhelmine, Valentins tochter; Konrad, Wilhelminens liebhaber; Wenzel, ein alter Pächter; Der amtmann;" etc. In "Der kluge mann" the characters are: "Hanns, ein armer holzhauer; Grete, seine frau; Lieschen, seine tochter erster ehe; Conrad, ein junger bauer; Wenzel, ein reicher pächter; Der amtmann." It is now easy to see how Schatz was led to his entry, though the texts are absolutely different.

A singspiel of the title, "Der kluge mann," was performed at Berlin by Koch on March 30, 1774. Schatz 771

Koenig der elfen. A. T. of Wranitzky's Oberon.

Koenig Saul, ein singspiel in zween aufzuegen, aufgefuehrt von der studirenden jugend des Katholischen schulhauses bey St. Salvator in Augsburg den 3. 4. und 6 ten des herbstmonates [September] 1798.

[*Augsburg*], *Joseph Anton Hueber, n. d.* [*16*] *p.* *18ᶜᵐ.*

Cast and "Vorbericht," mentioning Matthäus **Fischer** as composer. At head of title, "Kaiser Mauritius, ein trauerspiel . . . und." SCHATZ 3222

Der **koenig Theodor.** Tr. of Paisiello's Il re Teodoro in Venezia.

Der **koenig Theodor in Venedig.** Tr. of Paisiello's Il re Teodoro in Venezia.

Der **koenig Theodor zu Venedig.** Tr. of Paisiello's Il re Teodoro in Venezia.

Der **koenig und der pachter.** Tr. of Monsigny's Le roi et le fermier.

Gesaenge zu dem heroisch-komischen singspiel in drey aufzuegen: Die **koenigin der Schwarzen inseln** als fortzetzung vom Wohlthaetigen derwisch. Die musik ist vom herrn Suessmaier, und nach dem bekannten, und beliebten *Spiegel von Arkadien,* auf dieses singspiel adaptirt, weil des grossen aufwandes, und der schweren besetzung weger der Spiegel nicht auf allen theatern kann gegeben werden.

n. i., 1797. *16 p.* *16½ᶜᵐ.*

Text probably by Johann Schwaldopler. Not recorded by Schatz.

ML 50.2.K7S9

Der koenigliche printz aus Pohlen, Sigismundus, oder Das menschliche leben wie ein traum in einem singe-spiel. Auf dem Hamburgischen schau-platz vorgestellet. 1693.

n. i., n. d. *Unpaged.* *17¼ᶜᵐ.*

Three acts. By Christian Heinrich Postel. Neither he is mentioned nor the composer, Johann Georg **Conradi.** Argument and "Bericht an den leser," in which Postel says:

"Diese erzehlte geschicht, oder vielmehr dieses gedicht, guenstiger leser, ist durch eine hollaendische feder erstlich in einer comoedie auf den schauplatz gefuehrt, und weil es von sonderbarer artigkeit, hat man es in eine opera, aber versichert nicht ohne grosse muehe wollen uemkleiden, ob es nun vergnuegung oder missbehagen erwecken werde, will man mit der zeit erwarten . . . Wo aber einer gedencket hier eine vollkommene version der hollaendischen comoedie zu finden, betriegt er sich, weil man aus derselben nur den verstand genommen, doch mit ein und andern zusaetzen denselben ausgeziert. Ist nun jemand, der meinet, dass solches uebel gethan, der versuch es auf eine andere art. Geraeth es ihm denn besser, wol! *Phillida solus habebit.*" SCHATZ 2179

Der koenigliche printz Regnerus. In einer opera auff dem Hamburgischen schau-platz vorgestellet.

[*Hamburg*], *Conrad Neumann, 1702.* *Unpaged.* *16½ᶜᵐ.*

Three acts. Neither the author is mentioned (unknown to Schatz) nor the composer, Johann Christian **Schieferdecker.** Argument and scenario.

First performed, as indicated, 1702. SCHATZ 9602

Der koenigssohn aus Ithaka. Eine grosse heroisch-komische oper in 2 aufzuegen. Verfasst von hrn. Emanuel Schikaneder. In musik gesetzt von hrn. Franz Anton Hoffmeister.

Wien, Franz Anton Hoffmeister, 1797. *100, [2] p.* *16½ᶜᵐ.*

First performed at Vienna, Theater auf der Wieden. June 27, 1795. SCHATZ 4750

Der koenigssohn aus Ithaka—Continued.

— Gesaenge aus dem singspiele: **Telemach,** in vier abtheilungen. (Neu bearbeitet). In musik gesezt von Hofmeister.

Hamburg, Friedrich Hermann Nestler, n. d. 48 p. 15^{cm}.

Schikaneder's text is hardly to be recognized in this version by unknown editor. First performed at Hamburg, Theater b. Gänsemarkt, January 26, 1797.

SCHATZ 4751

— Arien und gesaenge aus **Telemach, koenigssohn aus Ithaka.** Eine heroisch-komische oper in zwey aufzuegen. Die musik ist von Franz Anton Hofmeister.

Frankfurt am Main, n. publ., 1798. 32 p. 16½^{cm}.

Follows Schikaneder's original text (at least of the arias) fairly closely. First performed at Frankfurt a/M, Nationaltheater, 1798. SCHATZ 4753

— **Telemach, prinz von Ithaka.** Eine heroisch-komische oper in zwei aufzuegen. Ganz neu bearbeitet. Die musik ist von Hofmeister. Aufgefuehrt zum ersten male den 11. februar 1797 auf dem Hoftheater zu Weimar.

Weimar, Hoffmann, 1797. 119 p. 15^{cm}.

This version was by Christian August Vulpius (not mentioned), who left practically nothing of Schikaneder's text. SCHATZ 4752

Der kohlenbrenner, ein lustspiel mit gesang in einem aufzug von Ludwig Ysenburg von Buri.

Neuwied, Gehra und Haupt, 1789. 48 p. 14½^{cm}.

Text and music by the above. First performed at Neuwied, Hoftheater, 1779. SCHATZ 1422

Die kolonie. Tr. of Sacchini's La colonie.

Gesaenge aus der oper Der **kopf ohne mann.** Eine grosse heroisch-komische zauber-oper in zwey aufzuegen nach der geschichte frey bearbeitet von Joachim Perinet . . . Die musik ist vom herrn Joseph Woelfl . . .

Wien, n. publ., 1798. 32 p. 16^{cm}.

First performed at Vienna, Theater auf der Wieden, December 3, 1798.

SCHATZ 11106

Kora und Alonzo, ein drama mit musik vermischt. Nach Marmontels erzaehlung frei bearbeitet. Die musik ist von herrn Winter. Mit begnehmigung eines kurfuerstl. Buecher-censurkollegiums.

[München], Joh. Paul Voetter, n. d. Unpaged. 16^{cm}.

Two acts. By Franz Joseph Marius von Babo, who is not mentioned. First performed at Ratisbon, Thurn & Taxische Schaubuehne im Ballhause, 1781.

SCHATZ 11038

Die kranckende liebe oder Antiochus und Stratonica. German T. of Graupner's L'amore ammalato.

Der krieg. Ein lustspiel des herrn Goldoni als eine komische oper in drey akten.

Leipzig, Adam Friedrich Boehme, 1773. 182, [1] p. 15^{cm}.

Goldoni's comedy was "La guerra." Saal's translation of this, revised by Carl Wilhelm Ramler, had been unsuccessful. Christian Felix Weisse saved the situation by adding songs and intermezzi which Johann Adam **Hiller** composed. In this form as singspiel, "Der krieg" was first performed at Berlin, Theater in der Behrenstrasse, August 17, 1772 (Schatz). SCHATZ 4723

Kriegs-liste des Bias. Tr. T. of Draghi's Gli stratagemi di Biante.

Der kurze irrthum. *See* Dezède's L'erreur d'un moment.

Labino, e Carlotta. Farsa per musica di Gaetano Rossi da rappresentarsi nel nobilissimo Teatro Venier in San Benedetto l'autunno dell' anno 1799.

    n. i., n. d. 40 p. 18ᶜᵐ.

Cast and name of Johann Simon **Mayr** as the composer. Pasted on p. 4 a page with the substitute aria "Amore è un ragazzo" (I, 9).

First performed, as indicated, October 9, 1799.   SCHATZ 6155

I ladri di spirito. Commedia per musica di Giuseppe Palomba da rappresentarsi nel Teatro de' Fiorentini nell' inverno di quest' anno 1769.

    Napoli, Stamperia Avelliniana, 1769. 78 p. 15ᶜᵐ.

Three acts. Scenario, cast, and name of the composer, Vincenzo **Curcio.**

         SCHATZ 2310

Il ladro convertito per amore. L. T. of Pergolesi's Livietta e Tracollo o sia La contadina astuta.

The lady of the manor. A comic opera: as it is performed at the Theatre-Royal in Covent-Garden. Written by Dr. Kendrick. The songs set to music by Mr. Hook. The second edition.

    London, E. and C. Dilly, J. Wilkie [etc.], 1778. 4 p. l., 64 p. 21ᶜᵐ.

Three acts. Cast and preface, in which the author says:

"The outline of the following opera (written about ten years ago, by way of relaxation from severer studies) was taken from the *Country Lasses* of Mr. Charles Johnson, particularly the pleasing and romantic episode, borrowed from the *Custom of the Country* of Beaumont and Fletcher . . ."

First performed November 23, 1778, as indicated.   LONGE 85

The entertainments, set to musick, for the comic-dramatick opera, called The lady's triumph. Written by Mr. Theobald, and set to musick by Mr. Galliard.

    London, Jonas Browne, 1718. 2 p. l., 27 p. 19ᶜᵐ.

In the acts one to four the "entertainments, set to musick" in this play were few and far between, the first, at least according to Browne's publication, occurring in the second act in form of a scene, with song; the second in the third act, as a "ballad sung by Mr. Pack." In the fifth act there occurred "The masque of *Decius* and *Paulina*," and the full text of this appears, with cast, on p. [12]–27 of this publication.

The piece evidently belongs to "The curious admixtures of masque and harlequinade" (Grove) which Rich produced, with music by **Galliard,** from about 1717 on as pantomimes.   LONGE 59

Der laecherliche printz Jodelet. [vignette.] In einem schertzhaften singspiele auf dem Hamburgischen Schau-Platz vorgestellet im jahr 1726.

    [Hamburg], mit Stromerischen schrifften, n. d. Unpaged. 19ᶜᵐ.

Five acts. Cast. Neither the author, resp. translator, Johann Philipp Praetorius, is mentioned, nor the composer Reinhard **Keiser.** The Italian text has been added to some of the arias. The text was based on Paul Scarron's "Jodelet ou Le maître valet."   SCHATZ 5100

Die laecherliche werbung. A. T. of Der militz.

Die lächerlichen gelehrten. Tr. of Astaritta's I visionari.

Der lahme husar. Eine comische oper in zwey acten von Friedrich Koch.

Dresden und Leipzig, Breitkopfische Buchhandlung, 1784. 62 p. 14^{cm}.

Bound in is an anonymous "Neujahrs-Vorspiel," p. [213]–230. Franz **Seydelmann**, the composer, is not mentioned.

First performed at Leipzig, Koch'sches Theater am Rannstaedter Thore, July 17, 1780, and at Dresden, Kleines Theater, in the same year. SCHATZ 9845

The laird in disguise. A. T. of Jamie and Bess.

Il Lamano. Drama per musica da rappresentarsi nel famoso Teatro Grimani di S. Gio. Grisostomo. Nel carnevale dell' anno 1719. Di Domenico Lalli . . .

Venezia, Marin Rossetti, 1719. 60 p. 15^{cm}.

Three acts. Author's dedication, "Ante fatto," cast, scenario, and name of Michel Angelo **Gasparini** as the composer. SCHATZ 3600

Lampedo, ein melodrama von herrn oberappellationsrath Lichtenberg in die musik gesetzet vom churpfaelzischen geistlichen rath und capellmeister Vogler, von dem Hofe aufgefuehrt zur feyer des 11ten julii, 1779.

Darmstadt, J. J. Will, n. d. 10 p. 15^{cm}.

One act. SCHATZ 10798

Lanassa's zweyter theil. *See* Marie von Montalban.

Das land der liebe. A. T. of Bierey's Der zauber-hain.

Der land-mann ein philosoph. Tr. of Galuppi's Il filosofo d campagna.

Landsbye-pigen fra Frascati. Tr. of Paisiello's La Frascatana.

La lanterna di Diogene. Drama per musica da rappresentarsi alle S. S. C. C. R. R. Maestà dell' imperatore Leopoldo et dell' imperatrice Claudia nel carnovale dell' anno MDCLXXIV. Musica dell Sr Ant. Draghi, M. di Cap. della M.^{tà} dell' imperatrice Eleonora. Con l'arie per li balli del Sr Gio. Henrico Schmelzer, V. M. di Cap. di S. M. Ces.

Vienna d'Austria, Matteo Cosmerovio, n. d. 4 p. l., 98 p. 15^{cm}.

In three acts, by conte Niccolò Minato, who is not mentioned. Argument and scenario. Lodovico Burnacini is mentioned as designer of the scenery; Santo Ventura of the ballets. A drama *à clef* (compare for the key Wotquenne, p. 90). The emperor Leopold I is said to have contributed one aria. SCHATZ 2798

La lanterna di Diogene. Commedia per musica di Giuseppe Palomba da rappresentarsi nel Teatro de' Fiorentini per terz' opera di questo corrente anno 1794.

Napoli, n. publ., 1794. 48 p. 15^{cm}.

Two acts. Cast and name of Pietro **Guglielmi** as the composer.

First performed at Venice, Teatro di S. Samuele, fall of 1793 with Palomba's text altered by Angelo Anelli, so that, as Schatz puts it, the revised opera was performed before the original. According to Piovano, the libretto was really by Nicolò Liprandi (pseud. of Angelo Anelli) and Palomba simply utilized it for the replica in Naples. SCHATZ 4250

La lanterna di Diogene—Continued.

— **La lanterna di Diogene.** Dramma giocoso per musica, da rappresentarsi nel Teatro elettorale di Sassonia.

Dresda, n. publ., 1796. 31 p. l., 72 p. 15½^{cm}.

Two acts. German title-page, "Die laterne des Diogenes," and detailed synopsis in German precede the Italian text translated with very many alterations from the Napoletan dialect into Italian. Pietro **Guglielmi** is mentioned as the composer.
First performed, as indicated, October, 1796. SCHATZ 4251

La lanterne veridique. Piece en un acte. Representée à la Foire Saint Laurent. 1732.

Le Théâtre de la foire, Paris, 1737, t. ix, 2, pl., [17]–71 p. 17^{cm}.

By Carolet. Largely *en vaudevilles*. The airs, selected or composed and arranged by Jean Claude **Gillier**, are printed at the end of the volume in the "Table des airs."
First performed August 19, 1732. ML 48.L2X

A'lantosok, vagy-is: A'vig nyomorúság. Egy vig Énekes Játék harom fel-vonásokban. Szabadon fordította, és muzsikára alkalmaztatta Szerelemhegyi András. A'muzsikáját pedig több ékesitö instrumentokkal bóvitette Reiman Úr.

Pesten, Füskúti Landerer Mihálynál, 1793. 73 p. 17^{cm}.

Title in English would be, "The lute player or Gay misery . . . set to music by András **Szerelemhegyi** . . ." SCHATZ 11530

Laodice. Dramma per musica, da rappresentarsi nel Teatro Giustiniano di S. Moisé l'autunno dell' anno MDCCXXIV.

Venezia, Marino Rossetti, n. d. 48 p. 15½^{cm}.

Three acts. By conte Angelo Schietti, who is not mentioned. Argument, cast, scenario, and name of Tommaso **Albinoni** as composer. SCHATZ 130

Laodicea. O. T. of Paër's Tegene e Laodicea.

Laodicea e Berenice. Drama per musica da recitarsi nel Teatro Vendramino di S. Salvatore l'anno 1695. Seconda impressione. Di Matteo Noris . . .

Venetia, Nicolini, 1695. front. 71 p. 13½^{cm}.

Three acts. Author's dedication, scenario, and notice to the reader with argument in which Noris enumerates the qualities that in his opinion make for a good libretto and says that for brevity's sake the original text has been modified in many places. Giacomo Antonio **Perti**, the composer, is not mentioned. SCHATZ 7951

Laomedonte. Drama per musica da rappresentarsi nel Teatro Giustinian à S. Moisè, l'autunno dell' anno MDCCXV . . .

Venezia, Marin Rossetti, 1715. 59 p. 14½^{cm}.

Three acts. Neither Giovanni Battista Gaizzardi, the author, is mentioned, nor Lorenzo **Baseggio**, the composer. Impresario's dedication, dated Venice, October 19, 1715, notice to the reader, argument, cast, scenario. SCHATZ 619

Larinda e Vanesio. *See* L'artigiano gentiluomo.

Larinda e Vanesio. O. T. of Hasse's L'artigiano gentiluomo.

The lass of the lakes. A. T. of Helvetic liberty.

Die last-tragende liebe, oder Emma und Eginhard, in einem sing-spiele auf dem Hamburgischen schau-platze anno 1728 aufgefuehret.

[*Hamburg*]. *Gedruckt mit Stromerischen schrifften, n. d.   Unpaged.*
18^{cm}.

Three acts. Note:
"Die music ist ein unvergleichliches meister-stuecke von dem nie genung geprie-senen herrn **Telemann** . . . Die poesie verfertigte C. G. Wend."
This is followed by the very odd
"Zuschrifft. Mein liebhaber . . . Gegeben auff dem Gosemarckte den 22. novembr. 1728. Deine getreue Die Hamburgische Opera" in which we read:
"Der verfasser hat zween beruehmte poeten des vorigen seculi, als den Schlesi-schen Hoffmannswaldau in seinen Helden-brieffen und den Hollaendischen Cats in seiner Manntragenden magd zu vorgaengern und ob er sich zwar fuer einen viel zu unwuerdigen nachfolger so grosser geister bekennet, so getrauet er sich doch zum wenigsten den fuerwurff damit abzulehnen, als ober sich an eine unwuerdige materie gemacht haette. Laeufft auch diese begebenheit schon nicht auff einen tugend-hafften endzweck hinaus, wie solches von eingien als ein unumgaengliches requisitum bey einer opera zum voraus gesetzet wird, so kan man doch dargegen nicht unbillig repliciren, dass wofern anders tugenden und laster in keiner andern absicht als zur resp. nachahmung und vermeidung in einem schauspiele fuergestellet werden, es gleich viel gelte, ob sie in dem ausgange, mittel oder anfange derselben ihre rolle spielen."   Schatz 10262

Die laterne des Diogenes. Tr. of P. Guglielmi's La laterna di Diogene.

Die launige kaffeeschenkinn. Tr. of Weigl's La caffettiera bizzarra.

Laura. Operette in drei akten. Zweiter band.

n. i., n. d.   16^{cm}.   p. [257]–314.

Detached from the works of freiherr Julius Soden v. Sassanfart (Berlin, Maurer, 1789), who says in a prefatory note:
"Die gesaenge dieser oper haben gefallen und sind sehr gut in musik gesezt worden. diess bewog mich, sie durchzusehen . . ."
No composer recorded by Schatz.   Schatz 11459

Laura Rosetti. Ein schauspiel mit gesang, von d'Arien.

Leipzig, Dyckische buchhandlung, 1777.   96 p.   16½^{cm}.

Three acts.
First performed, with music by Johann **André**, at Berlin, Döbbelinsches Theater, May 23, 1778.   Schatz 188

Lauretia, ballet. *See* Bertoni's Cajo Mario.

La **Lauretta,** ballet. *See* Caruso's Il matrimonio in commedia.

La **Lauretta,** ballet. *See* Gassmann's L'amore astigiano.

Lauretta, ballet. *See* P. Guglielmi's La serva innamorata.

Lauretta, ballet. *See* Tritto's L'Artenice.

Lauso e Lidia. Dramma per musica di Giuseppe Foppa da rappre-sentarsi nel Teatro La Fenice il carnovale dell' anno 1798.

Venezia, Stamperia Valvasense, n. d.   62 p.   17^{cm}.

Two acts. Argument, cast, scenario, and name of Joh. Simon **Mayr** as the com-poser. On p. [53]–62, cast and description of the ballet, "L'inutile precauzione," by Lauchlin Duquesny. The composer not mentioned.
First performed February 14, 1798.   Schatz 6156

Lauso e Lidia, ballet.　*See* Monza's Cajo Mario.

Lauso e Lidia, o sia Il trionfo dell' amicizia, ballet.　*See* Nasolini's Teseo a Stige.

Lauso e Lidia, ballet.　*See* Rust's Adriano in Siria.

Lauso e Lidia, ballet.　*See* Tarchi's L'impostura poco dura.

La lavandara.　L. T. of Galuppi's Il marchese villano.

La lavandara astuta.　L. T. of Galuppi's Il marchese villano.

La lavandarina.　Intermezzi per musica a cinque voci, da cantarsi nel Teatro alla Valle l'anno 1746 . . .
> *Roma, Komarek, 1746.　48 p.　16^{cm}.*

Two parts.　Dedication by Angiolo Lungi, cast, and name of Giovanni Battista **Casali** as composer.　The author is not known to Schatz.
First performed in January, as indicated.　　　　　　　　ML 48.A5　v. 3

Le lavarandine.　O. T. of Zannetti's Die waescherinnen, also of his Die waeschermaedchen.

Il Leandro.　Drama per musica del conte Camillo Badovero . . .
> *Venetia, Gio. Francesco Valvasense, 1679.　46, [1] p.　14½^{cm}.*

Three acts.　Author's dedicationi dated Venice, May 15, 1679, argument, notice to the reader, and scenario.　Francesco Antonio **Pistocchi,** the composer, is not mentioned.
The opera was performed, according to Schatz, at the Teatro sulle Zattere, with movable wooden figures, and the singers behind the scenes.　　　SCHATZ 8196

— **Gl'amori fatali.**　Dramma per musica da rappresentarsi nel Teatro di S. Moisè.　Del Co. Camillo Badovero . . .
> *Venetia, Gio. Francesco Valvasense, 1682.　46 p.　14½^{cm}.*

Lacks p. 33–40.
Three acts.　Impresario's dedication dated Venice, January 1682, printer's notice to the reader, mentioning this as a replica, and the name of "Francesco Antonio Pistochino" (**Pistocchi**) as the composer, argument and scenario.　This is with negligible differences the same text as that of "Il Leandro" and was performed in the same manner.　　　　　　　　　SCHATZ 8199

La leçon, ou La tasse de glaces.　Comédie en un acte et en prose, mêlée d'ariettes, représentée sur le Théâtre de la rue Feydeau, le 5 prairial, an 5.eme (24 mai, 1797, v. s.)　Paroles de M. Marsollier, musique de M. d'Alayrac.
> *Paris, Huet, an V, (1797, v. st.)　4 p. l., 48 p.　20½^{cm}.*

Cast.　In his Avertissement, which contains a very flattering "hommage" to Dalayrac, Marsollier says:
"Cette comédie, imitée d'un des jolis proverbes de M. Carmontelle, est la première que j'aie donnée sur le Théâtre italien, sous le nom de *la Fausse peur.* L'ouvrage réussit, et obtint même l'honneur d'une réprise, quoi-qu'il eût bien des défauts, et que la musique légère, agréable, mais foible, ne fût l'ouvrage que d'un enfant de quatorze ans, (le jeune Darcis) qui annonçait, il est vrai, les plus heureuses dispositions, et que la mort a enlevé à la fleur de l'âge.　Il étoit l'élève du célèbre Grétry . . . Voulant fair reparoître ce petit ouvrage . . . j'ai cru ne pouvoir mieux faire, que de l'embellir des charmes de la musique de M. d'Alayrac . . . il a bien voulu se charger de *la Leçon* . . ."　　　　　ML 50.2.L23D2

Lenardo und Blandine. Ein melodram von J. F. von Goetz. In musik gesezt von herrn Winter . . . Aufgefuert von einer gesellschaft adelicher kunstfreunde auf dem Stadttheater in Augsburg.

[Augsburg, Andreas Brinhausser, 1785.] *front., unpaged.* *15½ cm.*

Two acts. Argument and long "Vorbericht" (8 p.) dated January, 1785, which reads, in part:

"Vor acht Jahren, da der Geschmak an Melodramen in Teutschland sich auszeichnete, dachte ich dieser Art Schauspiele öfters nach, und konnte mich nicht enthalten zuweilen meine Anmerkungen über den Zweck und die innere Einrichtungen des Spiels, nebst den erforderlichen Masregeln der begleitenden Musik, öfentlich kund zu thun.

"Ich war weit entfernt, die Warscheinlichkeit eines Monologes von solcher Ausdenung zu behaupten. Allein, so wie eine philosophische Streitfrage, wobei der Gegensaz schon erwiesen angenommen ist, eh man sich darüber streitet, dem Verstande zu einer angenemen Beschäftigung wird: eben so dürfe ein leidenschaftlicher, idealisirter Monolog, welcher Säze enthält, die bei wirklichen Handlungen und Dialogen einzeln vorkommen können, in einer gedrängteren Reihe nicht ganz unangenem sein. Ueberdies könnte man ein Melodram als ein künstliches Solo ansehen, worin der Künstler seine Fertigkeit, reichhaltige Verbindung der Ideen und das Kreszendo seiner Kunst zu zeigen Gelegenheit nimmt. In den gewönlichen dramatischen Stüken dient dem Schauspieler zum Vorteil: dass sein Spiel durch Zwischenszenen oft vorteilhaft unterbrochen wird, und dem vom Sinne der Handlung erfüllten Zuschauer manche Bewegung nicht besonders auffällt, die der Spielende häufig bis zum Ekel widerholt. Ich habe diese Unvollkommenheit in den Vorstellungen verschiedener beliebten Melodramen zuweilen wargenommen, worin die spielenden Personen, teils bei dem Texte gegen den gehörigen Ausdruck gestikulirten, teils die hie und da mit Musik ausgedenten unwarscheinlichen Intervallen, wie abgerissene Perioden, begleiteten.

"In dieser Absicht stimte mich einst ein einsamer Spaziergang durch romantische Gegenden zu Lieblingsbildern dichterischer Auftritte, ein Zufal hielt mich bei Bürgers Lenardo und Blandine fest; und der Sinn dieses innigst durchgedachten Stoffes erhizte meine Einbildungskraft so nachdrüklich, dass ich eine ganze Reihe von Handlungen, die bei dieser Begebenheit sich vor odor nach ereignen konten, mir gleichsam im Geiste vorschweben sah. Im Schwunge dieser Ideen drängte michs zum Deklamiren, zum Gestikuliren, und endlich sas ich auf meinem Stule fest, und versuchte einige der vorgeschwebten Bilder mit Feder und Kreide zu entwerfen. Dabei ereignete sich der äusserst seltne Fal, dass mir die Arbeit den folgenden Morgen nicht ganz misfiel. Kunstfreunde ermunterten mich fortzufaren: und so ward nach und nach Lenardo und Blandine in dramatische Szenen eingeleitet, und von Punkt zu Punkt so niedergezeichnet, dass man die Folge von Zeichnungen, welche sich auf 160 Blat beläuft, als eine fortdauernde Handlung ansehen konte, die so oft zu erneuern war, als man Belieben trug, die Zeichnungen nach ihrer Reihe und Verbindung vor Augen zu legen.

"Ich war dabei bemühet den Grundursachen der menschlichen Bewegungen nachzuforschen, wornach sich die Stellung und Gesichtsausdrüke des menschlichen Körpers durch verschiedne Lagen drängen und verändern konten. Die Resultate dieser mühsamen Beobachtungen hab' ich bereits dem Publikum unter dem Titel: *Versuch leidenschaftlicher Entwürfe für empfind ame Kunst- und Schauspielfreunde* vorgelegt, und ich gestehe gerne dass die gütige Aufnahme dieses Versuches in verschidnen öfentlichen Blättern meiner Erwartung desto überraschender kommen muste, je mehr ich von der Beschränktheit meiner geringen Verdienste überzeugt bin.

"Meine Absicht dabei war vorzüglich den öfentlichen Redner und Schauspieler auf die feineren Reize des Geberdenspils und der Deklamazion aufmerksam, und dadurch das Gebiet des Seelenvermögens und seines unbegreiflichen Einwirkungskreises bekanter und gemeinnüzlicher zu machen. Diess war eigentlich die Hauptabsicht des Melodrams, welches ich bey seiner Entstehung keineswegs für eine öfentliche Vorstellung auf der Bühne, sondern blos zu einem Grundplan zur Zergliederung der Symtome und Auswüchse einer der bekantesten und algemeinsten Leidenschaften (ich meine die Liebe) bestimte. Es war demnach Zufall, und keineswegs meine Hauptabsicht, wenn dieses Stük auf verschiedenen Bühnen Teutschlands aufgefürt ward, und die Talente verschidner Musiker beschäftigt hatte, die Ruhepunkte der Affekte mit Melodien zu begleiten. Die Einrichtung jener Musik, welche unter meiner Aufsicht und nach meinen correcten Musikbegriffen ausgefürt worden, ist, (wie auf den Titel angemerkt ward) von Herrn Winter, einem Mann, welchen Teutschland noch zu wenig kennt, um ihm so viel Gerechtigkeit widerfaren zu lassen, als seine besonderen musikalischen Vorzüge verdienen, welche er in verschiednen

Lenardo und Blandine—Continued.

Werken an dem kurfürstl. Münchner und Manheimer Hofe bereits rümlichst gezeigt hat.

"Vileicht dürfte es einigen Kunstfreunden nicht unangenem seyn, wenn ich hier einige Ideen anmerke, wornach ich dem Tonkünstler bei diesem Melodram fortzuschreiten bat. Ich fand bei einigen Dramen und Rezitativen, welche mit Musik begleitet werden, den Feler: dass der begleitende Gesang der Instrumente entweder zu ser an einzelnen Bildern haftete, und allenfals die Bewegungen eines Stromes schilderte, welcher unter der ganzen Vorstellung der Natur warscheinlich auf seinem unveränderlichen Plaz fortrauschte, sich aber dennoch in der Musik in dem Augenblik nur hören liess, da der Schauspieler von Strome sprach. Ausser dieser Kleinmeisterei pflegen die Entwiklungen und Ausweichungen öfters so gedent zu werden, dass der Zuschauer und Schauspieler in Verlegenheit gesezt werden muss, was sie in diesen langen Zwischenraumen handlen oder denken sollen. Dadurch wird das vilfältige hin und her Traben, und manche absichslose Händebewegung bei einigen Monologen unvermeidlich. Meiner unmasgeblichen Meinung nach solte gerade so viel und nicht mer Musik zwischen den Redeintervallen angenommen und gehört werden, als warscheinliche Zeit die Seele in ihrer einmal angenommen Lage nötig hat, um Begriffe aus Begriffen zu folgern oder dadurch zu neuen Ideen überzugehen. Der Tonsezer sol sich lebhaft in die Lage der handlenden Person versezen und den sprachlosen Zustand mit sanften Akorden ausfüllen, worinnen das innere Gefül sich sammelt und ordnet. Er sol die Wirkung iener Momente studiren, worinn die Leidenschaft entweder noch nicht zu iener Höhe gestiegen ist, dass sie den Mund unwilkürlich öfnet, und zu sprechen drängt, oder wenn durch Uebergewicht des Gefüls die Sprache stoket.

". . . Diese wenigen Bemerkungen fand ich nötig bei Verfertigung der Musik zu meinem Drama vorauszusezen. Und einsichtsvolle Kenner der Tonkunst haben die von dem geschikten Tonsezer dadurch erreichten Wirkungen mit Beifal beglüket. Sie werden auch in den meisten Stellen der Musik finden, dass die Instrumente in dem nämlichen Grundtone beginnen, oder aufhören, in welchem die Stime der deklamirenden entweder einfält, oder vorhergegangen ist. Dadurch schmilzt Musik und Deklamazion harmonischer ineinander, und drängt den Sinn der Handlung ungezwungener fort. Aus diesem läst sich ohngefähr schliesen, wie genau Dichter, Tonsezer und Agirende auf einen Punkt zusammen wirken müssen, um einer Vorstellung Warheit und Ungezwungenheit zu geben . . ."

First performed, as indicated, at Augsburg, January 25, 1785; at Munich, National Schaubühne, June 25, 1779.   SCHATZ 11040

Die Leipziger messe. A. T. of Keiser's Le bon vivant.

Léon ou Le chateau de Montenero. Drame en trois actes et en prose mêlé d'ariettes. Représenté sur le Théâtre de l'Opéra-comique, ci-devant Théâtre-italien, le 24 vendémiaire, an VII de la République. Paroles du citoyen Hoffman. Musique du citoyen Dalayrac.

Paris, Vente, an 7 [1798–99]. 84 p. 19½ᶜᵐ.

Cast.

First performed, as indicated, October 15, 1798.   ML 50.2.L26D2

Leonida in Sparta. Drama da rappresentarsi in musica nel Regio Teatro di Torino l'anno 1689.

Torino, Bartolomeo Zappata, 1689. 88 p. 15ᶜᵐ.

Prologue and three acts. Argument, scenario, and prefatory note by the unknown author, who says:

"Per servire al genio di chi commanda, eccomi quel che non sono, e forzato à comparire quel che mai fui, cioè divenuto autore d'un drama, senza sapere tampoco quel che si sia teatro."

"Giovanni **Sebenico** mastro di capella di S. A. R." is mentioned as the composer.

SCHATZ 9812

Leonida in Tegea. Drama per musica da rappresentarsi nel Teatro Zane di S. Moisè l'anno MDCLXXVI del Co. Nicolo Minato . . .

Venetia, Francesco Nicolini, 1676. 64 p. 13½^{cm}.

In three acts. With impresario's dedication dated February 9, 1676, argument, scenario, and notice to the reader. He is informed that Minato's original libretto has been retouched "per compiacere al genio di questo Serenissimo Cielo," but that the alterations have been pointed out by quotation marks. He is also informed that Antonio **Draghi**'s music, originally composed for Vienna, June 9, 1670, has been retouched and adjusted, but it is not said that this duty fell to M. A. **Ziani**. The majority of the arias has either been added or changed. The very first, for instance, "Parto mio ardore," and the very last, "Il destin già s'è placato," are additions.

SCHATZ 2799

— Leonida zu Tegea. Gesungene vorstellung zu begaengnuss dess glorwuerdigen geburths-tag der roemischen Kayserlichen Mayestaet, Leopold dess Ersten . . . In sing-kunst gerichtet durch Antoni Draghi, Ihrer Mayestaet der verwittibten kayserin Capellmeistern. Und in teutsch uebersetzet.

Wienn, bey Mattheo Cosmerovio, 1670. 7 p. l., 63 p. 14½^{cm}.

In three acts, with the "Beurlaubung" (licenza). With argument and scenario. A German translation of Draghi's "Leonida in Tegea," as originally performed at Vienna, June 9, 1670. For this opera the emperor **Leopold I** composed the arias, "Io non so cangiar amor" and "Quand' era giovanetta." Both were published by Adler, 1892, in "Musikalische werke der kaiser Ferdinand III, Leopold I und Joseph I."

SCHATZ 2800

Leonida rè di Sparta. *See* M. Curzio.

Léonore, ou L'amour conjugal, fait historique, en deux actes et en prose mêlée de chants. Paroles de J. N. Bouilly, musique de P. Gaveaux, représentée pour la première fois, à Paris, sur le Théatre Feydeau, le 1er ventôse, an 6e de la République française [February 19, 1798].

Paris, Barba, an septième [1798–99]. 40 p. 19½^{cm}.

Cast.

SCHATZ 3649

[Lesbina e Milo] Nuovi intermedii per musica da rappresentarsi nel Teatro di Sant' Angelo. L'autunno dell' anno 1706 . . .

Venezia, Gio. Battista Chiarello, 1706. 17^{cm}*. 15*^{cm}.

Three parts. Dedication dated Venice, November 15, 1706, and signed Lesbina, one of the two characters. Cast. The intermedii were performed together with the opera, "Paride in Ida" (text by Francesco Mazzarà; music by Luigi Manza and Agostino Bonaventura Coletti), according to Schatz, to whom both author and composer of these intermedii are unknown.

SCHATZ 11345

Lesbina e Nesso.

Intermezzi (text by Nicola Serino; music by Leonardo **Leo**), interpolated in Haendel's "Rinaldo," Napoli, 1718, performed, with additions by Leo, on October 1, 1718. (Not listed by Leo.)

See SCHATZ 4495

La letteraria fanatica, ballet. *See* Cimarosa's L'impresario in angustie (Milano, 1789).

La lettre, comédie en un acte, en prose et vaudevilles, par C. J. Loeuillart-Davrigni; représentée pour la première fois, sur le Théâtre du Vaudeville, le 7 nivose l'an 3me de la République française [Dec. 27, 1794].

Paris, Chez le libraire, au Théâtre du Vaudeville, an troisième [1794–95]. 44 p. 20^{cm}.

Cast. A few of the airs notés are printed in the text—for instance, one by **Jadin**, "Pour la beauté." Not recorded by Cl. & L. or Schatz.

ML 48.M2L

Der letzte rausch.   Tr. of Gluck's L'ivrogne corrigé.

Leucippe, e Teonoe.   Tragedia per musica da rappresentarsi nel famoso Teatro Grimani di S. Gio. Grisostomo.   L'autunno dell' anno 1719.

Venezia, Marino Rossetti, 1719.   81 p.   15^{cm}.

Five acts. By Pietro Maria Suarez, who is not mentioned. Argument, long notice to the reader, cast, scenario, and name of Antonio **Pollaroli** as the composer.
SCHATZ 8262

Leucippo, favola pastorale per musica, rappresentata nella Regia Elettoral villa di Sant' Uberto, il felicissimo giorno natalizio della Maestà di Augusto III . . . li 7 ottobre l'anno MDCCXLVII.

n. i., n. d.   8 p. l., 163, [4] p.   17^{cm}.

At end, "Dresda . . . la vedova Stössel."
Three acts and licenza. Argument, scenario, cast, and names of Gio. Claudio Pasquini as author, of Johann Adolph **Hasse** as composer. German title page, "Leucippus," and text face Italian.
SCHATZ 4545

— Leucippo.   Favola pastorale per musica da rappresentarsi nel Teatro Grimani di San Samuele nella fiera dell' Ascensione l'anno MDCCXLIX.

Venezia, Al segno della scienza, 1749.   58 p.   15½^{cm}.

Three acts. Argument, cast, scenario, and name of Johann Adolph **Hasse** as the composer. The text seems to be practically the same as in Pasquini's text, Dresden, 1747.
SCHATZ 4591

Leucippus.   Tr. of Hasse's Leucippo.

La liaison de l'Amour et de Bachus, ballet.   *See* Traetta's Siroe.

La liberazione di Castruccio Castracane, ballet.   *See* Cimarosa's L'Olimpiade.

La liberazione di Lilla, ballet.   *See* Bertoni's Medonte.

La libertà gelosa di se stessa in persona di Annibale amante di patria.   *See* M. Curzio.

La libertà nociva.   Drama giocoso per musica da rappresentarsi nel Teatro Tron di S. Cassiano l'autunno dell' anno 1744.

Venezia, n. publ., n. d.   2 p. l., 88 p.   17^{cm}.

At end, p. 61 repeated, with variants.
Three acts by Giovanni Barlocci (not mentioned).   Cast and name of the composer, **Rinaldo di Capua.**
First performed at Rome, Teatro della Valle, January 17, 1740.   SCHATZ 8798

La libertà ramminga.   *See* M. Curzio.

La libertà sempre stabile nelle vicende del principato.   *See* M. Curzio.

La libertà trionfante.   *See* M. Curzio.

La libertà trionfatrice del tempo.   *See* M. Curzio.

Liberty-hall: or, A test of good fellowship. A comic opera, in two acts. As it is performed with the greatest applause at the Theatre-Royal in Drury-Lane.

London, Printed for the author, and sold by G. Kearsley, 1785. 3 p. l., 38 p. 21^{cm}.

Two acts. Cast. The author-composer, Charles **Dibdin**, is not mentioned. First performed February 8, 1785, as indicated. LONGE 95

Licinio imperatore. Drama per musica nel famosissimo Teatro Grimano in S. Gio. Grisostomo l'anno 1684. Di Matteo Noris . . .

Venetia, Francesco Nicolini, 1684. 84 p. 14^{cm}.

Three acts. Author's dedication, argument, and scenario. The composer, Carlo **Pallavicino**, is not mentioned. SCHATZ 7726

Il **Licurgo** overo Il cieco d'acuta vista, drama per musica da rappresentarsi nel Teatro di S. Angelo l'anno MDCLXXXVI.

Venetia, Francesco Nicolini, 1686. 57 p. 13½^{cm}.

Three acts. Neither Matteo Noris, the author, nor Carlo Francesco **Pollaroli**, the composer, is mentioned. The registration date is given as February 5, 1685. Scenario and notice to the reader, which reads:
"Per accomodarsi a i personaggi, che recitano, & per non poter per tal quale convalescenza dell' autore farsi dal medesimo qualche accordo finale di perfettione alla presente operetta, sono state aggionte canzoni, accorciate scene di maggior forza, con pregiudizio delle medesime, & fatte aggiongere altre segnate con queste linee ,, come vedrai; tanto ti basti."
This applies only to scenes ix and x of the third act. SCHATZ 8300

Die lieb des Arion gegen die Leucosie. Tr. T. of the ballet Les amours d'Arion & de Léucosie.

Die lieb kan alles. Tr. of L'amor può tutto.

Die liebe auf dem lande. Eine komische oper in drey aufzuegen von C. F. Weisse. Verbesserte ausgabe.

Leipzig, Dykische buchhandlung, 1776. 104 p. 17^{cm}.

The composer, Johann Adam **Hiller**, is not mentioned. Weisse based his piece on two French works, Madame Favart's "Annette et Lubin" and Anseaume's "La clochette."
First performed at Leipzig, Theater beim Rannstaedter Thore, May 18, 1768. SCHATZ 4724

— Die **liebe auf dem lande.** Eine komische oper in drey aufzuegen.

C. F. Weisse, Komische opern, Carlsruhe, 1778, th. i, p. [97]–188. 18½^{cm}.

On p. 98, the note: "Nach *Anette a Lubin* des herrn Favart und der *Clochette* des herrn Anseaume." The composer, **Hiller**, is not mentioned. ML 49.A2W2

Liebe aus dankbarkeit. A. T. of Seydelmann's Das ungeheuer.

Liebe aus haabsucht. Tr. of Seydelmann's Amor per oro.

Die liebe bey den handwerkern. Tr. of Gassmann's L'amore artigiano.

Liebe durch zauberei. A. T. of Grossheim's Titania.

Liebe erhaelt den sieg. A. T. of Grétry's Ferdinand und Nicolette.

Die **liebe fuer den kaiser,** ein laendliches schauspiel mit gesang von herrn Wagenseil. Die musik von herrn direktor Steudle. Hierauf folgt: Der prinzenraub, oder Kunz von Kauffungen, ein historisches schauspiel in 5 aufzeugen, von herrn Neumann.

　　Kaufbeuren, Dorn, 1790. Unpaged. 16½ cm.

　　At head of title: "Von der loebl. Agenten Gesellschaft A. C. wird Montags den 25 und Donnerstags den 28 Oktobr. auch Montags den 1sten novembris aufgefuehrt."
　　Cast and prefatory note. On p. 5, the title and note preceding title repeated with addition "an dem obrigkeitlich verordneten freudenfest wegen begluekter kaiserwahl Sr. Majestaet Leopold II." 　　　　Schatz 10062

Die **liebe gegen das vaterland** oder Der sterbende Cato. German title of Keiser's L'amore verso la patria.

Die **liebe im matrosenkleide.** Tr. of Weigl's L'amor marinaro.

Die **liebe im narrenhause.** Eine komische oper in zwey aufzeugen. In musik gesetzt von hrn. Ditters von Dittersdorf.

　　n. i., n. d. p. [257]–350. 17 cm.

　　By Gottlieb Stephanie, the younger. Detached from his Singspiele, 1792?
　　First performed at Vienna, Kärnthnerthor theater, April 12, 1787. Schatz 2599

— Gesaenge aus dem singspiele: **Orpheus der zweyte,** in drey aufzeugen, nach einer musik von Dittersdorf.

　　Hamburg, J. M. Michaelsen, 1788. 36 p. 16 cm.

　　Is "Die liebe im narrenhause," as altered by Friedrich Ludwig Schröder.
　　First performed as pasticcio at Hamburg, Theater b. Gänsemarkt, December 8, 1788. 　　　　Schatz 2600

Die **liebe in der Ukräne** oder Hier gehen die maedchen auf die freierei aus. Ein singspiel in vier aufzeugen.

　　Frankfurt am Main, Esslingersche Buchhandlung, 1786. 104 p. 16½ cm.

　　Neither the author, Heinrich Christian Pleissner, nor the composer, Stanislaus Franz Xaver **Spindler** is mentioned.
　　First performed at Innsbruck, Hoftheater, 1786. 　　　　Schatz 9976

Liebe macht alle stände gleich. A. T. of Gerl's Der bestrafte hochmuth.

Gesaenge zu der oper: **Liebe macht kurzen prozess,** oder Die heyrath auf gewisse art. In zwei aufzeugen von Joachim Perinet . . . 1799.

　　n. i., n. d. 27 p. 16 cm.

　　A pasticcio. The names of the following composers are indicated in the libretto: Johann Baptist **Hennerberg,** Joseph **Woelfl,** Matthias **Stegmayer,** Franz Anton **Hoffmeister,** Franz Xaver **Süssmayer,** Ignaz Xaver, ritter von **Seyfried,** Jacob **Haibel,** Joseph **Triebensee.**
　　First performed at Leipzig, Theater am Rannstädter Thore, 1799; at Vienna, Theater auf der Wieden, March 26, 1798. 　　　　Schatz 4633

Die **liebe ohne bossheit.** Tr. of Ottani's L'amore senza malizia.

Die **liebe und Psiche,** ballet. *See* Piccinni's Cato in Utica.

Die **liebe unter den gondoliren.** A. T. of Fliess' Die regata zu Venedig.

Die liebe unter den gondolieren. A. T. of Sander's Die regata zu Venedig.

Die liebe unter den handwerksleuten. Tr. of Gassmann's L'amore artigiano.

Liebe wagt alles. Tr. of Devienne's Les visitandines.

Liebe zum schein. Tr. of P. Guglielmi's I finti amori.

Die liebenden greise. Tr. of Anfossi's Gli amanti canuti.

Das liebesgrab. Ein schauspiel mit gesang in drey akten.
Heydelberg, Gebrueder Pfaehler, 1779. 4 p. l. (incl. front.), 152 p. 15½ᶜᵐ.

Neither the author, Wilhelm Gottlieb Becker, nor the composer, Friedrich **Schwindel**, is mentioned. SCHATZ 9779

Die liebesintrigue. A. T. of Paër's L'intrigo amoroso.

Der liebesteufel, oder Der alchymist. In einem akt. Nach Le Grand.
A. G. Meissner, Operetten, Leipzig, 1778. 79 p. 17ᶜᵐ.
Is the second of the three librettos in this collection. Meissner says, in his "Vorerinnerung:"
"Der gang dieser operette ist nach *L'amour diable* von Le Grand: Aber auch nicht vielmehr als den blossen gang der scenen, und selbst diesen nicht durchgaengig, hab' ich beybehalten; anfang und ende weichen vom franzoesischen original ganz, und auch hin und wieder der mittlere theil ab . . .
"Scenen mit gesang haben nothwendig einen ganz andern bau, als solche, die bloss gesprochen werden: Meistentheils nehmen sich diejenigen operetten beym auffuehren am wenigsten gut aus, die sich treflich lesen lassen, und zum glueck gilt dies auch oft umgekehrt; denn oft skitzirt der dichter nur, um dem feuer des ton-kuenstlers stof und raum zu geben."
No composer mentioned. The text became much better known under the alternative title. Schatz (with doubts) records a setting by Johann **André** under the above title at Schwerin, Theater im Rathhause, May 15, 1788. ML 49.A2M3

— Der **alchymist.** Operette. [vignette.]
Leipzig, Dykische Buchhandlung, 1778. 79 p. 16ᶜᵐ.
One act. Same "Vorerinnerung" as above. No composer mentioned.
SCHATZ 9742

— Arien und gesänge su der operette Der **alchymist.** 1778.
n. i., n. d. 16 p. 15½ᶜᵐ.
One act. Cast. Neither Meissner is mentioned, nor the composer, Johann **André.**
First performed at Berlin, Döbbelinsches Theater, April 11, 1778. SCHATZ 1770

— Arien und gesaenge aus der operette: Der **alchymist,** in einem aufzuge, vom herrn Meissner. Die musik ist vom herrn Schuster.
Hamburg, J. M. Michaelsen, 1779. 16 p. 15½ᶜᵐ.
First performed at Dresden March, 1778; at Hamburg, January 27, 1779.
SCHATZ 9742ᵃ

Die liebhaber auf der probe. Tr. of Piticchio's Gli amanti alla prova.

Der liebhaber von allen. Tr. of Galuppi's opera L'amante di tutte.

Der **liebhaber von funfzehn jahren.**   Tr. of Martini's L'amoureux de quinze aus.

Liebs betrug.   Tr. of Bertali's L'inganno d'amore.

The **life and death of Oliver Cromwell.**   A. T. of The restauration of King Charles II.

Lilla e Lubino ossia Una cosa rara, ballet.   *See* Tarchi's Antioco.

Linceo, ballet.   *See* Mortellari's Antigona.

Lindane e Dalmiro.   Dramma serio-comico per musica da rappresentarsi nel Real Teatro dell' Ajuda nel felicissimo giorno natalizio di Sua Majesta . . . Donna Maria I . . . li 17 decembre 1789.

[Lisboa], Stamperia Reale, n. d.   88 p.   16^cm.

Two acts. Scenario, cast, and names of Gaetano Martinelli as author, of João Cordeiro da **Silva** as composer.   Schatz 9882
                                                              Second copy.   ML 48.C6I

Das **lindenfest,** oder Das fest der freundschaft, eine laendliche operette in zweyen aufzeugen, fuer gesellschaftliche buehnen.

n. i., 1790.   64 p.   15^cm.

"Vorbericht" by the author, who is unknown to Schatz.   Composed by Peter von **Winter,** who is not mentioned.
Schatz records no performance.   Schatz 11041

Lindor et Ismene.   Entrée in Les fêtes liriques.

Lindor und Ismene.   Eine operette.

n. i., n. d.   4 p. l., 38 p.   15^cm.

Perhaps real title page with imprint "Anspach, Gapert, 1773" missing. Same dedication as in the 1771 edition. (*See* next entry.)
First performed with music by Nicolaus **Mühle** at St. Petersburg, Deutsches Theater, 1779.   Schatz 6873

Lindor und Ismene.   Eine operette.

n. i., n. d.   1771.   4 p. l., 39 p.   15^cm.

One act.   In the dedication the author (not mentioned), Friedrich Julius Heinrich, freiherr Soden von Sassanfart, says:
"Das bekannte gemaelde des reizenden Poussin hat mir die erste idee zu diesem stueck gegeben, einem zwitter der Romantischen und Schaeferoper.—Vielleicht koennte es auf dem theater durch die bezaubernde composition eines Hillers, durch die dekorationen und hauptsaechlich durch die taentze vorzuege bekommen, die ihm iezt fehlen."
Actually composed by Joseph Aloysius **Schmittbauer,** and first performed at Hanover, Schlosstheater, 1771.   Schatz 9657

— Ein **grab in Arkædien!**   Operette.   In musik gesezt von herrn capellmeister Schmittbauer.

Leipzig, n. publ., 1779.   39 p.   15^cm.

One act.   In the prefatory note "S——n" (freiherr Soden von Sassanfart) says:
"Als kind liess ich dieses unbedeutende ding [as "Lindor und Ismene"] drucken; ward auch deswegen von einigen journalisten wie billig jaemmerlich angegrinzt.
"Zufaelligerweise fiel es herrn kapellmeister Schmittbauer zu Carlsruhe in die haende. Seine vortreffliche composition, nach der es auf der hannoeverischen buehne oefters aufgefuehrt wurde, konnte allein mich bewegen, es wieder durchzusehen. Ich geb' es hier veraendert, so viel es bey dem zwang der composition und ohne vernichtung des ganzen, moeglich war. Niemand kan uebrigens mehr, als ich

Lindor und Ismene—Continued.

selbst, fuehlen, wie wenig es die ehre verdient, die ihm der hannoeverische theater-direktor durch herrn Gotters namen erwiess." SCHATZ 9658

—Arkadien. Operette. In musik gesezt von herrn capellmeister Schmittbauer.

n. i. p. [233]–258. (Freiherr Soden von Sassanfart, Schauspiele, bd. I, Berlin, 1788.) 16^{cm}.

A further revision of his "Lindor und Ismene," with the same (but condensed) prefatory note as in "Ein grab in Arkadien." SCHATZ 9659

Lionel and Clarissa. A comic opera. As it is performed at the Theatre-Royal in Covent Garden. The fourth edition.

London, W. Giffin, 1768. 4 p. l., 76 p. 20^{cm}.

Three acts. Cast, prefatory note, and dedication. Neither Bickerstaffe, the author, nor **Dibdin**, the compiler and composer, is mentioned. (*See* next entry.)
First performed February 25, 1768. LONGE 14

— The school for fathers; or, Lionel & Clarissa. A comic opera. By Isaac Bickerstaff. Adapted for theatrical representation, as performed at the Theatre-Royal Drury-Lane and Covent-Garden. Regulated from the prompt-book, by permission of the managers . . .

London, John Bell, 1791. front., 1 p. l., vi, [3], 107, [1] p. (J. Bell, British theatre, London, 1791–1797, t. 1.)

The engraved front. represents Mr. Parsons as Col. Oldboy and is dated January 27, 1791. The 1 p. l. is an engraved added title page with a scene from the opera and is dated January 6, 1791.

Three acts. Biographical note, editorial comment, Drury-Lane and Covent-Garden casts, and author's Advertisement. In this he says:

"it was the general opinion of all my friends, some of whom rank among the best judges, that of all my trifles, Lionel and Clarissa was the most pardonable (an estimate with which neither the public nor the editor does not agree) . . .

"When Mr. Garrick thought of performing this piece at Drury-Lane theatre [1770], he had a new singer to bring out, and every thing possible for her advantage was to be done; this necessarily occasioned some new songs and airs to be introduced; and other singers, with voices of a different compass from those who originally acted the parts, occasioned still more; by which means the greatest part of the musick unavoidably became new. This is the chief, and indeed the only alteration made in the opera; and even to that, I should, in many places, have been forced, much against my will, had it not given a fresh opportunity to Mr. **Dibdin** to display his admirable talents as a musical composer . . .

"The *School for fathers* is added to the title, because the plot is evidently double; and that of Lionel and Clarissa alluded to but one part of it . . ."

Following the text: "A table of the songs. With the names of the several composers. N. B. Those marked thus ** are new, both words and music: but those marked thus *, are only new set." According to this, the overture was a "new overture" by **Dibdin** and with exception of one number, "Ah! pry'thee spare me," with music by **Galuppi**, the entire first act was by **Dibdin**, "To rob them of strength" and "To tell you the truth" having one asterisk, "Ye gloomy thoughts" two. In the second act two numbers, "Talk not to me," and "Go, and, on my truth," were by **Vento**, one each by **Scolari** ("Indeed, forsooth"), **Arne** ("How cursedly vext"), and **Ciampi** ("Come then, pining, peevish lover"); all the others by **Dibdin**, "To fear a stranger" having one asterisk, "Ladies, pray admire," "Poor panting heart," and "We all say the man," two. The third act, with exception of one number ("Why with sighs"), by **Ciampi**, was by **Dibdin**, and was new with exception of the final chorus, "I wonder, I'm sure" and "O, bliss unexpected" having one asterisk, "How can you inhuman," "Hist, soft: let's hear," and "A rascal, a hussy" having two. However, the table of songs is not complete, half a dozen of the songs not being listed at all!

These are "Ah, how delightful the morning" (I, 1), "Immortal pow'rs protect me" (I, 6), "Indulgent pow'rs, if ever" (I, 11), "Hence with caution" (II, 6), "When love gets into a youthful brain" (III, 8), "O dry those tears" (III, 9).

Lionel and Clarissa—Continued.

"To fear a stranger," while listed under **Dibdin** (one asterisk) as in act II, in the text appears in act III, 2! In Johnston's vocal score of "A school for fathers . . . as performed at . . . Drury-Lane" this air also appears as in act II, but as composed by **Galuppi!**

Further comparison discloses some rather startling discrepancies. In the vocal score "Ah how delightful the morning" is attributed to **Scolari,** while the other anonymous airs are not printed. In the vocal score on p. 40 "Come then pining peevish lover" is attributed as in the libretto to **Ciampi,** but in the "table of the songs" of the vocal score it is attributed to **Vinci!** Finally, "Why with sighs" is attributed both in the text and the table of the vocal score to **Potenza** and not to Ciampi.   PR 1241.B4

Liretta e Giannino.   Commedia per musica di Saverio Zini da rappresentarsi nel Teatro de' Fiorentini per second' opera del corrente anno 1795.

Napoli, n. publ., 1795.   47 p.   16ᶜᵐ.

Two acts.   Cast and name of the composer, Valentino **Fioravanti.**

Lisandro.   Dramma serio per musica da rappresentarsi in Genova nel Teatro da S. Agostino il carnevale del 1790 . . .

Genova, Stamperia Gesiniana, n. d.   70, [1] p.   13½ᶜᵐ.

Three acts.   By Francesco Ballani, who is not mentioned and whose "Agesilao," with many alterations, this is.   Dedicatory sonnet by Pietro Maria Leverati, argument, cast, scenario, and name of Gaetano **Isola** ("musica nuova") as composer.   On p. 55–70, argument, cast, name of Vittorio Trento as composer of the music ("tutta nuova"), and description of Filippo Beretti's "Tamar e Selimo ossia Padre e figlio rivali sconosciuti, ballo eroico-tragico di lieto fine in cinque atti."

First performed January 24, 1790, as indicated.   SCHATZ 4906

Lisbeth, drame lyrique en trois actes et en prose, mêlée de musique; representé, pour la première fois, à Paris, sur le Théâtre de l'Opéra-comique de la rue Favart, le 21 nivôse an 5 de la République, ou le 10 janvier 1797, vieux style.   Paroles de Favières.   Musique de Grétry.

Paris, Barba, an VIII de la République [1799–1800].   32 p.   19½ᶜᵐ.

Cast.   SCHATZ 4197

Lise et Colin, ou La surveillance inutile, opéra en deux actes. Paroles de J. B. Eugène-Hus.   Musique de P. Gaveaux.   Représenté pour la première fois à Paris, sur le Théatre de la rue Faydeau, le 17 thermidor [August 4], an quatrième de la République.

Paris, A la Nouveauté, chez les frères Gaveaux, an 4. 1796.   64 p. 19½ᶜᵐ.

Cast and author's dedicatory poem to Dauberval, with footnote:

"J'ai fait cet opéra d'après un ballet charmant de la composition du célèbre Dauberval, donné à Londres, il y a quelques années, sous le titre de *la Fille mal gardée,* et depuis à Bordeaux, à Lyon, à Marseille, sous celui d' *Il n'est qu'un pas du mal au bien.*"

On the last two pages, a complimentary Note to the artists of the Théâtre Feydeau.
                                                                            ML 50.2.L4G2

Intermezzi di **Lisetta, ed Astrobolo.**

These three intermezzi (by unknown author; music by Carlo Francesco **Gasparini**) form p. 84–95 of the libretto of Caldara's opera "La verità nell' inganno," Vienna, November 4, 1717.   The intermezzi were previously performed at Venice Teatro di S. Cassiano, carnival, 1707.   SCHATZ 1490

Lisimaco.   Drama per musica.   Da rappresentarsi nel famoso Theatro Grimano a SS. Giovanni e Paolo.   L'anno MDCLXXIV . . .

Venetia, Francesco Nicolini, 1674.   front., 69 p.   15ᶜᵐ.

Three acts.   By Cristoforo Iwanovich, who is not mentioned.   Publishers' dedication dated December 10, 1673, and notice to the reader, with allusion to Giovanni Maria **Pagliardi** as the composer, argument, and scenario.   SCHATZ 7583

Lisimaco riamato da Alessandro. Drama per musica di Giacomo Sinibaldi da Roma. Riformato all' uso di Venetia da Aurelio Aureli per recitarsi nel Teatro Vendramino à S. Salvatore. L'anno MDCLXXXII . . .

Venetia, Francesco Nicolini, 1682. 60 p. $14\frac{1}{2}^{cm}$.

Three acts. Aureli's dedication dated Venice, January 23, 1682, argument, scenario, cast, and notice to the reader, with name of Giovanni **Legrenzi** as composer ("nova musica"), and remark that lack of time prevented him (Aureli) from writing a new drama,

"onde trà molti de' virtuosi forastieri, che mi sono capitati nelle mani, hò stimato bene lo sciegliere questo Lisimaco del Signor Sinibaldi, rappresentato l'anno passato in Roma avanti la Maestà della regina di Suezia." SCHATZ 5545

List über list. L. A. T. of Mozart's Figaros hochzeit.

Arien und gesaenge aus dem singspiel **List und ungefaehr,** oder Der glueckliche zufall. In drey aufzuegen, von Stephanie dem juengeren, in musik gesetzt von Ernst Lange.

Riga, Julius Conrad Daniel Müller, 1793. 20 p. 17^{cm}.

First performed at Riga, Vietinghof'sches Theater, February 25/March 8, 1793. SCHATZ 5415

Die **listige rache des Sueno.** A. T. of Keiser's Die gezwungene bestaendigkeit.

Die **listige wittwe.** Tr. of Leo's La vedova ingegnosa.

Lisuart und Dariolette oder Die frage und die antwort, eine operette in zwey aufzuegen.

[Wien], Zu finden im Krausischen buchladen, 1766. 46 p. 16^{cm}.

Neither the author, Daniel Schiebeler, nor the composer, Johann Adam **Hiller,** is mentioned. On p. [2], a note to the effect that the piece is based on Chaucer's "The tale of the wife of Bath," as edited by Dryden, and on which tale Voltaire based his "Ce qui plait aux dames."

First performed at Vienna, Kärnthnerthor Theater, January 6, 1767; at Leipzig, Theater beim Rannstaedter Thore, November 25, 1766. SCHATZ 4726

— **Lisuart und Dariolette.** Ein singestueck in drey acten.

Riga, Joh. Friedrich Hartknoch, 1773. 52 p. 18^{cm}.

Neither the author, Schiebeler, nor the composer, **Hiller,** is mentioned. The text is somewhat different from the Vienna text of 1766. For instance, the latter has not the arias, "Gieb, grausames geschick" (I, 1) and "Die prinzessin zu entdecken" (I, 2). This belongs to the three-act version, which Schiebeler brought out at Leipzig on January 7, 1767 (Calmus). SCHAÅZ 4734

— Arien aus **Lisuart und Dariolette,** in musik gesetzt von herrn Hiller. Nuernberg den 24 sten may 1780.

n. i., n. d. 23, [1] p. 16^{cm}.

An altered version of Schiebeler's text. SCHATZ 4727

The little gipsy. A. T. of Arne's May-day.

Little John and the giants: A dramatic opera.

n. i., n. d. 92 p.

A five-act ballad opera, the airs of which are indicated in the text by title. Text by Henry Brooke, vol. iv of whose collected works this appears to be. Acted originally March 27, 1749 at Dublin as "Jack the gyant quiller." Prohibited after first night. Altered in 1754 and again acted at Dublin. Printed 1778 as above. Text preceded by "Prologue" and "Prologue, spoken at the second representation." LONGE 131

The **livery rake, and country lass.** An opera. As it is perform'd by the company of comedians of His Majesty's revels, at the new Theatre in the Hay-Market. With the musick prefix'd to each song. *London, J. Watts, 1733. 2 p. l., 35 p. 21ᶜᵐ.*

One act. By Edward Phillips, who is not mentioned. Ballad opera. Cast and table of the 18 songs. The airs are printed in the text, two of them without title.

First performed, as indicated, October 15, 1733. ML 50.5.L49

Second copy. LONGE 37

Livietta e Tracollo o La contadina astuta.

Two intermezzi by **Pergolesi,** text by Mariani. The Naples, 1734, ed. is not in the L. of C., nor any other ed. with the original title. The work became known also under the alternative title, as "Tracollo," "La finta Polacca," "Tracollo, medico ignorante" (as in the Paris libretto of 1753).

First performed as intermezzi to Pergolesi's "Adriano in Siria" at Naples, Teatro di S. Bartolomeo, October 25, 1734; at Paris at the Académie royale de musique in May 1753.

In his Pergolesi biography Radiciotti has analized (not the original libretto, but) the score preserved at the Naples conservatory. Accordingly, this score (which is *not* Pergolesi's own original score) would seem to contain two singing parts "Livietta" and "Tracollo" besides the mute "Fulvia" and the following arias:

(Int. I) *Vi stò ben? Vi comparisco?* (Livietta); *A una povera Polacca* (Tracollo); *Ecco il povero Tracollo* (Tracollo); *Vado, vado, ed avrai core* (duet);

(Int. II) *Vedo l'aria che s'imbruna* (Tracollo); *Caro perdona mi, placa* (Livietta); *Non si muove, non rifiata* (Tracollo); *Sempre attorno qual palomba* (duet, in place of which other scores, according to Radiciotti, have "Per te ho io nel core" from Pergolesi's "Flaminio." For other final duets *see* below).

It should be noted that the arias "Vi stò ben? Vi comparisco?" and "Non si muove, non rifiata" appear also in Goldoni's "Amor fà l'uomo cieco" text dated 1731 by Wotquenne. As intermezzi of that title were composed by **Pergolesi** and performed with his "La Salustia" at the Teatro di S. Bartolomeo, Naples, winter 1731, it may be that those two arias made part of these intermezzi and that in 1734 they were again used for "Livietta e Tracollo." (*See* Amor fà l'uomo cieco.)

It appears from Radiciotti's analysis, that the Naples score of "Livietta e Tracollo" and presumably the Naples libretto do not agree with the score of "Tracollo, intermède "as published at Paris in 1753 nor with our score of "La contadina astuta, as transcribed from a score preserved at the Brussels Conservatory. The distinguishing feature between these two scores (which coincide completely) and the Naples score is that they contain a third singing part "Sulpizio" besides "Livia" and "Tracollo" resp. "Tracollo medico ignorante." The two scores contain (arias in italics):

(Int. I) *Lo voglio scannare* (Sulpizio) Al cospetto di tutti gl'elementi; *Vi stò ben? Vi comparisco* (Livia) Ma gli scherzi lasciam; *Ad un povero Polacco* (Tracollo) Si, dormono ancor ed io Misera, che ascoltai; *Tu sei troppo scelerato* (Livia) Pietà Livietta mia; *Ecco il povero Tracollo* (Tracollo) Livia se tanto barbara; *Vado, vado, ed avrai* (duet).

(Int. II) *Vedo l'aria che s'imbruna* (Tracollo) Affè che il far; *Questo—foglio, questa carta* (Livia) Questa è passata ben; *Caro, perdonami, placa* (Livia) Gli credo o non gli credo; *Non si muove, non rifiata* (Tracollo) Affè, ch'ella è già morta! *Io non posso resistere* (Livia) Comincia à intenerirsi; *A quella che t'adora* (duet).

— **Il finto pazzo.** Intermezzo per musica da rappresentarsi nel Theatro Nuovo dell' opera pantomima de piccoli Hollandesi del Nicolini.

Brunsviga, heredi di Keiteli, n. d. 15 unnumb. p. 20ᶜᵐ.

Two parts. By Tommaso Mariani. Cast and name of Giov. Battista **Pergolesi** as the composer.

The characters are Livietta, Tracollo and "Fulvia e Facenda, che non parlano" and the libretto contains the following (arias in italics):

(Int. I) *Vi stò ben? vi comparisco?* (Liv.) Ma lasciamo li scherzi; *Ad um povero Polacco* (Tracollo) Dormono a sonno pieno; *Senti . . . non sarà mai* (Liv.) Dunque, Livietta mia; *Bella mia, se son tuo sposo* (Tracollo. From Pergolesi's Il maestro di musica) Via, risolva una volta; *Vado a morte, ed avrai* (duet).

Livietta e Tracollo—Continued.

(Int. II) *Vedo l'aria, che s'imbruna* (Tracollo) Par che ci pigli gusto; *Caro perdonami, placa* (Livietta) Gli credo, o non gli credo; *Non si muove, non rifiata* (Tracollo) Ah Livietta mia; *Dimmi a me, Tu mi vuoi bene?* (duet).

First performed, as indicated, 1749; at Dresden Hoftheater, August 5, 1747.

Schatz 7891

— **Il ladro convertito per amore.** Farsa in musica da rappresentarsi per intermezzo nel Teatro Tron di S. Cassiano. Il carnovale dell' anno 1750.

Venezia, Modesto Fenzo, 1750. 19 p. 15^{cm}.

Two parts. Cast. Author not mentioned and unknown to Schatz, but the characters are "Livietta" and "Tracollo" and "Fulvia che non parla." Consequently, this pointed to a later title of **Pergolesi's** "Livietta e Tracollo," text by Mariani and a comparison of this and "Il finto pazzo" established the fact.

The characters are Livietta, Tracollo and the mute Fulvia. The libretto contains the following (arias in italics):

(Int. I) *Vi stò ben? Vi comparisca?* (Livietta) Ma lasciamo gli scherzi; *Ad un povero Polacco* (Tracollo) Dormono a sonno pien; Perche ridi, mustaccio; *Senti, non sarà mai* (*Livietta*) Via risolva una volta; *Deh non lasciarmi, ingrata* (Tracollo) Invano ti lusinghi; *Vado a morte, ed avrai* (duet).

(Int. II) *Vedo l'aria, che s'imbruna* (Tracollo) Par, che ci pigli gusto; *Caro perdonami, placa* (Livietta) Gli credo o non gli credo? *Non si muove, non rifiata* (Tracollo) Ah! Livietta mia; *Contento tu sarai* (duet, from Pergolesi's La serva padrone).

Schatz 7906

La locanda. Dramma giocoso per musica da rappresentarsi nel Teatro Giustiniani di S. Moisè il carnovale dell' anno 1771.

Venezia, Antonio Graziosi, 1771. 60, [1] p. 17½^{cm}.

Three acts. Cast, scenario, and names of Giovanni Bertati as author and of Giuseppe **Gazzaniga** as the composer.

Schatz 3668

La locanda. Commedia per musica in due atti. Da rappresentarsi nell' Teatro Reale di corte l'anno 1792.

Vienna, n. publ., n. d. 60 p. 17^{cm}.

Two acts. By Giovanni Bertati with revisions by Girolamo Tonioli, both unmentioned. **Paisiello** is mentioned as the composer.

First performed July 10, 1792, as indicated; at London, Little theatre in the Haymarket, February 14, 1792.

Schatz 7634

— **Il fanatico in berlina.** Dramma giocoso per musica da rappresentarsi nel Teatro di S. A. S. il Signor principe di Carignano nell' autunno dell' anno 1792.

Torino, Onorato Derossi, n. d. 51, [1] p. 15^{cm}.

Two acts. Giovanni Bertati's "La locanda" text with modifications. Cast and name of **Paisiello** as the composer.

First performed at Genoa, Teatro di S. Agostino, spring of 1791. Schatz 7635

— **La locanda:** A comic opera, as represented at the Theatre Royal, Hay-market.

London, H. Reynell, 1792. 75 p. 19^{cm}.

Two acts. Cast and note on p. [3]: "The music composed expressly for the occasion, by the celebrated **Paesiello** . . . the poetry by Signor Bertati, with additions and alterations by G. Tonioli." English text faces Italian.

First performed, as indicated, February 14, 1792.

Bound in with this is the libretto of Shield's The farmer, 8th ed., London, T. Cadell, 1791.

Schatz 7672

La locanda—Continued.

— Lo **strambo in berlina**; dramma giocoso per musica da rappresentarsi nel Reggio Teatro di S. Carlo della Principessa, la primavera dell' anno 1795.

Lisbona, Simone Taddeo Ferreira, 1795.   77 p.   15ᶜᵐ.

Two acts.   Bertati's text with modifications.   Cast and name of **Paisiello** as the composer.   SCHATZ 7685

La locandiera.   Dramma giocoso per musica da rappresentarsi nel Pubblico Teatro di Lucca l'autunno dell' anno 1798 . . .

Lucca, Bonsignori, 1798.   32 p.   17ᶜᵐ.

Two acts.   Cast, scenario, name of Alessandro **La Motte Foucher** as composer ("musica tutta nuova") and initials of the author, A. L., who says in a prefatory note that the text is based on Goldoni.   SCHATZ 5358

La locandiera.   Dramma giocoso per musica da rappresentarsi nel Piccolo Teatro di S. A. E. di Sassonia.

Dresda, n. publ., 1776.   157 p.   16ᶜᵐ.

Three acts.   By Domenico Poggi, who is not mentioned.   Scenario and name of Antonio **Salieri** as the composer.   German title-page, "Die gastwirthinn," and text by Ludwig Zehnmark face Italian.

First performed 1776 at Dresden, as indicated; at Vienna, Burgtheater, June 9, 1773; and at the Kärthnerthortheater, June 8, 1773.   SCHATZ 9301

La locandiera di spirito.   Commedia per musica da rappresentarsi nel Teatro Nuovo sopra Toledo nell' autunno del corrente anno 1768.

Napoli, Vincenzo Mazzola-Vocola, 1768.   2 p. l., 66 p.   16ᶜᵐ.

Three acts.   Author not mentioned and unknown to Schatz.   Scenario, cast, and name of Niccolò **Piccinni** as the composer.   SCHATZ 8128

La locandiera vivace, ballet.   *See* Gardi's Il nuovo convitato di pietra.

Lock and key: a musical entertainment, in two acts, performed at the Theatre Royal, Covent-Garden.   By Prince Hoare, Esq.

London, T. N. Longman, 1796.   48 p.   21ᶜᵐ.

Cast.   The compiler-composer, William **Shield**, is not mentioned.   In Preston and Son's vocal score the overture is headed as composed by William **Parke** and "For moments to view" as by **Paisiello**.

First performed February 2, 1796.   LONGE 238

Lodoiska, comédie en trois actes, en prose, mêlée d'ariettes.   Représentée, pour la première fois, par les Comédiens italiens ordinaires du roi, le premier août 1791.   Paroles de M. Jaure.   Musique de M. Kreutzer.

Paris, Fiévée, [etc.], 1792.   39 p.   20ᶜᵐ.   SCHATZ 5269

— La **Lodoiska**: Dramma per musica da rappresentarsi nel Regio Teatro di S. Carlo della Principessa in occasione di celebrare il felicissimo giorno natalizio di Sua Maestà Fedelissima D. Maria I . . . li 17 decembre 1796.

Lisbona, Simone Taddeo Ferreira, 1796.   189 p.   14½ᶜᵐ.

Two acts.   Portuguese and Italian text, of which a footnote on p. 5 says: "Tutti i versi virgolati sono dell' originale [!], tutti gli altri sono del Sig. cav. Baldinotti, poeta estemporaneo."

Cast and note on p. 7:

Lodoiska—Continued.

"La musica del dramma è del celebre Sig. maestro **Kreutzer** e d'altri autori rinomati, diretta dal Sig. Antonio Leal Moreira, compositore di musica della Real Camera di Sua Maestà Fedelissima . . ."

First performed at Monza, Teatro Arciducale, fall of 1793. SCHATZ 5269

La Lodoiska. Dramma per musica da rappresentarsi nel nobilissimo Teatro La Fenice il carnovale dell' anno 1796.

Venezia, Stamperia Valvasense, n. d. 72 p. 18^{cm}.

Three acts. On p. 7, "La poesia è tutta nuova del dott. F. G.[onella] di F.[errara]," and Joh. Simon **Mayr** is mentioned as the composer. Argument and cast. On p. [25]–39 preface, argument, cast, and description of Lauchlin Duquesny's "Cook, ossia Gl'Inglesi in Othaiti, ballo pantomimmo in cinque atti." The second ballet had the title, "Il mercato di Pozzuolo ossia Il speciale ingamato." The composers of the music are not mentioned.

First performed January 26, 1796. SCHATZ 6158

— Lodoiska. Dramma per musica da rappresentarsi nel Regio-Ducal Teatro alla Scala di Milano il carnevale dell' anno 1800 . . .

Milano, Gio. Batista Bianchi, n. d. 70 p. 60$\frac{1}{2}$^{cm}.

Two acts. Impresario's dedication, cast, scenario, and name of Joh. Simon **Mayr** as the composer. Sometimes attributed to Gaetano Rossi, but comparison with Schatz 6158 proves that it is but F. Gonella di Ferrara's text in two acts, with numerous alterations. For instance, the first scene of act first is entirely different in the two versions, but to scene second has been added everything preceding the words, "Principessa, se vuoi." The second act shows comparatively few changes in the dialogue, but in this act, too, most of the arias do not appear in the original version, and, for instance, in II, 5 the aria, "Quel nobil core," has been added, where originally there was none at all. On p. 35–42, prefatory note, argument, description, and cast of Gaspare Ronzi's "Ginevra di Scozia, ballo eroico pantomimo." The second ballet had the title, "Ergasto, ed Eurilla vinti dall' amore." The composers of the music are not mentioned.

First performed at Milan, La Scala, December 26, 1799. SCHATZ 6159

La Lodoiska, ballet. *See* Mayr's Telemaco.

Lodoiska, ballet. *See* Paër's La Rossana.

Lodoiska; an opera, in three acts, performed, for the first time, by His Majesty's servants, at the Theatre Royal, Drury-Lane, on Monday, June 9th, 1794. Written by J. P. Kemble. The music composed, and selected from Cherubini, Kreutzer, and Andreozzi, by Mr. Storace.

London, G. G. and J. Robinson, n. d. pl., 58 p. 20^{cm}.

Cast. LONGE 228

Lodovico Pio. Dramma per musica . . . Cantato per le vacanze del carnevale nel 1687. Nel nob. Collegio Tolomei di Siena da quei Signori convittori.

Siena, Stamp. del Publ., 1687. 6 p. l., 70, [1] p. 14^{cm}.

Three acts. Dedication dated Siena, February 3, 1687, and signed by the author, Girolamo Gigli, argument, cast, and notice to the reader, with name of Giuseppe **Fabbrini** as composer, and in which Gigli says:

"Eccomi . . . col terzo dramma, quando forse potea bastarmi avervi attediato con il secondo . . .

"Troverete, che Don Chisciotte usa tal volta versi presi, o dal Tasso, o dall' Ariosto. Non mi crediate sì temerario, che io pretenda mettere in burla due autori da meriveriti, e stimati come maestri della poesia; hò solamente voluto esprimere i pensieri del personaggio, co'versi di que' degni poeti, per far nascer il ridicolo dal contraposto, facendo servire una grande autorità, ad una gran follia . . ." ML 50.2.L4F2

Die löwenjagd. A. T. of Wenzel Müller's Die verschwoerung der Odaliken.

Die loewenritter. Erster theil. Ein schauspiel mit gesang in vier aufzuegen, nach der geschichte des herrn Spiess fuer die Marinellische schaubuehne von Karl Friedrich Hensler. Die musik ist von herrn Ferdinand Kauer . . .

> *Wien, gedruckt bey Mathias Andreas Schmidt, 1799.*   *104 p.*   *19½*^{cm}.

First performed at Vienna, Theater in der Leopoldstadt, September 5, 1799.

ML 50.2.L5K2

Lord Blunder's confession; or, Guilt makes a coward. A new ballad opera . . . By the author of Vanelia, an opera.

> *London, T. Reynolds, 1733.*   *67 p.*   *18½*^{cm}.

Three acts. Table of the 21 airs used in the opera indicated by title. Author unknown to Clarence. No performance recorded.   LONGE 176

Songs, duets, etc in the new pantomime called **Lord Mayor's day;** or, A flight from Lapland. As performed at the Theatre-Royal, in Covent-Garden, with the grand procession, etc.

> *London, T. Cadell, 1783.*   *23 p.*   *21*^{cm}.

Cast. One act, after which (p. 12–23), "A grand historical procession of the several Companies, with their respective pageants, and the chief magistrates belonging to the City of London from its foundation." Two glees, one indicated as composed by Dr. **Rogers,** one by William **Shields,** formed part of this. The text of the entertainment was by John O'Keefe. Neither he is mentioned, nor the composer, but William **Shield** is known to have been responsible for the music.

Performed November 25, 1782.   ML 52.2.L6

The lord of the manor, a comic opera, as it is performed at the Theatre Royal Drury-Lane, with a preface by the author.

> *London, T. Evans, 1781.*   *xxvi, 96 p.*   *21*^{cm}.

Three acts. Cast. By John Burgoyne, who is not mentioned. His lengthy but important preface after apologizing "to every man who has been charged with this foundling"—the anonymous piece had even been attributed to Sheridan—states that the piece "was written last summer in the country for mere amusement" without any satirical design on the recruiting service, and he then indulges in "a few thoughts upon opera, and particularly that species of it attempted in the ensuing pages." A few quotations will show that Burgoyne's ideas are worthy of notice by the historians of English opera:

"I have no hesitation in pronouncing an opinion, that the adopting what is called recitative into a language, to which it is totally incongruous, is the cause of failure in an English serious opera much oftener than the want of musical powers in the performers . . .

"I will not contend (though I have my doubts) that it is impossible for genius to invent, and for voice to deliver, a sort of recitative that the English language will bear. But it must be widely different from the Italian. If any specimens can yet be produced of it's having been effected, they will be found to consist only of a few lines introductive of the air which is to follow, and as such received by the ear just as symphony would be. Very few serious pieces, except Artaxerxes, can be recollected upon our Theatre where it has not entirely failed, even when assisted by action: in oratorios it is, with a few exceptions, and those sustained by accompaniment, a soporific that even the thunder of Handel's chorusses are hardly loud enough to overcome . . .

"I trust that in contending against musical dialogue in English, I shall not be understood to think that all music is inapplicable to the higher compositions of our stage. On the contrary I am convinced that under judicious management music is capable of giving them effect beyond what our best authors can attain without it—music can add energy to Shakespeare himself. Indignant as an English audience would be to hear King Lear deliver himself in recitative, I believe no person, who had a heart or taste, ever contemplated the mute groupe of Cordelia with the aged

The **lord of the manor**—Continued.

parent asleep in her lap, and the physician watching by, without an encrease of sensibility from the soft music which Mr. Garrick introduced into that scene . . .

"One branch of comic opera which meets with succes on our stage is evidently a graft from the Burletta of the Italians; and little as I may admire it in general, I will venture to say, respectively to the writing, it is improved in our soil. Midas, the Golden Pippin, and some others, considered as pieces of parody and burlesque, are much better than any Italian burletta I know . . .

"I cannot easily bring myself to allow the higher branch of our Comic Opera, to be of foreign extraction. From the time the Beggar's Opera appeared, we find pieces in prose, with songs interspersed, so approaching to regular comedy in plot, incident, and preservation of character, as to make them a distinct species from any thing we find abroad—and is it too much to add that the sense, wit, and humour to be found in some of them are sterling English marks by which we may claim the species as our own? . . .

"They who are unacquainted with the Paris theatre, are referred for judgement upon this subject to the Deserter, Zemira and Azor, and other direct translations; and to Daphne and Amintor, and Thomas and Sally, and other after-pieces, very good in their kind, but written after the French manner. The Padlock is above this class in display of characters; and the French have nothing upon their musical comic stage to compare as resembling comedy, with Love in a Village, or the Maid of the Mill, or to take still greater credit to our theatre, the Duenna.

"The Lord of the Manor, although the leading incident of the story is professedly taken from the Silvain of Marmontel, is an humble attempt at the species of opera which I have ventured to call English, and to describe as a drama the next in gradation below regular comedy, and which might perhaps be carried a step above it . . .

"In a representation which is to hold "a mirror up to nature," and which ought to draw its chief applause from reason, vocal music should be confined to express the feelings of the passions, but never to express the exercise of them. Song, in any action in which reason tells us it would be unnatural to sing, must be preposterous. To fight a duel, to cudgel a poltroon in cadence, may be borne in a burletta, upon the same principle that in the serious opera we see heroes fight lions and monsters, and sometimes utter their last struggles for life in song and die in strict time and tune: but these liberties would be totally inadmissable in the kind of drama which I am recommending . . .

"Music, therefore, if employed to express action, must be confined to dumb shew. It is the very essence of pantomime; and we have lately seen upon the opera stage how well a whole story may be told in dance; . . . It should always be the accessory and not the principal subject of the drama; but at the same time spring out of it in such a manner that the difference can hardly be discerned, and that it should seem neither the one nor the other could be spared . . . It would be affectation in me, as well as ingratitude to the public, to deny the pleasure I have had in the very favourable reception of this piece. At the same time I trust that I am duly sensible how much of the success is to be attributed to the exertions of the performers, the merits of the orchestra, and the excellence of Mr. [William] **Jackson's** composition . . ."

First performed at London, Drury Lane, December 27. 1780 (Genest), November 27, 1780 (Oulton).   Longe 91

— The **lord of the manor,** a comic opera, as it is performed at the Theatre Royal, Drury-Lane, with a preface by the author.
Philadelphia, William Spotswood, 1790.   xv, [16]–71 p.   15½*cm*.
Three acts. Without names of Burgoyne or **Jackson.**   ML 50.6.L62

— The **lord of the manor,** a comic opera, in three acts. As performed with universal applause, by the American company.
Philadelphia, H. Taylor, 1791.   63 p.   18½*cm*.
First performance in America unknown to Seilhamer and me.   ML 50.6.L63

The **lords maske.**   *See* A relation of the late royall entertainment.

Lorezzo, ballet.   *See* Campobasso's Antigona.

Lorezzo, ballet.   *See* Federici's L'Olimpiade.

Lotario.

Three-act opera, by Georg Friedrich **Händel.** Altered version of text by Matteo Noris, "Berengario, rè d'Italia."
First performed at London, Haymarket, December 2, 1729.
Not in L. of C.

— **Judith, gemahlin kayser Ludewigs des Frommen** oder Die siegende unschuld, in einer opera auf dem Hamburgischen schauplatze ao. 1732. vorgestellet. [vignette]

Hamburg, mit Stromerischen schrifften, n. d.   Unpaged.   18½^{cm}.

Three acts.   Argument and note that the translation of the recitatives is by Johann Georg Hamann, their composition by Georg Philipp **Telemann.**   It is not mentioned that the arias were taken from **Händel's** "Lotario" (by Matteo Noris) and F. **Chelleri's** "L'innocenza difesa" (by F. Silvani).   The German translation of the arias is added to the Italian text.
First performed, as indicated, November 27, 1732.   SCHATZ 4481

Lottchen am hofe.   Eine komische oper in drey aufzuegen von C. F. Weisse.   Dritte verbesserte auflage.

Leipzig, Dykische buchhandlung, 1776.   104 p.   16½^{cm}.

On p. [2], the note: "Nach der Ninette à la cour des herrn Favart."   The composer, Johann Adam **Hiller,** is not mentioned.
First performed at Leipzig, Theater am Rannstaedter Thore, May 7, 1767 (Schatz), April 24, 1767 (Calmus).   SCHATZ 4728

— Arien und gesaenge aus der comischen opera: **Lottchen,** oder Das bauernmaegdchen am hofe.   In dreyen akten.

Altona, 1770, n. publ.   20 p.   16½^{cm}.

Neither Weisse nor **Hiller** is mentioned.
First performed at Altona, Theater "Sansouci," 1770.   SCHATZ 4729

— **Lottchen am hofe.**   Eine komische oper in drey aufzuegen.

C. F. Weisse, Komische opern, Carlsruhe, 1778, th. i, 96 p.   18½^{cm}.

On p. [2], the note: "Nach der *Ninette à la cour* des herrn Favart."   The composer, **Hiller,** is not mentioned.   ML 49.A2W2

La lotteria militare.   A. T. of Le Messier's ballet Accampamento.

The lottery.   A farce.   As it is acted at the Theatre-Royal in Drury-Lane.   By His Majesty's servants.   With the musick prefix'd to each song.   The 3d ed., with the addition of a new scene.

London, J. Watts, 1732.   4 p. l., 36 p.   20^{cm}.

On p. [ii]-[iv], "Books printed for J. Watts," p. [iv] containing a list of ballad "Operas with the musick."   One act, prologue, and epilogue.   Cast and table of the 22 songs.   Ballad opera.   The airs are printed in the text, with their titles, except no. 1, "A lottery is a taxation;" no. 5, "How hapless is the virgin's fate;" no. 6, "Farewell ye hills and valleys;" no. 8, "When love is lodg'd within the hearts;" no. 9, "Alas! my Lord, you're too severe;" no. 10, "I've often heard;" no. 12, "Dear Sir, be not in such a passion;" no. 13, "Ah think, my Lord!" no. 15, "When the candidate offers;" no. 21, "Since you whom I lov'd," which are all marked as "set by Mr. **Seedo**;" and no. 22, "That the world is a lottery," which has neither title nor composer's name.   The text is by Henry Fielding, who is not mentioned.
First performed, as indicated, January 1, 1732.   ML 50.5.L68

— The **lottery.**   By Henry Fielding, Esq.

[292]-316 p.   19^{cm}.   (Collection of the most esteemed farces and entertainments, t. ii, Edinburgh, 1792.)

One act.   Drury Lane cast.   SCHATZ 11753B

Arien und gesaenge aus **Louise**. Eine oper in drey aufzuegen. In musik gesetzt von Friedrich Ludwig Benda.

Riga, Julius Conrad Daniel Mueller, 1794. 20 p. 17^{cm}.

The librettist, Ernst Friedrich Jester, is not mentioned.
First performed at Königsberg, Ackermann'sches schauspielhaus, January 16, 1791; at Riga on May 30 (June 10), 1794. Schatz 765

Love and innocence, a pastoral serenata. As performed at Marybone-Gardens. Set to music by Mr. Hook.

London, T. Becket and P. A. de Hondt, 1769. 2 p. l., 27, [1] p. 19^{cm}.

The last (unnumb.) p. contains publisher's booklist.
Two acts. Author not mentioned, and unknown to Clarence. Longe 40

Love and loyalty. An opera.

[237]–293 p. 21½^{cm}. (The miscellaneous works of A. M'Donald, London, J. Murray, 1791.)

Detached copy. Three acts. Neither a composer nor a performance recorded by Clarence. Longe 282

Love and magic. A. T. of The enchanter.

Love and money; or, The fair Caledonian. A musical farce, in one act, as performed at the Theatres-Royal, Drury-Lane, and the Haymarket, with universal applause. By the late Mr. Benson . . .

London, J. Wallis, n. d. 32, [8] p. 21^{cm}.

Cast. The [8] p. contain "addresses" and list of subscribers. The composer, Samuel **Arnold**, is not mentioned.
First performed August 29, 1795. Longe 246

Love and revenge; or, The vintner outwitted: an opera; as acted at the new Theatre in the Hay-Market.

London, 2 p. l., [3]–56 p. 19½^{cm}.

Three acts, with prologue, "spoke by Mr. Fielding." Author not mentioned and not recorded by Clarence. Ballad opera. The airs of the 37 songs are merely indicated by title. Cast and dedication.
First performed 1729, as indicated. ML 50.5.L69
Second copy. Longe 105

Love and riches reconcil'd, a masque. *See* Love's a lottery.

Love at first sight; a ballad farce, of two acts. As performed at the Theatre Royal in Drury Lane.

London, T. Becket and P. A. de Hondt, 1763. 2 p. l., 35, [1] p. 19½^{cm}.

Two acts. By Thomas King, who is not mentioned. Cast and prefatory note. The eleven airs, except the last, are indicated by title.
First performed, as indicated, October 17, 1763. Longe 36
Second copy (20½^{cm}.). Longe 193

Love at first sight: or, The wit of a woman. A ballad opera of two acts, by Joseph Yarrow, comedian . . .

York, Printed by Thomas Gent, 1742. 6 p. l., 108 p. 17½^{cm}.

On p. 54–68, "Nancy, or, the parting lovers" and nine other songs that have no connection with the play, and on p. [69]–108 the farce, "Trick upon trick, or, The vintner outwitted." A farce, as perform'd by the York company of comedians."
Two acts, prologue, epilogue. Dedication and list of subscribers. The 21 airs used are indicated by title in the text. Longe 321

The **love distracted maid.**   Tr. A. L. of Dalayrac's Nina.

Airs, duets, trios, etc in the new comic opera, called **Love finds the way.**   As performed at the Theatre-Royal in Covent-Garden.

London, J. Bell, 1777.   2 p. l., 24 p.   20^{cm}.

Three acts.   Cast.   The text is an abridgment of "The School for guardians" by Thomas Hull.   Neither he nor the composer is mentioned.

First performed, as indicated, November 18, 1777 (Genest).   ML 50.2.L6

Love in a camp or Patrick in Prussia.

Text by John O'Keefe, music selected and composed by William **Shield.**
First performed at London, Covent Garden, February 17, 1786 (Genest).
No libretto with the O. T. in L. of C.

— **Patrick in Prussia,** or Love in a camp; a comic opera, in two acts, with all the original songs; as performed at the Theatres Royal Covent-Garden, and Smock-Alley: being a sequel to the Poor Soldier, written by John O'Keefe, Esq . . .   From the author's original manuscript.

Dublin, G. Perrin, 1786.   35 p.   16$\frac{1}{2}$^{cm}.
Cast.   LONGE 148

Love in a riddle.   A pastoral.   As it is acted at the Theatre-Royal, by His Majesty's servants.   Written by Mr. Cibber.

London, J. Watts, 1719 [!].   2 p. l., 96 p.   20^{cm}.   [Bound with Gay, John.   The beggar's opera.   London, 1728]

Three acts, prologue, and epilogue.   Ballad opera.   Cast.   On verso of t.-p. a publisher's book list, dated January 3, 1728–9.   "The tunes to the songs" are printed on p. [75]–96, with their titles and numbered consecutively for each act: 15, 22, 18, total 55.   In the text the airs appear numbered but without title.   The air to which the epilogue was to be sung appears in the text.

The piece was printed 1729, not 1719 as in the title.   It was first performed as indicated, January 7, 1729.   (*See* Damon and Phillida.)   ML 50.5.B3

Love in a village; a comic opera.   As it is performed at the Theatre Royal in Covent-Garden.

London, Printed by W. Griffin for J. Newbery and W. Nicoll [etc.], 1763.   3 p. l., 78 p.   19^{cm}.

Three acts.   Cast.   By Isaac Bickerstaffe, who is not mentioned and who says in his dedication to Mr. Beard:

"If this opera is considered merely as a piece of dramatic writing, it will certainly be found to have very little merit: in that light no one can think more indifferently of it than I do myself; but I believe I may venture to assert, on your opinion, that some of the songs are tollerable; that the music is more pleasing than has hitherto appeared in any composition of this kind; and the words better adapted, considering the nature of the airs, which are not common ballads, than could be expected, supposing any degree of poetry to be preserved in the versification . . ."

The text was based on "The village opera" and other old plays.   Thomas Aug. **Arne,** who partly composed, partly compiled the music, is not mentioned, nor are other composers mentioned in this edition.

First performed on December 8, 1762, as indicated.   LONGE 42

— . . . **Love in a village;** a comic opera.   As it is performed at the Theatre Royal in Covent-Garden.   Distinguishing also the variations of the theatre.   Regulated from the prompt-book, by permission of the managers, by Mr. Wild, prompter.

London, John Bell, 1781.   front., iv, [2], 57, [1] p.   18$\frac{1}{2}$^{cm}.

The front. is a port. of Mrs. Wrighten as Madge.   Cast, Bickerstaff's dedication to Beard, and "A table of the [42] songs, with the names of the several composers."

Love in a village—Continued.

These are **Abel, Agus, Abos, Arne, Baildon, Boyce, Bernard, Carey, Festing, Galuppi, Geminiani, Giardini, Händel, Howard, Paradies, Weldon.** Almost one half of the music was by Thomas Augustine **Arne.**

From this table it appears that Abel's overture was "new," that Howard's "Oh had I been by fate decreed" and "How much superior beauty awes," Arne's "Still in hopes to get the better," "Believe me dear aunt," "Go, naughty man, I can't abide you," and "Well come let us hear" "were composed on purpose for this opera" and that the ballad tunes "Larry Gorgan" and "St. Patrick's day" were introduced. It is curious to note that Walsh's vocal score does not mention Bernard, Abel, Carey, Weldon on title page and that Longman & Broderip's vocal score does not mention Abos and Bernard, but adds **Oswald.** LONGE 322

— **Love in a village.** A comic opera. By Isaac Bickerstaff. Adapted for theatrical representation, as performed at the Theatre-Royal, Covent-Garden. Regulated from the prompt-book, by permission of the managers . . .

London, John Bell, 1791. front., 1 p. l., 5, [10]–90, [3] p. 15ᶜᵐ. (J. Bell, British Theatre, London, 1791–1797, v. 1.)

The front. represents Mrs. Billington as Rosetta in this opera. The 1 p. l. is an engraved serial title page with a scene from the same opera. The front. is dated September 28, 1790, the serial title page, January 6, 1791. Author's dedication, prefatory note, Drury-Lane and Covent-Garden casts. PR 1241 B4

— **Love in a village.** A comic opera. Written by Mr. Bickerstaff. As performed at the New theatre, in Philadelphia.

[Philadelphia] From the press of M. Carey, March 1, 1794. 58 p. 16½ᶜᵐ.

Three acts. Cast, and on p. 3. "Table of the [42] songs, with the names of the several composers:" **Abel, Abos, Argus, Arne, Baildon, Bernard, Boyce, Carey, Festing, Galuppi, Geminiani, Giardini, Händel, Howard, Larry Grogan [!], Paradies, Weldon.**
First performed in America at the Southwark Theatre, Philadelphia, March, 1767. ML 50.6.L72

Love in every age. A. T. of The four seasons.

Love in low life. A. T. of Carey's The press gang.

Love in Mexico. A. T. of Arnold's New Spain.

Love in the city; a comic opera. As it is performed at the Theatre Royal in Covent-Garden. The words written, and the music compiled by the author of Love in a village. The second edition.

London, W. Griffin, 1767. 2 p. l., iii, [1], 69, [3] p. 19½ᶜᵐ.

The [3] p. at end contain a book list by the publisher.
Three acts. Cast, dedication, and preface in which Isaac Bickerstaffe says:
"To those who find fault with an opera, merely for being such, it will be in vain to say any thing in defence of this; indeed the absurdity attach'd to the musical drama is so glaring, that there seems no great penetration necessary to discover it; and consequently any one who will cry out sing-song or tweedle-dee, is capable of turning it into ridicule. Yet it should be considered, that its absurdity, gross as it is, constitutes, in a great measure, its power of pleasing . . .
"The music of this piece is almost totally comic, and generally characteristic; I would therefore advise those of my auditors, who do not taste it at the first hearing, to give it a second, nay a third or a fourth; and after that, should they never desire to hear it again, I can only tell them they happen to dislike what has been repeatedly approved, by all the polite nations of Europe . . ."
Charles **Dibdin** (not mentioned) assisted Bickerstaffe in the musical make-up of this pasticcio, which became better known in an altered version as "The romp." The vocal score mentions in the headings (besides Dibdin): **Vento, Cocchi, Galuppi, Piccinni, Barthelemon, Pergolesi** and **Jommelli.**
First performed, as indicated, February 21, 1767. LONGE 32

Love in the East; or, Adventures of twelve hours: A comic opera, in three acts. Written by the author of The stranger at home. As performed at the Theatre-Royal, Drury-Lane.

London, W. Lowndes, 1788. 3 p. l., 81 p. 20^{cm}.

Cast and dedication, dated E. J. H., March 4, 1788, by J.[ames] C.[obb], to Thomas **Linley,** who composed the music.
First performed February 25, 1788, as indicated.   LONGE 110

The lover his own rival. A ballad opera. As it is perform'd at the New Theatre in Goodman's Fields. By.Mr. Langford.

London, J. Watts, 1736. 4 p. l. 32, [3] p. 20½ ^{cm}.

One act, prologue sung to the second part of the "Dutch skipper," epilogue sung to the tune of "Sir Thomas I cannot." Cast, preface in which Abraham Langford expresses his appreciation of the "kind reception" given to his piece, due largely to the "care and chearfulness" of the performers, inducing him "probably [to] produce another attempt of the same kind," and table of the 17 songs. Ballad opera, the airs of which are printed in the text with title, except song no. VI, "Like me, the tender dove laments," which is marked as "set by Mr. **Stanley.**"
First performed 1736, as indicated.   ML 50.5.L7

— The **lover his own rival.** A ballad opera. As it is perform'd at the Theatre Royal in Covent-Garden. By Mr. Langford.

London, J. Watts, 1753. 4 p. l., 32, [3] p. 20½^{cm}.

Except for the title page, exactly like the edition of 1736.   LONGE 198

The lovers opera. As it is performed at the Theatre-Royal, by His Majesty's servants. By Mr. Chetwood . . . The second edition, with alterations.

London, Printed and sold by A. Dodd, 1729. 3 p. l., 34 p. 19^{cm}.

One act, with prologue. Cast and same preface as quoted from the 3d ed., only somewhat shorter. No table of songs in this edition. Nor are the 39 [!] airs printed in the text. They are indicated only by title.
According to Clarence, first performed at Drury Lane, May 14, 1730, but the title page of this libretto would seem to establish 1729 as the year of performance, and, in fact, Tufts gives May 14, 1729, as date of first performance.   LONGE 49

— **The lovers opera.** As it is performed at the Theatre-Royal, by His Majesty's servants. By Mr. Chetwood . . . 3d ed., with alterations: and the musick prefix'd to each song.

London, J. Watts, 1730. 4 p. l., 40 p. 20^{cm}.

One act, with prologue. Cast, and preface in which William Rufus Chetwood says: "This attempt being begun soon after the run of the celebrated *Beggar's Opera* (to mention which gives me some confusion, while I am speaking of my own weak endeavors) the reader may perhaps find some new tunes since made use of in other entertainments of this kind. I must declare the songs thereto were made before I ever saw any such performances . . . The town, thro' their good-nature, having given this trifle a more favourable reception than I could have expected, the printer has, to compleat this third edition, been at the expence of adding the tunes to each song."
Ballad opera with table of the 32 songs. The corresponding airs are printed in the text with their titles, no. 29, "When beauty our courage will try," being marked as "compos'd by Mr. **Charke.**"   ML 50.5.L72

Love's a lottery, and a woman the prize. With a new masque, call'd Love and riches reconcil'd. As it was acted by His Majesties servants at the Theatre in Lincolns-Inn-Fields . . .

London, Daniel Brown and Edmund Rumball, 1699. 4 p. l., 40 p. 21½^{cm}.

The masque on p. 36–40. Neither the author, Joseph Harris, is mentioned, nor the composer of the music.
First performed 1699, as indicated.   LONGE 240

Love's labyrinth. A. T. of Arnold's The banditti.

Love's mistresse: or The Queens masque. As it was three times presented before both Their Majesties, within the space of eight dayes: In the presence of sundry forraigne ambassadors. Publikely acted by the Queenes comedians, at the Phoenix in Drury-Lane. The second impression, corrected by the author, Thomas Heywood . . .

London, Printed by John Raworth, for John Crouch, 1640. [72] p. 17ᶜᵐ.

Five acts. The masque is here entered without further comment, as it contains so few opportunities for music (dances and a few songs) as to be negligible for the present purpose. It is more a drama than a masque. LONGE 61

Love's paradice. A. T. of The grove.

The **loves of Mars and Venus;** a play set to musick: written by Mr. Motteux . . .

London, A. Bettersworth and F. Clay, 1722. [51]–84 p. 15ᶜᵐ.

Three acts and prologue. "An explanation of the fable" (p. 83–84), cast, dedication and preface in which Motteux says:
"This musical play or masque was written to be inserted into a very short farce, written by Mr. Ravenscroft, called The *Anatomist*, or the Sham doctor . . . I chose a subject never manag'd in a dramatick way before . . . Whatever the critics may think of the lines . . . there has not been more agreeable, nor more masterly music perform'd upon our stage . . ."
The prologue and third act are headed as composed by Godfrey **Finger**, acts 1–2 as by John **Eccles**.
First performed 1696 at Lincoln's-Inn-Fields. LONGE 205
Second copy. LONGE 277

The **loves of the deities.** A. T. of D. Purcell's Cinthia and Endimion.

The **loyal shepherds;** or, The rustic heroine, a dramatic poem. In one act. To which is affixed, several sonnets, ballads, acrostics, etc. Written by T. Goodwin.

[London], Printed for the author, n. d. 3 p. l., 39 p. 20½ᶜᵐ.

List of subscribers and prefatory acrostic with the name of the author, Thomas Goodwin.
No composer or performance recorded by Clarence. LONGE 303

Lucas et Colinette. A. T. of La fête d'amour.

Lucas und Bärbchen. L. T. of G. Benda's Der jahrmarkt.

Lucca liberata. *See* M. Curzio.

Lucile, comédie en un acte, mêlée d'ariettes. Représentée pour la première fois par les Comédiens italiens ordinaires du Roi, le 5 janvier 1769.

Paris, Merlin, 1769. 44 p. 19ᶜᵐ.

Neither Marmontel, the author, is mentioned, nor **Grétry**, the composer.
SCHATZ 4165

— **Lucile,** comédie en un acte, mêlée d'ariettes. Représenté pour la première fois par les Comédiens italiens ordinaires du roi, le 5 janvier 1769.

Paris, Veuve Duchesne, 1769. 36 p. 19ᶜᵐ.

On p. [33]–36, "Ariettes de Lucile": "Chantons deux époux," "On dit qu'à quinze ans." Cast. Neither **Grétry** is mentioned, nor Marmontel. ML 50.2.L8G7

Lucile—Continued.

— **Lucile**, comédie en un acte, meslée d'ariettes, représentée pour la premiere fois par les Comédiens italiens ordinaires du roi, le 5 janvier 1769.

> *Paris, Merlin, 1770. 40 p. 19ᶜᵐ.*
>
> Cast.   On p. 37 the air of "Chantons deux époux" followed on p. 38–40 by the duet, "On dit qu'à quinze ans."   Without names of Marmontel or **Grétry.**
>
> Schatz 11706

— **Lucile**, comédie en un acte, meslée d'ariettes, représentée pour la premiere fois par les Comédiens italiens ordinaires du roi, le 5 janvier 1769.

> *Paris, Merlin, 1774. 40 p. 18ᶜᵐ.*
>
> Cast.   The text is the same as in the 1770 ed.   Schatz 11707

— **Lucile**, ein singspiel in einem aufzuge aus dem franzoesischen uebersetzt und von dem uebersetzer selbst herausgegeben.

> *Frankfurt am Mayn, mit Andreäischen schriften, 1772. 60 p., 10 p. (music). 16½ᶜᵐ.*
>
> By Johann Heinrich Faber who is not mentioned.   The music (voices and bass) consists of "Wo kann man besser seyn" (Où peut-on être mieux, I, 4).   Schatz 4166

Lucinda.   Scherzo pastorale per musca . . .

> *Parma, Paolo Monti, 1713. vi, 7–48 p. 21 p.*
>
> Three acts.   Imprimatur dated July 14, 1713.   In a prefatory note the publisher mentions Vincenzio Nieri as the author and prints a letter by him, dated Lucca, April 19, 1713, in which he says:
>
> "nel passato carnevale alcuni amici, ed io risolvemmo di rappresentare per proprio divertimento questo piccolo dramma, il di cui motivo lo trassi . . . dall' opere del già famoso Moniglia; ma dopo alcune recite, fù sparsa voce, contenersi in esso qualche sentimento immodesto, e perciò indegno d'esser udito, benchè del continuo fosse il concorso degli uditori assai folto.   Fra gli altri si pose in testa, che cosi fosse, un certo *Satrapone Zelante*, il quale unito con altro soggetto suo pari, e senza averlo nè pur veduto, gli diede taccia di disonesto, e lascivo; e fece, per quanto fù in sua mano, ogni possibile sforza, acciò ne restasse sospesa la recita . . ."
>
> He then states that these unwarranted attacks failed and that the opera continued to be performed with success.   The composer is unknown to Schatz.   ML 50.2.L83

Lucio Giunio Bruto, ballet.   *See* Tarchi's La congiura Pisoniana.

Lucio Giunio Bruto primo consolo di Roma.   *See* M. Curzio.

Lucio Papirio.

> *Apostolo Zeno, Poesie drammatiche, Venezia, 1744, t. i, p. [271]–355 p. 19ᶜᵐ.*
>
> Three acts and licenza.   Argument.   No composer is mentioned.   In the "Catalogo" at end of t. x, date and place of first ed. are given as Vienna, 1719.   (Performed there on November 4, with music by **Caldara** as "Lucio Papirio dittatore.")
>
> ML 49.A2Z3

— **Lucio Papirio.**   Pubblicato per la prima volta in Vienna 1719.

> *Apostolo Zeno, Poesie drammatiche, Orleans, 1785–86, t. v, p. 86. 21ᶜᵐ.*
>
> Three acts.   Argument.   No composer is mentioned.   ML 49.A2Z4

Lucio Papirio. Dramma per musica da rappresentarsi in Copenhagen.—Lucius Papirius . . .

Copenhagen, Andreas Hartwig Godiche, 1756. 155 p. 15½^{cm}.

Three acts. Argument, cast, scenario and note: "La musica è di diversi autori." German text face the Italian of Apostolo Zeno.

First performed 1756, as indicated. SCHATZ 11346

Lucio Papirio. Dramma per musica da rappresentarsi nel Regio Teatro di Torino, nel carnovale del 1753 . . .

Torino, Pietro Giuseppe Zappata e figliuolo, 1753. 4 p. l., 56 p. 16^{cm}.

Three acts. Argument, cast, and scenario. Neither the composer, Ignazio **Balbi,** nor the librettist, Apostolo Zeno, are mentioned, but as composers of the ballet music are named Amedeo Rasetti and Rocco Gioannetti.

First performed as indicated, December 26, 1752 (Schatz). SCHATZ 557

Lucio Papirio. Drama per musica da rappresentarsi nel Teatro di Breslavia l'anno 1731–1732 . . .

n. i., n. d. 103 p. 17½^{cm}.

Three acts. Dedication by the composer, Antonio **Bioni,** argument. The librettist, Antonio Salvi, is not mentioned. German title-page, "Lucius Papirius, musicalische opera," and text face Italian. SCHATZ 1044

Lucio Papirio. Drama per musica del Signor dottor Antonio Salvi da Firenze, da rappresentarsi nella Sala de' Sign. Capranica nel carnovale dell' anno 1714.

Roma, Bernabò, 1714. 74 p. 15½^{cm}.

Three acts and three intermezzi (text on p. 65–74), "BARILOTTA E SLAPINA." Argument, cast, scenario, and name of Francesco **Gasparini** as composer. The intermezzi appear to be the same as Salvi's "Barillotto," first composed with music by Domenico **Sarro,** at Venice, Teatro di San Angelo, fall of 1712. ML 50.2.L85G2

Lucio Papirio. Dramma per musica da rappresentarsi nel Regio Teatro di Berlino . . .

Berlino, A. Haude, 1745. 133, [1] p. 16^{cm}.

Three acts. By Apostolo Zeno, who is not mentioned. Argument, scenario, and name of Carl Heinrich **Graun** as composer. German title-page, "Lucius Papirius," and text face Italian.

First performed, as indicated, January 4, 1745. SCHATZ 4104

Lucio Papirio. Dramma per musica da rappresentarsi nel Regio Teatro di Berlino . . .

Berlino, Haude e Spener, 1784. 109, [3] p. 16½^{cm}.

Three acts. By Apostolo Zeno, who is not mentioned. Argument, cast, scenario, and name of Joh. Ad. **Hasse** as the composer. German title page "Lucius Papirius," and text face Italian.

Performed, as indicated, January, 1784; previously there on January 24, 1766; first performed at Dresden, Hoftheater, January 18, 1742. SCHATZ 4546

Lucio Papirio. Dramma per musica da rappresentarsi in Firenze nella primavera dell' anno 1795 nel Regio Teatro degli Intrepidi detto della Palla a Corda . . .

Firenze, Ant. Gius. Pagani e comp., 1795. 26 p. 18^{cm}.

Two acts. Cast and name of Gaetano **Marinelli** as composer. Schatz attributes the text to Zeno. By comparison, it is, however, neither by him nor by Salvi.

First performed at Naples, Teatro di San Carlo, May 30, 1791. ML 48.A5 v. 16

Lucio Papirio. Dramma per musica da recitarsi nel Teatro Arciducale di Mantova nel carnovale dell' anno MDCCXVIII . . .

Mantova, Alberto Pazzoni, n. d. 61 p. 17^{cm}.

Three acts. Neither Antonio Salvi, the author, nor Giuseppe Maria **Orlandini**, the
composer, is mentioned. Impresario's (Francesco Bibiena!) dedication, argument,
cast, and scenario.
First performed at Naples, Teatro di S. Bartolomeo, December 11, 1717.

SCHATZ 7352

Lucio Papirio. Dramma per musica da rappresentarsi nel nobile
Teatro Tron di S. Cassiano nel carnevale dell' anno 1737 . . .

Venezia, Giuseppe Bettinelli, 1737. 6 p. l., 48 p. 15^{cm}.

Three acts. By Antonio Salvi, who is not mentioned. Domenico Lalli's dedication, argument, cast, scenario, and name of Nicolà Antonio **Porpora** as the composer.

SCHATZ 8371

Lucio Papirio. Dramma per musica del Sig. dottor Antonio Salvi
da Firenze, da rappresentarsi nel Teatro di Sant' Angelo il carnovale
dell' anno 1715 . . .

Venezia, Marino Rossetti, 1715. 59 p. 15^{cm}.

Three acts. By Antonio Salvi, who is not mentioned. Dedication by Antonio
Vivaldi, argument, cast, scenario, and name of the composer, Luca Antonio **Predieri**.
First performed at Pratolino, Teatro della Villa Medici, 1714.   SCHATZ 8457

Lucio Papirio dittatore. O. T. of Zeno's Lucio Papirio and Quinto
Fabio.

Lucio Papirio dittatore. Dramma per musica, da rappresen-
tarsi nella Cesarea corte per il nome gloriosissimo della Sac. Ces. e Catt.
Real Maestà di Carlo VI . . . La poesia è del Sig. Apostolo Zeno . . .
La musica è del Sig. Antonio Caldara . . .

Venezia, Domenico Lovisa, 1720. 63 p. 15^{cm}.

Three acts. With argument and scenario. Nicola Matteis is mentioned as composer of the ballet music.
First performed, as indicated, at Vienna November 4, 1719.   SCHATZ 1499

Lucio Papirio dittatore. Dramma per musica da rappresentarsi nel nuovo Ducal Teatro di Parma la primavera dell' anno
MDCCXXIX . . .

Parma, eredi di Paolo Monti, 1729. 71, [1] p. 16½^{cm}.

Three acts. By Apostolo Zeno, retouched by Carlo Innocente Frugoni, both mentioned by inference. Dedication, dedicatory sonnet by Frugoni ("Comante Eginetico
P. Arcade"), argument, notice to the reader with reasons for the alterations, cast,
scenario, and name of Geminiano **Giacomelli** as the composer.   SCHATZ 3809

Lucio Papirio dittatore. Dramma per musica da rappresentarsi
nel Real Teatro di Salvaterra nel carnovale dell' anno 1775.

[Lisboa, n. d.], Stamperia reale. 62 p. 15½^{cm}.

Three acts. Apostolo Zeno is mentioned as the author, **Paisiello** as the composer.
Cast, scenario, and argument.
First performed at Naples, Teatro di San Carlo, summer, 1767.   SCHATZ 7674

Lucio Papirio dittatore. Drama per musica da rappresentarsi nel famosissimo Teatro Grimani di S. Gio. Grisostomo il carnovale dell' anno 1721 . . .

Venezia, Marino Rossetti, 1721. 60 p. 14½ᶜᵐ.

Three acts. By Apostolo Zeno, who is not mentioned. Impresario's dedication, argument, cast, scenario, name of Antonio **Pollaroli** as composer, and notice informing the reader—

"Nella presente tragedia alcuni cambiamenti si sono dovuti fare, per accomodarla ad un altro Teatro, e ad un' altra musica, e finalmente ad altri virtuosi destinati a rappresentarla . . ."

and then follows the customary apology to the author and public, protesting that the intention was "solamente di mutare, non di correggere." In his lctter no. 538 Zeno speaks of this libretto as "mutilato dal Piovene."

First performed, as indicated, December 26, 1720. SCHATZ 8259

Lucio Silla. Dramma per musica da rappresentarsi nel nobilissimo Teatro di S. Samuele la fiera dell' Ascensione dell' anno 1774.

Venezia, Grazioli, n. d. 48 p. 17ᶜᵐ.

Three acts. By Giovanni de Gamerra, with cast, scenario, and name of composer, Pasquale **Anfossi**, but not of librettist. As first ballet was performed "Solimano II [o sia] La francese trionfante," author and composer not being mentioned.

SCHATZ 243

Lucio Silla. Dramma per musica da rappresentarsi all Corte elettorale Palatina in occasione del felicissimo giorno del nome del serenissimo elettore.

Mannheim, Stamperia elettorale, n. d. 77 p. 16ᶜᵐ.

Three acts. By Giovanni de Gamerra with alterations by Matteo Verazj in the second act. Argument, cast, scenario, and names of composer, Johann Christian **Bach** ("musica . . . nuova composizione"), and of librettist.

First performed at Mannheim, Hoftheater, November 4, 1773 (Schatz), preceding the performance mentioned by Mozart. SCHATZ 529

— Lucius Silla, eine opera aufgefuehret bei gelegenheit des hoechstbeglueckten namensfestes Seiner Kurfuerstl. Durchlaucht zu Pfalz.

Mannheim, Hof und Akademie Buchdruckerei, 1774. 80 p. 15½ᶜᵐ.

Argument, cast, scenario, and names of Joh. Christian **Bach** as composer and of Gamerra and Verazi as authors. On p. 69–70 a detailed description of the ballets, "Acis und Galatea," invented by Stephen Lauchery, music by Joseph Toeschi, and "Achilles und Ulysses auf der Insel Scyros," by the same author, music by Christian Cannabich. SCHATZ 530

Lucio Silla. Dramma per musica da rappresentarsi nel Regio Teatro di Torino nel carnovale del 1779 . . .

Torino, Onorato Derossi, n. d. viii, 42, [1] p. 16½ᶜᵐ.

Three acts. Giovanni de Gamerra is mentioned as the author of the text "adattata al comodo del compositor della musica," Michele **Mortellari.** Argument, cast, scenario. Vittorio Amedeo Canavasso is mentioned as the composer of the music for the ballets, which had no characteristic plot or title.

First performed, as indicated, December 26, 1778. SCHATZ 6682

Lucio Vero. O. T. of Zeno's text Vologeso.

Lucio Vero.

Apostolo Zeno, Poesie drammatiche, Venezia, 1744, t. iii, p. [87]–168 p. 19ᶜᵐ.

Three acts. Argument. No composer is mentioned. In the "Catalogo" at end of t. x, date and place of first ed. are given as Venice, 1700. (*See* below).

ML 49.A2Z3

Lucio Vero—Continued.

— **Lucio Vero.** Pubblicato per la prima volta in Venezia 1700.

Apostolo Zeno, Poesie drammatiche, Orleans, 1785–86, t. ii, p. 59–136.
21ᶜᵐ.

Three acts. Argument. No composer mentioned.　　　　ML 49.A2Z4

Lucio Vero. Dramma per musica da rappresentarsi nel·famoso
Ducal Teatro di Bronsevico nella fiera d'inverno dell' anno 1756.

[Bronsevico], Keitel, n. d. 151 p. 16ᶜᵐ.

Three acts. Argument, scenario. German title page, "Lucius Verus," and text
face Italian by Apostolo Zeno. Neither he nor the composer (unknown to Schatz)
is mentioned.　　　　　　　　　　　　　　　　　　　　SCHATZ 11347

Lucio Vero. Dramma per musica da rappresentarsi nel Teatro di
Sant' Angelo il carnovale dell' anno MDLCXXXV . . .

Venezia, Marino Rossetti, n. d. 58 p. 14½ᶜᵐ.

Three acts. By Apostolo Zeno. Impresario's dedication, cast, argument, scenario, and name of composer, Francesco **Araya,** but not of librettist.　　SCHATZ 306

Lucio Vero. Dramma per musica da rappresentarsi in Verona nell'
aprimento del Nuovo Teatro Filarmonico il carnovale dell' anno
MDCCLIV . . .

Verona, Giambattista Saracco, n. d. 56 p. 18ᶜᵐ.

Three acts. By Apostolo Zeno, who is not mentioned. Publisher's dedication,
argument, cast, scenario, and name of Davide **Perez** as the composer. SCHATZ 7873

Lucio Vero. Drama per musica da recitarsi nel Teatro Grimani di
S. Gio. Grisostomo, l'anno MDCC . . .

Venezia, Nicolini, 1700. 7 p. l., 56 p. 14½ᶜᵐ.

Three acts. Dedication with the initials of the author, Apostolo Zeno, argument,
and scenario. The composer, Carlo Francesco **Pollaroli,** is not mentioned.
　　　　　　　　　　　　　　　　　　　　　　　　　　SCHATZ 8301

Lucio Vero. Dramma per musica da rappresentarsi nel Real Teatro
di S. Carlo nel dì 13 agosto 1785 per festeggiarsi la nascita di S. M.
la regina . . .

Napoli, Vincenzo Flauto, 1785. 59 p. 15ᶜᵐ.

Three acts. By Apostolo Zeno, who is not mentioned. Dedication with same
date as in the title, argument, cast, scenario, and name of Antonio **Sacchini** as the
composer. On p. 9–26 argument, cast, and name of Antonio Rossetti as composer of
the music of Domenico Lefèvre's "D. Pedro, infante di Portogallo. Ballo tragico in
cinque atti." As second ballet was performed his "La festa di Flora, ballo pastorale."
First performed at the same theatre, November 4, 1764.　　SCHATZ 9242

Lucio Vero. Drama per musica da rappresentarsi in Monaco nel
autunno dell anno 1720. Nel Teatro Elettorale festeggiandosi il
felicissimo giorno del nome dell' Altezza Serenissima Elettorale di
Massimiliano Emanuele . . . il di 12. octob. 1720.

Monaco, Enrigo Teodoro di Cöllen, n. d. 68, [26] p. 15ᶜᵐ.

Three acts. By Apostolo Zeno, who is not mentioned. Argument, cast, and scenario. Pietro **Torri,** the composer, is not mentioned. The unnumb. pages contain
argument and scene by scene synopsis in German.　　SCHATZ 10366

Lucius Papirius. Tr. of Zeno's text Lucio Papirio, Copenhagen,
1756.

Lucius Papirius. Tr. of Bioni's Lucio Papirio.

Lucius Papirius. Tr. of Graun's Lucio Papirio.

Lucius Papirius. Tr. of Hasse's Lucio Papirio.

Lucius Silla. Tr. of Bach's Lucio Silla.

Lucius Verus. Tr. of Zeno's text Lucio Vero.

Lucius Verus, oder Die siegende treue: in einem singe-spiel auf dem Hamburgischen Schauplatze im jahr 1728 aufgefuehret.

[Hamburg], mit Stromerischen schrifften, n. d. Unpaged. 19^{cm}.

Three acts. Scenario, name of Reinhard **Keiser** as the composer, and "avertissement:"

"Die denen liebhabern zu gefallen, statt der hier eingedruckten deutschen, abzusingende wenige italiaenische arien, (deren inhalt sich zu der materie gantz ungezwungen schickt), werden verhoffentlich eine allgemeine approbation verdienen."

The author, Hinsch, who based his text on Zeno, is not mentioned.

First performed, as indicated, October 18, 1728.   SCHATZ 5101

The **lucky discovery:** or, The tanner of York. An opera. As it was acted at the theatre in York . . .

York, Printed for the author by Thomas Gent, 1737. 1 p. l., iii, [1], 26 p. 19^{cm}.

One act. Cast and preface signed by John Arthur as author. Ballad opera, the 9 airs of the songs being indicated by title.

Performed at Covent Garden, London, April 24, 1738.   LONGE 152

The **lucky mistake.** A. T. of The jealous clown.

Lucretia. *See* Keiser's Die kleinmuethige . . .

Lucrezia Romana. Dramma di tre atti per musica.

Carlo Goldoni, Opere teatrali, Venezia, Zatta e figli, 1788–95, v. 43, [295]–340 p. 18^{cm}.

See also his "Lugrezia Romana in Contantinopoli."   PQ

Il **Lucullo.** A. T. of A. Scarlatti's L' humanità nelle fere.

Ludovico il Moro, ballet. *See* Rispoli's Ipermestra.

Ludovico Sforza detto Il Moro, ballet. *See* Cimarosa's Volodomiro.

Die **luftschiffer** oder Der strafplanet der erde. Ein komisch-satirisches original singspiel in 3 aufzuegen von Max Blumhofer. Fuer das kaiserliche deutsche Hoftheater zu St. Petersburg bearbeitet.

Leipzig und Koeln, J. A. Imhofsche buchhandlung, 1787. 80 p. 16^{cm}.

In his long "Vorrede" (p. 3–9), dated Duesseldorf, August 21, 1786, Blumhofer says:

"Meine liebe zur musik, und besonders, zur theatermusik gab diesem singspiel das daseyn. Ich wollte mich in composition ueben und zeigen, und beschloss, mir ein stueck zu diesem endzweck zu verfertigen Ich nahm daher bey der ausarbeitung desselben sogleich auch auf die musik ruecksicht, welches wie es scheint, die meisten verfasser von singspielen versehen, oft versehen muessen, weil sie entweder keine musik verstehen, oder wenn sie sie verstehen, weil sie zu wenig gefuehl haben, um sich zum voraus in die lage des tonsetzers zu versetzen . . .

"Ich wollte versuchen, ob ich in Weissens fusstapfen tretten, und eine operette liefern koenne, die meiner eigenen musickcomposition und der auffuehrung wuerdig waere . . .

Die luftschiffer—Continued.

"Auch diese operette trug ich Sr. Excellenz dem freyherrn von D . . . [Dalberg] an. Aber ich unbesonnener dachte nicht darauf, dass in den opern und operetten, die in M . . . [Mannheim] aufgefuehrt werden, mord und tod, gift und dolch herrschen muessen; wie es die opern: *Guenther von Schwartzburg*, welche gewiss von jeder oper des Metastasio das gegenstueck ist, und *Rosemunde* beweisen; auch muss ueberdies das stueck arbeit aus eigener fabrique seyn. Ich verdenke also Sr. Excellenz nicht, dass Dieselben den antrag meiner operette keiner antwort wuerdig fanden.

"Aber was soll ich mit dir anfangen, liebes operettchen?—dich nach . . . M. [Muenchen] schicken?—Nein; du bist zu stolz um dich da von einer Excellenz, welche Helena und Paris so reichlich belohnte, beallmosen zu lassen; und ich selbst mag mit musickern, die den grossen Mozart verkleinerten, verachteten und beca-balirten, nichts zu thun haben.—Oder soll ich dich nach Wien schicken?—Freylich das gieng noch wohlan—Aber ich bin etwas misstranisch. Wien ist fuer manuscripte eine gefaehrliche stadt.—Weisst du was, liebes buechelchen; wandre du auch nach St. Petersburg.—Aber, dort ist keine deutsche operette, sagst du?—Naerrchen? Was thut das zur sache? Vor etlichen jahren war dort auch noch kein deutsches theater. Was nicht ist, das kann noch werden . . ."

Schatz records no performance.

ML 50.2.L9B4

Second copy. 14½^{cm}. Schatz 1108

Lugrezia Romana in Costantinopoli.

[217]–264 p. 16½^{cm}. (*Carlo Goldoni, Opere drammatiche giocose, t. iii, Torino, 1757.*)

See also his "Lucrezia Romana." First performed as below. ML 49.A2G6

Lugrezia Romana in Costantinopoli. Dramma comico da rappresentarsi in musica dalla Compagnia de Comici nel Teatro Grimani di S. Samuele il carnovale dell' anno 1737.

Venezia, Alvise Valvasense, 1737. 47 p. 14½^{cm}.

Three acts. Prefatory note. Neither the author, Carlo Goldoni, is mentioned, nor the composer, Giacomo **Macari**. Schatz 5811

Lukas und Bärbchen. L. T. of G. Benda's Der Jahrmarkt.

Lukas und Hannchen, eine operette . . . [vignette]

Braunschweig, Fuerstl. Waisenhausbuchhandlung, 1768. 2 p. l., 44 p. 16^{cm}.

One act. Dedicatory poem. Based, as the author, Johann Joachim Eschenburg, remarks in a note, on "Annette et Lubin" of Marmontel and still more on that of Mad. Favart. The composer, Johann Friedrich Gottlieb **Beckmann**, is not mentioned.

First performed at Braunschweig, Fürstl. Kleines Theater, in 1768. Schatz 685

Luminalia, or The festivall of light. Personated in a masque at Court, by the Queenes Majestic, and her ladies. On Shrovetuesday Night, 1637.

London, Printed by John Haviland for Thomas Walkley, 1637. 1 p. l., 21 p. 18^{cm}.

Text of the songs, minute description of the masque and of "Night," the anti-masque, and at end "the names of the masquers." The prefatory remarks read, in part:

"The kings Majesties masque being performed, the queene commanded Inigo Jones, surveyor of her Majesties works, to make a new subject of a masque for her selfe, that with high and hearty invention, might give occasion for variety of scenes, strange apparitions, songs, musick and dancing of severall kinds; from whence doth result the true pleasure peculiar to our English masques, which by strangers and travellers of judgement, are held to be as noble and ingenious, as those of any other nations: This being suddainly done and shewed her Majestie, and shee approving it, the worke was set in hand, and with all celerity performed in shorter time, than any thing here hath beene done in this kind."

The masque has been attributed to T. Lodge and Robert Greene and the music is credited to Nicholas **Laniere**. ML 52.2.L92

Arien aus dem singspiel: Der **lumpensammler,** oder Ein gutes herz ziert jeden stand in zwey aufzuegen. Die musik ist von herrn Weigl.

n. i., 1797. 14 p. 16^{cm}.

By Paul Weidmann, who is not mentioned.
First performed at Vienna, Burgtheater, October 15, 1792. SCHATZ 10940

O lunatico illudido. Novo drama adornado de musica, e tradu-zido do idioma italiano, para se representar no Theatro do Salitre.

Lisboa, José de Aquino Bulhoens, 1791. ·127 p. 14½^{cm}.

Three acts. Author not mentioned and unknown to Schatz. Cast and name of Marcos Antonio [**Portugal**] as composer. According to Carvalhaes, this is a Portu-guese version of Goldoni's "Il mondo della luna." In Portugal's catalogue of his works this opera figures as "O mundo da lua," with date of 1792 instead of 1791.
ML 50.2.L95P7

Der **lustige schuster** oder Der zweyte theil vom Teufel ist los. Eine komische oper in drey aufzuegen.

C. F. Weisse, Komische opern, Carlsruhe, 1778, t. ii, p. [105]–194. 18½^{cm}.

On p. 106 the note: "Nach dem *Merry cobler* oder *the Second part of the Devil to pay* des herrn Coffey."
Neither Johann **Standfuss,** who originally composed the music, nor Johann Adam **Hiller,** who revised it and partly composed the text anew, is mentioned.
First performed at Leipzig, Theater am Rannstädter Thore, 1766. With Standfuss' music first performed at Lübeck, January 18, 1759. ML 49.A2W2
Second (detached) copy. SCHATZ 4733

Die **lustigen weiber.** Ein singspiel in vier aufzuegen von Georg Roemer [vignette]. Die musik is von Peter Ritter.

n. i., 1792. 143 p. 14½^{cm}.

First performed at Mannheim, Nationaltheater, November 4, 1794. SCHATZ 8825

Das **lustlager.** Ein singspiel in zwei aufzuegen. Die musik ist vom herrn doktor Schuhbauer, dem verfasser der Dorfdeputirten.

Muenchen, Johann Baptist Strobl, 1784. 77 p. 16^{cm}.

By Franz Joseph Marius von Babo, who is not mentioned.
First performed at Munich, old opera house by St. Salvator, August 4, 1784.
SCHATZ 9711

Lycidas: a musical entertainment. As it is performed at the Theatre Royal in Covent Garden. The words altered from Milton . . .

London, W. Griffin, 1767. 1 p. l., 13, [1] p. 20½^{cm}.
One act. Cast. The text by the composer, William **Jackson,** of Exeter.
First performed November 4, 1767. LONGE 198
Second copy. LONGE 216

Epilogue. Being a new fancy after the old, and most surprising way of **Macbeth,** perform'd with new and costly machines, which were invented and managed by the most ingenious operator Mr. Henry Wright. P. G. Q.

London, Printed in the year 1674. 21½^{cm}. (In Thomas Duffet's "The Empress of Morocco," London, Simon Neal, 1674 as p. [25]–39.)

Cast. The composer of the music (only incidental) of the play is not mentioned. The play was a parody of Elkanah Settle's tragedy of the same title and was first per-formed in 1674. The "Macbeth" epilogue is said in Grove to be a parody of Davenant's version of "Macbeth,"[2] music by Mathew **Locke.** LONGE 271

Il **macchinista** ossia La susta matematica, ballet. *See* Martin y Soler's Vologeso.

Die **macht der feen.**   A. T. of Selim und Zelide.

Die **macht der liebe** oder Die von Paris entfuehrte Helena.   German title of Keiser's La forza dell' amore.

Il **Macedone continente.**   A. T. of M. A. Ziani's La virtù sublimata dal grande.

Macrina e Carfoglio.   Intermezzi in Vinci's Medea riconosciuta.

The **mad captain,** an opera as it is acted at the New Theatre in Goodman's-Fields.

London, Charles Corbett, 1733. 54 p. 19ᶜᵐ.

Title vignette port. of Addison.
One act. By Robert Drury, who is not mentioned. Cast. Ballad opera, the 33 airs of which are merely indicated by title in the text, airs 20–29 being incorrectly numbered 21–32.
First performed March 5, 1733.   LONGE 50

Madama Arrighetta.   Dramma giocoso per musica da rappresentarsi nel Teatro Formagliari il carnevale dell' anno 1761 . . .

Bologna, Sassi, 1760. 72 p. 15ᶜᵐ.

Three acts. By Antonio Palomba, who is not mentioned. Impresario's dedication, cast, and name of Niccolò **Piccinni** as the composer.
First performed, as indicated, January 7, 1761, at Naples; as "Monsieur Petitone" (Schatz), Naples, Teatro Nuovo, fall of 1758.   SCHATZ 8150

Madama Ciana.   Drama giocoso per musica da rappresentarsi nel Teatro di S. Cassano nell' autunno dell' anno 1744.

Venezia, n. publ., n. d. 2 p. l., 84, [4] p. 17ᶜᵐ.

Three acts. By Giovanni Barlocci, who is not mentioned. Cast and name of Gaetano Latilla as composer. The 4 additional p. contain the substitute arias, "D'ogni core la bellezza" for "Non si credano mai" (I, 6), "Il modo è questo" for "Si con giudizio" (II, 2), "Se mai perdete" for "L'idol mio tu fosti," and the additional arias, "Al pensier de torti miei" (II, 11) and "Disprezzata, abbandonata" (III, 1). According to Schatz, Barlocci's libretto was originally called "Donna Marzia."   SCHATZ 5447

— **Ciana.**   Dramma giocoso per musica.

Monaco, Giovanni Giacomo Vötter, 1749. 52 p. 15ᶜᵐ.

Three acts. The author, Barlocci, is not mentioned. Cast and name of Gaetano Latilla as composer. The text is somewhat different from that of Venice, 1744. For instance, I, 6 has the aria, "Quanto son pazze" instead of "Non si credano," and the aria, "Non mi burli," has been dropped from I, 9.
First performed, as indicated, July 13, 1749.   SCHATZ 5448

— **L'ambizione delusa.**   Dramma giocoso per musica da rappresentarsi in Torino nel Teatro di S. A. S. il Signor principe di Carignano nel carnovale dell' anno 1747.

Torino, Giuseppe Domenico Verani, n. d. 72 p. 14½ᶜᵐ.

Three acts. Cast and name of Gaetano Latilla as the composer. The text is Giovanni Barlocci's "Madama Ciana," though with many differences. For instance, the aria "Non si credano" (I, 6) has been replaced by "Quanto son pazze;" "Se tu mi sei fedele" (I, 7) by "Pupillette vezzosette;" "Sento cangiarsi in lagrime" (I, 8) by "Fiume che altero abbonda." These and others on mounted slips. SCHATZ 5462

Madama Prudenza. Farsetta per musica da rappresentarsi nel Teatro della Valle nel carnevale dell' anno 1749 . . .

Roma, Ottavio Puccinelli, 1749. 31 p. 15ᶜᵐ.

Two parts. Dedication by Angelo Lungi (as author?) and the printer, cast and name of Gregorio **Sciroli** as composer. ML 50.2.M2S2

A rehearsal of a new ballad-opera burlesqu'd, call'd The **madhouse.** After the manner of Pasquin. As it is now acting at the Theatre-Royal in Lincoln's-Inn-Fields. By a gentleman of the Inner-Temple.

London, T. Cooper, 1737. 47, [3] p. 20½ᶜᵐ.

Two acts, with introduction. In his dedication, R. Baker claims that "The madhouse [is] a subject of satyre never touched upon before in the dramatic way . . ."

Prologue and epilogue, followed by a "Prologue to the busy body, design'd to have been spoken by Mrs. Roberts, on Friday, May 22, 1737." The airs of the 18 songs are indicated by title.

First performed April 22, 1737. LONGE 192

Das maechtige geschick bei Lavinia und Dido. A. T. of Steffani's Il triumfo del fato.

Das maedchen im Eichthale. Ein laendliches hochzeitspiel in fuenf aufzuegen von Bock. Neue rechtmaessige auflage.

Hamburg, Heroldsche Buchhandlung, 1785. 104 p. 16ᶜᵐ.

Five acts. The composer, Johann *or* Georg Friedrich **Lampe,** is not mentioned. First performed at Hamburg, Theater beim Gänsemarkt, August 19, 1776.

SCHATZ 5384

Das maedchen im thurme. A. T. of Ruprecht's Das wuetende heer.

Das maedchen im thurme. A. T. of Schweitzer's Das wütende heer.

Die maedchen sind von Flandern. A. T. of Mozart's Weiber-treue.

Das maedchen von Fraskati. Tr. T. of Paisiello's La Frascatana.

Die maedchenliebe. Ein schauspiel mit gesang in drei akten.

Leipzig, n. publ., 1794. 152 p. 16½ᶜᵐ.

Not recorded by Schatz. Not found in "Deutsches Anonymen Lexikon."

SCHATZ 11632

Maedchenlist und liebe. A. T. of Mozart's Die wette.

Der maedchenmarkt. Komisches singspiel in drey aufzuegen nach Saintfoix.

Herklots, Operetten, III, (Berlin, 1793), p. [187]–296. 15ᶜᵐ.

Detached copy. Performed with music by **Dittersdorf** at Oels, Hoftheater, April 18, 1797.

SCHATZ 3601

Gesaenge aus dem singspiele: Der **maedchenmarkt,** in zwey aufzuegen, nach Saintfoix von Herklots. In musik gesezt vom reichs-grafen von Kospoth.

Hamburg, Joh. Matth. Michaelsens wittwe, 1793. 46 p. 15ᶜᵐ.

First performed at Hamburg, Theater beim Gänsemarkt, September 3, 1793.

SCHATZ 5220

Das **maedgen im thurme**.   A. T. of Schweitzer's Das wuetende heer.

Arien und gesaenge zur komischen oper: **Maegera**.   In zween auf- zuegen 1774.

n. i., n. d.   20 p.   17ᶜᵐ.

Without names of the composer, Johann **Bohm**, and the librettist, W. Philipp Haffner.

First performed at Berlin, Kochsches Theater, July 27, 1774.   Schatz 1115

La maestra.   Dramma bernesco per musica da rappresentarsi nel Teatro Tron di S. Cassiano il carnovale dell' anno 1754 . . .

Venezia, Modesto Fenzo, 1754.   72 p.   15ᶜᵐ.

Three acts.   By Antonio Palomba (not mentioned).   Dedication, scenario, cast, and name of the composer, Gioacchino **Cocchi**.

First performed at Bologna, Teatro Formagliari, summer 1747.   Schatz 2033

NB.   Cocchi's "La scaltra governatrice," which was first performed at Paris, Académie royale de musique, January 25 (Schatz), March 23 (de La Laurencie) 1753, was but a *rifacimento* of his "La maestra," both containing, for instance, the arias "Scelerata a me rispondi," "Cara Drusilla, Non goda quell' infida" etc.   As the L. of C. does not possess the original Bologna, 1747 text, I cannot point out, just what surgical operations the opera suffered at the hands of the Bambini company at Paris. The Venice, 1754 ed. contains in the first act the following arias and it is clear from a comparison with de La Laurencie's remarks on "La scaltra governatrice" in S. I. M., June 15, 1912, p. 32, that the Paris and Venice versions must have been strikingly different:

I, 1 *à, a, be, ce, qu . . . Oh diavolo.*
    Io sono una ragazza.
I, 2 *Mia Drusilla, all' or che.*
I, 5 *Più non chiamo ingiusto amore.*
I, 9 *Poverina! ha freddo il naso.*
I, 10 *Fiume, ch' alterno abbonda.*
I, 12 *No, non mi muove a sdegno.*
I, 13 *Se mai vi vedi andar vicino.*
I, 14 *Bella mano, or che ti stringo.*

The following arias cited by de La Laurencie are not in the Venice ed. of La maestra: *Vedovella poverella; Drusillina; O quanti maestri; Gli sbirri* (from Cocchi's La mascherata), *Non son piccina, Fra noi scende Imeneo.*

— La **maestra di scuola**.   Dramma giocoso per musica da rappresentarsi nel Regio Teatro di Berlino per ordine di Sua Maestà prussiana.

Berlino, Haude e Spener, 1763.   101, [3] p.   17½ᶜᵐ.

Three acts, with name of **Cocchi** as composer.   German title-page "Die schulmeisterin," and text face Italian, which differs somewhat from that of "La maestra." The first act now has only ten scenes, the two last arias mentioned above occurring in I, 9 and I, 10.   Furthermore I, 8 has the aria "Mentisca pure," I, 7 "Poverina! ha freddo," I, 5 "Se alla mia fè," I, 2 "Mia Drusilla" and in I, 1 the second aria was dropped.

First performed at Berlin, Schlosstheater, December 1763, and previously there in 1754 (Schatz).   Schatz 2034

— La **scuola moderna**, osia La maestra di buon gusto.   Dramma giocoso per musica da rappresentarsi nel Teatro Giustiniano di S. Moisè l'autunno dell' anno 1748.

Venezia, Modesto Fenzo, 1748.   front., 58, [1] p.   15ᶜᵐ.

Three acts.   Antonio Palomba's "La maestra," rewritten by Carlo Goldoni, according to Schatz, who records **Cocchi** as the composer, whereas Wiel leaves that point open.   This notice is addressed to the reader on p. 3:

"Non avendo servito il tempo per mutar tutta l'opera, come erasi divisato, si è mutata tutta la materia buffa, la quale, se non parerà bene intrecciata colla seria, ciò e provenuto per la necessaria brevità . . ."

La maestra—Continued.

The differences will appear from the list of characters. Originally they were: Drusilla, Fazio, Leonora, Ottavio, Flaminio, Checca, Pistone. In the revised version they are: Doralba, Rosmira, Ergasto, Drusilla, Belfiore, Leonora, Lindoro. For purposes of identification it may be further noticed that act I, sc. 2, now begins "Cara Drusilla mia" instead of "Ma che buona ragazza?" and that the opera now ends with "Io mi sento dal diletto" instead of "Grazia ad amore. Eh al nostro core." The additional page contains the substituted arias "Destrier che all' armi usato" (II, 7) and "Giovani cari amanti" (II, 9). SCHATZ 2048

La maestra di buon gusto. A. T. of Cocchi's La scuola moderna.

La maestra di scuola. L. T. of Cocchi's La maestra.

Il maestro di capella o sia Il tutore deluso, ballet. *See* Cimarosa's Il fanatico burlato.

Il maestro di capella. Dramma giocoso per musica da rappresentarsi nei Teatri privilegiati di Vienna l'anno 1771. Appresso il maestro di logge.

n. i., n. d. 64 p. 15½cm.

With scenario and name of Florian Johann Deller as composer. The author, Antonio Palomba, is not mentioned. Originally the title was "Orazio."
First performed at Vienna, Theater nächst der Burg, 1771. SCHATZ 2496

Il maestro di cappella. L. T. of Pergolesi's Il maestro di musica.

Il maestro di cappella burlato. O. T. of Lorazi's Der kapellmeister.

Il maestro di musica. A. T. of the ballet Le tuteur trompé.

Il maestro di musica.

Two acts. Author and exact date of performance unknown. Music by Giovanni Battista Pergolesi, composed, according to Radiciotti, probably during the winter 1733/34. Neither a copy of the original libretto has come to light, nor the original score or a copy of it. Consequently it is not known just what the score and the libretto contained. Not even the plot is perfectly clear, since the nearest known approach to Pergolesi's score does not contain any dialogue. It is the score of "Le MAITRE DE MUSIQUE opéra bouffon italien . . . Avec la belle ariette Cou-cou. Chantée dans la *Fausse suivante* del Sigᵣ Atilla [!]," Paris, Boivin, with the note below the imprint:
"Pour se conformer au goût du public, ou a cru devoir retrancher le récitatif. Gravé d'après la partition de l'auteur."
If this last sentence is to be taken literally, it would mean that the Boivin ed. was based on Pergolesi's own score. At any rate, it was evidently inserted in order to establish the authenticity of the Boivin ed., which contains the Italian text (and a French prose translation) of twelve arias, duets, etc., from Pergolesi's "Il maestro di musica," first performed at Paris, September 19 (de La Laurencie), October 3 (Schatz), October 19 (Cl. & L.) 1752, with an overture by Sammartini, which was not included in the score, and, as a supplement, the indicated cou-cou aria, "Colà sul praticello," from Latilla's "La finta cameriera." The twelve arias, etc., from "Il maestro di musica" are:
First act: (1) "Oh che sproposito (by Pietro Auletta, according to de La Laurencie);" (2) "A un gusto da stordire;" (3) "Vò dir lo basso;" (4) Bella mia, se son tuo sposo;" (5) "Vedo quel bel l'occhietto;" (6) "Come chi giocca alle palle." Second act: (7) "Le virtuose che son famose;" (8) "Quando sciolto avrò il contratto;" (9) "Se giammai da speco;" (10) "Splenda fra noi, seren" (chorus); (11) "Qual doppo insano" (duet); (12) "Caro signor maestro" (trio).
It may be added that the ms. score at Berlin (of which the L. of C. has a transcript) is identical with the Boivin ed., *i. e.*, it, too, lacks the dialogue.
The opera, "Orazio," given 1743 at Venice, with the names of Latilla and Pergolesi as composers in the libretto (entered in this catalogue under "Orazio"), is

Il maestro di musica—Continued.

clearly a very much expanded three-act version, with six characters instead of three, of the "Il maestro di musica" text. The author of the "Orazio" text is not mentioned in the libretto, but is said by Schatz to have been Antonio Palomba. As to the music of "Orazio," Radiciotti and others enter this opera under Pergolesi and Latilla, but, as a matter of fact, the libretto has Latilla first and Pergolesi second. The reason for this order becomes quite obvious from a comparison between the "Orazio" libretto and the Paris, Boivin ed. of the score of "Il maestro di musica:" *Of the twelve arias, etc., enumerated above, only the following four appear in the "Orazio" libretto:* (no. 1) in I, 1; (2) as "Ha un gusto da morire," in I, 1; (6) in I, 13; (10) as "Splenda fra noi seren," in II, 17. In other words, Pergolesi's share in "Orazio" would seem to have been very small, and the opera should henceforth be entered mainly under Gaetano Latilla.

In 1749, at Parma, "Il maestro di musica" had become "Orazio o La scolara alla moda," and at Florence, of course with further interpolations, alterations, etc., the opera was given (1760) as "La scolara alla moda."

— Il **maestro di cappella,** intermezzi per musica, da rappresentarsi nel Regio Teatro di Potsdam per ordine di Sua Maestà.

Berlino, Haude e Spener, 1756. 53 p. 17½ cm.

Three acts. German title page, "Der kapell-meister," and text face Italian. Schatz enters this under "Orazio," by Pergolesi and Latilla, but I fail to see the reason, since both texts, while having a few scenes and arias in common, differ widely, and much more than was customary, even in cases of replicas. For instance, the differences begin in the very first scene, when, instead of the aria, "Ha un gusto da morire," the Potsdam version has "Quanto comanda, si ubbidirò." Scene 2, "Costei troppo è vezzosa," has grown from half a page without aria to three with aria, "Finche suona il ritornello." Scenes 4 to 7 in "Orazio" are not in the Potsdam ed., so that I, 8, "Mi par mill' anni," has become I, 4, and then the two texts part company after a few lines, etc., etc. The composer, resp. author, responsible for this three-act version of Pergolesi's two-act "Il maestro di musica," if it may be called such, is not known. SCHATZ 5468

— Le **maître de musique,** comedie en deux actes, melée d'ariettes. Parodié de l'italien. Representée pour la première fois par les Comédiens italiens ordinaires du roi le 28 may 1758 [!]. Avec les changemens qui ont été faits depuis peu par l'auteur dans le second acte.

Bruxelles, J. J. Boucherie, 1758. 36 p. 21 cm.

Two acts. Neither Baurans, the author, is mentioned, nor **Pergolesi.** Cast. The arias in the libretto are as follows:

(1) Ah quel martire (I, 1=Oh che sproposito in "Il maestro di musica); (2) Un pilote battu de l'orage (I, 1 not traced by Wotquenne); (3) Quel délice ne trouve point (I, 1=A un gusto da stordire in M. di M); (4) Suis-je bien pour une actrice (I, 3=Vi stò bene? Vi comparisco? in Pergolesi's Tracollo); (5) Oui, nos chanteuses (I, 3=Le virtuose in M. di M.); (6) Je veux tout bas (I, 3=Vuò dir lo basso in M. di M.); (7) La pudeur qui me guide (I, 5=Io sono una donzella, in Sellitti's "Cinese rimpatriato "); (8) Si d'une ame propice (I, 5=Bella mia, se son tuo sposo, in M. di M.); (9) Le feu me monte au visage (I, 6=Come chi giuocha alle palle in M. di M.); (10) Oh la puissante querelle (II, 1 not traced by Wotquenne); (11) Le badinage, l'humeur volage (II, 1 not traced by Wotquenne); (12) Que c'est un plaisir extrême (II, 1 not traced by Wotquenne); (13) Non, je suis trop en colère (II, 2=Quando sciolto avrò il contratto in M. di M.); (14) Désormais, Je sçaurai mieux (II, 2 not traced by Wotquenne); (15) Qu' espère un amant (II, 2 not traced by Wotquenne); (16) Ingrat, je romps ma chaîne (II, 2 not traced by Wotquenne); (17) Ah! mon coeur soupire (II, 3 not traced by Wotquenne); (18) Grace, sois plus traitable (II, 4=Ad un povero Tracollo, in Pergolesi's Tracollo); (19) Que mille plaisirs. (Not traced by Wotquenne).

Of these nineteen arias, nos. 1–9, 13, 16, 18 are in the score, as printed by Bailleux, resp. De la Chevardiere, and nos. 10–12, 14, 15, 17, 19 are not. It should also be noted that "A telle qui t'entage," the last aria in the score, is not in the revised libretto. In other words, the aria belonged, as did the entire printed score, to the *first* version of Bauran's parody, and does not embody any of the alterations in the second act, which, as a footnote (on p. 20) informs us, had been found to be "trop sérieux & trop uniforme."

Il maestro di musica—Continued.

The Brussels 1758 ed. establishes still another important fact. The Conservatory at Brussels possesses, besides the printed score, one (no. 2028) that is in manuscript, with "sept morceaux de plus que le n° précédent, tous au second act." Beyond this remark, Wotquenne ventured no conjectures. It turns out, from comparison, that six of these nos. in the manuscript score are identical with nos. 10–12, 14, 15, 17 in the libretto of the revised version, and only one aria ("Mais il faut enfin prendre un parti") does not appear therein. This manuscript score therefore represents the revised version of the opera, and Brussels possesses, therefore, the score of both versions.

The first version was first performed at Paris May 28, 1755; the second version on March 7, 1757; and at Bruxelles, Théatre de la Monnaie in 1757. ML 50.2.M3P3

— Le maitre de musique, comédie, mêlée d'ariettes, parodiées de l'italien par Baurans.

Paris, Au bureau de la petite bibliotheque des théatres, 1784. 1 p. l., iv, 50 p, 15 p. (music) 13ᶜᵐ.

Two acts. Argument, date of first performance as May 28, 1755 (Paris, Comédie italienne), and "Jugemens et anecdotes sur le Maitre de musique" which read, in part:

"Cette piece n'est encore qu'une parodie d'un intermede italien, en deux actes, donné à l'Opéra, sous ce titre: Il *maestro di musica*, le 3 octobre 1752. Le public accueillit très-bien, à la Comédie italienne, cette seconde traduction de Baurans, et lui sut gré d'avoir puisé deux fois dans la même source, pour lui procurer de nouveaux plaisirs, inconnus jusqu'alors en France. Le maître de musique n'eut cependant, pas le même succès qu'avoit eu la Servante maîtresse . . .

"Le sujet du Maître de musique a été traité en ballet-pantomime, par Sabadini . . . Ce ballet, composé sur la musique italienne, fut donné, après la seconde représentation de la Servante maîtresse, le 17 août 1754, et il réussit beaucoup."

The text is followed by these "Airs du Maître de musique": "Quel délice, ne trouve point" (="A un gusto da stordire," in "Il maestro di musica"), "La pudeur qui me guide" (="Io sono una donzella" in Sellitti's "Cinese rimpatriato"), "Si d'une ame propice" (="Bella mia, se son tuo sposo" in "Il maestro di musica"). The text is the same as in the Brussels (1758) edition, belonging, therefore, to the revised version of 1757.   SCHATZ 5467

La maga Circe.

One act farsetta, by unknown author, music by Pasquale **Anfossi**.

First performed at Rome, Teatro Capranica, carnival 1788 together with Basili's "La bella incognita" and original libretto printed together with libretto of the latter on p. 28–55. (*See* "La bella incognita.")   ML 50.2.B28B2

—La maga Circe. Dramma giocoso per musica in un atto da rappresentarsi nel Teatro della nobiliss. Accademia degl' Intronati nel carnevale 1792 . . .

Siena, n. publ., 1792. 23 p. 16½ᶜᵐ.

With cast and name of Pasquale **Anfossi** as composer but not of librettist, who is unknown to Schatz. On p. 5 the titles of three ballets by Giuseppe Bossi: "Il generoso perdono, ballo eroico pantomimo; musica del rinomato Sig. Francesco Giuliani, Livornese," "La burla di D. Pacconio a Parigi," and "La filosofa olandese."
      SCHATZ 262

— La maga Circe, commedia in musica di un solo atto da rappresentarsi nel Regio teatro di S. Carlo della Principessa l'autunno dell' anno 1797.

Lisbona, Simone Taddeo Ferreira, 1797. 84 p. 16ᶜᵐ.

Cast, scenario, and name of **Anfossi** as composer. Italian and Portuguese text.
      SCHATZ 263

La maga fulminata. Favola di Benedetto Ferrari dalla Tiorba. Rappresentata in musica in Bologna, e in Venetia. In questa quarta impressione dall' autore corretta.

n. i., n. d. *[53]–110 p. 13½ᶜᵐ.* (*Benedetto Ferrari, Poesie drammatiche, Milano, 1644.*)

Detached copy. Three acts. Dedication by the composer, Francesco **Manelli**, dated Bologna, April 20, 1641, six sonnets by Angelo Botti, Francesco Sbarra, Francesco Peruzzi, Angelo de' Rossi, conte Paolo Bossio, and Lelio Altogradi, all addressed to Ferrari, the author, argument, prologue, list of characters, and poem by the printer, G. P. Ramellati, to Ferrari. Manelli says in his dedication:
"La Maga fulminata del Sig. Ferrari, una delle peregrine opere, c'habbiano calcate le scene reali. Fù già da me vestita della musica; hora l'hò con maggiore studio raffinata . . ."
First performed at Venice, Teatro Cassano, carnival 1638.   SCHATZ 5888

Le magazin des modernes, opera-comique en un acte; représenté pour la premiere fois sur le Théâtre de la Foire, en 1733.

Charles François Pannard, Théâtre, Paris, Duchesne, 1763, v. 2, [281]–326 p. 17ᶜᵐ.

Prose and vaudevilles. Some of the airs printed in the text. Composer not recorded by Parfaict, who dates first performance February 3, 1736! PQ 2019.P3

Die magd als frau im hause. Tr. of Pergolesi's La serva padrona.

Magdelon. Comédie épisodique, en prose et en un acte, mêlée d'ariettes. Représentée, pour la première fois, à Paris, le 16 prairial an VII, et pour la 26ᵉ fois, le 3 vendémiaire suivant, par les comédiens du Théâtre du Palais Egalité, *dit* Montansier. Paroles et musique du Cousin-Jacques.

Paris, Moutardier, an VIII [1799–1800]. 21½ᶜᵐ. 2 p. l., 35, [1] p. 21½ᶜᵐ.

Cast and Avant-propos, in which Cousin Jacques (Beffroy de Reigny) calls this of all his pieces the easiest to play and pays a special tribute to the Magdelon of Madame Barroyer.
First performed, as indicated, June 4, 1799.   SCHATZ 706

Il maggior impossibile. A. T. of Pallavicino's Bassiano.

La maggior impresa d'Ercole o sia Admeto ed Alceste, ballet. *See* Pio's Nettuno ed Egle.

Magia contro magia, ballet. *See* Bernardini's L'ultima che si perde è la speranza.

Magia contra magia, ballet. *See* P. Guglielmi's L'Azzardo.

Le magistrat du peuple. A. T. of Ladurner's Wenzel.

The magnet. A musical entertainment, as sung at Marybone Gardens.

London, T. Becket, 1771. 29, [3] p. 20ᶜᵐ.

The [3] p. contain a publisher's book list.
One act. Neither author nor composer recorded by Schatz.
Performed 1771, as indicated.   LONGE 190

Der magnetstein der herzen. Tr. of Salieri's La calamita de cuori.

Le **magnifique,** comédie en trois actes, en prose et en vers, mise en musique, terminée par un divertissement. Par M. Sedaine. La musique est de M. Grétry. Représentée à Paris, pour la première fois, par les Comédiens italiens du Roi, le lundi 4 mars 1773, & à Versailles en présence de Sa Majesté, le 26 mars 1773.

Paris, Claude Herissant, 1773. 52 p. 19ᶜᵐ.

Cast and same *avertissement* as in the next. The "ariette" here on p. 50–52.

ML 50.2.M2G7

— Le **magnifique,** comédie en trois actes, en prose et en vers, mise en musique, terminée par un divertissement. Par M. Sedaine. La musique est de M. Grétry. Représentée à Paris, pour la première fois, par les Comédiens italiens du roi, le lundi 4 mars 1773, & à Versailles en présence de Sa Majesté, le 26 mars 1773.

Paris, Claude Herissant, 1773. 56 p. 18ᶜᵐ.

Cast. In the "Avertissement" Sedaine says that he wrote his libretto without ever having seen Houdart de la Mothe's piece of the same title (1731). At the end of the avertissement, these esthetic or dramaturgie remarks are of interest:

"Il faut quelque réflexion pour s'appercevoir des soin avec l'auteur du drame écarte les moyens de paroître aux dépens de son associé, comme il se replie, comme il s'efface, combien enfin il a fait de sacrifices pour n'être que le piédestal de la statue qu'il lui éleve. Il est besoin, il est vrai, que le piédestal soit solide, & je n'ose m'en flatter . . . J'ai mis avec une sorte d'affectation le jeu du théatre, & la pantomime qui occupe la scene pendant les ritournelles (toujours trop longues pour tout auditeur qui n'est pas musicien . . ."

On p. 53–56, the "*Ariette,* Jour heureux, douce espérance" (III, 8). SCHATZ 4167

— Le **magnifique,** comédie en trois actes, en prose et en vers, mise en musique, terminée par un divertissement. Par M. Sedaine. La musique est de M. Grétry. Représentée à Paris, pour la première fois, par les Comédiens italiens ordinaires du roi, le lundi 4 mars 1773, & à Versailles en présence de Sa Majesté, le 26 mars 1773.

Paris, Hérissant, 1782. 56 p. 19ᶜᵐ.

Cast and same avertissement. On p. 53–56, the ariette, "Jour heureux, douce espérance" (III, 8). SCHATZ 11708

— Der **praechtige freygebige,** ein singspiel in drey aufzuegen aus dem franzoesischen uebersetzt, mit musik.

Frankfurt am Mayn, mit Andreäischen schriften, 1774. 88 p., 12 p. (folded music). 15½ᶜᵐ.

By Joh. Heinr. Faber, who is not mentioned. Cast. The music (voice and bass) consists of "Ach! wie ist das pferd so schön" ("Ah! c'est un superbe cheval," I, 6) and "Ach ja, eifersucht quält ihn" ("O ciel! quel air de courroux!" III, 6).

SCHATZ 4168

Songs, duets, trios, finales, etc in **Mahmoud.** A musical romance, in three acts; as performed at the Theatre Royal, Drury-Lane. The musick by the late Mr. Storace. With a few selections from Sarti, Haydn, etc.

n. i., 1796. 24 p. 21ᶜᵐ.

Cast. By Prince Hoare, who is not mentioned. The score was prepared for performance by Michael Kelly.

First performed April 30, 1796. LONGE 234

718 LIBRARY OF CONGRESS

The **maid of the mill.** A comic opera. As it is performed at the Theatre Royal in Covent Garden. The music compiled, and the words written by the author of Love in a village.

London, J. Newberry, R. Baldwin [etc.], 1765. 1 p. l., iv, ii, [2], 75, [1] p. 19^{cm}.

On last page, publishers' advertisement of tenth [!] ed. of "Love in a village."
Three acts. By Isaac Bickerstaffe. Cast, preface, with statement that the text is based on Richardson's "Pamela," and dedication, in which Bickerstaffe says:

". . . How far the Comic Opera, under proper regulations, has a right to be acknowledged for a junior offspring of the Drama, and as such become candidate for a share of public encouragement, I shall not pretend to determine; but if it can be rendered an agreeable amusement, the English Theatre has never scrupled to adopt, what was capable of pleasing there; and though as a work of genius, it is by no means to be set in competition with good tragedies and comedies, it may, I apprehend, be permitted as an occasional relief to them, without bringing either our taste or understanding into question.

"I need not inform your Royal Highness, that in France, where the stage has been cultivated with more care, and success, than in any other country, this species of entertainment is receiving very great applause; nor is it thought any injury to Corneille, and Moliere, that the pieces of Anseaume and Favart, meet with success. It is true, among the French, comic operas have very often the advantage of being extremely well written, of which, *On ne S'avise jamais de tout, Le Roy et le Fermier,* and some others are an instance; nor would the best composition of the greatest master, make a very contemptible poem pass on an audience: I wish I could assert with truth, that in this respect, we fall nothing behind our neighbours, and that what I here present to your Royal Highness, might lay claim to some degree of merit, even in the writing; but though I cannot do this, permit me to say, I have attempted to render it a little interesting, and not wholly undiverting, as far as the music, my principal care, would give me leave . . ."

Neither Samuel **Arnold,** who assisted Bickenstaffe in the selection and arrangement of the music, is mentioned, nor any other composer on whose works they drew for this pasticcio. "The table of the songs" in Preston and Son's vocal score mentions besides Arnold the following composers: Earl of **Kelly** (Overture), **Abos, Bach, Ciampi, Cocchi, Duni, Galuppi, Giardini, Hasse, Jommelli, Laschi, Monsigny, Pergolesi, Philidor, Piccinni, Rinaldo di Capua, Scarlatti, Vinci** and "the late elector of Saxony."

First performed, January 31, 1765, as indicated. LONGE 46
Second copy. AC 901.M5

— The **maid of the mill.** A comic opera. By Isaac Bickerstaff. Adapted for theatrical representation, as performed at the Theatre Royal, Covent-Garden, regulated from the prompt book, by permission of the managers . . .

London, John Bell, 1791. front., 1 p. l., vii, [4], 12–102 p. 15^{cm}. (J. Bell, British Theatre, London, 1791–1797, v. 1.)

The front. is a port. of Mr. Blanchard as Ralph in the "Maid of the Mill." The p. l. is an engraved title page of the series with a scene from the same opera. Both engravings are dated January 4, 1791. Author's dedication, biographical sketch of the author, editorial estimate, preface, Drury-Lane and Covent-Garden casts.
PR 1241.B4

— The **man of the mill.** A new burlesque tragic opera. The musick compiled, and the words written, by Seignior Squallini.

London, J. Cooke, 1765. 1 p. l., 42 p. 20^{cm}.

Three acts. A parody of "The maid of the mill." Author not recorded by Clarence. Not performed. LONGE 125

The **maid of the oaks:** a new dramatick entertainment. As it is performed at the Theatre-Royal, in Drury-Lane . . .

London, T. Becket, 1774. 6 p. l., 68 p. 19^{cm}.

The **maid of the oaks**—Continued.

Five acts with considerable incidental music, prologue and epilogue. Cast and preface. By John Burgoyne. Neither he is mentioned, nor François Hippolyte Barthelemon, who partly composed, partly selected the music from **Rousseau**, **Philidor**, and **La Borde**.

First performed, as indicated, November 5, 1774.   LONGE 48

La **maison isolée**, ou Le vieillard des Vosges, comédie en deux actes, en prose, mélée d'ariettes, représentée sur le Théâtre Italien, le 22 floréal, an 5, 11 mai 1797, (vieux style)   Paroles de Marsolier. Musique de Dalairac.

Paris, Barba, An cinquième de la République [*1797*].   *46,* [*2*] *p.   20^{cm}*.

The 2 additional p. contain Barba's "Pièces de Théâtre."   Cast.   SCHATZ 2363

Le **maître de musique**.   Parody of Pergolesi's Il maestro di musica.

Le **maître en droit**, opera-comique, en deux actes, représenté pour la premiere fois sur le Théâtre de l'Opéra-comique de la Foire S. Germain, le 13 février 1762.

Paris, Duchesne, 1762.   31 p.   19½^{cm}.

Neither the author, Lemonnier, is mentioned, nor the composer, **Monsigny**. First performed, as indicated, February 13, 1760 (Cl. & L.), February 14. 1760 (Wotquenne), February 23, 1760 (Schatz, as in next entry).

ML 50.2.M31M6

—Le **maître en droit**, opéra-comique, en deux actes; représenté pour la première fois sur le Théâtre de l'Opéra-comique de la Foire S. Germain, le 23. février 1760.

Paris, Duchesne, 1764.   38 p.   19^{cm}.

Neither the author, Pierre Réné Lemonnier, nor the composer, **Monsigny**, is mentioned.   SCHATZ 6577

Le **major Palmer**, drame, en trois actes, en prose.   Par Pigault-Lebrun.   Musique du citoyen Bruni.   Représenté, pour la première fois, sur le Théâtre Feydeau, le 7 pluviôse [January 26] de l'an cinquième de la République.

Paris, Huet, an cinquième (*1797*).   *2 p. l., 72 p.   21^{cm}*.

Cast and dedicatory poem to Mademoiselle Lesage, who took the part of "Amalie."

ML 50.2.M32B7

Malmosor.   O. T. of Buini's Artanaganamenone.

Man kann es ja probieren.   A. T. of Schweitzer's Walmir und Gertraud.

The **man of the mill**.   Parody of The maid of the mill.

Man sieht niemals alles voraus.   Tr. of Monsigny's On ne s'avise jamais de tout.

Mandame.   *See* Mandane.

[**Mandane**] **Mandame** [!]   Dramma per musica da rapresentarsi nel Teatro di S. Angelo nel carnovale dell' anno 1736.

Venezia, Domenico Tabacco, 1736.   60 p.   14½^{cm}.

Three acts. By Bartolomeo Vitturi, who is not mentioned. Argument, notices to the reader, scenario, cast, and name of the composer, Ignazio **Fiorillo**.

SCHATZ 3203

Il **manescalco**, ballet.　*See* Rust's Adriano in Siria.

Il **maniscalco francese**, ballet.　*See* Mortellari's Semiramide.

Il **maniscalco francese**, ballet.　*See* Zingarelli's Alsinda.

Manto la fée, opera représenté par l'Academie royale de musique l'an 1711.　Les paroles de M. Menesson, & la musique de M. Batistin. LXXVI. opera.

> *n. i., n. d.　pl., 253–314 p.　14ᶜᵐ.　(Recueil général des opéra, t. X, Paris, 1714.)*

Detached copy.　Prologue and five acts.　Music by Jean Batistin **Stuck**.
First performed January 29, 1711, as indicated.　　　SCHATZ 10123
　　　　　　　　　　　　　　　　　　　　Second copy.　ML 48.R4

Marc' Antonio.　*See* M. Curzio.

Marcello in Siracusa.　Drama per musica nel famoso Teatro Grimano l'anno MDCLXX di Matteo Noris . . .

> *Venetia, Francesco Nicolini, 1670.　front., 107 p.　13½ᶜᵐ.*

Last page incorrectly paged 197, with running heading *Secondo* instead of *Terzo*. Three acts.　Author's dedication, notice to the reader with name of the composer Giovanni Antonio **Boretti**, argument, and scenario.　　　SCHATZ 1220

Il **marchese Carbonaro.**　Dramma giocoso per musica di Filippo Livigni da rappresentarsi nel Teatro Giustiniani in S. Moisè il carnovale dell' anno 1776.

> *Venezia, Gio. Battista Casali, n. d.　64 p.　16½ᶜᵐ.*

Three acts.　Cast, scenario, and name of Francesco **Salari** as the composer.　On p. 31–32, a brief description of Gio. Battista Martein's ballet (title not given), performed as primo ballo.　The second, by Bartolamio Cambi, was called "Le peregrine erranti."　The composers of the music are not mentioned.　　　SCHATZ 9267

Il **marchese del Bosco.**　Intermezzi per musica da rappresentarsi nel Teatro Giustiniano di S. Moisè.　Nella fiera della Ascensione dell' anno 1747.

> *Venezia, Modesto Fenzo, 1747.　21 p. (incl. front.)　14½ᶜᵐ.*

Three parts.　Author and composer not mentioned and unknown to Schatz.　The intermezzi were performed with the anonymous opera, "La finta pazza" (Wiel).
　　　　　　　　　　　　　　　　　　　　　　SCHATZ 11349

Il **marchese di Castel Verde.**　Dramma giocoso per musica da rappresentarsi nel nobil Teatro delle Dame nel carnevale dell' anno 1779 . . .

> *Roma, 1779, Si vendono da Luigi Bendio.　60 p.　15ᶜᵐ.*

Three acts.　Dedication, cast, scenario, and name of composer, Agostino **Accorimboni**, but not of librettist, who is unknown to Schatz.　The dedication states that the opera was to be performed at Rome "per la prima volta."　　　SCHATZ 13

Il **marchese di Spartivento**, ovvero Il cabalista ne sa' men del caso.　Farsetta per musica da rappresentarsi nel Teatro della Valle nel carnevale dell' anno 1747 . . .

> *Roma, Si vendono da Muzio Bona, 1747.　36 p.　15ᶜᵐ.*

Two parts.　Author not mentioned.　Dedication, cast and name of Pietro **Auletta** as composer, with note that "per comodo de' Signori musici" "alcune arie" marked with asterisk were composed by Benedetto **Micheli**, but only "Perchè il tempo di vincersi" has an asterisk.　　　ML 50.2.M37A9

Il **marchese di Tulipano** o sia Il matrimonio inespetato. L. T. of Paisiello's Il matrimonio inaspettato.

Il **marchese Sgrana.** Drama per musica di Antonio Palomba Napoletano. Da rappresentarsi nel Teatro nuovo sopra Toledo nella primavera di quest' anno 1738 . . .

Napoli, Nicola di Biase, 1738. 69 p. 15ᶜᵐ.

Three acts. Dedication, cast, and name of Pietro **Auletta** as composer

SCHATZ 499

Il **marchese villano.** O. T. of Chiari's libretto I raggiri fortunati.

Il **marchese villano.** Dramma giocoso per musica da rappresentarsi ne' Teatri privilegiati di Vienna in tempo delle feste per li felicissimi sponsali di Ferdinando II di Borbone . . . e di Maria Giuseppe d'Austria l'anno MDCCLXVII.

Vienna, Ghelen, n. d. 65 p. 16ᶜᵐ.

Three acts. By Pietro Chiari, who is not mentioned. Scenario and name of Baldassare **Galuppi** as composer.

First performed at Vienna in September, 1767; at Venice, Teatro di S. Moisè February 2, 1762. SCHATZ 3458

— La **lavandara.** Dramma giocoso per musica da rappresentarsi nel Teatro di S. A. Serenissima il Signor principe di Carignano l'autunno dell' anno MDCCLXX.

Torino, Onorato Derossi, n. d. 50, [2] p. 16ᶜᵐ.

Three acts. Cast. Neither the author, Pietro Chiari, nor the composer, **Galuppi**, is mentioned. The dialogue follows that of "Il marchese villano" closely, but many arias are different. For instance, "Il marchese villano" has (I, 4), in the Vienna version, "Nina cara, Nina bella," whereas "La lavandara" has "Chi và a prender la consorte." SCHATZ 3515

— La **lavandara astuta.** Dramma giocoso da rappresentarsi in musica nel Regio-Ducal Teatro Nuovo di Mantova l'autunno dell' anno 1771. In occasione del felicissimo passaggio di Sua Altezza Reale il serenissimo Ferdinando Carlo arciduca d'Austria . . .

Mantova, Alberto Pazzoni, n. d. 56 p. 20ᶜᵐ.

Two acts. By Pietro Chiari, who is not mentioned. Cast, scenario, and name of **Galuppi** as composer. A condensation of "Il marchese villano," the third act having been practically suppressed. The two versions show also noticeable differences in the lyrical parts, and "La lavandara astuta" begins "Benedetta primavera." SCHATZ 3505

— Il **matrimonio per inganno.** Dramma giocoso per musica da rappresentarsi nel Teatro di S. Giacomo di Corfù nell' autunno dell' anno 1771 . . .

Venezia, Giambattista Casali, 1771. 60 p. 15½ᶜᵐ.

Three acts. By Pietro Chiari, who is not mentioned. Impresario's dedication, cast, scenario, and name of **Galuppi** as composer. Another version of "Il marchese villano." It begins, like "La lavandara astuta," with "Benedetta primavera." The fourth scene of act first opens, like the Vienna version of "Il marchese villano," with "Nina cara, Nina bella," but ends with "Sai che abbiamo un marchesato," instead of "Guardami in volto, e poi." SCHATZ 3506

La **marchesina di Nanchin ed il conte di Pelusio,** intermezzi. *See* Caldara's Camaide, imperatore della China.

72251°—VOL 1—14——46

M. Curzio. Dramma per musica nella solenne celebrazione de' Comizj della serenissima Repubblica di Lucca l'anno MDCCXCI.

Lucca, Francesco Bonsignori, n. d.   lxii p.   20½ᶜᵐ.

On p. lxi–lxii substitute arias "Al zelo, che m'accende" and "Alme amanti, a voi ritorno." Argument. Divided into "Giornata" I–III, each having two parts. Not recorded by Nerici, who, however, mentions Pasquale Antonio **Soffi,** Antonio **Puccini,** and Marco **Santucci** as composers on p. 335 of his "Storia della musica in Lucca" (1879).

Since 1431 the election of the city government was accompanied in Lucca by the national festivities of the "Comizj," popularly known as "le feste delle *Tasche*," in December, first biennial, then tri-ennial, and since 1750 every thirty months. The festivities lasted three days and took place at the government palazzo.

According to Nerici, the first definite news of the vocal and instrumental music used at the "feste delle Tasche" date from the year 1636, when Valerio Guami would seem to have been the composer of at least part of the music. With the fall of the republic of Lucca in 1799, the "feste delle tasche" died a natural death.

In the case of this "M. Curzio" there would seem to be little room for doubt that it was a bona-fide opera, yet the L. of C. possesses quite a few "Tasche" libretti of a similar character but which are designated as "concerto in musica," "applausi musicali," etc. They would lead to the impression that the works were not performed as operas with scenery and action, but as dramatic cantatas, with scenery perhaps, but without action, even though occasionally called "Dramma per musica" or "Componimento dramatico." A characteristic feature of these works was that practically without exception, text and music were the productions of native authors and composers. As a rule, each "giornata" was allotted to different authors and composers, if the subjects for each day were different and to different composers, even if the text of the whole formed a trilogy by *one* author.

The librettos were practically always printed without names of authors, composers and performers. Since these rare and curious texts sometimes figure as operas in reference books and since Nerici does not make it at all clear whether these festival works were operas or dramatic cantatas—my impression being that they were of the latter kind—it is perhaps best to give here a brief list of those in the L. of C. (those so far found all in ML 54.2.L9, chronologically arranged). The set is not quite complete, but it contains some texts unknown to Nerici.

1645   I–III *Applausi musicali.* Neither author nor composers known to me. Different in subject from Francesco Sbarra's text "Gli ossequi della fortuna" mentioned by Nerici under 1645.

1651   II La *visione,* poesia per musica. Text by Silvestro Torcigliani. Composer not mentioned by Nerici.

1654   I La *libertà trionfante,* applausi musicali. Text by Lodovico Breni, music by Marco Bigongiari. Not recorded by Nerici.

1654   II Il *porto della libertà,* concerto musicale. Text by Bartolomeo Beverini, music by Dom. Stiava. Not recorded by Nerici.

1654   III La *nave d'Argo,* idillio. Text, according to contemporary ms. note, by Francesco Sbarra, music by Bernardino Roncaglia.

1657   I L'*invidia abbattuta,* applausi musicali. Text by Celio Altogradi, music by Marco Bigongiari. Not recorded by Nerici.

1657   II *Hercole perseguitato,* idillio. According to contemporary ms. note, the text was by Bartolomeo Beverini, the music by Domenico Stiava. Nerici mentions Francesco Sbarra as the author.

1657   III La *pace,* concerto musicale. According to contemporary ms. note, the text was by Domenico Vanni, the music by Bernardino Roncaglia.

1660   I Gl'*avvanzi fortunati del mondo naufragante,* concerto musicale. Not recorded by Nerici. Author and composer unknown to me.

1660   II *Bruto costante,* concerto musicale. Not recorded by Nerici. According to contemporary ms. note, the author was Bartolomeo Beverini. The composer is not mentioned.

1660   III La *libertà trionfatrice del tempo.* Not recorded by Nerici. Author and composer unknown to me.

1663   I I *giganti abbattuti,* concerto musicale. Nerici mentions the author, Domenico Berti, but not the composer.

1663   II *Scipione Affricano,* concerto musicale. Not recorded by Nerici. Author and composer unknown to me.

M. Curzio—Continued.

1663　III La *fortuna incatenata*. Not recorded by Nerici. Author and composer unknown to me.

1666　I Il *vessillo della libertà*, concerto musicale. Text by Paolino Casoli, composer unknown to Nerici.

1666　II Gl'*amori politici della libertà raminga*, concerto musicale. Not recorded by Nerici. Composer unknown to me. Text, according to contemporary ms. note, by Vincenzo Cini.

1666　III *Horatio vero amatore della patria*, concerto musicale. Not recorded by Nerici. Author and composer unknown to me.

1669　I La *prudenza vittoriosa*, applausi musicali. Not recorded by Nerici. Text, according to contemporary ms. note, by Bartolomeo Beverini. Composer not mentioned.

1669　II La *città felice*, applausi musicali. Not recorded by Nerici. Text, according to contemporary ms. note, by Amadèo Saminiati. Composer unknown to me.

1669　III *Martio Cariolano*, applausi musicali. Not recorded by Nerici. Text, according to contemporary ms. note, by Leone Santucci. Composer not mentioned.

1672　I Gli *avantaggi della concordia*, applausi musicali. Not recorded by Nerici. Text, according to contemporary ms. note, by Nicolao Bartolini. Composer not mentioned.

1672　II Il *consiglio fedele*, applausi musicali. Not recorded by Nerici. Text, according to contemporary ms. note, by Amadeo Saminiati.

1672　III Il *merito riconosciuto*, concerto musicale. Composer unknown to Nerici, who records Giov. Vittorio Diversi as author.

1675　I Il *Fetonte*, applausi musicali. Text by Bernardo Moscheni, according to contemporary ms. note, by Ottavio Carli, according to Nerici, who does not mention the composer.

1675　II L'*amore della patria*, applausi musicali. Text by Bernardo Moscheni, composer not mentioned by Nerici.

1675　III *Mutio Scevola*, applausi musicali. Not recorded by Nerici. Text by Donato Antonio Leonardi, according to contemporary ms. note. Composer not mentioned.

1678　I Il *trionfo del ben pubblico*, applausi musicali. According to contemporary ms. note, the text was by Matteo Regali, the music by Bernardino Roncaglia.

1678　II Il *Temistocle*, applausi musicale. Not recorded by Nerici. Text by Giov. Nicolao Barsanti, according to contemporary ms. note. Composer not mentioned.

1678　III La *libertà raminga*, applausi musicali. Text by Michele di Poggio. Composer unknown to Nerici.

1681　I *Fabio vincitor di se stesso*, concerto in musica. Nerici (under 1678) mentions the author, Bartolemeo Andreucci, but not the composer.

1681　II *Trasibolo ateniese*, applausi musicali. Neither author nor composer known to Nerici.

1684　I *Decio sacrificato alla patria*, applausi musicali. Nerici mentions the author, Pier Francesco Boccella, but not the composer.

1684　II L'*idea del comando nel cuore di Germanico invincibile*, concerto in musica. Not recorded by Nerici. Author and composer unknown to me.

1684　III La *libertà gelosa di se stessa in persona di Annibale amante di patria*, applausi musicali. Nerici mentions the author, Michele Boccella, but not the composer.

1687　I–III *Marc' Antonio*, poesie per musica. Nerici mentions the author, Domenico Berti, but not the composer.

1690　I–III *Il Catone*, poesie per musica. Nerici mentions the author, Bernardino Moscheni, but not the composer.

1693　I La *libertà sempre stabile nelle vicende del principato*, concerto per musica. Nerici mentions the author, Paolo Sinibaldi, but not the composer. Imprint has date of December 4.

M. Curzio—Continued.

1693   III   *Horatio*, concerto per musica.   Not recorded by Nerici.   Imprint has date of December 7.

1735   I–III   *Lucio Giunio Bruto primo consolo di Roma*, componimento per musica. Nerici mentions the composers, Giovanni Antonio Canuti, Giuseppe Montuoli and Domenico Pierotti, but not the author for this year.

1741   I–III   *Solone*, dramma per musica.   Nerici mentions the composers, Pier Vincenzo Chiocchetti, Domenico Pierrotti and Giacomo Puccini, but not the author for this year.

1744   I–III   *Teramene*, dramma per musica.   Not recorded by Nerici, who mentions Giov. Lorenzo Fascetti, Domenico Pierotti and Giacomo Puccini as composers for this year, but not the author.

1755   I–III   *Marco Manlio Capitolino*, dramma.   Not recorded by Nerici who mentions as composers for this year—he has incorrectly 1756—Frediano Matteo, Pasquale Antonio Soffi and Giacomo Puccini.

1760   I–III   *Roma liberata dalla signoria de' re*, dramma.   By Giambattista Montecatini.   Nerici mentions Pasquale Antonio Soffi (due giornate) and Giacomo Puccini as composers for this year.

1765   I–III   *La confederazione de i Sabini con Roma*, dramma.   Nerici mentions Pier Angelo Trenta as author, Giacomo Puccini, Lelio Ignazio di Poggio and Luigi Boccherini as composers.

1768   I–III   *L'esilio di M. P. Cicerone*, dramma.   Nerici mentions Orazio Gherardi Scolopio as author, Giacomo Puccini and Lelio Ignazio di Poggio as composers.

1770   I–III   *Il Narsete, generale di Giustiniano imperatore*, dramma.   Not recorded by Nerici, who mentions Pellegrino Tomeoni, Giacomo Puccini and Antonio Puccini as composers for this year, but not the author.

1775   I–III   *Roma liberata dalla congiura di Catilina*, dramma.   Nerici mentions as composers for this year Florido Tomeoni and Antonio Micheli, but not the authors.

1777   I–III   *Marco Manlio Capitolino*, dramma.   Text by Bartolomeo Baroni, music by Antonio Puccini (June 7), Giacomo Puccini (June 8) and Pasquale Antonio Soffi (June 9).

1779   I–III   *Cesare nella Brettagna*, dramma.   Text by abate Serafini, music by Giuseppe Finucci (June 7), Antonio Puccini (June 8), Antonio Micheli.

1781   I–III   Il *Castruccio*, dramma per musica.   Nerici mentions as author, Carlo Provenzali, as composers Domenico Quilici (May 28), Antonio Puccini (May 29), and Giuseppe Finucci (May 30).   This is bound in with ML 48. A5, v.28.

1783   I–III   *Leonida rè di Sparta*, dramma.   Nerici mentions as author Francesco Franceschi, as composers Giuseppe Rustici (June 2), Antonio Puccini (June 3), Giuseppe Finucci (June 4).

1785   I–III   *L'Emilio*, dramma per musica.   Not mentioned by Nerici, who says that the music for second day (June 7) was composed by Pasquale Antonio Soffi, of the third day (June 8) by Antonio Benedetto Maria Puccini. That for the first day (June 6) was by Giuseppe Rustici.

1787   I–III   *Lucca liberata*, dramma.   Not recorded by Nerici, who says that the text was written by Alessandro Ottolini and the music composed by Pasquale Antonio Soffi (June 11), Antonio Puccini (June 12) and Domenico Quilici (June 13).

1789   I–III   *Bruto*, dramma.   Not recorded by Nerici, who mentions Luigi Vannucci as author, Domenico Quilici (June 25), Giuseppe Rustici (June 26) and Antonio Puccini (June 27) as composers.

1791   I–III   *M. Curzio*, as at beginning of this entry.

ML 54.2.L9   1791

Marco Manlio Capitolino.   *See* M. Curzio.

Le **maréchal**, ballet.   *See* P. Guglielmi's L'impostore punito.

Le **marechal ferrant,** opera comique en un acte; représenté pour
la première fois sur le Théâtre de l'Opera comique de la Foire Saint
Laurent le 22 août 1761. Par M. Quetant. La musique de M.
Philidor. Seconde edition, revûe, corrigée & augmentée par
l'auteur.

Paris, Claude Herissant, 1761. 1 p. l., 52, [2] p. 19^{cm}.

Cast. The [2] p. contain text of the "Vaudeville: L'amour se plaît."

YUDIN PQ

— Le **maréchal ferrant,** opéra-comique en un acte. Représenté,
pour la première fois, sur le Théâtre de l'Opera-comique de la Foire
Saint Laurent, le 22 août 1761. Par M. Quetant. Nouvelle édition.

Paris, Claude Herissant, 1765. 46 p. 19^{cm}.

The composer, **Philidor,** is not mentioned. SCHATZ 8018

— Le **maréchal ferrant,** opéra comique, en un acte, représenté pour
la première fois sur le Théâtre de l'Opéra comique de la Foire Saint-
Laurent, le 22 août 1761. Par M. Quétant. La musique de M.
Philidor.

Paris, Claude Hérissant, 1785. 48 p. 18^{cm}.

Cast. On p. 23–26, the ariette, "Charmant objet de ma flâme." SCHATZ 11741

— Der **hufschmied,** eine operette in einem aufzuge. Nach dem
franzoesischen des herrn Quetant. Die musik ist von herrn Philidor.

Frankfurth und Leipzig, Esslinger, 1772. 64 p., 4 p. (music). 15^{cm}.

Johann André's translation, who is not mentioned. The music consists of the
aria "Komm, ach komm zurück" and the vaudeville "Die liebe fordert heisse glut."

SCHATZ 8019

— Der **hufschmied,** eine komische oper in zwey akten, nach Quetant
und Philidor, aus dem franzoesischen uebersetzt von Heinr. August
Ottocar Reichard . . .

Riga, Gottlob Christian Froelich, 1785. 15 p. 16^{cm}.

Lyrics only.
First performed at Riga, Vietinghoff'sches Theater i. d. gr. Königsstrasse, 5/16
Sept. 1785. SCHATZ 8020

Margaretha, koenigin in Castilien. In einer opera auf dem
Hamburgischen Schau-platze aufgefuehret, den 10. Aug. 1730.

*[Hamburg], Gedruckt mit Stromerischen schriften, n. d. Unpaged.
18^{cm}.*

Five acts. Cast, names of Johann Georg Hamann as author, of Georg Philipp
Telemann as composer, and "Vor-erinnerung" which reads, in part:
"Diejenige, so der geschichte kundig, duerfften sich vielleicht einer russischen
prinzessin bey der Margaretha erinnern. Sie hat Olga geheissen und man setzet
ihre lebens-zeit in das achte jahrhundert. Sie verlor ihren gemahl, welcher Ingof
oder Igor geheissen, sehr zeitig; und liess sich nichts so sehr angelegen seyn, als
desselben tod zu raechen. Man hat wichtige bewegungs-gruende gehabt; wesswegen
man die begebenheit dieser heldin, in eine Spanische verwandelt; welche aber anzu-
fuehren man nicht fuer nothwendig haelt." SCHATZ 10263

Margery, or, A worse plague than the dragon: A burlesque opera.
Being the sequel to the Dragon of Wantley. As it is perform'd at
the Theatre Royal in Covent-Garden. Altered from the original
Italian by Signor Carini. Set to musick by Mr. John Frederick
Lampe. The third edition.

London, J. Shuckburgh, 1738. 2 p. l., 8–31 p. 20^{cm}.

Margery—Continued.

Three acts. By Henry Carey. Cast and argument which ends:
'The opera concludes, according to the custom of all operas, with the general reconciliation of all parties, no matter how absurd, improbable, or ridiculous.'
First performed December 9, 1738, as indicated.   LONGE 153

— The **dragoness**, a burlesque opera. Set to musick by Mr. John Frederick Lampe.

[115]–150 p. 22ᶜᵐ. (Henry Carey, Dramatick works, London, 1743.)

Later version of " Margery." Three acts. Argument with same remark as above.
The text of "The Dragoness" is noticeably different from that of Margery. For instance, the airs "The tongue is a dangerous weapon" and "No place shall conceal 'em" are not in II, 2, of "Margery," where instead we have "Wretched is a wife's condition." Also the dialogue of 1, 3 was shortened and the air I, 2 "The swain I adore" is now preceded by "Enter shepherd" with dialogue and air "Hark! I hear the midnight owl," etc., etc.   ML 49.A2C2

Le mari préferé. Piece d'un acte. Par Mr. Le S * *. Représentée à la Foire S. Laurent. 1736.

Le Théâtre de la foire, Paris, 1737, t. ix, [363]–421 p. 17ᶜᵐ.

By Le Sage. Largely *en vaudevilles.* The airs, selected or composed and arranged by Jean Claude Gillier, are printed at the end of the volume in the "Table des airs."
First performed Aug. 11, 1736.

     ML 48.L2IK

Le mariage caché. A. T. of Kohault's Sophie.

Le mariage d'Antonio, comédie en un acte et en prose, mêlée d'ariettes, représentée sur le Théâtre italien, le 29 juillet 1786. Les paroles sont de Mde. de Beaunoir. La musique est de Mlle. Gretry.

Paris, Vente, 1787. 17 p. 21½ᵐ.

The opera was instrumentated by Lucile Grétry's father, the famous composer.
     ML 50.2.M4G7

Le mariage de Momus ou La gigantomachie, opéra-comique en trois actes, représenté par les marionnettes de la troupe de Francisque, à la Foire Saint-Laurent, en 1722.

Alexis Piron, Oeuvres complettes, Liege, 1776, v. 5, 49 p. 17½ᶜᵐ.

In prose and *vaudevilles.* Composer not mentioned. *See also* Tirésias.
     PQ 2019.P6

Le mariage du caprice et de la folie. Piece d'un acte. Par M * * Représentée pour la première fois à la Foire Saint Laurent 1724. Et remise au théâtre en 1730.

Le Théâtre de la foire, Paris, 1731, t. viii, pl., [185]–238 p. 17ᶜᵐ.

By Alexis Piron. Largely *en vaudevilles.* The airs, selected or composed and arranged by Jean Claude Gillier, are printed at the end of the volume in the "Table des airs." Text by Piron.
First performed August 16, 1724.   ML 48.L2VIII

— Le **caprice**, opéra-comique, en un acte. Mêlé de prose & de vaudevilles. Représenté, pour la première fois, le 16 août 1724, sur le Théâtre de l'Opéra-comique.

Alexis Piron, Oeuvres complettes, Liege, 1776, t. 3, [223]–283 p. 17½ᶜᵐ.

Epitre dédicatoire aux dances. Same as the above.   PQ 2019.P6

Le mariage du diable. A. T. of Gluck's L'ivrogne corrigé.

Le mariage impromptu. A. T. of Gaveaux' Le petit matelot.

Le mariage par escalade, opera-comique, a l'occasion de la prise du Port-Mahon, representé pour la premiere fois sur le Théâtre de l'Opera-comique, le samedi 11 septembre 1756. Nouvelle edition, augmentée de couplets qui avoient été retranchés & de vaudevilles.

Paris, Duchesne, 1757. 56 p. 19ᶜᵐ. (Theatre de M. Favart, Paris, Duchesne, 1763–77, t. viii.)

One act. *En vaudevilles.* On p. 49–56 three "Airs du mariage par escalade" and two vaudevilles. According to Font, the couplets on the taking of Port-Mahon (1756) are by Piron. The play was first presented in honor of duc de Richelieu by Mme. de Mauconseil at Bagatelle, which explains Favart's dedication to her ("C'est par vos ordres que j'ai composé ce petit opéra-comique"). The dedication is preceded by an Avertissement, in which the author insists that he is under no contract to write exclusively for the Comédie italienne, and says:

"Cette petite piece n'a été composée que pour une fête particuliere que l'on préparoit pour le retour de M. le maréchal de Richelieu. Mais l'accueil favorable que le public à fait à tous les ouvrages qui ont paru sur la prise de Mahon, a donné lieu de penser qu'il auroit la même indulgence pour cette bagatelle.

"Quelques critiques ont trouvé que l'on ne menageoit pas assez les Anglois, que nous ne devions point rendre injure pour injure, ni imiter l'indécence des spectacles de Londres à notre égard; ce sentiment fait honneur à notre nation; mais une délicatesse trop scrupuleuse auroit empêché de faire parler les personnages selon leur caractere . . ."

Favart's musical collaborator is not mentioned by Font. ML 49.A2F1

— **Le mariage par escalade,** opera-comique à l'occasion de la prise du Port-Mahon; représenté pour la premiere fois sur le Théatre de l'Opéra-comique, le samedi 11 septembre 1756. Nouvelle edition.

Paris, la veuve Duchesne, 1777. 64 p. 19ᶜᵐ.

On p. 49–64 seventeen unaccompanied "Airs du Mariage par escalade." Same dedication and Avertissement. Sᴄʜᴀᴛᴢ 1197

Les mariages de Canada. *See* La première représentation.

Les mariages Samnites, drame lyrique en trois actes et en prose. Par M. de Rozoi . . . La musique de M. Grétry . . . Représenté pour la première fois par les Comédiens italiens ordinaires du Roi, le mercredi 12 juin 1776. Nouvelle édition.

Paris, la veuve Duchesne, 1776. xiii, 58 p. 18½ᶜᵐ.

Dedication, cast, and "Préface" in which the author first starts out with a kind of *argomento*, but then takes issue with his critics. He says, for instance:

"J'ai fait quelques changements à cet ouvrage depuis la première représentation. Ils consistent d'abord à avoir supprimé quelques phrases dans le rôle d'*Euphémie*, & un récit, par lequel je donnois à croire, qu' *Agathis*, après être retourné au combat, pouvoit s'être trop livré à son courage, & avoit reçu un coup mortel. La douleur d'*Eumene*, de *Céphalide*, & d'*Euphémie* amenoit un trio du plus grand effet musical . . . Le public a paru ne pas aimer ce récit . . . Sans doute, parce qu' un récit un peu tragique semble absolument étranger au *Théatre italien*, ou à l'Opéra comique . . .

"Le second détail dans lequel je dois entrer, est d'assurer, que l'indisposition seule de *M. Clairval* a retardé la seconde représentation de cet ouvrage . . ."

On p. 30–32, the "*Choeur des jeunes Samnites.* Dieu d'amour, en ce jour" (I, 7, and on p. 56–58, the air of "Vous, qui voyez un coeur éclorre" (III, 7). Sᴄʜᴀᴛᴢ 4169

— **Les mariages Samnites,** drame lyrique en trois actes, et en prose. Par M. de Rozoi . . . Représenté pour la première fois,

Les **mariages Samnites**—Continued.

par les Comédiens italiens ordinaires du roi, le mercredi 12 juin 1776.
Nouvelle edition.

Paris, la veuve Duchesne, 1776. xv, 56 p. 19^{cm}.

Same cast, etc., as in the last entry, but no music printed in the text.   Yudin PQ

— Les **mariages Samnites,** comédie héroïque, en trois actes et en
vers; mêlée d'ariettes. Par M. de Rozoi . . . Représentée en
prose pour la première fois . . . 12 juin 1776, remise au Théâtre en
1777 & 1780; & redonnée en vers le 22 mai 1782. La musique de
M. Grétry.

Paris, Belin, 1782. xiv, [2], 61 p. 20^{cm}.

Preface, list of errata, and cast. In the preface the author says:
"On m'avoit reproché de n'avoir point écrit en vers un sujet aussi héroïque: j'ai
cru devoir au public & à l'amitié, de me conformer à leur avis. Le succès, que cet
ouvrage a obtenu sur le Théâtre de Rouen, depuis que je l'ai mis en vers m'a déja
récompensé de mes peines."
Further on, he regrets "que l'on ne donne point au Théâtre la fin du deuxième acte,
telle que je l'avois composée, & telle qu' elle n'a jamais été représentée." On the
other hand, he congratulates himself on having reinserted the trio.   Schatz 4170

— Die **samnitische vermaehlungsfeyer.** Ein schauspiel mit
gesang. Aus dem franzoesischen. Nach der musik von Gretry, auf
dem Hoftheater . . . [zu] Schwedt . . . zum erstenmale aufgefuehrt.

Berlin, Christian Friedrich Himburg, 1780. 54 p. 16^{cm}.

German version, by Johann André and Friedrich Ludwig Wilhelm Meyer, who are
not mentioned.   Schatz 4171

La **Mariamme.** Drama per musica da rappresentarsi nel famosissimo Teatro di SS. Gio. e Paulo. Nell' anno MDCXCVI . . .

Venetia, Nicolini, 1696. 86 p. 14^{cm}.

Three acts. Notice to the reader, argument, scenario, and dedication, in which
the anonymous author calls this "questa prima adulatione del mio genio." The text
was by Lorenzo Burlini. The composer, Giov. Maria **Ruggeri,** is not mentioned.
   Schatz 9139

La **Mariane.** *See* Albinoni's Gl'eccessi della gelosia.

Marianne, comédie en un acte et en prose, mêlée d'ariettes; représentée pour la première fois sur le Théâtre de l'Opéra-comique de la
rue Favart, le 19 messidor, an 4e (7 juillet 1796, v. st.). Paroles de
Marsollier, musique de Dalayrac.

*Paris, chez Vente, [n. d.], De l'imprimerie de Chaignieau [!] ainé.
55 p. 21^{cm}.*

Cast, only two of the actors being called "Le c."[itoyen].   ML 50.2.M45D2

— **Marianne** . . . [same as in the above].

*Paris, chez Vente, [n. d.], De l'imprimerie de Chaigneau [!] ainé.
44 p. 21^{cm}.*

Same cast, all being now "C^{en}" and "C^{ne}," and same text.   ML 50.2.M45D21

Marie von Montalban, oder Lanassa's zweyter theil. Ein trauerspiel mit choeren in fuenf aufzuegen, von J. N. Komareck.

n. i., 1794. 86 p. 16^{cm}.

Author's dedication, dated Pilsen, am 1ten hornung [February], 1792. On p. 82–86,
"Nachrede." in which the author says that he was inspired to write this piece by

Marie von Montalban—Continued.

"Lanassa," the German version (by Pluemicke) of Le Mierre's "La Veuve de Mala-bar," and performed at Pilsen February 19, 1791, by the Vossische Schauspielergesell-schaft, which Komareck then criticizes violently for the liberties taken with pieces in the repertory, sometimes leaving, as he claims, nothing of the piece except its name. His wish for his own piece is—

"dass die musik zu den choeren nur fuer saenger, und fuer keine schnattergaense, wie wir sie und ein wildes miauen hier hoeren mussten, komponirt werden moechte, damit es Voss und konsorten nie einfallen koennte, sich daran zu versuendigen . . ."

First performed, with music by Peter von **Winter**, at Munich, Hof u. National-theater, January 28, 1800.   SCHATZ 11633

Le marin généreux. A. T. of Piccinni's L'esclave.

Songs, duets, trio and choruses, in the **Mariners,** a musical enter-tainment, in two acts. As performed at the King's Theatre, Hay-Market . . .

London, C. Lowndes, 1793. 16 p. 20ᶜᵐ.

Neither the author, Samuel Birch, is mentioned, nor the composer, Thomas **Attwood**, who, as appears from Longman & Broderip's vocal score partly com-posed this *pasticcio*, partly compiled it from **Shaw, Martini** (Martin y Soler?), **Ferrari, Mozart,** Miss **Bannister, Dittersdorf.**

First performed May 10, 1793.   LONGE 227

Mario e Felice, ballet. *See* Bianchi's Ines de Castro.

Vollstaendiger musik-text zur grossen komischen oper in 2 auf-zuegen: Die **marionettenbüde,** oder Der jahrmarkt zu Gruenwald. Die musik ist von herrn Th. Weigl, dem juengern.

Salzburg, Franz Xaver Duyle, 1797. 30 p. 17ᶜᵐ.

The author, Carl Friedrich Hensler, is not mentioned.

First performed at Vienna, Theater in der Leopoldstadt, March 17, 1795.

ML 50.2.M455W3

Il maritato fra le disgrazie. Commedia per musica di Giuseppe Palomba da rappresentarsi nel Teatro de' Fiorentini nell' autunno del corrente anno 1774.

Napoli, n. publ., 1774. 69 p. 15ᶜᵐ.

Three acts. Argument, scenario, cast, and name of Gaetano **Latilla** as composer.

SCHATZ 5464

Il marito che non ha moglie. Dramma giocoso per musica di Giovanni Bertati da rappresentarsi nel Teatro Giustiniani di San Moisè nell' autunno dell' anno 1774.

Venezia, Antonio Graziosi, 1774. 63 p. 17ᶜᵐ.

Three acts. Cast, scenario, and name of Gennaro **Astaritta** as composer.

SCHATZ 373

Il marito disperato. Dramma giocoso di Giambatista Lorenzi P. A. da rappresentarsi nel Teatro de' Fiorentini per seconda com-media del corrente anno 1785.

Napoli, n. publ., 1785. 64 p. 15ᶜᵐ.

Two acts. Cast and name of the composer, Domenico **Cimarosa.** SCHATZ 1942

— Arien und gesaenge aus der komischen oper in zwey akten: Die **bestrafte eifersucht.** Die musik ist von Cimarosa.

Berlin, n. publ., 1794. 45 p. 16ᶜᵐ.

Translated by Friedrich Hildebrand von Einsiedel (Schatz). Cast.

First performed at Berlin, Nationaltheater, September 4, 1794.   SCHATZ 1943

Il **marito geloso**　Dramma giocoso per musica da rappresentarsi in Livorno nel Nuovo teatro detto dagli Armeni il carnevale dell' anno 1784.

Livorno, Antonio Lami e comp., n. d.　93 p. (incl. h.-t.).

Two acts. Cast, scenario, name of Felice **Alessandri** as composer. Author unknown to Schatz.　　　　　　　　　　　　　　　　SCHATZ 147

Il **marito geloso.**　Dramma giocoso per musica di Giovanni Bertati da rappresentarsi nel Teatro Giustiniani in S. Moisè per la seconda opera dell' autunno l'anno 1781.

Venezia, n. publ., n. d.　64 p.　17cm.

Two acts.　Cast and name of Luigi **Caruso** as composer ("La musica sarà").
　　　　　　　　　　　　　　　　　　　　　SCHATZ 1645

Il **marito giogatore** [!], e la **moglie bacchettona.**　Intermezzi per musica da rappresentarsi nel Teatro di S. Angelo il carnevale dell' anno 1719.

Venezia, Marino Rossetti, 1719.　16 p.　15cm.

No cast, but it is well known to have been the same as at Brussels in 1728. (*See* below).　Neither the author of the text is mentioned nor the composer.　Schatz attributes the text to Antonio Salvi and the music to Giuseppe Maria **Orlandini**. First performed as intermezzi in Chelleri's "*Amalasunta*" on December 24, 1718, according to Schatz.　　　　　　　　　　　　　SCHATZ 7337

　　The outlines of the text are (arias in Italics):

(Int. Primo)　*Si si maledetta.*
　　　　　　　Disgraziato Bacocco.
　　　　　　　Un consorte sciagurato.
　　　　　　　O Bacocco, se questa è la vigilia.
　　　　　　　Serpilla diletta (duet).
(Int. Sec.)　Serpilla indiavolata.
　　　　　　　Signor giudice.
　　　　　　　Alzatevi madonna, e non piangete.
　　　　　　　Questo è quell' nomo (duet).
(Int. Terzo)　*A questa pellegrina.*
　　　　　　　La vergogna, il dispetto.
　　　　　　　Io già sento.

　　Under no. 2372 of the Brussels Conservatory catalogue Mr. Wotquenne lists the score of "*Serpilla e Baiocco o vero Il marito giocatore e la moglie bacchettona*, inter-mezzi comici musicali da rappresentarsi in Bruselle nell' opera di *Lucio Papirio* il 1728 dalla Sig. Rosa Ungarelli di Bologna e dal Sig. Antonio Maria Ristorini di Firenze."　Mr. Wotquenne adds that this is not really the title of this score, of which the L. of C. has a transcript with title "Il Giocatore," but that it is a "titre copié d'après le livret."　He means the libretto published at Brussels for the performances (first: November 4) 1728 of "Lucio Papirio," music by Orlandini [!] and of the inter-mezzi under discussion.　The text of the Brussels libretto, I know from a private communication to me by Mr. Wotquenne, is the same as in the original Venice libretto of 1719 "Il marito giogatore e la moglie bacchettona."　This means that it does not contain in the second intermezzo the aria, etc. "Con tanto stranutare," which is the distinguishing feature of the Brussels score no. 2372, the text of which is otherwise the same as in the librettos mentioned.　As Georgy Calmus pointed out, a manuscript note (not in our transcript of the Brussels score) says that this aria, etc., was taken from "Il vecchio pazzo in amore."　The statement is correct, since the aria (and part of the connecting dialogue) appears in the libretto of this title (*See* Schatz 11376) in the first of the three intermezzi first performed with "La caduta di Leone Impe-rator d'Oriente" (music by Paganelli) at Venice, Teatro Giustiniano di S. Moisè, carnival 1731.　Neither author or composer are mentioned in the libretto and both are unknown to Schatz.

　　Possibly this was not the first performance of "Il vecchio pazzo in amore," but until an earlier performance is discovered, this Venice performance of 1731 must be considered the first known.　Therewith the date of the anonymous Brussels score with the interpolated aria from "Il vecchio pazzo in amore" is approximately fixed as not earlier than 1731.　It follows that the anonymous score was *not* used at Brussels in 1728, though Mr. Wotquenne has given it the title of the Brussels, 1728 libretto,

Il marito giogatore [!], e la moglie bacchettona—Continued.

the text of which does not contain the interpolated aria "Con tanto stranutare" but coincides fully with the original Venice, 1719 libretto.

Below, there is listed under "The gamester," London, 1736, another edition of the text which coincides fully with the original text. This London version of "Il marito giogatore" is positively attributed in the libretto to Orlandini. It would follow, it seems to me, that we do not have the right to attribute any score exclusively to Orlandini, the text of which does not coincide fully with the text of the London libretto. Scores like the Brussels score with its interpolated matter, therefore, represent, *if at all*, **Orlandini's** setting, *not in its original form, but in a later, adulterated form.* This means that as yet Orlandini's score in its original form has not come to light again and that no historical arguments can be based on interpolations for which he was not responsible!

In his catalogue of "Handschriften nebst den älteren Druckwerken der Musik-Abtheilung der Herzogl. Bibliothek zu Wolfenbüttel," 1890, Emil Vogel has, under no. 257, this entry:

"Erste Hälfte des 18. Jahrh. VINCI, Leonardo. Intermezzo: *Bacocco e Serpillo*[!] . . . Partitur. *Der Componist dieses Intermezzo war bisher nicht bekannt . . .*" and under no. 258 another copy with title "Serpilla e Bacocco" and remark "Partitur, dieselbe wie No. 257, doch mit veränderter Schlüsselvorzeichnung in den Singstimmen."

Our transcript of one of these scores includes a note—presumably in Vogel's hand: "Die hier vorliegende Partitur ist—wenn nicht überhaupt die einrige erhaltene—sicher die einzige, welche den Namen des Componisten angiebt."

The text of this score, too, coincides fully with the text of the original "Il marito giogatore" libretto, Venice, 1719. For this reason and because these scores bear the name of Vinci one might feel inclined to conclude that the intermezzos were originally composed by **Vinci.** This conclusion would be hasty, first, because the Wolfenbüttel scores bear, not the original title, but two later titles of the work; secondly, because the text of the original libretto as stated above, coincides also fully with the text of the London (1736) libretto "The gamester" (Il giocatore) described below, and the title page of this explicitly calls Orlandini the composer. Under the circumstances we must assume, until proof to the contrary is adduced, that at London a setting by Orlandini was actually used. Consequently we must further assume that both Vinci and Orlandini composed the same (original and unadulterated) text at a very early date, but we can not as yet definitely attribute the earliest setting, that for Venice, season of 1718–19, to either one or the other.

The commentary above and below in part supersedes the author's article on "Il giocatore" in the "Musical Antiquary," April 1913, p. 160–174 and also his remarks in controversy with Georgy Calmus in "Sammelbände der I. M. G. 1912/13, y. 14, p. 170–173. I wish to add here that in my opinion it is dangerous to deduct the comparative age of fairly contemporary scores from a fuller or thinner orchestration of such copies as have been preserved but are not the autograph scores of the composers. Many of the scores of that period have come down to us not in their original form, but with the "Partitur-Bild" simplified for purposes similar to those for which later on "Klavierauszüge," Vocal scores, "Partitions, chant et piano," etc., became the customary substitutes. How dangerous such arguments of appearance or even style are, if in this given case the priority of Vinci is to be deducted from a comparison of the appearance of his scores with "Giocatore" scores *attributed* to Orlandini, may be illustrated by the fact that of the two composers Orlandini is the earlier and that his first known opera antedates by several years the first known opera by Vinci!

— **Serpilla e Bacocco.** Intermezzi comici musicali. Da rappresentarsi la seconda volta, che si esibisce il drama.

n. i., n. d. 15 p. 14½ cm.

Three parts. Neither author nor composer is mentioned. The text is practically identical with Schatz 7337. Cast. On a fly-leaf Schatz has written this note:

"Dieses intermezzo wurde als zwischenspiel zu der 2ten aufführung von T. Albinoni's oper "I veri amici" zu München, am 27/x 1722, zur vermählungsfeier des churprinzen Carl Albert mit der erzherzogin Maria Amalia, gesungen.

"Ursprünglich war dieses Textbuch demjenigen der vorstehenden oper angeheftet & folgte auf das erste, "Vespetta e Pimpinone" betitelte zwischenspiel."

SCHATZ 7338

— The **gamester.** An interlude. Performed by Signora Anna Maria Faini, and Signor Antonio Lottini, at the King's Theatre in the

Il marito giogatore [!], e la moglie bacchettona—Continued.
Hay-Market. The musick is composed by Sig. Giuseppe Maria
Orlandini . . .

London, J. Chrichley, 1736. 23 p. 17^{cm}.

Italian text under the title of "Il *giocatore*" faces the English.
First performed January 1/12, 1737, as indicated.
The text is practically identical with that of "Il marito giocatore," Venice, 1719.
According to Burney "Il *giocatore*," first performed at London, Haymarket, Jan-
uary 1, 1737, was the first "intermezzo, or comic interlude which was ever introduced
between the acts of an Italian opera [Hasse's Siroe] in England."   SCHATZ 7339

— Le **joueur**, parodie. Par les Srs. Dominique & Romagnesi . . .
Représentée pour la premiere fois, par les Comédiens italiens ordinaires du roi, le 21 juillet 1729.

*Les parodies du Nouveau théâtre italien, Nouv. éd., Paris, 1738,
t. iv, [183]–202 p. 16½^{cm}.*

One act. A note on p. 185 says:
"Cette petite parodie de l'Opera du Joueur faisoit cidevant la scene xviii de la
Comédie des Debuts, jouée avec les Paysans de qualité."
The characters were (as in all the "Il giocatore" librettos) Bacocco and Serpilla,
and much of the text was in Italian, even text sung to the French airs. (They are
printed at end of the volume, in the "Table des airs," 92 p., of which p. 49–72 are
wanting. To this intermezzo was added, as an afterpiece, on August 17, 1729, "Don
Micco e Lesbina. Intermede.") As comparison proves, *some, but not many,* of the
Italian lines are the same, or nearly the same, as in the Venice (1719) edition of "Il
marito giocatore." It is therefore qute possible that where *French* airs are not indicated in the text the parodists used corresponding music in "Il marito giocatore,"
performed at Paris, Académie royale de musique, June 7, 1729, by Rosa Ongarelli
(Ungarelli) and Antonio Maria Ristorini. However, the abundance of French airs,
including those to Italian text, that imitate text in "Il marito giocatore" excludes
the possibility that much of the original music was used for the parody. Indeed, even
the possibility of the use of some of it becomes doubtful, in view of the report in the
"Mercure du mois de Juillet 1729" (quoted by Parfaict):
"Toute la musique qu' on trouve très çonvenable, est de la composition du Sieur
Mouret . . ."   ML 48.P3

— **Il giocatore**. Intermezzo per musica. In tre atti. Da representarsi in Parigi, n'ell Theatro, Opera, il 1752.—Le joueur. Intermede en musique en trois actes. Représenté [!] à Paris, sur le
Théatre de l'Opéra en 1752.

Paris, la veuve Delormel & fils, 1752. 27, [1] p. 16½^{cm}.

On last page, the Approbation, dated Versailles, August 20, 1752. Cast. (Serpilla:
Anna Tonelli; Baccocco: Pietro Manelli.) French prose text faces Italian. The
arias are not distinguished typographically from the recitatives in this libretto, and I
can not guarantee that the following outlines of the text (arias in italics) are complete:

(Atto I)   *Si, si maledetta.*
            Ah sei qui bona lana?
            (?) *Si ravviva nel mio core.*
            La buona moglie Fà buono il marito.
            Serpilla diletta (duet).
(Atto II)   Serpilla indiavolata.
            Oh che risa, oh che piacere.
            (?) *Di potermi vendicar.*
            Speri fors' anche un di.
            Uh! che alcun non c'ascolti.
            Quest' è quel uomo (duet).
(Atto III) Jo son fuor di me stesso.
            A questa pellegrina.
            La vergogna, il rispetto.
            (?) *Ecco disciolti i lacci.*
            Ahi finito.
            Contento tu sarai.

Il **marito giogatore** [!], e la **moglie bacchettona**—Continued.

This text differs strikingly from the original "Il marito giogatore" text. True, "Si, si maledetta," the first aria, and the duet, "Serpilla diletta," are the same in both texts. Also, the second intermezzo in both begins with "Serpilla indiavolata," and ends with the duet, "Questo è quell' uomo." Furthermore, the aria, "A questa pellegrina," is in the third intermezzo in both texts, but the aria, "Un consorte sciagurato," is not in the first intermezzo of the Paris (1752) ed., nor "Signor giudice giustizia" in the second, nor the final duet, "Io già sento," in the third. The dialogue, while for lines at a time is the same in both, very much more often is not the same; and Baccocco's monologue, at the beginning of the third intermezzo ("Io son fuor di me stesso"), is only in the Paris (1752) edition. If the text in the latter (which unquestionably is Salvi's "Il marito giogatore," though considerably altered) was actually used in the performances of 1752 at Paris, then the entry in Clément et de Laporte's "Anecdotes dramatiques," Paris, 1775 (Supplement):

"JOUEUR, (le) Opéra bouffon italien, dont la musique est d'Orlandini, jouée à l'Opéra en 1752" [first on Tuesday, August 22, *not* on August 12, preceding Campra's Aréthuse] needs to be modified, because it would have been impossible to use Orlandini's score without quite a few interpolations and alterations.

As a matter of fact, the Paris version used was a *pasticcio*. According to the *Mercure*, quoted by De La Laurencie (*S. I. M.* 1912, no. 6, p. 27):

"La musique de cet intermède, tel qu'il a été joué, est de differents auteurs," and the *Mercure* attributes the recitatives, the duets in the first two actes ("Serpilla diletta" and "Quest' è quel' uomo"), and the arias, "Si, si maledetta" and "A questa pellegrina," specifically to **Orlandini**. Contant d'Orville (I, 10, not 11) mentions **Pergolesi** as one of the composers of this pasticcio, and since the text of the final duet in the printed Paris (1752) libretto, "Contento tu sarai," is indeed from his "La serva padrona," there is no reason for disputing the accuracy of Contant d'Orville's remark. We know, however, from the *Mercure* that this duet was replaced at the third performance by another piece (the duet, "Pace con un laccio," of the Doletti score?). At least one more composer figured in the pasticcio, namely, Giuseppe Maria **Buini**, since De La Laurencie has traced the "Oh che risa" in the second act to him. He adds Pietro **Auletta**, but without any proof whatsoever of his identity with **Doletti**. (*See* below.)

If at the third performance "Contento tu sarai" was dropped, "Signor giudice" added to the second act, and if, as reported, other changes took place, then the text in the Paris (1752) ed. can not have been used as printed. These doubts become stronger still in view of the score of:

"Les ARIETTES DU JOUEUR, opera bouffon italien. Del Sg.r Doletti. Réprésenté à l'Opera de Paris en 1752" Paris, M.e Boivin, Mr. Le Clerc, M.lle Castagnarie. (Undated! 1 p. l., 32 p., fol.) Below the privilege: "Gravé d'après la partition de l'auteur."

The text of the eight arias and duets in this score is identical with that of the 1719 libretto, except that of the two last numbers, "Pace con un laccio" and "Spera fors' anch' un di." These are not in the "Il marito giogatore" libretto. On the other hand, the last aria in the 1719 libretto, "Io già sento," is not in the Doletti score. At any rate, with exception of two out of eight numbers, the text of all is identical with the texts as found in the Wolfenbüttel Vinci scores and in the London Orlandini libretto and the Venice (1719) libretto. But the title page not only attributes the opera to one **Doletti** (of whom absolutely nothing else seems to be known to Fétis, Wotquenne, Eitner), but says that the Paris score was engraved after his (the author's, *i. e.* composer's) score! Here, then, is a new puzzle! Now, it is a singular fact that of those two arias one, "Spera (speri) fors' anch' un di," appears in the Paris (1752) "Il giocatore" libretto. In view of this fact, and in view of the other fact, already mentioned, that with the third performance of "Il giocatore" Pergolesi's "Contento tu sarai" was replaced by another duet, the conjecture may be ventured that (the otherwise unknown) **Doletti** composed these two arias, and that in some manner the whole score came to be attributed to him.

We know, however, that of the other six arias (act I) "Si, si, maledetta," "Un consorte sciagurato," "Serpilla diletta" [duet]; (act II) "Signor giudice," "Quest' è quel' uomo [duet]; (act III) "A questa pellegrina", the music of five is the same as in the Wolfenbüttel scores bearing **Vinci**'s name and in the Brussels "Giocatore" score no. 2372, barring transposition of key, etc. The aria "Si, si, maledetta," in the Doletti score is the same as in the Brussels score, but it is different from that in the Vinci score. Consequently as early as 1731 (*see* above) a setting of "Si, si, maledetta" existed which was not by Vinci. This aria is one of those expressly attributed by the *Mercure* to Orlandini. Since the recitatives in the Vinci scores are nearly all different from those in the Brussels score (the Doletti score has no recitatives), again some composer other than Vinci must have composed these recita-

Il marito giogatore [!], e la moglie bacchettona—Continued.

tives of the Brussels score. This conclusion recalls to our mind the fact that the *Mercure* expressly attributed the recitatives as used at Paris (1752) to Orlandini. Therefore, if the Mercure was wholly mistaken in assigning the arias identical in the Vinci scores and the Brussels and the Doletti score (duets "Serpilla diletta" and "Quest' è quel' uomo" and the aria "A questa pellegrina," *i. e.*, as sung at Paris, 1752) to Orlandini, and if Leonardo Vinci, instead of Orlandini, should have to be considered their composer, the pasticcio character of the Paris (1752) "Giocatore" would have grown still more pronounced. If De La Laurencie adds to the composers so far traced Pietro Auletta, on the theory of his identity with Doletti, this identity is merely an assumption, and has not been supported by any evidence.

ML50.2.G4O7

—**Baiocco et Serpilla**, parodie du Joueur; intermede en trois actes. Représentée pour la premiere fois par les Comédiens italiens ordinaires du roi, le jeudi 6 mars 1753. Nouvelle édition.

Paris, N. B. Duchesne, 1760. 48 p. 19ᶜᵐ. (Theatre de M. Favart, Paris, Duchesne, 1763–77, t. ii.)

Cast, note, and music the same as in the 1771 ed.   ML 49.A2F1

—**Baiocco et Serpilla**, parodie du Joueur, intermede en trois actes. Représentée pour la premiere fois par les Comédiens italiens ordinaires du roi, le jeudi 6 mars 1753.

Paris, la veuve Duchesne, 1771. 38 p. 17ᶜᵐ.

Cast and note:

"Cet intermede est une traduction littérale de Baiocco e Serpilla ò del Giocatore, opéra bouffon, mis en musique par Mr. [Carlo] **Sodi**, & représenté ci-devant à la Comédie italienne."

On p. 3–5 the airs of "Ah! ah! ma cassette" (I, 1); p. 6, "On n'a jamais vu de femme" (I, 2); p. 11, duo "Je ne puis plus durer" (I, 2); p. 14–16, "Ma femme fait la diablesse" (II, 1); p. 17–20, "C'est un traître, un vaurien" (II, 2); p. 24–27, "Ah! perfide, barbare!" (III, 1); p. 28–32, "Ingrate, tu me fuis en vaine" (III, 2); p. 33–38, the duo "Mon bonheur est extrême" (III, 2).

This parody, though originally based on that of 1729, no longer has anything in common with it. Parfaict narrates under Sodi the origin of the new parody thus:

"La nouvelle musique de la parodie du *Joueur*, intermède italien qui a été représentée deux fois à la cour avec beaucoup de succès. Les anciens vaudevilles ayant déplu à la derniere reprise de cette parodie, les Comediens Italiens prirent le parti de charger le Sieur **Sodi** de composer de nouvelle musique sur les mêmes paroles, & le mélange d'italien & de françois ayant encore déplu dans les paroles, ils supprimèrent tout l'italien, & y substituèrent des paroles françoises de la composition de M. Favart qui fut obligé de parodier la musique du Sieur **Sodi**." . . .

(Substantially the same remarks are to be found in the pref. to "Theatre de M. Favart," Paris, 1763–77, t. I, p. xviii.) Sodi's score as published (in L. of C.) agrees with the libretto.   SCHATZ 9929

Il marito indolente. Dramma giocoso per musica da rappresentarsi nel Teatro Giustiniani di S. Moisè il carnevale dell' anno 1778.

[Venezia], n. publ., n. d. 62 p. 18ᶜᵐ.

Two acts. By Caterino Mazzolà, who is not mentioned. Cast and name of Alfonso **Santi** as the composer ("La musica sarà"). With the opera was performed, composer of the music not mentioned, Riccardo Blèck's ballet "L'Indiana a Londra."   SCHATZ 9393

Il marito indolente. Dramma giocoso per musica da rappresentarsi nel Piccolo Teatro di S. A. E. di Sassonia, di Caterino Mazzolà . . .

Dresda, n. publ., 1782. 141 p. 15½ᶜᵐ.

Two acts. Joseph **Schuster** is mentioned as the composer. German title-page, "Der gleichgueltige ehemann," and text face Italian.

First performed 1782, as indicated.   SCHATZ 9747

Il **marito indolente**—Continued.

— Gesaenge aus dem singspiele Der **gleichgueltige ehemann,** in zwei aufzuegen, nach dem italienischen von J. Andrée. In musik gesezt von Schuster.

*Hamburg, J. M. Michaelsen, 1788. 32 p. 16*cm*.*

First performed at Hamburg, Theater beim Gänsemarkt, September 22, 1788; at Berlin, Nationaltheater, May 26, 1788. SCHATZ 9748

Il **marito ravveduto,** ballet. *See* Bianchi's Piramo e Tisbe.

Il **marito umiliato** ossia La moglie di spirito, ballet. *See* Cimarosa's 'Li amanti comici.

Markedet i Venedig. Tr. of Salieri's La fiera di Venezia.

Der **markt von Venedig.** Tr. of Salieri's La fiera di Venezia.

O **marquez de Tulipano** ou O casamento inesperado. Tr. of Paisiello's Il matrimonio inaspettato.

The **marriage act:** a farce. In two acts. As it is performed at the Theatre Royal in Covent Garden.

*London, G. Kearsley, 1781. 2 p. l., 40 p. 21*cm*.*

Cast. A reduced version of Charles **Dibdin's** "The Islanders" (1780).
First performed September 17, 1781 (Schatz and Oulton); September 18, 1781 (Genest). LONGE 91

Marriage at last. A. T. of The fortunate prince.

Marriage by proxy. A. T. of The court medley.

The **marriage of Peleus and Thetis,** masque. *See* Windsor castle.

The **marriage promise** or The disappointed virgin. *See* The intriguing courtiers.

Marsia.

*p. 217–242. 15½*cm*. (Ottavio Tronsarelli, Drammi musicali, Roma, Francesco Corbelletti, 1632.)*

Three parts. Argument. No composer mentioned. ML 49.A2T7

Marsia deluso. Favola pastorale. Da rappresentarsi in musica nel famoso Teatro Grimani de' SS. Gio. e Paolo il carnovale dell' anno 1714.

*Venezia, Marino Rossetti, n. d. 72 p. 14½*cm*.*

Five acts. Neither the author, conte Agostino Piovene, nor the composer, Carlo Francesco **Pollaroli,** is mentioned. Notice to the reader, cast, and scenario.
First performed December 26, 1714, as indicated. SCHATZ 8302

Marte deluso. L. T. of M. A. Ziani's La Falsirena.

Marte, Venere e la Gloria, ballet. *See* M. A. Valentini's Solimano.

Marthesie, premiere reine des Amazones, tragedie representée par l'Academie royale de musique. l'an 1699. Les paroles de M. de la Mothe, & la musique de M. Destouches. XLVIII. opera.

front., p. 413–468.   (Recueil général des opéra, t. vi, Paris, 1703.) *14ᶜᵐ.*

Detached copy. Five acts and prologue with dedicatory poem to the king and "Avertissement."
First performed, as indicated, November 29, 1699; at Fontainebleau in the king's private theatre, October 25, 1699.   SCHATZ 2548
Second copy. ML 48.R4

Martin Velten.   Eine komische oper in drey aufzügen.

n. i., n. d.   p. [273]–352.   16ᶜᵐ.

Detached copy. Neither the composer, Carl Christian **Agthe,** is mentioned, nor the author, who is unknown to Schatz.
First performed at Reval, 1778.   SCHATZ 62

Martio Coriolano.   *See* M. Curzio.

Martio Coriolano. Drama per musica di Frencasco Valsini da rappresentarsi nel famoso Teatro Grimano de Ss. Gio. e Paolo. L'anno MDCLXXXIII . . .

Venetia, Francesco Nicolini, 1683.   48 p.   14½ᶜᵐ.

Three acts. Dedication signed Frencasco Valsini [=Francesco Silvani] and dated Venice, January 20, 1683, argument, scenario, notice to the reader with name of Giacomo Antonio **Perti** as the composer, and remark "eccoti il mio secondo drama."
SCHATZ 7957

Marzio Coriolano. Drama per musica. Da rappresentarsi nel famoso Teatro di S. Gio. Grisostomo. L'anno 1698. Di Matteo Noris . . .

Venezia, Nicolini, 1698.   front., 82 p.   14½ᶜᵐ.

Three acts. Author's dedication dated Venice, January 18, 1697. M. V. [=1698], argument, notice to the reader, and scenario. The composer, Carlo Francesco **Pollaroli,** is not mentioned.   SCHATZ 8303

Masagniello furioso. Oder: Die neapolitanische fischer-empoerung. Musicalishes schau-spiel.

Barth. Feind's Deutsche gedichte, Stade, 1708, pl., p. [251]–320. *17ᶜᵐ.*

Three acts. Date of first performance as June, 1706, and "Vorbericht" with remark:
"Die italiaenischen arien wird ein dieser sprache kuendiger, umsonst anderswo als auff diesen blaettern suchen"
which implies Feind's own authorship. The composer, Reinhard **Keiser,** is not mentioned.   ML 49.AF2

— Masagniello furioso. Drama musicale, da rappresentarsi nel famosissimo Theatro d'Hamburgo, Die neapolitanische fischer empoerung . . .

Hamburg.   Unpaged.   18ᶜᵐ.

(Imprint partly cut off by binder.)
Three acts. To a few of the arias the Italian text has been added. Neither the author, resp. translator, Barthold Feind, is mentioned, nor the composer, Reinhard **Keiser.**
First performed, as indicated, June, 1706.   SCHATZ 5125

Masagniello furioso—Continued.

— Masagniello furioso. Drama musicale, da rappresentarsi nel famosissimo Teatro d'Amburgo. [port.] Die neapolitanische fischer-empoerung . . .

Hamburg, Friderich Conrad Greflinger, 1714. Unpaged. 19ᶜᵐ.

The port. is supposed to be a likeness of "Masaniello, vischer zu Napels. 1647." The Italian text has been added to some arias. Schatz calls this the second version, but at least the text is the same as in the 1706 edition. Neither Feind is mentioned nor **Keiser.** SCHATZ 5126

— Masagniello furioso, oder Die neapolitanische fischer-empoerung, in einem sing-spiele auf dem Hamburgischen Schau-platze vor-gestellet im jahr 1727.

[Hamburg], mit Stromerischen schrifften, n. d. Unpaged. 19ᶜᵐ.

Three acts. Cast, scenario. Schatz calls this "III. ausgabe." Neither the author, resp. translator, Barthold Feind, is mentioned, nor the composer, Reinhard **Keiser.** To some of the arias the Italian text has been added. The text is the same as in the editions of 1706 and 1714. SCHATZ 5102

La maschera levata al vitio. Drama per musica da rappresentarsi nel Teatro Tron in S. Casciano l'autunno dell' anno 1704 . . .

Venetia, Marin Rossetti, 1704. 59 p. 14½ᶜᵐ.

Three acts. Dedication signed and dated by the author, Francesco Silvani, Venice, November 2, 1704, argument, cast, and scenario. The composer, Carlo Francesco **Gasparini,** is not mentioned. SCHATZ 3571

La mascherata.

[261]–318 p. 16½ᶜᵐ. (Carlo Goldoni, Opere drammatiche giocose, t. i, Torino, 1757.)

Three acts. For first composer, *see* below. ML 49.A2G6

— La mascherata. Dramma di tre atti per musica.

Carlo Goldoni, Opere teatrali, Venezia, Zatta e figli, 1788–95, v. 42, [47]–108 p. 18ᶜᵐ. PQ

La mascherata. Dramma comico per musica di Polisseno Fegejo Pastor Arcade da rappresentarsi nel Teatro Tron di S. Cassiano. Il carnovale dell' anno 1751.

Venezia, Modesto Fenzo, 1751. 70 p. 15ᶜᵐ.

Three acts. By Goldoni. The composer is not mentioned. Cast and scenario. Attributed by some to **Galuppi,** by others to Gioacchino **Cocchi.** Pages 3–4, with Goldoni's dedication, dated December 24, 1750, are missing in this copy. SCHATZ 3487

Massenzio. Drama per musica nel Teatro Vendramino à S. Salvatore. Del Bussani . . .

Venetia, Francesco Nicolini, 1673. 80 p. (incl. front.) 15ᶜᵐ.

Three acts. Author's dedication, argument, and scenario. The composer, Antonio **Sartorio,** is not mentioned.
First performed carnival, 1673, as indicated. SCHATZ 9494

Massilie, ou La fondation de Marseille. Opéra en cinq actes.

Venard de la Jonchère, Théâtre lyrique, Paris, 1772, t. ii, p. [145]–212. 18½ᶜᵐ.

"Avant-propos" (p. 147–159). No composer mentioned, nor is any recorded by Cl. & L. ML 49.A2L2

Massimiano. Dramma per musica da rappresentarsi nel famosissimo Teatro Grimani di S. Gio. Grisostomo nell' carnevale dell' anno 1731 . . .

Venetia, Carlo Buonarigo, n. d. 66 p. 14½ᶜᵐ.

Three acts. Originally written as "Costantino" by Zeno and Pariati, retouched under the above title by Giovanni Boldoni, neither of whom is mentioned. Impresario's dedication, argument, scenario, cast, and name of Giuseppe Maria **Orlandini** as the composer. SCHATZ 7351

Massimo Puppieno. Drama per musica da rappresentarsi nel famosissimo Teatro Grimano di SS. Gio. e Paolo. Seconda impressione con nuova aggiunta . . .

Venetia, Francesco Nicolini, 1685. 64 p. 14ᶜᵐ.

Three acts. Dedication dated Venice, December 28, 1684, and signed by the author, Aurelio Aureli, argument, and scenario. The composer, Carlo **Pallavicino,** is not mentioned. SCHATZ 7727

The **master of the opera.** Tr. of Sarro's L'impresario.

Mastino della Scala, ballet. *See* Paër's L'oro fa tutto.

A match for a widow: or, The frolics of fancy. A[!] A comic opera, in three acts. As performed at the Theatre Royal, Dublin.

London, C. Dilly, 1788. vii, [1], 61, [2] p. 20ᶜᵐ.

The [2] p. contain the "Original epilogue," "spoken by Mrs. Melmoth, in 1786." Cast and dedication by the author, Joseph Atkinson (not mentioned), to Richard Daly, the patentee and manager of the Theatre Royal, Dublin:

"You remember that it was originally written and presented to you in the winter of 1785, as an after-piece, acknowledged to be suggested from a little French drama of one act, without songs (intitled, *L'heureuse erreur*), and that in borrowing the idea I totally altered and augmented the dialogue, incidents, and situation of *that* plot, and for the first time, attempted the introduction of a *Yankee* character on the European stage . . . you earnestly recommended and urged me instead of confining it to an after musical piece, to extend the design to a compleat comic opera, by the assistance of new characters and an underplot . . .

"In the course of the week, I again presented you, and read the opera in its present state, with the additional episode, characters and songs . . . It was then . . . transmitted to Mr. [Charles] **Dibdin** in London, who embellished it with his harmony: thus with the ornament of new scenery and dresses, and the then musical strength of **y**our company, you, in the spring of 1786, gave it a fair trial before an Irish audience . . ."

The Yankee character introduced is that of Jonathen, who, in the course of the play, sings a "Song (air, *Yankee tune* [which is not mentioned]): 'He found me in a country now famous in story,'" and "Song (tune, *Yankee doodle*): 'For when I dwelt in Boston bay / I liv'd in peace and plenty.'" LONGE 110

Il **matematico,** ballet. *See* Pampani's Demofoonte.

La **matinée des boulevards,** ambigu-comique. Premiere partie.—La soirée des boulevards, . . . Seconde partie—La nuit des boulevards . . . Troisième partie—Le bal des boulevards . . . quatrième partie.

Paris, Cailleau, n. d. 122 p. 21ᶜᵐ.

Casts. SCHATZ 11498

La **matinée et la veillée villageoisie,** ou Le sabot perdu, divertissement en deux actes et en vaudevilles, par MM. de Piis & Barré; représenté pour la première fois par les Comédiens italiens ordinaires du roi, le mardi 27 mars 1781.

Paris, Vente, 1784. 32 p. 19ᶜᵐ.

Cast. Arranger of the music not recorded by Schatz. SCHATZ 11499

I matrimoni in ballo. Farsetta per musica di Pasquale Mililotti da rappresentarsi nel Teatro Nuovo nel carnevale di quest' anno 1776.

n. i., n. d. p. [29]–51. 14½ cm.

A detached copy of **Cimarosa's** operatic farce, played at the end of his "I sdegni per amore" (Schatz 1993). SCHATZ 1984

I matrimoni in cantina. A. T. of Neri Bondi's I viaggiatori.

I matrimoni in maschera. Dramma giocoso per musica da rappresentarsi nel Teatro Tron di S. Cassano nell' autunno dell' anno 1765 . . .

Venezia, Modesto Fenzo, 1765. 59 p. 15 cm.

Three acts. Author not mentioned and unknown to Schatz. Cast, scenario, and name of Ruttini (Giovanni Marco **Rutini**) as the composer. SCHATZ 9192

— Il matrimonio in maschera. Dramma giocoso per musica. Da rappresentarsi nel Piccolo Teatro di S. A. E. di Sassonia. Dresda, nel carnevale dell' 1767.

n. i., n. d. 149 p. 16 cm.

Three acts. Cast, scenario, and name of Giovanni [Marco] **Rutini** as the composer. German title-page, "Die eheverbindung in der maske," and text face Italian, which is with very few modifications the same as in the Venice (1765) version. SCHATZ 9187

— Il tutore burlato o sia I matrimonii in maschera. Dramma giocoso per musica da rappresentarsi nel Regio Teatro Danese—Den bedragne formynder eller De under masken sluttede giftermaale . . .

Kiøbenhavn, L. N. Svare, 1768. 125 p. 17½ cm.

Three acts. Cast and name of Ruttini [Giovanni Marco **Rutini**] as the composer. First performed 1768, as indicated. SCHATZ 9188

I matrimonj per fanatisimo [!] Dramma giocoso per musica da rappresentarsi nel Real Teatro del Fondo di Separazione per terza opera di quest' anno 1788 . . .

Napoli, n. publ., 1788. 60 p. 15 cm.

Two acts. Impresario's dedication dated Naples, Nov. 6, 1788, cast, and name of Pasquale **Anfossi** as composer, but not of librettist, who is unknown to Schatz. On p. 5–13, a detailed description with argument and cast of "Astarbea ossia Pimmalione vendicato, ballo tragico in cinque atti, inventato, e composto dal Sig. Giambattista Giannini . . . La musica è tutta nuova del Signor D. Pietro Dutillieu." SCHATZ 259

I matrimonii per inganno. Commedia per musica di Giuseppe Palomba da rappresentarsi nel Real Teatro del Fondo di Separazione. Nell' inverno di questo anno 1779.

Napoli, n. publ., 1779. 64 p. 15 cm.

Three acts. Cast and name of the composer, Giuseppe Maria **Curcio** ("Curci") SCHATZ 2302

I matrimonj per inganno, ballet. *See* Nicolini's Gli Sciti.

I matrimonj per magia. Commedia per musica da rappresentarsi nel Teatro de' Fiorentini per quart' opera del corrente anno 1797.

Napoli, n. publ., 1797. 24 p. 15½ cm.

One act. Author not mentioned and unknown to Schatz. Cast and name of the composer, Valentino **Fioravanti**.
First performed at Naples, Teatro di Fondo, 1794. SCHATZ 3135

Li matrimonj per sorpresa. Farsa per musica a 5. voci da rappresentarsi nel Teatro Valle degl' illustrissimi Signori Capranica il carnevale dell' anno 1788 . . .

Roma, Gioacchino Puccinelli, n. d. 58 p. 15cm.

Two acts. Author not mentioned and not known to Schatz. Dedication, cast and name of Luigi **Platone** as composer. ML50.2.M46P4

Il matrimonio cinese, ballet. *See* Anfossi's Gengis-Kan.

Il matrimonio de' Groelandesi, ballet. *See* Rispoli's Nitteti.

Il matrimonio de' Groenlandesi, ballet. *See* Rossetti's Olimpiade.

Il matrimonio di Figaro. A. T. of Portugal's La pazza giornata.

Il matrimonio improvviso. Commedia con musica d'un atto solo ridotta da Giuseppe Foppa. Da rappresentarsi nel nobilissimo Teatro Giustiniani in San Moisè il carnovale dell' anno 1794.

n. i., n. d. 24 p. 18cm.

Cast and name of Ferdinando Pè (**Päer**) as the composer. SCHATZ 7563

— **Il matrimonio improviso** o I due sordi, dramma giocoso per musica da rappresentarsi nel Teatro della molto Ile. città di Barcellona l'anno 1798.

Barcellona, Francesco Généras, n. d. 54 p. 14½cm.

Two acts. Cast and name of Per (**Paer**) as the composer. Foppa, the author, is not mentioned. SCHATZ 7564

Il matrimonio inaspettato, ballet. *See* Valentini's Le sorelle rivali.

Il matrimonio in commedia. Dramma giocoso per musica da rappresentarsi nel Teatro grande alla Scala di Milano, la primavera dell' anno 1782 . . .

Milano, Gio. Batista Bianchi, n. d. 4 p. l., 51 ,[1] p. 15½cm.

The additional p. contains a substitute aria ("A forze di mortello") for I, 7. Two acts. By Giuseppe Palomba, who is not mentioned and whose much altered "Le nozze in commedia" this is. Dedication, cast, scenario, and name of Luigi **Caruso** as the composer. Gaspero Angiolini is mentioned as the author and composer of the following ballets: "I geni riuniti," "Il Solimano Secondo," "Il diavolo a quattro, ossia La doppia metamorfosi," and "La Lauretta." These are called "Balli da rappresentarsi alternativamente."

First performed, as indicated, April 7, 1782; at Rome, carnival 1782.

SCHATZ 1646

— **Li sposi in commedia.** Dramma giocoso per musica da rappresentarsi nel nobile Teatro di S. Samuele il carnovale dell' anno 1786.

Venezia, Modesto Fenzo, 1786. 48, 14 p. 17½cm.

Two acts. Altered version of Palomba's "Il matrimonio in commedia." Cast, scenario, and name of Francesco **Bianchi** as composer, but replaced by that of Luigi **Caruso** on a printed slip of paper pasted over Bianchi's name. The additional 14 p. contain argument, cast, and detailed description of "Ballo primo. Rossana. Ballo tragico in cinque atti da rappresentarsi nel Nobile Teatro di San Samuele il carnovale dell' anno 1786. Condotto, e diretto dal Signor Eusebio Luzzi." The composer of the ballet music is not mentioned. SCHATZ 1647

Il matrimonio in contrasto. Commedia per musica di Giuseppe Palomba da rappresentarsi nel Teatro de' Fiorentini nell' està del corrente anno 1776.

Napoli, n. publ., 1776. 69 p. 15^{cm}.

Three acts. Argument cast, scenario, and name of Pietro **Guglielmi** as the composer. SCHATZ 4252

Il matrimonio in maschera. L. T. of G. M. Rutini's I matrimoni in maschera.

Il matrimonio inaspettato. Dramma giocoso per musica da rappresentarsi nel Teatro di Camenoi-Ostroff. di S. A. I. Monsignor il gran duca—Le mariage imprévu . . .

n. i., n. d. 93 p. 18^{cm}.

One act. Based on "Il marchese villano" by Pietro Chiari, who is not mentioned. Argument and name of **Paisiello** as composer. French text faces Italian.
First performed at St. Petersburg, 1779, as indicated. SCHATZ 7636

— **Il marchese di Tulipano** o sia Il matrimonio inespetato [!] Farzeta in musica, per representarci nel Theatro della rua do Condes, nel anno di 1790 . . .

Lisbona, Simão Thaddeo Ferreira, 1790. 91 p. 15^{cm}.

Two acts. By Chiari, who is not mentioned. Dedication, cast, scenario, and name of **Paisiello** as the composer. Portuguese title page, "O marquez de Tulipano, ou O casamento inesperado," and text face Italian. SCHATZ 7688

— Das **witzige landmaedchen,** oder Der geadelte landmann. Eine komische oper in zwey aufzuegen. Aufgefuehrt auf der schaubuehne der Kaiserl. freyen reichsstadt Nuernberg.

Nuernberg, n. publ., 1787. 54 p. 15½^{cm}.

With name of **Paisiello** as the composer.
First performed 1787, as indicated. SCHATZ 7638

Il matrimonio non è per i vecchi. A. T. of Longarini's La donna ne sa più del diavolo.

Il matrimonio per astuzia, ballet. *See* Bianchi's Il Chinese in Italia.

Il matrimonio per astuzia. Dramma giocoso per musica da rappresentarsi nel nobilissimo Teatro di S. Benedetto l'autunno dell' anno MDCCLXXI.

Venezia, Modesto Fenzo, n. d. 56 p. 17^{cm}.

Three acts. Author not mentioned, and unknown to Schatz. Cast, scenario, and name of Andrea **Luchesi** as composer.
First performed in October 1771, as indicated. SCHATZ 5740

Il matrimonio per concorso. Dramma giocoso per musica da rappresentarsi in Lisbona nel Teatro della rua dos Condes nell' autunno dell' anno 1773.

[Lisbona], Stamperia reale, n. d. 84 p. (incl. h.-t.) 16½^{cm}.

Three acts. By Gaetano Martinelli, who is not mentioned. Cast, scenario, and name of Felice **Alessandri** as composer. The libretto mentions as "Ballo secondo," "La vedova scaltra," based on Goldoni's comedy of this title, by Giuseppe Magni.
First performed at Venice, Teatro di S. Moisè, during carnival of 1767. SCHATZ 148

Il matrimonio per concorso, ballet. *See* P. Guglielmi's L'impresa d'opera.

Il matrimonio per concorso. Dramma giocoso per musica da rappresentarsi nel Regio Ducal Teatro di Milano nell' autunno dell' anno 1768 . . .

Milano, Giovanni Montani, n. d.   4 p. l., 51 p.   14ᶜᵐ.

Three acts.   Dedication, cast, and names of Gaetano Martinelli as the author, of Niccolò **Jommelli** as the composer.
First performed at Ludwigsburg, Hoftheater, November 4, 1766 (the date 1744 is very improbable).   SCHATZ 4864

Il matrimonio per concorso, ballet. *See* Pugnani's Achille in Sciro.

Il matrimonio per concorso, ballet. *See* Zingarelli's Ifigenia in Aulide.

Il matrimonio per contrattempo. Dramma giocoso per musica da rappresentarsi in Livorno nel Nuovo Teatro detto dagli Armeni il carnevale dell' anno 1785 . . .

Livorno, Antonio Lami e comp., n. d.   61 p.   14½ᶜᵐ.

Two acts.   Author not mentioned and unknown to Schatz.   Dedication by the impresario, Giovanni Albertini, cast, and name of Angelo **Tarchi** as the composer. With the opera were performed, composers of the music not mentioned, Giacomo Gentili's ballets "Aci e Galatea" and "Il tutore in scompiglio."   SCHATZ 10237

Il matrimonio per forza, intermezzo per musica, da rappresentarsi nel Nuovo Regio Teatro di Potsdam . . .

Potsdam, C. F. Boss, 1748.   39 p.   16ᶜᵐ.

Three parts.   Cast.   German title page, "Die erzwungene ehe," and text face Italian.   Author and composer not mentioned and unknown to Schatz.
First performed at Venice, Teatro di San Cassiano, fall of 1729.   SCHATZ 11350

Il matrimonio per gratitudine, ballet. *See* Marinelli's L'interesse gabba tutti.

Il matrimonio per industria. Dramma giocoso per musica da rappresentarsi nel nobile Teatro di Varese l'autunno dell' anno 1793 . . .

Milano, Gio. Batista Bianchi, n. d.   60 p.   17ᶜᵐ.

Two acts.   Dedication by the author (??), Pietro Astolfi, cast, and name of Ferdinando **Rutini** as the composer.   With the opera were performed Eusebio Luzzi's ballets "Il convitato di pietra" and "Il geloso in cimento," the composers of the music not being mentioned.
First performed at Florence as "Il matrimonio per industria o sia Il servo astuto," Teatro via della Pergola, fall of 1792.   SCHATZ 9184

Il matrimonio per inganno. Dramma giocoso per musica da rappresentarsi nel nobile magnifico Teatro delle Grazie di Vicenza nel corrente mese di settembre 1780 . . .

Vicenza, n. publ., n. d.   55 p.   17ᶜᵐ.

Last p. numbered incorrectly 41.   Two acts.   By Giovanni Bertati.   Impresario's dedication, cast, and name of Pasquale **Anfossi** as composer, but not of librettist. Original title of Bertati's libretto: "Le industrie amorose."
First performed at Paris, Académie royale de musique, on September 30, 1779, but previously, according to our transcript of the score at the Paris Conservatoire National at the Cocomero, Florence, spring of 1779.   SCHATZ 244

Il **matrimonio per inganno**—Continued.

— Il **matrimonio per inganno.** Dramma giocoso per musica da rappresentarsi nel Piccolo Teatro di S. A. S. di Brunsvic-Luneburg.

*Brunsvic, n. publ., 1782. 135 p. 16½*cm*.*

Two acts. Name of **Anfossi** as composer. German title-page, "Die heyrath durch betrug," and text face Italian. Schatz 245

Il **matrimonio per inganno.** L. T. of Galuppi's Il marchese villano.

Il **matrimonio per scomessa** ossia La guerra aperta. Dramma giocoso per musica di Filippo Casari da rappresentarsi nel nobile Teatro di San Samuele l'autunno dell' anno 1795.

*Venezia, Casali, 1795. 64 p. 18*cm*.*

Cast and name of **Della Maria** as composer. Schatz 2494

Il **matrimonio segreto.** Dramma per musica in due atti, da rappresentarsi nel Teatro Elettorale.

*Dresda, n. publ., 1792. 127 p. 15*cm*.*

Two acts. With name of the composer, Domenico **Cimarosa,** but not of the author, Giovanni Bertati. German title-page, "Die heimlich geschlossene ehe," and text face Italian.
First performed at Dresden, October 3, 1792; at Vienna, Hoftheater n. d. Burg, February 7, 1792. Schatz 1948

Matroco, drame burlesque. En quatre actes et en vers. Mêlée d'ariettes, et de vaudevilles; représenté devant Leurs Majestés, par les Comédiens italiens ordinaires du roi, en 1777. Et à Paris, par les mêmes Comédiens le 4 février 1778. Les paroles sont de M. Laujon . . . La musique de M. Grétry.

*Paris, Ruault, 1778. 42 p. 19*cm*.*

Cast.
According to Schatz, the opera was first performed at Fontainebleau, November 12, 1777, and at Paris, Comédie italienne, February 23, 1778. ML 50.2.M465G7

. . . Die **matrosen,** ein schauspiel mit gesang in zwey aufzuegen.

*n. i., n. d. [97]–160 p. 15*cm*.*

Detached copy. Schatz attributes text and music to Ernst Karl Ludwig Ysenburg von **Buri.** Schatz 1423
First performed at Neuwied, Hoftheater, 1778.

Matthatia, der eiferer fuer Gottes ehre, ein singspiel in zween aufzuegen, aufgefuehret von der studirenden jugend des katholischen schulhauses zu Augsburg bey St. Salvator den 4. 5. und 6ten herbstmonder [Sept.] 1797.

*[Augsburg], Joseph Anton Hueber, n. d. [10] p. 18*cm*.*

Cast and "Vorbericht," mentioning Matthäus **Fischer** as composer. At head of title: "Der gluckliche vater, ein buergerliches schauspiel . . . und" Schatz 3223

I **matti gloriosi.** Intermezzo giocoso in musica da rappresentarsi nel nobil Teatro Tron di San Cassiano il carnovale dell' anno MDCCLXXXIII.

*Venezia, Modesto Fenzo, 1783. 40 p. 17*cm*.*

Two acts. Author unknown to Schatz. Cast, scenario, and name of the composer, Angelo **Gagni.** After the first act Gaspero Burchi's ballet "I divertimenti dei Calabresi," after the second Leopoldo Campilli's ballet "Il divertimento de' Quaqueri nella China." The composers of the music are not mentioned. Schatz 3412

Li matti per amore. Dramma giocoso per musica da rappresentarsi nel Teatro Grimani di S. Samuel l'autunno dell' anno 1754 . . .

Venezia, Modesto Fenzo, 1754. 60 p. 15ᶜᵐ.

Three acts. Dedication, cast, scenario, and name of Gioacchino **Cocchi** as composer. The libretto, according to Schatz, is a later version of Gennaro Antonio Federico's "Amor vuol sofferenza."   Sᴄʜᴀᴛᴢ 2035

— **Li matti per amore.** Dramma giocoso per musica da rappresentarsi nel Regio Theatro di Berlino per ordine di Sua Maestà prussiana.

Berlino, Haude e Spener, 1764. 91, [3] p. 17½ᶜᵐ.

Three acts. **Cocchi** is mentioned as the composer. German title-page, "Die narren für liebe," and text face Italian. The first ballet of the three performed with the opera in January, 1764, was called "Le bien et le mal tiré des contes de la Fontaine."   Sᴄʜᴀᴛᴢ 2036

Il matto Don Narciso. L. T. of Jommelli's L'uccellatrice.

Il Mauritio. Drama da rappresentarsi in musica nel famoso Teatro Vendramino di S. Salvatore l'anno 1687. Ristampata con nuove aggiunte . . .

Venetia, Francesco Nicolini, 1687. 69 p. (incl. front.). 14½ᶜᵐ.

Three acts. By Adriano Morselli, who is not mentioned. Impresario's dedication dated Venice, December 25, 1686, notice to the reader with name of Domenico **Gabrieli** as composer, argument, and scenario.   Sᴄʜᴀᴛᴢ 3399

— **Il Maurizio,** drama da rappresentarsi in musica nel Teatro dell' illustriss. Sign. Co. e Cav. Giuseppe Secco Svardo . . .

Bergamo, li fratelli Rossi, 1689. 72 p. 13ᶜᵐ.

Three acts. Dedication by Giacomo Cipriotti, dated Bergamo, January 12, 1689, "istoria," scenario. Neither the author is mentioned, nor the composer, but comparison showed that this is Morselli's text as composed by **Gabrieli.**

    ML 50.2.M47G2

Le mauvais plaisant ou Le drole de corps, opera-comique, en un acte, par M. Vadé, représenté pour la premiere fois sur le Théâtre de l'Opera-comique de la Foire S. Laurent, le mercredi 17 août 1757.

Paris, Duchesne, 1757. 60, [4] p. 19½ᶜᵐ.

On the [4] p. a list of plays published since 1747.
Cast. Prose and *en vaudevilles.* Composer unknown to me. On p. 57–60 the same airs as below.   ML 50.2.M48

— **Le mauvais plaisant,** ou Le drole de corps, opera-comique. En un acte, par M. Vadé. Représenté pour la première fois sur le Théâtre de l'Opéra-comique de la Foire S. Laurent le mercredi 17 août 1757.

La Haye, Pierre Gosse junior, 1759. 63 p. 16ᶜᵐ. (Vadé, Oeuvres, La Haye, 1759, t. iv.)

One act, largely *en vaudevilles.* Cast. On p. 60–63, the *airs notés,* "Oui oui, vous le pouvez," "Daignés donc m'apprendre," "Je vous aime: prononcez de même."   ML 49.A2V2

— **Le mauvais plaisant,** ou Le drole de corps, opéra-comique en un acte, représenté pour la premiere fois sur le Théatre de l'Opéra-comique de la Foire S. Laurent, le mercredi 17 août 1757.

Paris, la veuve Duchesne, 1766. 60 p. 19ᶜᵐ.

On p. 57–60, the "airs," "Oui, oui, vous le pouvez," "Daignez donc m'apprendre."   Sᴄʜᴀᴛᴢ 11500

May-day: or, The little gipsy. A musical farce of one act. To which is added The theatrical candidates. A musical prelude. As they are both performed at the Theatre-Royal, in Drury-Lane.

London, T. Becket, 1775. 4 p. l., 40 p. 18½ᶜᵐ.

One act each. Casts. "The theatrical candidates" on p. [31]–40. Both pieces by David Garrick, who is not mentioned. He says of "May-day," in a prefatory note, that

"it was merely intended to introduce the Little Gipsy [Miss Abrams] to the public, whose youth and total inexperience of the stage, made it necessary to give as little dialogue to her character as possible, her success depending wholly upon her singing . . ."

The half title of the other piece, on p. [31], reads: "Upon the opening and alterations of the theatre," Drury-Lane [Sept. 23, 1775], where "May-Day" was first performed on August 28, 1775 (Cummings); October 28 (Schatz). "May Day" was composed by Thomas Augustine **Arne**, "The theatrical candidates" by William **Bates**, neither of whom is mentioned.   LONGE 78

— **May-day;** or The little gipsy. A musical farce, of one act. By David Garrick, Esq.

[137]–157 p. 19ᶜᵐ. (Collection of the most esteemed farces and entertainments, t. vi, Edinburgh, 1792.)

Drury-Lane cast.   SCHATZ 11753

Mazet, comedie en deux actes en vers, mêlées d'ariettes, par Mr. Anseaume. Représentée pour la premiere fois par les Comédiens italiens ordinaires du roi, le jeudi 24 septembre 1761. La musique est de M. Duny.

Bruxelles, Pierre Paupié, 1763. 47 p. 19ᶜᵐ.   ML 50.2.M48D9

— **Mazet,** comédie en deux actes et en vers, mêlée d'ariettes. Par M. Anseaume. Représentée pour la premiere fois par les Comédiens italiens ordinaires du Roi, le jeudi 24 Septembre mil sept soixante-un.

Paris, Par la compagnie des libraires, 1769. 43 p. 19ᶜᵐ.

The composer, **Duni,** is not mentioned.   SCHATZ 2847

— **Mazet,** comédie en deux actes, en vers, mêlée d'ariettes, par Mr. Anseaume. La musique est de Mr. Duny.

Paris, la veuve Duchesne, 1771. 43, 4 p.

Cast. The last 4 p. contain the ariette, "Avec un Turc, un corsaire" (I, 4).

SCHATZ 11696

Le mbroglie de le bajasse. O. T. of Paisiello's La serva fatta padrona.

Medea. Ein drama mit musicalischen accompagnements, vom hrn. legations-secretair Gotter. Die musik ist vom hrn. capelldirektor Benda.

Hamburg, n. publ., 1776. 16 p. 16ᶜᵐ.

One act.

First performed at Hamburg, Theater b. Gänsemarkt, December 10, 1776; at Leipzig, Theater beim Rannstaedter Thore, May 1, 1775.   SCHATZ 774

— **Medea.** Ein musikalisches drama von herrn Gotter. Die musik ist von herrn Georg Benda.

n. i., n. d. [51]–74 p. 14½ᶜᵐ.

Detached copy of no. III of "Melodramen," pub. by Joseph Johann Morgensaeuler, Pilsen und Klattau, 1791, as appears from our copy of Benda's "Pygmalion."

SCHATZ 774a

Medea e Giasone. Drama per musica da rappresentarsi nel Teatro di Sant' Angelo nel carnovale dell' anno 1726.

Venezia, Marino Rossetti, 1726. 48 p. 16ᶜᵐ.

In three acts, by Giovanni Palazzi (not mentioned). Argument, cast, and name of the composer, Giovanni Francesco **Brusa**.

First performed December 26, 1726 (Schatz).   SCHATZ 1374

Medea e Giasone—Medée et Jason, ballet. *See* Jommelli's La Didone abbandonata.

Medea in Atene. Drama per musica ristampata con nuove aggiunte per il Teatro novissimo in S. Angelo. L'anno MDCLXXVIII. Di Aurelio Aureli. Opera decima ottava . . .

Venetia, Francesco Nicolini, 1678. 59 p. 14ᶜᵐ.

Prologue and three acts. Dedication by Francesco Santorini, dated December 30, 1677, argument, scenario. Antonio **Zannettini**, the composer, is not mentioned.

First performed at Venice, Teatro di S. Moisè, fall of 1675.   SCHATZ 11144

— **Teseo in Atene.** Drama rappresentato in musica nel novissimo Teatro Ducale di Parma . . . Poesia di Aurelio Aureli.

Parma, Stamperia Ducale, 1688. 85 p. 16ᶜᵐ.

Three acts. Dedication by Giuseppe Calvi, argument, scenario, and Aureli's notice to the reader, in which he says:

"Fù questo drama con titolo di *Medea in Atene* rappresentato già 12 anni in Venetia [1675] . . . E se ben variato di titolo, non cangia però la sua essenza primiera, benche con aggiungervi il novo personaggio della Vecchia l'abbia aricchito d'alquante nove ariette poste miralbilmente in musica dalla virtù del Sig. D. Bernardo **Sabadini** . . . Vieni ad ascoltar il drama se brami d'udire una delle più armoniose, e bizarre musiche, ch'abbia giamai composta il Sig. Gio. Antonio Gianettini [**Zannettini**] . . ."

This version of "Medea in Atene" does not begin with the prologue of 1678, or even with the first scene in that edition. It begins with "Vincesti amico, e di tua spada," which is not in the 1678 version, and the first scene in this, "E svanita dal mio core," is now the third scene. There are many other minor differences of a similar nature between the two texts.   SCHATZ 11143

Medea riconosciuta. L. T. of Vinci's Medo.

Medea und Jason. Tr. T. of the ballet Medée et Jason.

Medea und Jason, ballet. *See* Bach's Temistocle.

Le **medecin de l'amour,** opera-comique. En un acte; par M. Anseaume, mis en musique par M. La Ruette; représenté pour la premiere fois sur le Théâtre de la Foire St. Laurent, le 22 septembre 1758 . . .

Paris, N. B. Duchesne, 1758. 64 p. 20ᶜᵐ.

Cast and footnote on p. 2 that scene 6 and the *canevas* of scenes 7 and 8 were by Marcouville. On p. 60–64 the airs "Accourez, garçons joyeux" (I, 8), "C'est bien dit compère" (I, 8), "Le mariage où l'on m'engage" (I, 9), "Vous jaloux, que viens-je" (I, 9), "Deviez vous m'éclaircir" (I, 9). Of the twelve "Ariettes notées," which one might expect, none is given.   SCHATZ 5438

Le **medecin de l'amour,** opera-comique en un acte en vers, remis en musique par M. Van Maldere.

Bruxelles, J. J. Boucherie, 1766. 46, [1] p. 19ᶜᵐ.

Cast. The authors, Anseaume and de Marcouville, are not mentioned.

First performed at Brussels, Théâtre de la Monnaie, 1766.   SCHATZ 5867

Medée, tragedie. En musique. Representée par l'Academie royalle de musique. Suivant la copie imprimée a Paris.

Amsterdam, Antoine Schelte, 1695. 69 p. (incl. front.). 13ᶜᵐ.

Prologue and five acts. Neither the author, Thomas Corneille, is mentioned, nor the composer, Marc' Antoine **Charpentier.**
First performed, as indicated, December 4, 1693. ML 50.2.M5C2

— **Medée,** tragedie representée par l'Academie royale de musique l'an 1694. Les paroles de M. T. Corneille, & la musique de Mᵣ Charpentier. XXXI. opera.

n. i., n. d. front., 345–420 p. 14ᶜᵐ. (Recueil général des opéra, Paris, 1703, t. iv.)

Detached copy. Five acts with prologue. Sᴄʜᴀᴛᴢ 1801
Second copy. ML 48.R4

Médée, tragédie en trois actes, en vers, paroles de Hoffmann, musique de Cherubini. Représentée sur le Théâtre Feydeau, le 23 ventôse [March 13].

Paris, Huet, an vᵉ. 1797. 2 p. l., 48 p. 21½ᶜᵐ.
Cast. ML 50.2.M5C3

Medée et Jason. Tr. T. of the ballet Medea e Giasone.

Medée et Jason—Medea und Jason, ballet. *See* Bernasconi's Demetrio.

Medée et Jason, tragedie représentée par l'Academie royale de musique l'an 1713. Les paroles de M. la Rocque & la musique de M. Salomon. LXXXI. opera.

n. i., n. d. pl., 545–609, [3] p. 14ᶜᵐ. (Recueil général des opéra, t. x, Paris, 1714.)

Detached copy. Prologue and five acts with cast. Schatz mentions as joint-author Simon Joseph de Pellegrin. His reasons do not appear. Parfaict attributes the text to abbé de Pellegrin "sous le nom de la Rogue" and he is also mentioned as the author in the Anecdotes dramatiques. It is safer to follow the libretto, as Antoine de la Roque was not a fictitious person but a well-known littérateur.
First performed, as indicated, April 24, 1713. Sᴄʜᴀᴛᴢ 9343
Second copy. ML 48.R4

— **Medée et Jason.** Représenté pour la premiere fois par les Comédiens italiens ordinaires du roi, le 28 may 1727.

Les parodies du Nouveau théâtre italien, Nouv. éd., Paris, 1738, t. iii, [219]–266 p. 16½ᶜᵐ.

One act. Parody of the opera "Medée et Jason" by Dominique, Lelio fils and Romagnesi (*see* t. I.) The airs and vaudeville are printed at the end in the "Table des airs" (84 p.). ML 48.P3

Il medico parigino o sia L'amaloto per amore. Dramma giocoso per musica da rappresentarsi nel nobilissimo Teatro della nobil Donna Tron Veronese in San Cassiano il carnovale dell' anno 1792.

Venezia, Modesto Fenzo, 1791. 56 p. 17½ᶜᵐ.

Two acts. Cast, scenario, and name of Gennaro **Astaritta** as composer, but not of librettist. According to Schatz this is a later version of Giuseppe Palomba's text, "Le nozze in commedia." Sᴄʜᴀᴛᴢ 374

Medo. Dramma per musica da rappresentarsi nel Regio Teatro di Torino, nel carnovale del 1753 . . .

> *Torino, Pietro Giuseppe Zappata e figliuolo, 1753.* 4 p. l., 56, [1] p. 15½*cm*.

Three acts. Cast, scenario, and name of composer, Girolamo **Abos**. Libretto attributed by Schatz to Carlo Innocenzio Frugoni. With the opera were performed three ballets, music by Amedeo Rasetti and Rocco Gioannetti.   SCHATZ 10

Medo. Dramma per musica di Comante Eginetico Pastore Arcade da rappresentarsi nel Nuovo Ducal Teatro di Parma la primavera dell' anno 1728 . . .

> *Parma, gl'eredi di Paolo Monti, 1728.* 80 p. 17*cm*.

Three acts. By Carlo Innocenzio Frugoni. Dedication, dedicatory sonnet by Frugoni to the princess Enrichetta d'Este, argument, scenario, cast, and name of Leonardo **Vinci** as the composer.   SCHATZ 10748

— **Medea riconosciuta.** Da cantarsi nel Teatro privilegiato da S. M. C. e Cat. in Vienna nell' anno MDCCXXXV. Nel mese di decembre.—Die wieder erkannte Medea . . .

> *Wien, Johann Peter v. Ghelen, n. d.* 111 p. 16*cm*.

Three acts (though not so designated) and two intermezzi with "Macrina" and "Carfoglio" as the main characters. Argument. German text faces Italian, which is Frugoni's "Medo," but with alterations. For instance, "Tu del mio regno sei" has been dropped from I, 3, and "Dal tuo gentil sembiante" has been added to I, 4.

The composer, Leonardo **Vinci**, is not mentioned.   SCHATZ 10753

Medonte. Dramma per musica da rappresentarsi nel Regio Teatro di Torino nel carnovale del 1778 alla presenza delle Maestà Loro.

> *Torino, Onorato Berossi, n. d.* viii, 56 p. 15½*cm*.

Three acts, with argument, cast, scenario, and name of composer, Ferd. Giuseppe **Bertoni**, but not of the librettist, Giovanni de Gamerra. On p. 53–56, description of the ballet, "La liberazione di Lilla," in four acts, by Domenico Ricciardi; music by Vittorio Amedeo Canavasso.

First performed, as indicated, December 26, 1777.   SCHATZ 923

Medonte, ballet. *See* Cavi's La prepotenza delusa.

Medonte. Dramma per musica da rappresentarsi nel Real Teatro di S. Carlo nel dì 30. maggio 1779 festeggiandosi il glorioso nome di Ferdinando IV . . .

> *Napoli, Vincenzo Flauto, 1779.* 60 p. 16*cm*.

Three acts. By Giovanni de Gamerra, who is not mentioned. Impresario's dedication, dated May 30, 1779, argument, cast, scenario, and name of Giacomo **Insanguine** as the composer. With the opera were performed, composers of the music not mentioned, Carlo Lepicq's ballet, "Orfeo sul Monte Rodope," and Gaetano Mariottini's ballet "L'incostanza degli amanti."   SCHATZ 4836

Medonte, ballet. *See* Salari's L'amore rammingo.

Medonte. Dramma per musica da rappresentarsi nel Real Teatro di S. Carlo nel dì 30 maggio 1783 festeggiandosi il glorioso nome di Ferdinando IV . . .

> *Napoli, Vincenzo Flauto, 1783.* 71 p. 15*cm*.

Three acts. By Giovanni de Gamerra, who is not mentioned. Dedication, with same date as in title, argument, scenario, name of Giuseppe **Sarti** as the composer, and note:

"L'arie segnate di asterisco ['Sento al cor la dolce fiamma' (I, 2), 'Prendi l'estremo addio' (I, 6), etc.] sono state presentate per la musica, e per la poesia da' cantanti

Medonte—Continued.

istessi. I due irregolari versi di carattere corsivo nel rondò ['Son pur fiere le mie pene,' etc.] non si son corretti, per non farne perder la musica."

On p. 10–15, argument, cast, description, and name of Mattia Stabingher as the composer of the music ("tutta nuova") of Gio. Antonio Cianfanelli's "Il trionfo di Alessandro o sia La disfatta di Dario, ballo eroico in quattro atti," and on p. 16–17, argument and name of Giovanni Francesco Giuliani as composer of the music ("tutta nuova") of Giuseppe Trafieri's "Il fido amante, ballo pastorale."

First performed at Florence, Teatro della Pergola, September 13, 1777, with the title, "Medonte, rè di Epiro." SCHATZ 9447

Medonte, rè d'Epiro. O. T. of libretto of Mortellari's Arsace.

Medonte rè di Epiro. Dramma per musica da rappresentarsi nel Teatro alla Scala il carnevale 1790 . . .

Milano, Gio. Batista Bianchi, n. d. 70 p. 16^{cm}.

Three acts. By Giovanni de Gamerra, who is not mentioned. Impresario's dedication, dated Milan, January 30, 1790, argument, cast, scenario, and name of Antonio **Pio** as the composer.

With the opera were performed Francesco Clerico's comic ballet, "Il convalescente innamorato," and his five-act "La caduta di Troja, ballo tragico pantomimo," of which a description with prefatory note and argument appears on p. [61]–70.

The composers of the music are not mentioned. SCHATZ 8187

Medonte re di Epiro. Dramma per musica da rappresentarsi nel nobilissimo Teatro di S. Benedetto il carnovale dell' anno 1778.

Venezia, Modesto Fenzo, 1778. 60 p. 17^{cm}.

Three acts. By Giovanni de Gamerra, who is not mentioned. Argument, cast, scenario, and name of Giuseppe **Radicchj**. On p. [25]–34, argument, cast, and description (without name of the composer of the music) of Giuseppe Canziani's "L'arrivo di Venere nell' isola di Cipro, ballo eroico pantomimo." SCHATZ 8539

Medonte, rè di Epiro. O. T. of Sarti's Medonte.

Il **Medoro** d'Andrea Salvadori. Rappresentato in musica nel palazzo del Serenissimo G. Duca di Toscana in Fiorenza. Per la elezione all' imperio della Sacra Cesarea Maestà dell' imperatore Ferdinando Secondo . . .

Fiorenza, Pietro Cecconcelli, 1623. 4 p. l., 46 p. 19½^{cm}.

Three acts. Introductory poem, argument, and dedication to Ferdinando Gonzaga, duke of Mantova, of date Florence, January 1, 1623, in which Salvadori says: "Il Medoro (Serenissimo Signore) ricordevole dell' onore al quale l'aveva destinato V. A. all' ora che nel felicissimo maritaggio della Sacra Cesarea Maestà dell' imperatrice Sua sorella, ella lo volse far degno d'esser rappresentato in Mantova; poiche per la subita partita di quella Maestà in Germania, egli non potè conseguire così segnalata grazia, si contentava più tosto di starsi celato appresso il suo autore, che comparire in luce con minor ventura. Ora sentendo io, che essendo stata trascritta una parte di esso, e divulgata in vari luoghi, correva non solamente risico di esser rappresentato, ma dato ancora alle stampe molto diverso da quello, che era appresso di mè, hò giudicato ben fatto, che egli con publica comparsa, qualunque egli si sia, venga à rassegnarsi à V. A. per Suo. Ella lo vedrà molto vario da quello, che la prima volta fu veduto in scena, e se potrà parer povero ne miei versi, la veste della musica, onde l'hà nuovamente arrichito il Sig. **Marco da Gagliano**, lo renderà appresso di Lei, e riguardevole, e grato . . ."

From this dedication it becomes evident, as Solerti correctly remarks, that the performance of 1622 at Mantova, recorded by Vogel, did not take place. Vogel (*see* his biography of Marco da Gagliano) did not know this edition of the libretto and based his remarks on letters written by Marco da Gagliano to the duchess of Mantova January 31 and February 7, 1622, to the effect that he was sending her the desired transcript of his score. Before Vogel discovered these letters, it was not known that Marco da Gagliano was the composer of "Il Medoro," first performed 1619 for the festivities mentioned in the title of the opera and alluded to in the dedication and more specifically, as Solerti has found from contemporary documents, on September

Il **Medoro**—Continued.

25, 1619. (An undated libretto for these performances exists, but it does not mention any composer.) From this document may be gleaned another fact not known to Vogel, Wotquenne, Schatz, etc., namely, that Jacopo **Peri** composed part of the original music. To quote the passus in Tinghi's "Diario," as excerpted by Solerti in his "Musica, ballo e drammatica all a Corte Medicea dal 1600 al 1637":

"Et adì 25 detto [settembre] S. A. . . . avendo alli passati giorni l'allegrezza della creazione del nuovo imperatore, et per ciò ordinò si facesse una festa per recitarsi in guisa di comedia cantata in musica, et sendo detta opera all' ordine et ordinato in detto di si recitasse nel palazzo de' Pitti nella sala grande de' forestieri, dove era fatto una prospettiva in forma di selve et boschi con finte finte [sic], la quale opera era nominata *Lo sposalizio di Medoro et Angelica*, recitata et cantata tutta in musica; fatta l'opera da Andrea Salvadori, poeta, et la musica fatta parte da Messer **Marco da Galliano**, maestro di cappella, et da Jacopo **Peri**, et vi cantò molte donne et castrati et tutti i musici di S. A. in diversi abiti . . ."

Which parts were composed by Peri, and which by Marco da Gagliano is not known, since no score appears to be extant, or, at any rate, the score has not yet been found. Apparently Peri's share was not large and, so to say, not worth mentioning later on, even if Marco da Gagliano retained it in 1622. From Marco da Gagliano's letters to the duchess of Mantova we know at least that, at the suggestion of Salvadori, he changed the choruses in order not to make the opera "troppo grave" for the contemplated revival at Mantova.   ML 48.M2F

Il **Medoro.** Drama per musica di Aurelio Aureli nel Teatro a SS. Gio. e Paolo. Favola quarta . . .

Venetia, Francesco Nicolini, 1658. front., 80 p. 13½ᶜᵐ.

Three acts and prologue. Dedication by the impresario, Francesco Piva, dated Venice, January 11, 1658, argument, scenario, and notice to the reader with name of Francesco **Luccio** as composer.   SCHATZ 5744

Medus, roy des Mèdes, tragedie representée par l'Académie royale de musique l'an 1702. Les paroles de M. de la Grange & la musique de M. Bouvard. LV. opera.

n. i., n. d. front., p. 345–390. 14ᶜᵐ. (Recueil général des opera, Paris, 1703, t. vii.)

Detached copy. Prologue and five acts.
First performed, as indicated, July 23, 1702.   SCHATZ 1274
Second copy.   ML 48.R4

Méduse. Tragedie, representée par l'Academie royale de musique l'an 1697. Les paroles sont de M. Boyer & la musique de M. Gervais. XXXX. opera.

n. i., n. d. front., p. 415–468. (Recueil général des opera, t. v, Paris, 1703.) 14ᶜᵐ.

Detached copy. Five acts and prologue.
First performed, as indicated, January 13, 1697.   SCHATZ 3792
Second copy.   ML 48.R4

Mehr als grosmuth! Schauspiel mit gesang. Aufgeführt von der Döbbelinschen gesellschaft in Berlin den 24 sten Jänner 1781.

Berlin, Arnold Wever, 1782. 24 p. 17ᶜᵐ.

One act. Prefatory note. Neither composer, Johann **André**, nor author mentioned in the libretto. The author is unknown to Schatz.   SCHATZ 189

De **meid meesteres.** A. T. of Pergolesi's Pandolfus en Zerbina.

La **melancholique.** Entrée in Mouret's Les Graces.

Méléagre, tragedie représentée par l'Academie royale de musique l'an 1709. Les paroles de M. Jolly & la musique de M. Batistin. LXXIII. opera.

n. i., n. d.   pl., 62 p.   14^{cm}*.   (Recueil général des opéra, t. x, Paris, 1714.)*

Detached copy. Prologue and five acts. In his "avertissement," Antoine François Jolly enumerates the sometimes radical changes made by him in his text since the performances of the piece. For instance, he says:

"Pour établir donc les caracteres des principaux personnages, & leurs differents interêts, & sur tout ceux de Plexippe, qui n'étoient point assez marquez, & qui est le personnage le plus essentiel de la piece puis qu'il en fait le noeud & le dénoüment; j'ay fait un premier acte avec un nouveau divertissement.

"Du premier acte j'en ay composé le second . . . Le troisième acte est entièrement changé au divertissement près qui est le même . . . Dans le quatrième acte les deux premières scenes sont changées . . . A l'égard du cinquième acte, la première scene est beaucoup plus étenduë . . ."

He concludes by saying:

"Cet ouvrage que j'ose appeller nouveau, puisqu'il n'a conservé que le texte & les vers."

Jean Batistin **Stuck**'s score was printed before these radical alterations took place, and a comparison between the score and the revised libretto is very confusing.

First performed May 24, 1709, as indicated.   SCHATZ 10124

Second copy.   ML 48 R4

Meleagro. Drama per musica da rappresentarsi nel Teatro di Sant' Angelo il carnovale dell' anno MDCCXVIII.

Venezia, Marino Rossetti, 1718.   45 p.   15½^{cm}*.*

Three acts. Argument, cast, scenario. Neither the author, Pier Antonio Bernardoni, is mentioned, nor the composer, Tommaso **Albinoni**.   SCHATZ 122

Il **Meleagro,** ballet. *See* Sarti's Mitridate a Sinope.

Il **Meleagro.** Drama pastorale da rappresentarsi nel Teatro dell' Illma Accademia . . .

Brescia, Gio. Maria Rizzardi, 1710.   52 p.   15^{cm}*.*

Three acts. By Pietro Antonio Bernardoni, who is not mentioned. Dedication and notice to the reader as argument. Marc' Antonio **Ziani,** the composer, is not mentioned.

First performed at Vienna, Burgtheater, July 26, 1706.   SCHATZ 11202

Meleagro. Dramma per musica da rappresentarsi nel Teatro alla Scala il carnevale dell' anno 1798, v. s., correndo l'anno VI. repubblicano.

Milano, Gio. Batista Bianchi, n. d.   48, [7] p.   16½^{cm}*.*

Three acts. Author not mentioned, and unknown to Schatz. Argument, cast, scenario, and name of Nicola Antonio **Zingarelli** as the composer. The seven unnumb. pages contain the description of Filippo Beretti's "L'Italia rigenerata, ballo eroico pantomimo in quattro atti." His second ballet was called "Il reclutamento nel villaggio." The composers of the music are not mentioned.

First performed, as indicated, in January, 1798.   SCHATZ 11254

Melide, oder Der schiffer. Tr. of Philidor's Mélide ou Le navigateur.

Mélide, ou Le navigateur, comédie en deux actes et en vers, mêlée d'ariettes, la musique est de Mr. Philidor.

Paris, Chez les Libaires [!] associés, 1774.   32 p.   18½^{cm}*.*

By Charles Georges Fenouillot de Falbaire de Quingey; arranged by de Relly (Schatz). On p. 6–9, the air of "Tu ne sçais pas beauté."

Date of first performance not mentioned by Wotquenne, but, according to Schatz, the opera was first performed at Fontainebleau Octobre 30, 1773, as "Lémire et Mélide, ou Les fausses infidélités."   SCHATZ 8033

Mélide, ou Le navigateur—Continued.

— **Melide** oder Der schiffer. Ein lustspiel mit gesang in zwey aufzuegen; in musik gesetzt von A. D. Philidor, und für die Seylerische schaubuehne, aus dem franzoesischen uebersetzt, von Grossmann und Neefe.

Frankfurt, n. publ., 1778. 45 p. 16½^{cm}.

On p. 3–6, a preface by the translators, in which they point to the growing favor of "Operetten" with the German public, comment on the difficulty of translating French librettos into German, and say:

"Wenn sich der reim nicht von selbst darbot, haben wir ihn auch nicht ängstlich gesucht, und ueberhaupt mehr frey als woertlich, mehr musikalisch brauchbar, als poetisch schoen uebersetzen wollen.

"Die gedruckte musik, welche wir bald zu liefern denken, ist ein auszug der singstimmen, den man zum gebrauch fuer die theater-direktoren, fuer den klavier-akkompagnisten, die saenger und saengerinnen beym einlernen, und fuer die liebhaber, die dieses und jenes lied zu hause nachsingen wollen, bequem genug finden soll . . ."

SCHATZ 8034

— Arien und gesaenge aus **Melide**, oder Der schiffer, eine ernsthafte oper, in zwey akten, aus dem franzoesischen uebersetzt, mit beybehaltung der original-musik des herrn Philidor, von Johann Heinrich Faber. Aufs neue verbessert von Christian Gottfried Thomas.

Riga, Gottlob Christian Froelich, n. d. 15 p. 16^{cm}.

First performed at Riga, Vietinghoff'sches Theater i. d. Königsstrasse, 16/27, November, 1786.

SCHATZ 8035

Mélidore et Phrosine, drame lyrique en trois actes, paroles du citoyen Arnault, musique du citoyen Méhul. Représenté, pour la première fois, sur le Théâtre lyrique de la rue Favart, le 17 Germinal, l'an second de la République [April 6, 1794].

Paris, Maradan, An second de la République [1794]. 2 p. l., 52 p. 21½^{cm}.

Cast.

SCHATZ 6277

Melinda. Favola romanzesca in musica di Giovanni Bertati . . . da rappresentarsi nel nobilissimo Teatro Venier in San Benedetto l'autunno dell' anno 1798.

Venezia, Modesto Fenzo, 1798. 64 p. 18^{cm}.

Two acts. Cast, scenario, and name of Sebastiano **Nasolini** as the composer ("musica tutta nuova"). On p. 64 a note to the effect that the score contains arias and verses not to be found in the libretto:

"cio accade per la circostanza, a cui per il meglio si è creduto di doversi adattare, onde facilitare il compimento della musica, dopo che il libretto medesimo era già stato riveduto, e licenziato."

On p. [33]–40 argument, cast, and description of Giovanni Monticini's "Abduramel, ballo tragico eroico pantomimo di cinque atti," music ("tutta nuova") by Giuseppe Nucci.

SCHATZ 7022

Melinda e Tiburzio. O. T. of Orlandini's La donna nobile.

Melissa schernita. Intermezzo. *See* Orefici and Mancini's L' Engelberta.

La mélomanie, comédie en vers et en un acte, mêlée d'ariettes. Poeme de M. * * *. Musique de M. S. Champein. Nouvelle édition.

Toulon, Mallard, 1787. 31 p. 20^{cm}.

Cast. Text by Grenier.

First performed at Versailles, January 23, 1781; at Paris, Théâtre italien, January 29, 1781.

ML 50.2.M52C4

Melpomene et Linus. Entrée in Quinault's Les amours des Déesses.

Das menschliche leben wie ein traum. A. T. of Conradi's Der koenigliche printz aus Pohlen, Sigismundus.

Il Meraspe. A. T. of Pallavicino's Il tiranno humiliato.

Il mercato d'Amacari Danase, ballet. *See* Boroni's Le orfane svizzere.

Il mercato di Malmantile. Dramma di tre atti in versi.

Carlo Goldoni, Opere teatrali, Venezia, Zatta e figli, 1788–95, v. 44, [123]–181 p. 18ᶜᵐ.

For first composer *see* below.   PQ

Il mercato di Malmantile. Dramma giocoso per musica di Polisseno Fegejo [Carlo Goldoni] Pastor Arcade da rappresentarsi nel Teatro Grimani di S. Samuele il carnovale dell' anno 1758.

Venezia, Modesto Fenzo, 1758. 58 p. 14½ᶜᵐ.

Cast, scenario, and name of Domenico **Fischietti** as composer.   ScHATZ 3231

— Il **mercato di Malmantile.** Dramma giocoso per musica, di Polisseno Fegeio, P. A. da rappresentarsi nel Piccolo Teatro di S. A. E. di Sassonia. Dresda, nel carnevale del 1766.

n. i., n. d. 143 p. 15ᶜᵐ.

Cast, scenario, name of the translator, H. A. Busius, and of the composer: "La musica è del celebre maestro Signor Domenico **Fischietti** di Napoli, e dall' istesso autore in molte parti rimodernata." German title-page, "Der jahrmarkt zu Magerndorff," and text face Italian.   ScHATZ 3232

— Il **mercato di Malmantile,** dramma giocoso in musica da rappresentarsi nel Teatro Reale di Sua Maestà d'Inghilterra etc etc. Hannover l'inverno del 1770.

n. i., n. d., 107 p. 16½ᶜᵐ.

Cast, scenario, and name of **Fischietti** as the composer. German title, "Der jahrmarkt zu Malmantile," and text face Italian. Considerably altered version. For instance, the characters "Il conte della Rocca," "La marchesa Giacinta," and "Cecca" of the original have been dropped entirely.   ScHATZ 3238

Il mercato di Malmantile. Dramma giocoso per musica di Polisseno Fegejo, Pastor Arcade. Da rappresentarsi nel Teatro Grimani di S. Samuele il carnovale dell' anno 1758.

Venezia, Modesto Fenzo, 1758. 58 p. 14½ᶜᵐ.

Three acts. By Goldoni. Cast, scenario, and name of Giuseppe **Scarlatti** as the composer.
First performed at Vienna, Burgtheater, 1757.   ScHATZ 9550

— Il **mercato di Monfregoso,** dramma giocoso per musica da rappresentarsi nel Reggio Teatro di S. Carlo della Principessa, l'estate dell' anno 1795.

Lisbona, Simone Taddeo Ferreira, 1795. 141 p. 15ᶜᵐ.

Two acts. Author not mentioned. Cast, scenario, and name of Nicola **Zingarelli** as composer. With the opera was performed, composer of the music not mentioned, Pietro Angiolini's ballet "L'arrivo opportuno." Portuguese text faces Italian.   ML 50.2.M55Z3

Il mercato di Monfregoso. Dramma giocoso per musica da rappresentarsi nel Teatro alla Scala l'autunno dell' anno 1792 . . .

Milano, Gio. Batista Bianchi, n. d. 58, [10] p. 16½ᶜᵐ.

Two acts. Scenario, cast, name of Nicola **Zingarelli** as composer, dedication by the impresario Gaetano Maldonati of date Milan, September 22, 1792, in which he says:
"Per desiderio di dare un maggiore risalto alle rappresentazioni, ed un migliore soddisfacimento al pubblico . . . ho intrapreso di fare scrivere un' opera a bella posta per questo teatro e per questa compagnia," and Avviso which reads:
"Un ben noto dramma giocoso del celebre Sig. Goldoni serve per fondamento del libro della presente opera. Si è sequitato più che è stato possibile l'originale, e colla traccia del medesimo si sono fatti tutti que' cambiameti creduti adattati al gusto dell' opera buffa del giorno d'oggi. Si è mutato nel titolo il luogo del mercato al solo oggetto, che lo spartito di questa nuova musica non potesse confondersi coll' antico, che era intitolato *Il Mercato di Malmantile*."
The [10] p. contain the scene "Saggia mia figlia vieni" with sextet, substituted for scene II, 8 "Vla venite in tribunale" and argument, cast, and description of Antonio Pitrot's four act "Adelasia ballo eroico pantomimo." Neither of this nor of his comic ballet "Don Chisciotte, che anderà in scena dopo alcuni giorni" is the composer mentioned. ML 50.2.M55Z2

Il mercato di Pozzuolo ossia Il speciale ingannato, ballet. *See* Mayr's Lodoiska.

Mercato fiammengo, ballet. *See* Cherubini's Ifigenia in Aulide.

Mercurio, e Marte. Torneo regale fatto nel superbissimo Teatro di Parma nell' arrivo della sereniss. Margherita Medici, moglie del sereniss. duca Odoardo Farnese.

Parma, Seth. & Erasmo Viotti, 1628. [43] p. 21½ᶜᵐ.

Schatz attributes the libretto to Claudio Achillini, and the music to Giulio **Caccini,** but as Caccini died in December, 1618, and as this *masque* was first performed at the inauguration of the Teatro Farnese, December 21, 1628, Caccini's connection is more than doubtful. At any rate, Ehrichs does not mention this among Giulio Caccini's works. Certainly Schatz found nothing to support his claim of Caccini's connection with "Mercurio e Marte" in Ferrari's "Spettacoli . . . in Parma," and I fail to see that Ferrari's rather cursory remarks even oblige us to attribute the text to Achillini. Ferrari mentions neither author nor composer. SCHATZ 1448

La mere embarrassée, opera-comique; représenté pour la premiere fois sur le Théâtre de la Foire, en 1734.

Charles François Pannard, Théâtre, Paris, Duchesne, 1763, v. 2, [327]–382 p. 17ᶜᵐ.

In prose and vaudevilles. Composer not recorded by Parfaict, who dates first performance June 26, 1734. PQ 2019.P3

La mere jalouse. Piece en un acte. Representée à la Foire Saint Laurent 1732.

Le Théâtre de la foire, Paris, 1737, t. ix, 2 pl., [123]–167 p. 17ᶜᵐ.

By Carolet, who is not mentioned. Largely *en vaudevilles*. The airs, selected or composed and arranged by Jean Claude **Gillier,** are printed at the end of the volume in the "Table des airs."
First performed September 19, 1732. ML 48.L2X

Meride. Dramma per musica da rappresentarsi nell' apertura del Nuovo gran Teatro della residenza Palatina. . . . l'anno MDCCXLII. La poesia è del Sig. abbate Giovan Claudio Pasquini . . . la musica è del Sig. Carlo Pietra Grua . . .

Mannheim, Stamperia Maieriana, [1742]. 5 p. l., 102, [1] p. 18½ᶜᵐ.

Three acts. Argument, cast, scenario. Alessandro Toeschi is mentioned as the composer of the incidental ballet music. On the last unnumb. p., a notice to the

Meride—Continued.

reader, asking his indulgence for misprints, since the printer did not know "una sola voce" of the Italian language.

First performed January 17, 1742, as indicated.   SCHATZ 8167

Meride e Selinunte.

Apostolo Zeno, Poesie drammatiche, Venezia, 1744, t. iii, p. [345]–438. 19ᶜᵐ.

Five acts and licenza. Argument. No composer is mentioned. In the "Catalogo" at end of t. x, date and place of first ed. are given as Vienna, 1721. (First performed at Laxemburg, Favorita, August 28, 1721, with music by Giuseppe *Porsile.*)

ML 49.A2Z3

— **Meride e Selinunte.** Pubblicati per la prima volta in Vienna 1721.

Apostolo Zeno, Poesie drammatiche, Orleans, 1785–86, t. v, p. 257–344. 21ᶜᵐ.

Five acts and licenza. Argument. No composer is mentioned.   ML 49.A2Z4

Meride e Selinunte. Dramma per musica da rappresentarsi nel famosissimo Teatro Grimani di Sᴺ Gio. Grisostomo nel carnevale 1744 . . .

[Venezia], n. publ., n. d.   1 p. l., 56 p.   15ᶜᵐ.

Three acts. By Apostolo Zeno. With argument, scenario, cast, and name of the composer, Pietro **Chiarini**, but not of the author.   SCHATZ 1851

Meride e Selinunte. Drama per musica da rappresentarsi nel famosissimo Teatro Grimani a S. Gio. Grisostomo. Nel carnovale dell' anno 1726.

Venezia, Marino Rossetti, 1726.   58 p.   15ᶜᵐ.

Three acts. By Apostolo Zeno, who is not mentioned. Argument, scenario, cast, and name of Nicolà Antonio **Porpora** as the composer.   SCHATZ 8372

Il merito riconosciuto. *See* M. Curzio.

Merlin in love: or, Youth against magic. A pantomime opera. **In** five acts.

[319]–342 p. 21ᶜᵐ. (Aaron Hill, Dramatic works, London, T. Lownds, 1760, vol. I.)

No composer or performance recorded by Clarence.   LONGE 325

Merope.

Apostolo Zeno, Poesie drammatiche, Venezia, 1744, t. i, p. 81–171. 19ᶜᵐ.

Three acts. Argument. No composer is mentioned. In the "Catalogo" at end of t. x, date and place of first ed. are given as Venice, 1712. (*See* below.)

ML 49.A2Z3

— **Merope.** Pubblicata per la prima volta in Venezia 1712.

Apostolo Zeno, Poesie drammatiche, Orleans, 1785–86, t. iv, p. 95–184. 21ᶜᵐ.

Three acts. Argument. No composer is mentioned.   ML 49.A2Z4

Merope. Drama per musica da rappresentarsi nella Gran Sala del Reggio Palazzo il dì 1. ottobre 1716. In cui si festeggiano gl'anni di S. M. Ces. e Cat. Carlo VI. imperatore regnante . . .

Nap., Michele Luigi Muzio, 1716. 6 p. l., 55 p. 13½ᶜᵐ.

Three acts and prologue. Argument, cast, scenario. Dedication, dated Naples, October 1, 1716, is signed by Nicola Serino, whom Schatz incorrectly records as the author, since this is clearly Apostolo Zeno's "Merope." The composer is not mentioned, and is unknown to Schatz.   ML 50.2.M6

La Merope. Dramma per musica da rappresentarsi in Verona nel nuovo Teatro dell' Accademia Filarmonica nel carnovale dell' anno 1763 . . .

Verona, Dionisio Ramanzini, 1763. 48 p. 18ᶜᵐ.

Three acts. By Apostolo Zeno, but with very many alterations. For instance, "Vane alla ingrata, e digli" (I, 4) is not by Zeno at all, and "Sprezza il furor del vento" (I, 5) is from Metastasio's "Adriano in Siria." Also, Zeno's character, Licisco, is missing entirely.

Francesco Puttini's dedication ("per la prima volta comparendo sopra le scene del cospicuo Filarmonico teatro il presente dramma"), argument, cast, scenario, and note: "La musica di diversi celebri autori."   ML 50.2.M62

Merope. An opera. As perform'd at the Royal Theatre in the Hay-market.

London, J. Chrichley, 1736. 69 p. 17ᶜᵐ.

Three acts. By Apostolo Zeno (not mentioned). Dedication, argument, cast, but without the name of the composer, Riccardo **Broschi**. English text faces the Italian.

First performed, as indicated, January 8/19, 1737; at Turin, Regio Teatro, carnevale, 1732.   Schatz 1341

Merope. Dramma per musica da rappresentarsi nel grande Real Teatro di S. Carlo nel dì 20. gennaro 1748 . . .

Napoli, Domenico Langiano, 1748. 6 p. l., 52 p. 14ᶜᵐ.

Three acts. By Apostolo Zeno. Impresario's dedication, dated Naples, January 20, 1748, argument, cast, scenario, and name of the composer, Gioacchino **Cocchi**, but not of the author.   Schatz 2049

Merope. Drama da rappresentarsi per musica nel famoso Teatro Tron di San Cassano il carnevale dell' anno 1711 . . .

Venezia, Marino Rossetti, 1711. 72 p. 14½ᶜᵐ.

Three acts. By Apostolo Zeno, who is not mentioned. Dedication, argument cast, scenario, and name of Carlo Francesco **Gasparini** as the composer.   Schatz 3573

Merope. Dramma per musica da rappresentarsi nel Teatro Giustiniani di S. Moisè il carnovale dell' anno 1757.

Venezia, Modesto Fenzo, 1757. 58 p. 15ᶜᵐ.

Three acts. By Apostolo Zeno, who is not mentioned. Cast and name of Florian Leopold **Gassmann** as the composer.   Schatz 3619

Merope. Dramma per musica da rappresentarsi nel famosissimo Teatro Grimani di San Gio. Grisostomo. Nel carnovale dell' anno MDCCXXXIV . . .

Venezia, Marino Rossetti, 1734. 71 p. 15ᶜᵐ.

Three acts. By Zeno, who is not mentioned. Dedication, argument, cast, scenario, and name of Geminiano **Giacomelli** as the composer.   Schatz 3807

Merope. Tragedia per musica da rappresentarsi nel Regio Teatro di Beriino per il felicissimo giorno natalizio della Sacra Real Maestà di Sofia Dorotea, regina madre . . .

Berlino, Haude e Spener, 1756. 123, [2] p. 16½^{cm}.

Three acts. Giampietro Tagliazucchi is mentioned as the author and Carl Heinrich **Graun** as the composer. The text, however, is merely the Italian version of a French text by Frederick the Great, based on Voltaire. German title-page and text (by Grugnanelli, according to Mennicke) face Italian.

First performed, as indicated, March 27, 1756. Schatz 4105

Merope. Drama per musica da rappresentarsi nel nobilissimo Teatro di S. Benedetto il carnovale dell' anno MDCCLXXIII.

Venezia, Modesto Fenzo, 1773. 2 p. l., 55 p. 17^{cm}.

Three acts. By Apostolo Zeno, who is not mentioned. Argument, cast, scenario, and name of Giacomo **Insanguine**, called Monopoli.

First performed, as indicated, December 26, 1772. Schatz 4834

Merope. Dramma per musica da rappresentarsi nel famosissimo Teatro Grimani di S.ª Giõ. Grisostomo il carnovale 1742 . . .

[Venezia], n. publ., n. d. 71 p. 15^{cm}.

Three acts. By Apostolo Zeno, who is not mentioned. Argument, cast, scenario, and name of Niccolò **Jommelli** as the composer.

First performed, as indicated, December 26, 1741. Schatz 4865

— Merope, ein musicalisches schauspiel. Vorgestellet auf der Kaiserl. Koeniglichen privilegirten schaubuehne in Wien, 1749.

Wien, Joh. Peter van Ghelen, n. d. 62, [1] p. 15^{cm}.

Three acts. Neither J. L. van Ghelen, the translator, nor **Jommelli,** the composer, is mentioned. Cast, argument, scenario. Second version of the "Merope" of 1741. Schatz 4866

Merope. Dramma per musica da rappresentarsi nel nobilissimo Teatro Venier in San Benedetto il carnovale dell' anno 1796.

Venezia, Modesto Fenzo, 1796. 45 p. 17½^{cm}.

Three acts. By Mattia Botturini, who is not mentioned. Cast, scenario, and name of Sebastiano **Nasolini** as the composer.

First performed, as indicated, January 21, 1796. Schatz 7005

La Merope. Dramma per musica da rappresentarsi in Bologna nel Teatro Formaliari l' autunno dell' anno MDCCXVII . . .

Bologna, li Rossi e compagni, n. d. 77, [1] p. 16^{cm}.

Three acts. Apostolo Zeno is mentioned as author, Giuseppe Maria **Orlandini** as the composer. Impresario's dedication dated Bologna, October 16, 1717, cast, argument, and scenario.

First performed, according to Schatz, on October 24, 1717. Schatz 7348

Merope. Dramma per musica da rappresentarsi nel famosissimo Teatro Grimani di S. Gio. Grisostomo nell' autunno dell' anno MDCCL.

Venezia, In merceria, n. d. 66 p. 15^{cm}.

Three acts. By Apostolo Zeno, who is not mentioned. Argument, scenario, cast, and name of Davide **Perez** as the composer. Schatz 7874

La Merope. Dramma per musica da rappresentarsi nel Regio-ducal Teatro di Milano per il carnovale dell' anno 1776 . . .

Milano, Giovanni Montani, n. d. 5 p. l., 46 p. 14½^{cm}.

Three acts. Impresario's dedication, argument, cast, and name of "Traeta" (Tommaso **Traetta**) as composer, but not of librettist, Apostolo Zeno. The ballets were invented by Noverre. In the dedication the opera is called the "secondo spettacolo del corrente carnovale." Schatz 10412

The **merry beggars.** A. T. of The jovial crew, 1767.

The merry cobler: or, The second part of The devil to pay. A farcical opera of one act. As it is perform'd at the Theatre-Royal in Drury-Lane, by His Majesty's servants. By Mr. Coffey, author of the first part . . .

London, J. Watts, 1735. 4 p. l., 32 p. 21^{cm}.

Cast, table of the 17 songs, and dedication to Lady Walpole, in which Charles Coffey says:

" 'Tis true it wants many imbellishments of the former, and is entirely unassisted by the force of magick, which might probably render it more diverting, as affording to poet an unbounded liberty; but as all spells and charms are supernatural and unreasonable, 'tis presumed, that the native simplicity of this, and its great affinity to true nature, will entitle it to bear some proportion of merit to its parent, that met with so much success before it: For the nearer any dramatick piece comes up to nature, the more it shou'd undoubtedly please."

Ballad opera, the airs of which are printed in the text with their titles.

First performed, as indicated, May 6, 1735.   ML 50.5.M3

Second copy. Longe 32

Airs, duetts, and chorusses, in the operatical pantomime of **Merry Sherwood** or Harlequin forrester. Now performing at the Theatre-Royal, Covent-Garden. Third edition.

London, T. N. Longman, 1795. 20 p. 21^{cm}.

Cast. Neither authors, M. Lonsdale and John O'Keefe, metnioned, nor the composer, William **Reeve**.

First performed December 21, 1795.   Longe 234

Mesenzio rè d'Etruria. Dramma per musica da rappresentarsi nel Regio Teatro di via della Pergola nell' autunno del MDCCLXXXII . . .

Firenze, Giovanni Risaliti, 1782. 47 p. 16^{cm}.

Three acts. By Ferdinando Casori. Cast and name of the composer, **Cherubini** ("musica . . . tutta nuova"). The author is not mentioned. On p. 4–8 argument and description of Antonio Muzzarelli's ballet "Adelasia Riconosciuta." The composer of the music is not mentioned.

First performed, as indicated, September 8, 1782.   Schatz 1846

Messalina. Drama per musica da rappresentarsi nel Teatro Vendramino di San Salvatore l' anno MDCLXXX del dottor Piccioli. Ristampato con nuove aggiunte . . .

Venetia, Francesco Nicolini, 1680. 72 p. 14^{cm}.

Three acts. Author's dedication dated Venice, February 8, 1679, argument, notice to the reader, and scenario. The composer, Carlo **Pallavicino**, is not mentioned.   Schatz 7728

Die **messe zu Venedig.** Tr. of Salieri's La fiera di Venezia.

Le **metamorfosi odiamorose in birba trionfale** nelle gare delle terre amanti. Dramma per musica di Gonanto Rinoi, tra gl' Accademici di Campalto Infelicio Scordato. Da rappresentarsi nel famoso Teatro Grimani in San Samuel il carnovale 1732 . . .

Venezia, Alvise Valvasense, 1732. 36 p. 14^{cm}.

Three acts. By Antonio Rigo [anagram as in title]. Dedication, argument, cast, scenario, name of Salvatore **Apolloni** as composer, and notice to the reader in which the author calls this his second "parto bamboleggiante in fasce," written "in trè sole ore."   Schatz 301

The **metamorphoses.** A comic opera. In two acts. As it is performed at the Theâtre-Royal in the Hay-Market. The music by Mr. Dibdin.

London, T. Lowndes, 1776. 2 p. l., 36 p. 20ᶜᵐ.

Cast and prefatory note by Charles Dibdin to the effect that about one third of the piece is borrowed from Molière's *Sicilien* and *George Dandin.* Dibdin says:
"I have repeatedly assured the public, that they shall be faithfully acquainted from whence I borrow any materials to work up my dramatic trifles."
First performed August 26, 1776 (Oulton and Schatz); August 26, 1775 (Genest, with reason why 1776 is impossible). Longe 214

Second copy. Longe 244

Metilda ritrovɛ ta. L. T. of Anfossi's L'incognita perseguitata.

La **meuniere de Gentilly,** comédie en un acte, meslée d'ariettes; par M. Le Monnier. Représentée pour la première fois par les Comédiens italiens, le jeudi 13 octobre 1768.

Paris, Vente, 1768. 75 p. 19ᶜᵐ.

Cast. The composer, Jean Benjamin de **La Borde,** is not mentioned. On p. 22–27, 40–42, 46–48, 73–74 the same airs as below printed in the text.

ML 50.2.M63L2

— La **meuniere de Gentilly,** comédie. En un acte, mêlée d'ariettes. Par Monsieur Le Monier. Représentée pour la première fois par les Comédiens italiens ordinaires du roi, le jeudi 13 octobre 1768.

Avignon, Louis Chambeau, 1768. 36 p. 19½ᶜᵐ.

The composer, Jean Benjamin de **La Borde,** is not mentioned.

ML 50.2.M63L22

— La **meuniere de Gentilly,** comedie en un acte, meslée d'ariettes; par M. Le Monnier. Représentée pour la première fois par les Comédiens italiens, le jeudi 13 octobre 1768.

Paris, Vente, 1770. 54, [1] p. 18ᶜᵐ.

The add. p. contains advertisement of F. J. Desseur, Liège.
The composer, Jean Benjamin de **La Borde,** is not mentioned. On p. 16–20 the ariette "La garde d'une fille" (I,5), on p. 29–31 "Amour, que tu me fais souffrir' (I, 7), on p. 34–36 "Quand pour nous rendre heureux" (I, 8), and on p. 52–54 the vaudeville (I, 13) "Nous avons dans notre jeune age." Schatz 5346

— La **meuniere de Gentilly,** comédie en un acte, mêlée d'ariettes; par M. Le Monnier. Représentée pour la première fois par les Comédiens italiens, le jeudi 13 octobre 1768.

Paris, Vente, 1779. 54 p. 17½ᶜᵐ.

Cast. On p. 16–20 the ariette "La garde d'une fille," 29–31 "Amour, que tu me fais souffrir," p. 34–35 "Quand pour nous rendre heureux," and on p. 32–33 the vaudeville "Nous avons dans notre jeune âge." Without name of de **La Borde.**

Schatz 11718

— Die **muellerinn,** ein singspiel in einem aufzuge aus dem franzoesischen uebersetzt, mit musik.

Frankfurt am Mayn, mit Andreaeischen schriften, 1773. 99 p., 10 p. (fold. music). 16½ᶜᵐ.

Cast. La Borde's "La meunière de Gentilly" translated by Johann Heinrich Faber. The folded music contains (voice and bass): "Ach! mein kummervoller stand" (I, 1="Vainement en filant mon lin"), "Stille wasser gruenden schlecht" (I, 5="Il n'est pis que l'eau qui dort"), and "Spielten wir in den jungen jahren" (I,13="Nous avons dans notre jeune age"). Schatz 5347

Der **meyerhof.** Tr. of Scolari's La cascina.

Midas; an English burletta. As it is performed, at the Theatre-Royal, in Covent-Garden.

London, G. Kearsly, W. Griffin, J. Coote, T. Lownds and W. Nicoll, 1764. 4 p. l., 66 p. 22^{cm}.

Ballad opera. Three acts. By Kane O'Hara, who is not mentioned. He is supposed to have selected and adapted the tunes used, as indicated in the headings of the Airs, but quite a few of the Airs were to be sung "To its own tune." These airs apparently composed for the occasion are: (Act I) "To happy ignorance," "Be by your friends advised," "Since you mean to hire"; (Act II) "Wondrous timber"; (Act III) "If in the courts your suit," "If a rival thy character draw" (headed Duetto and the name of Henry **Carey's** has been added in pencil as the composer), "Now I'm seated" and others. The tunes used included several French and Italian. The text is preceded by the cast, by the humorous "Prologue" as a plea for English drama and English music and by an editorial prefatory note which reads in part:

"The editor of the following piece thinks proper to observe, that the first idea of it was conceived, and the plan in some measure executed by a gentleman in Dublin, for the private entertainment of some persons of distinction in that kingdom, at a time, when Italian burlettas were blended with the exhibitions of the theatre, and almost triumphed over the best productions in our language. The public spirit of those, for whom it was originally intended, prevailed upon the author to enlarge his design. Accordingly, *Midas* adventured on the stage, and met with uncommon success for a series of nights . . . The public, with their usual candour, will consider the particular scope of this piece, and will decide nothing till they have heard the musick, to which it is adapted." ML 50.2.M65

— **Midas:** An English burletta. In two acts. As it is performed, at the Theatre Royal in Covent-Garden. The third edition.

London, W. Griffin, W. Nicoll, [etc.], 1766. 32 p. 19^{cm}.

Two acts. Cast. By Kane O'Hara, who is not mentioned. The tunes are not indicated in this edition.

First performed at Dublin, Theatre Royal, 1762, and at London, Covent Garden, February 22, 1764. LONGE 46

— **Midas,** a burletta. In two acts. By Kane O'Hara, Esq.

[342]–365 p. 19^{cm}. (Collection of the most esteemed farces and entertainments, t. II, Edinburgh, 1792.)

Two acts. Covent-Garden and Edinburgh (1782) casts. SCHATZ 11753B

— An improved edition of the songs in the burletta of **Midas,** adapted to the times . . .

London, John Stockdale, 1789. 38, [2] p. 20^{cm}.

An anonymous political satire with Pitt, Sheridan, the Prince of Wales, etc., as characters. The last (unnumb.) page contains advertisement of Stockdale's edition of Shakespeare's works. LONGE 195

The **midnight wanderers:** a comic opera. In two acts. Performed at the Theatre-Royal, Covent-Garden. Written by Mr. Pearce . . .

London, T. N. Longman, 1793. 2 p. l., 45 p. 20½^{cm}.

Cast and Advertisement with name of William **Shield** as composer, but Longman & Broderip's vocal score says "Composed by **Paisiello, Grétry,** and **Shield,**" and the overture is headed as being that by **Naumann** "for the celebrated opera of Amphion."

First performed February 25, 1793. LONGE 221

Mietitori. Commedia per musica di Saverio Zini da rappresentarsi nel nuovo Teatro de' Fiorentini per second' opera di questo corrente anno 1781.

Napoli, n. publ., 1781. 60 p. 15^{cm}.

Three acts. Cast and name of Pietro **Guglielmi** as the composer.
First performed at Naples, as indicated, October 20, 1781. SCHATZ 4291

Il miglior d'ogni amore per il peggiore d'ogni odio. Drama per musica da rappresentarsi nel Teatro Tron di S. Casciano. L'autunno dell' anno 1703. Di Francesco Silvani . . .

Venezia, Gio. Battista Zuccato, 1703. 72 p. 15^{cm}.

Three acts. Dedication signed by the author, Francesco Silvani, and dated Venice, November 6, 1703, argument, notice to the reader with name of Carlo Francesco **Gasparini** as the composer, cast, and scenario.   SCHATZ 3572

Das milchmaedchen und die beiden jaeger. Tr. of Duni's Les deux chasseurs et la laitière.

Das milchmaedgen und die zween jaeger. Tr. of Duni's Les deux chasseurs et la laitière.

Die mildigkeit des Titus. Tr. of Jommelli's La clemenza di Tito.

The Milesian, a comic opera. In two acts. As it is performed at the Theatre-Royal in Drury-Lane.

London, J. Wilkie, 1777. 1 p. l., 44 p. 21^{cm}.

Cast. Neither the author, Isaac Jackman, is mentioned, nor the composer, Thomas **Carter.**

First performed March 20, 1777, as indicated.   LONGE 86

Le milicien, comédie en un acte, meslée d'ariettes, par M. Anseaume. La musique de M. Duny. Représentée pour la première fois à Versailles devant Leurs Majestés, le 29 Décembre 1762, & à Paris sur le Théâtre de la Comédie italienne le 1 janvier 1763.

Bruxelles, Pierre Paupié, 1763. 48 p. 20^{cm}.   SCHATZ 2848

— **Le milicien,** comédie en un acte, meslée d'ariettes, par M. Anseaume, représentée pour la premiere fois à Versailles devant Leurs Majestés, le 29 décembre 1762, & à Paris sur le Théâtre de la Comédie italienne le 1 janvier 1763.

Paris, la veuve Duchesne, 1774. 47 p. 19^{cm}.

Duni, the composer, is not mentioned.   SCHATZ 11697

— **Der militz** oder Die laecherliche werbung, ein singspiel in einem aufzuge aus dem franzoesischen uebersetzt, mit musik.

Frankfurt am Mayn, mit Andreäischen schriften, 1775. 84 p., 7 p. (folded dated music). 16^{cm}.

German version by Johann Heinrich Faber.

The musical supplement contains the arias (voice and bass): "Ist die liebe vergnügt" ["Quand l'amour est content"], p. 1–3; "Vögeln ländeln und spielen" ["Ces oiseaux de passage"], p. 4–7.   SCHATZ 2849

First performed at Frankfurt a/M, Theater im Junghof, 1772.

Il militare amante. Dramma giocoso per musica da rappresentarsi nel nobil Teatro delle Dame il carnevale dell' anno 1781 . . .

Roma, Puccinelli, n. d. 72 p. 15½^{cm}.

Three acts. Author not mentioned and unknown to me. Cast, scenario, prefatory note and name of Francesco **Piticchio** as the composer. On p. 36–41 cast, argument, description (music "tutta nuova" by Mattia Stabingher) of Domenico Ricciardi's "Il trionfo di Alessandro o sia La prigionia di Dario."   ML 50.2.M66P4

Il **militare bizzaro.** Dramma giocoso per musica in due atti composto da Tommaso Grandi detto il pettinaro comico. Da rappresentarsi in Venezia nel nobile Teatro di San Samuele il carnovale dell' anno 1778.

Venezia, Modesto Fenzo, 1778. 62 p. 16½cm.

Two acts. Cast, scenario, and name of Giuseppe **Sarti** as the composer. On p. 37 argument without name of the composer of the music of Giuseppe Fabiani's "I prodigi d'amore, favola pastorale, ballo pantomimo."
First performed, as indicated, December 27, 1777. SCHATZ 9448

Der **militz** oder Die laecherliche werbung. Tr. of Duni's Le milicien.

La **milorda.** Chelleta per museca, da rappresentarese à lo Triato nuovo ncoppa Toleto nchisto vierno de st' anno 1728 . . .

Napoli, Agnolo Vocola, n. d. 52 p. 14½cm.

Three acts. Author not mentioned and unknown to Schatz. Impresario's dedication, notice to the reader, cast, and name of Peppo [Giuseppe] de **Majo** as composer. SCHATZ 5863

Milton und Elmire, ein singspiel in einem aufzuge. Von einem jungen cavalier verfertiget.

Frankfurt und Leipzig, Johann Georg Fleischer, 1775. 46 p. 17cm.

By H., graf von Spaur.
First performed with music by Joseph **Michl** at Frankfurt a/M, Schauspielhaus i. Junghofe, 1773. SCHATZ 6486

— **Milton und Elmire** eine original-oper, in zween aufzuegen. Aufgefuehrt von der Seipp und Bullaischen gesellschaft der deutschen schauspieler auf dem allhiesigen opernhause.

Augsburg, n. publ., 1780. 40 p. 17cm.

The same text as above, but retouched by Wilhelm Friedrich Hermann Reinwald (Schatz). **Michl** is not mentioned.
First performed at Meiningen, Hoftheater, 1776. SCHATZ 6487

— Arien aus **Milton und Elmire,** eine original-oper in zwei aufzuegen aufgefuehrt von der Rossnerischen gesellschaft deutscher schauspieler. Die musik ist von dem beruehmten herrn Michel in Muenchen.

n. i., 1782. 16 p. 16½cm. SCHATZ 6487a

Milziade. Dramma per musica da rappresentarsi nel famosissimo Teatro Grimani à SS. Gio. e Paulo il carnevale dell anno MDCXCIX. Del dottor Lotto Lotti . . .

Venetia, Girolamo Albrizzi, 1699. 60 p. 14cm.

Three acts. Author's dedication dated Venice, February 24, 1699, argument, scenario, and notice to the reader with the name of Giovanni Maria **Ruggeri** as the composer. SCHATZ 9140

Minervens ankunft bey den Musen. Ein analogisches singspiel von F. G. v. Nesselrode. Die musik ist von herrn Paul Kirzinger, Aufgefuehrt auf dem fuerstlich Taxischen Theater in Regensburg. 1780.

[Regensburg], Im Montagischen buchladen, n. d. 23 p. 16cm.
SCHATZ 5340

De **minnaer standbeeld.** Tr. of Dalayrac's L'amant statue.

Minona oder Die Angelsachsen. Ein tragisches melodrama in vier akten. Die musik vom herrn kapellmeister J. A. P. Schulz.

Hamburg, Benjamin Gottlob Hoffmann, 1785. 190, [1] p.

By Heinrich Wilhelm von Gerstenberg (not mentioned) whose "Erlaeuterungen und anmerkungen" on p. 169–190. SCHATZ 9724

Minosse rè di Creta o sia La fuga d'Arianna e di Fedra, ballet. *See* Martin y Soler's In amor ci vuol destrezza.

Intermedi [**Mirena e Floro**] cantati dalli Signori Livia Constantini detta Polacchina **e** Lucretio Borsari . . . Traduction des intermedes italiens en françois . . .

Dresde, Jean Riedel, & Jean Conrad Stössel, 1718. Unpaged. 21cm.

The three intermezzi, whose title appears in caption, form on appendix to the libretto of Lotti's opera "Gl' odi delusi dal sangue," Dresda, 1718. The author of the intermezzi is unknown and the composers, Carlo Francesco **Gasparini** and Giovanni Battista **Bononcini**, are not mentioned.

First performed at Naples, Teatro di S. Bartolomeo, 1699. SCHATZ 5707

The **mirror**; or, Harlequin everywhere. A pantomimical burletta, in three parts. As it is performed at the Theatre-Royal in Covent-Garden.

London, G. Kearsley, 1779. 2 p. l. (incl. front.), 39 p. 21cm.

Cast. The author-composer, Charles **Dibdin**, is not mentioned.

First performed, as indicated, November 30, 1779. LONGE 102

Mirsa, ballet en action, par M. Gardel. Représenté sur le Théâtre de L'Académie de musique, le jeudi 8 novembre 1779.

Paris, chez les marchands de piéces de théâtre, 1779. 10, [1] p. 20½cm.

Three acts. Cast. Act by act synopsis of the plot. Composer of the music not recorded by Lajarte, who rectifies the error that the plot of this ballet had anything to do with our war for independence. ML 52.2.M4

Mirtil, pastorale en musique, ornée de ballets; représentée par les pensionnaires dans les Plaisirs du roy.

Dresden, Joan Conrad Stössel, 1721. Unpaged. 20½cm.

One act. The Avertissement reads:

"Les vers & la musique de cette petite pastorale ont été composez en moins d'une semaine: ainsi on peut dire, que c'est un impromptu de poësie & de musique. La promptitude, sur tout, du maitre de musique, n'est pas ordinaire; car quoyqu'il y ait dans ce divertissement, plus de travail que dans deux actes d'un opera françois, il n'a employé que quatre jours à le mettre en musique. Et voila ce que fait l'envie d'obéïr, & de plaire à un grand roy, à un bon maître. On a inseré dans cette petite piece tout ce que l'on a cru de plus propre à exercer le talent d'un maître de musique; & le Sieur [Louis] **Andre** qui a été recu, depuis peu, au service de Sa Majeste, l'a souhaitté ainsi, pour avoir occasion de faire connoitre son genie. Les vers sont du Sieur Poisson. La musique est du Sieur **André**. Les ballets sont du Sieur Debargues."

First performed, as indicated, February 23, 1721. ML 50.2.M67A5

Mirzele. *See* Mondonville's Les projets de l'amour.

Il **misantropo** o sia Il poter delle donne, ballet. *See* Cimarosa's Giunio Bruto.

Miss Lucy in town.   A sequel to The virgin unmasqued.   A farce; with songs.   As it is acted at the Theatre-Royal in Drury-Lane, by His Majesty's servants.

London, A. Millar, 1742.   2 p. l., 44 p.   20½ᶜᵐ.

One act.   Ballad farce.   Cast and table of the eight songs, the airs of which are not indicated.   By Henry Fielding, who is not mentioned.

First performed May 5, 1742, as indicated.   ML 50.5.M4

Der misslungene braut-wechsel oder Richardus I, koenig von England.   Tr. of Händel's Riccardo I rè d'Inghilterra.

Mistevojus.   [vignette]   In einem sing-spiele auf dem Hamburgischen Schau-platze vorgestellet im jahr 1726.

[Hamburg], Stromerische schrifften, n. d.   Unpaged.   19ᶜᵐ.

Five acts.   Cast, scenario, and "avertissement, which reads, in part:
"Wenn der herr verfasser dieser opera gegenwaertig und nicht in einer ruehmlichen bedienung abwesend waere, wuerde er ohne zweifel in einer gelehrten vorrede den innhalt der gantzen geschichte auf das umstaendlichste angezeigt haben . . .   Man ist in allem dem hn. verfasser nachgegangen, ohne dass man hie und da einige italiaenische arien eingeschoben und im 5ten acte die mit astericis bezeichnete worte, zur introduction des noch nie in solcher vollkommenheit gesehenen prospects der Stadt Hamburg, von J. P. P. [Johann Philipp Praetorius] inserirt worden . . .   Die vortreffliche music ausser etlichen wenigen arien, ist von . . . Reinhard Kaeyser [Keiser].   Die poesie ist von dem herrn [Johann Samuel] Müller . . ."
He based it on Zeno and Pariati's "Antioco."   Schatz 5103

Mit dem glockenschlag: zwoelf! ernsthafte operette in drey akten . . .

Anspach, Haueisen, 1781.   80 p.   16½ᶜᵐ.

Neither the author, freiherr Soden von Sassanfart, nor the composer, Nicolaus **Mühle,** is mentioned.   Schatz 6871

Mithridates.   Tr. of Graun's Mitridate.

Mitridate.

Apostolo Zeno, Poesie drammatiche, Venezia, 1744, t. v, p. [95]–196. p. 19ᶜᵐ.

Four acts and licenza.   Argument.   No composer is mentioned.   In the "Catalogo," at end of t. x, date and place of first ed. are given as Vienna, 1728.   (*See* below.)   ML 49.A2Z3

— Mitridate.   Pubblicato per la prima volta in Vienna 1728.

Apostolo Zeno, Poesie drammatiche, Orleans, 1785–86, t. vii, p. 153– 248.   21ᶜᵐ.

Five acts and licenza.   Argument.   No composer is mentioned.   ML 49.A2Z4

Mitridate.   Dramma per musica, da rappresentarsi nella Cesarea corte per il nome gloriosissimo della Sac. Ces. e Catt. Real Maestà Carlo VI . . .   L'anno MDCCXXVIII.   La poesia è del Sig. Apostolo Zeno . . .   La musica è del Sig. Antonio Caldara . . .

Vienna d'Austria, Gio. Pietro van Ghelen, n. d.   4 p. l., 82 p.   16½ᶜᵐ.

Five acts, with licenza.   Argument and scenario.   Niccola Matteis is mentioned as the composer of the ballet music.

First performed, as indicated, November 4, 1728.   Schatz 1494

Mitridate. Dramma per musica da rappresentarsi nel famosissimo Teatro Grimani di S. Gio. Grisostomo nel carnevale dell' anno MDCCXXX . . .

Venezia, Carlo Buonarigo, n. d. 72 p. 14½^{cm}.

Five acts. By Apostolo Zeno, with indicated alterations "di pochissime arie." Impresario's dedication, notice to the reader, cast, scenario, argument, and name of Giovanni Antonio **Giai** as the composer. SCHATZ 3815

Mitridate. Tragedia per musica da rappresentarsi nel Regio Teatro di Berlino . . .

Berlino, Haude e Spener, 1750. 95 p. 17½^{cm}.

Three acts. Leopoldo de Villati is mentioned as the author, and Carl Heinrich **Graun** as the composer. Argument and scenario. German title page, "Mithridates," and text face Italian.

First performed, as indicated, Friday, January 1, 1751 (Schatz); December, 1750 (Mennicke). SCHATZ 4106

— **Mitridate.** Opera. Representée devant Sa Majesté à Berlin, le 1 janvier 1751.

Berlin, Edienne de Bourdeaux, 1751. 30 p. 16^{cm}.

Three acts. Argument, scenario, and names of Villati and **Graun.** SCHATZ 4107

Mitridate. Drama per musica di Filippo Vanstryp da recitarsi nella Sala degl' illustrissimi Signori Capranica nel carnevale dell' anno 1730 . . .

Roma, Antonio de' Rossi, n. d. 72 p. 16^{cm}.

Three acts. Impresario's dedication, argument, cast, scenario, and name of Nicolà Antonio **Porpora** as the composer. SCHATZ 8373

Mitridate a Sinope. Dramma per musica da rappresentarsi in Firenze nel Regio Teatro degl' Intrepidi detto della Palla a corda dai fondamenti eretto, ed aperto per la prima volta nell' autunno del 1779 . . .

[Firenze], Anton Giusep. Pagani, n. d. 6 p. l., 50 p. 18½^{cm}.

Three acts. Dedication, argument, cast, and name of Giuseppe **Sarti** as composer. The author is not mentioned, and is unknown to Schatz. At end, no substitute arias in this, the obviously first edition of the next entry, and, like this, giving details about the ballet, "Il Meleagro." ML 48.A5 v. 30

— **Mitridate a Sinope.** Dramma per musica da rappresentarsi in Firenze nel Regio Teatro degl' Intrepidi detto della Palla a corda dai fondamenti eretto, ed aperto per la prima volta nell' autunno del 1779 . . .

[Firenze], Anton. Giusep. Pagani, n. d. 7 p. l. (incl. front.), 52 p. 19^{cm}.

Three acts. Author not mentioned, and unknown to Schatz. Dedication, argument, cast, name of Giuseppe **Sarti** as composer, and prologue-poem. On p. 51–52, the substitute arias, "Lasciami in abbandono" (I, 5), "Se oppresso l'indegno" (I, 6), and "In un mar di tante pene" (III, 7). On p. l. 4–5, argument and name of Luigi Marescalchi as composer of the music ("sara tutta nuova") of Onorato Viganò's ballet, "Il Meleagro." SCHATZ 9449

Il **Mitridate Eupatore.** Tragedia per musica da rappresentarsi nel famosissimo Teatro Grimani di S. Gio. Grisostomo l'anno 1707 . . .

Venezia, Marino Rossetti, 1707. 84 p. 14½^{cm}.

Five acts. Dedication by the author, conte Girolamo Frigimelica Roberti, argument, cast, scenario, notice to the reader, and name of Alessandro **Scarlatti** as the composer. SCHATZ 9524

Mitridate in Sebastia. Dramma per musica da rappresentarsi in Firenze nel carnevale del 1704.

Firenze, Vincenzio Vangelisti, n. d. 70 p. 15^{cm}.

Three acts. Argument, cast, and scenario. Neither the author, Giacomo **Maggi**, is mentioned, nor the composer, Giuseppe Antonio Vincenzo **Aldrovandini**.
First performed at Genoa, fall of 1701, at the Teatro del Falcone.   SCHATZ 139

Mitridate rè di Ponto, dramma per musica da rappresentarsi nel Regio Teatro di Torino nel carnovale del 1767. Alla presenza di S. S. R. M.

Torino, Onorato Derossi, n. d. viii, 63, [1] p. 16^{cm}.

Three acts. Argument, cast, scenario, and names of the author, Vittorio Amedeo Cigna-Santi, and of the composer, Quirico **Gasparini**.   SCHATZ 3604

Mitridate rè di Ponto vincitor di sè stesso. Drama da cantarsi nel celebre Teatro Grimani in S. Gio. Grisostomo. Nel carnovale MDCCXXIII di Merindo Fesanio Past. Arc.

Venezia, Marino Rossetti, 1723. 63 p. 16½^{cm}.

Three acts. By Benedetto Pasqualigo. Argument, cast, scenario, and name of the composer, Giovanni Maria **Capello**.   SCHATZ 1592

Le Mitron et la Mitronne, ou Les amours de Gonesse, comedie en un acte, meslée d'ariettes, par Mrs. * * * Représentée pour la premiere fois, par les Comédiens italiens ordinaires du roi, le 8 mai 1765.

Paris, Duchesne, 1765. 30 p. 19^{cm}.

Neither the author (unknown to Schatz) is mentioned, nor the composer, Jean Benjamin de **La Borde**.   SCHATZ 5349

The mock doctor: or, The dumb lady cur'd. A comedy done from Moliere. As it is acted at the Theatre Royal in Drury-Lane, by His Majesty's servants. With the musick prefix'd to each song. The fourth edition, with additional songs and alterations.

London, J. Watts, 1753. 3 p. l., 33, [1] p. 20^{cm}.

One act and epilogue. Ballad opera, in which airs v ("O cursed power of gold"), vii ("Thus, lovely patient"), and viii ("If you hope by your skill") were "set by **Mr. Seedo**." Cast, dedication, and preface, in which Henry Fielding (not mentioned) says:

"Le *Medicin malgré lui* of Molière hath been always esteemed in France the best of that author's humorous pieces . . . The English theatre owes this farce to an accident not unlike that which gave it to the French. And I wish I had been as able to preserve the spirit of Molière, as I have, in translating it, fallen short even of that very little time he allowed himself in writing it . . . .

"One pleasure I enjoy from the success of this piece, is a prospect of transplanting successfully some others of Molière of great value. How I have done this, any English reader may be satisfy'd by examining an exact literal translation of the *Medecin malgré lui*, which is the second in the second volume of *Select comedies of Moliere*, just published by John Watts."

The preface is followed by cast and table of the nine songs.
First performed at Drury-Lane, September 8, 1732.   ML 50.5.M58

—— **The mock doctor:** or, The dumb lady cur'd. A comedy. Done from Moliere. As it is acted at the Theatre-Royal in Drury-Lane. By His Majesty's servants. With the musick prefix'd to each song. A new ed. With additional songs and alterations.

London, A. Millar, 1761. 3 p. l., 31, [1] p. 19½^{cm}.

Contents appear to be practically identical with the 1753 ed.   MD 50.5.M6

The **mock doctor**—Continued.

— The **mock doctor** or, The dumb lady cur'd. In two acts. By Henry Fielding, Esq.

[135]–161 p. 19^{cm}. (Collection of the most esteemed farces and entertainments, t. I, Edinburgh, 1792.)

Original Drury-Lane and Edinburgh casts. Ballad opera. The airs, "O cursed power of gold" and "If you hope by your skill," were "set by Mr. **Seedo**."

SCHATZ 11753A

The **mock governor.** A. T. of Sancho at court.

The **mock lawyer.** As it is acted at the Theatre Royal in Covent Garden. Written by Mr. Phillips . . . To which is added, the musick engraved on copper plates.

London, T. Astley, n. d. 2 p. l., 3½ p., 8 p. (music). 16^{cm}.

One act. Cast. Ballad opera, the airs of the 20 songs being indicated in the text by title, and the airs engraved in supplement without titles.

First performed at Covent Garden, London, April 27, 1733. LONGE 73

The **mock-tempest:** or, The enchanted castle. Acted at the Theatre Royal. Written by T. Duffett . . .

London, William Cademan, 1675. 3 p. l., 56 p. 20½ ^{cm}.

Five acts with introduction, prologue, and epilogue. Freely interspersed with songs, etc. Written as a parody of Dryden's "Tempest." LONGE 194

La **moda.** Dramma giocoso per musica. Da rappresentarsi nel Teatro Giustiniani di San Moisè. Il carnovale dell' anno 1754.

Venezia, Modesto Fenzo, 1754. 48 p. 15^{cm}.

Three acts. Argument, cast, scenario, and name of Ferdinando Giuseppe **Bertoni** as composer. The librettist, Domenico Benedetti, is not mentioned.

SCHATZ 922

La **moda.** Dramma giocoso per musica di Pietro Cipretti A. P. Fiorentino, Accademico Appatista da rappresentarsi nel Teatro Giustiniani di S. Moisè il carnovale dell' anno MDCCLXIX.

Venezia, Modesto Fenzo, 1769. 59 p. 15^{cm}.

Three acts. Cast, scenario, and name of the composer, Antonio **Boroni**.

SCHATZ 1249

Die **mode,** oder Die haeuslichen zwistigkeiten, ein lustiges singspiel, aufgefuehret auf den privilegirten schaubuehnen der Kaiserl. koenigl. haupt- und residenzstadt Wien im jahre 1771.

Wien, Gedruckt mit von Ghelenschen schriften. 59 p. 17^{cm}.

Three acts. Scenario and note: "Die musik ist von verschiedenen meistern, vorzueglich aber von herrn Anton Salini" [! instead of **Salieri**]. The original Italian text, "La moda, ossia I scompigli domestici," is by Pietro Cipretti, who is not mentioned. SCHATZ 9337

Modern fine lady. A. T. of The female rake.

Modern gallantry. A. T. of The humours of the court.

Modern honour; or, The barber duellist. A comic opera in two acts. As it is now performing with great applause, at the Theatre Royal, in Smock-Alley, Dublin. Written by a gentleman of that city.

London, J. Williams, 1775. iv, [3], 10–33, [1] p. 21^{cm}.

Prologue, cast, dedication dated Dublin, November 23, 1775, and prefatory note, in which this is called a "first attempt." Composer not recorded by Schatz.

LONGE 251

La **modista** ossia La scuffiaja. L. T. of Paisiello's La modista raggiratrice.

La **modista raggiatrice.** Commedia per mucia da rappresentarsi nel Teatro de' Fiorentini per terz' opera di quest' anno 1787.

Napoli, n. publ., 1787. 59 p. 16^{cm}.

Three acts. By Giambattista Lorenzi, who is not mentioned. Cast and name of **Paisiello** as the composer. Schatz 7642

— La **modista** ossia La scuffiaja, dramma giocoso per musica. Da rappresentarsi il carnovale del 1790 nel Teatro del nob. Signor Filippo de Bandeu in Gorizia . . .

Gorizia, Valerio de' Valerj e figli, n. d. 2 p. l., 53 p. 17^{cm}.

A condensation of Lorenzi's text by suppressing the two scenes of the original third act and by substituting as scene xiii of the second act "Incomincio a sperar" and as scene xiv (the last) "Nè Cicotto? dove andiamo," both of which are not in the original. Cast and impresario's dedication dated Gorizia, January 29, 1790. **Paisiello** is not mentioned. Schatz 7643

Les **moeurs du bon vieux temps.** A. T. of Grétry's Aucassin et Nicolette.

La **moglie bizzarra.** L. T. of Galuppi's L'amante di tutte.

La **moglie capricciosa.** Dramma giocoso per musica da rappresentarsi nel Teatro di S. A. E. di Sassonia.

Dresda, n. publ., 1786. 159 p. 15½^{cm}.

Two acts. By Filippo Livigni. Giuseppe **Gazzaniga** is mentioned as the composer. German title page, "Die eigensinnige ehefrau," and text face Italian.
First performed, as indicated, March 18, 1786; at Venice, Teatro di S. Moisè, fall of 1785. Schatz 3672

— La **moglie capricciosa.** Intermezzo a sei voci da rappresentarsi in Firenze nel R. Teatro degl' Infuocati posto in via del Cocomero nel carnevale dell' anno 1792 . . .

Firenze, Ant. Gius. Pagani e comp., 1791. 55 p. 16½^{cm}.

Two acts. Cast and name of Giuseppe **Gazzaniga** as composer. Livigni is not mentioned. ML 48.A5 v.24

— La **moglie capricciosa.** Opera buffa in musica da rappresentarsi nel Teatro dei nobili Signori fratelli Prini di Pisa nel carnevale dell' anno 1795.

Pisa, Francesco Pieraccini, 1795. 16½^{cm}.

Incomplete. Lacks the pages after p. 32.
Two acts. By Filippo Livigni, who is not mentioned. Cast and name of Giuseppe **Gazzaniga** as the composer. Schatz 3671

— A **mulher caprichosa.** Drama jocoso em musica para se representar no Theatro da rua dos Condes no estio do anno de 1791.

Lisboa, Simão Thaddeo Ferreira, 1791. 179 p. 14½^{cm}.

Two acts. By Filippo Livigni, who is not mentioned. Portuguese text faces Italian. Cast and name of Giuseppe **Gazzaniga** as the composer. Schatz 3678

La **moglie di spirito.** A. T. of the ballet Il marito umiliato.

La moglie nemica. Drama per musica da rappresentarsi nel Teatro Vendramino di S. Salvatore, l' anno 1694. Di Francesco Silvani . . .

Venetia, Nicolini, 1694. front., 64 p. 14½cm.

Three acts. Author's dedication dated Venice, January 10, 1694, argument, and scenario. The composer, Marc' Antonio **Ziani,** is not mentioned. SCHATZ 11203

La moglie padrona. Dramma giocoso per musica da rappresentarsi ne' Teatri privilegiati di Vienna. L'anno 1768.

Vienna, Ghelen, n. d. 88 p. 16cm.

Two acts. Author not mentioned and unknown to Schatz. Scenario and name of Giuseppe **Scarlatti** as the composer. SCHATZ 9559

La moglie virtuosa, ballet. *See* Cristiani's La città nuova.

La mogliere fedele. Commeddea pe mmuseca da rappresentarese a lo Teatro Nuovo ncoppa Monte Cravaneo nchist' autunno dell' anno corrente 1731 . . .

Napole, A spese de li impressarie, 1731. 60 p. 15cm.

Three acts. Author not mentioned and unknown to Schatz. Impresario's dedication, argument, cast, and note to the effect that the music is by Leonardo **Vinci,** except all the recitatives and certain indicated arias, which were by Giuseppe **Sellitti.** These arias are "Quanta furie scatenate" (I, 10), "Non serve cchiu a penzare" (II, 13), "E'no scuoglio chisto core" (III, 10). At the end of the libretto is this note: "Nell' atto primo Sc. xii noagno de l'area 'Frà le sciure,' etc. se pò dicere la seguente aria posta mmuseca da lo Sio Angelo Antonio **Trojano,** 'Se chisto affritto core' . . . Pulli che ritrovi in qualche margine, è il Sig. Pietro **Pulli** famosissimo sonatore di arceliuti e contrapontisto."

This remark applies to the arias "Povera pecorella" (I, 6), "So n'astritto rescegnuolo" (I, 17), "Chi cade dint' all' acqua" (II, 2), "Non si stracqus turco cano" (II, 15), "Me conzola no penziero" (III, 2), "Che d'è chesto? che m'e dato?" (III, 4). Even therewith the pasticcio character of the opera is not exhausted because the aria "E n'ancunia sto core" has in margin Leonardo **Leo's** name. SCHATZ 10755

Der mohr. Tr. of Salieri's Il moro.

Les moissonneurs, comédie en trois actes, melée d'ariettes. Représentée pour la premiere fois par les Comédiens italiens ordinaires du roi, le 27 janvier 1768. Par M. Favart. La musique est de M. Duni.

Paris, la veuve Duchesne, 1768. 61 p. 19cm.

With Favart's dedication and "Avertissement." No cast and no music printed in the text. SCHATZ 2850

— Les **moissonneurs,** comedie en trois actes et en vers, meslée d'ariettes . . . Représentée pour la premiere fois par les Comédiens italiens ordinaires du roi, le 27 janvier 1768. Par M. Favart. La musique est de M. Duni.

Paris, la veuve Duchesne, 1768. 91, [4] p. 3 pl. 19cm. (Theatre de M. Favart, Paris, Duchesne, 1763–77, t. x.)

Cast. On p. 89–90 the "Vaudeville. Rustant et Nicole" ("Des biens que votre main"). The [4] p. "Catalogue général des théâtres" and a list of "Pieces a ariettes et vaudevilles" arranged by title. Text preceded by same dedication and avertissement. Font claims that Voisemon retouched the text. ML 49.A2F1

— Die **schnitter.** Ein schauspiel in drey aufzeugen mit arietten aus dem franzoesischen des hrn. Favart uebersetzt von Johann Heinrich Faber . . .

Frankfurt am Mayn, Johann Georg Esslinger, n. d. 88 p. 17cm.

Les moissonneurs—Continued.

The text is preceded by Faber's rebuttal (dated Mayence, May 20, 1769) of a violent criticism of his tragedy "Inkle und Yariko" and a "Vorbericht," in which he expresses in vigorous terms his contempt for critics in general and a certain Schmidt in particular. This edition of Faber's translation evidently was issued previous to its first performance in 1771, noted below.   ML 50.2.M75D94

— Die **schnitter,** ein singspiel in drey aufzuegen aus dem franzoesischen uebersetzt, mit musik.

Frankfurt am Mayn, mit Andreaeischen schriften, 1772.   110 p., 8 p. (folded dated music).   16½cm.

German version by Johann Heinrich Faber (not mentioned).   With cast.

The musical supplement contains the arias (voice and bass): "O! wie schön sind doch" ["Que Rousine est touchante"], p. 1–3; "O! wie erfreut die erndte-zeit" [O le bon temps que la moisson], p. 3–4; "Ich geh gern jeden morgen" ["Ma démarche est légere], p. 4–7; "Candorn soll der Himmel schonen" ["Mon coeur jouit d'un bien suprême"], p. 7–8.   SCHATZ 2851

First performed at Frankfurt a/M, Theater im Junghof, 1771.

Il **molaforbici.**   Commedia per musica di Giuseppe Palomba da rappresentarsi nel Teatro nuovo sopra Toledo per prim' opera di quest' anno 1782.

Napoli, n. publ., 1782.   55 p.   15½cm.

Three acts.   Cast and name of Gaetano **Monti** as the composer.   SCHATZ 6602

Os **moleiros.**   Tr of Paër's I molinari.

La **molinara.**   Dramma giocoso per musica di Filippo Livigni da rappresentarsi nel nobile Teatro di San Samuele il carnovale dell' anno 1778.

Venezia, Modesto Fenzo, 1778.   52 p.   17cm.

Two acts.   Cast, scenario, and name of Domenico **Fischietti** as composer.   Between the acts was performed "Amore e Psiche.   Ballo eroico" by Giuseppe Fabiani, the composer of the music not being mentioned.   SCHATZ 3233

La **molinara.**   O. T. of Piccinni's La Molinarella and Il Cavaliere Ergasto.

La **molinara** o sia L'amor contrastato.   L. T. of Paisiello's L'amor contrastato.

La **molinara spiritosa.**   Commedia per musica di Saverio Zini da rappresentarsi nel Real Teatro del Fondo di Separazione per second' opera di quest' anno 1787 . . .

Napoli, n. publ., 1787.   48 p.   15cm.

Two acts.   Cast, notice to the public, impresario's dedication, and name of Giacomo **Tritto** as the composer.   With the opera was performed Giambattista Giannini's ballet "L'isola de' cannibali."   The composer of the music not mentioned.
          SCHATZ 10476

La **molinarella.**   Dramma giocoso per musica da rappresentarsi in Lisbona nel Teatro della rua dos Condes nella primavera dell' anno 1773.

[Lisbona], Stamperia Reale, n. d.   87 p.   16½cm.

Three acts.   The author is not mentioned and is unknown to Schatz.   Argument, cast, scenario, and name of Niccolò **Piccinni** as the composer.   The opera became known also as "Il cavaliere Ergasto" (Fedeli).

As "La Molinara" first performed at Naples, Teatro Nuovo, fall of 1766.
          SCHATZ 8099

I molinari. Commedia con musica d'un atto solo di Giuseppe Foppa da rappresentarsi nel nobilissimo Teatro Giustiniani in San Moisè il carnovale dell' anno 1794.

Venezia, Modesto Fenzo, 1794. 38 p. 18^{cm}.

Cast and name of Ferdinando Pèr (**Paër**) as the composer. SCHATZ 7515

— **Os moleiros:** comedia com musica em hum so' acto, para se representar no Real Theatro de S. Carlos, no dia 4 de janeiro de 1796. Em beneficio de Domingos Caporalini . . . Traduzida do italiano por N. N.

Lisboa, Simão Thaddeo Ferreira, 1795. 107 p. 14½^{cm}.

Prefatory note and name of Fernando Per (**Paër**) as the composer. The author, Foppa, is not mentioned. Portuguese text faces the Italian. SCHATZ 7558

I molinari francesi, ballet. *See* Monza's Sesostri.

Momus. Intermède in Bourgeois' Les plaisirs de la paix.

Momus exilé. *See* Destouches and Lalande's ballet Les élémens.

Momvs turn'd fabulist: or, Vulcan's wedding. An opera: after the manner of the Beggar's opera. As it is perform'd at the Theatre-Royal in Lincolns-Inn Fields. With the musick prefix'd to each song.

London, J. Watts, 1729. 4 p. l., 70 p. 18½^{cm}.

Three acts and introduction. The p. l. contain half-title, publisher's list, with date Nov. 12, 1729, title page, publisher's list, dated October 28, 1729, cast, and "introduction," in which the *gentleman* says:

"Sir, I was my self an eye-witness of it, being in France when this piece first appear'd on the stage and saw it represented several nights with a considerable share of pleasure, which put me upon rendering it into English. In this performance I have taken the liberty of turning the fables which were spoke in France, into ballads to be sung, and have heighten'd several of the scenes by the addition of other ballads, suitable to the present taste of the town. In short, I have made that an English opera, which was but a French farce."

By Ebenezer Forrest, after a farce by Fuzelier and Le Grand. The 42 airs are printed in the text, with their titles.

First performed, as indicated, December 3, 1729. ML 50.5.M63

Second copy. LONGE 50

Le monde renversé. Pièce d'un acte. Par Mrs. le S * *. & D'Or * *. Sur le plan de M. de la F. Représentée à la Foire de Saint Laurent 1718.

Le Théâtre de la foire, Paris, 1737, t. iii, pl., [201]–267 p. 17^{cm}.

By Le Sage and d'Orneval. Largely *en vaudevilles.* The airs, selected or composed and arranged by Jean Claude **Gillier**, the "compositeur" of the theatre, are printed at the end of the volume in the "Table des airs." ML 48.L2III

Das monden-reich. Eine operette von drey handlungen. Die musik ist von herrn Frischmuth.

n. i., n. d. [40] p. 16½^{cm}.

Author unknown to Schatz.

First performed at Berlin (Doebbelin), Theater Monbijou, 1769. SCHATZ 3373

Das mondenreich. Tr. of Piccinni's Il regno della luna.

Il **mondo al rovescio,** o sia Le donne che comandono.

[1]–52 p. 16½^cm. (*Carlo Goldoni, Opere drammatiche giocose, t. I, Torino, 1757.*)

Three acts. First composed by *Galuppi.* (*See* below.)　　　ML 49.A2G6

— Il **mondo alla roversa,** o sia Le donne che comandano. Dramma di tre atti per musica. Rappresentato per la prima volta in Venezia l'anno MDCCL.

Carlo Goldoni, Opere teatrali, Venezia, Zatta e figli, 1788–95, v. 41, [61]–114 p. 18^cm.　　　PQ

Il **mondo alla roversa** o sia Le donne che comandono. Dramma giocoso per musica da rappresentarsi nel Teatro Nuovo di S. Samuele. Il carnovale dell' anno 1753.

Venezia, Modesto Fenzo, 1753. 48 p. 16½^cm.

Three acts. By Goldoni, who is not mentioned. Impresario's dedication, dated February 17, 1753, cast, scenario, but not the name of the composer, Baldassare **Galuppi.** The opera became known later on also under the title, "Il regno delle donne."
First performed at Venice, Teatro di S. Cassiano, fall, 1750.　　SCHATZ 3459

— Il **mondo alla roverscia.** Dramma giocoso per musica. Di Polisseno Fegeio P. A. da rappresentarsi nel Piccolo Teatro di S. A. E. di Sassonia. Dresda, l'anno del 1768.

n. i., n. d. 135 p. 15½^cm.

Three acts. Cast, scenario, and the name of **Galuppi** as composer. German title page, "Die verkehrte Welt," and text face Italian text, which is noticeably different in the arias from the Venice (1753) edition. For instance, this has (I, 6) "Feriteme, piagatemi" instead of "In quel volto siede un nume," and (III, 4) "E un dolce tesoro" instead of "Chi troppo ad amor crede."
First performed at Dresden, Brühl'sches Theater, June 25, 1754.　　SCHATZ 3460

Il **mondo della luna.**

[5]–62 p. 16½^cm. (*Carlo Goldoni, Opere drammatiche giocose, t. II, Torino, 1757.*)

Three acts. First composed by *Galuppi.* (*See* below.)　　　ML 49.A2G6

— Il **mondo della luna.** Dramma di tre atti per musica. Rappresentato per la prima volta in Venezia il carnovale dell' anno MDCCLII. [!]

Carlo Goldoni, Opere teatrali, Venezia, Zatta e figli, 1788–95, t. 40, p. [113]–169. 18^cm.　　　PQ

Il **mondo della luna.** Dramma giocoso per musica da rappresentarsi nel Teatro Giustiniani di San Moisè nel carnovale dell' anno 1775.

Venezia, Antonio Graziosi, 1775. 64 p. 17½^cm.

Three acts. By Goldoni. Cast, scenario, and name of the composer Gennaro **Astaritta,** but not of the author.　　　SCHATZ 383

Il **mondo della luna.** Dramma giocoso per musica di Polisseno Fegejo, Pastore Arcade, da rappresentarsi nel Real Teatro di Salvaterra nel carnovale dell' anno 1765.

Lisbona, Stamperia Ameniana, n. d. 66 p. 15^cm.

Three acts. By Carlo Goldoni. Cast, scenario, and name of composer, Pietro Antonio **Avondano.**　　　SCHATZ 510

Il **mondo della luna.** Dramma giocoso per musica di Polisseno Fegejo Pastor Arcade. Da rappresentarsi nel Teatro Giustinian di S. Moisè. Il carnovale dell' anno 1750.

Venezia, Modesto Fenzo, 1750. 59 p. 14½^{cm}.

Three acts. By Goldoni. Neither he nor the composer, Baldassare **Galuppi**, is mentioned. Cast and scenario.

First performed, as indicated, January 29, 1750.

Schatz 3461

— Il **mondo nella luna.** Drama giocoso, da rappresentarsi sopra il Teatro di S. M. B.

London, G. Woodfall, 1760. 93, [1] p. 20^{cm}.

Three acts. The last p. contains the aria, "Bella mia, se son tuo sposo," substituted for "Io ho un vespaio" (I, 4). English transl. faces the Italian of Goldoni, who is not mentioned. Cast, name of Baldassare **Galuppi** as composer, and note that "the translator has thought proper to give some of the scenes almost literally, in order the more to facilitate to the reader the intelligence of the original."

The text does not mention the fact that about one-half of the arias are not from this or any other play by Goldoni. It is clear that also the music was more or less a pasticcio, the substituted aria, for instance, being from **Pergolesi's** "Il maestro di musica."

First performed at London, Haymarket, November 22, 1760. ML 48.M2H

— Die **welt im Monde.** Eine komische oper in drey aufzuegen. Aus dem italiaenischen uebersetzt. Die musik ist von dem herrn Balthasar Galuppi.

Oels, Samuel Gottlieb Ludwig, [17—]. 79 p. 16^{cm}.

Three acts. Translator unknown to Schatz. Schatz 3462

Il **mondo della luna.** L. T. of Paisiello's Il credulo deluso.

Il **mondo festeggiante.** Balletto a cavallo fatto nel Teatro congiunto al palazzo del serenissimo granduca per le reali nozze de' serenissimi principi Cosimo Terzo di Toscana e Margherita Luisa d'Orleans.

G. A. Moniglia, Poesie drammatiche, parte prima, Firenze, Vincenzio Vangelisti, 1689, v. 1, [257]–297 p. 24^{cm}.

A prose description by Alessandro Segni of this remarkable affair (invented by Alessandro Carducci), interspersed with Moniglia's "parole per tanto de' pienissimi cori e quelle di tutti i passati canti." Domenico **Anglesi** is mentioned as the composer.

According to Allacci, printed 1641, which is impossible, since Cosimo III's marriage took place in 1661. ML 49.A2M7

Monsieur de Porsugnac. Intermezzi comici musicali da rappresentarsi nel Teatro di Sant' Angelo l'autunno dell' anno MDCCXLI.

Venezia, Marino Rossetti, 1741. 19 p. 14½^{cm}.

Two parts. Author not mentioned, and unknown to Schatz, and Giuseppe Maria **Orlandini**, the composer, not mentioned.

First performed at Venice, Teatro di S. Samuele, May, 1727. Schatz 7341

— **Pourceaugnac and Grilletta.** An interlude. Performed by Sig. Anna Maria Faini, and Signor Antonio Lottini, at the King's Theatre in the Hay-Market. The musick is composed by Sig. Giuseppe Maria Orlandini . . .

London, J. Chrichley, 1737. 31 p. 17^{cm}.

English text faces Italian, which is much altered from the original.

First performed January, 1737, as indicated. Schatz 7342

Monsieur Petiton. Intermezzo.

[257]–276 p. 16½cm. (Carlo Goldoni, Opere drammatiche giocose, t. iv, Torino, 1757.)

Two parts. Not mentioned by Wiel. Schatz records without composer's name a performance at the Teatro di San Samuele, 1736.   ML 49.A2G6

— **Monsieur Petiton.** Intermezzo di due parti per musica.

Carlo Goldoni, Opere teatrali, Venezia, Zatta e figli, 1788–95, v. 35, [207]–229 p. 18½cm.   PQ

Monsieur Petitone. O. T. of Piccinni's Madama Arrighetta.

Li **montanari nel Perù,** ballet. *See* Rispoli's Idalide.

Montezuma. Tragedia per musica da rappresentarsi nel Regio Teatro di Berlino . . . nel carnovale del MDCCLXXI.

Berlino, Haude e Spener, 1771. 131, [3] p. 16½cm.

Three acts. By Frederick the Great, whose French prose text was translated into Italian by Giampietro Tagliazucchi. Neither he nor the king is mentioned. Argument, scenario, and name of Carl Heinrich **Graun** as the composer. German title-page and text face Italian.

Performed as indicated; previously performed there January 6, 1755. SCHATZ 4108

The **monument in Arcadia:** A dramatic poem, in two acts: By George Keate, Esq. . . .

London, J. Dodsley, 1773. x, [2], 43 p. 26cm.

Dedication, preface. No composer or performance recorded by Clarence.

LONGE 186

Der **morgen des europaeischen glueckes,** oder Aurora, an dem hohen gebuhrts-tage des . . . herrn Joseph I, erwaehlten roemischen kaeysers . . . in einem schaeffer-spiel auf dem grossen Hamburgischen schau-platz vorgestellet, im jahr 1710, den 26 julii.

Hamburg, Friedrich Conrad Greflinger, n. d. Unpaged. 19cm.

Five acts. Scenario and congratulatory "vorbericht." Neither the author, Breymann, is mentioned, nor the composer, Reinhard **Keiser.** To some of the arias Italian text has been added.

First performed, as indicated, July 26, 1710.   SCHATZ 5104

Il **Moro.** Commedia per musica da rappresentarsi nel Teatro elettorale di Sassonia.

Dresda, n. publ., 1797. 157 p. 16½cm.

Two acts. Antonio **Salieri** is mentioned as the composer. Giovanni de Gamerra, the author, is not mentioned. German title-page, "Der mohr," and text face Italian.

First performed at Dresden, July, 1797; at Vienna August 7, 1796, at the Burgtheater.   SCHATZ 9303

Il **moro di corpo bianco** ossia Lo schiavo del proprio onore, ballet. *See* P. Guglielmi's La sposa contrastata.

Il **moro di corpo bianco** o sia Lo schiavo del proprio onore, ballet. *See* Marinelli's Amore aguzza l'ingegno.

La **mort d'Hercule.** L. T. of Lully and Marais' Alcide.

La **mort di Licomède.** Tr. T. of the ballet La morte di Licomede.

La **morte d'Agamemnone,** ballet. *See* Andreozzi's Ines de Castro.

La morte d'Egisto ossia Le furie d'Oreste, ballet. *See* Caruso's Antigono.

La morte d'Ercole—Der tod des Hercules, ballet. *See* Jommelli's Semiramide.

La morte d'Ercole, ballet. *See* Nasolini's Adriano in Siria.

La morte d'Ettore, ballet. *See* Nasolini's Gl' Indiani.

La morte d'Ippolito e Fedra, ballet. *See* Geraci's Vologeso.

La morte d'Oloferne. Tragedia sacra per musica da rappresentarsi nel Real Teatro del Fondo di Separazione nella quadragesima di quest' anno 1791.

> *Napoli, Vincenzo Flauto, n. d. 34 p. 15ᶜᵐ.*

Two parts. Cast and name of Pietro **Guglielmi** as composer. In an "Avviso" the anonymous author says:
". . . E siccome l'istesso sacro fatto è stato scenegigiato dall' in signe abate Pietro Metastasio, sotto il titolo della Betulia Liberata, così ha creduto ben fatto lo scrittore della presente tragedia, dove l'è riuscito servirsi de' sentimenti d'un si immortale autore, non defraudarne il publico, con trascriverli fedelmente." ML 50.2.M8G92

— **La morte di Oloferne.** Componimento per musica.
> *Roma, Arcangelo Casaletti, 1791. 1 p. l., xxxvii p. 27ᶜᵐ.*

Two parts. Text based on "La Betulia liberata" by Metastasio. The author is not mentioned. Pietro **Guglielmi** is mentioned as the composer.
First performed at Rome, Palazzo Colonna, April 22, 1791. ML 50.2.M8G93

— **Il trionfo di Giuditta** o sia La morte d'Oloferne. Dramma sacro per musica da rappresentarsi nel Regio Teatro di via della Pergola la quadragesima del MDCCXCV . . .
> *Firenze, Stamperia Albizziana, 1795. 32 p. 16½ᶜᵐ.*

Two acts. Cast, name of Pietro **Guglielmi** as the composer and same "avviso" according to which the anonymous author helped himself freely to Metastasio's "Betulia liberata." SCHATZ 4277

— **Il trionfo di Giuditta** o sia La morte d'Oloferne. Dramma sacro per musica da rappresentarsi nel Regio Teatro degli Avvalorati in Livorno la quadragesima dell' anno 1796.
> *[Livorno], Tommaso Masi e compagno, n. d. 46 p. 15ᶜᵐ.*

Two acts. Cast, scenario, and same prefatory Avviso.
Pietro **Guglielmi** is mentioned as the composer. SCHATZ 11712

La morte d'Orfeo, ballet. *See* Gius. Scarlatti's Pelopida.

La morte di Arrigo Sesto, rè d'Inghilterra, ballet. *See* G. Giordani's Elpinice.

La morte di Attila, ballet. *See* Fioravanti's L'astuta in amore ossia Il furbo malaccorto.

La morte di Calisto, ballet. *See* Paër's Cinna.

La morte di Cesare. Dramma per musica del Signor abate D. Gaetano Sertor da rappresentarsi nel nobilissimo Teatro di San Samuele il carnovale dell' anno 1789 . . .
> *Venezia, Modesto Fenzo, 1788. 80 p. 17ᶜᵐ.*

La morte di Cesare—Continued.

Three acts with *licenza*. Author's dedication, argument, scenario, cast, and name of the composer, Francesco **Bianchi**. On p. 31–35 argument of the ballet "Il convito di Cesare," p. 56–65 argument, cast, and full description of the ballet "Timugino, gran Kan de' Tartari, in quattro atti." Both ballets were by Domenico Ricardi, the composers of the music not being mentioned.

First performed, as indicated, December 27, 1788. Schatz 1005

— **Giulio Cesare.** Dramma per musica del Signor abate D. Gaetano Sertor da rappresentarsi nel Reg. Teatro di Trieste nella primavera dell' anno MDCCXC.

Trieste, Stamperia governale, n. d. 63 p. 16½ᶜᵐ.

Three acts. Impresario's dedication, dated April 21, 1790, argument, cast, scenario, and name of Francesco **Bianchi** as composer. The text is a later version of Sertor's "La morte di Cesare." Schatz 1006

La morte di Cesare. Dramma per musica da rappresentarsi nel Teatro grande alla Scala il carnevale 1791 . . .

Milano, Gio. Batista Bianchi, n. d. 64 p. 16½ᶜᵐ.

Pages 17–18 supplied in ms.

Three acts. By Gaetano Sertor, who is not mentioned. Impresario's dedication, dated Milan, December 19, 1790, argument, cast, scenario, and name of Nicola Antonio **Zingarelli** as the composer. With the opera was performed Giuseppe Traffieri's ballet "Edipo," composer of the music not mentioned and the libretto of which does not appear at the end, as announced in a footnote.

First performed, as indicated, December 26, 1790 (Schatz). Schatz 11263

La morte di Cleopatra. Dramma per musica da rappresentarsi nel Real Teatro di S. Carlo nel dì 30. maggio 1798 per festeggiare il nome glorioso di Ferdinando IV . . .

Napoli, Stamperia Flautina, 1798. 51 p. 15ᶜᵐ.

Two acts. Argument, cast, scenario, name of Pietro **Guglielmi** as the composer, and dedication, dated May 30, 1798, in which the impresario, Onorato Balsamo, says: "Per la seconda volta, mediante il vostro sovrano clementissimo beneplacito, comparisce sulle scene del vostro Real Teatro il dramma intitolato: *La morte di Cleopatra.*"

By whom the text was first composed and when it was first performed as indicated, Schatz does not mention, but Piovano proved that the libretto is by Antonio Simone Sografi, that it was composed by Nasolini, 1791, and that Guglielmi's opera was first performed at Naples, Teatro di San Carlo, June 22, 1796. The libretto contains also, on p. 38–47, cast and description of Gaspare Ronzi's "Enea e Lavinia, ballo eroico pantomimico," in five acts, and on p. 48–51 of his "Amor vince tutto, ballo comico pantomimo in un solo atto." The composers of the music are not mentioned.

Schatz 4253

La morte di Cleopatra. O. T. of Nasolini's Cleopatra, regina d'Egitto.

La morte di Cleopatra, ballet. *See* Rust's Gli antiquari in Palmira.

La morte di Clitennestra. A. T. of the ballet Oreste.

La morte di Danao. A. T. of the ballet Ipermestra.

La morte di Dimone o sia L'innocenza vendicata. Dramma seriogiocoso per musica da rappresentarsi nel nuovo Teatro Tron in S. Cassano l'autunno dell' anno MDCCLXIII.

Venecia, Paolo Colombani, 1763. 77 [1] p. 17ᶜᵐ.

Three acts. Prefatory note with argument, cast, and note: "Il dramma è del Sig. Giuseppe de [Joseph Felix von] Kurtz impresario, e posto in versi italiani dal Sig. Giovanni Bertati. La musica è del Sig. Antonio **Tozzi** . . ."

La **morte di Dimone**—Continued.

In his preface Kurtz says:

"Ecco qual sia il dramma, ch'io ho destinato di far rappresentare in questo nuovo teatro. Molto dire dovrei del dramma medesimo, il di cui genere forse potrà strano sembrare al pubblico, dopo che l'Italia si è dimenticata delle rappresentazioni, che facevansi ne' suoi teatri il secolo scorso. Solamente però io mi ristringerò a dire, che non cerco, e non pretendo con questa mia composizione d'introdurre un nuovo gusto sulle scene italiane; ma che a me si conveniva di appigliarmi ad una rappresentazione di questo tal genere, affine d'introdurvi que' spettacoli, e quelle decorazioni, ch'io aveva destinato di produrre in questa città; ed ecco per questo introdotte nuovamente sulle scene le Deità, e la moltiplicità di personaggi." SCHATZ 10385

La **morte di Geta**, ballet. *See* Portugal's Alceste.

La **morte di Licomede**—Là mort de Licomède, ballet. *See* Jommelli's Demofoonte.

La **morte di Meleagro**, ballet. *See* Tritto's L'equivoco.

La **morte di Mitridate**, tragedia per musica del Signor Sografi poeta del Teatro La Fenice e del Teatro comico Sant' Angelo l'estate dell' anno 1797.

Venezia, Stamperia Valvasense, n. d. 55 p. 17½ᶜᵐ.

Two acts. Cast and name of Nicola Antonio **Zingarelli** as the composer ("La musica tutta nuova"). On p. [25]–33, argument, cast, and description of Filippo Beretti's ballet, "L'esilio di Tarquinio il Superbo VII. rè di Roma," music by Vittorio Trento. The second ballet was called "Chi la fa l'aspetta." SCHATZ 11269

La **morte di Pirro**, ballet. *See* Bertoni's Nitteti.

La **morte di Semiramide**. Tragedia per musica da rappresentarsi nel Teatro grande alla Scala il carnevale 1791 . . .

Milano, Gio. Batista Bianchi, n. d. 4 p. l., 57, [16] p. 16½ᶜˣ.

Three acts. By Antonio Simone Sografi. Impresario's dedication dated Milan, February 9, 1791, cast, scenario, and names of the composer, Giovanni Battista **Borghi**, and the librettist (in h.-t.). The unnumb. additional pages contain preface, cast, argument, and detailed description of Giuseppe Traffieri's "Le Danaidi, ballo tragico-pantomimo" in five acts and the argument of his ballet "Rinaldo d'Asti." The composers of the music are not mentioned. SCHATZ 1234

— La **morte di Semiramide**, ossia La vendetta di Nino. Tragedia per musica da rappresentarsi nel Regio Teatro di S. Carlo della Principessa la primavera dell' anno 1799.

Lisbona, Simone Taddeo Ferreira, 1799. 4 p. l., 99 p. 14ᶜᵐ.

Cast, scenario, and name of composer, **Borghi**. Portuguese text faces Italian. SCHATZ 1240

La **morte di Semiramide** ossia La vendetta di Nino. Dramma per musica da rappresentarsi nel Ces. Reg. Teatro di Trieste l'autunno dell' anno 1795.

Trieste, Stamperia governiale, n. d. 48 p. 16½ᶜᵐ.

Three acts. By Antonio Simone Sografi, who is not mentioned, and is not to be confused with the author or rather arranger of the text with same title as composed 1802 by **Nasolini**, who is not mentioned, but is known to be the composer of this earlier opera, too. Dedicatory poem by the impresario dated Trieste, October 3, 1795, cast, and scenario. With the opera was performed Michele Fabiani's "Il trionfo d'Arbace, ballo eroico in cinque atti," music ("scritta espressamente") by "Mons. d'Anglois, virtuoso di S. M. il rè di Sardegna."

First performed at Rome, Teatro Argentina, carnival 1792, under the title "Semiramide." SCHATZ 7013

La **morte di Semiramide.** L. T. of Prati's La vendetta di Nino.

La **morte ed il rinascimento del pastore Adone,** ballet. *See* Bach's Artaserse.

Les **mortels.** Entrée in Brassac's L'empire de l'amour.

I **morti fatti sposi,** ballet. *See* Cimarosa's Gli Orazi e i Curiazi.

Les **morts vivans.** A. T. of Le Petit's Le combat nocturne.

Moschetta e Grullo. Intermezzi in Sarro's Siroe, rè di Persia.

Il **mostro,** ossia Da gratitudine amore. Dramma per musica da rappresentarsi nel Teatro Elettorale, composta da Caterino Mazzolà . . .

Dresda, n. publ., 1786. 135 p. 15½ᶜᵐ.

Two acts. Franz **Seydelmann** is mentioned as the composer. German title-page "Das ungeheuer, oder Liebe aus dankbarkeit," and text face Italian. First performed 1786, as indicated.   SCHATZ 9846

Motezuma. Dramma per musica da rappresentarsi nel nobilissimo Teatro di S. Benedetto per la fiera dell' Ascensione dell' anno 1772.

Venezia, Modesto Fenzo, 1772. 56 p. 16½ᶜᵐ.

Three acts. Argument with name of the author, Vittorio Amedeo Cigna-Santi, cast, scenario, and name of Baldassare **Galuppi** as composer. ("La musica sarà del.") First performed May 27, 1772, as indicated.   SCHATZ 3463

Motezuma. Dramma per musica da rappresentarsi nel Regio Teatro di Torino nel carnovale del 1780 . . .

Torino, Onorato Derossi, n. d. viii, 60 p. 15½ᶜᵐ.

Three acts. Argument, cast, scenario, and names of Vittorio Amedeo Cigna-Santi as author, of Giacomo **Insanguine** as composer. With the opera were performed, libretto published separately in French and Italian, Sebastiano Gallet's ballets "Il tempio della pazzia," "Bacco ed Arianna," and "Il guerrier generoso," music by Vittorio Amedeo Canavasso.   SCHATZ 4835

Motezuma. Dramma per musica da rappresentarsi nel Regio Teatro di Torino nel carnovale del 1765 . . .

Torino, Gaspare Bayno, n. d. 8 p. l., 60 p. 16½ᶜᵐ.

Three acts. Argument, cast, scenario, and names of Vittorio Amedeo Cigna-Santi as author, of Giovanni Francesco de **Majo** as composer of the opera, and of Giuseppe Antonio Le Messier as composer of the three incidental ballets.   SCHATZ 5858

Motezuma. A serious opera. To be performed at the King's Theatre in the Hay-Market. The music, entirely new, by Signor Sacchini. The translation by Bottarelli, jun. teacher of languages.

London, T. Cadell, 1775. iv, 53, [1] p. 19ᶜᵐ.

This title on p. [1]. It is preceded by the iv p. with the author, Giovan Gualberto Bottarelli's, dedication (dated February 1, 1775) to the duke of Dorset. The last unnumb. page contains "Proposals for printing by subscription several Odes of Horace, translated into Italian verse by G. G. Bottarelli and set to music by Messrs. Bach, Vento, Giordani, Boroni, Holtzbauer, Barthelemon, and others . . ."

The cast is preceded by G. G. Bottarelli's notice to the reader with a very brief argument, and reading in part:

"I do not see what objections can arise against Motezuma's dying on the *opera-stage*, breathing the language of *harmony*, when *actors* die on other stages in *tragedy*, speaking the language of the *Muses*.

Motezuma—Continued.

"I hope the British nation (I mean such as are inspired by Apollo, and whose genius's are happily composed to form the learned world) will take in good part these attempts of an *honest man*, who has laboured these *seven and twenty years*, both night and day, either to add *new* pleasures to the entertainment, or to give a new face and form to the *old ones*." SCHATZ 9232

Motezuma. Drama per musica da rappresentarsi nel Teatro. di Sant' Angelo nell' autunno dell' anno 1733.

Venezia, Marino Rossetti, n. d. 60, [1] p. 15ᶜᵐ.

Three acts. By Alvise Giusti, who is not mentioned. Argument, cast, scenario, and name of Antonio **Vivaldi** as the composer. The additional page contains the substitute aria, "A svenare il mostro gl'empi" (I, 16), and the additional aria, "Il nochiero coraggioso" (II, 2). SCHATZ 10773

The recitatives, airs, etc. in the new pantomime entertainment of **Mother Shipton.** As it is now performing at the Theatre-Royal in Covent-Garden. The second edition.

London, n.·publ., 1771. 8 p. 21ᶜᵐ.

Cast. Neither the author (unknown to Clarence) nor the composer, Samuel **Arnold**, is mentioned.
First performed 1770. ML 52.2.M6

Moulinet premier, parodie de Moulinet Second, tragédie.

Paris, Prault fils, 1739. 2 p. l., 56 p. 19ᶜᵐ. (Theatre de M. Favart, Paris, Duchesne, 1763–77, t. vi.)

One act. Text (in prose and vaudevilles) preceded by "Epistre. Moulinet a Mahomet" and followed, on p. 55–56, by "Compliment de Moulinet au public. A la clôture du Théâtre de l'Opéra-comique, le 21 mars 1729," with "Nota. La parodie a été représentée pour la premiere fois, le 15 mars 1739." Parody of de la Noue's "Mahomet II," first played at the Théâtre-Français on February 23, 1739. Font does not mention Favart's musical collaborator. ML 49.A2F1

Songs, duets, choruses etc in The **mountaineers;** a play, in three acts. Performed at the Theatre. Royal, Hay-Market. Second edition.

London, T. Cadell, 1793. 1 p. l., 5–20 p. 20ᶜᵐ.

Neither the author, George Colman, jun., is mentioned, nor the composer, Samuel **Arnold.**
First performed August 3, 1793. LONGE 227

— The **mountaineers;** a play, in three acts; written by George Colman; (the younger) and first performed at the Theatre Royal, Haymarket, on Saturday, August 3, 1793.

London, J. Debrett, 1795. 2 p. l., 90, [2] p. 20ᶜᵐ.

The [2] p. contain booklists of Debrett. Cast. LONGE 231

Mountaineers of Switzerland. A. T. of Carr's The archers.

The **mouth of the Nile;** or, The glorious first of August, a musical entertainment. By T. Dibdin. As performed at the Theatre-Royal, Covent-Garden. The second edition.

London, J. Barker, 1798. 26, [2] p. 21ᶜᵐ.

On the [2] p., Barker's booklists. One act. Cast and prologue. The composer, Thomas **Attwood,** is not mentioned.
First performed October 25, 1798. LONGE 254

Die muellerin. Tr. of de La Borde's La meunière de Gentilly.

Die **müllerin** oder Die streitig gemachte liebe.   Tr. of Paisiello's **La** molinara o sia L'amor contrastato.

Das **muendel.**   Ein lustspiel mit gesaengen, in zwey aufzuegen, von Ch. G. K. [orb]

> *Altona, J. H. S. Hellmann, 1783.   56, [1] p.   16½ᶜᵐ.*
> Not recorded by Schatz.   ML 50.2.M86

A **mulher caprichosa.**   Tr. T. of Gazzaniga's La moglie capricciosa.

Les **Muses,** ballet représenté par l'Academie royale de musique l'an 1703.   Les paroles de M. Danchet & la musique de M. Campra. LIX. Opéra.

> *n. i., n. d.   front., 111–172 p.   14ᶜᵐ.   (Recueil général des opéra, Paris, 1706, t. viii.)*
> Detached copy.   Prologue and four entrées, called "La pastorale," "La satyre," "La tragédie," "La comédie."
> First performed, as indicated, October 28, 1703.   • SCHATZ 1558
> > Second copy.   ML 48.R4

— **Amarillis,** pastorale, représentée par l'Academie royale de musique, à la place de celle qui se trouve dans Le ballet des Muses. Composée par MM. Danchet & Campra.

> *n. i., n. d.   173–180 p.   14ᶜᵐ.   (Recueil général des opera, Paris, 1706, t. viii.)*
> Detached copy.   One act.   At end, the remark, "Cette pastorale finit par le divertissement de la première pastorale, cy devant page 124," i. e., "le ballet des Muses."
> First performed at Paris, Académie royale de musique, September 10, 1704.
> > SCHATZ 1542
> > Second copy.   ML 48.R4

— Les **Muses,** ballet.   Représenté par l'Académie royale de musique le 8 octobre 1703.

> *[193]–263 p.   17½ᶜᵐ.   (Antoine Danchet, Théâtre, t. ii, Paris, 1751.)*
> Prologue and the same four entrées.   **Campra,** the composer, is not mentioned.
> > PQ 1972.D2

— **Amarillis,** pastorale, représentée, par l'Académie royale de musique, à la place de celle, qui se trouve dans Le ballet des Muses.

> *[255]–263 p.   ibidem.*   PQ 1972.D2

The **Muses in mourning.**   An opera.

> *[3]–17 p.   21ᶜᵐ.   (Aaron Hill, Dramatic works, London, T. Lownds, 1760, vol. ii.)*
> One act.   No composer or performance recorded by Clarence.   LONGE 326

Das **muster rechtschaffener ehelichen liebe.**   A. T. of Händel's Zenobia.

La **muta per amore.**   A. T. of Moneta's Il capitan Tenaglia.

La **muta per amore.**   Dramma giocoso per musica di Cerilo Orcomeno P. A. della Colonia Renia.   Da rappresentarsi nel nobile Teatro di San Samuele nel carnovale dell' anno 1781 . . .

> *Venezia, Modesto Fenzo, 1781.   72, [1] p.   16½ᶜᵐ.*
> Two acts.   Dedication, cast, scenario, and name of Michele **Mortellari** as the composer.   Author's real name not mentioned by Wotquenne.   SCHATZ 6693

Mutio Scevola. *See* M. Curzio.

Mutio Scevola. Drama per musica nel Teatro a S. Salvatore l'anno 1665 . . .

   Venetia, Guliani, 1665. front., 94 p. (incl. pl.) 14½ᶜᵐ.

Three acts with prologue. By conte Niccolò Minato. Author's dedication dated Venice, January 26, 1665, preface, argument, and scenario. The composer, Pietro Francesco **Cavalli,** is not mentioned. SCHATZ 1739

Mutius Scaevola. Tr. of Mattei, Bononcini and Händel's Muzio Scevola.

Il muto per astuzia. Farsa giocosa per musica di Giuseppe Foppa da rappresentarsi nel nobile Teatro Giustiniani in San Moisè il carnovale dell' anno 1799.

   [Venezia], n. publ., n. d. 36 p. 17½ᶜᵐ.

One act. Cast and name of **Bernardini** (Marcello di Capua) as composer. SCHATZ 851

Mutter Natur in ihren kindern. A. T. of Piccinni's Der glueckswechsel.

Il Muzio Scevola. Dramma per musica del nobile Signore Carlo Giuseppe Lanfranchi Rossi, patrizio Pisano, da rappresentarsi nel Nuovo Teatro della città di Padova per la solita fiera dell' anno 1762 . . .

   Padova, Conzatti, 1762. 62, [2] p. 17ᶜᵐ.

Three acts. Impresario's dedication, argument, scenario, cast, and name of Baldassare **Galuppi** as composer. ("La musica è nuova.") The additional pages contain the substitute arias (II, 6) "Almen la sorte arrida" and "*Aria di Tito.* Veggo nel gran cimento."

First performed in June, 1762, as indicated. SCHATZ 3464

Muzio Scevola, drama per musica, da rappresentarsi nel Teatro d' Hamburgo, l'anno 1723—Mutius Scaevola . . .

   Hamburg, Caspar Jakhel, n. d. Unpaged. 18½ᶜᵐ.

Three acts and prologue. Argument, cast, scenario. The prologue has German text only; the three acts German (author unknown to Schatz) and Italian (by Paolo Antonio Rolli). Neither he is mentioned, nor any composer.

Chrysander, when speaking of the first performance of the opera at London, Haymarket, April 15, 1721, in his Händel biography, proved that the single acts were composed by Filippo **Mattei** (*called* Pippo), Giovanni Battista **Bononcini** (who also composed the overture published by Walsh), and Georg Friedrich **Händel**, in the order named. The error of naming Attilio **Ariosti** (who was not in England at the time) as one of the collaborators instead of Mattei is due to Hawkins (V, 277) and Burney (IV, 258). Also Filippo **Amadei** has been mentioned as composer of the first act. That would not add to the controversy if the claim of Schatz is correct, that Filippo Amadei was merely the real name of Filippo Mattei.

First performed at Hamburg, January 7, 1723; at London, as above. SCHATZ 168

— **Muzio Scevola.**

   [37]–99 p. 17ᶜᵐ. (Rolli, Componimenti poetici, Nuova edizione, Verona, G. Tumermani, 1744.)

Three acts. Argument and dedication. ML 49.A2R7

Il Muzio Scevola. Drama per musica . . .

   Napoli, Dom. Ant. Parrino e Michele Luigi Muzio, 1698. 71 p. 13ᶜᵐ.

Il **Muzio Scevola**—Continued.

Three acts. By conte Niccolò Minato, who is not mentioned. Impresario's dedication, argument, cast, and scenario. The composer, Alessandro **Scarlatti**, is not mentioned. Dent says: "ascribed by Florimo and others to A. Scarlatti without any apparent documentary evidence."
First performed at Naples, Teatro di S. Bartolomeo, 1698.   SCHATZ 9528

My grandmother; a musical farce, in two acts, as performed at the Theatre Royal, Haymarket. The music composed by Mr. Storace.

n. pl., Printed for the curious, 1794. 19, [1] p. 17½ᶜᵐ.

Cast. The author, Prince Hoare, not mentioned.
First performed December 16, 1793.   LONGE 233

Myndlingen og Sladdreren. Tr. of d'Avossa's La pupilla ed il ciarlone.

Myrrha und Elvira oder Das opferfest. L. T. of Winter's Das unterbrochene opferfest.

Myrtil et Lycoris, pastorale. Représentée devant Leurs Majestés à Choisy, en septembre 1778.

[Paris], P. R. Christophe Ballard, 1778. 4 p. l., 22 p. 21ᶜᵐ.

One act. Cast. Bocquet de Liancourt and Maximilien Jean Boutellier are mentioned as authors, [Leopold Bastien] **Desormery** as composer.
First performed at Fontainebleau, November 4, 1777; at Paris, Académie royale de musique, October 2, 1777.   ML 50.2.M92D2

Myrtillo. *See* Venus and Adonis.

Mysis ed Eufrasia ossia I due gemelli, ballet. *See* Trento's opera Bianca de' Rossi.

The **mysteries of the castle:** a dramatic tale, in three acts; as performed at the Theatre-Royal, Covent-Garden. Written by Miles Peter Andrews, Esq.

London, T. N. Longman, 1795. 1 p. l., 89, [3] p. 20ᶜᵐ.

Cast, prologue, epilogue, and prefatory note, of date February 24, 1795, stating that the prologue and song in praise of Hawking is by Capt. Topham. William **Shield**, who partly selected, partly composed the numerous songs, glees, etc., is not mentioned.
First performed January 31, 1795.   LONGE 229

Der **nachlaessige.** Tr. of Ciampi's Il negligente.

Die **nacht.** Tr. of Piccinni's Notte critica.

Die **nachtmusik.** A. T. of Mitscha's Adrast und Isidore.

Naïs, ballet-héroïque, avec un prologue, représenté, pour la premiere fois, par l'Academie-royale de musique le mardi 22 avril 1749, et remis au Théâtre le mardi 7 août 1764.

Paris Aux dépens de l'Académie, chés de Lormel, 1764. 59, [1] p. 22½ᶜᵐ.

Three entrées and prologue, called "L'accord des dieux." Cast, brief argument, and names of Louis de Cahusac as author, of Jean Philippe **Rameau** as composer.
                                              ML 52.2.N22

La **naissance de Venus,** opera. Representée par l'Academie royale de musique l'an 1696. Les paroles sont de M. Picque & la musique de M. Collasse. XXXIX. opera.

n. i., n. d. front., 353–414 p. 14ᶜᵐ. (Recueil général des opéra, Paris, t. v, 1703.)

Detached copy. Five acts and prologue.
First performed May 1, 1696, as indicated. Schatz 2101
Second copy. ML 48.R4

Der name thut nichts zur sache. A. T. of Schack's Die beiden Antone and originally of Anton der dumme gaertner.

Nancy: or, The parting lovers. An interlude. Set to music by the author.

[245]–254, [2] p. 22ᶜᵐ. (Henry Carey, Dramatick works, London, 1743.)

One act. Argument, in which Carey says that the subject of his interlude is based on an actual occurrence, and that from it:

"the author drew the following sketch, and form'd it into an interlude, a kind of entertainment formerly in great request, but now almost a stranger to the English stage. The Italians still preserve it under the name of Intermezzo, which is equal to the word Interlude. These little starts of fancy, not only afford a present diversion, and supply a vacancy on the stage, while other entertainments are getting ready; but, by encouragement and improvement, sometimes become entertainments themselves."

First performed at Drury Lane 1739; revived in 1755, as "The press gang, or Love in low life," "on the prospect of a war, and frequently brought forward on similar occasions under the title of *True Blue*" (Grove). ML 49.A2C2

Nanette et Lucas, ou La paysanne curieuse, comedie en prose, mêlée d'ariettes, en un acte; représentée pour la première fois par les Comédiens italiens le 14 juin 1764. Les paroles sont de M. Framery. La musique de M. le chevalier d'Herbain.

Paris, Claude Herissant, 1754 [!] *51 p. 19ᶜᵐ.*

Cast and Framery's complimentary "Epître a Messieurs les acteurs de Nanette et Lucas." ML 50.2.N17H3

— **Nanette et Lucas,** ou La paysanne curieuse, comédie en prose, mêlée d'ariettes, en un acte; représentée pour la premiere fois par les Comédiens italiens le 14 juin 1764. Les paroles sont de M. Framery. La musique de M. le chevalier d'Herbain.

Paris, Claude Herissant, 1775. 40 p. 19ᶜᵐ.

On p. 18–19, the air of "Cet amour qu' en vous voyant" (I, 7). Schatz 4644

Nanine, soeur de lait de la reine de Golconde; pastorale en trois actes; en ariettes et vaudevilles choisis.

Genève et se trouve à Paris, chez la veuve Duchesne, 1773. 64 p. 21ᶜᵐ.

Argument. On p. 57–64 the "Airs détachés": "Nos plus beaux jours," "Où suis-je transporté?" "Non, je ne puis plus." Neither the author, Desfontaines de Lavallée, is mentioned, nor the composer, Jean Joseph **Rodolphe.**
First performed at Fontainebleau, Théâtre de la Cour, 1773. ML 50.2.N2R7

Nannerl bei hofe. A. T. of Der verliebte eigensinn.

Li Napoletani in America. Dramma giocoso per musica da rappresentarsi nel Real Teatro dell' Ajuda in occasione di festeggiarsi il felicissimo giorno natalizio di Sua Reale Maestà . . . D. Marianna Vittoria . . . nella primavera dell' anno 1775.

Lisbona, Stamperia reale, n. d.   88 p.   15^{cm}.

Three acts. Cast, scenario, and names of Francesco Cerlone as author, of Niccolò **Piccinni** as composer.

First performed March 31, 1775, as indicated; at Naples, Teatro de' Fiorentini, June 10, 1768.   SCHATZ 8133

Narbale. Dramma per musica da rappresentarsi nel Teatro Giustiniani di San Moisè nella fiera dell' Ascensione dell' anno 1774.

Venezia, Modesto Fenzo, 1774.   47 p.   17^{cm}.

Three acts. Argument, cast, scenario, and name of the composer, Ferdinando Giuseppe **Bertoni,** and of the author, Metastasio. The argument contains this ludicrous but characteristic remark:

"Questo atto eroico diede occasione al rinomatissimo Metastasio di formarne il dramma, che ha per titolo: L'*Eroe cinese.* Per le convenienze poi di questi cantanti, e le circostanze del teatro, che non poterono accomodarsi al vestito e scena Cinesi, si è pensato mutare e scena e nomi de' personaggi, e per conseguenza anche il titolo del dramma, conservandone tutta l'azione."

With the opera was performed (composer of the music not mentioned) Domenico Ricciardi's ballet, "Il ratto delle Sabine," description and cast of which on p. 20–22.

First performed, as indicated, May 25, 1774.   SCHATZ 940

Narciso.

p. 9–55.   15½^{cm}.   (Ottavio Tronsarelli, Drammi musicali, Roma, Francesco Corbelletti, 1632.)

Prologue and five acts. Argument. No composer mentioned.   ML 49.A2T7

Il Narciso.

Apostolo Zeno, Poesie drammatiche, Venezia, 1744, t. vii, p. [293]–358. 19^{cm}.

Five acts. Argument and prefatory note referring to the first edition of this "dramma pastorale" published at "Aspac, per Geremia Kretschmann nel 1697," with Francesco Antonio *Pistocchi's* name as composer, etc. It is further said that Pistocchi performed the part of Narciso and that Zeno wrote the play in fifteen days. In the "Catalogo" at end of t. x is this note: "in Aspac. 1696. Ediz. assai guasta, e storpiata." As a matter of fact, the Anspach ed. is not dated.   ML 49.A2Z3

— **Il Narciso,** publicato per la prima volta in Aspac 1696.

Apostolo Zeno, Poesie drammatiche, Orleans, 1785–86, t. i, p. 103–158. 21^{cm}.

Five acts. Argument. No composer is mentioned.   ML 49.A2Z4

Il Narciso. Favola boschereccia rappresentata in musica nella città di Lodi . . .

Lodi, Menletti, n. d.   4 p. l., 80 p.   15^{cm}.

Three acts with prologue. By Francesco de Lemene, who is not mentioned. Dedication dated Lodi, September 29, 1676, and signed by the composer, Carlo **Bortio.**   SCHATZ 1254

Il Narciso. Pastorale per musica da rapresentarsi nel novissimo Teatro di corte d'Anspach, consegrata all' Altezza Serenissima Elettorale di Madama Soffia Charlotte . . . da Francesco Antonio Pistocchi, mastro di capella dell' Altezza Serenissima il Margravio di Brandenburgo.

Anspach, Geremia Kretschmann, n. d.   Unpaged.   19^{cm}.

Five acts. Composer's dedication, notice to the reader with Apostolo Zeno's name as the author and of Johann Christian Rau as author of the German translation

Il **Narciso**—Continued.

that faces the Italian text. Argument, scenario, and cast, in which Giuseppe Maria Cassani's name was added on a printed slip for the character of the originally blank Lesbino.

First performed in 1697, as indicated. SCHATZ 8197

Il **Narciso,** drama pastorale, da rappresentarsi sul Regio Teatro Danese, il carnovale dell' anno 1763.—Narcissus . . .

Kiøbenhavn, Lars Nielsen Svare, n. d. 109 p. 15½^{cm}.

Three acts. Argument, cast, and names of Apostolo Zeno as author, of Giuseppe **Sarti** as composer ("La musica è tutta nuova"). Danish text faces Italian.

SCHATZ 9450

Narciso et Ecco immortalati. Opera drammatica di Oratio Persiani rappresentata in musica in Venetia . . .

Venetia, Antonio Bariletti, 1642. 81, 18 p. 14^{cm}.

The last page of the libretto incorrectly numbered 65. In three acts with prologue. Author's dedication, dated Venice, January 30, 1642. The additional 18 p. contain the "Argomento et scenario . . ." The composer, Pietro Francesco **Cavalli,** is not mentioned.

First performed at Venice, 1642, Teatro a SS. Giovanni e Paolo, as indicated.

SCHATZ 1747

Narcissus. Tr. of Sarti's Il Narciso.

Die **narren für liebe.** Tr. of Cocchi's Li matti per amore.

Die **narrheiten der eifersucht.** Tr. of Anfossi's Le pazzie de'gelosi.

Il **Narsete, generale di Giustiniano imperatore.** *See* M. Curzio.

Il **natal d'Apollo.** Componimento drammatico per festeggiare la nascita di S. A. R. il principe ereditario delle Sicilie.

Napoli, Stamperia reale, 1775. front., 78 p. 19½^{cm}.

Two acts and licenza. Vignettes, etc. Argument, scenario, cast, names of Saverio Mattei as author, of Pasquale **Cafaro** as composer. The two acts were separated by "La gara degli atleti, ballo." The componimento was followed by Carlo Lepicq's five-act "Adelaide di Guesclin, ballo eroico," of which, without name of the composer of the music, cast, argument, and scene by scene description.

First performed, as indicated, January 4, 1775, Teatro di San Carlo.

ML 48.M2G

Il **natal d'Ercole** di Michelagnolo Buonarroti. Favola rappresentata al serenissimo Signor Don Alfonso da Este, principe di Modana, e all' eccellentissimo Signor Don Luigi suo fratello, nella venuta loro a Firenze. Da Madama serenissima di Toscana. Nel palazzo dell' Eccellentiss. Sig. D. Antonio Medici. [coat of arms]

Firenze, Giunti, 1605. 4 p. l., 51 p. 21^{cm}.

Prologue and five acts. Buonarroti's dedication is dated Florence, October 22, 1605. Since he speaks of "Questa mia favola del Natal d'Ercole, rappresentata a V. A. S. e all' eccellentiss. Sig. D. Luigi suo fratello, ben che al presente comparisca fuori spogliata de gli ornamenti dell' apparato, e per se poco adorna . . ." The performance would seem to have taken place *before* October 22, 1605, but a contemporary diary of court happenings, which Solerti quotes in "Musica . . . alla Corte Medicea dal 1600 al 1637" make it quite clear that October 22, 1605, was the date of first performance. The diary does not mention the composer. Nor is he mentioned in the libretto, nor by Solerti, Eitner, Vogel, Corazzini, yet Schatz attributes the music to Jacopo **Peri.** The words of "Il natal d'Ercole" do not appear with any of his published music. SCHATZ 7920

Second copy. ML 48.M2 I

Il natal di Giove.

Metastasio, Poesie, Parigi, vedova Quillau, 1755, t. ii, [431]–454 p.
16ᶜᵐ.

One act.   ML 49.A2M42

— **Il natal di Giove.**   Azione teatrale, rappresentata la prima volta, con musica del Bonno, negli appartamenti dell' Imperial Favorita dalle reali arciduchesse Maria Teresa (poi imperatrice regina), e Marianna di lei sorella, dal R. principe Carlo di Lorena, e da una dama, ed un cavalier della corte, alla presenza de' sovrani, per festeggiàre il giorno di nascita dell' imperator Carlo VI, il dì primo ottobre 1740 . . .

[359]–384 p.   26ᶜᵐ.   (Pietro Metastasio, Opere, t. i, Parigi, vedova Herissant, 1780.)

One act.   Argument.   ML 49.A2M44

Il natale augusto.   Dramma per musica per celebrare il felicissimo nascimento di S. A. Serenissima Donna Maria, principessa della Beira.   Da cantarsi in atto di umilissimo ossequio in casa di Anselmo Jose da Crus Sobral.

Lisbona, Simone Taddeo Ferreira, 1783.   4 p. l., 38 p.   16ᶜᵐ.

Prologue, two acts.   Gaetano Martinelli is mentioned as the author, Antonio Leal **Moreira** as the composer.   The princess was born April 29, 1793.
First performed, as indicated, Lisbon, May, 1793.   Schatz 6637

Il natale di Minerva.   Dramma musicale.

Girolamo Bartolommei Smeducci, Drammi musicali morali, Firenze, 1656, v. i, p. [59]–99.   23ᶜᵐ.

Prologue and three acts.   Argument, allegoria, and dedication to duke Ferdinand of Bavaria, beginning:
"Queste mie musicali favole, che nel tempo delle fortunatissime nozze di V. A. S. giunsero in penna a farle divotissima offerta, ritornano, rinnovate con la stampa, a dedicarsi all' A. S. Sereniss. . . ."   ML 49.A2B3

Nature et patrie.   A. T. of Grétry's Callias.

Naturens røst.   Et syngestykke i tre akter.   Lyrisk omarbejdet efter Armands original: Le cri de la nature, komoedie i een akt.   Af E. Falsen.   Musiken af hr. kapelmester Kundzen.

Kjøbenhavn, Johan Fredrik Schultz, 1799.   100 p.   15½ᶜᵐ.

First performed at Copenhagen, Royal Theatre, December 3, 1799.   Schatz 5327

Le naufrage au port, comédie en un acte, mêlée de vaudevilles par les CC. Pain et Midet; représentée pour la première fois sur le Théâtre du Vaudeville le 13 Fructidor, l'an 2ᵐᵉ de la République française.

Paris, au Théâtre du Vaudeville, an troisième, [1794–95].   39 p.   20ᶜᵐ.

Cast.   On p. 38, the air of the vaudeville, "Pour voir accueillir."
First performed, as indicated, August 30, 1794.   ML 48.M2H

Il naufragio di Cipro.   Dramma pastorale per musica, nuovamente composto per essere rappresentato sul Regio Teatro di Copenaga, nel carnevale dell' anno 1764.—Skibbruddet ved Cypren . . . Oversadt paa dansk, af R. Soelberg . . .

Kiøbenhavn, Lars Nielsen Svare, n. d.   95 p.   16ᶜᵐ.

Three acts.   Argument, cast, and names of Pietro Antonio Zani as author ("La poesia è tutta nuova"), and of Giuseppe **Sarti** ("La musica è tutta nuova").   Danish text faces Italian.
First performed, as indicated, in January, 1764.   Schatz 9451

Il **naufragio felice,** ballet. *See* Borghi's La donna instabile.

The **naval pillar:** A musical entertainment. Performed at the Theatre-Royal, Covent-Garden, with unbounded applause. By T. Dibdin . . .

> *London, J. Barker, 1799. 27, [1] p. 21½ᶜᵐ.*

Cast, prefatory note, and name of "Mr. [John] **Moorehead**" as composer of "the overture, new songs, and music of the dance." He also utilized a few national and old airs and the "Glee and chorus: When Britain first her flag uprear'd," by **Callcott.**
First performed October 7, 1799. (Genest.) LONGE 258

La **nave d'Argo.** *See* M. Curzio.

Le **navigateur.** A. T. of Philidor's Mélide.

Die **neapolitanische fischer-empoerung.** A. T. of Keiser's Masagniello furioso.

Nebucadnezar, koenig zu Babylon. *See* Keiser's Der bestuerzte und wieder erhoehte . . .

La **necessità non ha legge.** Dramma giocoso per musica da rappresentarsi in Bologna nel Teatro Marsigli Rossi nel' estate dell' anno 1784 . . .

> *Bologna, Sassi, n. d. 54 p. 15ᶜᵐ.*

Two acts. Author unknown to Schatz. With impresario's dedication, cast, scenario, and name of the composer, Vincenzo **Fabrizj.** Practically the same text as:
SCHATZ 2976

— La **necessità non ha legge.** Dramma giocoso per musica da rappresentarsi nel Teatro di S. A. E. di Sassonia.

> *Dresda, n. publ., 1786. 119 p. 15ᶜᵐ.*

Two acts. Author unknown to Schatz. German text and title-page, "Noth hat kein gesetz," face Italian. With cast and name of the composer, Vincenzo **Fabrizj.**
SCHATZ 2969

Il **negligente.**

> *[173]–218 p. 16½ᶜᵐ. (Carlo Goldoni, Opere drammatiche giocose, t. ii, Torino, 1757.)*

Three acts. First composed by **Ciampi** as below. ML 49.A2G6

— Il **negligente.** Dramma di tre atti per musica. Rappresentato per la prima volta in Venezia l'anno 1753. [!]

> *Carlo Goldoni, Opere teatrali, Venezia, Zatta e figli, 1788–95, v. 44, [183]–231 p. 18ᶜᵐ.* PQ

Il **negligente.** Dramma comico per musica da rappresentarsi nel Teatro Giustinan di S. Moisè l'autunno dell' anno 1749.

> *Venezia, Modesto Fenzo, 1749. front., 48 p. 14½ᶜᵐ.*

Three acts. By Goldoni, with alterations. Cast and name of composer, Legrenzio Vincenzo **Ciampi.** SCHATZ 1886

— Il **negligente,** drama per musica. Tradotto dall' italiano in tedesco da Marco Soralli, maestro della lingua italiana in Norimberga.—Der nachlaessige, eine musicalische opera. Ubersetzt aus dem italiaenischen ins teutsche und verbessert von Marco Soralli . . .

> *n. i., n. d. 109 p. 17ᶜᵐ.*

Three acts. German text faces the Italian. The cast is that of Füerst Thurn und Taxis private company, managed by Girolamo Bon, which first performed the opera

Il negligente—Continued.

at Frankfort o/M, Theaterbude am Rossmarkt, October 5, 1754. A foot-note on p. [2] reads:
"La musica delle arie, duetti, terzetti e quartetti sono del celebre Signor Vincenzo **Ciampi,** Maestro napolitano."
    The text is not quite the same as in "Il negligente," Venezia, 1749. For instance, the aria, "Se il foco mi accende" (I, 6) is not in the text as composed by Ciampi, where we have "Senza sentir il danno," and in III, 5, "Levarsi dopo il Sole" instead of "Non voglio imbrogli," as in III, 4 of the Soralli version.   SCHATZ 1889

Le négociant de Nantes.   A. T. of Solié's Le Franc Breton.

Nel perdono la vendetta. Melodramma da rappresentarsi nel Teatro Giustiniano di S. Moisè per la fiera dell' Ascensione dell' anno 1728.

    Venezia, Aloise Valvasense, 1728. 46 p. 15^{cm}.

    Pages 3–4 perhaps missing.
    Three acts. Notice to the reader as argument, and scenario. Neither the author, Carlo Paganicesa, nor the composer, Giovanni **Porta,** is mentioned.
    First performed in May, 1728, as indicated.   SCHATZ 8384

Le nemiche degli uomini, ballet. *See* Tarchi's Dorval e Virginia.

I nemici generosi o sia Il duello per complimento. Dramma giocoso per musica da rappresentarsi nel Regio Teatro di via della Pergola la primavera del 1797 . . .

    Firenze, Stamperia Albizziniana, 1797. 52 p. 16½^{cm}.

    Two acts. Without names of the composer, **Cimarosa,** or author, who is unknown to Schatz. On p. 4–10, argument, cast, and detailed description of Gio. Batista Giannini's four-act "La fata benefica. Ballo persiano favoloso." Paisiello and Ercolani are mentioned as the composers of the music.
    First performed at Rome, Teatro Valle, carnival, 1796.   SCHATZ 1957

— **I nemici generosi.** Dramma giocoso per musica, da rappresentarsi nel Teatro Elettorale di Sassonia.

    Dresda, n. publ., 1797. 27 p. l., 64 p. 16^{cm}.

    Two acts with name of the composer, **Cimarosa.** German title-page, "Die grossmuethigen feinde," faces Italian, and most of the p. l. are taken up by the very detailed "Innhalt."
    First performed, as indicated, January 18, 1797.   SCHATZ 1958

— **Il duello per complimento.** Farsa giocosa per musica d'un atto solo da rappresentarsi nel Teatro Giustiniani in San Moisè.

    Venezia, Modesto Fenzo, Anno primo della libertà italiana [1797]. 32 p. 18½^{cm}.

    One act. Cast and name of **Cimarosa** as the composer. The farce is followed by Luigi Olivieri's "Ernesta e Daon, ballo pantomimo in tre atti," with cast, argument, and description, but without name of the composer of the music, and "Chi l'avrebbe mai creduto." Then comes, on p. 39–64, with cast, the libretto of "Il SECRETO, farsa giocosa per musica d'un atto solo da rappresentarsi nel Teatro Giustiniani in S. Moisè del cittadino Giuseppe Foppa . . . La musica è del celebre maestro Simeone **Mayr.**"   SCHATZ 2002

Il nemico amante. L. T. of Buini and Chelleri's La pace per amore.

Il nemico delle donne. L. T. of Galuppi's L'inimico delle donne.

Neptune et Amymone.   *See* Mouret's Les amours des dieux.

Nerina. Favola pastorale da rappresentarsi nel Teatro Grimani di S. Samuel nella fiera dell' Ascensione dell' anno 1728 . . .

Venezia, Carlo Bonarrigo, 1728. 47 p. 15½ᶜᵐ.

Three acts. Dedication by Domenico Lalli as impresario, who is supposed to have altered the text by Pietro d'Averara, who is not mentioned; argument, cast, scenario, and name of Antonio **Pollaroli** as the composer. Schatz 8263

Nero. *See* Händel's Die durch blut und mord erlangete liebe.

Nero. Tr. of Orlandini's Nerone.

Nerone. Tragedia per musica rappresentata nel famoso Teatro Grimani di S. Gio. Grisostomo il carnovale dell' anno 1721.

Venezia, Marino Rossetti, 1721. 59 p. 15½ᶜᵐ.

Three acts. By conte Agostino Piovene, who is not mentioned. Argument, cast, scenario, and name of Giuseppe Maria **Orlandini** as the composer. Schatz 7343

— Nero, in einem sing-spiele auf dem Hamburgischen schauplatze vorgestellet. Im jahr 1729.

n. pl., Gedruckt mit Stromerschen schrifften, n. d. Unpaged. 18ᶜᵐ.

Three acts. Scenario. Translated by Johann Mattheson, who is not mentioned. The arias have also Italian text. "Die music (ausser den wenigen mit dem * bezeichneten arien) ist von dem hrn. **Orlandini** . . ." The starred arias are "Affetti del mio sposo" (I, 1), "Già tutto valore" (I, 5), "Spirto eccelso, con valore" (I, 9), "Bella destra" (I, 12), "Amor e gelosia" (II, 3), "D'antico Amor le faci" (II, 6). The composers of these arias are not mentioned. Schatz 7344

Il Nerone. Drama per musica, nel nuovo Teatro Grimano di S. Gio. Grisostomo. L'anno 1679. Di Giulio Cesare Corradi . . .

Venetia, Francesco Nicolini, 1679. 71 p. 14ᶜᵐ.

Three acts. Author's dedication, argument, notice to the reader with name of Carlo **Pallavicino** as the composer and scenario. Schatz 7729

Nerone fatto Cesare. Drama per musica da rappresentarsi nel famoso Teatro di S. Salvatore. L'anno MDCXCIII. Di Matteo Noris . . .

Venetia, Nicolini, 1693. 89 p. 13½ᶜᵐ.

Three acts. Author's dedication, notice to the reader with name of Giacomo Antonio **Perti** as the composer, and scenario.
First performed, carnival 1693, as indicated. Schatz 7952

Netley Abbey, an operatic farce in two acts, as performed at the Theatre-royal, Covent-Garden. Written by Mr. Pearce . . .

London, T. N. Longman, 1794. 3 p. l., 35, [1] p. 20ᶜᵐ.

Cast, dedication, dated November 22, 1794, and note appreciative of the "comic exertions," "vocal powers" of the cast and of "the beautiful air" by Mr. **Baumgarten,** in the first act, and Mr. **Shield's** striking composition of "England, a world within itself" in the second. No other composers are mentioned in the libretto, but the title page of Longman and Broderip's vocal score says "partly selected and partly composed by Mr. **Baumgarten,** Mr. W. **Parke,** Sigʳ **Paisiello,** Mr. **Howard,** and Mr. **Shield,**" and the individual numbers are headed accordingly.
First performed on April 10, 1794 (Schatz); April 22, 1794 (Genest). Longe 229

Nettuno ed Egle. Favola pastorale per musica da rappresentarsi nel Real Teatro dell' Ajuda per celebrare gli augustissimi sposalizi de' serenissimi Signori infanti di Portogallo e di Spagna Don Giovanni con Donna Carlotta Gioacchina, e Donna Marianna Vittoria con Don Gabriele Antonio la primavera dell' anno 1785.

[Lisboa], Nella stamperia reale, n. d. 52 p. 15ᶜᵐ.

Two acts. By Gaetano Sertor (Schatz). Argument, cast, scenario, and name of the composer, João de Sousa **Carvalho.** It is said that "il drammatico componimento, è d'un Veneto incognito autore." Schatz 1671

Nettuno ed Egle. Favola pastorale per musica da rappresentarsi nel nobilissimo Teatro di S. Benedetto la fiera dell' Ascensione dell' anno 1783 . . .

*Venezia, Modesto Fenzo, 1783. 57 p. 17½*cm.

Two acts. Dedication by the author, Gaetano Sertor, argument, cast, scenario, and name of Antonio **Pio** as the composer. On p. 29–32 cast, description, and name of Carlo Canobio as the composer of the music of "Cupido trionfatore o sia Apollo e Dafne, ballo pastorale pantomimo composto dal Signor Giuseppe Canziani" and on p. 55–57 of "La maggior impresa d'Ercole o sia Adureto ed Alceste, ballo tragico eroico pantomimo" by the same author and composer.   SCHATZ 8188

Das neu-beglueckte Sachsen durch die erfreuliche geburt eines Chur-Saechsischen printzen, auf veranstaltung des koenigl. Pohln. und Chur-fuerstl. Saechs, Geheimen Secretairs herrn Koenigs, als er eben in Hamburg anwesend war, in einem von ihm verfertigten Prologo vor seiner opera Sancio zu allerunterthaenigster freuden-bezeugung auf dasigem schau-platze oeffentlich vorgestellt.   1730.

*Hamburg, [Piscator], n. d.   Unpaged.   18*cm.

Publisher's name cut off in binding.

Cast, names of the author and of the composer, Georg Philipp **Telemann,** and sonnet by Christoph Gottlieb Wend, dated "Hamburg, im October 1730" and addressed to Johann Ulrich Koenig.   From the dedication it appears that this libretto was printed after the performance on October 30, 1730, in honor of the prince's birth, on August 25, 1730.   The libretto is followed by:

— FORSETZUNG DES PROLOGI, an statt der opera Sancio, dabey vorzustellen.   1730. Hamburg, gedruckt mit Piscators schrifften.

Cast.   SCHATZ 10272

Der neu-modische liebhaber Damon, in einem scherzhaften singespiele auf der Hamburgischen schau-buehne zum erstenmale vorgestellet 1724.

*[Hamburg], Caspar Jakhel, n. d.   Unpaged.   18*cm.

Three acts. Argument. Neither the author (unknown to Schatz) nor the composer, Georg Philipp **Telemann,** is mentioned.   SCHATZ 10264

Musiktexte aus dem Neusonntagskinde nach dem Furchtsamen des weil. herrn Hafner.   Als singspiel neu fuer das k. k. privil. Marinellische Theater bearbeitet [von] Joachim Perinet . . .   Die musik ist vom herrn Wenzel Mueller . . .   Aufgefuehrt den 10 ten des weinmonates [Oct.] 1793.   Dritte auflage.

*Wien, Mathias Andreas Schmidt, 1794.   40 p.   17*cm.

Cast.   SCHATZ 6947

— Gesaenge aus dem singspiele: Das **sonntagskind** in zwey aufzuegen.   In musik gesetzt von Wenzel Mueller.

*Hamburg, Rabe und Freystatzky wittwe, 1798.   32 p.   16*cm.

Joachim Perinet is not mentioned.

First performed at Hamburg, Theater beim Gänsemarkt, February 3, 1795.

                                                               SCHATZ 6948

— Arien und gesaenge aus der oper: Das **neue Sonntags-kind.** Ein komisches singspiel in zwey aufzuegen.   Die musik ist vom herrn kapellmeister Mueller in Wien.

*Berlin, n. publ., n. d.   46 p.   15½*cm.

Cast.   Perinet is not mentioned.

First performed at Berlin, Koenigl. National Theater, May 6, 1796.   SCHATZ 6949

Der neue gutsherr.   A. T. of Dittersdorf's Der schiffspatron.

Der **neue gutsherr.** In drey akten. Komponirt vom herrn musik-direktor Hiller.

n. i., n. d. 134 p. 17cm.

In his "Vorrede," dated Leipzig, July 6, 1781, [Johann Gottfried] Dyk says: "Die franzoesische und deutsche komische oper ist ein sonderbar ding. Zwar ist es etwas sehr gewoehnliches, zumal unter den Franzosen, liederchen bey spaziergaengen und mahlzeiten zu singen; aber im gespraech mit andern faellt man doch nie aus rede in gesang. Indess, die gattung ist einmal da und gewaehrt vergnuegen . . . Um aber das unnatuerliche in der form so viel als moeglich zu mindern, sollte man die scene immer auf das land, oder in die fabelhaften und ritter zeiten legen; hier laesst sich der gesang noch am ehsten ohne gar zu grosse widersinnigkeit anbringen. Aus dem itzigen staedtischen leben entlehnte suejets, sollten wir Deutsche uns um so mehr enthalten mit gesaengen zu verbraemen, da wir unsern dialog in prosa schreiben und da unser gesang, eben weil er ungleich mehr gesang ist als der franzoesische, auch deshalb ungleich greller von der rede absticht. Die Italiener, in deren opern alles gesang ist, koennen ihre suejets freyer waehlen: hingegen muessen sie auf alle entwicklung der charaktere und leidenschaften verzicht thun, welche das recitativ nicht zulaesst. Bey dieser manier kann der dichter nur durch die situationen interes-siren oder belustigen: bey der franzoesischen und deutschen kann er es auch in etwas durch die charaktere . . . Ausgefuehrte arien vollends darf man nur in ruhepunk-ten, etwann gegen das ende eines akts, anbringen: in der mitte einer scene haelt eine solche arie den fortgang der handlung zu lange auf. Nach diesen grundsaetzen habe ich zu arbeiten gesucht, und nicht sowohl auf einen kuenstlich verflochtenen plan und ausgefuehrte charaktere, als auf gemaelde und kontrastirende situationen und empfindungen mein absehn gerichtet . . . Der stoff meines stuecks ist aus dem *Paysan parvenu* von Marivaux gezogen; und die ausfuehrung der gesaenge gehoert einem meiner freunde, dem verfasser des Huldreich Wurmsamen von Wurmfeld, [Johann Friedrich Jünger], ohne dessen beyhuelfe ich es nicht wuerde gewagt haben, eine oper zu schreiben . . . Herr Hiller will die gefaelligkeit fuer mich haben, musik zu den gesaengen zu setzen: ein klavierauszug dieser musik wird im druck erscheinen."

A performance is not recorded by Schatz. Schatz 4730

Der **neue herr** oder Die hoeflichen bauern. Ein singspiel in zwey akten nach der Ankunft des herrn neu bearbeitet.

Breslau und Hirschberg, Johann Friedrich Korn, dem aeltern, 1788. 94 p. 14cm.

Not recorded by Schatz. Not found in "Deutsches Anonymen Lexikon." Rie-mann has "Der neue Herr, Singspiel von Georg Braun (Eichstätt, ca. 1790)." Schatz 11637

Der **neue krumme teufel.** Ö. T. of Haydn's Asmodeus der krumme teufel.

Der **neue richter.** A. T. of Weissflog's Das fruehstueck auf der jagd.

Das **neue sonntagskind.** L. T. of Wenzel Müller's Das neu sonntagskind.

Die **neuen Amazonen,** ein allegorisch pantomimisches ballet von C. Schulz. Die musik ist vom kapellmeister Schweitzer.

Theater Journal fuer Deutschland, Fuenftes stueck, Gotha, 1778, p. 46–53.

Two acts. Identical with the ballet "Die Amazonen" composed between 1772 and 1775 (Maurer)? Schatz 11754

Die **neuen Arkadier.** L. T. of Süssmayer's Der spiegel von Arkadien.

The **new rehearsal.** A. T. of Barthélemon's A peep behind the curtain.

New Spain; or, Love in Mexico: an opera in three acts; as performed at the Theatre-Royal in the Hay-Market. First acted on Friday, July 16, 1790.

> *London, G. G. J. and J. Robinson, 1790. 3 p. l., 61 p. 22^{cm}.*

Neither the author, John Scawen, nor Samuel **Arnold,** the composer, is mentioned.
ML 50.2.N43
Second copy.   LONGE 238

Nicaboro in Jucatan. Dramma per musica di Domenico Piccinni da rappresentarsi nel Real Teatro di S. Carlo nel dì 12. gennaro 1799. Festeggiandosi la nascita di Ferdinando IV . . .

> *Napoli, Stamperia Flautina, 1799. 48 p. 15$\frac{1}{2}$^{cm}.*

Two acts. Impresario's dedication, dated Naples, January 12, 1799, argument, scenario, cast, and name of Giacomo **Tritto** as the composer. According to a footnote, the text of the first part of scene 1, act I, was not by Piccinni. On p. 8–18, argument, cast, without name of the composet of the music, and description of Gaspare Ronzi's "Giulietta e Romeo, ballo pantomimo tragico-urbano." His second ballet was called "Li Zingani in fiera."   SCHATZ 10463

Nicaise, opera-comique en un acte. Par M. Vadé. Représenté sur le Théâtre de l'Opera-comique à la Foire S. Germain le 7 février 1756.

> *Paris, Duchesne, 1756. 70 p. 19$\frac{1}{2}$^{cm}.*

Largely *en vaudevilles.* Cast. On p. 65–70 the "Airs choisis" as below. On cover of this title the music is attributed to [Felice] **Bambini.**   ML 50.2.N3

— **Nicaise,** opera-comique en un acte, par M. Vadé. Représenté sur le Théatre de l'Opéra-comique à la Foire St. Germain le 7 février 1756.

> *La Haye, Pierre Gosse, junior, 1760. 85 p. 16^{cm}. (Vadé, Oeuvres, La Haye, 1759, t. iv.)*

Largely *en vaudevilles.* Cast. On p. 79–85, the "Airs choisis:" "Pour d'autres instans," "Non, je n'aimerai jamais."   ML 49.A2V2

— **Nicaise,** opéra-comique, en un acte. Représenté sur le Théatre de l'Opéra-comique, à la Foire S. Germain le 7 février 1756.

> *Paris, la veuve Duchesne, 1766. 72 p. 19^{cm}.*

On p. 67–72, the airs: "Pour d'autres instants gardez," "Non, je n'aimerai jamais que vous."   SCHATZ 11501

Nice, imitation de Stratonice; en un acte, en prose, melée de vaudevilles; représentée pour la première fois sur le Théâtre du Vaudeville le mercredi 6 juin 1792.

> *Paris, Maret, 1793. 27 p. 20^{cm}.*

Cast. Not recorded by Cl. & L., Schatz or Towers.   ML 48.M2H

Nicodème dans la lune, ou La révolution pacifique. Folie en prose et en trois actes, mêlée d'ariettes et de vaudevilles. Représentée pour la première fois à Paris, au Théâtre français, comique et lyrique, le 7 novembre 1790, et, pour la cent cinquante-sixième fois, le mardi 27 septembre 1791. Par le Cousin-Jacques. Troisième édition.

> *Paris, Froullé et chez l'auteur, 1791. 104 p. 21^{cm}.*

Cast. On p. 97–104, "Quelques réflexions de l'auteur" on the history, etc., of this famous piece, which is "selon tout le monde, une production très originale, soit en mal, soit en bien."   SCHATZ 707

Nicola e Cirilla, ballet. *See* Gardi's Il finto Stregone.

Nicomede. Dramma serio per musica da rappresentarsi in Genova nel Teatro da S. Agostino il carnevale del 1790 . . .

Genova, Stamperia Gesiniana, n. d. 53 p., 13, [1] p. 13½ᶜᵐ.

Three acts. Eustachio Manfredi is mentioned as the author, and Giuseppe **Giordani** as the composer ("musica nuova"). Dedicatory poem, argument, scenario, and cast. The additional pages contain the argument, cast, and description of Filippo Beretti's five-act ballo tragico, "Ipermestra ossia La morte di Danao." The composer of the music is not mentioned. SCHATZ 3847

Il Nicomede in Bitinia. Drama per musica da rappresentarsi nel Teatro Zane. L'anno MDCLXXVII. Del dottore Gio. Matteo Giannini . . .

Venetia, Francesco Nicolini, 1677. front., 71 p. 14ᶜᵐ.

Three acts. Poem dedicated to the empress Eleonara by Giannini and dated Venice, February 4, 1677, argument, scenario, and notice to the reader, with name of Carlo **Grossi** as the composer, and remark to the effect that the drama, on account of the "apparenze e machine," could not be performed in its original form, for want of space. Hence the necessity to condense and mutilate it "in quella parte, che nobilita i drami, ed allettando l'occhio, invaghisce gl'animi, oggidè assuefatti à i prodigi." SCHATZ 4218

La Nicopoli. Drama musicale da rappresentarsi nel Theatro Domestico in S. Fantino l'anno 1700 del dottor Francesco Rossi . . .

Venetia, Gio. Maria Rossi, 1700. front., 48 p. 15ᶜᵐ.

Three acts. Author's dedication, argument, prefatory note, with name of the composer, Bernardo **Borgognini.** SCHATZ 1241

Nicoraste. Dramma per musica da rappresentarsi nel nobilissimo Teatro di S. Benedetto nella fiera dell' Ascensione dell' anno 1769.

Venezia, Modesto Fenzo, 1769. 46 p. 15½ᶜᵐ.

Three acts. By Bartolomeo Vitturi (not mentioned), with alterations. Argument, cast, and name of Antonio **Sacchini** as the composer. SCHATZ 9233

Nicoraste rè di Tracia. Dramma per musica da rappresentarsi nel Teatro di S. Angelo la fiera dell' Ascensione dell' anno 1745.

Venezia, Modesto Fenzo, 1745. 48 p. 15ᶜᵐ.

Three acts. By Bartolomeo Vitturi, who is not mentioned. Impresario's dedication, dated Venice, May 22, 1745, argument, cast, scenario, and name of Giovanni Battista **Pattoni** as the composer. SCHATZ 7785

Nilus, der grossmuethige veraechter der welt, ein singspiel in einem aufzuge von der kleineren congregation unter tem titel der Unbefleckten Empfaengniss Mariae aufgefuehrt im Maerzmonde 1785 zu Augsburg.

[Augsburg], Joseph Simon Hueber, n. d. 10 p. 19½ᶜᵐ.

At head of title: "Martinez oder Die besiegte rachbegierde, ein christliches trauerspiel in dreyen aufzuegen, und."

With cast and "Vorbericht." Michael **Demler** is mentioned as composer. The author is not mentioned, and is unknown to Schatz. SCHATZ 2508

Nina, ou La folle par amour, comédie en un acte, en prose, mêlée d'ariettes, par M. M. D. V. Musique de M. Dalayrac. Réprésentée, pour la premiere fois, par les Comédiens italiens ordinaires du roi. le 15 mai 1786.

Paris, Brunet, 1788. 47 p. 21ᶜᵐ.

Cast. Text by B. J. Marsollier. ML 50.2.N4D2

Nina—Continued.

— **Nina**; or, The love distracted maid: A comedy in one act. Translated from the French of M. M. D. V.

London, G. Goulding, 1787.   2 p. l., 40 p.   21ᶜᵐ.

On p. 39–40, a list of "New music published by G. Goulding." In a prefatory note this translation is called, "entire and unmutilated: no deviation whatever has been attempted from the fable or connection of the excellent original . . ." He apparently alludes to Marsollier's "Nina, ou La folle par amour," first performed at Paris, with Dalayrac's music, 1786.

No performance of this English version, by unknown translator, recorded by Clarence.   Longe 99

— **Nina** oder Wahnsinn aus liebe. Ein schauspiel mit gesang in einem aufzuge. Nach dem franzoesischen mit beybehaltener musik von B. C. d'Arien.

Hamburg, n. publ., 1787.   56 p.   17ᶜᵐ.

Dalayrac is not mentioned.
First performed at Hamburg, Theater beim Gänsemarkt, January 31, 1787.

Schatz 2367

— **Nina** oder Wahnsinn aus liebe. Ein schauspiel mit gesang in einem akt.

Mainz, n. publ., 1787.   2 p. l., 66 p.   14½ᶜᵐ.

"Vorerinnerung . . . Der uibersetzer," according to Schatz, Heinrich Gottlieb Schmieder. **Dalayrac** is not mentioned.
First performed at Mannheim, June 17, 1787.   Schatz 2368

— Arien und gesaenge aus **Nina** oder Wahnsinn aus liebe. Singspiel in einem aufzuge. Aus dem franzoesischen. Die musik ist vom herrn Dallairac.

Berlin, n. publ., 1790.   16 p.   16ᶜᵐ.

German version by Joh. André (Schatz).
First performed at Berlin, Nationaltheater, May 3, 1788.   Schatz 2369

— **Nina**; oder: Was vermag die liebe nicht? Ein singspiel in einem aufzuge. Nach dem franzoesischen von L. Die musik ist von Dallirak.

Berlin, n. publ., 1789.   62 p.   15ᶜᵐ.

First performed at Charlottenburg, Schlosstheater, July 31, 1789.   Schatz 2370

Nina or The love distracted maid. Tr. of Dalayrac's Nina ou La folle par amour.

Nina o sia La pazza per amore. Commedia in prosa, ed in verso per musica, tradotta dal francese. Da rappresentarsi nel Teatro de' Fiorentini per seconda opera di quest' anno 1790.

Napoli, Vincenzo Flauto, 1790.   47 p.   18ᶜᵐ.

Two acts. Cast, name of **Paisiello** as composer, and preface by the author, Giambattista Lorenzi. In this he refers to the first performance at Caserta, Teatro del Reale Sito di Belvedere, summer of 1789, for which, by royal command, he wrote and Paisiello composed several additional numbers. The opera was there performed in one act, without intermissions. For this replica, he continues, it was found necessary to divide the opera in two parts, and, incidentally, to write and compose further additional numbers. All these additions are marked with an asterisk in the libretto. They are:

"Con voi divide" (I, 8), "Mormora il ruscelletto allor più grato" (I, 9), "Gli armenti suoi raccoglie" (I, 9), "Senza il caro mio tesoro" (I, 9), "L'amo tanto, che per lei" (II, 1), "Se non prendo un pò di fiato" (II, 3), "Conti-con voi . . . con lei" (II, 7).   Schatz 7645

Nina o sia La pazza per amore—Continued.

— **Nina**, o sia La pazza per amore. Dramma giocoso per musica, da rappresentarsi nel Teatro di S. A. E. di Sassonia.

Dresda, n. publ., 1791. 99 p. 15½ᶜᵐ.

Two acts. **Paisiello** is mentioned, but not Lorenzi. German title page, "Nina, oder Wahnsinn aus liebe," and text face Italian.

First performed January 7, 1792, as indicated. Schatz 7646

Nina oder Wahnsinn aus liebe. Tr. of Dalayrac's Nina ou La folle par amour.

Nina oder Wahnsinn aus liebe. Tr. of Paisiello's Nina o La pazza per amore.

Nina oder Was vermag die liebe nicht? Tr. of Dalayrac's Nina ou La folle par amour.

Nina pazza per amore, ballet. *See* Andreozzi's Amelia ed Ottiero.

Nina pazza per amore, ballet. *See* Andreozzi's Argea.

Nina pazza per amore, ballet. *See* Astaritta's Il curioso accidente.

La **Nina pazza per amore,** ballet. *See* Guglielmi's Enea e Lavinia.

Ninetta, o sia La contadina nel palazzo signorile, ballet. *See* Sarti's Siroe.

Ninette à la cour. A. T. of Le caprice amoureux.

Ninette a la cour, ballet en action; par M. Gardel, L. . . . Représenté, devant Leurs Majestés, à Choisy, pour la premiere fois, & à Fontainebleau en 1777.

[Paris], Pierre Robert Christophe Ballard, 1777. 2 p. l., 19 p. 21ᶜᵐ.

Three acts. Cast. Act by act synopsis of the action. Composer of the music not recorded by Lajarte, who merely says: "*Ninette à la cour* fut parodié par Favart sur la musique de Ciampi (*Bertoldo alla Corte*). Quelques airs sont restés dans le ballet, qui eut du succès."

First performed at Paris, Académie royale de musique, August 18, 1778.

ML 52.2.N4

La **ninfa Apollo.** O.T. of L' inganno felice, 1730; with same prefatory note.

La **ninfa Apollo** del conte Lemene. Favola pastorale da rappresentarsi nel Teatro Grimani di S. Samuele nella fiera dell' Ascensione dell' anno 1734 . . .

Venezia, Marino Rossetti, n. d. 34 p. 15½ᶜᵐ.

Three acts. Retouched by Giov. Boldini, who is not mentioned. Impresario's dedication, cast, scenario, and name of **Galuppi** as composer.

First performed, as indicated, May 30, 1734. Schatz 3488

La **ninfa Apollo.** Scherzo scenico pastorale per musica da rappresentarsi nel Teatro Tron di S. Cassano l' ultima sera del carnovale dell' anno MDCCIX. Poesia del co. Francesco de Lemene, Lodigiano.

Venezia, Marino Rossetti, 1709. 24 p. 14½ᶜᵐ.

Three acts. Cast. The composer, Carlo Francesco **Gasparini,** is not mentioned.

First performed February 12, 1709, as indicated. Schatz 3574

La ninfa Apollo. Pastorale da recitarsi in musica l' anno 1726. Per la ricreazione del carnovale da Signori Accademici Librali . . .

Venezia, Antonio Bortoli, 1726. 46 p. 15ᶜᵐ.

Three acts. Without list of characters! Dedication and notice to the reader: "Eco la Ninfa Apollo parto della celebre penna del Sig. Francesco di Lemene, ma non già quale resci dalle mani del suo autore. L' aggiunta d' un personaggio, la mutazione delle ariette, e la variazione e trasposizione di qualche scena, la rendono in buona parte da quella diversa. Sappia però chi legge, che un tale cambiamento non è gia effetto di poca stima verso un così illustre poeta, ne presunzione di migliorar la poesia, ma pura necessità di accomodarla al numero, ed alla abilità di chi deve rappresentarla, ed all' uso, ed al gusto della musica del moderno teatro . . ." The composer, Francesco **Rossi**, is not mentioned. SCHATZ 8888

La ninfa avara di Benedetto Ferrari dalla Tiorba. Rappresētata in musica in Venetia. Posta in musica dall' istesso autore.

n. i., n. d. p. [205]–237 (Poesie drammatiche di Benedetto Ferrari, Milano, 1644). 13½ᶜᵐ.

Detached copy. Three acts and prologue. Author's dedication and argument. First performed at Venice, Teatro di San Moisè, carnival 1641. SCHATZ 3066

La ninfa bizzarra. Dramma pastorale del Signor Aurelio Aureli. Musica del Sig. Marc' Antonio Ziani. Da rappresentarsi il mese di Settembre nel rinovato Teatro Accademico dell' Aurora in Cento l' anno MDCCI . . .

Modona, Demetrio Degni, 1701. 48 p. 15½ᶜᵐ.

Three acts. By Aurelio Aureli, who is not mentioned. Cast, scenario, and dedication dated Cento, September 8, 1701, which begins: "La ninfa bizzarra, che nel fine dello spirato secolo sù la Brenta fece di sè medesima delizioso spettacolo agl' occhj dell' adriatica nobiltà . . ." This refers to the performances at Venice, Teatro di Dolo sopra la Brenta, October, 1697. SCHATZ 11190

Le ninfe di Diana, ballet. *See* Bianchi's Calto.

Ninias tiranno di Babilonia punito da Zoroastro o sia Piramo e Tisbe, ballet. *See* Anfossi's Gli amanti canuti.

Nino. Dramma per musica da rappresentarsi nel Teatro di S. Angelo. Nel carnovale dell' anno 1732 . . .

Venezia, Carlo Buonarrigo, n. d. 55 p. 15ᶜᵐ.

Page 55 contains Buonarrigo's announcement of publication of "un esatto catalogo di tutti li drammi musicali recitati in Venezia." Three acts. Dedication, argument, scenario, cast, and name of the composer, Francesco **Courcelle**. The libretto was originally by Ippolito Zanelli and was revised by Vincenzo Cassani (Schatz). SCHATZ 2283

Niobe. *See* Bertali's Theti.

Niobe, koenigin in Thebe . . . gesungener vorgestellet im jahr 1688.

Muenchen, Johann Jaecklin, n. d. 6 p. l., 92 p. 18½ᶜᵐ.

Three acts. Dedication to the "Churfuerstliche Durchleuchten" dated Munich, January 1, 1688, and signed by Ludwig (Luigi) Orlandi, argument, scenario, list of machines. The composer, Agostino **Steffani**, is not mentioned. Orlandi's Italian title was "Niobe, regina di Thebe." First composed January 5, 1688 (Riemann). SCHATZ 10033

Niobe, regina di Thebe. O. T. of Steffani's Niobe, koenigin in Thebe.

Nitetis. Tr. of Sarti's La Nitteti.

Nitetti. Dramma per musica del celebre Sig. Pietro Metastasio. Da rappresentarsi nell' Imperial Teatro di Pietroburgo.

St. Pietroburgo, Nella Stamperia dell' Academia delle Scienze, n. d. 217 p. 19ᶜᵐ.

Three acts. Argument, cast, and name of Giovanni **Paisiello** as composer. French title page, "Nitetis," and text face Italian.
First performed January, 1788, as indicated. ML 50.2.N46P2

Nitocri.

Apostolo Zeno, Poesie drammatiche, Venezia, t. iii, p. [249]–344 p. 19ᶜᵐ.

Three acts and licenza. Argument. No composer is mentioned. In the "Catalogo" at end of t. x, date and place of first ed. are given as Vienna, 1722. (*See* below.)
ML 49.A2Z3

— Nitocri. Pubblicata per la prima volta in Vienna 1722.

Apostolo Zeno, Poesie drammatiche, Orleans, 1785–86, t. v, p. 345– 436. 21ᶜᵐ.

Three acts and licenza. Argument. No composer is mentioned. ML 49.A2Z4

Nitocri. Drama per musica da rappresentarsi nel Regio Teatro di Torino, nel carnovale del 1752. alla presenza di S. S. R. M.

Torino, Pietro Giuseppe Zappata e figliuolo, 1751. 4 p. l., 68 p. 15½ᶜᵐ.

Three acts. By Apostolo Zeno. Argument, cast, scenario, and names of the author and the composer, Gioacchino **Cocchi**.
First performed, as indicated, December 26, 1751. SCHATZ 2050

Nitocri. Dramma per musica da rappresentarsi nel famoso Teatro Grimani di S. Gio. Grisostomo il carnevale dell' anno MDCCXXXIII.

Venezia, Carlo Buonarigo, n. d. 69 p. 15ᶜᵐ.

Three acts. By Apostolo Zeno. Dedication by Domenico Lalli (who, according to Schatz, altered the text) argument, notice to the reader, scenario, name of the composer, Giuseppe **Sellittti**, and cast.
First performed at Venice with modifications (indicated by an asterisk) of the original libretto as used at Vienna 1722 ("è rimasta soggetta alla solitta mutazione di alcune arie"). SCHATZ 9827

Nitocri, koenigin in Egypten. An dem glorwuerdigsten geburtstag der Roem. Kais. wie auch Koen. Spanis. Cathol. Majestaet Elisabethae Christinae . . . In der kaiserlichen Favorita welsch gesungener vorgestellet. Im jahr 1722. Poësi des herrn Apostolo Zeno . . . Die music zu denen worten ist von dem hrn. Antonio Caldara . . .

Wienn, Johann Peter Van Ghelen, n. d. 4 p. l., 72 p. 14½ᶜᵐ.

Three acts and licenza. Argument and scenario. The ballet music was composed by Niccola Matteis. Translation only of Caldara's "Nitroci." SCHATZ 1486

Nitteti. Dramma scritto dall' autore in Vienna, per la Real corte cattolica; ed ivi . . . rappresentato la prima volta con musica del Conforti, sotto la magistrale direzione del celebre cavalier Carlo Broschi, l'anno 1756.

pl., [105]–206 p. 26ᶜᵐ. (Metastasio, Opere, t. viii, Parigi, vedova Herissant, 1781.)

Three acts. Argument. ML 49.A2M44

La Nitteti.   Nuovo dramma per musica del Signor abbate D. Pietro Metastasio.

Napoli, Domenico Lanciano, 1756.   72 p.   15½ᶜᵐ.

Three acts.   Argument, scenario, and dedicatory sonnet to Farinelli.   No composer is mentioned.   Evidently published for the closet, not for the stage.

ML 50.2.N46

La Nitteti.   Dramma per musica da rappresentarsi nel nobilissimo Teatro di S. Benedetto la fiera dell' Ascensione dell' anno 1780.

Venezia, Modesto Fenzo, n. d.   54 p.   17½ᶜᵐ.

Three acts.   By Metastasio.   Argument, cast, scenario, and name of composer, Pasquale **Anfossi**, but not of librettist.   On p. 22–35: "Descrizione del primo ballo. Gabriella di Vergy ballo tragico-pantomimo in cinque atti d'invenzione, e direzione del Sig. Francesco Clerico . . ." with cast and argument, but not the name of the composer of the music.   SCHATZ 276

Nitteti.   Dramma per musica da rappresentarsi nel nobilissimo Teatro di San Samuele il carnovale dell' anno 1789.

Venezia, Modesto Fenzo, 1789.   64 p.   18ᶜᵐ.

Two acts!   Argument, cast, scenario, and name of the composer, Ferdinando Giuseppe **Bertoni**, but not of the librettist, Metastasio.   On p. 25–32 argument, cast, and full description of "La morte di Pirro, ballo eroico in quattro atti," by Domenico Ricciardi, music by Vittorio Trento.   SCHATZ 941

Nitteti.   Dramma per musica da rappresentarsi nel Teatro alla Scala di Milano nella primavera 1789.   In occasione delle faustissime nozze delle Loro Altezze Reali l'arciduchessa Maria Teresa d'Austria ed il duca d'Aosta . . .

Milano, Gio. Batista Bianchi, n. d.   72 p.   16½ᶜᵐ.

Three acts.   By Metastasio.   Impresario's dedication, argument, cast, scenario, and name of Francesco **Bianchi** as composer.   On p. [61]–72 cast, argument, and description of "Amore e Psiche, ballo eroico pantomimo" in five acts by Gaspero Angiolini, who also composed the music.

First performed, as indicated, April 20, 1789.   SCHATZ 1003

La Nitteti.   Dramma per musica da rappresentarsi nel Real Teatro di S. Carlo nel dì 20 gennaro 1783 per festeggiare la nascita . . . [di] Carlo III . . .

Napoli, Vincenzo Flauto, 1783.   72 p.   15ᶜᵐ.

Three acts.   By Metastasio.   Dedication dated Naples, January 20, 1783, argument, cast, scenario, and name of the composer, ("Curci") Giuseppe Maria **Curcio**. With the opera were performed Paolo Franchi's "Urtado e Miranda, ballo tragico pantomimo in cinque atti" with argument, cast, and description and Giuseppe Trafieri's ballet "Il cambio felice o sia Pulcinella sposo deluso."   The composers of the music are not mentioned.   SCHATZ 2300

La Nitteti.   Dramma per musica da rappresentarsi in Firenze nel Teatro di via della Pergola nell' autunno dell' anno 1758 . . .

Firenze, Stamperia dirimpetto all' Oratorio di S. Filippo Neri, n. d. 63 p.   15ᶜᵐ.

Three acts.   By Metastasio, who is not mentioned.   Argument, cast, scenario, and name of Johann Adolph **Hasse** as the composer.

First performed at Venice, Teatro di S. Benedetto, carnival 1758.   SCHATZ 4547

La Nitteti.   Dramma per musica da rappresentarsi nel Real Teatro dell' Ajuda nel felicissimo giorno natalizio del fedelissimo monarca D. Giuseppe I . . . nel dì 6 giugno 1770.

Lisbona, Stamperia reale, n. d.   85 p.   16ᶜᵐ.

Three acts.   Argument, scenario, cast, and names of Metastasio as author, of Niccolò **Jommelli** as composer.

First performed at Stuttgart, Hoftheater, February 11, 1759.   SCHATZ 4891

La Nitteti. Dramma per musica da rappresentarsi nel Real Teatro di S. Carlo nel dì 30. maggio 1764. Festeggiandosi il nome della S. R. M. di Fernando IV . . .

Napoli, Francesco Morelli, 1764.   70, [1]   15½ᶜᵐ.

Three acts. By Metastasio, who is not mentioned. Impresario's dedication, dated Naples, May 30, 1764, argument, scenario, cast, name of Antonio Maria **Mazzoni** as the composer, and "avvertimento," which reads, in part:

"non meno i versi de' recitativi, che l'arie segnate colle virgolette si tralasciano per la maggior possibile brevità. In qualche scena poi si sono aggiunti pochi versi di recitativo, a solo oggetto, che l'attore senza cantar quell' aria, che si tralascia, abbia un positivo concludente per partir dalla scena. Questi pochi versi non vengono stampati nell' interno del libro, ove la scena si chiede; ma nell' ultima pagina divisi, per quella venerazione, che si deve al non mai lodato abbastanza rispettabilissimo autore di questo dramma."   Schatz 6227

La Nitteti. Dramma per musica da rappresentarsi nel Regio Ducal Teatro di Milano nel carnovale dell' anno 1771 . . .

Milano, Giovanni Montani, 1771.   v, 56 p.   15ᶜᵐ.

Three acts. By Metastasio, who is not mentioned. Dedication, argument, scenario, cast, and name of Carlo **Monza** as the composer.   Schatz 6615

Nitteti. Dramma per musica da rappresentarsi nel Regio Teatro di Torino nel carnovale del 1783 . . .

Torino, Onorato Derossi, n. d.   viii, 63, [1] p.   15½ᶜᵐ.

Three acts. By Metastasio, who is not mentioned. Argument, cast, scenario, and names of Salvatore **Rispoli** as the composer of the opera, of Vittorio Amedeo Canavasso as composer of Innocenzo Gambuzzi's ballets, "La favola d'Apollo e Dafne," "Il matrimonio de' Groelandesi," and "Di popolo egizio." A description of the first is printed on p. 58–62, the argument of the second on p. 63.

First performed, as indicated, December 26, 1782.   Schatz 8812

La Nitteti. Dramma per musica, da rappresentarsi sul Regio Teatro Danese, l'autunno dell' anno 1761.—Nitetis . . .

Kiøbenhavn, Lars Nielsen Svare, n. d.   143 p.   16ᶜᵐ.

Three acts. Argument, cast, and names of Metastasio as author, of Giuseppe **Sarti** as composer. Danish text faces Italian.

First performed, as indicated, October 12, 1761.   Schatz 9452

— La Nitteti. Dramma per musica da rappresentarsi nel Teatro di S. Benedetto per la fiera dell' Ascensione dell' anno 1765.

Venezia, Giorgro Fossati, n. d.   64 p.   17½ᶜᵐ.

Three acts. By Metastasio, who is not mentioned. Argument, cast, scenario, and name of Giuseppe **Sarti** as the composer. The text follows the original of 1761 closely, but it is characteristic that for the performances in Venice the chorus, "Si scordi i suoi tiranni" (I, 6), was dropped.   Schatz 9475

La Nitteti. Ultimo dramma per musica del Sig. abate Pietro Metastasio, Poeta Cesareo. Da rappresentarsi nel Teatro dell' illustrissimo pubblico di Reggio per la Fiera dell' anno 1757 . . .

Reggio, Giuseppe Davolio, n. d.   5 p. l., 64 p.   17½ᶜᵐ.

Three acts. Dedication dated Reggio, April 29, 1757, argument, cast, scenario, and name of Tommaso **Trajetta** as composer.   Schatz 10403

Li nnamorate correvate. Commeddea de notà Pietro Trinchera, posta mmuseca da lo Sio Don Gregorio Sciroli, masto de cappella de S. Ece. lo Segnore prencepe de Besegnano. Da rappresentarese a lo Teatro Nuovo a Mmonte Cravario nchisto prencipio de vierno dell' anno 1752.

Napoli, Domenico Lanciani, 1752.   83 p.   15½ᶜᵐ.

Three acts. Cast and notice to the reader:

"sta commeddeja . . . è cchella stessa, che a lo carnevale dell' anno passato co lo titolo de lo FINTO PERZIANO, ncontraje la sciorte de dare sfazione . . . E pe cosirela

Li nnamorate correvate—Continued.

ncuollo a st'aute personàggie, è stato necessario cagnare la parte de la primma donna, e chella de la seconda da Napolitano, Ntoscano.   La museca è tutta nuova, fatta da lo Sio Don Gregorio **Sciroli** . . . a riserba de ll'arie segnate co llo segno §, che sò de lo primmo autore."

Accordingly, "Picarone, a un cavaliero" (I, 4), "Chi llo birbo malenato" (I, 8), "Celia mia, meglio de chillo" (I, 11), etc., were by Nicola **Logroscino**.

SCHATZ 9785

No magick like love.   A. T. of The British enchanters.

Songs, duets, trio and finales, in **No song no supper.**   As performed at the Theatre-Royal, Drury-Lane.   The music chiefly composed by Mr. Storace: The rest selected from Pleyel, Gretry, Dr. Harington, Giordani, Gluck, etc.

n. i., 1790.   18 p.   19½ cm.

Two acts. Cast. The author, Prince Hoare, is not mentioned. Storace utilized his opera "Gli equivoci" for this.

First performed, as indicated, April 16, 1790.   LONGE 206

—— **No song, no supper.**

—— *Same title, same imprint, same cast, same text, but 1 p. l., [1], 6–17 p.   18 cm.*   LONGE 215

—— **No song no supper.**   An opera in two acts.   As performed at the Theatre Royal Drury-Lane.

Dublin, P. Byrne, 1792.   34 p.   17½ cm.

Cast. Neither Prince Hoare, the author, nor Stephen **Storace**, the composer, is mentioned.   SCHATZ 10085

Second copy.   LONGE 223

Noah's flood, or, The destruction of the world.   An opera.   . . . By Edward Ecclestone, Gent.   ...

London, Printed by M. Clark and sold by B. Tooke, 1679.   9 p. l., 52 p.   21 cm.

Of the 9 p. l., the 3d (end of the dedication) and 9th (list of characters) are wanting in this copy. On p. l. 2–3, "The epistle dedicatory;" on p. l. 4–5, poems to "Mr. Edward Ecclestone," by Richard Saunders, John Leanerd, and John Morton; on p. l. 6–8 the preface to this five-act play, in which the author says:

". . . Mr. Dreydon's State of Innocency and fall of Man, is of the same nature with this, from whose incomparable piece I drew this rugged draught . . ."

John Leanerd begins his poem:

"Milton reviv'd, or rather Dryden trac'd;
"Each step found out and follow'd, though in haste.
"A second op'ra to the world is brought,
"Full of quick sence, smooth fancy, subtle thought."

Listed by Clarence in "The Stage" as a miracle play.   ML 50.2.N74

Second copy, lacking 9th p. l., and trimmed to 19 cm.   LONGE 241

The **noble peasant,** a comic opera, in three acts; as performed at the Theatre-Royal, in the Haymarket.   By Thomas Holcroft.

London, George Robinson, 1784.   2 p. l., iii, [4]–68 p.   21 cm.

Three acts. Cast and preface dated August 14, 1784, in which the author lavishes his praise on William **Shield**, who composed the overture and almost all the songs, etc., except two glees by **Cooke** and **Smith**, an "Ancient glee, composed in the year 1500," and two songs to music by **Duni** and **Sacchini**.

First performed August 2, 1784, as suggested.   LONGE 93

The **noble pedlar:** or, The fortune hunter. A burletta. As acted at the Theatre Royal, Drury-Lane, set to music by Mr. Barthelemon. Second edition.

London, W. Nicoll, 1771. 20 p. 23ᶜᵐ.

Two parts. Cast. The author, George Saville Carey, is not mentioned.
First performed, as indicated, May 13, 1771. Longe 213

Le **noble roturier,** comédie en un acte, mêlée de vaudevilles; par J. B. Radet. Représentée sur le Théatre du Vaudeville, le 24 ventose de l'an deux de la république françoise une et indivisible.

Paris, chez le libraire, au Théâtre du vaudeville, An deuxième. [1793–94] *54 p. 20ᶜᵐ.*

—— *Variantes du Noble roturier. n. i., n. d. 12 p. 20ᶜᵐ.*

Cast. Many of the airs are printed in the text. Not recorded by either Cl. & L. or Schatz.
First performed, as indicated, March 14, 1794. ML 48.M2K

La **noce interrompue.** Parody of Lully's Alceste.

Les **noces d'Arlequin et de Silvia** ou Thetis et Pelée déguisés. Parody of Colasse's Thetis et Pelée.

A **noiva fingida.** Drama jocoso em musica para se representar no Theatro do Salitre. Anno de 1790.

Lisboa, José de Aquino Bulhoens, 1790. 74 p. 15ᶜᵐ.

Three acts. Portuguese translation of Giuseppe Maria Diodati's "Le trame deluse."
Cast and name of Marcos Antonio [**Portugal**] as the composer. Schatz 8431

Non irritare le donne ovvero Il chiamantesi filosofo. Farsa giocosa per musica originale di Giuseppe Foppa da rappresentarsi nel nobile Teatro Giustiniani in San Moisè il carnovale dell' anno 1799.

Venezia, Modesto Fenzo, 1798. 41 p. 18½ᶜᵐ.

Cast and name of Marcos **Portugal** as the composer.
The opera was followed by Giuseppe Cajani's ballet, "L'amante in cimento," the composer of the music not being mentioned.
First performed, as indicated, December 27, 1798 (Carvalhaes). Schatz 8438

Non son quella, è la difesa. Drama per musica da rappresentarsi nel Teatro di Sant' Angelo nell' autunno dell' anno MDCCX . . .

Venezia, Gio. Battista Zuccato, 1710. 60 p. 14½ᶜᵐ.

Three acts. Dedication dated Venice, November 29, 1710, argument, and scenario. Neither the author, Giorgio Antonio Falier, nor the composer, Giov. Maria **Ruggeri,** is mentioned. Schatz 9132

Les **nopces de Pelée et de Thetis.** *See* Caproli's Le nozze di Teti e di Peleo.

Airs, duets, etc., in the new pantomime, called the **Norwood gypsies.** Performing at the Theater-Royal in Covent-Garden. Second edition.

London, Printed in the year 1777. 1 p. l., 5–16 p. 20ᶜᵐ.

Neither the author is mentioned (unknown to Clarence), nor the composer, John Abraham **Fisher.** Longe 124

Noth hat kein gesetz. Tr. of Fabrizj's opera La necessità non ha legge.

Il **nottambulo,** ballet.   *See* Sarti's L'Idalide.

La **notte critica.**   Dramma di tre atti per musica.   Rappresentato per la prima volta in Venezia il carnovale dell' anno MDCCLXVI con musica del Boroni.

Carlo Goldoni, Opere teatrali, Venezia, Zatta e figli, 1788–95. t. 39 [*127*]*–188 p.   18^{cm}.*   FQ

La **notte critica.**   Dramma giocoso per musica del Signor dottor Carlo Goldoni da rappresentarsi nel Teatro Tron di S. Cassano il carnovale dell' anno 1766 . . .

Venezia, Modesto Fenzo, 1766.   70 p.   14$\frac{1}{2}$^{cm}.

Three acts.   Impresario's dedication, cast, scenario, and name of the composer, Antonio **Boroni.**   SCHATZ 1246

— La **notte critica.**   Dramma giocoso per musica di Polisseno Fegeio, P. A. da rappresentarsi nel Piccolo Teatro di S. A. E. di Sassonia.

Dresda, n. publ., 1768.   159 p.   15$\frac{1}{2}$^{cm}.

Cast and name of the composer, **Boroni.**   German title-page, "Die critische nacht," and text face Italian.   SCHATZ 1247

La **notte critica.**

Three acts.   By Goldoni.   Music by Florian Leopold **Gassmann.** First performed at Vienna, Burgtheater, January 5, 1768.
Not in L. of C.

— Die **unruhige nacht,** ein komisches singspiel in drey aufzuegen. Aus dem italienischen.   Auf die musik des verstorbenen herrn Florian Gassmann uebersetzt.   Aufgefuehrt in Kais. Koenig. National- Hoftheater.

Wien, beym Logenmeister, 1783.   69 p.   16$\frac{1}{2}$^{cm}.

Three acts.   German version by Johann Joachim Eschenburg. First performed, as indicated January 10, 1783.   SCHATZ 3616

La **notte critica.**   Dramma giocoso per musica da rappresentarsi nel Teatro del Pubblico della città di Pisa il carnovale dell' anno MDCCLXIX.

Pisa, Pompeo Polloni, e comp., 1769.   78 p.   19^{cm}.

Three acts.   By Goldoni, who is not mentioned.   Cast, scenario, and name of Filippo **Gherardesca** as the composer.   SCHATZ 3801

Notte critica.   Dramma giocoso per musica di Polisseno Fegejo, P. A. da rappresentarsi nel Real Teatro di Salvaterra nel carnevale dell' anno 1767.

Lisbona, Michele Maneschal da Costa, n. d.   98 p.   16^{cm}.

Three acts.   By Goldoni.   Argument, cast, scenario, and name of Niccolò **Piccinni** as the composer.   This libretto, therefore, undermines Cametti's claim that "Notte critica" was really an opera of Niccolo Piccinni's "secondogenito, Luigi," who was born, by the way, in 1766!!   SCHATZ 8100

— Gesaenge aus der komischen oper: Die **nacht,** in zwey aufzuegen, nach dem italienischen des Dr. Goldoni.   Die musik von Piccini.

Hamburg, J. M. Michaelsen, n. d.   36 p.   15^{cm}.

Translated by Johann Joachim Eschenburg.
First performed at Berlin, Koch'sches Theater i. d. Behrenstrasse, November 10, 1774.   SCHATZ 8101

Le nouveau d'Assas, trait civique, en un acte et en prose, mêlé de chants. Représenté pour la première fois, par les Comédiens italiens ordinaires du roi, en octobre 1790. Les paroles sont de M * * *. La musique est de M. Berton.

Paris, Vente, 1790. 32 p. 21^cm.

Label of Duchesne, an VII, pasted over imprint. Cast. Text by Dejaure. First performed October 15, 1790. ML 50.2.N6B2

Le nouveau Don-Quichotte, opéra-bouffon, en deux actes, paroles de M. Boissel. Musique de M. Champein; représenté, pour la première fois, à Paris, sur le Théâtre de Monsieur, aux Thuileries, le lundi 25 mai 1789; & à Nantes, dans les premierers jours de novembre 1790.

A Nantes, et se trouve à Bruxelles, ches J. L. de Boubers, 1792. 35 p. 21½^cm.

Cast. ML 50.2.N62C3

Le nouveau magasin des modernes, comédie en un acte, en prose, mêlée de vaudevilles. Représentée, pour la première fois sur le Théâtre du Vaudeville le 18 Frimaire, an 7 [December 8, 1798].

Paris, chez le libraire du Théâtre du vaudeville, an VII. [1798–99]. 47 p. 20^cm.

Cast. "Avec 14 airs notés," printed in the text. Not recorded by either Cl. & L. or Schatz. ML 48M2K

Le nouveau marié, ou Les importuns, opera comique en un acte; représenté pour la premiere fois, par les Comédiens italiens ordinaires du roi, le 20 september 1770. Les paroles sont de Monsieur de Cailhava. La musique de Monsieur Bacelli.

Paris, veuve Duchesne, 1771. 31 p. 18^cm.

Cast and (on p. 25–31) music. Schatz 520

La nouvelle Bastienne, opera comique en un acte, suivi du Divertissement de la Fontaine du Jouvence. Par Mr. Vadé. Représenté pour la premiere fois sur le Théatre de l'Opéra-comique le 17 septembre 1754.

La Haye, Pierre Gosse, 1760. 44, 24 p. 16^cm. (Vadé, Oeuvres, t. ii, La Haye, 1760.)

En vaudevilles. The 24 p. contain seven "Airs de la Nouvelle Bastienne": "Tant qu'on verra la riviere," "Donn' moi ta main," "Mon Bastien va perir," "Aga! ces gens la faut," "Ne vla-t-il pas de bieaux appas," "Esprit farouche, rien ne te touche," and "Quand j'avons engagé"; three "Airs chantans de La fontaine de Jouvence": "Tendre Amour reçois l'hommage," "Ah! qu'il est affreux de vieillir," and "Sois favorable à nos désirs"; and "Fontaine de Jouvence. Duo. Parodie du Regne amour": "Chante un dieu, que j'adore." The divertissement was "composed" by Jean George Noverre. The arranger of the music unknown to me. ML 49.A2V2

— **La nouvelle Bastienne,** opéra-comique en un acte, suivi du Divertissement de la Fontaine de Jouvence. De M. Vadé. Représenté pour la premiere fois sur le Théatre de l'Opéra-comique le 17 septembre 1754.

Paris, la veuve Duchesne, 1766. 56 p. 19^cm.

On p. 33–44, seven "Airs de La nouvelle Bastienne," and on p. 45–56, four "Airs de La fontaine de Jouvence." Schatz 11503

Nouvelle chasse du cerf, divertissement en musique; composé de plusieurs airs parodiés sur les opera d'Angleterre: avec différentes symphonies étrangeres.

p. [297]–[315]. 19½ᶜᵐ. (Jean de Serré de Rieux, Les dons des enfans de Latone, Paris, 1734.)

The text is preceded by an "Avertissement," which reads in part:

"L'idée n'est pas nouvelle; elle a paru avec succès dans le divertissement de la Chasse du cerf imprimé chés Ballard il y a plus de vingt-cinq ans . . . en même tems l'idée est venuë d'offrir aux personnes qui pourvoient dans la suite entendre cette seconde Chasse, un genre de nouveauté en musique si différent, qu' elle ne pourroit diminuer le prix ni balancer la réputation acquise à la musique de M. Morin auteur de la premiere . . .

". . . Toute la différence qu'il y a entr'eux, ne consiste que dans la composition de la musique. Il n'y a dans cette seconde Chasse que les seuls recitatifs, qui font la liaison de l'action, & les choeurs, qui sont composés par un auteur françois: toutes les symphonies sont étrangeres, tirées de différens auteurs italiens connus, & tous les airs chantans sont parodiés sur un nombre d'airs choisis dans les opera d'Angleterre de la composition de M. Hendel (**Händel**).

". . . Comme sa composition infiniment sage & gratieuse semble s'approcher de notre gûot plus qu'aucune autre, dans le principe où l'on estque tout ce qui est essentiellement bon en musique doit le paroître tel à toutes les nations sensées, on a voulu faire l'essay de voir si les paroles françoises mises avec exactitude pourroient sous un masque étranger recevoir encore de nouvelles graces . . ."

This preface is slightly contradicted by the "Table des air a chanter, avec violons" at end, where after the airs by "Hendel" is listed "Volez, tendres Zéphirs" as by "**Fago**, Napolitain" and "Que tes jeux sont charmans, *trio*." as from "2. L. de Son. **Le Clair**."

Not recorded by De La Vallière.   ML 63.S36

La nouvelle école des femmes, comedie en trois actes, meslée d'ariettes, avec un divertissement par M. de Moissy. La musique de M. Philidor. Représentée pour la premiere fois par les Comédiens italiens ordinaires du roi, le lundi 22 janvier 1770.

Paris, la veuve Duchesne, 1770. 61 p. 18ᶜᵐ.

Cast. On p. 53–61, the airs of the *ariettes*, "Je veux qu'on m'aime" (I, 1), "Laure a de la beauté" (I, 5), "Ce n'est plus à Cythère" (II, 6).   Sᴄʜᴀᴛᴢ 8021

La nouvelle soirée des boulevards, ambigu mêlé de chants & de danses; nouvellement corrigée & augmentée, & telle que les Comédiens italiens ordinaires du roi viennent de la remettre au théatre.

Bordeux, Jean Chappuis, 1769. 46 p. 19ᶜᵐ.   Sᴄʜᴀᴛᴢ 11504

Le nouvelliste dupé, opera comique en un acte; représenté pour la premiere fois sur le Théâtre de la Foire, en 1737.

Charles François Pannard, Théâtre, Paris, Duchesne, 1763, v. 2, [179]–226 p. 17ᶜᵐ.

In prose and vaudevilles. Composer not found.   PQ 2019.P3

Il novello Giasone. L. T. of Cavalli's Giasone.

Le nozze. O. T. of Goldoni's text I pretendenti delusi, better known as Fra i due litiganti il terzo gode. Also the same as Le nozze di Dorina.

Le nozze. Dramma di tre atti per musica.

Carlo Goldoni, Opere teatrali, Venezia, Zatta e figli, 1788–95, v. 37, [315]–364 p. 18½ᶜᵐ.

For first composer and performance *see* next entry.   PQ

Le nozze. Dramma giocoso per musica di Polisseno Fegejo, Pastor Arcade, da rappresentarsi nel Teatro Grimani di S. Samuele per il carnovale 1757.

Venezia, Modesto Fenzo, 1757. 48 p. 14½ cm.

Three acts. By Goldoni, who is not mentioned. Cast, scenario, and name of Baldassare **Galuppi** as composer.

First performed at Bologna, Teatro Marsigli Rossi, summer, 1755, but Piovano says that the Teatro Fo magliari was the theatre. Schatz 3465

Le nozze a dispetto. Commedia per musica di Giuseppe Palomba da rappresentarsi nel Real Teatro del Fondo di Separazione per la prima opera del corrente anno 1797.

Napoli, Stamperia Flautina, 1797. 55 p. 15½ cm.

Two acts. Impresario's dedication dated Naples, July 17, 1797, cast, and name of the composer, Giuseppe Maria **Curcio**. On p. 47–55, argument, preface, description, cast of "Elisabetta e Blech, ballo eroico pantomimo diviso in cinque atti," by Giuseppe Cajani, who also composed the music. As second ballet, was performed "I finti filosofi." Schatz 2303

Le nozze alla Mira. Farsa con arie in musica che si rappresenta nel Teatro Tron di San Cassano il carnovale 1780.

Venezia, Modesto Fenzo, 1780. 48 p. 16½ cm.

Two acts. Author unknown to Schatz. Cast. Angelo **Gagni** is mentioned as the composer of the opera and of the ballets. Schatz 3413

Le nozze americane, ballet. *See* Colla's Andromeda.

Le nozze d'Enea con Lavinia. Tragedia di Giacomo Badoaro N. V. Rappresentata nel Teatro di S. S. Gio. e Paolo l'anno 1641. Posta in musica da Claudio Monteverde, maestro di capella della Basilica di S. Marco.

Unpaged ms, probably 17th cent. 13½ cm.

Five acts, with prologue. The opera was first performed as indicated.
Schatz 6596

Le nozze d'Ercole, e d'Ebe. Dramma per musica per i lietissimi, e faustissimi sponsalizi dell' Augusta infanta di Spagna D. Carlotta di Borbon coll' infante augusto di Portogallo D. Giovanni e dell' augusta infanta di Portogallo D. Marianna Victoria coll' augusto infante di Spagna D. Gabriel Antonio di Borbon.

Lisbona, Francesco Luiggi Ameno, 1785. 5 p. l., 27 p. 16½ cm.

Two acts. The title proper, on 1st p. l., the rest on 2d p. l. On 3d p. l., "Da cantarsi ai [13] d'Aprile del 1785. Nel palazzo dell' eccellentissimo Signor conte di Fernan Nuñez." On p. l. 4, cast and note that the music is by Jeronymo Francisco de **Lima**, "il poetico componimento è del Sig. * * * poeta romano" (name unknown to Schatz). Schatz 5618

Le nozze d'Ercole, e d'Ebe. Serenata per musica da rappresentarsi nel famosissimo Teatro Grimani a S. Gio. Grisostomo l'ultima sera del carnevale.

Venezia, n. publ., 1744. 14 p. 18 cm.

Two parts. Cast and name of Nicolà Antonio **Porpora** as the composer. The author not mentioned, and unknown to Schatz.

First performed February 18, 1744, as indicated. Schatz 8374

Le nozze degli Dei. Favola dell' ab.' Gio. Carlo Coppola nelle reali nozze de Sereniss. gran duchi di Toschana Ferdinando II. e Vittoria principessa d'Urbino.

Firenze, Amadore Massi e Lorenzo Landi, 1637. 4 p. l., 104 p., 7 pl., 50, [1] p., 1 pl. 23ᶜᵐ.

The ornamental t. p. and the 7 pl. were designed by Alfonsus Pariginus, engraved by Stefanus Della Bella. The pl. at end of the volume has the legend "Trattato di Carlo Blasis" and hardly belonged originally with this volume.

Prologue and five acts. Author's dedication dated Florence, August 1, 1737, and "A' lettori argomento, which reads in part:

"Sappia il benigno lettore, che io nel comporre, e stampare questa opera non hò havuto altro fine, che di ubbidire al comandamento del Serenissimo Gran Duca, à cui servo; il quale mentre ch'io era con l'animo più che mai alieno da simili poesie, mi comàdò, che componessi la comedia, la quale si dovea rappresentare in musica nelle sue felicissime nozze. Mi ristrinse à breve spazio di tempo per condurla a fine, come quegli, che havea gusto di vederla compita avàti la sua partenza per Pisa. M'ordinò soggetto allegro, quale si conviene à nozze, e per dar maggior campo all' inventor delle machine di abbellirla con varietà, e vaghezza di prospettiva; volle che contenesse festa in cielo, in mare, e nell' inferno: Ond' io presi per soggetto le Nozze degli Dei, trattandone quattro più celebrate da' poeti . . .

"Così pensai sodisfare alle volontà del Serenissimo Gran Duca il quale trà sette giorni vide la comedia finita, l'udì letta da me, e mostrò nõ poco gradirla. Spero che la brevità del tempo, nel quale è stata composta scuserà le imperfezioni . . . Non tralascerò di dire, che per fuggir la lunghezza, che portan seco le musiche, e le machine, e per la stagione molto calda, e poco atta agli spettacoli, e per la brevità delle notti, quella che si rappresentò fù in gran parte scemata, e variata da questa, che si stampa . . ."

This argumento is followed by the list of "Interlocutori. Chori. Balli." The text of the opera ending on p. 104, with instructions to the binder is followed by

— "Relazione delle Nozze degli Dei. Favola dell' abate Gio. Carlo Coppola . . . In Firenze Nella nuova stamperia del Massi, e' Landi. 1637."

The author was Francesco di Raffaello Rondinelli, who signs the dedication. His very minute description of this extraordinarily spectacular opera begins with the antecedents of the text, already narrated by Coppola and then he says:

"Piacuto il concetto si diede ordine à cinque compositori principali della città (accioche il sentirsi varietà di stile apportasse maggior diletto à chi àscoltava) che metessero in musica questa poesia; i quali corrisposero con l'artifizio del contrappunto, e con la vaghezza dell' arie alla bellezza della favola. Il che fatto furono distribuite le parti à migliori, che si trovassero nella città; nè si deve tralasciare, che un' opera così grande, nella quale intervennero circa 150. cantori, si fece senza chiamare alcun musico forestiero; essendosi presi tutti de' provisionati da S. A. e dello Stato, e città di Firenze. La cura della musica fù del Sig. Balè Ferdinando Saracinelli, sopraintendente di essa per S. A. quella delle machine l'ebbe Alfonso Parigi, e de' balli Agnolo Ricci veterano in condurre con isquisitezza simili trattenimenti. Per ispiegare questa machina fù eletto il cortile del Palazzo de' Pitti, il quale essendo per tutta Europa celebrato (come in verità egli è) per una fabrica ammirabile, sarebbe cosa superflua, come notissimo il descriverlo.

"Risolutesi tutte queste cose il Sereniss. G. Duca se n'andò à Pisa, lasciando la cura di perfezionare quest' opera al Sereniss. Sig. principe Gio. Carlo suo fratello . . . Fattasi pertanto la coronazione della Sereniss. Sposa, fù giudicato opportuno il rappresentarla in questo tempo, accioche essendo i popoli in somma allegrezza per questa solennità della nuova Gran Duchessa à tanto giubilo, e così universale, corrispondesse festa di straordinaria magnificenza . . ."

The relation is followed by the names "de i cavalieri, che operavano nell' abbattimento, e ne balli della commedia" and on the unnumb. p. by the imprimatur, dated September 5, 1637, that of the opera itself (on p. 104) being dated July 14, 1637.

Neither Schatz nor Solerti have anything to say about the identity of the five composers. If Schatz dates the first performance as September, 1637, he overlooked the fact that the text of the opera was published after the performances. The correct date is July 8, 1637, as appears from Solerti's "Musica, ballo e drammatica alla Corte Medicea dal 1600 al 1637."   Schatz 11351

Le nozze de' Sanniti, ballet. *See* G. Giordani's La disfatta di Dario.

Le **nozze della Bita.** Dramma giocoso per musica da rappresentarsi in Firenze nel Teatro di via del Cocomero nell' autunno dell' anno 1778 . . .

Firenze, Anton Giuseppe Pagani, 1778. 59 p. 16½cm.

Two acts. Cast. Niccolò Tassi is mentioned as the author, Bernard(in)o **Ottani** as the composer. SCHATZ 7362

Le **nozze di Amore e di Norizia.** Italian O. T. of Sales' Das hochzeitsfest des Amors und der Norizia.

Le **nozze di Dorina.** Same as Goldoni's text Le nozze.

Le **nozze di Dorina.** L. T. of Sarti's I pretendenti delusi.

Le **nozze di Figaro.** Comedia per musica tratta dal francese in quattro atti. Da rappresentarsi nel Teatro di corte l'anno 1786.

Vienna, Giuseppe Nob. de Kurzbeck, n. d. 99 p. 16½cm.

Da Ponte is mentioned as the author, **Mozart** as the composer. In his preface, Da Ponte says:

"Il tempo prescritto dall' uso alle drammatiche rappresentazioni, un certo dato numero di personaggi comunemente praticato nelle medesime; ed alcune altre prudenti viste, e convenienze dovute ai costumi, al loco, e agli spettatori, furono le cagioni per cui non ho fatto una traduzione di quella eccellente comedia [by Beaumarchais], ma una imitazione piuttosto, o vogliamo dire un estratto.

"Per questo sono stato costretto a ridure a undeci attori i sedici che la compongono, due de' quali si possono eseguire da uno stesso soggetto, e ad ommettere, oltre un intiero atto di quella, molte graziosissime scene, e molti bei motti, e saletti ond'è sparsa, in loco di che ho dovuto sostituire canzonette, arie, cori ed altri pensieri, e parole di musica suscettibili, cose che dalla sola poesia, e non mai dalla prosa si sommistrano. Ad onta però di tutto lo studio, e di tutta la diligenza e cura avuta dal maestro di cappella, e da me per esser brevi, l'opera non sarà delle più corte che si sieno esposte sul nostro teatro al che speriamo che basti di scusa la varietà delle fila onde è tessuta l'azione di questo dramma, la vastità e grandezza del medesimo, la moltiplicità de' pezzi musicali, che si son dovuti fare, per non tener di soverchio oziosi gli attori, per scemare la noja, e monotonia dei lunghi recitativi, per esprimere tratto tratto con diversi colori le diverse passioni che vi campeggiano, e il desiderio nostro particolarmente di offerire un quasi nuovo genere di spettacolo ad un pubblico di gusto sì raffinato, e di sì giudizio intendimento. *Il Poeta.*"

First performed, as indicated, May 1, 1786. SCHATZ 6826

— Le **nozze di Figaro** o sia La folle giornata. Comedia per musica tratta dal francese in quattro atti, da rappresentarsi ne' Piccoli Teatri di S. M. il rè di Prussia messo in musica dal Sign. Wolfgango Mozart . . .

Berlino, Haude e Spener, 1790. 165 p. 15½cm.

Da Ponte is not mentioned. German title page, "Figaro's hochzeit oder Der tolle tag," and text (after Vulpius) face Italian.
First performed at Potsdam, as indicated, 1790. SCHATZ 6827

— Gesaenge aus dem singspiele **Figaro's heyrath,** in vier aufzuegen, aus dem italienischen uebersetzt vom freyherrn von Knigge. In musik gesetzt von Mozart.

Hamburg, Joh. Matth. Michaelsen, 1791. 56 p. 16cm.

First performed at Hamburg April 4, 1791. SCHATZ 11396

— Die **hochzeit des Figaro.** Eine nach dem italienischen freibearbeitete operette in vier aufzuegen von C. A. Vulpius. Die musik ist von Mozart.

Leipzig, Johann Samuel Heinsius, 1794. 110 p. 14½cm.

First performed at Weimar, herzogl. Hoftheater, October 24, 1793. SCHATZ 6829

Le **nozze di Figaro**—Continued.

— Die **hochzeit des Figaro.** Ein singspiel in vier aufzuegen. Mit beybehaltung der musik von Mozart. Aus dem italienischen übersetzt. Fuer das Kaiserl. Koenigl. Hoftheater.

Wien, Johann Baptist Wallishausser, 1798. 102 p. 16^{cm}.

German version, by Adolph Friedrich freiherr von Knigge and Philippine Eregine, freiin von Knigge.

First performed at Vienna, as indicated, July 10, 1798; at Hanover, Schlosstheater, by the G. F. W. Grossmann'sche Gesellschaft, May 18, 1789. SCHATZ 6828

— **Figaros hochzeit,** oder List über list. Ein scherzhaftes singspiel in 4 aufzügen. Nach Mozzarts musik. Aus dem italiänischen des abbate da Ponte.

Passau, Niklas Ambrosi, 1793. 109 p. 17½^{cm}.

"Karakter und kleidung der personen" on p. [4–9]. The stage-business is printed in red! SCHATZ 6860

Le **nozze di Monsù Fagotto.** Intermezzi per musica a tre voci da rappresentarsi nel Teatro alla Valle nel carnevale dell' anno 1754 . . .

Roma, Libraria di S. Michele, 1754. 24 p. 15^{cm}.

Two parts. Author not mentioned. Text perhaps written by Angelo Lungi, who together with the book-seller G. Puccinelli signed the dedication. Cast and name of Gioacchino **Cocchi** as composer. The first intermezzo begins with the aria "Perchè son bella, Perchè son cara," the second with the aria "Se si mette una pedina."

ML 50.2.N7C6

Le **nozze di Paride.** Spettacolo poetico, e musicale dell' abate Pietro Chiari Bresciano poeta di S. A. Sereniss. di Modona. Da rappresentarsi nel Teatro di San Gio. Grisostomo l'autunno dell' anno 1756.

Venezia, Modesto Fenzo, 1756. 56 p. 17^{cm}.

"Azioni della mattina—del mezzogiorno—della sera." Sonnet by Antonio Codognato, cast, name of **Galuppi** as composer, and notice to the reader, which begins: "Ecco un componimento poetico di cui non s'è ancora veduto su teatri nostri l'esempio; ma che non lascia però d'esser giustificato dalla ragione, e dall' uso."

On p. 8, a substitute aria, "Se mi volete oppressa" (II, 12). SCHATZ 3489

Le **nozze di Peleo e di Theti.**

Prologue and three acts. Text by Francesco Buti, music by Carlo **Caproli** *del Violino.* Not to be confused with Cavalli's "Le nozze di Teti e di Peleo."

First performed at Paris, Salle du Petit-Bourbon, April 14, 1654 (*not* January 26, 1654).

Not in L. of C.

— Les **nopces de Pelée et de Thetis.** Comedie italienne en musique, entre-meslée d'un ballet sur le mesme sujet, dansé par Sa Majesté.

Paris, Robert Ballard, 1654. 43 p. 21½^{cm}.

Prologue and three acts. Names of the nobility participating. A note at end says: "Ce qui suit est la comedie italienne, traduite en vers françois par un autre que par celuy qui a fait ceux du ballet."

The text of the "comedie" does *not* follow in this copy. The caption title on p. 3 reads:

"VERS DU BALLET ROYAL, avec l'argument de chaque scene de la comedie, qui donne occasion à chaque entrée du ballet."

The text of the ballet was by Benserade. The "comedie italienne en musique," as the scene by scene argument proved, was NOT identical with Cavalli's "Le nozze di Teti e di Peleo," text by Orazio Persiani.

First performed at Paris, January 26, 1654.

Chouquet and others confuse Caproli's opera with the ballet intermezzos as represented by this entry. The composer of the ballet I have not found mentioned, but Prunières claims that Jean Baptiste de **Lully** collaborated. ML 52.2.N67

Le **nozzi di Peleo e di Theti**—Continued.

— The **nuptials of Peleus and Thetis.** A new Italian comedy, whence the preceding mask was extracted; made English by a nearer adherence to the original, then to the French translation . . .

   London, Henry Herringman, 1654. 2 p. l., 25 p. 21½ᶜᵐ.

Three acts and prologue. Obviously a translation of Buti's text by James Howell, who is not mentioned.   Longe 241

Le **nozze di Peleo e Teti,** ballet. *See* Cimarosa's Artemisia.

Le **nozze di Perseo e d'Andromeda,** ballet. *See* Casali's Antigona.

Le **nozze di Teti, e di Peleo.** Opera scenica del Signor Oratio Persiani . . .

   Venetia, Giacomo Sarzina, 1639. 108, 23 p. 14ᶜᵐ.

Three acts, with prologue. Author's dedication dated Venice, January 24, 1639. The 23 additional pages contain "Breve espositione della festa teatrale del Signor Oratio Persiani, posta in musica dal Sig. Francesco **Cavalli** da recitarsi nel Teatro di S. Casciano. L'opera è intitolata Le nozze di Teti e di Peleo." Schatz 1748

Le **nozze disturbate.** L. T. of Naumann's La villanella incostante.

Le **nozze disturbate.** Dramma giocoso per musica del Signor. Gaetano Martinelli Romano da rappresentarsi nel Teatro Giustiniani di San Moisè il carnovale dell' anno 1766.

   Venezia, Modesto Fenzo, 1766. 71 p. 14½ᶜᵐ.

Three acts. Cast, scenario, and name of **Paisiello** as the composer. Schatz 7696

Le **nozze in campagna.** Dramma giocoso di Logolcardoni Colodisce da rappresentarsi nel Teatro Giustiniani di S. Moisè l'autunno dell' anno 1768.

   Venezia, Modesto Fenzo, 1768. 70 p. 15ᶜᵐ.

Three acts. By Carlo Goldoni, according to Schatz and Wiel, but none of the arias listed in Wotquenne's Verzeichnis under Goldoni. Cast, scenario, and name of Gregorio **Sciroli** as the composer. Schatz 9782

Le **nozze in commedia.** O. T. of G. Palomba's text Il medico parigino.

Le **nozze in commedia.** Commedia per musica di Giuseppe Palomba da rappresentarsi nel Nuovo Teatro de' Fiorentini per terz' opera di quest' anno 1781.

   Napoli, n. publ., 1781. 70 p. 15ᶜᵐ.

Three acts. Cast and name of Pietro **Guglielmi** as the composer. Schatz 4254

Le **nozze in contrasto.** Dramma giocoso per musica di Giovanni Bertati da rappresentarsi nel Teatro Giustiniani in S. Moisè l'autunno dell' anno 1779.

   Venezia, n. publ., n. d. 63 p. 18ᶜᵐ.

Two acts. Dedication by Bertati, cast, and name of Giovanni **Valentini** as the composer. ("La musica sarà.") Schatz 10582

— Le **nozze in contrasto.** Dramma giccoso per musica da rappresentarsi nel Piccolo Teatro di S. A. E. di Sassonia.

   Dresda, n. publ., 1782. 109 p. 15½ᶜᵐ.

Two acts. Giovanni **Valentini** is mentioned as composer. German title-page, "Die streitige heurath," and text faces Italian, which is practically the same as in the Venetian version of 1779.

First performed, as indicated, 1782. Schatz 10583

Le nozze in contrasto—Continued.

— Le nozze in contrasto. Dramma giocoso per musica da rappresentarsi in Firenze nel Nuovo Regio Teatro degl' Intrepidi detto La Palla a Corda nell' autunno del 1785 . . .

Firenze, Stamperia Bonducciana, 1785. 52 p., [2] l.   17½ᶜᵐ.

Two acts. Cast and name of the composer, Giovanni **Valentini.** The 2 l. contain substituted matter for I, 7.   ML 48.A5 v.24

Le nozze in garbuglio. Commedia per musica di G. M. D. da rappresentarsi nel Teatro Nuovo sopra Toledo per terz' opera di questo corrente anno 1793.

Napoli, n. publ., 1793. 39 p.   15ᶜᵐ.

Two acts. By Giuseppe Maria Diodati. Cast and name of Giacomo **Tritto** as the composer.   SCHATZ 10473

Le nozze in villa. Intermezzo per musica da rappresentarsi nel Teatro alla Valle degl' illm̃i Sigg. Capranica nel carnevale dell' anno 1792.

Roma, Michele Puccinelli, n. d. 54 p.   16ᶜᵐ.

Two acts. Author not mentioned and unknown to Schatz. Cast and name of Silvestro **Palma** as composer.   ML 50.2.N72P2

Le nozze inaspettate. Commedia per musica da rappresentarsi nel Teatro de' Fiorentini per terza opera di questo corrente anno 1793.

Napoli, 1793. 56 p.   15½ᶜᵐ.

Two acts. Cast and name of composer, Gaetano **Andreozzi**, but not of librettist, who is unknown to Schatz.   SCHATZ 208

Numa, dramma per musica da rappresentarsi alla Regia elettoral corte di Dresda, il carnovale dell' anno MDCCXLIII.

n. i., n. d.   (double) 54, [14] p.   15ᶜᵐ.

Three acts. By Stefano Benedetto Pallavicini, who is not mentioned. Argument, scenario, and name of Johann Adolph **Hasse** as the composer. German title page, "Numa . . . Dresden, gedruckt . . . bey der verwitt . . . Stoesselin," and text face Italian. The fourteen additional pages contain Italian and German text of the "intermedio PIMPINELLA E MARCANTONIO—Pimpernelle und Marcantonius," by the same author and composer.

Performed, as indicated, January 14, 1743; first performed at Hubertusburg, Schlosstheater, October 7, 1741.   SCHATZ 4548

Numa Pompilio. Poemetto drammatico nel felicissimo giorno natalizio della Sac. Ces. R. Maestà di Leopoldo I. Augustissimo imperador de' Romani.

Pietro Antonio Bernardoni, Poemi drammatici, parte terza, Vienna, van Ghelen, 1707, p. 91–106.   16½ᶜᵐ.

Argument. The composer is not mentioned by von Weilen.
First performed at Vienna, June 9, 1707, as indicated.   ML 49.A2B4

Numa Pompilio. Drama per musica da rappresentarsi nel famoso Teatro Grimano. L'anno MDCLXXIV. Di Matteo Noris . . .

Venetia, Francesco Nicolini, 1674. 96 p.   14½ᶜᵐ.

Three acts. Author's dedication dated Venice, January 11, 1674, argument, notice to the reader, and scenario. The composer, Giovanni Maria **Pagliardi**, is not mentioned.   SCHATZ 7584

Numa Pompilio II rê de Romani. Serenata per musica da cantarsi nel Real palazzo di Lisbona li 24 giugno 1789 . . .

[Lisbona], Nella stamperia reale, n. d. 26 p. 15^{cm}.

One act. "Succinto drammatico componimento" by Gaetano Martinelli. Argument, cast, and names of the composer, João de Sousa **Carvalho,** and the author.

SCHATZ 1672

Numitore.

36 p. 17^{cm}. (Rolli, Componimenti poetici, Nuova edizione, Verona, G. Tumermani, 1744.)

Three acts. Argument. The composer, Giovanni **Porta,** is not mentioned.
First performed at London, Haymarket, April 2 (Fassini), April 13 (Schatz), 1720.
See also "Die helden-muetige schaefer Romulus und Remus."   ML 49.A2R7

La nuova della pace, ballet. *See* Cherubini's Ifigenia in Aulide.

La nuova Giannetta. Dramma giocoso per musica da rappresentarsi in Parma nel R. D. Teatro di corte il carnevale dell' anno MDCCXXXVII . . .

Parma, Carmignani, n. d. vii, 43, [1] p. 17^{cm}.

Imprimatur dated February 5–6, 1787.
Two acts. A later version of "L'incognita perseguitata," by Giuseppe Petrosellini. Cast and name of "Ferdinando **Robuschi** Colornese" as the composer, of whom the impresario in the dedication says:
"la carriera, con tanto applauso intrapresa dal giovine autor della musica, è segnata dalla sovrana munificenza."   SCHATZ 8841

Il nuovo convitato di pietra. Dramma tragicomico da rappresentarsi nel nobile Teatro di San Samuele il carnovale dell' anno MDCCLXXXVII.

Venezia, Modesto Fenzo, 1787. 64 p. 18^{cm}.

Two acts. Author not mentioned, and unknown to Schatz. Cast, scenario, and name of Francesco **Gardi** as the composer. With the opera were performed the ballets, by Antonio Muzzarelli, "Il Beverlei o sia Il giouocatore inglese" (music by **Pietro** Dutillieu) and "La locandiera vivace" (composer of the music not mentioned).

SCHATZ 3540

Il nuovo D. Chisciotte. L. T. of Leo's Il fantastico.

Il nuovo Figaro. Dramma giocoso per musica da rappresentarsi in Parma nel R. D. Teatro di corte il carnevale dell' anno MDCCXCIV . . .

Parma, Carmignani, n. d. viii, 86 p. 18^{cm}.

Four acts. A slightly altered version of Lorenzo da Ponte's "Le nozze di Figaro." Impresario's dedicatory poem, scenario, and name of Ferdinando Per (**Paër**) as the composer.
On p. 75–86, preface, argument, cast, and description of Giovanni Monticini's "Il trionfo di Gustavo rè di Svezia, ballo eroico-tragico pantomimico in cinque atti." The composer of the music is not mentioned.
First performed January, 1794, as indicated.   SCHATZ 7565

Il nuovo savio della Grecia. Dramma giocoso per musica di Domenico Mantile da rappresentarsi nel Real Teatro del Fondo di Separazione per terz' opera del corrente anno 1796 . . .

Napoli, n. publ., 1796. 2 p. l., 47 p. 15½^{cm}.

Two acts. Impresario's dedication, dated November 4, 1796, cast, and name of the composer, Giuseppe **Farinelli.** On p. [3]–13, argument, cast, and description of "Zulima o sia La famiglia riunita, ballo pantomimo in cinque atti, composto e diretto dal Sig. Lauchlin Dusquesney . . . la musica . . . tutta nuova, scritta dal Signor Pleyel."   SCHATZ 3019

The **nuptials of Peleus and Thetis.**   *See* Caproli's Le nozze di Peleo e di Theti.

Les **nymphes.**   Entrée in Duval's Les genies.

Les **nymphes de Diane,** opéra comique, par Mr. Favart.   Nouvelle édition.

> *Paris, Aux dépens de la compagnie, 1755.   39 p.   19½^{cm}.*
> *En vaudevilles.*   On cover of this copy the music is attributed to J.[ean] B.[aptiste] Moulinghem (**Moulinghen**), who, under the circumstances, can only have arranged the music.   ML 50.2.N9M6

— Les **nymphes de Diane,** opera-comique en un acte.   Représenté pour la premiere fois tout en vaudevilles sur le Théâtre de l'Opéra-comique de la Foire S. Laurent le 22. septembre 1755.   Par M. Favart.

> *Paris, Duchesne, 1755.   56, [8] p.   19^{cm}.   (Theatre de M. Favart, Paris, Duchesne, 1763–77, t. viii.)*
> Cast.   The [8] p. contain eight "Airs choisis des Nimphes de Diane—Vaudeville" ("Je voulois vaincre").   Favart's musical collaborator is not mentioned by Font, who says that the opera was first performed at Bruxelles in 1747, after having been forbidden for performance at Paris, Foire St. Laurent, in 1741.   ML 49.A2F1

— Les **nymphes de Diane,** opéra-comique en un acte.   Représenté pour la premiere fois tout en vaudevilles sur le Théatre de l'Opéra-comique de la Foire St. Laurent le 22 septembre 1755.

> *Paris, la veuve Duchesne, 1766.   68 p.   19^{cm}.*
> On p. 55–68, eight "Airs des Nymphes de Diane."   Neither the author, Favart, is mentioned, nor the arranger of the airs, etc.   SCHATZ 11502

Oberon oder Koenig der elfen, ein romantisches singspiel in drey aufzuegen nach Wieland.   Von Friederike Sophie Seyler.   Herrn Schroeder, Director des Hamburger Theaters, zugeeignet.   Die musik ist von Paolo Wranitzky.   Dritte auflage.

> *Hamburg, Herold, 1792.   95, [1] p.   15½^{cm}.*
> Page 95 incorrectly numbered 79.   The last page contains instructions for an altered performance of the third act.
> The dedication is dated Schleswig, July, 1788.   In it the authoress does not mention the fact that Heinrich Gottlieb Schmieder added a few arias, which were composed by Carl David **Stegmann.**
> First performed at Frankfurt a/M, Nationaltheater, October 15, 1790, and at Hamburg, Theater beim Gänsemarkt, October 17, 1791.   SCHATZ 11112

Obert e Melina, ballet.   *See* Mayr's cantata Temira e Aristo.

L'**obstacle favorable.**   *See* Les comediens corsaires.

Octavia.   *See* Keiser's Die roemische unruhe.

Odervik, ballet.   *See* Zingarelli's Il ritratto.

Gl'**odj delusi dal sangue.**   Drama per musica . . . da rappresentarsi in Dresda nel carnevale 1718.

> *Dresda, Giovanni Riedel & Giovanni Stoessel, n. d.   Unpaged.   21^{cm}.*
> Three acts.   Dedication signed by the author, Antonio Maria Luchini, and dated Dresda, Febraro, 1718, argument, cast, scenario, and name of Antonio **Lotti** as composer of the opera; of "Signor Woulmyer" as composer of the ballet music.   French title page, "La haine vaincue par la force du sang," and text face Italian.   Following the text of the opera is printed that of the three "Intermedi cantati . . . Dresde, chez Jean Riedel & Jean Conrad Stössel, 1718," called "MIRENA E FLORA."   These, too, have Italian and French texts on opposite pages.   SCHATZ 5707

Gl'odj delusi dal sangue. Drama per musica da rappresentarsi nel Teatro di S. Angelo nella fine del carnovale 1728.

Venezia, Marin Rossetti, n. d. 41 p. 14ᶜᵐ.

Three acts. By Antonio Maria Lucchini, who is not mentioned. Argument, cast, scenario, and names of **Galuppi** as the composer of acts I and III, and of Giov. Battista **Pescetti** of act II.

First performed on February 4, 1728. SCHATZ 3521

Gli odii fraterni. A. T. of Pacelli's Il finto Esaù.

L'odio l'amor. Drama per musica. Da rappresentarsi nel famosissimo Teatro Grimani in S. Gio. Grisostomo l'anno 1703. Di Matteo Noris.

Venezia, Marino Rossetti, 1703. 1 p. l., 79 p. 15ᶜᵐ.

Three acts. Preface and scenario. The composer, Carlo Francesco **Pollaroli**, is not mentioned. SCHATZ 8304

L'odio e l'amore. Melodrama di Matteo Noris da rappresentarsi in Napoli nel Teatro di S. Bartolomeo in quest. anno 1704 . . .

Napoli, Michele Luigi Mutio, 1704. 4 p. l., 64 p. 13½ᶜᵐ.

Three acts. Dedication by Nicola Serino, cast, scenario, name of Giuseppe [Antonio Vincenzo] **Aldrovandini** as composer, and notice (by Serino?) to the reader, according to which the present edition is an altered version of Noris' libretto "per l'aggiunzioni di rappresentanti e tra per la variazione d'arie." It is also stated that the music of the following arias was not by Aldrovandini but was new: "A l'armi, a l'armi" (I, 2), "Mi fà guerra, e mi combatte" (I, 3), "Voi piangete ò luci belle" (I, 6), "Sapessi almen dov'è" (I, 6), and many others. Their composer is not mentioned. SCHATZ 136

L'odio placato. Drama per musica da recitarsi nel Teatro di S. Angelo l'anno 1730.

Venezia, Alvise Valvasense, 1730. 47 p.

Three acts. By Francesco Silvani, who is not mentioned. Argument, notice to the reader, cast, scenario, and name of **Galuppi** as composer.

First performed, as indicated, December 27, 1729. SCHATZ 3490

L'odio vinto dalla costanza. Dramma per musica da rappresentarsi in Parma nell' Imperial-ducale Teatro il carnovale dell' anno 1739 . . .

Parma, Gozzi, n. d. 48 p. 17ᶜᵐ.

Three acts. Author not mentioned and unknown to Schatz. Dedication by the impresario, Domenico Maria Creta, dated Parma, January 24, 1739, argument, cast, scenario, and note:

"La musica è scelta da diversi autori."

The text is perhaps the same as Antonio Marchi's, another title of which was "La costanza trionfante degl' amori e degl' odii." SCHATZ 11352

L'odio vinto dalla costanza. L. T. of Vivaldi's La costanza trionfante degl' amori e degl' odii.

L'Odoacre. Drama per musica di Novello Bonis. Da rappresentarsi nel Teatro di Sant' Angelo. L'anno MDCLXXX . . .

Venetia, Francesco Batti, 1680. 60 p. 14ᶜᵐ.

Three acts (running title of third incorrectly numbered second). Author's dedication dated Venice, January 4, 1679, argument, scenario, and notice to the reader:

"Doppo il mio Dario ravvitato non hebbi altra fortuna di servirti. Hora vedrai l'Odoacre. Compatiscilo poichè e barbaro. Ammolirà le sue durezze l'armonia delle note del Signor Giovanni **Varischino** nipote, e discepolo di quel D. Giovanni Lerenzi, ch'immobilisce la fama sul' arco de' stupori." SCHATZ 10593

Odoacro, primo rè d'Italia, ballet.   *See* Piccinni's Il servo padrone.

Odoardo.   Drama per musica da rappresentarsi nel Teatro di Sant'
Angelo l'anno MDCXCVIII . . .

 Venezia, Girolamo Albrizzi, 1698.   6 p. l. (incl. front.), 57 p.   14ᶜᵐ.

Three acts.   Dedication by Apostolo Zeno as author, though "Odoardo" does
not appear in his collected works nor any of the arias in Wotquenne's Verzeichnis
under Zeno.   Argument, and scenario.   The composer, Marc' Antonio **Ziani,** is not
mentioned.

First performed, as indicated, carnival 1698.   SCHATZ 11191

Oedip zu Colonos.   Tr. of Sacchini's Oedipe à Colone.

Oedipe a Colone, tragédie lyrique en trois actes.

 n. i., n. d.   p. [1]–32.   18½ᶜᵐ.

Three acts.   On p. [1] this note: "Le poëme est du C. Guillard.   La musique de
Sacchini."   C. stands obviously for Citoyen, which would fix the date of this edition
as 1792 or later.

First performed at Versailles, Théâtre de la Cour, January 4, 1786, and at Paris,
Académie royale de musique, February 1, 1787.   SCHATZ 9234

— Oedip zu Colonos.   Lyrisches drama in drey aufzuegen zur
beybehaltenen musik von A. Sacchini, aus dem franzoesischen uebersetzt von C. Herklots.

 Berlin, n. publ., 1798.   55 p.

Cast and "Vorerinnerung."

First performed at Berlin, Kgl. National Theater, October 17, 1797.   SCHATZ 9235

Die oesterreichische grossmuht oder Carolus V.   Auf das hoechst-
erfreuliche kroenungs-fest . . . Caroli VI. erwaehlten roemischen
kaeysers . . . in einem musicalischen schauspiele auf dem grossen
Hamburgischen Theatro vorgestellet am tage Caroli MDCCXII.

 n. i., n. d.   Unpaged.   19ᶜᵐ.

Three acts and epilogue.   Scenario and laudatory "vorbericht."   Neither the
author, Johann Ulrich Koenig, is mentioned, nor the composer, Reinhard **Keiser.**

First performed, as indicated, January 28, 1712.   SCHATZ 5108

Ogus, o sia Il trionfo del bel sesso.   Dramma giocoso per musica,
da rappresentarsi nel Teatro Elettorale.

 Dresda, n. publ., 1796.   22 p. l., 60 p.   16ᶜᵐ.

Two acts.   By Giovanni Bertati, who is not mentioned and whose title originally
was "La forza delle donne."   German title-page, "Ogus, oder Der triumph des
schoenen geschlechts," and scene-by-scene synopsis precedes the Italian text.   Peter
von **Winter** is mentioned as the composer.

First performed, as indicated, March 5, 1796; at Prague, Nationaltheater, 1795.

SCHATZ 11058

Oithona: A dramatick poem, taken from the prose translation of
the celebrated Ossian, as performed at the Theatre Royal in the
Hay-Market.   Set to musick by M. Barthelemon.

 London, T. Becket and P. and A. de Hondt, 1768.   23 p.   21ᶜᵐ.

Three acts.   Author not recorded by Baker.   LONGE 163

L'Olandese in Italia.   Dramma giocoso in musica da rappresentarsi nel Teatro da rua dos Condes nel anno 1766 . . .

 Lisbona, Pietro Ferreira, n. d.   94 p.   15ᶜᵐ.

Incomplete, p. 1–8 missing.   The t.-p. supplied in transcript.

Three acts.   Niccolò Tassi is mentioned as the author, Giovanni Marco **Rutini** as
the composer.

First performed at Florence, Teatro di via del Cocomero, spring of 1765.

SCHATZ 9190

An old fool worse than any. A. T. of He wou'd if he cou'd.

An old man taught wisdom: or, The virgin unmask'd. A farce. As it is perform'd at the Theatre-Royal, by His Majesty's servants. By Henry Fielding, Esq; with the musick prefix'd to each song. The second edition.

London, J. Watts, 1735. 39 p. 19ᶜᵐ.

One act. Cast and table of the twelve songs. Ballad opera, the airs printed in the text, with their titles. Later on, the piece became known almost exclusively under the alternative title.

First performed at Drury Lane, 1734 (Clarence); January 6, 1735 (Tufts).

ML 50.5.O42

— **The virgin unmasked.** A musical entertainment, in one act. By Henry Fielding, Esq. With alterations. As performed at the Theatres-Royal in Drury-Lane, and Covent-Garden.

London, T. Payne and son [etc.], 1786. 27, [5] p. 21ᶜᵐ.

The [5] p. contain a table of the 11 songs and a four-page booklist of W. Lowndes. Casts of 1786, with the N. B.: "Some parts of this entertainment are performed only at Drury-Lane, and other passages only at Covent-Garden." Ballad opera, most of the airs being indicated by title. LONGE 97

— **The virgin unmask'd.** By Henry Fielding, Esq.

[120]–141 p. 19ᶜᵐ. (Collection of the most esteemed farces and entertainments, t. ii, Edinburgh, 1792.)

Drury-Lane and Edinburgh (1782) casts. Ballad opera. SCHATZ 11753B

The old woman weatherwise, an interlude; as performed at the Theatre Royal in Drury-Lane.

London, S. Bladon, 1788. 18 p. 21ᶜᵐ.

One act. Cast. Neither the author, G. Saville Carey, is mentioned, nor the composer (not recorded by Schatz). Genest under Drury Lane 1769–70 says: "Old women weatherwise. This contemptible interlude is attributed to G. S. Carey—it was acted at D. L. in the course of 1770." LONGE 251

Olimpia, ballet. *See* Winter's Catone in Utica.

Olimpia placata. L. T. of Freschi's Olimpia vendicata.

Olimpia vendicata. Drama per musica da rappresentarsi nel Teatro di S. Angelo l'anno MDCLXXXII. Di Aurelio Aureli opera XXII . . .

Venetia, Francesco Nicolini, 1682. 55 p.

Three acts. Author's dedication dated Venice, November 20, 1681, author's notice to the reader, with name of Giovanni Domenico **Freschi** as composer, scenario, and arguments preceding each act. SCHATZ 3352

— **Olimpia placata.** Drama rappresentato in musica nel novissimo Teatro ducale di Parma . . . Poesia di Aurelio Aureli.

Parma, nella Stamperia ducale, 1687. 88 p. 16ᶜᵐ.

Three acts. Impresario's dedication, argument, scenario, and author's notice to the reader, in which he says:

"La brevità del tempo stabilito alle recite non le hà permesso di poter questa prima volta farsi vedere con nuova fatica. Onde è stata dalla necessità costretta à portarti l'*Olimpia* mio drama già un lustro composto, e rappresentato con non picciolo agradimento in Venetia . . . hò inserita la Vecchia, che nel primo drama non v'era, per il che m'e convenuto riformarlo in gran parte con mutar totalmente non solo il suo fine ma cangiarli ancora il primo titolo d'*Olimpia vendicata* in *Olimpia placata*. Le nuove

Olimpia vendicata—Continued.

aggiunte tutte sono state poste in musica dalla virtù ammirabile del Sig. D. Bernardo **Sabadini** . . . l'armonia delle cui note avrà aggiunto nuovo splendore alla musica singolare della prima Olimpia composta dal Sig. D. Domenico **Freschi** . . .''

The libretto is one of the early instances in which not only the "l'inventore delle scene" (in this case, "Ferdinando Galli detto il Bibiena") is mentioned, but also the "inventor de balli" (Federico Crivelli) and the "inventore, e fabbricatore degl' habiti" (Gasparo Torrelli).   Schatz 5359

L'Olimpiade.

[227]–297 p. 19ᶜᵐ. (Pietro Metastasio, Opere drammatiche, Venezia, Giuseppe Bettinelli, 1733–37, t. 1.)

Three acts and licenza. Argument. No composer is mentioned.   ML 49.A2M4

— Olimpiade.

Metastasio, Poesie, Parigi, vedova Quillau, 1755, t. II, 104 p. 16ᶜᵐ.
Three acts and licenza. Argument.   ML 49.A2M42

— Olimpiade. Dramma rappresentato con musica del Caldara la prima volta nel giardino dell' Imperial Favorita, alla presenza degli augusti regnanti, il dì 28 agosto 1733, per festeggiare il giorno di nascita dell' imperatrice Elisabetta . . .

pl., [3]–120 p. 26ᶜᵐ. (Pietro Metastasio, Opere, t. II, Parigi, vedova Herissant, 1780.)
Three acts and licenza. Argument.   ML 49.A2M44

L'Olimpiade. Drama per musica da rappresentarsi nel nobilissimo Teatro di S. Benedetto il carnovale dell' anno MDCCLXXIV

Venezia, Modesto Fenzo, 1774. 62 p. 17ᶜᵐ.
Three acts. By Metastasio. Argument, cast, scenario, and name of **Pasquale Anfossi** as composer, but not of librettist. Between the first and second acts was performed "L'Ipermestra o Le Danaidi. Ballo tragico pantomimo, d'invenzione e composizione di Monsieur Giovanni Favier." The composer of the music is not mentioned. A detailed description of the ballet on p. 21–30.
First performed, as indicated, December 26, 1774. (Schatz.)   Schatz 246

L'Olimpiade. Dramma per musica da rappresentarsi nel Teatro Tron di S. Cassiano il carnovale dell' anno 1765.

Venezia, Modesto Fenzo, 1765. 54 p. 18ᶜᵐ.
Three acts. Argument, cast, scenario, and name of composer, Ferdinando Giuseppe **Bertoni,** but not of the librettist, Metastasio.   Schatz 915

Olimpiade. Dramma per musica da rappresentarsi nel Teatro grande alla Scala di Milano, il carnevale dell' anno 1782 . . .

Milano, Gio. Batista Bianchi, n. d. 48 p. 15½ᶜᵐ.
Three acts. By Metastasio. Dedication ("per l'apertura delle recite del carnevale entrante"), argument, cast, scenario, and name of composer, Francesco **Bianchi.**
First performed, as indicated, December 26, 1781.   Schatz 1004

L'Olimpiade. Dramma per musica da rappresentarsi in Firenze nel nuovo Regio Teatro degl' Intrepidi detto La Palla a corda nella primavera del 1785 . . .

Firenze, Stamperia Bonducciana, 1785. 1 p. l., iv, 37 p. 16½ᶜᵐ.
Two acts. By Metastasio, with argument, cast, and name of the composer, Giovanni Battista **Borghi** ("musica nuova"). Two ballets by Domenico Ricciardi were performed with the opera, one of which was composed by Gius. Horban and was called "Giasone e Medea."
First performed at Modena, Teatro Rongoni, December 26, 1784.   Schatz 1235

L'Olimpiade. Dramma per musica da rappresentarsi nel Regio Teatro di Torino nella primavera del 1737 per le regie nozze.

Torino, Pietro Giuseppe Zappata e figliuolo, 1737. *4 p. l., 76, 1 p.* *15½ᶜᵐ.*

By Metastasio. Three acts. Argument, scenario, cast, and name of the composer, Giuseppe Ferdinando **Brivio**. Alessio Rasetti is mentioned as composer of the ballet music. SCHATZ 1326

Olimpiade. Dramma rappresentato con musica del Caldara la prima volta nel giardino dell' Imperial Favorita, alla presenza degli augusti regnanti, il dì 28 agosto 1733, per festeggiare il giorno di nascita dell' imperatrice Elisabetta, d'ordine dell' imperator Carlo VI.

n. i., n. d. *pl., 106 p.* *17ᶜᵐ.*

Evidently detached from an edition of Metastasio's works not in the L. of C. Three acts and Licenza. Argument. ML 50.2.O5C2

L'Olimpiade del celebre Sig. abate Pietro Metastasio . . . Dramma per musica da rappresentarsi nel Pubblico Teatro di Lucca nell' autunno dell' anno MDCCLXXXIV.

Lucca, Francesco Bonsignori, n. d. *63 p.* *14½ᶜᵐ.*

Two acts. Argument, scenario, cast, and name of the composer, **Cimarosa**. On p. 57–63 description of Antonio Muzzarelli's "La liberazione di Castruccio Castracane." The composer of the music is not mentioned.
First performed at Vicenza, Nuovo Teatro Eretenio, July 10, 1784. SCHATZ 1960

— **L'Olimpiade** del celebre Signor abate Pietro Metastasio . . . Dramma per musica da rappresentarsi nel Nuovo Teatro di Vicenza l'autunno MDCCXCIV.

Vicenza, Vendramin Mosca, n. d. *48 p.* *18ᶜᵐ.*

Two acts. Dedication referring to the first performance in 1784, argument, cast, scenario, and name of Domenico **Cimarosa** as composer. ("La musica sarà.")
SCHATZ 11686

L'Olimpiade. Dramma per musica da rappresentarsi nel Regio Teatro di Torino nel carnovale del 1790. Alla presenza di S. S. R. M.

Torino, Onorato Derossi, n. d. *viii, 51 p.* *15½ᶜᵐ.*

Three acts. By Metastasio. With argument, cast, scenario, and name of the composer, Vincenzo **Federici**. On p. [47]–51 "Descrizione de' balli inventati, e composti, come pure la musica de' medesimi dal Signor Gaspare Angiolini" with argument, cast, and description: (1) "Sargine," (2) "Lorezzo," (3) "I vincitori de' giuochi olimpici."
First performed at Turin, as indicated, December 26, 1789. SCHATZ 3046

L'Olimpiade. Dramma per musica da rappresentarsi nel Teatro Grimani a S. Samuele nella Fiera dell' Ascensione dell' anno 1745.

n. i., n. d. *1 p. l., 48 p.* *15ᶜᵐ.*

Three acts. By Metastasio. Argument, cast, scenario, and name of the composer, Ignazio **Fiorillo**.
First performed, as indicated, Venice, May, 1745. SCHATZ 3205

— **L'Olimpiade.** Drama per musica da recitarsi sul famosissimo Teatro di Braunsviga nella fiera d'estate l'anno 1749.—Die olympischen spiele . . .

Wolfenbuettel, Christian Bartsch wittwe u. erben, n. d. *Unpaged.* *18½ᶜᵐ.*

Three acts. By Metastasio. Argument (in German only), scenario, and name of the composer, Ignazio **Fiorillo**. German text faces Italian. SCHATZ 3202

L'Olimpiade. Dramma per musica del Signore abbate Pietro Metastasio da rappresentarsi in Siena nel Teatro della virtuosissima Accademia degl' Intronati nell' estate dell' anno 1763 . . .

*Siena, Bonetti, 1763.   58 p.   15½*cm.

Three acts. Impresario's dedication, argument, cast, scenario, and name of Galuppi as composer.

First performed, as indicated, July 24, 1763; at Milan, Regio Ducal Teatro, December 26, 1747.   SCHATZ 3496

L'Olimpiade.   Dramma per musica da rappresentarsi nel nobilissimo Teatro di S. Benedetto il carnovale dell' anno MDCCLXVII . . .

*Venezia, Modesto Fenzo, 1767.   64 p.   17½*cm.

Three acts. By Metastasio, who is not mentioned. Impresario's dedication dated Venice, December 26, 1766, argument, cast, scenario, and note: "La musica è di tre celebri maestri di capella." These were Pietro Guglielmi, Antonio Gaetano Pampani, and Francesco Brusa.

Whether the first act was that of Guglielmi's "L'Olimpiade," Naples, 1763, or whether it was a new setting, is not known.   SCHATZ 4316

Olimpiade.   Dramma per musica da rappresentarsi nel Regio elettoral Teatro di corte nel carnevale dell' anno MDCCLVI.   La musica è del Sig^r. Gio. Adolfo Hasse . . .

*Dresda, la vedova Stoessel e Giovanni Carlo Krause, n. d.   7 p. l., (double) 91 p.   23*cm.

Three acts. By Metastasio, who is not mentioned. Argument, cast, and scenario. German title page, "Das olympische spiel," and text face Italian.

First performed, as indicated, February 16, 1756.   SCHATZ 4549

—— **L'Olimpiade.**   Dramma per musica da rappresentarsi nel Regio Teatro di Torino nel carnovale del 1765 . . .

*Torino, Gaspare Bayno, n. d.   viii, 68 p.   16*cm.

Three acts. Argument, cast, scenario, and name of Joh. Ad. Hasse as the composer. The text is not quite the same as in the original Dresden (1756) edition. For instance, the whole scene I, 4, "Quanto importuno è questo," has been dropped as also the aria, "Parto: ma so che degno," from II, 2. On p. 67–68 brief descriptions of the ballets by Francesco Salomoni, the second of which, music by Giuseppe Antonio Le-Messier, was called "I cacciatori burlati."

First performed, as indicated, December 26, 1764.   SCHATZ 4550

L'Olimpiade.   Dramma per musica da rappresentarsi nel Teatro ducale di Stutgard festeggiandosi il felicissimo giorno natalizio di Sua Altezza Serenissima Carlo, duca regnante di Wirtemberg e Teck, etc.   La poesia è del Signor abbate Pietro Metastasio . . .   La musica è nuovamente composta dal Signor Nicolò Jommelli . . . I balli sono inventati dal Signor Giovanni Giorgio Noverre . . .

*Stutgard, Cotta, 1761.   181, [7] p.   18*cm.

Three acts, preceded by (17 p.) "Prologo." German title page, "Die olympische spiele," and text face Italian. Preceding p. 72, two unnumbered pages, with a brief description of "I capricci di Galatea, ballo pastorale." The 7 add. p. contain a description of "Admeto ed Alceste, ballo tragico." The composers of the music are not mentioned. Abert says that, in addition, between second and third acts Noverre's ballet "Rinaldo," music by Rudolph, was performed.

First performed, as indicated, February 11, 1761.   SCHATZ 4867

—— **L'Olimpiade.**   Dramma per musica da rappresentarsi nel Real Teatro dell' Ajuda in occasione di festeggiarsi il felicissimo giorno natalizio di Sua Real Maestà l'augustissima Signora D. Marianna Vittoria . . . nella primavera dell' anno 1774.

*[Lisbona], Stamperia Reale, n. d.   88 p.   15*cm.

Three acts. Argument, scenario, cast, and names of Metastasio as author, of Niccolò Jommelli as composer. The text seems to follow closely that of 1761.

First performed, as indicated, March 31, 1774.   SCHATZ 4885

L'Olimpiade, dramma per musica da rappresentarsi nel Teatro Tron di S. Cassiano l'autunno dell' anno MCCLII . . .

[Venezia], n. publ., n. d.   1 p. l., 48 p.   16^cm.

Three acts. By Metastasio, who is not mentioned. Impresario's dedication, argument, cast, scenario, and name of Gaetano **Latilla** as composer.   Schatz 5449

L'Olimpiade, ballet.   *See* Meucci's Telemaco.

L'Olimpiade. Dramma per musica da rappresentarsi nel famoso Teatro Grimani di S. Gio. Grisostomo nell' autunno dell' anno 1738 . . .

Venezia, Marino Rossetti, 1738.   69 p.   15^cm.

Three acts. By Metastasio, who is not mentioned; neither is **Pergolesi,** the composer. Domenico Lalli's dedication, argument, cast, and scenario.
First performed at Rome, Teatro Tor di Nona, carnival (January), 1735.

Schatz 7904

L'Olimpiade. Dramma da rappresentarsi ne' Regi Teatri di S. M. il rè di Prussia.   Messo in musica dal Sign. G. F. Reichardt . . .

Berlino, Haude e Spener, 1791.   107 p.   16½^cm.

Three acts. German title-page, "Die Olympiade . . .vom herrn abt Metastasio," and text face Italian. Argument, cast, and note that "molti cambiamenti furono fatti al dramma del Metastasio si per commodo della musica, che per quello de' Signori attori."
First performed at Berlin, as indicated, on October 3, 1791.   Schatz 8649

Olimpiade. Dramma per musica da rappresentarsi nel Teatro Interinale di Milano il carnovale dell' anno 1778 . . .

Milano, Gio. Batista Bianchi, n. d.   59, 24 p.   14½^cm.

Three acts. By Metastasio, who is not mentioned. Impresario's dedication, argument, cast, scenario, and name of Antonio **Rossetti** as the composer. The 24 p. contain cast, argument, description, and name of Luigi Gatti ("musica tutta nuova") as composer of the music of Innocenzo Gambuzzi's "Germanico in Germania, ballo eroico-pantomimo," in five acts, the argument of Gambuzzi's "Il matrimonio de' Groenlandesi," and the title of his third ballet, "Giaccona."
First performed December 27, 1777, as indicated.   Schatz 8885

L'Olimpiade. Dramma per musica da rappresentarsi nel nobilissimo Teatro di S. Benedetto l'autunno dell' anno MDCCLXXXVI.

Venezia, Modesto Fenzo, 1786.   55 p.   17^cm.

Three acts. By Metastasio, who is not mentioned. Argument, cast, scenario, and name of **Sacchini** as the composer, with remark, "alcuni pezzi di musica sono di altri celebri maestri."
First performed at Padova, Teatro Nuovo, June, 1763.   Schatz 9238

— **L'Olympiade** ou Le triomphe de l'amitié, drame héroique en trois actes et en vers, mêlé de musique; représenté, pour la premiere fois, par les Comédiens italiens oridnaires du roi, le 2 octobre 1777, & à Fontainebleau, devant Leurs Majestés, le 24 du même mois.

Paris, la veuve Duchesne, 1777.   2 p. l., 24 p.   19^cm.

Cast and names of Nicolas Etienne Framery as the author of this French version, of **Sacchini** as the composer.   Schatz 9239

L'Olimpiade. Dramma per musica da rappresentarsi nel Teatro Grimani di S. Benedetto l'autunno dell' anno 1760.

Venezia, Antonio Comino, 1760.   55 p.   15^cm.

Three acts. By Metastasio, who is not mentioned. Argument, cast, scenario, and name of Gregorio **Sciroli** as the composer.   Schatz 9783

L'Olimpiade. Dramma per musica da rappresentarsi nel Teatro Giustiniani di S. Moisè il carnovale dell' anno 1747.

Venezia, Valvasense, 1747. 48 p. 15½^{cm}.

Three acts. By Metastasio, who is not mentioned. Argument, cast, scenario, and name of Giuseppe **Scolari** as the composer.   SCHATZ 9797

Olimpiade. Dramma per musica del Sig. abbate Pietro Metastasio, Poeta Cesares. Da rappresentarsi in Verona nel nuovo Teatro dell' Accademia filarmonica nell' autunno dell' anno 1758 . . .

Verona, Dionisio Ramanzini, n. d. 51 p. 17½^{cm}.

Three acts. Impresario's dedication, argument, cast, scenario, and name of Tommaso **Trajetta** as the composer. ("La musica è tutta nuova.") SCHATZ 10404

— Olimpiade. Dramma per musica da rappresentarsi in Firenze nel Teatro di via della Pergola nell' autunno dell' anno 1767 sotto la protezione di Sua Altezza Reale Pietro Leopoldo, arciduca d'Austria . . .

n. i., n. d. vi, 60 p. 21½^{cm}.

Vignettes.
Three acts. Argument, cast, and name of Tommaso **Traetta** as composer. The music is called "tutta nuova," which possibly means that this is a second setting of the text by Metastasio, who is not mentioned.
First performed October 15, 1767, as indicated.   SCHATZ 10396
Second copy.   ML48.M2C

L'Olimpiade. Dramma per musica di Pietro Metastasio, poeta di S. M. C. C., fra gl'Arcadi Artino Corasio. Da rappresentarsi nel Teatro di Sant' Angelo nel carnovale dell' anno MDCCXXXIV.

Venezia, Marino Rossetti, 1734. 72 p. 15^{cm}.

Three acts. Argument, cast, scenario, and name of Antonio **Vivaldi** as the composer.   SCHATZ 10774

Olimpie, tragédie lyrique en trois actes, poème du c^{en} Guillard, musique du c^{en} Kalkbrenner; représentée pour la première fois à Paris, sur le Théâtre de la République et des Arts, le 18 frimaire an 7 . . .

Paris, Charles Honel, an VII [1798–99]. 2 p. l., 40 p. 26^{cm}.

First performed, as indicated, December 18, 1798.   SCHATZ 4998

L'Olindo. Commedia per musica di Antonio Palomba Napoletano da rappresentarsi nel Teatro di Forentini nel carnevale di quest' anno 1753.

Napoli, Domenico Lanciano, 1753. 83 p. 14½^{cm}.

Three acts. Cast and (on p. [4]) the remark:
"La musica è del Signor D. Niccolò **Conti**, a riserba dell' ultima cavatina di Masillo, Finale dell' atto secondo e l'intiero terz atto, come anco la sinfonia, e l'arie con questo segno §, che sono del Sig. D. Matteo **Capranica**, ambo maestri di cappella Napoletani."   SCHATZ 2208

Olindo e Sofronia. L. T. of Andreozzi's Sofronia e Olindo.

L'Olympiade da rappresentarsi in musica nel Teatro Nouvo [!] di corte.—nel carnovale 1764. Trasposte in versi tedeschi. La poesia è del Signor abbate Pietro Metastasio.—La musica è del Sig. Andrea di Bernasconi . . .

Monaco, Giov. Giac. Vötter, n. d. 211 p. 15^{cm}.

Three acts. Argument. German title, "Die olympischen spiel," and text face Italian.
First performed at Munich, January 20, 1764.   SCHATZ 859

Die **Olympiade.**   Tr. of Reichardt's L'Olimpiade.

L'**Olympiade** ou Le triomphe de l'amitié.   French version of Sacchini's Olimpiade.

Das **olympische spiel.**   Tr. of Hasse's Olimpiade.

Die **olympische spiele.**   Tr. of Jommelli's L'Olimpiade.

Die **olympischen spiel.**   Tr. of Bernasconi's L'Olympiade.

Die **olympischen spiele.**   Tr. of Fiorillo's L'Olimpiade.

L'**ombra di Nino** ossia L'impostore scoverto.   Da rappresentarsi nel Real Teatro di S. Cecilia, per la prima opera nell' autunno di quest' anno 1796 . . .

Palermo, Stamperia Valenza, n. d.   48 p.   14½^{cm}.

Two acts.   The author, Michelangelo Prunetti, is not mentioned.   Impresario's dedication, cast, and name of Francesco **Ruggi** as the composer.

First performed at Naples, Teatro del Fondo, 1794.   S̲c̲h̲a̲t̲z̲ 9145

L'**ombre du cocher poëte.**   Prologue des deux pièces suivantes. Representé par les Marionettes êtrangères à la Foire de S. Germain 1722 . . .

Below the title this Avertissement:

"Les auteurs de l'Opéra comique, voyant encore une fois leur spectacle fermé, plus animez par la vengeance que par un esprit d'interêt, s'avisèrent d'acheter une douzaine de marionettes, & de loüer une loge, où, comme les assiégez dans leurs derniers retranchemens, ils rendirent encore leurs armes redoutables.   Leurs ennemis poussez d'une nouvelle fureur, firent de nouveaux efforts contre Polichinelle chantant; mais ils n'en sortirent pas à leur honneur."

— Le **remouleur d'amour.**   Pièce d'un acte.   Representée par les Marionettes etrangeres à la Foire de S. Germain 1722.

— **Pierrot Romulus,** ou Le ravisseur poli.   Representée par les Marionettes etrangeres à la Foire de S. Germain 1722.   Cette pièce est une parodie de la tragédie de Romulus que l'on joüoit en ce tems-là.

Le Théâtre de la foire, Paris, 1724, t. v, 3 pl., [47]–140 p.   17^{cm}.

The plays in t. v. were written by Le Sage, Fuzelier, d'Orneval, according to a note on 2d p. l. of t. iv.   Largely *en vaudevilles.*   The airs, selected or composed and arranged by Jean Claude **Gillier,** are printed at the end of the volume in the "Table des airs."   ML 48.L2V

Omphale, tragedie.   Representé par l'Academie royale de musique l'an 1701.   Les paroles de M. de la Mothe, & la musique de M. Destouches.   LIV. opera.

n. i., n. d.   front., p. 277–344 (Recueil général des opéra, t. vii, Paris, 1703.)   14^{cm}

Detached copy.   Five acts and prologue, with dedicatory "Epistre" to the duke of Burgundy.

First performed, as indicated, November 10, 1701.   S̲c̲h̲a̲t̲z̲ 2549

Second copy.   ML 48.R4

— **Omphale,** tragedie, représentée pour la premiere fois par l'Académie royale de musique, en 1701.   Reprise en 1721 & en 1733. Remise au Théâtre le 14 janvier 1752.

Paris, Aux dépens de l'Académie chez la V. Delormel & fils, 1752. 60 p.   24^{cm}.

With cast.   Author and composer are mentioned on p. 2.   S̲c̲h̲a̲t̲z̲ 2549A

Omphale—Continued.

— **Fanfale,** parodie d'Omphale, en cinq actes; avec des divertissements. Par Mrs. Favart & Marcouville. Représentée pour la
premiere fois par les Comédiens italiens ordinaires du roi, le mercredi
8 mars 1752.
> *Paris, N. B. Duchesne, 1759.   60, [4] p.   19^{cm}.   (Theatre de M.
> Favart, Paris, Duchesne, 1763–77, t. I.)*

Cast. *En vaudevilles.* Many of the airs are printed in the text. The arranger of
the music is not mentioned by Font. The [4] p. contain "Privilège du roi" and a
"Catalogue de parodies & opera comiques."   ML 49.A2F1

— **La fileuse,** parodie d'Omphale, par Mr. Vadé.   Représentée pour
la premiere fois sur le Théatre de l'Opéra comique le 8 mars 1752.
> *La Haye, Pierre Gosse, 1760.   38, [1] p.   16^{cm}.   (Vadé, Oeuvres, La
> Haye, 1760, t. I.)*

One act, *en vaudevilles.* The added page contains the air of the vaudeville, "Si
l'amant qui vous rend."   ML 49.A2V2

— **La fileuse,** parodie d'Omphale, représentée pour la premiere fois
sur le Théatre de l'Opéra-comique, le 8 mars 1752.
> *Paris, la veuve Duchesne, 1766.   32 p.   19^{cm}.*

One act. On p. 29–30, the "Vaudeville de La fileuse:" "Si l'amant qui vous rend
hommage." The author, Jean Joseph Vadé, is not mentioned.   SCHATZ 11492

— **Hercule filant.**   Parodie d'Omphale.   Comedie représentée pour
la premiere fois, par les Comédiens italiens ordinaires du Roi, le jeudi
15. may 1721.
> *Les parodies du Nouveau Théatre italien, Nouv. éd., Paris, Briasson,
> 1738, t. II, [41]–86 p.   16½^{cm}.*

One act. Louis Fuzelier mentioned in t. I as author. The airs and vaudeville
used are printed at the end of the volume in the "Table des airs" (60 p.).
                                                                 ML 48.P3

Omphale, in einem sing-spiele auf dem Hamburgischen Schau-platze
zum erstenmale im jahre 1724 aufgefuehret.
> *[Hamburg], Caspar Jakhel, n. d.   Unpaged.   18^{cm}.*

Prologue and five acts. Cast, scenario, and notice to the reader, who is informed:
"Es hat zwar dem hiesigen Schau-platze bissher an allerhand abwechslungen, so
wohl in ansehung des innhaltes der opern als auch der music, taenze, kleidungen, ver-
wandlungen und anderen zierraten nicht gemangelt; ob aber jemahls alhier ein werk
hervor getreten, dass so viele und so weit von einander entfernete veraenderungen in
sich gehalten als das gegenwaertige, daran moegte wohl gezweifelt werden. Seinen
ursprung nimmt es von Mr. de la Motte . . . Gleich wie nun in itztgedachtem [the
text] ein bestaendiger wechsel herrschet, also ist auch in der musicalischen ausarbeitung solches in acht genommen und der hauptinnhalt nach italiaenischer was aber zu
den aufzuegen gehoeret, nach franzoesischer art eingerichtet worden."
The reader is further informed that, for the sake of brevity, the music was cut in
three places, besides in the last scene, "damit das spiel ein freudiges ende nehme,"
as was also done in France. The absent translator is said to have reported that his
translation is literal, except for the interpolation of arias of his own make in imitation
of Italian models, or excisions in order to better balance the "Odaischen saetze" or
"wenn er, da ihm in der gedruckten franzoesischen music etwas von dem originale
abweichendes in die augen gefallen, diesem mehr, als jenem nachzugehen ursache
gefunden."
The German version was made by the composer Georg Philipp **Telemann,** who is
not mentioned.   SCHATZ 10265

On ne s'avise jamais de tout, opéra-comique, représenté à Versailles devant Leurs Majestés, le mercredi 2 décembre 1761. Et ci-devant sur le Théâtre de la Foire St. Laurent, le lundi 14 septembre 1761. Par M. Sedaine. La musique de M. M * * * [Monsigny]. Toisième [!] édition augmentée.

Avignon, Louis Chambeau, 1764. 35 p. 19ᶜᵐ.

Cast of September 14, 1761. SCHATZ 6578

— **On ne s'avise jamais de tout,** opera-comique, par M. Sedaine. Représenté par les Comédiens françois de la cour sur le Nouveau Théatre de S. A. E. de Saxe à Dresde, 1766.

[Dresde], George Conrad Walther, n. d. 60 p. 18ᶜᵐ.

Monsigny is not mentioned. SCHATZ 11729

— **On ne s'avise jamais de tout,** opera comique, en un acte en prose, mêlé de musique; par Mr. Sedaine. Représenté pour la premiere fois sur le Théatre de la Foire St. Laurent, le 14 septembre 1761.

Paris, Claude Herissant, 1775. 46 p. 17½ᶜᵐ.

On p. [40]–46, "Ariettes et vaudevilles:" "Un chanteur n'est pas un Caton," "Une fille est un oiseau," "Vous qui croyez que des tendres." Music by **Monsigny,** who is not mentioned. SCHATZ 11728

— **Man sieht niemals alles voraus,** ein singspiel in einem aufzuge aus dem franzoesischen uebersetzt mit musik.

Frankfurt am Mayn, mit Andreäischen schriften, 1772. 64 p., 10 p. (folded music). 16½ᶜᵐ.

Johann Heinrich Faber's version. The 10 p. of music (bass and voice) contain: "Lise kann nicht mehr lang verweilen," "Alles, was ich nur erblicke," "Junge maedchen sind fuerwahr," "Ihr, die ihr meint." SCHATZ 6579

Het onderaardsch gewelf. A. T. of Dalayrac's Camille.

L'onestà trionfante. A. T. of the ballet La sposa in equivoco.

Der onkel aus Amsterdam. Tr. of Cimarosa's Il pittore parigino.

Onorio. Dramma per musica da rappresentarsi nel famosissimo Teatro Grimani di S. Gio. Grisostomo nell' autunno dell' anno MDCCXXIX . . .

Venezia, Carlo Buonarigo, n. d. 1 p. l., 69 p. 15ᶜᵐ.

Three acts. Dedication signed by Domenico Lalli, scenario, cast, and notice to the reader (with name of Francesco Čiampi as composer) which says:
"Da una penna fu ideata la presente drammatica composizione, e da un' altra intieramente verseggiata."
Schatz records as authors Lalli and Giovanni Boldini. SCHATZ 1874

Onorio in Roma. Drama da rappresentarsi in musica nel famosissimo Teatro di S. Gio. Grisostomo l'anno 1692 . . .

Venetia, Nicolini, 1692. front., 67 p. 14ᶜᵐ.

Three acts. Dedication dated Venice, February 2, 1692, with the initials of the author, Giovanni Matteo Giannini, argument, scenario, and notice to the reader with the remark:
"E stata ideata in momenti: sceneggiata in ore: verseggiata in meno di un giorno: Reso armoniosa dal Signor Carlo [Francesco] Polaroli in poco più d'una settimana. Non dico favole: Lo creda chi vuole; ma è cosi in verità." SCHATZ 8305

L'opéra.   Entrée in Campra's Les festes vénitiennes.

Opera buffa.   Ein komisches singspiel in zwey akten.

*n. i., n. d.   p. [95]–218.   (C. F. Bretzner, Singspiele, Leipzig, 1796.)
16^{cm}.*

The composer, Georg Ernst Gottlieb **Kallenbach,** is not mentioned.

SCHATZ 4999

L'opéra comique, opera-comique en un acte, en prose et ariettes,
par J. Ségur le jeune, et Em. Dupaty; représenté pour la première
fois sur le Théâtre de l'Opéra comique national, rue Favart, le 21
messidor an 6 de la République [July 9, 1798].

Paris, Huet, an VI. [1797–98]   55 p.   19^{cm}.

Cast.   The composer, P. A. D. **Della Maria,** is not mentioned.   ML 50.2.O6D2

— **L'opéra comique,** opéra comique en un acte, en prose et ariettes;
par J. Ségur le jeune, et Em. Dupaty; musique de Domenico Della
Maria.   Représenté, pour la première fois, sur le Théâtre de l'Opéra-
comique-national, rue Favart, le 21 messidor an VI de la République.

Toulouse, Brouilhiet, an septieme [1798–99].   24 p.   19½^{cm}.

Cast.   ML 50.2.O6D22

L'opera comique assiegé.   Piece d'un acte.   Par M^{rs} le S * *
& d'Or * *   Representée à la Foire Saint Germain 1730 . . .

Le Théâtre de la foire, Paris, 1731, t. vii, pl., [403]–436 p.   17^{cm}.

By Le Sage and d'Orneval.   Largely *en vaudevilles.*   The airs, selected or composed and arranged by Jean Claude **Gillier,** are printed at the end of the volume in
the "Table des airs."   Below the title the Avertissement:
    "Cette pièce fut faite à l'occasion d'un nouveau procès que les Comédiens françois
s'avvisèrent d'intenter à l'Opéra comique, & dans lequel ils eurent le démenti."
    First performed March 26, 1730.   ML 48.L2VII

L'opéra en province.   Parody of Gluck's Armide.

L'opera in prova alla moda.   Drama giocoso.

Amsterdam, Enrico Boussiere, 1753.   205, [3] p.   15^{cm}.

French title page, "La répétition ordinaire de l'opéra," and text face Italian.
Three acts with cast, followed by three acts with cast and argument of "*Urganostocor,*
tragedia tragichissima ma di lieto fine," this, too, with Italian text and French translation.   The 3 additional p. contain substitute arias.   Neither the author, Giovanni
Fiorini, is mentioned, nor the composer, Gaetano **Latilla.**   The following avviso
precedes the text:
    "Non essendo possibile d'eseguire l'intero libro in una sola sera, si è giudicato
bene di spartirlo in quattro recite; nella di cui 1. La prova intiera, colla prima
azzione della tragedia.   Nella 2. La stessa prova colla seconda azzione della tragedia.
Nella 3. I medesimi atti della prova colla terza azzione della tragedia.   4. La scena
unica del terzo atto della prova, e le tre azzioni della tragedia . . ."
    First performed at Amsterdam, 1753; at Venice, Teatro S. Moisè, carnival, 1751.

SCHATZ 5450

L'opera nuova.   Dramma giocoso per musica di Giovanni Bertati
da rappresentarsi nel Teatro Giustiniani in S. Moisè per la seconda
opera di carnovale l'anno 1781.

Venezia, n. publ., n. d.   62 p.   17^{cm}.

Two acts.   Cast and name of Matteo **Rauzzini** as the composer.   SCHATZ 8613

L'opera seria.   O. T. of Calsabigi's text La critica teatrale.

L'opera seria. Dramma giocoso per musica da rappresentarsi in Firenze nel Teatro di via del Cocomero, nella primavera dell' anno 1771 . . .

[*Firenze*], *Ant. Giuseppe Pagani, n. d.   front., 1 p. l., 64 p.   16½*^{cm}.

Three acts. Neither the author, Ranieri de' Calsabigi, nor the composer, Florian Leopold **Gassmann**, is mentioned. Scenario and dedication. The opera is a satire on the foolish practices of composers, rhymesters, stars, impresarios, etc., and the libretto is dedicated to them in words that leave nothing to be desired in bluntness.

The front. is a portrait by An. Piattoli, engraved by F. Gregori, of Pietro Leopoldo I, arciduca d'Austria.

First performed, according to Schatz, at Vienna, Teatro di Corté, 1769.

SCHATZ 3623

The operator.   A ballad opera.

London, Printed for the author, 1740.   2 p. l., 36 p.   22^{cm}.

One act. The airs of the 10 songs not even indicated by title. Author not recorded by Tufts, who says: "intended to satirize Dr. Taylor, an oculist."   LONGE 128

Die operisten in Nanking. Tr. of Alessandri's La compagnia d'opera a Nanchino.

Opernverwalter von den Canarischen inseln. A. T. of Leo's Der impresarius.

Das opfer der Nymphen, ein vorspiel. Am geburtsfeste des koenigs von Preussen, den 24. januar 1774 auf dem Deutschen Theater zu Berlin aufgefuehret.

Berlin, George Ludewig Winters wittwe, n. d.   11 p.   20½^{cm}.

One act. Neither the author, Carl Wilhelm Ramler, nor the composer, Johann Abraham Peter **Schulz**, is mentioned.   SCHATZ 9725

Das opfer der treue. Ein vorspiel mit gesaengen. Aufgefuehrt am geburtstage Seiner Majestaet des koenigs, den 24 jenner 1776 von der Waeserschen Schauspielergesellschaft in Breslau.

Breslau und Leipzig, Christian Friedrich Gutsch, 1779.   16 p.   15½^{cm}.

One act. Neither the author, Karl Emil Schubert, is mentioned, nor the composer, Franz Andreas **Holly**.   SCHATZ 4771

Das opferfest. A. T. and L. T. of P. v. Winter's Das unterbrochene opferfest.

I oprørt vand er godt at fiske. Tr. of Sarti Fra i due litiganti il terzo gode.

L'oracolo, ballet. *See* Nasolini's Il trionfo di Clelia.

L'oracolo di Velleda. Poemetto drammatico nel giorno del gloriosissimo nome della Sacra Real Maestà di Amalia Willelmina regina de' Romani.

Pietro Antonio Bernardoni, Poemi drammatici, parte terza, Vienna, van Ghelen, 1707, p. 45–64.   16½^{cm}.

Argument. The composer is not mentioned by von Weilen.

First performed July 10, 1706?   ML 49.A2B4

L'oracolo in Messenia. Dramma per musica da rappresentarsi nel Teatro di S. Angelo nel carnovale dell' anno 1738.

Venezia, Marino Rossetti, n. d.   70 p.   14½^{cm}.

Three acts. Later version of "Merope," by Apostolo Zeno, who is not mentioned. Argument, cast, scenario, and name of Antonio **Vivaldi** as the composer.

SCHATZ 10775

L'oracolo in sogno. Drama in musica da rappresentarsi nel Teatro di Sant' Angelo l'anno 1700. Poesia di Francesco Silvani . . .

Venezia, Nicolini, 1700. 60 p. 14½ᶜᵐ.

Three acts. Silvani's dedication, dated Venice, January 11, 1700, argument, cast, scenario, and notice to the reader, who is informed by Silvani that he was forced to mutilate his text so much "ch'egli è appena riconoscibile per quello, che recitato in Mantova, ebbe la fortuna d'incontrare il compatimento di quella Serenissima Altezza, che hà voluto clementissimamente rimunerarlo col dichiararmi suo Servidore Attuale . . ." SCHATZ 11353

Composer not mentioned, and unknown to Schatz.

Oraklet. Et syngespil i to handlinger. Indrettet til det Danske Theaters Brug efter det franske af Saint Foix og det tydske af Gellert.

n. i., n. d. 44 p. 17ᶜᵐ.

Paolo **Scalabrini** is mentioned as the composer. Author unknown to Schatz. First performed at Copenhagen, Courttheater, April 23, 1776. SCHATZ 9517

Gli **Orazi e i Curiazi,** ballet. *See* Basili's Il ritorno d'Ulisse.

Gli **Orazi e i Curiazi.** Tragedia per musica del Signor Antonio Sografi, poeta del nobilissimo Teatro la Fenice e del Teatro comico Sant' Angelo composta per il teatro sudetto per il carnovale 1797.

Venezia, Stamperia Valvasense, n. d. 70 p. 16½ᶜᵐ.

Three acts. Cast and name of the composer, **Cimarosa.** ("La musica tutta nuova.") On p. 61–70, argument, cast, and detailed description of Lorenzo Panzieri's "Cha-Gian in Dely ballo eroico in cinque atti." The composer of the music is not mentioned. The second ballet was called "I morti fatti sposi." First performed at Venice, La Fenice, December 26, 1796. SCHATZ 1961

Gli **Orazi e I Curiazi.** Tragedia per musica del Signor Sografi da rappresentarsi nel nobilissimo Teatro La Fenice l'autunno 1798.

Venezia, Valvasense, n. d. 45 p. 17ᶜᵐ.

Three acts. Cast and name of Marcos **Portugal** as the composer ("La musica tutta nuova"). On p. [25]–28, cast, argument, and name of Vittorio Trento as the composer of the music of Salvatore Vigano's ballet, "Giorgio principe della Servia, ballo eroicomico pantomimo."

First performed at Ferrara, Teatro Comunale, September 2, 1798 (Schatz and Carvalhaes). SCHATZ 8442

Orazio. Dramma giocoso per musica.

Venezia, Modesto Fenzo, 1748. 57 p. 14½ᶜᵐ.

Three acts. Scenario and name of Pietro **Auletta**, composer, but not of librettist, Antonio Palomba (Schatz).

First performed at Venice, Teatro di S. Angelo, spring, 1748. SCHATZ 500

Orazio. O. T. of Deller's Il maestro di cappella.

Orazio. Opera bernesca in musica da rappresentarsi in Venezia nel Teatro di S. Moise nell' autunno dell' anno 1743.

Venezia, Girolamo Bortoli, 1743. 66 p. (incl. front.) 15½ᶜᵐ.

Three acts. By Antonio Palomba, who is not mentioned. Cast, scenario, and names of "Gaetano **Latilla** e Signor Pargolesi" (**Pergolesi**) as composers. *See* Pergolesi's "Il maestro di musica."

Latilla's "Orazio" was first performed at Rome, Teatro Valle, spring of 1738. SCHATZ 5466

Orazio. Drama per musica da rappresentarsi nel famosissimo Teatro Grimano di San Gio. Grisostomo. L'anno MDCLXXXVIII . . .

Venetia, Francesco Nicolini, 1688. 71 p. 14^{cm}.

Three acts. Dedication dated Venice, January 16, 1688, and signed "F. A. L." Neither the author, Vincenzo Grimani, is mentioned, nor the composer, Giuseppe Felice **Tosi.** Notice to the reader, argument. The "Intermedii" are mentioned in the nature of "Gioco di soldate con lotte, e spadoni," the first act, "Combattimento de tre Orazij e tre Curiazij," second act, etc. SCHATZ 10377

Orazio Curiazo. Drama per musica da rappresentarsi nel Teatro Grimani a S. Samuelle per la fiera dell' Ascenj^{ne} l'anno 1746 . . .

[Venezia], n. publ., n. d. 46 p. 15$\frac{1}{2}$^{cm}.

Three acts. Argument, scenario, cast, and Ferdinando **Bertoni**'s name as "direttore della musica," not as composer. Librettist not mentioned and unknown to Schatz. SCHATZ 924

Orbecch, ballo eroico favoloso. *See* Fioravanti's Gl'inganni fortunati.

Oreste. Dramma per musica da rappresentarsi nel Real Teatro di S. Carlo nel dì 13 agosto 1783 per festeggiarsi la nascita di S. M. la regina . . .

Napoli, Vincenzo Flauto, 1783. 55 p. 15^{cm}.

Three acts. Luigi Serio is mentioned as author of this "nuovo dramma" in the dedication dated Naples, August 13, 1783. Argument, cast, scenario, and name of **Cimarosa** as composer. On p. 10–15 argument, cast, and detailed description of Gio. Antonio Cianfanelli's "Il trionfo di Alessandro o sia La disfatta di Dario, ballo eroico in quattro atti . . . La musica è tutta nuova del Sig. Mattia Stabingher." SCHATZ 1966

L'Oreste. Dramma serio in musica da rappresentarsi nel Regio Teatro della nobile Academia dei Costanti della città di Pisa nella primavera dell' anno 1798.

Pisa, Stamperia Pieraccini, n. d. 38 p. 17^{cm}.

Two acts. "La poesia è del Sig. D. F.[rancesco] G.[onella] autore del Ritorno di Serse, della Lodoiska . . . La musica è del celebre Sig. Giuseppe **Moneta** . . ." Cast. SCHATZ 6555

Oreste. Dramma per musica da rappresentarsi nel Regio Teatro di Torino nel carnovale del 1766 . . .

Torino, Onorato Derossi. viii, 52, [2] p. 17^{cm}.

Date of publication, if any, torn off.

Three acts. A later version of "Ifigenia in Tauride" by Mattia Verazj, who is not mentioned. Argument, cast, scenario, and names of Carlo **Monza** as the composer of the opera, and of Giuseppe Antonio Le Messier as the composer of the music for Giovanni Battista Marten's ballets "Bradamante e Ruggero" and "Amor Corsaro." SCHATZ 6611

Oreste o sia La morte di Clitennestra, ballet. *See* Giordani's Fernando nel Messico.

Oreste o sia La morte de Clitennestra, ballet. *See* Rust's Il baron di Terra Asciuta.

Oreste e Pilade. O. T. of Agricola's I Greci in Tauride.

L'Oreste in Sparta. Drama primo per musica del dottor Pompeo Luchesi . . .

Reggio, Prospero Vedrotti, 1697. 88 p. 15½cm.

Three acts. Dedication dated Reggio, April 29, 1697, notice to the reader with the name of Carlo Francesco **Pollaroli** as the composer ("nuovo saggio del suo spiritoso talento nella musica"), cast, and scenario. On p. 87–88 the "Arie proprie de' signori virtuosi": "Più che preghi meno intendo" (I, 3), "Vezzosetto nume alato" (I, 7), "Chi è rubello ad amor" (I, 28), and "Delizie de l'alma" (III, 21).

SCHATZ 8306

Orestes: a dramatic opera. As it is acted at the Theatre-Royal in Lincoln's Inn-Fields. Written by Mr. Theobald . . .

London, John Watts, 1731. 4 p. l., 77, [2] p. 19cm.

Cast. Five acts, prologue, and epilogue by Henry Fielding, in which the line occurs: "Love for soft hearts, —— and musick for soft brains." Why this drama with its negligible few songs, etc., is called an opera is difficult to see. The composer is not mentioned and is not recorded by Schatz.

First performed, as indicated, April 3, 1731.   LONGE 191

Le orfane svizzere. Dramma giocoso per musica da rappresentarsi nel Teatro Giustiniani di S. Moisè l'autunno dell' anno 1770 dell' abbate Pietro Chiari.

Venezia, Antonio Graziosi, 1770. 52 p. 13½cm.

Three acts. Impresario's dedication, cast, scenario, and name of the composer, Antonio **Boroni**. Innocente Gambuzzi's ballets, composers not mentioned, were performed with the opera, "La pescatrice fedele" and "Il mercato d'Amacari Danase."   SCHATZ 1248

L'orfanella americana. Commedia per musica in quattro atti di Giovanni Bertati da rappresentarsi nel Teatro in S. Moisè per la prima opera dell' autunno 1787.

Venezia, Gio. Battista Casali, n. d. 56 p. 18cm.

Four acts. Cast and name of Pasquale **Anfossi** as composer.   SCHATZ 270

L'orfanella americana. Dramma giocoso per musica, da rappresentarsi nel Teatro di S. A. E. di Sassonia.

Dresda, n. publ., 1790. 119 p. 15½cm.

Two acts. By Giovanni Bertati, who is not mentioned. Composed by Friedrich Christopher **Gestewitz**, as appears from the libretto. German title page, "Die verwaiste Amerikanerin," face the Italian.

First performed, as indicated, in January, 1791.   SCHATZ 3796

L'orfano, ballet. *See* Tarchi's Giulio Sabino.

L'orfano cinese. Dramma per musica da rappresentarsi nel nobilissimo Teatro di S. Benedetto la fiera dell' Ascensione dell' anno MDCCLXXXVII.

Venezia, Modesto Fenzo, 1787. 72 p. 16cm.

Three acts. Cast, scenario, and name of composer, Francesco **Bianchi**. Librettist unknown to Schatz. On p. 33–36, description of Antonio Muzzarelli's ballet, "Ulisse al Monte Etna." Neither of this nor the second ballet, "L'amante del studio," is the composer mentioned.

First performed, according to an *avviso* (p. 3), at the same theatre during carnival (January 30), 1787.   SCHATZ 979

L'orfano della China, ballet. *See* Bertoni's Cajo Mario.

L'orfano nella China, ballet. *See* Bianchi's Eurione.

Orfeo.

[363]–394 p.   17ᶜᵐ.   (Rolli, Componimenti poetici, Nuova .edizione, Verona, G. Tumermani, 1744.)

Three acts. According to Burney "a new pasticcio . . . the airs . . . chiefly selected from the works of **Hasse, Vinci, Araja** and **Porpora.**" From the six "Favourite Songs" published by Walsh we know that **Araja** composed "Felice ai di sereni" (III, 5) and **Vinci** "E follia, se nascondete" (III, 4), which is but a paraphrase of Metastasio's text in his "Catone in Utica." The aira "Vaga stella pallidita" headed by Walsh as composed by **Porpora,** does not seem to be in Rolli's text of 1744.

First performed at London, Haymarket, March 2, 1736.   ML 49.A2R7

Orfeo.   L. T. of Bertoni's Orfeo ed Euridice.

Orfeo.   Abbr. T. of Gluck's Orfeo ed Euridice.   *See* the third act of his Le feste d'Apollo.

Orfeo.   Tragedia per musica da rappresentarsi nel Regio Teatro di Berlino per il felicissimo giorno natalizio della Sacra Real Maestà di Sofia Dorotea, regina madre . . .

Berlino, Haude e Spener, 1752.   92, [3] p.   17ᶜᵐ.

Three acts. Leopoldo de Villati is mentioned as the author, and Carl Heinrich **Graun** as the composer. Haude & Spener's privilege, argument, and scenario. German title-page, "Orpheus," and text face Italian.

First performed, as indicated, March 27, 1752.   Schatz 4115

— **Orfeo.**   Tragedia per musica.—Orpheus, ein musicalisches trauerspiel.

Hamburg, Conrad Jacob Spieringk, 1764.   63 p.   17ᶜᵐ.

Three acts. Neither the author, Leopoldo de Villati, nor the composer, Carl Heinrich **Graun,** is mentioned. German text faces Italian.

Performed at Hamburg, Theater b. Gänsemarkt, 1764.   Schatz 4109

Orfeo, ballet.   *See* Paisiello's La disfatta di Dario.

L'Orfeo.   Drama per musica nel Teatro Vendramino à S. Salvatore. Di Aurelio Aureli.   Opera decima settima . . .

Venetia, Francesco Nicolini, 1673.   72 p.   14ᶜᵐ.

Prologue and three acts. Author's dedication, dated Venice, December 14, 1672, argument, scenario, and name of Antonio **Sartorio** as the composer.   Schatz 9483

— **Orpheus,** in einer italiaenischen opera auf dem Schau-platz zu Braunschweig vorgestellet und daraus in das teutsche uebersetzet.

Braunschweig, Christoph Friedrich Zilliger, 1690.   Unpaged.   15ᶜᵐ.

Prologue and three acts. A "Symbolum" by the translator, "Johann Kristof Lorber," pasted on the leaf preceding the title page. He is r.ot mentioned in the text, nor is the composer. According to Schatz, it is "probably" Antonio **Sartorio's** "Orfeo" in a German version (with alterations) of Aureli's text.

Evidently performed at Brunswick, 1690.   Schatz 9484

Orfeo a torto geloso overo Amore spesso inganna.   Drama per musica da rappresentarsi nel Teatrino di Savoia l'anno MDCXCVII . . .

Bologna, Pier-Maria Monti, n. d.   front., 67 p.   13½ᶜᵐ.

Three acts. Dedication signed by Giacomo Maggi, and dated Turin, April 20, 1697. Argument and scenario. Schatz attributes the music to Antonio **Sartorio** and the text to Aurelio Aureli, neither of whom is mentioned. As a matter of comparison, so little of Aureli's "Orfeo" text (Venice, 1672; music by Sartorio) appears in this

Orfeo a torto geloso—Continued.

Bologna edition that they are practically two different librettos. For instance, in the original, I, 6 begins, "Aristeo, che t'affligge," and the aria is, "Al foco d'amore," whereas in this Bologna libretto these words open the eleventh scene of the first act, and the aria is, "Amor spietato arciere."

First performed at Bologna, Teatro Formagliari, carnival, 1695.   SCHATZ 9485

Orfeo e Euridice.   Ballet, music by Le Messier.   *See* Galuppi's La clemenza di Tito.

Orfeo ed Euridice.   Dramma per musica da rappresentarsi nel nobil Teatro di San Benedetto di Venezia nell' estate dell' anno MDCCLXXVI.

Venezia, Modesto Fenzo, 1776.   xxvii p. $20\frac{1}{2}^{cm}$.

One act.   Argument, cast, scenario, and name of composer, Ferdinando Giuseppe **Bertoni,** but not of the librettist, Ranieri de' Calsabigi.   The opera had been previously performed at the same theatre during carnival (January) of the same year (1776), as appears from the libretto "Aristo e Temira e Orfeo ed Euridice." (Schatz, 934–935.)   According to the preface of the latter, "Orfeo" had first been performed at Vienna, but this can refer only to Gluck's setting, Vienna, 1762.

First performed, as indicated, June 3, 1776.   The libretto of Bertoni's opera was also printed, and performed together with Joh. Simon Mayr's "Temira e Aristo" (Venezia, Stamperia Valvasense, 1795, p. [29]–51 [Schatz 6203]).   SCHATZ 916

— Orfeo.   Dramma per musica con li balli analoghi da rappresentarsi nel Regio Teatro di Berlino.

Berlino, Haude e Spener, [1788].   63 p. 16^{cm}.

Three acts.   Argument, cast, scenario, and names of the composer, **Bertoni,** and the librettist.   It is stated that the Italian text is by Calsabigi "mit einigen zu der jezigen aufführung anbefohlnen einschaltungen."   **Reichardt** is mentioned as the composer of these interpolations.   German title-page, "Orpheus," and text face Italian.

First performed at Berlin, Kgl. Operntheater, January 31, 1788.   SCHATZ 917

Orfeo ed Euridice, ballet.   *See* Gazzaniga's La disfatta de' Mori.

Orfeo, ed Euridice.   Azione teatrale per musica da rappresentarsi nel Teatro privilegiato vicino alla Corte nell' autunno del 1762.

Vienna, Ghelen, n. d.   [34] p. 19^{cm}.

T.-p. preceded by half-title with quotation from Virgil.   Text of first act headed, of the two other acts followed, by vignettes.   On t.-p. above imprint Orpheus resting under a tree with his lyre.

Argument, scenario, cast, and names of "Cav. Cristofano **Gluck**" as composer, of Gaspero Angiolini as "inventore e direttore de' balli," a brief description of which follows.   The author of this famous libretto, Ranieri de' Calsabigi, is not mentioned.

First performed, as indicated, October 5, 1762.   ML 50.2.O7G4

— Orfeo.   Forms third part of Gluck's Le feste d'Apollo, Parma (1769).   SCHATZ 3897

— Orfeo ed Euridice e **Aristo e Temira,** drammi per musica da rappresentarsi in Bologna nel Nuovo Pubblico Teatro nella primavera dell' anno MDCCLXXI.

Bologna, Sassi, n. d.   32, 32, vii, [1] p. 20^{cm}.

One act.   By Calsabigi, who is not mentoined.   Argument, cast, and name of **Gluck** as the composer.

Of the one act "Aristo e Temira" Carlo **Monza** is given as the composer after the argument and cast.   Conte De Salvioli, the author, is not mentioned.   At the end a description of Giovanni Favier's "Gli amori di Marte, e di Venere o la Furina di Vulcano nell' isola di Lenno.   Ballo eroico pantomimo."   The composer of the music is not mentioned.   SCHATZ 3934

Orfeo, ed Euridice—Continued.

— **Orpheus and Eurydice,** a musical drama in imitation of the ancient Greek theatrical feasts. As performed at the King's Theatre in the Haymarket. The poetry by the celebrated councellor Calsabigi with additions and alterations by Signor A. Andrei.

London, J. Jarvis, 1785. 55 p. 23ᶜᵐ.

Argument, cast, explanation of the ballets, and autobiographic *captatio benevolentiae* by the "Orpheus" Giusto Ferdinando Tenducci, dated May 7, 1785. If he therein says "I have resolved humbly to present . . . that same Orpheus, which was so much applauded at Florence" and where he had sung the same part, he not only contradicts himself later on but on p. [8] shows that the London version was a pasticcio of the worst sort:

"The music by cav. Christopher **Gluck**: with the additions of the late celebrated John Christian **Bach**: and with the choice of several favorite pieces of Mr. **Handel.** The whole (with many new additions and alterations) under the direction of Signor Pasquale **Anfossi.**"

English text faces the Italian. SCHATZ 3926

— **Orpheus und Euridice.** Eine tragische oper in drey acten.

458–481 p. Cramer's Magazin der musik, Feb. 21, 1785. 17ᶜᵐ.

According to a footnote this translation was by Johann Joachim Eschenburg.
First used at a concert at Breslau in the Zwinger, August 29, 1770 (Schatz).

SCHATZ 3912

— **Orphée et Euridice,** drame-héroïque en trois actes, représenté, pour la premiere fois, par l'Academie-royale de musique, le mardi 2 août 1774.

Paris, Et se vend a Marseilles, chez Sube et Laporte, 1775. 28 p. 19½ᶜᵐ.

Cast and argument with remark:
"M. Calzabigi est l'auteur du poëme italien. On a suivi aussi littéralement qu'il étoit possible l'original dans la traduction: Ce foible ouvrage semble exiger plus d'indulgence qu'aucun autre, par l'extrême difficulté d'adapter la poësie française à la musique expressive d'un opéra, qui a déjà été représenté avec succès sur les principaux théâtres de l'Europe."
Moline is mentioned as translator, **Gluck** as composer. ML 50.2.O7G45

— **Orphée et Euridice,** opéra à grand spectacle . . . par Mᵣ le chevalier Gluck.

Paris, Veuve Duchesne, 1782. 32 p. 20ᶜᵐ.

Three acts. By Pierre Louis Moline, who is not mentioned.

ML 48.M2H

— **Roger-Bontems et Javotte,** parodie d'Orphée et Euridice, pièce en un acte, mêlée d'ariettes, par MM. Moline e D'Orvigny représentée pour la premiere fois par les Comédiens italiens ordinaires du roi, le samedi 13 mai 1775.

Paris, la veuve Duchesne, 1775. 32 p. 19ᶜᵐ.

On p. 32 the air of "Eh, messieurs! laissez-vous toucher." The composer, resp. arranger, of the music not recorded by Cl. & L. and Schatz. SCHATZ 11510

Orfeo ed Euridice—Orphée & Euridice, ballet. *See* Jommelli's La Didone abbandonata.

Orfeo ed Euridice, ballet. *See* Mizliweczek's Il Bellerofonte.

Orfeo ne'll inferi—Orphée aux enfers. *See* Campra's Le carnaval de Venise.

Orfeo sul Monte Rodope, ballet. *See* Insanguine's Medonte.

Oriana. Tr. of Händel's Amadigi di Gaula.

Origille. Opera bernesca in musica da rappresentarsi nel Teatro di S. Moisè l'autunno dell' anno 1744.

Venezia, Pietro Bassaglia, 1744. 46 p. 14½ᶜᵐ.

Three acts. By Antonio Palomba, who is not mentioned. Notice to the reader, scenario, cast, and note "La musica è di diversi autori," who are not mentioned. Antonio **Palella** is known as one of them. SCHATZ 7713

L'origine degli amori di Marc Antonio nell' arrivo di Cleopatra in Tarso, ballet. *See* Anfossi's Ezio.

L'Orimonte. Drama per musica del Co. Nicolo Minato . . .

Venetia, Valuasense, 1650. 100 p. (incl. front.) 14ᶜᵐ.

Three acts, with prologue. Author's dedication, dated Venice, February 20, 1650, argument, notice to the reader, and scenario. Without name of the composer, Pietro Francesco **Cavalli.**
First performed, as indicated, at the Teatro S. Cassiano. SCHATZ 1723

Orion, tragedie representée par l'Academie royale de musique, l'an 1728. Paroles de M. Pellegrin. Musique de M. de la Coste. CIX. opera.

n. i., n. d. 14ᶜᵐ. pl., 189–252 p. (Recueil général des opéra, t. xiv, Paris, 1734.)

Detached copy. Five acts and prologue. Schatz gives as joint author Joseph de Lafont.
First performed, as indicated, February 17, 1728. SCHATZ 5355
Second copy. ML 48.R4

Orion oder Der fuerst und sein hofnarr. Ein hofgemaelde in vier aufzuegen fuer das k. k. priv. Schikanedersche Theater frey bearbeitet von Joachim Perinet . . . [vignette].

Wien, n. publ., 1798. 4 p. l., 103 p. 16ᶜᵐ.

Sentimental dedication to the public of Vienna, without name of Ignaz Xaver, ritter von **Seyfried,** as the composer.
First performed at Vienna, Theater auf der Wieden, January 8, 1798.
SCHATZ 9858

L'Orione. Dramma di Francesco Melosio da Città della Pieve. Fatto rappresentare nel Teatro Regio di Milano l'anno 1653 . . .

Venetia, n. publ., 1653. 72 p. 13½ᶜᵐ.

Pages 3–4 appear to be missing. Presumably they contained the dedication, the argument, and possibly the name of the composer, Pietro Francesco **Cavalli.**
First performed, as indicated, in June, 1653. SCHATZ 1740

L'Oristeo. Drama per musica di Giovanni Faustini Favola ottava.

Venetia, Gio. Pietro Pinelli, 1651. 80 p. 14½ᶜᵐ.

Three acts, with prologue. Author's dedication and argument. Pietro Francesco **Cavalli,** the composer, is not mentioned.
First performed at Venice, Teatro di S. Apollinare, carnival, 1651. SCHATZ 1752

— **L'Oristeo travestito.** Favola dramatica per musica di Giovanni Faustini . . . [coat of arms]

Bologna, Giacomo Monti, 1656. 92 p. 14ᶜᵐ.

Three acts, with prologue. Dedication by Pier' Antonio Cerua, dated Bologna, January 2, 1656, argument, and notice to the reader, who is informed that this is

L'Oristeo—Continued.

Faustini's Oristeo, but much altered, "per così dire, mascherato." As a matter of fact, the first eleven scenes of both are practically identical, then I, 12 in Bologna begins, "Qual rumor," whereas Venice has "Pargoletti germani," and the differences become too numerous for enumeration, though the original text is not lost sight of. For instance, III, 1 in the Venice ed., "Dove, dove m'aggiro," has become III, 4 in the Bologna ed. The composer of "quest' operetta," as it is called in the dedication, is not mentioned, but most likely was **Cavalli**, except, of course, for the new text. The matter is summed up in these words: "Condona cortese la multiplicità de gli episodii aggionti per dilettarti, e compatisci le digressioni talora soverchie, necessarie però nel diversificarsi le scene, e multiplicarsi le machine."   SCHATZ 1724

Orithia. Favola scenica del conte Maiolino Bisaccioni . . .

     Venetia, Milochi, 1650. 72 p. 14½cm.

Prologue and three acts. Author's dedication, dated February 1, 1650, notice to the reader, argument, and scenario. The composer, Gasparo **Sartorio**, is not mentioned.   SCHATZ 9497

Orlando. Drama per musica da rappresentarsi nel Teatro di Sant' Angelo l'autuno dell' anno MDCCXXVII.

     Venezia, Marino Rossetti, 1727. 60 p. 15cm.

Three acts. By Grazio Braccioli, who is not mentioned. (Somewhat altered version of his "Orlando furioso.") Cast, scenario, and name of Antonio **Vivaldi** as the composer.   SCHATZ 10776

Orlando finto pazzo. Drama P. musica da rappresentarsi in S. Angelo l'autunno 1714 del dottor Grazio Braccioli . . .

     Venetia, Marino Rossetti, n. d. 72 p. 13½cm.

Three acts. Author's dedication, dated Venice, November 10, 1714, argument, cast, scenario, and name of Antonio **Vivaldi** as the composer. Not the same text as "Orlando."   SCHATZ 10777

Orlando furioso. Dramma per musica da rappresentarsi nel Teatro Arciducale di Mantova il carnovale dell' anno MDCCXXV . . .

     Mantova, Alberto Pazzoni, n. d. 52 p. 16cm.

Three acts. By Grazio Braccioli, who is not mentioned. Impresario's dedication, argument, cast, scenario, and name of Orazio **Polarolli** as the composer.   SCHATZ 8257

Orlando furioso. Dramma per musica da rappresentarsi nel Teatro di S. Angelo l'autunno del 1713. Del dottor Grazio Braccioli . . .

     Venezia, Marino Rossetti, 1713. 71 p. 14½cm.

Three acts. Author's dedication dated Venice, November 7, 1713, argument, cast, scenario, and name of Giovanni Alberto **Ristori** as the composer.   SCHATZ 8818

Orlando generoso. O. T. of Steffani's Der grossmuethige Roland.

Orlando Paladino. Dramma eroicomico per musica, da rappresentarsi nel Teatro Elettorale.

     Dresda, n. publ., 1792. 115 p. 15½cm.

Three acts. By Nunziato Porta, who is not mentioned. German title page, "Ritter Roland," and text face Italian. Joseph **Haydn** is mentioned as the composer.

First performed at Dresden, Churfuerstl. Theater, November 28, 1792; at Esterhaz, August, 1782.   SCHATZ 4612

Orlina ossia La famiglia riunita, ballet. *See* Zingarelli's Carolina e Mexicow.

L'Ormindo. Favola regia per musica di Giovanni Faustini . . .

Venetia, Francesco Miloco, 1644. 95 p. 12½ᶜᵐ.

Three acts with prologue. Author's dedication and argument. Without name of the composer, Pietro Francesco **Cavalli.**

First performed at Venice, Teatro di S. Cassiano, carnival, 1644. Schatz 1725

Ormisda. O. T. of Zeno's Cosroe text.

Ormisda.

Apostolo Zeno, Poesie drammatiche, Venezia, 1744, t. iv, p. 92. 19ᶜᵐ.

Three acts and licenza. Argument. No composer is mentioned. In the "Catalogo" at end of t. x, date and place of first ed. are given as Vienna, 1721. *See* below. The text is preceded (on p. xiv) by count Gozzi, the editor's prefatory comment on the vicissitudes of librettos, etc. . . ." ML 49.A2Z3

— Ormisda. Pubblicato per la prima volta in Vienna 1721.

Apostolo Zeno, Poesie drammatiche, Orleans, 1785–86, t. v, p. 167–256. 21ᶜᵐ.

Three acts. Argument. No composer is mentioned. ML 49.A2Z4

Ormisda. Dramma per musica, da rappresentarsi nella Cesarea corte per il nome gloriosissimo della Sac. Ces. e Catt. Real Maestà di Carlo VI . . . L'anno MDCCXXI. La poesia è del Sig. Apostolo Zeno . . . La musica è del Sig. Antonio Caldara.

Vienna d'Austria, Gio. Pietro Van Ghelen, n. d. 4 p. l., 82 p. 15ᶜᵐ.

Three acts and licenza. Argument and scenario. Niccola Matteis is mentioned as composer of the ballet music.

First performed, as indicated, November 4, 1721. Schatz 1501

Ormisda. Dramma per musica da rappresentarsi nel Teatro Tron a' San Cassiano nel carnovale dell' anno 1728.

Venezia, Marino Rossetti, 1728. 60 p. 15ᶜᵐ.

Three acts. By Apostolo Zeno. Argument, cast, scenario, and name of the composer, "Bartolamio Cornans" [**Cordans**]. Schatz 2226

L'Ormonda costante. A. T. of Grossi's L'Artaserse.

Ornospade.

Apostolo Zeno, Poesie drammatiche, Venezia, 1744, t. ii, p. [281]–363 p. 19ᶜᵐ.

Three acts and licenza. Argument. No composer is mentioned. In the "Catalogo" at end of t. x, date and place of first ed. are given as Vienna, 1727. (*See* below.) ML 49.A2Z3

— Ornospade. Pubblicato per la prima volta in Vienna 1727.

Apostolo Zeno, Poesie drammatiche, Orleans, 1785–86, t. vii, p. 82. 21ᶜᵐ.

Three acts and licenza. Argument. No composer is mentioned. ML 49.A2Z4

Ornospade. Dramma per musica, da rappresentarsi nella Cesarea corte per il nome gloriosissimo della Sac. Ces. e Catt. Real Maestà Carlo VI . . . L'anno MDCCXXVII. La poesia è del Sig. Apostolo Zeno . . . La musica è del Sig. Antonio Caldara . . .

Vienna d'Austria, n. publ., n. d. 4 p. l., 63, [1] p. 16ᶜᵐ.

Three acts and licenza. Argument and scenario. Niccola Matteis is mentioned as composer of the ballet music.

First performed, as indicated, November 4, 1727. Schatz 1503

L'oro fa tutto. Dramma giocoso per musica da rappresentarsi nel Teatro alla Scala l'autunno dell' anno 1793 . . .

Milano, Gio. Batista Bianchi, n. d. 68, [8] p. 16ᶜᵐ.

Two acts. By Angelo Anelli, who is not mentioned. Impresario's dedication, cast, scenario, and name of Ferdinando Për (**Paër**) as the composer.

With the opera were performed the ballets "La contadina astuta" and "Mastino della Scala," by Giuseppe Banti. Of the first, music by Vittorio Trento, the 8 unnumbered p. contain prefatory note, cast, and description of the four acts.

SCHATZ 7521
Second copy. ML 48.A5 v. 1

— **L'oro fa tutto.** Dramma giocoso per musica, da rappresentarsi nel Teatro Elettorale.

Dresda, n. publ., 1795. 127 p. 15½ᶜᵐ.

Two acts. **Paer** is mentioned as the composer, but Anelli is not mentioned. German title page, "Geld ist die loosung," and text face Italian. SCHATZ 7522

Oro non compra amore o sia Il barone di Mosca bianca. Dramma giocoso per musica da rappresentarsi nel nobilissimo Teatro Venier in San Benedetto l'autunno dell' anno 1794.

Venezia, Modesto Fenzo, 1794. 78 p. 18½ᶜᵐ.

Two acts. By Angelo Anelli, who is not mentioned, and who based his text on Bertati's "La villanella rapita." Cast, scenario, and name of the composer, **Luigi Caruso.** Between the acts were performed Giuseppe Trafieri's ballet, "Lo sposalizio de' Morlacchi." The composer of the music is not mentioned.

First performed, as indicated, November 26, 1794. SCHATZ 1649

L'Orode. Drama per musica da recitarsi nel Teatro di Casale l'anno 1675 . . .

Milano, Lodovico Monza, n. d. 93 p. 14½ᶜᵐ.

Three acts. Dedication, notice to the reader, mentioning Sig. Marchese Giacomo Natta as author, the latter's notice to the reader, informing him that the opera was originally intended for performance by the "cavalieri . . . per loro divertimento," and that "Pietro Paolo **Forni**, mastro di capella insigne del duomo di Casale," composed the music. Argument, and scenario. SCHATZ 3301

L'Oronta. Drama per musica da rappresentarsi nel Teatro di S. Bartolomeo in questo carnovale dell' anno 1728 . . .

Napoli, Francesco Ricciardi, 1728. 60 p. 14¼ᶜᵐ.

Three acts and (on p. 21–26, 38–43) the two intermezzi "PERICHITTA E BERTONE." Authors of the texts not mentioned, of the intermezzi unknown to Schatz, of the opera given by him as Claudio Nicola Stampa. Dedication, argument, scenario, casts and name of Francesco **Mancini** as composer. On p. 60 "aria di Perichitta" "Io però non son di quelle" substituted for "Dolce stral del dio bambino" in the first intermezzo. ML 50.2.O7M2

Oronte. Dramma di tre atti per musica. Rappresentato per la prima volta in Venezia il carnovale dell' anno MDCCXL.

Carlo Goldoni, Opere teatrali, Venezia, Zatta e figli, 1788–95, v. 36, [145]–203 p. 18½ᶜᵐ.

As "Oronte rè de' Sciti" with music by **Galuppi,** first performed at Venice, Teatro Grimani di S. Grisostomo, December 26, 1740. PQ

L'Oronte di Menfi. Drama per musica da rappresentarsi nel famoso Teatro Formagliari l'anno 1676 di Tomaso Stanzani. Seconda impressione con aggiunta.

Bologna, per l'erede di Domenico Barbieri, n. d. 71, [1] p. 13ᶜᵐ.

Three acts. Argument, scenario, and notice to the reader, with name of Petronio **Franceschini** as composer. SCHATZ 3318

Oronte rè de' Sciti.   O. T. of Galuppi's Oronte.

Orontea, regina d'Egitto.   Drama musicale del Sig. dottor Giacinto Andrea Cicognini . . .

> *Venetia, n. publ., n. d.   72 p.   14^{cm}.*

Prologue and three acts. Published after 1649 (*see* next entry) by Bartolomeo Lupardi, the Roman bookseller, who speaks in his dedication of "la presente operetta dell' Orontea regina d'Egitto, di nuovo peregrina, e vagante per mezo delle stampe." The composer, Marc' Antonio **Cesti,** is not mentioned.

First performed as "Orontea" at Venice, Teatro di SS. Apostoli, carnival, 1649.

ML 50.2.O73C2

— Orontea, regina d'Egitto.   Drama musicale del dottor Iacint' Andrea Cicognini . . .   Fatto rappresentare dal Sign. Gio. Battista Abbatoni in Torino.

> *Torino, Bartolomeo Zavatta, 1662.   1 p. l., 69, [3] p.   13½^{cm}.*

Three acts, with prologue. Impresario's dedication, scenario, but without the name of the composer, Marc' Antonio **Cesti.** The three additional pages contain "Aggionte nell' opera dell' Orontes:" Act I, 11, "Qual vaneggiante ardire," with aria, "Credere à femine è vanità."   Act II, 1, "Dimmi Amor, che t'hò fatt' io;" II, 5 (Creonte), "Odami il mondo tutto amo Alidoro. Ah! l'amerai si, mà con tuo danno;" II, 12, "Un dolcissimo sorriso."   Act III, 4, "Trionfa mia core;" III, 7, "Da me che più volete;" III, 22, "Giovinetti lascivi."   It is said in the dedication that "il presente drama musicale" met with applause "in tutte le parti d'Italia."

SCHATZ 1781

Orphée.   Entrée in Grenet's Le triomphe de l'harmonie.

Orphée, tragedie en musique, représentée par L'Academie royale de musique.   Suivant la copie imprimée à Paris.

> *[Amsterdam, Antoine Schelte], 1690.   48 p. (incl. front.)   13½^{cm}.*

Prologue and three acts. Neither the author, Du Boullay, is mentioned, nor the composer, Louis de **Lully.**

First performed, as indicated, April 8, 1690.   ML 50.2.O75L9

Orphée, tragedie representée par l'Academie royale de musique l'an 1690.   Les paroles de M. Du Boulay, & la musique de M. Louis de Lully.   XXV. opera.

> *n. i., n. d.   14^{cm}.   front., 1–50 p.   (Recueil général des opéra, t. iv, Paris, 1703.)*

Detached copy. Three acts and prologue.

First performed, as indicated, April 8, 1690.   SCHATZ 5783
          Second copy.   ML 48.R4

Orphée aux enfers.   *See* Campra's Le carnaval de Venise.

Orphée et Euridice.   Tr. T. of the ballet Orfeo ed Euridice.

Orphée et Euridice.   *See* Gluck's Orfeo ed Euridice.

Orphée et Euridice.   Mélo-drame en un acte, en prose par Mons. Duplessis, au service de S. A. R. le duc de Parme.   Musique de Mr Pär.   1791.

> *n. i., n. d.   [17] p.   18^{cm}.*

Printed in a most unusual manner, in three parallel columns, the first containing musical indications, as, for instance, "Musique frissonante & plaintive," or "Quelques coups d'archet," with figures referring to the respective place in the prose text; the second containing indications of *durée* (duration), as, for instance, "6 secondes" or "2 minutes"; the third containing the prose text.

First performed, as indicated, at Parma, Teatrino di Corte.   SCHATZ 7550

L'orpheline villageoise. A. T. of Fridzeri's Les deux miliciens.

Orpheus, burletta. *See* Barthélemon's A peep behind the curtain.

Orpheus. Ein singspiel in drey aufzuegen, von L. In musik gesetzt von Friedrich Benda.

n. i., 1785. 22 p. 15½ᶜᵐ.

Name of author unknown to Schatz.
First performed at Berlin, at a concert in January, 1785. **SCHATZ 766**

Orpheus. Tr. of Bertoni-Reichardt's Orfeo.

Orpheus. Tr. of Graun's Orfeo.

Orpheus.

First performed in five acts, text by Friedrich Christian Bressand, music by **Keiser**, at the Courttheatre, Brunswick, 1798, under the above title, according to Schatz. Repeated (with alterations) in two parts of three acts each at Brunswick in 1699 as "Die sterbende Eurydice," resp. "Die verwandelte leyer des Orpheus." Then at Hamburg, Opernhaus beim Gänsemarkte, 1702, as follows:

— Die **sterbende Eurydice** oder Orpheus erster theil. In einem singespiel auff dem Hamburgischen Schau-platz vorgestellet.

Hamburg, Conrad Neumann, n. d. Unpaged. 18ᶜᵐ.

Three acts. Neither the author, Friedrich Christian Bressand, nor the composer, Reinhard **Keiser**, is mentioned. **SCHATZ 5106**

— **Orpheus,** ander theil. In einem singe-spiel auf dem Hamburgischen Schau-platz vorgestellet.

Hamburg, Conrad Neumann, n. d. Unpaged. 18ᶜᵐ.

Three acts. Without name of the author, Bressand, or **Keiser**, the composer. **SCHATZ 5107**

— Die **biss in und nach dem todt unerhoerte treue des Orpheus.** [vignette] In einem singe-spiel auf dem grossen Hamburgischen Schau-platze vorzustellen. Im jahr 1709.

Hamburg, Joh. Nic. Gennagel, n. d. Unpaged. 18½ᶜᵐ.

Five acts. Scenario and name of Reinhard **Keiser** as the composer. The author, resp. translator, Friedrich Christian Bressand, is not mentioned. The Italian text has been added to many of the arias.

In the very nature of the case, this five-act version is not a mere condensation of the version in two parts of three acts each. For instance, scenes I, 1–6, in Schatz 5106 are not in Schatz 5105. I, 3 of the latter, "Ach, Aristaeus, welch verkehrter blick," and I, 4, "Dein für mich dunckles wort," are the same as I, 6, and I, 7, in Schatz 5106. In the latter I, 8 (the last scene of the act), has the aria, "Bey mir wancken," which is not in the corresponding scene I, 5, of Schatz 5105. This is followed, as last of the act, by scene I, 6, "Angenehmste liebeskertzen," with aria, "Dolce mia vita—Angenehmstes leben," which scene is not in Schatz 5106. The second act is the same in both versions, but after that the differences become very numerous again. It is curious to see that, whereas the fourth act begins with "Lass Orpheus die vernunfft," etc., in Schatz 5105, this whole scene is made part of III, 11, in Schatz 5106. The first scene in Schatz 5107 in common with Schatz 5105, seems to be the latter's IV. 7, "Schöner ort, glückseelge felder" (chorus) which is the first scene of second act in Schatz 5107. **SCHATZ 5105**

The masque **Orpheus and Euridice.**

See act III, scene 2 of Martin Bladen's tragi-comedy, "Solon or Philosophy no defence against love," *London, R. Smith, 1705, p. 28–33.*

No performance recorded by Clarence. **LONGE 79**

Orpheus and Eurydice. With the pantomime entertainment. As acted at the Theatre-Royal in Lincoln's-Inn-Fields. By Mr. Henry Sommer . . .

> *London, C. Corbett, 1740. viii, 28 p. 17½*^{cm}.

One act. In his preface the author refutes the charges of plagiarism brought by "Mr. Hill the apothecary" against the impresario, Mr. Rich. Sommer says that he wrote the piece eleven years ago, and that in 1734 he had occasion to submit it to Rich, who then described to him the plan of his own entertainment of the same title, with the "several tricks and escapes" which he intended to introduce. The same season (1734) Sommer made overtures to Mr. Fleetwood, who, however, could only offer to take the piece for the season following, and to purchase several of Sommer's "modules," which offer he rejected. Thereupon he entered into negotiations with Mr. Giffard, who, in 1736, agreed to produce the piece

"and the modules were carried to Lincoln's-Inn-Fields Play-house, in order to be got up with all expedition. And Mr. Giffard judging the *pantomime* part was long enough without the addition of a *serious*, because there was so great a variety, declined playing this as being too expensive.

"In January, towards the latter end, the *harlequinade* of my piece was performed with applause . . . I have reason to hope that Mr. Hill will not be so hardy to say, I have borrow'd any thing from his . . ."

The composer, John Frederick **Lampe**, not mentioned, and not recorded by **Schatz**.
LONGE 199

Orpheus and Eurydice. Tr. of Gluck's Orfeo ed Euridice.

Orpheus der zweyte. A pasticcio principally by Dittersdorf. *See his* "Die liebe im narrenhause."

Orpheus og Euridice. Et syngespil i tre acter. Poesien er af C. D. Biehl. Musiquen af hr. Nauman. Paa regisseur Hansens Forlag.

> *Kiøbenhavn, Johan Friderich Morthorst, 1790. 40 p. 16*^{cm}.

First performed at Copenhagen, Kongl. Theater, January 31, 1786. SCHATZ 7052

— **Orpheus und Euridice.** Eine tragische oper. Nach dem daenischen von Carl Friedrich Cramer. Die musik vom herrn capellmeister Naumann.

> *Kiel und Hamburg, bey dem verfasser, n. d. xxxi, [1], 54 p. 15*^{cm}.

The first seventeen p. of the "Vorrede" bring quotations from Virgil and Ovid, to show the origin of the plot. Then Carl Friedrich Cramer, the author of the German text, dwells at length on the dramaturgic problems presented by the theme of Orpheus and Euridice, and finally he points out wherein and why his text differs from the Danish original. On p. xxvi particularly he gives his reasons for weakening still more than the Danish original the impression of a "ganz grundloser eigensinn" in the mere "Frauenzimmer" Euridice. This "Vorrede" is well worth reading. Cramer's Tr. also in his Magazin d. Musik, 1786, p. 1085–1145. SCHATZ 7053

Orpheus und Eurydice. Tr. of Gluck's Orfeo ed Euridice.

Orpheus und Euridice. Tr. of Naumann's Orpheus og Euridice.

Gli Orti Esperidi.

> *[319]–356 p. 19*^{cm}. *(Pietro Metastasio, Opere drammatiche, Venezia, 1733–37, v. 3.)*

Two parts. No composer mentioned.
First performed with music by *Porpora* at Naples, Real Palazzo, August 28, 1721.
ML 49.A2M4

Gli **Orti Esperidi**—Continued.

— Gli **Orti Esperidi**.

Metastasio, Poesie, Parigi, vedova Quillau, 1755, t. ix, [101]–146 p. 16^{cm}.

Two parts. ML 49.A2M42

— Gli **orti Esperidi**.

[47]–86 p. 26^{cm}. (Metastasio, Opere, t. x, Parigi, vedova Herissant, 1782.)

Two parts. ML 49.A2M44

Gli **Orti Esperidi**. Serenata per musica da cantarsi . . . per celebrare il felicissimo giorno natalizio di Sua Maestà fedelissima l'augusta D. Marianna Vittoria regina madre nella primavera dell' anno 1779.

[Lisbona], Stamperia reale, n. d. 30 p. 16^{cm}.

Two parts. Cast and names of Metastasio as author, of Jeronymo Francisco de Lima as composer.
First performed, as indicated, March 31, 1779. SCHATZ 5620

Gli **orti Esperidi**. Drama per musica del Signore abate Pietro Metastasio da cantarsi nella Real Villa di Queluz. Nell' anno 1764.

Lisbona, Stamperia Sosiana, n. d. 23 p. 16½^{cm}.

Two parts. "Luciani Xavier" (Luciano Xavier dos Santos) is mentioned as the composer. SCHATZ 9396

The airs, duets, choruses and argument of the new ballet pantomime, (taken from Ossian) called **Oscar and Malvina;** or The hall of Fingal. As performed at the Theatre-Royal, Covent-Garden. The third edition.

London, T. Cadell, 1791. 19 p. 18^{cm}.

Cast. According to Grove's Dict., William Reeve completed William Shield's unfinished music.
First performed August 20, 1791 (Clarence), October 20 (Genest). LONGE 218

Oscar e Malvina, ballet. *See* Trento's Bianca de' Rossi.

Osiride, dramma per musica, in occasione delle felicissime nozze di S. A. S. il principe Antonio, duca di Sassonia, etc. e di S. A. R. la principessa Carolina, figlia di S. M. il rè di Sardegna. Del Sigr. Caterino Mazzolà . . .

Dresda, n. publ., 1781. 4 p. l., 79 p. 19^{cm}.

Two acts and Licenza. Argument and name of Johann Gottlieb Naumann as the composer. German title page, "Osiris," and text face Italian.
First performed as indicated, October 27, 1781. SCHATZ 7054

Osiris. Tr. of Naumann's Osiride.

Osiris. Entrée in Rameau's Les fêtes de l'Himen et de l'Amour.

Osmanns serail. Tr. of Ghinassi's Il serraglio di Osmano.

Osmane. Dramma per musica da rappresentarsi nel nobilissimo Teatro di S. Benedetto il carnovale dell' anno 1784 . . .

Venezia, Modesto Fenzo, 1784. 51 p. 17½^{cm}.

Three acts. By Gaetano Sertor, who is mentioned as author and Giuseppe Giordani as the composer. Author's dedication, argument, cast, and scenario. On p.

Osmane—Continued.

23–29 cast and description of "Giasone e Medea. Ballo eroico-tragico d'invenzione del celebre Sig. Noverre rimesso in scena dal Sig. Vestris; dato in Venezia dal Sig. Le Picq; e adesso rimesso in scena dal Sig. Domenico Le Fevre," whose ballet "Gli amori di Mirtillo con Silvanzia" was also performed. The composers of the music are not mentioned. SCHATZ 3848

L'ospedale de' pazzi, ballet. *See* Giordani's Don Mirtillo contrastato.

Ottaviano Ces. Augusto. Melodrama da rappresentarsi nel Teatro ducale dell' Altezza Serenissima di Mantova. L'anno MDCLXXXII.

Venetia, Francesco Nicolini, 1682. 1 p. l., 60 p. 21ᶜᵐ.

Three acts. Argument, cast, scenario, and notice to the reader with the name of Giovanni **Legrenzi** "novo Anfione del nostro secolo" as the composer and stating that the author of "L'Annibale in Capua, il Tito, il Genserico & l'Eraclio "is also the author of this, which accordingly would be count Nicola Beregani.
Lacks the p. l. (an ornamental t.-p.) which is in our second copy (ML 50.2.P78L3.)
First performed, as indicated, May, 1682. SCHATZ 5537

L'Ottavio. Commedia per musica di Gennarantonio Federico Napoletano. Da recitarsi nel Teatro de' Fiorentini nell' inverno di questo anno 1733 . . .

Napoli, Nicola di Biase, n. d. 57 p. 14½ᶜᵐ.

Three acts. Impresario's dedication, cast, and name of Gaetano **Latilla** as the composer. SCHATZ 5452

Otto. Tr. of Händel's Ottone.

Ottocaro, ballet. *See* Nicolini's Il trionfo del bel sesso.

Ottone. Dramma per musica da rappresentarsi nel famosissimo Teatro Grimani di S. Gio. Grisostomo il carnovale dell' anno 1740.

Venezia, Marino Rossetti, 1740. 48 p. 15ᶜᵐ.

Three acts. By Antonio Salvi, who is not mentioned. Argument, cast, scenario and name of Gennaro d' Alessandro (**Alessandri**) as composer. SCHATZ 157

Ottone.

Three-act opera by Georg Friedrich **Händel.** Text was an altered version by Nicola Francesco Haym of Stefano Benedetto Pallavicini's "Teofane."
First performed at London, Haymarket, January 12, 1723.
Not in L. of C.

— Otto, in einem sing-spiele auf dem Hamburgischen Schau-platze vorgestellet im jahr 1726.

[Hamburg], Gedruckt mit Stromerschen schrifften, n. d. Unpaged. 19½ᶜᵐ.

Three acts. Argument, name of Georg Friedrich **Händel** as the composer. The arias are printed with Italian and German texts. The translator, Glauche, is not mentioned. SCHATZ 4482

Ottone. Tragedia per musica fatta da rappresentarsi nel Teatro di S. Gio. Grisostomo. L'anno MDCXCIV . . .

Venetia, Nicolini, 1694. 84 p. (incl. front.). 16ᶜᵐ.

Five acts. Dedication by the author, conte Girolamo Frigimelica Roberti, notice to the reader, scenario, and arguments preceding each act. The composer, Carlo Francesco **Pollaroli,** is not mentioned. SCHATZ 8307

Ottone il Grande. Drama per musica da recitarsi nel famoso Teatro de' S. S. Gio. e Paolo l'anno MDCLXXXIII di Frencasco Valsini . . .

Venetia, Francesco Nicolini, 1683. 60 p. 14½ᶜᵐ.

Three acts. Author's dedication (dated December 5, 1682), notice to the reader, argument but without name of the composer, Paolo **Biego**. Francesco Valsini stands for Francesco Silvani, who calls this "il primo parto della mia penna."

SCHATZ 1015

Our way in France. A. T. of Fontainebleau.

The Oxford act, a new ballad-opera. As it was perform'd by a company of students at Oxford . . . The second edition.

London, L. Gulliver, 1733. 2 p. l., 44 p. 19ᶜᵐ.

Three acts. Table of the 37 songs, the airs of most of which indicated by title in the text. Author not mentioned, and not recorded by Clarence. LONGE 49

The Oxford roratory. A. T. of The ragged uproar.

La pace. *See* M. Curzio.

La pace fra la virtù e la bellezza.

Metastasio, Poesie, Parigi, vedova Quillau, 1755, t. vii, [337]–362 p. 16ᶜᵐ.

One act. ML 49.A2M42

— La pace fra la virtù e la bellezza. Azione teatrale, scritta dall' autore in Vienna per ordine sovrano, l'anno 1738, ed eseguita la prima volta con musica del Predieri nella grande anticamera dell' Imperial residenza . . . per festeggiare il giorno di nome di S. A. R. Maria Teresa, arciduchessa d'Austria, poi Imperatrice regina.

[369]–392 p. 26ᶜᵐ. (Pietro Metastasio, Opere, t. iii, Parigi, vedova Herissant, 1780.)

One act. ML 49.A2M44

La pace fra le tre dee. Festa teatrale, scritta dall' autore in Vienna l'anno 1765 per uso della Real corte cattolica, in occasione delle felicissime nozze delle Loro Altezze Reali D. Carlo di Borbone . . . e Donna Luisa di Borbone . . .

[211]–232 p. 26ᶜᵐ. (Metastasio, Opere, t. xi, Parigi, vedova Herissant, 1782.) ML 49.A2M44

La pace fra Tolomeo e Seleuco. Drama per musica da rappresentarsi nel famoso Teatro Grimano di S. Gio. Grisostomo l'anno 1691 . . .

Venetia, Nicolini, 1691. front., 64 p. 14ᶜᵐ.

Three acts. Dedication, with the initials of the author, Adriano Morselli, argument, notice to the reader, with the name of Carlo Francesco **Pollaroli** as the composer, and scenario. SCHATZ 8308

— Il Seleuco. Drama per musica d'Adriano Morselli da rappresentarsi nel famosissimo Teatro di Torre di Nona l'anno MDCXCIII . . .

Roma, Gio. Francesco Buagni, 1693. front., 72 p. 13ᶜᵐ.

Three acts. Dedication by the bookseller, Francesco Leone, argument, cast, and scenario. The composer, Carlo Francesco **Pollaroli,** is not mentioned. A considerably altered version of Morselli's "La pace fra Tolomeo & Seleuco." For instance, the latter begins, "Per beltà non vista mai;" "Il Seleuco" begins, "Non veduta ancor, m'impiaga;" and sceneIII, "Dal pin fugace usciti," has become scene IV.

SCHATZ 8309

La pace generosa. Drama per musica da recitarsi nel famoso Teatro di S. Salvatore l'anno 1700. Poesia di Francesco Silvani . . .

Venetia, Nicolini, 1700. *83, [1] p.* *14½^{cm}.*

Imprint at end.

Three acts. Author's dedication, dated Venice, February 10, 1700, argument, notice to the reader, cast, and scenario. The composer, Marc' Antonio **Ziani**, is not mentioned. SCHATZ 11192

La pace per amore. Drama per musica da rappresentarsi nel Teatro Giustiniano di S. Moisè l'anno 1719.

Venezia, Marino Rossetti, 1719. *55 p.* *15^{cm}.*

Three acts. By conte Angelo Schietti. Argument, cast, and scenario, but without the names of the composers, Giuseppe Maria **Buini** and Fortunato **Chelleri,** or of the librettist. SCHATZ 1400

— Il nemico amante. Drama per musica da rappresentarsi nel Teatro Giustiniano di S. Moisè. L'anno 1724 . . .

Venezia, Mario Rossetti, n. d. *48 p.* *15^{cm}.*

Three acts. Argument, cast, and scenario. A "ristampa" of "La pace per amore," as appears from the impresario's dedication:

"Havendo rissoluto di fare novamente rappresentare nel Teatro Giustiniano di S. Moisè il drama presente, che nello stesso gl'anni decorsi sotto altro titolo riportò l'applauso universale, come anco lo consegui in altre città d'Italia per esser parto di penna erudita, e benissimo nota . . ."

The alterations are numerous. For instance, I, 7 now has the aria, "Nel giardin di piante adorno," instead of "Quando arricchito," and I, 8 "La mia fiamma và dicendo" instead of "Ingegnoso è pur Amore." Neither the composers, **Buini** and **Chelleri,** are mentioned, nor Schietti, the author. SCHATZ 1401

The padlock: A comic opera: As it is perform'd by His Majesty's servants, at the Theatre Royal in Drury-Lane. A new edition [title vignette].

London, W. Griffin, n. d. *vi, [2], 31 p.* *19^{cm}.*

Two acts. By Isaac Bickerstaffe, who is not mentioned. Cast, dedication to the King of Denmark, in which Bickerstaffe says:

"It is my lot to produce the only new dramatic performance, while this kingdom is honored with Your Majesty's presence. I lay it at your feet, as a mark of hommage from the English stage,"

and preface, in which Bickerstaffe mentions as source of "this petty drama" Cervantes' novel, "The jealous husband," thanks the artists who performed it, especially Mrs. Arne, "our best English singer," and says:

"The music of this piece being extremely admired by persons of the first taste and distinction, it would be injustice to the extraordinary talents of the young man who assisted me in it, was I not to declare, that it is, under my direction, the entire composition of Mr. **Dibdin,** whose admirable performance in the character of Mungo, does so much credit to himself and me . . ."

First performed October 3, 1768, as indicated. LONGE 46

— The padlock. In two acts. By Mr. Isaac Bickerstaff.

[266]–289 p. *19^{cm}.* *(Collection of the most esteemed farces and entertainments, Edinburgh, 1792, t. iii.)*

Drury-Lane and Edinburgh (1783) casts. SCHATZ 11753

Padmani e Mirda, ballet. *See* Minoja's Tito nelle Gallie.

Padmani e Mirda, ballet. *See* Monza's Enea in Cartagine.

Il **padre crudele.** A. T. of the ballet Tancredi.

Padre e figlio rivali sconosciuti. A. T. of the ballet Tamar e Selimo.

Il padre e il figlio rivali. The father and the son rivals; a comic opera as perform'd at the King's Theatre in the Hay-Market. The music entirely new by Signor Tomaso Giordani, a Neapolitan composer.

London, W. Griffin, Dec. 1769. 67, [1] p. 19½^{cm}.

Three acts. Made up, as appears from the notice to the reader, by Giovanni Gualberto Bottarelli from the "Incognita perseguitata," by Petrosellini and Casori's "Amore industrioso":

"The merit of invention, I do not, therefore, presume to claim; but the reduction of one complete drama, from two imperfect and confused ones, with five principal actors, and three inferiors who all contribute to accomplish the action, is the produce of my own industry."

Cast. English text faces Italian. SCHATZ 3851

Il paese della Cucagna.

[5]–51 p. 16½^{cm}. (Carlo Goldoni, Opere drammatiche giocose, t. iii, Torino, 1757.)

Three acts. First composed by *Galuppi* as below. ML49.A2G6

— **Il paese della Cuccagna.** Dramma di tre atti per musica.

Carlo Goldoni, Opere teatrali, Venezia, Zatta e figli, 1788–95, v. 44, [287]–338 p. 18^{cm}.

PQ

Il paese della Cuccagna. Dramma giocoso per musica.

Vienna, Gi. Tomaso de Trattnern, 1770. Unpaged. 16^{cm}.

Three acts. Author (Carlo Goldoni) and composer (unknown to Schatz) not mentioned.

First performed at Vienna, 1770. SCHATZ 11354

Il paese della Cuccagna. Commedia per musica. Di Polisseno Fegejo, Pastor Arcade. Da rappresentarsi nel Teatro Giustiniani di S. Moisè. Per la fiera dell' Ascensione l'anno 1750.

Venezia, Modesto Fenzo, 1750. front., 48, [2] p. 15^{cm}.

Three acts. By Goldoni. Galuppi, the composer, is not mentioned. Cast and scenario. The two additional pages contain the substitute arias "Innocente saì, che sono" (I, 5), "Ad ogni bel diletto" (I, 11), "Se ne avesse mille intorno" (III, 5), and "Imparare non voglio (III, 10).

First performed, as indicated, May 7, 1750. SCHATZ 3492

Le palais de Flore. Ballet. Dansé à Trianon le [*blank* 6.] janvier 1689. Suivant la copie imprimée, a Paris.

[Amsterdam, Antoine Schelte], 1689. 24 p., incl. front. 13½^{cm}.

Five entrées. Argument, beginning:

"Le roy, entre les autres marques de son extrème satisfaction au retour de Monseigneur le Dauphin, a voulu luy donner une feste dans cét agreable palais que l'on a tant de raison de nommer le Palais de Flore . . ."

Neither the author nor the composer is mentioned by de La Vallière, or in modern reference books. ML52.2.P2

Il palazzo d'Osmano. L. T. of Gazzaniga's Il seraglio d'Osmano.

Palaemon ein schaeferspiel mit gesaengen in zween akten von J. W. A. Schoepfel.

Frankfurt und Leipzig, Christian Gottlieb Hertel, 1774. xxii, 151, [1] p. 17^{cm}.

The xxii p. contain a "Vorrede" dated Leipzig, March 22, 1774, which throws a curious side light on the author's esthetic creed. He begins with a dissertation on taste regretting that the preference of Germans for "die franzoesische jacke" and

Palaemon—Continued.

"den Frack" "des Englaenders" in literary matters. He then launches into an esthetic comparison between the merits (and popularity) of the "Singspiel" and of comedy and tragedy. He finally champions the "Schaeferspiel" and finds fault with those who call "Das schaeferspiel . . . hirngespinnst, leere, traeumerey und das zeitalter, in welchem die handlung vorgeht, ein Ding, das nie wirklich, sondern immer nur in den koepfen der dichter existirt hat." Not recorded by Schatz. No composer known to me.   ML 50.2.P16

Pallade trionfante in Arcadia.   Dramma pastorale per musica da rappresentarsi nel Teatro Grimani di S. Samuele.   Il carnovale dell' anno 1714 . . .

Venezia, Marino Rossetti, 1714.   43 p.   14½^{cm}.

Three acts. Tommaso Ristori's dedication, argument, scenario, and name of Giovanni Alberto **Ristori** as the composer. The author, conte Otto Mandelli, is not mentioned.   SCHATZ 8819

Il palladio conservato.   Componimento drammatico rappresentato in musica nell' Imperial corte il dì 4. novembre 1735 per festeggiare il glorioso nome di Carlo VI . . .

[13]–24 p.   19^{cm}.   (*Pietro Metastasio, Opere drammatiche, Venezia, Giuseppe Bettinelli, 1733–37, v. 4.*)

One act. Argument. No composer mentioned.   ML49.A2M4

— **Il palladio conservato.**

Metastasio, Poesie, Parigi, vedova Quillau, 1755, t. vii, [259]–278 p. 16^{cm}.

One act.   ML49.A2M42

— **Il palladio conservato.**   Azione teatrale, allusiva alle vicende di quel tempo, scritta dall' autore in Vienna l'anno 1735 . . . e rappresentata la prima volta con musica del Reütter negli interni privati appartamenti dell' Imperial Favorita dalle Altezze Reali di Maria Terese . . . dell' arciduchessa Marianna di lei sorella, e da una dama della Cesarea Corte, per festeggiare il dì primo d'ottobre, giorno di nascita dell' imperatore Carlo VI.

[341]–358 p.   26^{cm}.   (*Pietro Metastasio, Opere, t. v, Parigi, vedova Herissant, 1780.*)

One act. Argument.   ML49.A2M44

Il palladio conservato, dramma per musica da cantarsi nella Real Villa di Queluz il giorno di S. Pietro del' anno de 1771.   Autore delle parolle il Signore abbate Piëtro Metastasio.   La musica è del Signore Luciano Xavier dos Santos.

Lisbona, Stamperia Sosiana, n. d.   3 p. l., 14 p.   16^{cm}.

One act. Argument.
First performed, as indicated, October 19, 1771.   SCHATZ 9397

Palma, ou Le voyage en Grèce, opéra en deux actes; représenté pour la premiere fois sur le Théâtre de la rue Feydeau, le 5 fructidor an 6. [Aug. 22, 1798] Par P. E. L. . . . Musique de Plantade.

Paris, Au Bureau dramatique, an VII [1798–99]   39, [1] p.   20^{cm}.

Cast. By Pierre Edouard Lemontey.   ML50.2.P2P4

La **palma d'amore**. Favoletta dramatica del Sig. Francesco Berni, rappresentata nel Teatro di S. Lorenzo in Ferrara con musica, e macchine in occasione delle nozze de gl'illustrissimi Signori Co. Francesco Miria estense Mosti, e D. Caterina Pia di Sauoia. Nel carnevale dell' anno 1650 e da Gio. Bascarini dedicata alli medesimi.

Ferrara, Giuseppe Gironi, 1650. 4 p. l., 62 p. 19½^{cm}.

Dedication and notice to the reader, in which the author says:
"Questo componimento fu destinato al teatro, non alla stampa. Nacque per la musica, non per la lettura"
in less than nine days. The customary *protesta* in this notice is neatly turned:
"Credi pure, che versarebbe il proprio sangue, come Christiano, chi ha sparso quest' inchiostro, come poeta."
The composer, Andrea **Mattioli**, is not mentioned. SCHATZ 6104

Palmira. Tr. of Salieri's Palmira, regina di Persia.

Palmira di Tebe. Serenata per musica da cantarsi nella Real Villa di Queluz per celebrare il felicissimo giorno natalizio del Serenissimo Signore D. Giuseppe principe del Brasile li 21 agosto 1781.

[Lisbona], Stamperia reale, n. d. 38 p. 15^{cm}.

One act. Gaetano Martinelli is mentioned as author, Luciano Xavier di Santi [dos Santos] as composer. Argument and cast. SCHATZ 9399

Palmira, koenigin von Persien. Tr. of Salieri's Palmira, regina di Persia.

Palmira regina di Persia. Dramma eroi-comico da rappresentarsi negl' Imperiali Regi Teatri di corte l'anno 1795.

Vienna, Mattia Andrea Schmidt, n. d. 62 p. 18^{cm}.

Two acts. Giovanni de Gamerra is mentioned as the author, Antonio **Salieri** as the composer.
First performed at Vienna, Kärnthnerthortheater, October 14, 1795.
SCHATZ 9305

— **Palmira, regina di Persia.** Dramma eroi-comico da rappresentarsi nel Teatro Elettorale di Sassonia.

Dresda, n. publ., 1797. 127 p. 16^{cm}.

Two acts. Antonio **Salieri** is mentioned as the composer, but the author, Giovanni de Gamerra, is not. The text follows the original closely. German title-page, "Palmira, koenigin von Persien," and text face Italian.
First performed at Dresden, as indicated, March 18, 1797. SCHATZ 9306

— **Palmira**, eine grosse oper in vier aufzuegen; aus dem italiaenischen des K. K. hofdichters Gamera, uebersezt von Schlotterbek, herzogl. hofdichter. Die musik ist vom kapellmeister Salieri. Auf dem grossen herzogl. Theater zu Stuttgart zum erstenmale aufgefuehrt bei gelegenheit der festlichen heimfuehrung Ihrer Koenigl. Hoheit, der frau erbprinzessin Charlotte Auguste Mathilde.

Stuttgart, gebrueder Maentler, 1797. 2 p. l., 73, [1] p.

Cast, argument, and "anmerkung," which reads, in part:
"Die verse dieser oper sind nach dem rhytmus des italienischen originals und der Salierischen musik uebersezt, einige wenige stellen ausgenommen, welche, da die launen des kompositeurs mich zu sehr fesselten, in der partitur anders lauten."
First performed, as indicated, April 7, 1797. SCHATZ 9307

Palmire, ballet héroïque en un acte; représenté devant Leurs Majestés, à Fontainebleau, le 24 octobre 1765.

[*Paris*], *Christophe Ballard, 1765. 32 p. 20½*ᶜᵐ. (*Journal des Spectacles, t. ii, Paris, 1766.*)

One act.   Cast and names of Chamfort (de Chanfort) as author of the text, of Bernard de **Bury** as the composer of the music, and of Laval père et fils as "composers" of the ballets.   On p. [21]–32, cast and program of (by the same authors):

— La **vengeance de l'amour,** ou Diane et Endimion, pantomime héroïque, en trois actes; exécuté devant Leurs Majestés, à Fontainebleau, à la suite de Palmire.

[*Paris*], *Christophe Ballard, 1765.*

ML 48.J7

Pandolfo.   L. T. of Hasse's Il tutore.

Il **Pandolfo.**   Commedia per musica da rappresentarsi in Venezia. Nel Teatro Grimani a S. Samuele l'autunno dell' anno 1745.

*Venezia, Antonio Mora, 1745.   46 p.   16*ᶜᵐ.

Three acts.   Giuseppe **Scolari** is mentioned as the composer.   A prefatory note informs us:

"Essendosi accinto un poeta incognito a ridure in cinque soli personaggi la Commedia in commedia già rappresentata in varii teatri; Dopo aver con tale idea scritti alcuni versi cangiò pensiero, e più agevole gli fu di scriver questa, che ti presento, dove di quella non v'e se non la scena appunto della Commedia, che si finge alla presenza di Pandolfo, ma diversamente condotta.   Ti serva l'avviso per sapere come siavi entrata l'accennata scena, quando essendo tutto il resto nuovo . . ."

Schatz 9798

Pandolfus en Zerbina of De meid meesteres.   Tr. of Pergolesi's La serva padrona.

I **panduri accampati,** ballet.   *See* **Pugnani's** Tamas Koulikan nell India.

Pane e Siringa, ballet.   *See* Piccinni's La pescatrice.

Pantaleone e Carlotta.   O. T. of Hasse's La finta Tedesca.

Panurge dans l'isle des lanternes, comédie-lyrique, en trois actes et en vers, représentée, pour la premiere fois, par l'Académie royale de musique, le mardi 25 janvier 1785.

*n. i., n. d.   48 p.   21*ᶜᵐ.

Cast, name of **Grétry** as the composer, and Avertissement.   The author, resp. authors, Etienne Morel de Chefdeville and the comte de Provence (later Louis XVIII) are not mentioned.   A note on p. [2] says: "Les paroles sont de M. M * * *." The Avertissement reads in part:

"On n'ignore point les préventions qui subsistent encore contre le genre comique, sur le Théâtre de l'Opéra; mais on sait aussi que le public ne se laisse point entraîner par les opinions particulières, et qu'il applaudit au genre qui l'amuse comme à celui qui l'intéresse . . ."   ML 50.2.P25G7

Il **Paolo Emilio.**   Drama per musica da rappresentarsi nel Teatro di Canalreggio l'anno MDCLXXXXIX . . .

*Venetia, Gio. Battista Tramontin à i Frati, n. d.   48 p.   13½*ᶜᵐ.

Three acts.   Anonymous dedication, argument, and notice to the reader.   Neither the author, Francesco Rossi, nor the composer, Pietro Romolo **Pignatta,** is mentioned.   Schatz 8170

Die **parforcejagd.** A. T. of Karoline.

Die **parforsjagd.** A. T. of Maier's Wallrad und Evchen.

Il **Paride,** opera musicale dedicata alle Serenissime Altezze di Christiano Ernesto, marggravio di Brandenburgo . . . et Erdmude Sofia, principessa di Sassonia . . . nella celebratione delle loro nozze di Gio. Andrea Bontempi, Perugino.

Dresda, Melchior Bergen, 1662. [*256*] *p.* *27½*^{cm}.

Five acts. By the composer, whose dedication is dated Dresden, **November 3, 1662.** Scene by scene argument and notice to reader, in which Bontempi says:

"Il mio poetare non si stende più oltre, che nel formar qualche soggetto apparte nente alla musica, e ciò più per uso de' miei proprii componimenti, che de gl' altrui;- più per mancanza de' poeti, che per professione . . . Alcuni lisci poetici, (se pur tali sono) da' quali, con lunga serie di versi, si cagiona la prolissità de' recitativi, che mi costituisce partiale, più della poesia, che della musica, son nati e dalla brevità della tessitura, per la disunione degl' atti, e perchè, havendo dovuta esser tradotta in lingua tedesca, per intendimento diquei, che non hanno cognitione della favella italiana, è da credere, che la lettura habbia da essere il principale oggetto: massimamente dove simili componimenti, non hanno fatto ancora spettacolo di se stessi, fra iluminosi splendori del teatro. Onde ne viene in consequenza che se quest' opera, non havra tessiture artificiose, accidenti improvisi, varietà di metri, frequenza d'inventioni, brevità di recitativi, spessezza di canzonette, inganni, viluppi, discioglimenti, sottigliezze, capricci, motti, allegorie, metafore, sentenze, traslati, e finalmente tutti quegli abbellimenti, che debbono havere i drami musicali, composti per allettare & adulare il genio del secolo; non havrà ne meno spettatori nauseati, come altrove, dalla frequenza di tante e tante opere, che l'ascoltino . . . [Then speaks of his ambition and intention to write an opera totally different from all others.]

"Non è comedia; poiche la materia, che contiene, non è tratta da attioni civili e private. Non è tragedia; poiche non esprime, ne conclude casi atroci, e miserabili. Non è tragicomedia; poiche non partecipa, ne della comedia, ne della tragedia. Dovrebl' esser drama; ma la qualità del soggetto, e della tessitura, non ammette ragionevolmente l'imposition di questo nome. Sarei per nominarla, *Erotopegnio Musicale* (Ερωτοπαίγνιον musicum; quod est ludus de amore, ad musicam pertinens) ma per esser nome inusitato, quantunque fondato su la ragione, no so se sia (lettore) per sodisfarti . . ."

At the end of the libretto of the opera a note by the translator and list of errata. German title page, "Paris, ein gedicht zur musica," and text face Italian. The libretto of the opera is followed by a number of prose monologues addressed to the "Hochverständige richter" in German by Nimrod, Sol, Mars, Diana, Venus, etc. Apparently an allegorical-mythological pageant followed the opera. The "Cartel zum ballet des Parnasses" with an address by "Fama" ends the volume. The performances of Bontempi's ambitious work took place at Dresden, November 3 and 13, 1662. SCHATZ 1209

Paride. Drama per musica da rappresentarsi nel famoso Teatro Grimani di S. Gio. Grisostomo. Il carnovale dell' anno 1720.

Venezia, Mariano Rossetti, 1720. *72 p.* *14½*^{cm}.

Five acts. By Francesco Muazzo, who is not mentioned. Argument, notice to the reader, cast, scenario, and name of Giuseppe Maria **Orlandini** as the composer. According to the author, this text was originally "in his tender years" written for his own pleasure as a tragedy. Upon suggestion of his friends he remodelled it into the text for an opera, adding arias and "per le convenienze della scena moderna . . . di bel nuovo alcune picciole scene." SCHATZ 7345

Paride ed Elena. Dramma per musica da rappresentarsi in Napoli nella nobile Accademia di musica dedicato a' Signori cavalieri che la compongono.

Napoli, Vincenzo Mazzola-Vocola, 1777. *5 p. l., 41 p.* *31*^{cm}.

Five acts. The author, Ranieri de' Calsabigi, is not mentioned. Argument, scenario and prefatory remarks by the marchese di Corleto (dated Naples, **December 17, 1777**), which reads as follows:

Paride ed Elena—Continued.

"L'aver io promossa in Napoli, e stabilita con successo una unione di cavalieri dilettanti di musica, mi ha fatto lusingare di ricavarne non solo un'onesto, e nobile divertimento, ma ben'anche di far rivivere il gusto in questo generé, che pare sia quasi assopito. Infatti la maggior parte de' forestieri intendenti rimangono stupiti di non trovare nelle orchestre di Napoli nè l'esattezza, nè l'espressione; e tanto più che mantenendosi ne' conservatorii una continua sorgente di musica, sembra che quest'arte dovesse nella nostra città portarsi al più eccelso grado di perfezione. Ma il numero immenso dei professori, che ne ha avvilite le paghe, e la moltiplicità delle musiche, nata appunto dalla poca spesa che importano, han prodotta corrispondentemente la sazietà negl'i ascoltanti, e la svogliatezza dell' arte nei professori. Chi crederebbe mai che un buon soprano canti per la miserabile paga di dieci carlini? E che sia solo per metà piena una chiesa, dove fra scelti, e numersoi cori d'istrumenti, si sente cantare un mottetto all' incomparabile Aprile, o a Cafarelli? Queste necessarie conseguenze dell' attuale sistema armonico di Napoli, sono da altra parte sintomi troppo chiari della decadenza di un' arte, che ha sempre formato uno de' preggi, ed ornamenti della nazione. Ho creduto dunque che eccitando l'emulazione nei professori, ed il genio nella nobiltà, si potesse por' reargine al torrente della corruzzione, che minaccia alla musica la totale rovina. Non ho trovato un mezzo più adattato per riuscirvi, quanto quello di formare la detta unione di nobiltà, dove sull' esempio delli stessi cavalieri dilettanti si animano i professori a distinguersi, e colla scelta delle migliori composizioni si risveglia generalmente il gusto, e la passione per la musica. A questo fine ho voluto ancora adoprarmi, con far eseguire nella nostra accademia il tanto rinomato Paride del cavalier Cristofaro Gluch (**Gluck**), del quale è superfluo decantarne i preggi a chi deve sentirlo. L'espressione della musica connaturale al detto compositore, brilla ancor maggiormente in questa sua opera, dove non trovando egli, come nell' Alceste passioni violenti da maneggiare, ha intrapreso di far spiccare il contraposto dei caratteri di Paride, e di Elena, esprimendo in essi l'indole delle due nazioni Frigia, e Spartana; essendo rimarchevole, che nell' adattarsi alla ruvidezza, e semplicità di quest' ultima, si sostenga meravigliosamente, senza punto cader nel triviale. Se non mi fosse pienamente nota l'abilità dei professori, che con tanta cura si sono scelti per servizio della nostra accademia, temerei con ragione del successo di una composizione così delicata, e che merita la maggior esattezza nell' esecuzione; ma questa volta mi lusingo, non ostante l'assenza del compositore; che dice lo stesso cavalier Gluch essere del pari necessario per il buon regolamento, che la presenza del sole nelle opere della natura; sia il Paride eseguito in modo, da farne spiccare tutta l'arte, e le bellezze . . .

First performed at Vienna, Burgtheater, November 3, 1770.   ML 50.2.P27G5

Paride in Ida. Drama per musica da rappresentarsi nel Teatro di S. Angelo l'autunno dell' anno 1706.

Venezia, Marino Rossetti, 1706. 52 p. 14½ᶜᵐ.

Three acts. Argument and scenario. Neither the author, Francesco Mazzari, nor the composers, Luigi **Manza** and Agostino Bonaventura **Colletti**, are mentioned.

First performed at Parma, Teatro Ducale, 1696.   Schatz 5917

Il Pariggino in Italia. Intermezzo in musica da reppresentarsi nel nobile Teatro Tron Veronese a San Cassiano il carnovale dell' anno 1784 . . .

Venezia, Modesto Fenzo, 1784. 40 p. 16½ᶜᵐ.

Two acts. Cast, scenario, and name of composer, Lorenzo **Baini**. Librettist unknown to Schatz. Not identical with "Il finto Parigino."   Schatz 553

Paris. Tr. of Bontempi's Il Paride.

Der Pariser mahler. Tr. of Cimarosa's Il pittor parigino.

Il Parnaso accusato e difeso.

Metastasio, Poesie, Parigi, vedova Quillau, 1755, t. vii, [279]–306 p. 16ᶜᵐ.

One act.   ML49.A2M42

Il **Parnaso accusato e difeso**—Continued.

— Il **Parnaso accusato, e difeso**. Componimento drammatico, scritto dall' autore in Vienna l'anno 1738 . . . ed eseguito la prima volta con musica del Reütter nella galleria dell' Imperial Favorita . . . per festeggiare il dì 28 d'Agosto, giorno di nascita dell' imperatrice Elisabetta.

[359]–380 p. 26^{cm}. (*Pietro Metastasio, Opere, t. v., Parigi, vedova Herissant, 1780.*) ML49.A2M44

Il **Parnaso confuso**. Festa teatrale, scritta . . . dall' autore in Vienna, e rappresentata la prima volta con musica del Gluck negl' interni appartamenti dell' Imperial soggiorno di Schönbrunn dalle AA. RR. di quattro arciduchesse d'Austria . . . in occasione delle nozze delle SS. RR. MM. di Giuseppe II d'Austria, e di Maria Giuseppe di Baviera, . . . l'anno 1765.

[345]–368 p. (*Metastasio, Opere, t. viii, Parigi, vedova Herissant, 1781.*)

One act. ML49.A2M44

Il **Parnaso confuso** del Sig. ab. Metastasio P. Ces., azione teatrale rappresentata in musica nell' interno della imperiale corte in occasione delle felicissime nozze delle Sacre Reali Maestà di Giuseppe II d'Austria e di Maria Gioseffa di Baviera; Rè e regina de' Romani.

Milano, Giuseppe Cairoli, 1765. 19 p. 17^{cm}.

One act. The composer, **Gluck**, is not mentioned.
First performed at Schönbrunn, January 24, 1765. SCHATZ 3936

Parodie, tragi-comedie. Représentée pour la premiere fois, par les Comédiens italiens ordinaires du roi, le 23. mai 1723.

Les Parodies du Nouveau Théâtre italien, Nouv. éd., Paris, 1738, t. ii, [207]–250 p. 16$\frac{1}{2}$^{cm}.

One act. By Fuzelier (*see* t. I). The airs and vaudeville used are printed at the end of the volume in the "Table des airs" (60 p.). ML48.P3

La **parodie au Parnasse**, opera-comique en un acte. Représenté pour la premiere fois sur le Théâtre de l'Opéra-comique de la Foire Saint Germain le 20 mars 1759 . . .

Paris, Duchesne, 1759. 53, [2] p. 19^{cm}. (Theatre de M. Favart, Paris, Duchesne, 1763–77, t. viii.)

The [2] p. contain lists of plays, etc.; p. 50–53, four airs. One act. Cast. Prose and vaudevilles. Font does not mention Favart's musical collaborator. Numerous footnotes give the key to the personal allusions, etc., in the text. The preface of the "Theatre (t. I, p. xxvi) says about this play:

"Satyre ingénieuse & très fine. M. Favart n'avoue point cette pièce, telle qu'elle est imprimée ici, quoique le fond, le quadre, la plus grande partie des couplets, & presque tous les détails lui appartiennent. Un anonyme ayant eu, on ne sçait comment, une copie de cet opera-comique, représenté en 1740 sous le titre de *La barriere du Parnasse ou de La muse chansonniere*, & ne sçachant pas que M. Favart en étoit l'auteur, crût pouvoir se l'approprier. Il y insera la critique des ouvrages dramatiques qui paroissoient alors, critique un peu trop vive, & qu'assurement M. Favart, qui n'y est pas ménagé lui-même au sujet de Petrine, ne se seroit pas permise. La scène de Diogène est une personnalité, & l'on n'en trouvera dans aucune des productions de notre auteur. On avoit judicieusement retranché cette scene à la représentation: elle n'auroit pas dü reparoître ici." ML49.A2F1

Parpagnacco. Intermezzi comici musicali da rappresentarsi nel Teatro Tron di San Cassano il carnovale dell' anno MDCCVIII.

Venezia, Marino Rossetti, 1708. 12 p. 13½^{cm}.

Three intermezzi. Neither the author, Pietro Pariati, nor the composer, Carlo Francesco **Gasparini**, is mentioned.

First performed at Venice, with the opera, "Flavio Anicio Olibrio," carnival, 1707.
SCHATZ 3575

— **Pollastrella & Parpagnacco.**

Under this title, with Italian and German texts, Pariati's Intermezzi, as composed by **Gasparini** (though he is not there mentioned), form part of the unpaged libretto of Riccardo Broschi's opera, "Adriano in Siria" (Stuccarda, 1737). Some differences are noticeable. For instance, the first aria, "Che piacere che diletto," supplanted "Non si vanti di beltà."   SCHATZ 1338

— **L'astrologo.** Intermezzi per musica da rappresentarsi nel Teatro di S. Angelo il carnovale 1731.

[At end] Venezia, Carlo Buonarigo, 1731. [12] p. 15^{cm}.

Three intermezzi. A somewhat altered version of "Parpagnacco." For instance, the aria in the third intermezzo is now "Io sono guerriero," instead of "Sogle donne amar e disamar," and "Di Venere il monte," in the second, has replaced "Da questa linea io vedo." Neither Pariati nor **Gasparini** mentioned.   SCHATZ 3590

Partenope. Festa teatrale, scritta . . . dall' autore in Vienna, e rappresentata la prima volta con musica dell' Hasse . . . per celebrare i regi sponsali di Ferdinando IV di Borbone . . . e di Maria Giuseppa arciduchessa d'Austria, nell' autunno dell' anno 1767.

[331]–390 p. 26^{cm}. (Metastasio, Opere, t. ix, Parigi, vedova Herissant, 1781.)

Two parts. Argument.   ML49.A2M44

La **Partenope.** Drama per musica da rappresentarsi nel famosissimo Teatro Grimani in San Gio. Crisostomo. Il carnovale dell' anno MDCCVII.

Venezia, Marino Rossetti, n. d. 59, [1] p. 14½^{cm}.

Three acts. By Silvio Stampiglia (not mentioned). Somewhat altered from the Naples (1699) edition of the text, as appears from the publisher's notice to the reader: "Chi hà dovuto per un grande comandamento ridurlo all' uso di queste scene hà servata religiosamente l'intentione del celeberrimo autore, che l'hà composto, non alteratovi punto l'ordine delle scene, nè con accrescervi del suo, nè con lo scemarvi cos'alcuna di ciò ch'ha ritrovato nell' esemplare stampato in Napoli l'anno 1699, che fù il primo, in cui fù rappresentato. Solamente vi hò levati gl'intramezzi, ed alcune ariette à titolo della voluta brevità nel luogo delle quali hà posto due versi di recitativo. Alcune altre nè hà mutate per accommodarsi alla musica . . ."

Argument, cast, and scenario, but without the name of the composer, Antonio **Caldara.** On the last page "Opere musicali sin' ora stampate in Venezia da Antonio Bortoli . . ."

First performed at Venice, as indicated; at Naples, January, 1699. SCHATZ 1495

Partenope. Drama. Da rappresentarsi nel Regio Teatro di Haymarket.

Londra, Tomaso Wood, 1730. 77, [1] p. 18^{cm}.

Three acts. Neither the author, Silvio Stampiglia, nor the composer, Georg Friedrich **Händel**, is mentioned. Argument and cast. English title, "Parthenope," and text face Italian. The additional page contains the additional aria "Seguaci di Cupido" for the last scene of the opera.

First performed February 24, 1730, as indicated.   SCHATZ 4483

Partenope—Continued.

— **Partenope**. Drama per musica con prologo nel felicissimo di natalizio dell' Altezza Serenissima di Elisabeta Sofia Maria, duchessa vedova di Braunsviga-Luneburgo . . .—Parthenope . . . Vorgestellet auf dem Theatro des fuerstlichen Lust-hauses zu Saltzthal den 12. september 1731.

n. i., n. d. Unpaged. 18½ᶜᵐ.

Three acts. Argument, scenario, and name of Hendel (Georg Friedrich **Händel**) as the composer. German translation faces Italian, which seems to follow Stampiglia's text closely. SCHATZ 4484

— **Parthenope**, in einem sing-spiele auf dem Hamburgischen schauplatze fuergestellet.

[Hamburg], Gedruckt mit Spieringkischen schrifften, 1733. Unpaged. 18½ᶜᵐ.

Three acts. "Vorbericht" with argument and note that C. G. Wendt translated the text, that Reinhard **Keiser** composed the recitatives and Hendel (Georg Friedrich **Händel**) the arias. The Italian text is added to the arias.
First performed October 27, 1733, as indicated. SCHATZ 4485

Partenope. Festa teatrale da rappresentarsi in musica nell' Imperial regio Teatro festeggiandosi i felicissimi sponsali di Ferdinando IV. di Borbone rè delle Due Sicilie e di Maria Giuseppa d'Austria l'anno MDCCLXVII.

n. i., n. d. Unpaged. 21ᶜᵐ.

At end: "Vienna, nella stamperia di Ghelen 1767." The frontispiece, ornamental title page, head and tail pieces, etc., were designed by J. Bidermann, engraved by J. C. de Reinsperger. Two acts. Argument, cast, and names of Metastasio as author, of Johann Adolph **Hasse** as composer.
First performed, as indicated, September 9, 1767. SCHATZ 4551

— **Partenope**, dramma per musica da rappresentarsi nel Regio Teatro del Nuovo Sans-Souci nell' estate del 1775 . . .

Berlino, Haude e Spener, 1775. 69, [3] p. 17ᶜᵐ.

Two acts. Argument, cast, and names of Metastasio as author, of **Hasse** as composer. German title page, "Parthenope," and text face Italian, which follows the original Vienna (1767) edition closely, except that the aria for II, 2, "Ah! più di te confusa," has been replaced by "Caro . . . l'affanno mio" and that the nuptial allusions after the chorus, "Si tutto il cielo," were, of course, dropped.
First performed, as indicated, July 18, 1775. SCHATZ 4552

Partenope componimento drammatico dell' abbate Pietro Metastasio da cantarsi nell' Accademia di musica di Dame e Cavalieri.

Napoli, Stamperia Raimondiana, 1782. 47 p. 19ᶜᵐ.

Two acts. Cast, name of Vincenzo Martini (**Martin y Soler**) as the composer, and on p. 5 "Protesta," in which alterations from Metastasio for brevity's sake and "per comodo della musica" are acknowledged. SCHATZ 6013

Partenope. Drama per musica da rappresentarsi nel Regio Teatro di Torino nel carnovale del 1749 . . .

Torino, Pietro Giuseppe Zappata e figliuolo, n. d. 4 p. l., 62 p. 15ᶜᵐ.

Three acts. By Silvio Stampiglia, who is not mentioned. Argument, scenario, cast, and names of Giuseppe **Scarlatti** as composer of the opera. of Alessio Rasetti of the music for the three ballets, "Caccia di Diana," etc. SCHATZ 9556

Partenope sul lido etrusco. Azione teatrale di Cristoforo Boccella, patrizio lucchese.

Lucca, Francesco Bonsignori, 1785. 25 p. 26ᶜᵐ.

Exquisite vignettes. One act. Cast, argomento, and name of composer, Gaetano Andreozzi.
First performed at Lucca, Teatro Castiglioncelli, 1785.   SCHATZ 197

La partenza d'Enea, o sia Didone abbandonata, ballet. *See* Gazzaniga's Zon-Zon principe di Kibin-Kin-Ka.

La partenza di Berenice. A. T. of the ballet Tito.

La partenza e il ritorno de' marinari. Dramma giocoso per musica da rappresentarsi nel Teatro Giustiniani di San Moisè il carnovale dell' anno 1765 . . .

Venezia, Modesto Fenzo, 1765. 71 p. 14½ᶜᵐ.

Three acts. Author unknown to Schatz. Cast, scenario, and name of **Galuppi** as composer.
First performed December 26, 1764, as indicated.   SCHATZ 3466

La partenza inaspettata. Intermezzo in musica a cinque voci da rappresentarsi nel Teatro Valle dell' illᵐⁱ Signori Capranica. Nel carnevale dell' anno 1779 . . .

Roma, Agostino Palombini, 1779. 46 p. 15ᶜᵐ.

Two acts. The author, Giuseppe Petrosellini, is not mentioned. Cast and name of Antonio **Salieri** as composer.   ML 50.2.P28S2

— **La partenza inaspettata.** Commedia per musica da rappresentarsi nel Teatro di Monza l'autunno dell' anno 1781 . . .

Milano, Gio. Batista Bianchi, n. d. 69 p. 15½ᶜᵐ.

Two acts. By Giuseppe Petrosellini, who is not mentioned. Cast, scenario, and name of Antonio **Salieri** as the composer. With the opera was performed Raineri Pazzini's ballet "Vindemmia."

    SCHATZ 9310

— **La partenza inaspettata.** Intermezzo in musica a cinque voci da rappresentarsi nel Piccolo Teatro di S. A. E. di Sassonia.

Dresda, Stamperia elettorale, 1781. 141 p. 16ᶜᵐ.

Two acts. Antonio **Salieri** is mentioned as the composer. German title-page, "Die unerwartete abreise," and text face Italian.
First performed 1781 at Dresden, as indicated.   SCHATZ 9311

Le parterre merveilleux. Prologue du Rival de lui-même. Représenté à la Foire Saint Laurent. 1732.

Le Théâtre de la foire, Paris, 1737, t. ix, 2, 2 pl., [73]–122 p. 17ᶜᵐ.

— **Le rival de lui-même.** Piece en un acte en vers. Representée par les petits Comediens de l'Opera comique à la Foire Saint Laurent 1732.

By Carolet. Largely *en vaudevilles*. The airs, selected or composed and arranged y Jean Claude **Gillier**, are printed at the end of the volume in the "Table des airs."
First performed August 19, 1732.   ML 48.L2X

Parthenope. Tr. of Händel's Partenope.

Parthenope. Tr. of Hasse's Partenope.

The **parting lovers.** A. T. of Carey's Nancy.

La Pasife o vero L'impossibile fatto possibile. Drama per musica del Signor D. Giuseppe Artale . . .

Venetia, Giacomo Batti, 1661. 72 p. 13½ cm.

Three acts with prologue. Dedication, argument, allegoria, and name of the composer, Daniele **Castrovillari.**
First performed at Venice, Teatro di S. Salvatore, carnival, 1661. SCHATZ 1689

Le passioni per troppo amore. Drama per musica da rappresentarsi nel Teatro di Sant' Angelo. Nel carnovale dell' anno 1713. Di Matteo Noris.

Venezia, Marino Rossetti, 1713. 72 p. 15 cm.

Three acts. Prefatory note, scenario, and name of Johann David **Heinichen** as the composer. SCHATZ 4703

Il pastor fido, ballet. *See* Alessandri's Il vecchio geloso.

Il pastor fido. Tragicommedia pastorale del cavalier Guarini compendiata al tempo, ed al modo di cantarsi nel Teatro a S. Angelo nel carnovale dell' anno 1721.

Padoa, Gio. Battista Conzatti, 1721. 79, [1] p. 17½ cm.

Five acts. Edited by Benedetto Pasqualigo, who is not mentioned. Argument, cast, scenario, and name of Carlo [Luigi] **Pietragrua** as the composer. The additional page contains the substitute aria "Da noi il ciel più non dimanda" (V, 7). SCHATZ 8164

Il pastor regio. Drammà del Signor Benedetto Ferrari, rappresentato in musica in Venetia nell' anno MDCXXXX . . .

Venetia, Antonio Bariletti, 1640. 1 p. l., 58 p. 14½ cm.

Three acts and prologue. Author-composer's dedication dated Venice, Jan. 23, 1640, and argument. SCHATZ 3067

— Il **pastor regio** di Benedetto Ferrari dalla tiorba. Rappresentato in musica in Venetia, et in Bologna. Posto in musica dall' istesso autore. In questa terza impressione dall' autore ampliato, e corretto.

n. i., n. d. 13 cm. [161]–207 p. (B. Ferrari, Poesie drammatiche, Milano, 1644.)

Detached copy. Three acts, the "Prologo d'Amore, rappresentato in Venetia," and the "Prologo d'Apollo rappresentato in Bologna," dedication signed by Camillio Cevenini and dated Bologna, May 18, 1641, argument and sonnet by the publisher Ramellati to Ferrari "per il suo Pastor regio." SCHATZ 11700

La pastorale. Entrée in Campra's Les Muses.

. . . **Pastorale mise en musique,** par le Sieur Cambert. Representée au village d'Issy près Paris, & au chasteau de Vincennes devant Leurs Maiestez en Avril 1659.

Perrin, Les oeuvres de poesie, Paris, Estienne Loyson, 1661, [291]– 312 p. 14½ cm.

Five acts. At head of title "Premiere comedie françoise en musique, representee en France," at the château of M. de la Haye. Until recently Pierre Perrin and Robert Cambert were considered the founders of French opera, but in the *S. I. M.,* 1908, y. 4, nos. 4–5, Henri Quittard published an essay, "La première comédie française en musique," in which he called attention to the extremely rare libretto "Le triomphe de l'amour sur des bergers et bergeres . . . mis en musique par De La Guerre . . . A Paris . . . Charles Chenault . . . 1654." This one act pastorale was reprinted 1661 or shortly afterwards. The text was by Charles de Beys, the

La **pastorale**—Continued.

music by Michel de la Guerre (*d*. 1679). Quittard goes into the history of this fore-runner of Perrin and Cambert's pastorale, reprints the text, and dates the first performance as January 22, 1655.

In his "Oeuvres," Perrin precedes the text of his own pastorale on p. 273–290 by his "Lettre ecrite a Monseigneur l'archevesque de Turin. Apres la representation de la comedie suivante. De Paris ce 30. avril 1659." Unfortunately, this very interesting and important historical document is too long for quotation here. It is easily accessible *in extenso* in Pougin's "Les vrais créateurs de l'opéra français, Perrin et Cambert" (Paris, 1881, p. 56–68). Of course, the letter is in the nature of a campaign manifesto for French opera against Italian. For English-speaking people his sixth "deffaut" (defect) pointed out against the cultivation of Italian opera in France is particularly *à propos*. Perrin says:

"Le sixieme qui les fera toújours échoüer sur nostre theatre, est le deffaut inévitable de chanter en une langue étrangere & inconnuë à la meilleure partie des spectateurs, qui leur ravit la plus belle partie du plaisir de la comedie, qui est celuy de l'esprit, & qui fait à leur égard ce qui arrive à peu près à ceux qui voyent danser sans entendre les violons . . ."   PQ 1879.P3

Il **pastore d'Anfriso**. Tragedia pastorale per musica da rappresentarsi nel Teatro Grimano di San Gio. Grisostomo l'anno MDCXCV . . . Seconda impressione.

Venetia, Nicolini, 1695.   front., 71 p.   14^{cm}.

Five acts with intermezzi. Dedication signed by the author, conte Girolamo Frigimelica Roberti, who, as was his custom, comments on his dramaturgic intentions in his notice to the reader, which is followed by the argument and scenario. The composer, Carlo Francesco **Pollaroli**, is not mentioned.   SCHATZ 8310

La **pastorella al soglio**. Opera postuma di Giulio Cesare Corradi. Da rappresentarsi per musica nell' antichissimo Teatro Tron di San Casciano per l'autunno dell' anno 1702.

Venezia, Marino Rossetti, 1702.   59 p.   15^{cm}.

Three acts. Argument, scenario. Composer not mentioned and unknown to Schatz. Orefice's opera, mentioned by Towers, is of date 1710.   SCHATZ 11355

La **pastorella al soglio**. Drama per musica di Gio. Carlo Paganicesa. Da rappresentarsi nel Teatro Giustiniano di S. Moisè nella fiera dell' Ascensione MDCCLI.

[Venezia], n. publ., n. d.   1 p. l., 48 p.   15^{cm}.

Three acts. Argument, cast, and name of Gaetano **Latilla** as composer.

SCHATZ 5465

La **pastorella fedele**, ballet. *See* Bianchi's La villanella rapita.

La **pastorella illustre**. Azione per musica in due parti da rappresentarsi nel Ducal Teatro di Stuttgardt per ordine di Sua Altezza Serenissima Carlo, duca regnante di Wirtemberg e Teck etc il di 4. novembre 1763 . . . La poesia è del Signor de Tagliazucchi . . . La musica è nuovamente composta dal Signor Nicolò Jommelli . . . I balli sono inventati e diretti dal Signor Giovanni Giorgio Noverre . . .

[Stuttgardt], Cotta, n. d.   111 p.   18^{cm}.

Two acts. Argument, cast, and scenario. German title page, "Die vornehme schaeferin," and text face Italian.   SCHATZ 4868

— La **pastorella illustre**. Azione teatrale per musica in due parti da rappresentarsi nel Real Teatro di Salvaterra nel carnovale dell' anno 1773.

Lisbona, Stamperia Reale, n. d.   51 p.   15^{cm}.

Two acts. Argument, scenario, cast, and names of Tagliazucchi as author, of Niccolò **Jommelli** as composer. Text seems to follow text of 1763 closely.

SCHATZ 4836

La pastorella impertinente, ballet. *See* Anfossi's Il curioso indiscreto.

La pastorella nobile. Commedia per musica di Saverio Zini da rappresentarsi nel Real Teatro del Fondo di Separazione per prim' opera di quest' anno 1788 . . .

Napoli, n. publ., 1788. 48 p. 14½^{cm}.

Two acts. Dedication dated Naples, April 15, 1788, cast, and name of Pietro Guglielmi as the composer. On p. 6-9 cast and argument of Giambattista Giannini's "L'Aurora vendicata, ballo eroico favoloso," without name of the composer of the music. SCHATZ 4255

— **La pastorella nobile.** Dramma giocoso per musica, da rappresentarsi nel Teatro di S. A. E. di Sassonia.

Dresda, n. publ., 1791. 115 p. 15^{cm}.

Two acts. Pietro Guglielmi is mentioned as the composer. German title-page, "Die adliche schaeferin," and text face Italian, which shows alterations of Zini's text. For instance, the aria, "Di qua vedi un milordino," I, 3, has been replaced by "Perchi mai t'ò fatto nascere," and the second act begins "Questo mio figlio m'à sconvolto il cerebro" instead of "No, no, german, in questo punto."
First performed, as indicated, February 12, 1791. SCHATZ 4256

— **La pastorella nobile.** Dramma giocoso per musica da rappresentarsi nel magnifico Teatro della illustrissima Accademia degli Erranti di Brescia il carnovale 1792 . . .

Brescia, Pasini, n. d. 60 p. 16½^{cm}.

Two acts. Impresario's dedicatory sonnet, cast, scenario, and name of Pietro Guglielmi as composer. Zini is not mentioned. ML48.A5v.12

La pastorella rapita da' corsari, ballet. *See* Paisiello's Il rè Teodoro in Venezia.

La pastorella scaltra. Intermezzi per musica a tre voci da rappresentarsi nel Teatro alla Valle nel carnevale dell' anno 1753 . . •.

Roma, Marcello Silvestri, n. d. 24 p. 15½^{cm}.

Two parts. Author not mentioned and unknown to Schatz Dedication signed by G. Puccinelli and Angelo Lungi, the latter perhaps being the author. Cast and name of Nicola Logroscino as composer. ML 50.2.P286L6

Le pastorelle d'Arcadia. Festa campestre nelle augustissime nozze delle Altezze Reali de reale infante di Spagna Don Ferdinando di Borbone . . . e della reale archiduchessa d'Austria Maria Amalia. [vignette]

Parma, Stamperia reale, 1769. 74, [1] p. front. 23½^{cm}.

Dedicatory poem, a "Relazione della festa campestre . . ." and names of the nobility participating precede the text which is in two parts with two "Cantate introdotte a guisa d'intermedj." Not recorded by Schatz. ML48M2A

Le pastorelle difese, ballet. *See* Valentini's Le sorelle rivali.

Li pastori d'Arcadia, ballet. *See* Gnecco's Lo sposo di tre.

I pastori delle Alpi. Dramma serio-giocoso per musica da rappresentarsi nel Regio Teatro di Trieste l'autunno dell' anno MDCCLXXX . . .

Gorizia, Giacomo Tommasini n. d. 58 p. 17½^{cm}.

Two acts. Antonio Pasquale Valli is mentioned as the author and Giuseppe Moneta as "compositore dilettante di musica, il quale recentemente ed a bella posta l'ha scritta." Impresario's dedicatory poem dated Trieste, October 17, 1780, cast, and scenario. SCHATZ 6557

Li pastori per allegrezza impazziti. Pastorale giocosa da rappresentarsi nel Nuovo Teatro in Dresda, festeggiandosi il giorno del glorioso nome di Sua Maestà d'Augusto III . . . l'anno MDCCLV.

Dresda, la vedova Stössel, ed aderente Giovanni Carlo Krause, n. d. 109, [2] p. 17^cm.

Two acts and licenza. Cast. German text faces Italian. Author and composer not mentioned, and unknown to Schatz and Fürstenau.

First performed, as indicated, August 5, 1755. SCHATZ 11356

Patie and Peggy: or, The fair foundling. A Scotch ballad opera. As it is acted at the Theatre-Royal in Drury-Lane. By His Majesty's servants . . . With the music prefix'd to each song.

London, J. Watts, 1730. 4 p. l., 34, [2] p. 20^cm.

One act, prologue, and epilogue. Cast and author's preface, signed T.[eophilus] C.[ibber] and dated "Theatre-Royal April the 20th, 1730," which reads, in part:

"That I am indebted to Mr. Ramsay's *Gentle Shepherd* (a Scotch pastoral comedy, wrote originally in five acts) for the greatest part of the following piece, was not owing to my idleness, but a doubt of my abilities to produce any thing entirely new of this kind, that might plead to much pretence to favour . . ."

He decided

"to turn it into a ballad opera . . . in bringing the tale within the compass of one act, adding to the number of the songs, and changing it into the English dialect without which, it had not been intelligible to our auditors; nor indeed had I time to vary it more, my benefit being fix'd before I had laid my design, which was plan'd and finish'd in *one day* . . .".

The 22 airs are printed in the text, with their titles.

First performed, according to Clarence ("The Stage encyclopaedia"), and Tufts, on May 31, 1731, but this is obviously incorrect, as this performance must have taken place before April 20, 1730. ML 50.5.P18

Second copy. LONGE 49

Patrick in Prussia or Love in a camp. *See* Love in a camp.

Patro Tonno d'Isca. Chelleta marenaresca a muodo de dramma pe museca de lo dottore Agasippo Mercotellis, da recetarese à lo Teatro de li Shiorentine nchist' anno 1714 . . .

Mmenezia, Francisco Ricciardo, 1714. 4 p. l., 64 p. 15^cm.

Last p. incorrectly numbered 74. Three acts. By Giuseppe Martoscelli. Dedication by the composer, Giovanne Veneziani (Giovanni **Veneziano**), dated September 26, 1714, notice to the reader, and cast.

First performed at Naples, Teatro de' Fiorentini, as indicated. ML 50.2.P29V2

The patron: or, The statesman's opera, of two acts, as 'tis acted by the company of comedians at the New Theatre in the Hay-Market. By Mr. Odell . . . To which is added the musick to each song . . .

London, Printed by W. Pearson, for John Clarke, n. d. 3 p. l., 38, [2] p. 19^cm.

The [2] p. contain Clarke's book list. Two acts. Cast, dedication, epilogue. Ballad opera. The 19 (unnumbered) airs used are printed in the text, with their titles.

First performed 1729, as indicated. LONGE 262

Second copy, with a half-title as 4th p. l. LONGE 321

Paul et Virginie. Opéra en trois actes. Musique de Kreutzer.

Hambourg, G. F. Schniebes, 1796. 20 p. 15½^cm.

By Etienne Guillaume François Favières, who is not mentioned.

First performed at Hamburg, Théâtre de la Société-française, October 23, 1795; at Paris, Théâtre de la Comédie italienne, January 15, 1791. SCHATZ 5266

Il **Pausania.** Drama per musica da rappresentarsi l'anno MDCLXXXII nel famosissimo Teatro Vendramino à S. Salvatore . . .

Venetia, Francesco Nicolini, 1682. 63 p. (incl. front.) 14½^{cm}.

Three acts. Dedication by the author, Girolamo Frisari, dated Venice, December 8, 1681, argument, scenario, and notice to the reader, with name of Giovanni **Legrenzi** as composer. SCHATZ 5546

La **pauvre femme,** comédie en un acte et en prose, mêlée de musique. Représentée pour la premiere fois, sur le Théâtre de l'Opéra-comique national, le 19 germinal, an troisième de la Republique. [April 8, 1795]. Paroles du citoyen Marsollier. Musique du citoyen Dalayrac.

Paris, chez les Marchands de nouveautés, An V [1796–97]. 28 p. 20^{cm}.

ML 50.2.P295D2

La **paysanne curieuse.** A. T. of d'Herbain's Nanette et Lucas.

La **pazza giornata** ovvero Il matrimonio di Figaro. Dramma comico per musica di Gaetano Rossi da rappresentarsi nel nobilissimo Teatro Venier in San Benedetto il carnovale dell' anno 1800.

Venezia, Fenzo, 1799. 88 p. 18^{cm}.

Two acts. Cast, notice to the reader, and name of Marcos **Portugal** as the composer ("Musica tutta nuova"). On p. [49]–52, cast, argument, and name of Giuseppe Nucci as the composer of the music ("tutta nuova") of "L'infausto Matrimonio balletto di Giovanni Monticini."

First performed, as indicated, December 26, 1799 (Carvalhaes). SCHATZ 8439

La **pazza per amore,** ballet. *See* Nasolini's La Calliroe.

La **pazza per amore.** A. T. of Paisiello's Nina.

I **pazzi per disimpegno.** Dramma giocoso per musica di Camidio Matiaglauro P. A. da rappresentarsi nel Teatro Giustiniani in S. Moisè per la seconda opera del carnevale l'anno 1782.

Venezia, n. publ., n. d. 60 p. 17^{cm}.

Two acts. Cast and name of composer, Gaetano **Andreozzi.** By Pietro Antonio Bagliacca, whose Arcadian name the above was. SCHATZ 222

La **pazzia in trono** ovvero Caligola delirante. O. T. of text of Pagliardi's Caligula delirante.

Le **pazzie amorose,** ballet. *See* Bianchi's La villanella rapita.

Le **pazzie amorose,** ballet. *See* P. Guglielmi's L'impostore punito.

Le **pazzie de' gelosi.** Farsetta per musica a cinque voci da rappresentarsi nel Teatro alla Valle degl' illmi Sig. Capranica nel carnevale dell' anno 1787.

Roma, Gioacchino Puccinelli, 1787. 48 p. 15^{cm}.

Two acts. Author not mentioned and unknown to Schatz. Cast and name of Pasquale **Anfossi** as composer.

First performed February 6, 1787, as indicated. ML 50.2.P3A5

— Le **pazzie de' gelosi.** Dramma giocoso per musica da rappresentarsi nel Teatro di S. H. E. di Sassonia.

Dresda, n. publ., 1788. 127 p. 15½^{cm}.

Two acts. Name of Pasquale **Anfossi** as composer, but without that of librettist, who is unknown to Schatz. German title-page, "Die narrheiten der eifersucht," and text face Italian. SCHATZ 247

Le pazzie degl' amanti. Drama da rappresentarsi in musica in Rovigo l'autunno dell' anno 1711. Nel Teatro dell' illustrissimo Signor Co: Marc' Antonio Monfardini. Di Francesco Passarini.

> *Venezia, Antonio Bortoli, 1712.*   *46 p.*   *15^{cm}.*

Three acts. Argument and notice to the reader with the name of Carlo **Francesco Pollaroli** as the composer.

First performed at Vienna, Teatro della Cesarea Corte, February, 1701.

                 SCHATZ 8311

Le pazzie di Orlando. Dramma giocoso da rappresentarsi nel Regio Ducal Teatro di Milano l'autunno dell' anno 1773 . . .

> *Milano, Gio. Battista Bianchi, n. d.*   *51, [1] 6.*   *14½^{cm}.*

Three acts. By Carlo Francesco Badini, who is not mentioned. Dedication, cast, and name of Pietro **Guglielmi** as the composer. The unnumb. pages contain a noteworthy comment by Gasparo Angiolini on his "Solimano II," a specimen of "la commedia ballata nella sua simplicità," of which, with exception of one aria, he also composed the music.

First performed at London, Haymarket, 1771.   SCHATZ 4301

Il pazzo glorioso. Dramma giocoso per musica da rappresentarsi nella presente stagione nel teatro di questa nobilissima città . . .

> *Casal maggiore, Giuseppe Braglià, n. d.*   *35 p.*   *14½^{cm}.*

Two acts. Cast and names of composer, **Bernardini** (Marcello di Capua), and librettist, Giovanni Bertati. A contemporary hand has added 1790 to the title.

                 SCHATZ 850

Il pazzo glorioso. Dramma giocoso per musica da rappresentarsi nel Teatro Tron di S. Cassiano l'autunno dell' anno 1753.

> *Venezia, Modesto Fenzo, 1753.*   *60 p.*   *15½^{cm}.*

Three acts. According to Schatz, Liviano Lantino's (*anagram* of Antonio Villano) "Lo stravagante," but altered by Goldoni. Cast, scenario, and name of Gioacchino **Cocchi** as composer.   SCHATZ 2053

— **Il pazzo glorioso.** Dramma giocoso per musica. Nell' anno 1758.

> *Monaco, Gio. Giac. Vötter, n. d.*   *40 p.*   *15½^{cm}.*

Reduced to two acts. With name of the composer, Giovanni [!] **Cocchi**.

                 SCHATZ 2037

Un pazzo ne fa cento. Dramma giocoso per musica da rappresentarsi nel Teatro Giustiniani in S. Moisè il presente autunno MDCCLXII.

> *Venezia, Francesco Valvasense, n. d.*   *48 p.*   *15½^{cm}.*

Three acts. Author not mentioned and unknown to Schatz. Scenario, cast, and name of Florian Leopold **Gassmann** as the composer.   SCHATZ 3624

Un pazzo ne fa cento. Dramma giocoso per musica di Giuseppe Foppa da rappresentarsi nel nobilissimo Teatro in S. Samuele l'autunno dell' anno 1796.

> *Venezia, Stamperia Valvasense, n. d.*   *78, [1] p.*   *18^{cm}.*

Three acts. Cast and name of Joh. Simon **Mayr** as the composer. On. p. [39]–45 argument, cast, and description of Gio. Battista Checchi's "Alessandro, e Campaspe, ballo eroico." The composer of the music is not mentioned.

First performed, as indicated, October 8, 1796.   SCHATZ 6176

Il **pazzo per forza.** Dramma giocoso per musica da rappresentarsi nel Teatro Elettorale, composto da Caterino Mazzolà . . .

Dresda, n. publ., 1783. 135 p. 15ᶜᵐ.

Two acts. Joseph **Schuster** is mentioned as composer. German title-page, "Er soll und muss ein narr seyn," and text face Italian.
First performed, as indicated, January, 1784. Schatz 9751

Le **pêcheur suédois.** A. T. of Bruni's Toberne.

Les **pêcheurs,** comedie en un acte et en vers. Mêlée d'ariettes. Représentée sur le Théâtre des Comédiens italiens ordinaires du roi, le 7 juin 1766. La musique est de M. F. J. Gossec.

Avignon, Louis Chambeau, 1766. 26 p. 19½ᶜᵐ.

Cast. Text by the marquis de La Salle, who is not mentioned. ML 50.2.P305G7

— Les **pêcheurs,** comédie. En un acte, melée d'ariettes, représentée sur le Théatre des Comédiens italiens ordinaires du Roi, le 7 juin 1766. La musique est de M. F. J. Gossec.

Paris, Vente, 1767. 37 p. 19ᶜᵐ.

Cast. Text by the marquis de La Salle, who is not mentioned. Schatz 4010

— Les **pêcheurs,** comedie en un acte, mêlée d'ariettes, représentée sur le Théatre des Comédiens italiens ordinaires du roi, le 7 juin 1766. La musique est de Mr. F. J. Gossec.

Paris, Vente, 1771. 35 p. 19ᶜᵐ.

Cast. On p. 14–16 the ariette "L'âge en vain sembloit," p. 17–18 "De la richesse l'éclat." The author, marquis de La Salle, is not mentioned. Schatz 11702

— Les **pêcheurs,** comédie en un acte, mêlée d'ariettes; représentée sur le Théatre des Comédiens italiens ordinaires du roi, le 7 juin 1766. La musique est de Mʳ F. J. Gossec.

Paris, Vente, 1782. 32 p. 19ᶜᵐ.

Cast. On p. 15–16 the ariette "De la richesse, l'éclat." The text is the same as in the 1771 ed., except that the ariette "L'âge en vain sembloit" is given without the music. The author is not mentioned. Schatz 11701

— De **visschers,** zangspel. Naar het fransche gevolgd door Bartholomeus Ruloffs.

Amsterdam, J. Helders en A. Mars, 1793. 7 p. l., 48, [4] p. 17ᶜᵐ.

The p. l. contain dedication, a poem by the translator, dated 1793, a notice to the reader with **Gossec**'s name as the composer, privilege notice, dated October 15, 1792, and the four additional pages contain "Byvoegzel tot de Visschers . . ."
First performed at Amsterdam, Stads Schouwburg, May, 1793. Schatz 4015

Le **pédant amoureux.** A. T. of Duni's La fille mal gardée.

A **peep behind the curtain;** or, The new rehearsal. As it is now performed at the Theatre Royal in Drury-Lane.

London, T. Becket and P. A. de Hondt, 1767. 2 p. l., 46 p. 20ᶜᵐ.

Prologue and two acts. The only operatic part of this farce by David Garrick (not mentioned) is in the second act, in form of "The burletta of *Orpheus*." The composer is not mentioned, but is known to be François Hippolyte **Barthélemon.**
First performed, as indicated, October 23, 1767. ML 50.2.P31

A peep behind the curtain—Continued.

— **A peep behind the curtain;** or, The new rehearsal. As it is now performed at the Theatre Royal in Drury-Lane. New edition.
London, T. Becket, 1772. 2 p. l., 46 p. 20ᶜᵐ.
Apparently the same as the 1767 ed.   LONGE 27

A peep into the seraglio. A. T. of Bickerstaffe's text The sultan.

A peep into the tower. A. T. of Harlequin Mungo.

Peeping Tom of Coventry, a comic opera. As it is performed at the Theatre Royal, Smock-Alley. By John O'Keefe, Esq.
Dublin, Colles, Wilkinson, Byrne [etc.], 1786. 2 p. l., 43 p. 17½ᶜᵐ.
Two acts. Cast. The composer, Samuel **Arnold,** is not mentioned.
First performed September 6, 1784, at the Hay-Market, London.   LONGE 149

— **Peeping Tom of Coventry;** a comic opera, as it is performed at the Theatre-Royal, Smoke-alley.
[Dublin], Printed for the booksellers, 1787. 28 p. 17½ᶜᵐ.
Two acts. Cast. Neither O'Keefe is mentioned, nor **Arnold.**   SCHATZ 338

Les peines et les plaisirs de l'amour, pastorale representée par l'Académie royale de musique en l'an 1672. Les paroles sont de M. Gilbert & la musique de M. Cambert. II. opera.
n. i., n. d. front., 49–100 p. 14ᶜᵐ. (Recueil général des opera, Paris, 1703, t. i.)
Detached copy. Five acts and prologue.   SCHATZ 1520
                                        Second copy. ML 48.R4

Le peintre amoureux de son modéle, piece en deux actes, parodiée dal *Pittore innamorato,* intermede italien: Représentée pour la premiere fois sur le Théâtre de l'Opera-comique de la Foire S. Laurent, le mardi 26 juillet 1757. Par M. Anséaume.
Paris, Duchesne, 1757. 38, [2] p. 19½ᶜᵐ.
Prose, ariettes and vaudevilles. Cast. On p. 3 the same foot-note as in next entry. The [2] p. contain lists of plays.   ML 50.2.P32D9

— **Le peintre amoureaux de son modéle,** piece en deux actes, Représentée pour la première fois sur le Théâtre de l'Opéra-comique de la Foire St. Laurent, le mardi 26 juillet 1757. Par M. Anseaume. Nouvelle edition.
Paris, la veuve Duchesne, 1767. 28 p. 19ᶜᵐ.
In footnote on p. 3: "Les ariettes sont parodiées sur la musique de l'intermède italien ['Il pittor innamorato'], de la composition del Signor **Duny,** compositeur de musique de l'Infant Don Philippe, duc de Parme, etc."   SCHATZ 2853

— **Der verliebte maler,** ein singspiel in zween aufzuegen aus dem franzoesischen uebersetzt, mit musik.
Frankfurt am Mayn, mit Andreäischen schriften, 1773. 52 p., 23 p. (folded music, dated 1775). 16ᶜᵐ.
German version, by Johann Heinrich Faber. With cast.
The musical supplement contains the arias (voice and bass): "Ja ich war ein mädchen" ["Quand j'étois jeunette"], p. 1–5; "Auf einmal ward entzündet" ["Un instant a fait naître"], p. 6–11; "Endlich singt der gott der liebe" ["De l'amour je sens la flamme"], p. 12–16; "Ist sie eine coquette" ["Si c'est une coquette"], p. 16–23.
First performed at Frankfurt, Theater im Junghof, 1773.   SCHATZ 2854

Pelarina. Intermezzo.

[*79*]–*109 p. 16½^{cm}. (Carlo Goldoni, Opere drammatiche, t. iv, Torino, 1757.)

Three parts. ML 49.A2G6

— La **pelerina.** ˚Intermezzo di tre parti per musica. Rappresentato per la prima volta a Feltre l'anno MDCCXXIX.

Carlo Goldoni, Opere teatrali, Venezia, Zatta e figli, 1788–95, v. 35, [5]–37 p. 18½^{cm}.

Three parts. According to Schatz, first performed with music by unknown composer at Venice, Teatro Grimania S. Samuele in 1734. PQ

Les pelerins de la Mecque. Piece en trois actes. Par M^{rs} le S** & d'Or** Representée à la Foire S. Laurent 1726 & ensuite sur le Théâtre du Palais royal.

Le Théâtre de la foire, Paris, 1728, t. vi, pl., [123]–230 p. 17^{cm}.

By Le Sage and d'Orneval. Largely *en vaudevilles*, a few of which are marked as by "M. l'Abbé." The airs, selected or composed and arranged by Jean Claude **Gillier,** the "compositeur" of the company, are printed at the end of the volume in the "Table des airs." Parfaict adds, as author, Fuzelier.

First performed July 29, 1726. ML 48.L2 VI

Il **pellegrinaggio** o sia La vindemmia fiamminga, ballet. *See* Sarti's Il trionfo della pace.

Il **pellegrino.** Drama musicale rappresentato nelle camere della serenissima granduchessa Vittoria di Toscana per solennizzare il giorno natalizio del serenissimo Cosimo Terzo granduca di Toscana.

G. A. Moniglia, Poesie drammatiche, seconda parte, Firenze, Cesare e Francesco Bindi, 1690, p. [295]–323. 24^{cm}.

Three acts. Argument and prefatory note according to which this "piccolo componimento dramatico ristretto in due soli personaggi" was composed by Lorenzo **Cattani** and was sung by "due fanciulle di camera della serenissima granduchessa." First performed in 1685 as indicated. ML 49.A2M7

Pelope. Dramma per musica da rappresentarsi nel Teatro Ducale di Stutgart festeggiandosi il felicissimo giorno natalizia di Sua Altezza Serenissima Carlo, duca regnante di Wirtemberg e Tech etc. . . . La poesia è di Mattia Verazi . . . La musica è del celebre Sig. Nicolò Jommelli . . .

Stutgart, Cotta, 1755. 94 p. 18½^{cm}.

Three acts. Argument, cast, scenario. German title-page, "Pelops," and text face Italian.

First performed, as indicated, February 11, 1755. Schatz 4869

Pelopida. Dramma per musica da rappresentarsi nel Regio Teatro di Torino nel carnevale del 1763 . . .

Torino, Gaspare Bayno, n. d. viii, 56 p. 16^{cm}.

Three acts. By Gaetano Roccaforte, who is not mentioned. Argument, cast, scenario, and name of Giuseppe **Scarlatti** as the composer. On p. 53–56 brief descriptions of Augusto Huss' ballets, music by Giuseppe Antonio Le Messier, "I selvatici" and "La morte d'Orfeo." Schatz 9551

Pelops. Tr. of Jommelli's Pelope.

La pena degl' occhi. Drama per rappresentarsi nel Teatro Zane di San Moisè l'anno MDCLXXXVIII . . .

Venetia, Francesco Nicolini, 1688. 56 p. 14ᶜᵐ.

Three acts. The anonymous author asks in a prefatory note for the reader's indulgence because he has "composto in poch'ore il presente drama." Argument and scenario. The composer, Francesco **Rossi,** is not mentioned. SCHATZ 8889

Penelope. Drama per musica in applauso delle augustissime nozze delle Sacre Cesaree Reali Maestà dell' imperatore Leopoldo et imperatrice Claudia Felice. Fatto rappresentare dal serenissimo Sig. duca di Mantova, Monferrato etc l'anno 1674.

Mantova, gli Osanni, n. d. 1 p. l., 75, [1] p. 20ᶜᵐ.

Prologue and three acts. Argument. Author and composer not mentioned and unknown to Schatz. SCHATZ 11357

Penelope, a dramatic opera, as it is acted at the new Theatre in the Hay-Market.

London, Printed, and sold by Tho. Green and Charles Davis, 1728. 4 p. l., [1], 18–60, [1] p., 15 p. (music). 19ᶜᵐ.

Three acts. By John Mottley and Thomas Cooke, who are not mentioned. Preface, prologue, cast, and epilogue. The 15 p. of music (engraved on one side) contain the overture in score and 14 numbered ballad airs with their titles, corresponding to the numbered songs in text (without the titles of the airs). LONGE 152

Penelope. Dramma serio per musica da rappresentarsi nel Regio Teatro dell' Accademia degli Avvalorati in Livorno l'autunno dell' anno 1795.

[Livorno], Tommaso Masi e compagno, n. d. 42 p. 18ᶜᵐ.

Two acts. By Gius. Maria Diodati, who is not mentioned. Impresario's dedication, argument, cast, scenario, and name of Domenico **Cimarosa** as composer. First performed at Naples, Teatro del Fondo, December 26, 1794. SCHATZ 1967

Penelope, tragicommedi. Denen . . . majestaeten . . . zur fassnachts-unterhaltung welsch-gesungener vorgestellet im jahr 1724. Poësi, des hrn. Pariati . . . In die music verfasset von hrn. Francesco Conti . . .

Wien, Johann Peter van Ghelen, n. d. 55 p. 15ᶜᵐ.

Three acts. Argument, cast, scenario. German text only. First performed at Vienna, Hoftheater, February 6, 1724. SCHATZ 2202

Penelope la casta, drama per musica, da rappresentarsi per opera seconda nel Teatro di S. Angelo il carnevale dell' anno 1716. Di Matteo Noris, recitato la prima volta nel famoso Teatro di S. Gio. Chrisostomo l'anno 1685 . . .

Venezia, Marino Rossetti, 1716. 60 p. 15ᶜᵐ.

Three acts. Dedication, argument, cast, name of the composer, Fortunato **Chelleri** and notice to the reader. He is informed (in the dedication) that this is

"la più fortunata composizione drammatica del Sig. Matteo Noris, intitolata la Penelope, la quale con tanto applauso nell' anno 1685 si vidde rappresentata nel Teatro di S. Gio. Chrisostomo."

and in the notice:

"Se la ritrovi in qualche parte mutata, e nell' arie, e nelli versi, non si è fatto ad altro fine, che per accomodarla, così all' uso moderno del teatro, come alla compagnia che deve rappresentarla." SCHATZ 1813

Penelope la casta. Drama per musica da rappresentarsi nel famosissimo Teatro Grimano in S. Gio. Chrisostomo. L'anno MDCLXXXV. Di Matteo Noris . . .

Venetia, Francesco Nicolini, 1685. 84 p. 14ᶜᵐ.

Three acts. Publisher's dedication dated Venice, January 28, 1685, argument, and scenario. The composer, Carlo **Pallavicino,** is not mentioned. SCHATZ 7730

La Penelope moderne. Piece en deux actes. Par Mʳˢ le S * * F * * & d'Or * *. Representée à la Foire Saint Laurent 1728.

Le Théâtre de la foire, Paris, 1731, t. vii, pl., 1 p. l., 84 p. 17ᶜᵐ.

By Le Sage, Fuzelier, and d'Orneval. Largely *en vaudevilles.* The airs, selected or composed and arranged by Jean Claude **Gillier,** the "compositeur" of the company, are printed at the end in the "Table des airs."
First performed September 6, 1728. ML 48.L2VII

Penelope nella partenza da Sparta. Dramma per musica per celebrare il felicissimo giorno natalizio di . . . Donna Maria I . . . li 17 decembre 1782.

[Lisbona], Nella stamperia reale, n. d. 32 p. 15ᶜᵐ.

One act with licenza. By Gaetano Martinelli. Cast, argument, and names of the composer, João de Sousa **Carvalho,** and the author. SCHATZ 1673

Penelope und Ulysses, ander theil, in einem sing-spiel vorgestellet.

Hamburg, Nicolaus Spieringk, 1702. Unpaged. 19ᶜᵐ.

Three acts. Neither the author, Friedrich Christian Bressand, is mentioned, nor the composer, Reinhard **Keiser.**
First performed at Brunswick, February, 1696. SCHATZ 5109

Il pentimento amoroso, ballet. *See* Astaritta's L'isola di Begodi.

Il pentimento generoso. Drama per musica da rappresentarsi nel Teatro di Sant' Angelo per ultim' opera del carnevale 1719. **Di** Domenico Lalli . . .

Venezia, Marino Rossetti, 1719. 55 p. 15ᶜᵐ.

Three acts. Author's signed preface, "Al lettore," cast, scenario, and name of the composer, Stefano Andrea **Fiorè,** "Milanese, Maestro di cappella attuale della Real Corte di Torino; & Accademico Filarmonico." SCHATZ 3194

Le pere rival. Piece en un acte. Representée sur le Théatre de l'Opera comique à la Foire S. Germain, le 24 mars 1734.

Le Théâtre de la foire, Paris, 1737, t. ix, 2, pl., [323]–383 p. 17ᶜᵐ.

By Carolet. Largely *en vaudevilles.* The airs, a few of which by **Corette,** are printed at the end of the volume in the "Table des airs."
First performed March 30, 1734. ML 48.L2X

Le peregrine erranti, ballet. *See* Salari's Il marchese Carbonaro.

Peribea in Salamina. Drama per musica da rappresentarsi nel Nuovo Teatro delle Grazie in Vicenza. Per la fiera del maggio 1712 . . .

Padova, Penada, 1712. 60 p. 15ᶜᵐ.

Three acts. Author not mentioned and unknown to Schatz. Dedicatory sonnet, argument, cast, scenario, and name of Carlo Francesco **Pollaroli** as the composer.
SCHATZ 8312

Perichitta e Bertone, intermezzi. *See* Mancini's L'Oronta.

Pericle effeminato. Drama per musica, di Giacomo Castoreo, per recitarsi nel Teatro di S. Appolinare . . .

Venetia, Giacomo Batti, 1653.   89 p. (incl. front.)   14^{cm}.

Three acts and prologue.   Author's dedication dated Venice, January 7, 1653, argument, and notice to the reader, in which he incidentally deplores "la deprovata corutella del secolo, nel quale la facoltà poetica, che altre volte fù stromento d' intimorir i tiranni con la civiltà de costumi, non trovi mezo per dilettarti che con la sfacciatagine de moti inhonesti . . ."
The composer, Francesco **Luccio,** is not mentioned.   SCHATZ 5747

Péronne sauvée, opera en quatre actes, représenté, pour la première fois, par l'Académie-royale de musique, le mardi 27 mai 1783.

Paris, P. de Lormel, 1783.   65 p.   23½^{cm}.

With cast and "Avertissement."   "Les paroles sont de M. de S * * *Sauvigny].
La musique est de M. **Dezède.**"   SCHATZ 2526

Persée, tragedie.   Representée par l'Academie royale de musique. Suivant le copie imprimée.   A Paris.

[Amsterdam, Antoine Schelte], 1685.   60 p. (incl. front.)   13½^{cm}.

Prologue and five acts.   Neither Quinault, nor **Lully** mentioned.

ML 50.2.P33L9

— Persée, tragedie representée par l'Academie royale de musique l'an 1682.   Les paroles de M. Quinault, & la musique de M. de Lully. XIV. opera.

n. i., n. d.   front., 299–368 p.   14^{cm}.   (Recueil général des opéra, t. ii, Paris, 1703).

Detached copy.   Prologue and five acts.
First performed, as indicated, April 17, 1682.   SCHATZ 5769
                                      Second copy.   ML 48.R4

— Persée, tragedie representée par l'Académie royale de musique, le 17 avril 1682. & ensuite à Versailles au mois de Juin.

Le théatre de Monsieur Quinault, Paris, 1739, t. v., pl., p. [12]–193. 17^{cm}.

Prologue and five acts.   **Lully** is not mentioned.   PQ 1881.A1   1739

— Arlequin Persée.   Comedie représentée pour la premiere fois par les Comédiens italiens ordinaires du roi, le vendredi 18. décembre 1722.

Les parodies du Nouveau Théatre italien, Nouv. éd., Paris, Briasson, 1738, t. ii, [87]–150 p.

Three acts.   By Fuzelier (*see* t. I).   The airs and vaudeville used are printed at the end of the volume in the "Table des airs" (60 p.).   ML 48.P3

Persée & Andromede, ballet.   *See* Traetta's Siroe.

Perseo.   Drama per musica di Aurelio Aureli, favvola decimaterza. Rappresentato in musica nel Teatro Grimano l'anno 1665 . . .

Venetia, Francesco Nicolini, 1665.   front., 6 p. l., 79 p.   14^{cm}.

Three acts and prologue.   Author's dedication, argument, and scenario.   The composer, Andrea **Mattioli,** is not mentioned.   SCHATZ 6103

Perseo trionfante.   Dramma musicale.

Girolamo Bartolommei Smeducci, Drammi musicali morali, Firenze, 1656, v. i, p. [101]–130.   23^{cm}.

Prologue and three acts.   Argument and allegoria.   ML 49.A2B3

Perseus and Andromeda with The rape of Colombine: or, the flying lovers. The five interludes; three serious, and two comic. The serious compos'd by Mons. Roger, and the comic by Mr. John Weaver, dancing masters. As it is perform'd at the Theatre Royal in Drury-Lane. The cloaths, scenes and machines, entirely new.

London, W. Trott, 1728. 5 p. l., 12 p. 19^{cm}.

Cast, argument, description, and the words of "A song sung by Mr. Ray to the tune of *Thomas I cannot* . . . the words by Mr. Weaver—In London Town there liv'd, well known." This was composed by John Christopher **Pepusch**, as perhaps the entire work. In his "History of the mimes and pantomimes" (1728) John Weaver calls "Perseus and Andromeda" "A burlesque entertainment in dancing, in grotesque characters. Composed by J. Weaver and first performed in Drury-Lane, 1716."

LONGE 191

— **Perseus and Andromeda.** As it is performed at the Theatre Royal in Lincoln's-Inn-Fields. Adorn'd with copper-plates . . . The fourth edition; to which is added the Sailor's ballad.

London, Tho. Wood, 1730. 5 p. l. (incl. 2 pl.), 18 p. 19^{cm}.

One act. Cast and argument. Neither author nor composer mentioned.

LONGE 40

Il pertinace. Drama per musica da rappresentarsi nel famoso Teatro. Vendramino di San Salvatore l'anno 1689 . . .

Venetia, Nicolini, 1689. 66 p. 14½^{cm}.

Three acts. Publisher's dedication, argument, and scenario. Neither the composer, Paolo **Biego**, nor the librettist is mentioned. Schatz considers Pietro d'Averara as the librettist, but Wotquenne points out that "Il pertinace" is not the same as d'Averara's "Publio Elio Pertinace."

SCHATZ 1016

The Peruvian; a comic opera, in three acts. As performed at the Theatre Royal Covent-Garden. By a lady. The music chiefly composed by Mr. Hook.

London, J. Bell, 1786. 3 p. l., 81 p. 21^{cm}.

Cast and Advertisement, in which the unidentified author calls herself "not a resident of England."

First performed March 18, 1786, as indicated.

LONGE 97

Li pescatori, ballet. *See* Sarti's La giardiniera brillante.

La pescatrice. L. T. of Pietro Guglielmi's La bella pescatrice.

La pescatrice ovvero L'erede riconosciuta. Farsa per musica a quattro voci da rappresentarsi nella Real Villa del Poggio a Cajano nella primavera dell' anno 1772.

Firenze, Stecchi e Pagani, 1772. 1 p. l., 56 p. 17^{cm}.

Two acts. Niccolò **Piccinni** is mentioned as the composer. Author unknown.

First performed at Rome, Teatro Capranica, January 9, 1766. SCHATZ 8102

— **La pescatrice.** Operetta per musica da rappresentarsi ne' Teatri privilegiati di Vienna il carnovale dell' anno 1769.

Vienna, Ghelen, n. d. 46 p. 17^{cm}.

Two acts. Niccolò **Piccinni** is mentioned as the composer.

First performed at Vienna, Kärnthnerthor Theater, January 23, 1769.

SCHATZ 8103

La pescatrice—Continued.

— L'erede riconosciuta. Dramma giocoso per musica da rappresentarsi nel nobilissimo Teatro di S. Benedetto l'autunno dell' anno MDCCLXXI.

Venezia, Modesto Fenzo, n. d. 55 p. 17½^{cm}.

Expanded to three acts. Cast, scenario, and names of Niccolò **Piccinni** and Salvador **Perillo** as the composers, the latter being responsible for the additional music only. This consists of: "Ajuto buona gente" and "Deh concedi, o caro padre" (I, 1), "Vi vuol altro che bravati" (I, 4), "Un pensier mi nasce in testa" (I, 5), "Un amante rispettoso" (I, 7, "Quella stizza lascia andare" (II, 1), "Voi altre femmine" (II, 2), "Delle donne il core è fatto" (II, 3), "Oh che giorno di contento" (II, 4), "Dal tuo costante amore" (II, 11), "Più non sento gli anni miei" (III, 3). With the opera were performed Giovanni Antonio Sacco's ballets, "Pane e Siringa" and "La sposa gronlandese," of which short descriptions, without name of the composers of the music, are given in the libretto.　　　　　　　　　　SCHATZ 8104

— Das fischermaedchen. Ein singspiel in zween aufzuegen. Auf dem hochfuerstlich Thurn- und Taxischen Theater allhier aufgefuehrt.

Regensburg, Gedruckt mit Breitfeldischen schriften, n. d. 48 p. 16^{cm}.

Two acts. Translator unknown.
First performed, as indicated, carnival, 1777.　　　　　　　SCHATZ 8105

La **pescatrice fedele.** L. T. of Anfossi's La vera costanza.

La **pescatrice fedele,** ballet. *See* Boroni's Le orfane svizzere.

La **pescatrice in Jassa,** ballet. *See* Gardi's Il contravveleno in Jassa.

Le **pescatrici.**

[*107]–160 p. 16½^{cm}. (Carlo Goldoni, Opere drammatiche giocose, t. iii, Torino, 1757.)*

Three acts. First composed by *Bertoni*, as below.　　　　ML 49.A2G6

— Le **pescatrici.** Dramma di tre atti in musica.

Carlo Goldoni, Opere teatrali, Venezia, Zatta e figli, 1788–95, v. 44, [233]–286 p. 18^{cm}.　　　　　　　　　　　　　　　PQ

Le **pescatrici.** Dramma giocoso per musica da rappresentarsi nel Teatro posto in contrada di San Samuele. Il carnovale dell' anno 1752 . . .

Venezia, Giuseppe Bettinelli, 1752. 59 p. 15^{cm}.

Three acts. Impresario's dedication, dated Venice, December 24, 1751, cast, scenario. Neither the author, Carlo Goldoni, is mentioned, nor the composer, Ferdinando Giuseppe **Bertoni.**　　　　　　　　　　SCHATZ 921

[Le **pescatrici.**]

Torino, 1754. 62 p. 15^{cm}.

Title page missing.
Three acts. By Carlo Goldoni, who is not mentioned. Cast, scenario, and name of Rocca **Gioanetti** as the composer.
First performed at Turin, Teatro del principe di Carignano, spring, 1754.
　　　　　　　　　　　　　　　　　　　　　　SCHATZ 3831

Das **Petermaennchen.** Ein schauspiel mit gesang in vier aufzuegen. Nach der geister geschichte des herrn Spiess bearbeitet von Carl Friedrich Hensler. Die musik dazu ist ganz neu verfasst von herrn Joseph Weigl . . . Erster theil.

Wien, Johann Baptist Wallishauser, 1794. 83 p. 18^{cm}.

This copy lacks the front. ("Ich will indess sein vater seyn"). A second copy (Schatz 11942a) contains it, but the copy was cut down to 16^{cm}. by a binder.
First performed at Vienna, Theater in der Leopoldstadt, April 8, 1794.

SCHATZ 10942

— Das **Petermaennchen.** Ein schauspiel mit gesang in vier aufzuegen . . . Zweyter theil.

Wien, Johann Baptist Wallishauser, 1794. 75 p. 18^{cm}.

First performed at Vienna, Theater in der Leopoldstadt, May 20, 1794.

SCHATZ 10943

Peters Bryllup. Et syngespil i to akter ved Thomas Thaarup. Sat i musik af hr. capelmester J. A. P. Schulz.

Kiøbenhavn, Johan Frederik Schultz, 1793. 60 p. 18^{cm}.

First performed at Copenhagen, Royal Theatre, December 12, 1793. SCHATZ 9726

Le **petit commissionnaire.** A. T. of Bruni's Claudine.

Le **petit-maître en province,** comédie en un acte et en vers, avec des ariettes. Par M. Harny. La musique est de M. Alexandre. Représentée pour la premiere fois par les Comédiens italiens ordinaires du roi, le 7 octobre 1765.

Paris, la veuve Duchesne, 1765. 38 p. 19$\frac{1}{2}$^{cm}.

Cast and author's preface which reads:
"Je ne dois sans doute qu'au jeu des acteurs le succès de cette piece. Je saisis avec plaisir l'occasion de leur en marquer ma reconnoissance. Quelques personnes cependant ont trouvé mauvais que j'aie fait représenter cette comédie sur le Théâtre Italien. Il faut me justifier. Les acteurs de ce théâtre se font un devoir d'accueillir, d'encourager les auteurs; on n'y connoît point l'usage de faire desirer pendant deux ans l'honneur d'une lecture, l'homme de lettres n'est point obligé de jouer le rôle de suppliant dans l'antichambre d'un semainier. Ces raisons sont suffisantes pour un homme qui ne se sent point d'humeur à souffrir les tracasseries, & sur-tout l'humiliation. On peut y joindre cependant des vues particulieres. La musique paroît aujourd'hui tenir le premier rang dans nos spectacles; sero tice déplaire au public que de tâcher de l'allier avec la peinture de nos moeurs? Pourquoi nous borner aux païsans? Pourquoi ne pas essayer tous les tous? Quittons le village, la ville nous offrira plus d'un tableau intéressant. J'espere que l'on ne prendra point ceci pour un trait de satyre contre les auteurs qui n'ont travaillé que dans le premier genre. Un talent en annonce toujours un autre. L'auteur de *la Chercheuse d'Esprit* a fait *l'Anglois a Bordeaux*. Chacune de ces pièces est un chef-d'oeuvre. On me pardonnera aisément de citer par préférence M. Favart. Il est permis à un écolier d'avoir quelque prédilection pour son maître. C'est lui qui m'a donné les premieres leçons de l'art dramatique. *Bastien* a été fait sous ses yeux. Il est facile de s'en appercevoir, & cette derniere piece vaudroit sans doute beaucoup mieux, si j'avois pu profiter de ses avis pendant le cours de la composition. Quelques critiques m'ont accusé d'avoir copié le méchant dans la scene où le marquis tourne en ridicule le baron & la baronne. Ils se sont trompés. Cette situation est tirée du conte des *Rémois* de la Fontaine." ML 50.2.P337A4

— Le **petit-maître en province,** comedie en un acte et en vers, avec des ariettes par Mr. Harny. Représentée pour la premiere fois par les Comédiens italiens ordinaires du Roi, le 7 octobre 1765. La musique est de Mr. Alexandre.

Paris, la veuve Duchesne, 1771. 40 p. 18$\frac{1}{2}$^{cm}.

One act. Cast and the music of some of the airs, as follows: "Les dehors les plus seduisants," "Les premiers moments d'une belle," "L'eclat est le moyen de plaire."

SCHATZ 159

Le petit-maitre malgré lui. A. T. of Favart's La répétition nterrompue.

Le petit matelot, ou Le mariage im-promptu, comédie, en un acte en prose, mêlée de chant. Par le C. Pigault-Lebrun. Musique du C. Gavau [!]. Représentée pour la première fois sur le Théâtre de la rue Faydau, le 7 nivôse, l'an 4me de la République.

　　Paris, Huet, 1796. 46 p. 20ᶜᵐ.

Préface. Cast. Composed by Pierre **Gaveaux**. The date in the title would be December 28, 1795, but is probably a misprint for 17 nivose, which would be January 7, 1796, in accordance with the date in the printed score and accepted by the reference books.　　　　　　　　　　　　　　　　　　　ML 50.2.P34G2

— Le **petit matelot,** ou Le mariage impromptu, comédie en un acte et en prose, mêlée de chant; par le citoyen Pigault-Lebrun, musique du citoyen Gavau [!] Représentée pour la première fois, sur le Théâtre de la rue Faydeau, le 7 nivôse, l'an quatrième de la République.

　　Paris, Huet, 1796. 40 p. 19½ᶜᵐ.

The same cast, preface, and text which is printed in a somewhat smaller type than the other edition of 1796.　　　　　　　　　　　　SCHATZ 3641

— Le **petit matelot,** ou Le mariage impromptu. Comédie en un acte et en prose; mêlée de chants. Par le C. Pigaut-Lebrun. Musique du C. Gavau.[!] Représentée pour la premiere fois sur le Théâtre de la rue Feideau, le 7 nivôse, l'an 4e de la République.

　　Avignon, les frères Bonnet, l'an cinquième de la République [1796–97]. *32 p. 20ᶜᵐ.*　　　　　　　　　　　　　　　　ML 50.2.P34G22

La petite Nannette. Opéra-comique, en deux actes, représentée pour la première fois à Paris, au Théatre Feydeau, le 19 frimaire, an 5me. (Vendredi 9 décembre 1796, vieux style) Paroles et musique du Cousin Jacques . . .

　　Paris, Moutardier, an V.—1797. 75 p. 19½ᶜᵐ.

Cast.　　　　　　　　　　　　　　　　　　　　　SCHATZ 703

Les petites maisons. Piece en un acte. Representée à la Foire S. Germain. 1732.

　　Le Théâtre de la foire, Paris, 1737, t. ix, 2, pl., [433]–488 p. 17ᶜᵐ.

By Carolet. Partly *en vaudevilles.* The airs are printed at the end of the volume in the "Table des airs." Composed according to Parfaict, by **Travenol.**

　　　　　　　　　　　　　　　　　　　　　　ML 48.L2X

Les petits comédiens, opera-comique en un acte; représenté pour la premiere fois sur le Théâtre de la Foire, en 1731.

　　Charles François Pannard, Théâtre, Paris, Duchesne, 1763, v. 2, [129]–178 p. 17ᶜᵐ.

In prose and vaudevilles. Composer not recorded by Parfaict, etc. PQ 2019.P3

Petrine. Parody of Lully's Proserpine.

Die pfleg-tochter. Tr. of Garcia's La pupilla.

Pflicht und liebe im streit. A. T. of Mederitsch' Rose.

Phaedon und Naide, oder Der redende Baum. Ein singspiel in zwey aufzuegen.

83 p. 14½ᶜᵐ. (Johann Georg Jacobi, Theatralische Schriften Nachtrag zu seinen saemtlichen werken, Leipzig, G. J. Goeschen, 1792.)

First performed with music by Franz Friedrich Siegismund August, reichsfreiherr **Boecklin von und zu Boecklinsau,** at Freiburg i/Br., Stadttheater, January 5, 1790.
SCHATZ 1113

Phaeton. Tr. of Graun's Fetonte.

Phaeton. Tr. of Jommelli's Fetonte.

Phaëton, tragedie en musique, representée par l'Academie royale de musique devant Sa Majesté à Versailles, le sixième jour de janvier mil six cens quatre-vingts-trois. Suivant la copie imprimée, a Paris.

[Amsterdam, Antoine Schelte], 1683. 58 p. (incl. front.) 13½ᶜᵐ.
Prologue and five acts. Neither Quinault, the author, is mentioned, nor **Lully,** the composer.
ML 50.2.P347L9

— **Phaëton,** tragedie en musique, representée par l'Academie royale de musique. Devant Sa Majesté à Versailles. Suivant la copie imprimée à Paris.

[Amsterdam, Antoine Schelte], 1686. 58 p. (incl. front.) 13½ᶜᵐ.
Prologue and five acts. Neither the author, Philippe Quinault, is mentioned, nor the composer, Jean Baptiste de **Lully.**
First performed at Versailles, January 6, 1683; at Paris, Académie royale de musique, April 27, 1683.
ML 50.2.P347L92

— **Phaeton,** tragedie representée par l'Academie royale de musique l'an 1683. Les paroles sont de M. Quinault, & la musique de M. de Lully, XV. opera.

n. i., n. d. 14ᶜᵐ. pl., 369–430 p. (Recueil général des opéra, t. ii, Paris, 1703.)
Detached copy. Five acts and prologue.
SCHATZ 5777
Second copy. ML 48.R4

— **Phaëton,** tragedie en musique. Representée devant le roi au mois de Janvier 1683. & ensuite par l'Académie de musique le 27 avril suivant.

Philippe Quinault, Theatre, Paris, 1739, t. v., pl., p. [195]–251. 17ᶜᵐ.
Prologue and five acts. **Lully** is not mentioned.
PQ 1881.A1 1739

— **Arlequin Phaëton,** parodie. Par les Srs. Dominique & Romagnesi . . . Représentée pour la premiere fois, par les Comédiens italiens ordinaires du roi, le 22 février 1731.

Les parodies du Nouveau théâtre italien, Nouv. éd., Paris, 1738, t. iv, [271]–312 p. 16½ᶜᵐ.
One act. Called in the table of contents the "second parodie" of the opera, but, according to Wotquenne, the third. The airs and vaudeville printed at end of the volume in the "Table des airs" (92 p.).
ML 48.P3

Die phantasten. Tr. of Paisiello's I visionari.

Phaon, drame lyrique. En deux actes, en vers mêlé d'ariettes, représenté devant Leurs Majestés, à Choisy en Septembre 1778.

[Paris], P. R. C. Ballard, n. d. 3 p. l., 46 p. 20ᶜᵐ.
Two acts. By Claude Henri Watelet, who is not mentioned. Cast and name of Niccolò **Piccinni** as the composer.
SCHATZ 8158

Pharamundus, in einer opera vorgestellet auf dem grossen Braunschweigischen Theatro in der Laurentii Messe, anno 1746.

Wolffenbuettel, Christian Bartsch wittwe, n. d.

Three acts. A German version of Aposto Zeno's "Faramondo," with the Italian text of the arias added to the German. Argument and note that the music "anlangend die symphonia und die meisten arien" was composed by Johann Adolph **Hasse.**

First performed as indicated, August 15, 1746. SCHATZ 4553

Pharao und Joseph, in einem sing-spiele auf dem Hamburgischen Schau-platze vorgestellet. Im jahr 1728.

[Hamburg] Gedruckt mit Stromerschen schrifften, n. d. Unpaged. 18½ cm.

In five acts, by Johann Samuel Müller. With cast and names of the author and of Antonio **Caldara** as composer of the arias, to which the Italian text has been added. Really a free translation of Zeno's "Gianguir," performed, with Caldara's music, at Vienna in 1724. SCHATZ 1483

Le **Pharaon.** Pièce d'un acte. Par Monsieur F * * *. Représentée à la Foire de Saint Germain 1717.

Le Théâtre de la foire, Paris, 1737, t. ii, pl., [399]-448 p. 17 cm.

By Fuzelier. The airs, selected or composed and arranged by Jean Claude **Gillier,** the "compositeur" of the theatre, are printed at the end of the volume in the "Table des airs." ML 48.L2II

Pharnaces: an opera. Altered from the Italian. By Thomas Hull. As it is performed at the Theatre Royal in Drury-Lane . . .

London, J. and R. Tonson and T. Lownds, 1765. vi, [2], 39 p. 19 cm.

Three acts. Cast and dedication, dated London, January 1, 1765. The composer, William **Bates,** is not mentioned. Presumably altered from Lucchini's "Farnace."
LONGE 50
Second copy. LONGE 203

Pharnaces: or, The revenge of Athridates. An English opera. As it was to have been performed at the Theatre Royal, Edinburgh. The music selected from the most capital composers, and adapted by Mr. Tenducci. The third edition.

Edinburgh, Printed by Martin & Wotherspoon, 1769. 47 p. 16½ cm.

Three acts. Cast and this note:
"As Mr. Gilson is extremely ill, the part of Athridates is obliged to be left out, and part of Pompey—and of Gilades—and all the recitatives (except Mr. Tenducci's, with accompanyments), as they would be tedious to the audience."
The original text presumably was Antonio Maria Lucchini's "Farnace." The English version is not that by Thomas Hull. LONGE 277

Phebe or The beggar's wedding. *See* The beggar's wedding.

Phedre, tragédie-lyrique, en trois actes; représentée à Fontainebleau le 26 octobre 1786. Remise sur le Theatre de l'Academie de musique le mardi 21 novembre 1786. Paroles du Sieur * * * Musique du Sieur Le Moine.

Bordeaux, Philippean, 1786. 28 p. 21 cm.

Text by François Benoit Hoffman. ML 50.2.P35L2

Le **Phénix.** A. T. of La bonne femme.

Philander. A dramatic pastoral. By the author of the Female Quixote.

London, A. Millar, 1758. vii, [8]–48 p. 19^{cm}.

Two acts. Dedication, dated London, November 20, 1757, by the author, Charlotte Lenox. No composer and no performance recorded by Clarence. Longe 52

Philander. Tr. of Porpora's Filandro.

Philémon et Baucis. A. T. of Les bons et les méchans.

Philemon und Baucis, oder Gastfreiheit und Armuth. Eine original-operette in zween aufzuegen: von Johann Christoph v. Zabuesnig. Aufgefuehrt auf der Schaubuehne zu Augsburg unter der direktion herrn Voltolini.

Augsburg, Conrad Heinrich Stage, 1792. 61 p. 17^{cm}.

The composer, Johann Christian **Kaffka,** is not mentioned.
First performed, as indicated, 1792. Schatz 4985

Philippe et Georgette.

One act. By Monvel; music by **Dalayrac.**
First performed at Paris, December 28, 1791.
Not in L. of C.

— Gesaenge aus der oper: **Philipp und Georgette,** in einem aufzuge, nach dem franzoesischen singspiele gleichen namens bearbeitet von Herklots. Die musik ist von d'Alairac.

Hamburg, Rabe und Freystatzky wittwe, 1798. 16 p. 15^{cm}.

First performed at Hamburg, Theater beim Gänsemarkt, October 2, 1798.

Schatz 2372

Phillis at court; a comic opera of three acts. As it is now performing, with great applause, at the Theatre-Royal in Crow-street, Dublin. The music by Signor Tomaso Giordani.

London, J. Williams, 1767. 40 p. 19½^{cm}.

Cast and Advertisement:
"It may be proper to take notice, that the title given this piece, at present, is copied from the French of Monsieur Favart; whose 'Caprices d'amour, ou Ninette a la cour,' the author, Mr. Lloyd, confesses was the ground-work of his piece, called the 'Capricious lovers.'
"In order to make that piece entertaining, (and in conformity with the Italian burletta) musical dialogues have been added towards the end of each act; these are known among the Italians by the word *finale,* and are deemed indispensably necessary in an entertainment of this sort. It is now presented to the public with many alterations. Several airs have been added, others again suppressed; and adapted to the talents of the different performers, some of them being foreigners . . . it was necessary to alter the title of this opera, to that of *Phillis at court,* on account of the alterations . . ."

First performed, as indicated, February 25, 1767 (Lawrence). Longe 36

Philomele, tragedie, représentée pour la première fois par l'Academie royale de musique, le 20. du mois d'octobre 1705.

Amsterdam, Henri Schelte, 1706. 68 (incl. front.), [3] p. 14^{cm}.

Five acts, prologue and avertissement. Cast. Neither the author, Roy ("Cet ouvrage est l'essai d'une Muse naissante") is mentioned, nor the composer, **La Coste.** ML 50.2.P36L2

Philomele—Continued.

— **Philomele**, tragedie représentée par l'Académie royale de musique l'an 1705. Remise au theatre le mardy 8me octobre 1709. Les paroles de M. Roy & la musique de M. de la Coste. LXV. opera.

n. i., n. d. 14cm. front., 64 p. (Recueil général des opéra, t. ix, Paris, 1710.)

Detached copy. Five acts and prologue. Cast.   SCHATZ 5356
                                        Second copy. ML 48.R4

— **Philomele**, tragedie representée par l'Academie royale de musique de Paris, les vingt octobre 1705, huit octobre 1709, & dix-neuf octobre 1734. Et par l'Academie royale de musique de Lyon en 1742.

Lyon, Aimé Delaroche, 1742. 67 p. 23cm.

Five acts, without prologue. Avertissement and cast. Neither Roy nor **La Coste** are mentioned. The text is the same as in the ed. of the Recueil des opéra, 1710.
                                                SCHATZ 5356a

— **Philomele**, parodie en trois actes; précédée d'un prologue, donnée au Théâtre italien en 1723.

Alexis Piron, Oeuvres complettes, Liege, 1776, v. 5, [321]-392 p. 17½cm.

In prose and vaudevilles. A parody of **Lacoste's** opera of the same title.
First performed, according to Parfaict, who does not record a composer, June 12, 1723.   PQ 2019.P6

Le **philosophe bridé**. A. T. of Aristote amoureux.

Die **philosophen**. Tr. of Paisiello's I filosofi immaginari.

Phoebe. A pastoral opera. Set to music by Dr. Greene.
London, n. publ., 1748. 27 p. 20½cm.
Three acts. The author, James Hoadley, is not mentioned.
No performance recorded by Schatz.   LONGE 274

La **pianella perduta**. A. T. of the ballet L'inverno.

La **pianella perduta**, ballet. *See* Paër's La Rossana.

La **pianella perduta**, ballet. *See* Paisiello's Le gare generose.

La **pianella persa**. A. T. of L'inverno.

La **pianella persa**. Farsa giocosa per musica d'un atto solo da rappresentarsi nel Teatro della magnifica Accademia Filarmonica di Verona nella corrente primavera . . .
Verona, Dionigi Ramanzini, 1798. 36 p. 18cm.
By Giuseppe Palomba, who is not mentioned. Dedication, cast and name of Francesco **Gardi** as composer ("La musica è tutta nuova").
First performed at Venice, Teatro di S. Moisè, fall of 1797.   ML 50.2.P38G2

Airs, duetts, and chorusses, arrangement of scenery, and sketch of the pantomime, entitled The **picture of Paris**. Taken in the year 1790. As performed at the Theatre-Royal, Covent-Garden.
London, T. Cadell, 1790. 20 p. 20cm.
Two acts. Cast. Neither the author of the dialogue and songs, Merry, is mentioned, nor the compiler-composer, William **Shield**. The title page of Longman and

The picture of Paris—Continued.

Broderip's vocal score says "part . . . taken from the celebrated opera of *Amphion*, composed by the Sigr. **Naumann** and the rest composed by William **Shield**." It is interesting to note that he introduced *Ça ira*.

First performed December 20, 1790.   LONGE 207

La piece a deux acteurs, opera-comique en un acte, avec un prologue, représenté pour la premiere fois sur le Théâtre de la Foire, en 1738.

Charles François Pannard, Théâtre, Paris, Duchesne, 1763, v. 3, [139]–202 p. 17ᶜᵐ.

In prose and vaudevilles. According to Parfaict, who does not record a composer and dates the first performance February 6, 1738, the original title was "L'armoire ou La piece a deux acteurs."   PQ 2019.P3

Pierrot Romulus ou Le ravisseur poli. *See* L'ombre du cocher poète.

La pietà di Sabina. Drama musicale.

G. A. Moniglia, Poesie drammatiche, seconda parte, Firenze, Cesare e Francesco Bindi, 1690, p. [149]–216. 24ᶜᵐ.

Three acts. Argument with remark:
"Questo drama fu composto per servire alla serenissima granduchessa Vittoria di Toscana, e messo in musica dal padre Lorenzo **Cattani** . . . ma per ancora non è comparito su le scene, nè alle stampe."   ML 49.A2M7

La pietà inaspettata, ballet. *See* Bertoni's Andromaca.

La pietra simpatica. Commedia per musica da rappresentarsi nel Teatro de' Fiorentini per terz' opera del corrente anno 1796.

Napoli, n. publ., 1796. 59 p. 15½ᶜᵐ.

Two acts. By Giambattista Lorenzi, who is not mentioned. Cast and name of Silvestro di **Palma** as composer.
First performed, according to Schatz, at the same theatre, fall of 1795.

ML 50.2.P4P2

Pietro il Grande ossia Il trionfo dell' innocenza. Dramma eroico del Signor Antonio Simon Sografi . . . da rappresentarsi nel Teatro privato di Sua eccellenza Co. Alessandro Pepoli la primavera dell' anno 1793.

Venezia, Dalla Nuova tipografia, n. d. 48 p. 17½ᶜᵐ.

Three acts. Name of Giuseppe **Rossi** as composer and author's dedication to conte Pepoli, from which it appears that the drama was ordered by the count for his private theatre and that he performed the part of Alessio. Says Sografi:
"Desidero che in qualche parte egli possa metter in mostra quel singolare talento, che tra i molti e vari la fa distinguere nella bell' arte del canto. Conoscendo la di Lei somma capacità nella teatrale declamazione, spero di non essermi ingannato nello scriverle la parte di Alessio."   SCHATZ 8893

Pigmalion, ou La statue animée, opera-comique en vaudevilles; représenté pour la premiere fois sur le Théâtre de la Foire, en 1733.

Charles François Pannard, Théâtre, Paris, Duchesne, 1763, v. 2, [227]–280 p. 17ᶜᵐ.

According to Parfaict, who does not record a composer, the text was written jointly by Pannard and Laffichard, first performed as "Pygmalion" on March 26, 1735 [!] and revived on March 6, 1736, under the above title.   PQ 2019.P3

Pigmalion oder Die reformation der liebe, ein lyrisches drama in zwey handlungen von Carl Herklots.

Berlin, Friedrich Maurer, 1794. front., 6, [2], 127 p. 16^{cm}.

No composer or performance recorded by Schatz. In his "Vorbericht" of date "Ostermesse 1794" Herklots says that his play is clearly intended for "musikalische composition," but that the possibility of "theatralische darstellung" is questionable, though he kept this possibility constantly in mind. He continues by saying what his main object was

"Seine hauptabsicht was die, einem gefühlvollen tonsezzer gelegenheit zu ver-schaffen, sein talent für richtigen ausdruck wechselnder leidenschaften zu zeigen, und diese absicht verräth schon zur genüge, dass er sich nicht arien nach italiänischem zuschnitt, sondern jene edlere gattung von tonkunst gedacht hat, von deren herz-erschütternden wirkung der unsterbliche Gluck seinen landsleuten so vortreffliche muster hinterliess."

"Der verfasser hat die stellen, die er für eigentlichen gesang, und die er für rezi-tation bestimmte, durch grössere und kleinere drucklettern bezeichnen lassen, aus gründen aber, hat er nur den drey hauptpersonen die leztere art des vortrags gegeben, und überdem vieles, was seinem inhalt gemäss, rezitativ seyn müsste, nach art der, in italiänischen opern gewöhnlichen schlussscenen, lyrisch behandelt; durch welche vermischung er keiner inkonsequenz schuldig zu seyn glaubt, da Reichardt, Salieri, und andere denkende componisten schon praktisch gezeigt haben, dass diese form den edlen und richtigen musikalischen ausdruck keinesweges ausschliesst."

                ML 50.2.P411

Pigmalion, acte de ballet, représenté devant La Majesté, à Fon-tainebleau, le samedi 24 octobre 1772.

[Paris], Pierre Robert Christophe Ballard, 1772. 18 p. 18$\frac{1}{4}$^{cm}.

Cast and names of Houdar de La Motte as author of the text, of Jean Philippe **Rameau** as composer, and of de Laval as "composer " of the ballets. The text is Ballot de Sauvot's revised version under the above title of the fifth entrée, "La sculpture," in de La Motte's ballet text "Le triomphe des arts."   ML 48.B2

Pigmalion, monologue. Par Jean Jacques Rousseau.

n. i., n. d., 1772. 21 p. 18^{cm}.

The text is followed by a folded sheet of engraved music, with title "Airs [d]e Pigmalion." First comes an "Andantino," air with acc., with name of Jean Jacques **Rousseau** as composer, and below this an "Andante par M. **Coignet.** Doit etre belle" and "Amoroso par M. **Coignet.** De ce qui n'est pas," both unaccompanied. Compare next entry.   ML 50.2.P41R7

— **Pygmalion,** par J. J. Rousseau, scène lyrique.

"A Genève, et se vend à Lyon, ainsi que la musique, chez Castaud . . . MDCCLXXXVI." 16 p. 20^{cm}.

With publisher's preface, in which this quotation from a letter to him by Coignet: "Ce n'est point un opéra . . . l'auteur l'a intitulée *Scène lyrique:* Les paroles ne se chantent point, & la musique ne sert qu'à remplir les intervalles des repos néces-saires à la déclamation. Rousseau vouloit donner par ce spectacle, une idée de la mélopée des Grecs, de leur ancienne déclamation théatrale . . . Je dois cependant à l'exacte vérité d'annoncer que dans les vingt-six ritournelles qui composent la musique de ce drame, il y en a deux que Rousseau a faite lui-même . . . Je déclare que l'andante de l'ouverture, & que le premier morceau de l'interlocution qui carac-terise le travail de Pygmalion, appartiennent à Rousseau. Le surplus de la musique est de M. Coignet, amateur."

First performed at Paris, Théâtre de la Comédie-Française, October 30, 1775.

              SCHATZ 2095

— **Pygmalion,** eine lyrische handlung aus dem franzoesischen des hrn. J. J. Rousseau mit begleitung der musik des hrn. Coignet, uebersetzt und mit taenzen vermehrt fuer die National-schaubühne zu Mannheim.

Mannheim, C. F. Schwan, 1778. 19 p. 16$\frac{1}{2}$^{cm}.

Translation by Otto Heinrich reichsfreiherr von Gemmingen, with "Inhalt."
First performed as indicated, March 29, 1778.   SCHATZ 2096

Il **Pigmalione,** ballet. *See* G. Giordani's Atalanta.

Pigmalione, ballet. *See* Mortellari's Arsace.

Die **pilgrime von Mecca** (Mekka). A. T. of Gluck's Die unvermutete zusammenkunft.

A **pill for the doctor:** or, The triple wedding. A musical entertainment, as performing at the Royalty-Theatre.

London, D. Steel, 1790. 17 p. 21ᶜᵐ.

One act. Cast. Neither author nor composer recorded by Clarence.

LONGE 273

Pimmalione. Scena drammatica tratta dalla Scena lirica di Monsieur J. J. Rousseau per li Signori Matteo Babini, e Carolina Pitrot dal Signor Sografi e posta in musica dal Signor Gian Battista Cimador da rappresentarsi la sera di 26 gennaro 1790.

Venezia, n. publ., 1790. xvi p. 18ᶜᵐ.

On p. iii: ". . . si è ritenuta soltanto l'idea principale del celebre autore."

SCHATZ 1903

Pimmalione vendicato. A. T. of the ballet Astarbea.

Pimpernelle und Marcantonius. Tr. of Hasse's Pimpinella e Marcantonio.

Pimpinella e Marcantonio. Intermezzi by Hasse for his opera Numa.

Pimpinone. Intermezzi comici musicali da rappresentarsi nel Teatro Tron di S. Cassiano l'autunno dell' anno MDCCVIII.

Venezia, Marino Rossetti, 1708. 12 p. 15ᶜᵐ.

Three parts. By Pietro Pariati, who is not mentioned. Composed by Tommaso **Albinoni,** performed with his opera, "Astarto," and bound in with its libretto (Schatz 110). The cast of the intermezzi there printed after the cast of the opera.

SCHATZ 111

— **Vespetta, e Pimpinone.** Intermezzi comici musicali. Da rappresentarsi la prima volte, che si esibisce il drama.

n. i., n. d. 16 p. 15ᶜᵐ.

Three parts. Cast.
Performed, with Tommaso **Albinoni's** opera, "I veri amici," at Munich October 24, 1722.

SCHATZ 100

Pirame et Thisbé, tragedie, représentée par l'Academie royale de musique, l'an 1726. Paroles de M. La Serre. Musique de Messieurs Francoeur & Rebel. CVII. opera.

n. i., n. d. pl., p. 61–122. (Recueil général des opera, t. 14, Paris, 1734.) 14ᶜᵐ.

Detached copy. Five acts and prologue.
First performed, as indicated, October 17, 1726.

SCHATZ 3336
Second copy. ML 48.R4

Pirame et Thisbé—Continued.

— **Pirame et Thisbé.** Par le Sr. R. R. * * * Représentée pour la premiere fois, par les Comédiens italiens ordinaires du roi, le 13 novembre 1726.

Les parodies du Nouveau théâtre italien, Nouv. éd., Paris, 1738, t. iii, [319]–366 p. 16½^{cm}.

One act. Parody, by Dominique, Romagnesi, and Riccoboni, of the opera. The airs and vaudeville printed at end of the volume in the "Table des airs" (84 p.).

ML 48.P3

— **Pirame et Thisbé**, tragedie. Représentée par l'Académie royale de musique de Lyon. Au mois de janvier de l'année 1741.

[Lyon], Aymé Delaroche, 1741. 59 p. 25^{cm}.

Five acts, without prologue. Neither the author, Jean Louis Ignace de La Serre, mentioned, nor the composers, François **Francoeur** and François **Rebel**.

ML 50.2.P43R2

Piramo e Tisbe. A. T. of the ballet Ninias tiranno di Babilonia punito da Zoroastro.

Piramo e Tisbe. Dramma per musica da rappresentarsi nel nobilissimo Teatro di S. Benedetto il carnovale [Jan.] dell' anno 1783 . . .

Venezia, Modesto Fenzo, 1783. 48 p. 17½^{cm}.

Three acts. Dedication by the author, Gaetano Sertor, argument, cast, scenario, and name of the composer, Francesco **Bianchi**. The ballets were called "Alonso e Cora. Estratto dalla storia dell' Incas del Signor di Marmontel," by Domenico Ricciardi; music ("tutta nuova") by Antonio Capuzzi. He is not mentioned as the composer of Ricciardi's second ballet, "Il marito ravveduto." SCHATZ 980

Piramo e Tisbe, ballet. *See* Colla's Didone.

Piramo e Tisbe, tragedia per musica in due atti da rappresentarsi nel Regio Teatro appresso Potsdam . . . nell' estate dell' anno MDCCLXXI.

Berlino, Haude e Spener, 1771. 61 p. 16^{cm}.

Two parts. Argument, cast, scenario, and names of Marco Coltellini as author, of Johann Adolf **Hasse** as composer. German title page "Piramus und Thisbe" and text face Italian.

First performed, as indicated, in March, 1771; at Vienna, Burgtheater, November, 1768. SCHATZ 4555

Piramo e Tisbe, ballet. *See* Piccinni's La Griselda.

Piramus und Thisbe. Tr. of Hasse's Piramo e Tisbe.

Piramus und Tisbe. Ein melo-drama. Bearbeitet nach Fabri dem juengern, und in die musik gesetzt von Franz Spindler.

n. i., n. d., 1788. p. [459]–476. 16^{cm}.

Detached copy.
First performed at Innsbruck, Hoftheater, 1785. SCHATZ 9977

Songs, duets, trios, chorusses, etc in the **Pirates.** An opera. In three acts, now performing at the King's Theatre, Haymarket.

London, E. Cox, 1792. 1 p. l., 29 p. 20½^{cm}.

Cast. Neither the author, James Cobb, is mentioned, nor the composer, Stephen **Storace**, who used parts of his opera "Gli equivoci."
First performed November 21, 1792 (Schatz), November 11 (Genest). LONGE 220

Pirithous, tragedie representée par l'Academie royale de musique l'an 1723. Paroles de M. de la Serre. Musique de M. Mouret. CI. opéra.

n. i., n. d. 1 pl., p. 195–262 (Recueil général des opéra, t. xiii, Paris, 1734). 14^{cm}.

Detached copy. Three acts and prologue. Seguineau is supposed to have been joint author with de La Serre.

First performed, according to Schatz, January 17, 1723, but the engraved score gives January 26, 1723.   Schatz 6743

Second copy. ML 48.R4

— Le **serdeau des théatres.** Comedie. Représentée pour la premiere fois, par les Comédiens italiens ordinaires du roi, le samedi 19. février 1723.

Les parodies du Nouveau théatre italien, Nouv. éd., Paris, Briasson, 1738, t. ii, 151–206 p. 16½^{cm}.

One act. By Fuzelier (*see* t. I). who in this comedy also parodied the opera "Pirithoüs." The airs and vaudeville used are printed at the end of the volume in the "Table des airs" (60 p.).   ML 48.P3

Pirrhus, tragedie representée par l'Academie royale de musique, l'an 1730. Paroles de M. Fermelhuis. Musique de M. Royer. CXIII. opera.

n. i., n. d. pl., 397–462 p. 14½^{cm}. (Recueil général des opéra, t. xiv, Paris, 1734.)

Detached copy. Five acts and prologue. Cast and avertissement.

First performed, as indicated, October 26, 1730 (Schatz), but the score says October 19, 1730.   Schatz 9110

Second copy. ML 48.R4

Pirro.

Apostolo Zeno, Poesie drammatiche, Venezia, 1744, t. vii, p. [201]–292 p. 19^{cm}.

Five acts. Argument and prefatory note, in which Zeno apologizes for this drama, practically written in ten days. No composer is mentioned. In the "Catalogo" at end of t. x, date and place of first ed. are given as Venice, 1704. (*See* below.)

ML 49.A2Z3

— **Pirro.** Pubblicato per la prima volta in Venezia 1704.

Apostolo Zeno, Poesie drammatiche, Orleans, 1785–86, t. iii, p. 88. 21^{cm}.

Five acts. Argument. No composer is mentioned.   ML 49.A2Z4

Pirro. Drama per musica da rappresentarsi nel Teatro di S. Angelo, l'anno MDCCIV . . .

Venezia, Marino Rossetti, 1704. 72 p. 12.*

Five acts. Dedication signed by A[postolo] Z[eno] as author, argument, scenario, notice to the reader, in which this drama is said to have been written in ten days. The composer, Giuseppe Antonio Vincenzo **Aldrovandini,** is not mentioned.

First performed during carnival, 1704, as indicated.   Schatz 137

Pirro. L. T. of Zingarelli's Pirro, rè di Epiro.

Pirro e Demetrio. O. T. of Morselli's text La forza dell' amicizia.

Pirro e Demetrio. Drama da rappresentarsi in musica nel famoso Teatro Grimano di S. Gio. Grisostomo l'anno 1690 . . .

Venetia, Nicolini, 1690. 70 p. 14ᶜᵐ.

Three acts. Dedication signed with the initials of the author, Adriano Morselli, argument, cast, scenario, and notice to the reader with name of [Giuseppe Felice] **Tosi** as the composer.　　　　　　　　　　　　SCHATZ 10378

Pirro rè di Epiro. Dramma per musica da rappresentarsi nel Teatro alla Scala il carnevale dell' anno 1792 . . .

Milano, Gio. Batista Bianchi, n. d. 67 p. 16ᶜᵐ.

Three acts. Impresario's dedication, dated Milan, December 26, 1791, argument, cast, scenario, name of Nicola Antonio **Zingarelli** as the composer, and note by the author, Giovanni de Gamerra (not mentioned by name) that this is his "Pirro" with "essential alterations," and he refers the reader to the seventh volume of his "nuovo Teatro" for the text in its original form.　　　　　　SCHATZ 11261

— **Il Pirro.** Dramma eroico per musica da rappresentarsi in Parma nel R. D. Teatro di Corte il carnevale dell' anno MDCCIC . . .

Parma, Stamperia Carmignani, n. d. 2 p. l., 48 p. 17½ᶜᵐ.

Three acts. By Giovanni de Gamerra, who is not mentioned. Cast and name of Nicola Antonio **Zingarelli** as the composer. On p. [43]–48, prefatory note, cast, and description of Giovanni Battista Checchi's "La generosità d'Alessandro ossia Apelle e Campaspe, ballo eroico-pantomimo," the composer of the music not being mentioned. First performed at Milan, Scala, December 26, 1791.　　　　SCHATZ 11253

Pisistrato. Dramma di tre atti per musica. Rappresentato per la prima volta in Venezia in tempo dell' Ascensione l'anno MDCCXXXVI.

Carlo Goldoni, Opere teatrali, Venezia, Zatta e figli, 1788–95, v. 36, [27]–66 p. 18½ᶜᵐ.

See also "La generosità politica."　　　　　　　　　　　　PQ

Il pittor burlato, ballet. *See* Anfossi's Zenobia in Palmira.

Il pittor parigino. Dramma gioccoso per musica da rappresentarsi nel Piccolo Teatro di S. A. E. di Sassonia.

Dresda, n. publ., 1782. 133 p. 15½ᶜᵐ.

Two acts. By Giuseppe Petrosellini (not mentioned). Name of the composer, **Cimarosa.** German title-page, "Der Pariser mahler," and text face Italian. First performed at Dresden February 22, 1783; at Rome, Teatro Valle dei Signori Capranica, January, 1781, as "Il pittore parigino."　　　　　SCHATZ 1969

— **Il pittor parigino.** Dramma giocoso per musica da rappresentarsi nel Reggio Teatro di S. Carlo della Principessa, l'autunno dell' anno 1794.

Lisbona, Simone Taddeo Ferreira, 1794. 169 p. 16ᶜᵐ.

Two acts. The author, Giuseppe Petrosellini, is not mentioned. Portuguese text faces Italian. Cast, scenario, and names of Domenico **Cimarosa** as composer of the opera; of Giuseppe Cajani of the music of his own "ballo eroico-magico-pantomimo intitolato Armida e Rinaldo."　　　　　　　　　　ML 50.2.P46C3

— **Il barone burlato.** Commedia per musica da rappresentarsi al Teatro Nuovo nell' inverno dell' anno 1784.

Napoli, n. publ., 1784. 54 p. 15ᶜᵐ.

A later version, in three acts, of "Il pittor parigino." Cast and name of the composer, **Cimarosa,** and the remark: "I pezzi nuovi sono del Sig. D. Francesco **Cipolla** . . . e si contrasegnano coll asterisco." These are: (I, 3) "Si discioglie, e si sconnette;" (I, 5) "La nostra signorina;" (I, 7) "Son modestina;" (II, 1) "Ad un amante savio;" (II, 2) "Semplicetta contadina," "Cricca mio, colla cognata." Giovanni Bonito is said to have made the changes in the libretto.　　　　SCHATZ 1979

Il pittor parigino—Continued.

— **Der onkel aus Amsterdam.** Eine comische oper in zwei aufzuegen. Nach dem italienischen: Il pittore parigino frei bearbeitet
und der musik des Cimarosa untergelegt. Aufgefuehrt von der
Secondaschen Gesellschaft in Leipzig und Dresden.

*Riga und Mitau, Wilhelm Christian Andreas Mueller, 1796. vi,
104 p. 16½ cm.*

German version, by G[eorg] C[arl] Claudius, who dates his preface Leipzig, May,
1795. In this he speaks of his deviations from the Italian original, and says:
Der Pariser Maler (Il pittore parigino) von Cimarosa machte eine geraume Zeit
hindurch auf dem kaiserl. königl. Hoftheater in Wien, selbst bei seinen vielfältigen
Wiederhohlungen gleichsam immer ein neues Glück, und dieses ist die Ursache,
warum man ihn in ein deutsches Gewand einzukleiden suchte. Da unsere deutsche
Original-Oper immer noch so arm bleibt, und, allem jetzigen Anscheine nach, auch
nicht sonderlich reicher werden dürfte, so bedarf es also schon einer Entschuldigung
weniger, wenn man ausländische Producte auf inländischen Boden verpflanzt. Dass
dergleichen Arbeit immer selbst bei allem Fleisse, selbst bei einem ziemlich gefüllten
Magazin von Erfahrungen, ein Wagstück bleibe, ist nicht zu läugnen. Denn der
Inhalt der ital. Opern, und die meist so sonderbare Bearbeitung ihrer Gegenstände
stossen gemeinhin so sehr wider den deutschen Geschmack, dass mit selten Nation
gegen Nation ungerecht wird, sich beiderseits verkennen, und am Ende selbst den
Wald-vor Bäumen nicht sehen. Die Deutschen haben bereits an unserm Eschenburg
einen vortrefflichen Vorgänger, wie der Friede zwischen beiden Partheien zu erhalten
sey, und wie man jeder sein Recht geben könne. Robert und Kalliste wird ewig
davon ein schönes Beispiel bleiben. Auch Herr D. Schmieders Versuche sind von
den deutschen Theatern mit Beifall aufgenommen worden. Ich würde mich freuen,
wenn mann meine Arbeit nicht so ganz überflüssig finden wollte. Ueber Cimarosas
Musik will ich hier nichts sagen, da ich nur mit meiner eigenen Sache zu thun habe.
"Die Aenderung des Titels: Der Pariser Maler, schien mir schon die erste Nothwendigkeit; denn der Maler in diesem Stück kann aus allen Weltgegenden herseyn,
da ihm der ital. Entwurf keine Eigenheit beimisst, warum er gerade aus Paris seyn
muss. Selbst für sonst neugierige Liebhaber des Theaters würde dieser Titel keinen
besondern Reiz gehabt haben, da die Emigranten anjetzt eben nicht die freudigste
Theilnahme erregen. Ich bestimmte den Titel nach der Hauptintrique des Stücks,
weil ich glaube, dass es mit Titeln so gemacht werden sollte, obgleich unsere
neuere Zeit auch über diese alte wahre Regel, ohne sich darum zu bekümmern, ihren
rüstigen Geniesprung gemacht zu haben scheint . . .
"Wenn trotz allen diesen Bemühungen diese Oper immer noch manches Unge-
reimte an sich tragen sollte, so war es schlechterdings unmöglich, solches ganz zu
verdrängen, weil man alsdann eine neue Musik hätte dazu componiren müssen, und
der schönen Musik wegen wurde diese Oper ja einzig nur verdeutscht.
"Schlüsslich bitte ich alle Künstler, die in diesem Stück eine Rolle zu spielen
haben, solche genau zu memoriren, was die Opernsänger, wie die Erfahrung sagt,
immer so leichtsinnig unterlassen sollen. Der Dialog muss Schlag auf Schlag gehen;
hängts aber da, so muss ich im voraus versichern, dass man sich selbst in den Hinter-
grund stellen, und einzig daran Schuld seyn wird, wenn man weniger gefällt."
First performed at Oels, Hoftheater, May 13, 1797.   SCHATZ 1970

Il più bel dono, inutile. Dramma giocoso per musica di un atto
solo di Giovanni Bertati da rappresentarsi nel Teatro Giustiniani in
S. Moisè il carnovale dell' anno 1779.

n. i., n. d. 30 p. 17½ cm.

Composed by Antonio **Rossetti**, who is not mentioned. This was performed
together with the one act "I Quaqueri" by the same author and composer and published with it in one volume with separate pagination.   SCHATZ 8884

La più costante tra le maritate. A. T. of Il D. Gastone.

Il più fedel frà i vassalli. Drama per musica. Da recitarsi nell'
antichissimo Teatro Tron di S. Casciano l'anno 1703. Poesia di
Francesco Silvani . . .

Venezia, li eredi Nicolini, 1703. 72 p. 14½ cm.

Il più fedel frà i vassalli—Continued.

Three acts. Author's dedication, dated Venice, February 3, 1703, notice to the reader with name of Carlo Francesco **Gasparini** as the composer, and scenario.

SCHATZ 3579

— Il più fedel fra i vassalli. Drama per musica da rappresentarsi nel Teatro di Sant' Angelo il carnoval dell' anno 1716.

Venezia, Marino Rossetti, 1716. front., 60 p. 14½^{cm}.

Three acts. Cast, scenario, and notice to reader, alluding to the performances of 1703, and stating:

"Lo scorgerai quello stesso, che ebbe la gloria di piacerti, nè vi troverai altra alterazione, che nelle canzoni in parte variate, per adattarle a' virtuosi, che devono rappresentarlo."

Neither Silvani nor **Gasparini** is mentioned.   ML 48.M2O

Il più fedel tra' gl'amici. Dramma per musica da rappresentarsi nel famosissimo Teatro Grimani di San Gio. Grisostomo. L'anno 1724 . . .

Venezia, Marino Rossetti, 1724. 70 p. 15½^{cm}.

Three acts. By Francesco Silvani, who is not mentioned. Publisher's dedication, "Motivo istorico," cast, scenario, and name of "Michel Angelo **Gasparini** Luchese" as the composer.   SCHATZ 3602

Il più fedel tra vassalli. Melodrama da rappresentarsi nel Teatro di S. Bartolomeo di Napoli in quest' anno 1705 . . .

Napoli, Michele Luigi Mutio, 1705. 4 p. l., 52 p. 13½^{cm}.

Three acts. Scenario, cast, and name of Giuseppe Antonio Vincenzo **Aldrovandini** as composer. It appears from Nicola Serino, the manager's notice to the reader, that the libretto (originally written by Francesco Silvani) was modified to the extent 'of adding the characters *Creperio* and *Bellina,* of replacing many arias by new ones from Giulio Convò's pen and by inserting a complete scene (III, 6) written by Silvio Stampiglia.   SCHATZ 138

Il più infedele trà gli amanti. Drama per musica da rappresentarsi nel Teatro Dolfin in Treviso per il prossimo autunno 1731 . . .

Venezia, Carlo Buonarrigo, 1731. 36 p. 15^{cm}.

Three acts. By Angelo Sorietti, who is not mentioned. Dedication by Antonio Martinelli, argument, cast, name of Tommaso **Albinoni** as composer, and notice that the performances would begin on October 6.   SCHATZ 123

Il Pizarro nell' America ossia La conquista del Perù, ballet. *See* Tarchi's Demofoonte.

Pizichi, oder Fortsetzung des Fagottisten. Ein singspiel in drey aufzuegen, von Joachim Perinet. Die musik ist vom hrn. Wenzel Mueller, kapellmeister dieses theaters. Aufgefuehrt auf dem k. k. priv. Marinellischen Theater. Zweyte verbesserte auflage.

Wien, Mathias Andreas Schmidt, 1793. 90 p. 18^{cm}.

The dedicatory preface by the author "dem besten publikum gewidmet" is dated Vienna, January 28, 1793, and reads, in part:

"Ich weiss, dass dieses spektakelstueck keinen auspruch auf regelmaessigkeit zu machen hat, aber ich denke, wenn es eine zeit im jahre giebt, die man die Fassnacht heisst, an der auch der vernuenftige mann zuweilen antheil nimmt, so mag wohl auch dann und wann so eine zauber komoedie mit unterlaufen, um sich zu zerstreuen, und Aug und ohr darinn zu ergoetzen . . . ich bin sehr entschlossen, mit einer Zauberruthe, dem chaos im dritten theile, ein erwuenschtes ende zu machen. . . . widme ich Ihnen hier die zweyte auflage, so wie sie auf dem hiesigen theater, der zu langen dauer wegen, abgekuerzt gegeben wurde . . ."

First performed, as indicated, October 2, 1792.   SCHATZ 6956

Pizzarro. Dramma per musica da rappresentarsi nel nobilissimo Teatro di San Samuele il carnovale dell' anno 1788.

Venezia, Modesto Fenzo, 1787. 55 p. 17½^cm.

Three acts. Argument, cast, scenario, and name of the composer, Francesco **Bianchi.** The librettist is not mentioned and unknown to Schatz. On p. [23]–32, argument, cast, and full description of "Cresfonte, rè di Scizia, ballo eroico in cinque atti" by Domenico Ricciardi, music ("tutta nuova") by Antonio Capuzzi. The second ballet, also by Ricciardi, the composer not being mentioned, was called "L'italiano maritato a Parigi."

First performed, as indicated, December 26, 1787. SCHATZ 999

Pizzarro nell' Indie o sia La distruzione del Perù. Dramma per musica da rappresentarsi in Firenze la primavera dell' anno 1784 nel nuovo Regio Teatro degl' Intrepidi detto La Palla a Corda . . .

Firenze, Stamperia Bonducciana, 1784. 40 p. 17^cm.

Two acts. Author not mentioned and unknown to Schatz. Argument, cast, scenario, and name of Giuseppe **Giordani** as the composer. ("La musica è tutta nuova.") SCHATZ 3849

Le plaisir et l'innocence, opera-comique en un acte. Par M. Parmentier. Représenté pour la première fois sur le Théâtre de l'Opéra-comique, le 14 août 1753.

Paris, Duchesne, 1753. 41, 7 p. 18½^cm.

En vaudevilles. Cast. The 7 p. contain eight engraved "Airs," the last being headed "Vaudeville de Mr. **Laruette**," who may have arranged the whole opera. In a note on p. 2 Parmentier says:

"Après avoir fait en société avec M. Favart la parodie de Mahomet Second, tragédie de M. de la Noüe, celle de l'opera Hyppolite, Le cocq de village, & quelques autres pièces qui n'ont pas été imprimées; j'ai cru pouvoir hazarder seul Le plaisir et l'innocence . . ." ML 50.2.P47L2

Les plaisirs de la campagne, ballet, representé par l'Academie royale de musique l'an 1719. Paroles de M. Pellegrin-Barbier. Musique de M. Bertin. XCVII opéra.

n. i., n. d. pl., 449–503 p. (Recueil général des opéra, t. xii, Paris, 1734).

Detached copy. Three *entrées* and prologue by Simon Joseph de Pellegrin and Mlle. Marie Anne Barbier.

First performed at Paris, Académie royale de musique, August 10, 1719.

SCHATZ 881
Second copy. ML 48.R4

Les plaisirs de la paix, balet représenté pour la première fois, par l'Académie royale de musique, le lundi 29. avril 1715. Les paroles de M. [*blank*] & la musique de M. Bourgeois. LXXXVII. opéra.

n. i., n. d. pl., [301]–353 p. 14^cm. (Recueil général des opéra, Paris, 1720, t. xi.)

Detached copy. By Mennesson. Prologue, three entrées "L'assemblée," "Feste de buveurs," "Le jaloux puni ou La serenade" and four intermèdes "Les Cyclopes," "Bacchus," "Momus," "Mascarade." The Avertissement says:

"Quoique chaque entrée ait son sujet particulier, on a pris soin de les lier toutes par des intermedes; ensorte que la piece & le prologue ne sont qu'un même sujet."

SCHATZ 1273
Second copy. ML 48.R4

Platée, ballet bouffon en trois actes, précédé d'un prologue; représenté devant le roi, en son château de Versailles; le mercredi 31 mars 1745.

[Paris], Ballard, 1745. 58 p. 25^{cm}.

Cast and names of "Hautreau, et Vallois" [Jacques Autreau and A J. Le Valois d'Orville] as authors, of Jean Philippe **Rameau** as the composer. With the text, retouched by Balot de Sauvot, the work was revived under the title of "Platée ou Junon jalouse" on February 4, 1749.   ML 52.2.P5

Plautilla.   Drama per musica da rappresentarsi nel famoso Teatro Grimani di S. Gio. Grisostomo. L'autunno dell' anno 1721 . . .

Venezia, Marino Rossetti, 1721. 60 p. 16^{cm}.

Three acts. Dedication signed by Vincenzo Cassani as author, argument, cast, scenario, name of Antonio **Pollaroli** as composer, and notice to the reader which reads, in part:

"Gia ti son noti i vincoli, onde viene ristretto un povero poeta dramatico. Numero preciso di mutazioni, e quasi di versi; ariette, che a richiesta de maestri, e de musici devono cambiarsi secondo il loro canto, ancorche guastino tal volta il componimento della scena, e faccino mutare il carattere, oltre tanti altri, che ben tu sai."   Schatz 8264

A playhouse to be lett.   A. T. of The stage-mutineers.

The plot.   As it is performed by His Majesty's Company of comedians at the Theatre-Royal in Drury-Lane. With the musick prefix'd to each song.

London, John Watts, 1735. 28, [2] p. 19^{cm}.

One act, prologue, and epilogue. Cast and table of the 10 songs, the airs of which are printed in the text with their titles. Attributed to John Kelly.
First performed at Drury Lane, January 22, 1735.   Longe 293

Plymouth in an uproar.   A musical farce, as it is performed at the Theatre-Royal in Covent-Garden. The music composed by Mr. Dibdin. The third edition.

London, G. Kearsley, 1779. 2 p. l., 41 p. 20^{cm}.

Cast. By Neville, who is not mentioned.
First performed October 21, 1779, as indicated.   Longe 153

Pocahontas.   Schauspiel mit gesang, in fuenf akten.

Jamestown, 1784. 80 p. 16^{cm}.

The prefatory note begins:
"Dieses schauspiel ruht schon laenger, als es Horaz verlangte, im pulte des verfassers, der es vor dreyzehn jahren, einem freunde zu gefallen, verfertigt hatte"
and ends:
"Dass das wilde maedchen witzig redet, wird niemand befremden, der aus Kap. Smiths Reise weiss, dass witz ein hervorstechender zug im charakter der Virginierinnen war."
Published at Ansbach, 1784, and written by Johann Wilhelm Rose. No composer recorded by Schatz.   Schatz 11641

Il poeta di campagna.   Commedia per musica di Saverio Zini da rappresentarsi nel Teatro Nuovo sopra Toledo per prim' opera di questo corrente anno 1792.

Napoli, Vincenzo Flauto, 1792. 46 p. 15^{cm}.

Two acts. Cast and name of Pietro **Guglielmi** as the composer.   Schatz 4263

Il **poeta di campagna**—Continued.

— Lo **sciocco poeta di campagna.** Dramma giocoso per musica da rappresentarsi nel Teatro alla Scala l'autunno dell' anno 1793 . . .

Milano, Gio. Battista Bianchi, n. d. 58 p. 16½^{cm}.

Two acts. Impresario's dedication, cast, scenario, and name of Pietro **Guglielmi** as the composer. Zini's text has been altered noticeably. For instance, I, 5, begins now "Che sposo vago, e bello," instead of "Col più profondo, ed umile." With the opera were performed, composers of the music not mentioned, Giuseppe Banti's "ballo eroico Zima" and his "ballo comico Il Posilipo di Napoli." Schatz 4264

— Lo **sciocco poeta di campagna:** Farsa prima per musica da rappresentarsi nel Reggio Teatro di S. Carlo, della Principessa nel carnovale dell' anno 1794 . . .

Lisbona, Simone Taddeo Ferreira, 1794. 95 p. 15^{cm}.

One act. By Saverio Zini, who is not mentioned. Portuguese text faces Italian. Impresario's dedication, cast, name of Pietro **Guglielmi** as composer, and scenario. With the opera were performed (composer of the music not mentioned) Pietro Angiolini's ballets, "Ciro in Timbraja" and "Li finti filosofi." ML 50.2.S38G9

Il **podestà di Tufo antico** o sia Il tutore burlato. Farsetta per musica da rappresentarsi nel Teatro Valle degl' illustriss. Sigg. Capranica nell' estate dell' anno 1786 . . .

Roma, Michele Puccinelli, n. d. 66 p. 15^{cm}.

Two acts. Cast, scenario, and names of the author, Francesco Ballani, and Agostino **Accorimboni** as composer. Schatz 17

Il **poeta di villa.** Farsetta in musica a cinque voci da rappresentarsi nel rinnovato Teatro di Palla [!] Corda la primavera dell' anno 1786 . . .

Roma, Arcangelo Casaletti, n. d. 57, [1] p. 14½^{cm}.

Two acts. Cast and name of the composer, Luigi **Caruso.** Author unknown to Schatz. Schatz 1658

Il **poeta melodrammatico in Parnaso.** Dramma eroicomico per musica da rappresentarsi nel magnifico Teatro dell' Accademia Filarmonica di Verona nel carnovale dell' anno MDCCLXXXVI . . .

Verona, Dionigi Ramanzani, 1786. 56 p. 17^{cm}.

Two acts. Impresario's noteworthy prefatory note, cast, name of Luigi **Caruso** as composer ("la musica tutta nuova" and note "La poesia è del Sig. A. A." ML 50.2.P48C2

Le **poète supposé,** ou Les préparatifs de fête, comédie en trois actes et en prose, mêlée d'ariettes et de vaudevilles, représentée, pour la première fois, par les Comédiens italiens ordinaires du roi, le 25 avril 1782. Seconde édition. Paroles de M. Laujon. Musique de M. Champein.

Paris, Duchesne, Brunet, n. d. 1 p. l., 124, 2 p. 21^{cm}.

Page 124 incorrectly numbered 224. The 2 add. p. contain three "Airs notés dans le divertissement." On p. 119–124, "Remplacement de la scène VIII, et en prose, de cet acte [III], par le présent duo" ("Ce cher Bailli"). ML 50.2.P5C3

Le **poirier,** opera comique. Par M. Vadé, représenté pour la premiere fois sur le Théâtre de la Foire S. Laurent, le 7 août 1752.

Paris, Duchesne, 1752. 56 p. 21½^{cm}.

One act. On p. 53–56, the airs notés, "Du jeune objet que j'adore," "Pour me plaire il faut," and the vaudeville, "Pretextant une bonne affaire." The arranger of the music not recorded by Parfaict. ML 50.2.P53S2

Le **poirier**—Continued.

— Le **poirier,** opera comique par Mr. Vadé. Représentée pour la premiere fois sur le Théatre de la Foire St. Laurent; le 7 août 1752.

La Haye, Pierre Gosse, 1760. 64 p. 16^cm. (Vadé, Oeuvres, La Haye, 1760, t. i.)

One act, *en vaudevilles.* Cast.   ML 49.A2V2

Le **poisson d'avril.** *See* Le public vengé.

Polidore, tragedie, representée par l'Academie royale de musique, l'an 1720. Paroles de M. de Laserre. Musique de M. Baptistin. XCVIII. opera.

n. i., n. d. pl., 64 p. 14^cm. (Recueil général des opéra, t. xiii, Paris, 1734.)

Detached copy. Prologue and five acts. Schatz mentions Simon Joseph de Pellegrin as joint author, without stating his reasons. The composer was Jean Batistin **Stuck.**
First performed February 15, 1720, as indicated.   SCHATZ 10125
Second copy. ML 48.R4

Polidoro. Tragedia da rappresentarsi in musica nel famoso Teatro Grimani de' SS. Gio. e Paolo il carnovale dell' anno 1714.

Venezia, Marino Rossetti, n. d. 71 p. 15^cm.

Five acts. Cast, scenario, and argument, in which the author, conte Agostino Piovene (not mentioned), acknowledges his indebtedness to the drama by conte Torelli. The composer, Antonio **Lotti,** is not mentioned.   SCHATZ 5708

Polidorus, in einem sing-spiele auf dem Hamburgischen Schauplatze fuergestellet.

[Hamburg], Gedruckt mit Spieringischen schrifften, 1735. Unpaged. 18^cm.

Five acts. Johann Samuel Müller's free German version of Co. Agostino Piovene's "Polidoro." Argument and name of Carl Heinrich **Graun** as the composer.
First performed at Hamburg, Theater b. Gänsemarkt, November 23, 1735; at Brunswick, August 13, 1731 (Schatz); Sommermesse, 1726 (Mennicke).
SCHATZ 4110

Il **Polifemo.** Dramma per musica da rappresentarsi nel Real Teatro del Fondo di Separazione per quart' opera di questo anno 1786 . . .

Napoli, n. publ., 1786. 36 p. 15^cm.

Three acts. By unknown author. Dedication, argument, and cast. The remark, "La musica è diretta dal . . . Francesco **Cipolla,**" does not, as Schatz would have it, establish him clearly as the composer.   SCHATZ 2013

Il **Polifemo.** Opera drammatica del Sig. Paolo Rolli. Da rappresentarsi nel Regio Teatro del Buon-Ritiro . . . in questo carnevale dell' anno MDCCXLVIII.

[Madrid], Lorenzo Francesco Mojados, n. d. [11], 12–101 p. 23^cm.

Three acts. Argument, cast, scenario, and the names of the composers, Francesco **Corselli** (act I), Francesco **Corradini** (act II), Giovanni Battista **Mele** (act III). Spanish title-page, "El Polifemo," and text face Italian.   SCHATZ 2253

Polifemo.

[295]–333 p. 17^cm. (Rolli, Componimenti poetici, Nuova edizione, Verona, G. Tumermani, 1744.)

Three acts. The composer, Nicolò **Porpora,** is not mentioned.
First performed at London, Haymarket, January 1, 1735 (Fassini).
ML 49.A2R7

Polipodio e Rucchetta. Intermezzi da cantarsi nel Teatro alla Torre Argentina nel carnevale dell' anno 1738. Musica del Sig. Gaetano Latilla.

> [*Rome*], *n. publ., n. d.   16 p.   15*^{cm}.

Two parts. Not recorded by Schatz. Author unknown to me. Intermezzo I begins with the aria "Se l'illustrissima Dicono a me," Intermezzo II "Certi amorini asciutti."   ML 50.2.P54L2

Politicks in miniature: or, The humours of Punch's resignation. A tragi-comi-farcical-operatical puppet-show with a new scene of Punch's levee, and the surprising metamorphosis of his puppets. To which is added, the Political rehearsal Harlequin Le Grand: or, The tricks of Pierrot Le Premier. With the cheats and adventures of Punchinello, Mezotin, Scaramouch, Pantaloon, and others. Being a tragi-comi-pantomimical performance of two acts. In which are introduced, An heroic scene of Female Honour, and a very majestic pantomime scene of kicking. The whole interspers'd with, patriots, chorus of patriots; courtiers, chorus of courtiers; songs; observations, critical and political. Taken from the Westminster Journal of March 20, 1741–2, Oct. 30, & Nov. 6, 1742.

> *London, J. Mechell, n. d.   38 p.   16½*^{cm}.

Two acts.   LONGE 277

Polixene et Pirrhus, tragedie représentée par l'Academie royale de musique l'an 1706. Les paroles de M. de la Serre, & la musique de M. Collasse. LXVIII. opera.

> *n. i., n. d.   (Recueil général des opéra, Paris, t. ix, 1710.)   front., 169–226 p.   14*^{cm}.

Detached copy. Five acts and prologue.
First performed, as indicated, October 21, 1706.   SCHATZ 2102
                                        Second copy.   ML 48.R4

Poll of Plympton.   A. T. Carter's The constant maid.

Pollastrella & Parpagnacco.   L. T. of Gasparini's Parpagnacco.

Pollastrella & Parpagnocco, intermezzi.   *See* Broschi's Adriano in Siria.

Polly: an opera. Being the second part of the Beggar's opera. Written by Mr. Gay . . .

> *London, Printed for the author, 1729.   1 p. l., vii, [1], 72 p., 31 p. (music).   23½*^{cm}.

Three acts and introduction. Ballad opera. Seventy-one songs, the airs of which are indicated in the text by title. They are printed with their basses in the supplement without title, but with number corresponding to that in the text and with the words to which they were to be sung in "Polly."

The text is preceded by Gay's preface, dated March 15, 1729, in which he narrates his experiences with the Lord Chamberlain who refused to grant permission of performance, though "everything was ready for a rehearsal," but "the Lord Chamberlain sent an order from the country to prohibit Mr. Rich to suffer any play to be rehears'd upon his stage till it had been first of all supervis'd by his Grace." Gay then in parallel columns lists the errors in the copy delivered to the Lord Chamberlain and the Emendations on revising the piece for the press. He takes pains to prove that there was no attempt on his part to deceive the Lord Chamberlain as to the actual text of the piece. On Dec. 7, 1728, he desired to read the opera to His Grace, but was ordered to leave the manuscript with him, and on Dec. 12, 1728, received word from the Lord Chamberlain

Polly—Continued.

"that it was not allow'd to be acted, but commanded to be supprest. This was told me in general without any reasons assign'd, or any charge against me of my having given any particular offence.

"Since this prohibition I have been told that I am accused, in general terms, of having written many disaffected libels and seditious pamphlets . . . I have been inform'd too, that in the following play, I have been charg'd with writing immoralities; that it is fill'd with slander and calumny against particular great persons, and that Majesty itself is endeavour'd to be brought into ridicule and contempt.

". . . to justify and vindicate my own character, I thought my-self obliged to print the opera without delay in the manner I have done.

"As the play was principally design'd for presentation, I hope when it is read it will be considered in that light: And when all that hath been said against it shall appear to be intirely misunderstood or misrepresented; if, some time hence, it should be permitted to appear on the stage, I think it necessary to acquaint the publick, that as far as a contract of this kind can be binding; I am engag'd to Mr. Rich to have it represented upon his theatre." [Lincoln's Inn Fields, not Covent Garden, built 1732, as pointed out by Tufts.]

John Christopher **Pepusch**, who selected and arranged the music, is not mentioned.

The piece was not performed until June 19, 1777, at the Haymarket (Genest), and then, it is generally claimed, altered by Colman. Tufts adds: "**Arnold** supplied six new airs."   ML 50.5.P74

— **Polly: an opera.** Being the second part of the Beggar's opera. Written by Mr. Gay . . .

London, Jeffery Walker, n. d. 3 p. l., [v]–vii, [1], 70 p. 20ᶜᵐ. [Bound with his Beggar's opera. London, 1728.]

Three acts and introduction. The same preface as in the dated 1729 ed. Contains no music. The (71) airs are merely indicated in the text by title.

ML 50.5.B3
Second copy.   LONGE 103

— **Polly.** An opera, as written by John Gay. Being the second part of the Beggar's opera.

London, John Bell, 1777. 84 p. 17ᶜᵐ.

At head of title: "Bell's edition." On p. 83–84 "Table of the songs." On p. 3–5 Gay's preface dated "March 25, 1729."

This 1777 edition contains the same text and the same 71 airs indicated by title as in the 1729 eds.! Consequently, it is not Colman-Arnold's version, first performed on June 19, 1777, at the Haymarket.   SCHATZ 7865

Poltis oder Das gerettete Troja, eine komische oper in drey aufzeugen.

Leipzig, bey Friedrich Gotthold Jacobaeern, 1773. 119, [1] p. 15½ᶜᵐ.

On the last unnumbered page the note that "diese komische oper von herr **Hillern** in musik gesetzt wird." Text preceded by quotation from Pope, by way of argument. The text is by Gottfried Samuel Brunner, who revised a manuscript play by Steinel and added arias. Schatz does not record a performance of this work.

SCHATZ 4731

Polyxena. Ein lyrisches monodrama. Von F. J. Bertuch.

Weimar, Im verlage des Industrie-comptoirs, 1793. 16 p. 22ᶜᵐ.

Dedication, dated Weimar, April 6, 1793, and Einleitung (dated Weimar, March 20, 1793), in which Bertuch says that he wrote this trifle 1774; that it was published in the same year in the Teutsche Merkur; that it was composed by several musicians, among whom Anton **Schweitzer**; and that the text was now reprinted, after nineteen years, because of the fact that Schweitzer's music was now to appear for the first time.

SCHATZ 11757

Polyxena—Continued.

— **Polyxena,** ein lyrisches monodrama von Bertuch. In musik gesetzt von Schweizer.

Hamburg, Freystatzky und Rabe, 1794. 13 p. 15½ᶜᵐ.

"Einleitung" (argument).

First performed at Gotha, Schlosstheater im Ballhause, April 7, 1775, and at Hamburg, Theater beim Gänsemarkt, February 19, 1778. SCHATZ 9778

Les pommiers et le moulin, comédie-lyrique en un acte, représenté pour la premiere fois par l'Academie royale de musique, le vendredi 22 janvier 1790. Paroles de M. Forgeot. Musique de M. Lemoine.

Paris, P. Delormel, 1791. 23 p. 21½ᶜᵐ. ML 50.2.P56L2

Pomone. Pastorale representée par l'Academie royalle en 1671. Les paroles sont de M. Perrin & La musique de M. Cambert. I. Opera

n. i., n. d. front., 48 p. 14ᶜᵐ. (Recueil général des opéra, Paris, 1703, t. i.)

Detached copy. Five acts and prologue.

First performed at Sèvres, at the palace of the marquis de Sourdeac, June 12, 1670, and at Paris, Salle au Jeu de Paume de la Bouteille, March 3, 1671. SCHATZ 1519

Second copy. ML 48.R4

Il Pompeo. Dramma per musica da rappresentarsi nel Teatro del Falcone di Genova . . .

Genova, Antonio Scionico, 1691. 71 p. 13ᶜᵐ.

Three acts. Conte Nicolo Minato, the author, not mentioned. Dedication signed by the composer, Giacomo Antonio **Perti,** who is not otherwise mentioned, argument, scenario, and cast. SCHATZ 7958

Il Pompeo. Dramma per musica da rappresentarsi nel Teatro di Ravenna nel present' anno 1685 . . .

Ravenna, Bernardino e Matteo Pezzi, 1685. 76 p. 14ᶜᵐ.

Three acts. Dedication, dated Ravenna, May 10, 1685, of this drama ("poch' anni sono da un ingegno più ameno fatto comparire su la magnificenza de' teatri di Roma, [1683] & hora dà noi su la picciolezza del nostro"), argument. Neither the author, *conte* Niccolò Minato, is mentioned, nor the composer, who is unknown to Schatz. At Rome, the composer was Alessandro **Scarlatti,** and probably, under the circumstances, his music was also used at Ravenna. ML 48.A5 v. 3

Pompeo in Armenia. Dramma per musica da rappresentarsi nel Teatro di S. Angelo il carnovale dell' anno 1747.

Venezia, Modesto Fenzo, 1747. 48 p. 14½ᶜᵐ.

Three acts. By Bartolomeo Vitturi, who is not mentioned. Argument, cast, scenario. Giuseppe **Scarlatti,** the composer, is not mentioned. SCHATZ 9552

Pompeo Magno. Drama per musica nel Teatro à S. Salvatore per l'anno 1666 . . .

Venetia, Francesco Nicolini, 1666. 86 p. 14½ᶜᵐ.

Three acts, with prologue. Author's dedication signed with conte Niccolò Minato's initials and dated Venice, February 20, 1666, argument, notice to the reader, and scenario. The composer, Pietro Francesco **Cavalli,** is not mentioned. SCHATZ 1732

Pompeo Magno in Cilicia. Drama per musica da rappresentarsi nel Teatro di Sant 'Angelo l'anno MDCLXXXI. Di Aurelio Aureli opera XXI.

Venetia, Francesco Nicolini, 1681. 57, [1] p. 14½ᶜᵐ.

Three acts. Author's dedication dated January 22, 1681, his notice to the reader, with name of Giovanni Domenico **Freschi** as composer, argument, and scenario.

SCHATZ 3353

Ponce de Léon. Opéra-bouffon, en trois actes; paroles et musique de M. Lebreton [!] Représenté pour la première fois, sur le Théâtre de l'Opéra-comique national, rue Favart, le 25 ventôse an. V. [March 15, 1797]

Paris, Barba, 1797. 60 p. 19½ᶜᵐ.

Cast. The score published in 1797 gives Henri Montan **Berton** as author and composer.

SCHATZ 896

The poor soldier, a comic opera. In two acts. With all the original songs. Written by John O'Keefe, Esq. . . . As acted at the Theatre Royal, Covent Garden. A new edition. Improved and carefully corrected.

Dublin, Printed and sold by the booksellers, 1785. 1 p. l., 32 p. 16½ᶜᵐ.

Cast. Largely a ballad opera, the resp. airs of the 19 songs being indicated by title. The music partly compiled and partly composed by William **Shield**, who is not mentioned.

First performed at Dublin, Smock Alley, March 28, 1783, as "The Shamrock or Revels on St. Patrick's Day" (Lawrence); as "The Shamrock, or, The anniversary of St. Patrick," London, Covent Garden, April 7, 1783 (Schatz), May 7, 1783 (Lawrence); under the above title, November 4, 1783 (Genest), December 1783 (Lawrence). According to Tufts, the 1798 ed. of O'Keefe's works gives the date as 1782.

LONGE 168

— **The poor soldier.** A comic opera.

[175]-200 p. 16ᶜᵐ. (A volume of plays, Dublin, 1791.)

Without name of author or composer.

PR 1269.V6

Poor Vulcan, a burletta, in two acts, as performed at the Theatre-Royal in Covent-Garden.

London, G. Kearsley and W. Nicoll, 1778. 2 p. l., 45 p. 21ᶜᵐ.

Cast. The author-compiler-composer, Charles **Dibdin,** is not mentioned. In Johnston and Randall's vocal score "When the sergeant" is headed as composed by **Dr. Arne** and "Joys that wordly mortals" as by Dr. **Arnold.**

First performed February 4, 1778, as indicated.

LONGE 87

Popolo d'Argo, ballet. *See* Rispoli's Ipermestra.

Poro. Drama per musica da rappresentarsi nel Regio Teatro di Torino nel carnovale del 1745. Alla presenza di Sua Maestà.

Torino, Pietro Giuseppe Zappata e figliuolo, n. d. 4 p. l., 68 p. 15½ᶜᵐ.

Three acts. Altered from Metastasio, who is not mentioned by name. Argument, scenario, cast, and names of **Gluck** as the composer of the opera, of Alessio Rasetti as composer of the ballet music.

First performed December 26, 1744, as indicated.

SCHATZ 3933

Poro rè d'Italia. O. T. of Händel's Porus.

Porsena. Drama per musica da rappresentarsi nel Teatro di S. A. S. E. di Baviera nel carnevale dell' anno MDCCXXV.

Monaco, Giovanni Luca Straub, n. d. 79, [1] p. 15ᶜᵐ.

Three acts. Argument, cast, scenario. Author and composer not mentioned and unknown to Schatz.   SCHATZ 11358

Porsenna. Drama per musica da rappresentarsi nel Teatro di S. Bartolomeo il giorno 19. novembre 1713.   In cui si festeggia il glorioso nome di S. M. Ces. e Catt. Elisabetta . . .

Napoli, Michele Luigi Muzio, 1713. 68 p. 14ᶜᵐ.

Three acts. Dedication by the impresario, Nicola Serino, argument, scenario, cast, and footnote on p. 10:
"Musica del Signor Antonio **Lotti**; accomodata e diretta dal Sig. Alessandro **Scarlatti**, primo maestro della Real Cappella."
The author, conte Agostino Piovene, is not mentioned.
Lotti's opera was first performed at Venice, Teatro di S. Giov. Grisostomo, carnival, 1712.   SCHATZ 5711

Porsugnacco e Grilletta. Intermezzi in Hasse's Gerone tiranno di Siracusa.

Li portentosi effetti della gran Madre Natura. A. T. of L'innocenza protetta dal Cielo.

I portentosi effetti della Madre Natura.

[271]–332 p. 16½ᶜᵐ. (Carlo Goldoni, Opere drammatiche giocose, t. ii, Torino, 1757.)

Three acts. First composed by *Scarlatti*, as below.   ML 49.A2G6

— I portentosi effetti della Madre Natura. Dramma di tre atti per musica.

Carlo Goldoni, Opere teatrali, Venezia, Zatta e figli, 1788–95, v. 42, [263]–325 p. 18ᶜᵐ.

                                                                    PQ

I portentosi effetti della Madre Natura. Dramma giocoso per musica da rappresentarsi nel Teatro Nuovo di S. Samuele l'autunno dell' anno 1752 . . .

Venezia, Modesto Fenzo, 1752. 2 p. l., 64 p. 17ᶜᵐ.

Three acts. Cast, scenario, and Carlo Goldoni's dedication dated November 11, 1752, in which he says:
"Questi giocosi drammi per musica sono in oggi per tutta l'Italia desiderati, e con piacere intesi, e le persone nobili, e colte v'intervengono frequentemente, trovando in esse alla melodia del canto, unito il piacere dell' onesto ridicolo, il che forma un divertimento assai più allegro del solito."
The composer, Giuseppe **Scarlatti**, is not mentioned.   SCHATZ 9554

— I portentosi effetti della Madre Natura. Dramma bernesco per musica. Nell' anno 1758.

Monaco, Giov. Giac. Vötter, n. d. 76 p. 15ᶜᵐ.

Three acts. By Goldoni, who is not mentioned. Neither is Giuseppe **Scarlatti**, the composer. The text differs slightly from the original Venice, 1752, ed. For instance, "Donna, vi lascio il cor" (I, 11) has become "Non temer, che avanti à lei" and "Se tal' un mi dice bella" (I, 13) has become "Non son bella—non sono vezzosa."
                                                                    SCHATZ 9553

Il porto della libertà. *See* M. Curzio.

The **portait;** a burletta. As it is performed at the Theatre Royal, in Covent-Garden. The music by Mr. Arnold.

London, T. Becket and co., MCCCLXX [!] *2 p. l., 32 p. 20^cm.*

Three acts. By George Colman, who is not mentioned. Cast and same prefatory note as in next entry.

First performed November 22, 1770, as indicated.   ML 50.2.P59A7

— The **portrait;** a burletta. As it is performed at the Theatre Royal, in Covent-Garden. The music by Mr. Arnold. A new edition.

London, T. Becket and co., MCCCLXX [!] *2 p. l., 28 p. 20^cm.*

Two acts. Cast and prefatory note, according to which this edition of "The Portrait" ("founded on a French piece, called Le tableau parlant" by Anseaume) differs from the first by omission of the "superfluous" part of Pierrot and the reduction of the burletta to two acts. The author, George Colman, is not mentioned.

LONGE 26

Porus. An opera as it is perform'd at the Theatre Royal in Covent-Garden. The fourth edition, with additions.

London, T. Wood, 1736. 67 p. 17^cm.

Three acts. Argument and cast. The Italian title, "Poro rè dell' Indie," heads the Italian text which faces the English. According to a footnote on p. 3 the arias, etc., "Tiranna la sorte" (I, 2), "Poro, se sull' Idaspe / Sortì illeso Alessandro" (III, 5), indicated in the text and others on "the leaf of alterations" which is not in this copy, were not composed by **Händel.** The text is based on "Alessandro nell' Indie" by Metastasio, who is not mentioned.

First performed, as indicated, December 8, 1736; originally at the same theatre, February 2, 1731.   SCHATZ 4486

— **Triumph der grossmuth und treue,** oder Cleofida, koenigin von Indien, in einem sing-spiele auf der Hamburgis. Schau-buehne fuergestellet. Anno MDCCXXXII.

Hamburg, mit Stromerschen schrifften, n. d. Unpaged. 18½^cm.

Three acts. In his "Vorbericht," which contains also the argument, C. G. Wend, the translator, says that this "Porus" has nothing to do with an opera of the same title previously performed at Hamburg, that in his translation of **Händel's** "Porus," though but "eine eilfertige arbeit," care was taken "ein theil derer arien (sonderlich solcher, die sich im gemeinen leben appliciren lassen,) in teutsche reime zu bringen und unter die music zu legen, damit sie allenfalls liebhaber, die eben keine abgoetter von italiaenischen worten sind, auch teutsch singen hoeren, oder selbst auf der kammer nachsingen koennen." He then comments on the difficulty Italian verses "musicalisch zu parodiren." Characteristic is his remark:

"Dass unser herr **Telemann** die teutsche recitative unter noten gebracht, brauche ich wohl nicht erst zu melden, weil so ein grosser meister dergleichen etwas wohl im schlafe zu verrichten faehig ist, und ich folglich seinen sonst hohen verdiensten durch meldung eines so geringen fast unrecht anthun wuerde."

The Italian text of the arias has been added to the German.

First performed, as indicated, Theater beim Gänsemarkt, February 25, 1732.

SCHATZ 4487

Porzia, ballet. *See* Alessandri's Calliroe.

Il **Posilipo di Napoli,** ballet. *See* P. Guglielmi's Lo sciocco poeta di campagna.

Pourceaugnac and Griletta. Tr. of Orlandini's Monsieur de Porsugnac.

Le **pouvoir de l'amour.** A. T. of the ballet Le premier navigateur.

Le **pouvoir de l'amour.** A. T. of Méhul's Euphrosine et le tyran corrigé.

Il **povero superbo.** Dramma giocoso per musica da rappresentarsi nel Teatro Grimani di S. Samuel nel carnovale dell' anno 1755 . . .

Venezia, Modesto Fenzo, 1755. 59 p. 15ᶜᵐ.

Three acts. Author unknown to Schatz. Impresario's dedication, cast, scenario, and name of Baldassare **Galuppi** as composer. According to Piovano, the text is taken from Goldoni's "Castalda." Schatz 3467

Der **praechtige freygebige.** Tr. of Grétry's Le magnifique.

Prassitele in Gnido. Drama pastorale per musica d'Aurelio Aurelii da rapresentarsi in Rovigo nel Teatro novissimo dell' illustriss. Signor Co. Marc' Antonio Monfredini l'anno 1700 . . .

Venezia, Marino Rossetti, 1700. front., 48 p. 14½ᶜᵐ.

Three acts. Dedication, argument, cast, scenario, and Aureli's notice to the reader, in which he mentions the "bizzarra musica del Signor Agostino Bonaventura **Colletti,** virtuoso Luchese," and says:

"Se giammai nel numero di 62 drami da me composti fin ora per la musica, me n'è caduto dalla pena alcuno che meriti il titolo d'allegro; questi (ò benigno lettore) à mio credere può dirsi uno di quelli . . ." Schatz 2113

Prassitele in Gnido. Drama pastorale per musica da rappresentarsi in Venetia nel Teatro Novissimo di Santi Appostoli l'anno 1707 . . .

Venetia, Gio. Maria Rossi, 1707. 55 p. 15ᶜᵐ.

Three acts. By Aurelio Aureli, who is not mentioned. Impresario's dedication, argument, notice to the reader, and scenario. The composer, Girolamo **Polani,** is not mentioned. Schatz 8255

Il **pregiudizio che nasce dal mancare di parola.** A. T. of C. F. Pollaroli's Almansore.

Le **premier navigateur,** ou Le pouvoir de l'amour, ballet d'action, en trois actes par M. Gardel l'aîné. Représenté sur le Théatre de l'Académie de musique, le mardi 26 juillet 1785.

Paris, n. publ., 1785. 13 p. 20½ᶜᵐ.

Cast and scene by scene synopsis of the action of the three acts. No composer mentioned, but Lajarte, charging Gardel with plagiarism on Philidor, says: "Musique tirée des oeuvres de **Grétry."** ML 52.2.P6

La **premiere representation.** Prologue. Pour précéder la pièce suivante. Par Mʳ Le S * * *. Représentée à la Foire S. Laurent. 1734.

— Les **mariages de Canada.** Piece d'un acte. Par Mʳ Le S * *. Représentée à la Foire S. Laurent. 1734.

Le Théâtre de la Foire, Paris, 1737, t. ix, p. [275]–362. 17ᶜᵐ.

By Le Sage. Largely *en vaudevilles.* The airs, selected or composed and arranged by Jean Claude **Gillier,** are printed at the end of the volume in the "Table des airs." ML 48.L21X

Il **prencipe giardiniero** di Benedetto Ferrari dalla tiorba . . . Rappresentato in musica in Venetia. Posto in musica dall' istesso autore.

n. i., n. d. p. [239]–291. (Poesie drammatiche di Benedetto Ferrari, Milano, 1644.) 13½ᶜᵐ.

Detached copy. Three acts. Author's dedication, argument, two sonnets addressed to the author, and "Prologo. Hercole su' L'idra."
First performed at Venice, Teatro de' SS. Gio. e Paolo, December 30, 1643. Schatz 3068

Les **préparatifs de fête.** A. T. of Champein's Le poète supposé.

La prepotenza delusa. Dramma giocoso per musica in due atti d'Antonio Piazza Venetiano da rappresentarsi nel nobilissimo Teatro di S. Samuele nel carnovale dell' anno 1777.

> *Venezia, Gio. Battista Casali, 1777. 64 p. 17½ cm.*
>
> Cast, scenario, and name of Giovanni **Cavi** as composer. On p. [31]–42, preface, cast, scenario, and detailed description of Innocenzo Gambuzzi's "Medonte, ballo eroico." Baldassare Filippo Mattei is mentioned as the composer of the music.
>
> SCHATZ 1757

La presa di Granata. Dramma serio per musica da rappresentarsi nel Regio Teatro dell' Accademia degli Avvalorati in Livorno l'autunno dell' anno 1795.

> *[Livorno], Tommaso Masi e compagno. 46 p. 17½ cm.*
>
> Two acts. By Mario Ballani. Argument, cast, and names of the composer, Giuseppe Maria **Curcio,** and the author. On a flyleaf a curious "protesta" of Sig. Girolamo Braura has been pasted:
> "che la parte di Lara . . . non corrisponda alle sue convenienze e carattere, protesta di avere accettata la detta parte spontaneamente, e per mera compiacenza alle istanze stategli fatti a tale effetto."
>
> SCHATZ 2305

— **La conquista di Granata.** Dramma per musica da rappresentarsi nel Regio Teatro di via della Pergola l'autunno del 1796 . . .

> *Firenze, Pietro Fantosini, 1796. 32 p. 17 cm.*
>
> Three-act version of the above. Argument, cast, and name of Giuseppe Maria **Curcio** as composer. The third act simply consists of the two last scenes of the second act. With the opera was performed Antonio Cianfanelli's ballet, "La diserzione per equivoco." The composer of the music is not mentioned.
>
> SCHATZ 2306

La presa de Marochini, ballet. *See* Della Maria's Chi vuol non puole.

The **press gang** or Love in low life. L. T. of Carey's Nancy.

Le **Pressoir.** *See* Floquet's Le seigneur bienfaisant.

Presumptuous love: A dramatick masque. As it is performed at the New Theatre in Lincoln's Inn-Fields, 1716.

> *London, Edw. Nutt, n. d. 24 p. 21 cm.*
>
> Two acts. Cast and preface, in which the author (not recorded by Clarence) says:
> "I own here is a great deal of room for fine machinery decoration of the stage, and the like; but as that wou'd have encreas'd the expences of the house too considerably, we hope the musick to this masque will prove as agreeable an entertainment to the town, as hath been produced in this kind some years; for the composing of which, we own ourselves obliged to Mr. William **Turner,** who hath a happy genius in naturalizing Italian musick into a true English manner, without losing the spirit and force of the original in the imitation, or the masterly touches of the art in the composition."
>
> LONGE 138

I pretendenti burlati. Dramma giocoso per musica esposto a diporto villereccio dal nobil uomo D. Gian-Carlo Grossardi nel suo privato teatrino di Medesano l' estate dell' anno 1793.

> *n. i., n. d. 4 p. l., 77 p. 20½ cm.*
>
> Two acts. Author not mentioned, and unknown to Schatz. Cast (of amateurs), scenario, and name of Ferdinando Pär (**Paër**) as the composer. ("La musica tutta nuova.")
>
> SCHATZ 7566

I pretendenti delusi. L. T. of Sarti's Fra i due litiganti il terzo gode.

Le prétendu, comédie en trois actes, en vers, mêlée de musique; par M. Riccoboni. Représentée, pour la premiere fois, sur le Théâtre des Comédiens italiens ordinaires du roi, le jeudi 6 novembre 1760.

Paris, de Lormel, 1760. 72 p. 19^{cm}.

Cast and name of Pierre **Gaviniés** as composer. ML 50.2.P63G2

Les prétendus, comédie-lyrique en un acte, représentée pour la premiere fois, par l'Académie royale de musique, le mardi 2 juin 1789.

Paris, P. de Lormel, 1789. viii, 55 p. 23^{cm}.

One act. By Marc Antoine Jacques Rochon de Chabannes, who is not mentioned. "Avertissement," name of **Le Moine** as composer, and cast. SCHATZ 5487

Les preux chevaliers. *See* Dorothée.

La preziosa ridicola. Intermezzi in Il Radamisto, Firenze, 1728.

La preziosa ridicola. Intermezzi comici musicali da rappresentarsi nel Teatro di S. Angelo il carneval dell' anno 1719.

Venezia, Marino Rossetti, 1719. 20 p. 15$\frac{1}{2}$^{cm}.

Three parts. Neither the author, marchese Trotti, nor the composer, Giuseppe Maria **Orlandini,** is mentioned.

First performed at Bologna, Teatro Formigliari, June 14, 1718. SCHATZ 7346

Le preziose umiliate, ballet. *See* Winter's Belisa.

Le prie del'oiseau ou du papegai, ballet. *See* Bernasconi's Didone abbandonata.

La prigionia di Dario. A. T. of Stabingher's ballet Il trionfo di Alessandro.

Il prigioniero fortunato. Drama per musica di Francesco Maria Paglia . . .

Napoli, Dom. Ant. Parrino e Michele Luigi Mutio, 1698. 70 p. 14^{cm}.

Three acts. Author's dedication, notice to the reader, cast, and scenario. The composer, Alessandro **Scarlatti,** is not mentioned.

First performed at Naples, Teatro di San Bartolomeo, December 14, 1698.

SCHATZ 9529

— **Il prigioniero fortunato.** Drama per musica da rappresentarsi in Mantova l' anno 1699 . . .

[Mantova], Gio. Batt. Grana, n. d. 91, [2] p. 15$\frac{1}{2}$^{cm}.

Three acts. Dedication, notice to the reader, cast, scenario, and names of Paglia as the author, of Alessandro **Scarlatti** as the composer. On the [2] p. "Arie mutate": "Segni d'un bel valore" instead of "Cangia il cielo," "Ben mio tù non vedrai" instead of "Quell' ardore" (both act I), "Son nata per quegl' occhi" instead of "Mi tormenta," "Saprò svenar con l' armi" instead of "Flagellate" (both act II), and in act III "Quanto sarei beata" instead of "Folli amanti" and "Bella prova de la mia fede" instead of "M' incatena." ML 50.2.P65S2

La prima età dell' innocenza o sia La Rosaja di Salency, ballet. *See* Borghi's Artaserse.

Primislao, primo rè di Boemia. Drama per musica. Da rappresentarsi nel Teatro di S. Cassiano l' anno 1698. Di Giulio Cesare Corradi . . .

Venetia, Per il Nicolini, 1697. 60 p. 14½^{cm}.

Three acts. Author's dedication dated Venice, November 9, 1697, argument, scenario. The composer, Tommaso **Albinoni**, is not mentioned. Schatz 124

Il primo giorno dell' anno nella China, ballet. *See* Tarchi's Ifigenia in Aulide.

Il primo navigatore, ballet. *See* Minoja's Tito nelle Gallie.

The prince of Arragon. A. T. of Arnold's The birth-day.

The princess of Tarento. A comedy in two acts.

[189]–236 p. 21½^{cm}. (The miscellaneous works of A. M'Donald, London, J. Murray, 1791.)

Interspersed with airs, songs, etc., composed by **Corelli, Vanhall, Gluck, Giardini, Millico, Händel, Harrington.** Longe 282

La princesse d'Elide, ballet heroique, representé par l'Academie royale de musique, l'an 1728. Paroles de M. Pellegrin. Musique de M. Villeneuve. CX. opera.

n. i., n. d. pl. 253–296 p. 14^{cm}. (Recueil général des opéra, t. xiv, Paris, 1734).

Detached copy. Prologue and three acts.
First performed, as indicated, July 20, 1728. Schatz 10738
Second copy. ML 48.R4

La princesse de Carizme. Pièce en trois actes. Par Monsieur le S * *. Représentée à la Foire de Saint Laurent 1718. Et pendant le cours de la même foire, sur le Théâtre de l'Opéra, par ordre de S. A. Royale Madame.

Le Théâtre de la foire, Paris, 1737, t. iii, pl., [95]–199 p. 17^{cm}.

By Alain René Le Sage. Largely *en vaudevilles.* The airs selected or composed and arranged by Jean Claude **Gillier,** the "compositeur" of the theatre, are printed at the end of the volume in the "Table des airs." ML 48.L2 III

La princesse de la Chine. Piece en trois actes. Par M^{rs} le S * * & d'Or * * representée à la Foire Saint Laurent 1729.

Le Théâtre de la Foire, Paris, 1731, t. viii, pl., [121]–212 p. 17^{cm}.

By Le Sage and d'Orneval. Largely *en vaudevilles.* The airs, selected or composed and arranged dy Jean Claude **Gillier,** are printed at the end of the volume in the "Table des airs."
First performed June 25, 1729. ML 48.L2 VII

La princesse de Navarre, comédie-ballet; feste donnée par le roy en son château de Versailles, le mardi 23. février 1745. Cette pièce est du Sr. Arrouet de Voltaire.

[Paris], Ballard fils, n. d. 88 p. 21^{cm}.

Prologue, three acts, and final Divertissement. The latter was intended entirely for music, whereas in the comédie-ballet proper music figured only incidentally in the form of dances and choruses. The composer, Jean Philippe **Rameau,** is not mentioned. Cast and Avertissement, reading, in part:

"Le Roi a voulu donner à Madame la Dauphine une Fête qui ne fût pas seulement un de ces Spectacles pour les yeux, tels que toutes les Nations peuvent les donner, & qui passant avec l'éclat qui les accompagne. ne laissent après eux aucune trace. Il a

La **princesse de Navarre**—Continued.

commandé un Spectacle qui pût à la fois servir d'amusement à la Cour, & d'encouragement aux beaux Arts, dont il sçait que la culture contribue à la gloire de son Royaume. M. le Duc de Richelieu, Premier Gentilhomme de la Chambre en exercice, a ordonné cette Fête magnifique.

"Il a fait élever un Théâtre de cinquante-six pieds de profondeur dans le grand Manege de Versailles, & a fait construire une Salle, dont les décorations & les embellissemens sont tellement menagés, que tout ce qui sert au Spectacle doit s'enlever en une nuit, & laisser la Salle ornée pour un Bal paré, qui doit former la Fête du lendemain.

"Le Théâtre & les Loges ont été construits avec la magnificence convenable, & avec le goût qu'on connoît depuis long-tems dans ceux qui ont dirigé ces préparatifs.

"On a voulu réunir sur ce Théâtre tous les talens qui pourroient contribuer aux agrémens de la Fête, & rassembler à la fois tous les charmes de la déclamation, de la Danse & de la Musique, afin que la Personne Auguste, à qui cette Fête est consacrée, pût connoître tout d'un coup les talens qui doivent être doresnavant employés à lui plaire.

"On a donc voulu que celui qui a été chargé de composer la Fête, fît un de ces ouvrages Dramatiques, où les divertissemens en musique forment une partie du sujet, où la plaisanterie se mêle à l'Heroïque, & dans lesquels on voit un mélange de l'Opéra, de la Comédie, & de la Tragédie.

"On n'a pû ni dû donner à ces trois genres toute leur étenduë; on s'est efforcé seulement de réunir les talens de tous les Artistes qui se distinguent le plus, & l'unique mérite de l'Auteur a été de chercher à faire valoir celui des autres . . .

"Ce Divertissement a été exécuté le 23. Février de cette année 1745. vers les six heures du soir. Le Roi s'est placé au milieu de la Salle, ayant auprès de lui, la Reine, Monsieur le Dauphin, Madame la Dauphine & Mesdames.

"Les Princes & les Princesses du Sang achevoient le cercle. Les Grands Officiers de la Couronne étoient derriere la Famille Royale.

"Il eût été à désirer qu'un plus grand nombre de Français eût pû voir cette assemblée, tous les Princes de cette maison qui est sur le Trône long tems avant les plus anciennes du monde, cette foule de Dames parées de tous les ornemens qui sont encore des chef-d'oeuvres du goût de la Nation, & qui étoient effacés par elles; enfin cette joye noble & décente qui occupoit tous les coeurs & qu'on lisoit dans tous les yeux.

"On est sorti du Spectacle à neuf heures & demie dans le même ordre qu'on étoit entré, & alors on a trouvé toute la façade du Palais & des Ecuries illuminée. La beauté de cette Fête n'est qu'une foible image de la joye d'une Nation qui voit réunir le sang de tant de Princes ausquels elle doit son bonheur & sa gloire.

"Sa Majesté, satisfaite de tous les soins qu'on a pris pour lui plaire, a ordonné que ce Spectacle fût représenté encore une seconde fois." ML 52.2.P7

Il **principato custodito dalla frode.** Drama per musica da rappresentarsi nel Teatro Tron in S. Casciano l'anno 1705 . . . Poesia di Francesco Silvani . . .

Venezia, Marino Rossetti, 1705. 72 p. 15^cm.

Three acts. Author's dedication, dated Venice, January 31, 1705, argument, notice to the reader, cast, scenario, and name of the composer, Carlo Francesco **Gasparini.**

SCHATZ 3577

Il **principe di Lago Nero** ossia La contadina in corte, ballet. *See* di Palma's Gli amanti della sorte.

Il **principe di Taranto.** Dramma giocoso per musica da rappresentarsi nel Teatro Elettorale di Sassonia.

Dresda, n. publ., 1798. 155 p. 15½^cm.

Two acts. Ferdinando Francesco **Paër** is mentioned as the composer. The author, Filippo Livigni, is not mentioned. German title page, "Der fuerst von Taranto," and text face Italian. The text is an altered version of Livigni's "La finta principessa."

First performed March 24, 1798, as indicated; previously at Parma, Teatro Ducale, carnival, 1797.

SCHATZ 7524

Il **principe selvaggio**. Drama per musica da rappresentarsi nel Teatro di Sant' Angelo. L'anno 1695 . . .

   Venetia, Nicolini, 1695. 66 p. 14^{cm}.

Three acts. Dedication signed by the author, Francesco Silvani, with his initials and dated Venice, January 10, 1695, notice to the reader, argument, and scenario. The composer, Michel Angelo **Gasparini**, is not mentioned.   SCHATZ 3603

La **principessa di Amalfi**. O. T. of Weigl's La contessa di Amalfi.

La **principessa di Tingi**, ballet. *See* Insanguine's Calipso.

La **principessa fedele**. Drama per musica da rappresentarsi nel Teatro Tron di San Cassiano per l'autunno dell' anno 1709 . . .

   Venezia, Marino Rossetti, n. d. 65 p. 15^{cm}.

Three acts. Neither the author, conte Agostino Piovene, nor the composer, Carlo Francesco **Gasparini**, are mentioned. Dedicatory poem, argument, cast, and scenario.   SCHATZ 3578

La **principessa filosofa** ossia Il contravveleno. Commedia ridotta ad uso melodrammatico da rappresentarsi nel nobilissimo Teatro Venier in S. Benedetto l'autunno dell' anno 1794.

   Venezia, Andrea Albrizzi, n. d. viii, 56, [12] p. 18½^{cm}.

Two acts. By Antonio Simone Sografi, who is not mentioned. Impresario's dedication, cast, and name of Gaetano **Andreozzi** as composer. Vittorio Trento is mentioned as composer of the music for the ballets "Fallaride, tiranno d'Agricento, ballo eroico tragico pantomimo" and "Il ratto delle castellane fatto dai Triestini." Of the first a complete synopsis of plot is given by its author; Giuseppe **Trafieri** on the unnumbered pages of the libretto.

First performed, as indicated, October 6, 1794.   SCHATZ 198

Le **printemps**, divertissement pastoral en un acte et en vaudevilles par MM. de Pils & Barré; représenté pour la première fois, à Marly, devans Leurs Majestés, le samedi 29 mai 1781, & à Paris, le mardi 22 du même mois, par les Comédiens italiens ordinaires du roi.

   Paris, Cailleau, 1784. 24 p. 18½^{cm}.

The composer, Félix Jean **Prot**, is not mentioned.   SCHATZ 8471

The **prisoner**: a musical romance, in three acts. First performed by His Majesty's company from the Theatre-Royal, Drury-Lane, at the King's Theatre, Hay-market, on Thursday, October 18th, 1792.

   London, C. Lowndes, n. d. 2 p. l., 28 p. 21½^{cm}.

Cast. The air "Where the banners of glory" is headed as by **Mozart**. Neither the author, John Rose, is mentioned, nor the composer, Thomas **Attwood**. In Longman & Broderip's vocal score the last finale is headed as by "**Giornovichi** and **Attwood**".

    LONG E 236

The **prisoner** or The resemblance. Tr. of Della Maria's Le prisonnier ou La ressemblance.

Le **prisonnier**, ou La ressemblance, comédie. En un acte et en prose, mêlée de chants; jouée sur le Théâtre Favart, le 10 pluviose, an VI. [January 29, 1798]. Parole [!] du citoyen Alex. Duval, musique du citoyen Domenico della Maria.

   Amsterdam, Le Franc, an. VI—1798. 36 p. 19½^{cm}.

With cast.   SCHATZ 2485

Le **prisonnier**—Continued.

— The **prisoner**; or, The resemblance. (From the French.) A comic opera, in one act. Adapted to the English stage by Henry Heartwell, Esq.

London, Cadell and Davies, 1799. viii, [9]–40 p. 21ᶜᵐ.

Cast and preface which makes it clear that the translation had not yet been performed and in which Heartwell says:

"Very few liberties have been taken with the original ["Le prisonnier, ou La ressemblance," text by Duval, music by Della Maria] which, to stamp its celebrity, boasts of one hundred successive representations in the year 1798. It does not open with Rosina's song; has no change of scene; with those exceptions, the situation, interest, and, it is hoped, simplicity, will be found faithfully preserved."

This translation was found to be too simple for the English stage. With the cooperation of George Colman for the text and Thomas **Attwood** for the music "The prisoner" was much altered and expanded to two acts. In this form it was first performed as "The castle of Sorrento" at the Haymarket, July 13, 1799. (*See* this under its title.)   LONGE 254

— Arien und gesaenge aus der oper: Der **arrestant,** in einem aufzuge. Aus dem franzoesischen uebersetzt von Ihlee. Die musik ist von Domenico della Maria.

Frankfurt am Main, n. publ., 1799. 16 p. 16½ᶜᵐ.

First performed at Francfort o/M, Nationaltheater, January 23, 1800.

SCHATZ 2486

Le **prix de Cythere,** opera-comique; par M. le marquis D. P. & M. Favart; représenté pour la premiere fois sur le Théâtre du fauxbourg S. Germain, le 12 février 1742. Nouvelle édition.

Paris, Duchesne, 1761. 72 p. 19ᶜᵐ. (Theatre de M. Favart, Paris, Duchesne, 1763–77, t. vi.)

Prologue, one act. Prose, vaudevilles, and original ariettes, which are printed in the text. Written in collaboration with the marquis de Paulmy. Font does not mention their musical collaborator. He gives February 13, 1742, instead of February 12 as the date of first performance.   ML 49.A2F1

The **prize,** or, 2, 5, 3, 8. A musical farce in two acts. Written by Prince Hare [!], Esq. The music by Storace.

Dublin, Patrick Conner, 1793. 44 p. 17½ᶜᵐ.

Cast. By Prince Hoare.
First performed at London, March 11, 1793.   LONGE 233

Proceguimento ou Segunda parte do Falador. Tr. of Marescalchi's Il proseguimento del Chiarlone.

Procris et Cephale. Tr. of Reichardt's Cephalus und Prokris.

Procris och Cephal, opera uti tvô acter, uti deras Kongl. Majestäters och Kongl. Husets närvaro första gången upförd den 8 jannarii 1778.

Stockholm, Kongl. Tryckeriet, 1778. 18 p. 22ᶜᵐ.

Cast and prefatory note, according to which the text was based on Marmontel's "Procris et Cephale," by Gudmund Göran Adlerbeth, who is not mentioned, and the music partly selected by Lars Samuel **Lalin** from "goda mästares arbeten," partly composed, "recitativerne och en del chorer," by the court conductor, Henrik Filip **Johnsen.**   SCHATZ 4967

Procris und Cephalus in einem singe-spiel vorgestellet.
Hamburg, Nicolaus Spieringk, 1701. [54] p. 18^{cm}.
Three acts. By Friedrich Christian Bressand. Neither he is mentioned, nor the composer, Georg **Bronner**.
First performed at Hamburg, Opernhaus b. Gänsemarkt, in 1701; at Brunswick, Hochfürstl. grosses Theater, in 1694.					SCHATZ 1333

I prodigi d'amore, ballet. *See* Sarti's Il militare bizzarro.

I prodigi dell' innocenza. Drama per musica rappresentato in Firenze nel carnevale dell' anno 1708 . . .
Firenze, Vincenzo Vangelisti, 1707. 64 p. 15½^{cm}.
Three acts. Argument, cast, scenario, and prefatory note, in which the unknown author acknowledges his indebtedness to the text ["Ottone"] by conte Roberto Frigimelica, for "pensieri" not only, but in many places for "sue parole medesime." Composer not mentioned, and unknown to Schatz.
First performed, as indicated, Teatro in via della Pergola.					SCHATZ 11359

Il prodigio dell' innocenza. Drama per musica da rappresentarsi nel Teatro Grimano de Ss. Gio. e Paolo. L'anno 1695 . . .
Venetia, Per il Nicolini, 1695. 70, [1] p. 14½^{cm}.
Three acts. By Fulgenzio Matteo Gualazzi. Neither he is mentioned, nor the composer, Tommaso **Albinoni**. Dedication, argument, scenario, notice to the reader.
					SCHATZ 104

Progne e Filomene, o sia Tereo, tiranno di Nasora, ballet. *See* Nasolini's Timoleone.

The **progress of a harlot.** A. T. of The jew decoy'd.

Les projets de l'Amour, ballet-héroïque, en trois actes; représenté, à Versailles, devant Sa Majesté, le mercredi 29 mai 1771
[Paris], Pierre Robert Christophe Ballard, 1771. 4 p. l., 51 p. 21½.^{cm}
Cast and name of Jean Joseph Cassanea de **Mondonville** as composer. The author of the text is not mentioned and is not recorded. The single acts were called "L'Himen et l'Amour," "Jupiter et Calisto," and "Mirzele."					ML 52.2.P75

Prologue des deux pièces suivantes. Representé par la Troupe du Sieur Francisque à la Foire de Saint-Germain. 1721 . . .
Below the title, the Avertissement:
"Quelques personnes de la premiere distinction s'étant interessés pour cette troupe, on la laissa joüer ce prologue & les deux pièces qui le suivent en prose, mêlée de vaudevilles."

— **Arlequin Endymion.** Pièce d'un acte. Representée par la Troupe du Sieur Francisque à la Foire de Saint Germain 1721 . . .
Below the title, this Avertissement:
"Les comédiens italiens dans ce temps-là représentèrent devant le roi une pièce intitulée *Diane & Endymion,* ce qui donna occasion de faire celleci, qui contient quelques scenes parodiées."

— **La forêt de Dodone.** Representée par la troupe du Sieur Francisque à la Foire de Saint Germain 1721.
Le Théâtre de la foire, Paris, 1724, t. iv, 3 pl., [213]–251 p. 17^{cm}.
From 264 the pagination jumps, by printer's error, to 295! According to a note on 2d p. l., the plays in t. iv were by Le Sage, Fuzelier, and d'Orneval. The "prologue" is entirely in prose; the two other plays *en prose, mêlée de vaudevilles.* The airs, selected or composed and arranged by Jean Claude **Gillier,** the "compositeur" of the theatre, are printed at end of the volume in the "Table des airs."
					ML 48.L2 IV

Prologue des Indes galantes. *See* Rameau's Les Indes galantes.

La promessa serbata al primo. Drama per musica da rappresentarsi nel Teatro de' SS. Gio. e Paolo l'anno 1697.

Venetia, Nicolini, 1697. 4 p. l., 48 p. 15^{cm}.

Three acts. Author unknown to Schatz. Argument, notice to the reader, scenario. The composer, Antonio **Caldara**, is not mentioned.   SCHATZ 1496

Les promesses de mariage, suite de L'épreuve villageoise, opéra bouffon en deux actes et un vers, par M. Desforges. Musique de M. Berton. Représenté, pour la première fois, par les Comédiens italiens ordinaires du roi, le 4 juillet, 1787.

Paris, Brunet, 1788. 26 p. 19½^{cm}.   SCHATZ 902

The prophetess or, The history of Dioclesian. Written by Francis Beaumont and John Fletcher. With alterations and additions, after the manner of an opera. Represented at the Queen's theatre, by Their Majesties servants.

London, Jacob Tonson, 1690. 2 p. l., 74, [2] p. 21^{cm}.

Five acts and epilogue. The operatic adaptation was made by Thomas Betterton. Neither he nor the composer, Henry **Purcell**, is mentioned. This copy contains no preliminary matter of any kind except the title page and list of characters.

First performed in the early summer of 1690.   ML 48.M2D

— **The prophetess;** or, The history of Dioclesian. A dramatic opera, with all the new songs, and the masque. As performed at the Theatre-Royal in Covent-Garden.

London, J. and R. Tonson, 1759. 72 p. 16^{cm}.

Five acts. Cast. Neither authors nor composer mentioned, but Cummings lists this modernization under the works of Thomas Aug. **Arne.**   LONGE 72

Il proseguimento del Chiarlone, dramma giocoso per musica di Giacomo Fiorini, da rappresentarsi nel Teatro rua dos Condes in Lisbona l'autunno dell' anno 1766 . . .

Lisbona, Pietro Ferreira, n. d. 8 p. l., 179 p. 14½^{cm}.

Three acts. Author's dedication, cast, scenario, and name of Luigi **Marescalchi** as the composer. Portuguese title-page, "Proceguimento, ou Segunda parte do Falador," and text face the Italian.   SCHATZ 5947

Proserpina rapita. Intermedio pe rmusica di Benedetto Ferrari dalla Tiorba.

n. i., n. d. p. [293]–30³ (Poesie drammatiche di Benedetto Ferrari, Milano, 1644.) 13½^{cm}.

Detached copy. One act, composed by the author, as appears from the sonnet addressed to the author on p. 295.

First performed at Bologna, Teatro Guastavillani, 1645.   SCHATZ 3069

Proserpina rapita. Intermedii in musica per la pastorale da recitarsi in casa de gl'illustriss. Signori Co. Costante, et Alessandro Bentivogli. D. C. R. C.

Bologna, per gli heredi di Giovanni Rossi, 1613. 30 p. 19½^{cm}.

Prologue and four intermedii. The dedication "Ad Amore" contains no special data. No composer recorded by Ricci or Schatz, but from Solerti's "L'origine del melodramma," p. 236, it appears that conte Ridolfo Campeggi was the author and Girolamo **Giacobbi** perhaps the composer.   ML 50.2.P68

Proserpine, tragedie en musique, ornée d'entrées de ballet, de machines, & de changements de theatre. Representée devant Sa Majesté à Saint Germain en Laye le [*blank*] de fevrier 1680.

Paris, Christophe Ballard, 1680. 7 p. l. (inc. front.), 70 p. 23^{cm}.

Bound in with Bellerophon, 1679, also composed by **Lully.**
Prologue and five acts. Casts. Neither the company nor the author, Philippe Quinault, is mentioned.
First performed, as indicated, February 3, 1680 (Schatz), February 5 (Prunières), and at Paris, Académie royale de musique, November 15, 1680. ML 50.2.B35L9

— **Proserpine,** tragedie en musique, ornée d'entrées de ballet, de machines, & de changements de theatre. Representé devant Sa Majesté à Saint Germain en Laye. Suivant la copie imprimée, à Paris.

[Amsterdam, Antoine Schelte], 1688. 72 p. (incl. front.) 13½^{cm}.

Five acts and prologue. Cast. Neither Quinault nor **Lully** are mentioned.
ML 50.2.P7L9

— **Proserpine,** tragedie representée par l'Academie royale de musique l'an 1680. Les paroles de M. Quinault, & la musique de M. de Lully. XII. opera.

n. i., n. d. 14^{cm}. front., 197–268 p. (Recueil général des opéra, t. ii, Paris, 1703.)

Detached copy. Prologue and five acts. Schatz 5770
Second copy. ML 48.R4

— **Proserpine.** Tragedie en musique ornée d'entrées de ballet, de machines & de changemens de théatre. Représentée devant Sa Majesté à Saint Germain en Laye, le 3. février 1680.

Quinault, Théatre, Paris, 1739, t. v., pl., 68 p. 17^{cm}.

Five acts. Without name of **Lully** as the composer. PQ 1881.A1 1739

— **Proserpine,** tragédie, représentée devant le roi, a Saint Germain en Laye, en 1680; et par l'Académie-royale de musique, en juillet 1699. Mars 1715. Janvier 1727. Janvier 1741. Et remise au théâtre, le mardi 14 novembre 1758.

Paris, Aux dépens de l'Académie, chez la V. De Lormel & fils, 1758. 71 p. 22½^{cm}.

Five acts without prologue. Cast. Names of Quinault and **Lully.**
ML 50.2.P72L9

— **Petrine,** parodie de Proserpine. Représentée pour la premiere fois par les Comédiens italiens ordinaires du roi, le 13 janvier 1759.

Paris, N. B. Duchesne, 1759. 64 p. 19^{cm}. (Theatre de M. Favart, Duchesne, 1763–77, t. iv.)

One act. Prose and vaudevilles. Many airs printed in the text. Cast. The arranger or composer is not mentioned and is unknown to Font. According to the preface (v. I, p. xix) some of the couplets were written by Sedaine. According to Font "Petrine" is merely a much altered version of Favart's "Farinette," a parody (performed March 9, 1741) of Lully's "Proserpine," revived January 31, 1741. The original version was "tout en vaudevilles." ML 49.A2F1

La prosperità di Elio Sejano. O. T. of Minato's libretto La generosità di Tiberio.

La prosperita di Elio Seiano. Dramma per musica nel Teatro a S. Salvatore l'anno MDCLXVII . . .

*Venetia, Bortolo Tramontino, 1667. 72 p. 14½*cm.

Three acts. Dedication by the author, conte Nicolò Minato, and dated Venice, January 15, 1666, argument, scenario, and notice to the reader which reads, in part:

"A questo drama, nominato La prosperità di Seiano, doveva la sera immediatamente vedersi l'altro intitolato La caduta di Seiano, mà per non ritardarti il godimento de gl'insigni virtuosi che v'intervengono, & il diletto della musica del Signor Antonio **Sartorio** . . . s'è voluto prevenire con questa, per farti poi in breui giorni sentire anco l'altra compositione."

This notice, therefore, would cancel the one at the end of the text:

"Segue poi l'opera intitolata La Caduta di Seiano, che si rappresenta la sera seguente alla recita di questa."   SCHATZ 9486

La prosperità infelice di Giulio Cesare dittatore. Opera musicale di Gio. Francesco Busenello.

*Venetia, Andrea Giuliani, 1656. 64 p. 15*cm.

Five acts, with prologue. Argument and scenario, but without name of the composer. Music attributed by Schatz and Wiel (in the "Musical Antiquary") to Pietro Francesco **Cavalli**. Both date the first performance 1646, Teatro Novissimo, Venice, though the libretto plainly has date of 1656.   SCHATZ 1726

Proteo sul Reno. Poemetto drammatico nel giorno del gloriosissimo nome della Sac. Real Maestà di Giuseppe I. rè de' Romani.

*Pietro Antonio Bernardoni, Poemi drammatici, parte terza, Vienna, van Ghelen, 1707, p. 79–90. 16½*cm.

The composer, Giovanni Battista **Bononcini**, is not mentioned.
First performed at Vienna, Hoftheater, as indicated, March 19, 1703.

ML 49.A2B4

Protesilao. Dramma per musica in due atti con cori e balli analoghi composto dal Signor abate Sertor di Venezia e messo in musica dal Signor Amedeo Naumann . . . da rappresentarsi nel Regio Teatro di Berlino il carnovale dell' anno 1793.

*Berlino, Haude e Spener, n. d. 73 p. 16½*cm.

Argument and cast. German title page, "Protesilaus," and text face Italian. (*See* next entry.)

First performed, as indicated, in January, 1793.   SCHATZ 7055

Protesilao. Dramma per musica in due atti con cori e balli analoghi. Composto dal Signor abate Sertor di Venezia. E messo in musica il primo atto: dal Sign. Gio. Feder. Reichardt . . . ed il second' atto dal Signor Amadeo Naumann . . . Da rappresentarsi nel Regio Teatro di Berlino il carnovale MDCCLXXXIX.

*Berlino, Haude e Spener, n. d. 73, [2] p. 16*cm.

Argument and cast. German title-page, "Protesilaus," and text face Italian.
First performed, as indicated, January 26, 1789.   SCHATZ 8654

Protesilaus. Tr. of Naumann's Protesilao, also of his and Reichardt's opera of this title.

Il protettor del poeta. Intermezzi per musica a tre voci da rappresentarsi nel Teatro alla Valle nel carnevale dell' anno 1754 . . .

*Roma, Si vendono nella Libraria di S. Michele, 1754. 24 p. 15½*cm.

Two parts. Author not mentioned and unknown to Schatz. Dedication signed by G. Puccinelli and Angelo Lungi, cast and name of Gaetano **Latilla** as composer.

ML 50.2.P73L2

Il protettore alla moda. Dramma comico per musica da rappresentarsi nel Teatro Tron di S. Cassiano l'autunno dell' anno 1749.

Venezia, Modesto Fenzo, 1749. 60 p. 15^{cm}.

Three acts. A new version of "Chi non fà non falla," by Giuseppe Maria **Buini**, who is not mentioned, and who also was responsible for the music (Bologna, 1729). For the replica, **Galuppi** reset more or less the whole libretto, but it is probable that, besides Buini and Galuppi's music, music by several other composers was used in this pasticcio (Piovano). The libretto for this further replica of 1749 contains no reference to the composers.   SCHATZ 3520

La prova del dramma serio. Dramma giocoso per musica da rappresentarsi in Firenze nel R. Teatro di via del Cocomero nel carnevale dell' anno 1797 . . .

Firenze, Anton Giuseppe Pagani e comp., 1797. 19 p. 16$\frac{1}{2}$^{cm}.

One act. Author not mentioned, and unknown to Schatz. Cast and name of Ferdinando **Rutini** as the composer. ("La musica è tutta nuova.")   SCHATZ 9185

La prova del vero amore. A. T. of the ballet Le due rivali.

La Provençale. Entrée in Mouret's Les festes de Thalie.

La Provençale. For Duni's parody of this, *see his* La fille mal gardée.

The prude, a comic opera . . .

n. i., n. d. [97]–176 p. 20^{cm}.

Three acts. By Eliza Ryves, who is not mentioned, and from whose Poems on several occasions (London, 1777), this appears to be detached. She says, in a footnote on p. [97]:

"The author hopes her readers will be so indulgent, as to consider that this opera was intended for the stage, and most of the airs composed for particular tunes . . ."

The titles of these are given on p. 175–176, in a table of the "Old tunes, to which the airs are adapted."   LONGE 197

La prudenza vittoriosa. *See* M. Curzio.

Prunella: an interlude perform'd in the The Rehearsal, at the Theatre-Royal in Drury-Lane. The sense and musick collected from the most famous masters. By Mr. Airs, for the advantage of Mr. Estcourt . . .

London, Printed for Bernard Lintott, n. d. 2 p. l., 16 p. 21$\frac{1}{2}$^{cm}.

A prefatory note by Estcourt precedes the list of characters. The interlude has four scenes spread over the four acts of "The Rehearsal," a comedy by George Villiers, duke of Buckingham. In the margin some of the airs are indicated to which the airs in "Prunnella" were to be sung. The indicated airs were taken from Clayton's "Arsinoe," from Bononcini's "Camilla" and from "Thomyris." Also popular airs (ballad airs?) seem to have been used! On the title page is this

"Note, that an opera, of which this is but a part, will be soon finished and printed, with a prologue and epilogue; and a preface in praise of the fineness and delicacy of operas, and the difference between an Italian opera and an opera in Italy."

According to Clarence "Printed before 1713 . . . Acted Drury Lane, Februray 12, 1708," the same date as given by Genest.   ML 50.2.P74

La pruova reciproca. Commedia per musica di Giuseppe Palomba da rappresentarsi nel Teatro de' Fiorentini per second' opera di quest' anno 1789.

Napoli, n. publ., 1789. 48 p. 14$\frac{1}{2}$^{cm}.

Two acts. Cast and name of Giacomo **Tritto** as the composer.   SCHATZ 10474

Psiche, componimento musicale cantato in Vienna, a di 19. novembre 1720 e replicato nel 1721.

Apostolo Zeno, Poesie drammatiche, Venezia, 1744, t. vii, p. [359]–390. 19ᶜᵐ.

No composer is mentioned. (The music was composed by *Fux* and *Caldara.*) In the "Catalogo" at end of t. x it is said of this text: "ora per la prima volta stampata."

ML 49.A2Z3

— **Psiche,** componimento musicale cantato in Vienna.

Apostolo Zeno, Poesie drammatiche, Orleans, 1785–86, t. xi, p. 349–382. 21ᶜᵐ.

One act. No composer is mentioned.

ML 49.A2Z4

La **Psiche.** Poemetto drammatico nel giorno del gloriosissimo nome della Sac. Ces. Real Maestà dell' imperadrice Eleonora Maddalena Teresa.

Pietro Antonio Bernardoni, Poemi drammatici, parte terza, Vienna, van Ghelen, 1707, p. 107–121.

Argument. The composer, Carlo Agostino **Badia,** is not mentioned.
First performed at Vienna, Hoftheater, February 21, 1703, as indicated.

ML 49.A2B4

La **Psiche.** Dramma musicale di Francᵒ di Poggiᵒ Cantato in Lucca nell anno MDCVL . . .

Lucca, Francescᵒ. Marescandoli, 1654. 1 p. l., 76 p. 21ᶜᵐ.

The publisher's dedication, Lucca, 1654, is followed by a notice to the reader, a dedication by "Li sei Accademici deputati" dated October 25, 1648, beginning "Esce finalmente questa nuova Psiche da' Teatri alle stampe," but from the publisher's dedication and notice to the reader it appears that the publication was delayed until 1654. Madrigal (words) by Antonio Fortini, argument, "Allegoria della favola," "Distributione dell' apparato." Architettura di Paulo Lipparelli, list of characters, prologue and five acts. The "Distributione" reads, in part:

"Fv' promosso il trattenimento di quest' Opera in Lucca, per gl'otij Carneualeschi del 1645. dalla Accademia delli Accesi; e fù espresso nella Sala del Palazzo de' Borghi, che nella sua mole antica, non punto violata da gl'anni, confessa d'hauer assistito à i nobili natali di questa Etrusca Figlia di Roma. Alla Poesia di Francesco di Poggio successe la Musica spiritosa di Tomaso **Breni;** che articolata con viuacissima leggiadria, fù poi cantata con straordinaria lode da varij Cantori, tanto nationali, che forestieri; ma trà tutti, dal Caualiere Nicolò Margheritoni, virtuoso Seruitore dell' Eccellentiss. Sig. Prencipe di Massa, che con energia molto efficace, vestitosi delle tenere conditioni di Psiche, seppe violentar al diletto egualmente, & alla commiseratione l'vniuersal sentimento delli Ascoltanti. Paulo Lipparelli, soggetto di celebrato grido, adempiendo le parti d'officiosissimo Accademico, arrichì lo spettacolo con merauigliose inuentioni di Apparato, & di Machine; di che all' altrui curiosità qui à parte si disegnano le memorie; & Francesco Sbarra, quell' ingegno grande, che nelle sue numerose, & bizzarre compositioni Drammatiche hà saputo erudire i costumi del nostro secolo, con arti non più godute sopra le Scene, hebbe gusto di sopr' intendere alla vniuersale Economia di tutta l'Attione rappresentatiua. Con appassionata applicatione inseruirono à quest' Opera molti altri Accademici, & soggetti di qualità; ma trà tutti si vide risplendere con singolarità di vantaggio la persona dell' Arcidiacono Francesco Sardi, che con larga contributione d'affetto, & d'oro, le adornò la comparsa, & le assicurò opportunamente ogni applauso." Sᴄʜᴀᴛᴢ 1315

Psiche. Tragicomedia rappresentata in musica, et dedicata alla serenissima Isabella Clara arciduchessa d'Austria, etc nelle sue augustissime nozze col serenissimo Carlo Secondo, duca di Mantova . . .

Mantova, Osanna, 1649. 1 p. l., 96 p. 22ᶜᵐ.

Prologue and five acts. Dedication by the editor, Francesco Bulgarini of date Mantova, October [*blank*], 1649, with name of Diamante Gabrielli as author, Alle-

Psiche—Continued.

goria, and editor's lengthy notice to the reader on the character of this drama, including remark:

"essendo il drama composto da rappresentarsi in musica, e con machine apparenti, poca vaghezza havrebbe avuta, cominciandosi dopo che Psiche fosse tornata dall' inferno: come all' incontro era necessario il farlo breve diversi, perche, portando lunghezza la musica, non havessero i Serenissimi prencipi, che v'intervennero, à stare à disaggio. Non durò più di tre hore in quattro; tempo nondimeno aggiustato alle sceniche poesie; di modo che al sentire d'Angelo Ingegneri nel luogo sopracitato, se più durassero, benche dilettevoli, sempre noiose riuscirebbono. Si potrebbe aggiungere, che il tesser lunga la favola, è cosi senza la mira, che possa commodamente recitarsi in musica, è difetto; che se bene oggidì si recitano spesso i drami senza musica, non è il dovere, che si tolga loro il potersi almeno in musica rappresentare . . ."

On p. 91–96 laudatory sonnets, etc. The composer, Alessandro **Leardini**, is not mentioned.

First performed in September, 1649, as indicated.   ML 50.2.P78L3

La **Psiche**, o vero Amore innamorato. Drama per musica rappresentato nel Real Palazzo, in ossequio del compleaños della Maestà della Regina Madre nostra signora, (che Dio guardi.) . . .

     Napoli, Carlo Porsile, 1683. 6 p. l., 68 p. 14^{cm}.

Three acts. Argument, cast, "Apparenze," name of Alessandro **Scarlatti** as composer, and dedication signed by Filippo Schor, Nicola Vaccaro, e Francesco della Torre and dated, Naples, December 21, 1683:

"La Psiche, che affidata nella protezzione dell' E. V. altre volte nel idioma spagnuolo fece pompa de suoi tragici avecenimenti, trasportata hora da un humilissimo servitore di V. E. nella favella italiana nõ ardirebbe esporsi di nuovo sù le scene senza la benigna assistēza del primiero suo protettore . . ."

Mentioned by Dent? Not recorded by Schatz.   ML 50.2.P78S2

Psiche ed Amore, intermedii. *See* Descrizione de gl'intermedii.

Psyché, tragedie. Representée par L'Academie royale de musique. Suivant la copie imprimée à Paris.

     [*Amsterdam, Antoine Schelte*], *1688. 60 p. (incl. front.) 13$\frac{1}{2}$^{cm}.*

Prologue and five acts and the dedication "L'Académie royale de musique au roy." Neither Corneille nor **Lully** is mentioned.   ML 50.2.P8L92

— **Psyché**, tragedie representée par l'Academie royale de musique l'an 1678. Les paroles sont de Mr Corneille & la musique de M. de Lully. X. opera.

     n. i., n. d. 14^{cm}. pl., 69–134 p. (Recueil général des opéra, t. ii, Paris, 1703.)

Detached copy. The dedicatory poem, prologue, and five acts. Fontenelle is sometimes said to have been a joint author, but Prunières questions this. He claims that Thomas Corneille simply turned his and Molière's "Psyché" of 1671, for which Lully had composed the intermèdes, etc., into an opera. Lully composed the necessary new music in three weeks. In this form "Psyché" was first performed, as indicated, April 9, 1678 (Schatz), April 19 (Prunières).   SCHATZ 5771

                Second copy. ML 48.R4

Psyché. L. T. of Mondonville's L'Amour et Psyché.

Psyche. Singespiel in zwei aufzuegen von Karl Muechler [portrait vignette].

     Berlin, Friedrich Maurer, 1789. 1 p. l., 86 p. 16$\frac{1}{2}$^{cm}.

The title page contains the portrait of "Friederike Auguste Conradine Unzelmann geb. Flittner." The composer, Carl Bernhard **Wessely**, is not mentioned.

First performed at Berlin, Nationaltheater, November 18, 1789.   SCHATZ 10990

Publio Cornelio Scipione. Dramma per musica da rappresentarsi nel Regio Teatro di Torino l'anno MDCCXXVI . . .

Torino, Francesco Antonio Gattinara, n. d. 60, [1] p. 15ᶜᵐ.

Three acts. Dedication, "notizie storiche," cast, and scenario. Neither the author, Antonio Salvi, nor the composer, Giovanni Antonio Giai, is mentioned. First performed, as indicated, December 26, 1725.   Schatz 3817

Publio Cornelio Scipione. Drama per musica da rappresentarsi nel famoso Teatro Grimani di S. Gio. Grisostomo nel carnovale dell' anno 1712 . . .

Venetia, Marino Rossetti, n. d. 79 p. 15ᶜᵐ.

Five acts. Neither the author, conte Agostino Piovene, nor the composer, Carlo Francesco Pollaroli, is mentioned. Dedicatory sonnet, historical notes, cast, and scenario.   Schatz 8313

Pub. Elio Pertinace. Drama per musica da rappresentarsi nel Teatro Vendramino di San Salvatore l'anno MDCLXXXIV . . .

Venetia, Francesco Nicolini, 1684. 70 p. (incl. front.) 14ᶜᵐ.

Three acts. Dedication by the author, Pietro d'Averara, argument, cast, scenario, and name of Giovanni Legrenzi as composer.   Schatz 5538

Second copy.   ML 48.M2O

Il Pubᵒ Scipione. Dramma per musica. MDCCLXXXVIV.

Author's manuscript. [61] p. 20½ᶜᵐ.

Two acts. Text preceded by the list of characters, argument, and the anonymous author's dedicatory "Lettera al Sig. Deifebo Romagnoli." According to Piovano, in the Supplement to Eitner, the composer, Deifebo Romagnoli, since 1795 organist at the cathedral of Siena, was also a poet. If that is correct, it is possible that he is the author of this libretto, since the "Lettera" is written in a curiously facetious, self-ironical tone. At any rate, the libretto appears to have been written at the request of Romagnoli for his use. Whether or not he composed it, is not known to me.

ML 48.A5 v. 32

Le **public vengé,** comédie-vaudeville en un acte, avec un prologue; représentée pour la premiere fois, par les Comédiens italiens ordinaires du roi, à la rentrée du 9 avril 1782.

Paris, la veuve Ballard & fils, 1782. 96, [4] p. 20ᶜᵐ.

Cast. The prologue is called "Le poisson d'avril." The 4 p. contain the vaudevilles "Loin d'ici la morale" and "Autheurs que la cabale." Composer and authors unknown to me.   ML 50.2.P85

Die **puecefarbnen schuhe** oder Die schoene schusterinn. Ein komisches singspiel in zwey aufzuegen. Aus dem franzoesischen des herrn baron v. Serrieres frey uebersetzt und bearbeitet von Stephanie dem juengern. Die musick ist neu gemacht vom herrn kapellmeister Umlauf. Aufgefuehrt im K. K. Nationaltheater.

Wien, beym Logenmeister, 1779. 69 p. 15½ᶜᵐ.

Haas says that Stephanie took over, without alterations, several arias in Joh. André's translation of de Serrières's "Les souliers mordorés" (1776). First performed, as indicated, June 19, 1779 (Schatz), June 22, 1779 (Haas).

Schatz 10529

— Die **schoene schusterinn.** Ein komisches singspiel in zwey aufzuegen.

n. i. p. 1–68. 16½ᶜᵐ. (Gottlieb Stephanie d. jüng., Singspiele, Liegnitz, 1792.)   Schatz 10530

Die **puecefarbnen schuhe**—Continued.

— Arien und gesaenge aus der operette in zwey aufzuegen: Die **schoene schusterinn**, oder Die schuhe à la Marlborough. Aus dem franzoesischen des baron dů [!] Serrieres. Die musik vom herrn Umlauf . . .

Berlin, n. publ., 1794.   24 p.   15½cm.

Cast.
First performed at Berlin, Kgl. Nationaltheater, 1794.   SCHATZ 10531

La pulcella d'Orleans.   A. T. of Andreozzi's Giovanna d'Arco.

Pulcinella, cavaliere d'industria, ballet. *See* Monza's Ifigenia in Tauride.

Puntigli, e gelosie tra moglie, e marito.   Commedia per musica di Giuseppe Palomba da rappresentarsi nel Teatro Nuovo nell' autunno dell' anno 1784.

Napoli, n. publ., 1784.   59 p.   14½cm.

Three acts.   Cast and name of the composer, Luigi **Caruso**.   SCHATZ 1650

I puntigli gelosi.   Dramma giocoso per musica di Filippo Livigni. Da rappresentarsi nel nobile Teatro in San Samuele il carnovale dell' anno 1783.

Venezia, Modesto Fenzo, 1783.   62, [1] p.   17½cm.

Two acts.   Cast, scenario, and name of Felice **Alessandri** as composer.   The "Secondo ballo" was entitled, "Il trionfo d'Arianna o sia Arianna abbandonata da Teseo, e soccorsa da Bacco d'invenzione del Sig. Onorato Viganò."   SCHATZ 154

Il puntiglio amoroso.   Dramma giocoso per musica da rappresentarsi nel Teatro Giustiniani di S. Moisè il presente carnovale MDCCLXIII.

Venezia, Francesco Valvasense, n. d.   56 p.   15½cm.

Three acts.   The author is not mentioned.   Cast, scenario, and name of **Galuppi** as the composer.   Schatz and Wotquenne attribute the text to Carlo Gozzi, Pavan to Gaspare Gozzi, Wiel and Piovano leave the question open.
First performed, as indicated, December 26, 1762.   SCHATZ 3507

La pupilla.   Intermezzo.

[176]–192 p.   16½cm.   (Carlo Goldoni, Opere drammatiche giocose, t. iv, Torino, 1757.)

Two parts.   First composer not recorded by Allacci, Wiel or Schatz.

                                                  ML 49.A2G6

— **La pupilla.**   Intermezzo di due parti per musica.   Rappresentato per la prima volta in Venezia l'autunno dell' anno MDCCXXXIV.

Carlo Goldoni, Opere teatrali, Venezia, Zatta e figli, 1788–95, t. 35, [51]–70 p.   18½cm.   PQ

La pupilla.   O. T. of d' Avossa's La pupilla ed il Ciarlone and Il Ciarlone.

La pupilla.   Farsetta in musica a tre voci a recitarsi nel Teatro alla Valle il carnevale dell' anno 1755 . . .

Roma, Ottavio Puccinelli, 1755.   22 p.   15½cm.

Two parts.   Author not mentioned and unknown to Schatz.   The text is neither by Ant. Palomba nor by Goldoni, though "Signor tutore, non dubitare" has been

La pupilla—Continued.

borrowed from his "La pupilla" and "Al mio ben si tu dirai" from his "Il filosofo di campagna." None of the other arias listed in Wotquenne's Verzeichnis. They are "Luci care, luci belle," "Non mi state a infastidire," "Va cantando l'augellino," etc. Cast, name of Francesco Saverio **Garcia** as composer and dedication by (the author?) Angelo Lungi. ML 50.2.P9G2

— Die **pfleg-tochter,** ein lustig musicalisches zwischen-spiel zu drey stimmen so auf gnaedigstem befehl Ihro Churfuerstl. Durchlaucht aufgefuehrt worden. den 21ten novembris 1758.

Mannheim, Churfuerstliche Hof- und cantzley-buchdruckerei, n. d. 67 p. 16½ᶜᵐ.

"Francesco Saverio Gurzia [!] der sogenannte Spagnoletto" is mentioned as the composer. Consequently a German version of Francesco Saverio **Garcia's** "La pupilla." The translator is not mentioned and is unknown to Schatz. SCHATZ 3555

La pupilla astuta. Dramma giocoso per musica da rappresentarsi nel nobiliss. Nuovo Teatro di Padova l'autunno dell' anno 1794 . . .

Padova, fratelli Conzatti, n. d. 81 p. 17ᶜᵐ.

Two acts. Neither the author (unknown to Schatz) nor the composer, Giuseppe **Elia,** is mentioned. Cast. Because of the radical changes in Harnaud's "Follie amorose" the anonymous author says "posso dirmi più compositore, che traduttore." First performed at Palermo, Teatro di S. Cecilia, fall of 1792. SCHATZ 2913

La pupilla, ed il ciarlone, dramma giocoso per musica da rappresentarsi nel Regio Teatro danese.—Myndlingen og Sladdreren, et lystigt synge-spil . . .

Kiøbenhavn, L. N. Svare, 1769. 177 p. 17½ᶜᵐ.

Three acts. Danish text faces Italian. By Antonio Palomba, who is not mentioned. Cast and name of Giuseppe Abbos (=Giuseppe **d'Avossa**) as composer. First performed at Naples, Teatro dei Fiorentini, carnival, 1763, as "La pupilla." SCHATZ 511

— Il **ciarlone.** Dramma giocoso per musica da rappresentarsi nei Teatri privilegiati di Vienna nell' anno 1770.

Vienna, Giovanni Tomaso di Trattnern, n. d. 64 p. 16½ᶜᵐ.

Argument, but without name of composer, Giuseppe **d'Avossa,** or librettist, Ant. Palomba. SCHATZ 512

La pupilla rapita. Dramma giocoso per musica da rappresentarsi nel Teatro Giustiniani di S. Moise il presente autunno MDCCLXIII.

Venezia, n. publ., n. d. 69 p. 15ᶜᵐ.

Three acts. Author not mentioned and unknown to Schatz. Cast, scenario, and note:
"La musica sarà tutta nuova del Sig. maestro Saverio **Laurenti** romano, eccettuate alcune arie, che saranno pure nuove del Sig. maestro Antonio **Boroni** romano a mottivo della ristrettezza del tempo per la absenza del Sig. maestro Gio. Battista Ruttini, e saranno contradistinte dal segno *."
The only arias thus marked are: "Ah sposina mia carina" (III, 12), "Le donne col cervello" (III, 6), "Oh che bile, oh che tremore" (II, 11), "Quel piacer d'esservi sposa" (II, 6), "Vo mostrarvi alla francese" (I, 7). SCHATZ 5473

La pupilla scaltra. Dramma giocoso per musica da rappresentarsi nel nobilissimo Teatro Venier in San Benedetto il carnovale dell' anno 1795.

Venezia, Modesto Fenzo, 1795. 88 p. 18½ᶜᵐ.

Two acts. Author not mentioned and unknown to Schatz. Cast, scenario, and name of Pietro **Guglielmi** as the composer. On p. 50–59 argument, cast, and descrip-

La pupilla scaltra—Continued.

tion of Giuseppe Traffieri's "Bianca de' Rossi, ballo tragico pantomimo" in five acts, music ("tutta nuova") by Vittorio Trento. Traffieri's second comic ballet was called "Rosa e Nicola."

First performed as indicated, January 8, 1795.   Schatz 4257

The purse; or, Benevolent tar. A musical drama, in one act, as performed at the Theatre Royal in the Hay-Market. By J. C. Cross. (The music by Mr. Reeve.)

London, Printed by William Lane, 1794. 32 p. 20ᶜᵐ.

Cast and prefatory note.

First performed February 8, 1794.   Longe 227

Pursignacco e Grilletta. *See* Orlandini's Pourceaugnac and Grilletta.

Die puzmacherinn. Eine operette in drei akten von J. W. A. Schoepfel, und in musik gesezt von Friedrich Preu.

Baireuth, Johann Andreas Luebeks erben, 1790. 176 p.

On p. 174–176 sale's catalogue of the publisher.   Schatz 8465

Pygmalion. Ein monodrama von J. J. Rousseau. Neu uebersetzt von herrn Gotter. Die musik ist von herrn Georg Benda.

24 p. 14½ᶜᵐ. (No. I. of " Melodramen," Joseph Johann Morgensaeuler, Pilsen und Klattau, 1791.)

First performed at Gotha, Hoftheater, September 20, 1779.   Schatz 775

Pygmalion. *See* Coignet and Rousseau's Pigmalion.

The comick masque of Pyramus and Thisbe. As it is perform'd at the Theatre in Lincoln's-Inn Fields . . .

London, W. Mears, 1716. 4 p. l., 16 p. 19ᶜᵐ.

One act. Cast, argument, and preface signed by the author, Richard Leveridge, in which he says:

"As diversion is the business of the stage, 'tis variety best contributes to that diversion . . . And as our present encouragers of this part of the theatrical labours, have for some late years been chiefly regaled with high recitative and buskin airs; I have here endeavoured the quite reverse of those exalted performances; and hope I may challenge some small excuse for this exotick essay, from no less than example and precedent.

"If the first founders, the Italians, in the grandest of their performances, have introduced lions, bears, monkies, dragons etc as their doughty fables require: I know no reason why I may not turn moonshine into a minstrel; the lion and stone wall into songsters; and make them as diverting as a dance of chairs and butterflies have been in one of our most celebrated British entertainments . . ."

At the end of the argument Leveridge says that Shakespeare's "The Midsummer night's dream" he "made bold to dress out . . . in recitative, and airs, after the present Italian mode, hoping I have given it the same comical face, though in a musical dress." **Leveridge** also composed the music.

First performed October 29, 1716, as indicated.   Longe 54

Pyramus und Thisbe. Ein musikalisches duodram. Für das K. K. National-Hoftheater.

Wien, Johann Baptist Wallishausser, 1795. 16 p. 17ᶜᵐ.

Author unknown to Schatz. Composed by Anton **Eberl,** who is not mentioned.

First performed, as indicated, December 7, 1794; privately, 1793, at the Gesellschaftstheater of count v. Stockhammer.   Schatz 2889

Pyramus und Thisbe. Ein musikalisches duodram.

Halle, Hemmerdesche buchhandlung, 1787. v, [6]–32 p. 15^{cm}.

One act. Prefatory note, dated "K . . n [Koeln] im maerz 1787," and signed by the author [Friedrich Anton Franz] B[ertra]nd. He says:

"Wer kennt nicht Ariadne auf Naxos, und Medea-durch herrn Benda's meisterhafte komposizion, zwo der treflichsten deutschen originalstuekke? Ich wuenschte Pyramus und Thisbe auf gleiche art bearbeitet zu sehen, schrieb den gegenwaertigen text, und theilt' ihn herrn Benda mit . . . ich erhielt die schmeichelhafte versicherung: sowohl gegenstand als behandlung desselben wuerden vorzueglich sein musikalisches talent aufgefordert haben, der deutschen buene in jener manier ein drittes stueck zu liefern;—haetten ihn nicht vorfaelle mit derselben entzweit, die mir von zu grossem gewicht scheinen, als dass ich so indiskret seyn sollte, sie ohne des mannes erlaubnis vor's angesicht des publikuns zu bringen. Vielleicht ist diese arbeit so gluecklich, dass sie—versoehnt sich herr Benda selbst nicht noch in der folge mit dem theater;—irgend eine andre meisterhand der vollendung nicht unwerth haelt . . ."

Composed by Daniel Gottlob **Türk**, who is not mentioned. Schatz records no performance. SCHATZ 10512

Pyrrhus and Demetrius. An opera. As it is perform'd at the Queen's Theatre in the Hay-Market.

London, Jacob Tonson, 1709. 3 p. l., 52 p. 22^{cm}.

Three acts. Cast and dedication by "Owen Swiny" (Owen McSwiney). His text is practically a translation of Adriano Morselli's "Pirro e Demetrio." It does not include the seventeen English aria translations by Armstrong, printed by Walsh in the "Songs in . . . Pyrrhus and Demetrius." The libretto contains the Italian text and the English translation of all the arias, etc., that were sung in English, those sung in Italian remaining untranslated. The music was largely that composed by Alessandro **Scarlatti** for Naples (1694), but the overture and not less than twenty-one arias were by Nicolo Francesco **Haym**, as appears from Walsh's "Songs."

First performed at London December 14, 1708. ML 50.2.P95

Second copy. LONGE 208

Pythias und Damon, ein singspiel von zween aufzuegen, aufgefuehrt von den schuelern der ersten rhetorik am Katholischen schulhause bey St. Salvator im Aprilmonathe 1781.

Augsburg, Joseph Simon Hueber, n. d. 8 p. 18½^{cm}.

With "Vorbericht," cast, and name of the composer, Johann Evangelist **Drexel**. The author unknown to Schatz. Preceded by "Der patriotismus, ein trauerspiel." SCHATZ 2819

Il **quacquero** burlato, ballet. *See* Caruso's Gli amanti dispettosi.

Il **quadro animato,** ballet. *See* Portugal's Lo spazzacamino principe.

Il **quadro movibile,** ballet. *See* Galuppi's L'amante di tutte.

The **quaker;** a comic opera. As performed at the Theatre-Royal in Drury-Lane.

London, John Bell, 1777. 3 p. l., 44 p. 21^{cm}.

On first p. l. a portrait of Mr. Bannister in the character of Steady. Two acts. Cast. The author-composer, Charles **Dibdin**, is not mentioned. In Johnston's vocal score, "The face which frequently displays," is headed as "composed by Mr. **Linley**."

First performed April 3, 1775 (Clarence), October 7, 1777 (Schatz), May 3, 1775 (Genest). LONGE 87

La **quakera spiritosa.** Commedia per musica di Giuseppe Palomba da rappresentarsi nel Teatro de' Fiorentini per second' opera in quest-anno 1783.

Napoli, n. publ., 1783. 58 p. 14½^{cm}.

Three acts. Argument, cast, and name of Pietro **Guglielmi** as the composer. SCHATZ 4258

The **quaker's opera.** As it is perform'd at Lee's and Harper's great theatrical booth in Bartholomew-fair. With the musick prefix'd to each song.

London, Printed for J. W. and sold by J. Roberts [etc.], 1728. 3 p. l., 49 p. 20cm.

Three acts and introduction. By Thomas Walker, who is not mentioned. The text is preceded by a table of the 26 songs. Ballad opera, the airs of which are printed in the text with their titles, except no. 8 "And when we come unto the whit" and 19 "O Johnny, thou hast done me wrong," which have none.

According to Tufts, altered from "The Prison-breaker or The adventures of John Sheppard" (printed in 1725 but not acted.) ML 50.5.Q91

Second copy. LONGE 47

I **Quaqueri.** Dramma giocoso per musica di un atto solo di Giovanni Bertati. Da rappresentarsi nel Teatro Giustiniani in S. Moisè il carnovale dell' anno 1779.

n. i., n. d. 32 p. 17½cm.

Composed by Antonio **Rossetti** ("La musica sarà"). This was followed by "IL PIÚ BEL DONO INUTILE," also in one act, by the same author and composer and forming part of the same publication. SCHATZ 8883

Le **quart-d'heure de Rabélais,** comédie en un acte, en prose, mêlée de vaudevilles. Par les CC. Dieu-la-Foy et Prévôt-d'Iray. Représentée pour la première fois, sur le Théâtre du Vaudeville le 25 nivôse, an 7. [Jan. 14, 1799.]

Paris, chez le libraire au Théâtre du Vaudeville, an vii. [1798–99.] 64 p. 20cm.

Cast. "Avec 9 airs notés," printed in the text. Not recorded by either Cl. & L. or Schatz. ML 48.M2K

Il **quartiere fortunato.** Intermezzo di tre parti per musica.

Carlo Goldoni, Opere teatrali, Venezia, Zatta e figli, 1788–95, v. 35, [159]–180 p. 18½cm.

No composer recorded by Schatz. PQ

Der **Quasi-mann,** eine komische oper in zwey aufzuegen. In musik gesetzt von herrn Franz Danzi . . .

Muenchen bey Joseph Lindauer, 1789. 62 [1] p. 16cm.

With "Vorbericht," dated April, 1789, in which [Matthias Georg] Lambrecht says: "Le *naufrage, ou: Les funérailles de Crispin,* wurde in Wien unter dem titel: *Treue und undank,* neu bearbeitet. Man fand, dass dieses nachspiel zu sehr farçe sey; auch erinnere ich mich nicht, dass es auf einem andern deutschen theater in diesem neuen gewande sey gegeben worden. Mir schien der stoff zur komischen oper unverbesserlich. Ich denke, man wird ihm itzt den vorwurf des uebertriebenen nicht machen, da man sich sogar an italienische opern hat gewoehnen koennen. Am musikalischem interesse wird es ebenfalls nicht fehlen, da herr **Danzi** sich schon als ein mann von talent, dem publiko bekannt gemacht hat."

First performed at Munich, Opernhaus bei St. Salvator, August, 1789.

SCHATZ 2410

Les **quatre saisons,** divertissement de musique & de danco, pour célébrer le mariage de Son Altesse Royale de Pologne & Electorale de Saxe 1719.

Dresde, Jean Conrad Stössel, n. d. Unpaged. 17½cm.

Prologue and five entrées. Argument, cast, names of Jean Poisson as author and of Johann Christoph **Schmidt** as the composer and "avant-propos," which says that the king himself, wanting for the festivities "un espèce d'opera français," selected the sujet, formed the plan, and designated the list of characters, thus leaving to the

Les **quatre saisons**—Continued.

poet practically only the versification. The spoken and danced parts were all taken by members of the nobility, almost sixty persons, whereas for the chorus and orchestra the king's musicians, more than one hundred persons, were employed.

First performed September 23, 1719, at Dresden in the Royal Gardens.

SCHATZ 9641

Li **quattro elementi**: Carrosello tra le feste celebrate in Dresda per comando di S. M. in occasione delle nozze di L. L. A. A. R. R.

Dresda, G. C. Stössel, n. d. Unpaged. 18ᶜᵐ.

French title-page "Carrousel des quatre elemens," and text face Italian, the author of which is not mentioned. A prefatory note says:

"Cangiato in anfiteatro il giardino degli aranci contiguo al Regio elettoral palazzo servendo à ciò mirabilmente la magnifica loggia, che regna intorno ad esso giardino, comparisce Giove sopra macchina mobile rappresentante il Caos, introducendo nell' anfiteatro suddetto con ordinata, e vaga marchia quattro quadriglie . . ."

The names of the noblemen taking part in these, representing the four elements, are given on the next pages together with the name of Antonio **Lotti** as composer of Giove's monologue.

First performed during the marriage festivities for prince Friedrich August and Maria Gioseffa, princess of Austria, on September 15, 1719.

SCHATZ 5725

Le **quattro nazioni**. L. T. of Bernardini's La donna di spirito.

Le **quattro stagioni**. Commedia per musica di Giuseppe Palomba da rappresentarsi nel Real Teatro del Fondo di Separazione . . .

Napoli, n. publ., 1784. 58 p. 15ᶜᵐ.

Three acts. Impresario's dedication, dated Napoli, June 12, 1784, cast, and name of the composer, Luigi **Caruso**.

SCHATZ 1651

Que ne peut pas l'amour? Comédie lyrique.

Le magasin des modernes, La Haye, Propice, [1768]. p. 51–98, 67 p. 14ᶜᵐ.

One act. The text proper on p. 53–94. In the prefatory remarks it is said that "cette petite piece . . . n'est faite que pour paroître dans l'asile d'une société." Interesting is also the remark:

"J'ai donc fait un opera-comique; ou plutôt, comme l'on dit aujourd'hui, une comédie lyrique."

The 67 p. contain the *airs notés* belonging to the piece. Neither author nor composer is mentioned. Not recorded by Schatz.

ML 20.M14

The **Queens masque**. A. T. of Loves mistresse.

Quello che può accadere. Dramma giocoso per musica da rappresentarsi nel nobile Teatro di San Samuele il carnovale dell' anno 1784.

Venezia, Gio. Battista Casali, n. d. 63 p. 18ᶜᵐ.

Two acts. Cast, scenario, and name of composer, Gaetano **Andreozzi**, but not of librettist, who is unknown to Schatz.

SCHATZ 218

La **querelle des theatres**. Prologue. Par Messieurs le S** & de la F*. Représenté à la Foire de Saint Laurent 1718. Et ensuite sur le Théâtre de l'Opéra, par ordre de Son A. R. Madame.

Le Théâtre de la foire, Paris, 1737, t. iii, pl., [37]–59 p. 17ᶜᵐ.

By Le Sage and Lafont. The airs, selected or composed and arranged by Jean Claude **Gillier**, the "compositeur" of the theatre, are printed at the end of the volume in the "Table des airs."

ML 48.L2III

La **queuë de verité**. *See* Le diable d'argent.

Quinto Fabio. Dramma per musica da rappresentarsi nel nobilissimo nuovo Teatro di Padova nella fiera di Giugno dell' anno 1778 . . .

Padova, n. publ., 1778. 48, [1] p. 17½ᶜᵐ.

The additional unnumbered page contains Volunnio's aria (I, 4), "Dell' amico i perigli." Three acts. Impresario's dedication, argument, cast, scenario, and name of Ferdinando Giuseppe **Bertoni** as composer ("musica sarà tutta nuova"). Apostolo Zeno not mentioned as author of the libretto, which in its original version was called "Lucio Papirio dittatore."

First performed at Milan, Teatro Interinale, January, 1778 (Schatz).　　SCHATZ 932

Quinto Fabio. Dramma per musica da rappresentarsi nel nobilissimo Teatro di Torre Argentina il carnevale dell' anno 1783 . . .

Roma, Cannetti, 1783. 36 p. 15½ᶜᵐ.

Three acts. By Apostolo Zeno. Originally called "Lucio Papirio dittatore." Argument, scenario, cast, and name of the composer, **Cherubini.** Onorato Viganò's ballets (music by Luigi Mareschalchi), "La dolce vendetta" and "Il rè de' ciarlatani," were performed with the opera.

First performed in January, 1783, as indicated.　　SCHATZ 1847

Quinto Fabio. Dramma per musica da rappresentarsi nel Regio Teatro dell' Accademia degli Avvalorati in Livorno l'autunno dell' anno 1794.

[Livorno], Tommaso Masi e compagno, n. d. 46 p. 17½ᶜᵐ.

Two acts. Author of this complete modernization of Zeno's "Lucio Papirio dittatore" not mentioned, and unknown to Schatz. Impresario's dedication, argument, cast, scenario, and name of Nicola Antonio **Zingarelli** as the composer ("La musica è tutta nuova"). With the opera were performed Carlo Augusto Favier's ballets, "Ezio" and "La contadina spiritosa," the composers of the music not mentioned.

SCHATZ 11255

Quinto Lucrezio proscritto. Dramma musicale fatto rappresentare da' Signori Accademici del Carino per festeggiare il giorno natalizio del sereniss. principe Francesco Maria di Toscana.

Firenze, Vincenzo Vangelisti, 1681. 4 p. l., 104 p. 16½ᶜᵐ.

Three acts. By Giov. Andrea Moniglia, who is not mentioned. Dedication dated November 12, 1681 (the prince's birthday), notice to the reader, with name of Lorenzo **Cattani** as composer, argument.　　SCHATZ 1713

— **Quinto Lucrezio proscritto.** Drama musicale fatto rappresentare da' Signori Accademici del Casino per festeggiare il giorno natalizio del sereniss. principe cardinale Francesco Maria di Toscana.

G. A. Moniglia, Poesie drammatiche, parte prima, Vincenzio Vangelisti, Firenze, 1689, p. [503]–593. 24ᶜᵐ.

Three acts. Argument and prefatory note with name of Lorenzo **Cattani** as composer. The text is followed on p. 584–593 by "Lettera apologetica per lo Quinto Lucrezio Proscritto. Scritta da F. N. all' autore."　　ML 49.A2M7

Les quiproquo nocturnes, opéra bouffon, en deux actes. Paroles de J. G. A. Cuvelier, musique de L. Morange. Représentée, pour la première fois, le 23 frimaire, an 6, [Dec. 13, 1797] sur le Théâtre Montansier.

Paris, Barba, (1798) An VI. 38 p. 20½ᶜᵐ.

Cast.　　SCHATZ 6627

Gesaenge aus dem singspiele: Der **rabe,** in vier aufzuegen nach dem italienischen des grafen Gozzi. In musik gesetzt von Andreas Romberg.

Hamburg, Freystatzky und Rabe, 1794. 31 p. $15\frac{1}{2}^{cm}$.

By Schwick, who is not mentioned.

First performed at Hamburg, Theater beim Gaensemarkt, April 7, 1794.

SCHATZ 8870

Les **racoleurs,** opera-comique en un acte. Par M. Vadé. Représenté pour la premiere fois sur le Théâtre de l'Opéra-comique à la Foire S. Germain le 11 mars 1756.

Paris, Duchesne, 1756. 61, [3] p. $19\frac{1}{2}^{cm}$.

On the [3] p. lists of plays by Vadé, etc. Prose and *en vaudevilles.* Cast. On p. 60–61 the airs of "D'un faraut de note quartier," and "Le zèle ardent nous engage." Composer unknown to me. ML 50.2.R15

— Les **racoleurs,** opéra comique, en un acte, représenté, pour la premiere fois, sur le Théâtre de l'Opéra comique, à la Foire Saint-Germain, le 11 mars 1756.

[181]–250 p. $15\frac{1}{2}^{cm}$. (Jean Joseph Vadé, Oeuvres complettes, t. iii, Nouv. éd., Troyes, an VI [1798].

The arranger of the music is not mentioned. PQ2068.V2

Il **Radamisto.** Drama per musica da rappresentarsi in Firenze nel Teatro di via del Cocomero l'estate dell' anno MDCCXXVIII . . .

Firenze, Melchiorre Alberighi e Giuseppe Pagani, 1728. 88 p. $15\frac{1}{2}^{cm}$.

Three acts. Impresario's dedication, dated Florence, June 18, 1728, argument, cast, scenario. On p. [71]–88 text of the three intermezzi "LA PREZIOSA RIDICOLA." Not recorded by Schatz and not found elsewhere by me. ML 48.A5 v.18

Radamisto. Musicalisches zwischenspiel . . . Vorgestellet im jahr 1734. im monat october.

n. i., n. d. 34 p. 15^{cm}.

The title is followed by argument and list of characters. At end of the text the note: "Die buechlein seynd zu bekommen in dem kaiserlich-privilegirten theatro bey dem Kaerntner-Thor" [Vienna]. Not recorded by von Weilen. SCHATZ 11643

Radamisto. Drama per musica da rappresentarsi nel Teatro di S. Angelo l'anno 1698. Di Antonio Marchi . . .

Venetia, Nicolini, 1698. 63 p. 14^{cm}.

Three acts. Author's dedication dated Venice, November 11, 1698, notice to the reader, argument, scenario. The composer, Tommaso **Albinoni,** is not mentioned.

SCHATZ 97

Il **Radamisto.** Drama per musica fatto rappresentare nel Teatro di Piedemonte . . . in occasione degli acclamati sponsali dell' eccellentiss. Sig. D. Antonio di Sangro . . . coll' eccellentiss. Signora D. Cecilia Gaetano d'Aragona . . . e à medesima consacrato dall' abb. Nicolò Giuvo.

Venetia, Per il Prodocimo, 1707. 4 p. l., 76 p. $13\frac{1}{2}^{cm}$.

Three acts. Author's dedication, argument, cast, scenario, and name of the composer, "Nicolò **Fago,** detto il Tarantino." SCHATZ 2981

Radamisto.

Three-act opera by Georg Friedrich **Händel.** Text by Nicola Francesco Haym. First performed at London, Haymarket, April 27, 1720.

— **Zenobia,** oder Das muster rechtschaffener ehelichen liebe, in einer opera auf dem Hamburgischen Schau-platze vorgestellet im jahr 1726.

[Hamburg], Gedruckt mit Stromerschen schrifften, n. d. Unpaged. 19½ᶜᵐ.

Three acts. Argument. Neither Johann Mattheson, the translator of Haym's "Radamisto," nor the composer, Georg Friedrich **Händel,** is mentioned. Italian text of the arias is added to the German.

First performed at Hamburg, 1722.   SCHATZ 4502

The **raft;** or, Both sides of the water, a musical drama. As performed with universal applause at the Theatre-Royal, Covent-Garden. By J. C. Cross . . . The music composed by Mr. Reeve.

London, J. Barker, 1798. 29, [3] p. 21ᶜᵐ.

The [3] p. contain advertisements.
One act. Cast.
First performed, March 31, 1798.   LONGE 246

The **ragged uproar:** or, The Oxford roratory: A new dramatick satire; in many scenes, and one very long act . . . Originally plann'd by Joan Plotwell; and continued by several truly eminent hands, well vers'd in the art of designing . . .

London, G. Pote, n. d. 32 p. 20ᶜᵐ.

In form almost of a ballad-opera, the airs being indicated by title. Author unknown to Clarence, who records neither date of publication nor a performance. LONGE 195

Il raggiratore di poca fortuna. Commedia per musica di Giuseppe Palomba da rappresentarsi nel Nuovo Teatro de' Fiorentini per prim' opera del corrente anno 1779.

Napoli, n. publ., 1779. 72 p. 15ᶜᵐ.

Three acts. Prefatory note, cast, and name of Pietro **Guglielmi** as the composer.
First performed, as indicated, August 1, 1779.   SCHATZ 4259

I raggiri d'amore. L. T. of Tritto's Le vicende amorose.

I raggiri fortunati. Farsa di un atto solo del Signor abate Pietro Chiari da rappresentarsi nel nobilissimo Teatro Venier in San Benedetto il carnovale dell' anno 1795.

Venezia, Modesto Fenzo, 1795. 40 p. 18ᶜᵐ.

Cast, scenario, and name of Sebastiano **Nasolini** as the composer. The text is an altered version of Chiari's "Il marchese villano."
First performed, as indicated, February 5, 1795.   SCHATZ 7029

Li raggiri fortunati. L. T. of Robuschi's Castrini, padre e figlio.

I raggiri scoperti. Dramma giocoso per musica da rappresentarsi nel Teatro della molto ille. città di Barcellona, l'anno 1792.

Barcell., Francesco Generas, n. d. 78 p. 15ᶜᵐ.

Two acts. Author not mentioned and unknown to Schatz. Cast and name of Giacomo **Tritto** as composer.
First performed at Rome, Teatro alla Valle, carnival 1791.   ML 50.2.R17T8

Il Ramiro in Norvegia. A. T. of M. A. Ziani's Gl'amori tra gl'odii.

Raol de Crequi, ballet.   *See* Winter's Belisa.

Raollo, signore di Crequi. Tr. of Dalayrac's Raoul, sire de Crequi.

Raoul, Barbe Bleue, comédie en prose et en 3 actes, mêlée d'ariettes; par M. Sedaine. Musique de Mr. Grétry. Représentée pour la première fois par les Comédiens italiens ordinaires du roi, le lundi 2 mars 1789.

Amsterdam, Gabriel Dufour, 1791. 40 p. 20½^{cm}.
Label of Vente pasted over imprint.
                                           ML 50.2.R22G72

— **Raoul Barbe Bleue,** comédie en trois actes et en prose, représentée pour la première fois, par les Comédiens italiens ordinaires du roi, le lundi 2 mars 1789. Paroles de M. Sedaine. Musique de M. Grétry.

Bruxelles, Loiseau, 1791. 39 p. 20^{cm}.
Label of Vente pasted over imprint.
                                           ML 50.2.R22G73

Raoul, herr von Crequi oder Die verhinderte grausamkeit. Tr. of the ballet Raul, signore di Crechi o sia La tirannide repressa.

Raoul, sire de Créqui, comédie en trois actes, en prose. Par Mr Monvel. Représentée pour la première fois par les Comédiens italiens ordinaires du roi, le samedi 31 octobre 1789. Mise en musique par Mr Dalayrac.

Paris, n. publ., 1790. 75 p. 19^{cm}.
                                           ML 50.2.R24D3

— Arien und gesaenge aus **Rudolph von Creki.** Ein singspiel in drey aufzuegen. Nach dem franzoesischen. Die musik ist von d'Alayrac.

Riga, Julius Conrad Daniel Müller, 1792. 16 p. 16½^{cm}.
German version, by Heinr. Gottlieb Schmieder.
First performed at Riga, Theater i. d. gr. Königstrasse, 1/12, Febr. 1793; at Mayence, Nationaltheater, Dec. 17, 1791.   SCHATZ 2374

— **Raollo, signore di Crequi,** tragi-commedia in prosa di tre atti, mista d'arie per musica, e tolta dal francese da reppresentarsi nel Reggio Teatro di S. Carlo . . . li 17 decembre dell' anno 1795.

Lisbona, Simone Taddeo Ferreir, 1795. 187 p. 15^{cm}.
Italian version, by Giuseppe Carpani, with his name and those of Monvel and **Dalayrac.** Portuguese text faces Italian.   SCHATZ 2376

The **rape of Colombine** or The flying lovers. *See* Perseus and Andromeda.

The **rape of Europa by Jupiter.** A masque as it is sung at the Queens Theatre in Dorset-Garden. By their Majesties servants.
London, M. Bennet, 1694. 2 p. l., 8 p. 21^{cm}.
One act. Cast and argument. Author not known to Clarence. Composer not mentioned, and unknown to me.   ML 50.2.R2

The **rape of Helen,** a mock opera. As it is acted at the Theatre Royal in Covent-Garden. By John Breval, Esq. . . .
London, J. Wilford, 1737. 2 p. l., 48 p. 19^{cm}.
One act. Ballad opera, but quite a few of the 25 songs lack indication of the air to be sung.
First performed May 19, 1733, as indicated.   LONGE 52

The **rape of Proserpine**: as it is acted at the Theatre-Royal in Lincoln's-Inn-Fields. Written by Mr. Theobald. And set to musick by Mr. Galliard.

London, T. Wood, 1727. viii, 17 p. 17½ cm.

One act. Cast and J. Rich's dedication, recommending his "part in this work" (the design of it), and dated "Lincoln's-Inn-Fields, Feb. 10, 1726." This dedication, to Thomas Chamber, reads in part:

"Though my inclination to musick frequently leads me to visit the Italian opera; yet, I confess, it is not in the power of the present excellent performers to prevent my falling into the very common opinion, that there are many essential requisites still wanting, to establish that entertainment on a lasting foundation, and adapt it to the taste of an English audience.

"For not to mention the trite objection of the performances being in Italian, and the general ill choice of the subjects for those compositions, it is evident that the vast expence of procuring foreign voices, does necessarily exclude those various embellishments of machinery, painting, dances, as well as poetry it self, which have been always esteemed (except till very lately in England) auxiliaries absolutely necessary to the success of musick; and, without which, it cannot be long supported, unless by very great subscriptions, of which we naturally grow tired in a few years.

"It seems, therefore, the only way by which musick can be establish'd in England, is to give it those assistances from other arts which it yet wants, and by that means to adapt it still more to the public taste; to moderate, as much as possible, the expence of it, and thereby to make it a general diversion, which hitherto it has not been.

"You will perceive, Sir, that in the following entertainment, the vocal parts of which are here presented to you, I have endeavoured to introduce that variety, which has usually been thought agreeable on the stage; and have attempted to form the serious part of it upon the above mentioned plan, as a specimen of what may not be displeasing to an English audience, and from which the town may be able to form a judgment of the effect an opera wou'd have, if conducted (by an abler hand) in the same manner.

"As for the other parts, it might, perhaps, seem an affectation in me to detain you with the history of the ancient pantomime entertainments, or to make a long apology for the revival of them at present. Thus much, however, may be said in their favour, that this theatre has of late ow'd its support in great measure to them. I own my self extremely indebted to the favour with which the town is pleas'd to receive my attempts to entertain them in this kind; and to engage, for my own part, that whenever the publick taste shall he disposed to return to the works of the drama, no one shall rejoice more sincerely than my self . . ."

According to Grove's Dict., this pantomime was first performed in 1725, forming part of "Harlequin sorcerer," as "The loves of Pluto and Proserpine." "The rape of Proserpina" is not mentioned by Genest.   ML 50.2.R24

Il **rapimento di Cefalo** rappresentato nelle nozze della Christianissima Maria Medici regina di Francia è di Navarra. Di Gabriello Chiabrera [vignette].

Firenze, Giorgio Marescotti, 1600. [3], 4-27, [1] p. 21 cm.

At end, on the unnumb. p. printer's mark. Five acts. On p. [2] Interlocutori, on p. [3]–4 Prologo. No composer is mentioned, but Michelangelo Buonarroti in his very minute and interesting "Descrizione," 1600, of the festivities (quoted by Solerti) says:

"Giulio **Caccini** ebbe il carico di tutta la musica, e funne il componitore; se non che dei cori, il primo da Stefan **Venturi del Nibbio**, insieme con una gran musica delli Dei simili a coro, ed il terzo e'l quarto da Messer Luca **Bati** maestro della cattedral cappella composti furono. Il secondo per maggiormente onorarsi musica e scena reale, di fare compiacquesi il Signor Pietro **Strozzi**, gentiluomo non solamente di tale arte, ma di ogni nobile facoltà adornissimo: per la cui opera altresì ricevette molto giovamento l'esercizio di tale impresa, siccome per quella del Signor Cosimo de' Medici ancora."

Caccini did not mention these facts when he published part of his music in his "Nuove musiche," 1601 [1602], p. 19–24 with these introductory remarks:

"Non havendo io potuto per molti impedimenti far' istampare com' era il desiderio mio il Rapimento di Cefalo composto in musica da me per comandamento del Serenissimo Gran Duca mio signore . . . mi è parso ora con l'occasione di quest' altre mie musiche aggiugnere à quelle l'ultimo coro di esso Rapimento . . ."

Il **rapimento di Cefalo**—Continued.

Besides this chorus "Ineffabile ardore" he published the arias "Muove si dolce," "Caduca fiamma," "Qual trascorrendo," and the chorus "Quand il bell' anno." After the first two arias the chorus "Ineffabile ardore" was repeated. The whole publication, therefore, forms what might be termed the *finale* of "Il rapimento di Cefalo."

Final rehearsal on October 7, 1600; first performance on October 9, 1600.

SCHATZ 1449

Il **rapimento di Proserpina,** ballet. *See* G. F. de Majo's Catone in Utica.

Il **rapitore punito,** ballet. *See* P. v. Winter's I sacrifizi di Creta.

Le **rappel de la Foire à la vie.** Pièce d'un acte. Par Mrs le S * *. & D'Or * * . . .

Le Théâtre de la foire, Paris, 1737, t. iii, pl., [411]–454 p. 17ᶜᵐ.

By Le Sage and D'Orneval. Largely *en vaudevilles*. The airs, selected or composed and arranged by Jean Claude **Gillier,** the "compositeur" of the theatre, are printed at the end of the volume in the "Table des airs." A note on the title page reads:

"Les auteurs de cette pièce l'avoient composée pour le début de l'Opéra comique, qui s'est rétabli à la Foire de S. Laurent de cette présente année 1721: mais comme la permission de r'ouvrir ce théâtre n'a pas été accordée aux acteurs qu'on auroit souhaité, on n'a pas voulu la faire représenter. Le lecteur sera peut-être bien aise de voir par où ces auteurs se proposoient de recommencer les représentations de ce spectacle."

First performed Sept. 1, 1721.

ML 48.L2III

Rappresentanza allegorica che serve d'introduzione alla festa di ballo da darsi nel Real Casino delle cascine e nell' annesso parterre la sera de' iv luglio MDCCXCI. In occasione delle pubbliche feste di gioia date da S. A. R. Ferdinando III Gran-duca di Toscana ec. ec. ec. nelle cascine dell' isola i giorni iii. iv. e v del detto mese di luglio.

Firenze, Grazioli, n. d. 24 p. 23½ᶜᵐ.

The text is preceded by a kind of argument. Neither the author nor the composer is mentioned. The allegory deals with Diana, Cerere, Flora, and Bacco.

ML 48.M2A

Le **rapt des Sabines,** ballet. *See* P. Guglielmi's L'impostore punito.

The **raree show:** or, The fox trap't. An opera. The second edition, with alterations. Written by Joseph Peterson, comedian . . .

Chester, Printed by Roger Adams, for the author, 1740. 4 p. l., 31, [1] p. 19ᶜᵐ.

Two acts. Dedication, prologue, and two epilogues. Largely a ballad opera, the airs used in which are indicated by title. According to Tufts, acted at York, 1739.

LONGE 271

Die **rasereyen des Rolands.** Tr. of Touchemolin's I furori di Orlando.

Raton et Rosette. Parody of Mondonville's Titon et l'Aurore.

Il **ratto della sposa,** ballet. *See* Baroni's Artaserse.

Il **ratto della sposa.** Dramma giocoso per musica del Signor Gaetano Martinelli Romano da rappresentarsi nel Teatro Giustiniani di San Moisè l'autunno dell' anno 1765.

Venezia, Modesto Fenzo, 1765. 60 p. 14ᶜᵐ.

Three acts.   Cast, scenario, and name of Pietro **Guglielmi** as the composer.

SCHATZ 4280

— Il **ratto della sposa.** Dramma giocoso per musica da rappresentarsi nel Real Teatro dell' Ajuda in occasione di festeggiarsi il giorno natalizio del fedelissimo monarca D. Giuseppe I . . . nel di 6. giugno MDCCLXVII.

Lisbona, Michele Manescal da Costa, n. d.   16ᶜᵐ.

Imperfect, wanting the pages after p. 82. .
Three acts.   By Gaetano Martinelli, who is not mentioned.   Cast, scenario, and name of Pietro **Guglielmi** as composer.   ML 50.2.R27G9

Il **ratto delle castellane fatto dai Triestini,** ballet. *See* Andreozzi's La principessa filosofa.

Il **ratto delle Sabine.** Drama per musica nell' augusto Teatro Grimani di S. Gio. Crisostomo l'anno MDCLXXX del Bussani . . .

Venetia, Francesco Nicolini, 1680.   66 p.   14½ᶜᵐ.

Three acts.   Dedication, argument, scenario, cast, and name of composer, Pietro Simone **Agostini.**   The dedication signed in full by Giacomo Francesco Bussani. The composer is referred to as Augustini.   SCHATZ 65

Il **ratto delle Sabine,** ballet. *See* Bertoni's Narbale.

Il **ratto delle Sabine.** Drama per musica, nel giorno natalizio della S. C. R. M.ᵗᵃ dell' imperatore Leopoldo. . . l'anno MDCLXXIV . . .   Posto in musica dal Sʳ Antonio Draghi . . . con l'arie per li balli del Sig. Gio. Enrico Smelzer . . .

Vienna d'Austria, Gio. Christoforo Cosmerovio, n. d.   7 p. l., 129 p. 15ᶜᵐ.

Three acts.   Argument.   By conte Nicolò Minato, who, in his dedication, dated June 9, 1674 (the emperor's birthday), calls this "il primo tributo della mia penna," and who, in a prefatory note to the reader, says:

"Questo drama fù concepito per le scene dell' Adria, mà direttione d'astri più fortunati l'hà scorto sù quelle di Cesare . . .   Lo vederai framezato con l'introduttione de' Giuochi olimpici, per dividerne in due giorni la rappresentatione: à causa di non recar' in una sol volta incommodo alle M. M. Augustissime in staggione di troppo fervidi giorni.   Comtisci la debolezza della mia penna, già da te conosciuta: e se à IX mie dramatiche compositioni in Venetia, & ad altre XIV in questa Cesarea Reggia porgesti il dono del tuo cortese gradimento, non defraudarne anco questo, che dalla tua benignità se lo spera: e vivi felici."   ML 50.2.R28D7

Il **ratto delle Sabine,** ballet. *See* Mortellari's Semiramide.

Il **ratto delle Sabine.** Dramma per musica di Gaetano Rossi da rappresentarsi nel nobilissimo Teatro La Fenice per prima del carnovale 1800.

Venezia, Stamperia Valvasense, 1799.   84, [1] p.   17½ᶜᵐ.

Two acts.   Cast, name of Nicola Antonio **Zingarelli** as the composer, and prefatory note by the author, Gaetano Rossi, who says:

"Quando si rifletta, che un povero autore è oggidi obbligato a servire alla musica, alla scena, ma più di tutto alle ognor nuove *Convenienze teatrali* (a queste capricciose e irragionevoli distruggitrici dell' ordine drammatico) non si potrà, non compatirlo, e tacciarlo di prolissità, e d'arbitrio."

Il **ratto delle Sabine**—Continued.

On p. [39]–44, prefatory note, argument, cast, and name of Vittorio Trento as composer of the music of Lorenzo Panzieri's "Kildar, ballo tragico pantomimo." The second ballet was called "Gl'inganni delusi."

First performed, as indicated, December 26, 1799.   SCHATZ 11256

Il **ratto di Prosperpina.** Favola per musica da eseguirsi nella nobile Accademia de' Rinnovati il carnovale dell' anno 1791.

Venezia, Typografia Valvasense, n. d. 16 p. 19½^{cm}.

Two acts. By Mattia Botturini. Names of the author and the composer, Giovanni Battista **Cimador.**   SCHATZ 1902

Il **ratto di Prosperpina,** ballet. *See* Naumann's Ipermestra.

Il **ratto di Prosperpina.** Dramma per musica da cantarsi nella Real Villa di Queluz per celebrare il felicissimo giorno natalizio della serenissima Signora Donna Maria Francesca Benedetta principessa del Brasile li 25 luglio 1784.

[Lisboa], Stamperia reale, n. d. 35 p. 15^{cm}.

One act. Argument, cast, and names of Gaetano Martinelli as author, of João Cordeiro da **Silva** as composer.   SCHATZ 9884

Der **rauchfangkehrer,** oder Die unentbehrlichen verraether ihrer herrschaften aus eigennutz. Ein musikalisches lustspiel in drey aufzuegen. In musik gesetzt von herrn Anton Salieri . . . Aufgefuehrt im K. K. Nationaltheater.

Wien, beym Logenmeister, 1781. 108, [1] p. 16^{cm}.

Three acts. By Leopold von Auernbrugger, who is not mentioned.

First performed at Wien, Burgtheater, April 30, 1781 (Schatz), April 20, 1781 (Haas).   SCHATZ 9313

Raul, signore di Crechi o sia La tirannide repressa, ballet. *See* Himmel's Semiramide.

Le **ravisseur poli.** A. T. of Pierrot Romulus.

Il **ravvedimento del figliuol prodigo,** dramma sacro in musica di Giuseppe Palomba da rappresentarsi al Teatrino del largo del Castello nella quaresima di quest' anno 1790.

Napoli, n. publ., n..d. 46 p. 14^{cm}.

Two acts. Cast and name of the composer, Giuseppe **Coppola.**   SCHATZ 2211

Il **re alla caccia.** Dramma di tre atti per musica. Rappresentato per la prima volta in Venezia l'autunno dell' anno MDCCLXIII, con musica del Buranello.

Carlo Goldoni, Opere teatrali, Venezia, Zatta e figli, 1788–95, v. 37, [71]–135 p. 18½^{cm}.   PQ

Il **rè alla caccia.** Dramma giocoso di Polisseno Fegejo da rappresentarsi nel Teatro di S. Samuelle l'autunno dell' anno MDCCLXIII.

Venezia, Antonio Bassanese, n. d. 66 p. 15½^{cm}.

Three acts. By Goldoni. Notice to the reader, cast, scenario, and name of Baldassare **Galuppi** as composer.   SCHATZ 3475

Il **rè alla caccia,** ballet. *See* Naumann's Solimano.

Il rè alla caccia. Commedia per musica di Pasquale Mililotti da rappresentarsi nel Teatro Nuovo sopra Toledo nell' autunno del corrente anno 1780.

Napoli, n. publ., 1780. 66 p. 15ᶜᵐ.

Three acts. Cast and name of Angelo **Tarchi** as the composer.   Schatz 10224

Il rè alla caccia, ballet. *See* Tarchi's Giulio Sabino.

Il rè de' ciarlatani, ballet. *See* Cherubini's Quinto Fabio.

Il rè infante. Drama per musica da rappresentarsi nel famosissimo Teatro Grimano di San Gio. Grisostomo. L'anno MDCLXXXIII. Di Matteo Noris. Ristampata con riforma . . .

Venetia, Francesco Nicolini, 1683. 80 p. 14ᶜᵐ.

Three acts. Author's dedication and scenario. The composer, Carlo **Pallavicino,** is not mentioned.   Schatz 7734

Il rè infante. Drama per musica da rappresentarsi nel Teatro Malvezzi l'anno 1694. Del Sig. Matteo Noris . . .

Bologna, Giulio Borzaghi, n. d. 87. 14ᶜᵐ.

Three acts. Dedication dated Bologna, January 18, 1694, and signed by Giacomo Antonio **Perti** and Ceare Bonazzoli apparently as impresarios, scenario, and notice to the reader which reads, in part:

"Lo vedrai cangiato in varij luoghi con nuove ariette . . . Averti ancora, che si è posto in scena nella maniera, che fù scritto di prima impressione supponendo questa la vera intentione del medesimo autore."

The words in the dedication "eccolo, che, dovendo ritornar alle stampe, e di nuovo comparir sopra le scene in Bologna" make it clear that the opera must have been performed there before 1694. Bound in is the following (same imprint, 21 p.):

Intermezzi, et aggiunte al drama intitolato Il rè infante, che si rappresenta nel Teatro Malvezzi l'anno 1694.

The reader is informed that, in order to please the audience, in many places of the opera arias have been cancelled and others "di maggior genio de' virtuosi cantanti" have been substituted, also that

"vi si sono ancora aggiunti due intermezzi, acciochè più ti sia grato il serio, vedendovi framezzato il faceto."

The characters in these intermezzi are "Dircea, poi Gildo" and "Gildo, poi Despina e Livio." The substitute arias printed are "Mercè de la mia fè" (I, 5), "Sembra riso, ed è sol pianto" (I, 7), "Se costante è la mia bella" (I, 11), "Sol per voi fogli amorosi" (I, 12), "Vaghi rai del mio bel Sole" (II, 1), "Quand un ayme tendrement" and "Les amantes, qui sont fidèles" (II, 3), "Rissolvi ò cor tradito" (II, 5), "Come al Polo si rivolge" (II, 17), "Sei vago, sei vezzoso" (II, 17), "Nel seno amante" (III, 2), "Beltà costante" (III, 3), "Fiero Pluto de l'Inferno" (III, 3), "Bel gioia, gioia soave" (III, 24). Schatz attributes the music to **Perti,** probably because he signed the dedication. Comparison proves that, barring many alterations, the text is the same as the one performed 1683 at Venice, the setting of which is attributed also by Schatz to Carlo Pallavicini. If correctly attributed to him, it therefore may be that Perti either did not compose the text for Bologna (1694) at all or that he was merely responsible for the additional music, etc.   Schatz 7953

Il rè pastore.

Metastasio, Poesie, Parigi, vedova Quillau, 1755, t. v, [359]–425 p. 16ᶜᵐ.

Three acts. Argument.   ML 49.A2M42

— **Il re pastore.** Dramma scritto dall' autore in Vienna . . . rappresentato la prima volta con musica del Bonno da giovani distinte dame, e cavalieri nel teatro dell' Imperial Giardino di Schönbrunn . . . nella primavera dell' anno 1751.

pl., [107]–180 p. 26ᶜᵐ. (Metastasio, Opere, t. vii, Parigi, vedova Herissant, 1780.)

Three acts. Argument.   ML 49.A2M44

Il re pastore. Dramma per musica da rappresentarsi nel Teatro di Lucca nell' autunno dell' anno MDCCLXV.

Lucca, Filippo Maria Benedini, n. d. 63 p. 14½ᶜᵐ.

Three acts. By Metastasio. Argument, scenario, cast, and note: "La musica è di diversi celebri autori." On p. 62, a schedule of the performances from August 17 to October 16; on p. 63, the substituted arias, "Al tuo pensier richiama" (I, 1) and "In mezzo a tanti affanni" (III, 4).   ML 50.2.R29

Il re pastore, ballet. *See* Anfossi's Gli artigiani.

Il rè pastore, ballet. *See* Anfossi's Gengis-Kan.

Il rè pastore, ballet. *See* Borghi's Creso rè di Lidia.

Il rè pastore. Dramma per musica da rappresentarsi nel nobil Teatro di San Benedetto di Venezia nell' estate dell' anno MDCCLXIX.

Venezia, Modesto Fenzo, 1769. 45 p. 19ᶜᵐ.

Two acts. Argument, cast, scenario, and names of Metastasio as author and of Baldassare **Galuppi**. An adaptation of the original drama, as remarked on p. 8. On p. 25–28 and 41–45, a description of the ballets, the second being called "Rinaldo nella isola incantata d'Armida."

First performed at Parma, Teatro Ducale, April, 1762 (Schatz); at Milan, Teatro Ducale, April, 1758 (Piovano).   SCHATZ 3468

Il rè pastore. Dramma per musica da rappresentarsi nel nobilissimo Teatro di S. Benedetto nella fiera dell' Ascensione dell' anno 1767 . . .

Venezia, Modesto Fenzo, 1767. 54 p. 17ᶜᵐ.

Three acts. By Metastasio, who is not mentioned. Impresario's dedication, argument, cast, scenario, and name of Pietro **Guglielmi** as the composer.

First performed at Turin, Teatro Carignano, fall of 1765, according to Schatz and others, but Piovano makes it clear that this is a mistake; that the composer of the Turin opera of that title is not known; and that Guglielmi's opera was probably first performed as indicated in the title of the Venetian libretto.   SCHATZ 4302

Il re pastore. Dramma per musica da recitarsi nella Regia elettorale villa di Sant' Uberto, per festeggiare il felicissimo giorno natalizio di S. S. R. M. il rè di Polonia Augusto III . . . li 7 ottobre dell' anno 1755 . . .

Dresda, la vedova Stoessel e Giovanni Carlo Krause, n. d. 3 p. l., 58, [2] p. 21ᶜᵐ.

Three acts and licenza. By Metastasio, who is not mentioned. Argument, cast, scenario, and name of Johann Adolph **Hasse** as the composer.   SCHATZ 4556

— **Il re pastore.** Dramma per musica da rappresentarsi nel Regio Teatro di Sans Souci . . .

Berlino, Haude e Spener, 1770. 107, [4] p. 16ᶜᵐ.

Three acts. German title-page, "Der im schaefer verborgene koenig," and text face Italian, which follows the original Dresden (1755) edition closely, except that a prologue has been added as "Vorspiel zu der oper der Koenigliche schaefer. Aus dem franzoesischen uebersetzt." Joh. Ad. **Hasse** is mentioned as composer of the opera.

First performed, as indicated, October 1, 1770.   SCHATZ 4557

Il re pastore. Dramma per musica del Sig. abate Pietro Metastasio . . . Da rappresentarsi nel Teatro Giustiniani di San Moisè il carnovale dell' anno 1753.

Venezia, n. publ., 1753. 47 p. 15^{cm}.

Three acts. Argument, cast, scenario, and name of Giuseppe **Sarti** as the composer.
First performed at Pesaro, Teatro del Sole, carnival, 1752. SCHATZ 9466

Il rè pastore, ballet. *See* Sarti's Fra i due litiganti il terzo gode, Milano, (1795).

Il rè pastore, ballet. *See* Sarti's Giulio Sabino.

Il re Teodoro in Venezia. Dramma eroi-comico per musica da rappresentarsi nel Teatro alla Scala la quaresima dell' anno 1788 . . .

Milano, Gio. Batista Bianchi, n. d. 1 p. l., 80 p. 16½^{cm}.

Two acts. By Giambattista Casti, who is not mentioned. Dedication, argument, scenario, and name of Giovanni **Paisiello** as the composer. With the opera were performed (composers of the music not mentioned) Ranieri Pazzini's ballet, "La pastorella rapita da' Corsari" and Giuseppe Scalesi's "Gelosia per gelosia."
First performed at Vienna, Burgtheater, August 23, 1784. ML 50.2.R3P22

— **Il rè Teodoro in Venezia.** Dramma eroico-comico, da rappresentarsi nel Teatro di Monsieur.—Le roi Théodore à Venise. Opéra héroi-comique, représenté pour la première fois, le 21 février 1789, sur le Théatre de Monsieur.

Paris, de L'imprimerie de Monsieur, 1789. (double) 62 p. 21^{cm}.

Two acts. Not Dubuisson's translation. French text faces Italian. Cast, name of Giovanni **Paisiello** as the composer and Avertissement:
"En traduisant ce poème, l'on s'est proposé deux principaux objets, l'un, de faciliter aux personnes peu versées dans la langue italienne, l'intelligence du texte, que l'on a suivi d'aussi près qu'il a été possible; l'autre, d'établir des distinctions sensibles entre le récitatif simple, le récitatif obligé, et les airs. On a donc rendu en prose le récitatif simple, et le reste en vers blancs ou non rimes . . . Si les personnes qui lisent pendant la représentation, éprouvent que cette forme de version distrait moins leur oreille du rythme musical, que ne le feroit de la prose absolue, on ne regrettera pas de s'être imposé cette contrainte de plus." ML 50.2.R3P27

— **Le roi Théodore a Venise,** opéra-héroï-comique en trois actes, . . . représenté devant Leurs Majestés, à Fontainebleau, le 28 octobre, & à Versailles, le 18 novembre 1786. Musique du célèbre Pasiélo [!]; Paroles imitées de l'italien par M. Dubuisson.

Versailles, Le Coutre, 1787. 66 p. 18^{cm}. ML50.2.R3P25

— **Der koenig Theodor in Venedig.** Ein aus dem italiaenischen uebersetztes grosses sing-spiel in zween aufzuegen mit der musik des kapellmeisters Paisiello, aufgefuehrt von der schauspieler gesellschaft des herrn Boehm.

Koeln am Rhein, gedruckt mit Langischen schriften, 1785. 62 p. 16½^{cm}.

Cast. Two acts. By Johann Boehm.
First performed 1785, as indicated. SCHATZ 7651

— **Der koenig Theodor zu Venedig.** Eine komische oper. Auf dem Hoftheater vorzustellen.

Stuttgart, Buchdruckerei der Herzogl. Hohen Carls-Schule, 1785. 189 p. 15½^{cm}.

Two acts. **Paisiello** is mentioned, but not Casti. Argument in German and Italian as is the text.
First performed 1785, as indicated. SCHATZ 7682

Il re **Teodoro in Venezia**—Continued.

— Gesaenge aus dem singspiele: **Koenig Theodor in Venedig**, in zwey aufzuegen. In musik gesetzt von Paisiello. Nach dem italienischen des abbate Casti, frey bearbeitet von d'Arien.

Hamburg, J. M. Michaelsen, 1788. 54 p. 16½^{cm}.

First performed at Hamburg, Theater b. Gänsemarkt, April 14, 1788.

Schatz 7653

— Gesaenge aus dem singspiele Der **Koenig Theodor** in zwey aufzuegen. Aus dem italienischen. In musik gesetzt von Paisello.

n. pl., n. publ., 1792. 40 p. 15^{cm}.

Schatz 7683

— Arien und gesaenge aus dem singspiel: **Theodore in Venedig**, mit der musik des kapellmeisters Paesiello.

Berlin, n. publ., 1799. 47 p. 16^{cm}.

Two acts. Boehm's version with modifications.
Performed in 1799 at Berlin, Kgl. National theater; first performed there August 7, 1786.

Schatz 7652

The **reapers**: or The Englishman out of Paris. An opera.

London, T. Carnan, 1770. 1 p. l., 63 p. 21^{cm}.

Three acts with prologue. According to prefatory note the piece is practically "a translation, or rather an imitation" of "Les Moissonneurs" (by Favart, music by Duni). Neither author nor performance recorded.

Longe 204

Das **recht des lehnsherrn**. Tr. of Martini's Le droit du seigneur.

Il **reclutamento in villaggio**, ballet. *See* Zingarelli's Meleagro.

Le **reclute d'amore**, ballet. *See* Tritto's Apelle e Campaspe.

Le **reclute del villaggio**, ballet. *See* Martin y Soler's L'accorta cameriera.

Le **reclute per inganno**, ballet. *See* Della Maria's Chi vuol non puole.

Le **reclute villane**, ballet. *See* Caruso's Gli amanti dispettosi.

La **reconciliation**. A. T. of Beffroy de Reigny's Le club des bons-gens.

The **reconciliation**; or The triumph of nature. A comic opera, in two acts by Peter Markoe.

Philadelphia, Prichard & Hall, 1790. viii, [9]–48 p. 20^{cm}.

A ballad opera, the tunes indicated in the text. The dedication (p. [III]) reads:
"To His Excellency Thomas Miflin, Esq., President of the State of Pennsylvania; and to the Honorable Thomas M'Kean, Chief Justice of the said State; this comic opera approved of by them in their official capacity according to law; but withdrawn from the managers of the theatre, after it had remained in their hands more than four months; is . . . inscribed."
In his preface (p. [v]–vi) Markoe says:
"A revisal and correction of "Erastus," literally translated by a native of Germany, lately arrived in Pennsylvania, gave rise to the following piece.
"The happy simplicity of the German original, written in one act by the celebrated Gesner, suggested an enlargement of the plan. A new character is added, songs are introduced, and the dialogue so modelled as to be rendered (it is presumed) pleasing to an American ear. Those who understand the German and the English languages will, on comparing the two pieces, readily perceive the difference between them . . ."

ML 50.6.R28
Second copy. Dram. Pamphl. v. 7

La **réconciliation généreuse,** ballet. *See* Bernasconi's La clemenza di Tito.

Die **recrouten auf dem lande,** eine komische oper in drey acten.
*Wittenberg und Zerbst, Samuel Gottfried Zimmermann, 1781. 135 p.
17ᶜᵐ.*

Neither the author (unknown to Schatz) nor the composer, Carl David **Stegmann,**
is mentioned.
First performed, as "Die rekruten auf dem Lande," at Königsberg, Ackermann'sches Schauspielhaus, 1775.　　　　　　　Schatz 10041

The **recruiting serjeant.** A musical entertainment as it is perform'd at the Theatre-Royal in Drury-Lane [vignette].
London, William Griffin, 1770. 28 p. 19½ᶜᵐ.
One act. Cast and prefatory note stating that Charles **Dibdin** composed the
music, and that
"This piece was performed last summer at Ranelagh; but, though very much
approved by the best judges of musical composition, by being performed in an
orchestra, lost the better part of its effect.
"It was thought it would please more in action upon the theatre; and with the
addition of a new scene and chorus, and a ballet suitable to the subject; is now,
accordingly, once more presented to the public . . . ."
The author, Isaac Bickerstaffe, is not mentioned.
First performed 1769, as indicated; at Drury Lane, January 19, 1771.
　　　　　　　　　　　　　　　　　　　　　　　Longe 37

— The **recruiting serjeant.** A musical entertainment. By Isaac
Bickerstaff, Esq.
*[333]–342 p. 19ᶜᵐ. (Collection of the most esteemed farces and
entertainments, t. vi, Edinburgh, 1792.)*
One act. Drury-Lane cast. The composer, **Dibdin,** is not mentioned.
　　　　　　　　　　　　　　　　　　　　　　Schatz 11753F

Der **redende baum.** A. T. of Boeklin von und zu Boeklinsau's
Phaedon und Naide.

Das **redende gemaehlde.** Tr. of Grétry's Le tableau parlant.

Die **redende statue.** A. T. of Mozart's Don Juan.

Die **reformation der liebe.** A. T. of Herklots' play Pigmalion.

Arien und gesaenge aus dem singspiele Die **Regata zu Venedig,**
oder: Die liebe unter den gondoliren in zwey akten. Komponirt
vom herrn doktor Fliess.
Berlin, n. pub., 1798. 35 p. 15ᶜᵐ.
By Samuel Gottlieb Bürde. Cast.
First performed at Berlin, Kgl. Nationaltheater, August 3, 1798.　Schatz 3247

Die **Regata zu Venedig** oder Die liebe unter den gondolieren.
Eine oper in drei aufzeugen von S. G. Buerde.
Koenigsberg, Friedrich Nicolovius, 1795. 112 p. 17ᶜᵐ.
Three acts. The composer, F. Sigismund **Sander,** is not mentioned in the "Vorbericht," which describes the Venetian regattas, and states that
"der vorfall, welcher die entwicklung des gegenwaertigen schauspiels ausmacht,
sich bei einer Regata im jahr 1784 wirklich ereignet hat."　　　Schatz 9372

La **reggia d' Imenèo**. Festa teatrale per le felicissime nozze del serenissimo principe Antonio di Sassonia, e della serenissima arciduchessa Maria Teresa di Austria.

Dresda, Stamperia elettorale, 1787. 45 p. 21½ᶜᵐ.

One act. Giannambrogio Migliavacca is mentioned as the author, Gio. Amadeo [Johann Gottlieb] **Naumann** as the composer. German title page, "Die burg Hymens," and text face Italian.

First performed, as indicated, October 21, 1787. Schatz 7056

I **regii equivoci**. Drama per musica da rappresentarsi nel famoso Teatro di Sant' Angelo l' anno 1697 . . .

Venezia, Nicolini, 1697. 2 p. l., 72 p. 14½ᶜᵐ.

Three acts. Dedication by the author, Matteo Noris, argument, notice to the reader, and scenario. The composer, Carlo Francesco **Pollaroli**, is not mentioned.

Schatz 8314

Le **regiment de la Calotte**. Pièce d'un acte. Représentée par l'Opera comique à la Foire de S. Laurent le 1. septembre 1721. avec *Les funerailles de la foire* & son *Rappel à la vie*. Et ces trois pièces furent joüées au Palais royal par ordre de S. A. R. Madame le 2. octobre suivant.

Le Théâtre de la foire, Paris, 1724, t. v, pl., 46 p. 17ᶜᵐ.

According to a note on 2d p. l. of t. iv, the plays in t. iv–v were written by Le Sage, Fuzelier, and d'Orneval. *Largely en vaudevilles.* The airs, selected or composed and arranged by Jean Claude **Gillier**, are printed at the end of the volume in the "Table des airs." The final vaudeville was composed by **Aubert**. The text is preceded by this Avertissement:

"Le 22. du mois d'Août le Privilege de l'Opera Comique fut ôté à la troupe qui l'avoit, & donné à celle du Sieur Francisque; qui commença ses représentations en vaudevilles le I. de Septembre suivant.

"Pour mettre au fait du Regiment de la Calotte ceux qui n'y sont pas, ils sauront que c'est un regiment metaphysique, inventé par quelques esprits badins, qui s'en sont fait euxmêmes les principaux officiers. Ils y enrôlent tous les particuliers, nobles & roturiers, qui se distinguent par quelque folie marquée, ou quelque trait ridicule. Cet enrôlement se fait par des brevets en prose ou en vers qu'on a soin de distribuer dans le monde. Mais la plûpart de ces brevets sont l'ouvrage de poëtes téméraires, qui de leur propre autorité font des levées de gens, qui deshonoreroient le corps par leur merite & par leur sagesse, si le commissaire ne les cassoit point aux revûës." ML 48.L2 V

La **regina creduta rè**. Drama per musica da rappresentarsi nel Teatro di Sant' Angelo l'anno 1706. Di Matteo Noris.

Venetia, Gio. Battista Zuccato, 1706. 70 p. 14ᶜᵐ.

Three acts. Prefatory note and scenario. The composer, Marc' Antonio **Bononcini**, is not mentioned. Between p. 8–9 a page inserted with alterations.

Schatz 1205

Regina de' Volsci. L. T. of M. A. Bononcini's Il trionfo di Camilla, regina de' Volsci.

La **regina Sant** [!] **Orsola** del Sr Andrea Salvadori Rappresᵗᵃ nel Teatro del sereniss. Gran duca di Toscana al sereniss. Principe Vladislao Sigismondo, Principe di Polonia e di Suetia. Aggiuntivi i Fiori del Calvario dello stesso autore . . .

Fiorenza, Pietro Cecconcelli, 1625. 5 fold. pl., 168 p. (incl. 2 engraved t.-p.) 14½ᶜᵐ.

Five acts and prologue. Author's dedication dated Florence, January 29, 1625, sonnet by Salvadori to the Polish prince, two sonnets by abate Agnolo Capponi, ode by Gabriello Chiabrera, argument, "Persone, che recitano" (without cast), and, finally, remarks on the scenery, after which:

La regina Sant [!] Orsola—Continued.

"Quest azzione, acciò possa recitarsi senza musica, è stata dal suo autore più allungata in stampa; di quello che fù cantata in scena. Le musiche furono del Sig. **Marco da Gagliano.**

"La scena, e le macchine de Sig. Giulio Parigi.

"L'abbattimento e'l ballo del Signor Agnolo Ricci."

The plates were engraved by Alfonso Parigi. In the argument we read:

"L'azzione eroica di questa real Vergine, e per episodio gl'accidenti del principe Ireo, spiegati in poesia drammatica, sotto le note di musica recitativa, due volte con pompa degna dell' antica grandezza Romana; è stata rappresentata a due de' maggiori principi d'Europa: la prima volta al sereniss. arciduca Carlo d'Austria, & ultimamente al serenissimo Vladislao Sigismondo, principe di Polonia, e di Suezia, sotto l'ombra della cui protezzione è venuta in luce. Nè forse è poca gloria del nome Toscano, che si come sotto gl'auspici de' sereniss. gran duchi, prima in questo teatro fù rinovato l'uso de gl'antichi drammi di Grecià in musica, cosi oggi in questo medesimo, sia stato aperto un nuovo campo, di trattare con più utile, e diletto lasciate le vane favole do Gentili, le vere, e sacre azzioni Cristiane."

Performed, as indicated, at the Palazzo Pitti, January 29, 1625; first performed, as indicated, at the same theatre during fall of 1624, but under the title "Santa Orsola, Vergine e Martire."

On p. [103]–168 of the book:

FIORI DEL CALVARIO. Sonetti del S. Andrea Salvadori nella Santiss. Passione di Nostro Sig. dedicati alla principessa M. Maddalena di Toscana."

Salvadori's dedication is dated Florence, December 20, 1623. On p. 167–168 "Tavola de sacri misteri contenuti ne' Fiori del Calvario," which comprise a "Prefazione" and 56 sonnets. SCHATZ 3410

— **La regina Sant' Orsola** d'Andrea Salvadori, recitata in musica nel Teatro del sereniss? Gran duca di Toscana dedicata al serenissimo principe Ladislao Sigismondo principe di Polonia, e di Suezia.

Fiorenza, Pietro Cecconcelli, 1625. 6 p. l. (incl. engraved t.-p.), 104 p. 23½ᶜᵐ.

Prologue and five acts. Contents the same as of the 168 p. ed. except that Salvadori's sonnet to Prince Sigismondo has been dropped and that neither the "Fiori del Calvario" appear in the 104 p. ed. nor Parigi's plates. ML 50.2.R34

Le regina di Macedonia. L. T. of Gasparini's Statira.

Il regio schiavo o sia La Dori. L. T. of Cesti's La Dori.

Il regno della luna. Dramma giocoso da rappresentarsi nel Regio Ducal Teatro di Milano nella corrente primavera . . .

Milano, Gio. Batista Bianchi, 1770. 83, [1] p. 15ᶜᵐ.

Three acts. Author not mentioned and unknown to Schatz. Dedication, cast, and name of Niccolò **Piccinni** as the composer. On p. [69]–83 cast and description of the ballets "Aci e Galatea" and "Gli Americani." The composers of the music are not mentioned.

The imprimatur on the last p. is dated April 14, 1770.

Cametti is wrong in attributing this text to Goldoni. It is a pasticcio with next to no arias, if any, from Goldoni, but, for instance, "Non vi piacque, ingiusti Dei" (I, 5) from Metastasio's Siroe or "Meglio rifletti al dono" (I, 10) from Metastasio's Antigono. SCHATZ 8106

— **Il regno della luna,** dramma giocoso per musica da rappresentarsi nel Piccolo Teatro di S. A. S. E. di Sassonia.

Dresda, n. publ., 1773. 141 p. 17ᶜᵐ.

Three acts. Niccolò **Piccinni** is mentioned as the composer. German title-page "Das mondenreich" and text face Italian, from which the arias "Ah sta un esercito" (II, 6), and "Ve', ve' di Florido" (III, 3), and the whole scene "Vaneggia? Delisa" (II,10) have been dropped. Otherwise the text is the same as in the original version.

First performed 1773, as indicated. SCHATZ 8107

Il **regno delle Amazoni.** Dramma giocoso per musica da rappresentarsi nel Regio Teatro di via della Pergola l'estate del MDCCLXXXIV . . .

Firenze, Si vende da Giovanni Risaliti, 1784. 48 p. 16^cm^.

Two acts. By Giuseppe Petrosellini, who is not mentioned. Scenario, cast of the ballet "Il divertimento transburghese," name of Agostino **Accorimboni** as composer.

First performed on July 16, 1784, as indicated; at Parma, Teatro Ducale, December 27, 1783. SCHATZ 14

Il **regno delle donne.** L. T. of Galuppi's Il mondo alla roversa o sia Le donne che comandono.

Il **regno galante.** Melodrama per musica da recitarsi nel Teatro Giustiniano a S. Moisè l'autunno dell' anno 1727 . . .

Venezia, Marino Rossetti, 1727. 59 p. 14^cm^.

Three acts. Dedication, with name of Giovanni **Reali** as the composer, dated Venice, October 25, 1727, and signed by cav. Michel Angiolo Boccardi di Mazzera as author, argument, cast, scenario, and again name of the composer SCHATZ 8619

Regulus. Tr. of Metastasio's text Attilio Regolo.

The **rehearsal:** or, Boys in petticoats. A comedy in two acts. As it is performed at the Theatre Royal in Drury-Lane. Written by Mrs. Clive. The music composed by Dr. Boyce.

London, R. Dodsley, 1753. 43 p. 21½^cm^.

The second act only contained music. Cast and prefatory note by C. Clive that she wrote the piece about 1750 for her benefit performance (March 15, 1750).

LONGE 270

Reinald. Tr. of Dalayrac's Renaud d'Ast.

Reinald und Armide, ballet. *See* Holzbauer's Hadrian in Syrien.

La **reine de Golconde.** L. T. of Monsigny's Aline reine de Golconde.

La **reine des Péris.** Comédie persane, representé par l'Academie royale de musique, l'an 1725. Paroles de M. Fuselier. Musique de M. Aubert. CIII. opera.

n. i., n. d. pl., 319–392 p. (Recueil général des opéra, Paris, 1734, t. xiii.)

Detached copy. Five acts and prologue.

First performed, as indicated, April 10, 1725. SCHATZ 486

Second copy. ML 48.R4

La **reine du Barostan.** Piece d'un acte. Par M^rs^ le S * * & d'Or * *. Representée à la Foire Saint Germain 1730.

Le Théâtre de la foire, Paris, 1731, t. vii, pl., [351]–401 p. 17^cm^.

By Le Sage and d'Orneval. Largely *en vaudevilles*. The airs, selected or composed and arranged by Jean Claude **Gillier,** are printed at the end of the volume in the "Table des airs."

First performed February 28, 1729 (Parfaict). ML 48.62 VII

Reinold und Armida. O. T. of P. v. Winter's Armida und Rinaldo.

Die **rekruten auf dem lande.** O. T. of Stegmann's Die recrouten auf dem lande.

Der **rekruten-aushub.** A. T. of Dieter's Die familien-heirath.

A relation of the late royall entertainment given by the Right Honorable the Lord Knowles, at Cawsome House neere Redding: to our most Gracious Queene, Queene Anne, in her progresse toward the Bathe, upon the seven and eight and twentie dayes of Aprill, 1613. Whereunto is annexed the description, speeches and songs of the Lords Maske, presented in the banquetting-house on the marriage night of the High and Mightie, Count Palatine, and the Royally descended the Ladie Elizabeth. Written by Thomas Campian.

London, John Budge, 1613. 32 unnumbered pages. 19ᶜᵐ.

Inigo Jones is mentioned as having invented the machines, etc. The composers of the music, Thomas **Campion** himself, and perhaps Jeremy **Hearn**, Robert **Johnson**, Giov. **Coperario**, Thomas **Giles**, Thomas **Lupo** are not mentioned.

ML 52.2.R38

Le remouleur d'amour. *See* L'ombre du cocher poète.

Renaud, tragedie, representée par l'Academie royale de musique, l'an 1722. Paroles de M. Pellegrin. Musique de M. Desmarests. C. opera.

n. i., n. d. pl., p. 117–194. (Recueil général des opéra, t. xiii, Paris, 1734.) 14ᶜᵐ.

Detached copy. Prologue and five acts, with long "Argument de la tragedie" (p. 119–122).

First performed, as indicated, March 5, 1722.   Schatz 2533

Second copy. ML 48.R4

Renaud. French version of Sacchini's Armida.

Renaud d'Ast, comédie en deux actes et en prose, mêlée d'ariettes. Représentée pour la premiere fois par les Comédiens italiens ordinaires du roi, le jeudi 19 juillet 1787. Les paroles de MM. Radet & Barré. La musique de M. d'Alayrac.

Paris, Prault, 1788. 37 p. 21ᶜᵐ.

Last p. incorrectly numbered 33.

Cast.   ML 50.2.R39D21

— **Renaud d'Ast,** comédie, en deux actes et en prose, mêlée d'ariettes; par MM. Radet & Barré. Musique de M. d'Alayrac. Représentée pour la premiere fois par les Comédiens italiens ordinaires du roi, le jeudi 19 juillet 1787.

Paris, Brunet, 1788. 56 p. ·19ᶜᵐ.

Cast.   ML 50.2.R39D22

— **Renaud d'Ast.** Syngespil i to acter. Musiken af D'almirac. [!]

n. i., n. d. 88 p. 16ᶜᵐ.

Cast.

First performed at Copenhagen, April 16, 1793.   Schatz 2379

— **Gesaenge aus dem singspiele Reinald,** in zwey aufzuegen, nach dem franzoesischen. In musik gesetzt von d'Alayrac.

Hamburg, Johann Matthias Michaelsen, 1790. 30 p. 15ᶜᵐ.

German version by H. G. Schmieder. (Schatz.)

First performed at Hamburg, Theater beim Gänsemarkt, January 12, 1790; at Mayence, National theater, November 1788.   Schatz 2378

Renaud d'Ast, comédie en deux actes, meslée d'ariettes, représentée devant Leurs Majestés à Fontainebleau, le 12 octobre 1765.

[*Paris*], *Christophe Ballard, 1765. 60 p. 20½*cm. (*Journal des spectacles, t. i, Paris, 1766.*)

Cast and names of Le Monnier as author, of **Trial** and Pierre **Vachon** as composers.

ML 48.J7

La **rencontre.** A. T. of Della Maria's Le vieux château.

La **rencontre imprevue.** A. T. of Le trompeur trompé.

La **rencontre imprévue,** opera bouffon en trois actes et en prose, tiré des Pélerins de la Mecque, rédigé par M. Dancourt & mis en musique par M. le chevalier Gluk [!] . . .

*Paris, la veuve Duchesne, 1776. 56 p. 18½*cm.

By L. H. Dancourt. At the end (on p. 52–56) the airs of "J'ai fait un rêve" and "Sans l'espérance du retour."

First performed at Vienna, Theater n. d. Burg, January, 1764. SCHATZ 3919

— **Die unvermuthete zusammenkunft** oder Die pilgrime von Mecca, ein singspiel in drey aufzeugen aus dem franzoesischen uebersetzt, mit musik.

*Frankfurt am Mayn, mit Andreaeischen schriften, 1772. 109 p., 14 p. (music). 16½*cm.

By Johann Heinrich Faber, who is not mentioned. Cast. The fourteen p. of music at end (voice and bass): "Das schicksal bringt mich itzt zurück," "So kommt, so kommt, holder jungfrau'n chöre" and "Einen bach, der fliesst" proved that this is a German version of the opera by **Gluck.** SCHATZ 3920

— **Det uventede møde.** Et lystigt syngestykke i tre acter, taget af herr Dancourts, Pilligrimene fra Mekka. Musikken er of ridderen herr Gluck. til samme musik oversat of P. T. Wandall.

*n. i., n. d. 96 p. 17*cm.

First performed at Copenhagen, Hoftheater i Christiansborg Slot, November 26, 1776. SCHATZ 3922

Das **rendezvous in der neuen alee.** A. T. of Tuczek's Hanns Klachl.

Il **Reno sacrificante,** attione dramatica in musica del Sig. Co. Ridolfo Campeggi.

*Bologna, Sebastiano Bonomi, 1617. 35 p. 20*cm.

On p. 3: "Fatta rappresentare in Bologna per honore de gli illustriss. & reverendiss. Signori cardinali Caponi legato, et Ludovisi arcivesc., di detta città, et per diporto de i suoi nobilissimi cavallieri & bellissime dame, dalla magnanimità de gl'illustri, & eccelsi Signori Anziani, Cons. e confaloniero di giustitia del popolo bolognese, per lo secondo bimestre dell' anno MDCXVII . . . Fece la musica il Sig. Girolamo Giacobbi maestro di capella di San Petronio di Bologna. Sovraintese alla scena, machine, ed habiti il Sig. Gio. Luigi Valesio."

First performed as indicated, Teatro della Sala, April 28, 1617. SCHATZ 3804

La **répétition interrompue,** opera-comique en un acte; avec un prologue. Représenté pour la premiere fois sur le Théâtre de la Foire, en 1735.

*Charles François Pannard, Théâtre, Paris, Duchesne, 1763, v. 2, [383]–444 p. 17*cm.

In prose and vaudevilles. Composer not recorded by Parfaict, who dates the first performance August 6, 1735, and attributes the text jointly to Pannard and Favart. *See* next entry. PQ 2019.P3

La répétition interrompue, ou Le petit-maitre malgré lui. Opera-comique, représenté pour la premiere fois sur le Théâtre de la Foire S. Germain, le 14 mars 1757. Et reprise le 3 février 1758.

Paris, N. B. Duchesne, 1758. 93, [3] p. 19cm. (Theatre de M. Favart, Paris, Duchesne, 1763–77, t. viii.)

Prologue and one act. In prose and vaudevilles. Casts. On p. 81–93 seven airs and a duo; on the [3] p. the approbation and lists of plays. Favart's musical collaborator is not mentioned by Font.

This is Favart's much altered version of "La répétition interrompue" written originally by him in collaboration with Pannard and first performed at Paris, Foire St. Laurent, August 6, 1735. The original version was incorporated in Pannard's works, as published by Duchesne in 1763. *See* preceding entry.   ML 49.A2F1

La répétition ordinaire de l'opéra. Tr. of Latilla's L'opera in prova alla moda.

The reprisal; or, The tars of Old England. In two acts. By Dr. Smollet.

[30]–63 p. 19cm. (Collection of the most esteemed farces and entertainments, t. ii, Edinburgh, 1792.)

Drury-Lane and Edinburgh (1780) casts.
Composer not mentioned by W. Barclay Squire.   SCHATZ 11753B

The resemblance. A. T. of Della Maria's The prisoner.

La ressemblance. A. T. of Della Maria's Le prisonnier.

La ressource comique, pièce en un acte, mêlée d'ariettes; précédée d'un prologue. Par M. Anseaume. La musique de M. Merault. Représentée pour la première fois par les Comédiens italiens ordinaires du roi, le Samedi 22 août 1772.

Paris, la veuve Duchesne, 1772. 80 p. 21½cm.

Cast. On p. 75–80, the airs of the ariettes, "Je le veux, et cela suffit," "De l'ordre exprès d'un petit dieu," and "Suis-je digne." The composer's correct name is Jean Nicolas Amédée Le Froid de Méreaux.   ML 50.2.R42M2

La ressource des théâtres, piece en un acte. Par M. C * * * représenté pour la premiere fois sur le Théâtre de l'Opera-comique, le 31 janvier 1760.

Paris, Duchesne, 1760. 42, [6] p. 19cm.

Cast. Running title calls this a prologue. Prose, vaudevilles, and ariettes, some of which are printed in the text, as, for instance, the final vaudeville, "Toujours suivre avec uniformité," of which a foot-note says: "L'air & les couplets du vaudeville sont de M. **Favart.**" In fact, the preface of the "Theatre" (v. I, p. xxvii) informs us that this was Favart's only contribution to the play, "mais ce vaudeville a fait presque seul tout le succès de la pièce." The real author is mentioned neither in this preface nor by Font, who is silent also on the musical collaborator. The [6] p. contain lists of plays, etc.   SCHATZ 11509

— **La ressource des théâtres,** piece en un acte. Par M. C * * * Représenté pour la premiere fois sur le Théâtre de l'Opéra-comique, le 31 janvier 1760.

Paris, Duchesne, 1760. 42, [6] p. 19cm. (Theatre de M. Favart, Paris, Duchesne, 1763–77, t. viii.)

Prose, vaudevilles, etc., precisely the same as the foregoing.   ML 49.A2F1

The **restauration of King Charles II.** or, The life and death of Oliver Cromwell. An histori-tragi-comi ballad opera. As it was forbid to be acted at the New Theatre in the Hay-Market . . .

London, R. Walker, 1732. 2 p. l., vii, [1], 54, [2] p. 18½ᶜᵐ.

Three acts. Dedication by the author, Walter Aston, and his preface. According to this, Aston submitted the play to Mr. Potter, "master" of the New Theatre in the Hay-Market, who told him that

"nothing must be play'd there till a gentleman of the treasury, and another of the exchequer, had read and approv'd it."

They were approached. They claimed to have "not time to look over such things," but if their friend, who had approached them in behalf of Aston, "was satisfied, there was no offence, there should not be any stop put to it." Thereupon Aston

"distributed the parts [the proposed cast on the last [2] p.], printed bills and tickets, and had it rehearsed thrice; but unexpectedly a message came, to stop the performance [which was planned for May 4th]; for the actors should be all taken up: That now they dare not play treason, they put treasonable titles to their bills; and that the *Restauration of King Charles II. was a treasonable title.*

"I confess I am so stupid, I cannot apprehend what they mean . . ." When Aston protested and asked for the censor's reasons, the final answer he reports to have been, "the story is too recent."

The 23 airs used in this ballad opera are indicated by title. LONGE 275

La rete di Vulcano, ballet. *See* Sacchini's Creso.

Le retour. Entrée in Boismortier's Les voyages de l'amour.

Le retour de l'opera-comique, en un acte. Par Monsieur * * * Représenté pour la premiere fois sur le Théâtre de l'Opera-comique de la Foire saint Laurent, le 28 juin 1759.

Paris, Duchesne, 1759. 56 p. 19ᶜᵐ. (Theatre de M. Favart, Paris, Duchesne, 1763–77, t. viii.)

Cast. Prose, vaudevilles, and ariettes. Several of the airs are printed in the text. Font does not mention Favart's musical collaborator. ML 49.A2F1

Le retour de l'Opera comique au faubourg S. Germain. Piece en un acte servant de prologue. Representée le 27 février 1734 à la Foire Saint Germain.

Le Théâtre de la foire, Paris, 1737, t. ix, 2, pl., [287]–321 p. 17ᶜᵐ.

By Carolet. Largely *en vaudevilles.* The airs, a few of which by **Corette,** are printed at the end of the volume in the "Table des airs." ML 48.L2 X

Le retour de tendresse, comédie. En un acte et en vers. Melée d'ariettes. Représentée devant Leurs Majestés, à Fontainebleau le 17 octobre 1777. Les paroles du Sieur Anseaume. La musique du Sieur Mereau.

Paris, Ruault, 1778. 37, [1] p. 19½ᶜᵐ.

Cast. ML 50.2.R4M3

Le retour du seigneur dans ses terres. *See* Floquet's Le seigneur bienfaisant.

Die reue vor der hochzeit. Singspiel in einem aufzuge.

Berlin, Friedrich Maurer, 1782. 56 p. 16½ᶜᵐ.

The author, Fr. L. W. Meyer, is not mentioned. No composer or performance recorded by Schatz. ML 50.2.R44

Die reue vor der that. *See* Dezède's L'erreur d'un moment.

Le rêve, opera-comique en un acte; représenté pour la premiere fois sur le Théâtre de la Foire, en 1738.

Charles François Pannard, Théâtre, Paris, Duchesne, 1763, v. 3, [203]–258 p. 17ᶜᵐ.

In prose and vaudevilles. Composer not recorded by Parfaict, who dates first performance February 15, 1738. PQ 2019.P3

Le reveil de l'opéra-comique. Prologue. Representé à la Foire Saint Laurent. 1732.

Le Théâtre de la foire, Paris, 1737, t. ix, 2, pl., 15 p. 17ᶜᵐ.

By Carolet. Largely *en vaudevilles.* The airs, selected or composed and arranged by Jean Claude **Gillier,** are printed at the end of the volume in the "Table des airs." First performed August 13, 1732. ML 48.L2 X

The revenge, a burletta; acted at Marybone Gardens, MDCCLXX. With additional songs. By Thomas Chatterton.

London, T. King, H. Chapmann, J. Egerton, 1795. 1 p. l., 47 p. 21ᶜᵐ.

On p. [41]–47 the additional "Songs." Two acts. A prefatory note says:
"This burletta, and the songs which follow it, were printed from an original manuscript, in the hand-writing of the celebrated Chatterton, who received five guineas for the composition from the proprietors of Marybone Gardens, July 6, 1770."
The composer, Samuel **Arnold,** is not mentioned. Longe 296
Second copy, lacking the leaf with the prefatory note. ML 50.2.R45

The revenge of Athridates. A. T. of the pasticcio Pharnaces.

La révolution pacifique. A. T. of Beffroy de Reigny's Nicodème dans la lune.

Rex et Pontifex: being an attempt to introduce upon the stage a new species of pantomime.

London, M. Cooper, 1745. 15 p. 20ᶜᵐ.

By R. Dodsley, who is not mentioned. ML 52.2.R4

Rhea Sylvia, in einem singespiele auf dem Hamburgischen Theatro vorgestellet im jahr 1720.

Hamburg, Caspar Jakhel, n. d. Unpaged. 18½ᶜᵐ.

Three acts. Argument and scenario. Neither the author (resp. translator, unknown to Schatz) nor the composer, Melchior **Hofmann,** is mentioned.
First performed at Leipzig, Opernhaus im Brühle, 1714; at Hamburg, Opernhaus beim Gänsemarkt. Schatz 4760

Rhea Sylvia. L. T. of Porta's Numitore.

La ricca locandiera. Intermezzi per musica a quattro voci da rappresentarsi nel Teatro Capranica nel carnevale dell' anno 1759 . . .

Roma, Giuseppe e Nicola Grossi, n. d. 35 p. 15½ᶜᵐ.

Two intermezzi. Dedication by the bookseller, Agostino Palombini, of "il presente scherzo di poesia," cast, and name of Pietro **Guglielmi** as composer. The author is unknown to Schatz. ML 48.A5 v.3

Il Riccardo. Drama per musica da rappresentarsi nel Teatro de' Fiorentini nel carnevale del corrente anno 1743 . . .

[Napoli], Nicola de Biase, n. d. 71 p. 14½ᶜᵐ.

Three acts. Author not mentioned and unknown to Schatz. Impresario's dedication, cast, and name of Nicola **Logroscino** as composer. Schatz 5674

Riccardo, Cor di Leone. Tr. of Grétry's Richard Coeur de Lion.

Riccardo Cor di Leone. Commedia per musica da rappresentarsi nel nobile Teatro Giustiniani in San Moisè per la prima opera del carnovale 1790. Tratta dall' originale francese di M. Sedaine e ridotta per uso del Teatro suddetto.

Venezia, Modesto Fenzo, 1789. 49 p. 18ᶜᵐ.

Two acts. Cast and name of Ferdinando **Robuschi** as the composer. First performed December 26, 1789, as indicated. SCHATZ 8844

Riccardo I rè d'Inghilterra.

Three acts. By Georg Friedrich **Händel.** Text by Paolo Antonio Rolli. First performed at London, Haymarket, November 11, 1727. Not in L. of C.

— Der **misslungene braut-wechsel,** oder Richardus I, koenig von England, in einem sing-spiele auf dem Hamburgischen Schau-Platze fuergestellet anno 1729.

[Hamburg], mit Stromerschen schrifften, n. d. Unpaged. 18½ᶜᵐ.

Three acts. With names of C. G. Wend as translator of Rolli's "Riccardo I, rè d'Inghilterra," and author of the "untergemischten teutschen poesie," of Georg Philipp **Telemann** as the composer of the German arias and of **Händel** as composer of the Italian, German translation of which is added to the Italian texts. Concerning the "untergemischte teutsche poesie," Wend says in the "Vorbericht" (with argument):

"die hinzugefuegte comische untermischung wird der geneigte leser sich desto weniger missfallen lassen, weil dergleichen abwechselung nunmehro nicht nur zur mode, sondern auch fast zur nothwendigkeit geworden ist, womit man sich zugleich zu dessen bestaendiger gewogenheit empfiehlet und sich einer frequenten gegenwart getroesten will."

First performed, as indicated, Theater beim Gänsemarkt, February 3, 1729.

SCHATZ 4488

Richard Coeur de Lion. Comédie en trois actes, en prose et en vers, mise en musique. Représentée, pour la première fois, à Paris, par les Comédiens italiens ordinaires du roi, le 21 octobre 1784; & à Fontainebleau, devant Leurs Majestés, le 25 octobre 1785.

Paris, Brunet, 1786. 48 p. 20ᶜᵐ.

Neither the author, Michel Jean Sedaine, is mentioned, nor the composer, **Grétry.**

ML 48.M2H

— **Richard, Coeur de Lion,** comédie en trois actes en prose et en vers, mis en musique. Représentée, pour la première fois, à Paris, par les Comédiens italiens ordinaires du Roi, le 21 octobre 1784; & à Fontainebleau, devant Leurs Majestés, le 25 octobre 1785. Nouvelle édition.

Paris, Didor, l'ainé, 1787. 34 p. 19ᶜᵐ.

Neither the author, Sedaine, nor the composer, **Grétry,** is mentioned.

SCHATZ 4177

— **Richard Coeur de Lion.** An historical romance. From the French of Monsr. Sedaine. As performed at the Theatre Royal, Drury-Lane.

London, J. Debrett, 1786. 52 p. 20½ᶜᵐ.

Three acts. Cast and Advertisement, stating this to be an adaptation to the English stage without "adventitious matter," except that "the discovery of Richard's confinement being now given to Matilda in place of Blondel . . . ."

Richard Coeur de Lion—Continued.

Neither John Burgoyne is mentioned, who translated and adapted Sedaine's text, nor Thomas **Linley,** who adapted **Grétry's** music.   Not to be confused with Shield's adaptation, performed at Covent Garden in the same year:
First performed at London October 24, 1786, as indicated.   LONGE 98

— . . . Arien und gesaenge aus dem singspiel **Richard Löwenherz,** in drei aufzuegen.   Nach dem französischen des Sedaine.   Musik von Gretry.   Nach anordnung der königl. General-intendantur.

Berlin, n. publ., n. d.   31 p.   15^{cm}.

By Johann André.
First performed at Berlin, Kgl. Nationaltheater, February 9, 1790.   SCHATZ 4179

— **Riccardo Cor di Leone.**   Commedia per musica da rappresentarsi nel Teatro di Monza l'autunno dell' anno 1787 . . .

Milano, Gio. Batista Bianchi, n. d.   64 p.   16^{cm}.

Three acts.   Sedaine and **Grétry** are mentioned by the anonymous translator in his interesting "Avvertimento del traduttore" (p. 7–12) after the dedication.   He speaks of the extraordinary difficulty of translating the "scarsa, laconica, e tronca . . . lingua de' Francesi . . . atta a rinchiudere molto senso in pochi monosillabi" into Italian and adjusting it to the score without changing a single bar of the music, the first time, so he claims, that this had been tried by a translator.   SCHATZ 4201

Richard Löwenherz.   Tr. of Grétry's Richard, Coeur de Lion.

Richardus I, koenig von England.   A. T. of Händel's Der misslungene braut-wechsel.

Ricimero.   Drama per musica da rappresentarsi nel nobilissimo Teatro di S. Benedetto l'autunno dell' anno MDCCLXXIII.

Venezia, Modesto Fenzo, 1773.   1 p. l., 55 p.   17^{cm}.

Three acts.   By Francesco Silvani (not mentioned).   Text originally called "La fede tradita e vendicata."   In the present libretto Umblo has become Grimoaldo, and Scandone has become Rodoaldo.   Argument, cast, scenario, and name of the composer, Giov. Batt. **Borghi.**   On p. 20–27, cast, argument, and detailed description of Antonio Trancart's "Ajace e Cassandra, ballo eroitragico," in thirteen scenes, on p. 41–47 of his ballet, "Le feste o Le gelosie del seraglio."   The composers of the music are not mentioned.
First performed November 26, 1773.   SCHATZ 1236

— **Ricimero.**   Dramma per musica da rappresentarsi nel Teatro dell' illustrissima Accademia Filarmonica di Verona nel carnovale dell' anno 1778 . . .

Verona, Dionisio Ramanzin, n. d.   47 p.   17½^{cm}.

Three acts.   By Silvani, who is not mentioned.   Impresario's dedication, argument, scenario, cast and name of **Borghi** as composer.   ML 50.2.R47B6

Ricimero.   Dramma per musica da rappresentarsi nel Regio Teatro di Torino nel carnevale del 1756 alla presenza di S. S. R. M.

Torino, Zappata e Avondo, n. d.   viii, 61, [2] p.   15½^{cm}.

Three acts.   Author unknown to Schatz.   Argument, cast, scenario, and name of the composer, Giacinto **Calderara.**   Vincenzo Saunier is mentioned as the "compositore" of the three ballets, Rocco Gionatti [Gioanetti] as the "compositore delle arie de' balli."   The first was entitled, "Cerere e Trittolemo," and is described on p. 20–21.   The second is called "Giudicio di Paride," and is described on p. 41–42, and the third, "Sacrificio detto Taurobolio pella elezione ed inaugurazione di un re di Norvegia," and is described on p. 60–61.   The two additional pages contain some changes introduced in the third act.
First performed, as indicated, December 26, 1755.   SCHATZ 1507

Ricimero. *See also* Galuppi's Ernelinda.

Ricimero. Dramma per musica da rappresentarsi nel Real Teatro di S. Carlo nel dì 13 di agosto 1789 per festeggiarsi la nascita di S. M. la regina . . .

Napoli, Vincenzo Flauto, 1789. 60 p. 15^cm.

Two acts. Argument, cast, scenario, name of Giacomo **Siri** as the composer, and impresario's dedication, in which this is called a replica of
"Ricimero, ma ridotto in una forma tutta nuova: ciò si è fatto a solo fine di adattarlo al gusto, che corre pe' spettacoli."
The author, Francesco Silvano, is not mentioned whose "La fede tradita e vendicata" this is in a modernized version.   SCHATZ 9896

Ricimero re de' Goti. Drama per musica da rappresentarsi il carnevale dell' anno 1740 nel Teatro a Torre Argentina . . .

Roma, Antonio de' Rossi, n. d. 62 p. 16^cm.

Three acts. *Rifacimento* of Zeno and Pariati's "Flavio Anicio Olibrio." Argument, cast, scenario and name of Niccolò **Jommelli** as composer.
First performed as indicated, January 16, 1740.   ML 50.2.R48J6

Ricimero rè de' Goti. Drama per musica da rappresentarsi in Roma nel nobil Teatro delle Dame nel corrente carnevale dell' anno MDCCLIX.

Roma, Stamperia de' Rossi, n. d. 49 p. 16^cm.

Three acts. Author not mentioned and unknown to Schatz. Dedication, argument, scenario, cast, and name of Giovanni Francesco de **Majo** as composer.
First performed at Parma, Teatro Ducale, carnival, 1758.   SCHATZ 5859

Ricimero, rè de Vandali. Drama per musica nel famosissimo Teatro Grimano in S. Gio. Grisostomo l' anno 1684. Di Matteo Noris . . .

Venetia, Francesco Nicolini, 1684. 79 p. 14^cm.

Three acts. Author's dedication, argument, and scenario. The composer, Carlo **Pallavicino**, is not mentioned.   SCHATZ 7731

Il **riconoscimento di Teseo** ossia Teseo e Medea, ballet. *See* G. Giordani's Ariarate.

Il **riconoscimento inaspettato,** ballet. *See* Jommelli's L' isola disabitata.

Le **rien.** Parody of Mondonville's Titon et L'Aurore.

I **rigiri delle cantarine.** Dramma giocoso per musica da rappresentarsi nel Teatro di S. Cassiano. L' autunno dell' anno 1745 . . .

Venezia, Modesto Fenzo, 1745. 60 p. 15½^cm.

Three acts. By Bartolomeo Vitturi, who is not mentioned. Impresario's dedication, cast, scenario, and name of Francesco **Maggiore** as composer. SCHATZ 5833

Les **rigueurs du cloitre,** comédie en deux actes, en prose, mêlée d'ariettes; représentée pour la première fois par les comédiens italiens ordinaires du roi, le 23 août 1790. Paroles de M. Févée. Musique de M. Berton.

Paris, J. L. de Boubers, 1793. 24 p. 18½^cm.

Cast.   SCHATZ 898

Rinaldo. Dramma per musica da rappresentarsi nel nobilissimo Teatro Venier in San Benedetto il carnovale dell' anno 1789.

Venezia, Modesto Fenzo, 1789.　40 p.　19½cm.

Two acts. By Giuseppe Foppa, who is not mentioned. Argument, cast, and name of Pietro **Guglielmi** as the composer. On p. [17] 24 cast, argument, and description without name of the composer of the music of Francesco Clerico's "I sacrifizi di Tauride, ballo serio pantomimo." The second ballet was called "Il filosofo deriso."

First performed, as indicated, January 28, 1789.　　　　　Schatz 4303

Rinaldo, an opera.　Perform'd at the Queen's Theatre in London. MDCCXI.

[71]–143 p.　21cm.　(Aaron Hill, Dramatic works, London, T. Lownds, 1760, vol. I.)

Three acts. Cast and argument. In his dedication to the Queen Aaron Hill says "This opera is a native of Your Majesty's dominions" and speaks of his "endeavour to see the English opera more splendid than her mother, the Italian." In his preface, Hill, mentioning Hendel (Georg Friedrich **Händel**) as the composer, gives the peculiar history of this Rinaldo text:

"The deficiencies I found, or thought I found, in such Italian opera's, as have hitherto been introduced among us, were, first, that they had been composed for tastes and voices, different from those who were to sing and hear them on the English stage; and secondly, that wanting the machines and decorations, which bestow so great a beauty on their appearance, they have been heard and seen to very considerable disadvantage.

"At once to remedy both these misfortunes, I resolved to frame some drama, that, by different incidents and passions, might afford the music scope to vary and display its excellence, and fill the eye with more delightful prospects, so at once to give two senses equal pleasure.

"I could not chuse a finer subject than the celebrated story of *Rinaldo and Armida*, which has furnished opera's for every stage and tongue in Europe . . . It was a very particular happiness, that I met with a gentleman so excellently qualify'd as Signor Rossi, to fill up the model I had drawn, with words so sounding and so rich in sense, that if my translation is in many places led to deviate, 'tis for want of power to reach the force of his original . . ."

This is followed by Giacomo Rossi's notice "Il poeta al lettore" in which he pays not the slightest attention to Hill, apologizes for the defects of his "parto di poche sere" due to lack of time

"poiche il Signor Hendel, Orfeo del nostro secolo, nel porla in musica, a pena mi diede tempo di scrivere, e viddi, con mio grande stupore, in due sole settimane armonizata da quell' ingegno sublime, al maggior grado di perfezzione un opera intiera."

Rossi's Italian text is faced by Hill's English translation.

First performed at London, Haymarket, February 24, 1711.　　　　Longe 325

— Rinaldo, [vignette].　Musicalisches schau-spiel, auf dem grossen Hamburgischen Theatro im monath novembr. 1715.

Hamburg, Friedrich Conrad Graeflinger, n. d.　Unpaged.　18½cm.

Publisher's name cut off in binding.

Three acts. In the lengthy "Kurtzer vor-bericht" Barthold Feind (not mentioned by name) states that he made his translation of Rossi's "Rinaldo" in five days; that this will account for its shortcomings; but that, on the other hand, he followed Rossi "fast sclavisch," so not to miss a single note of Hendel's music. He means, of course, Georg Friedrich **Händel**. This incidental remark may be of interest:

"En fin, weil noch kein Teutscher als Hendel einen Rinaldo aus der italiaenischen sprache in die music gesetzet, wird ihm wohl niemand den glorieusen musicalischen titel eines Orfeus dieses seculi, als der neid selber disputirlich machen; wiewol ich mich dabey mit plaisir erinnere, dass alhier ein herr von den gens de qualité, welcher einen staatscaracter mit besonderm ruhm bekleidet und dem bey muessigen stunden die music sein zeitvertreib ist, vor einigen jahren in der allerzartesten bluethe seines alters eine von mir auf befehl seines nunmehr in Gott ruhenden herrn vaters *Excellence* verfertigte italiaenische opera, "Virginia generosa, e Don Camillo incostante" benahmet in die music gesetzt und der Hochseeligsten Koenigin Anna, glor-wuer-

Rinaldo—Continued.

digsten andenckens, seine vertû dergestalt gezeiget, dass ihm der titul eines *Amphions* von vielen Grossen der music kundigen in London beygelegt worden . . ."

SCHATZ 4489

— **Rinaldo.** In einem singe-spiele auf dem Hamburgischen Schauplatze im jahr 1723 vorgestellet.

[Hamburg], Caspar Jakhel, n. d. Unpaged. 18ᶜᵐ.

Three acts. Neither Feind, the author, nor **Händel**, the composer, is mentioned. Schatz calls this "II. veraenderte ausgabe," but comparison proves the text to be identical with that of 1715, except that the Italian text of the arias has been more consistently added to the German. SCHATZ 4501

— **Rinaldo.** Drama per musica da rappresentarsi nella gran sala del Real Palazzo il di 1. ottobre 1718 in cui si festeggiano gli anni di S. M. Ces. e Cat. Carlo VI . . .

Napoli, Michele Luigi Muzio, 1718.

Prologue and three acts. Nicola Serino's dedication, dated October 1, 1718, scenario, cast, and publisher's notice to the reader, which reads, in part:

"L'idea dell' autore ne alterò alcuni personaggi, al che non s'è potuto dar rimedio per servirsi in buona parte della musica del Signor Giorgio Federico Hendel (**Händel**); che primo la pose in musica. Molte scene aggiuntevi, come ancora tutte le buffe, quali ritroverai segnate con il § sono musica del Sign. Leonardo **Leo**, che n'ebbe il pensiero di deriggerla."

Accordingly, Leo composed "Ove ridon nel prato li fiori" (prol.), the scenes (I, 10) "Già per la mia grand' arte," (II, 4) "Esser non può, che l'Averno," (II, 11) "Ahi! Pur riveggo il caro sposo," etc., and more particularly the scenes between "Lesbina" and "Nesso" exclusively, which act as interpolated intermezzi, "Oh sconsolato Nesso" (I, 11), "E non si arriva mai, poter di Bacco" (II, 12), "Io per me mi strasecolo" (III, 8), and "Trombe, fischi, tamburri" (III, 11). These comic scenes, etc., Schatz attributes to Serino. SCHATZ 4495

Il **Rinaldo,** ballet. *See* Marescalchi's L'Alessandro nell' Indie.

Rinaldo. Dramma per musica da rappresentarsi nel Teatro Vendramin in S. Salvatore nella fiera dell' Ascensione dell' anno 1775 . . .

Venezia, Gio. Battista Casali, 1775. 44 p. 17ᶜᵐ.

Three acts. Dedication, cast, scenario, and name of Antonio **Tozzi** as the composer. ("La musica sarà del tutto nuova.") Author not mentioned, and unknown to Schatz. SCHATZ 10386

Rinaldo and Armida.

Noverre, Jean George, Works, Tr. from the French, London, 1783, v. 3, [29]–51 p. 21½ᶜᵐ.

"Preliminary discourse" and detailed description of the three scenes.

GV 1787.N8

Rinaldo d'Aste. Commedia con musica d'un atto solo da rappresentarsi nel nobilissimo Teatro Giustiniani in San Moisè il carnovale dell' anno 1794.

Venezia, Modesto Fenzo, 1794. 40 p. 18ᶜᵐ.

By Giuseppe Carpani, who is not mentioned. Cast and name of Marco Portogalli (**Portugal**) as the composer.

First performed, as indicated, January 4, 1794 (Carvalhaes). SCHATZ 8428

— **Rinaldo d'Aste.** Dramma giocoso per musica da rappresentarsi nel Regio Teatro di S. Carlo della Principessa nel felicissimo

Rinaldo d'Aste—Continued.

giorno natalizio di Sua Altezza Reale . . . D. Carlotta Gioacchina . . . li 25 d'aprile 1799.

Lisbona, Simone Taddeo Ferreira, 1799.   109 p.   14^{cm}.

Two acts.   Cast and name of Marcos **Portugal** as the composer, and note:
"Questo dramma in un solo atto in prosa, è stato accresciuto, e ridotto a due atti in verso dal Sig. Giuseppe Caravita, poeta del Teatro."
Portuguese text faces Italian.   SCHATZ 8429

Rinaldo d'Asti, ballet.   *See* Borghi's La morte di Semiramide.

Rinaldo e Armida, ballet.   *See* Salieri's La cifra.

Rinaldo nel giardino incantato d'Armida, ballet.   *See* Bianchi's Trionfo della pace.

Rinaldo nella isola incantata d'Armida, ballet.   *See* Galuppi's Il rè pastore.

Rinaldo nella selva incantata, ballet.   *See* Sarti's Siroe.

Rinaldo und Alcina.   Eine komische oper in drei aufzeugen von Ludwig v. Baczko.

Koenigsberg, Hartung, 1794.   71 p.   15^{cm}.

Composed by Maria Theresia **Paradies,** who is not mentioned.
First performed at Prag, Altstaedter National Theater, 1796.   SCHATZ 7770

Der ring der liebe oder Zemirens und Azors ehestand, ein singspiel in drey aufzeugen.   Aufgefuehrt im k. k. Theater naechst dem Kaernthnerthore.

Wien, beym Logenmeister, 1786.   77 p.   16^{cm}.

Neither Schatz nor Haas know the author.   They record Ignaz **Umlauf** as the composer.   A foot-note on p. [2] reads:
"Die musik ist auf ein waelsches singspiel geschrieben; ein deutscher dichter hat auf die musik einen neuen stoff gebaut.   Kenner wissen die beschwerlichkeit."
First performed, as indicated, December 3, 1786.   SCHATZ 10533

La rinovata Camilla o sia Camilla, regina de' Volsci.   L. T. of M. A. Bononcini's Il trionfo di Camilla, regina de' Volsci.

Il ripiego in amore.   Farsetta per musica da rappresentarsi nel Teatro alla Valle nel carnevale dell' anno 1751 . . .

Roma, Ottavio Puccinelli, 1751.   [28] p.   15½^{cm}.

Two parts.   Author not mentioned and unknown to Schatz.   Cast, name of **Rinaldo di Capua** as composer and dedication signed by Angelo Lungi and the publisher.   ML 50.2.R49R4

Il riposo interotto, ballet.   *See* Gluck's Il trionfo di Clelia.

Il ripudio d'Ottavia.   Drama per musica, da rappresentarsi nel Teatro Grimani in S. Gio. Grisost. l'anno MIDCC . . .   Di Matteo Noris.

Venetia, Nicolini, 1699.   72 p., incl. front.   15^{cm}.

Three acts.   Author's dedication, notice to the reader, and scenario.   The composer, Carlo Francesco **Pollaroli,** is not mentioned.   SCHATZ 8315

Le risa di Democrito.   Da cantarsi nel Teatro privilegiato da S. M. C. e Cat. in Vienna.   Nell' anno MDCCXXXVII.   Nel mese di settembre.—Das gelaechter des Democritus . . .

Wien, Johann Peter v. Ghelen, n. d.   81 p.   14^{cm}.

Three acts.   Argument and text in German faces Italian.   Neither the author, conte Nicola Minato, nor the composer, Francesco Antonio **Pistocchi,** is mentioned. First performed at Vienna, Hoftheater, carnival, 1700.   SCHATZ 8200

La rispettosa tenerezza.   Componimento dramatico, scritto in Vienna dall' autore . . . ed eseguito con musica del Reutter negl' interni appartamenti del palazzo di Schönbrunn dalle AA. RR. di tre arciduchesse d'Austria . . . in occasione di festeggiare il giorno di nome della madre loro augustissima l'anno 1750.

[197]–204 p.   26^{cm}.   (Metastasio, Opere, t. xi, Parigi, vedova Herissant, 1782.)   ML 49.A2M44

I riti d'Apollo Leucadio.   A. T. of Mayr's Saffo.

I riti della Baja Dushy, ballet.   *See* Bianchi's La cappricciosa ravveduta.

La ritornata di Londra.   Dramma di tre atti per musica.   Rappresentato per la prima volta in Venezia il carnovale dell' anno MDCCLVI.

Carlo Goldoni, Opere teatrali, Venezia, Zatta e figli, 1788–95, v. 44, [5]–62 p.   18^{cm}.   PQ

La ritornata di Londra.   Dramma giocoso per musica di Polisseno Fegejo P. A. [Goldoni]   Da rappresentarsi nel Teatro di S. Samuele il carnevale dell' anno MDCCLVI.

Venezia, Angiolo Geremia, n. d.   60 p.   15½^{cm}.

Three acts.   Cast, scenario, and name of the composer, Domenico **Fischietti.**
SCHATZ 3234

— **La ritornata di Londra,** dramma giocoso per musica, da rappresentarsi nel Nuovo Teatro in Dresda nell' estade dell' anno MDCCLVI.—Die zurueckkunft aus Londen, ein musicalisches lustspiel . . .

[Dresden], Stoesselin und Joh. Carl Krause, n. d.   175 p.   16^{cm}.

Three acts.   Cast added in ms., scenario, and name of Domenico **Fischietti** as composer.   German text faces Italian.
First performed July 20, 1756.   SCHATZ 3235

Il ritorno d'Agamemnone, ballet.   *See* P. Guglielmi's Arsace.

Il ritorno d'Angelica nell' Indie.

p. 143–154.   15½^{cm}.   (Ottavio Tronsarelli, Drammi musicali, Roma, Francesco Corbelletti, 1632.)

One act.   Argument.   No composer mentioned, but Lady Morgan, in her work on Salvator Rosa, affirms that the above was performed at Rome, with music by one **Cignani,** who is not mentioned by Eitner.   ML 49.A2T7

Il ritorno d'Ulisse.   Dramma per musica da rappresentarsi nel Regio Teatro di via della Pergola nell' autunno del 1798 . . .

Firenze, Pietro Fantosini, 1798.   49 p.   16½^{cm}.

Il ritorno d'Ulisse—Continued.

Three acts. Argument, cast, and name of Francesco **Basili** as composer. Librettist is unknown to Schatz. On p. 5–12, a detailed description, with cast, of "Gli Orazi, e i Curiazi. Ballo eroico tragico pantomimo in cinque atti composto e diretto da Gaetano Gioja." Composer of the music not mentioned. The second ballet, also by Gioja, was called "La volubile."

First performed September 1, 1798, as indicated.   Schatz 629

Il ritorno d'Ulisse. Componimento dramatico rappresentato nella sala dal palazzo del sereniss. granduca in Pisa per festeggiare il giorno natalizio della sereniss. granduchessa Vittoria di Toscana.

G. A. Moniglia, Poesie drammatiche, parte prima, Firenze, Vincenzio Vangelisti, 1689, p. [435]–501. 24^{cm}.

Three acts and prologue. Argument with name of Jacopo **Melani** as composer.
First performed as indicated, 1656.   ML 49.A2M7

Il ritorno della primavera, ballet. *See* Colla's Andromeda.

Il ritorno di Astrea in terra. Dramma per musica per i lietissimi e faustissimi sposalizi dell' augusta infanta di Spagna D. Carlotta Gioacchina coll' infante Augusto di Portogallo D. Giovanni: e dell' augusta infanta di Portogallo D. Marianna Vittoria coll' augusto infante di Spagna D. Gabriele Antonio.

Lisbona, Francesco Luigi Ameno, 1785. 5 p. l., 15 p. 16^{cm}.

The title on the 1st p. l., the rest on the 2d. On 3d p. l., "Da cantàrsi ai [15] de Giugno del 1785 nel palazzo dell' eccellentissimo Signor conte di Fernan Nuñez." Argument, cast, and name of José **Palomino** as the composer. The author is not mentioned, and is unknown to Schatz.   Schatz 7751

Il ritorno di D. Calandrino. Intermezzo in musica a cinque voci da rappresentarsi nel Teatro Valle dell' illmi Signori Capranica. Nel carnevale dell' anno 1778 . . .

Roma, Arcangelo Casaletti, 1778. 60 p. 15^{cm}.

Two parts. Author not mentioned, and unknown to Schatz. Dedication by the impresario, Palombini, cast, and name of **Cimarosa** as composer.   ML 50.2.R5C3

Il ritorno di Rinaldo presso Armida o sia La vendetta di Armida vinta dall' amore, ballet. *See* Bianchi's Cajo Mario.

Il ritorno di Ulisse a Penelope. Dramma per musica composto da Ant. Filistri de' Caramondani . . . e messo in musica dal Sign. Felice Alessandri . . . da rappresentarsi nel Regio Teatro di Berlino il carnovale dell' anno 1790.

Berlino, Haude e Spener, n. d. 151 p. 15$\frac{1}{2}$^{cm}.

German title-page, "Ulysses rückkunft zur Penelope," and text face Italian. Three acts. Argument, cast, and indication of the cuts adopted for the performance after a number of copies of the libretto without such indication had been published, so a special note informs us. From a comparison with the score it would appear as if Alessandri never composed these cuts.

First performed, as indicated, January 25, 1790.   Schatz 149

Il ritorno opportuno, ballet. *See* Martin y Soler's L'accorta cameriera.

Il ritratto. Commedia per musica di Saverio Zini da rappresentarsi nel Real Teatro del Fondo di Separazione per second' opera di questo corrente anno 1791.

Napoli, Vincenzo Flauto, n. d. 33 p. 15^{cm}.

Il **ritratto**—Continued.

Two acts. Cast and name of composer, Francesco **Bianchi**. On p. 5–7, cast, description of the ballet, "Gl'Inglesi in America Ballo di carattere inventato, et composto dal Sig. Gio. Battista Giannini", music ("tutta nuova") by Giuseppe Ercolano.

First performed at Naples, Teatro Nuovo, in 1787. Schatz 981

Il **ritratto**. Dramma giocoso in musica da rappresentarsi nel Teatro alla Scala di Milano l'autunno del 1799.

Milano, Gio. Batista Bianchi, n. d. 72 p. 17cm.

Two acts. By Luigi Romanelli, who is not mentioned. Cast and name of Nicola Antonio **Zingarelli** as the composer. With the opera was performed Gaspare Ronzi's ballet, "Odervik," the composer of the music not mentioned.

First performed, as indicated, October 12, 1799. Schatz 11257

La **ritrosía disarmata**. Componimento drammatico, scritto dall' autore in Vienna l'anno 1759, per uso della Real corte di Spagna.

[105]–118 p. 26cm. (Metastasio, Opere, t. xi, Parigi, vedova Herissant, 1782.)

One act. Composer unknown to me. ML 49.A2M44

Ritter Roland. Tr. of Haydn's Orlando Paladino.

Ritter Willibald, oder Das goldene gefaess. Ein romantisches singspiel in zwey aufzuegen. Von Karl Friedrich Hensler. Aufgefuehrt auf der Kais. Koenigl. privil. Marinellischen Schaubuehne. Die musik ist von Ferdinand Kauer.

Wien, Ignaz Goldhann, 1794. 78 p. 17cm.

First performed, as indicated, June 13, 1793. Schatz 5053

The **rival candidates:** a comic opera in two acts; as it is now performing at the Theatre Royal in Drury-Lane. By the rev. Henry Bate.

London, Printed: sold by T. Becket and W. Griffin, 1775. 4 p. l., 37 p. 19½cm.

Two acts with epilogue. Cast, dedication of "this my first essay" to Mrs. Garrick, dated Hendon, Middlesex, February 9, 1775, and Advertisement:

"The *Rival candidates* is an attempt of the dramatic kind, undertaken by the writer from no motive of literary variety, but in order to introduce to the world, a young musical composer, whose taste he conceived might do honour to his profession . . ."

He means Thomas **Carter**.

First performed, as indicated, February 1, 1775. Longe 32

— The **rival candidates**. In two acts. By the Rev. Henry Bates.

[130–154] p. 19cm. (Collection of the most esteemed farces and entertainments, t. iv, Edinburgh, 1792.)

Drury-Lane and Edinburgh (1783) casts. Schatz 11753

Le **rival confident,** comédie en deux actes et en prose, mêlée d'ariettes; par M. Forgeot, musique de M. Grétri; Représentée, pour la première fois, par les Comédiens italiens ordinaires du roi, le 26 juin 1788.

Paris, Prault, 1788. 2 p. l., 65, [3] p. 21cm.

Cast. The [3] p. contain advertisements. ML 50.2.R58G7

Le **rival de lui-même**. *See* Le parterre merveilleux.

The **rival milliners:** or, The humours of Covent Garden. A tragi-comi-operatic pastoral farce. As it was acted at the theatre in the Hay-Market. By Robert Drury, Gent. . . . The third edition corrected.

> *London, R. Spavan, n. d. 48 p. 15^{cm}.*
>
> Two acts. Cast. Ballad opera, the airs of the 25 songs of which are indicated in the text by title.
> First performed at London, Little theatre in the Hay Market, 1735. LONGE 76

I rivali delusi. A. T. of Hasse's Eurimedonte e Timocleone.

I rivali delusi. Intermezzo per musica a quattro voci, da rappresentarsi nel Teatro alla Valle l'anno 1752 . . .

> *Roma, Ottavio Puccinelli, 1752. 22, [1] p. 15½^{cm}.*
>
> Two parts. Author not mentioned and unknown to Schatz. Text *not* by Goldoni. Contains arias like "Se son ragazza tenera," "Bella tu sei di questo core," "Divertirse a spese d'altri," etc. Cast, name of Niccolò **Jommelli** as composer and dedication by Agostino Valle.   ML 50.2.R59J6

I rivali generosi.

> *Apostolo Zeno, Poesie drammatiche, Venezia, 1744, t. v, p. [267]–352 p. 19^{cm}.*
>
> Three acts and licenza. Argument. No composer is mentioned. In the "Catalogo" at end of t. x, date and place of first ed. are given as Venice, 1697. (*See* below.)
>   ML 49.A2Z3

— **I rivali generosi,** pubblicati per la prima volta in Venezia 1697.

> *Apostolo Zeno, Poesie drammatiche, Orleans, 1785–86, t. i, p. 159–234. 21^{cm}.*
>
> Three acts. Argument. No composer is mentioned.   ML 49.A2Z4

I rivali generosi. Drama per musica da rappresentarsi nel Reg. Teatro della Munitione di questa Nob. e Fedel. città di Messina l'anno 1712 . . .

> *Messina, Stamp. di Vinc. d'Amico, 1712. 82 p. 13½^{cm}.*
>
> Three acts. By Apostolo Zeno. With impresario's dedication, argument, notice to the reader, cast, and scenario. Neither Zeno nor the composer, Michele **Facco,** is mentioned.   SCHATZ 2979

I rivali generosi. Drama per musica da rappresentarsi nel Teatro Grimani di S. Samuele l'anno 1726. Per la festa dell' Ascensione.

> *Venezia, Marino Rossetti, 1726. 57 p. 14½^{cm}.*
>
> Three acts. By Apostolo Zeno, who is not mentioned. Argument, cast, scenario, and name of Giuseppe **Vignati** as the composer.   SCHATZ 10724

I rivali generosi. Drama per musica da rappresentarsi nel Teatro di S. Salvatore l'anno MDCXCVII . . .

> *Venetia, Nicolini, 1697. 6 p. l., 48 p. 15^{cm}.*
>
> Three acts. Dedication signed by A[postolo] Z[eno] as author, his dramaturgic preface, argument, and scenario. The composer, Marc' Antonio **Ziani,** is not mentioned.
> First performed, as indicated, carnival, 1697.   SCHATZ 11206

Le rivali placate. Da cantarsi nel Teatro privilegiato da S. M. C. e Cat. In Vienna nell' anno MDCCXXXVIII. Nel mese di Gennaio.—Die besaenftigte mitbuhlerinnen . . .

> *Wien, Johann Peter v. Ghelen, n. d. 75 p. 13½^{cm}.*
>
> Three acts. Argument. German text faces Italian. Author and composer not mentioned and unknown to Schatz. Not recorded by von Weilen. SCHATZ 11360

Li rivali placati. Dramma giocoso per musica da rappresentarsi nel Teatro di questa elettorale corte . . .

Bonn, Rommerskirchen, 1774. Unpaged. 15^{cm}.

Three acts. Cast, scenario, and name of Pietro **Guglielmi** as the composer. The author, Gaetano Martinelli, is not mentioned.
First performed, as indicated, 1774 at Venice, Teatro di S. Moise, fall of 1764.
SCHATZ 4261

— I rivali placati; drama giocoso per musica da rappresentarsi nel Regio Teatro—De forsonede medbeylere . . .

Kiøbenhavn, H. J. Graae, 1777. 139 p. 16½^{cm}.

Three acts. Cast and name of Pietro **Guglielmi** as the composer. Danish text faces Italian.
First performed, as indicated, December 18, 1777.
SCHATZ 4262

Li rivali ridicoli. Dramma giocoso per musica di Giovanni Bertati da rappresentarsi nel Teatro Giustiniani in S. Moisè per la prima opera dell' autunno 1780.

Venezia, n. publ., n. d. 64 p. 17½^{cm}.

Three acts. Cast and name of Michele **Mortellari** as the composer.
SCHATZ 6691

The rivals, or, The green-room controversy; a musical prelude, as performed at the Salisbury Theatre, 1776.

Salisbury, J. Hodson, n. d. 12 p. 19^{cm}.

One act. Cast and dedication dated November 6, 1776. **Author and composer** not mentioned. Not recorded by Clarence or by Schatz.
ML. 50.2.R6

La robe de dissention, ou Le faux-prodige, opéra-comique en deux actes, joué à la Foire Saint-Germain, en 1726.

Alexis Piron, Oeuvres complettes, Liege, 1776, v. 4, [255]–335 p. 17½^{cm}.

En vaudevilles. Composer not recorded by Parfaict.
First performed, as indicated, September 7, 1726.
PQ 2019.P6

Robert und Kalliste oder Der triumph der **treue.** **Tr.** of P. Guglielmi's La sposa fedele.

Robin Hood. An opera. As it is perform'd at Lee's and Harper's Great Theatrical Booth in Bartholomew-fair. With the musick prefix'd to each song.

London, J. Watts, 1730. 45 p. 19^{cm}.

Three acts. Table of the 19 songs, the airs of which are printed in the text, with their titles. Author unknown to Squire and Tufts.
LONGE 49

Robin Hood. A new musical entertainment. As it is perform'd at the Theatre-Royal in Drury-Lane. The musick compos'd by the Society of the Temple of Apollo.

London, Printed and sold at the Theatre, 1751. 24 p. 20½^{cm}.

Two acts. Cast. By Moses Mendez, who is not mentioned. According to Grove, the music was composed by Charles **Burney,** who was a member of the Society of the Temple of Apollo.
First performed December 13, 1750, as indicated.
AC 901.M5 v.519

Robin Hood; or, Sherwood forest: A comic opera. As it is performed at the Theatre-Royal, in Covent-Garden. By Leonard Mac Nally, Esq.

London, J. Almon, 1784. 74 p. 21^{cm}.

Three acts. Cast and dedication to William **Shield,** composer to the Theatre-Royal, Covent-Garden (in which capacity he also composed and partly compiled the music for this piece). Mac Nally says:

"The three principal ideas which combine the subject are not original, but borrowed from the ballads of *Robin Hood,* the *Nutbrown maid,* and the *Hermit of the dale:* I adopted them as being popular. It was my first intention to have taken all the songs from old ballads; those I have selected are, I trust, not ill chosen, or unapplicable to the piece . . ."

In Bland's vocal score "The stag through the forest" is headed as composed by Henry **Harington,** "If to me" as by **Anfossi** and "Friendship claims the name" as by **Bertoni.** The overture is ascribed by a contemporary hand to **Baumgarten.**
First performed, as indicated, April 17, 1784.   LONGE 93

— **Robin Hood** or Sherwood forest: A comic opera. As it is performed at the Theatre-Royal, in Covent Garden. By Leonard Macnally, Esq. The fifth edition. With alterations, and additions, as it is now performed.

London, J. Almon, 1787. [3], 6–62 p. 21^{cm}.

Three acts. Casts of 1784 and 1787. **Shield** is not mentioned.
    ML 50.2.R62S3

La **Rodelinda.** Drama per musica da rappresentarsi in Venezia nel Teatro di San Moisè l'autunno del' anno MDCCXXXI . . .

Venezia, Carlo Buonarigo, 1731. 48 p. 14½^{cm}.

The publisher's name has been effaced.
Three acts. By Antonio Salvi (not mentioned). Dedication, argument, notice to reader, cast, and scenario. The composer, Bortolamio **Cordans,** is not mentioned.
    SCHATZ 2227

Rodelinda.

Three-act opera. By Georg Friedrich **Händel.** Text was an altered version by Nicola Francesco Haym of Antonio Salvi's "Rodelinda, regina de' Longobardi."
First performed at London, February 13, 1725.
Not in L. of C.

— **Rodelinda, koenigin in der Lombardey,** in einem sing-spiele auf dem Hamburgischen schau-platze im jahr 1734 vorgestellet.

[Hamburg], Gedruckt mit Spieringischen schrifften, n. d. Unpaged. 18½^{cm}.

Three acts. Argument, with name of Georg Friedrich **Händel** as composer of the Italian arias, the Italian text of which is added to the German. Neither the composer of the German recitatives nor C. G. Wend, the translator of the Italian by Salvi-Haym, is mentioned.
First performed, as indicated, Theater beim Gänsemarkt, November 29, 1734.
    SCHATZ 4490

Rodelinda, koenigin in der Lombardey. Tr. of Händel's Rodelinda.

Rodelinda, regina de' Longobardi. Dramma per musica da rappresentarsi nel nuovo Regio Teatro della Corte . . .

[Berlino], Ambrogio Haude, 1741. 6 p. l., 95 p. 19½^{cm}.

Three acts. Giovanni Gualberto Bottarelli is mentioned as the author, and he signs the dedication as such, remarking that he wrote the libretto by demand of the king, but from the "Avvertimento" in the 1778 ed. it would appear that he simply retouched a drama by Zeno. As a matter of fact, Zeno never wrote a Rodelinda, nor

Rodelinda, regina de' Longobardi—Continued.

did he write the arias in this particular Rodelinda. The text utilized by Bottarelli was really that by Antonio Salvi. The avvertimento is preceded by the cast, the argument, and the names of Carl Heinrich **Graun** as the composer, and of "Giovanni Cristoforo Rost" as the author of the German version, "Rodelinde, königinn der Longobarden," which faces the Italian.

First performed, as indicated, December 13, 1741.   Schatz 4117

— **Rodelinda, regina de' Longobardi.** Dramma per musica da rappresentarsi nel Regio Teatro della Corte . . .

  Berlino, Haude e Spener, 1778. 95, [3] p. 16ᶜᵐ.

Three acts. By Giovanni Gualberto Bottarelli (who is not mentioned), but the "Avvertimento" reads as follows:

"Quantunque questa tragedia [Pertharit, di P. Cornelio] sia forse la più debole di quante ne ha scritte quel chiarissimo tragico, parve ad Apostolo Zeno, ch'ella potesse servire di degno soggetto ad un dramma per musica, e ne fece un opera che si trova fra le altre di quell' insigne autore.

"Quei che nell' anno 1744 serviva da poeta nel Regio Teatro di Berlino, trasformò malamente l'opera dello Zeno, e la diè fuori mutilata e guasta com' ell' è anche al presente . . ."

This is entirely incorrect, as the note for the 1741 ed. proves. Argument, cast, scenario, and name of Carl Heinrich **Graun** as the composer. Though the *avvertimento* says that a revival was ordered "nel presente anno 1778," the performance took place, according to Schatz, December 19, 1777. German title-page, "Rodelinde, koeniginn der Longobarden," and text face Italian.   Schatz 4111

Rodelinde, königinn der Longobarden. Tr. of Graun's Rodelinda, regina de' Longobardi.

Il Roderico. Dramma per musica da rappresentarsi nel Teatro della Pace di Roma. L'anno MDCXCIV . . .

  Roma, Buagni, 1694. 64 p. 13ᶜᵐ.

Three acts. Author not mentioned and unknown to Schatz and Wotquenne. Carlo Francesco **Gasparini** is mentioned as the composer in the dedication. Argument and scenario.

First performed, as indicated, January 25, 1694.   Schatz 3580

Rodoaldo, rè d'Italia. Drama da rappresentarsi nel nuovo Teatro Zane à S. Moisè l'anno MDCLXXXV. Di Tomaso Stanzani . . .

  Venetia, Francesco Nicolini, 1685. 56 p. (incl. front.) 14½ᶜᵐ.

Three acts. Author's dedication dated Venice, January 10, 1685, argument with name of Domenico **Gabrieli** as composer, and scenario.   Schatz 3400

Rodomonte sdegnato. Dramma per musica. Da rappresentarsi nel Teatro di S. Angelo. Il carnovale dell' anno 1714. Del dottor Grazio Braccioli . . .

  Venezia, Marino Rossetti, 1714. 72 p. 14ᶜᵐ.

Three acts. Dedication signed by Antonio Vivaldi and dated Venice, January 20, 1714, argument, cast, scenario, and name of Michel Angelo **Gasparini** as the composer.   Schatz 3601

Rodrigo Ecimene. A. T. of the ballet L'eroe castigliano.

Das roemische April-fest. Musicalisches lust und tantz-spiel, zu allgemeiner freuden-bezeugung ueber die im April erfolgte heilsame gebuhrt Sr. roemisch-kayserl. und catholischen Majestaet Caroli VI erstgebohrnen . . . Leopoldi I . . . im junio 1716 auf dem Hamburgischen Schau-platz vorgestellet.

  Hamburg, Friderich Conrad Greflinger, n. d. Unpaged. 19ᶜᵐ.

Das roemische April-fest—Continued.

Five acts. Lengthy historical preface without names of the author, Barthold Feind, or composer, Reinhard **Keiser**. To some of the arias the Italian text has been added.   Schatz 5127

Die roemische grossmuht, oder Calpurnia. Tr. of Heinichen's Calfurnia.

Die roemische unruhe, oder Die edelmuehtige Octavia. In einem sing-spiel auf dem grossen Hamburgischen Schau-platz aufgefuehret.

[Hamburg], Gedruckt im jahr, 1705. Unpaged. 18½^{cm}.

Three acts. Neither the author, resp. translator, Barthold Feind, is mentioned, nor the composer, Reinhard **Keiser**. To some of the arias the Italian text has been added.
First performed, as indicated, August 5, 1705.   Schatz 5128

— **Die roemische unruhe.** Oder: Die edelmuehtige Octavia, musicalisches schauspiel.

Barth. Feind's Deutsche gedichte, Stade, 1708, pl., p. [115]–174 17^{cm}.

Three acts. Date of first performance, Hamburg, August 5, 1705, and "Vorbericht," in which Feind first compares other librettists like Postel, Hunold, and Bressand, and then says:
"Das sujet dieses schau-spiels ist zuerst in Weissenfels, ehe und bevor Nero all hier aufgefuehret, verfasset und biss auf die helffte ausgearbeitet worden. Nachdem man mir aber das werck gezeiget und an bey dessen vollziehung aufgetragen, so habe bey der durchlesung befunden, dass es die umstaende schwerlich zuliessen, des herrn verfassers propos auszufuehren, ich auch lieber etwas neues selbst machen wollte, als andre arbeit zumustern: darum ich ausser den namen der Octavia, und einige reflexions auf die auffuehrung des Piso, nichts behalten . . ."
The composer, Reinhard **Keiser,** is not mentioned. Quite a few of the arias have Italian and German texts. This the "Vorbericht" explains, as follows:
"Weil auch bissher die delicatesse der italiaenischen sprache in andern opern die ohren der zuschauer durch eine verborgene kitzlung an sich gelocket, so habe aus dieser ursache einige hinzu gefueget. Wer solcher kuendig, mag solche als die erste fruechte von dergleichen arbeit ansehen, und Kein zu strenges urtheil faellen, denn sie haetten endlich bey mehr gegebner zeit wol koennen verbessert werden."
     ML 49.A2F2

Roger-Bontems et Javotte. Parody of Gluck's Orphée et Euridice.

Roger de Sicile, surnommé Le roi sans chagrin. Piece en trois actes. Par M^{rs} Le S * *. & d'Or * * *. Représentée à la Foire S. Laurent 1731.

Le Théâtre de la foire, Paris, 1737, t. ix, 115 p. 17^{cm}.

By Le Sage and d'Orneval. Largely *en vaudeville.* The airs, selected or composed and arranged by Jean Claude **Gillier,** are printed at the end of the volume in the "Table des airs."   ML 48.L2IX

Rogerius auf der insel der Alcine, ballet. *See* Bach's Temistocle.

Le roi et le fermier, comédie en trois actes, mêlée de morceaux de musique. Représentée pour la premiere fois par les Comédiens italiens ordinaires du roi, le lundi 22 novembre 1762. Par M. Sedaine.

Bruxelles, Pierre Paupié, 1765. 52 p. 19½^{cm}.

The composer, **Monsigny,** is not mentioned.   ML 50.2.R7M7

Le roi et le fermier—Continued.

— **Le roi et le fermier.** Comedie en trois actes. Mêlée de morceaux de musique. Par M. Sedaine. Représentée par les Comédiens françois de la cour sur le Nouveau Théatre de S. A. E. de Saxe, à **Dresde,** 1766.

> [*Dresde*], *George Conrad Walther, n. d. 78 p. 16½^{cm}.*
>
> The composer, **Monsigny,** is not mentioned. The text is the same as in our Paris ed. of 1768.
> First performed at Dresden, June 13, 1766.   SCHATZ 11732

— **Le roi et le fermier,** comédie en trois actes, mêlée de morceaux de musique. Représentée pour la premiere fois par les Comédiens italiens ordinaires du roi, le lundi vingt-deux novembre 1762. Par M. Sedaine.

> *Paris, Claude Herissant, 1768. 52 p. 19^{cm}.*
>
> In his "Avertissement" Sedaine says:
> "Jamais bon ou mauvais ouvrage n'a eu tant de peine que celui-ci a paroître au théatre. Il avoit en lui-même la première difficulté. Il falloit que je trouvasse un grand artiste, un musicien habile, qui voulût bien avoir un peu de confiance en moi, enfin un ami qui voulût bien risquer un genre nouveau en musique; & quelque rares que soient les poêtes en ce nouveau genre, les musiciens le sont encore plus."
> He continues by saying that his piece was based on an English tale, that it was performed with ill-advised changes, and that it is here published as written by him originally. The composer was **Monsigny.**   SCHATZ 11730

— **Le roi et le fermier,** comédie en trois actes, mêlée de morceaux de musique. Représentée pour la premiere fois par les Comédiens italiens ordinaires du Roi, le lundi 22 novembre 1762. Par M. Sédaine.

> *Paris, la veuve Duchesne, 1779. 56 p. 19½^{cm}.*
>
> Cast. The composer, **Monsigny,** is not mentioned. With the airs of "Ami, laisse là la tendresse" (I, 4), and "Le mylord m'offre des richesses" (I, 8).   SCHATZ 6580

— **Der koenig und der pachter.** Ein comisches singspiel in drey aufzuegen. Aus dem franzoesischen des herrn Sedaine uebersetzt.

> *Frankfurt und Leipzig, Johann Gottlieb Garbe, 1766. 94 p. 17^{cm}.*
>
> Conrad Gottlieb Pfeffel's version of **Monsigny's** opera.   SCHATZ 6581

— **Der koenig und der pachter,** ein singspiel in drey aufzuegen aus dem franzoesischen uebersetzt, mit musik.

> *Frankfurt am Mayn, mit Andreäischen schriften, 1773. 102 p. 14 p. (folded music). 16½^{cm}.*
>
> Dialogue by Johann Heinrich Faber, the lyrics by Pfeffel. The music (bass and voice) consists of: "Der milord wies mir kostbarkeiten" (I, 8), "Des reicht ums pracht" (I, 8), "Ce que je dis est la vérité même,") "Lasst uns schaaf und trift verzehren" (III, 12, "Que le soleil dans la plaine").
> Version used by Theob. Marchand's Churpfälz. deutsche Hofschauspiel-Gesellschaft.   SCHATZ 6582

Le roi Théodore à Venise. Tr. of Paisiello's Il rè Teodoro in Venezia.

Roland, tragedie en musique. Representée devant Sa Majesté à Versailles, le huitième janvier 1685. Suivant la copie imprimée à Paris.

> [*Amsterdam, Antoine Schelte*], *1685. 69 p. 13½^{cm}.*
>
> Prologue and five acts. Neither Quinault, the author, is mentioned, nor Jean Baptiste de **Lully,** the composer.   ML 50.2.R65L9

Roland—Continued.

— **Roland,** tragedie representée par l'Academie royale de musique l'an 1685. Les paroles sont de M. Quinault, & la musique de M. de Lully, XVII. opera.

n. i., n. d.   14ᶜᵐ.   front., 1–72 p.   (Recueil général des opéra, t. iii, Paris, 1703.)

Detached copy.   Five acts and prologue.
First performed, as indicated, March 8, 1685; at Versailles, January 18, 1685.
SCHATZ 5778
Second copy.   ML 48.R4

— **Roland,** tragedie représentée devant Sa Majesté, à Versailles, le huitième [!] jour de janvier 1685.   Remise au Theatre par l'Academie royale de musique le 12 fevrier 1705, 15 novembre 1709, 15 decembre 1716, 11 novembre 1727; et le jeudi 17 decembre 1743.

Paris, Jean Baptiste Christophe Ballard, 1743.   x, 66 p.   22½ᶜᵐ.

Over the last date on the title page has been pasted a slip with the correct date of performance, December 19, 1743.
Prologue and five acts with cast.   On p. iii the note:
"Il n'y a rien de nouveau dans cette remise, qu'un mot au dernier vers de la page 3, on y lit *Quand je trouvay Medor*, il faut lire *Quand j'apperçûs Medor:* même page au huitième vers, lire *Roland renverse*.   On peut accoler ou rayer les retranchements qu'on a jugé a propos de faire aux pages suivantes" [follows an extensive list].
SCHATZ 5780

— **Roland.**   Tragedie en musique.   Representée à la Cour le 18 janvier 1685. & par l'Académie de musique le 8. fevrier suivant.

Philippe Quinault, Théâtre, Paris, 1739, t. v., pl., p. [313]–378 p. 17ᶜᵐ.

Prologue and five acts.   **Lully** is not mentioned.   PQ 1881.A1   1739

— **Arlequin Roland.**   Par les Srs. Dominique & Romagnesi . . . Représenté pour la premiere fois par les Comédiens italiens ordinaires du roi, le 31 décembre 1727.

Les parodies du Nouveau théâtre italien, Nouv. éd., Paris, Briasson, 1738, t. iii, [367]–408 p.   16½ᶜᵐ.

One act.   Parody of the opera "Roland."   The airs and vaudeville printed at end of the volume in the "Table des airs" (84 p.).   ML 48.P3

— **Roland,** parodie.   Représentée pour la premiere fois par les Comédiens italiens ordinaires du roi, le 20 janvier 1744.

Charles François Pannard, Théâtre, Paris, Duchesne, 1763, v. 1, 48 p.   17ᶜᵐ.

En vaudevilles.   Parody of Lully's opera.   Composer not recorded by Parfaict, who attributes the text jointly to Sticotti and Pannard.   PQ 2019.P3

Roland, tragédie-lyrique mise en trois actes, avec quelques changemens, representée pour la premiere fois, par l'Académie royale de musique, le mardi 27 janvier 1778.   Le poëme est de Quinault.   La musique est de M. Piccini.

Paris, Aux dépens de l'Academie, 1778.   31 p.   21ᶜᵐ.

Cast.   ML 50.2.R65P3

Roma liberata dalla congiura di Catilina.   *See* M. Curzio.

Divertissements du ballet des **Romans,** et Les amours de Ragonde, comedie en musique.   En trois actes.   Mis au Théâtre de l'Académie royale de musique, de Lyon.   En l'année 1742.

Lyon, Aimé Delaroche, 1742.   1 p. l., 26 p.   23ᶜᵐ.

Contains only "La *bergerie,* acte du ballet des Romans" with cast.   Neither the author, Michel de Bonneval, nor the composer, **Niel,** is mentioned.

The ballet, "Les Romans," of which "La bergerie" forms the first *entrée,* was first performed at Paris, Académie royale de musique, August 23, 1736.   Schatz 7161

— Les **romans,** ballet-heroique représenté par l'Académie royale de musique, l'an 1736.   Paroles de Mr Bonn * * * Musique de Mr Niel.   CXXVI. opera.

n. i., n. d.   281–370 p.   14½ᶜᵐ.   (Recueil général des opéra, Paris, 1745, t. xvi.)

Detached copy.   Prologue and the entrées "La bergerie," "La chevalerie," "La féerie," "Le roman merveilleux, nouvelle entrée, ajoutée aux précédentes, le 23 septembre 1736," with note replying to the reproach "d'avoir introduit dans ses romans des noms & des divinités du paganisme" and stating that this added act is partly by another author.   At end of text a note that the Académie now performs "La bergerie" as third and "La féerie" as first entrée.   ML 48.R4

Le **roman merveilleux.**   Entrée in Niel's Les romans.

Rome excis'd.   A new tragi-comi ballad-opera.   Of three acts.   As it now acting with general applause.   By a polite company of courtiers.   *Ezekiel,* xxvii. 36 [follows quotation]

London, Printed for Cyrenius Taxall, and sold by T. Jones, 1733. vii, [1], 9–48 p.   21ᶜᵐ.

A political attack on the excise bill in form of a ballad opera with eighteen songs, tunes indicated by title.   The plot is laid in Rome in the times of "Augustus Caesar, Emperor of Rome."   The tenor of the play and of the "Dedication" (p. iii–vii) is obvious from the heading "To all true lovers of old English liberty."

Of course, no performance is recorded and the author seems to be unknown.

Longe 172

Romeo e Giulia.   Dramma per musica in II. atti del Sanseverino. Seconda edizione.

Berlino, la vedova di Giorgio Lodovico Winter, 1776.   40 p.   20½ᶜᵐ.

The two acts are preceded by "Prologo della Musa Melpomene a S. A. R. Monignore il principe Henrico di Prussia."   The text is followed by:

— **Romeo et Julie.**   Drame en musique en deux actes, traduit de l'italien composé par Sanseverino.

Berlin, la veuve Winter, 1776.   44 p.   20½ᶜᵐ.

Same prologue, but in French.   For a composer of the text *see* next entry.

ML 50.2.R67

Romeo e Giulia.   Drama per musica in due atti del Sign. Sanseverino da cantarsi per commando al Palazzo Ducale di Brunsviga.

Brunsviga, n. nubl., 1778.   55 p.   16ᶜᵐ.

Johann Gottfried **Schwanberg** is mentioned as the composer.   German titlepage, "Romeo und Julie," and text face Italian.

First performed, as indicated, March, 1778.   Schatz 9766

Romeo e Giulia—Continued.

— **Romeo e Giulia.** Dramma per musica in due atti del Sign. Sanseverino. La musica è del Sigr. Schwanenberg. Da cantarsi nel Concerto dei dilettanti di musica in Berlino 1780.

n. i., n. d. *55 p.* *16½*^{cm}.

German title-page, "Romeo und Julie," and text by Eschenburg face Italian.

SCHATZ 9766

Roméo et Juliette, opera en trois actes. Paroles du C. J. A. Ségur, musique du C. Steibelt. Représenté, pour la première fois, à Paris, sur le Théâtre de la rue Feydeau, le 10 septembre (v. st.), l'an deuxième de la République, une & indivisible.

Paris, Huet [etc], L'an second de la République [1793–94] *44 p.* *21*^{cm}.

Cast. Pages 33–44 stitched in twice.

ML 50.2.R68 S8

— **Roméo et Juliette,** opera en trois actes. Paroles du C. J. A. Ségur, musique du C. Steibelt. Représenté, pour la première fois, à Paris, sur le Théâtre de la rue Feydeau, le 10 septembre (v. st.), l'an deuxième de la République française. Seconde édition.

Paris, Huet, An troisième de la République [1794–95]

Same cast and same text, which is corrected in many places by a contemporary hand. Evidently used for performances. Provenience perhaps explained by the label on the binding "Theatre Feydeau. Sageret." ML 50.2.R68 S82

Romeo und Julie. Ein schauspiel mit gesang in drey aufzuegen [vignette]

Leipzig, Dyk, 1779. *76 p.* *16½*^{cm}. ("*Singspiele von Friedrich Wilhelm Gotter, erstes baendchen*")

In a "Nachricht," following a poem "An Madam Unzer, geborne Ackermann," the first Julie, Gotter says:

"**Benda's** musik mag meine schuzschrift bey denjenigen seyn, die es fuer entweihung halten, ein suejet der tragischen Muse auf die opernbuehne zu versezen."

This prefatory note is dated Gotha, October, 1778," and Gotter takes pains to point out that his text is indebted to Shakespeare and not to German dramatists.

First performed with Georg Benda's music at Gotha, Hoftheater, September 25, 1776. SCHATZ 776

— Arien und gesaenge aus **Julie und Romeo,** einem schauspiele mit gesang in drey aufzuegen, vom herrn Geheimen legations-secretair Gotter. In musik gesetzt vom herrn kapelldirector George Benda.

Berlin, n. publ., 1796. *16 p.* *16*^{cm}.

Cast.

Performed at Berlin, Nationaltheater in the year of publication; first performed at Berlin, Döbbelin'sches Theater, February 8, 1779 (Schatz). SCHATZ 777

Romeo und Julie. Tr. of Schwanberg's Romeo e Giulia.

Romilda. Dramma per musica da rappresentarsi nel Teatro Giustiniano di S. Moisè nel carnevale dell' anno 1731.

Venezia, Carlo Buonarigo, n. d. *43 p.* *14½*^{cm}.

Three acts. By Carlo Paganicesa (not mentioned). Impresario's dedication, argument, cast, scenario, and name of the composer, Bortolamio **Cordans**.

SCHATZ 2229

La Romilda. Drama regio musicale del Co. Pietro Paolo Bissari K.
Vicenza, Giacomo Amadio, 1659. front., 91 p. 14^{cm}.

Prologue and three acts. Imprimatur dated January 3, 1659, argument. On p. 90 additional verses for Adrasto, between I, 14, and I, 15. On p. 91 cuts are indicated, for instance, II, 8, and III, 11. The composer, Carlo **Grossi**, is not mentioned.

Schatz 4219

Il Romolo. Drama per musica nel felicissimo giorno natalizio della S. C. R. M^{ta} di Leopoldo I. . . . l'anno MDCCII. Posto in musica dal Sig^r Marc' Antonio Ziani . . . con l'arie per li balletti del Sig^r Gio. Gioseffo Hoffer . . .
Vienna d'Austria, appresso gl'eredi Cosmeroviani, n. d. 77 p. 14$\frac{1}{2}$^{cm}.

Three acts and licenza. Dedication by the author, Donato Cupeda, dated Vienna, June 9, 1702, argument, scenario.

Schatz 11193

Romolo e Tazio. Drama per musica da rappresentarsi nel famosissimo Teatro Grimani di S. Gio. Grisostomo. Nell' autunno 1722. Di Vicenzo Cassani . . .
Venezia, Marin Rossetti, 1722. 56 p. 15^{cm}.

Three acts. Author's dedication, cast, argument, scenario, and name of Carlo Luigi **Pietragrua** as the composer.

Schatz 8166

Romolo ed Ersilia. Dramma scritto dall' autore in Vienna . . . e rappresentato . . . la prima volta con musica dell' Hasse, nel Teatro dell' Imperial palazzo della città d'Inspruch . . . in occasione delle felicissime nozze, che ivi si celebrarono, delle Altezze Reali dell' Arciduca Leopoldo d'Austria, e dell' infanta donna Maria Luisa di Borbone, l'anno 1765.
[95]–176 p. 26^{cm}. (*Metastasio, Opere, t. ix, Parigi, vedova Herissant, 1781.*)

Three acts. Argument.

ML 49.A2M44

Romolo ed Ersilia. Dramma per musica rappresentato in occasione delle felicissime nozze delle AA. LL. Reali l'arciduca Leopoldo d'Austria e l'infanta D. Maria Luisa di Borbon, celebrate in Inspruch . . . l'anno MDCCLXV.
Roma, Carlo Barbiellini, 1765. 5 p. l., 55, [1] p. 21^{cm}.

Three acts. Dedication, argument, cast, scenario, and names of Metastasio as author, of Joh. Adolph **Hasse** as composer.
First performed at Innsbruck, Theatre in the Imperial palace, August 6, 1765.

Schatz 4589

Il Romolo e'l Remo. Drama di Giulio Strozzi.
Venetia, Gio. Battista Surian, 1645. 96 p. 13$\frac{1}{2}$^{cm}.

Three acts with prologue. Dedication dated Venice, February 5, 1645, argument, but without name of the composer, Pietro Francesco **Cavalli**. The single acts bear the technical titles "La proposta," "Il nodo," and "Lo scioglimento."
First performed, as indicated, at the Teatro a S. S. Giovanni e Paolo, February 5, 1645.

Schatz 1727

The romp. O. T. of Love in the city.

The **romp.** A musical entertainment in two acts. Altered from Love in the city, by Mr. Bickerstaff. As it has been acted at the Theatres Royal in Dublin and York, and now performed at the Theatre-Royal in Drury-Lane.

London, W. Lowndes, 1786. 32 p. 21ᶜᵐ.

Cast and dedication. Charles **Dibdin,** who had assisted the author in the compilation of the music of this pasticcio, is not mentioned.
First performed at Covent Garden, March 28, 1778. LONGE 97

— The **romp.** A comic opera. In two acts. Altered from Love in the City, by Mr. Bickerstaff.

[239]–262 p. 19ᶜᵐ. (Collection of the most esteemed farces and entertainments, t. vi, Edinburgh, 1792.)

Drury-Lane and Edinburgh casts. SCHATZ 11753F

Rosa e Nicola, ballet. *See* P. Guglielmi's La pupilla scaltra.

Rosalia. Ein nachspiel mit arien von Schink.

Gotha, Carl Wilhelm Ettinger, 1777. 39 p. 17ᶜᵐ.

One act. The composer, Joseph **Schubert,** is not mentioned.
First performed at Berlin, Döbbelinsches Theater, March 8, 1777. SCHATZ 9704

Rosalinda, a musical drama. As it is performed at Hickford's Great Room, in Brewer's Street. By Mr. Lockman. Set to music by Mr. John Christopher Smith. To which is prefixed, an enquiry into the rise and progress of opera and oratorios, with some reflections on lyric poetry and music.

London, Printed by W. Strahan for the author, 1740. 4 p. l., xxiv, [2], 9–19 p. 23ᶜᵐ.

One act. Cast and dedication by John Lockman. ML 50.2.R72

La Rosalinda. Drama per musica da rappresentarsi nel novissimo Teatro di S. Angiolo l'anno 1692. M. V. d'Antonio Marchi . . .

Venetia, Girolamo Albrizzi, 1693. front., 71 p. 14½ᶜᵐ.

Three acts. Author's dedication dated Venice, November 11, 1692, argument, scenario, and notice to the reader, in which Marchi calls this "un primo parto d'ingegno . . . scritto più per capriccio, che per genio" and mentions Marc' Antonio **Ziani** as the composer. SCHATZ 11210

Rosamond; an opera. (Altered from Mr. Addison.) The music entirely new set by Mr. Arnold.

London, L. Davis and C. Reymers, 1767. 40 p. 19½ᶜᵐ.

Reduced from three to two acts. Cast. Author of the alterations not mentioned by Genest.
First performed at Covent Garden, April 21, 1767. ML 50.2.R73A7

Rosamund. Ein singspiel in drey aufzeugen. Fuer die Chur-Pfaelzische Hof-singbuehne.

Mannheim, C. F. Schwan, 1778. Unpaged. 15½ᶜᵐ.

Three acts. Cast, vorbericht, and names of Wieland as the author, of Anton **Schweitzer** as the composer of the opera and of Cannabich as composer of Lauchery's incidental "ballet, welches die hoellenfarth des Herkules um Alcesten zuruecckzuhohlen vorstellt."
First performed at Mannheim, Nationaltheater, January 20, 1780, the death of the sovereign interfering with first performance in 1778. SCHATZ 9774

La **Rosaura**. Dramma per musica da rappresentarsi nel Teatro di S. Angelo l'anno 1689 . . .

Venetia, Nicolini, 1689. front., 67 p. 14^{cm}.

Three acts. Author's dedication by Antonio Arcoleo, notice to the reader with Giacomo Antonio **Perti**'s name as the composer, argument, and scenario. Arcoleo says:

"Mi è stato necessario addattarmi ad alcune scene già dipinte; ad abiti preparati, al numero stabilito de personnaggi, alle sodisfattioni di tutti, ed in tanta angustia, di tempo." SCHATZ 7954

La **Rosaura**. Commedia per musica di Gennarantonio Federico Napoletano. Da rappresentarsi nel Teatro de' Fiorentini nell' inverno di quest' anno 1736 . . .

Napoli, Nicola di Biase, 1736. 72 p. 15^{cm}.

Three acts. Impresario's dedication, cast, and name of Domenico **Sarro** as the composer. SCHATZ 9419

La **Rosaura**. A. T. of A. Scarlatti's Gli equivoci in amore.

La **Rosaura** overo Amore figlio della gratitudine, drama. Da rappresentarsi in musica da ajutante & ajutanti di camera avanti la S. R. Maestà di Eleonora, regina di Polonia . . . l'anno MDCXCII. Posto in musica dal Sign. Carlo Augustino Badia . . .

Insprugg, Giacomo Christoforo Wagner, n. d. 61 p. 14$\frac{1}{2}$^{cm}

Three acts. By conte Ottavio Malvezzi, who is not mentioned. SCHATZ 542

Rosbale. Dramma per musica da rappresentarsi nel famosissimo Teatro Grimani di S. Gio. Grisostomo nell' autunno dell'anno 1737 . . .

Venezia, Marino Rossetti, n. d. 60 p. 14^{cm}.

Three acts. Dedication by Domenico Lalli, argument, cast, scenario, and name of Nicolà Antonio **Porpora** as the composer. Text by Claudio Nicola Stampa, who is not mentioned. The title originally was "Eurene."

In his own catalogue Schatz recorded as first performance Arezzo, Teatro della Città, 1736, but in the ms. of his opera dictionary he gives the above. SCHATZ 8360

Roschen und Colas. Tr. of Monsigny's Rose et Colas.

La **rose** ou Les jardins de l'Hymen. O. T. of the following:

— La **roze** ou Les festes de l'Hymen, opera comique, représenté sur le Théâtre de l'Opéra comique, le 8 mars 1752.

Paris, Duchesne, 1754. 56 p. 18$\frac{1}{2}$^{cm}.

Prologue and one act. *En vaudevilles.* Not recorded by Schatz. Parfaict refers from the title to the alternative title, but has no entry there. Desboulmiers, in his "Histoire du théâtre de l'Opéra-comique" (1769, t. i) has a few pages on Piron's "La rose ou Les jardins de l'Hymen; Opéra comique en un acte, en prose, mêle de vaudevilles, suivi d'un divertissement & précédé d'un prologue," which was performed on March 5, 1745, after some difficulties with the police authorities. Comparison of the present libretto with Desboulmiers' analysis of Piron's piece proved them to be identical. I have not found "La roze" elsewhere mentioned in the reference books. ML 50.2.R87

— La **rose**, opéra-comique en un acte, avec un prologue.

Alexis Piron, Oeuvres complettes, Liege, 1776, v. 3, [347]–418 p. 17$\frac{1}{2}$^{cm}.

En vaudevilles. PQ 2019.P6

The rose. A comic opera, in two acts, as it is performed at the Theatre Royal, in Drury-Lane. The words by a Gentleman commoner of Oxford. The music by doctor Arne.

London, E. and C. Dilly and W. Griffin, 1773. 4 p. l., 28 p. 19½ᶜᵐ.

Two acts. Cast and preface, in which the anonymous author says:
"My attendance at college being indispensible, I have committed this trifle to the care of my friend, Dr. **Arne**."
whom Grove and others consider the real author.
First performed December 2, 1772, as indicated.						LONGE 37

Rose, oder Pflicht und liebe im streit. Ein komisches singspiel in drey aufzuegen. Aufgefuehrt im kaiserl. koenigl. National-Hoftheater.

Wien, Joseph, edler von Kurzbeck, 1783. 86 p. 16ᶜᵐ.

Neither the author, Gottlieb Stephanie d. J. is mentioned nor the composer Johann **Mederitsch.**
First performed, as indicated, February 9, 1783.						ML 50.2.R74M3

Rose and Colin, a comic opera, in one act. As it is performed at the Theatre-Royal in Covent Garden.

London, G. Kearsley, 1778. 28 p. 21ᶜᵐ.

Cast and prefatory note by the author-composer, Charles **Dibdin**:
"The following little piece is an imitation of the French comic operas of one act, which are generally characterized, either by their natural simplicity, or some single striking incident, and little or nothing more is designed. It is now first attempted to introduce this species of entertainment on the English theatre, as containing excellent situations for light airs . . ."
First performed September 18, 1778, as indicated.						LONGE 87

Rose et Colas, comedie en un acte, prose et musique, représentée pour la premiere fois par les Comédiens italiens ordinaires du roi, le 8 mars 1764.

Paris, Claude Herissant, 1764. 4 p. l., 62, [2] p. 18ᶜᵐ.

Cast, Herissant's privilege, on the [2] p. a list of plays and preface by the author Sedaine, who is not mentioned, in which he states:
"Je fais imprimer cette pièce avant qu'elle soit représentée, & je la fais distribuer le propre jour de la représentation."
He took this precaution, he says, not because of "un amour-propre très indiscret" but in order to give "à l'auditeur toute la facilité de suivre la musique sur les paroles."
The preface is interesting, as it gives an inside-view of Sedaine's ambitions and methods. He says, for instance:
"Ce petit genre a l'ambition de joindre la flûte d'Euterpe au masque de Thalie, tels que les Grecs l'ont unie au sceptre de Melpomène. Ses efforts tendent à introduire la vraie comédie, ne faisant qu'un avec les morceaux de musique nécessairement enchaînés à la scène, & vicieux dès que le concours heureux de l'harmonie ne donne pas à l'action de la chaleur, du mouvement, & de la précision, sur-tout dans ces momems rapides sur lesquels la tragédie & la comédie n'osent & ne peuvent appuyer . . ."
Sedaine forgot completely to mention his musical partner, **Monsigny.**
						ML 50.2.R74M6

— Rose et Colas, comédie en un acte, prose et musique, représentée pour la premiere fois par les Comédiens italiens ordinaires du roi, le 8 mars 1764.

Paris, la veuve Duchesne, 1770. 52 p. 18ᶜᵐ.

Cast. Neither Sedaine, the author, nor **Monsigny,** the composer, is mentioned. Contains the airs of "Pauvre Colas" (I, 1), "C'est ici que Rose respire" (I, 12).
						SCHATZ 6583

Rose et Colas—Continued.

— **Rose et Colas,** comédie en un acte, prose et musique; représentée pour la premiere fois par les Comédiens italiens ordinaires du roi, le 8 mars 1764.

Paris, la veuve Duchesne, 1779. 43 p. 19^{cm}.

Cast. On p. 3–6, the ariette, "Pauvre Colas." Neither the composer, **Monsigny,** is mentioned, nor Sedaine, the author. SCHATZ 11733

— **Roschen und Colas,** ein singspiel in einem aufzuge aus dem franzoesischen uebersetzt.

Frankfurt am Mayn, mit Andreäischen schriften, 1772. 88 p., 15 p. (music). 16½^{cm}.

Johann Heinrich Faber's version of Monsigny's opera. The music (voice and bass) contains: "Viel lieber an einem fädchen" (I, 5, "Sans chien & sans houlette"); "Hier wohnt sie, wo ich zitternd schleiche" (I, 12, "C'est ici, que Rose respire"); "Es war einst ein vogel draus" (I, 13, "Il étoit un oiseau gris"). Version used by Theob. Marchand's Churpfälzische Hofschauspiel gesellschaft. SCHATZ 6584

— Den **forstilte tvistighed,** efter den franske: Rose og Colas. Et comisk synge-spil af Sedaine i een handling; musiken af Monsigny; til samme musik oversat af Niels Krog Bredal.

n. i., n. d. 95 p. 16^{cm}.

First performed at Copenhagen, January 10, 1777. SCHATZ 6585

Rosemunde. Ein melodrama in einem akt von Bretzner. (Die musik von J. Ch. Kaffka.)

p. 65–89. 18½^{cm}. (Litteratur und Theater Zeitung, Berlin, 1780, 3ter jahrg., 1ster Th.)

First performed at Breslau, Neues Wäser'sches Theater, January, 1782. SCHATZ 4772

Das **rosenfest.** Eine operette in drey aufzuegen. Aus dem franzoesischen nach dem singspiele des hrn. Favart, La rosière de Salenci. Dritte veraenderte auflage.

Weimar, Carl Ludolf Hoffmann, 1774. 2 p. l., 188 p. 15½^{cm}.

By Gottlob Ephraim Heermann (not mentioned), who says in the preface that he had neither patience nor time to thoroughly overhaul the text again for a third edition, and that he contented himself with condensing now and then the text and with marking those parts which in performance might be omitted. The composer, Ernst Wilhelm **Wolf,** is not mentioned.

First performed at Weimar, Schlosstheater in der Wilhelmsburg, 1770. SCHATZ 11083

— Das **rosenfest.** Eine operette in drey aufzügen. Aus dem französischen nach dem singspiele des Herrn Favart, La rosière de Salenci.

[Weimar?] n. publ., 1776. 112 p. 16½^{cm}.

Neither G. E. Heermann is mentioned, nor Ernst Wilhelm **Wolf.**

ML 50.2.R75W6

Das **rosenfest zu Salenci.** Tr. of Grétry's La rosière de Salenci.

Das **rosenmaedchen,** oder Das fest der weiblichen tugend. Tr. of La rosière de Salenci by Blaise, Philidor and Duni.

La **Rosiere,** ballet-d'action, en deux actes, de la composition de M. Gardel, l'aîné, Maître des ballets. Représentée, pour la première fois, sur le Theatre de l'Académie de musique, le mardi 29 juillet 1783.

Paris, à la Salle de l'Opéra, 1783.   16 p.   18½^{cm}.

Two acts.   Cast added by contemporary hand.   Scene by scene description of the action.   The composer of the music is not mentioned in the libretto nor by Lajarte.

ML 48.B2

La **rosiere de Salenci,** comédie, en trois actes, mêlée d'ariettes; par M. Favart: représentée devant Sa Majesté à Fontainebleau, le 25 octobre 1769.   Et à Paris, par les Comédiens ordinaires du roi, le 14 décembre 1769.

Paris, la veuve Duchesne, 1770.   viii, 104 p.   19^{cm}.   (Theatre de M. Favart, Paris, Duchesne, 1763–77, t. x.)

Cast.   On. p. 97–98 the air of the "Vaudeville de la Rosiere de Salenci" ("Vous qui cherchez à mériter") and on p. 102–104 the "Air: Menuet d'Exaudet" sung to the words "Cet étang, qui s'étend."   The text is preceded by an "Éclaircissement historique sur la Fête de la rose" and by an "Avis du libraire" which begins:

"La Rosière de Salenci a déja été imprimée; mais les exemplaires étoient uniquement destinés pour la cour.

"Depuis plusieurs années bien des auteurs se plaignent de voir leurs ouvrages contrefaits dans presque toutes les grandes villes du royaume, remplis de fautes, de contre-sens insoutenables, qui les défigurent au point qu'eux-mêmes ont bien de la peine à les reconnoître.   Ces contrefactions . . . se débitent même jusques sur les théâtres de la capitale: c'est pourquoi, pour garantir le public de toute supercherie à cet égard, nous nous croyons obligés de l'avertir de s'adresser directement aux libraires désignes sur les titres des pièces qui s'impriment à Paris . . ."

The music is attributed principally to **Blaise, Duni,** and **Philidor,** who are not mentioned.

ML 49.A2F1

— Das **rosenmaedchen,** oder, Das fest der weiblichen tugend, ein singspiel in drey aufzuegen aus dem franzoesischen uebersetzt, mit musik.

Frankfurt am Mayn, mit Andreäischen schriften 1772.   128 p., 11 p. (folded dated music).   16½^{cm}.

German version by Johann Heinrich Faber.   With cast.

The musical supplement contains the arias (voice and bass): "Dieser teich malet" ["Cet etang qui s'étend"] p. 1–4, "Kätchen hat mir dumm geschienen" ["Nicole a l'air bien novice"], p. 4–8; "Mädchen, lasst euch die freude schmecken" ["Amusés vos jeunes"], p. 9–10; "Man giebt uns den unterricht" ["On nous donne des leçons"], p. 10–11.

First performed at Frankfurt a/M, Theater im Junghof, 1772.			SCHATZ 2860

La **rosière de Salenci,** pastorale en trois actes, mêlée d'ariettes; représentée, pour la première fois, par les Comédiens italiens ordinaires du roi, le lundi 28 février 1774: précédée de Réflexions sur cette pièce, mêlés de quelques Observations générales sur les spectacles.

Paris, Delalain, 1774.   xxviii, 67 p.   21^{cm}.

Cast.   By Alexandre Frédéric Jacques Masson, marquis de Pézay, who is not mentioned.   His preface is very interesting and full of side lights on olden times and manners.   **Grétry,** the composer, comes in for some complimentary remarks, and those who were jealous of his successes for some rather uncomplimentary remarks.   Nor does the author spare his own critics when defending his piece in detail against their attacks.   Still, the criticism levelled at the piece can not have been wholly unreasonable, because the author himself in a foot-note on p. xx remarks that even after contracting the two first acts of the original four into one, the piece may be too long with its three acts.   The date of performance in the title is that of the original four acts at the Comédie italienne, Paris, whereas the three-act version was first performed there on June 18, 1774.   The present three-act libretto was printed, as appears from

La **rosière de Salenci**—Continued.

remarks on p. xvii, before this performance but, of course, after that of the four-act version. Of the libretto printed for the original performances at Fontainebleau (exact date not recorded) the author says that it was "trop fautive pour valoir même la peine d'être désavouée."

For the present purpose the following quotations from Masson de Pézay's frank and noteworthy "Réflexions" must suffice:

". . . La présence inattendue de Madame la Dauphine, avoit favorablement disposé le Public à la première représentation de la Rosière à Paris; on est indulgent quand on est heureux. Quelques mois auparavant cette Pièce avoit été donnée à Fontainebleau, & n'avoit pas eu pour elle, à beaucoup près, le plus grand nombre des suffrages. Il y a plusieurs exemples, au Théâtre, de cette apparente contradiction entre les jugemens de la Cour & ceux de la Ville. J'en donnerai plus d'une raison plausible, avant de me prévaloir de celle que l'esprit malin de la Capitale se plaît à accréditer. Je ne l'allégue point, parce qu'elle me paroît fausse . . .

"Une de ces circonstances les plus marquées, est sans doute l'usage qui proscrit les applaudissemens toutes les fois que Sa Majesté honore le Spectacle de sa présence. Il ne nous appartient pas de décider si ce silentieux hommage du respect compense bien celui qu'il interdit à l'amour; s'il peut être, pour un Monarque, beaucoup de tableaux plus doux que tout mouvement passionné des coeurs qui lui appartiennent; & si des ris & des larmes libres ne développeroient pas toujours, avec un nouvel avantage, aux yeux du Roi, le caractère du peuple charmant & sensible dont il est maître? Ce que je sais, c'est que l'étiquette a fixé cet usage; c'est qu'il est glaçant pour l'Acteur; c'est que l'Acteur ne se glace point sans réfroidir celui qui l'écoute, & que de froideur en froideur, & de contrainte en contrainte la toile se lève & s'abaisse ainsi, sans que l'ame engourdie à ce Théâtre se permette l'élan, qui seul lui donne le droit de juger, parce que seul il lui permet de sentir . . .

"Il est une autre observation particulière aux Pièces en musique, c'est qu'elles ne sont données à Versailles ou à Fontainebleau qu'une fois, deux au plus, & qu'il est impossible de juger les effets d'harmonie à une première, & même à une seconde représentation . . .

"Aux obstacles communs à toutes les Pièces en musique données à la Cour, il s'en est joint quelques-uns de particuliers à la mienne. Un devoir militaire m'occupoit à l'Isle de Rhé, au moment où l'on se disposoit à la donner à Fontainebleau. Je ne pouvois pas trop décemment repasser la mer pour venir veiller à la répétition. Quelques mois auparavant, je m'étois contenté d'envoyer un manuscrit exact, accompagné de notes indispensables. J'ignore par quelle fatalité il se trouva perdu avant que la Pièce fût sûe, & par conséquent représentée. Au défaut du manuscrit égaré, on eut recours à un autre très-raturé, où les nouvelles corrections, relatives aux ariettes seulement, étoient portées. Elles s'y trouvoient malheureusement en contradiction avec l'ancien dialogue: delà résulta, à la représentation, mille petites absurdités plus piquantes les unes que les autres, & un galimathias dont toute la bonne volonté des rivaux auroit eu bien de la peine à sauver le ridicule à l'Auteur mutilé & absent.

"Ce manuscrit étoit depuis cinq ou six ans entre les mains de M. **Gretri**. Je saisis cette occasion de rapporter la date de mon importante production; je me crois obligé d'en faire part aux esprits bien intentionnés, qui ont eu grand soin de faire remarquer à des Juges, dont une seule pensée ne peut être indifférente, combien peu le métier d'un Aide-Maréchal Général-des-Logis de L'Armée est de faire des Opéra-comiques. C'est à ces donneurs d'avis bénévoles que j'observe qu'il y a six ans sur-tout, ces distractions pouvoient encore m'être permises; qu'aujourd'hui même je serois aussi loin d'en rougir que de m'enorgueillir du succès le plus entier dont elles pourroient être suivies . . .

"J'ai tardé long-tems à faire imprimer la Rosiere: peut-être ne l'aurois-je pas fait imprimer du tout, si des critiques verbales, même imprimées, ne m'avoient fait connoître que toute Pièce où il y a de la musique n'est jamais bien entendue, ni même comprise avant d'avoir été lûe: c'est pour l'intelligence de la Scène que je me détermine à cette nouvelle publicité, & non par la conviction que de telles miseres puissent jamais mériter les honneurs durables de la presse . . ." ML 50.2.R8G71

— La **rosière de Salenci,** pastorale en trois actes, mêlée d'ariettes. Représentée pour la première fois par les **comédiens** italiens ordinaires du Roi le lundi 28 février 1774.

Paris, Delalain, 1775. 52 p. 18ᶜᵐ.

Neither the author nor the composer **Grétry** is mentioned. Contents as in next entry.
SCHATZ 4182

La rosière de Salenci—Continued.

— La **rosière de Salenci**, pastorale en trois actes, mêlée d'ariettes. La musique de M. Grétry. Représentée pour la première fois par les Comédiens italiens ordinaires du roi, le lundi 28 février 1774.

Paris, Delalain, 1785. 54 p. 18ᶜᵐ.

Same cast. Does not contain Masson de Pézay's "Reflexions." On p. 3–6, the air of the ariette, "Quel beau jour se dispose" (I, 1). On p. 52–54 of the "*Ronde*, pendant laquelle on danse. Chantez, dansez, amusez-vous" (III, 5).

ML 50.2.R8G73

— Das **rosenfest zu Salenci**, ein singspiel in drey aufzuegen aus dem franzoesischen uebersetzt, mit musik.

Frankfurt am Mayn, mit Andreaischen schriften, 1775. 109 p., 8 p. (folded music). 16½ᶜᵐ.

By Joh. Heinr. Faber, who is not mentioned. The music (voice and bass) consists of "Im wankenden kahne" ("Ma barque flottante," II, 7) and "Singet und tanzet, freuet Euch" ("Chantez, dansez, amusez-vous," III, 5). SCHATZ 4183

La Rosilda. Dramma favoloso da recitarsi in musica l'anno 1707. Nel Teatro di S. Fantin in Venezia. Di Bartolomeo Pedoni . . .

Venezia, Gio. Maria Rossi, 1707. 48 p. 15ᶜᵐ.

Three acts. Author's dedication, argument, scenario, and notice to the reader, with the name of Girolamo **Polani** as the composer. SCHATZ 8251

La Rosilena. Drama per musica di Aurelio Aureli, favola duodecima. Rappresentata nel novissimo Teatro Grimano l'anno 1664 . . .

Venetia, Francesco Nicolini, 1664. 71 p. 14½ᶜᵐ.

Prologue and three acts. Author's dedication dated January 4, 1664, argument, and scenario. **Rovettino,** the composer, is not mentioned. SCHATZ 9109

Rosilena ed Oronta. Drama per musica da rappresentarsi nel Teatro di Sant' Angelo nel carnovale dell' anno 1728 . . .

Venezia, Antonio Bortoli, 1728. 58 p. 15ᶜᵐ.

Three acts. By Giovanni Palazzi, who is not mentioned. Impresario's dedication, argument, cast, scenario, and name of Antonio **Vivaldi** as composer.

SCHATZ 10778

La Rosilla. Tragicommedia di Filostrato Lucàno Cinnèo. Da rappresentarsi nel nuovo Teatro di sopra la strada di Toledo in questo autunno del corrente anno 1733 . . .

Napoli, n. publ., 1733. 72 p. 15ᶜᵐ.

Three acts. Real name of the author is Antonio Soliva, according to Wotquenne after Florimo), but Piovano says that it is an anagram of Francesco Antonio Tulli. Impresario's dedication, cast, argument, and note:

"La musica è del Signor Antonio **Orefici**, a riserva dell' arie con questo segno § che sono del Signor Lionardo **Leo** . . ."

This would apply to "Se i miei strali fosser tali" (I, 4), "Il vincitore : Lascia, ch'io parli al core" (I, 7), "Po fa la Ddea, che a chisto core" (I, 13), "In libertate lasciami il core" (I, 15), "Vincerai, non paventar" (II, 7), "Quell' amor, che nel cimento" (II, 9), "Ma non gli affetti miei" (II, 11), "Sento là speme" (II, 15), "Non fa, ch'io porri immora" (III, 1), "Dove spero aver la sorte" (III, 3), "Dolce ben mio" (III, 9), "Bell' alme innamorate" (III, 14).

The sign § frequently stands not at the beginning of an aria but somewhere in the middle or towards the end. Since there appears no reason for having misplaced it, the lines have been quoted, which are actually distinguished by the sign. Thus part of an aria would seem to have been by Orefici, part by Leo! This sort of thing was not customary even in pasticcios, though it was not unprecedented.

SCHATZ 7293

Rosimonda. Tragedia per musica da rappresentarsi nel Teatro Grimano di San Gio. Grisostomo l'anno MDCXCVI . . .

Venetia, Nicolini, 1696. front., 84 p. 14ᶜᵐ.

Five acts. Dedication by the author conte Girolamo Frigimelica Roberti, one of his lengthy notices to the reader, argument, and scenario. The composer, Carlo Francesco **Pollaroli**, is not mentioned.

First performed at the same theatre, fall of 1695. SCHATZ 8316

Rosina, a comic opera, in two acts. Performed at the Theatre-Royal in Covent-Garden.

London, T. Cadell, 1783. 46, v–vi p. 21ᶜᵐ.

Cast. The p. v–vi at end contain an Advertisement to the effect that "some of the songs and a few short passages of the dialogue" which were omitted in the performance are restored, also that the fable of the piece is taken from the book of Ruth, and that both Thomson and Favart's works on the same subject were utilized as far as the difference of the plan would allow.

Neither the author, Mrs. Brooke, nor the composer-compiler, William **Shield**, is mentioned. In Napier's vocal score "The morn returns" is headed as composed by Stephen **Paxton**, "Henry cull'd the flowrets" as by **Sacchini**

First performed December 31, 1782, as indicated. LONGE 91

Rosina consolata o sia L'innocenza protetta. Intermezzo a quattro voci del Signor abate Pietro Antonio Bagliaca tra gl'Arcadi Cancidio Matiglauro. Da rappresentarsi nel Teatro di San Cassiano l'autunno dell' anno 1781 . . .

Venezia, n. publ., 1781. 40 p. 16½ᶜᵐ.

Two acts. Pages 29–30 supplied in ms. Impresario's dedication, cast, and name of Giovanni **Valentini** as the composer. SCHATZ 10584

Rosmira. Dramma per musica da rappresentarsi in Firenze nel Teatro di via del Cocomero nell' carnevale dell' anno 1746 . . .

Firenze, Gio. Batista Stecchi, 1746. 55 p. 15ᶜᵐ.

Three acts. Impresario's dedication, argument, cast, and scenario. Neither author nor composer mentioned. Schatz attributes the music to Giuseppe Antonio **Paganelli** and says that the composer sang the part of "Armindo." The list of characters says: "Il Sig. Giuseppe Paganelli di Forli," but since the composer was from Padua, the two do not appear to be identical. (*Comp. also* Eitner.)

By comparison I find that the text is a pasticcio text. Much of the dialogue is identical with Silvio Stampiglia's "La Rosmira fedele." Also a few arias are identical with arias in this, but most are not, and of these quite a few can be traced to Metastasio. SCHATZ 7575

Rosmira. Dramma per musica da rappresentarsi nel Teatro di S. Angelo il carnovale 1738 . . .

Venezia, Marino Rossetti, 1738. 48 p. 15ᶜᵐ.

Three acts. Dedication by the composer, Antonio **Vivaldi**, argument, cast, and scenario. Silvio Stampiglia is mentioned by Vivaldi as the author. SCHATZ 10779

La Rosmira fedele. Dramma per musica di Silvio Stampiglia, da rappresentarsi nel Teatro di S. Samuele per la fiera dell' Ascensione dell' anno MDCCLIII.

Venezia, Angiolo Geremia, n. d. 33 p. 16ᶜᵐ.

Three acts. Argument, cast, and name of the composer, Gioacchino **Cocchi**. SCHATZ 2044

La **Rosmira fedele.** Dramma per musica di Silvio Stampiglia tra gli Arcadi Palemone Licurio. Da rappresentarsi nel Teatro celebre Grimani in S. Gio. Grisostomo il carnovale MDCCXXV . . .

Venezia, Marino Rossetti, n. d. 57 p. 15½ᶜᵐ.

Three acts. Impresario's dedication, cast, argument, scenario, and name of Leonardo **Vinci** as the composer. SCHATZ 10751

La **Rossana.** A. T. of the ballet "La vittoria di Tamerlano contro Bajazette.

Rossana, ballet. *See* Caruso's Li sposi in commedia.

La **Rossana.** Dramma per musica da rappresentarsi nel Teatro alla Scala il carnevale dell' anno 1795 . . .

Milano, Gio. Batista Bianchi, n. d. 50, [15] p. 16ᶜᵐ.

Three acts. Author not mentioned and unknown to Schatz. Impresario's dedication dated Milan, January 31, 1795, argument, cast, scenario, and name of Ferdinando Për (**Paër**) as the composer.

With the opera were performed Paolino Franchi's "ballo eroico-tragico Lodoiska," his "ballo eroico-pastorale Gli amori di Angelica e Medoro" and "La pianella perduta." The unnumbered pages contain the description of the first and the argument of the second. The composers of the music are not mentioned. The last unnumbered page contains the substitute aria, etc. (I, 6) "Un tenero accento."

SCHATZ 7561

Le **rossignol,** opera comique an un acte, de Messieurs * * * Représenté pour la premiere fois le 15 septembre 1752, & jours suivans, jusqu'à la clôture du Théatre du Faubourg Saint-Laurent; et continué le 3 février 1753, pour l'ouverture du Théatre du Faubourg Saint-Germain.

Paris, Prault fils, 1753. 31 p. 19ᶜᵐ.

En vaudevilles. In the Avertissement (p. [4–5]) the authors say:

"Parlons maintenant d'une autre pièce qui s'est débitée à Paris dans l'intervalle des deux foires, intitulée de même: *Le Rossignol, opera comique, représenté pour la premiere fois sur le théatre de Rouen*, le 8 octobre 1751, & imprimé dans la *même ville en 1752.*

"Ce titre annonçant à notre Rossignol, un rival d'autant plus dangereux qu'il paroît fortifié du droit d'aînesse, les deux auteurs se sont, comme on peut croire, empressés à le lire, & ce n'est pas sans surprise, qu'entr'autres imitations, ils y ont vû un de leurs couplets, copié presqu'en entier . . . Il est question du monologue "Que pour mon coeur ces lieux ont d'attraits . . . Or, comme il seroit difficile de se persuader qu'une ressemblance si parfait soit un pur effet du hazard, les deux auteurs appréhendant, avec raison, que le reproche d'un plagiat aussi caractérisé ne retombât sur eux, ont fait toutes les démarches nécessaires pour éclaicir la vérité; & ils ont été assez heureux pour recouvrer un des doubles de la pièce de Rouen, revêtu de l'approbation d'un censeur de Paris, dans lequel double, le couplet, dont il s'agit, n'existe point, ce qui est une preuve, sans replique, que cet auteur l'a ajouté après coup, & que c'est lui par conséquent qui est le plagiaire . . ."

They then ask the public to choose between their "Rossignol de Paris" and the "Rossignol provincial." According to Parfaict (*see* t. vii):

"L'avis au lecteur qui précède la pièce est fait pour justifier les auteurs de l'accusation d'avoir pris l'idée & même quelques morceaux d'une pièce du même nom, composée par M. Bavières de Rouen . . ."

Clément and de Laporte give Baillère as the name of the author. They and Schatz attribute the text of the Parisian Rossignol to the abbé de Latteignant and others. Schatz does not mention the composer, resp. the arranger, of the music. According to Schatz there was played on November 18, 1751, at Berny, at the palace of the comte de Clermont a one-act comédie mêlée d'ariettes by Charles Collé, music by J. B. de La Borde, which might easily be confused with the two other Rossignols, since its title was "Rossignol ou Le mariage secret." ML 48.A4

Das **rothe kaeppchen** oder Hilft's nicht, so schadt's nicht. Ein komisches singspiel in drei aufzuegen von herrn von Dittersdorf.

>*Koeln am Rheine, Langen, 1791. 78 p. 16^{cm}.*
>
>By the composer after Livigni's "Giannina."
>First performed at Breslau, Wäsersches Theater, May 26, 1790. SCHATZ 2603

— Das **rothe kaeppchen.** Eine komische operette in zwei aufzuegen. Die musik ist von herrn Dieter von Dittersdorf. Aufgefuehrt zum erstenmal den 7. Junius 1791 auf dem Hoftheater zu Weimar.

>*Weimar, Hoffmannische buchhandlung, 1792. 88 p. 16$\frac{1}{2}$^{cm}.*
>
>Altered by Vulpius who in the unsigned "Vorrede" says:
>"Das original dieser operette, welches man als manuskript mit der partitur erhaelt, mag wohl allein die guten buehnen von der auffuehrung derselben bisher abgeschreckt haben. Das war auch der fall bei uns, und daher enstand diese neue bearbeitung deren guenstige aufnahme gar nicht zweifelhaft geblieben ist. Die angenehme musik dieser operette verdiente alleine schon eine umaenderung des textes . . ." SCHATZ 2604

The **rover;** or, Happiness at last: A pastoral drama, as it was intended for the theatre . . .

>*London, M. Cooper, W. Reeve, and H. Dood, 1752. 1 p. l., ii, [2], 24 p. 21$\frac{1}{2}$^{cm}.*
>
>One act. Poem to Francis Delavall, list of subscribers and Advertisement in which this play "the author's first essay of this kind," is said to have
>"gain'd the commendation of the manager of the Theatre Royal; but, as it was intended to succeed the representation of a play, the length of it prevented its having the honour of appearing on the stage."
>The author, S. Boyce, is not mentioned. LONGE 160

Les **routes du monde.** *See* L'industrie.

Royal clemency. A. T. of The deserter of Naples.

The **royal garland.** A new occasional interlude, in honour of His Danish Majesty. Set to music by Mr. Arnold. And performed at the Theatre Royal, Covent-Garden.

>*London, T. Becket and P. A. de Hondt, 1768. [6]–24 p. 19$\frac{1}{2}$^{cm}.*
>
>By Isaac Bickerstaffe, who is not mentioned.
>First performed October 1, 1768, as indicated. LONGE 36

The **royal merchant:** an opera. Founded on Beaumont and Fletcher. As it is performed at the Theatre Royal, in Covent-Garden.

>*London, William Griffin, 1768. 3 p. l., 68 p. 19$\frac{1}{2}$^{cm}.*
>
>Three acts. Cast and prefatory note, in which the author, Thomas Hull (not mentioned), says that in utilizing the old play ["The beggar's bush"]
>"he was the rather tempted to make this experiment, from the romantic turn of the fable, and singularity of the characters in this play, which appeared to him peculiarly calculated for an opera . . ."
>The composer, Thomas **Linley,** is not mentioned. (*See also* his "The camp.")
>First performed December 14, 1767 (Schatz), February 24, 1767 (Tufts). LONGE 197

The **royal shepherd,** an English opera; as it is performed at the Theatre-Royal in Drury-Lane. The music composed by Mr. Rush. The second edition.

>*London, W. Owen and C. Moran, n. d. 2 p. l., 41, iii–iv p. 19$\frac{1}{2}$^{cm}.*

The **royal shepherd**—Continued.

Three acts. Taken by R. Rolt from Metastasio's "Il rè pastore," neither of whom is mentioned. The iii–iv p. contain table of the songs.
First performed, as indicated, February 24, 1764.   Longe 37

— The **royal shepherd**. An English opera; as it is performed at the Theatre-Royal in Drury-Lane. The music composed by Mr. Rush. The third edition.

London, W. Owen and C. Moran, n. d.   2 p. l., 41, xlii–xliii p.   20½ cm.

Three acts. Argument, cast, and at end table of the songs, etc. By Richard Rolt.
                                                                    Longe 192
                                                    Second copy. Longe 216

— **Amintas**. An English opera. As perform'd at the Theatre-Royal in Covent-Garden.

London, T. Lowndes, 1769.   2 p. l., 28 p.   19½ cm.

Three acts. Cast and argument. This is Richard Rolt's "The Royal shepherd," as altered by Giusseppe Ferdinando Tenducci. Music by George **Rush**, with interpolations from Pietro **Guglielmi** and others. One of the telling differences between this and "The Royal shepherd" is that the latter has, in I, 2, the aria, "A shepherd, though I am," whereas "Amintas" has "Altho' this humble garb I wear."
First performed December 15, 1769, as indicated.   Longe 37

— **Amintas**; an English opera.

[293]–311 p.   19 cm.   (Collection of the most esteemed farces and entertainments, t. vi, Edinburgh, 1792).

Three acts. Covent-Garden cast.   H   ATZ 11753F

La **roze** ou Les festes de l'Hymen. *See* Piron's text La rose.

Der **ruchlose**. A. T. of Righini's Das steinerne gastmahl.

Rudolph von Creki. Tr. of Dalayrac's Raoul, sire de Créqui.

Rübenzahl, o sia Il vero amore. Dramma giocoso per musica da rappresentarsi nel Teatro di S. A. E. di Sassonia del Signor Caterino Mazzolà.

Dresda, n. publ., 1789.   131 p.   15½ cm.

Two acts. Joseph **Schuster** is mentioned as composer. German title-page, "Ruebenzahl, oder Die wahre liebe," and text face Italian.
First performed, as indicated, February 14, 1789.   Schatz 9752

Ruggiero. Dramma per musica da rappresentarsi nel Teatro Vendramin di S. Salvatore nella fiera dell' Ascensione dell' anno 1769.

Venezia, Modesto Fenzo, 1769.   47 p.   16 cm.

Three acts. By Caterino Mazzolà, who is not mentioned. Cast, scenario, and name of Pietro **Guglielmi** as composer of the "musica tutta nuova."
First performed May 3, 1769, as indicated.   Schatz 4304

Il **Ruggiero** o vero L'eroica gratitudine. Questo dramma manca nell' edizione torinese, perchè non era ancora scritto quando il decimo volume di essa fu pubblicato. Il compose l'autore d'ordine dell' imperatrice regina in Vienna; ed ivi uscì . . . dalla stamperia del Ghelen; e fu rappresentato con musica dell' Hasse immediatamente in Milano, in occasione delle felicissime nozze delle AA. RR. di Ferdinando arciduca d'Austria, e dell' arciduchessa Maria Beatrice d'Este . . . l'anno 1771.

pl., [177]–266 p.   26 cm.   (Metastasio, Opere, t. ix, vedova Herissant, 1781.)

Three acts.   ML 49.A2M44

Il **Ruggiero** o vero L'eroica gratitudine. Dramma per musica da rappresentarsi in occasione delle felicissime nozze delle Altezze Loro Reali . . . Ferdinando arciduca d'Austria e . . . Maria Beatrice d'Este . . . In Milano l'anno MDCCLXXI.

Vienna, Stamperia di Ghelen, 1771. Unpaged. 25 cm.

The imprint, together with Metastasio's name as author, appears on a leaf preceding the ornamental title page, which, as were the head and tail pieces, was designed by J. Bidermann and engraved by J. C. de Reinsperger.

Three acts and licenza. Scenario, cast, and name of Johann Adolph **Hasse** as the composer.

First performed at Milan, Regio-Ducal Teatro, October 18, 1771 (Schatz), October 16, 1771 (Mennicke). SCHATZ 4558

Die **ruinen von Portici.** Ein allegorisches singspiel in zwey acten von C. A. Herbst.

Breslau, Ernst Gottlieb Meyer, 1798. 112 p. 17 cm.

Dedication, "Vorschläge zu anordnung des costums," "An das publicum:" "Die grundidee zu dieser operette ist aus dem kleinen franzoesischen roman des Cazotte 'Biondetta' entlehnt."

First performed, with music by A. Joseph **Fischer,** Stuttgart, Hoftheater, May 10, 1807. SCHATZ 3210

La **rupture du carnaval.** *See* Destouches' Le carnaval et la folie.

La **ruse d'amour,** ou L'épreuve, comédie en un acte et en vers, mêlée d'ariettes. Par M. Maillé de Marencour. Musique de M. Chardiny . . . Représentée pour la premiere fois à Paris, par les Comédiens de S. A. S. Monseigneur le conte de Beaujolois, au Palais-Royal, le jeudi 25 août 1785, & à Saint Cloud; devant Leurs Majestés, le 28 septembre 1785.

Paris, Brunet, 1786. 13, [1] p. 20½ cm. ML 50.2.R9C3

La **ruse de carnaval.** A. T. of Les deux morts.

La **ruse villageoise,** opéra-comique, en un acte, en prose et en vaude-villes. Par le C. A. B. Sewrin, représenté, pour la première fois, à Paris, sur le Théâtre de la rue de Louvois, le 2 juillet 1793 (vieux style).

Paris, la citoyenne Toubon, 1794. 32 p. 20½ cm.

Cast. Not recorded by Cl. & L. or Schatz. An opera of the same title (music by Charles **Ots**) was performed at Ghent, January 2, 1796. SCHATZ 11511

The **rustic heroine.** A. T. of The loyal shepherds.

Sabinus, tragédie-lyrique, en cinq actes, représentée, devant Sa Majesté, à Versailles, le 4 décembre 1773.

[Paris], P. Robert Christophe Ballard, 1773.

Cast. With name of the composer, François Joseph **Gossec,** but not of the author, Michel Paul Gui de Chabanon de Maugris. SCHATZ 4011

Le **sabot perdu.** A. T. of La matinée et la veillée.

Les **sabots,** opéra-comique en un acte, meslé d'ariettes. Par Mrs. C . . . et Sedaine. Représenté pour la premiere fois par les Comédiens italiens ordinaires du roi, le mercredi 26 octobre 1768.

Paris, Claude Herissant, 1769. 22 p. 19 cm.

Cast. **Duni,** the composer, is not mentioned. Jacques Cazotte collaborated with Sedaine. ML 50.2.S2D9

Les **sabots**—Continued.

— Les **sabots,** opéra-comique en un acte, meslé d'ariettes.　Par Mrs.
C. . . . et Sedaine.　Représenté pour la première fois par les
Comédiens italiens ordinaires du roi, le mercredi 26 octobre 1768.

Paris, Claude Herissant, 1770.　24 p.　18ᶜᵐ.

Cast.　**Duni,** the composer, is not mentioned.　　　　　　　SCHATZ 2855

— Les **sabots.**　Opéra-comique en un acte, mêlé d'ariettes; par
Mrs. C. . . . & Sédaine.　Représenté pour la première fois par les
Comédiens italiens ordinaires du roi, le mercredi 26 octobre 1768.

Paris, Claude Herissant, 1777.　24 p.　18ᶜᵐ.

Cast.　On p. 14–16, the ariette, "Qu'ils sont heureux, ces oiseaux!"　The composer, **Duni,** is not mentioned.　　　　　　　　　　　　　SCHATZ 11698

Sabrina.　An opera for the Theatre Royal in the Hay-Market.　By
Paul Rolli, F. R. S.

London, J. Chrichley, 1737.　61 p.　17ᶜᵐ.

Three acts.　Preface, like the text, in Italian, with English translation.　Burney
IV, 412, mentions this opera, without naming the composer.　Schatz enters it under
Giov. Battista **Pescetti** and others.

First performed, as indicated (April 26), May 7, 1737.　　　SCHATZ 8859

— **Sabrina.**

*[425]–460 p.　17ᶜᵐ.　(Rolli, Componimenti poetici, Nuova edizione,
Verona, G. Tumermani, 1744.)*

Three acts.　Argument.　No composers mentioned.　　　　　ML 49.A2R7

I sacrifizi di Creta o sia Arianna e Teseo.　Dramma per musica da
rappresentarsi nel Regio Teatro di via della Pergola la **primavera**
del MDCCXCIII . . .

Firenze, Stamperia Albizziniana, 1793.　32 p.　16ᶜᵐ.

Three acts.　By Pietro Pariati (not mentioned), but modernized.　Argument, cast,
and name of Peter von **Winter** as the composer.　With the opera was performed
Giuseppe Trafieri's "Il rapitore punito, ballo eroicomico pantomimo" (composer of
the music not mentioned).

First performed at Venice, Teatro di S. Benedetto, carnival, 1792.　SCHATZ 11051

I sacrifizi di Tauride, ballet.　*See* P. Guglielmi's Rinaldo.

Sacrifizio detto Taurobolio pella elezione ed inaugurazione di un
rè di Norvegia, ballet.　*See* Calderara's Ricimero.

Il sacrifizio interrotto.　Tr. of P. v. Winter's Das unterbrochene
opferfest.

Saed ossia Il serraglio.　L. T. of Paër's L'intrigo amoroso.

Der **saeuffer.**　Tr. of Hasse's Il bevitore.

Saffo.　*See* Traetta's Le feste d'Imeneo.

Saffo o sia I riti d'Apollo Leucadio, dramma per musica del **Signor**
Sografi da rappresentarsi nel nobilissimo Teatro della Fenice il carnovale dell' anno 1794.

Venezia, Modesto Fenzo, 1794.　43 p.　17½ᶜᵐ.

Two acts.　Cast, scenario, and name of Joh. Simon **Mayr** as the composer.

　　　　　　　　　　　　　　　　　　　　　　　　　　SCHATZ 6171

La saggia pazzia di Giunio Bruto. Drama per musica da rappresentarsi nel famosissimo Teatro Grimani à Santi Gio. e Paolo l'anno 1698 . . .

*Venetia, Nicolini, 1698. front., 60 p. 14½*cm.

Three acts. Dedication dated by the author Lotto Lotti, Venice, November 24, 1698, scenario and notice to the reader with name of Giovanni Maria **Ruggeri** as the composer. SCHATZ 9141

. . . The **sailor's farewell**; or, The Guinea outfit. A comic opera, in three acts. With great improvements.

*Liverpool, Printed and sold by T. Schofield, n. d. 45 (incl. front.), [3] p. 17*cm.

The [3] p. contain prologue and publisher's book-list. At head of title: "Second edition." By T. Boulton, who is not mentioned. No composer recorded by Clarence. LONGE 323

The **sailor's opera**: or, A trip to Jamaica.

*London, Printed for the author, 1745. 1 p. l., 46 p. 16*cm.

Five acts. Ballad opera, the 27 airs in which are indicated by title. Author not recorded by Clarence, who dates first performance as London, Drury Lane, May 12, 1731. LONGE 168

The **sailor's rehearsal.** A. T. of Britons, strike home.

The **sailor's return.** A. T. of Thomas and Sally.

St Patrick's day; or, The scheming lieutenant. A comic opera: as it is acted at the Theatre-Royal, Smoke-Alley.

*[Dublin], Printed for the booksellers, 1788. 27 p. 15½*cm.

Bound in by mistake are p. 47–50 of an edition of the "Castle of Andalusia."
Two acts. Neither the author, Richard Brinsley Sheridan, is mentioned, nor the composer.
First performed at London, Covent Garden, May 2, 1775. LONGE 223

Les saisons. *See* Ballet des saisons.

Les salamandres. Entrée in Duval's Les genies.

Salomon. A. T. of Keiser's Die ueber die liebe triumphirende weissheit.

Salustia. L. T. of Bernasconi's Alessandro Severo.

Die **samnitische vermaehlungsfeyer.** Tr. of Grétry's Les mariages Samnites.

Sancho at court. By a gentleman late of Trinity College, Dublin. As it was design'd to be acted at Drury Lane.

*2 p. l., 56 p. 19*cm.

Title page wanting. Title copied from Tufts, who says under 1742 "Ascribed to James Ayres." I have found the opera mentioned also with the title "Sancho at court or The mock governor."
Three acts. Ballad opera, the 20 airs in which are indicated by title. In a preface, the bookseller, Mr. Torbuck, tells the reader that
"The author is a gentleman of Trinity College, Dublin, who has publish'd several small pieces that have had a favourable reception, and, as I am inform'd, is in no small reputation with the inimitable Dean, who, as he himself told me, had the inspection and chastisement of the play"

Sancho at court—Continued.

He goes on to say that he submitted the piece to the manager of Drury-Lane, who advised judicious cuts and who recommended Chetwood for the purpose. This was done, but when the piece was submitted to the Chamberlain's office with Chetwood's alterations, no answer was forthcoming from the censor for eight months, and when Torbuck wanted the manuscript back he "could not have it, it being left at a place not then to be come at." Thereupon he decided to print the piece. He winds up by saying:

"However, the trouble I have had in this affair will be a sufficient caution to me (and may be so to others) not to undertake the bringing a play on the stage; for as things are now circumstanced, viz. the approbation of the players, the licensing-office and the ill-natur'd critic, not to say any thing of the publick, an author has but a small chance of succeeding."   LONGE 189

Sancho Panca dans son isle, opera bouffon, en un acte, par M. Poincinet le jeune. La musique est de M. Philidor. Représentée pour la premiere fois par les Comédiens italiens ordinaires du roi, le 8 juillet 1762.

Avignon, Louis Chambeau, 1768. 39 p. 19½^{cm}.   ML 50.2.S2P4

—Sancho Pança dans son isle, opera bouffon en un acte, par Mr. Poinsinet, le jeune, représenté pour la premiere fois par les Comediens italiens ordinaires du roi, le 8 février 1762. La musique est de Mr. Philidor.

Paris, la veuve Duchesne, 1771. 56 p. 18^{cm}.

Cast. On p. 18–22 the ariette "Je vais seulette en mon jardin" (I, 5), on p. 35–38 the romance "Je m'en revenais chantant" (I, 12) and the vaudeville "Je vais revoir ma chère" in last scene.

The date of first performance in the title is incorrect; it should be July 8, 1762.
                                                                      SCHATZ 8022

— Sanko Panssa: eine operette. Aus dem franzoesischen uebersetzt.

Halberstadt, Johann Heinrich Gross, 1776. 72 p. 15^{cm}.

Argument with names of Poinsinet as author and **Philidor** as the composer. Translated by Friedrich Wilhelm Eicholz, who is not mentioned.   SCHATZ 8023

Sancio, oder Die siegende grossmuth. In einem sing-spiele auf dem Hamburgischen Schau-platze vorgestellet. Im jahr 1727.

[Hamburg], Gedruckt mit Stromerschen schrifften, n. d. Unpaged. 18^{cm}.

Three acts. Argument, cast, scenario, and names of Joh. Ulrich Koenig as the author, of Georg Philipp **Telemann** as the composer. Koenig based his text on Francesco Silvani's "Il miglior d'ogni amore per il peggiore d'ogni odio."
                                                                      SCHATZ 10266

Den sande bestandighed. Tr. of Anfossi's La vera costanza.

Sanko Panssa. Tr. of Philidor's Sancho Panca.

Sansome, ballet. *See* Cimarosa's I tre amanti.

Sansonnet et Tonton. O. T. of Favart's parody L'amour impromptu.

La Santa Eugenia. A. T. of L'innocenza vendicata.

Sapho. Opéra en trois actes.

Venard de La Jonchère, Théâtre lyrique, Paris, 1772, t. ii, p. [275]–340. 18½^{cm}.

"Avant-propos" (p. 277–294). No composer mentioned. Nor is any recorded by Clément & Larousse. ML 49.A2L2

Sara, ou La fermiere écossoise, comédie en deux actes et en vers, mêlée d'ariettes; par M. C. . .D. . .M. . . Représentée pour la premiere fois par les Comédiens italiens ordinaires du roi, le 8 mai 1773. La musique est de M. Vachon.

Paris, J. A. Durand Dufrenoy, 1774. 45, [2] p. 19^{cm}.

Cast. By Jean Baptiste Collet de Messine. The 2 unnumb. pages contain the air "Le dieu d'amour, le dieu du vin" (II, 5). Schatz 10571

Sardanapalo. Drama per musica. Da recitarsi nel Teatro di San't Angelo l'anno 1679. Di Carlo Maderni . . .

Venetia, Francesco Nicolini, 1679. 60 p. 14½^{cm}.

Three acts. Impresario's dedication, argument, notice to the reader with name of Giovanni Domenico **Freschi** as composer and scenario. Schatz 3654

Sardanapalo, rè degli Assirj, ballet. *See* Andreozzi's Agesilao.

Il **sargente burlato,** ballet. *See* Cimarosa's Le donne rivali.

Sargine, ballet. *See* Federici's L'Olimpiade.

Sargines, ou L'élève de l'amour, comédie en quatre actes, en prose, par M. Monvel. Représenté pour la première fois à Paris, par les Comédiens italiens ordinaires du roi, le mercredi 14 mai 1788. Mise en musique par M. d'Alayrac.

Paris, J. L. de Boubers, 1789. 46 p. 18½^{cm}. Schatz 2380

Die **satire.** A. T. of Preu's Bella und Fernando.

I **satiri in Arcadia.** O. T. of Conti's Cloris und Tirsis.

I **satiri puniti.** A. T. of the ballet Egle e Cloco.

Satiro & Amore. Intermedio in Cavalli's Il novello Giasone.

Les **saturnales.** Entrée in Colin de Blamont's Les festes grecques et romaines.

La **satyre.** Entré in Campra's Les Muses.

Les **sauvages.** A. T. of Dalayrac's Azémia.

Les **sauvages.** Entrée in Rameau's Les Indes galantes.

La **sauvagesse.** *See* Les desesperés.

Le **savetier et le financier,** opera comique, en deux actes, en prose, mêlée d'ariettes; représenté devant Leurs Majestés, à Marly, en octobre 1778.

[Paris], R. R. C. Ballard, n. d. 3 p. l., 75 p. 23^{cm}.

Cast, dedicatory poem, and name of Henri Joseph **Rigel** as composer. The author, Jean Baptiste Lourdet de Santerre, is not mentioned.

First performed October 23, 1778, as indicated; at Paris, Comédie italienne, October 30, 1778 (Schatz), November 9 (Cl. & L.). ML 50.2.S3R3

Il savio delirante. Comico divertimento per musica da rappresentarsi nel Teatro Formagliari il carnevale dell' anno 1726.

Bologna, Costantino Pisarri, n. d. 58, [1] p. 15ᶜᵐ.

Three acts, in Bolognese dialect. The composer, Giuseppe Maria **Buini,** to whom Schatz attributes the text, is not mentioned. Notice to the reader. The *imprimatur* is dated January 16, 1726. SCHATZ 1385

— Le frenesie d'amore. Divertimento per musica da rappresentarsi nel Teatro Giustiniano di S. Mosè. Nelli mesi di maggio, e giugno 1726.

Venezia, Maria Rossetti, 1726. 56 p. 12ᶜᵐ.

Three acts. Practically the same as "Il savio delirante," though beginning with an aria, "Barbare stelle infide," which is not in the original. **Buini** is not mentioned. SCHATZ 1386

Lo sbarco de' Spagnuoli nell' America, ballet. *See* G. M. Rutini's Sicotencal.

La scaltra avventuriera. Commedia per musica di Giuseppe Palomba da rappresentarsi nel Teatro de' Fiorentini per quart' opera di quest' anno 1788.

Napoli, n. publ., 1788. 55 p. 15ᶜᵐ.

Three acts. Argument, cast, and name of Giacomo **Tritto** as the composer. SCHATZ 10477

La scaltra governatrice. L. T. of Cocchi's La maestra.

La scaltra letterata. Dramma giocoso per musica da rappresentarsi nel Real Teatro di Salvaterra nel carnovale dell' anno 1772.

Lisbona, Stamperia Reale, n. d. 80 p. 15ᶜᵐ.

Three acts. Antonio Palomba is mentioned as the author; Niccola **Piccinni** as the composer. Cast and scenario. With the opera were performed Francesco Sauveterre's ballets, "La statua animata" and "Li vendemmiatori." The composers of the music are not mentioned.

First performed at Naples, Teatro Nuovo, winter of 1758. SCHATZ 8139

— La scaltra spiritosa. Dramma giocoso per musica da rappresentarsi nel Teatro di S. A. Serenissima il Signor principe di Carignano nell' autunno dell' anno MDCCLXI.

Torino, Gaspare Bayno, n. d. 70 p. 15ᶜᵐ.

Three acts. Cast, scenario, and name of Niccolò **Piccinni** as the composer. The dialogue follows fairly closely that of Palomba's "La scaltra letterata," but many arias are different. For instance, this has in I, 4, "D'ogni timor già sento," and in III, 3, "T'amo a segno o mio tesoro," whereas "La scaltra letterata" has "De dolci affetti miei," resp. "No, non vedrete mai," the "T'amo a segno" being in III, 1.

First performed with this title at Bologna, Teatro Marsigli Rossi, fall of 1760.

SCHATZ 8148

La scaltra spiritosa. L. T. of Piccinni's La scaltra letterata.

Scamandre. Pastorale héroique en quatre actes, avec un prologue.

Venard de La Jonchère, Théâtre lyrique, Paris, 1772, t. ii, p. [77]–144. 18½ᶜᵐ.

"Avant-propos" (p. 79–95). From a publisher's "Avis aux musiciens" ("Ceux qui auroient dessein de mettre en musique quelques-uns des opéra contenn dans ce recueil . . ." it would appear that the text had not yet been composed in 1772. Nor is any composer recorded by Cl. & L. ML 49.A2L2

Scanderberg, tragedie, représentée par l'Académie royale de musique, l'an 1735. Paroles de feu Monsieur de la Mothe; achevées par M. de Laserre. Musique de Messieurs Rebel et Francoeur. CXXIV. opera.

*n. i., n. d.   145–204 p.   14½*ᶜᵐ*.   (Recueil général des opera, Paris, 1745, t. xvi.)*

Detached copy. Five acts and prologue.
First performed, as indicated, October 27, 1735.   ML 48.R4

— **Scanberberg,** tragédie, représentée devant Leurs Majestés, à Fontainebleau le 22 octobre 1763.

*[Paris], Christophe Ballard, 1763.   4 p. l., 62 p.   19*ᶜᵐ*.*

Five acts. Cast and names of "feu M. de la Mothe, avec les changemens qui ont été jugés necessaires" as author; of François **Rebel** and François **Francoeur** as composers. In view of this libretto, Cl. & L.'s statement, "Cet opéra n'a jamais été repris," should be modified.   ML 50.2.S34R2

Schach Wampum oder Die wuensche.   L. T. of Stegmann's Sultan Wampum oder Die wuensche.

Die **schadenfreude,** ein kleines lustspiel fuer kinder mit liederchen.

*[101]–130 p.   16*ᶜᵐ*.   (Der kinderfreund.   Ein wochenblatt, Tuebingen, 1778.)*

In caption on p. [103]: "LXXI. bis LXXIII. stueck, den 11. bis 25. november 1776." Neither the author, Christian Felix Weisse, nor the composer, Georg Peter **Weimar,** is mentioned.   SCHATZ 10963

Schattenspiel an der wand.   Ein singspiel in zwey akten.

*94 p.   (C. F. Bretzner, Singspiele, Leipzig, 1796.)   16½*ᶜᵐ*.*

This detached copy contains the title page of the collection and the "Vorbericht" (p. iii–v), in which Bretzner says:
"Mozart ward dem deutschen theater zuerst durch *die Entfuehrung* bekannt: vielleicht weckt auch eins dieser stuecke irgend ein noch schlafendes musikalisches genie auf, und dann hab ich doch wenigstens das verdienst, es aufgeweckt zu haben. Zwar haben, bereits vor drei jahren, zwey kompositeurs die komposition der beyden ersten stuecke [this and his "Opera buffa"] uebernommen: allein da sie in langer zeit, trotz meiner erinnerung um zuruecksendung der manuscripte, nichts haben von sich hoeren lassen: so kann ich nicht anders vermuthen, als dass sie—die lust dazu verloren haben . . . Dass ich meine singspiele nach italienischer form gemodelt habe? es ist die gegenwaertig beliebte modeform, ohne welche sich selten ein produkt dieser art glueck versprechen kann . . ."
The composer, Georg Ernst Gottlieb **Kallenbach,** is not mentioned.
Schatz records no performance.   SCHATZ 5000

Der **schatzgraeber.**   A. T. of Kaffka's Der aepfeldieb.

Die **schatzgraeber** oder Wer andern eine grube graebt, faellt selbst darein.   Ein lustspiel in drey aufzuegen mit arien.

*n. i., 1789.   64 p.   17*ᶜᵐ*.*

Not recorded by Schatz. Not found in Deutsches Anonymen Lexikon.
                                                      SCHATZ 11647

Der **schauspieldirektor.**   Ein gelegenheitsstück in einem aufzuge. Musik von Mozart.

*Liegnitz, David Siegert, 1792.   p. [351]–395.   16½*ᶜᵐ*.*

At head of title the figure 5. The words from "Musik" to "1792" are pasted over the original title page which was without imprint. The libretto in this form is merely a detached copy from Gottlieb Stephanie's "Singspiele" with special title-page. A

Der **schauspieldirektor**—Continued.

prefatory note preceding the title page has been likewise extracted therefrom and pasted on a fly leaf. It reads:

"Der Schauspieldirektor, welcher bey gelegenheit eines festes in Schönbrunn gegeben wurde, und wozu Seine Majestät, der Hoechstselige Kaiser Joseph der Zweijte, mir selbst die idee angaben, fand, so oft er hernach in Wien gegeben wurde, den ausserordentlichsten beyfall. Da nur eine kleine zahl bücher davon gedruckt worden sind, so ist es auswaerts so gut als gar nicht bekannt; auch sind die dritte und fuenfte scene hier voellig neu. Vorhin waren statt derselben scenen aus bekannten stücken. Dem ohngeachtet, dass es blos als gelegenheitsstück erschien, hat es doch herr Schröder mit vielem beyfalle in Hamburg aufgefuehrt. **Mozart** setzte die darinn vorkommenden singstuecke in musik."

First performed at Schönbrunn, Orangerie, February 7, 1786.   Schatz 6840

Der **schauspieldirektor in der klemme.** Tr. of Cimarosa's L'impresario in angustie.

Die **schellenkappe.** A. T. of Schack's Der wohlthätige derwisch.

Die **schelmen.** Tr. of Fiorillo's Li birbi.

The **scheming lieutenant.** A. T. of St. Patrick's day.

Scherz, list und rache. Ein singspiel. Von Goethe. Ächte ausgabe.

Leipzig, Georg Joachim Göschen, 1790. 1 p. l., 96 p. 17½ᶜᵐ.

Four acts. Edition without "Göschen's Schriften," with "Er ist bitter" on p. 37 and with Ä in title.   PT 1958.S4 1790

— **Scherz, list und rache.** Ein singspiel. Von Goethe. Ächte ausgabe.

Leipzig, Georg Joachim Göschen, 1790. 1 p. l., 96 p. 16ᶜᵐ.

Four acts. Edition with Ä in title, on p. 37 "Es ist bitter." Without "Göschen's Schriften."

First performed with music by Peter von **Winter,** at the private theatre of Graf Anton von Törring at Schloss Seefeld (near Munich), 1790.   PT 1958.S4 1790a

Gli scherzi di fortuna. Drama per musica subordinato al Pirro di Aurelio Aureli, favola nona. Rappresentato nel famoso Theatro Grimano l'anno 1662 . . .

Venetia, Francesco Nicolini, 1662. 78 p. 14ᶜᵐ.

Prologue and three acts. Author's dedication dated Venice, January 12, 1662, argument, and scenario. The composer, Pietro Andrea **Ziani**, is not mentioned.

   Schatz 11218

La **schiava.** L. T. of Piccinni's Gli stravaganti.

La **schiava americana,** ballet. *See* Paisiello's Le vane gelosie.

La **schiava amorosa.** Farsetta in musica a quattro voci da rappresentarsi nel Teatro Capranica nel carnevale dell' anno 1770 . . .

Roma, Ottavio Puccinelli, n. d. 52 p. 16ᶜᵐ.

Two parts. Impresario's dedication, argument, cast and names of Marcello di Capua as author, of Giovanni Battista **Borghi** as composer.   ML 50.2.S41B6

La **schiava astuta.** Intermezzi per musica a tre voci da rappresentarsi nel Teatro Alibert detto delle Dame, nel carnevale dell' anno 1765 . . .

Roma, Ottavio Puccinelli, n. d. 15 p. 15½ᶜᵐ.

Two parts. Author not mentioned and unknown to Schatz. Cast and name of Marcello di Capua (**Bernardini**) as composer. Contains arias like "Via buon zitello," "Fra tante mie pene," "Una ragazza semplice," etc. ML 50.2.S42B3

La **schiava fedele.** A. T. of Cesti's La Dori.

La **schiava fortunata.** Drama per musica da rappresentarsi nel portentoso Teatro Zane à San Moisè l'anno MDCLXXIV . . .

Venetia, Francesco Nicolini, 1674. 56 p. 14ᶜᵐ.

Three acts. Francesco Santorini's dedication, dated Venice, January 1, 1674, notice to the reader, argument, scenario, and name of the composer, Marc' Antonio **Cesti.** Originally by Gio. Andrea Moniglia, the libretto was "ritoccata [by Giulio Cesare Corradi] d'ariette, introduttione, intermedij, e qualche picciola scena, che smaltata con natural bizzarria dall' armonico stile del Sign. Marc' Antonio **Ziani,** le ridusse in figura del moderno universal compiacimento, e fece maggiormente spiccare il suo antico pretioso valore." First performed at Vienna, Hoftheater, 1667, according to Schatz. Von Weilen fails to record such a performance. Schatz 1782

La **schiava fortunata.** Commedia per musica da rappresentarsi nel Teatro Nuovo sopra Toledo per quart' opera nel corrente carnovale 1796.

Napoli, n. publ., 1796. 48 p. 15ᶜᵐ.

Two acts. Author not mentioned, and unknown to Schatz. Cast and name of the composer, Valentino **Fioravanti.** First performed at Rome, Teatro Capranica, 1791. Schatz 3130

La **schiava liberata.** Dramma serio-comico per musica da rappresentarsi nel Real Teatro dell' Ajuda in occasione di festeggiarsi il felicissimo giorno natalizio di Sua Reale Maestà . . . D. Marianna Vittoria . . . nella primavera dell' anno 1770.

Lisbona, Stamperia reale, n. d. 98 p. 15½ᶜᵐ.

Three acts. Scenario, cast, and names of Gaetano Martinelli as author, of Niccolò **Jommelli** as composer. First performed, as indicated, March 31, 1770; at Ludwigsburg, Hoftheater, December 18, 1768. Schatz 4898

La **schiava liberata.** Dramma serio comico per musica del Sigr. Gaetano Martinelli da rappresentarsi nel Piccolo Teatro di S. A. E. di Sassonia.

Dresda, l'anno 1777, n. publ. 135 p. 16ᶜᵐ.

Three acts. Joseph **Schuster** is mentioned as the composer. German title-page, "Die befreyte sklavinn," and text face Italian. First performed October 2, 1777, as indicated. Schatz 9754

— Die **befreyte sklavin.** Ein singspiel nach dem italienischen des herrn Cajetan Martinelli. In drey aufzuegen. Die musik ist vom herrn Joseph Schuster . . .

p. 1–72. 17ᶜᵐ. (Joh. Christ. Kaffka, Sammlung auslaendischer theaterstuecke, in die deutsche buehne, bearbeitet, Breslau, Wilhelm Gottlieb Korn, 1784.)

Detached copy. First performed at Breslau, Wäser'sches Theater, 1784. Schatz 9755

La schiava per amore. Comedia per musica di Tomaso Mariani Romano. Da rappresentarsi nella Sala Latina al vicolo de Leutari nel carnevale del presente anno 1746.

Roma, Giovanni Zempel, 1746. 60 p. 16½^{cm}.

Three acts. Argument and name of Francesco Maria **Paci** as the composer.

SCHATZ 7379

La schiava riconosciuta. L. T. of Piccinni's Gli stravaganti.

La schiava riconosciuta. Dramma giocoso per musica da rappresentarsi nel Teatro Grimani di S. Samuele il carnovale dell' anno 1766 . . .

Venezia, Modesto Fenzo, 1766. 48 p. 17^{cm}.

Three acts. Impresario's dedication, cast, scenario, and names of Giuseppe **Scolari** as composer ("La musica è nuova"), and of Alcindo Isaurense, P. A. as author, whose real name is not mentioned by either Wotquenne or Schatz. SCHATZ 9805

Gli schiavi per amore. A. T. and L. T. of Paisiello's Le gare generose.

La schiavitù fortunata. Drama per musica da rappresentarsi nel Teatro di S. Angelo. L'anno 1694 . . .

Venetia, Nicolini, 1694. 64 p. 14^{cm}.

Three acts. Dedication by the author, Fulgenzio Mattia Gualazzi, who is not mentioned by name, argument, scenario, and notice to the reader, which reads, in part:

"Il primo drama fù cõposto per questo medesimo teatro, poi accomodato per necessità à quello di Padova. Il presente, come usci dalla penna, cosi vien dato alla luce."

The composer, Carlo Francesco **Pollaroli**, is not mentioned. SCHATZ 8317

Lo schiavo del proprio onore. A. T. of the ballet Il moro di corpo bianco.

Lo schiavo reggio. A. T. of Cesti's La Dori.

Der schiffbruch, ein maehrchen in vier akten von dem verfasser von Fremore und Melime, die musik von Franz Hugo, freiherrn von Kerpen.

Frankfurt am Mayn, mit Andreaeischen schriften, 1778. 93 p. 16^{cm}.

By Graf H. von Spaur.

First performed at Mayence, Schauspielhaus a. d. gr. Bleiche, January, 1778.

SCHATZ 5142

Der schiffer. A. T. of Philidor's Melide.

Gesaenge aus dem singspiele: **Der schiffspatron** oder **Der Gutscherr,** in zwey aufzuegen. In musik gesezt von Dittersdorf.

Hamburg, Freystatzky und Rabe, 1794.

Schatz attributes this version to Jünger. Comparison with the next entry proves that it is practically the original version as condemned by "C."

First performed at Hamburg, Theater beim Gänsemarkt, April 28, 1794; at Vienna, Theater auf der Wieden, 1790. SCHATZ 2608

— **Der schiffspatron** oder Der neue gutsherr. Eine komische oper in zween aufzügen. Neubearbeitet. Die musik ist von herrn Ditters von Dittersdorf.

Leipzig, Wilhelm Heinsius der jungere, 1793. 118, [1] p. 16^{cm}.

Der **schiffspatron**—Continued.

On p. [103]–118, signed "Ostermesse, 1793. C.," the editor's reasons for subjecting the original text to such a thorough revision. To prove "die geschmacklosigkeit des alten textes," he then quotes several scenes of the original version. For instance, the opera began, "*Amtmann:* Doch unmasgeblich meynt das Oberamt" instead of, as in his version, "*Der Schöffer.* Hiermit wird männiglich heut publicirt," and instead of the aria,

"O Eifersucht! O Eifersucht
Mein Herz willst Du zerstören!"

he has:

"O Eifersucht! O Eifersucht!
Du Qual verliebter Herzen."

In general, he says: "habe ich dem ganzen mehr haltung zu geben, und die scenen überhaupt besser zu verbinden gesucht."

Schatz attributes the original version to Johann Friedrich Jünger, and mentions a later version, "neubearbeitet," by Vulpius. SCHATZ 2607

Gesaenge aus der oper: Der schlaftrunk. In zwei aufzuegen von C. F. Bretzner. Die musik ist von G. B. Bierey.

Breslau, Grass und Barth, n. d. 36 p. 16½ᶜᵐ.

First performed at Dresden, Theater vor dem schwarzen Thore, August 4, 1797.

SCHATZ 1028

Der schlaftrunk. Ein komisches singspiel in 2 aufzuegen. Von C. F. Bretzner. In musik gesetzt von G. E. G. Kallenbach.

Altona, gebrueder Meyn, n. d. Unpaged. 16ᶜᵐ.

Printed before 1800?
Schatz records no performance. SCHATZ 5001

Das schlangenfest in Sangora. Eine heroisch komische oper in zwey aufzuegen, von Karl Friedrich Hensler. Die musik ist von Wenzel Mueller, Kapellmeister.

Wien, Schmidt, 1797. 86 p. 16½ᶜᵐ.

"Aufgefuehrt auf der K. K. privil. Marinellischen schaubühne in Wien," December 15, 1796. SCHATZ 6959

Die schlaue wittwe oder Die beiden angefuehrten thoren. Tr. of Portugal's La vedova raggiratrice o siano I due sciocchi delusi.

Gesaenge aus dem singspiele: Der schleyer, in drey aufzuegen, von Vulpius. In musik gesetzt von dem herzogl. Sachsen-Weimarischen kapellmeister Wolf.

Hamburg, Johann Matthias Michaelsen, 1788. 22 p. 16½ᶜᵐ.

First performed at Hamburg, Theater beim Gänsemarkt, May 22, 1788.

SCHATZ 11084

— Der schleier.

n. i., n. d. 110 p. 14½ᶜᵐ. (Vulpius, Opern, 1. baendchen, Baireuth & Leipzig, 1790.)

Detached copy. Three acts. The composer, Ernst Wilhelm **Wolf**, is not mentioned. SCHATZ 11084a

Der schlosser. Tr. of Kohault's Le serrurier.

Gesaenge aus dem singspiele Der schlosser. In zwey aufzuegen. In musik gesetzt von herrn Piccini.

n. i., 1793. [8] p. 16½ᶜᵐ.

Not recorded by Schatz under Piccinni. SCHATZ 11756

Die **schnitter.** Tr. of Duni's Les moissonneurs.

Die **schnitter.** Eine komische oper in drey aufzuegen. Von P. F. I.
Rostock, Mueller, 1779. [8] p. 18cm.

By P. F. Ilgener. Perhaps a German version of Favart's play "Les moissonneurs,"
music by **Duni.**   Schatz 11462

Die **schoene Arsene.** Tr. of Monsigny's La belle Arsene.

Die **schoene Arsene.** *See* Seydelmann's Arsene.

Das **schoene fischermaedchen.** Tr. of Pietro Guglielmi's **La**
bella pescatrice.

Die **schoene marketenderinn.** Ein militaerisches original-singspiel in zwey aufzuegen fuer die Marinellische schaubuehne von Karl
Friedrich Hensler. Die musik von herrn Wenzel Mueller, kapellmeister.
Wien, Mathias Andreas Schmidt, 1795. 36 p. 16cm.

Cast.
First performed, as indicated, October 13, 1795.   Schatz 6961

— Die **schoene marketenderin.** Ein militairisches original-singspiel in zwey aufzuegen vom Karl Friedrich Hensler; die musik ist
vom herrn Wenzel Mueller, kapellmeister.
n. pl., n. publ., 1798. 32 p. 16cm.   Schatz 6961a

Die **schoene muellerin.** Tr. of Paisiello's L'amor contrastato.

Die **schoene schusterinn.** A. T. and also L. T. of Umlauf's Die
puecefarbnen schuhe.

Die **schöne und getreue Ariadne.** O. T. of Postel's text Die
betrogene und nachmals vergoetterte Ariadne.

Schoenheit und ehrbarkeit. A. T. of Martin y Soler's Etwas
seltsames.

Schoenheit und tugend. A. T. of Martin y Soler's Die seltenheit.

Schoenheit und tugend. A. T. of Martin y Soler's Die seltne
sache.

The **school for fathers** or Lionel and Clarissa. L. T. of Lionel and
Clarissa.

De **schoone Arsine.** Tr. of Monsigny's La belle Arsène.

Der **schorsteinsfeger Peter** oder Das spiel des ohngefaehrs. Tr. of
Portugal's Lo spazzacamino principe.

Die **schuhe à la Marlborough.** A. T. of Umlauf's Die schöne
schusterinn.

De **schulden.** Tr. of Champein's Les dettes.

Die **schule der ehemaenner.** Tr. of Isouard's L'aviso ai maritati.

Die schule der eifersucht. Tr. of Salieri's La scola de' gelosi.

Die schule der eifersuechtigen. Tr. of Salieri's La scola de gelosi.

Die schule der jugend. Tr. of Duni's L'école de la jeunesse.

Die schule der liebhaber. A. T. of Mozart's Eine (ist) (machts) wie die andere.

Die schulmeisterin. Tr. of Cocchi's La maestra di scuola.

Der schulze im dorfe, oder Der verliebte herr doctor. Eine comische oper in drey aufzuegen.
   Weimar, Karl Ludolf Hoffmann, 1779. 112 p. 15ᶜᵐ.
   Author unknown to Schatz. Composed by Christian Ludwig **Dieter**.
   First performed at Stuttgart, kl. Schauspielhaus, May 10, 1779.   Schatz 2580

Der schulze im dorfe, oder Der verliebte herr doctor. Eine comische oper in drey aufzuegen.   Die musik ist von herrn Lacher . . .
   n. i., 1789. 112 p. 16ᶜᵐ.
   Author and date of first performance unknown to Schatz.   Schatz 5363

Der schuss von Gaensewiz. A. T. of Zumsteeg's Der betrug aus liebe.

Gesaenge aus den [!] Schusterfeierabend. Eine [!] komisches singspiel in drey aufzuegen. Die musik dazu ist von herrn Wolaneck, musikdirektor zu Prag. **Aufgefuehrt von der Mihuleschen gesellschaft.** Augsburg 1794.
   n. i., n. d. 31 p. 16ᶜᵐ.
   Author not mentioned and unknown to Schatz.
   First performed at Prague, Vaterlaendisches Theater, December 31, 1793.
                                             Schatz 11073

Schwarz und weiss. Singspiel in zwei aufzuegen, nach Saintfoix.
   n. i., n. d. [57]–176 p. 15ᶜᵐ. (Carl Alexander Herklots, Operetten, Berlin, 1793.)
   Detached copy. No composer recorded by Schatz.   Schatz 11649

Die schwestern von Prag. Als singspiel in zwey aufzuegen, nach dem lustspiele des weyland herrn Hafner, für dieses theater neu bearbeitet von Joachim Perinet . . . Die musik ist vom herrn Wenzel Mueller . . .
   Wien, Mathias Andreas Schmidt, 1794. 100 p. 15ᶜᵐ.
   Cast and prefatory note which ends:
   "Dass die ausdrücke und die sprache im oesterreichischen dialekte sind, entschuldigt nur die bestimmung, dass es in und fuer Oesterreich geschrieben wurde."
   At end of the text: "Aufgefuehrt auf dem k. k. privil. Marinellischen Theater in der Leopoldstadt," March 11, 1794.   Schatz 6963

Lo scialacquatore. Intermezzi per musica a tre voci da rappresentarsi nel Pubblico Teatro di Lucca nel carnevale dell' anno MDCCLXIII. In occasione delle recite in prosa da farsi dall' Accademia de' dilettanti della Comica.
   Lucca, Francesco Antonio Berchielli, 1763. 22 p. 15 ᶜᵐ.
   Two parts. Author unknown to Schatz. (Text not that of Schatz 6521.) Cast and name of Lorenzo **Minuti** as composer.   Schatz 6521

Lo scialaquatore alla fiera. Dramma giocoso da rappresentarsi nel Teatro di S. Cassiano l'autunno dell' anno 1745 . . .

Venezia, Modesto Fenzo, 1745. 57 p. 15^{cm}.

Three acts. By Ambrosio Borghesi, who is not mentioned. Impresario's dedication, cast, and note:
"La musica del Sig. maestro [Giuseppe Maria] **Orlandini,** e d'altri."

SCHATZ 7347

La sciocchezza in amore. L. T. of Piccinni's Le contadine bizarre.

Lo sciocco poeta di campagna. L. T. of P. Guglielmi's Il poeta di campagna.

Scipio in Kartagena. Tr. of Sacchini's Scipione in Cartagena.

Scipione.

[187]–220 p. 17^{cm}. (Rolli, Componimenti poetici, Nuova edizione, Verona, G. Tumermani, 1744.)

Three acts. Argument. The composer, **Händel,** is not mentioned.
First performed at London, Haymarket, March 12, 1726.   ML 49.A2R7

Scipione. Dramma per musica da rappresentarsi nel nuovissimo e nobilissimo Teatro dell' eccellentissima casa Balbi in Mestre l'autunno dell' anno 1778 . . .

Venezia, Modesto Fenzo, 1778. 56 p. 17^{cm}.

Three acts. Eugenio Giunti's "Scipione in Cartagena" (not mentioned) with alterations. Dedication, argument, cast, scenario, and name of Giuseppe **Sarti** as the composer. ("La musica è tutta nuova.") On p. [23]–32 dedication, argument, cast, name of Luigi Boccherini as composer of the music, and description of Onorato Viganò's "Cefalo e Procri, ballo eroico-tragico pantomimo."   SCHATZ 9474

Scipione Affricano. *See* M. Curzio.

Scipione Affricano. Dramma per musica recitato nel Teatro novo di Roma, in Tordinona l'anno 1671 . . .

Roma, per i success. al Mascardi, 1671. 6 p. l., 82, [1] p. 14^{cm}.

Prologue and three acts with two intermezzi ("GROTTE DI VULCANO" and "LA BELLEZZA SOPRA D'UN CARRO"). The author, conte Niccolò Minato, is not mentioned, whose text was very much altered. Argument, notice to the reader, scenario, and dedication by the book-dealer, Bartolomeo Lupardi, dated January 1, 1671. Schatz attributes the music to Alessandro **Scarlatti,** but, if he was born in 1658 or 1659, Schatz presumably was mistaken. Dent does not mention this opera.

SCHATZ 9537

Scipione Africano drama per musica nel Teatro à SS. Gio. e Paolo l'anno 1664 . . .

Venetia, Steffano Curti e Franc. Nicolini, 1664. 5 p. l., 74, [1] p. 14^{cm}.

Three acts. By Co. Niccolò Minato. Author's dedication dated Venice, February 9, 1664, argument, and scenario. Notice to the reader with name of Pietro Francesco **Cavalli** as composer.   SCHATZ 1741

— Scipione Africano. Drama per musica nel famoso Teatro Grimano à SS. Gio. e Paolo l'anno MDCLXXVIII . . .

Venetia, Francesco Nicolini, 1678. 72 p. 14^{cm}.

Three acts, altered by Tebaldo Fattorini. Editor's dedication, argument, scenario, and notice to the reader, in which we are informed that to adapt **Cavalli's** opera "maggiormente al genio corrente è stato necessario di ridurlo à qualche brevità, ed accrescerlo nelle canzoni." The composition of these alterations was entrusted to Bonaventura **Viviani.** For purposes of identification it may be noted that this 1678 ed. contains 20, 21, and 24 scenes instead of 20, 20, and 20.   SCHATZ 1754

Scipione il giovane. Dramma per musica da rappresentarsi nel famosissimo Teatro Grimani di S. Giõ. Grisostomo nell' autunno dell' anno 1731 . . .

Venezia, Carlo Buonarigo, n. d. 1 p. l., 60 p. 15ᶜᵐ.

Three acts. By Giovanni Francesco Bortolotti, who is not mentioned. Author's dedication, argument, scenario, cast, name of Luca Antonio **Predieri** as the composer, and notice to the reader which reads:

"Per l'ordinaria necessità di accomodarsi alla voce, ed al genio de virtuosi cantanti, essendosi dovute mutare alcune dell' arie del presente dramma, ne potendolo par l'autore per le sue gravi occupazioni, è convenuto ad altra penna impiegarsi per sodisfarli."

These arias or parts of arias are designated by asterisks, as for instance: "L'ardente mia fiamma" (III, 1) or "Ingrata mi sprezzi" (II, 5). SCHATZ 8458

Scipione in Cartagena. O. T. of Eugenio Giunti's text Scipione.

Scipione in Cartagena, dramma per musica da rappresentarsi nel Nuovo Teatro di Corte . . . nel carnevale dell' anno MDCCLXX. La poesia è del Signor Eugenio Giunti . . . La musica è del Sig. Antonio Sacchini.

Monaco, Maria Maddalena Mayrin, n. d. 125 p. 19ᶜᵐ.

Three acts. Argument, scenario, and cast. German title-page, "Scipio in Kartagena," and text face Italian. With the opera were performed the ballets, "L'alliance de Romulus et de Tatius—Der fried zwischen Romulo und Tatzio," and "Les amans réunis—Die wieder vereinigten freier."

First performed, as indicated, January 8, 1770—not at Padua, where the opera was not performed until June, 1770. SCHATZ 9240

Scipione in Cartagine nuova, dramma per musica da rappresentarsi nel nuovo Ducal Teatro di Piacenza, in occasione, che si riapre la fiera la primavera dell' anno 1730 . . . Poesia di Carlo Innocenzio Frugoni . . .

Parma, Stamperia di S. A. S., n. d. 8 p. l., 72 p. 17ᶜᵐ.

Three acts. Dedication and Frugoni's dedicatory sonnet, argument, cast, scenario and name of Geminiano **Giacomelli** as the composer.

First performed at Parma in 1728. SCHATZ 3808

Scipione nelle Spagne.

Apostolo Zeno, Poesie drammatiche, Venezia, 1744, t. iv, p. [93]–189. 19ᶜᵐ.

Three acts and licenza. Argument. No composer is mentioned. In the "Catalogo" at the end of t. x, date and place of first ed. are given as "in Barcellona. 1710. E in Vienna. 1722." According to Schatz both times *Caldara's* score was used.

ML 49.A2Z3

— Scipione nelle Spagne. Pubblicato per la prima volta in Barcelona 1710.

Apostolo Zeno, Poesie drammatiche, Orleans, 1785–86, t. iv, p. 94. 21ᶜᵐ.

Three acts and licenza. Argument. No composer is mentioned. ML 49.A2Z4

Scipione nelle Spagne. Dramma per musica, da rappresentarsi nel Teatro Grimani di S. Samuele nell fiera dell' Ascensione. L'anno 1724.

Venezia, Marino Rossetti, 1724. 57 p. 14½ᶜᵐ.

Three acts. Argument, cast, scenario, name of Tommaso **Albinoni** as composer, and notice to the reader, in which this is called an altered and reduced version of Zeno's text as first performed at Vienna in 1722. SCHATZ 125

Scipione nelle Spagne. Dramma per musica da rappresentarsi nel Teatro di S. Angelo l'autunno dell' anno 1746.

Venezia, Modesto Fenzo, 1746. 34 p. 15^{cm}.

Three acts. The author is not mentioned. Argument, scenario, cast (also for the "Intermezzi"), and name of **Galuppi** as composer. The intermezzi, "La donna giudice e parte," were composed by Giovanni **Cingoni.** The composer of the other "Il conte Nespola" unknown to Piovano. The original title of conte Agostino Piovene's libretto (music by C. F. Pollaroli, Venice, 1712) was "Publio Cornelio Scipione."

First performed, as indicated, in November, 1746 (Pavan).   SCHATZ 3493

Gli Sciti, ballet. *See* Arioli's Cinna.

Gli Sciti. Nuovo dramma da rappresentarsi in musica nel Teatro grande alla Scala di Milano il carnevale del 1799. Correndo l'anno VII. repubblicano.

Milano, Gio. Batista Bianchi, n. d. 48 p. 15$\frac{1}{2}$^{cm}.

Two acts. By Gaetano Rossi, who is not mentioned. Cast, scenario, and name of Giuseppe **Nicolini** as the composer.

With the opera were performed Urbano Garzia's "ballo eroi-tragico Gonzalvo in America" and "ballo comico I matrimonj per inganno." The composers of the music are not mentioned.   SCHATZ 7133

Gli Sciti, ballet. *See* Paisiello's Ipermestra.

Der sclavenhaendler, ein singspiel in zwei aufzuegen. In musik gesezt von Peter Ritter.

Mannheim, C. F. Schwan und G. C. Goetz, 1790. 92 p. 18^{cm}.

Prefatory note, dated Mannheim, January 20, 1790, by the author, Christian Friedrich Schwan, who says that about twenty years previously he translated from the French the popular comedy, "Der kaufmann von Smyrna." This he subsequently turned into a one-act singspiel, produced successfully with Vogler's music at Mannheim, but it could not be continued, because Vogler went to Italy with the only score. In the meantime Carl David Stegmann (1773) published the vocal score of his own setting of the text, and in 1775 Andreas Holly his. Schwan continues:

"Dadurch wurde nun dieses kleine singspiel allgemeiner gemacht, und verschiedene Jahre lang auf mehreren buehnen gegeben, bis es endlich auch wie andere seines gleichen, nach und nach in vergessenheit gerieth.

"Ich lasse es nun auf veranlassung eines unserer hiesigen schon ruehmlich bekanten tonkuenstlers, zum dritten male in einer sehr veraenderten gestalt, und in einem etwas laengerem gewande, unter dem titel, Der *sclavenhaendler,* auf der buehne erscheinen."

First performed at Mannheim, Nationaltheater, April 11, 1790.   SCHATZ 8830

Die sclavin und der grossmuethige seefahrer. Tr. of Piccinni's Gli stravaganti.

La scola de' gelosi. Dramma giocoso per musica da rappresentarsi nel Teatro Giustiniani in S. Moisè il carnovale dell' anno 1779.

n. i., n. d. 72 p. 18^{cm}.

Two acts. By Caterino Mazzolà, who is not mentioned. Antonio **Salieri** is mentioned as the composer.   SCHATZ 9314

— La **scola de gelosi.** Opera in musica da rappresentarsi nel Piccolo Theatro di S. A. S. di Brunsvic Luneburg.

Brunsvic, n. publ., 1782. 159 p. 17^{cm}.

Two acts. Without name of Caterino Mazzolà, the author, but with name of Antonio **Salieri,** the composer. German title-page, "Die schule der eifersuechtigen," and text face Italian, which is practically the same as in the original edition.

First performed 1782, as indicated.   SCHATZ 9315

La scola de' gelosi—Continued.

— Die **schule der eifersucht,** oder Liebe hasst allen zwang. Ein singspiel, in zwei aufzuegen; von herrn Pr. Zehnmark.

Koeln am Rheine, Johan Godschalk Langen, 1787. 75, [4] p. 16ᶜᵐ.

At end, 3 unnumb. p. of "Nachricht," with a list of Langen's theatrical publications. The composer, Antonio **Salieri,** is not mentioned.

First performed at Vienna, Kärthnerthortheater, November 19, 1784.

SCHATZ 9316

— Gesaenge aus Der **schule der eifersuechtigen,** ein singspiel in vier aufzuegen, nach Mazzola, von C. F. Bretzner. In musick gesetzt von Salieri.

Hamburg, J. M. Michaelsen, 1787. 32 p. 18ᶜᵐ.

First performed at Hamburg, Theater b. Gänsemarkt, November 23, 1785.

SCHATZ 9317

— **A escola dos ciosos.** Drama giocoso em hum só acto, traduzido livremente do idioma italiano em versos portuguezes para se representar em musica no Real Teatro de S. Carlos, offerecido ao publico por Francisco Marquesi no dia do seu beneficio: A musica he do celebre mestre de capella o Senior Salieri.

Lisboa, Simão Thaddeo Ferreira, 1795. 66 p. 15ᶜᵐ.

Cast.

First performed 1795, as indicated.

SCHATZ 9318

La scola di musica. A. T. of Bernardini's Le tre orfanelle.

La scolara alla moda. L. T. of Pergolesi's Il maestro di musica; also A. T. of Latilla and Pergolesi's Orazio, which is a very much altered and expanded version of "Il maestro di musica."

La scolara fatta maestra. Intermezzi per musica da rappresentarsi nel Real Teatro di Potsdam, per ordine di Sua Maestà.

Potsdam, C. F. Voss, 1749. 53 p. 16½ᶜᵐ.

Three parts. Cast. The author is unknown to Schatz. German title-page, "Die zur meisterin gewordene schuelerin," and text face Italian. The composer, Giovanni **Cingoni,** is not mentioned. The two last parts of the text are clearly based on the intermezzo, "La donna giudice e parte." The first part may also have been taken from some intermezzo, or may have been written for the occasion. SCHATZ 2010

La sconfitta delle Amazoni, ballet. *See* Salieri's La fiera di Venezia.

La scoperta d'un isola nell' America del capitano Durson Inglese, ballet. *See* Crippa's Le confusioni per somiglianza.

Lo scroccatore smascherato. A. T. of di Palma's Chi mal fa mal aspetti.

Lo scoprimento inaspettato. Dramma giocoso per musica da rappresentarsi nel Teatro Nuovo nel carnevale del corrente anno 1787.

Napoli, n. publ., 1787. 58 p. 15ᶜᵐ.

Three acts. By Vicenzo di Stefano, who is not mentioned. Cast and name of Pietro **Guglielmi** as the composer. SCHATZ 4265

La scuffiaja. A. T. of Paisiello's La modista.

La **scuffiara.**   *See* Tritto's Li due gemelli.

Lo **scultore.**   Intermezzi a tre voci da rappresentarsi in Firenze **nel** Teatro di via del Cocomero nell' autunno dell' anno 1761.

   Firenze, Anton Giuseppe Pagani, 1761.   24 p.   15ᶜᵐ.

   Two parts.   Cast.   Neither author nor composer known to Schatz.

ML 48.A5   v. 16

La **scuola degli amanti.**   A. T. of Mozart's Cosi fan tutte.

La **scuola degli amanti.**   Commedia per musica da rappresentarsi nel Teatro Nuovo sopra Toledo per quart' opera di quest' anno 1783.

   Napoli, n. publ., 1783.   60 p.   15ᶜᵐ.

   Three acts.   By Giuseppe Palomba, who is not mentioned.   Cast and name of Giacomo **Tritto** as composer.

SCHATZ 10478

La **scuola de' gelosi.**   Dramma giocoso per musica nella prossima primavera dell' anno 1780.   Nel Teatro Filarmonico di Verona . . .

   Verona, Dionigio Ramanzini, n. d.   72, 6, [1] p.   17½ᶜᵐ.

   Two acts.   Impresario's dedication, cast, names of Catterino Mazzolà as author, of Antonio **Salieri** as composer.   The 6 p. contain libretto of Gaspero Angiolini's "Alessandro trionfante nell' Indie, ballo eroico pantomimo," composer of the music not mentioned.

ML 50.2.S46S2

La **scvola di magia,** balletto alle Dame.   Amore riconscendo le Dame si volubili e legiere viene ne la scuola di magia da Zoroastro Mago, acciò trasformi con incanti, inusitati oggetti per appagar il loro inconstante desio.

   n. i., n. d.   folio broadside.

ML 52.2.S39

La **scuola di scultura,** ballet.   *See* Cimarosa's I due supporti conti.

La **scuola moderna.**   Dramma di tre atti per musica rappresentato per la prima volta in Venezia l'autunno dell' anno MDCCXLVIII.

   Carlo Goldoni, Opere teatrali, Venezia, Zatta e figli, 1788–95, v. 42, [207]–261 p.   18ᶜᵐ.

   But see Cocchi's La maestra, text by Ant. Palomba.

PQ

La **scuola moderna** osia La maestra di buon gusto.   L. T. of Cocchi's La maestra.

La **scuola olandese** ossia L'amante in statua, ballet.   *See* Portugal's La donna di genio volubile.

Scylla, tragedie representée par l'Academie royale de musique l'an 1701.   Les paroles de M. Duché & La musique de M. Theobal. LIII. opera.

   n. i., n. d.   front., p. 215–276 (Recueil général des opéra, t. vii, Paris, 1703).   14½ᶜᵐ.

   Detached copy.   Five acts and prologue.   Composed by Teobaldo di **Gatti,** called as above.

   First performed, as indicated, September 16, 1701.

SCHATZ 3633
Second copy.   ML 48.R4

Gli **sdegni amorosi.**   A. T. and L. T. of Goldoni's text Il gondoliere.

Li sdegni cangiati in amore: Dramma da rappresentarsi nel Teatro Giustiniano di S. Moisè. Il carnevale dell' anno MDCCXXV . . .

Venezia, Marino Rossetti, n. d.   47 p.   15½ᶜᵐ.

Three acts. By Francesco Silvani (not mentioned), but completely altered according to this notice to the reader:

"S'è convenuto per accomodarsi al numero degli attori ridurre il drama à sei, mentre il suo autore l'haveva composto in sette ed altresì per maggior brevità levarle moltissimi versi, che s'havrebbero interlineati, ma per comodo de chi legge lasciati senza stamparli. Tutte l'arie sono state mutate, alla risserva di alcune . . ."

Schatz attributes these changes of Silvani's "Il duello d'amore e di vendetta" to the composer, Giuseppe Maria **Buini,** who is not mentioned. Impresario's dedication, argument, cast, scenario. Schatz 1394

I sdegni per amore. Commedia per musica di un' atto di Giuseppe Mililotti da rappresentarsi nel Teatro Nuovo nel carnevale di quest' anno 1776.

Napoli, n. publ., 1776.   52 p.   15ᶜᵐ.

Cast and name of the composer, **Cimarosa.** On p. [3] the notice:

"Questa commedia, che ora comparisce di un solo atto, doveva farsi in due, ma per vari accidenti, e sopratutto per la mancanza del tempo si è dovuta ridurre in un atto solo."

Pages [29]-51 contain the libretto with cast of **Cimarosa's**

"I MATRIMONI IN BALLO. Farsetta per musica di Pasquale Mililotti. Da rappresentarsi nel Teatro Nuovo nel carnevale di quest' anno 1776" Schatz 1993

La secchia rapita. Dramma eroi-comico per musica composto da Niccolò Liprandi da rappresentarsi nel nobilissimo Teatro di San Samuele il carnovale dell' anno 1794.

Venezia, Modesto Fenzo, 1794.   64 p.   17½ᶜᵐ.

Two acts. Author's dedication, cast, scenario, and name of Francesco **Bianchi** as composer. In the dedication Angelo Anelli (pseud. Liprandi) says of the text, written for Milan, fall of 1793:

"ho dovuto rifarlo presso che tutto di novo, non conservando, che alcune cose, cioè l'introduzione, e i finali di quello esposto in Milano: anzi nè stessi finali ho dovuto aggiungere, e togliere alcune cose in maniera, che men fatica mi sarebbe stata il comporli di novo." Schatz 982

La secchia rapita. Dramma eroi-comico di Gio. Gastone Boccherini, poeta Arcade, da rappresentarsi ne' Teatri privilegiati di Vienna l'anno 1772.

[Vienna], Giuseppe Kurtzboeck, n. d.   77 p.   16ᶜᵐ.

Three acts. Argument, cast, scenario, and name of Antonio **Salieri** as the composer ("La musica è tutta nuova").

First performed at Vienna, Burgtheater, October 21, 1772. Schatz 9319

— **La secchia rapita.** Dramma eroicomico di Gio. Gastone Boccherini poeta Arcade da rappresentarsi nel Piccolo Teatro di S. A. E. di Sassonia.

Dresda, n. publ., 1775.   135 p.   16ᶜᵐ.

Three acts. Antonio **Salieri** is mentioned as the composer. German title-page, "Der geraubte eymer," and text face Italian, which is slightly different from the original edition. For instance, the latter does not have the chorus, "Viva, viva: trombette e tamburi" (I, 6).

First performed January 3, 1775, as indicated. Schatz 9321

— **Der geraubte eymer,** eine heroisch-komische oper aufgefuehret am kurpfaelzischen hofe im jahre 1774.

Mannheim, Hof und Akademie buchdruckeri, n. d.   72, [5] p.   15ᶜᵐ

La **secchia rapita**—Continued. .

Three acts. Argument, scenario, and name of Antonio **Salieri** as the composer. This is a separate edition of the German translation of his "La secchia rapita," first performed at Mannheim, November 5, 1774, as indicated. At end descriptions of the ballets "Die von Amor beschuezten liebhaber" and "Das seefest oder Die unvermuthete zusammenkunft." SCHATZ 9320

La **secchia rapita**. Dramma giocoso per musica da rappresentarsi nel Teatro alla Scala l'autunno dell' anno 1793 . . .

Milano, Gio. Batista Bianchi, n. d. 68 p. 16½ᶜᵐ.

Two acts. By Angelo Anelli, who is not mentioned. Impresario's dedication, argument, cast, scenario, name of Nicola Antonio **Zingarelli** as the composer, and footnote that this text is an absolutely new treatment of the subject, and not to be confused with the former drama of the same title. With the opera was performed Giuseppe Banti's ballet, "Zima," the composer ot the music not being mentioned. ·
First performed, as indicated, September 7, 1793. SCHATZ 11258

— La **secchia rapita**. Dramma giocoso per musica da rappresentarsi nel Teatro Elettorale.

Dresda, n. publ., 1795. 15 p. l., 58 p. 15½ᶜᵐ.

The p. 1. contain detailed "Innhalt." German title page, "Der geraubte eimer," faces Italian. **Zingarelli** is mentioned as the composer.
First performed, as indicated, 1795. SCHATZ 11259

Second thought is best. An opera of two acts, performed at the Theatre Royal in Drury-Lane. Addressed to R. B. Sheridan, Esq. by J. Hough, of the Inner Temple, in which is introduced the song rejected by the Lord Chamberlain.

[London], Murray and Greenlaw, 1788 [!]. 43 p. 21½ᶜᵐ.

The date is a misprint for 1778.
Cast and dedication. The composer is not mentioned, and is unknown to Schatz.
First performed, as indicated, March 30, 1778. LONGE 270

The **secret enlarged.** *See* The agreeable surprise.

Il **secreto,** opera by Joh. Simon Mayr. *See* Cimarosa's Il duello per complimento, Venezia, (1797). SCHATZ 2002

Das **seefest** oder Die unvermuthete zusammenkunft; ballet. *See* Salieri's Der geraubte eymer.

Il **segreto,** ballet. *See* Nicolini's Il trionfo del bel sesso.

Il **seguito tra l'armi** o sia La donna militare, ballet. *See* Salari's L'amore rammingo.

Der **sehende Cupido.** Tr. F. of the ballet L'amour clairvoyant.

I **sei gigli.** *See* Manelli's La Filo.

Le **seigneur bienfaisant,** opéra, composé des actes du Retour du seigneur dans ses terres, du Pressoir, ou Des fêtes de l'automne, de L'incendie et du Bal, représenté pour la première fois par l'Académie-royal [!] de musique le lundi 23 décembre 1782.

Paris, P. de Lormel, 1782. viii, 58 p. 23ᶜᵐ.

Rochon de Chabannes is mentioned as author, Etienne Joseph **Floquet** as the composer. Cast and "avertissement," which begins:
"L'Académie royale de musique m'avoit engagé plusieur fois à faire un nouvel acte **au** *Seigneur Bienfaisant* pour tâcher de completter la durée du spectacle, & remédier

Le seigneur bienfaisant—Continued.

ainsi à l'embarras d'y joindre un acte étranger, d'autant plus difficile à trouver, qu'il falloit toujours qu'il fut sans ballet . . . Je ne dirai plus rien de cet acte, sinon qu'il m'a facilité les moyens d'amener naturellement un spectacle militaire & par conséquent un tableau différent de ceux des trois anciens derniers actes . . ."

The opera is based on incidents in the life of Henri IV.

The original three-act version was first performed at Paris, Palais Royal, December 14, 1780, and later at the Salle de la Porte Saint Martin, November 15, 1781.

SCHATZ 3249

Seila. Componimento dramatico d'Inalbo Laerzio P. A. Posto in musica dal Sig. Jacopo Scolart, maestro di capella in Cingoli e cantato in Cesena nella sera del di 7 settembre 1787.

Faenza, Lodovico Genestri, n. d. 29 p. 19½cm.

Two acts. Real name of the above unknown to Schatz, and this Arcadian name not entered by Wotquenne.

SCHATZ 9807

Seldano, duce degli Svedesi. Dramma per musica da rappresentarsi nel Teatro di San Benedetto l'autunno dell' anno 1797.

Venezia, Anno primo della Libertà italiana, Modesto Fenzo, n. d. 40 p. 18½cm.

Two acts. Author unknown to Schatz. Argument, cast, and name of the composer, Giuseppe **Farinelli**. On p. [21]–26, cast and description of the ballet, "I bacchanali, composto e diretto da Onorato Vigano . . . la musica tutta nuova è del maestro Giuseppe Nucci.

SCHATZ 3030

Il Seleuco. L. T. of C. F. Pollaroli's La pace fra Tolomeo e Seleuco.

Seleuco. Drama per musica nel Teatro à San Salvatore, per l'anno 1668 . . .

Venetia, Francesco Nicolini, 1668. 4 p. l., 78 p. 14cm.

Three acts. Dedication by the author, conte Niccolò Minato and dated Venice, January 16, 1668, argument, scenario, and notice to the reader:

"Questo drama comparve fin hora mascherato sotto simulazione di cittadino del cielo di Napoli; hora ch'egli è stato eletto à nuovamente servirti, no hò gusto, ch'egli rimanga con l'oscura nota d'occulti, e menzogneri natali. Egli è parto di quella stessa penna, che ti fece vedere il Xerse, L'Artemisia, L'Antioco, Lo Scipione, il Mutio, il Pompeo & ultimamente la Caduta, e la Prosperità di Seiano. L'autore nascose volontieri la di lui origine all' hora che doveva farlo comparire insieme col suo Pompeo, temendo, che, se fossero ambo stati conosciuti per figli d'una senna medesima, potesse egli restar ripreso di partialità con l'uno più, che con l'altro."

The composer, Antonio **Sartorio**, is not mentioned.

First performed at the same theatre, carnival, 1666, the dedication in the 1666 libretto being dated January 16, 1666. (*See* Wotquenne, who does not mention the author.)

SCHATZ 9487

Seleuco. Dramma per musica da rappresentarsi nel Teatro di S. Angiolo l'anno MDCCXXV . . .

Venezia, Marino Rossetti, n. d. 59 p., [1] l. 15½cm.

Three acts. Argument, cast, scenario, and dedication with Apostolo Zeno's name as author. His collaborator, Pietro Pariati, is not mentioned. The original title of their text was "Antioco." The composer Giovanni **Zuccari**, is not mentioned as composer.

SCHATZ 11286

Seleuco, rè di Siria. Dramma per musica da rappresentarsi nel nobilissimo Teatro Venier in San Benedetto il carnovale dell' anno 1792.

Venezia, Modesto Fenzo, 1791. 64 p. 18cm.

Three acts. Cast, scenario, and name of the composer, Francesco **Bianchi**, but not of the librettist, Mattia Botturini. On p. [19]–39 argument, cast, and full description

Seleuco, rè di Siria—Continued.

of "Alfredo il Grande, rè degli Anglo-Sassoni, ballo tragico pantomimo in cinque atti" by Paolino Franchi, music ("tutta nuova ed espressamente scritta") by Vittorio Trento. The second ballet, also by Franchi, composer not mentioned, was called "Solimano II."

First performed, as indicated, December 26, 1791.   SCHATZ 1000

The self-conquest of Alexander.   A. T. of Noverre's ballet Apelles and Campaspe.

Selim og Mirza.   Originalt skuespil med musik i tre acter af P. A. Heiberg.   Musiken af herr O. Zink.

*Kiøbenhavn, Christian Frederik Holm, 1790.   viii, 72 p.   17½*cm.

Cast and noteworthy "forerindring."

First performed at Copenhagen, Royal Theatre, February 1, 1790.   SCHATZ 11272

Selim und Zelide, oder Die macht der feen.   Eine romantisch-komische oper in zwey aufzeugen.   Unter der direktion der herrn Mihule und Butteau aufgefuehrt auf dem Kleinseitner Theater montags den 30 november 1789.

*Prag, Joseph Emanuel Diesbach, n. d.   Unpaged.   17½*cm.

Author and composer unknown to Schatz.   SCHATZ 11463

Selima & Azor, a Persian tale, in three parts: as performed at the Theatre-Royal in Drury-Lane . . .

*London, J. Bell, 1784.   4 p. l., 39 p.   21*cm.

By Sir G. Collier, who is not mentioned.   Cast, dedication dated West-Hill, January 12, 1784, and Advertisement dated January 13, 1784, in which the author says:

"The following little piece (which is an imitation of the French *Zemire & Azor*) [by Marmontel] was the production of some leisure hours, in a journey which the author made a few years ago . . ."

The success of the piece, during his absence from England, he says, was owing

"most particularly to the taste and judgment of Mr. Sheridan in several judicious alterations; and to the excellent music of Mr. **Linley** . . ."

As a matter of fact, Thomas Linley utilized Grétry's score to a considerable extent.

First performed at Drury-Lane, October 6, 1776 (Schatz); December 5, 1776 (Genest).   LONGE 95

Selin.   Gran signor de' Turchi.   Drama per musica da rappresentarsi nel Nuovo Teatro di S. Margherita il carnovale dell' anno 1730 . . .

*Venezia, Carlo Buonarrigo, 1730.   47 p.   14*cm.

Three acts.   Impresario's dedication, argument, scenario.   Author (Antonio Maria Lucchini) and composer not mentioned.   Schatz records this as a pasticcio.

SCHATZ 11361

Der **seltene fall.**   Tr. of Martin y Soler's Una cosa rara.

Die **seltenheit** oder Schoenheit und tugend.   Tr. of Martin y Soler's Una cosa rara.

Der **seltne fall.**   Tr. of Martin y Soler's Una cosa rara.

Die **seltne sache** oder Schoenheit und tugend.   Tr. of Martin y Soler's Una cosa rara.

La **selvaggia** ovvero Adelia e Roberto, ballet.   *See* Paër's L'intrigo amoroso.

Il **selvaggio eroe.** Tragicomedia eroico-pastorale da rappresentarsi in musica nel famosissimo Teatro Grimano di S. Gio. Grisostomo l'anno 1707.

Venezia, Marino Rossetti, n. d. 72 p. 14^{cm}.

Five acts. By conte Girolamo Frigimelica Roberti, who is not mentioned. Publisher's prefatory note, author's "Notizia poetica" (p. 4–9), argument, cast, scenario, and name of the composer, Antonio **Caldara.**   Schatz 1497

I **selvatici,** ballet. *See* Gius. Scarlatti's Pelopida.

Sémélé, tragedie représentée par l'Academie royale de musique l'an 1709. Les paroles de M. de la Mothe, & la musique de M. Marais. LXXII. opera.

n. i., n. d. front., p. 387–437, [3] (Recueil général des ópera, t. ix, Paris, 1710.) 14^{cm}.

Detached copy. Five acts and prologue.
First performed, as indicated, April 9, 1709. The three additional pages contain the "Privilège général."   Schatz 5921
Second copy. ML 48.R4

Semiramide.

Metastasio, Poesie, Parigi, vedova Quillau, 1755, t. v, [265]–357 p. 16^{cm}.

Three acts and lizenza. Argument. "Nella forma in cui sono stati ridotti dall' autore" (*See* note on p. 169 of v. vi.) Same as his "Semiramide riconosciuta," which *see* for characteristic differences between the original and the later version.
Same, t. vii, [119]–240 p. 16cm. "Come . . . nell' altre edizioni" (Note, VI, 169).   ML 49.A2M42

— **Semiramide.** Dramma scritto dall' autore in Roma, ed ivi rappresentato con musica del Vinci la prima volta, nel Teatro detto delle Dame, il carnevale dell' anno 1729.

pl., [3]–106 p. 26^{cm}. (Metastasio, Opere, t. vii, Parigi, vedova Herissant, 1780.)

Three acts and licenza. Argument.   ML 49.A2M44

Semiramide. Pubblicata per la prima volta in Vienna 1725.

Apostolo Zeno, Poesie drammatiche, Orleans, 1785–86, t. vi, p. 233– 310. 21^{cm}.

Five acts and licenza. Argument. No composer is mentioned. Same as "Semiramide in Ascalona."   ML 49.A2Z4

Semiramide. Dramma per musica del Signor abate Pietro Metastasio. Da rappresentarsi nel Teatro di Lucca nell' autunno dell' anno 1751.

Lucca, Filippo Maria Benedini, 1751. 92, [1] p. 16^{cm}.

Three acts. Argument, cast, scenario. Composer not mentioned and unknown to Schatz. The last p. contains the schedule of performances, which began on August 29, 1751.   Schatz 11362

Semiramide, ballet. *See* Anfossi's Antigono.

Semiramide. Dramma per musica da rappresentarsi nel Nuovo Teatro di Corte . . . in occasione del reale sposalizio della Sacra Real Majestà di Gioseppe . . . e dell' imperial prencipessa, Maria Gioseppa . . .

Monaco, Gioseppe Francesco Thuille, 1765. 135, [17] p. 15½^{cm}.

Semiramide—Continued.

Three acts. By Metastasio and *licenza* by Eugenio Giunti. Cast, argument, scenario, and names of composer, Andrea **Bernasconi**, and librettists. The *licenza* is followed by the description of the ballets invented by Du Buisson de Chalandray. German title-page, "Semiramis," and text face Italian.

First performed, as indicated, January 5, 1765.   Schatz 860

La Semiramide. Drama musicale.

G. A. Moniglia, Poesie drammatiche, seconde parte, Firenze, Cesare e Francesco Bindi, 1690, p. [440]–504. 24^{cm}.

Three acts. Scenario and argument with remark this drama:

"ebbe la sua nascita per servire alle nozze del serenissimo arciduca Sigismondo, ma per la morte dell' A. S. prima di celebrare i regij sponsali, fù tolto ancor' esso alla luce. Fù comandato all' autore di comporlo dal serenissimo principe Leopoldo di Toscana, ed' il Signor cavaliere [Marc'] Antonio **Cesti** [*d.* 1669] l'arricchì maraviglio- samente co'l metterlo in musica."   ML 49.A2M7

Semiramide. Dramma per musica da rappresentarsi nel Nuovo Teatro in Padova per la solito fiera di Giugno 1759 . . .

Padova, Conzatti, 1759. 64 p. 18^{cm}.

Three acts. By Metastasio. Dedication signed by Domenico Fischietti e Prospero Olivieri, argument, cast, scenario, and name of **Fischietti** as composer ("La musica tutta nuova").   Schatz 3243

Semiramide. Drama per musica da rappresentarsi nel Regio Teatro di Berlino per il felicissimo giorno natalizio della Sacra Real Maestà di Sofia Dorotea, regina madre . . .

Berlino, Haude e Spener, 1754. 135 p. 16½^{cm}.

Three acts. Giampietro Tagliazucchi is mentioned as the author and Carl Hein- rich **Graun** as the composer. Argument, and scenario. German title-page "Semi- ramis," and text face Italian.

First performed at Berlin, Kgl. Opern theater, March 27, 1754.   Schatz 4112

Semiramide. Dramma da rappresentarsi con musica del Signor Himmel . . . nel gran Teatro Reale di Berlino il carnovale dell' anno 1797 . . .

Berlino, Haude e Spener, n. d. 89 p. 16^{cm}.

Two acts. Author not mentioned and unknown to Schatz. German title page "Semiramis" and text face Italian. Argument and cast. On p. [78]–89 cast and description of "Raul Signore di Crechi osia La tiranide repressa. Ballo tragicomico in tre atti, composto dal Sign. Salvatore Viganò. La musica è del medesimo.—Raoul, herr von Crequi, oder Die verhinderte grausamkeit."

First performed, as indicated, February 18, 1797.   Schatz 4738

Semiramide. Dramma per musica da rappresentarsi nel famosis- simo Teatro Grimani di S^a Giõ. Grisostomo nel carnevale 1743 . . .

[Venezia], n. publ., n. d. 1 p. l., 48 p. 15^{cm}.

Three acts. By Francesco Silvani, who is not mentioned. Argument, cast, scenario, and name of Niccolò Jumelli (**Jommelli**) as composer. It should be noted that this text, attributed by Wiel to Silvani, is totally different from Metastasio's "Semiramide riconosciuta." Therefore, Jommelli's "Semiramide," Venice, 1743, should no longer be confused with his "Semiramide riconosciuta," first performed at Turin, December 26, 1741, as appears from the original libretto in possession of Manoel de Carvalhaes. (This settles definitely the questions left half-open by Abert on p. 46, 78 of his Jommelli biography.)   Schatz 4880

Semiramide. Dramma per musica da rappresentarsi nel Teatro Ducale di Stutgard festeggiandosi il felicissimo giorno natalizio di Sua Altezza Serenissima Carlo, duca regnante di Wirtemberg e Teck,

Semiramide—Continued.

etc. . . . La poesia è del Signor abbate Pietro Metastasio . . . La musica è nuovamente composta dal Signor Nicolò Jommelli . . . I balli sono inventati dal Signor Giovanni Giorgio Noverre . . .

[Stutgard], Cotta, 1762. *170, [5] p.* *18ᶜᵐ.*

Three acts. Argument, cast, scenario. German title page, "Semiramis," and text face Italian. On p. [66]–73, cast and description of "Amore e Psiche, ballo eroico—Amor und Psyche . . ." On p. [122]–131 of the ballet, "La morte d'Ercole— Der tod des Hercules." The 5 add. p. contain brief explanation and cast of "Le feste persiane—Das persianische freuden-fest." The composers of the music are not mentioned, but Abert mentions as composer of the first two Rudolph.

Schatz calls this opera Jommelli's second setting of "Semiramide," first performed (*see* Schatz 4880) as "Semiramide riconosciuta" at Turin, December 26, 1741; at Stuttgart, as indicated, February 11, 1762.   SCHATZ 4870

— **Semiramide.** Dramma per musica da rappresentarsi nel Real Teatro di Salvaterra nel carnovale dell' anno 1771.

Lisbona, Stamperia reale, n. d. *72 p.* *16ᶜᵐ.*

Three acts. Argument, cast, scenario, and names of Metastasio as author, of Niccolò Jommelli as composer. The text is slightly different from that of 1762. For instance, the aria, "Come all' amiche arene" has been dropped at end of I, 8.

First performed, as indicated, January 25, 1771.   SCHATZ 4892

La Semiramide, ballet. *See* Jommelli's Armida abbandonata.

Semiramide. Dramma per musica da rappresentarsi nel Teatro alla Scala il carnevale dell' anno 1785 . . .

Milano, Gio. Batista Bianchi, n. d. *67, [1] p.* *16ᶜᵐ.*

Three acts. Author not mentioned, and unknown to Schatz. Dedication, argument, cast, scenario, and name of Michele **Mortellari** as the composer. With the opera were performed Sebastiano Gallet's ballets, "Il ratto delle Sabine," "Il maniscalco francese," and a third without characteristic title. The composers of the music are not mentioned.

First performed, as indicated, December 26, 1784.   SCHATZ 6692

Semiramide. Dramma per musica. Da rappresentarsi nel famoso Teatro Grimani di S. Gio. Grisostomo. Il carnovale dell' anno 1714 . . .

Venezia, Marino Rossetti, 1714. *58 p.* *14½ᶜᵐ.*

Three acts. Dedication by the author, Francesco Silvani, who is not mentioned by name, argument, cast, scenario, and name of Carlo Francesco **Pollaroli** as the composer. First performed, as indicated, December 26, 1713.   SCHATZ 8318

Semiramide. Dramma per musica da rappresentarsi nel Teatro Nuovo di corte per comando di S. A. S. E. Carl Teodoro conte Palatino del' Reno, duca dell' Alta è Bassa Baviera . . . nel carnovale MDCCLXXXII.

[Munich], n. publ., n. d. *157 p.* *15ᶜᵐ.*

Three acts. Metastasio is mentioned as author, Lorenz Hübner as translator and **Salieri** as composer. Argument, cast. German t.-p. "Semiramis" and text face Italian.

First performed in January, 1782, as indicated.   ML 50.2.S48S2

Semiramide. Dramma per musica, da rappresentarsi sul Regio Teatro Danese, l'autunno dell' anno 1762.—Semiramis . . .

Kiøbenhavn, Lars Nielsen Svare, n. d. *127 p.* *15½ᶜᵐ.*

Three acts. Argument, cast, and names of Metastasio as author, of Giuseppe **Sarti** as the composer ("La musica è tutta nuova").   SCHATZ 9463

Semiramide—Continued.

— Semiramide.   Dramma per musica da rappresentarsi nel Teatro Vendramino di S. Salvatore la fiera dell' Ascensione dell' anno 1768.

Venezia, Modesto Fenzo, 1768.   46 p.   15ᶜᵐ.

Three acts.   By Metastasio, who is not mentioned.   Argument, cast, scenario, and name of Giuseppe **Sarti** as the composer.   The text is noticeably different from the original text of 1762.   The first act, for instance, had only ten scenes instead of thirteen, the tenth being "Come? qual foggia è questa," which was not in the 1762 version.

SCHATZ 9476

Semiramide.   Dramma per musica del Signor abate Pietro Metastasio, Poeta Cesaro da rappresentarsi nel Teatro Tron di S. Cassano il carnovale dell' anno 1765 . . .

Venezia, Modesto Fenzo, 1765.   64 p.   17½ᶜᵐ.

Three acts.   Impresario's dedication, argument, cast, scenario, and name of Tommaso **Trajetta** as composer.   SCHATZ 10413

La Semiramide.   Drama per musica nel famoso Teatro Grimano à S. Gio. e Paolo.   Per l'anno MDCLXXI . . .

Venetia, Nicolini, 1671.   front., 72 p.   15ᶜᵐ.

Three acts.   Publisher's dedication, dated Venice, December 11, 1670, argument, scenario, and notice to the reader, informing him that the text is by Gio. Andrea Moniglia, with alterations "per aggiustar all' uso di Venetia il presente drama."   The alterations were by Matteo Noris (Schatz).   Neither he nor the composer, Pietro Andrea **Ziani**, is mentioned.   SCHATZ 11223

Semiramide in Ascalona.

Apostolo Zeno, Poesie drammatiche, Venezia, 1744, t. ii, p. [365]–443, [1] p.   19ᶜᵐ.

Five acts and licenza.   Argument.   No composer is mentioned.   In the "Catalogo" at end of t. x, date and place of first ed. are given as Vienna, 1725.   Same as his "Semiramide."   First performed August 28, music by **Caldara.**

ML 49.A2Z3

Semiramide in bernesco.   Same as Jommelli's Il cacciatore deluso.

La Semiramide in India.   Dramma del conte Maiolino Bisaccioni . . .

Venetia, Francesco Miloco, 1648.   89 p.   15ᶜᵐ.

Three acts, with prologue.   Author's dedication, dated Venice, January 4, 1649, notice to the reader, and argument.   Francesco Paolo **Sacrati,** the composer, is not mentioned.   SCHATZ 9254

La Semiramide riconosciuta.

[71]–148 p.   19ᶜᵐ.   (Pietro Metastasio, Opere drammatiche, Venezia, Giuseppe Bettinelli, 1733–37, v. 2.)

Three acts.   Argument.   No composer mentioned.   Same as his "Semiramide."
This is one of the texts which Metastasio later on partly rewrote.   Here are a few telling differences: The original version has in I, 6 the aria "Maggior follia non v'è," which the later version dropped.   In I, 8 of the original version the scene begins with "Amico, in rivederti" and has the aria "Come all' amiche arene"; in the later version the scene begins "Come! e tu non ravoisi" and has no aria.   In the original version I, 10 begins "Signor, brama Scitalce" and has no aria, in the later version it begins "Signor, quali predici" and has the aria "Se intende si poco" which occurs in the original version in I, 11.   ML 49.A2M4

Semiramide riconosciuta. Dramma per musica da rappresentarsi nel Teatro novissimo di San Benedetto nel carnevale dell' anno
MDCCLVI.

Venezia, Angiolo Geremia, n. d. 70 p. 15½ cm.

Three acts. By Metastasio. Argument, scenario, and cast, but without name of
the composer, Francesco **Brusa.** SCHATZ 1377

Semiramide riconosciuta. Dramma per musica da rappresentarsi nel Teatro Tron di San Cassiano. Il carnovale dell' anno
1753 . . .

Venezia, Modesto Fenzo, 1753. 64 p. 14½ cm.

Three acts. By Metastasio. Dedication, argument, cast, and name of the composer, Gioacchino **Cocchi.** SCHATZ 2045

La **Semiramide riconosciuta,** dramma per musica da rappresentarsi nel Regio-Ducal Teatro di Milano, nel carnovale dell' anno
1749 . . .

Milano, Giuseppe Richino Malatesta, 1749. 6 p. l., 55 p. 14 cm.

Three acts. By Metastasio, who is not mentioned. Impresario's dedication, dated
Milan, January 25, 1749, argument, cast, scenario, and name of Baldassare **Galuppi**
as composer. SCHATZ 3469

Second copy. ML 48.A5 v. 3

Semiramide riconosciuta. Dramma per musica da rappresentarsi nel famosissimo Teatro Grimani di S. Giŏ. Grisostomo nel carnevale 1745 . . .

n. i., n. d. 72 p. 15½ cm.

Three acts. Dedication, argument, cast, scenario, name of Johann Adolph **Hasse**
as the composer, and apology for the (perhaps in some places) excessive cuts in Metastasio's masterpiece.

First performed, as indicated, at Venice December 26, 1744. SCHATZ 4559

— La **Semiramide riconosciuta,** dramma per musica, da rappresentarsi nel Reggio Teatro in Dresda nell' occasione delle felicissime
nozze del serenissimo real principe Luigi Delfino di Francia colla serenissima Giuseppa Delfina di Francia, principessa real di Polonia . . .
anno 1747.

n. i., n. d. 8 p. l., (double) 111, [2] p. 16½ cm.

Three acts and licenza. Argument and name of Johann Adolph **Hasse** as the
composer. German title page, "Die entdeckte Semiramis," and text face Italian,
which is not quite the same as in the original Venice (1745) version. For instance,
the aria, "Maggior follia non v'è," has been added to I, 6, and the aria, "Ei d'amor
quasi delira," has been added to I, 12. Mennicke (but not Schatz) calls this Hasse's
second version of his opera.

First performed, as indicated, January 11, 1747. SCHATZ 4560

— La **Semiramide riconosciuta.** Dramma per musica da rappresentarsi nel Regio Teatro di Varsavia per il gloriosissimo giorno
natalizio di Sua Maestà Augusto III . . . In Varsavia a' VII
d'ottobre MDCCLX.

[Varsavia], Presso Micaele Groell, n. d. Unpaged. 16½ cm.

Three acts and licenza. Argument, scenario, and names of Metastasio as the
author, of Joh. Ad. **Hasse** as the composer. French title page, "Semiramis," and
text face Italian, which is neither quite the same as in the Dresden version of 1747,
nor as in the original Venice version of 1745. For instance, the aria, "Ardo per te d'a-
more," in I, 11 of Venice ed. has been replaced by "Se intende si poco" of the Dresden
ed. On the other hand, the additional arias in I, 6 and I, 12 of the Dresden version
have been dropped, and the original text has been restored. SCHATZ 4572

Semiramide riconosciuta.　O. T. of Jommelli's Semiramide, 1762.

Semiramide riconosciuta.　Drama per musica.　Da rappresentarsi nel Teatro, detto delle Dame nel carnevale dell' anno 1741 . . .

Roma, gli eredi del Ferri, 1741.　84 p.　14^{cm}.

Three acts.　Impresario's dedication, argument, cast, scenario, and names of Metastasio as author, of Giovanni Battista **Lampugnani** as composer.
First performed, as indicated, January, 1741.　　　　Schatz 5389

La Semiramide riconosciuta.　Dramma per musica dell' abbate D. Pietro Metastasio da rappresentarsi nel Regal Teatro di S. Carlo il dì 20. gennajo 1751 . . .

Napoli, gli eredi di Mosca, 1751.　6 p. l., 72 p.

Three acts.　By Metastasio, who is not mentioned.　Impresario's dedication, dated Naples, January 20, 1751, argument, cast, scenario, and name of Giuseppe de **Majo** as composer.　　　　Schatz 5864

La Semiramide riconosciuta.　Dramma per musica, da rappresentarsi nel nobil Teatro del Bairo Alto nel autunno dell' 1765.

Lisbona, Pietro Ferreira, n. d.　8 p. l., 133 p.　16^{cm}.

Three acts.　By Metastasio, who is not mentioned.　"La musica è tirata da uno spartito del . . . David **Perez**."　Argument, cast, and scenario.　Portuguese title page, "A Semiramis reconhecida," and text face Italian.
First performed at Rome, Teatro Alibert, carnival, 1749.　　　　Schatz 7875

Semiramide riconosciuta.　Dramma per musica di Artino Corasio, Pastore Arcade, da rappresentarsi nel famosissimo Teatro Grimani di S. Gio. Grisostomo nel carnevale del 1729.

Venezia, Carlo Buonarigo, n. d.　1 p. l., 72 p.　14½^{cm}.

Three acts.　By Metastasio, who is not mentioned.　Dedication by Domenico Lalli, argument, cast, scenario, and name of Nicolà Antonio **Porpora** as the composer.　　　　Schatz 8361

Semiramide riconosciuta.　Drama per musica di Pietro Metastasio frà gli Arcadi Artino Corasio.　Da rappresentarsi nel carnevale dell' anno 1729 nel Teatro detto delle Dame . . .

Roma, Zempel e de Mey, n. d.　84 p.　15^{cm}.

Three acts.　Dedication, argument, cast, scenario, and name of Leonardo **Vinci** as composer.　　　　Schatz 10752

Semiramis.　Tr. of Bernasconi's Semiramide.

Semiramis, tragedie, representée par l'Academie royale de musique l'an 1718.　Paroles de M. Roy.　Musique de M. Destouches.　XCVI. opera.

n. i., n. d. pl., p. 377–448.　(Recueil général des opéra, t. xii, Paris, 1734.)　14^{cm}.

Detached copy.　Five acts and prologue with "Avertissement."
First performed, as indicated, December 4, 1718.　　　　Schatz 2550
　　　　　　　　　　　　　　　Second copy.　ML 48.R4

Semiramis.　Tr. of Graun's Semiramide.

Semiramis.　Tr. of Hasse's La Semiramide riconosciuta.

Semiramis.　Tr. of Himmel's Semiramide.

Semiramis.   Tr. of Jommelli's Semiramide.

Semiramis.   Tr. of Salieri's Semiramide.

Semiramis.   Tr. of Sarti's Semiramide.

A Semiramis reconhecida.   Tr. of Perez' La Semiramide riconosciuta.

La semplice.   A. T. of von Schacht's Il tutore deluso.

La semplice ovvero La virtù premiata, dramma eroicomico d'un atto solo originale di Giuseppe Foppa da rappresentarsi nel nobile Teatro Giustiniani in San Moisè il carnovale dell' anno 1799.

> *Venezia, Modesto Fenzo, 1798.   36 p.   15ᶜᵐ.*
>
> Cast and name of Francesco **Gardi** as the composer. After the opera Giuseppe Cajani's ballet "L'isola piacevole" (composer of the music not mentioned).
>
> SCHATZ 3541

La semplice ad arte.   Commedia per musica di Giuseppe Palomba da rappresentarsi nel Nuovo Teatro de' Fiorentini per prim' opera di quest' anno 1782.

> *Napoli, n. publ., 1782.   58, [1] p.   14½ᶜᵐ.*
>
> Three acts.   Cast and name of Pietro **Guglielmi** as the composer.
> First performed, as indicated, May 12, 1782.   SCHATZ 4266

La semplice burlata ballet.   *See* Andreozzi's Arsinoe.

La semplice fortunata.   L. T. of Paisiello's L'innocente fortunata.

La semplice spiritosa.   Dramma giocoso per musica da rappresentarsi nel Teatro Giustinian di S. Moisè l'autunno dell' anno 1748.

> *Venezia, Modesto Fenzo, 1748.   60, [2] p.   14½ᶜᵐ.*
>
> Three acts.   Cast, scenario.   The 2 unnumb. p. contain substitute arias.   Author and composer not mentioned and unknown to Schatz.   SCHATZ 11363

Senocrita, dramma per musica.

> *n. i., n. d.   70 p.   15ᶜᵐ.*
>
> At end: Dresda . . . la vedova Stoessel.   MDCCXXXVII.
> Three acts.   By Stefano Benedetto Pallavicini, who is not mentioned.   Argument and name of Johann Adolph **Hasse** as the composer.
> First performed at Dresden, Hoftheater, February 27, 1737.   SCHATZ 4561

La sepolta viva.   A. T. of Dalayrac's Camilla.

A sequel to the opera of Flora.   As it is now acted at the Theatre Royal in Lincoln's-Inn-Fields.   To which is added, the musick engraved on copper plates.   Written by the author of Flora.

> *London, A. Bettesworth and C. Hitch and T. Wood, 1732.   1 p. l., 31, 8 p.   15ᶜᵐ.*
>
> Two acts.   By Colley Cibber, *not* by John Hippesley, who played Sir Thomas Testy.   The 8 p. contain without titles Airs 1–15.   The titles of the airs are indicated in the text.
> First performed on March 20, 1732, as indicated.   ML 50.5.S3

La sera sposa del sole.   A. T. of Sacrati's La Delia.

The **seraglio;** a comic opera, in two acts: as performed at the Theatre-Royal in Covent-Garden.

London, T. Evans, 1776. 1 p. l., 31 p. 20^{cm}.

Cast. Author-composer, Charles **Dibdin.** Johnston's vocal score says, "chiefly composed by C. Dibdin," and heads "What shall I do?" "I simply wait for your commands," and "Away with tyrant laws" as composed by Samuel **Arnold,** and "Ah what avails?" as by A. [John Abraham] **Fisher.**
First performed November 14, 1776.   LONGE 124

— Airs, chorusses, in the new musical entertainment of **The seraglio;** as it is performed at the Theatre-Royal in Covent-Garden.

London, T. Evans, 1776. 16 p. 19^{cm}.

Two acts. Cast and note:
"On account of the unusual number of songs originally performed in this piece, it has been found expedient, in order to shorten the time of representation, to take out some of the airs, among which are those sung by Mr. Mattocks, his part has therefore been given to Mr. Robson."   ML 50.2.S48

Il **seraglio di Osmano.** Dramma giocoso per musica di Giovanni Bertati da rappresentarsi nel Teatro Giustiniani in S. Moisè per prima opera del carnevale 1785.

Venezia, Antonio Casali, n. d. 62 p. 17^{cm}.

Two acts. Cast, scenario, and name of the composer, Giuseppe **Gazzaniga.**
First performed, as indicated, December 26, 1784.   SCHATZ 3676

— Il **palazzo d'Osmano:** Dramma giocoso per musica da rappresentarsi nel Reggio Teatro di S. Carlo, della Principessa il **carnevale** dell' anno 1795.

Lisbona, Simone Taddeo Ferreira, 1795. 191, [2] p. 14½^{cm}.

Two acts. **Gazzaniga** is mentioned as the composer. Portuguese text faces **the** Italian by Bertati, who is not mentioned.   SCHATZ 3680

Le **serdeau des théâtres.** Parody of Pirithoüs.

La **sérénade vénitienne.** *See* Campra's Trois nouvelles entrées.

Serenaden eller De sorte naeser. Syngestykke i tre optoge af **O.** Pram sat i musik af hr. regimentsquarteermester Wedel.

Kiøbenhavn, Johan Frederik Schultz, 1795. 80 p. 16^{cm}.

First performed at Copenhagen May 15, 1795.   SCHATZ 10919

Les **serenades & les joueurs.** Entrées in Campra's Les festes venitiennes.

Die **serenate.** A. T. of Preu's Adrast und Isidore.

Le **serenate noturne,** ballet. *See* Anfossi's Le gelosie villane.

La **serietà in conflitto,** ballet. *See* Rust's La caccia d'Enrico IV.

Serpilla e Bacocco. L. T. of Il marito giogatore e la moglie bacchettona.

Il **serraglio.** A. T. of Paër's Saed.

Il serraglio di Osmano. Dramma giocoso per musica da rappresentarsi nel Teatro di S. A. E. di Sassonia.

Dresda, n. publ., 1787. 143 p. 15½^{cm}.

Two acts. By Giovanni Bertati, who is not mentioned. Stefano **Ghinassi** is named as the composer. The German title page, "Osmanns serail," and text face Italian. SCHATZ 3803

Le serrurier, opera bouffon; représenté pour la premiere fois par les Comédiens italiens ordinaires du roi, le 20 décembre 1764. Les paroles sont de M. Quétant.

Paris, Duchesne, 1765. 47 p. 21^{cm}.

One act. Cast and note on p. 2:
"Le sujet de cette bagatelle est originairement de M. de la Ribardiere. La pièce avoit été présentée aux Italiens qui n'en firent point usage: l'auteur l'ayant abandonnée à M. **Kohault,** ordinaire de la musique de Monseigneur le prince de Conti, je la refis comme elle est actuellement pour l'amusement de S. A. S."
On p. 10–12, the ariette, "Le tendre coeur de ta bergere." On p. 38–40, the vaudeville, "Bannissons le soupçon jaloux." On p. [43]–47, an "Essai sur l'opera-comique," in which Quétant defines this form of art and gives his advice as routinier on suitable subjects, on the "intrigues," the dialogue, the proper place for ariettes, etc.
First performed at Paris, Théâtre de la Comédie-italienne, December 20, 1764. SCHATZ 5205

— **Le serrurier,** opera bouffon; représenté pour la premiere fois par les Comédiens italiens ordinaires du roi, le 20 décembre 1764. Les parolles sont de M. Quetant.

Paris, Duchesne, 1766. 31 p. 19^{cm}.

One act. On p. [2], the same note as above.
On p. [28]–31 the "Essai sur l'opera-comique." SCHATZ 11716

— **Le serrurier,** opera bouffon, représenté pour la premiere fois par les Comédiens italiens ordinaires du roi, le 20 décembre 1764. Les paroles sont de M. Quetant.

Paris, Duchesne, 1771. 32 p. 19^{cm}.

One act. Cast. The essay on the opéra-comique is not in this edition, the text of which is the same as in the ed. of 1766 with the addition of the unaccompanied airs of "Le tendre coeur de ta bergère," on p. 8–11 and on p. 28–31 the vaudeville with chorus "Bannissons le soupçon jaloux." SCHATZ 11717

— **Der schlosser,** ein singspiel in einem aufzuge aus dem franzoesischen uebersetzt. Mit musik.

Frankfurt am Mayn, mit Andreaeischen schriften, 1772. 60 p., 9 p. (music). 16½^{cm}.

Cast. Neither the translator, Johann Heinrich Faber, nor the composer, Joseph **Kohault,** is mentioned. The music supplement (voice and bass) contains: "Wenn mich armen mann" (I, 5="Tandis que, du matin au soir") and the vaudeville "Eifersucht, argwohn und verdacht" (I, 13="Bannissons le soupçon jaloux"). SCHATZ 5206

La serva astuta. Intermezzi per musica a tre voci da rappresentarsi nel Teatro di via del Cocomero nel carnevale dell' anno 1756.

Firenze, Gaetano Albizzi, 1756. 30 p. 15^{cm}.

Two parts. Neither author nor composer mentioned and both unknown to me. The text is *not* by Goldoni. ML 48.A5 v.16

La serva astuta o sia Il filosofo in campagna. L. T. of Galuppi's Il filosofo di campagna.

La serva bacchettona. Commedia per musica di Antonio Palomba Napoletano da rappresentarsi nel Teatro de' Fiorentini, nella primavera di quest' anno 1749 . . .

Napoli, Domenico Langiano, 1749. 4 p. l., 63 p. 14½ cm.

Three acts. Impresario's dedication ("commedia, che prima comparisce in quest' anno sul mio teatro"), cast, and name of the composer, Gioacchino **Cocchi**.

SCHATZ 2040

La serva fatta padrona. Commedia per musica da rappresentarsi nel Teatro de' Fiorentini nell' està di quest' anno 1769.

Napoli, Stamperia Avelliniana, 1769. 72 p. 15½ cm.

Three acts. Cast, name of **Paisiello** as the composer, and preface by the author, Pasquale Mililotti, in which he says that the impressario was compelled to abandon his plan of presenting a new work and "di replicare la presente commedia, tanto, pochi anni sono, dall' eccellentissima nobiltà e dal pubblico compatita; ed acciocchè possa maggiormente aggradire, come spera, ha proccurato di farla in buona parte innovare sì di poesia, come di musica, come si osserverà da chi cortese degnerasse di leggerla."

Accordingly, these performances of 1769 can not have been the first, at least not in the original form of the opera, and it is known that the title of the original dialect version was "Le mbroglie de le bajasse." SCHATZ 7671

La serva favorita. Dramma per musica da rappresentarsi in Firenze nel Teatro di via del Cocomero, nell' autunno del 1741 . . .

Firenze, Anton M. Albizzini, n. d. 65 p. 14½ cm.

Three acts. By Giov. Cosimo Villafranchi, with dedication signed by Giovanni Ghinzer (**Chinzer**) as impresario and cast. Author unknown to Schatz. Composed by the impresario, who does not mention the fact.

First performed at Florence, Teatro via di Cocomero, carnival, 1727.

SCHATZ 1864

La serva innamorata: Dramma giocoso per musica da rappresentarsi nel Reggio Teatro di S. Carlo della Principessa, l'estate dell' anno 1794.

Lisbona, Simone Taddeo Ferreira, 1794. 165 p. 14½ cm.

Two acts. By Giuseppe Palomba, who is not mentioned. Cast, scenario, and name of Pietro **Guglielmi** as the composer. With the opera was performed, composer of the music not mentioned, Carlo Bencini's ballet "Lauretta."

First performed at Naples, Teatro de' Fiorentini, summer, 1790. SCHATZ 4294

La serva nobile. Drama civile fatto rappresentare in musica dagl' illustrissimi Signori Accademia Immobili nel loro teatro . . .

n. i., n. d. [185]–298 p. 15½ cm.

Detached apparently from Moniglia's Poesie drammatiche, 1689–90, third part which is wanting in our set. Three acts. By Giovanni Andrea Moniglia, who is not mentioned. Argument, name of Domenico **Anglesi** as composer in the prefatory note, and on p. 279–29, "Dichiarazione La serva nobile de' proverbi, e vocaboli usati dalla plebe fiorentina, de' quali per legittima imitazione s'è valso l'autore." Why Pavan attributes the music to Jacopo **Melani** is unknown to me.

First performed at Florence, as indicated, in 1660. SCHATZ 288

La serva onorata. Dramma giocoso per musica da rappresentarsi nel Teatro de' Fiorentini per seconda opera del corrente anno 1792.

Napoli, Vincenzo Flauto, n. d. 58 p. 15 cm.

Two acts. Cast and name of Niccolò **Piccinni** as the composer. On p. 3 this anonymous note:

La **serva onorata**—Continued.

"Il presente dramma è una imitazione, o sia estratto del libro intitolato le Nozze di Figaro. Nell' originale francese l'azione fu condotta da sedici interlocutori, e poi dal Sig. ab. da Ponte questi si ridussero a undici . . . ora comparisce sopra queste scene ristretta l'azione a sei attori."

According to Schatz Giambattista Lorenzi is responsible for this version.

SCHATZ 8129

La **serva padrona.** Intermezzo per musica da rappresentarsi nel Teatro Giustinian di S. Mosè.

Venezia, Modesto Fenzo, 1748. 20 p. (incl. front.). 14½ᶜᵐ.

Two parts. Neither Gennaro Antonio Federico is mentioned as author, nor G. B. **Pergolesi** as the composer. Cast. The text is exactly the same as in the score edited at Paris by Rousseau in 1752. It agrees also, it seems, with the text of the original libretto (Naples, 1733) as analyzed by Radiciotti, except that the final duet, "Per te io ho nel core," has been substituted from act III of Pergolesi's "Flaminio" for the original final duet of "La Serva Padrona," "Contento tu sarai." In the replicas, "Per te io ho nel core" appears to have been used oftener than the original.

The libretto contains (arias in italics):
(Int. I) 1. *Aspettare e non venire.*
              Questa è per me disgrazia.
          2. *Sempre in contrasti.*
              In somma delle somme.
          3. *Stizzoso, mio.*
              Benissimo, hai tu inteso?
          4. *Lo conosco a quelli occhietti* (duet).
(Int. II)   Or che fatto.
          5. *A Serpina penserete.*
              Ah quanto mi.
          6. *Son imbrogliato io già.*
              Favorisca, signor, passi.
          7. *Per te ho io nel core* (duet).

First performed at Naples, Teatro di S. Bartolomeo, August 28, 1733.

SCHATZ 7892

— La **serva padrona.** Intermezzo in musica da rappresentarsi sopra il Theatro Nuovo dell' opera pantomima del Nicolini.—Die als magd gewordene frau . . .

Braunschweig, Keitel, n. d. Unpaged. 18½ᶜᵐ.

Cast. German text faces Italian. **Pergolesi** is not mentioned. Contains the substituted final duet, "Per te io ho nel core."

Performed 1749, as indicated.

SCHATZ 7894

— La **serva padrona**, intermezzo per musica. Stampato a spese degli musici italiani e riveduto da Marco Soralli, maestro della lingua italiana.

n. i., n. d. 63 p. 16½ᶜᵐ.

An altered version of **Pergolesi**'s 2-act intermezzo. Soralli or somebody else made this version begin with an "Intermezzo primo. SERPINA E ANTIMONIO. *Serp.* 'Di grazia signore conte.'" After this comes the original "Intermezzo primo," and called such! The second intermezzo is followed by "Intermezzo terzo. UBERTO, POI SERPINA, etc. *Uber.* 'Il prender moglie,'" in which again the *conte* figures. Apparently two different works were combined to produce this hybrid affair. German title page, "Die herrschende magd," and text face Italian.

First performed at Frankfurt a/M, Theaterbude am Rossmarkt, April 4, 1755, by the opera company of prince Thurn & Taxis under the management of Girolamo Bon.

SCHATZ 7902

— La **servante maitresse.** Comedie en deux actes. Melée d'ariettes, parodies de La serva padrona, intermède italien. Repré-

La serva padrona—Continued.

sentée pour la première fois par les Comediens italiens ordinaires du roi, le mércredi 14 août 1754.

Paris, P. G. Le Mercier, 1754. 31, [1] p. 19^{cm}.

Pergolesi is not mentioned. On p. 3, this four-liner:
> "A Mlle Favart.
> Nature un jour épousa l'art;
> De leurs amours nâquit Favart.
> Qui semble tenir de sa mere.
> Tout ce qu'elle doit à son pere."

The parody resp. transl. was by N. Baurans, who is not mentioned.

The score was published by the widow Delormel. Both the score and the libretto contain the arias

I, 1. *Longtemps attendre* (=1 in La Serva Padrona).
I, 2. *Eh bien! Finiras tu?* (source unknown to Wotquenne).
   Sans fins, sans cesse (=2 in S. P.).
   Eh, mais ne fait-il pas? (=3 in S. P.).
   Je devine a ces yeux (=4 in S. P.).
II, 1. *Vous gentilles jeunes filles* (According to Wotquenne=*Donne belle che bramate* in "Amor mascherato," intermezzo by unknown composer).
II, 2. *Charmant espoir qui nous* (Source unknown to Wotquenne).
II, 3. *A Zerbine laissés par grace* (=5 in S. P.).
II, 4. *Quel est mon embarras* (=6 in S. P.).
II, 5. *Me seras tu fidèle?* (=*Contento tu sarai*, the original final duet of S. P.).

"La serva padrona" was first performed at Paris, Comédie italienne, October 4, 1746, with an overture by Paganelli, and again at Paris, Academie royale de musique, with an overture by Telemann on August 1, 1752, before a ballet-pantomime and after Lully's "Acis et Galatée." SCHATZ 7895

— **La servante maitresse,** comédie en deux actes. Mêlée d'ariettes parodiées de la Serva padrona, intermede italien. Représentée pour la premiere fois, par les Comediens italiens ordinaires du roi, le mercredi 14 août 1754.

La Haye, Pierre Paupié, 1755. 36 p. 19^{cm}.

Baurans translation. **Pergolesi** is not mentioned. ML 48.A4

— **La servante maitresse,** comedie en deux actes, mêlée d'ariettes, traduite de la Serva Padrona, interméde italien.

Paris, la veuve Duchesne, 1771. 32 p. 16^{cm}.

Transl. by N. Baurans. **Pergolesi** is not mentioned. Cast. On p. 27–32, "Airs de la Servante maitresse," *viz,* "Sans fin, sans cesse" (I, 2), "Vous, gentilles jeunes filles" (II, 1). SCHATZ 7895a

— **La servante maitresse,** comedie en deux actes, melée d'ariettes, traduite de la Serva padrona, intermède italien.

Bruxelles, J. J. Boucherie, n. d. 35, [1] p. 19^{cm}.

Cast. Neither **Pergolesi** is mentioned, nor Baurans, the translator, resp. parodist. On p. 31–35, "Airs choisis de la Servante Maitresse." ML 50.2.S51P3

— **Die magd als frau im hause,** ein musicalisches mittel-spiel.
n. i., n. d. [16] p. 15½^{cm}.

Cast and date, "Dresden im jahr 1740." **Pergolesi** is not mentioned.
First performed at Dresden, Hoftheater, February 8, 1740. SCHATZ 7893

— **Pandolfus en Zerbina,** of De meid meesteres, zangspel. Naar het fransche La servante maitresse gevolgd door Bartholomeus Ruloffs.

Amsteldam, J. Helders en A. Mars, 1793. 7 p. l., 32 p. 16½^{cm}.

Prefatory poem by the translator, followed by his historical preface. SCHATZ 7896

La serva padrona. Intermezzo in due atti da rappresentarsi in musica nella Sala del Signor Bartolomeo Cambi detto Meo . . . Posto in musica dal Sig. maestro Vittorio Trento.

Venezia, n. publ., 1795. 20 p. 16ᶜᵐ.

By Gennaro Antonio Federico, who is not mentioned. Composer's dedication and cast.

First performed 1795, as indicated. SCHATZ 10429

La serva per amore. Dramma giocoso per musica di Filippo Livigni, da rappresentarsi nel Teatro di San Samuelle l'autunno dell' anno 1773.

Venezia, Modesto Fenzo, 1773. 54 p. 17½ᶜᵐ.

Three acts. Cast, scenario, and name of **Galuppi** as the composer. SCHATZ 3508

La serva scaltra. Dramma giocoso per musica da rappresentarsi nel Teatro Giustiniani di S. Moisè. Nell' autunno dell' anno MDCCLIX.

Venezia, Modesto Fenzo, 1749. 70 p. 15ᶜᵐ.

Three acts. Author not mentioned, and unknown to Schatz. Impresario's dedicatory poem, cast, scenario, and name of Giuseppe **Scarlatti** as the composer.

SCHATZ 9555

La serva sposa. Intermezzi per musica a tre voci da rappresentarsi nel Teatro alla Valle nel carnevale dell' anno 1753 . . .

Roma, Marcello Silvestri, n. d. 23 p. 15½ᶜᵐ.

Two parts. Author not mentioned and unknown to Schatz. Publisher's dedication, cast and name of **Rinaldo di Capua** as composer. Contains arias: "Più sono in amore," "Sbagliate Sor conte," "D'amore nella rete," "Più rimiro quel visino," etc. ML 50.2.S5R4

La servante justifiée, Opéra comique. De Messieurs F*** et F***

Paris, Prault fils, 1744. 48 p. 19ᶜᵐ. (Theatre de M. Favart, Paris, Duchesne, 1763–77, t. vi.)

One act. Prose and vaudevilles. By Favart and Fagan. "Suivi de 12 airs et du duo du Tictac, gravés en musique," says Font, but they are not in this reissue of Prault's edition, at least not in our copy, which does not show signs of imperfection. Font does not mention Favart's musical collaborator. Towers lists an opera of the above title as composed by J. B. Moulinghem (**Moulinghen**).

First performed at the Foire St. Germain March 19, 1740. ML 49.A2F1

— **La servante justifiée,** opéra-comique en un acte. Représenté pour la premiere fois sur le Théatre de l'Opéra-comique, le 19 mars 1740.

Paris, la veuve Duchesne, 1766. 68 p. 19ᶜᵐ.

On p. 45–68, twelve "Airs de La servante justifiée" and "Le tictac. Duo. Comme on voit notre moulin." Without names of the authors, Fagan and Favart, or the composer. SCHATZ 11513

La servante maitresse. Parody of Pergolesi's La serva padrona.

Le serve rivali. Dramma giocoso per musica del Signor abate Pietro Chiari da rappresentarsi nel Teatro Giustiniani di S. Moisè l'autunno dell' anno 1767.

Venezia, Modesto Fenzo, 1767. 70 p. 14½ᶜᵐ.

Three acts. Argument, cast, scenario, name of Tommaso **Trajetta** as composer, and description of the ballets, whose composer is not mentioned.

First performed at Venice, as indicated, but previously at Venice, Teatro di S. Moisè, fall of 1766. SCHATZ 10397

Il **servo astuto.** A. T. of Ferd. Rutini's Il matrimonio per industria.

Il **servo di due padroni,** ballet. *See* Martin y Soler's Ifigenia in Aulide.

Il **servo padrone** ossia L'amor perfetto. Dramma giocoso per musica da rappresentarsi nel nobilissimo Teatro di San Samuele il carnovale dell' anno 1794.

Venezia, Modesto Fenzo, 1794. 68, [1] p. 18^cm.

Two acts. Impresario's dedication with Caterino Mazzolà's name as the author of the text, scenario, cast, and name of Niccolò **Piccinni** as the composer.

On p. 37–43 argument, cast, and description of Giuseppe Trafieri's five act "Odoacre, primo rè d'Italia, ballo tragico eroico pantomimo . . . La musica tutta nuova è del Signor maestro Vittorio Trento."

First performed January 17, 1794, as indicated. SCHATZ 8152

Il **servo padrone,** ossia L'amor perfetto. Dramma giocoso per musica, da rappresentarsi nel Teatro Elettorale, del Signor Caterino Mazzolà . . .

Dresda, n. publ., 1792. 173 p. 15½^cm.

Two acts. Joseph **Schuster** is mentioned as composer. German title-page, "Der herr als bedienter oder Die wahre liebe" and text face Italian.

First performed January 5, 1793, as indicated. SCHATZ 9756

Sesostri. Dramma per musica da rappresentarsi nel Regio Teatro di Torino nel carnevale del 1755 alla presenza di S. S. R. M.

Torino, Zappata ed Avondo, n. d. viii, 62, [1] p. 15½^cm.

Three acts. Argument, cast, scenario, and name of composer, Ferdinando Giuseppe **Bertoni,** but not of Apostolo Zeno and Pietro Pariati, the authors. The ballets, of which the second was called "Coronazione d'Apollo, e Dafne," were by Gaetano Vestri, music by Rocco Gioannetti.

First performed at Turin, December 26, 1754. SCHATZ 918

— **Sesostri, rè d'Egitto.** Dramma per musica da rappresentarsi nel Reggio Teatro di Praga, in decembre dell' anno 1766 . . .

Praga, Carlo Giuseppe Jaurnich, n. d. 5 p. l., 119 p. 15^cm.

Three acts. Impresario's dedication, cast, scenario, and name of composer, **Bertoni.** Zeno and Pariati are not mentioned. German title-page, "Sesostris, könig in Egypten," and text face Italian. SCHATZ 919

Sesostri. Dramma per musica da rappresentarsi nel Teatro Grimani di S. Benedetto l'autunno dell' anno 1757.

Venezia, Modesto Fenzo, 1757. 47 p. 15^cm.

Three acts. By Apostolo Zeno and Pietro Pariati, who are not mentioned. Argument, cast, scenario, and name of **Galuppi** as composer.

First performed, as indicated, November 26, 1757. SCHATZ 3494

Sesostri, an opera; to be perform'd at the King's Theatre in the Hay-Market. For the benefit of Signora Campolini, and Signor Guglielmi, composer to the opera. The music was composed on purpose for this benefit by the above Signor Guglielmi. The poetry taken from an old book, is quite alter'd and adapted to the present taste by Giovan Gualberto Bottarelli.

London, W. Griffin, 1768. 47, [1] p. 20^cm.

Three acts. Italian text and English translation. Cast and argument.

First performed, as indicated, 1768.

It is not known in just what relation this "Sesostri" stood to Guglielmi's opera of the same title, text by Zeno and Pariati, as first performed at Venice, Teatro di S. Salvatore, May 7, 1766. SCHATZ 4267

Sesostri, rè di Egitto.

Apostolo Zeno, Poesie drammatiche, Venezia, 1744, t. ix, p. [201]– 292. 19ᶜᵐ.

Three acts. Argument. Written in collaboration with Pietro Pariati. No composer is mentioned. In the "Catalogo" at end of the t. x, date and place of first ed. are given as Venezia, 1710, *but see* below.   ML 49.A2Z3

— Sesostri. Pubblicato per la prima volta in Venezia 1708.

Apostolo Zeno, Poesie drammatiche, Orleans, 1785–86, t. x, p. 199– 287. 21ᶜᵐ.

Three acts. Argument. No composer is mentioned. Written in collaboration with Pietro Pariati.   ML 49.A2Z4

Sesostri, rè d'Egitto—Sesostris, könig in Egypten. L. T. of Bertoni's Sesostri.

Sesostri rè d'Egitto. Drama per musica da rappresentarsi nel Regal Teatro di S. Carlo a di 30. maggio 1752 . . .

Napoli, Domenico Lanciano, 1752. 48 p. 14ᶜᵐ.

Three acts. By Apostolo Zeno and Pietro Pariati, who are not mentioned. Impresario's dedication, dated Naples, May 30, 1752, argument, cast, scenario, and name of the composer, Gioacchino **Cocchi.**   Schatz 2046

— Sesostri re d'Egitto, dramma per musica da rappresentarsi nel Nuovo Teatro di Padova per la solita fiera di giugno dell' anno 1756 . . .

Venezia, Modesto Fenzo, 1756. 48 p. 17ᶜᵐ.

Three acts. Dedication, argument, scenario, cast, and name of Gioachino **Cocchi** as composer. Zeno and Pariati, the authors, are not mentioned.   Schatz 11687

Sesostri, rè di Egitto. Drama per musica, da rappresentarsi nella Cesarea corte . . . nel carnevale dell' anno MDCCXVII. La poesia sì del drama, come degl' intramezzi è del Sig. dottor Pietro Pariati . . . La musica pure sì del drama, come degl' intramezzi è del Sig. Francesco Conti.

Vienna d'Austria, Gio. Van Ghelen, n. d. 80 p. 14½ᶜᵐ.

Argument, scenario, and note that at the end of the play would be performed a "ballo di fanciulli," music by Nicola Matteis, and the *intramezzi* after the first act, the second act and during the first change of scenery in the third. The subject of these *intramezzi* (p. 69–80) was "Grilletta e Pimpinone" (Schatz 2198). It should be noted that in Zeno's collected works "Sesostri, rè di Egitto" appears as written jointly by him and Pariati.

First performed, as indicated, February, 1717.   Schatz 2197

Sesostri, rè d'Egitto. Drama per musica, da rappresentarsi nel Teatro di S. A. S. di Carignano, nel carnevale dell' anno 1717 . . .

Torino, P. G. Zappata, 1717. 4 p. l., 72 p. 15ᶜᵐ.

Three acts. By Apostolo Zeno and Pariati, who are not mentioned. Dedication, argument, cast, notice to the reader asking his pardon for the liberties taken with "la gloriosa penna dell' autore," scenario, and name of the composer, Stefano Andrea **Fiorè.**   Schatz 3192

Sesostri rè di Egitto. Drama per musica da rappresentarsi nel Teatro Tron di San Cassano nel carnovale dell' anno 1709 . . .

Venezia, Marino Rossetti, n. d. 68 p. 15ᶜᵐ.

Three acts. By Apostolo Zeno and Pariati, who are not mentioned. Impresario's dedication, argument, cast, scenario, and name of Carlo Francesco **Gasparini** as the composer.   Schatz 3581

Sesostri rè d'Egitto, dramma per musica da rappresentarsi nel Regio Ducal Teatro di Milano, nel carnovale dell' anno 1760 . . .

Milano, Giuseppe Richino Malatesta, 1759. 5 p. l., 36, [1] p. 14½^{cm}*.*

Three acts. By Zeno and Pariati, who are not mentioned. Dedication, argument, cast, and name of Carlo **Monza** as the composer. On the additional page the substitute aria for III, 6, "Che pena, che affanno." With the opera were performed Sonié's ballets "Venere ed Adone," "I molinari francesi," and "Il giudizio di Paride." The composers of the music are not mentioned.

First performed, as indicated, December 26, 1759.   SCHATZ 6612

Sesostri re d'Egitto.   Drama per musica da rappresentarsi in Roma nel Teatro delle Dame nel carnevale dell' anno MDCCLI . . .

Roma, Fausto Amidei, n. d. 65 p. 15^{cm}*.*

Three acts. By Zeno and Pariati, who are not mentioned. Dedication, argument, scenario, cast, and name of **Terradellas** as composer.   ML 50.2.S55T2

Sesostris, könig in Egypten.   Tr. of Bertoni's Sesostri, rè d'Egitto.

Sesto Tarquinio.   Drama per musica.   Nel famoso Teatro Vendramino di San Salvatore, l'anno MDCLXXIX.   Del dottore Camillo Badovero . . .

Venetia, Francesco Nicolini, 1679. 78 p. 14^{cm}*.*

Three acts. Author's dedication, dated December 5, 1678, argument, scenario, and notice to the reader:

"Questo è il mio primo drama, che nove anni sono scrissi per mio diporto, sceneggiato però con altro ordine di quello, che lo ritrovi al presente. Per incontrare le sodisfattione de molti, hò pregiudicato alla mia, è l'uso corrente della moltiplicità delle arie, hà fatto correr in aria le sostanze del più buono recitativo . . . sì, per essere primo aborto della mia penna, come ti dissi, come per essere stato lacerato più volte, e gli errori . . . sarebbe rimasto finalmente estinto, se la virtù singolarissima del illustre Sig. Gio. Battista **Tomasi** Virtuoso di camera del Serenissimo Duca di Mantova non gli havesse sominstrato il balsamo vitale della sua musica. Respira dunque questo à sola forza de sospiri; sono le note i suoi giorni; spera passare al tuo aggradimento à favore de passaggi, e far punto al periodo delle sue avversitadi cõ il solo contrapunto. Il Sig. Tomasi ancora per colpa di tante mutationi è stato necessitato a rendere in qualche parte dura la solita sua dolcezza, che però se ti ferirà l'orrecchio alcuna diversità, di tuono accusa il troncamento delle scene, le aggiunte doppo la perfettione, che per altro non può fallire chi insegna."   SCHATZ 10359

Li sforzi d'ambizione e d'amore.—Drama per musica, da rappresentarsi nel Teatro Giustiniano di S. Moise.   Nel carnovale 1724.

Venezia, Carlo Buonarrigo, n. d. front., 48 p. 14½^{cm}*.*

The title appears separate as frontispiece.

Three acts. By Antonio Maria Lucchini, who is not mentioned. Argument, cast, scenario, and name of Giovanni **Porta** as the composer.   SCHATZ 8392

The sham captain.   A. T. of The boarding-school.

The shamrock or The anniversary of St. Patrick.   O. T. of Shield's The poor soldier.

The shamrock or Revels on St. Patrick's Day.   O. T. of Shield's The poor soldier.

The sheep-shearing: or, Florizel and Perdita.   A pastoral comedy. Taken from Shakespear.   As it is acted at the Theatre-Royal in Smock-alley.   The songs set by Mr. Arne.

Dublin, Peter Wilson, 1755. 27, [1] p. 16^{cm}*.*

Two acts, prologue, and epilogue. By MacNamara Morgan, who is not mentioned.   LONGE 201

First performed at London, Covent Garden, March 25, 1754 (Genest).

The **sheep-shearing**—Continued.

— Florizel and Perdita; or, The Sheepshearing: A dramatic pastoral. In two acts. (Altered from Shakespeare's Winter's tale.

[*87*]–*103 p.* *19ᶜᵐ.* (*Collection of the most esteemed farces and entertainments, t. i, Edinburgh, 1792.*)

Drury-Lane and Edinburgh (1781) casts. Neither MacNamara Morgan is mentioned, nor **Arne.** SCHATZ 11753A

The **shepherd's artifice**, a dramatic pastoral. As it is perform'd at the Theatre Royal in Covent Garden. The words written and the music compos'd by Mr. Dibdin.

London, T. Becket and P. A. De Hondt, 1765. *32 p.* *19ᶜᵐ.*

Two acts. Cast.
First performed Friday, May 21, 1762, at Covent Garden. LONGE 52

The **shepherd's lottery.** A musical entertainment. As it is perform'd by His Majesty's Company of comedians at the Theatre-Royal in Drury-Lane. The music compos'd by Dr. Boyce.

London, M. Cowper, 1751. *24 p.* *19ᶜᵐ.*

Two parts. By Moses Mendez, who is not mentioned.
First performed November 19, 1751, as indicated. LONGE 54

The **shepherd's wedding.** A. T. of Stanley's Arcadia.

The **shepherdess of the Alps:** a comic opera, in three acts. As it is performed at the Theatre-Royal in Covent-Garden.

London, G. Kearsly, 1780. *1 p. l., 86 p.* *20½ᶜᵐ.*

Cast. The author-composer, Charles **Dibdin,** is not mentioned.
First performed January 18, 1780, as indicated. LONGE 126

Sherwood forest. A. T. of Shield's Robin Hood.

La **sibille,** représentée, devant Sa Majesté, a Fontainebleau, le jeudi 25 octobre 1770.

[*Paris*], *Pierre Robert Christophe Ballard, 1770.* *2 p. l., 15 p.* *21¼ᶜᵐ.*

One act. Cast and names of De Moncrif as author, of Antoine **Dauvergne** as composer.
First performed at Paris, Académie royale de musique, August 8, 1758, and previously at Fontainebleau November 13, 1753, as first act of a ballet called "Les fêtes d'Euterpe." (*See also his* La coquette trompée.") ML 50.2.S59D2

Der sich raechende Cupido. L. T. of Keiser's Die entdeckte verstellung.

The **Sicilian romance:** or, The apparition of the cliffs, an opera, by Henry Siddons. As performed with universal applause at the Theatre Royal, Covent-Garden.

London, J. Barker, 1794. *1 p. l., 44 p.* *21½ᶜᵐ.*

Three acts. Cast, prologue, and dedication. The composer, William **Reeve,** is not mentioned.
First performed May 28, 1794. LONGE 239

Sicotencal. Dramma per musica da rappresentarsi nel Nuovo Teatro de' quattro Signori associati cavalieri e patrizj della Regia città di Pavia nella primavera dell' anno 1776 . . .

Pavia, Porro, Bianchi e compagni, n. d. *41, [1] p.* *17ᶜᵐ.*

Sicotencal—Continued.

Three acts. By Cesare Oliveri. Impresario's dedication, argument, cast, scenario, and names of the author and the composer, Giuseppe **Colla** ("La musica sarà tutta nuova"). The ballets, of which the first was called "Arianna," were by Giuseppe Salomoni; the music by Giuseppe Sighizzelli. SCHATZ 2110

Sicotencal. Dramma per musica da rappresentarsi nel Regio Teatro di Torino nel carnovale del 1776 . . .

Torino, Onorato Derossi, n. d. viii, 60 p. 16½ cm.

Three acts. Argument, cast, scenario, and names of Cesare Oliveri as author, of Giovanni Marco **Rutini** as composer. With the opera were performed (music by Giuseppe Antonio Le Messier) Giuseppe Canziani's ballets, "Le dissensioni d'amore nel campo," "L'amante travestita," and "Lo sbarco de' Spagnuoli nell' America." SCHATZ 9191

Sidney e Silly, ballet. *See* Bianchi's Eurione.

Sidonio. Drama per musica da rappresentarsi nel Teatro Tron di S. Cassano l'autunno dell' anno 1706 . . .

Venezia, Marino Rossetti, 1706. 70 p. 15 cm.

Three acts. By Pietro Pariati, who is not mentioned. Dedication, argument, cast, scenario, and name of Antonio **Lotti** as composer. SCHATZ 5722

Sidonio e Dorisbe. Drama di Francesco Melosio. Honorato di musica dal Sig. Nicolò Fontei e rappresentato nel Teatro di S. Moisè l'anno [1642].

Venetia, Gio. Battista Surian [MDCXLII]. 106 p. 13 cm.

Dates partly filled out in pencil. On p. 106 (incorrectly numbered 104), a mounted notice to the reader:

"Scusa gli errori della stampa, che sono infiniti, occorsi, per hauer l'autore lasciata ad altri la cura di correggere."

Three acts and prologue. Author's dedication, dated February 16, 1642, argument, author's notice to the reader, and "Scherzo avanti il prologo." SCHATZ 3290

Der sieg der bescheidenheit auf der insel des vergnuegens. A. T. of Kauer's Kaspars zoegling.

Der sieg der Clelia. Tr. of Michl's Il trionfo di Clelia.

Der sieg der natur ueber die schwaermerey. A. T. of Phanty's Don Sylvio von Rosalva.

Der sieg der natur ueber die schwaermerey. A. T. of F. S. Sander's Don Sylvio von Rosalva.

Der sieg der natur ueber die schwaermerey. A. T. of Ulbrich's Der blaue schmetterling.

Sieg der schoenheit, in einem singspiele auf dem Hamburgischen Schau-Platz vorgestellet 1722.

Hamburg, Philipp Ludwig Stromer, n. d. Unpaged. 18 cm.

Three acts. According to Schatz, originally written by Christian Heinrich Postel as "Der grosse könig der afrikanischen Wenden Gensericus als Roms und Karthagos ueberwinder," but first performed at Hamburg in 1693 as "Gensericus," with music by Johann Georg **Conradi.** The text was then partly rewritten by Weichmann, and further altered for the performances of 1722 by Georg Philip **Telemann,** who composed the new music. Under its original title, "Der grosse koenig," etc., Telemann's version of Conradi's opera was then performed at Braunschweig in February, 1725. It was repeated, so Schatz claims, at Braunschweig in February, 1732, as "Sieg der

Sieg der schoenheit—Continued.

schoenheit." Schatz' statements do not quite agree with those of Ottzenn, who, in his monograph on Telemann, mentions a score preserved at Berlin headed "Genserich Opera, so zu Braunschweig anno 1732, in der Winter Messe representiret worden. Componirt von kapellmeister Telemann in Hamburg." This would seem to imply that Telemann composed an opera, "Genserich," performed at Braunschweig in 1732, and that this opera is not identical with Conradi's "Sieg der schoenheit," as revised by Telemann.

Cast, scenario, and *avertissement*, which indicates cuts and states:

"Ferner hat man für gut befunden [das] in der dritten handlung am ende des zehenden auftritts befindliche B[allet] nicht vorzustellen, an dessen statt aber soll vor dem schluss-chore ein *Gr[and] Balleten chaconne* von den sämtlichen taentzern und taentzerinnen hin [zu] gefueget und also das gantze werck mit solcher pracht geschlossen werden, [wie] es anfaenget."

The composer, Johann Georg **Conradi**, is not mentioned.   SCHATZ 2180

Sieg der weissheit ueber die liebe.   A. T. of Telemann's Calypso.

Le **siege de Tyr.**   Tragédie en cinq actes.

Venard de La Jonchère, Théâtre lyrique, Paris, 1772, t. ii, 76 p.

"Avant-propos" (p. 3–12). No composer mentioned, nor is any recorded by Clément & Larousse.   ML 49.A2L2

Songs, duets, trios, chorusses, etc., in the **Siege of Belgrade.** An opera, in three acts, now performing at the Theatre-Royal, Drury Lane.

London, J. Jarvis, 1791.   2 p. l., 27 p.   20cm.

Cast. Neither the author, James Cobb, is mentioned, nor Stephen **Storace,** who partly composed the music, partly compiled it from **Martin y Soler's** "Una cosa rara," and other works. Dale's vocal score mentions in the headings besides Martin y Soler, **Paisiello, Salieri,** and **Kelly.**

First performed January 1, 1791, as indicated.   LONGE 207

— The **siege of Belgrade;** a comic opera, in three acts. As it is performed at the Theatres Royal, in London and Dublin . . .

Dublin, Printed and sold by the booksellers, n. d.   48 p.   17½cm.

Cast. Neither author nor composers mentioned.   LONGE 233

           Second copy.   SCHATZ 6020

— Songs, duets, trios, chorusses, etc., in the **Siege of Belgrade.** An opera, in three acts. Now performing at the Theatre Royal, Drury-Lane. The music by the late Mr. Storace.

London, Printed by C. Lowndes, and sold in the theatre, n. d.   23 p. 21½cm.

Cast. As Storace died 1796, this would be the earliest possible date for this edition.   LONGE 263

The **siege of Gibraltar:** A musical farce, in two acts. As it is performed at the Theatre-Royal in Covent-Garden. The second edition. By F. Pilon.

London, G. Kearsley, 1780.   2 p. l., 42 p.   21cm.

Cast and prefatory note, in which Frederick Pilon acknowledges the "very favourite song of 'How stands the glass around, my boys?'" as not his own. The composer, William **Shield,** who partly selected the music from others, is not mentioned.

First performed April 25, 1780, as indicated.   LONGE 95

The siege of Rhodes: the first and second part; as they were lately represented at His Highness the Duke of York's Theatre in Lincolns-Inn Fields. The first part being lately enlarg'd. Written by Sir William D'avenant.

London, Printed for Henry Herringman . . . 1663. 4 p. l., 46 p., 1 l., [2], 61, [2] p. 22^cm.

Signatures: pt. 1: A in four, A₂–F in fours; pt. 2: 2 l. unsigned, B–I in fours.

The second part has special t.-p. and separate paging.

The first part consists of "Entry" first to fifth, preceded by the author's dedication to the Earl of Clarendon, and "The persons represented." The second part consists of five acts, prologue, and epilogue.

This edition contains no allusion to the fact that this was (practically) the first opera produced by D'avenant in 1656 after he obtained permission "for the performance of operas." Especially does this edition not contain the particulars given in the first edition of the libretto, 1656. (*See* Prendergast in "English music," 1906), as, for instance, "a representation by the art of prospective in scenes, and the story sung in *recitative* musick," nor that the vocal music of the first and fifth "entry" of the first part was composed by Henry **Lawes,** of the second and third, by Captain Henry **Cook,** and the fourth, by Matthew **Locke,** nor further, that the instrumental music was composed by Charles **Coleman** and George **Hudson.** The music of this first English opera seems to be lost.   ML 50.2.S62

Die siegende Atalanta. A. T. of Steffani's Die vereinigten mitbuhler.

Die siegende bestaendigkeit. A. T. of Keiser's Bretislaus.

Die siegende grossmuth. A. T. of Telemann's Sancio.

Der siegende Phaeton, in einem sing-spiel auf dem Hamburgischen Schau-platz vorzustellen.

Hamburg, Nicolaus Spieringk, 1702. Unpaged. 18½^cm.

Three acts. Neither the author, Nothnagel, is mentioned, nor the composer, Reinhard **Keiser.**

First performed at Hamburg, 1700, as "Der gedemüthigte Phaeton."

     SCHATZ 5110

Die siegende treue. A. T. of Keiser's Lucius Verus.

Die siegende unschuld. A. T. of Händel's Chelleri and Telemann's Judith, gemahlin Kayser Ludewigs des Frommen.

Der siegreiche koenig der Gothen Alaricus. Als uberwinder des maechtigen Roms, in einem singe-spiel auff dem Hamburgischen Schau-Platze vorgestellet.

Hamburg, Conrad Neumann, n. d. Unpaged. 16½^cm.

Three acts. Argument. Neither the author, Nothnagel, nor the composer, Johann Christian **Schieferdecker,** is mentioned.

First performed, as indicated, 1702.   SCHATZ 9603

Siface. Dramma per musica da rappresentarsi nel Teatro di Sant' Angelo per la solita fiera dell' Ascensione dell' anno 1761.

Venezia, Modesto Fenzo, 1748 [!] 46 p. 14½^cm.

Three acts. Cast, scenario, argument, and name of the composer, Domenico **Fischietti.**

The author of the text is not mentioned, but comparison showed it to be a *rifacimento* of Metastasio's text for Porpora's "Siface," which itself was but a *rifacimento* of some earlier text by unknown author. (*See* below.) Metastasio's dialogue was kept largely intact, but most of his arias have disappeared and others were replaced by texts from other operas of his. For instance I, 4 "Potria fra tanto" if from his

Siface—Continued.

"Achille in Sciro," II, 4 "Più temer non posso ormai" from his "Ipermestra," II, 8 "Io veggo in lontananza" from his "Semiramide." Fischietti's "Siface" has in I, 2 "Della mia sorte altera," Porpora's I, 2 has "Se ti scopro il foco mio," Fischietti's II, 3 has no aria, Porpora's II, 3 has "Porto è vero il sen piagato," Fischietti's II, 4 has "Più temer non deve ormai," Porpora's has "Come nave in mezzo all' onde" and Porpora's III, 9 "Quel basso vapore" was moved to III, 7. Other original "Siface" arias in Fischietti's opera are "Son pellegrin errante" (II, 5), "Rendimi i lacci miei" (II, 11), "Sempre in soglio" (final chorus). "A gli oltraggi della sorte" (II, 14) which is listed by Wotquenne as from Zeno's "Ornospade" (I, 1) appears in Fischietti's "Siface" in II, 13 and in Porpora's "Siface" in II, 14!

It should be noted that Schatz claims Porpora not to have been the first to compose Metastasio's "Siface." He records a setting by Francesco Feo for Naples, Teatro di S. Bartolomeo, spring 1723.

The date in the imprint is a misprint, as the first performance took place as indicated, on April 29, 1761.   SCHATZ 3242

Siface. Dramma per musica da rappresentarsi in Rovigo nel Teatro Venezij per la fiera l'anno MDCCXLIV.

Bologna, Costantino Pisarri, n. d. 1 p. l., 55, [2] p. 14½ cm.

The imprint on first add. p. On second add. p. a list of "Comedie diverse stampate da Costantino Pisarri."

Three acts. By Metastasio, who is not mentioned. (*See* above and next entry.) Dedication by the impresario, Alessandro Paghetti, dated Rovigo, October 10, 1744, argument, cast, scenario, and name of Francesco **Maggiore** as composer.

SCHATZ 5834

Siface. Drama per musica da rappresentarsi nel famosissimo Teatro Grimani di S. Gio. Grioostomo nel carnevale dell' anno MDCCXXVI.

Venezia, Marino Rossetti, 1726. 60 p. 15 cm.

Three acts.

No author is mentioned. Quadrio was the first to attribute the text to Metastasio, who then had this to say about his authorship in a letter written on June 29, 1772, to abbate Vincenzo Cammillo Alberti:

"E un dramma fatto senza volerlo fare: l'idea era di raffazzonare un antico libretto a istanza del maestro **Porpora** (but *see* above) e nel raffazzonarlo fu interamente cambiato . . . ma pure non è mio, ben chè non credo che vi sia rimasto alcun verso del primo autore."

It is unknown to me whose text Metastasio undertook to *raffazzonar*. However, it is a curious fact that the aria "A gli oltraggi della sorte" in II, 14 of "Siface" also occurs and only slightly different in I, 1 of Zeno's Ornospade! This fact was overlooked by Wotquenne, who failed to incorporate several "Siface" arias in his "Verzeichnis" (*See above* Fischietti's Siface.)

Argument, cast, scenario, and name of Nicolà Antonio **Porpora** as the composer. First performed at Milan, Regio Ducal Teatro, December 26, 1725. SCHATZ 8362

— **Syphax,** in einem sing-spiele auf dem Hamburgischen Schauplatze vorgestellet. Im jahr 1727.

[Hamburg], Gedruckt mit Stromerschen schrifften, n. d. Unpaged. 19 cm.

Three acts. Cast, argument, and names of Nicolà Antonio **Porpora** as the composer "der Arien," of Johann Philipp Praetorius as the translator. The arias are printed with Italian and German text.   SCHATZ 8363

Siface e Sofonisba. Dramma per musica da cantarsi nella Real Villa di Queluz per celebrare il felicissimo giorno natalizio di S. M. fedelissima l'augusto D. Pietro III. rè di Portogallo . . . li 5. luglio 1783.

n. pl., n. d., Nella stamperia reale. 34 p. 15 cm.

One act. Argument and cast. Gaetano Martinelli is mentioned as the author, Antonio Leal **Moreira,** maestro del Real Seminario di Lisbona, as the composer.

SCHATZ 6632

Sigismondo primo al diadema. Dramma musicale da rappresentarsi nel famosissimo Teatro di SS. Gio. e Paolo, nell' anno MDCLXXXXVI . . . Composto in musica dal Sign. D. Pietro Romolo abbatte Pignatta.

Venetia, Nicolini, 1696. 62 p. 16^{cm}.

Three acts. Composer's dedication and argument. Text from a "penna illustre" *scil.* Giovanni Grimani, who is not mentioned by name.   SCHATZ 8171

Il signor benefico, ballet. *See* Salieri and Rust's Il talismano.

Il signor benefico, ballet. *See* Tarchi's Il trionfo di Clelia.

Il signor dottore. Dramma di tre atti per musica. Rappresentato per la prima volta in Venezia l'anno MDCCLVIII.

Carlo Goldoni, Opere teatrali, Venezia, Zatta e figli, 1788–95, t. 40, [57]–112 p. 18^{cm}.
See next entry.   PQ

Il signor dottore. Dramma giocoso per musica di Polisseno Fegejo, Pastor Arcade [Goldoni] da rappresentarsi in Monaco di Baviera. nel anno 1760.

[*Monaco*], *Giuseppe Francesco Thuille, n. d. 64,* [1] *p. 15*^{cm}.

Three acts. With name of Domenico **Fischietti** as composer. The additional page contains the substitute arias (I, 6) "Donne belie avete il vanto" and (II, 2) "È un grandissimo piacere."
First performed at Venice, Teatro di San Moisè, fall of 1758.   SCHATZ 3236

— **Il signor dottore.** Dramma giocoso per musica. Da rappresentarsi nel Piccolo Teatro di S. A. E. di Sassonia. Dresda, l'inverno del 1768.

n. i., n. d., 141 p. 16^{cm}.

Three acts. Cast, scenario, and names of Goldoni as author, of Domenico **Fischietti** as composer. German title-page, "Der herr doctor, ein lustiges singspiel," and text face Italian. Differs considerably from the Munich version.   SCHATZ 3237

Il signore benefico, ballet. *See* Zingarelli's Alsinda.

Silla. Drama da rappresentarsi nel Teatro di Sant' Angelo. L'anno MDCLXXXIII . . .

Venetia, Francesco Nicolini, 1683. 58 p. 14½^{cm}.

Three acts. By Andrea Rossini, who is not mentioned. Impresario's dedication, dated Venice, February 4, 1683, argument, scenario, and author's notice to the reader, in which he mentions Giovanni Domenico **Freschi** as the composer, and says:
"Per agiustare il presente drama alla necessità, che seco porta l'angustia del teatro, e la brevità desiderata ne tempi correnti, hò convenuto renderlo come uno scheletro spolpato dalla maggior forza degl' accidenti, essendosi levati non solo moltissimi versi, mà ancora l'intiere mutationi di scena."   SCHATZ 3355

Silla. Drama per musica da rappresentarsi nel Regio Teatro di Berlino per il felicissimo giorno natalizio della Sacra Real Maestà di Sofia Dorotea, regina madre . . .

Berlino, Haude e Spener, 1753. 107, [1] *p. 16½*^{cm}.

Three acts. In the preface the court poet, Giampietro Tagliazucchi, says:
"Venutami leggiadramente in francese scritta [by Frederick the Great, based on Duché's 'Scylla'] mi è convenuto darle l'ornamento della italiana dramatica poesia, perchè sia dell' altro della musica soggettibile."
The composer, Carl Heinrich **Graun**, is not mentioned. German title-page and text (by Francesco Grugnanelli, according to Mennicke) face Italian.
First performed, as indicated, March 27, 1753.   SCHATZ 4116

Silla—Continued.

— **Sylla.** A dramatic entertainment, presented at the King's Theatre in Berlin, on the 27th day of March, 1753. Being the birthday of the Queen Mother. Translated from the French of the king of Prussia, by Mr. Derrick.

London, P. Vaillant, J. Bouquet, [etc.], 1753. vii, [1], 39, [1] p. 19ᶜᵐ.

Three acts. Dedication by Samuel Derrick, dated London, July 11, 1753, translation of Tagliazucchi's "address to the reader," in which he makes it clear that he simply translated the French prose text by Frederick the Great in order to adapt it to the "beauties of Italian music" and to render it fit for a theatrical representation," and "A short account of Sylla." **Graun**, the composer, is not mentioned. English text only.

Not performed in England. LONGE 262

Silvain, comédie en un acte, meslée d'ariettes; par M. Marmontel . . . La musique est de M. Gretry. Représentée pour la première fois par les Comédiens italiens ordinaires du Roi, le 19 février 1770.

Paris, Merlin, 1770. 40 p. 18ᶜᵐ.

Cast. On p. 33–40, the ariettes, "Nos coeurs cessent de s'entendre" (I, 1), "Ne crois pas qu'un long ménage" (I, 3). SCHATZ 4184

— **Silvain,** comédie en un acte, mêlée d'ariettes; par M. Marmontel, de l'Académie Françoise. La Musique est de M. Grétry. Represente pour la premire [!] fois par les Comédiens Italiens ordinaires du Roi, le 19 Février 1770.

Paris, Merlin, 1770. 55 p. 19½ᶜᵐ.

Cast. On p. [47]–55, the "Ariettes de Silvain:" "Nos coeurs cessent," "Ne crois pas qu'un long ménage." The approbation is dated February 21, 1770.

ML 50.2.S63

— **Silvain,** ein singspiel in einem aufzuge aus dem franzoesischen uebersetzt, mit musik.

Frankfurt am Mayn, mit Andreaeischen schriften, 1772. 52 p., 16 p. (folded music). 16½ᶜᵐ.

Neither Marmontel nor **Grétry** nor the translator (Joh. Heinr. Faber) mentioned. The music (bass and voice) consists of "Glaube mir, was ich Dir sage" ("Ne crois pas qu'un long ménage," I, 3), "Ich weiss nicht, ob die schwesterliebe" ("Je ne sçais pas si ma soeur aime," I, 3), and "Er hat längst diesen trieb gespürt" ("Hé comment ne pas le chérir," I, 3). SCHATZ 4185

— **Sylvain,** ein singspiel in einem aufzuge uebersetzt aus dem franzoesischen. Die musik ist vom herrn Grétry. Aufgefuehrt auf dem K. K. Nationaltheater.

Wien, zu finden beym logenmeister, 1778. 39 p. 16½ᶜᵐ.

Translator not mentioned, and unknown to Schatz.
First performed, as indicated, November 18, 1778. SCHATZ 4186

— **Erast und Lucinde.** Eine operette in einem aufzuge. Nach dem Silvain des herrn Marmontel. Neue durch herrn Eschenburg veraenderte auflage. Die musik ist von herrn Gretry.

Muenster, Perrenon, 1777. 43 p. 14½ᶜᵐ.

First performed at Berlin, Theater i. d. Behrenstrasse, October 16, 1773.

SCHATZ 4187

Silvia; or, The country burial. An opera. As it is performed at the Theatre-Royal in Lincoln's-Inn-Fields. With the music pre-fix'd to each song.

London, J. Watts, 1731. 4 p. l., 77, [1] p. 19^{cm}.

Three acts. Ballad opera. Dedication by the author, George Lillo, and table of the 63 songs, the airs of which are printed in the text, with their titles.
First performed November 10, 1730. LONGE 262

La Silvia. Drama pastorale da rappresentarsi nel Teatro Gius-tinian di S. Moisè l'autunno dell' anno 1730 . . .

Veneiazia [!], Carlo Buonarigo, n. d. 45 p. 14½^{cm}.

Three acts. By conte Enrico Bissari (not mentioned). Argument, dedication, cast, notice to the reader. The dedication is dated October 28, 1730. The composer, Bortolamio **Cordans**, is not mentioned.
First performed at Vicenza, Teatro nuovo di Piazza, 1710 (Schatz). SCHATZ 2228

Silvia. Opera pastorale. Da rappresentarsi in musica in Ratis-bona . . .

Ratisbona, n. publ., 1690. Unpaged. 20^{cm}.

Three acts and prologue. With dedication to the participants in the Reichs-versammlung at Ratisbon, February, 1690, signed by the author, Ruggiero **Fedeli**, who also composed the music. German title-page, "Silvia," and text face the Italian.
SCHATZ 3038

Silvie, opéra en trois actes; avec un prologue. Représenté devant Leurs Majestés, à Fontainebleau, le 17 octobre 1765.

[Paris], Christophe Ballard, 1765. 56 p. 20½^{cm}. (Journal des Spectacles, t. ii, 1766.)

Prologue and three acts. Cast and names of Laujon as author, of Le Berton (Pierre Montan **Berton**) and Jean Claude **Trial** as composers.
First performed, as indicated, at the Académie royale de musique, November 18, 1766—not, as incorrectly in the libretto, November 11 (Schatz). ML 48.J7

La sincerità con la sincerità ovvero Il Tirinto. Favola dramma-tica per musica composta e fatta rappresentare dagli Accademici Sfaccendati. Nell' Aricia, l'anno 1672 . . .

Cosmopoli [Roma], 1672. 84 p. 13½^{cm}.

Three acts. Dedication, argument, scenario. Authors and composers not known to Schatz. SCHATZ 11364

Ein singspiel ohne titel in drey aufzuegen.

n. i., n. d. 108 p. 16^{cm}.

Possibly printed after 1800. Neither the author, Leopold Hiesberger, nor the composer, Johann Baptist **Schenck**, is mentioned.
First performed at Vienna, Theater auf der Wieden, November 4, 1790.
SCHATZ 9594

Die singschule oder Drei heirathen an einem tage. Eine komische oper in drei aufzuegen von Ludwig v. Baczko.

Koenigsberg, Hartung, 1794. 84 p. 15½^{cm}.

"Die musik ist von herrn musikdirektor Mile" (Nicolaus **Mühle**).
First performed at Koenigsberg, Ackermannsches Theater, 1794. SCHATZ 6872

Sir Politick Ribband. A. T. of The state juggler.

Sirita.

Apostolo Zeno, Poesie drammatiche, Venezia, 1744, t. vi, p. [183]–269. 19ᶜᵐ.

Three acts and licenza. Argument. No composer is mentioned. In the "Catalogo," at end of t. x, date and place of first ed. are given as Vienna, 1719. (*See* below).

ML 49.A2Z3

— Sirita. Pubblicata per la prima volta in Vienna 1719.

Apostolo Zeno, Poesie drammatiche, Orleans, 1785–86, t. v, p. 87–166. 21ᶜᵐ.

Three acts. Argument. No composer is mentioned. ML 49.A2Z4

Sirita, dramma per musica, da rappresentarsi nell' imperial favorita . . . per le felicissime nozze de serenissimi principi Maria Gioseffa arciduchessa d'Austria e Federico Augusto, principe ereditario di Sassonia. La poesia è del Sig. Apostolo Zeno . . . La musica è del Sig. Antonio Caldara . . .

Vienna d'Austria, Gio. Van Ghelen, 1719. 4 p. l., 72 p. 15½ᶜᵐ.

Three acts and licenza. Argument and scenario. The ballet music was composed by Niccola Matteis.

First performed, as indicated, at Laxenburg, August 20, 1719. Schatz 1487

Il Siroe.

70 p. 19ᶜᵐ. (Pietro Metastasio, Opere drammatiche, Venezia, Giuseppe Bettinelli, 1733–37, v. 2.)

Three acts. Argument. No composer mentioned. ML 49.A2M4

— Siroe.

Metastasio, Poesie, Parigi, vedova Quillau, 1755, t. iii, [111]–215 p. 16ᶜᵐ.

Three acts. Argument. ML 49.A2M42

— Siroe. Rappresentato con musica del Vinci la prima volta in Venezia, nel carnevale dell' anno 1726.

pl., [223]–336 p. 26ᶜᵐ. (Pietro Metastasio, Opere, t. iii, Parigi, vedova Herissant, 1780.)

Three acts with licenza. Argument. ML 49.A2M44

— Siroes.

Metastasio, Tragedies opera, Vienne, 1751, t. iii, 127 p. 14ᶜᵐ.

Three acts. Richelet's translation of "Siroe." ML 49.A2M47

Il Siroe. Dramma per musica da rappresentarsi nel Gran Ducal Teatro di Bronsevigo nella fiera d'estate del anno MDCCLXVII.

n. i., n. d. 151 p. 15½ᶜᵐ.

Three acts. Argument, scenario. German title page, "Der Siroes," and text face Italian. A 19th cent. ms. note on the t.-p. reads: "Gedichtet von Metastasio. In musik gesetzt von **Vinci, Händel, Wagenseil, Bioni, Hasse,** Vivaldi, u. s. w." Of course, this "in musik gesetzt" is misleading, since the music of this pasticcio was not composed for the occasion, but selected. Schatz 11365

Siroe. Dramma per musica da rappresentarsi nel Teatro di S. Benedetto nel carnevale dell' anno MDCCLXXI.

Venezia, Modesto Fenzo, n. d. 62 p. 18ᶜᵐ.

Siroe—Continued.

Three acts. By Metastasio. Argument, cast, scenario, and name of the composer, Giovanni Battista **Borghi.** On p. 27–30 detailed description of Charles Lepicq's ballet "Gli amanti protetti dall' Amore." The composer of the music is not mentioned.

First performed in January 1771 as indicated.   SCHATZ 1237

Siroe. Dramma per musica da rappresentarsi nel famosissimo Teatro Grimani di S. Gio. Grisostomo, nel carnovale dell' anno 1750.

Venezia, All' insegna della scienza, n. d. 59 p. 15^{cm}.

Three acts. By Metastasio. Cast, scenario, and name of the composer, Gioacchino **Cocchi.**   SCHATZ 2041

Siroe. *See* Hasse's Siroe, rè di Persia.

Siroe. Dramma per musica da rappresentarsi nel Nuovo Teatro in Padova per la solita fiera di giugno 1753 . . .

Padova, Conzatti, 1753. 78 p. 17½^{cm}.

Three acts. By Metastasio, who is not mentioned. Dedication, argument, cast, scenario, and name of Gaetano **Latilla** as composer.

First performed at Rome, Teatro delle Dame, carnival, 1740.   SCHATZ 5451

Siroe. Dramma per musica da rappresentarsi nel famosissimo Teatro Grimani di Sr Giõ. Grisostomo nel carnevale 1743 . . .

n. i., n. d. 1 p. l., 60 p. 15½^{cm}.

Three acts. By Metastasio, who is not mentioned. Argument, scenario, cast, and name of Gennaro **Manna** as composer.   SCHATZ 5902

Siroe. Dramma per musica da rappresentarsi nel Regio Teatro di Torino nel carnovale del 1780 . . .

Torino, Onorato Derossi, n. d. viii, 60 p. 15½^{cm}.

Three acts. By Metastasio, who is not mentioned. Argument, cast, scenario, and name of Giuseppe **Sarti** as composer. With the opera were performed, music by Vittorio Amedeo Canavasso, Sebastiano Gallet's ballets "Rinaldo nella Selva incantata," "Ninetta, o sia La contadina nel palazzo signorile," and "L'incoronazione di Siroe," descriptions of which are noted to have been published separately.

First performed, as indicated, December 26, 1779.   SCHATZ 9464

Siroe. Drama per musica da rappresentarsi nel Regio Teatro di Torino nel carnovale del 1750 . . .

Torino, Pietro Giuseppe Zappata e figliuolo, n. d. 4 p. l., 61 p. 16^{cm}.

Three acts. By Metastasio, who is not mentioned. Argument, scenario, cast, and names of Giuseppe **Scarlatti** as composer of the opera, of Alessio Rasetti of the three ballets, which had no specific titles.

First performed December 26, 1749, as indicated; at Florence, Teatro in via della Pergola, summer of 1742.   SCHATZ 9557

Il Siroe. Dramma per musica da rappresentarsi nel Nuovo Teatro di corte . . . nel carnovale 1767. La poesia è del Signor abbate Pietro Metastasio . . . La musica è del Signor Tommaso Trajetta . . .

Monaco, appresso Marie Magdalene Mayrin, n. d. 173, [24] p. 16^{cm}.

Three acts. German title page "Siroes" and text face Italian. Argument, scenario, cast. On the [24] p. description (in German and French) and cast of Chalandray's two ballets "Persée & Andromede" and "La liaison de l'Amour et de Bachus."

                    ML 50.2.S6T8

Siroe, rè di Persia. Drama per musica, da rappresentarsi nel Regio Teatro di Torino nel carnovale del 1730 . . .

Torino, Gio. Battista Valetta, n. d. 3 p. l., 54, [1] p. 15½ᶜᵐ.

Three acts. By Metastasio. Argument, scenario, cast, and name of the composer, Stefano Andrea **Fiorè**, "maestro di cappella di S. M. il rè di Sardegna, etc."

First performed, as indicated, December 26, 1729. SCHATZ 3193

Siroe, rè di Persia.

Text by Metastasio; music by **Hasse.**
His so-called first setting first performed at Bologna, May 2, 1733.
Not in L. of C.

— Siroes, king of Persia. An opera perform'd at the King's Theatre in the Hay-Market.

London, Charles Bennet, 1736. 83 p. 17ᶜᵐ.

Three acts. Argument and cast. English text faces the Italian. Neither Metastasio, the author of "Siroe" (as in caption title), nor Johann Adolph **Hasse**, the supposed composer, is mentioned. (*See* next entry.)

First performed, as indicated, November 23, 1736. SCHATZ 4587

— Siroe, dramma per musica da rappresentarsi nel Regio Teatro di Dresda per il gloriosissimo giorno di nome di Sua Maestà Augusto III . . . La poesia è del Sig. abbate Metastasio. La musica è del Sig. Hasse . . .

Dresda, Stamperia regia, 1763. 3 p. l., 87, [2] p. 17ᶜᵐ.

Three acts and licenza. Argument and scenario. Schatz and Mennicke call this Hasse's second version of the text, which is not quite the same as in the London (1736) edition. For instance, London has, in I, 1, the aria, "Dovea svenarti allora", (from Metastasio's Catone in Utica), whereas Dresden has "Se il mio paterno amore;" London has, in I, 3, the aria, "Dille pur che il suo riposo," which is not in the Dresden edition, and is not by Metastasio at all; Dresden has, in I, 5, the aria, "D'ogni amator la fede," whereas London has "Ancor io pensai d'amore," which is also not by Metastasio; Dresden has, in I, 8, the aria, "O placido il mare," whereas London has "Nel cor il mio pensier," which is not by Metastasio. Considering that Metastasio's dialogue has been freely tampered with, and that so many arias are neither from his "Siroe" nor by him at all, it becomes clear that this London "Siroe" (by Schatz and Mennicke so-called first version of the "Siroe" text) was really a pasticcio, and though Hasse presumably composed the new numbers, at its best, a Hasse pasticcio, though Burney (IV, 400) says: "Composed by Hasse. This is the first time that I ever perceived the composer of an opera named in the advertisements and bills of the day."

First performed at Dresden, as indicated, August 3, 1763. SCHATZ 4562

— Siroës. Opera, qui sera representé au Théatre Royal de Varsovie au carnaval de l'an MDCCLXIII.

Varsovie, Michel Groell, n. d. Unpaged. 16½ᶜᵐ.

Three acts. Argument and scenario. The composer, Joh. Ad. **Hasse,** is not mentioned. German title page, "Siroes," and text faces this French translation of Metastasio's text. The opera was, of course, performed in Italian. SCHATZ 4592

Siroe, rè di Persia. Drama per musica da rappresentarsi nel Teatro detto delle Dame nel carnovale dell' anno 1727 . . .

Roma, Bernabò, n. d. 72 p. 15ᶜᵐ.

Three acts. By Metastasio, who is not mentioned. Argument, scenario, cast, name of Niccola **Porpora** as composer, and dedication to "Clementina regina della Gran Bretagna," in which this is called the second opera of the season.

ML 50.2.S64P6

Siroe, rè di Persia. Drama per musica di Artino Corasio Pastore Arcade da rappresentarsi nel Teatro di S. Bartolomeo nel carnevale dell' anno 1727 . . .

Napoli, Angelo Vocola, 1727. 64 p. 14½ cm.

Three acts. By Metastasio. Impresario's dedication, argument, scenario, cast, and name of Domenico **Sarro** as the composer also of the two intermezzi by an unknown author, on p. 57–64, "MOSCHETTA E GRULLO," performed with the opera.

SCHATZ 9420

Siroe, rè di Persia. Drama per musica di Artino Corasio Pastore Arcade. Da rappresentarsi nel famosissimo Teatro Grimani di S. Gio. Grisostomo nel carnevale dell' anno 1731 . . .

Venetia, Carlo Buonarigo, n. d. 70 p. 14 cm.

Three acts. By Metastasio. D dication by Domenico Lalli, argument, cast, and scenario. The composer, Leonardo **Vinci,** is not mentioned.

First performed at Venice, same theatre, carnival, 1726.   SCHATZ 10749

Siroe, rè di Persia. Drama per musica da rappresentarsi nel Teatro dell' illustriss. pubblico di Reggio in occasione della fiera dell' anno MDCCXXVII . . .

Reggio, li Vedrotti, 1727. 72 p. 16½ cm.

Three acts. By Metastasio (not mentioned). Impresario's dedication, dated Reggio, April 29, 1727, argument, cast, scenario, name of Antonio **Vivaldi,** and note to the effect that "per comodo della musica," the arias, "Non si presto il suo colore" (I, 9) and "Vado con alma sorte" (II, 13) were substituted.   SCHATZ 10780

Siroes. Tr. of Metastasio's Siroe text.

Siroës. *See* Hasse's Siroe, rè di Persia.

Siroes. Tr. of Traetta's Siroe.

Siroes, king of Persia. *See* Hasse's Siroe, rè di Persia.

Il Sismano nel Mogol. Dramma serio per musica da rappresentarsi in Cremona nel Teatro Nazari il carnevale dell' anno 1785.

Cremona, Manini, n. d. 46 p. 15 cm.

Three acts. Impresario's dedication, argument, cast, scenario, and names of Giovanni de Gamerra as the author, of **Paisiello** as the composer. With the opera were performed Luigi Corticelli's ballets "Adelaide" and "Il tutore ingannato." The composer of the music is not mentioned.

First performed at Milan, Regio Ducal Teatro, January, 1773.   SCHATZ 7697

Skibbruddet ved Cypren. Tr. of Sarti's Il naufragio di Cipro.

Den skiønne Arsene. Tr. of Monsigny's La belle Arsene.

The skirts of the camp. A. T. of Shield's Hartford-Bridge.

Skovhuggeren eller De tre ønsker. Tr. of Philidor's Le bucheron.

Slaves in Algiers; or, A struggle for freedom: A play, interspersed with songs, in three acts, by Mrs. Rowson. As performed at the New Theatres, in Philadelphia and Baltimore.

Philadelphia, Printed for the author, 1794. 2 p. l., ii, 72, [2] p. 16 cm.

Three acts, prologue, and epilogue. Dedication of "this first dramatic effort" "to the citizens of the United States of North America;" cast and preface in which Susanna Rowson says that her play is founded in part on Cervantes, that she hopes some

Slaves in Algiers—Continued.

alterations made since the first performance have improved her play, that she returns her thanks to the performers, "since it was chiefly owing to their exertions that the play was received with such unbounded marks of approbation." As to Alexander **Reinagle** she acknowledges her obligation "for the attention he manifested, and the taste and genius he displayed in the composition of the music."

First performed at Philadelphia, New Theatre, December 22, 1794.

PR 1241.D7 v.9

La smorfiosa. Intermezzi per musica a tre voci da recitarsi nel Teatro alla Valle nel carnevale dell' anno 1756 . . .

Roma, Ottavio Puccinelli, 1756. 24 p. 15^{cm}.

Two parts. Author not mentioned and unknown to Schatz. Cast, name of **Rinaldo di Capua** as composer and dedication signed by the publisher and Angelo Lungi. Contains arias: "Signor Tenente non serve niente," "Se a un bel canto lusinghiero," "Cosi per terra," etc. ML 50.2.S66R4

— La smorfiosa. Intermezzi per musica a tre voci da rappresentarsi nel pubblico Teatro di Lucca nel carnevale dell' anno MDCCLXII. In occasione delle recite in prosa da farsi dall' Accademia de' dilettanti della Comica . . .

Lucca, Filippo M. Benedini, 1762. 26 p. 15^{cm}.

Two acts. Author unknown to Schatz. Composed by **Rinaldo di Capua**, who is not mentioned. SCHATZ 8799

La smorfiosa. Intermezzi à tre voci da recitarsi nel Teatro alla Valle il carnevale dell' anno 1748 . . .

Roma, Ottavio Puccinelli, 1748. 21 p. 15^{cm}.

Two intermezzi. Author not mentioned and unknown to **Schatz**. Dedication by Angelo Lungi and the publisher, cast and name of Gregorio **Sciroli** as composer. Contains the arias: "Lasciate fare, non dubitare," "Gia mi fà Galeno al core," "Qual colomba innamorata," "E nemico, e non amante," etc. Entirely different text from that of Rinaldo di Capua's opera. ML 50.2.S66S2

The smugglers; a musical drama, in two acts. As it is performed at the Theatre Royal, Drury Lane. By Samuel Birch.

London, C. Dilly, 1796. 2 p. l., 37, [1] p. 21^{cm}.

Cast and prefatory note. The composer, Thomas **Attwood,** is not mentioned. In Longman & Broderip's vocal score "My fathers before me" is headed as "Sung and composed by Mr **Suett**." LONGE 238

First performed April 13, 1796, as indicated.

The snake in the grass: A dramatic entertainment, of a new species; being neither tragedy, comedy, pantomime, farce, ballad, nor opera.

[87]–114 p. 21^{cm}. (Aaron Hill, Dramatic works, London, 1760, vol. ii.)

One act. No composer or performance recorded by Clarence. LONGE 326

The snuff box; or, A trip to Bath. A comedy of two acts, as it was performed at the Theatre Royal in the Hay-Market. By William Heard . . . [vignette]

London, Printed for the author), 1775. 4 p. l., 26 p. 21^{cm}.

Prologue, dedication, dated Martlet-Court, Bow-street, May 13, 1775, in which this is called "the first effort of an inexperienced Muse" and preface, from which it appears that the piece was "intended for a comic opera" (and it is so printed), but that it was performed without "the embellishments of music" except the song "With head thrown back," composed "in a most elegant style" by James **Hook**. LONGE 310

So bessert sie sich. Tr. of Martin y Soler's La capricciosa corretta.

So prellt man alte fuechse. Eine komische operette in einem aufzuge, nach dem franzoesischen des Moliere. Die musik dazu ist von Johann Christoph Kaffka.

n. i., n. d. p. [127]–180. (Sammlung auserlesener theaterstücke, Breslau, 1784.) 17^cm.

Detached copy. Text by August Gottlieb Meissner and the composer.
First performed at Breslau, Neues Wäsersches Theater, 1782.　　Schatz 4987

Socrate immaginario. Commedia per musica da rappresentarsi nel Piccolo Teatro di S. A. E. di Sassonia.

Dresda, n. publ., 1781. 183 p. 15½^cm.

Three acts. By Ferdinando Galiani and Giambattista Lorenzi, who are not mentioned. German title-page, "Der eingebildete Sokrates and text face Italian."
First performed 1781, as indicated; at Portici, Teatro di Corte, December 23, 1775; and at Naples, Teatro Nuovo sopra Toledo in October of the same year.　Schatz 7658

Il Socrate immaginario. Dramma giocoso per musica da rappresentarsi nel nobile Teatro di San Samuele il carnovale dell' anno 1776.

Venezia, Gio. Battista Casale, 1776. 32 p. 17½^cm.

One act. Author not mentioned and unknown to Schatz. Cast and name of the composer, Giacomo **Rust.**　　　　　　　　　　　　　　　Schatz 9170

Sofonisba. Dramma per musica del Sig. Mattia Verazzi, poeta e secretario intimo di S. A. E. Elettoral Palatina da rappresentarsi nel Teatro Vendramino di S. Salvatore la fiera dell' anno 1764 . . .

Venezia, Modesto Fenzo, 1764. 58 p. 14½^cm.

Three acts. Dedication, argument, cast, scenario, and name of the composer, Antonio **Boroni.**　　　　　　　　　　　　　　　　Schatz 1251

Sofonisba. Drama per musica da rappresentarsi nel famosissimo teatro Grimani di S. Gio. Grisostomo. L'autunno dell' anno MDCCVIII. Consegrato . . . da Francesco Silvani.

Venezia, Marino Rossetti, 1708. 71, [1] p. 14½^cm.

Three acts. With author's dedication dated Venice, November 22, 1808, argument, notice to the reader with name of Antonio **Caldara** as composer, cast, and scenario.
　　　　　　　　　　　　　　　　　　　　　　　　Schatz 1500

Sofonisba. Dramma per musica da rappresentarsi nel Regio Teatro di Torino nel carnovale del 1764 . . .

Torino, Gaspare Bayno, n. d. viii, 55, [1] p. 16^cm.

Three acts. By Matteo Verazj, who is not mentioned. Argument, cast, scenario, and name of Baldassare **Galuppi** as composer. With the opera were performed Augusto Huss' ballets "La contribuzione sforzata," "La costanza affricana soccorsa dall' arte magica," and "Le allegrezze per le vittorie di Scipione," music by Giuseppe Antonio Le Messier. The ballets are described on p. 53–55.　　Schatz 3470

La Sofonisba. Dramma per musica da rappresentarsi nel Regio Ducal Teatro di Milano nel carnovale dell' anno 1744 . . .

Milano, Giuseppe Richino Malatesta, 1744. 6 p. l., 51, [1] p. 15^cm.

Three acts. Recitatives by Francesco Silvani, most of the lyrics from Metastasio's works. (*Comp.* Wotquenne). Dedication dated Milan, January 13, 1744, argument, cast, scenario, and the name of **Gluck** as the composer.　Schatz 3932

Sofonisba. Drama per musica da rappresentarsi nel famosissimo Teatro Grimani di S. Gio. Grisostomo nel carnevale MDCCXLVI.

[Venezia], n. publ., n. d. 1 p. l., 60 p. 14½ᶜᵐ.

Three acts. By Antonio and Girolamo Zanetti, who are not mentioned. Argument, cast, scenario, and name of Niccolò **Jommelli** as the composer.
(Abert incorrectly 1749, on p. 5; correctly 1746, on p. 46.) SCHATZ 4871

Sofonisba. Drama per musica da rappresentarsi nel Teatro di S. Bartolomeo nel carnevale dell' anno 1718 . . .

Napoli, Michele Luigi Muzio, 1718. 75 p. 13½ᶜᵐ.

Three acts. Dedication by Nicola Serino, dated Naples, January 22, 1718, argument, scenario, cast, and name of Leonardo **Leo** as composer. The author, Francesco Silvani, is not mentioned. SCHATZ 5555

Sofronia, ed Olindo. Azione tragica per musica di Carlo Sernicola, P. A. da rappresentarsi nel Real Teatro di S. Carlo nella Quaresima del 1793 . . .

Napoli, Vincenzo Flauto, 1793. 39 p. 18½ᶜᵐ.

Two acts. Impresario's dedication dated Naples, February 17, 1793, cast, and name of Gaetano **Andreozzi** as composer. SCHATZ 200

— Olindo e Sofronia. Dramma per musica da rappresentarsi nel Teatro Venier in San Benedetto la primavera dell' anno 1798.

Venezia, Modesto Fenzo, 1798. 50 p. 18ᶜᵐ.

Two acts. Cast, scenario, and name of composer, Gaetano **Andreozzi**, but not of librettist. Pages 37–50 contain cast and detailed description of "Riccardo cuor di Lione, ballo eroico pantomimo in sei atti" by Salvatore Vigano. Giuseppe Waigel [!] is mentioned as the composer of the music. SCHATZ 220

Il sogno. Componimento drammatico, scritto d'ordine sovrano dall' autore in Vienna l'anno 1756, ed eseguito la prima volta con musica del Reütter ne' privati appartamenti dell' imperatrice regina, dall' A. R. dell' arciduchessa Marianna, e da due dame della sua corte.

[417]–430 p. 26ᶜᵐ. (Pietro Metastasio, Opere, t. 4, Parigi, vedova Herissant, 1780.)

One act. Argument. ML 49.A2M44

Il sogno. Nuovo componimento dramatico del Sig. abbate Pietro Metastasio, Poeta Cesareo, da cantarsi dalla Serenissima arciduchessa Marianna figlia primogenita delle LL. MM. Imp. e da due dame dell' imperial corte di Vienna l'anno 1757. [vignette]

Pisa, Gio. Paolo Giovanelli e comp., n. d. 1 p. l., xv p. 22½ᶜᵐ.

Vignettes, head and tail pieces. On p. [2] medaillon portrait "Pietrus Metastasius. Poeta. Caesareus. / Apollini Austriaco MDCCLIV."
One act. Argument and name of Georgio Reutter (Johann Adam Joseph **Carl Georg Reutter**) as the composer.
First performed at Vienna, privately before Maria Theresia, 1757. SCHATZ 8696

Il sogno di Scipione.

Metastasio, Poesie, Parigi, vedova Quillau, 1755, t. ii, [405]–430 p. 16ᶜᵐ.

One act and licenza. ML 49.A2M42

— Il sogno di Scipione. Azione teatrale, allusiva alle sfortunate campagne delle armi Austriache in Italia; rappresentata la prima volta con musica del Predieri nell' Imperial Favorita, alla presenza

Il sogno di Scipione—Continued.

de' Sovrani, il di primo ottobre 1735, per festeggiare il giorno di nascita dell' imperator Carlo VI . . .

[335]–358 p. 26ᶜᵐ. (Pietro Metastasio, Opere, t. i, Parigi, vedova Herissant, 1780.)

One act and licenza. Argument. ML 49.A2M44

Il sogno di Scipione. Drammatico componimento da rappresentarsi nel Regio Teatro di Berlino per ordine di Sua Maestà.

Berlin, A. Haude, 1746. 45, [2] p. 16ᶜᵐ.

Two parts. The Italian title page is preceded by German title page, "Der traum des Scipio," and German text faces Italian. Neither Metastasio, the author, nor Christoph **Nichelmann,** the composer, is mentioned.

First performed, as indicated, March 27, 1746. SCHATZ 7103

La soirée à la mode. A. T. of Le cercle.

La soirée des boulevards, ambigû mêlé de scenes, de chants, & de danses. Représentés pour la premiere fois par les Comédiens italiens ordinaires du roi, le 13 novembre 1758.

Paris, N. B. Duchesne, 1759. 36 p. 19ᶜᵐ.

One act. Cast. Neither the author, Charles Simon Favart, is mentioned, nor the arranger of the popular airs, etc, who, according to Font, also contributed original music. SCHATZ 11514

— La soirée des boulevards, ambigu mêlé de scenes, de chants, & de danses; représenté pour la premiere fois par les Comédiens italiens ordinaires du roi, le 13 novembre 1750 [!]. Nouvelle édition.

Paris, N. B. Duchesne, 1759. 60, [4], 16 p. 19ᶜᵐ. (Theatre de M. Favart, Paris, Duchesne, 1763–77, t. iv.)

One act. Again the composer and arranger of the music is not mentioned. The [4] p. contain catalogues of plays and opera music. The 16 p. contain six "Airs et vaudevilles de la Soirée des boulevards." They are followed by

— Supplément de la Soirée des boulevards; représentée pour la premiere fois, par les Comédiens italiens, ordinaires du roi, le 10 mai 1760.

Paris, Duchesne, 1760. 64 p. 19ᶜᵐ.

One act. Cast. Several of the airs and vaudevilles are printed in the text. According to Font, the text of this sequel was partly by Panard and Guérin

ML 49.A2F1

La soirée orageuse, comédie en un acte et en prose, mêlée d'ariettes; par M. Radet; musique de M. d'Alayrac: représentée pour la première fois par les Comédiens italiens ordinaires du roi, le samedi 29 mai 1790.

Paris, Brunet, 1791. 40 p., [14] l. 19½ᶜᵐ.

Cast. The unnumb. l. contain (printed on inside p.) seven airs and one vaudeville from the opera, all, with one exception, with guitar accompaniment, and all, with two exceptions, with Imbault's imprint. ML 50.2.S67D2

Il solachianello. A. T. of Pietro Guglielmi's La finta zingana.

Der soldat als zauberer. Tr. of Philidor's Le soldat magicien.

Le **soldat magicien**, opera-comique en un acte; représenté pour la première fois sur le Théâtre de l'Opéra-comique de la Foire S. Laurent, le 14 août 1760.

> *Paris, Duchesne, 1760. 76 p. 20ᶜᵐ.*

Cast. Neither Anseaume, the author, is mentioned, nor **Philidor**, the composer. On p. 67–76 the same airs as below. ML 50.2.S68P4

— Le **soldat magicien**, opera-comique en un acte; représenté pour la premiere fois sur le Théâtre de l'Opéra-comique de la Foire S. Laurent, le 14 août 1760.

> *Paris, la veuve Duchesne, 1775. 51 p. 18½ᶜᵐ.*

On p. 43–51, "Airs choisis du Soldat magicien": "Femme qu'on offense" (I, 3), "Tous les voeux d'une fillette" (I, 7), "L'hymen est à craindre" (I, 10). Neither Anseaume, the author, nor **Philidor**, the composer, is mentioned. Schatz 8024

— Der **soldat als zauberer**, eine komische oper in einem aufzuge aus dem franzoesischen uebersetzt von F. W. M. Die musik ist von Hn. Philidor.

> *Mannheim, C. F. Schwan, 1772. 80 p. 14ᶜᵐ.*

Transl. by Friedrich Ludwig Wilhelm Meyer. Schatz 8025

— Arien der komischen operette: Der **zaubernde soldat**. In einem akte.

> *n. i., n. d. 14 p. 16ᶜᵐ.*

On p. 3, this note:
"Das stueck ist aus dem franzoesischen, und die arien unter die musik des herrn **Philidor** von dem uebersetzer des Sancho Panssa untergelegt," which points to Johann Joachim Eschenburg. Schatz 8026

Il **soldato per forza impazzito per amore**. Intermezzo a quattro voci da rappresentarsi nella presente stagione nel Teatro di questa città . . .

> *Pavia, Porro, Bianchi e comp., n. d. 36 p. 16ᶜᵐ.*

Imprimatur dated at end, April 22, 1775 or 1774.
Two acts. Antonio **Sacchini** is mentioned as the composer. The author, Tommaso Mariani, is not mentioned.
First performed, as "Il finto pazzo per amore," at Rome, Teatro aila Valle, spring of 1765. Schatz 9221

— Der **verstellte narr aus liebe**. Ein singspiel in zwey aufzuegen. Aus dem italiaenischen uebersetzt, auf die musick des herrn Ant. Sacchini . . . Aufgefuehrt in dem K. K. National-Theater.

> *Wien, beym Logenmeister, 1779. 52 p. 16ᶜᵐ.*

Two acts. Transl. by Gottlieb Stephanie d. jüng.
First performed, as indicated, April 6, 1779. Schatz 9222

Soliman. Tr. of Hasse's Solimano.

Soliman den Anden. Comoedie i tre acter, efter hr. Favarts Soliman Second. Med nye arier forøget, hvortil musiken er sat af hr. secretaire Thomas Christian Walter.

> *n. i., n. d. 111 p. 16½ᶜᵐ.*

By Charlotte Dorothea Biehl, who is not mentioned.
First performed at Copenhagen, Court theater, February 17, 1778. Schatz 10867

Soliman der Zweite, oder Die drei sultaninnen. Ein singspiel in zwey aufzuegen. Nach dem franzoesischen des herrn Favart bearbeitet von Franz Xaver Huber. Die musik ist von hrn. Franz Xav. Suessmayer . . . Aufgefuehrt auf den k. k. Hoftheatern.

Wien, J. B. Wallishauser, 1799. 88 p. 16½cm.

First performed October 5, 1799, as indicated. SCHATZ 10182

Soliman Second, comédie en trois actes, en vers; par M. Favart: représentée pour la premiere fois par les Comédiens italiens ordinaires du roi, le 9 avril 1761. Et remise au Théâtre de 19 décembre de la même année.

Paris, Duchesne, 1762. 4 p. l., 118 p. 19cm. (Theatre de M. Favart, Paris, Duchesne, 1763–77, t. iv.)

The 4 p. l. contain besides the t.-p., catalogues of plays, etc., and Favart's dedication to the duc de Richelieu. No cast! On p. 100–102 the Divertissement, a *fête turque* and errata, on two unnumb. p. Favart's privilege and then on p. 103–118 six "Airs de Soliman Second et de la Feste turque." The arranger and composer of the music, Paul César **Gibert,** is not mentioned. ML 49.A2F1

— Soliman second; ou, Les trois sultanes, comédie en trois actes et en vers par M Favart. Représentée pour la première fois par les Comédiens italiens, ordinaires du roi le 9 avril 1761 & remise au Théâtre le 19 Décembre de la même année. Nouvelle édition.

Paris, Didot l'aîné, 1772. 64 p. 19cm.

The composer, Paul César **Gibert,** is not mentioned. For the revival of January 16, 1777, he partly set the text anew. ML 48.M2N

Solimano. Dramma per musica da rappresentarsi nel Regio Teatro di Torino nel carnovale del 1782 . . .

Torino, Onorato Derossi, n. d. viii, 63, [1] p. 17cm.

Three acts. Argument, cast, scenario, and name of the composer, Giuseppe Maria **Curcio** ("Curci"). The author is unknown to Schatz. With the opera were performed Sebastiano Gallet's "Aci e Galatea, favola ridotta in ballo eroico," "La fiera di Batavia, ballo comico," and "Il Beiram, o sia Il carnovale turco," music of all three by Vittorio Amedeo Canavasso.

First performed, as indicated, January 19, 1782. SCHATZ 2301

Solimano. Dramma per musica da rappresentarsi nel Teatro Giustinian di S. Moisè nel carnovale 1755.

Venezia, Modesto Fenzo, 1755. 58 p. 15cm.

Three acts. By Giannambrogio Migliavacca, who is not mentioned. Cast, scenario, and name of Domenico **Fischietti** as composer. SCHATZ 3240

Solimano. Drama per musica da rappresentarsi nel Teatro della Regia elettoral corte di Dresda, nel carnevale dell' anno MDCCLIII. La poesia è del Sigʳ Giannambrogio Migliavacca . . . La musica è del Sigʳᵉ Gio. Adolfo Hasse . . .

Dresda, la vedova Stössel, n. d. 4 p. l., 92 p. 19cm.

Three acts. Argument, cast, and scenario.

First performed, as indicated, February 5, 1753. SCHATZ 4563

— Solimano. Dramma per musica da rappresentarsi nel Teatro della Regia elettoral corte di Dresda, nel carnevale dell' anno MDCCLIV. La poesia è del Sigʳᵉ Giannambrogio Migliavacca . . . La musica è del Sigʳᵉ Gio. Adolfo Hasse . . .

Dresda, la vedova Stössel, n. d. 7 p. l., (double) 92 p. 23cm.

Solimano—Continued.

Three acts. Argument, cast, scenario. German title page, "Soliman," and text face Italian, which is practically the same as in the 1753 edition.

First performed, as indicated, January 7, 1754.   SCHATZ 4564

Solimano. Drama per musica da rappresentarsi nel nobilissimo Teatro di S. Benedetto il carnovale dell' anno MDCCLXXIII.

Venezia, Modesto Fenzo, 1773. 52 p. 17½^{cm}.

Three acts. Author not mentioned and unknown to Schatz. Argument, cast, scenario, and name of Johann Gottlieb **Naumann** as the composer.

On p. 24 brief description of the ballet "Il rè alla caccia" by Gasparo Angiolini, who also composed the music.   SCHATZ 7062

Solimano. Dramma per musica da rappresentarsi nel Real Teatro dell' Ajuda in occasione di festeggiarsi il felicissimo giorno natalizio di Sua Reale Maestà . . . D. Marianna Vittoria . . . nella primavera dell' anno 1768.

Lisbona, Michele Maneschal da Costa, n. d. 70 p. 18^{cm}.

Three acts. Author not mentioned and unknown to Schatz. Argument, cast, scenario, and name of David **Perez** as the composer.

Performed as indicated, March 31, 1768; previously at Lisbon, Theatro provisional do Barracão da Ajuda, 1757.   SCHATZ 7877

Solimano. Dramma per musica da rappresentarsi nel nobilissimo Teatro Tron di S. Cassano l'autunno dell' anno 1766.

Venezia, Modesto Fenzo, 1766. 56 p. 16^{cm}.

Three acts. Author not mentioned and unknown to Schatz. Dedication signed A. C. and dated Venice, November 22, 1766, argument, cast, and name of Gregorio **Sciroli** as the composer.   SCHATZ 9784

Solimano. Dramma per musica da rappresentarsi nel Regio Teatro di Torino nel carnovale del 1756 . . .

Torino, gli Zappata et Avondo, n. d. x, [2], 76 p. 15½^{cm}.

Three acts. By Giannambrogio Migliavacca, who is not mentioned. Argument, cast, scenario, and name of Michel Angelo **Valentini** as composer. With the opera were performed (brief descriptions in the libretto) three ballets by Vincenzo Saunier, music by Rocco Gioanetti, "Di selvaggi," "Del Bezestan, o Mercato di schiavi" and "Di Marte, Venere e la Gloria."   SCHATZ 10587

Solimano II, ballet. *See* Bianchi's Seleuco.

Il **Solimano Secondo,** ballet. *See* Caruso's Il matrimonio in commedia.

Il **Solimano secondo,** ballet. *See* Gassmann's L'amore artigiano.

Solimano II, ballet. *See* P. Guglielmi's Le pazzie di Orlando.

Solimano II o sia La francese trionfante, ballet. *See* Anfossi's Lucio Silla.

Il **solitario reso sociabile per amore,** ballet. *See* Cimarosa 's Il convito.

Solone. *See* M. Curzio.

La somiglianza, ossiano I gobbi. Drama giocoso per musica, da rappresentarsi nel Teatro Elettorale.

Dresda, n. publ., 1793. 135 p. 15ᶜᵐ.

Two acts.. The author, Cosimo Mazzini, is not mentioned. **Portugal is men-tioned** as the composer. German title-page, "Die taeuschende aehnlichkeit oder Die buckeligen," and text face Italian.

First performed at Dresden on December 4, 1793, as indicated; at Florence, Teatro Palla a Corda, spring of 1793, under the title, "La confusione della somiglianza ossiano I due gobbi" as probably the first of Portugal's operas performed in Italy.

SCHATZ 8400

— **I due gobbi.** Dramma giocoso in musica da rappresentarsi nel nobilissimo Nuovo Teatro di Padova l'autunno dell' anno 1793 . . .

Padova, li fratelli Conzatti, n. d. 51 p. 18ᶜᵐ.

Two acts. Dedication, cast, and name of Marcos **Portugal** as the composer.
With this title, the opera was first performed in Siena spring of 1793.

SCHATZ 8445

— Arien und gesaenge aus dem komischen singspiel **Verwirrung durch aehnlichkeit** in zwey aufzuegen aus dem italienischen frey uebersetzt von C. Herklots. Die musik ist von Marco Portogallo.

n. i., 1795. 46 p. 16ᶜᵐ.

Two acts. Cast.
First performed at Berlin, Kgl. Nationaltheater, August 3, 1795. SCHATZ 8401

The **son-in-law**, a comic opera: as it acted at the Theatres Royal in London and Dublin.

Dublin, Printed for the booksellers, 1788. 32 p. 15½ᶜᵐ.

Two acts. Neither the author, John O'Keefe, is mentioned, nor the composer, Samuel **Arnold**.
First performed at London, Haymarket, August 14, 1779. LONGE 223

Il **sonambulo**, ballet. *See* Andreozzi's Amleto.

Das **sonnenfest der Braminen.** Ein heroisch-komisches original-singspiel in zwey aufzuegen, fuer die k. k. privil. Marinellische schau-bühne von Karl Friedrich Hensler. Die musik ist von herrn **Wenzel Mueller**, kapellmeister.

Wien, Schmidt, 1790. 60 p. 17ᶜᵐ.

Cast and dedication dated "Im herbstmonat 1790."
First performed, as indicated, September 9, 1790. SCHATZ 6965

— Het **feest der Braminen**, zangspeel.

Amsteldam, I. Helders en A. Mars, 1798. 3 p. l., 79, [1] p. 17ᶜᵐ.

Dedicatory sonnet by the translator, Salomon Bos.
First performed at Amsterdam, Nationale Stads schouwburg, 1798. SCHATZ 6966

Das **sonntagskind.** L. T. of Wenzel Müller's Das neusonntagskind.

Sophie, ou Le mariage caché, comédie en trois actes, mêlée d'ariettes. La musique est de M. Kohaut. Représentée pour la premiere fois par les Comédiens italiens ordinaires du roi, en 1770.

Paris, veuve Duchesne, 1771. 46 p. 16½ᶜᵐ.

By Madame Riccoboni, who is not mentioned.
Date above incorrect; first performed there June 4, 1768. SCHATZ 5207

Sophie et Moncars, ou L'intrigue portugaise; comédie lyrique en trois actes et en prose, mêlee de chants: Représentée pour la premiere fois à Paris sur le Théâtre de la rue Feydeau, le 9 vendémiaire an VI de la République (30 septembre 1797). Par J. H. Guy. Mise en musique par P. Gaveaux.

Paris, Tiger, an VI (1797. v. st.).   2 p. l., 60 p.   21ᶜᵐ.
Cast.   ML 50.2.S7G2

Sophie et Sigismond.   *See* Les desesperés.

Sophonisbe: ein musikalisch drama, mit historischem prolog und choeren von A. G. Meissner.

Leipzig, Dykische buchhandlung, 1776.   32 p.   15ᶜᵐ.

One act. "Die musikbegleitung ist von herrn musik direktor **Neefe.**" In the "Vorbericht," dated Dresden, July 23, 1776, the author dwells at considerable length on the problem of "diese art von drama," meaning the "melodrama" of Benda, Neefe, etc. At the end he says that he had contemplated going more into detail about the dramaturgic problem of prologues for purposes of dramatic exposition, but gave up the idea since he heard that a similar work was to leave the press soon.

First performed at Frankfurt a/M, Theater im Junghof, 1778.   Schatz 7072

— **Sophonisbe.**   Ein musikdrama von herrn Meissner.   Die musik ist von herrn Neefe.

n. i., n. d.   [109]–129 p.   14½ᶜᵐ.
Detached copy.   From his Collected works, published after 1800?   Schatz 11724

Le sorcier, comedie lyrique, meslée d'ariettes en deux actes: représentée pour la premiere fois par les Comédiens françois ordinaires du roi, le [*blank*] 1767 . . .

Copenhague, Cl. Philibert, 1767.   68 p.   19ᶜᵐ.

Cast, author's dedication, names of **Philidor** as composer and of Poinsinet as author, who says, in a note:

"Je profite de cette occasion pour avertir le public au sujet de l'équivoque qu'a souvent occasionné la conformité du nom de mon cousin avec le mien; c'est pour la prevenir désormais que M. Poinsinet de Sivri, auteur de l'élégante traduction des poëtes lyriques Grecs . . . ne prendra plus que le nom de Sivri . . ."

According to Tiersot, Philidor helped himself to music from Gluck's Orpheus.
For date of first performance, *see* next entry.   Yudin PQ

— **Le sorcier,** comédie lyrique, meslée d'ariettes, en deux actes, représentée pour la premiere fois par les Comédiens italiens ordinaires du roi, le lundi 2 janvier 1764.

Paris, la veuve Duchesne, 1770.   67 p.   17½ᶜᵐ.

Neither the author, Poinsinet is mentioned, nor **Philidor,** the composer. On p. 55–67, the air of the vaudeville "Loin de l'objet de ma tendresse" (II, 12) and the "Airs du Sorcier:" "Jeune fillette" (I, 4), "Sur les gazons" (II, 2), "Dans le sein de la liberté" (II, 12), "Rien ne peut bannir," substitute air for "Non ma mère" (I, 3).   Schatz 8027

— **Der zauberer,** ein singspiel in zween aufzuegen aus dem franzoesischen uebersetzt, mit musik.

Frankfurt am Mayn, mit Andreaeischen schriften, 1772.   110 p., 12 p. (music)   16ᶜᵐ.

Cast.   Transl. for Theod. Marchand's company by Johann Heinrich Faber.   Neither he nor **Philidor** is mentioned.   The music (voice and pf.) consists of "Faengt der stahl nur an zu glühn" (I, 1, "De ce linge que je repasse"), "Am baum dort" (II, 2, "Sur les gazons"), "Als mir das schicksal" (II, 12, "Dans le sein de la liberté").
                                                              Schatz 8028

Le sorelle rivali. Dramma giocoso per musica da rappresentarsi nel Teatro di Monza l'autunno dell' anno 1782 . . .

Milano, Gio. Batista Bianchi, n. d. 63 p. 15½cm.

Three acts. By Giovanni Bertati, who is not mentioned. Dedication, cast, scenario, and note: "Musica in buona parte del Sig. maestro [Giovanni] **Valentini** ed in parte d'altri celebri autori." With the opera were performed Antonio Bertini's ballets, "Il matrimonio inaspettato" and "Le pastorelle difese," the composers of the music not being mentioned.

First performed at Brescia, Teatro dell' Accademia degli Erranti, 1781; at Venice, Teatro di S. Moisè, December 26, 1780, as "La statua matematica." SCHATZ 10586

De sorte naeser. A. T. of Wedel's Serenaden.

Il sospetto senza fondamento. Dramma pastorale fatto rappresentare da gli Accademici Oscuri per festivo applauso al giorno natalizio del Sereniss. principe Ferdinando di Toscana.

Firenze, Stamperia di S. A. S. alla Condotta, 1691, Ad istanza di Andrea Orlandini. 43 p. 16½cm.

Three acts. Dedication signed by Andrea Orlandini, whom Schatz calls the author. Composer not mentioned, and unknown to Schatz.

First performed, as indicated, August 9, 1691. SCHATZ 11366

The sot. A burletta, in two parts. As it is performed at the Theatre Royal in the Hay market. Altered from Fielding. The music composed by Dr. Arne.

London, Cox and Bigg, 1775. 2 p. l., [1], 10–35 p. 20½cm.

The caption title is "'Squire Savage. Part the first." The prefatory advertisement reads:

"The characters and design of this piece are taken from a ballad opera, written by Henry Fielding, Esq.

"Some of the songs are likewise written by that celebrated author; but many others, with the quintetto and chorus necessarily added, and the measure of the dialect is obliged to be changed throughout, on account of its being delivered in recitative.

"Dr. Arne is sensible of the disadvantage attending all dramatic performances, deprived of their greatest ornaments, viz.—Action, characteristic, dress and scenes; but a restrictive Act of Parliament, (intended chiefly to prevent strolling vagabonds from infesting the town with their paltry attempts; but no way meant to suppress native genius, when displayed by persons of undoubted establishment and reputation) has unfortunately prevented the Dr. from displaying his productions in the most advantageous manner, he humbly hopes (supposing it was difficult to draw a line between the two extremes) that the public, ever favourable and indulgent, will, as in oratorios, by the assistance of printed books, supply with their ever fertile imagination, this unavoidable deficiency which, as now, will hereafter give him a fair opportunity to exert his best endeavours towards the entertainment of his gracious patrons, without infringing the interdicts of the said Act."

The piece was advertised for first performance on March 16, 1772, as "a new burletta, called *'Squire Badger''* (Cummings), and, according to Clarence, was printed in 1772 under that title. LONGE 274

Il sotteraneo ossia Catterina di Coluga, ballet. *See* Nasolii's Len feste d'Iside.

Les souliers mors-dorés ou La cordonniere allemande, comédie lyrique en deux actes; représentée pour la premiere fois sur le Théatre des Comédiens italiens ordinaires du roi, le jeudi 11 janvier 1776.

Paris, Vente, 1776. 63 p. 19cm.

Cast. Neither de Ferrières, the author, nor **Fridzeri,** the composer is mentioned in the libretto. On p. 59–63 the melodies of the "*Air.* Bien loin d'oser douter" and the "*Vaudeville.* Chez l'etranger, on apprécie." SCHATZ 3372

Le **souterrain.** A. T. of Dalayrac's Camille.

Airs, duets, trios and finale, introduced in the comedy of The **Spanish barber.** As performed at the Theatre-Royal in the Hay-Market. The third edition.

> *London, T. Cadell, 1783. 12 p. 21*ᶜᵐ.

Text by George Colman (who is not mentioned) and founded on Beaumarchais' "Barbier de Seville." Samuel **Arnold,** who partly composed, partly adapted the music, is not mentioned.

First performed, August 30, 1777. LONGE 91

The **Spanish lady,** a musical entertainment, in two acts. Founded on the plan of the old ballad. As perform'd at the Theatre Royal in Covent-Garden . . .

> *London, J. Cooper, n. d. 35 p. 18½*ᶜᵐ.

Cast, dedication, and preface dated, Theatre-Royal, Covent-Garden, December 8, 1769, which reads in part:

"The following scenes were written on receiving the news of a signal conquest, gained in the Spanish West Indies, by the English forces in the year 1762, and intended as a small tribute to the noble family who had the direction of that important expedition. It was accordingly licensed and rehearsed, when some public commotions in the theatrical world, prevented the intended exhibition; since which, it has been once acted for a performer's benefit.

"It has now undergone some few changes and abridgments, and is to be considered merely as the story of the Spanish lady, in a dramatic dress . . . With the aid of the music (which has been selected under the inspection of an eminent composer), it is hoped the piece may not prove unentertaining to a delicate and susceptible mind . . ."

The author, Thomas Hull, is not mentioned. The composer, who selected the music, is not recorded by W. Barclay Squire.

First performed May 2, 1765, as indicated. LONGE 150

The **Spanish rivals.** A musical farce, in two acts, as performed at the Theater-Royal in Drury-Lane.

> *London, J. Almon, 1784. 1 p. l., 34 p. 21*ᶜᵐ.

Cast and dedication, in which the author, Mark Lonsdale, calls this the "first offering of a Cumbrian Muse." The composer, Thomas **Linley,** is not mentioned. He utilized, as appears from Thompson's vocal score, a number of folk-dances.

First performed November 4, 1784 (Schatz); November 5 (Tufts). LONGE 95

Spartaco. Dramma per musica, da rappresentarsi nell' Imperial Corte . . . nel carnevale dell' anno MDCCXXVI. La poesia è del Sig. abate Giovan Claudio Pasquini. La musica è del Sig. Giuseppe Porsile . . .

> *Vienna d'Austria, Gio. Pietro Van Ghelen, n. d. 4 p. l., 70 p. 16½*ᶜᵐ.

Three acts. Argument, scenario, and name of Niccola Matteis as composer of the ballet music.

First performed, as indicated, February 21, 1726. SCHATZ 8377

La **Spartana generosa,** ovvero Archidamia, dramma per musica rappresentato . . . in occasione delle doppie auguste nozze celebrate in Dresda. L'anno MDCCXXXXVII. La poesia è del Sign. abbate Gio. Claudio Pasquini . . .

> *n. i., n. d. 7 p. l., 174 p. 15½*ᶜᵐ.

At end: "Dalla Stampa regia per la vedova Stössel."

Three acts. Argument, cast, and scenario. Johann Adolph **Hasse,** the composer is not mentioned. German title page, "Die grossmuethige Spartanerin, oder Archidamia," and text face Italian.

First performed, as indicated, June 14, 1747. SCHATZ 4565

Lo **spazzacamino,** ballet. *See* Bianchi's Ines de Castro.

Lo **spazzacamino.** L. T. of Portugal's Lo spazzacamino principe.

Lo **spazzacamino principe.** Commedia con musica d'un atto solo da rappresentarsi nel nobilissimo Teatro Giustiniani in San Moisè il carnovale dell' anno 1794.

Venezia, Modesto Fenzo, 1794. 48 p. 18^{cm}.

By Giuseppe Foppa, who is not mentioned. Cast and name of Marcos **Portugal** as the composer. After the opera was performed Urbano Garzia's comic ballet "Il quadro animato." The composer of the music is not mentioned.
First performed, as indicated, January 4, 1794 (Carvalhaes).   Schatz 8417

— Lo **spazzacamino.** Commedia con musica d'un atto solo da rappresentarsi nel Teatro Elettorale.

Dresda, n. publ., 1794. 48 p. 16^{cm}.

By Giuseppe Foppa, who is not mentioned. Marco Portogalli (**Portogallo**) is mentioned as the composer.   Schatz 8418

— Il **barone Spazzacamino.** Farza in prosa di un solo atto da rappresentarsi nel Regio Teatro di S. Carlo offerto al rispettabil publico di Lisbona da Giuseppe Tavani nel giorno del suo benefizio ai 27 maggio 1799.

Lisbona, Simone Taddeo Ferreira, 1799. 103 p. 14½^{cm}.

Cast and name of Marco **Portogallo** as the the composer. Portuguese text faces Italian, which is practically Giuseppe Foppa's "Lo spazzacamino principe."
        Schatz 8433

— Der **schorsteinfeger Peter,** oder Das spiel des ohngefaehrs. Eine komische oper in zwei akten. Nach dem italiaenischen singspiele *lo Spazzacamino* frei bearbeitet von K. H. Zschiedrich.

Pirna, Arnold und Pinther, 1799. 2 p. l., 80 p. 15^{cm}.

Name of **Portogallo** as composer, and translator's preface, dated Dresden, May, 1799, in which he says that Brocchi selected Portugal's opera, "Lo spazzacamino," for his debut at Pillnitz (near Dresden), with great succ ss. He then continues:
"Hier sahe sie der bearbeiter derselben mit vergnuegen und glaubte dem teutschen operntheater nicht unnuetz zu werden, wenn er ihm dies lustige machwerk eignete.
"Dies geschahe mit mannichfaltigen noethigen abaenderungen des plans, mit veredlung des karakters der Donna Flora, der, unter der welschen maske, dem sittlichen vaterlaendischen zuschauer schwerlich behagen konnte und mit vertheilung *einer* handlung in *zwo;* jedoch unter beibehaltung der ganzen lokalitaet und der schoenen musik."
First performed at Dresden, Theater vor dem schwarzen Thore, May 22, 1799.
        Schatz 8419

Lo **spazzacamino principe.** Commedia con musica divisa in due atti' e tolta dal francese da rappresentarsi nel Teatro di Monza l'autunno 1790 . . .

Milano, Gaetano Motta, n. d. 4 p. l., 68 p. 16^{cm}.

Two acts. Dedication by the impresario, Antonio Puttini, in which he calls this "uno spettacolo che è il primo di questo genere, che compaja in Italia." The author, Giuseppe Carpani, who is not mentioned by name, takes his mouth still more full in his notice to the public. He, too, insists on the novelty saying of his version of "Le ramoneur prince:"
"non vi avendo musica, si poteva, col farvela tra noi, riunire per la prima volta ai pregj dell' opera francese la pompa, e le attrative della musica italiana, e dar cosi uno spettacolo, o signori, novissimo e ben degno di voi, e che imitato venendo produrrebbe all' Italia una quantità di attori, ed arricchir potrebbela di bellissime commedie alla musica accomodote."
On a slip pasted on p. l. 4, the note: "La musica sarà tutta nuova del cel. Sig. maestro Angelo **Tarchi**." With the opera was performed (composer of the music not mentioned) Urbano Garzia's ballet, "La cosa rara."   Schatz 10238

Il **speciale ingannato.** A. T. of the ballet Il mercato di Pozzuolo.

Les **spectacles malades.** Prologue. Par Mᵐ le S * * * d'Or * * représenté à la Foire Saint Laurent 1729.

Le Théâtre de la foire, Paris, 1731, t. vii, pl., [213]–240 p. 17ᶜᵐ.

By Le Sage and d'Orneval. Largely *en vaudevilles.* The airs, selected or composed and arranged by Jean Claude **Gillier,** the "compositeur" of the company, are printed at the end of the volume in the "Table des airs."

First performed August 29, 1729. ML 48.L2VII

Lo **speziale.** Dramma di tre atti per musica. Rappresentato per la prima volta in Venezia l'anno 1753 con musica del Pallavicini e del Fishietti.

Carlo Goldoni, Opere teatrali, Venezia, Zatta e figli, 1788–95, t. 42, p. [109]–158. 18ᶜᵐ. PQ

Lo **speziale.** *See also* Fischietti's Il bottanico novellista.

Lo **speziale.** Dramma giocoso per musica di Polisseno Fegejo pastor Arcade da rappresentarsi nel Teatro Grimani di S. Samuel, nel carnovale dell' anno 1755 . . .

Venezia, Modesto Fenzo, 1755. 48 p. 14½ᶜᵐ.

Three acts. By Goldoni. Impresario's dedication, cast, scenario, names of Vincenzo **Pallavicini** and Domenico **Fischietti** as composers, and notice to the reader, which reads:

"Ponendosi nel frontispizio il nome arcadico dell' autore, ben conosciuto, ha egli desiderato, che si faccia sapere al mondo, essere stato da lui composto il presente libretto tre anni sono in Bologna ad istanza del Sig. Francesco Baglioni e del Sig. Francesco Carratoli, in tempo che colà trovavasi colla compagnia del Sig. Girolamo Medebac.

"Tale protesta intende egli di fare per sua giustificazione verso di quelli, che lo caricano ingiustamente aver trascurato di scrivere per il Comico suo Teatro per lucrare con altri. Egli ha libertà di scrivere per teatri di musica. Il Filosofo di Campagna lo ha scritto nella Quaresima passata, in tempo, che non potea prevedere la malatia sofferta per cinque mesi. Ma a chi mai rende egli conto di ciò la gente oziosa, e maligna, che non ha che fare con lui."

First performed, according to Schatz, at Milan, Regio Ducal Teatro, 1754, *but see* above the entry from Goldoni's works. SCHATZ 7714

— Lo **speziale,** dramma giocoso per musica, da rappresentarsi nel Nuovo Teatro di Dresda l'anno MDCCLV. Der Apotheker . . .

[Dresden], Gedruckt bey der verwitt. . . . Stoesselin und . . . Johann Carl Krausen, n. d. 131 p. 16½ᶜᵐ.

Three acts. Cast and scenario. German text faces Italian. Neither Goldoni nor the composers, **Pallavicini** and **Fischietti,** are mentioned. The Dresden text seems to follow the original closely. SCHATZ 7715

Der **spiegel von Arkadien.** Eine grosse heroisch-komische oper in 2 aufzuegen. Von Emanuel Schikaneder.

n. i., 1796. 79 p. 15ᶜᵐ.

Franz Xaver **Suessmayr** is mentioned as the composer. *See also* his "Die koenigin der Schwarzen inseln.

First performed at Vienna, Theater auf der Wieden, November 14, 1794. SCHATZ 10183

— Der **spiegel von Arkadien.** Eine heroisch-komische oper in zwei aufzuegen. Unter dem titel: Die neuen Arkadier neubearbeitet und zum erstenmal auf dem Hoftheater zu Weimar den 2. februar 1796 aufgefuehrt. Die musik ist von Franz Suessmeyer.

Weimar, Hoffmannische Buchhandlung, 1796. 4 p. l., 120 p. 17ᶜᵐ.

Der **spiegel von Arkadien**—Continued.

This title page followed by a special t.-p. with the new title.

In his "Vorrede," Christian August Vulpius (not mentioned) under date of "Weimar, am tage Renata, 1796" says:

"Wer das original dieser oper kennt, deren bearbeitung ich hier liefere, der wird finden, was ich dabei geleistet habe, oder nicht. Ich habe anderswo (In den Rheinischen Musen, 5 bd., 1 St. S. 67-72) als ich diese arbeit begann, schon etwas darueber gesagt."

Vulpius then takes issue with Schikaneder for having given the piece an incorrect title, for having made of Arcadia an island and other such silly and absurd nonsense, and he continues:

"Der dialog aller handelnden personen ist groesstentheils ganz neu fuer gesittete und deutsche zuschauer geschrieben worden und die verse sind allenthalben abgeaendert . . . Freilich, die musik war da und der neue text musste derselben erst angepasst werden, und daher kamen die fesseln, in die ich mich sehr ungern schmiegen musste."   SCHATZ 10184

Gesaenge aus dem singspiele: Der **spiegelritter,** in drey aufzuegen, vom praesidenten von Kotzebue. In musik gesetzt von Ignaz Walter.

Hamburg, Freystatzky und Rabe, 1795. 51 p. 16½cm.

First performed at Hamburg, Theater beim Gänsemarkt, October 26, 1795; at Frankfurt a. M., Nationaltheater, September 11, 1791.   SCHATZ 10865

— Der **spiegelritter,** eine oper in drey aufzuegen.

n. i., n. d. front., [321]–448 p.

Obviously detached from some volume of an edition (before 1800?) of August von Kotzebue's collected works, as the opera libretto is followed on p. [449]–476, by his "Einige zuege aus dem leben des guten Musaeus von der hand seines schuelers entworfen." In the "Vorbericht" to the opera, Kotzebue says:

"Man hat mich oft aufgefordert, doch auch einmal eine oper nach heutigem zuschnitt zu verfertigen, und da habe ich denn endlich eine gemacht. Der leser wird hoffentlich finden, dass sie eben so naerrisch und abentheuerlich und albern ist, als ihre aeltern geschwister auf der deutschen buehne. Unter allen operibus eines schriftstellers ist eine solche oper das leichteste opus. Der himmel mache mich so gluecklich, als er die herren Eberl & consorten gemacht hat; das heisst: er schenke meinem Spiegelritter eine musik, wie die der Dittersdorffe, Mozart's, Martin's oder Reichard's, so wird sich der bursche wohl durch die welt helfen."

                                                                    SCHATZ 10865a

Das **spiel des ohngefaehrs.** A. T. of Portugal's Der schorsteinfeger Peter.

Lo **spirito di contraddizione.** Dramma giocoso per musica da rappresentarsi nel Teatro di S. A. E. di Sassonia, composto dal Signor Caterino Mazzolà . . .

Dresda, n. publ., 1785. 139 p. 15½cm.

Two acts. Joseph **Schuster** is mentioned as composer. German title-page, "Der geist des widerspruchs," and text face Italian.

First performed, as indicated, April 20, 1785.   SCHATZ 9757

Lo **spirito di contradizione.** Dramma giocoso per musica del Signor Gaetano Martinelli Romano. Da rappresentarsi nel Teatro Giustiniani di San Moisè il carnovale dell' anno 1766.

Venezia, Modesto Fenzo, 1766. 70 p. 15cm.

Three acts. Cast, scenario, and name of Pietro **Guglielmi** as the composer.

                                                                    SCHATZ 4305

Lo spirito di contradizione. Dramma giocoso per musica da rappresentarsi nel Real Teatro di Salvaterra nel carnovale dell' anno 1772.

Lisbona, Stamperia reale, n. d. 98 p. 16[cm].

Three acts. Argument, cast, scenario, and names of Gaetano Martinelli as author, of Girolamo Francesco Lima (Jeronymo Francisco de Lima) as composer.

Schatz 5616

The spoil'd child. A farce, in two acts. As performed at the Theatre in Boston. First American edition.

Boston, Thomas Hall, 1796. 28 p. 15½[cm].

Cast. Neither the author, Bickerstaffe, is mentioned, nor the composer of the incidental music.

First performed in America as a "musical farce" at Baltimore, October 27, 1794.

PR 1241.D7 v. 7

Li sponsali d'Enea. Drama per musica da rappresentarsi nel Teatro di S. Angelo nella Fiera dell' Ascensione . . .

Venezia, Girolamo Savioni, 1731. 48, [1] p. 14½[cm].

Three acts. Impresario's dedication, argument, notice to the reader cast and scenario. Neither the author, Francesco Passarini, nor the composer, Michele Fini, is mentioned.

Schatz 3104

La sposa bisbetica. Dramma giocoso per musica da rappresentarsi nel Teatro di S. A. S. il Signor principe di Carignano nella primavera dell' anno 1798.

Torino, Onorato Derossi, n. d. 4 p. l., 46, [4] p. 15[cm].

Two acts. Author not mentioned and unknown to Schatz and Piovano. Cast, scenario, and name of [Pietro Carlo] Guglielmi as the composer.

First performed at Rome, Teatro Valle, carnival, 1797.

Schatz 4312

— La sposa di stravagante temperamento. Dramma per musica da rappresentarsi nel nob. Teatro di S. Cassiano nella state 1798.

Venezia, Antonio Rosa, n. d. 17[cm].

Incomplete, ending with p. 46.

Two acts. Cast and name of Pietro [Carlo] Guglielmi as the composer. The text is that of his "La sposa bisbetica," but with alterations. For instance, I, 4, now begins "Fate largo, buona gente," instead of "Mie care donnette." Schatz 4313

La sposa bizzarra. Opera buffa di Egesippo Argolide, Pastore Arcade della Colonia Alfèa. Da rappresentarsi nel Teatro Giustiniani in S. Moisè per la terza opera di carnovale l'anno 1781.

Venezia, n. publ., n. d. 53 p. 17[cm].

Two acts. By Carlo Giuseppe Lanfranchi Rossi, who is not mentioned. Cast and name of Alfonso Santi as the composer. Schatz 9394

La sposa contrastata. Commedia per musica di Saverio Zini da rappresentarsi nel Real Teatro del Fondo di Separazione per terz' opera di questo corrente anno 1791.

Napoli, Vincenzo Flauto, n. d. 43 p. 14½[cm].

Two acts. Cast and name of Pietro Guglielmi as the composer. On p. 4–7, cast, prefatory note, and argument of Giovanni Battista Giannini's "Il moro di corpo bianco o sia Lo schiavo del proprio onore, ballo di carattere," music ("tutta nuova") by Giuseppe Ercolano. Schatz 4269

La sposa costante. A. T. of S. Viganò's La creduta vedova.

La sposa di stravagante. L. T. of P. C. Guglielmi's La sposa bisbetica.

La sposa fedele. Dramma giocoso per musica da rappresentarsi nella prossima primavera dell' anno 1765[?]. Nel Teatro in Cremona in proprietà di un nobile di detta città . . .

Cremona, Ricchini, n. d.   48 p.   17^{cm}.

Three acts. Cast and dedication. Neither the author, Pietro Chiari, is mentioned, nor the composer. If the date in the title is 1769, instead of 1765, then this might have been a replica of Pietro **Guglielmi's** opera of the same title, first performed at Venice 1767.   ML 50.2.S72

La sposa fedele. Dramma giocoso per musica da rappresentarsi in Lisbona nel Teatro della rua dos Condes nell' autunno dell' anno 1773.

[Lisbona], Stamperia reale, n. d.   85 p.   16^{cm}.

Three acts. By Pietro Chiari, who is not mentioned. Cast, scenario, and name of Pietro **Guglielmi** as the composer. With the opera was performed (composer of the music not mentioned) Giuseppe Magni's ballet "La vedova scaltra."
First performed at Venice, Teatro di S. Moisè, carnival, 1767.   SCHATZ 4270

— **La sposa fedele,** dramma giocoso per musica da rappresentarsi nel Regio Teatro Danese.—Den troe bruud . . .

Kiøbenhavn, Lars Nielsen Svare, 1768.   127 p.   17½^{cm}.

Three acts. Cast and name of Pietro **Guglielmi** as the composer. Chiari is not mentioned. Danish text faces Italian.
First performed, as indicated, 1768.   SCHATZ 4271

— **La sposa fedele.** Dramma giocoso per musica. Da rappresentarsi nel Piccolo Teatro di S. A. E. di Sassonia.

Dresda, n. publ., 1771.   131 p.   16½^{cm}.

Three acts. Name of Pietro **Guglielmi** as the composer. Chiari is not mentioned. German title-page, "Die getreue braut," and text, calling the composer "Don Petro Wilhelm," face Italian.
First performed, as indicated, 1771, but also previously, 1768.   SCHATZ 4272

— **Robert und Kalliste,** oder Der triumph der treue. Eine operette in drey akten. Nach dem inhalte der Sposa fedele von Johann Joachim Eschenburg.

Breslau und Leipzig, n. publ., 1776.   62 p.   15^{cm}.

Pietro **Guglielmi** is not mentioned as composer.
First performed at Berlin, Theater in der Behrenstr, April 8, 1775. SCHATZ 4273

La sposa gronlandese, ballet. *See* Piccinni's La pescatrice.

La sposa in equivoco. Dramma giocoso per musica da rappresentarsi nel nobile Teatro Giustiniani in San Moisè l'autunno dell' anno 1791.

Venezia, Modesto Fenzo, 1791.   84 p.   17^{cm}.

Two acts. By unknown librettist. Impresario's dedication ("Si riapre . . . questo teatro"), cast, scenario, and name of Francesco **Bianchi** as composer. On pages 45–53, argument, cast, and full description of "Le donne invidiose ossia L'onestà trionfante, ballo giocoso pantomimo," by Giuseppe Scalesi, music ("tutta nuova") by Vittorio Trento, and p. 80–84, of "Enrichetta, comico pantomimo," by the same authors.   SCHATZ 1007

La sposa invisibile. Dramma buffo per musica da rappresentarsi nel Teatro di S. A. E. di Sassonia.

Dresda, n. publ., 1788.   99 p.   15½^{cm}.

Two acts. Author unknown to Schatz. German text and title-page, "Die unsichtbare braut," face Italian. Vincenzo **Fabrizj** is mentioned as composer.
First performed, as indicated, February 20, 1788; at Rome, Teatro Capranica, carnival, 1786.   SCHATZ 2970

La sposa persiana. Drama giocoso ter[!] musica da rappresentarsi nel nobile Teatro di San Samuele nell' autunno dell' anno 1775.

Venezia, Carcani, n. d. 55 p. 16½ᶜᵐ.

Three acts, based on Goldoni's comedy of the same title, possibly by the impresario, Onorato Viganò, who signed the dedication. Cast and name of Felice **Alessandri** as composer. Carlo Canobbio is mentioned as the composer of the music of the first ballet.

SCHATZ 155

La sposa persiana, ballet. *See* Anfossi's Il curioso indiscreto.

La sposa peruviana, ballet. *See* Martin y Soler's Vologeso.

La sposa polacca. Dramma giocoso per musica da rappresentarsi nel Teatro di Sant' Angelo nella primavera dell' anno 1799.

Venezia, Casali, n. d. 62 p. 17½ᶜᵐ.

Two acts. Cast and name of composer, **Bernardini** (Marcello di Capua), who is also mentioned as librettist.

First performed at Rome, Nuovo Teatro di Apollo, December 26, 1795.

SCHATZ 852

La sposa rapita, ballet. *See* Portugal's La donna di genio volubile.

La sposa tra le imposture. Commedia per musica di Francesco Antonio Signoretti da rappresentarsi nel Teatro Nuovo sopra Toledo per prim' opera di quest' anno 1798.

Napoli, n. publ., 1798. 51 p. 15ᶜᵐ.

Two acts. Cast and name of Luigi **Mosca** as the composer.

SCHATZ 6725

La sposa volubile ossia L'amante imprudente. Dramma giocoso per musica per celebrare l'augusto nome di Sua Altezza Reale . . . D. Carlotta Gioacchina . . . da rappresentarsi nel Reggio Teatro di S. Carlo l'autunno dell' anno 1795.

Lisbona, Simone Taddeo Ferreir, 1795. 173 p. 15ᶜᵐ.

Two acts. Author unknown to Schatz. Cast, name of the composer, Luigi **Caruso,** and scenario. Portuguese text faces Italian.

First performed, as indicated, November 4, 1795; at Rome, Teatro della Valle, summer, 1789.

SCHATZ 1654

Lo sposalizio de' Morlacchi, ballet. *See* Caruso's Oro non compra l'amore.

Lo sposalizio per dispetto. Dramma giocoso per musica di Giovanni Bertati da rappresentarsi nel Teatro Giustiniani in S. Moisè per la prima opera del carnevale l'anno 1782.

Venezia, n. publ., n. d. 61 p. 17ᶜᵐ.

Two acts. Cast and name of Gaetano **Monti** as the composer.
First performed, as indicated, December 26, 1781.

SCHATZ 6600

Le spose ricuperate. A. T. of Caruso's I campi Elisi.

Li sposi contenti, ballet. *See* Martin y Soler's L'isola piacevole.

Gli sposi delusi dalle astuzie di Crespino, ballet. See Cimarosa's Artaserse.

Li sposi in commedia. L. T. of Caruso's Il matrimonio in commedia.

I sposi in rissa. Farsa di un' atto per musica di G. M. D.[iodati] La musica è del P. D. Bernardo di Fraja dilettante attual organista di M. Casino.

Napoli, n. publ., 1791. 24 p. 14½^{cm}.

Cast.
First performed at Naples, Teatro Nuovo, 1791.　　　　　　SCHATZ 3314

Gli sposi per inganno, ballet. *See* G. Giordani's Caio Ostilio.

I sposi perseguitati. Commedia per musica di Pasquale Mililotti da rappresentarsi nel Teatro Nuovo sopra Toledo per terza opera del corrente anno 1782.

Napoli, n. publ., 1782. 64, [1] p. 14½^{cm}.

Three acts. Cast and name of Niccolò **Piccinni** as the composer. On the additional page the substitute recitative and aria (I, 8) "Come li dentro intesi"—"Ahi, che parlar non posso" with this note:
"Non essendo l'aria di Vernold dell' atto primo confacente alla sua voce, e trasportandola, avrebbe perduta l'armonia."
On p. 3 this *avvertimento:*
"Essendosi stabilito dal sig. impresario di far rappresentare per terza opera la presente commedia rappresentata nello stesso Teatro nell' anno 1769. Per adattarlo alla presente compagnia, si son dovute tradurre in Toscano quattro parti Napolitane, cioè la parte di Bettina, di Melampo, di Nanella, che se le è dato il nome di Lesbina, e di Rina, a cui si è dato il nome di Ninetta. Le suddette parti sono state tradotte quasi ad literam per non uscir dalla favola, e non cambiare i pezzi di musica, che fecero allora una sorprendente riuscita."　　　　　　SCHATZ 8140

Li sposi ridicoli burlati, ballet. *See* Anfossi's Gli amanti canuti.

Lo sposo burlato, ballet. *See* Caruso's Il vecchio burlato.

Lo sposo burlato. *See* Dittersdorf's "Der gefoppte braeutigam."

Lo sposo burlato. Intermezzi in musica da rappresentarsi nei Teatri privilegiati di Vienna nell' anno 1770.

Vienna, Giovanni Tomaso di Trattnern, n. d. 54 p. 16^{cm}.

Two acts. Author not mentioned and unknown to Schatz. Niccolò **Piccinni** is mentioned as the composer.
First performed at Rome, Teatro della Valle, January 3, 1769.　　　SCHATZ 8153

Lo sposo deluso, ballet. *See* Astaritta's L'isola di Begodi.

Lo sposo di trè e marito di nessuna, dramma giocoso per musica, da rappresentarsi nei Teatri privilegiati in Vienna la primavera dell' anno MDCCLXVIII.

[Vienna], nella Stamperia Ghelen, n. d. 68 p. 15½^{cm}.

Three acts. By Antonio Palomba, who is not mentioned. On p. 2, the note: "La musica e del Signor Don Pasquale **Anfossi** . . . A riserva dell' introduzione, e de' tre finali, che sono del Sig. [Pietro] **Guglielmi**, e dell' arie segnate coll' asterisco che sono del Sig. Floriano **Gasman** . . ." but *no aria appears printed with asterisk!*
According to Schatz (no such performance in Florimo), the opera was first performed at Naples, Teatro Nuovo sopra Toledo, fall of 1763, music by Anfossi, except the introduction, the three finales, and the aria of the baronessa in the third act, which were by Pietro Guglielmi.　　　　　　SCHATZ 284

Lo sposo di tre e marito di nessuna. Commedia per musica di Antonio Palomba da rappresentarsi nel Teatro della citta' dell' Aquila.

Napoli, Amato Cons, 1781. 68 p. 15½^{cm}.

Lo sposo di tre e marito di nessuna—Continued.

Three acts. Cast. No composer mentioned, but Schatz and Florimo attribute the music to Pasquale **Anfossi**, Pietro **Guglielmi**, and Giuseppe **Giordano**. The text is a very much altered version of the Vienna (1768) ed. of "Lo sposo di trè," and in Neapolitan dialect. One distinguishing difference is that it no longer contains the famous "Son già trè dì che Nina."

First performed at Naples, Teatro del Fondo, 1781, as indicated. Schatz 285

Lo sposo di tre, e marito di nessuna. Dramma giocoso per musica di Filippo Livigni da rappresentarsi nel nobile Teatro di San Samuele l'autunno dell' anno 1783 . . .

Venezia, Gio. Battista Casali, n. d. 63 p. 17½cm.

Two acts. Cast, scenario, and name of the composer, **Cherubini**. Schatz 1848

Lo sposo di tre, e marito di nessuna. Dramma giocoso per musica da rappresentarsi nel Teatro alla Scala la quaresima dell' anno 1793 . . .

Milano, Gio. Batista Bianchi, n. d. 56 p. 16½cm.

Two acts. By Antonio Palomba, who is not mentioned. Impresario's dedication, cast, and name of Francesco **Gnecco** as the composer. With the opera were performed Giovanni Monticini's ballets, "La fata Urgella" and "Li pastori d'Arcadia." The composers of the music are not mentioned. Schatz 3965

Lo sposo disperato. Dramma giocoso per musica di Giovanni Bertati da rappresentarsi nel Teatro Giustiniani di S. Moisè l'autunno dell' anno 1777.

[Venezia], n. publ., n. d. 63 p. 18cm.

Two acts. Cast and name of Pasquale **Anfossi** as composer. Schatz 252

— Il zotico incivilito. Dramma giocoso per musica, da rappresentarsi nel Teatro Elettorale.—Der civilisirte bauer. Ein scherzhaftes singspiel . . .

Dresda, n. publ., 1792. 15½cm.

Two acts. Name of composer, **Anfossi**. Cast added in pencil. Text a later version of "Lo sposo disperato." German text faces Italian.

First performed at Dresden on December 12, 1792. Schatz 253

Lo sposo per equivoco. Intermezzo in musica da rappresentarsi nel nobil Teatro Tron Veronese di S. Cassiano l'autunno dell' anno MDCCLXXXIII.

Venezia, Pietro Sola, n. d. 50 p. 16½cm.

Two acts. Cast, scenario, and name of Pasquale **Anfossi** as composer, but not of librettist, who is unknown to Schatz.

First performed at Rome, Teatro Capranica, carnival, 1781. Schatz 277

Lo sposo senza moglie. A. T. of Cimarosa's I due supposti conti.

Sprigs of laurel: a comic opera. In two acts. As performed, with universal applause, at the Theatre-Royal, Covent-Garden. Written by John O'Keeffe[!] . . .

London, H. S. Woodfall, 1793. 3 p. l., 47 p. 20cm.

Cast, author's dedication, dated April 6, 1793, and "A card," dated Brompton, May 21, 1793, which reads:

"Mr. O'Keefe owes his first thought of writing this piece, to a circumstance he had heard of a centinel quitting his post, to follow the detachment from the Guards when it embarked at Greenwich: But whether a fact, or fiction, he is happy if it has afforded any pleasure from the popularity of the occasion, the sweet melodies of Mr. **Shield**, and the zealous exertion of the respective performers." Longman & Broderip's

Sprigs of laurel—Continued.

. vocal score says: "Consisting of German, Scotch, Irish, and English airs, one by a nobleman and others by **Handel, Anfossi, and Shield**."

First performed, as indicated, May 11, 1793, and, according to Genest, in an altered version as "The rival soldiers," at the same theatre, May 17, 1797.   LONGE 225

— **Sprigs of laurel:** a comic opera, in two acts. As performed, with universal applause, at the Theatre Royal, Covent-Garden. Written by John O'Keefe . . . A new edition.

London, G. Woodfall, 1794. 3 p. l., 47, [1] p. 20ᶜᵐ.

Same cast, dedication, and "card."   ML 50.2.S74S3

The Spring. Pastoral as it is now performing at the Theatre Royal in Drury Lane. The music by Mr. Handel, and other eminent masters . . .

London, T. Davies, n. d. 16 p. 21½ᶜᵐ.

Two acts. Text by James Harris, who is not mentioned in the Advertisement, which reads:

"As this pastoral was not originally designed for the theatre, it is thought proper to give the public some account of it, and by what means it has now found its way to the stage.

"The chorusses and airs were selected from Mr. **Handel** and several other eminent masters, by a gentleman whose taste and knowledge in music, is perhaps his least merit.

"Having conceived the design of a musical entertainment of this miscellaneous nature, he found himself obliged, in order to introduce the several airs and chorusses with propriety, to connect them by a recitative of his own composition: This naturally produced a kind of little drama; and the ease and elegance of the whole, is the more to be admired, when it is considered that the words were of necessity composed in perfect subservience to the music.

"The piece has been several times performed at Salisbury, and been greatly admired by many of the first rank and other acknowledged judges of music. The author, upon Mr. Norris (who performed a capital part in the pastoral) being engaged at the theatre, was applied to for leave to bring it on the stage, to which, he has most obligingly given his consent . . ."

The text is the same as of "Daphne and Amaryllis," 1766 (Longe 293).

First performed at Drury Lane October 22, 1762.   ML 50.2.S743H2

The springs glory, a maske. Together with sundry poems, epigrams, elegies, and epithalamiums. By Thomas Nabbs.

London, Printed by J. Dawson, 1639. 51 unnumbered p. 17½ᶜᵐ.

Second ed. Includes his "A presentation intended for the Prince his Highnesse on his birthday the 29 of May 1638," partly to be sung and danced. The text of the masque is preceded by Thomas Nabbes' dedication to "Guglielmo Balle [William Ball] filio natu majori Petri Balle armigeri" (therefore *not* dedicated to Peter Ball!), a dedicatory poem by "C. G. Oxon" to Nabbes and one by Robert Chamberlaine to Nabbes. No allusion to a composer is made. No performance recorded by Clarence.
ML 52.2.S76

Spurio Postumio. Drama per musica da rappresentarsi nel famosissimo Teatro Grimani di San Gio. Grisostomo il carnovale dell' anno 1712 . . .

Venezia, Marino Rossetti, n. d. 68 p. 15ᶜᵐ.

Three acts. By conte Agostino Piovene, who is not mentioned. Historical notes, cast, and scenario. The composer, Carlo Francesco **Pollaroli**, is not mentioned.
SCHATZ 8220

Squire Badger. *See* Arne's The sot.

Die staats-thorheit des Brutus. A. T. of Keiser's Die kleinmuehtige selbst-moerderin Lucretia.

The **stage-mutineers:** or, A play-house to be lett. A tragi-comi-farcical-ballad opera, as it is acted at the Theatre-Royal in Covent-Garden. By a gentleman late of Trinity-College, Cambridge . . .

London, Richard Wellington, 1733. 4 p. l., 40 p. 19ᶜᵐ.

One act, prologue, and epilogue. Cast. The airs used are indicated by title. The author is not recorded by Clarence.

First performed, as indicated, October 31, 1733. Longe 262

The **state juggler:** or, Sir Politick Ribband. A new excise opera. N. B. With this opera is given gratis, *Britannia excisa,* in two parts; and the *Excise Congress,* with three emblematical pictures, printed on a large sheet of fine paper, fit to be fram'd . . .

London, T. Reynolds, 1733. 1 p. l., [7]–43 p. 19ᶜᵐ.

Three acts. In form of a ballad-opera, the airs of the 21 songs in which are indicated by title. The *extras* mentioned in the title are not in this copy. No author or performance recorded. Longe 136

The **state of innocence, and fall of man:** an opera. Written in heroick verse; and dedicated to Her Royal Highness the Dutchess. By John Dryden . . .

London, Printed by H. H. for H. Herringman, 1684. 8 p. l., 38, [2] p. 22½ᶜᵐ.

"The author's apology for heroick poetry, and poetick licence" ([8] p. preceding p. 1) contains first Dryden's reasons for publishing "an opera which was never acted." One of them was his desire to protect his reputation as a poet:

"many hundred copies of it being dispers'd abroad, without my knowledge or consent; so that every one gathering new faults, it became at length a libel against me . . ."

This treatise is preceded by a poem "To Mr. Dryden, on his poem of Paradise" and by Dryden's dedication. At the end a two-page publisher's catalogue. No mention is made of a composer or of a performance and none are recorded.

ML 50.2.S745

The **statesman's opera.** A. T. of The patron.

The **statesman foil'd.** A musical comedy of two acts. Performed at the Theatre Royal in the Hay-Market. The musick composed by Mr. Rush.

London, T. Becket and co., 1768. 2 p. l., 42 p. 19½ᶜᵐ.

Two acts. By Robert Dossie, who is not mentioned. Cast.

First performed July 8, 1768, as indicated. Longe 37

Statira. Dramma di tre atti per musica rappresentato per la prima volta in Venezia l'anno MDCCXL.

Carlo Goldoni, Opere teatrali, Venezia, Zatta e figli, 1788–95, v. 36, [205]–247 p. 18½ᶜᵐ. PQ

The earliest setting recorded by Schatz is that by Pietro *Chiarini* for Venice, Teatro di San Samuele, spring 1741.

Statira.

Apostolo Zeno, Poesie drammatiche. Venezia, 1744, t. x, p. [205]–288. 19ᶜᵐ.

Three acts. Argument. Written in collaboration with Pietro Pariati. No composer is mentioned. In the "Catalogo" at end of vol. x date and place of first ed. is given as Venice, 1706, but *see* Gasparini's opera below. ML 49.A2Z3

Statira—Continued.

— Statira. Pubblicata per la prima volta in Venezia 1706.

Apostolo Zeno, Poesie drammatiche, Orleans, 1785–86, t. ix, p. 279–359. 21cm.

Three acts. Argument. No composer is mentioned. Written in collaboration with Pietro Pariati.   ML 49.A2Z4

Statira. Dramma per musica da rappresentarsi nel Teatro dell' Illustriss. Signori Capranica l'anno 1726 . . .

Roma, Rossi, n. d. 64 p. 15cm.

Three acts. By Apostolo Zeno and Pietro Pariati, who are not mentioned. Dedication by Giuseppe Polvini Falliconti, argument, cast, scenario, and name of Tommaso **Albinoni** as composer of the opera and of the intermezzi ("ed è questa la settantesima opera da lui posta in musica").   Schatz 98

Statira. Drama per musica da rappresentarsi nel Teatro Tron di S. Cassano il carnovale dell' anno MDCCV . . .

Venezia, Marino Rossetti, 1705. 60 p. 14½cm.

Three acts. Neither the authors, Zeno and Pariati, are mentioned, nor the composer, Carlo Francesco **Gasparini**. Dedication dated Venice, February 2, 1705, argument, and scenario.   Schatz 3582

— Le regine di Macedonia. Drama per musica da rappresentarsi nel famoso Teatro di S. Bartolomeo in quest' anno 1708 . . .

Napoli, Salvatore Votto, n. d. 5 p. l., 66, [1] p. 14cm.

Three acts. Impresario's dedication, notice to the reader, argument, cast, and scenario. Is Zeno and Pariati's "La Statira" as altered by Carlo de Pretis. The usual excuse is made to the "Amico Lettore," in which notice Giuseppe **Vignola** is named as the composer of the additional matter. **Gasparini** is not mentioned at all. A most unusual feature of this libretto is that on the additional page the arias by Giuseppe **Vignola** are enumerated by first line, *i. e.* (Act I) "Dalle pupille della mia bella," "Si, si consolami," "Fiero addio"; (Act II) "Pupille del mio bene," "Disperato questo core," "Co i lacci del tuo amor"; (Act III) "Di morte non cura il rigore," "Si godi, o cor," "Bella mi parto," "Cari sassi," "Scherza ridi," "Aure belle," "e tutte le scene buffe."   Schatz 3583

Statira. Dramma per musica del dottor Carlo Goldoni. Da rappresentarsi nel Teatro di Sant' Angelo. Nella fiera dell' Ascensione l'anno 1751.

Venezia, Modesto Fenzo, 1751. 45 p. 14½cm.

Three acts. Argument, cast, scenario, and note that "La musica de' recitativi con alcune arie segnate con la stelletta * sarà del Signor Francesco **Maggiore** maestro di capella napolitano, e direttore dell' opera. L'altre arie saranno poste a piacimento de cantanti."

Accordingly, Maggiore composed only the arias "Fidi amanti fortunati (III, 4), "Al caro Nume appresso" (III, 5) and no others.   Schatz 5832

Statira. Dramma per musica da rappresentarsi nel famosissimo Teatro Grimani di Sᵖ Giõ. Grisostomo il carnevale 1742 . . .

[Venezia], n. publ., n. d. 59 p. 15cm.

Three acts. By Francesco Silvani, who is not mentioned. Argument, scenario, cast, and name of Nicolà Antonio **Porpora** as the composer.   Schatz 8364

La Statira. Dramma per musica recitato nel Teatro di Torre di Nona. L'anno 1690.

Roma, Gio. Francesco Buagni, 1990 [!]. 68 p. 13cm.

Three acts. By cardinal Ottoboni, who is not mentioned. Impresario's dedication, argument, and scenario. The composer, Alessandro **Scarlatti**, is not mentioned.   Schatz 9536

Statira. Dramma per musica del dottor Carlo Goldoni da rappresentarsi nel Teatro Grimani di S. Samuele nella fiera dell' Ascensione l'anno MDCCLVI . . .

Venezia, Francesco Pitteri, n. d. 46 p. 15½^{cm}.

Three acts. Argument, cast, scenario, name of Giuseppe **Scolari** as composer, and Goldoni's, as always, charming dedication "alle nobilissime dame Veneziane," in which he says:

"Allora quando (Eccellentissime dame) su queste scene medesime fu per la prima volta rappresentata la mia Statira, nell' anno 1741, questo piccolo dramma era parto d'un' uomo che dir potevasi principiante, e da pochissimi conosciuto . . . Non mi sarei mai creduto vederla, dopo il corso di quindici anni, tratta dall' urna delle opere dimenticate, per farla nuovamente comparir sul teatro. So chi mi ha fatto si bel regalo; non ho potuto impedirlo, ma non vuò nemmeno dissimulare la dispiacenza, che ne risento. Ora quell' uomo, incognito nel 1741, è conosciuto un po troppo per suo malanno, e se in allora quest' operetta ebbe la fortuna che di lei si parlasse poco, ora chi sa, che di lei non si parli troppo? . . . Il zelo dunque di mia reputazione, il rispetto, che devo al pubblico . . . mi hanno stimolato a rivederlo, ad accrescerlo, a riformarlo, cosicchè poco del primo scheletro vi è rimasto . . .

"Aggiugnesi alle altre imperfezioni di questo dramma quella di essere in cinque personaggi soltanto, per accomodarsi alla brevità ricercata dalla stagione. Ma ciò sarebbe il minor male, se fosse poi ben tessuto, e dolcemente scritto; io non so fare nell' una, nè l'altra di queste due. Quando scrivo per musica l'ultimo, a cui pensi, son'io medesimo. Penso agli attori, penso al maestro di capella moltissimo, penso al piacere degli uditori in teatro, e se i miei drammi si vedessero rappresentate soltanto, e non venissero letti, spererei migliore destino . . ." Schatz 9799

La Statira principessa di Persia. Drama per musica impiego di hore otiose di Gio. Francesco Busenello . . .

Venetia, Andrea Giuliani, 1655. 94 p. (incl. front.) 14½^{cm}.

Three acts with prologue. Long author's dedication dated Venice, January 18, 1655, with name of Pietro Francesco **Cavalli** as composer, and argument.

First performed at Venice, Teatro di SS. Giovanni e Paolo, as indicated, carnival 1655. Schatz 1728

— La **Statira, principessa di Persia.** Drama per musica di Gio. Francesco Busenello.

Venetia, Andrea Giuliani, 1656. 70 p. 15^{cm}.

Prologue and three acts. Argument. The composer, Francesco **Cavalli,** is not mentioned. Schatz 11682

La statua animata, ballet. *See* Piccinni's La scaltra letterata.

La statua matematica. O. T. of Valentini's Le sorelle rivali.

La statua per puntiglio. Dramma giocoso per musica da rappresentarsi nel nobilissimo Teatro Giustiniani in San Moisè il carnovale dell' anno 1792.

Venezia, Modesto Fenzo, 1791. 55 p. 17^{cm}.

Two acts. Cast, scenario, and name of composer. **Bernardini** (Marcello di Capua), but not of librettist, who is unknown to Schatz. Schatz 835

Le statue. Dramma giocoso per musica da rappresentarsi nel Teatro Grimani di S. Samuele per il carnovale 1757.

Venezia, Modesto Fenzo, 1757. 60 p. 15^{cm}.

Three acts. Cast and scenario. Wiel mentions neither librettist nor composer. Schatz attributes text and music to Francesco **Brusa.**

First performed December 27, 1757, as indicated. Schatz 1378

La statue animée. A. T. of Pannard's text Pigmalion.

La **statue merveilleuse**. Pièce en trois actes. Tirée de l'arabe . . .
Le Théâtre de la foire, Paris, 1724, t. iv, pl., 94 p. 17cm.

By Le Sage and D'Orneval. Mostly *en vaudevilles.* The airs, selected or composed and arranged by Jean Claude **Gillier**, the "compositeur" of the theatre, are printed at the end of the volume in the "Table des airs." A note on the title page reads:

"Cette pièce avoit été composée par les auteurs du *Rappel de la foire à la vie,* pour être donnée avec ce prologue à l'Opéra-comique, dont ils espéroient le rétablissement à la Foire de S. Germain 1719. Mais ce spectacle demeurant supprimé, ils la firent représenter en prose par la troupe des danseurs de corde du Sieur Francisque, qui, ne se voyant pas inquitée par les Comédiens, la joüa à Foire de S. Laurent 1720."

ML 48.L2IV

Arien und gesaenge aus Dem stein der weisen, oder Die zauberinsel. Eine heroisch-komische oper in zwey aufzuegen.
Frankfurt am Main, 1796. 28 p. 16cm.

Neither the author, Johann Emanuel Schikaneder, nor the composer, Benedict **Schack**, is mentioned.

First performed at Frankfurt a/M. Nationaltheater, 1796; at Vienna, Theater auf der Wieden, September 11, 1790. SCHATZ 9570

Arien und gesaenge aus dem singspiele Die steinerne braut. Verfasst und in musik gesetzt vom freyherrn von Lichtenstein.
Dessau, n. publ., 1799. Unpaged. 16½cm.

Two acts. At end, "Gedruckt bey H. G. Heybruch."
First performed at Dessau, Hoftheater, April 25, 1799. SCHATZ 5599

Der **steinerne gast**. A. T. of Mozart's Don Juan.

Das **steinerne gastmahl** oder Der ruchlose. Tr. of Righini's Il convitato di pietra o sia Il dissoluto.

Der **sterbende Cato**. A. T. of Keiser's Die liebe gegen das vaterland.

Die **sterbende Eurydice** oder Orpheus. L. T. of Keiser's Orpheus.

Stoertebecker und Joedge Michaels. Erster theil, vorgestellet in einem singe-spiel auff dem Hamburgischen Schau-platz.
Hamburg, Nicolaus Spieringk, 1701. Unpaged. 18½cm.

Three acts. "Vorbericht," mentioning neither the author, Hotter, nor the composer, Reinhard **Keiser**.
First performed, as indicated, 1701. SCHATZ 5111

— **Stoertebecker und Joedge Michaels.** Zweyter theil, vorgestellet in einem singe-spiel auf dem Hamburgischen Schau-platz.
Hamburg, Nicolaus Spieringk, 1701. Unpaged. 18½cm.

Three acts. Neither Hotter is mentioned, nor **Keiser**.
First performed, as indicated, 1701. SCHATZ 5112

Den **store Tamerlan**. Tr. of Sarti's Il gran Tamerlano.

Der **strafplanet der erde**. A. T. of Blumhofer's Die luftschiffer.

Lo **strambo in berlina**. L. T. of Paisiello's La locanda.

The **strangers at home;** A comic opera, in three acts. As performed at the Theatre Royal in Drury Lane [vignette].

London, Harrison & co., 1786. 80 p. 21^{cm}.

Cast, dedication by the author, James Cobb, dated London, February 22, 1786, and Advertisement, with name of Thomas **Linley** as the composer.

First performed December 8, 1785, as indicated. LONGE 96

Die **strassenraeuber,** eine komische oper in drey aufzuegen. (Zum behuf des Hamburgischen Theaters.)

Hamburg und Bremen, Johann Henrich Cramer, 1770. 126 p. 16½^{cm}.

By E. E. Buschmann, who is not mentioned and who on p. 105–126 in an "Anhang" calls his play "eine kopie der beruehmten Bettlers-oper," pointing out the differences between his version and Gay's original and the reasons therefor and adding a few historical notes on the "Beggar's opera." No composer or performance recorded by Schatz. ML 50.2.S746

Les **stratagêmes de l'amour,** ballet representé par l'Academie royale de musique l'an 1726. Musique de M. Destouches. Paroles de M. Roy. CVI. opera. Tome XIV.

n. i., n. d. pl., p. 1–60. (Recueil général des opéras, Paris, 1734.) 14^{cm}.

Detached copy. Three acts and prologue with "Avertissement" as argument with this statement (on p. 7):

"Le prologue a été fait pour le mariage de Leurs Majestez. On a placé Le Roy au milieu de ses plus célèbres prédecesseurs qui doivent revivre en Luy."

First performed, as indicated, March 28, 1726. SCHATZ 2551

Second copy. ML 48.R4

Li **stratagemi amorosi.** Dramma per musica da rappresentarsi nel Teatro Giustiniano di S. Moisè. Il carnovale dell' anno 1730.

Venezia, Carlo Buonarrigo, 1730. 48 p. 15^{cm}.

Three acts. Argument, cast, scenario, notice to the reader with name of Tommaso **Albinoni** as composer and establishing Francesco Passarini as author. SCHATZ 131

Gli **stratagemi di Biante.**

By conte Nicola Minato, composed by Antonio **Draghi** for the birthday of the Empress, January 6, 1682, with insertion of arias by Leopold I.

Not in L. of C.

— **Kriegs-liste dess Bias.** An dem geburts-tag Ihrer Mayest. der regierenden roemischen kaiserin Eleonora Magdalena Theresia . . . Gesungener vorgestellt. In die music gesezt durch herrn Antoni Dragi, der verwittibten Kayserl. Mayest. capellmeistern. Mit der music zu den daenzen herrn Andre Antoni Schmelzer von Ehrenruef der Roem. Kayserl. Mayest, Cammer musici.

Wienn, bey Johann Christoph Cosmerovio, 1682. 80 p. 14½^{cm}.

Three acts. With dedication, dated "Wienn, den 6 jenner 1682" and signed Nicola Minato, "Inhalt," "Unterredente persohnen," "Veraenderungen der Schaubuehne" (by Lodovico Burnacini) and "Daenze" (arranged by the imperial ballet master, Domenico Ventura). On p. 10:

"*Zu mercken*

Dass die Reden, sozwischen disen zwey zeichen ( ) begriffen seyn, von niemand andern verstanden werden, als nur von dem, der sie selbst saget."

SCHATZ 2802

Stratira. Tragedia di Silvestro Branchi da Bologna, detto il Costante, nell' Accademia de 'Ravvivati . . . Rappresentata dalli Accademici, con gl'intermedii dell' istesso. Fatti in musica dal Sig. Ottavio Vernici, organista di S. Petronio.

Bologna, Gio. Domenico Moscatelli, 1617. 6 p. l., 231, [1] p. 18½^cm.

The last page contains the errata.

Prologue and five acts with five intermedi. Author's dedication dated September 2, 1617, sonnets by the author "alla sua tragedia," and to cardinal Capponi, to whom the text is dedicated, by Paolo Forti to the author, by the latter to the "signori protettori nel recitarsi la sua tragedia," argument and notice to the reader containing this *protesta*, certainly one of the earliest on record:

"E dove si ritroveranno in questo mio poema le voci fate, sorti, Dei, eterno, Angelo, & simili si devranno intendere conforme al' uso poetico; imperoche io voglio sottopormi sempre à l'ubbidienza de la santa Romana Chiesa . . ."

It is remarkable how this agrees with the later on so stereotyped formulas of *protesta*.   Schatz 10714

Stratonica. Drama per musica da rappresentarsi nel Teatro di San Bartolomeo nella primavera del corrente anno 1727 . . .

Napoli, Angelo Vocola, n. d. 48 p. 15½^cm.

Three acts. Publisher's dedication, scenario, cast, and notice to the reader, in which we read:

"Se diverso dal suo primo essere, ti verrà sotto l'occhio, il presente drama, sappi, che si è fatto per meglio accomodarsi agli attori, à libertà de quali s'è lasciato il poner l'arie à loro sodisfazione, e sono tutte quelle contrasegnate con il presente asterisco *, l'altre si sono fatte dipianta, non già per pregiudicare il suo degnissimo autore [Antonio Salvi?]; mà solo per incontrare il genio de' rappresentanti, e questo si è fatto dal Sig. Carlo de Palma . . ."

Accordingly the arias "T'inganna il tuo pensier" (II, 6), "In sen più non scintilla," (III, 4), etc., were selected by the singers for this pasticcio. On p. 19–23, 35–39 the text of two intermezzi with the characters "Valasco e Vespetta." Author and composer of these also unknown to me.   ML 50.2.S75

Lo stravagante. O. T. of Villano's libretto Il pazzo glorioso.

Lo stravagante. Commedia per musica da rappresentarsi nel Teatro de' Fiorentini nel carnevale di quest' anno 1764.

Napoli, Vincenzo Mazzola-Vocola, 1764. 71 p. 15^cm.

Three acts. By Liviano Lantini (*recte* Antonio Villano) who is not mentioned. Cast and name of Nicolò **Piccinni** as the composer.

First performed at Naples, same theatre, fall of 1761.   Schatz 8130

Lo stravagante Inglese. Dramma gjocoso per musica da rappresentarsi nel Teatro Ducale di Bronsvic.

Bronsvic, n. publ., 1788. 72 p. 16½^cm.

Two acts, with name of the composer, Francesco **Bianchi,** but not of the librettist, Giovanni Greppi.

First performed at Venice, Teatro di S. Moisè, fall of 1785.   Schatz 983

Gli stravaganti. Farsetta per musica a quattro voci da rappresentarsi nel Real Teatro dell' Ajuda per gli anni felicissimi di S. M. F. Don Giuseppe Primo nel giorno 6. di giugno del 1765.

Lisbona, Michele Maneschal da Costa, n. d. 4 p. l., 52 p. 15½^cm.

Two acts. Cast, scenario, and name of Niccolò **Piccinni** as the composer. Author not mentioned and unknown to Schatz.

First performed at Rome, Teatro Valle, January 1, 1764.   Schatz 8144

Gli **stravaganti**—Continued.

— Gli **stravaganti.** Intermezzo in musica con farsetta in prosa intitolata La falsa gelosia. Da rappresentarsi nel Teatro de' Fiorentini nell' està di quest' anno 1772 . . .

Napoli, Vincenzo Flauto, 1772. 70 p. 15^{cm}.

Two parts. Impresario's dedication and cast. The composer, Niccolò **Piccinni**, is not mentioned. The text is the same as of his "La schiava riconosciuta," of course, with the usual changes in the arias.   Schatz 8112

— La **schiava.** Azione comica per musica da rappresentarsi nel Teatro privilegiato vicino alla corte l'anno 1765.

Vienna, Ghelen, n. d. 44 p. 16^{cm}.

Two acts. Cast and name of Niccolò **Piccinni** as the composer.   Schatz 8151

— La **schiava.** Azzione comica in musica, da rappresentarsi nel Picolo Teatro di S. A. E. di Sassonia.

Dresda, L'autunno del anno 1765, n. publ. 3 p. l., 94 p. 15^{cm}.

Two acts. Cast and name of Niccolò **Piccinni** as the composer. German title-page, "Die gefangene," and text face Italian.
First performed October 15, 1765, as indicated.   Schatz 8110

— La **schiava,** a comic opera; as performed at the King's-Theatre in the Hay-Market. The music by Signor Piccini, directed by Signor Tomaso Giordani. With additions and alterations, by Giovan Gualberto Bottarelli.

London, W. Griffin, 1772. 59, [1] p. 18^{cm}.

Three acts. Cast. English translation faces Italian.
First performed at London, Hay-Market, under the above title, on November 5, 1767; under the original title, "Gli stravaganti," but with much interpolated music by other composers, October 21, 1766.   ML 50.2.S85P4

— La **schiava riconosciuta.** Dramma giocoso per musica da rappresentarsi nel Teatro dell' illustrissimo pubblico di Reggio per la fiera dell' anno MDCCLXX . . .

Reggio, Giuseppe Davolio, n. d. 56 p. 14½^{cm}.

Three acts. Dedicatory poem by the impresario, Francesco Guatelli, cast, and name of Niccolò **Piccinni** as the composer.
April 29, 1770, is given as the date of first performance in the libretto, which is (with the customary alterations) the same as "Gli stravaganti."   Schatz 8109

— La **schiava riconosciuta,** dramma giocoso per musica da rappresentarsi nel Teatro di Ratisbona . . .

[Regensburg], Gedruckt mit Zunkelischen schriften, n. d. 111 p. 15½^{cm}.

Two acts. Cast and name of Niccolò **Piccinni** as the composer. German title-page, "Die wieder erkannte sclavin, and text face Italian.
First performed, as indicated, carnival, 1777.   Schatz 8111

— L'**esclave,** ou Le marin généreux, intermede en un acte, rédigé de l'italien, et représenté en province. La musique est de M. N. Piccini . . .

Aux Deux-Ponts, et se trouve à Paris, chez la veuve Duchesne, 1774. 52 p. 18½^{cm}.

The "Notes" on p. 3–5 give the plot of "tout ce fatras qu'on nommoit les *Extravagans.*" The anonymous translator and editor waxes very sarcastic over this kind of Italian dramas, made "on dit . . . pour la plûpart, par des perruquiers," and he

Gli stravaganti—Continued.

briefly states his reasons for his own one-act version. He begins his "Notes" with these remarks:

"Ces especes de traductions devroient être moins rares: outre qu'elles rendroient notre scene lyrique plus variée, elles empêcheroient les larcins continuels d'une partie de nos musiciens, & aiguil loueroient l'emulation de l'autre."

On p. 38–52, the airs: "À votre âge, ce langage" (sc. 2), "Loin de son berger" (sc. 6), "En amour un tel hommage" (x 8).

First performed at Zweibrücken, Theatre de Société, 1774.　　　　SCHATZ 8114

— **Die ausschweifenden,** ein komisches singspiel, welches bei Gelegenheit des hoechstbeglueckten namens festes der durchlauchtigsten frauen churfuerstin an dem Churpfaelzischen Hof aufgefuehret worden.

Mannheim, Akademische buchdruckerey, 1771. 54 p. 15ᶜᵐ.

Two acts. Niccolò **Piccinni** is mentioned as the composer.
First performed November 19, 1771, as indicated.　　　　SCHATZ 8113

— Arien aus der oper Der **grossmuethige seefahrer.**

n. i., n. d. [8] p. 16ᶜᵐ.

Eschenburg's version of "Gli stravaganti."　　　　SCHATZ 8117

— Die **sclavin und der grossmuethige seefahrer.** Eine operette nach dem italiaenischen. Die musik ist von hrn. Piccini.

Mannheim, C. F. Schwan, 1773. 72, [4] p. 14ᶜᵐ.

The unnumb. p. contain advertising matter.
One act. Translated by Johann Joachim Eschenburg, who is not mentioned. He says in his preface:

"Die italiaenische operette selbst [Gli Stravaganti, perf. there 1772] hat mit gegenwaertiger ausser der anlage, die ueberhaupt nicht viel sagen will, sehr wenig aehnliches. Man hat nur die musik nutzen wollen und ist also von dem original so oft abgewichen, als es der deutsche plan zu erfordern schien. Ein hiesiger geschickter theatraldichter machte zuerst eine franzoesische nachahmung, die auch mit der musik gestochen worden; diese ist gewissermassen, besonders was die arien betrifft, hier zum grunde gelegt worden. Es wird immer zum voraus gesetzt, dass man den hrn. **Piccini** hoeren will, wenn man sich bei der vorstellung dieses stueckes einfindet und nicht den dichter, auf den man, wenn er noch so harmonisch gereimt haette kaum acht haben wird.

"Bey originalstuecken geht der dichter voran und der componist folgt ihm. Bey uebersetzungen aber und nachahmungen muss sich der dichter nach der bereits vorhandenen musik bequemen . . ."

First performed at Mannheim, Brettertheater auf dem Fruchtmarkt, by Theod. Marchand's company, January, 1773.　　　　SCHATZ 8115

— Die **sklavinn und der grossmuethige seefahrer.** Ein komisches singspiel, nach dem italienischen frey bearbeitet. Auf die musik vom herrn Piccini. Von herrn Stephanie dem juengern. Auf geführt auf dem k. k. Nazionalhoftheater.

Wien, Logenmeister, 1781. 57 p. 16½ᶜᵐ.

Two acts. First performed, as indicated, August 1, 1781.　　　　SCHATZ 8116

Le stravaganze del caso. Intermezzo per musica a quattro voci da rappresentarsi nel Teatro di S. Angelo.

Venezia, Modesto Fenzo, 1761.

Two parts. Author is not mentioned and is unknown to Schatz. Cast and name of Antonio [Maria] **Mazzoni** as the composer.
First performed at Bologna, Teatro Pubblico, carnival, 1760.　　　　SCHATZ 6228

Le **stravaganze del conte.** Commedia per musica di P. M. da rappresentarsi nel Teatro de' Fiorentini nel carnevale del corrente anno 1772.

Napoli, Vincenzo Flauto, 1772. 71 p. 15^cm.

Three acts. By Pasquale Milillotti. Scenario, cast, and name of the composer, Domenico Cimarosa. SCHATZ 1986

Der **streit der kindlichen pflicht und der liebe** oder Die flucht des Aeneas nach Latien. In einer opera auf dem Hamburgischen Schau-platz aufgefuehret.

[Hamburg], Gedruckt mit Stromerschen schrifften, 1731. Unpaged. 19^cm.

Three acts. Argument and names of Johann Georg Hamann as translator (of Metastasio's "Didone abbandonata"), of Georg Philipp Telemann as composer of the recitatives, and of Nicolà Antonio **Porpora** as composer of the "unvergleichliche *music* der arien." These are printed with Italian and German text.

The above was first performed, as indicated, November 19, 1731; the original, "Didone abbandonata," at Reggio, Teatro Pubblico, April 28, 1725. SCHATZ 8365

Die **streitig gemachte liebe.** A. T. of Paisiello's Die müllerin.

Die **streitig gemachte liebschaft.** Tr. of Paisiello's L'amor contrastato.

Die **streitige heurath.** Tr. of Valentini's Le nozze in contrasto.

A **struggle for freedom.** A. T. of Reinagle's Slaves in Algiers.

Lo **studente.** Commedia per musica di Saverio Zini da rappresentarsi nel Teatro Nuovo per second' opera di quest' anno 1783.

Napoli, n. publ., 1783. 47 p. 15^cm.

Three acts. Cast and name of Gaetano **Monti** as the composer. SCHATZ 6604

I **studenti.** Commedia per musica di Giuseppe Palomba da rappresentarsi nel Real Teatro del Fondo di Separazione per prim' opera del corrente anno 1796 . . .

Napoli, n. publ., 1796. 52 p. 15^cm.

Two acts. Impresario's dedication dated Naples, May 12, 1796, cast, and name of Gabriele **Prota** as the composer. On p. 6–14 prefatory note, argument, cast, description, and name of Vittorio Trento as the composer of the "musica tutta nuova" of Lauchelin Duquesney's "Ahtor ed Erma, ballo eroico in cinque atti," on p. 15–17 argument and cast without name of the composer of the music of Duquesney's "Ernesto ed Elisa, ballo pastorale." SCHATZ 8472

The **students whim.** A. T. of Don Sancho.

Gli **studi interotti**, ballet. *See* Salieri's La cifra.

The **sturdy beggars.** A new ballad opera. Humbly dedicated to the Right Honourable, and Right Worshipful, the Lord Mayor . . . and the worthy merchants and citizens of London . . .

London, J. Dormer, 1733. xii, [3], 14–80 p. 18^cm.

Three acts. The lengthy dedication of this political piece on the Excise Bill is signed *Civicus.* The airs of the 29 songs are indicated by title. The author unknown to Clarence. LONGE 200

Der **sturm**. Eine heroisch-komische oper in zwey aufzeugen, nach Schakespear fuer die Marinellische schaubuehne bearbeitet, von Karl Friedrich Hensler. Die musik ist vom herrn Wenzel Mueller, kapellmeister.

Wien, Matthias Andreas Schmidt, 1798. 86 p. 17^{cm}.

Krone gives the title as "Der Sturm oder Die zauberinsel."
First performed, as indicated, November 8, 1798.   SCHATZ 6967

Der **sturm** oder Die bezauberte insel. Ein singspiel in zwey aufzeugen. Nach dem Shakespearischen schauspiel: Der Sturm bearbeitet von J. W. D.

Cassel, Griesbachsche hofbuchhandlung, 1798. 100 p. 15^{cm}.

By Johann Wilhelm Doering. The composer, Peter **Ritter**, not mentioned.
First performed at Aurich, 1799.   SCHATZ 8831

Die **subordination**. A. T. of Walter's Graf von Waltron.

Il **suffi e lo schiavo**, ballet. *See* Calegari's Artemisia.

Le **suffisant**, par M. Vadé. Représentée pour la premiere fois sur le Théâtre de l'Opéra-comique, le 12. mars 1753.

Paris, Duchesne, 1753. 36 p. 18½^{cm}.

One act, *en vaudevilles*. The arranger of the music is unknown to me.
                     ML 50.2.S9

—Le **suffisant**, opera comique, par Mr. Vadé. Représenté pour la première fois sur le Théatre de l'Opéra comique le 12 mars 1753.

La Haye, Pierre Gosse, 1758. 60 p. 16^{cm}. (Vadé, Oeuvres, La Haye, 1760, t. i.)

One act, *en vaudevilles*.   ML 49.A2V2

Les **suites d'une erreur**. A. T. of Berton's Le délire.

La **suite de Julie**. *See* L'erreur d'un moment.

La **suite des Trois fermiers**. *See* Blaise et Babet.

Suite du comte d'Albert. *See* Grétry's Le comte d'Albert.

Sulpitia. Drama per musica nel giorno del gloriosissimo nome della S. C. R. M.^{tà} dell' augustissimo imperatore Leopoldo . . . l'anno MDCXCVII. Posto in musica dal Sr Antonio Draghi, maestro di cap. di S. M. C. con l'arie per li balletti del Sr Gio. Gioseffo Hoffer, violinista di S. M. C.

Vienna d'Austria, Susanna Cristina, vedova di Matteo Cosmerovio, n. d. 90 p. 14½^{cm}.

Three acts. By conte Nicola Minato, who is not mentioned. At end of the opera (p. 88–90), "La vittoria d'Ercole contro Anteo. Introduttione ad un real balletto, *per la licenza*." With argument, scenario (designed by Lodovico Burnacini). The dances were arranged by the imperial ballet master Sig^r Francesco Torti. The emperor Leopold I contributed the arias, "Taci, o core," "Amor di marito," and "O bella costanza," all three published by Adler, 1892.

Performed, as indicated, November 15, 1697; first performed at Vienna, Hoftheater, November 18, 1672.   SCHATZ 2803

Sulpizia fedele. Dramma per musica: Da rappresentarsi nel Theatro Grimani di S. Samuel. Nella fiera dell' Ascensione dell' anno 1729 . . .

Venezia, Carlo Buonarrigo, n. d. 36 p. 15^cm.

Three acts. Argument, cast, scenario, name of Antonio **Pollaroli** as the composer, and dedication signed by Domenico Lalli, who says:
" . . . gia che per ora non mi vien fatto col mio, ardisco almeno col merito dell' altrui virtuoso operare. In quest' opera adunque scritta dal Sig. Giovanne Boldini veneto cittadino, ed illustre poeta, della quale (come direttore delli Teatri Grimani) a me ne tocca la cura, in questa il mio tributo le porgo . . ."
On what authority Wiel and Schatz attribute the text jointly to Boldini and Lalli I do not know.   SCHATZ 8261

The **sultan,** or, a Peep into the seraglio. A farce in two acts. By Isaac Bickerstaffe . . . Acted at the Theatres Royal in Drury-Lane and Covent-Garden. The second edition.

[London], C. Dilly, 1787. 22, [2] p. 20½^cm.

The [2] p. contain the Epilogue spoken at the Theatre-Royal, Dublin, 1778.
Casts of Drury Lane, 1775 and 1787; Covent Garden, 1787, and Advertisement:
"The following petite piece, which is taken from Marmontel, was originally acted at Drury-Lane Theatre in the year 1775" [December 12].
Here entered because, on account of the less than half dozen songs, it sometimes figures as a musical entertainment.   LONGE 98

— The **sultan,** or A peep into the seraglio. In two acts.

[310]–339 p. 19^cm. (Collection of the most esteemed farces and entertainments, t. i, Edinburgh, 1792).

Dublin and Edinburgh (1782) casts.   SCHATZ 11753A

Sultan Wampum, oder Die wuensche. Ein orientalisches scherzspiel mit gesang, in drey aufzuegen. Von August von Kotzebue.

n. i., 1794. 88 p. 16^cm.

Carl David **Stegmann,** the composer, is not mentioned.
First performed at Mainz, Nationaltheater, March 7, 1791.   SCHATZ 10042

— Gesaenge aus **Schach Wampum,** oder Die wuensche, ein orientalisches scherzspiel mit gesang, in drey aufzuegen. In musik gesezt von Stegmann.

Hamburg, Joh. Matthias Michaelsen, 1792. 16 p. 16½^cm.

First performed at Hamburg, Theater beim Gänsemarkt, December 1, 1792.
                                                                             SCHATZ 10043

— **Sultan Wampum** oder Die wuensche. Ein orientalisches scherzspiel mit gesang in drey aufzuegen. (Erschien 1794.)

n. i., n. d. 98 p. 14^cm.

Neither the author, Kotzebue (evidently the copy is detached from an edition (before 1800?) of his collected works), nor the composer, Carl David **Stegmann,** is mentioned.   SCHATZ 11749

Le **sultane,** ballet. *See* G. Giordani's Atalanta.

Songs, trios, duetts and chorusses, in the comic opera of **Summer amusement;** or, An adventure at Margate. As it is performed at the Theatre Royal in the Hay-Market. Third edition.

London, T. Cadell, 1781. 23 p. 21^cm.

Three acts. Cast. Neither the authors, Peter Andrews and William Augustus Miles, are mentioned, nor Samuel **Arnold,** who partly composed, partly compiled the music from Dr. **Arne, Giordani,** and **Dibdin,** as appears from Thompson's vocal score. Arnold also utilized a few ballad airs.
First performed July 1, 1779, as indicated.   LONGE 91

The **summer's tale.** A musical comedy of three acts. As it is performed at the Theatre Royal in Covent-Garden . . .

London, J. Dodsley [etc], 1765. 2 p. l., 76 p. 19ᶜᵐ.

Three acts. Cast. By Richard Cumberland, who is not mentioned. A pasticcio with overture (by Abel) and 36 airs, music by the following composers mentioned in the heading: one air each by **Lampugnani, Boyce Potenza, Bertoni, Russell, Lampe,** St. **Germain, Granom, Dunn** (Duni?), **Stanley, Ciampi, Piccinni, Giardini, Vernon, Richter,** two each by **Howard, Hasse,** three anonymous, three each by **Bach** (Joh. Chr.) and **Cocchi,** four by Thomas Aug. **Arne,** and five by Samuel **Arnold.** Composed for the occasion were Arne's "From clime to clime" (II, 8), "In vain you attempt to engage" (II, 9), and "When a freak has got in" (III, 6); Arnold's "There lies your road" (I, 2), "Look back, behold" (II, 2), and "Give me back my heart" (III, 7); Bach's "So profound an impression" (II, 3).

First performed December 6, 1765, as indicated.

For a two-act condensation, *see* "Amelia," 1771.　　　　　　　　　LONGE 40

The **sun's darling:** A moral masque: as it hath been often presented at Whitehall, by Their Majesties servants; and after at the Cockpit in Drury-Lane, with great applause. Written by John Foard and Tho. Decker, Gent.

London, Printed by J. Bell, for Andrew Penneycuicke, 1656. 3 p. l., 43 p. 17ᶜᵐ.

First performed at Drury Lane, 1623–24.　　　　　　　　　LONGE 242

La superba corretta. Commedia per musica in due atti. Da rappresentarsi negl' Imper. Reg. Teatri di corte, l' anno 1795.

Vienna, Mattia Andrea Schmidt, n. d. 46 p. 17½ᶜᵐ.

Author unknown to Schatz. Pierre **Dutillieu** is mentioned as the composer.

First performed, as indicated, April 30, 1795.　　　　　　　　　SCHATZ 2876

La superba innamorata, ballet. *See* Nasolini's Adriano in Siria.

La superbia umiliata ossia L'egualità d'amore, ballet. *See* Cimarosa's I Traci amanti.

Il superbo deluso. L. T. of Gassmann's La contessina.

Les surprises de l'amour.

Three act ballet-opera by Gentil-Bernard, music by **Rameau.**
First performed at the Académie royale de musique, Paris, May 31, 1757.
Not in L. of C.

— Les **ensorcelés,** ou Jeannot et Jeannette, parodie des Surprises de l'amour. Par Mde. Favart & Mrs. Guerin & H ＊ ＊ ＊ Représentée pour la premiere fois par les Comédiens italiens ordinaires du roi, le jeudi premier septembre 1757.

Paris, la veuve Delormel & fils, 1758. 2 p. l., 52 p. 19ᶜᵐ.

The initial H. above stands for Harny de Guerville who, at least according to Schatz, was principally responsible for the selection and arrangement of the music for this parody. The dedication is signed by Mad. Favart alone.　　　SCHATZ 4454

— Les **ensorcelés** ou Jeannot et Jeannette, parodie; par Madame Favart & Mrs. Guerin & H . . . Représentée pour la premiere fois par les Comédiens italiens ordinaires du roi, le jeudi 1 septembre 1757. Nouvelle édition.

Paris, N. B. Duchesne, 1758. 75, [5] p. 19ᶜᵐ. (Theatre de M. Favart, Paris, Duchesne, 1763–77, t. v.)

The [5] p. contain catalogues (partly dated 1759) of plays and operas. One act. Dedication signed by Favart [!] and not by his wife. Cast. Only the airs of the ariettes are printed in the text, not of the vaudevilles.　　　ML 49.A2F1

The **surrender of Calais.** A play. In three acts. By George
Coleman, Jun. Esq. As performed at the little Theatre Hay-Market.
*Dublin, P. Byrne, 1792. 59 p. 17½*cm.

Cast. The composer, Samuel **Arnold,** is not mentioned.
First performed at London, as indicated, July 30, 1791.   LONGE 233
               Second copy.   SCHATZ 336

La **surveillance inutile.** A. T. of Gaveaux' Lise et Colin.

La **Svanvita.**

*Apostolo Zeno, Poesie drammatiche, Venezia, 1744, t. vii, p. [93]–200.
19*cm.

Three acts. Argument. No composer is mentioned. In the "Catalogo" at end
of t. x, date and place of first ed. are given as Milan, 1707. Schatz and Fehr attribute
the libretto to Apostolo Zeno and Pietro Pariati, whereas in Zeno's collected works it
appears as written by Zeno alone. Campanini attributes the text to Pariati alone.
(*See also* below.)   ML 49.A2Z3

— **Svanvita.** Pubblicata per la prima volta in Milano 1707.

*Apostolo Zeno, Poesie drammatiche, Orleans, 1785–86, t. iii, p.
177–276. 21*cm.

Three acts. Argument. No composer is mentioned.   ML 49.A2Z4

La **Svanvita.** Drama da rappresentarsi nel Regio Ducal Teatro di
Milano l'anno 1708 . . . Opera del dottore Pietro Pariati da
Reggio.

*Milano, Eredi Ghisolfi, n. d. 5 p. l., 71, [1] p. 14¼*cm.

Three acts. Impresario's dedication, dated December 26, 1707, argument, scenario,
and name of the composer, Stefano Andrea **Fiorè,** "maestro di Capella di S. A. R. di
Savoja."   SCHATZ 3195

Gli **sventurati amori di Cleide ed Almindo** o sia Il trionfo de'
Goti, ballet. *See* Bianchi's La vendetta di Nino.

Le **sventure fortunate.** Farsa per musica da rappresentarsi nel
Teatro de' Fiorentini nel carnevale di quest' anno 1785.

*Napoli, n. publ., 1785. 71 p. 15*cm.

One act. Author not mentioned, and unknown to Schatz. Cast and name of
Pietro **Guglielmi** as the composer. On p. [33]–71 is printed, with cast and the same
composer's name:

— **La finta Zingara.** Farsa per musica di Giambattista Lorenzi,
P. A. da rappresentarsi nel Teatro de' Fiorentini nel carnevale di
quest' anno 1785.

First performed, as indicated, January 10, 1785.   SCHATZ 4274

Il **Svizzero ingannato,** ballet. *See* Zannetti's Le cognate in
contesa.

Sylla. Tr. of Graun's Silla.

Les **sylphes** ou L'amour leger. Entrée in Duval's Les génies.

Les **sylphes supposés.** A. T. of Blaise's Isabelle et Gertrude.

Sylvain. Tr. of Grétry's Silvain.

Syphax. Tr. of Porpora's Siface.

The **syrens,** a masque in two acts, as performed at the Theatre Royal, Covent-Garden. Written by captain Thompson. The music composed by Mr. Fisher . . .

London, G. Kearsly, 1776. 4 p. l., [1], 4–32 p. 18ᶜᵐ.

Two acts. Cast, preface, and dedication, dated Kew, April 28, 1776.
First performed February 26, 1776 (Genest).   LONGE 200

Der **Tabaran.** Tr. of Hasse's Il Tabarano.

Il **Tabarano.** L. T. of Hasse's Don Tabarrano.

Le **tableau parlant,** comédie-parade, en un acte & en vers, mêlée d'ariettes; représentée pour la première fois par les Comédiens italiens ordinaires du roi, le mercredi 20 septembre 1769. Par Mr. Anseaume, la musique est de Mr. Grétry.

Paris, la veuve Duchesne, 1769. 48 p. 19ᶜᵐ.   SCHATZ 4188

— Das **redende gemaehlde,** eine operette in einem aufzug aus dem franzoesischen des hrn. Anseaume von F. W. M.[eyer]. Die musik ist von hn. Gretry.

Mannheim, C. F. Schwan, 1771. 88 p. 14½ᶜᵐ.

First performed at Mannheim, Theater a. d. Fruchtmarkt, 1771.   SCHATZ 4189

— Gesaenge und arien aus der komischen oper: Das **redende gemaehlde.** Die musik ist vom herrn Gretry.

Hamburg, J. M. Michaelsen, 1780. 16 p. 16½ᶜᵐ.

One act. German version by Heinrich August Ottokar Reichard, who is not mentioned.
First performed at Hamburg, Theater am Gänsemarkt, December 15, 1780; at Berlin, Theater i. d. Behrenst., May 31, 1774.   SCHATZ 4190

Tacere ed amare. Drama civile musicale rappresentato nell' Accademia de' Signori Infuocati.

n. i., n. d. p. [405]–504 p. 15½ᶜᵐ.

Three acts. Detached from the third vol. (not in L. of C.) of the "Poesie drammatiche" (1689–1690) by Giov. Andrea Moniglia, who is not mentioned. Argument, scenario, and preface, in which Jacopo **Melani** is mentioned as the composer, and the "Teatro di via del Cocomero da' SS. Accademici Infuocati," at Florence, is given as the place of first performance, which probably took place, not in 1674 (Schatz), but in 1673, since the dedication in the 1674 libretto, at Brussels, is dated Florence, January 7, 1673.   SCHATZ 6288

Taddaedl, der dreyssigjaehrige A. B. C. schuetz. Eine posse mit gesang in drey aufzuegen, nach einer burleske fuer die Marinellische schaubuehne bearbeitet von Karl Friedrich Hensler. Die musik ist vom herrn Wenzel Mueller kapellmeister.

Wien, Schmidt, 1799. 95 p. 16½ᶜᵐ.

First performed, as indicated, May 22, 1799.   SCHATZ 6968

Die **taeuschende aehnlichkeit** oder Die buckeligen. Tr. of Portugal's La somiglianza ossiano I gobbi.

Der **tag des heyls** oder Demetrius in Athen. Tr. of Wilderer's Il giorno di salute ovvero Demetrio in Athene.

Taican rè della Cina. Tragedia per musica da rappresentarsi nel Teatro Tron di S. Cassano l'anno 1707.

Venezia, Marino Rossetti, 1707. front., 82 p. 13½ᶜᵐ.

Five acts. By Urbano Rizzi, who is not mentioned. Argument, cast, name of Carlo Francesco **Gasparini** as the composer, scenario, and printer's notice to the reader, beginning:
"Per lascier tempo à gl'intermezzi ridicoli, & a' balli, si taceranno nella musica tutti li versi, che vedrai segnati nel margine." SCHATZ 3584

Les talens lyriques. A. T. of the ballet Les fêtes d'Hébé.

Talestri. Drama per musica da rappresentarsi in Roma nel **Teatro** delle Dame nel corrente carnevale dell' anno MDCCLII . . .

Roma, Fausto Amidei, n. d. 71 p. 14½ᶜᵐ.

Three acts. Dedication, argument, cast, scenario, and names of Gaetano Roccaforte as author, of Niccolò **Jommelli** as composer.
First performed, as indicated, December 28, 1751. ML 50.2.T13J6

Talestri, regina delle Amazoni. Opera drammatica. Di E.[rmelinda] T.[alèa] P.[astorella] A.[rcada].

Monaco, Giuseppe Francesco Thuille, 1760. 64 p. 16ᶜᵐ.

Orignal edition, and practically the same text, though without the licenza, as of next entry. SCHATZ 5950

— **Talestri, regina delle Amazzoni,** opera drammatica di E.[rmelinda] T.[alèa] P.[astorella] A.[rcada].

Dresda, C. S. Walther, 1770. 91, [3] p. 23½ᶜᵐ.

Three acts and licenza. Text and music by **Maria Antonia Walpurgis,** princess of Saxony, whose Arcadian name is indicated in the title.
First performed at Dresden August 24, 1763; at Nymphenburg, Theater des churf. Schlosses (near Munich), February 6, 1760. SCHATZ 5948

Der talisman. Ein singspiel in drey aufzeugen. Nach dem italiaenischen des Goldoni. Auf die musik des herrn Anton Salieri . . . für die Marinellische buehne frei uebersetzt von Ferdinand Eberl.

Wien, n. publ., 1789. 72 p. 17ᶜᵐ.

Dedication and "Erinnerung fuer die kritick," which reads, in part:
"Die ersten zwey arien des zweyten aufzugs befinden sich nur in der original Spartitur, und sind im gedruckten italiaenischen buechel ['Il talismano'] ganz andren textes."
First performed at Vienna, Theater in der Leopoldstadt, April 30, 1789. The original "Il Talismano," Goldoni's text partly rewritten by Da Ponte, was first performed at Vienna, Burgtheater, September 10, 1788. SCHATZ 9322

— Arien und gesaenge aus dem **Talisman,** oder Die zigeuner. Ein singspiel in zwey aufzeugen, nach dem italienischen. Die musik ist von herrn Salieri.

n. i., 1790. 40 p. 16ᵉᵐ.

Translation by Heinrich Gottlieb Schmieder, who is not mentioned.
First performed at Mayence, Nationaltheater, February 20, 1790. SCHATZ 9323

— Arien und gesaenge aus dem singspiel in drey aufzeugen Der **Talisman.** Die musik ist von Salieri.

Berlin, n. publ., 1798. 56 p. 17ᶜᵐ.

Cast. The translator, Adolph Franz Friedrich Ludwig, freiherr von **Knigge,** is not mentioned.
First performed at Berlin, Nationaltheater, May 20, 1796; at Hanover, Schlosstheater, June 4, 1790. SCHATZ 9324

Der **talisman.**   Tr. of Salieri's Il talismano.

Il **talismano.**   Dramma di tre atti per musica.

Carlo Goldoni, Opere teatrali, Venezia, Zatta e figli, 1788–95, v. 37, [5]–69 p.   18½^cm.

For first composers *see* next entry.   PQ

Il **Talismano.**   Dramma giocoso per musica da rappresentarsi nel Teatro alla Scala l'estate dell' anno 1785 . . .

Milano, Gio. Batista Bianchi, n. d.   67 p.   16½^cm.

Three acts.   By Carlo Goldoni, who is not mentioned.   Dedication, cast, scenario, and names of Antonio **Salieri** as composer of the first act, of Giacomo **Rust** of the second and third.   With the opera were performed "alternativamente" Sebastiano Gallet's ballets, "L'amor vincitore, ballo anacreontico," "Il signore benefico," "Il Bajram de' Turchi," the composers of the music not being mentioned.

First performed at Milan, Teatro alla Canobbiana, September, 1779.

SCHATZ 9336

Tamar e Selimo ossia Padre e figlio rivali sconosciuti, ballet. *See* Isola's Lisandro.

Tamas Kouli-Kan nell' India.   Dramma per musica da rappresentarsi nel Regio Teatro di Torino nel carnovale del 1772 . . .

Torino, Onorato Derossi, n. d.   viii, 63, [1] p.   16^cm.

Last page incorrectly numbered 93.

Three acts.   Argument, cast, scenario, and names of Vittorio Amedeo Cigna Santi as the author, of Gaetano **Pugnani** as the composer of the opera, and of Paolo Gebhard as the composer of the music for Giovanni Favier's ballets, "I panduri accampati," etc., briefly described on p. 61–63.   SCHATZ 8506

Il **tamburo.**   Commedia per musica di Giambatista Lorenzi, P. A. da rappresentarsi nel Teatro Nuovo nel carnevale di quest' anno 1784.

Napoli, n. publ., 1784.   58 p.   14½^cm.

Three acts.   Cast and name of **Paisiello** as the composer.

First performed at the same theatre, spring of 1773.   SCHATZ 7659

— Il **tamburo notturno.**   Dramma giocoso per musica da rappresentarsi nel Regio-Ducal Teatro di Parma il carnovale dell' anno MDCCLXXVIII.

Parma, Stamperia reale, n. d.   64 p.   20^cm.

Three acts.   Lorenzi's text with alterations by Giovanni Bertati, neither author being mentioned.   Cast and name of **Paisiello** as the composer.   On p. [61]–64 cast and program of Giuseppe Traffieri's "Amore premiato, ballo pastorale."   The composer of the music is not mentioned.

First performed, as indicated, December 26, 1777; at Venice, Teatro di San Moisè, fall of 1773.   SCHATZ 7660

— Il **tamburo notturno.**   Dramma giocoso per musica da rappresentarsi ne' Teatri privilegiati di Vienna nell' anno 1774.

[Vienna], Giuseppe Kurzbök, n. d.   78 p.   17^cm.

Three acts.   Lorenzi's poetry "tradotta dal dialetto napolitano nel idioma Toscano dal Signor Boccarini, poeta de' Cesarei **Teatri** di Vienna."   **Paisiello** is mentioned as the composer.

First performed May 17, 1774, as indicated.   SCHATZ 7661

Il **tamburo notturno.**   L. T. of Paisiello's Il tamburo.

Tamerlan.   Tr. of Händel's Tamerlano.

Tamerlane. Tr. of Händel's Tamerlano.

Tamerlano. Dramma per musica da rappresentarsi nel Teatro di San Samuelle il carnevale dell' anno MDCCLIV.

Venezia, Angiolo Geremia, n. d. 43 p. 16ᶜᵐ.

Three acts. By conte Agostino Piovene, who is not mentioned. Notice to the reader as argument, scenario, cast, and on p. 6 the statement:
"Il primo atto è posto in musica dal Signor Gioacchino **Cocchi**, il secondo dal Signor Giambattista **Pescetti**, il terzo parte da uno, e parte dall' altro di essi maestri."

SCHATZ 2054

Tamerlano. Tragedia per musica da rappresentarsi nel Teatro Tron di San Cassano l'anno 1710.

Venezia, Marino Rossetti, n. d. 65 p. 14½ᶜᵐ.

Three acts. Neither the author, conte Agosttino Piovene, nor the composer, Carlo Francesco **Gasparini** is mentioned. Notice to the reader, cast and scenario.

SCHATZ 3585

— Il Bajazet. Dramma per musica da rappresentarsi nel Teatro dell' illustrissimo pubblico di Reggio in occasione della fiera l'anno MDCCXIX . . .

Reggio, Ippolito Vedrotti, 1719. 77 p. 16½ᶜᵐ.

Three acts. Dedication dated Reggio, April 29, 1719, argument, Protesta, cast, scenario, and name of Carlo Francesco **Gasparini** as the composer. ("La musica è nuova.") The author, conte Agostino Piovene, is not mentioned, a considerably altered adaptation of whose "Tamerlano" this "Bajazet" is said to be in the Protesta, "particolarmente nell' arie, che sempre esigono d'essere accomodate a' nuovi musici." For instance, Tamur has been dropped from the list of characters and that of Clearco has been added. The aria ending scene IV, act I, "Custodite per mia figlia," has become "Forte, e lieto a morte andrei," the third scene begins "Un lieto annunzio" instead of "Prencipe, or orai i Greci," the third act has seventeen scenes instead of fifteen, etc., etc. Though the music is said to be *new*, presumably this is to be taken with a grain of salt. Probably "Il Bajazet" was not Gasparini's second setting of the Tamerlano text, but his first and only setting of the text with other music where the texts differed. Perhaps "Il Bajazet" was in reality a pasticcio. SCHATZ 3562

Il **Tamerlano.** Dramma per musica da rappresentarsi nel Teatro Vendramino di S. Salvatore la fiera dell' Ascensione dell' anno 1765.

Venezia, Modesto Fenzo, 1765. 56 p. 14½ᶜᵐ.

Three acts. By conte Agostino Piovene, who is not mentioned. Argument, cast, scenario, and name of Pietro **Guglielmi** as the composer. On p. 25–26 description without name of the composer of the music of Jean Baptiste Martein's ballet "La forza dell' amore e dell' amicizia."

SCHATZ 4306

Tamerlano: Drama. Da rappresentarsi nel Regio Teatro di Hay-Market, per La Reale Accademia di musica.

London, Printed and sold at the King's Theatre in the Hay-Market, 1724. 6 p. l., [3], 4–99 p. 18ᶜᵐ.

Three acts. Cast, argument, text both in Italian and in English. (Half-title on 1st p. l. is "Tamerlane, an opera.") The dedication in Italian only. In it Nicola [Francesco] Haym says:
"Avendo io per ubbidire agli ordini de' miei nobilissimi padroni i signori direttori della Reale Accademia di musica, accomodato per il loro teatro la presente opera di Tamerlano . . ."
Consequently, Haym did not claim to have been the author of the text, as charged in Grove's Dictionary and elsewhere. He does not mention conte Agostino Piovene nor the composer, Georg Friedrich **Händel**. English translation faces Italian text.
First performed at London, as indicated, October 31, 1724. ML 50.2.T23

Tamerlano—Continued.

— **Tamerlan,** in einem sing-spiele, auf dem Hamburgischen Schauplatze vorgestellet. Im jahr 1725.

[Hamburg], mit Stromerischen schrifften, n. d.   Unpaged.   18½ᶜᵐ.

Three acts. Cast, prefatory note, and names of Hendel (Georg Friedrich **Händel**) as the composer of the opera, of Georg Philipp **Telemann** as the composer of the "intermezzo," of Nicola Haym as author of the "italiaenische poesie" and Johann Philipp Praetorius as author of the translation, to which the Italian text of the arias has been added. Praetorius says, after mentioning Haym and "die ausbuendig schoene musique" Händel's:

"Doch hat eine illustre persohn durch geschickte composition der parthie des Bajazeths eine abermahlige probe ihrer vertu ablegē wollen. Das recitativ hat zwar der music nach bey der ubersetzung durch einē beruehmten mann geaendert werden muessen, doch sind in dem 10tē auftritt der 3ten handlūg einige zeilen unveraendert in italiaenis. sprache und nach der Hendelischen composition beybehalten wordē, weil worte uñ music gar zu schoen auch dem affect ein grosses abgehen duerffte, im fall die ubersetzung dem original nicht gleich kaeme . . ."   Schatz 4492

Tamerlano. Drama per musica, da rappresentarsi nel Regio Teatro di Torino nel carnovale del 1730 . . .

Torino, Gio. Battista Valetta, n. d.   3 p. l., 58 p.   15ᶜᵐ.

Three acts. By conte Agostino Piovene, who is not mentioned. Argument, scenario, cast, and name of Nicolà Antonio **Porpora** as the composer.   Schatz 8375

Tamira. Ein drama. Nebst einer abhandlung ueber das melodrama von D. Huber . . . [vignette].

Tuebingen, Cotta, 1791.   136 p.   17ᶜᵐ.

One act. Argument, dedicatory poem, and prefatory note, in which Huber says: "Dieses melodrama war vor zehn jahren fertig, nemlich die arbeit des dichters. Ich las es, wie meine meisten arbeiten in diesem und andern faechern, meinem ehrwuerdigen freunde vor, dem regierungs praesidenten von Gemmingen. Das drama schien ihm zu gefallen. Er machte mir sogar die hoffnung, die musik dazu zu verfertigen. Denn er war auch meister in dieser kunst. Er componirte wirklich eine tragische ouvertüre in dieser absicht. Ich harrte ein paar jahre mit geduldiger hoffnung auf die erfuellung des ganzen verspruchs. . . . Da hatte ich die freundliche bosheit, ihm mit dem druck des drama und einer zueignung zu drohen, die ihn der unerfuellten zusage beschuldigte . . . Es hatte die wirkung, dass er unsern hofmusikus **Zum Steeg** [!] bewog, die musikalische composition zu uebernehmen. Er that es, das stueck wurde zweymal auf hiesigem theater aufgefuehrt . . ."

First performed June 13, 1788. Huber's essay, "Etwas ueber das melo-drama," on p. 41–136. Schatz records the author as Ludwig Ferdinand Huber, other authorities as Johann Ludwig Huber.   Schatz 11295

Tamiri, drama per musica di Bartolameo Vitturi da rappresentarsi nel Teatro di S. Angelo nell' autuno dell' anno MDCCXXXIV . . .

Venezia, Marin Rossetti, n. d.   60 p.   15½ᶜᵐ.

Three acts. Impresario's dedication, argument, author's notice to the reader, cast, scenario, and name of **Galuppi** as composer.

First performed, as indicated, November 17, 1734.   Schatz 3495

Tancrede, tragedie representée par l'Academie royale de musique l'an 1702. Les paroles de M. Danchet & la musique de M. Campra. LVII. Opera.

n. i., n. d. front., 1–56 p.   14ᶜᵐ.   (Recueil général des opéra, Paris, 1706, t. viii.)

Five acts with prologue.

First performed, as indicated, November 7, 1702.   Schatz 1560

Second copy.   ML 48.R4

Tancrede—Continued.

— **Tancrede**, tragédie, representée, par l'Académie royale de musique, pour la premiere fois le 7 novembre 1702.

[133]–192 p.   17½cm.   (Antoine Danchet, Théâtre, Paris, 1751, t. ii.)
Prologue and five acts.   **Campra** is not mentioned.   PQ 1972.D2

— **Arlequin Tancrede.**   Parodie en un acte.   Par les Srs. Dominique & Romagnesi . . .   Représenté pour la premiere fois par les Comédiens italiens ordinaires du roi, le 19 mars 1729.

Les parodies du Nouveau théâtre italien, Nouv. éd., Paris, 1738, t. iv, [73]–120 p.   16½cm.

One act.   The airs and vaudeville used are printed at end of the volume in the "Table des airs" (92 p.)   ML 48.P3

Tancredi ossia Il padre crudele.   Ballo tragico in tre atti composto e diretto da M.ᵣ Domenico Lefevre da rappresentarsi nel magnifico Teatro dell' Accademia Filarmonica di Verona nel carnovale dell' anno 1793.

Verona, Dionigi Ramanzini, n. d.   20 p.   17cm.

Argument, cast, and scene by scene description of the plot.   Composer of the music not mentioned and unknown to me.   ML 52.2.T22

Tancredi.   Dramma per musica da rappresentarsi nel Regio Teatro di Torino nel carnovale del 1767.   Alla presenza di S. S. R. M.

Torino, Stamperia reale, n. d.   viii, 64, [1] p.   16½cm.

Three acts.   Argument, cast, scenario, and name of composer, Ferdinando Giuseppe **Bertoni**, but not of librettist, Balbis.   Three ballets by Vincenzo Galeotti, music by Giuseppe Antonio Le Messier, went with the opera, the first two being called "Il convitato di pietra" and "Amore e Psiche."
First performed, as indicated, December 26, 1766.   SCHATZ 930

Tancredi.   Tragedia per musica in tre atti di Alessandro Pepoli ad uso del medesimo nel suo Teatro privato.

Venezia, Tipografia Pepoliana, 1795.   40 p.   17½cm.

Francesco **Gardi** is mentioned as the composer.   In his curious preface, conte Pepoli says:
   "il libro (e tutti lo crederanno) fu da me composto a piacer mio, la musica egualmente vi fu applicata dal valente compositore a piacer mio, ed io alfine la reciterò, e la canterò a piacer mio."   SCHATZ 3542

Tancredi.   Dramma per musica da rappresentarsi nel Teatro Nuovo di Corte per comando di S. A. S. E. Carlo Teodoro conte Palatino del' Reno . . . nel carnovale MDCCLXXXIII.

n. i., n. d.   135 p.   14½cm.

Three acts.   Author not mentioned, and unknown to Schatz.   Argument, cast, and names of Ignaz **Holzbauer** as composer, of Lorenz Hübner as translator.   German title page, "Tankred," and text face Italian.
First performed, as indicated, at Munich, Hoftheater, January, 1783.
SCHATZ 4786

Il **Tancredi,** ballet.   See Tritto's La vergine del sole.

Tankred.   Tr. of Holzbauer's Tancredi.

The **tanner of York.**   A. T. of The lucky discovery.

Tanto va la gatta al lardo che si lascia lo zampino.   A. T. of Il calzettaro, ballet.

Tarar. Tr. of Salieri's Axur rè d'Ormus.

Tarara o sia La virtù premiata. Dramma per musica del Sig. abate Gaetano Sertor da rappresentarsi nel nobilissimo Teatro La Fenice nel carnovale dell' anno 1793.

Venezia, n. publ., 1792. [v]–viii, 48 p. 16ᶜᵐ.

Three acts. Cast and name of composer, Francesco **Bianchi.**
First performed at Venice, as indicated, December 26, 1792. Schatz 984

Tarare, opera en cinq actes, avec un prologue, représenté pour la premiere fois sur le Théatre de l'Academie royale de musique, le vendredi 8 juin 1787.

Amsterdam, César Noël Guerin, 1787. 88 p. 18ᶜᵐ.

Dedication and names of [Pierre Augustin] Caron de Beaumarchais as the author, of Antonio **Salieri** as the composer. Schatz 9325

— **Tarare,** an opera, in five acts: with a prologue. As it was performed for the first time at the Theatre of the Royal Academy of music, on Friday the 8th June, 1787.

London, R. Faulder, 1787. 96 p. 20½ᶜᵐ.

Five acts and prologue. Cast, translator's advertisement, names of Beaumarchais as author, and of Antonio **Salieri** as composer, and Beaumarchais's dedication to Salieri. Longe 299

— **Axur re d'Ormus.** Dramma tragicomico in cinque atti. Da rappresentarsi nei Teatri di Praga l'anno 1788.

[Praga], Giuseppe Emanuele Diesbach, n. d. 82 p. 16ᶜᵐ.

Name of Lorenzo da Ponte as author, of Antonio **Salieri** as the composer. This is a free Italian version of "Tarare," not a translation.
First performed at Vienna, Burgtheater, January 8, 1788. Schatz 9326

— **Axur, re d'Ormus.** Dramma tragicomico in due atti da rappresentarsi nel Theatro di S. A. E. di Sassonia.

Dresda, n. publ., 1789. 131 p. 15ᶜᵐ.

Two-act version of Da Ponte's text, who is not mentioned. Antonio **Salieri** is mentioned as the composer. German title-page, "Axur, koenig von Ormus," and text face Italian.
First performed, as indicated, November 21, 1789. Schatz 9329

— **Axur re d'Ormus.** Dramma tragicomico in musica da rappresentarsi in musica da rappresentarsi nel Teatro alla Scala la primavera dell' anno 1792 . . .

Milano, Gio. Batista Bianchi, n. d. 68 p. 16½ᶜᵐ.

Two acts. Cast, scenario, names of Da Ponte as author, and of Antonio **Salieri** as the composer, and impresario's dedication, which reads, in part:
". . . Axur re d'Ormus, lo stesso che fu rappresentato nel Teatro della R. I. Corte di Vienna. Benchè sia egli stato originariamente scritto in cinque atti separati, si è ora diviso in due sole parti, puramente per uniformarsi all' uso dei nostri teatri dell' Italia, ed acciochè non mancasse del solito divertimento dei balli."
The first of these, by Urbano Garzia (composer of the music not mentioned), was called "Federico II re di Prussia." Schatz 9331

— **Axur, koenig von Ormus.** Ein tragikomisches singspiel in fuenf aufzeugen. Uebersetzt von Sarker. Aufzufuehren im K. K. Hoftheater. Bei der vermaehlung S. K. H. Franz, erzherzogs von Oesterreich mit J. D. H. Elisabeth, princessinn von Wuertemberg.

Wien, n. publ., 1788. 58 p. 16½ᶜᵐ.

Names of Lorenzo da Ponte and of Antonio **Salieri.** This is Sarker's transl. of the Italian original first performed, as indicated, January 8, 1788. Schatz 9327

Tarare—Continued.

— **Axur, koenig von Ormus.** Eine heroische oper in fünf aufzügen, nach dem italiaenischen des herrn abbé da Ponte uebersetzt
und für das gräflich Erdoedysche operntheater eingerichtet von herrn
Giržick. Zum drucke befoerdert von herrn Joh. Nep. Schueller.
1788. Die musik ist von herrn Anton Salieri.

Pressburg, Weber, 1788. 80 p. 16^{cm}.

On p. 74–80: "Anhang das graeflich Erdoedische Operntheater betreffend.
Theater Personale—Folgende opern sind seit der eroeffnung des graeflichen theaters
aufgefuehrt worden." Dedication and cast. Schatz 9328

— **Axur, koenig von Ormus,** ein singspiel in vier aufzuegen. Nach
dem Tarar des Beaumarchais von D. Schmieder.

*Hamburg und Altona, Buchhandlung der Neuen Verlagsgesellschaft,
1799. 125 p. 16½^{cm}.*

Cast and notice to the reader by Schmieder, which reads:
"Dieses singspiel ist durch seine oefteren darstellungen auf allen grossen buehnen
Deutschlands bekannt genug. Neulich hat sich durch seine fleissige und prunkvolle
auffuehrung dieser oper, das Nationaltheater zu Altona, ein schoenes blatt, in seinen
noch frisch bluehenden kranz gewunden. Sie ward hier vom May bis July d. J.
eilfmal mit immer gleichem beyfall gegeben. Die Namen der hiesigen kuenstler
sind dem personenverzeichnisse, als ein zeichen der achtung, beygesetzt."
First performed at Frankfurt, Nationaltheater, August, 1790. Schatz 9332

— **Axur, koenig von Ormus.** Grosse oper in vier aufzuegen. Aus
dem italiaenischen. Musik von Anton Salieri.

n. i., n. d. 64 p. 16½^{cm}.

Later version with recitatives of Heinrich Gottlieb Schmieder's translation, who
is not mentioned. Possibly published after 1800. Schatz 9334

— Gesaenge aus dem singspiele: **Tarar,** in vier aufzuegen, nach dem
franzoesischen und italienischen des Beaumarchais und abbate Casti, [!]
von *D.* Schmieder. Die musik ist von Salieri.

Hamburg, Johann Matthias Michaelsen, 1791. 48 p. 16½^{cm}.

As "Tarar" first performed at Hamburg, Theater beim Gänsemarkt, December 28,
1791; as "Axur, koenig von Ormus" at Frankfurt a/M, Nationaltheater, August 14,
1790. Schatz 9330

Il **Tarconte, principe de' Volsci.** Drama per musica da rappresentarsi nel Teatro Formagliari l'autunno dell' anno 1716.

Bologna, Giulio Rossi, e comp., n. d. 48 p. 15^{cm}.

Three acts. Argument, notice to the reader, cast, scenario. Author and composer not mentioned and unknown to Schatz.
First performed, as indicated, November 7, 1716. Schatz 11367

The **tars of Old England.** A. T. of The reprisal.

Tarsis et Zelie, tragedie representée par l'Academie royale de
musique, l'an 1728. Paroles de M. de la Serre; musique de M^{rs}
Francoeur-Cadet, & Rebel fils. CXI opera.

*n. i., n. d. pl., p. 297–344 (Recueil général des opera, t. xiv, Paris,
1734). 14^{cm}.*

Detached copy. Five acts and prologue.
First performed, as indicated, October 19, 1728. Schatz 3337
Second copy. ML 48.R4

I **Tartari generosi,** ballet. *See* Bertoni's Bajazette.

Das tartarische gesez. Ein schauspiel mit gesang in zwey aufzügen. [vignette]

> *Leipzig, Dykische buchhandlung, 1779. 64 p. 16¼ᶜᵐ.*

Two acts. By Gotter, based according to his "Nachricht," dated "Gotha im
august 1778," on Gozzi's "Glückliche Bettler." The composer, Johann **André**, is
not mentioned.

First performed at Berlin, Döbbelinsches Theater, May 31, 1779.   SCHATZ 190

Il Tartaro generoso, ballet.   *See* Zannetti's Le cognate in contesa.

La tasse de glaces.   A. T. of Dalayrac's La leçon.

Taste à la mode.   A. T. of Harlequin restor'd.

The taste of the age.   A. T. of The fool's opera.

Téagene et Cariclée, tragedie en musique.   Représentée par l'Académie royale de musique.   Suivant la copie imprimée à Paris.

> *Amsterdam, Antoine Schelte, 1695. 60 p. (incl. front.) 13½ᶜᵐ.*

Prologue and five acts. Neither the author, Duché, is mentioned, nor the composer, **Désmarets.**

First performed, as indicated, February 3, 1695.   ML 50.2.T3D2

— **Téagene et Cariclée,** tragedie représentée par l'Academie royale
de musique l'an 1695.   Les paroles sont de M. Duché, & la musique
de M. Desmarets.   XXXIV. opera.

> *n. i., n. d. front., p. 67–134. (Recueil général des opéra, t. v, Paris,
> 1703.) 14ᶜᵐ.*

Detached copy. Prologue and five acts.   SCHATZ 2534
                                   Second copy.   ML 48.R4

Il teatro italiano alla China, ballet.   *See* Martin y Soler's
Andromaca.

Tegene e Laodicea.   Dramma per musica da rappresentarsi nel
Regio Teatro di via della Pergola il carnevale del 1799 . . .

> *Firenze, Stamperia Albizziniana, 1799. 28 p. 16ᶜᵐ.*

Three acts. By Giuseppe Foppa, who is not mentioned. Cast and name of Ferdinando Per (**Paër**) as the composer. With the opera were performed Domenico de
Rossy's ballets, "Alfonso di Castiglia" and "L'equivoco dei due mulinari." The
composers of the music are not mentioned.

Originally performed at Padua, Teatro Nuovo, June, 1793, as "Laodicea."

                                                    SCHATZ 7508

Telegone, tragedie, representée par l'Academie royale de musique,
l'an 1725.   Musique de M. la Coste.   Paroles de M. Pellegrin.
CV. opera.

> *n. i., n. d. 14ᶜᵐ. pl., 453–524 p. (Recueil général des opéra,
> t. xiii, Paris, 1734.)*

Detached copy. Five acts and prologue. Cast.

First performed, as indicated, November 6, 1725.   SCHATZ 5357
                                   Second copy.   ML 48.R4

Telemach.   Tr. of Grua's Telemaco.

Telemaco. Opera seria da rappresentarsi nel Teatro Nuovo di Corte . . . nel carnevale 1780. La poesia è del Signor conte Serimann. La musica è del Signor Paolo Grua . . .

Monaco, Francesco Giuseppe Thuille, n. d. 145 p. 15^{cm}.

Three acts. Argument, cast, and name of Giuseppe Toeschi as composer of the ballet music. German title-page, "Telemach," and text by Anton, graf von Toerring zu Seefeld, as indicated in the German title, face Italian.

First performed, as indicated, January 10, 1780. SCHATZ 4222

Telemaco. Dramma per musica di Carlo Sigismondo Capeci da rappresentarsi nella Sala dell' illustrissimo Signor Federico Capranica nel carnevale dell' anno 1718 . . .

Roma, Bernabò, 1718. 72 p. 14$\frac{1}{2}$^{cm}.

Three acts. Impresario's dedication, argument, cast, and name of Alessandro **Scarlatti** as the composer. ("Questa è la centesima nona opera teatrale da lui composta.") SCHATZ 9532

Telemaco ed Eurice nell' isola di Calipso. Dramma per musica da rappresentarsi nel nobilissimo Teatro di S. Benedetto nel carnovale dell' anno 1777.

Venezia, Modesto Fenzo, 1777. 62 p. 17$\frac{1}{2}$^{cm}.

Three acts. Argument, cast, scenario, and names of composer, Ferdinando Giuseppe **Bertoni**, and the author, *marchese* Giovanni Piudemonte, whose Arcadian name is given: "Echille Acanzio, P. A. della colonia Veronese." Both poetry and music are called "tutta nuova." On p. 23–36, description, with cast and argument, of "I tre Orazj e i tre Curiazj. Ballo tragico, composto ed eseguito da Monsieur Carlo Le Picq," and on p. 53–56, description of "L'amante generosa, ballo pantomimo d'invenzione ed esecuzione del Sig. Giuseppe Canciani." The composers of the music are not mentioned.

First performed, as indicated, December 26, 1776. SCHATZ 933

Telemaco in Sicilia. Dramma per musica del Signor Antonio Simon Sografi avvocato veneto.

(At end) Padova, Penada, 1792. 55, [1] p. 19$\frac{1}{2}$^{cm}.

Four acts. Sografi's dedication, dated Padova, June 20, 1792, begins: "Nell' idea di offerirvi questa nuova mia produzione (la quale posso chiamar nuova, perchè ad onta ch'io abbia trattato questo medesimo soggetto pel teatro d'una Real corte volli in questa occasione ridurlo ad uso del vostro . . ." Cast and name of Antonio **Calegari** as composer. SCHATZ 1508

Telemaco nell' isola di Calipso, ballet. *See* Bertoni's Il Bajazette

Telemaco nell' isola di Calipso, ballet. *See* P. Guglielmi's Alessandro nell' Indie.

Telemaco nell' isola di Calipso. Dramma per musica del Signor. Sografi, poeta del nobilissimo Teatro La Fenice e del Teatro comico Sant' Angelo. Composta per il teatro sudetto per il carnovale 1797.

Venezia, Stamperia Valvasense, n. d. 78 p. 17$\frac{1}{2}$^{cm}.

Three acts. Cast and name of Joh. Simon **Mayr** as the composer. On p. [67]–78, prefatory note, argument, cast, and description of Lorenzo Panzieri's "La Lodoiska, ballo eroico pantomimo in tre atti." The composer of the music is not mentioned.

First performed, as indicated, January 16, 1797. SCHATZ 6175

Telemaco nell' isola di Calipso. Dramma per musica del nobile Signore Carlo Lanfranchi Rossi, patrizio Pisano, da rappresentarsi in Firenze nel Teatro di via del Cocomero nell' autunno dell' anno 1773 . . .

Firenze, Anton Giuseppe Pagani, 1773. vi, 3–56 p. 17^{cm}.

Telemaco nell' isola di Calipso—Continued.

Three acts. Argument, cast, and scenario. On p. v, "La musica parte è propria, e parte sotto la direzione del Sig. Gio. Vincenzo **Meucci**, maestro di cappella Fiorent. Tutte quelle arie, che saranno notate con questo segno *non sono, che adattate dall' autore del libro a comodo della musica."

On p. 3–6, description and cast of Giuseppe Banti's "L'Olimpiade, ballo pantomimo-eroico," music by Gennaro Astaritta. SCHATZ 6400

Telemaco nell' isola di Calipso, ballet. *See* Piccinni's Tigrane.

Telemaco nella isola di Calipso. Dramma per musica da rappresentarsi nel Real Teatro del Fondo di Separazione per terza opera di questo anno 1785 . . .

Napoli, n. publ., 1785. 24 p. 15^{cm}.

Two parts. Dedication and cast. The remark, "La musica è diretta dal Sig. D. Francesco **Cipolla**" (p. 5), does not, as Schatz would have it, establish him as the composer. The author is unknown to Schatz. SCHATZ 2012

Télémaque, tragedie, fragments des modernes. Représentée pour la première fois par l'Academie royale de musique, l'onzième jour de novembre 1704.

Amsterdam, Henri Schelte, 1705. 48 p. 13^{cm}.

A pasticcio in five acts with prologue. The compilers Danchet and **Campra** are not mentioned. Same Avvertissement as below. ML 50.2.T34C3

— **Télémaque**, tragedie, fragments des modernes. Représentée par l'Academie royale de musique l'an 1704. Cette pièce a esté mise au Théatre par les soins de MM. Danchet & Campra. LXII. opera.

n. i., n. d. front., 291–332 p. (Recueil général des opéra, Paris, 1706, t. viii.)

Detached copy. A pasticcio in five acts with prologue. In the Avertissement Danchet says:

"Après avoir donné les FRAGMENTS DE MONSIEUR DE LULLY, qui eurent un succès favorable, je fus chargé de faire les FRAGMENTS DES OPERA MODERNES que l'on ne veut pas remettre entiers sur le théatre. Pour en faire quelque chose de singulier, j'entrepris de les rendre interessants en y mettant une action . . . J'ay choisi le sujet de Télémaque, j'en ai fait le plan d'une tragédie, que j'ai composée des plus beaux morceaux de musique, que les connoisseurs m'ont indiquez, ou que j'ay vû moymême aplaudir au théatre. Cet ouvrage peut être comparé à un cabinet paré de tableaux choisis de differents maîtres . . . J'ay marqué dans ce livre le nom des auteurs dont je me suis servy, & j'ay marqué par doubles virgules les vers de liaison que j'ay faits, & que Monsieur Campra a mis en musique."

Accordingly, for this pasticcio he utilized Fontenelle and **Colasse**'s "Enée & Lavinie," his own and **Campra**'s Arethuse, La Fontaine and **Colasse**'s Astrée, de La Mothe and **Colasse**'s Canente, Corneille and **Charpentier**'s Medée, Bernard and **Campra**'s Carnaval du Venise, Saint Jean and **Marais**' Ariane, Mlle Saintonge and **Desmarets**' Circé, Guichard and **Rebel**'s Ulysse. It is not mentioned that **Campra** composed the "vers de liason."

First performed at Paris, Académie royale de musique, November 11, 1704.

SCHATZ 1561
Second copy. ML 48.R4

— **Telemaque**, tragédie. Fragmens des modernes. Représentée par l'Académie royale de musique, l'an 1704.

[291]–333 p. 17½^{cm}. (Antoine Danchet, Théâtre, t. ii, Paris, 1751.)

Prologue and five acts. Practically the same avertissement. PQ 1972.D2

Telemaque, tragedie representée pour la premiere fois, par l'Académie royale de musique, le jeudi 6. decembre 1714. Les paroles de M. Pellegrin & la musique de M. Destouches. LXXXVI. opera.

n. i., n. d. pl., p. 233–300. (Recueil général des opéras, t. xi, Paris, 1720.) 14ᶜᵐ.

Detached copy. Five acts and prologue. The score, published 1714 as "Telemaque et Calypso," gives November 15, 1714, as the date of first performance, the "second edition" of 1715 gives December 6, 1714, and Chouquet and Schatz have November 29, 1714. Schatz 2552

Second copy. ML 48.R4

— Parodie de l'opera de **Telemaque.** Pièce d'un acte. Par Monsieur le S * *. Representée à la Foire de S. Germain 1715 avec *La ceinture de Venus.*

Le Théâtre de la foire, Paris, 1737, t. i, pl., [351]–384 p. 17ᶜᵐ.

By Alain René Le Sage. *En vaudevilles.* The melodies are printed in the "Table des airs" at the end of the volume. They were selected or composed and arranged by the "compositeur" of the theatre, Jean Claude **Gillier.** The overture and the tempest music was borrowed from **Marais'** opera "Alcione." ML 48.L2

Télémaque dans l'isle de Calipso, ballet-héroïque, en trois actes, par M. Gardel. Représenté pour la première fois sur le Théâtre de l'Académie de musique, le mardi 23 février 1790.

Paris, à la Salle de l'Opéra, 1790. 28 p. 18½ᶜᵐ.

Three acts. Cast. Scene by scene description of the action. The composer, **Miller** (according to Lajarte), is not mentioned. ML 48.B2

Telemaque dans l'isle de Calypso, ou Le triomphe de la sagesse, tragédie lyrique en trois actes. Représentée sur le Théâtre de la rue Feydeau, le [*blank*] floréal, an 4. [May 11, 1796].

Paris, Laurens ainé, an IV de la République [1795–96]. 56 p. 21ᶜᵐ.

Cast and names of Alphonse François Dercy as author, of **Le Sueur** as composer. ML 50.2.T35L3

Télémaque dans l'isle de Calypso, ballet. *See* Michl's Il trionfo di Clelia.

Telephe, tragedie représentée pour la premiere fois, par l'Académie royale de musique, le jeudy 23, novembre 1713. Les paroles de M. Danchet & la musique de M. Campra. LXXXIV. opera.

n. i., n. d. 111–176 p. 14ᶜᵐ. (Recueil général des opéra, Paris, 1720. t. xi.)

Detached copy. Five acts, with prologue. Schatz 1562

Second copy. ML 48.R4

— **Telephe,** tragedie.

[217]–280 p. 17½ᶜᵐ. (Antoine Danchet, Théâtre, Paris, 1751, t. iii.)

Prologue and five acts. **Campra** is not mentioned. PQ 1972.D2

Temira e Aristo. Cantata da eseguirsi nel nobilissimo Teatro della Fenice per la fiera dell' Ascensione dell' anno 1795.

Venezia, Stamperia Valvasense, 1795. 51 p. 19ᶜᵐ.

Nine scenes. Neither the author, conte de Salvioli, is mentioned, nor the composer, Joh. Simon **Mayr.** On p. [17]–28, prefatory note, argument, cast, and description of Lauchlin Duquesny's "Obert e Melina, ballo eroico-tragico in cinque atti," with music ("tutta nuova") by Vittorio Trento. On p. [29–51] the argument, cast, scenario, and Calsabigi's (not mentioned) text of "Orfeo ed Euridice," with name of Ferdinando **Bertoni** as the composer. The latter was first performed in 1776. Schatz 6203

Il **Temistocle.**   *See* M. Curzio.

Il **Temistocle.**

68 p. 19ᶜᵐ. (Pietro Metastasio, Opere drammatiche, Venezia, Giuseppe Bettinelli, 1733–37, v. 4.)

Three acts and licenza.   Argument.   No composer mentioned.   ML 49.A2M4

— **Temistocle.**

Metastasio, Poesie, Parigi, vedova Quillau, 1755, t. iv, [301]–403 p. 16ᶜᵐ.

Three acts and licenza.   Argument.   ML 49.A2M42

— **Temistocle.**   Rappresentato con musica del Caldara la prima volta in Vienna, nell' interno gran Teatro della Cesarea corte . . . il dì 4 novembre 1736, per festeggiare il nome dell' imperator Carlo VI . . .

pl., [235]–340 p. 26ᶜᵐ. (Pietro Metastasio, Opere, t. v, Parigi, vedova Herissant, 1780.)

Three acts and licenza.   Argument.   **ML 49.A2M44**

Temistocle.   Azione scenica.

Apostolo Zeno, Poesie drammatiche, Venezia, 1744, t. i, p. [449]–504 p. 19ᶜᵐ.

Three acts.   Argument.   No composer is mentioned.   In the "Catalogo" at end of t. x, date and place of first ed. are given as Vienna, 1700. (According to Schatz and Fehr first performed there on June 9, 1701, with music by M. A. *Ziani.*)
           ML 49.A2Z3

— **Temistocle.**   Azione scenica, pubblicata per la prima volta in Vienna 1700.

Apostolo Zeno, Poesie drammatiche, Orleans, 1785–86, t. ii, p. 58. 21ᶜᵐ.)

Three acts.   Argument.   No composer is mentioned.   ML 49.A2Z4

Temistocle.   Dramma per musica da rappresentarsi nel Regio Teatro di via della Pergola il carnevale del MDCCXCIII . . .

Firenze, Stamperia Albizziniana, 1793.   35 p.   16½ᶜᵐ.

Two acts.   Argument, cast, and note: "La musica è di diversi celebri autori." The author, Metastasio, is not mentioned.   ML 48.A5   v. 16

Temistocle.

Three acts.   By Metastasio.   Music by Johann Christian **Bach.**
First performed at Mannheim, November 4, 1772.
Not in L. of C.

— **Themistocles,** eine opera aufgefuehret bei gelegenheit des hoechstbeglueckten namensfestes Seiner churfuerstl. Durchlaucht zu Pfalz.

Mannheim, Hof und Akademie Buchdruckerei, 1772.   95 p.   16½ᶜᵐ.

According to note on p. [8], this is an adaptation "mit neuen arien, duetten und finalen bereichert," by Mattia Verazi, of Metastasio's drama as composed by Johann Christian **Bach.** Argument, cast, scenario. German text only. On p. 81–95, detailed description, with cast, of the ballets, "Rogerius auf der insel der Alcine" (music by Joseph Toeschi) and "Medea und Jason" (music by Christian Cannabich). Both were written by Stephan Lauchery.   SCHATZ 531

Temistocle. Dramma per musica da rappresentarsi nel famosissimo Teatro Grimani di Sn. Gio. Grisostomo nel carnevale 1744 . . .

[Venezia], n. publ., n. d. 57 p. 15ᶜᵐ.

Three acts. By Metastasio. Argument, cast, scenario, and name of composer, Andrea **Bernasconi**, but not of librettist. Schatz 861

— Temistocles. Vorgestellt [im] gesungnen schau-spiel auf dem neuen Hof-Schau-Platze . . . in der fassnacht 1754. Die poesie ist vom herrn abbt, Peter Metastasio, die musik ist vom herrn André Bernaskoni . . .

Muenchen, Johann Jacob Voetter, n. d. 191, [3] p. 14½ᶜᵐ.

Three acts. Argument, cast, and scenario. Italian text, "Temistocle," faces German. The opera was followed by "Urtheil des Paris, heroischer schaefer-tanz," apparently by Du Buisson de Charlandray.

First performed at Munich, as indicated. Schatz 862

Il Temistocle. Dramma per musica, da rappresentarsi nel gran Teatro dell' imperial Corte per il nome gloriosissimo della Sac. Ces. e Catt. Real Maestà di Carlo VI . . . L' anno MDCCXXXVI. La poesia è del Sig. abbate Pietro Metastasio . . . La musica è del Sig. Antonio Caldara . . .

Vienna d'Austria, Gio. Pietro Van Ghelen, n. d. 5 p. l., 72 p. 15ᶜᵐ.

Three acts and licenza. Argument and scenario. The ballet music was composed by Niccola Matteis.

First performed at Vienna, Hoftheater, November 4. 1736. Schatz 1488

Temistocle. Drama per musica da rappresentarsi nel Teatro Obizzi di Padova nel mese di giugno 1721 . . .

Padova, n. publ., 1721. 48 p. 15ᶜᵐ.

Three acts. By Apostolo Zeno. Impresario's dedication, argument, cast, scenario, name of Fortunato **Chelleri** as composer, and this notice to the reader, which covers a current practice of the time:

"Il presente Temistocle è un' azzione scenica fatta in Vienna per il giorno natalizio della S. C. R. M. di Leopoldo Primo Imperatore de Romani l'anno 1701, e per potere esprimere la sua perfezzione, basta il dire, che sia componimento uscito dalla famosa penna del Sig. Apostolo Zen [!] istorico e poeta di S. M. Imp. [music by Ziani]. Questo adunque essendosi dovuto accommodare rappresentabile nel Teatro Obizzi di Padova, è stato soggetto alla dura necessità di aggiunta di nuove scene, cambiamenti di arie, ed accrescimenti di mutazioni. Destino al quale ogni drama vien sottoposto, dopo la sua prima comparsa che egli fà sù i Teatri. Ma acioche questo non punto resti defraudato di ciò, che di venerazione si deve, a quello, ch' è parto d'un' così celebre, e rinomato autore, tutto quello che da altro poeta vi sarà tramischiato con piccole virgolette contrasegnato vedrassi. Vivi felice."

Accordingly, for instance, were added Temistocles' aria (I, 7) "Dell' aurora al primo albore," Palmide's entire scene (I, 10) "O dell' anime amanti" and the final chorus "Chi non sà che sia dolore" and many more. The revisor is not mentioned. Schatz 1815

Temistocle in bando. Drama per musica da rappresentarsi nel Teatro di San Casciano l' anno MDCLXXXIII . . .

Venetia, Francesco Nicolini, 1683. 59 p. 14ᶜᵐ.

Three acts. By Adriano Morselli (not mentioned) with indicated interpolations "per comodo delle mutationi, e per sodisfare à cantanti." These are "Quella è Sibari al certo," etc. (I, 14), and the whole III, 4, "Io vivo ancora? e invendicato io vivo?" Dedication, argument, and scenario. The composer, Antonio **Zannettini,** is not mentioned. Schatz 11147

Temistokles. Tr. of Bernasconi's Temistocle.

Der **tempel der wahrheit.** Ein vorspiel mit gesang und tanz. Aufgefuehrt zu Berlin am geburtsfeste S. K. H. des Prinzen von Preussen (des jetzt regierenden Koenigs Majestät) den 25ten September 1780.

[14]–26 p. (Annalen des theaters, erstes heft, Berlin, Friedrich Maurer, 1788.)

According to a foot-note the libretto was by Prof. [Friedrich Ludwig Wilhelm] Meyer of Göttingen and had not been published. The composer, Friedrich Wilhelm Heinrich **Benda**, is not mentioned. Schatz 767

Der **tempel des gedaechtnisses.** Ein scherzhaftes singspiel, aus dem franzoesischen uebersezt. Nebst einem historischen vorbericht von den comischen opern.

Frankfurt und Leipzig, n. publ., 1770. 103 p. 16½^{cm}.

In the unsigned "Historischer vorbericht von dem ursprung der scherzhaften singspiele, welche *Opera comique* genennet werden," it is said:

"Gegenwaertiges stueck ist aus dem sechsten theil des theaters *de la foire* genommen, welcher die herren le Sage, Fuzelier und d'Orneval zu verfassern hat; es hat daselbsten die zweyte stelle, und heisset *Le temple de memoire* oder Gedaechtnisstempel. Hier ist es theils uebersetzt, theils nachgeahmt. Von den *couplets* sind viele in der melodie franzoesischer *vaudevilles;* einige gehen nach teutschen gassenhauern; einige auch nach opern-arien vornehmer componisten; der dritte theil derselben aber ist, von herrn Johann Conrad **Elmer,** wohlbestellten organisten zu St. Martin in Memmingen, in die musique gesetzet worden." Schatz 2917

Der **tempel des schicksals.** Prolog vom herrn stadtgerichts sekretär Schubert in Breslau; vorgestellt auf dem hiesigen theater am ersten januar dieses jahres.

p. 193–200. 18½^{cm}. (Litteratur und Theater Zeitung, Berlin, 1779, 2ter jahrg., 1ster th.)

The composer, Franz Andreas **Holly,** is not mentioned.
First performed at Breslau, as indicated. Schatz 4772

The **tempest.** An opera. Taken from Shakespear. As it is performed at the Theatre-Royal in Drury-Lane. The songs from Shakespear, Dryden, etc. The music composed by Mr. Smith.

London, J. and R. Tonson, 1756. 4 p. l., 47 p. 20½^{cm}.

Three acts. The composer, John Christopher **Smith,** also compiled, resp. selected the text, probably aided by David Garrick. Argument and cast.
First performed February 11, 1756, as indicated. Longe 198
Second copy. Office

Il **tempio dell' eternità.**

Metastasio, Poesie, Parigi, vedova Quillau, 1755, t. vi, [391]–432 p. 16^{cm}.

One act. Argument. ML 49.A2M42

— Il **tempio dell' eternità.** Festa teatrale scritta dall' autore in Vienna l'anno 1731 . . . e sontuosamente rappresentata la prima volta con musica del Fux nel Giardino dell' Imperial Favorita, per festeggiare il dì 28 agosto, giorno di nascita dell' imperatrice Elisabetta.

[357]–394 p. 26^{cm}. (Pietro Metastasio, Opere, t. 4, Parigi, vedova Herissant, 1780.)

One act. Argument. Originally composed, performed and published, according to Köchel, under the title "Enea negli Elisi ovvero Il tempio dell' eternità," which *see*. ML 49.A2M44

Il tempio della gloria—O templo da gloria.

Lisboa, Simão Thaddeo Ferreira, 1790. 39 p. 15^{cm}.

On p. [2], "Da rappresentarsi nel Teatro della rua Dos Condes nel 17. di decembre 1790. Giorno natalizio di Sua Maestà Fedelissima Dona Maria I." Dedication, cast, and names of Eustachio Manfrede as author, of Carlo **Spontoni** as composer. Portuguese text faces Italian. SCHATZ 10017

Il tempio della morte. Ballo eroico-pantomimo da rappresentarsi nel magnifico Teatro dell' Accademia Filarmonica di Verona il carnovale dell' anno 1794. Composto e diretto dal Signor Filippo Beretti.

Verona, Dionigi Ramanzini, n. d. 14 p. 16½^{cm}.

Cast, argument, scene-by-scene description. Composer of the music not mentioned. ML 52.2.T32

Il tempio della pazzia, ballet. *See* Insanguine's Motezuma.

Le temple de l'ennuy. Prologue. Par Messieurs le S * * & F * * *. Representé à la Foire de S. Germain 1716.—Le **tableau du mariage.** Pièce d'un acte. Par Messieurs le S * * & F * * *. Représentée à la Foire de Saint Germain 1716.

Le Théâtre de la foire, Paris, 1737, t. ii, 2 p. l., [259]–315 p. 17^{cm}.

By Alain René Le Sage and Louis Fuzelier. The airs, selected or composed and arranged by Jean Claude **Gillier,** are printed at the end of the volume in the "Table des airs." ML 48.L2II

Le temple de la gloire, feste donnée à Versailles, le 27 novembre 1745.

[Paris], Jean Baptiste Christophe Ballard, 1745. viii, 48 p., 1 pl.

Head and tail-pieces, initials. Five acts. Preface, according to which the subject is taken from Metastasio. Neither Voltaire, the author, is mentioned, nor the composer, Jean Philippe **Rameau.**
First performed at Versailles, November 27, 1745; at Paris, Academie royale de musique, December 7, 1745. ML 50.2.T38R2

Le temple de la paix. Ballet. Dansé devant sa Majesté à Fontainebleau, le 15 d'Octobre 1685. Suivant la copie imprimée à Paris.

[Amsterdam, Antoine Schelte], 1686. 36 p. (incl. front.) 13½^{cm}.

Six entrées, with the names of the nobility participating. In his dedication **Lully** says:
"De tous les ouvrages que j'ay faits, & que j'ay eû l'honneur d'offrir à Vostre Majesté, voicy celui qui luy appartient le plus legitimement." ML 49.A2L9

— **Le temple de la paix,** ballet representé par l'Academie royale de musique l'an 1685. Les paroles de M. Quinault & la musique de M. de Lully. XIX. opera.

n. i., n. d. 14^{cm}. front., 91–120 p. (Recueil général des opéra, t. iii, Paris, 1703.)

Detached copy. Six entrées.
First performed, as indicated, October, 1685; at Fontainebleau, September 12, 1685 SCHATZ 5772
Second copy. ML 48.R4

— **Le temple de la paix.** Ballet dansé devant le roi à Fontainebleau le 15. octobre 1685.

Philippe Quinault, Théâtre, Paris, 1739, t. v., pl., p. [379]–411. 17^{cm}.

Six entrées. **Lully** is not mentioned. PQ 1881.A1 1739

Le temple de memoire. Piece d'un acte. Representée à la Foire de Saint Laurent 1725. & ensuite sur le Théâtre du Palais Royal.

Le Théâtre de la foire, Paris, 1728, t. vi, pl., [19]–69 p. 17ᶜᵐ.

Le Sage, Fuzelier, and d'Orneval are mentioned as the authors. Largely *en vaudevilles*. The airs selected or composed and arranged by Jean Claude **Gillier**, the "compositeur" of the troupe, are printed at the end of the volume in the "Table des airs."

First performed July 21, 1725. ML 48.L2VI

Le temple du destin. Pièce d'un acte. Par M. le S * * *. Representée à la Foire de S. Laurent 1715.

Le Théâtre de la foire, Paris, 1737, t. i, pl., [385]–427 p. 17ᶜᵐ.

By Alain René Le Sage. *En vaudevilles.* The melodies are printed in the "Table des airs" at the end of the volume. They were selected or composed and arranged by the "compositeur" of the theatre, Jean Claude **Gillier**.

First performed July 25, 1715. ML 48.L2 I

The temple of dullness. With the humour of Signor Capocchio, and Signora Dorinna. A comic opera of two acts. As it is perform'd at the Theatre-Royal in Drury-Lane. The music by Mr. [Th. Aug.] Arne.

London, J. Watts, 1745. 16 p. 21½ᶜᵐ.

Two acts. The author, Colley Cibber, is not mentioned. Text preceded by "a short preface by way of argument."

First performed, as indicated, January 17, 1745. ML 50.2.T39A7

The temple of love: a pastoral opera. English'd from the Italian. All sung to the same musick. By Signior J. Saggione. As it is perform'd at the Queen's Theatre in the Hay-Market. By Her Majesty's sworn servants. Written by Mr. Motteux.

London, Jacob Tonson, 1706. 2 p. l., 37, [1] p. 21ᶜᵐ.

Three acts, prologue, and epilogue. According to Burney (iv, 201), the music was by Giacomo **Greber**. Not only does the title page contradict this, but Walsh published songs from the opera, as composed by Giuseppe Fedeli **Saggione**.

First performed, as indicated, March 7, 1706. LONGE 294

O templo da gloria. Tr. of Spontoni's Il tempio della gloria.

Il tempo fa giustizia a tutti. Dramma giocoso per musica da rappresentarsi nel Teatro alla Canobiana il carnevale 1797 . . .

Milano, Gio. Batista Bianchi, n. d. 63 p. 16½ᶜᵐ.

Two acts. By Antonio Brambilla, who is not mentioned. Cast and name of Ferdinando Pher (**Paër**) as the composer.

First performed at Milan, as indicated, January 26, 1797; at Parma, Teatro Ducale, fall 1792. SCHATZ 7537

Ten thousand pounds for a pregnancy. A. T. of The wanton countess.

Teodelinda. Dramma per musica da rappresentarsi nel Regio Teatro di Torino nel carnovale del 1789 . . .

Torino, Onorato Derossi, viii, 64 p. 19ᶜᵐ.

Three acts. By Giandomenico Boggio. Cast, scenario, argomento, and names of librettist and composer, Gaetano **Andreozzi**. The ballets, the music for which was composed by Vittorio Amedeo Canavasso, are entitled "La costanza coniugale," "La fiera di Sinigaglia" and "Il Gastaldo burlato." They were by Giuseppe Banti, and a detailed description of the first is on p. 57–64 of the libretto. SCHATZ 211

Teodora Augusta. Drama per musica da rappresentarsi nel riformato Teatro Vendramino di S. Salvatore l'anno 1686. Ristampato con nuova aggiunta . . .

Venetia, Francesco Nicolini, 1686. 60 p. 14^{cm}.

Three acts. By Adriano Morselli, who is not mentioned. Impresario's dedication, argument, scenario, and author's notice to the reader, in which he mentions Domenico **Gabrieli** as the composer, and says:

"Fù dall'autore adornato di nove arie, e si sono alterate, & aggiunte alcune scene; onde benche sia lo stesso, sara però in qualche parte diversa. SCHATZ 3401

Teodorico. Dramma per musica da rappresentarsi nel Teatro Formagliari l'autunno dell' anno MDCCXXVII . . .

Bologna, Costantino Pisarri, n. d. 62, [1] p. 16½^{cm}.

Three acts. By Antonio Salvi. Impresario's dedication, dated Bologna, October 26, 1728, argument, cast, and scenario, but without name of the composers or librettist, but on p. 7, the note: "La musica sarà di diversi autori," and Schatz mentions Giuseppe Maria **Buini** as one of them. In the dedication the term "il presente *libretto*" is used. SCHATZ 1383

Teodorico. Drama per musica da rappresentarsi nel famoso Teatro Grimani di S. Gio. Grisostomo. L'autunno dell' anno 1720. Del dot. Antonio Salvi Fior. . . .

Venezia, Marino Rossetti, 1720. 60 p. 15^{cm}.

Three acts. Publisher's dedication, argument, cast, name of Giovanni **Porta** as the composer, and notice to the reader, who is informed that this text is but a somewhat altered version of a "drama, che uscito pochi anni sono, ben è vero con altro nome, dalla penna felice del Signor dottor Salvi Fiorentino." SCHATZ 8393

Teodosio. Drama per musica da rappresentarsi nel Teatro d'Hamburgo l'anno 1718.—Theodosius . . .

Hamburg, Caspar Jakhel, n. d. Unpaged. 19^{cm}.

Three acts. By Vincenzo Grimani, who is not mentioned. The "Innhalt" is in German only, but list of characters and the text are both in Italian and German. Schatz mentions as composers Johann Joseph **Fux**, Carlo Francesco **Gasparini**, and Antonio **Caldara**.

First performed, as indicated, November 14, 1718; at Brunswick on September 12, 1716, as "Teodosio ed Eudossa." SCHATZ 3392

Il Teodosio. Drama per musica da rappresentarsi nel Teatro di S. Cassiano in Venezia l'anno 1699.

Venezia, Nicolini, 1699. 59 p. 14½^{cm}.

Three acts. Argument, scenario, and publisher's prefatory note:

"Eccoti un drama abozzato molto tempo fà da una penna nobile [Vincenzo Grimani], che per esser volata al cielo non hà potuto compirlo. Hora te lo presento aggiustato in modo tale, che haverei speranza potesse esser compatito. Chi hà havuto la prima intentione di perfettionarlo, non hà havuto mai la seconda di mettertelo sotto l'occhio, mà la conguintura hà portato cosi . . ."

The composer, Marc' Antonio **Ziani**, is not mentioned.

First performed, as indicated, carnival, 1699. SCHATZ 11194

Teodosio ed Eudossa. O. T. of Fux, Gasparini and Caldara's Teodosio.

Teodosio il giovane. Dramma posto in musica dal Signor Filippo Amadei, e rappresentato in Roma l'anno 1711.

Roma, Antonio de' Rossi, n. d. 80 p. 16^{cm}.

Three acts. Argument and scenario. Librettist unknown to Schatz.

First performed at the Teatro di Tor di Nona, as indicated. SCHATZ 167

Teofane. Dramma per musica rappresentato nel Regio Elettoral Teatro di Dresda in occasione delle felicissime nozze de' Serenissimi principi Federigo Augusto . . . e Maria Gioseffa, arciduchessa d'Austria.

Dresda, Gio. Corrado Stössel, 1719. front, unpaged. 19ᶜᵐ.

Three acts. By Stefano Benedetto Pallavicini, who is not mentioned. Argument, cast, and names of Antonio **Lotti** as composer of the opera, of "Giambattista Woulmyer, mastro di concerto" as composer of the ballet music. French title page, "Theophane," and text face Italian. At end, a congratulatory scene (licenza), with chorus.

First performed, as indicated, September 13, 1719.   Schatz 5723.

Teramene. *See* M. Curzio.

Teraminta: an opera. Set to musick by Mr. John Christopher Smith.

[47]–88 p. 22ᶜᵐ. (Henry Carey, Dramatick works, London, 1743.)

Three acts. Argument with foot-note:
"The recitative of this opera was written originally in prose for expedition sake; since which time the author has alter'd it into blank verse, and made great improvement in the drama, as will appear by comparing it with the edition printed in the year 1732."

First performed at London, Lincoln's Inn Fields, November 20, 1732.
          ML 49.A2C2
          Second copy, detached.   Longe 127

Tereo, tiranno di Nasora. A. T. of the ballet Progne e Filomene.

Der ternengewinnst oder der gedemüthigte stolz. O. T. of Dittersdorf's Terno secco.

Terno secco, oder Der gedemuethigte stolz. Ein komisches singspiel in 2 aufzuegen, nach dem italiaenischen frey bearbeitet zu einer musik vom herrn von Dittersdorf.

Oels, Ludwig, n. d. 100 p. 17ᶜᵐ.

Text by the composer.
First performed at Oels, Hoftheater, February 11, 1797, as "Der ternengewinnst oder Der gedemüthigte stolz."   Schatz 2609

Il Teseo. Festa teatrale per le reali nozze de i serenissimi sposi Gio. Giorgio III, principe elettorale di Sassonia . . . ed' Anna Sofia, principessa reale ereditaria di Danimarca, e Norvvegia, de' Vandali, e Goti, etc.

G. A. Moniglia, Poesie drammatiche, seconda parte, Firenze, Cesare e Francesco Bindi, 1690, p. [355]–438. 24ᶜᵐ.

Prologue and five acts. Scenario and argument. No composer mentioned and not recorded by Schatz or Fürstenau. Possibly composed by Giovanni Andrea Angelini **Bontempi**, who was court composer at Dresden, where "Il Teseo" was first performed on January 27, 1667.   ML 49.A2M7

Teséo. Dramma per musica da cantarsi nella Real villa di Queluz per celebrare il felicissimo giorno natalizio del Serenissimo Signore D. Giuseppe, principe del Brasile li 21. agosto 1783.

[Lisbona], Stamperia reale, n. d. 32 p. 15½ᶜᵐ.

One act with licenza. Argument, cast, and names of Gaetano Martinelli as author, of Jeronymo Francisco de **Lima** as composer.   Schatz 5619

Teseo a Stige. Dramma tragico per musica da rappresentarsi nell'
Imperial Teatro di via della Pergola il carnevale del MDCCXCI . . .

   Firenze, Stamp. Albizziniana, 1791. front., 59 p. 17^{cm}.

Two acts. Author not mentioned and unknown to Schatz. Argument, cast, and
name of Sebastiano **Nasolini** as the composer ("La musica è tutta nuova"). On
p. 7–14 cast and description of Gaspero Ronzi's "Lauso e Lidia o sia Il trionfo dell'
amicizia, ballo eroico pantomimo in cinque atti." The composer of the music is
not mentioned.   SCHATZ 7021

Teseo e Medea, ballet. *See* Il riconoscimento di Teseo.

Teseo in Sicilia. Poetico componimento ad uso di serenata del Sig.
abate Gio. Domenico Co. di Cataneo. Posto in musica dal N. H.
Marc' Antonio Tiepolo per piacevole trattenimento delle figlie del
Pio Ospitale degl' Incurabili. L'anno MDCCLIV.

   Venezia, Modesto Fenzo, 1754. 32 p. 17^{cm}.

Two parts. Cast.   SCHATZ 10352

Teseo tra le rivali. Dramma per musica da rappresentarsi nel
Teatro à S. Angelo. Di Aurelio Aureli. Opera XXV . . .

   Venetia, Francesco Nicolini, 1685. 56 p. 13$\frac{1}{2}$^{cm}.

Three acts. Author's dedication dated Venice, February 7, 1685, argument, scenario, and author's notice to the reader, mentioning Giovanni Domenico **Freschi** as
composer.   SCHATZ 3348

A test of good fellowship. A. T. of Dibdin's Liberty-hall.

La testa riscaldata. Farsa giocosa per musica originale di Giuseppe Foppa da rappresentarsi nel nobilissimo Teatro Venier in San
Benedetto il carnovale dell' anno 1800.

   Venezia, Fenzo, 1799. 48 p. 18^{cm}.

One act. Cast and name of Ferdinando Per (**Paër**) as the composer. On p. 45–48
argument of Giovanni Monticini's "La vendetta d'amore, ballo allegorico," music
("tutta nuova") by Vittorio Trento.
First performed January 20, 1800, as indicated.   SCHATZ 7540

Das testament, eine komische operette in einem aufzuge.

   *[185]–246 p. 16^{cm}. (Zwo komische operetten von G * *, Chem-
nitz, 1773.)*

Not recorded by Schatz. For author's name, quotation from the preface, etc.,
see "Das vornehme Suschen."   SCHATZ 11655

Testoride Argonauta. Dramma per musica da rappresentarsi nel
Teatro della real villa di Queluz per festeggiare il felicissimo giorno
natalizio di sua maestà . . . D. Pietro III . . . li 5 luglio 1780.

   [Lisboa], Nella stamperia reale, n. d. 55 p. 15^{cm}.

Two acts. By Gaetano Martinelli. Scenario, cast, and names of the author and
the composer, João de Sousa **Carvalho.**   SCHATZ 1669

La tête-noire. *See* La fausse-foire.

Tetide. Serenata da cantarsi per le felicissime nozze delle LL. AA.
RR. l'arciduca Giuseppe d'Austria e la Principessa Isabella di Borbone per comando degli Augustissimi Regnanti.

   Vienna, Ghelen, 1760. Unpaged. 21^{cm}.

Embellished with exquisitely engraved vignettes, etc. The preliminary title
reads: "Tetide del Sig. Giannambrogio Migliavacca . . ." Argument, cast, and
name of **Gluck** as the composer.
First performed at Vienna, Redouten Saal of the palace, October 8, 1760.
        SCHATZ 3937

Tetide in Sciro. Drama per musica da rappresentarsi nel Teatro delle Grazie il maggio 1715 . . .

Vicenza, Tomaso Lavezari, 1715.   52 p.   16ᶜᵐ.

Three acts. By Carlo Sigismondo Capece, who is not mentioned. Dedication, argument, cast, and name of Carlo Francesco **Pollaroli** as the composer.

Schatz 8319

Der teufel ist los.   A. T. of Hiller's Die verwandelten weiber.

Der teufel ist los oder Die verwandelten weiber.   O. T. of Standfuss-Hiller's Die verwandelten weiber oder Der teufel ist los.

Teuzzone.

Apostolo Zeno, Poesie drammatiche, Venezia, 1744, t. iv, p. [355]–444.   19ᶜᵐ.

Three acts. Argument. No composer is mentioned. In the "Catalogo" at end of t. x, date and place of first ed. are given as, "in Milano. 1706. [Music of act I by Paolo *Magni*, of acts II–III by Clemente *Monari*.]   E in Ven. 1707. ma tronco" (*see* below).

ML 49.A2Z3

— **Teuzzone.**   Pubblicato per la prima volta in Milano 1706.

Apostolo Zeno, Poesie drammatiche, Orleans, 1785–86, t. iii, p. 89–176.   21ᶜᵐ.

Three acts. Argument. No composer is mentioned.

ML 49.A2Z4

Teuzzone.   Drama per musica, da rappresentarsi nel Teatro di S. A. S. di Carignano . . .

Torino, Pietro Giuseppe Zappata, 1716.   4 p. l., 69, [1] p.   14ᶜᵐ.

Three acts. Altered from Apostolo Zeno, as indicated on 3d p. l. Dedication, argument, cast, scenario, and names of Girolamo **Casanova** as composer of first and second acts, of Stefano Andrea **Fiorè** of the third.

First performed, as indicated, in September, 1716.

Schatz 1682

Teuzzone.   Drama da rappresentarsi per musica nel Teatro Tron di S. Cassano, il carnovale dell' anno MDCCVII.   Di A. Z.

Venezia, Marino Rossetti, n. d.   60 p.   14½ᶜᵐ.

Three acts. By Apostolo Zeno. Argument, cast, scenario, and name of Antonio **Lotti** as composer. The text is the one called above "tronco," but, as a matter of fact, it is exactly the same as in the Orleans edition.

Schatz 5709

— **L'inganno vinto dalla ragione.**   Drama per musica del Sig. A. Z.   Da rappresentarsi nel nuovo Teatro detto di S. Gio. de' Fiorentini nel giorno 19. di novembre, che si festeggia il nome della nostra regina . . .

Napoli, Michele Luigi Mutio, 1708.   50 p.   13½ᶜᵐ.

Three acts. Impresario's dedication, argument, scenario, cast, and notice to the reader, with name of Apostolo Zeno as author, but stating:

"la necessità, impostami da varie circostanze del tempo, del luogo, de' rappresentanti, e dal genio de gl'ascoltanti, mi hà costretto farci non picciola alterazione, cosi nel troncare dello stil recitativo, come nello aggiungervi ariette, e scene burlesche. Il tutto però si è fatto colla maggior discrezione possibile, senza alterare il principal tessuto del drama . . ."

which is an altered version of "Teuzzone." A further note then gives the names of Giuseppe **Vignola** as the composer of the alterations and additional burlesque scenes, and that of Antonio **Lotti** of the opera proper. In this *rifacimento* the character of "Troncone, imperadore della Cina" has been dropped. Begins "Dunque l'invitto rege" instead of "Nostro, amici, è'l trionfo" and has in this I, 1 the aria "Occhi non giova" which originally was in I, 3 has in II, 9 in addition to aria "Soffri costante" the aria "Fugge e vola" which is not in the original version, etc., etc.

Schatz 5727

Thalie au nouveau théatre, prologue en prose, en vers, ariettes & vaudevilles. La musique est de M. Grétry.

> *Paris, Brunet, 1783. 30, [2] p. 21½*^{cm}.

On the [2] p. a list of plays published by Brunet.
Cast. The author, Sedaine, is not mentioned.
First performed at Paris, Comédie italienne, rue Favart, April 28, 1783.

ML 50.2.T395G7

The theatrical candidates. *See* also May-day.

— The **theatrical candidates**, a musical prelude, upon the opening and alterations of the theatre, Drury-Lane, 1775. By David Garrick, Esq.

> *[159]–164 p. 19*^{cm}. (*Collection of the most esteemed farces and entertainments, t. vi, Edinburgh, 1792.*)

Cast. Music by William **Bates,** who is not mentioned.
First performed, as indicated, September 23, 1775. SCHATZ 11753F

— The **theatrical candidates:** a musical prelude, upon the opening and alterations of the theatre.

> *n. i., n. d. [31]–40 p. 21½*^{cm}.

Detached copy. Cast. Neither author nor composer mentioned. LONGE 239

Thémire, pastorale en un acte . . . par M. Sedaine. La musique de M. Duny. Représentée pour la premiere fois, devant Sa Majesté à Fontainebleau, le samedi 20 octobre 1770. Et à Paris, pour la première fois, par les Comédiens ordinaires du roi, le lundi 26 octobre 1770.

> *Paris, Claude Herissant, 1771. 24 p. 18½*^{cm}.

With cast. SCHATZ 2856

Thémistocle, tragédie lyrique, en trois actes; représentée, pour la premiere fois, devant Leurs Majestés, à Fontainebleau, le jeudi 13 octobre 1785.

> *[Paris], P. R. C. Ballard, 1785. 4 p. l., 55 p. 20*^{cm}.

Cast and names of Morel [de Chefdeville] as author, of François André Danican **Philidor** as composer.
First performed, as indicated; at Paris, Académie royale de musique, May 23, 1786.

ML 50.2.T4P3

Themistocles. Tr. of Bach's Temistocle.

Theodor in Venedig. Tr. of Paisiello's Il re Teodoro in Venezia.

Théodore & Paulin. Original title of Grétry's L'épreuve villageoise.

Theodosius. Tr. of Fux, Gasparini, and Caldara's Teodosio.

Theonoé, tragédie representée pour la premiere fois par l'Académie royale de musique le [*blank*] jour du mois de novembre 1715.

> *Paris, Pierre Ribou, 1715. xx, 58, [2], 4 p. 23*^{cm}.

Prologue and five acts. Argument and cast. For author, composer and date of first performance *see* next entry. On the [2] p. Ribou's privilege, on the 4 p. his "Catalogue des livres nouveaux."

ML 50.2.T43S2

Théonoé—Continued.

— **Théonoé**, tragedie représentée pour la premiere fois, par l'Académie royale de musique, le 3e decembre 1715. Les paroles de M. de la Rocque & la musique de M. Salomon. LXXXVIII. opera.

n. i., n. d. pl., [355]–418 p. 14^{cm}. (Recueil général des opéra, t. xi, Paris, 1720.)

Prologue and five acts. Avertissement as argument. Schatz (following Parfaiet) gives Simon Joseph de Pellegrin as author, but the Anecdotes dramatiques give Antoine de la Roque, and there seems to be no reason for not accepting his authorship.

SCHATZ 9344
Second copy. ML 48.R4

Theophane. Tr. of Lotti's Teofane.

Thereby hangs a tale. A. T. of Apollo turn'd stroller.

Thésée. Opéra en trois actes.

Venard de La Jonchère, Théâtre lyrique, Paris, 1772, t. ii, p. [213]–273. 18½^{cm}.

"Avant-propos" (p. 215–232). No composer mentioned, nor is any recorded by Clément & Larousse.

ML 49.A2L2

Thésée, tragédie-lyrique en quatre actes, représentée pour la première fois, par l'Académie-royale de musique le 11 janvier 1675. En Novembre 1707, en janvier 1721, en novembre 1729, en décembre 1744, en décembre 1754, en décembre 1765, en février 1779. Remise en musique par M. Gossec. Et au théâtre, le mardi 26 février 1782.

Paris, P. de Lormel, 1782. 62 p. 23^{cm}.

Cast. Quinault is mentioned as author, but his text was retouched by Etienne Morel de Chefdeville, who is not mentioned.

The correct date of the revival, according to Schatz, is March 1, 1782.

SCHATZ 4012

Thesée. Tragedie en musique ornée d'entrées de ballets, de machines, & de changements de théâtre. Representée devant Sa Majesté à Fontainebleau, le [blank] jour de janvier 1678.

Imprimée à Paris, & on les vend à Anvers, Henry van Dunwaldt, 1687. 72 p. 13^{cm}.

Prologue and five acts. Cast. Neither the author, Quinault, is mentioned, nor the composer, Jean Baptiste **Lully**.

First performed April, 1675, at Paris, Académie royale de musique; before the king at Saint-Germain en Laye, January 11, 1675 (Schatz), January 10 (Prunières).

SCHATZ 11722

— **Thesée.** Tragédie en musique. Ornée d'entrées de ballet, de machines, & de changemens de theatre. Representée devant Sa Majesté à Fontainebleau. Suivant la copie imprimée, à Paris.

[Amsterdam, Antoine Schelte], 1688. 81 p. (incl. front.) 13½^{cm}.

Prologue and five acts. Cast. Neither Quinault is mentioned, nor **Lully**.

ML 50.2.T45L92

— **Thesée**, tragedie representée par l'Academie royale de musique l'an 1675. Les paroles sont de M. Quinault, & la musique de M. de Lully. VI. opera.

n. i., n. d. 14^{cm}. pl., 273–346 p. (Recueil général des opéra, t. i, Paris, 1703.)

Detached copy. Prologue and five acts.

SCHATZ 5773
Second copy. ML 48.R4

Thesée—Continued.

— **Thesée**, tragedie. En musique. Ornée d'entrées de ballet, de machines & de changemens de théatre. Représenté devant Sa Majesté à Saint Germain en Laye, le 3. février [!] 1675.

Quinault, Théatre, Paris, 1739, t. iv, pl., p. [191]–265. 17cm.

Prologue and five acts. **Lully** is not mentioned.   PQ 1881.A1   1739

— **Thesée**, parodie nouvelle de Thesée; représentée pour la premiere fois sur le Théâtre de l'Opera comique, le 17 février 1745. Nouvelle édition, avec la musique.

n. i., n. d. 56 p. 19cm. (Theatre de M. Favart, Paris, Duchesne, 1763–77, t. vii.)

One act. *En vaudevilles*, quite a few of the airs being printed in the text, which was partly by Laujon and Parvi. Font does not mention the musical collaborator.
ML 49.A2F1

Thesée, tragédie en cinq actes; représenté pour la premiere fois devant Leurs Majestés, à Fontainebleau, le 7 novembre 1765.

[Paris], Christophe Ballard, 1765. 72 p. 20½cm. (Journal des spectacles, t. ii, Paris, 1766.)

Five acts. Cast, names of Quinault as author, of **Mondonville** as composer, who penned the following dignified and sensible Avertissement, as if he foresaw the unfair attacks on him ever since the first public performance of his work at the Académie royale de musique, January 13, 1767:

"On sçait qu'en Italie, les Musiciens sont en possession de mettre en musique le même poëme. On ne les soupçonne pas de travailler dans la vüe de déprimer ceux qui les ont devancés.

"Nous avons la même liberté en France pour les motets. Si nous pensons comme eux dans le genre Latin, pourquoi n'aurions nous pas le même privilége pour les poëmes françois? Cet usage encourageroit les talens, exciteroit l'émulation, & contribueroit peut-être à l'amusement du Public. Ces motifs que j'ai crû raisonnables, m'ont déterminé à choisir le poëme de Thesée, non comme un téméraire qui veut attaquer Lully, mais comme un enthousiaste des operas de Quinault. Il est vrai que pour me conformer au goût présent du Théâtre, j'ai été contraint d'abréger les scenes, & d'acroître les divertissemens, ce qui m'a obligé pour les liaisons d'ajoûter quelques vers qu'on reconnoîtra sûrement pour n'être pas de Quinault.

"À l'égard de la musique de Lully, ma délicatesse & mon admiration pour ce célébre auteur, m'ont défendu de l'employer. J'ai crû que n'en pas faire usage c'étoit la respecter.

"C'est dans ce sentiment que j'ai osé ouvrir une carriere nouvelle & avantageuse à tous les compositeurs. Heureux si l'on veut bien pardonner mon entreprise en faveur du motif."
ML 48.J7

Il Theseo. A. T. of P. A. Ziani's L'incostanza trionfante.

Theti. Favola dramatica, e **Niobe**, introduttione alla Barriera. Rappresentate in musica nel gran Teatro Ducale di Mantoua, per la venuta de' Ser.mi arciduchi d'Austria Ferdinando Carlo, Anna Medici sua consorte, e Sigismondo Francesco. Componimenti del senator Diamante Gabrielli . . .

Mantova, Osanna, 1652. 79 p. 17cm.

"Theti" (p. 3–54) has argument, prologue, and five acts; "Niobe" (Schatz 873). three acts. The composer, Antonio **Bertali,** is not mentioned.   SCHATZ 872–873

Thetis et Pelée, tragédie. En musique, representée par l'Academie royalle de musique.

Paris, Christophe Ballard, 1699[!]. front., 56 p. 22cm.

Prologue and five acts. Neither the author, Bernard Le Bovier de Fontenelle, is mentioned, nor the composer, Pascal **Colasse.**
First performed, as indicated, January 11, 1689, not 1699.   ML 50.2.T48C6

Thetis et Pelée—Continued.

— **Thetis et Pelée**, tragedie en musique, representée par l'Academie royalle de musique.   Suivant la copie imprimée à Paris.

[*Amsterdam, Antoine Schelte*], *1689.   60 p. (incl. front.).   13½cm.*
Prologue and five acts.   Neither de Fontenelle is mentioned, nor **Colasse.**

ML 50.2.T48C62

— **Thetis et Pelée**; tragedie representée par l'Academie royale de musique l'an 1689.   Les paroles de M. de Fontenelle & La musique de M. Colasse.   XXIV. opera.

n. i., n. d.   front., 331–394 p.   14cm.   (Recueil général des opéra, Paris, 1703, t. iii.)
Detached copy.   Five acts, with prologue.
First performed January 11, 1689.

SCHATZ 2103
Second copy.   ML 48.R4

— Les **amans inquiets,** parodie de Thetis et Pelée.   Représentée pour la première fois par les Comédiens italiens, ordinaires du roi, le 9 mars 1751.

Paris, La veuve Delormel & fils [etc.], 1751.   59, [1], 4 p.   18½cm.
One act.   Cast.   The 4 p. contain eight *airs notés.*   The piece, *toute en vaudevilles,* was written by Charles Simon Favart, who is not mentioned.   ML 48.P2

— Les **amants inquiets,** parodie de Thetis et Pelée.   Representée pour la premiere fois, par les Comédiens italiens ordinaire[!] du roi, le mardi 1751.   Seconde edition.

Paris, Prault, 1751.   59, [1], 2 p.   19cm.   (Theatre de M. Favart, Paris, Duchesne, 1763–77, t. i.)
One act.   En vaudevilles.   Cast.   The 2 p. contain six engraved airs.   The arranger of the music is not mentioned by Font.   ML 49.A2F1

— Les **noces d'Arlequin et de Silvia,** ou Thetis et Pelée déguisés. Parodie de l'Opera de Thétis & Pelée.   Par M. Dominique . . . Représentée pour la premiere fois, par les Comédiens italiens ordinaires du roi, le 18 janvier 1724.

Les parodies du Nouveau Théâtre italien, Nouv. éd., Paris, 1738, t. ii, [251]–278 p.
One act.   The airs and vaudeville used are printed at the end of the volume in the "Table des airs" (60 p.).   ML 48.P3

Thétis et Pélée, tragédie en cinq actes.   Représentée devant Leurs Majestés à Fontainebleau, le 10 octobre 1765.

[*Paris*], *Christophe Ballard, 1765.   68 p.   20½cm.   (Journal des spectacles, t. i, Paris, 1766.)*
Cast and name of de Fontenelle as author.   **Colasse** was not the composer, since we read, on p. 13 of the Journal: "la musique de M.   *   *   *   substituée à celle de Colasse."   Jean Benjamin de **La Borde** is known to have been the composer.

ML 48.J7

Thetis et Pelée deguisés.   A. T. of Les noces d'Arlequin et de Silvia.

Thetis och Pelee. Opera i fem acter, upfoerd på den Kongl. Svenska Theatren första gången, den 18 januarii, 1773.

Stockholm, Henr. Fougt, 1773. 8 p. l., 67 p. 19ᶜᵐ.

Johan Wellander is mentioned as the author, Francesco Antonio Baldassare **Uttini** as the composer. Dedicatory poem to the king by the author, argument, cast, and noteworthy preface, with this footnote:

"Herr Uttini hade förut componerat Kongl. Begrafnings-och Krönings-musiken, efter de, på nådigste befallning, af Författaren, dertil upgifne Skalde-stycken."

SCHATZ 10550

Thomas and Sally or the Sailor's return. A musical entertainment as performed at the Theatres Royal. A new edition. [vignette.]

London, W. Griffin, T. Lownds [etc.], n. d. 1 p. l., vii, [1], 19 p. 19½ᶜᵐ.

Two acts. Cast and preface by the author, Isaac Bickerstaffe (not mentioned), in which he says, among other things:

"He wrote it merely to comply with the request of a theatrical person, whom he had an inclination to oblige; it was designed and finished in somewhat less than a fortnight; and his excuse for now suffering it to appear in print (and he really thinks such excuse necessary) must be the nature of a musical entertainment, which requires, that the words should be put into the hands of the audience, who would otherwise find it impossible to accompany the performers in what they sing upon the stage . . ."

The composer, Thomas Aug. **Arne,** is not mentioned.

First performed at London, Covent Garden, November 28, 1760. LONGE 37

— **Thomas and Sally:** or, The sailor's return. A musical entertainment. As performed at the Theatres Royal. A new edition.

Dublin, James Williams, 1773. vii, [8]–23 p. 17ᶜᵐ.

Two acts. Cast and preface. Without name of Bickerstaffe or **Arne.**

AC 901.T5

— **Thomas and Sally.** In two acts by Mr. Isaac Bickerstaff.

A collection of the most esteemed farces . . . Edinburgh, 1792, v. 2, p. [235]–244. 19ᶜᵐ.

Covent Garden, Drury-Lane, and Edinburgh (1782) casts. SCHATZ 11753B

Thomyris, queen of Scythia. An opera. As it is perform'd at the Theatre in Lincolns-Inn-Fields. Written by Mr. Motteux. The fourth edition.

London, J. Tonson, 1719. 3 p. l., [1], 10–46 p. 18ᶜᵐ.

Three acts. Cast and preface:

"The delicacy of taste in musick which the English have of late Years arriv'd to, makes it necessary that all Entertainments of this kind shou'd be as exquisite as the Nature of the Thing will bear. For this Reason it is, that the Persons concern'd in the reviving of English Opera's lay before the Town the Scheme of their Undertaking; not without Hopes, from former Encouragements, that the World will come into so Agreeable and Innocent a Diversion.

"Their first and principal Design is to fix these Entertainments, and make them more lasting in England. It has been observ'd, that if we shou'd have the Misfortune to lose the best of the Italian Performers, either through Age, want of Health, or their Customary Inclination of returning to their Native Country, Opera's must necessarily fall. But it wou'd be happy if we had young People train'd up here in England, and instructed to sing after the Italian Manner; (and sure the Town will be willing to encourage such a Nursery, who may emulate those Excellent Performers:) This wou'd be a Means not only to establish but perpetuate these favourite Entertainments.

"To those who may perhaps mention the Difficulty of finding Native Voices for the English Theatre, we beg leave to observe that England has already supply'd us with Mrs. Tofts, Mrs. Barbier and Mrs. Robinson; who may stand in Competition with the most Eminent among the Italians: There have formerly been Men, who have given entire Satisfaction to the Publick on the Stage, and there is no Reason

Thomyris, queen of Scythia—Continued.

why others may not be found now, who will be glad to qualify themselves upon Encouragement. We cannot but remember one of late Years whose Voice, dedicated to more solemn Performances, the Italians themselves have own'd was not to be parallel'd; and if we may expect to be supply'd with the like, those Artificial Voices, which are the peculiar Product of Italy, may well be spared, and we are apt to believe the English will never regret the want of them in their own Country.

"As a moderate Price demanded will help to convince the Town that the Principal Aim is to divert the Publick upon the most easie and reasonable Terms the Nature of the Affair will admit; so at the same time the Persons concern'd confess they flatter themselves that this very Method will in the Event be serviceable to them. For they cannot conceive how any Diversion can be lasting that is so Burdensome, as are those Exorbitant Prices, Large Subscriptions, and frequent Benefit Days. These are Grievances that have been justly complain'd of, and which they are resolv'd shall never be charg'd upon them. They are determin'd to sit down satisfied with a moderate Gain, and if in the Prosecution of this Design they shall hereafter have occasion to make Application to the Publick for some additional Encouragement, they promise that it shall be in such moderate Terms as every Body may think well of.

"Now what they hope they may promise themselves in the Success, depends upon these three Particulars; The General Encouragement from the Town to what has been propos'd; The Reasonableness of the Performers in their Demands; and The good Oeconomy and sincere Design of Pleasing in those who have undertaken it."

Motteux wrote the text adapting it to arias by Alessandro **Scarlatti**, Giovanni Battista **Bononcini**, as Walsh's score informs us and to whom Hawkins adds **Steffani**, **Gasparini**, and **Albinoni**. **Pepusch** furnished the recitative (not printed) and arranged the music.

First performed, as indicated, April 1, 1707.   LONGE 200

Der thrazische printz Floridantes. Tr. of Händel's Floridante.

The three dukes of Dunstable. A. T. of H. Purcell's A fool's preferment.

Songs, etc., in a new musical farce, called Throw physick to the dogs! As performed at the Theatre-Royal, Hay-Market. The musick by Dr. Arnold.

London, Cadell and Davies, 1798.   14 p.   21^{cm}.

Two acts. By H. Lee, who is not mentioned. Also known as "Caleb Quotem and his wife."

First performed, as indicated, July 6, 1798.   ML 50.2.T52

Tiberio imperadore d'Oriente. O. T. of Pallavicino's text Le vicende d'amor e di fortuna.

Tiberio imperatore d'Oriente. Drama per musica da rappresentarsi nel Teatro di Santangelo l'anno 1702.

Venezia, Marino Rossetti, n. d.   48 p.   14½^{cm}.

Three acts. By Giovanni Domenico Pallavicino, who is not mentioned. Argument, printer's notice to the reader with the name of Carlo Francesco **Gasparini** as the composer, and scenario.   SCHATZ 3586

Tieteberga. Drama per musica da rappresentarsi nel Teatro Giustiniano di San Moisè l'autunno dell' anno MDCCXVII.

Venezia, Marino Rossetti, 1717.   58 p.   14½^{cm}.

Three acts. By Antonio Maria Lucchini, who is not mentioned. Argument, cast, scenario, and name of Antonio **Vivaldi** as the composer.   SCHATZ 10781

Tigrane. Dramma per musica da rappresentarsi nel Teatro di via della Pergola il carnevale del MDCCLXXI . .

Firenze, Gio. Risaliti, 1771.   56 p.   16½^{cm}.

Three acts. Cast, argument, scenario. Author and composer not mentioned and unknown to Schatz.   SCHATZ 11368

Il **Tigrane.** Dramma per musica Da rappresentarsi in Crema in occasione della Fiera di Settembre dell' anno 1743 . . .

Brescia, Gian Maria Rizzardi, n. d. 55 p. 12°.

Three acts. Argument, cast, scenario, and on p. 7: "La musica sarà di nuova composizione del Sig. Cristoforo Gluch" [**Gluck**]. In his essay, "Un opéra inconnu de Gluck" (Sammelbände d. I. M. G. 1907/8, p. 231–281), Piovano proves that: "Le texte du *Tigrane* est celui que l'abbé Francesco Silvani écrivit en 1691 sous le titre *La virtù trionfante dell' amore e dell' odio,* et qui fut successivement refondu en 1723 probablement par un poéte napolitain, et remanié en 1741 par Goldoni." The copy described by Piovano lacked the p. 35–36, which contain, according to *our complete* copy, scene I, 14, beginning "Deh, principessa, almeno" and ending with the aria "Priva del caro bene," also I, 15, beginning "Morire? tolga il ciel sì tristo evento" with the aria "Care pupille amate" and I, 16, beginning "Caro, invitto Tigrane."

ML 50.2.T56G3

Tigrane. Drama per musica da rappresentarsi nel Real Teatro di S. Carlo nel dì 4. novembre di quest' anno 1745. Per solennizare il glorioso nome di Sua Maestà.

Napoli, Cristoforo Ricciardi, n. d. 58 p. 14^cm.

Three acts. Dedication, argument, cast, scenario, and note: "La musica del recitativo della scena xi dell atto terzo, e tutte l'arie signate colla lettera S. sono del celebre maestro Sig. Gio. Adolfo Asse detto il Sassone [**Hasse**], quelle di tutti l'altri recitativi, sinfonia, ed alcune arie sono del Sig. Antonio **Palella,** maestro di cappella napolitano, direttore dell' opera."

The arias not by Hasse, accordingly, were, for instance, in the first act: "Coronato il crin d'alloro" (I, 1), "Scende dal monte il fonte" (I, 7), "Perfido non parlarmi" (I, 8). The text is a modernized version (utilizing perhaps Goldoni's final alterations of 1741) of Francesco Silvani's "La virtù trionfante dell' amore e dell' odio." Comparison with the Brescia, 1743, edition of "Tigrane" (as set by Gluck for Crema, 1743) shows, for instance, that the aria for I, 8, in this "Non mi parlar d'amore "has become "Perfido non parlarmi." The scene I, 9, now begins "L'odio di Cleopatra" and has the aria "Quando l'amore insegna" instead of "Si despera il mio core" resp. "Vezzi, lusinghe e sguarde," 'and Scene I, 10, beginning "Se sia, che un giorno stringa" has the aria "Se spunta amica face" instead of "Se spunta amica stella" and beginning "Non im ami Cleopatra."

First performed, as indicated, November 4, 1745, but previously under the same title at Naples, Teatro di San Bartolomeo November 4, 1723, and presumably without the final revisions by Goldoni, but with many alterations in Silvani's text and without Palella's music.

Schatz 4584

Tigrane. Dramma per musica da rappresentarsi nel Teatro di S. Angelo. Nella fiera della Ascensione dell' anno 1747 . . .

Venezia, Modesto Fenzo, 1747. 47 p. 15^cm.

Three acts. Impresario's dedication, argument, cast, scenario, and name of Giovanni Battista **Lampugnani** ("nuova composizione") as composer. The author is not mentioned, but comparison proved that this is substantially Goldoni's modernization (1741) under the title "Tigrane" of Francesco Silvani's "La virtù trionfante dell' amore e dell' odio."

First performed, as indicated, May 10, 1747.

Schatz 5390

Tigrane. Dramma per musica da rappresentarsi nel Teatro di S. Angelo il carnovale dell' anno 1733 . . .

Venezia, Aloise Valvasense, 2 p. l., 47 p. 15½^cm.

Three acts. Dedication signed by the author, Bartolo Vitturi, notice of the substitute aria (I, 11) "Agitata da più vanti," argument, notice to the reader, cast, and name of Giuseppe Antonio **Paganelli** as composer. Vitturi informs the reader that the drama really intended for this season had to be reserved for the next and that he found himself obliged to write "Tigrane" in five days. He goes on to say that this old theme has been treated by him independently of others and:

Tigrane—Continued.

"Il mio solito non è di servirmi delle scene migliori di cinque, o sei drammi, e poi per formarne uno, con una massa d'incompatibili errori unirle assieme. Tutto quello, che finora composi, fù parto della mia mente, ne vi sarà alcuno capace di dirne il contrario. Questa volta dovei fare diversamente . . . Dunque, qual esso sia cotesto dramma compatiscilo, se non altro à riguardo de virtuosi, che lo rappresentano . . ."

First performed, as indicated, February 10, 1733.   SCHATZ 7370

Tigrane. Dramma per musica. La rappresentarsi nel Regio Teatro di Torino nel carnevale del MDCCLXI . . .

Torino, Giacomo Giuseppe Avondo, n. d.   viii, 52 p.   16½cm.

Three acts. In the catalogue of his libretto collection Schatz gives Vittorio Amedeo Cigna-Santi as the author, but in his Piccinni "Chronologisches Verzeichnis" he says: "Text von Francesco Silvani, ursprünglich m. d. Titel. La virtù trionfante dell' amore, e dell' odio bearbeitet von Carlo Goldoni." Argument, cast, scenario, and name of Niccolò **Piccinni** as the composer. With the opera were performed Vincenzo Saunier ballets, music by Giuseppe Antonio Le Messier, "Telemaco nell' isola di Calipso," "Cadmo ed Ino," and "Cittadini di Sinope festeggianti le nozze di Mitridate." Of the last, which was a sequel to the opera's *finale*, a brief description is given on p. 52.   SCHATZ 8118

Tigrane. Dramma per musica da rappresentarsi nel Teatro di S. Angelo nella fiera dell' Ascensione dell' anno 1762.

Venezia, Modesto Fenzo, 1762.   48 p.   17½cm.

Three acts. Argument, cast, scenario, and name of Antonio **Tozzi** as composer ("La musica sarà tutta nuova"). The text is Francesco Silvani's "La virtù trionfante dell' amore e dell' odio" as rewritten under the above title by Carlo Goldoni, 1741.

First performed, as indicated, May 19, 1762.   SCHATZ 10387

Il Tigrane rè d'Armenia. Drama per musica da rappresentarsi nel Teatro di San Cassiano. L'anno 1697. Di Giulio Cesare Corradi . . .

Venezia, Per il Nicolino, 1697.   71 p.   14cm.

Three acts. Author's dedication, argument, scenario, and notice to the reader, with name of Tommaso **Albinoni** as composer.

First performed during carnival of 1697.   SCHATZ 126

Time turned oculist. A. T. of Albion restored.

The times; or, A fig for invasion: a musical entertainment in two acts. Dedicated to . . . William Pitt . . . by a British officer . . .

London, T. Becket, 1797.   6 p. (incl. front.), 48 p.   21cm.

Dedication dated January, 1797, and note to the public. Neither author, composer, nor performance recorded by Clarence.   LONGE 244

Timocrate. Dramma per musica da rappresentarsi nel Teatro di S. Angelo nel carnevale dell' anno 1723 . . .

Venezia, Francesco Storti, 1723.   57 p.   14½cm.

Three acts. Dedication signed by Domenico Lalli as author, argument, cast, scenario, and name of Leonardo **Leo** as composer.   SCHATZ 5560

Timoleone. Dramma serio per musica da rappresentarsi per la prima volta nel Teatro di Reggio la fiera dell' anno VI. Repubblicano.

Reggio, Davolio, n. d.   34 p.   19cm.

Two acts. "La poesia del dramma è affatto nuova del citt. Simon Antonio Sografi. La musica tutta nuova è espressamente composta in Reggio dal rinomato maestro citt.

Timoleone—Continued.

Sebastiano **Nasolini**.'' Impresario's prefatory note, dated ''Reggio 14 fiorile anno VI.'' (April 29, 1798), cast, and scenario. With the opera was performed Giovanni Monticini's ballet, ''Progne e Filomene, ossia Tereo, tiranno di Nasora.'' The composer of the music is not mentioned. SCHATZ 7026

Timugino, gran Kan de' Tartari, ballet. *See* Bianchi's Morte di Cesare.

I **Tintaridi,** dramma per musica da rappresentarsi in Firenze nel Teatro di via della Pergola nel carnevale dell' anno 1768 . . .

n. i., n. d. Unpaged. 21ᶜᵐ.

Same general appearance as the 1768 ''Enea e Lavinia'' libretto. Five acts. Dedication, argument, cast, scenario, and name of Tommaso **Traietta** as composer, and librettist, Carlo Innocente Frugoni. In the dedication the impresario says:

''Non potevano in miglior tempo uscire per la prima volta alla pubblica luce del Teatro fiorentino i Tintaridi, opera del celebratissimo abbate Frugoni ridotta all' ultima perfezione, quanto adesso . . .''

First performed, as indicated, January 3, 1768; at Parma, Teatro Ducale, April, 1760. SCHATZ 16400

La **tirannide abbattuta dalla virtù.** Festa musicale.

By conte Nicolò Minato, music by Antonio **Draghi,** Vienna, 1697, with some arias by the emperor, **Leopold I.**
Not in L. of C.

— Die durch die tugend gestuerzte wueterey. An den glorwuerdigsten namens-tag der Roem. Kayserl. Majestaet Eleonora Magdalena Theresia . . . gesungener vorgestellt in dem Lustgarten der Kayserlichen Favorita im jahr 1697. Mit der music zu denen worten herrn Antoni Drahy[!], der Roem. Kays. Mayest. capellmeisters. Zu den daenzen, herrn Johann Joseph Hoffer, der Roem. Kays. Mayest. Cammer-musici.

Wienn in Oesterreich, Bey Susanna Christina Cosmerovin, n. d. [50] p. 18ᶜᵐ.

One act. With argument and scenario (designed by Lodovico Burnacini).
First performed, as indicated, July 22, 1697. SCHATZ 2804

La **tirannide debellata.** Drama da rappresentarsi nel Regio-Ducal Teatro di Milano . . . nel carnevale dell' anno 1736.

Milano, Giuseppe Richino Malatesta, 1736. 56 p. 14½ᶜᵐ.

Three acts. Argument, scenario, cast, and name of the composer, ''Egidio **Duni,** Napoletano,'' but without name of the authors. The libretto is by Apostolo Zeno and **Pietro Pariati,** and originally had the title, ''Flavio Anicio Olibrio.''
SCHATZ 2857

La **tirannide dell' interesse.** Tragedia politicomorale di Francesco Sbarra, rappresentata in musica in Lucca nel Teatro de Borghi.

Lucca, Francesco Marescandoli, 1653. 192 p. 13½ᶜᵐ.

Prologue and five acts. Author's dedication, with date of Lucca, September 30, 1653, argument, anagram, and sixteen poems addressed to the author (p. 13–25), and his lengthy preface, which elucidates his reasons for writing a ''tragedia politicomorale.'' He starts in by saying:

''Io non compongo, che per mio gusto, ed il mio gusto è d'apportar più giovamento, che diletto, onde stimo megliore strada di caminar sù le regole de Sacri Oratori, che detestano i vitii. che il seguitar gl' esempi de profani poeti, che gli vanno adulando . . .''

and he lays stress on the fact that he deemed it fruitful

La **tirannide dell' interesse**—Continued.

"contro l'uso, e le leggi poetiche, che non ammettono le morti in scena sè non per racconto, esporre alla vista degl' auditori la Virtù per sua cagion moribonda, e l'Intelletto di sua man trucidato . . ."

The allegorical nature of the work may be inferred from the scenic indication: "La scena rappresenta la Reggia dell' Intelletto nell' Isola del Libero Arbitrio." The composer, Marco **Bigongiari**, is not mentioned.

First performed at Lucca, February 5, 1653. ML 50.2.T55

— La **tirannide dell' interesse.** Tragedia politico morale di Francesco Sbarra rappresentata in musica in Lucca nel Teatro de' Borghi . . .

Venetia, Nicolò Pezzana, 1658. 168 p. 13ᶜᵐ.

Five acts and prologue. Publisher's dedication (dated Venice, January 12, 1657), author's preface, and argument. Marco **Bigongiari**, the composer, is not mentioned. SCHATZ 1035

La **tirannide punita.** Drama per musica da rappresentarsi nel Teatro Obizi in Paova [!] il carnovale dell' anno 1721.

Padova, Gio. Battista Conzatti, 1721. 59 p. 15ᶜᵐ.

Three acts. Argument, cast, scenario, and prefatory note, according to which this is an altered version of a text previoulsy performed at Venice and, indeed, it is Giacomo Francesco Bussani's "Antonino e Pompejano."

Composer not mentioned and unknown to Schatz. SCHATZ 11369

La **tirannide repressa.** A. T. of the ballet Raul, signore di Crechi.'

Il **tiranno di Colco.** Drama musicale rappresentato nella Villa di Pratolino.

Firenze, Vincenzio Vangelisti, 1688. 76 p. 15ᶜᵐ.

Three acts. Argument. Neither the author, Giovanni Andrea Moniglia, nor the composer, Giovanni Maria **Pagliardi**, is mentioned SCHATZ 7585

Il **tiranno di Colco.** Drama musicale rappresentato nella villa di Pratolino [vignette]

G. A. Moniglia, Poesie drammatiche, parte seconda, Firenze, Cesare e Francesco Bindi, 1690, 1 p. l., 78 p. 24ᶜᵐ.

Three acts. Argument, scenario and prefatory note (p. 3–6) which contains details about "una non maravigliosa meno, che sontousissima macchina" used for a somewhat burlesque kind of prologue to the opera. We are told that the opera was performed eight times and:

"Fu questo drama composto nella villa di Pratolino, e dopo tre anni, nell' istessa tatto rappresentare dal serenissimo principe di Toscana: Io messe in musica con ammirabile armonia il Sig. Gio. Maria Palliardi (**Pagliardi**) . . . A questo drama fu fatta una amorevole censura, alla quale soggiunse l'autore una piccola difesa, che in piede dell' opera è registrata."

It is printed as "Lettera apologetica dell' autore" on p. 69–78 and is dated Pratolino, September 15, 1688, which proves that the opera cannot have been performed later than in the summer of 1688. ML 49.A2M7

Il **tiranno eroe.** Drama per musica da rappresentarsi nel Teatro Tron di S. Cassano l'anno 1710 . . .

Venezia, Marino Rossetti, 1710. 69 p. 14ᶜᵐ.

Three acts. Dedication signed by the author, Vincenzo Cassani, argument, notice to the reader, cast, scenario, and name of Tommaso **Albinoni** as composer. SCHATZ 127

Il tiranno humiliato d'Amore, overo il Meraspe. Drama p. musica nel Teatro Grimano . . .

Venetia, Bortolo Bruni, 1667. 1 p. l., 67, [1] p. 15ᶜᵐ.

Prologue and three acts. By Giovanni Faustini, music by Carlo **Pallavicino,** neither of whom mentioned. Imprimatur dated November 24, 1667.

First performed, as indicated, December 12, 1667. Schatz 7737

Tircis et Doristée. Parody of Lully's Acis et Galatée.

Tirésias, opéra-comique, en trois actes. Précédé d'un prologue. Donné à la Foire Saint-Laurent en 1722.

Alexis Piron, Oeuvres complettes, Liege, 1776, v. 4, [337]–468 p. 17½ᶜᵐ.

On p. 339–348 "Avertissement de l'éditeur, et anecdote sur la pièce de Tiresias, & sur Le mariage de Momus, ou La gigantomachie," informing the reader how Piron came to write "Tirésias" for Francisque, manager of the Opéra-comique, how Francisque defied the authorities by using spoken language in his theatre, how he was promptly arrested, how Piron sought to gain his release by a satirical lettre to M. d' Argenson, which is reprinted, etc., etc. The piece is partly in prose, partly *en vaudevilles*. Composer not recorded by Parfaict, etc. PQ 2019.P6

Tiridate. Drama per musica nel Teatro a S. Salvatore per l'anno 1668 . . .

Venetia, Francesco Nicolini, 1668. front., 67 p. 14ᶜᵐ.

Three acts. Dedication signed by Niccolò Minato and dated Venice, February 4, 1668, argument, and notice informing the reader:

"La composizione [*i. e.* drama] è d'insegne & erudita penna . . . la necessità di brevità l'hà fatta ridur meno ricca. Qualche cosa è stata aggiunta, come la parte della Bambina Fidalma, e qualche altra pocha novità per acomodarsi a' personaggi, che si havevano, e per tenersi all' uso di queste scene. Chi v'hà immischiato la penna [Minato?], l'hà fatto con espressa permissione dell' autore [marchese Ippolito Bentivoglio] . . ."

The composer, Giovanni **Legrenzi,** is not mentioned. Schatz 5539

Il Tirinto. A. T. of La sincerità con la sincerità.

Il Tirinto. Dramma musicale nuovamente rappresentato da' Signori Accademici Efimeri in Firenze l'anno 1692 . . .

Firenze, Vincenzio Vangelisti, 1692. 61 p. 14ᶜᵐ.

Three acts. Dedication signed by Domenico Piazzini, argument, and "protesta" which reads:

"Per accomodarsi al genio del presente secolo, che ne i divertimenti ancora ama la brevità, è stato necessario troncare gran parte de' versi del presente dramma, ed aggiungervi delle arie. Non s'è preteso in ciò dar regola all' autore, il quale se fosse stato presente da per se stesso avrebbe ridotta l'opera sua alla moda."

Author and composer unknown to Schatz. Schatz 11370

Tirsi. Drama pastorale da rappresentarsi in musica nel Teatro Giustiniano di San Moisè il carnovale dell' anno MDCCXXXIV.

Venezia, Marin Rossetti, n. d. 36 p. 14½ᶜᵐ.

Three acts. Author (Francesco Lemene) and composer (unknown to Schatz) not mentioned. Scenario and note that the idea and disposition of the text is wholly the author's own, wherefore no argument. Schatz 11371

Il Tirsi. Drama pastorale per musica da rappresentarsi nel Teatro di S. Salvatore l'autunno dell' anno MDCXCVI . . .

Venezia, n. publ., n. d. 6 p. l., 48 p. 14½ᶜᵐ.

Publisher's name and date, 1696, cut off in binding?

Five acts. Dedication signed with the initials of Apostolo Zeno as author, though no such text appears in his collected works. Argument, scenario. The composers, Antonio **Lotti,** Antonio **Caldara,** and Attilio **Ariosti** (Schatz), are not mentioned. Schatz 5728

Der tischler. Tr. of Cimarosa's Il falegname.

Titania oder Liebe durch zauberei.   Ein singspiel in zwey aufzügen.
   Cassel, Hampe, 1792.   2 p. l., 108 p.   17ᶜᵐ.

Prefatory note by the author, Oberst von Weber, who is not mentioned, with information to the effect that the text was composed by Georg Christoph **Grossheim**, and that the opera was first performed at Cassel, Hof-Operntheater, 1792.   SCHATZ 4215

Il Tito.   Melodrama da recitarsi nel famoso Teatro Grimano l'anno 1666 . . .
   Venetia, Steffano Curti, 1666.   front., 91, [1] p.   14½ᶜᵐ.

Three acts.   By conte Niccolò Beregani.   Publisher's dedication, dated Venice, February 13, 1666, author's preface, with clear allusions to his identity, name of Marc' Antonio **Cesti** as composer, argument, and scenario.   SCHATZ 1784

Tito o La partenza di Berenice, ballet.   *See* Tarchi's L'apoteosi d'Ercole.

Tito e Berenice, ballet.   *See* Borghi's Arbace.

Tito e Berenice.   Dramma per musica di Giuseppe Foppa da rappresentarsi nel nuovo e nobilissimo Teatro detto La Fenice la fiera dell' Ascensione dell' anno 1793.
   Venezia, Modesto Fenzo, 1793.   60 p.   17ᶜᵐ.

Two acts.   Argument, cast, scenario, and name of Sebastiano **Nasolini** as the composer.   On p. 25–28, argument of Francesco Clerico's "La conquista del vello d'oro, ballo eroico pantomimo in cinque atti," the composer of the music not being mentioned.   SCHATZ 7017

Tito Manlio.   Dramma per musica da rappresentarsi nel Teatro da S. Agostino il carnovale dell' anno 1784 . . .
   Genova, Stamperia Gesiniana, n. d.   72 p.   14½ᶜᵐ.

Three acts.   Author not mentioned, and unknown to Schatz.   Argument, scenario, cast, and name of Giuseppe **Giordani** as the composer.   ("La musica è di nuova composizione.")   On p. 59–72, description of "Enea nel Lazio ballo tragico-pantomimo d'invenzione . . . del Signor Michele Fabiani . . ."   The composer of the music is not mentioned.   SCHATZ 3841

Tito Manlio.   Drama per musica da rappresentarsi nel Regio Teatro di Torino nel carnovale del 1743 . . .
   Torino, Pietro Giuseppe Zappata e figliuolo, n. d.   4 p. l., 71 p. 19½ᶜᵐ.

Three acts.   By Gaetano Roccaforte, who is not mentioned.   Argument, cast, scenario, and names of Niccolò **Jommelli** as composer of the opera, of Alessio Rasetti as composer of the music of the three ballets, "Sposalizio rustico," etc.   On p. 70–71, the arias "Mi promette al cor la calma," substituted for "Confusi i miei pensieri," in I, 10;   "Languire, oh Dio! vi sento," substituted for "Spezza lo stral piagato," in I, 12;   and "Nel morir se mi vuoi forte," substituted for "Che legge tiranna," in II, 12.   SCHATZ 4881

Tito Manlio.   Drama per musica da rappresentarsi nel famosissimo Teatro Grimani a S. Gio. Grisostomo l'autunno dell' anno 1746.
   [Venezia], n. publ., n. d.   1 p. l., 48 p.   15ᶜᵐ.

Three acts.   Argument, cast, scenario, name of Niccolò **Jommelli** as the composer, and notice to the reader to the effect that
   "per accomodarsi poi sempre più al moderno Teatro ed alla nuova musica, comparisce questa volta il presente dramma, in qualche parte variato si nell' ordine, come nel portamento di qualche scena, di versi, ed ariete, ed accorciato in oltre, per opportunemente restringerlo alla solita prescritta brevità."
   Neither Matteo Noris is mentioned as author, nor conte Jacopo Sanvitale, who, according to Schatz, was responsible for the alterations.   Schatz also claims that this

Tito Manlio—Continued.

was Jommelli's second setting, with interpolation of pieces by Antonio **Zanetti,** but neither the libretto itself nor Wiel corroborate this claim. The text is so absolutely different from that of Turin (1743) as to have nothing in common with it except the scene in II, 3, "Ingiustissimi Numi," with the aria, "Da me che vorresti," which has become scene II, 4. Under the circumstances, it is clear that this "Tito Manlio" was not a second setting, but practically a new opera. SCHATZ 4900

Tito Manlio. Drama per musica rappresentato nella Villa di Pratolino.

  Firenze, Gio. Filippo Cecchi, 1696. 4 p. l., 72 p. 15^{cm}.

Three acts. Neither the author, Matteo Noris, nor the composer, Carlo Francesco **Pollaroli,** is mentioned. Argument and scenario. SCHATZ 8321

Tito Manlio. Dramma per musica da rappresentarsi in Firenze il carnovale dell' anno 1721 nel Teàtro di via della Pergola . . .

  Firenze, Stamperia di Domen. Ambrogio Verdi. Ad istanza di Gio. Angiolo Targioni, 1720. 79 p. 15^{cm}.

Three acts. Dedication by Michele Giusti, argument, cast, scenario. Neither the author, Matteo Noris, is mentioned, nor the composer, Luca Antonio **Predieri.**
           ML 48.A5 v.18

Tito nelle Gallie. Dramma per musica da rappresentarsi nel Teatro grande alla Scala il carnevale dell' anno 1787 . . .

  Milano, Gio. Batista Bianchi, n. d. 16½^{cm}.

Imperfect, stops with p. 44 (III, 5) and lacks therefore also the "programma" of the ballets.

Three acts. Author unknown to Schatz, who says that this is a much altered version of the "Giulio Sabino" text. Dedication, argument, cast, scenario, and name of Ambrogio **Minoja** as the composer. With the opera were performed Paolino Franchi's ballets "Padmani e Mirda," "Il primo navigatore," and "Fanfara militare." The composers of the music are not mentioned.

  First performed, as indicated, December 26, 1786. SCHATZ 6519

Tito Vespasiano ovvero La clemenza di Tito. O. T. of Hasse's La clemenza di Tito.

Titon et L'Aurore, pastorale-héroïque, représentée, pour la premiere fois, par l'Académie-royale de musique le mardi 9 janvier 1753. Remise au Theâtre le mardi 22 février 1763.

  Paris, Aux dépens de l'Académie. Chés de Lormel, 1763. 43 p. 22½^{cm}.

Prologue and three acts. Cast and name of Jean Joseph Cassanea de **Mondonville** as composer. The author, Antoine Houdart de La Motte, is not mentioned.
           ML 50.2.T59M7

— **Titon et L'Aurore,** pastorale héroique, mise en musique par Mr. Mondonville . . .

  Marseille, Jean Mossy, 1775. 28 p. 21^{cm}.

Prologue and three acts. De La Motte is not mentioned. ML 50.2.T59M73

— Le **rien,** parodie des parodies de Titon et l'Aurore. Représenté sur le Théâtre de l'Opera comique le 10 avril 1753.

  Paris, Duchesne, 1753. 16 p. 18½^{cm}.

One act, *en vaudevilles.* Neither the author, J. J. Vadé, nor the arranger of the music are mentioned.

See also Vadé's Oeuvres, 1760, t. ii. ML 48.P2

Titon et L'Aurore—Continued.

— Raton et Rosette, ou La vengeance inutile; parodie de Titon et l'Aurore; représentée pour la premiere fois par les Comédiens italiens ordinaires du roi, le mercredi 28 mars 1753. Troisième édition.

Paris, N. B. Duchesne, 1759. 88 p. 19ᶜᵐ. (Theatre de M. Favart, Paris, Duchesne, 1763–77, t. ii.)

Cast. One act. *En vaudevilles.* Many of the airs printed in the text and at the end of the text on p. [65]–88 ten "Vaudevilles, et ariettes italiennes, parodiées dans Raton et Rosette . . ."
The music is a mixture of old airs and such from **Mondonville's** opera.

ML 49.A2F1

Il Titone.   Drama per musica di Giovanni Faustini.

Venetia, Francesco Valvasense, 1645. 66 p. 14ᶜᵐ.

Three acts with prologue. Author's dedication. Pietro Francesco **Cavalli,** the composer, is not mentioned.
First performed at Venice, Teatro di S. Cassano, carnival, 1645.   SCHATZ 1749

Titus.   Tr. of Metastasio's text La clemenza di Tito.

Titus.   Tr. of Mozart's La clemenza di Tito.

To arms! or, The British recruit. A musical interlude. As performed at the Theatre Royal, Covent Garden. By Thomas Hurlstone . . .

London, J. Debrett, 1793. 16 p. 20½ᶜᵐ.

One act. Cast and prefatory note stating that the piece is the production of a few hours and that the music is by William **Shield** and Tommaso **Giordani.**
First performed, May 3, 1793.   LONGE 221

Toberne, ou Le pêcheur suédois, comedie en deux actes, mêlée de morceaux de musique; paroles du C. Patras, musique du C. Bruny, représentée sur le Théâtre de la rue Feydeau, en vendémiaire, 4ᵉ année de la République Française.

Paris, Maradan, cinquieme année de la République [1796–97]. 39 p. 19ᶜᵐ.

First performed, as indicated, December 2, 1795.   SCHATZ 1370

Der tod der Dido.

p. 497–510   18½ᶜᵐ.   (Litteratur und Theater Zeitung, Berlin, 1780, 3ᵗᵉʳ jahrg., 3ᵗᵉʳ th.).

At head of title: "Auch ein melodram mit chören und taenzen untermischt."
The editor of the magazine says in a footnote:
"Von dieser kurzweiligen satire, die vermuthlich das licht der welt am Rhein erblickt hat, ist mir ein gedrucktes exemplar von einem unbekannten zum einruecken in diese zeitung zugesandt worden."   SCHATZ 4772

Der tod des Hercules.   Tr. of the ballet, La morte d'Ercole.

Der tod des Hercules, ballet. *See* Salieri's Die messe zu Venedig.

Der tod des Orpheus.   Ein singspiel in drey aufzuegen.

n. i., n. d.   162 p.   14½ᶜᵐ.

Neither composer, Gottlob **Bachmann,** nor author mentioned in this copy, detached from J. G. Jacobi's Theater schriften, Leipzig, 1792.
First performed, according to Riemann, at Brunswick, in 1798.   SCHATZ 537

Toeffel und Dortchen.   *See* Blaise et Babet.

Der **töpfer,** eine komische oper in einem aufzuge. Verfertiget und in musick gesetzt von Johann André. Zweyte, verbesserte auflage. *Frankfurt und Leipzig, Johann Georg Esslinger, 1774. 96 p. 15½^{cm}.*

Dedication. In his prefatory note, dated "Offenbach, den 28. Brachmonats [June] 1774," André says:

"Der musick zu gefallen, weil sie in partitur gestochen ist, musst ich die arien ohnverändert lassen. Eine neue arie ['Bis eins gewinnt'] ist im dritten auftritt hinzugekommen, davon die partitur bey dem verleger geschrieben zu haben ist.

"Bey dieser gelegenheit finde ich dienlich zu erklären, dass ich nicht, wie im diesjährigen Almanach der deutschen Musen von mir gesagt wird, der uebersetzer der französischen operetten bin, welche seit einigen messen bey herrn Andräe in Frankfurth erscheinen."

First performed at Frankfurt a/M., Schauspielhaus im Junghof, October 29, 1773; at Hanau, according to the t.-p. of the engraved score, January 22, 1773.

SCHATZ 191

Toinon et Toinette, comédie, en deux actes en prose, meslée d'ariettes. Représentée pour la première fois, par les Comédiens italiens ordinaires du Roi, le 20 juin 1767.

Paris, la veuve Duchesne, 1768. 31 p. 19^{cm}.

Cast. By Des Boulmiers; music by **Gossec;** both not mentioned.

SCHATZ 4013

— **Toinon et Toinette,** comédie en deux actes, en prose, mêlée d'ariettes; représentée pour la première fois par les Comédiens italiens ordinaires du roi, le 20 juin 1767.

Paris, la veuve Duchesne, 1781. 40 p. 19^{cm}.

On p. 35–36, the vaudeville "La plus vive reconnaissance," on p. 37–40, the air of "Avec une epouse chérie." Neither Desboulmiers nor **Gossec** mentioned.

SCHATZ 11703

— **Anton und Antonette,** ein singspiel in zween aufzuegen aus dem franzoesischen uebersetzt. Aufgefuehrt auf dem churfuerstl. Theater zu Muenchen. [Nov.] 1778.

n. i., n. d. 40 p. 16½^{cm}.

Translated by Johann Heinrich Faber.
First performed at Francfort o/M., Theater im Junghofe, 1774. SCHATZ 4014

La **toison d'or.** A. T. of Colasse's Jason.

La **toison d'or,** tragedie lyrique, en trois actes, représentée, pour la premiere fois à Paris, sur le Théatre de l'Academie-royale de musique, le mardi 29 août 1786.

Paris, P. de Lormel, 1786. 45 p. 24^{cm}.

Cast and name of Johann Christoph **Vogel** as the composer.
The score bears as date of first performance September 5, 1786, and Schatz insists on this as correct. Cl. & L. have the date of the libretto. The author, Desriaux, is not mentioned. ML 50.2.T67V7

Der **tolle tag.** A. T. of Mozart's Figaro's hochzeit.

Tom Jones, comédie lyrique, en prose et en trois actes. La musique est de M. Philidor, et les paroles de M. Poinsinet.

Paris, Duchesne, 1766. 60 p. 19^{cm}. SCHATZ 11742

— **Tom Jones,** comédie lyrique, en trois actes, imitée du roman Anglois de M. Fielding, par M. Poinsinet. La musique, par Mr. A. D. Philidor. Représentée devant Leurs Majestés à Versailles par les

Tom Jones—Continued.

Comédiens italiens ordinaires du roi, le 30 mars; à Paris pour la première fois le 27 février 1765, & remise au Théatre le 30 janvier 2766[!].

Paris, la veuve Duchesne, 1769. 44, [2] p. 19ᶜᵐ.

It should de noted that "Tom Jones et Fellamar, suite de Tom Jones a Londres" Paris, 1787 is a comedy, not an opera.　　　ML 48.M2N

— **Tom Jones.** Comedie lyrique en trois actes imitée du roman anglois de M. Fielding par M. Poinsinet. La musique par Mr. A. D. Philidor. Representée à Florence au Théâtre dans la rue de S. Marie.

Florence, L'imprimerie Bonducciana, 1776. 47 p. 20ᶜᵐ.

ML 48.M2F

— **Tom Jones.** Comédie lyrique en trois actes, imitée du Roman anglais de M. Fielding, par M. Poinsinet. La musique par M. A. D. Philidor. Représentée devant Leurs Majestés à Versailles, par les Comédiens italiens ordinaires du roi, le 30 mars; à Paris, pour la premiere fois, le 27 février 1765, & remise au Théatre le 30 janvier 1776 [! instead of 1766]. Nouvelle édition.

Paris, la veuve Duchesne, 1778. 61 p. 17½ᶜᵐ.

On p. 59–60, the air of the vaudeville, "Je vous obtiens."　　　SCHATZ 8029

— **Tom Jones,** ein singspiel in drey aufzeugen aus dem franzoesischen uebersetzt, mit musik.

Frankfurt am Mayn, mit Andrealischen schriften 1773. 103 p., 18 p. (folded music). 16½ᶜᵐ.

Cast. Transl. for Theob. Marchand's company, by Johann Heinrich Faber. Neither he nor **Philidor** is mentioned. The music (voice and pf.) consists of: "Ach! ich fleh in Ihren armen" (I, 8, "Ah! ma tante, je vous prie"), "Wie stark ist Deine macht" (II, 4, "La pauvre fillette a beau faire"), "Oft, wenn im haus" (II,5, "Plus d'une fois"), "Vergönne, dass ich weine" (III, 2, "Ami, qu'en mes bras"), "Dich hab ich, dich, mir theurer" (III, 12, "Je vous obtiens").　　　SCHATZ 8030

— Gesaenge aus der oper: **Tom Jones.** In drey aufzuegen. Der inhalt von Poinsinet, die composition von Philidor.

Hamburg, J. M. Michaelsen, n. d. 24 p. 17ᶜᵐ.

The translator, Friedrich Wilhelm Gotter, is not mentioned.
First performed at Hamburg, Theater beim Gänsemarkt, April 26, 1779.

SCHATZ 8031

— **Tom Jones.** Ein lustspiel mit gesang in drey aufzuegen. Aus dem franzoesischen des hrn. Poinsinet. In musik gesetzt von A. D. Philidor.

Oels, Samuel Gottlieb Ludwig, n. d. 72 p. 16ᶜᵐ.　　　SCHATZ 8032

Tom Jones, a comic opera: as it is performed at the Theatre-Royal in Covent-Garden. By Joseph Reed.

London, Becket and De Hondt, 1769. 4 p. l., 62 p. 20ᶜᵐ.

Three acts. Cast and same preface as in next entry, which also *see* for composers.
First performed as indicated, January 14, 1769.　　　ML 50.2.T71

Tom Jones—Continued.

— **Tom Jones,** a comic opera: as it is performed at the Theatre Royal in Covent-Garden. By Joseph Reed. The second edition.

London, Becket and De Hondt, 1769. 4 p. l., 59 p. 20ᶜᵐ.

Three acts. Cast and preface, in which the author says:

"While I was writing the last act of this opera (which was in June, 1765), the French *Tom Jones* fell into my hands. I found its plan so very confined, and so materially different from mine, that I could reap little or no benefit from it. The only particulars, of which I have availed myself from Mons. Poinsinet, are the hint of legitimating Jones, and the thought, which gave rise to my second air."

By far most of the airs are headed by the names of these composers: **Arnold** (6), **Holcombe** (1), **Granom** (1), **Arne** (11), **Van Maldere** (1), Joh. Chr. **Bach** (3), **Händel** (1), **Galuppi** (1), **Baildon** (1), **Boyce** (1), **Abel** (1), **Pergolesi** (1), **Hasse** (1), **Corelli** (1), but some were to be sung to indicated popular tunes, and a few of the airs have no heading at all. LONGE 25

La tomba di Merlino. Dramma giocoso per musica da rappresentarsi nel Teatro Giustiniani di S. Moisè l'autunno dell' anno 1772 di Giovanni Bertati.

Venezia, Antonio Graziosi, 1772. 68 p. 17½ᶜᵐ.

Three acts. Impresario's dedication, cast, scenario, and name of the composer, Giuseppe **Gazzaniga**. SCHATZ 3673

Le tombeau de Nostradamus. *See* Arlequin Mahomet.

Tomiri. Dramma per musica per celebrare il felicissimo giorno natalizio di Sua Maestà Fedelissima l'augusta Donna Maria I . . . li 17. Dec. 1783.

[Lisbona], Nella stamperia reale, n. d. 33 p. 15ᶜᵐ.

One act, with licenza. By Gaetano Martinelli. Argument, cast, and names of the author and the composer, João de Sousa **Carvalho**. SCHATZ 1675

Tomiri. Dramma per musica da rappresentarsi nel nobilissimo Teatro Venier in San Benedetto l'autunno dell' anno 1795.

Venezia, Modesto Fenzo, 1795. 49 p. 17½ᶜᵐ.

Two acts. Author not mentioned, and unknown to Schatz. Argument, cast scenario, and name of Pietro **Guglielmi** as the composer. On p. 25–32, argument, cast, and synopsis of "Alcide negli orti Esperidi, ballo favoloso eroico pantomimo."

First performed, as indicated, December, 1795. SCHATZ 4276

Tomiri. Drama per musica da rappresentarsi nel Teatro di S. Casciano l'anno MDCLXXX di Antonio Medolago . . .

Venetia, Francesco Nicolini, 1680. front., 60 p. 14ᶜᵐ.

Three acts. Argument, scenario, author's dedication dated Venice, January, 1679, and his notice to reader, in which he says:

"Tutto ciò, che troverai di lascivo in questo drama credilo posto solo per seguire l'uso corrente, e non per genial propensione. L'angustia della scena (in cui non ponno farsi apparenze di pompa) & altri difetti gli remetto tutti alla tua gentilezza . . . La musica è del S. D. Angelo **Vitali**, nelle noti del cui bizzaro contrapunto conoscerai, che non hà degradato dà gli altri suoi spiritosi talenti." SCHATZ 10758

Le tonnelier. Opéra-comique mêlé d'ariettes. Représenté par les Comédiens italiens ordinaires du roi, le 16 mars 1765.

Paris, Duchesne, 1765. 56 p. 18½ᶜᵐ.

Cast. On p. 52–56 the airs of "C'est cependant le cours" and of the three airs mentioned in next entry, which compare for further details. On p. [3] a note reads: "La pièce est un mélange de l'ancien & du nouveau genre," meaning that it is partly *en vaudevilles* and partly not. An Avertissement on p. [2] reads:

Le **tonnelier**—Continued.

"On a représenté, à l'Opéra-Comique, dans la dernière année de la Foire Saint-Laurent, une pièce intitulée: le Tonnelier, dont le succès ne fut pas heureux. Quelques situations théâtrales & de bons morceaux de musique qui s'y trouvoient, firent naître l'idée de la remettre au théâtre, avec des changemens. Ceux qu'on y a faits, sont devenus si considérables, qu'on pourroit la donner aujourd'hui comme tout-à-fait nouvelle. Cependant pour n'avoir point de reproche à recevoir ni à se faire sur cet article, on a eu soin de marquer ici, avec des guillemets, tout ce qui subsiste de l'ancien Tonnelier.

C'est d'après des épreuves favorables & réitérées en plusieurs endroits, qu'on ose présenter cette ·pièce au public; plus appuyés néanmoins sur les exemples de son indulgence, que sur le mérite de l'ouvrage . . ."

Accordingly "C'est pour le dieu du vin," "Climène, au cabaret," "Dans un verger, Colinette," "Quand je vois Fanchette," "Près de moi dans la boutique," etc., had been retained by Quétant-**Gossec** from **Audinot**'s original version. Indeed, this applies to most of the ariettes, etc., in the libretto. As to the "nouvelle édition augmentée" of the next entry, the 1767 ed. has thirteen scenes only, whereas the 1765 has fourteen! Furthermore, while the dialogue in scene 7 is somewhat longer in the 1767 ed., the songs "En revenant de Clarenton" and "Je veux bien m'en fier à foi" in scenes second and third have been dropped. The final scene differs very much in both editions, the 1767 ed. having, for instance, the vaudeville "Trop occupé de mon ouvrage," the 1765 ed. "Auprès d'un tendron." The score published by De La Chevardière coincides with the 1767 ed. of the libretto, not with the 1765 ed.

ML 50.2.T68

— Le **tonnelier**, opéra-comique, mêlé d'ariettes. Représenté par les Comédiens italiens ordinaires du roi, le 16 mars 1765, & à Bruxelles le 20 avril 1767. Nouvelle édition augmentée.

Paris, Veuve Duchesne, 1767. 48 p. 19^{cm}.

Originally written and composed by Nicolas Médard **Audinot** and first performed at the Opéra-comique on September 28, 1761, this one-act opera was revised for the performances mentioned above by François Quétant and François Joseph **Gossec**. On p. 44–48 the music of the vaudeville "Auprès d'un tendron" and the three airs "Dans un verger Colinette," "Près de moi, dans la boutique," and "Un tonnelier vieux."   SCHATZ 487

— Le **tonnelier**, opéra-bouffon, en un acte, mêlé d'ariettes; revu, corrigé, & tel qu'il a été représenté à Paris par les Comediens italiens ordinaires du roi.

Paris, par la Compagnie des libraires, 1768. 38 p. 19^{cm}.

Neither Audinot nor **Gossec** mentioned.   SCHATZ 11672

— Le **tonnelier**, opéra bouffon, en un acte, mêlé d'ariettes; revu, corrigé, & tel qu'il a été représenté à Paris par les Comédiens italiens ordinaires du Roi. Nouvelle édition.

Paris, par la Compagnie des libraires, 1768. 38 p. 18½^{cm}.

Neither Audinot nor **Gossec** mentioned.   SCHATZ 11674

— Le **tonnelier**, opera-comique, meslé d'ariettes, représenté par les Comédiens italiens ordinaires du roi, le 16 mars 1765, & à Bruxelles le 20 avril 1767. Nouvelle édition, augmentée.

Paris, la veuve Duchesne, 1770. 44 p. 19^{cm}.

On p. 39–44 the vaudeville "Auprès d'un tendron, à votre âge," and the airs "Dans un verger Colinette," "Près de moi, dans la boutique," and "Un tonnelier vieux." The text seems to be the same as in the Paris, 1768, ed.   SCHATZ 11673

— Arien und gesaenge aus der komischen oper: Der **fassbinder**, in einem akt.

Berlin, n. publ., 1796. 15 p. 16^{cm}.

First performed at Berlin in 1796 at the Nationaltheater, but previously at the Döbbelinsches Theater, November 2, 1781 (Schatz).   SCHATZ 489

Le **tonnelier**—Continued.

— Der **fassbinder,** ein singspiel in einem aufzuge aus dem franzoesischen uebersetzt mit musik.

Frankfurt am Mayn, Andreae, 1773. 71 p, 10 (fold. music). 17ᶜᵐ.

Cast. The music (voice and bass) consists of the arias "Einen weinstock, der
voll trauben," "Seiner arbeit abzuwarten," "Ein büttner alt," "Ein alter mann
von euren jahren." This is Johann Heinrich Faber's translation of "Le tonnelier."
First performed at Frankfort o/M., Theater au d. Junghofe, 1773.   SCHATZ 488

Too civil by half, a farce in two acts, as performed with universal
applause, at the Theatre-Royal, Drury-Lane. By John Dent . . .

London, J. Stockdale, 1783. 4 p. l., 39, [1] p. 21ᶜᵐ.

Cast, dedication, and prefatory note. Interspersed with six songs, the composer
of which not recorded by Clarence.
First performed November 5, 1782.   LONGE 92

La **Torilda.** Drama del Rincorato, Academico Olympico.

Venetia, Francesco Valvasense, 1648. 127, [1] p. 14½ᶜᵐ.

Three acts with prologue. Long historico-esthetic preface by the author, Pietor
Paolo Bissari. Argument and scenario. The composer, Pietro Francesco **Cavalli,**
is not mentioned.
First performed at Venice, Teatro di S. Cassiano, carnival, 1648.   SCHATZ 1733

Die **totale mondfinsterniss,** ein komisch singspiel in zwey aufzuegen, von Carl Friedrich Zimdar . . . In musik gesezt von C. G.
Weber . . .

*Stuttgart, Buchdruckerei der herzoglichen Hohen Carls-Schule, 1786.
92 p. 15½ᶜᵐ.*

First performed at Stuttgart, Herzogl. Kleines Schauspielhaus auf der Planie, 1786.
                                                              SCHATZ 10915

Totila. Drama per musica nel famosissimo Teatro Grimano di SS.
Gio. e Paolo. L'anno MDCLXXVII. Di Matteo Noris . . .

Venetia, Francesco Nicolini, 1677. 79 p. 14ᶜᵐ.

Three acts. Author's dedication, argument, scenario. The composer, Giovanni
Legrenzi, is not mentioned.   SCHATZ 5547

The songs, chorusses, etc in The **touchstone,** or, Harlequin traveller.
An operatical pantomime. As it is performed at the Theatre-Royal
in Covent-Garden. The third edition.

London, G. Kearsley, 1779. 2 p. l., 15 p. 21ᶜᵐ.

Text and music by Charles **Dibdin,** who, in a prefatory note, speaks of the dialogue
as "considerably improved, by the advice and assistance of some ingenious friends."
First performed January 4, 1779, as indicated.   LONGE 102

Il **Trace in catena,** drama per musica da rappresentarsi nella Sala
de' Signori Capranica l'anno MDCCXVII.

Roma, Bernabò, 1717. 72 p. 15ᶜᵐ.

Three acts. Author not mentioned and unknown to Allacci. Prefatory note,
scenario, cast and note: "La musica è del Sig. Francesco **Gasparini,** e di dui suoi
allievi."   ML 50.2.T73G2

I **Traci amanti.** Dramma giocoso per musica da rappresentarsi nel
Teatro di S. A. S. il Signor principe di Carignano nel carnovale dell'
anno 1794.

Torino, Onorato Derossi, n. d. iv, 56 p. 14½ᶜᵐ.

Two acts. By Giuseppe Palomba, who is not mentioned. Cast, scenario, and
name of **Cimarosa** as composer. On p. 44-56, description, with argument and cast.

I Traci amanti—Continued.

but without name of the composer of the music of Federico Terrades "Eschila e Timoleone ossia La caduta di Timofane, tiranno di Corinto, ballo eroico-tragico diviso in tre atti." His second ballet was called "La superbia umiliata ossia L'egualità d'amore."

First performed at Naples, Teatro Nuovo, 1793.   ML 50.2.T73C2

— Gli **Turchi amanti,** dramma giocoso per musica da rappresentarsi nel Reggio Teatro di S. Carlo della Principessa il carnovale dell' anno 1796.

Lisbona, Simone Taddeo Ferreira, 1796. 135 p. 14½^{cm}.

Two acts. Cast and names of the author, Giuseppe Palomba, and the composer, **Cimarosa.** A later version of their "I Traci amanti."   SCHATZ 1999

Tracollo. L. T. of Pergolesi's Livietta e Tracollo o sia La contadina astuta.

Il tradimento premiato. Favola pastorale, da recitarsi in musica l'autunno dell' anno 1709. Nel Teatro di Sant' Angelo . . .

Venetia, Gio. Battista Zuccato, 1709. 56 p. 14^{cm}.

Three acts. By Giov. Battista Candi, who is not mentioned. Publisher's dedication, argument, and scenario. The composer, Girolamo **Polani,** is not mentioned.
                    SCHATZ 8252

Il tradimento punito, ballet. *See* Piccinni's La Griselda.

Il tradimento tradito. Drama per musica. Da rappresentarsi nel Teatro di S. Angelo l'anno MDCCIX . . .

Venetia, Zuccato, 1709. 4 p. l., [5]–60 p. 15^{cm}.

Three acts. Dedication signed by the author, Francesco Silvani, and dated Venice, December 29, 1708, argument, cast, scenario. The composer, Tommaso **Albinoni,** is not mentioned.   SCHATZ 103

Il tradimento traditor di se stesso. Drama per musica da rappresentarsi nel famosissimo Teatro Grimani di S. Gio. Grisostomo l'anno MDCCXI . . . Di Francesco Silvani.

Venezia, Marino Rossetti, 1711. 72 p. 15^{cm}.

Three acts. Author's dedication, dated Venice, January 17, 1711, argument, scenario, cast. The composer, Antonio **Lotti,** is not mentioned. A contemporary ms. note on p. [2] reads: "è lo stesso che la Statira t? A."   SCHATZ 5710

— **Artaserse rè di Persia.** Drama per musica da rappresentarsi nel Real Palaggio, nel dì primo ottobre 1713. Giorno festivo per gli anni, che compie la Maestà Ces. e Catt. del nostro invittissimo imperadore Carlo VI . . .

Napoli, Michele Luigi Muzio, 1713. 6 p. l., 57 p. 14^{cm}.

Prologue and three acts. Dedication signed by Serino as impresario, argument, scenario, cast, and notice to the reader, stating:

"La necessità d'avervisi adaggiungere le parti di Farfalletta, e di Dragasso, hà fatto, che più cose vi si fussero tolte, aggiunte, e variate, non meno per attendersi alla brevità che uniformarsi al genio de' rappresentanti, e di questa città.

"Anche la musica è di celebre compositore [**Lotti**], mà ti avvertisco, che tutte le scene buffe, e tutte le arie che vedrai con questo segno §, sono state poste in musica dal Signor Francesco **Mancini** . . ."

Accordingly, he composed, for instance, the arias, "Superba; vedrai" (I, 3), "Aure, fonti, erbetti, e fiori" (I, 4), "Sai, ch'un ombra è la bellezza" (I, 6), "Sovvengati, spietata" (I, 9), and many others. The text, with the indicated alterations, is Silvani's "Il tradimento traditor di se stesso."   SCHATZ 5712

La tragédie. Entrée in Campra's Les Muses.

The **tragedy of Chrononhotonthologos**: being the most tragical tragedy that ever was tragediz'd by any company of tragedians. Written by Benjamin Bounce, Esq; . . .

London, J. Shuckburgh and L. Gilliver [etc], n. d. 30, [1] p., incl. front.

Cast. One act, prologue and epilogue. By Henry Carey. On p. [8]: "The tunes of ye songs." (only four)

First performed at London, "little theatre" in the Haymarket, February 22, 1734.

ML 50.2.C47

— **Chrononhotonthologos**: The most tragical tragedy that ever was tragediz'd by any company of tragedians.

[151]–182 p. 22ᶜᵐ. (Henry Carey, Dramatick works, London, 1743)

Prologue and one act. Without the tunes.

ML 49.A2C2

— **Chrononhotonthologos**: The most tragical tragedy that ever was tragedized by any company of tragedians. The seventh edition.

London, T. Lowndes, T. Calson [etc.], 1770. 32 p. 19ᶜᵐ.

One act and prologue. No music printed in this ed.

LONGE 54

— **Chrononhotonthologos.** By Mr. Henry Carey.

[245]–258 p. 19ᶜᵐ. (Collection of the most esteemed farces and entertainments, t. ii, Edinburgh, 1792.)

One act.

SCHATZ 11753B

Traiano. Drama per musica da rappresentarsi nel famoso Teatro Grimano di SS. Gio. e Paolo. L'anno MDCLXXXIV. Di Matteo Noris . . .

Venetia, Francesco Nicolini, 1684. 69 p. 14ᶜᵐ.

Three acts. Author's dedication and scenario. Giuseppe Felice **Tosi**, the composer, is not mentioned.

SCHATZ 10380

Le **traité nul**, comédie en un acte et en prose, mêlée d'ariettes, représentée le 5 messidor, an 5, sur le Théatre Feydeau. [June 23, 1797] Paroles de M. Marsollier, musique de M. Gavaux.

Paris, Huet, an V (ou 1797). 64 p. 21ᶜᵐ.

Cast.

ML 50.2.T77G2

— Le **traité nul**, comédie en un acte et en prose, mêlée d'ariettes, représentée le 5 messidor, an V, sur le Théatre Feydeau. Paroles de M. Marsollier, musique de M. Gavaux.

Paris, Huet, an VIIᵉ [1798–99] 48 p. 21ᶜᵐ.

Same cast and text.

ML 50.2.T77G22

— Het **vernietigd verdrag**, zangspel. Door G. Brender à Brandis.

Amsteldam, Abraham Mars, 1799. 87, [1] p. 16½ᶜᵐ.

Author's preface dated "den 11ᵈᵉⁿ van Lentemaand 1799" with names of the author and the composer.

First performed at Amsterdam, Stadt Schouwburg, March, 1799. SCHATZ 3644

Le **trame deluse.** Drama giocoso in due atti da rappresentarsi nel Teatro di Corte l'anno 1787.

Vienna, Gioseppe nob. de Kurzbek, n. d. 84 p. 16½ᶜᵐ.

Two acts. With name of the composer, Domenico **Cimarosa**, but not of the author, Gius. Maria Diodati.

First performed at Vienna, Nationalhoftheater n. d. Burg, May 7, 1787; at Naples, Teatro Nuovo, carnival, 1786.

SCHATZ 1972

Le **trame deluse**—Continued.

— Le **trame deluse**. Dramma giocosa per musica da rappresentarsi nel Teatro di S. A. E. di Sassonia.

> *Dresda, n. publ., 1788. 127 p. 15½^{cm}.*
>
> Two acts, with name of the composer, **Cimarosa**. German title-page, "Die vereitelten raenke," and text face Italian.
> First performed at Dresden, January 3, 1789.   SCHATZ 1973

Le **trame deluse**. O. T. of text of Portugal's A Noiva fingida.

Le **trame per amore**. Commedia per musica di Francesco Cerlone da rappresentarsi nel Teatro Nuovo per terza opera di quest' anno 1783.

> *Napoli, n. publ., 1783. 60 p. 15^{cm}.*
>
> Three acts. Cast, name of **Paisiello** as the composer and note that "per brevità" the third act had to be shortened and would end with the terzetto and that for the same reason minor arias would be dropped.
> First performed at Naples, Teatro Nuovo, October, 1770.   SCHATZ 7681

Le **trame spiritose**. Dramma giocoso per musica da rappresentarsi in Genova nel Teatro da S. Agostino la primavera del 1793 . . .

> *Genova, Stamperia Gesiniana, n. d. 65 p. 14^{cm}.*
>
> Two acts. By Giuseppe Palomba, who is not mentioned. Cast, name of Giacomo Tritta (**Tritto**) as composer and impresario's dedication, in which he says that the opera was heard with applause in the previous pear at Naples, at the Teatro Nuovo.
>   SCHATZ 10475

La **tranquillità disturbata**, ballet. *See* Borghi's Creso rè di Lidia.

Gesaenge aus dem singspiele Der **transport im koffer**, in drey aufzuegen. In musik gesezt von Edmund Weber.

> *Hamburg, Johann Matthias Michaelsen, 1791. 32 p. 16½^{cm}.*
>
> Author not mentioned and unknown to Schatz.
> First performed at Hamburg, Theater beim Gänsemarkt, May 30, 1791.
>   SCHATZ 10916

Trapolin's vagaries. A. T. of The devil of a duke.

Trasibolo Ateniese. *See* M. Curzio.

Trattenimento musicale d'*Apollo con il Reno* nelle nozze sonttuose delli Ill. et Ecc. SS^{ri} il Sig^r Co. Federico Rossi Co. di San Secondo et la Sig^{ra} Donna Orsina Pepoli: *la coronatione d'Apollo per Dafne conversa in lauro* Baletto: *Amore guerriero per la Rocca incantata* Bariera. Pensieri del Sig. Silvestro Branchi il Costante nell' Accademia di Ravvivati, et alcune ottave per le medesime nozze del Sig^r N. S. . . .

> *Bologna, Gio. Paolo Moscatelli, 1621. [72] p. 15^{cm}.*
>
> Pictorial title page. Branchi's dedication is dated Bologna, May 30, 1621. The first piece is divided into "Uscita" 1–2, "Amore guerriero" is one long scene ("barriera") followed by a baletto and the "Coronatione d'Apollo" consists of Uscita 1–6 with the baletto in the last. Ricci attributes all these texts to Silvestro Branchi. He does not mention the composer or composers. That Silvestra Branchi wrote and Ottavio **Vernizzi** (probably) composed at least "La coronatione d'Apollo "is clear since in 1623 an edition of the text was published by the same publisher for performance in the Teatro della Sala in which Branchi is called the author and Vernizzi the composer. In 1623 the text was divided into four "intermezzi," for Branchi's play "L'amorosa innocenza." (*See* "La coronatione d'Apollo").   ML 52.2.T7

Der **traum des Scipio.** Tr. of Nichelmann's Il sogno di Scipione.

The **travellers in Switzerland.** A comic opera, in three acts: as performed at the Theatre Royal, Covent-Garden. By Mr. Bate Dudley . . .

London, J. Debrett, 1794. 80 p. 20^{cm}.

Cast, author's dedication, dated Bradwell Lodge, March 20, 1794, and prefatory note, with name of William **Shield** as composer resp. compiler, and statement that "several of the airs, and all the choruses" were "written to compiled music."
First performed February 22, 1794. Longe 227

Gesaenge zu dem schauspiele Der **travestirte Hamlet,** in drey akten. In musik gesetzt von Tuzeck.

n. i., 1799. 14 p. 16½^{cm}.

The author, Johann Georg Carl Ludwig Giesecke, is not mentioned.
First performed at Vienna, Theater auf der Wieden, July 10, 1794. Schatz 10506

I **tre amanti.** Dramma giocoso per musica da rappresentarsi nel Teatro di via della Pergola nella primavera del MDCCLXXVII . . .

Firenze, Gio. Risaliti, 1777. 66 p. 16^{cm}.

Two acts. Cast and name of **Cimarosa** as the composer. The author is unknown to Schatz. On p. 5–16, cast and description of "Sansone, ballo tragico di invenzione, e composizione del Sig. Antonio Pitrot, posto in scena per la prima volta . . . 1777." The composer of the music is not mentioned. Pitrot remarks (p. 16), "si sono nobilitati i personaggi per maggior proprietà del soggetto!"
First performed at Rome, Teatro Valle dei Signori Capranica, carnival, 1777.
Schatz 1975

— I **tre amanti.** Intermezzo in musica a cinque voci da rappresentarsi nel Piccolo Teatro Elettorale.

Dresda, Stamperia elettorale, 1781. 125 p. 15½^{cm}.

Two acts, with name of the composer, **Cimarosa.** German title-page, "Die drey liebhaber," and text face Italian.
First performed, as indicated, March 10, 1781. Schatz 1976

Li **tre amanti ridicoli.** Dramma per musica di Ageo Liteo da rappresentarsi nel Teatro della Fama de' Nobili di Gubbio nel corrente carnevale dell' anno 1765 . . .

Gubbio, Giuseppe Bartolini, n. d. 53 p. 15½^{cm}.

Three acts. By Antonio Galuppi who is not mentioned. Cast, dedication, and name of Baldassare **Galuppi** as composer.
First performed at Venice, Teatro di S. Moisè, carnival, 1761. Schatz 3471

Le **tre burle.** A. T. of Salieri's Falstaff.

Li **tre cicisbei ridicoli.** Dramma giocoso per musica da recitarsi nella fiera dell' Ascensione dell' anno 1748. Nel Teatro di Sant' Angelo.

Venezia, Modesto Fenzo, 1748. 59 p. 15^{cm}.

Three acts. By Carlo Antonio Vasini, who is not mentioned. Cast and name of Natale **Resta** as the composer. Additional or substitute arias, "Arsa d'interno adore" (p. 45) and "Basta cosi, t'intendo" (p. 59), are inserted on slips.
Schatz 8692

I tre difensori della patria. Dramma per musica da rappresentarsi nel Teatro di Sant' Angelo l'autunno dell' anno MDCCXXIX . . .

Venezia, Marino Rossetti, 1729. *46 p.* *15½ᶜᵐ.*

Three acts. By Adriano Morselli, who is not mentioned, and whose original title was "Tullo Ostilio." Dedication, argument, scenario, cast, and name of Giovanni Battista **Pescetti** as the composer. Schatz 7961

— Tullo Ostilio. Dramma per musica da rappresentarsi nel Teatro di San Angelo l'anno 1740 . . .

Venezia, Marino Rossetti, 1740. *48 p.* *15ᶜᵐ.*

Three acts. Neither Adriano Morselli, the author, nor Giovanni Battista **Pescetti**, the composer, is mentioned. Impresario's dedication, argument, and cast. Noticeably different from the earlier "I tre difensori della patria." For instance, the opening chorus in the latter, "Queste spoglie, o invitta Roma," is absent from the 1740 ed. Schatz 7962

Li tre Eugenj. Commedia per musica di un atto di G. B. L., P. A. Da rappresentarsi nel Teatro Nuovo sopra Toledo nel carnovale del corrente anno 1778.

Napoli, n. publ., 1778. *39 p.* *15ᶜᵐ.*

Text by Giovanni Battista Lorenzi. Cast and name of Francesco **Lenzi** as composer. Schatz 5551

Le tre fanatiche. Commedia per musica di Giuseppe Palomba da rappresentarsi nel Real Teatro del Fondo di Separazione nel carnovale di quest' anno 1785 . . .

Napoli, n. publ., 1785. *48 p.* *15½ᶜᵐ.*

Two acts. Cast and name of composer, Gaetano **Andreozzi**. The impresario's dedication is dated January 25, 1785. Schatz 204

I tre gobbi rivali. Intermezzo a quattro voci da cantarsi dalla compagnia de' Comici Lombardi nel Teatro de' Fiorentini nel carnovale del 1783.

Napoli, n. publ., 1783. *21 p.* *15ᶜᵐ.*

Two acts. A much altered, shorter version of "La favola de' tre gobbi," by Carlo Goldoni, who is not mentioned. Dedicatory poem, cast, and remark: "La sinfonia e la musica segnata col segno + è del Sig. D. Vincenzo **Fabrizi** Romano." This applies to "Mi corrono d'intorno," "Dico bene-certo ardore," "Per servirvi, e cortegiar," etc. The text of these arias does not appear to be by Goldoni. In the first intermezzo only his "Vezzosa gradita" was retained. In the second, whereas the arias "Corpo di Bacco / Son Parpagnacco," "Vi prego di core" and "Se vi guardo ben" are in the original version, "Seu tanto benedetti" and "Che bella cosa ch'è" are not by Goldoni at all. Schatz 2972

I tre matrimoni. Commedia in musica da rappresentarsi nel Teatro Grimani di S. Samuele l'autunno dell' anno MDCCLVI.

Venezia, Modesto Fenzo, 1756. *52 p.* *14½ᶜᵐ.*

Cast, scenario, and name of the composer, Nicola **Calandra**, *detto* Frascia. Librettist unknown to Schatz. Schatz 1474

De tre ønsker. A. T. of Philidor's Skovhuggeren.

I tre Orazj e i tre Curiazj, ballet. *See* Bertoni's Telemaco ed Eurice.

Le tre orfanelle o sia La scola di musica. Dramma giocoso di un atto solo per musica del Sig. Giovanni Bertati . . . da rappresentarsi nel nobilissimo Teatro Venier in San Benedetto l'autunno dell' anno 1798.

Venezia, Modesto Fenzo, 1798. 32 p. 18ᶜᵐ.

Cast and name of **Bernardini**, (Marcello di Capua) as composer. Sᴄʜᴀᴛᴢ 847

Li tre Orfei. Dramma giocoso per musica da rappresentarsi nel nobile Teatro Tron in S. Cassiano nell' autunno dell' anno 1787.

Venezia, n. publ., n. d. 60 p. 16ᶜᵐ.

Two acts. Cast. Neither the composer, Marcello **Bernardini** (Marcello di Capua) is mentioned, nor the author, who is unknown to Schatz.
First performed at Rome, Teatro della Palla a Corda, carnival, 1784. Sᴄʜᴀᴛᴢ 848

Gli tre pretendenti. Dramma giocoso per musica da rappresentarsi in Bologna nel Teatro Marsigli Rossi la primavera dell' anno 1777 . . .

Bologna, Sassi, n. d. 67 p. 15ᶜᵐ.

Three acts. Impresario's dedication, cast, scenario, and name of the composer, Giovanni Battista **Borghi**, but not of the librettist. The *imprimatur* is dated May 21, 1777.
Schatz lists this as being the same as Giovanni Bertati's text of "La donna instabile." The two texts, indeed, begin "Don Testaccio mio carissimo" and they have now and then other matter in common, as, for instance, the finale of the second act, "Non si faccia più rumore." It is therefore clear, that the "Gli tre pretendenti" text is somewhat related to that of "La donna instabile," but on the whole the two texts have very little in common and are practically two different texts. Sᴄʜᴀᴛᴢ 1230

I tre rivali in amore. Farsa per musica a 5. voci da rappresentarsi nel Teatro Valle degl' illm̃i Sig. Capranica. Il carnevale dell' anno 1789.

Roma, Gioacchino Puccinelli, n. d. 48 p. 16½ᶜᵐ.

Two acts. The author not mentioned and unknown to Schatz. Cast and name of Ferdinando **Robuschi** as the composer. Sᴄʜᴀᴛᴢ 8845

Li tre vagabondi. Dramma giocoso per musica da rappresentarsi nel nobile Teatro Tron di San Cassiano nell' autunno dell' anno 1776 . . .

Venezia, Gio. Battista Casali, 1776. 63 p. 17ᶜᵐ.

Three acts. Author not mentioned and unknown to Schatz. Impresario's dedication, cast, scenario, and name of Salvatore **Perillo** as the composer. Sᴄʜᴀᴛᴢ 7927

Treu in der untreue. Tr. of Cimarosa's L'infedeltà fedele.

Die treuen koehler, eine operette in zwey aufzuegen, von herrn Herrmann in Weimar. In musik gesezt von herrn musikdirektor Knecht in Biberach. Wird den 29 juni auch 2ten und 4ten julii 1789 allhier zu Kaufbeuren auf dem gewoehnlichen Theater der burgerlichen Agenten A. C. aufgefuehrt.

Kaufbeuren, Dorn, n. d. Unpaged. 16ᶜᵐ.

Cast and "historischer vorbericht," at end of which price of tickets, rules about admission, etc.
First performed at Biberach, Theater der evangelischen Meister Sänger Gesellschaft im Schlachthause, February 2, 1786. Sᴄʜᴀᴛᴢ 5198

Die **treuen koehler,** eine operette in zween aufzuegen von Heermann. In musik gesezt von L. Schubaur der medizin doktor. Aufgefuehrt auf dem churfuerstl. Nationaltheater in Muenchen 1786.

Muenchen, Joseph Lindauer, n. d. 1 p. l., 120 p. 15½ᶜᵐ.

Dedication signed by the composer, Lukas **Schubauer,** and his "Vorrede" in which he narrates "die geschichte des saechsischen prinzenraubes," on which the operetta is based.

First performed, as indicated, September 29, 1786.   SCHATZ 9712

Die **treuen koehler,** eine operette in zween aufzuegen.

Weimar, Carl Ludolf Hoffmann, 1773. 7 p. l. (incl. front.), 182 p. 14½ᶜᵐ.

By Gottlob Ephraim Heermann, who is not mentioned. Dedication, argument, name of Ernst Wilhelm **Wolf** as the composer, and note:

"Auf dem herzoglichen Hoftheater zu Weimar, von der zur zeit anwesenden koenigl. Grosbritannischen Seilerischen Gesellschaft aufgefuehret, den 2ten des Brachmonats."

First performed at Weimar, Schlosstheater in der Wilhelmsburg, July 14, 1772.   SCHATZ 11085

Le **tribunal de la chicane.** A. T. of Philidor's L'huitre et les plaideurs.

Il **tributo campestre.** Componimento pastorale drammatico da rappresentarsi in musica nel Regio Ducale Teatro nuovo di Mantova in occasione del felicissimo passaggio di Sua Maestà Maria Carolina . . . sposa di Sua Maestà Ferdinando IV. di Borbone, rè delle Due Sicilie [engraved ports. of both]

Mantova, per l'erede di Alberto Pazzoni, 1768. 5 p. l. (incl. front.), 30 p. 23ᶜᵐ.

One act. Numerous vignettes, cast, and names of Tommaso **Trajetta** as composer and of librettist, Giovanni Battista Buganza.   SCHATZ 10401

Tributo di rispetto e d'amore. Componimento drammatico, scritto dall' autore . . . l'anno 1754, ed eseguito con musica del Reutter nell' interno della Corte imperiale dalle tre AA. RR. . . . festeggiando il giorno di nascita dell' augusto loro genitore.

[189]–196 p. 26ᶜᵐ. (Metastasio, Opere, t. xi, Parigi, vedova Herissant, 1782.)   ML 49.A2M44

Trick for trick. A comedy of two acts. As it is perform'd at the Theatre-Royal in Drury-Lane, by His Majesty's servants. By R. Fabian . . .

London, J. Watts, 1735. 4 p. l., 36 p. 19ᶜᵐ.

Interspersed with ten songs, sung to popular airs, which are printed in the text, with their titles. Cast, table of the songs, and dedication.

First performed, as indicated, May 10, 1735.   ML 50.5.T84

Second copy. LONGE 40
Third copy. LONGE 262

A **trick to cheat the devil.** A. T. of Imposture defeated.

Le **triomphe d'Alcide.** A. T. of Lully's Alceste.

Le **triomphe de Flore.** *See* Dauvergne's Eglé.

Le **triomphe de l'amitié.** A. T. of Sacchini's L'Olympiade.

Le triomphe de l'amour. Divertissement en musique orné de ballets pour le carnaval de l'année 1725.

Dresde, Jean Conrad Stössel, n. d. [56] p. 19ᶜᵐ.

Prologue and five entrées. Cast, names of Poisson as author, of Louis **André** as composer, and Avertissement, which reads, in part:
"Ceci n'est point ouvrage dramatique, qui renferme un sujet intrigué, suivi, & denoüé; ce n'est à proprement parler que ce qu'on nomme un ballet: On y trouvera cependant tous les spectacles, & tous les agrémens de nos grands opera françois . . ."
First performed at Dresden, Hoftheater, February 12, 1725.   ML 50.2.T7
Second copy.   SCHATZ 193

Le triomphe de l'amour. Ballet, dansé devant Sa Majesté à S. Germain en Laye. Suivant la copie imprimée à Paris.

[Amsterdam, Antoine Schelte], 1686. 47 p. (incl. front.). 13½ᶜᵐ.

Twenty entrées, with the names of the participants. On p. [29]–47, the "Vers pour la personne et le personnage de ceux qui sont du ballet du Triomphe de l'Amour." Neither authors nor composer mentioned. *See* next entry.   ML 49.A2L9

— **Le triomphe de l'amour,** ballet representé par l'Academie royale de musique l'an 1681. Les paroles sont de M. Quinault & la musique de M. de Lully, XIII. opera.

n. i., n. d. 14ᶜᵐ. front., 269–298 p. (Recueil général des opéra, t. ii, Paris, 1703.)

Detached copy. Twenty entrées. Text partly by Benserade. (*See* his Oeuvres, t. ii.)
First performed, as indicated, April 15, 1681 (Schatz), May 6 (Prunières); at Saint-Germain en Laye, before the court, January 21, 1681. On September 11, 1705, the ballet was revived, but reduced to four entrées and prologue by Danchet and Campra.   SCHATZ 5774
Second copy.   ML 48.R4

— **Le triomphe de l'Amour,** ballet dansé devant Sa Majesté, à Saint Germain en Laye le . . . janvier 1681.

Le Théatre de Monsieur Quinault, Paris, 1739, t. v., pl., [69]–104 p. 17ᶜᵐ.

Twenty entrées. On p. [105]–126: "Vers pour la personne et le personnage de ceux qui sont du ballet du Triomphe de l'Amour." Those participating are mentioned by name. **Lully,** the composer, is not mentioned.   PQ 1881.A1 1739

Le triomphe de l'Amour sur Bacchus. Entrée in Duplessis' Les festes nouvelles.

Le triomphe de l'harmonie, ballet-heroique représenté par l'Académie royale de musique, l'an 1737. Paroles de Mʳ Le Franc, musique de Mʳ Grenet. CXXVIII. opera.

n. i., n. d. 429–478 p. 14½ᶜᵐ. (Recueil général des opéra, Paris, 1745, t. xvi.)

Detached copy. Prologue and entrées, "Orphée," "Hylas," "Amphion."
First performed, as indicated, May 9, 1737.   ML 48.R4

Le triomphe de la raison sur l'amour, pastorale mise en musique par Monsieur de Lully . . . Representée à Fontainebleau.

Amsterdam, Henry Schelte, 1699. 15 p. (incl. front.). 15ᶜᵐ.

One act. Author not mentioned, and unknown to Schatz. The composer was Jean Baptiste de **Lully,** the younger.
First performed, as indicated, October 25, 1696.   ML 50.2.T8L9

Le triomphe de Thalie. *See* Mouret's Les festes de Thalie.

Le **triomphe de Vénus.**　*See* Campra's Trois nouvelles entrées.

Le **triomphe des arts,** ballet representé par l'Academie royale de musique l'an 1700.　Les paroles de M. de la Mothe, & la musique de M. d la Barre.　XLIX. opera.

> *n. i., n. d.　front., 48 p.　14ᶜᵐ.　(Recueil général des opéra, Paris, 1703, t. vii.)*
>
> Five entrées.　Dedicatory poem and "avertissement," with argument.
> First performed at Paris, Académie royale de musique, May 16, 1700.
>
> Schatz 5344
> Second copy.　ML 48.R4

Le **triomphe des sens.**　*See* Mouret's Le ballet des sens.

I **trionfi del fato.**　O. T. of Steffani's Il trionfo del fato.

I **trionfi di Goffredo in Gerusalemme.**　Cantata da rappresentarsi nel Teatro del Pubblico della città di Pisa in occasione del primo faustissimo arrivo in detta città di S. A. R. Francesco III . . . granduca di Toscana.

> *Pisa, Evangelista Pugli, 1739.　35 p.　20½ᶜᵐ.*
>
> Dedication, argument, "Annotazioni" (p. 19–24, 34–35), argument, "Interlocutori," name of cavaliere avvocato Pio dal Borgo as author and Michele **Fini** as composer.
>
> Schatz 3106

Il **trionfo d'amore.**　Questa festa teatrale fu, sotto il titolo di Asilio d'Amore, scritta dall' autore in Vienna, e rappresentata la prima volta in Lintz l'anno 1732 . . .　L'anno 1765 poi venne in gran parte cambiata dall' autore medesimo per adattarla col nuovo titolo di *Trionfo d'amore* alla circostanza delle reali nozze di Giuseppe II, e Maria Giuseppa di Baviera . . . e fra le altre festive solennità fu da cantori, e cantatrici con musica del Gasman eseguita . . . negli appartamenti dell' imperial soggiorno di Schönbrunn.

> *[267]–292 p.　26ᶜᵐ.　(Metastasio, Opere, t. ix, Parigi, vedova Herissant, 1781.)*
>
> One act.　　　　　　　　　　　　　　　　　　　　　　ML 49.A2M44

Il **trionfo d'amore.**　Azione teatrale rappresentata in musica nella Imperial Regia Corte in occasione delle felicissime nozze delle Sacre Reali Maestà di Giuseppe II. d'Austria e di Maria Gioseffa di Baviera . . . l'anno MDCCLXV.

> *Milano, Giuseppe Cairoli, n. d.　42, [1] p.　17ᶜᵐ.*
>
> One act.　Neither Metastasio, the author, nor Florian Leopold **Gassmann**, the composer, is mentioned.　The imprimatur is dated February 27, 1765.
> First performed at Schönbrunn, Schlachtensaal of the Imperial palace, January 25, 1765.　　　　　　　　　　　　　　　Schatz 3628

Il **trionfo d'amore.**　Azione pastorale in un solo atto da rappresentarsi nel teatro novamente costrutto a questo solo fine in una delle corti del Ducal Palazzo di Luisburgo all' occasione, ed in seguito della superba festa ivi data li 16 febbraio 1763.　La poesia è del Signor de Tagliazucchi . . .　La musica è di nuova composizione del Signor Jommel i . . .　I balli sono del Signor Noverre . . .

> *[Stuttgardt], Cotta, n. d.　53 p.　18ᶜᵐ.*
>
> One act.　Argument, cast.　German title-page, "Der triumph des Amors," and text face Italian.　Not to be confused with Jommelli's "L'Endimione."　Schatz 4872

Il trionfo d'amore. A. T. of Jommelli's L'Endimione.

Il trionfo d'amore. Favola pastorale da rappresentarsi in musica in Mantova l'anno MDCCIV . . .

   Mantova, Alberto Pazzoni, n. d. 72 p. 15^{cm}.

   Three acts. Author not mentioned and unknown to Schatz. Dedication dated Mantova, December 19, 1703, cast, scenario, and (at end) note: "La musica è del Sig. Antonio **Quintavalle**, organista di camera del Ser. padrone." On p. 69–71 text of eight "Arie mutate." ML 50.2.T81Q3

Il trionfo d'amore. *See* Traetta's Le feste d'Imeneo.

Il trionfo d'Arbace, ballet. *See* Nasolini's La morte di Semiramide.

Il trionfo d'Arianna con balli, e cori analoghi al soggetto. Dramma per musica del nobile Signore Carlo Lanfranchi Rossi . . . frà gli Arcadi Egesippo Argolide da rappresentarsi nel Teatro Giustiniani in San Moisè per la fiera dell' Ascensione dell' anno 1781.

   Venezia, Modesto Fenzo, n. d. 44 p. 17^{cm}.

   Two acts. Author's dedicatory sonnet, argument, cast, and name of Pasquale **Anfossi** as composer. SCHATZ 271

Il trionfo d'Arianna. Dramma con cori e balli analoghi composto d'ordine sovrano da Antonio de' Filistri . . . e messo in musica dal Signor Vincenzo Righini . . . da rappresentarsi nel gran Teatro Reale di Berlino.

   Berlino, Haude e Spener, 1796. 111 p. 16½^{cm}.

   Three acts. Argument and cast. German title-page, "Der triumph der Ariadne," and text face Italian.

   Performed in 1796, as indicated; first performed at the same theatre, December 28, 1793. SCHATZ 8788

Il trionfo d'Arianna o sia Arianna abbandonata da Teseo e soccorsa da Bacco, ballet. *See* Alessandri's I puntigli gelosi.

Il trionfo d'Armida. Drama per musica da' rappresentarsi nel Teatro Giustiniano A. S. Moisè l'anno 1726.

   Venezia, Marino Rossetti, n. d. 43 p. 15½^{cm}.

   Three acts. By Girolamo Colatelli, who is not mentioned. Scenario and notice to the reader with name of Tommaso **Albinoni** as composer.

   First performed in the fall of 1726, as indicated. SCHATZ 132

Il trionfo d'Augusto in Egitto. Opera in musica. Dedicata, e cantata all' Ecc.^{ma} Sig.^{ra} D. Anna Antonia . . . nelle sue nozze coll' Ecc.^{mo} Sig.^r D. Gaspar Teller Girone, Gomez di Sandovale, duca d'Ossuna . . . Nel Regio Teatro di Milano l'anno 1672.

   Milano, Marc' Antonio Randolfo Malatesta, n. d. 4 p. l., 107 p. 16^{cm}.

   Prologue and three acts. Dedication to the ladies and sonnett to D. Anna Antonia. Author (Carlo Maria Maggi) and composer (unknown to Schatz) not mentioned. SCHATZ 11372

Il trionfo d'Ercole in Troia o sia Esione liberata, ballet. *See* Martin y Soler's Una cosa rara.

Il trionfo de' Goti. A. T. of the ballet Gli sventurati amori di Cleide ed Almindo.

Il trionfo de' pupilli oppressi. Commedia per musica di Pasquale Mililotti da rappresentarsi nel Nuovo Teatro de' Fiorentini per quart' opera di questo corrente anno 1782.

Napoli, n. publ., 1782. 56 p. 15ᶜᵐ.

Three acts. Cast and name of Salvatore **Rispoli** as the composer. SCHATZ 8813

Il trionfo de' Spagnoli o sia La disfatta de' Marrocchini, ballet. *See* Bernardini's Amore per incanto.

Il trionfo del bel sesso. Dramma giocoso in musica da rappresentarsi nel Teatro alla Scala di Milano l'autunno del 1799.

Milano, Gio. Batista Bianchi, n. d. 76, [2] p. 16½ᶜᵐ.

Two acts. By Luigi Romanelli, who is not mentioned. Cast, scenario, and name of Giuseppe **Nicolini** as composer. On p. [69]–76, argument, cast, and description of Gaspare Ronzi's "Ottocaro, ballo eroico pantomimo in cinque atti." Neither of this, nor of his "ballo comico Il segreto," is the composer of the music mentioned.

First performed, as indicated, August 20, 1799. SCHATZ 7138

Il trionfo del bel sesso. A. T. of P. v. Winter's Ogus.

Il trionfo del ben pubblico. *See* M. Curzio.

Il trionfo del valore. A. T. of the ballet Amor può tutto.

Il trionfo dell' amicizia. A. T. of the ballet Lauso e Lidia.

Il trionfo dell' amore & della costanza. Der triumph der liebe und bestaendigkeit, wurde [vignette] in einem sing-spiel auf dem Hamburgischen Schau Platz fuergestellet im monath Januarius, 1718.

Hamburg, Friedrich Conrad Greflinger, n. d. Unpaged. 19ᶜᵐ.

German version by Johann Joachim Hoe, with scenario and very long argument, in which we read:

". . . dieses von fuernehmer hand herstammende schau-spiel [ist] auf dem Schauplatz zu Wien, wiewohl auf eine gantz andere art, in welscher sprache fuergestellet und von dem beruehmten kayserl. capellmeister Mons. Conty [Francesco Bartolomeo **Conti**] in die music gebracht worden: Selbige ist von dem verfasser der teutschen poesie, anlangend die Arien ausser zwey oder drey schertzhaffte durchgehends behalten worden, um den versuch zu thun, ob man nicht einige teutsche dem italiaenischen metro gleichfoermige arien, verfertigen koenne, welche der schoenheit der music, dem von dem musico wohl beobachteten nachdrucke der woerter und der reinlichkeit [!!] der teutschen sprache nicht entgegen stuenden . . ."

The libretto contains practically only German text, but about half of the arias appear also in Italian.

The Italian original, by Francesco Ballerini (von Weilen), was first performed at Vienna, Hoftheater, January 21, 1711. SCHATZ 2199

Il trionfo dell' Amore fra i pastori, ballet. *See* Sarti's Giulio Sabino.

Il trionfo dell' Arno. Componimento drammatico fatto rappresentare nel Teatro del Pubblico della città di Pisa da XII cavalieri . . . per festeggiare il primo faustissimo arrivo in detta città de serenissimi sposi Pietro Leopoldo, arciduca d'Austria . . . e Maria Luisa, infanta di Spagna . . . in Pisa l'anno MDCCLXVI.

[Pisa], Pompeo Polloni, n. d. xxvii p. 25ᶜᵐ.

Two acts. Dedication. Cav. Pio dal Borgo is mentioned as author, Giovanni Gualberto **Brunetti** as composer. SCHATZ 1366

Il trionfo dell' innocenza. A. T. of Gius. Rossi's Pietro il Grande.

Il trionfo della continenza. Drama per musica da rappresentarsi nel famosissimo Teatro di SS. Gio. e Paolo l'anno 1691 di Giulio Cesare Corradi . . .

Venetia, Nicolini, 1691. 60 p. 14^cm.

Three acts. Argument, scenario, and name of Francesco Paris **Algisi** as composer. Schatz gives the fall of 1690 as time of first performance, which would seem to be contradicted by the information in the title and the date of imprint. Schatz 161

Il trionfo della costanza. Dramma semi-serio da rappresentarsi in musica nel Teatro di S. A. Serenissima il Signor Principe di Carignano nella primavera dell' anno MDCCLXIX.

Torino, Onorato Derossi, n. d. 52 p. 14½^cm.

Three acts. Cast, scenario, name of the author, G. M. d'Orengo, and of the composer, Carlo **Defranchi** (Franchi). Schatz 3329

Il trionfo della costanza. Opera tragicomica per musica, composta . . . da Domenico Poggi per solennizare il giorno natalizio di S. A. Reale Filippina Carlotta . . .

Bronsvic, n. publ., 1790. 76 p. 16^cm.

Two acts. Argument, scenario, and name of Johann Gottfried **Schwanberg** as the composer.

First performed at Brunswick, Hoftheater, March 13, 1790. Schatz 9767

Il trionfo della costanza in Statira vedova d'Alessandro. Drama per musica da rappresentarsi nel Teatro di S. Angelo. Il carnovale dell' anno 1731.

Venezia, Carlo Buonarrigo, n. d. 36 p. 14½^cm.

Three acts. By Bartolomeo Vitturi, who is not mentioned. Cast, name of Antonio **Galeazzi** as composer, scenario, and argument, in which we read: "Della Statira di Monsieur Pradon furono tratti i caratteri, e l'argomento del presente dramma, ma poi diversamente sceneggiato per accomodarlo all' uso dell' Italiano Musicale Teatro." Schatz 3418

Il trionfo della fedeltà. Dramma pastorale per musica di E.[rme-linda] T.[alèa] P.[astorella] A.[rcada]

Dresda, la vedova Stössel e Giovanni Carlo Krause, 1754. 8 fold. pl. (of which the last six numbered 1–6 and incl. front.), port., 63 p. 22½^cm.

The plates were engraved by L. Zucchi after paintings by (1–5) B. Müllers and (6–8) J. Roos. The portrait was designed by Steffano Torelli and engraved by L. Zucchi. It represents in profile "Ermelind. Tal. P. A.," indicating as in the title-page the Arcadian name of Maria Antonia Walpurgis, princess of Saxony, who wrote both text and music of this opera, though neither was wholly her work. It is known from her letters that she submitted her text to Metastasio for corrections and that **Hasse,** her teacher, composed part of the music, though his name appears neither in the libretto nor in the published score of the opera.

First performed at Dresden, Regio Elettoral Teatro, summer of 1754. Schatz 5949

Il trionfo della innocenza. Drama per musica da rappresentarsi nel Teatro di S. Angelo, l'anno 1692. Di D. Rinaldo Cialli . . .

Venetia, Nicolini, 1692. 58 p. 15^cm.

Three acts. Author's dedication, argument, scenario, and notice to the reader with name of Antonio **Lotti** as composer. Schatz 5724

Il trionfo della libertà. Tragedia per musica. Da rappresentarsi nel famosissimo Teatro Grimano di S. Gio. Grisostomo. L'anno 1707.

Venezia, Marino Rossetti, 1707. 84 p. 15^cm.

Five acts. By conte Girolamo Frigimelica Roberti, who is not mentioned and who filled 24 of the 84 p. with lengthy notices to the reader, notizia istorica, notizia poetica, L'azione, Il nodo, etc., etc. Scenario and name of Alessandro **Scarlatti** as the composer. Schatz 9525

Il **trionfo della pace.** Festa teatrale per musica da rappresentarsi nel Regio Teatro di Torino nella primavera del 1782 alla presenza delle Maestà Loro.

Torino, Onorato Derossi, n. d. viii, 40 p. 15½cm.

Two acts. Argument, cast, scenario, and names of the composer, Francesco **Bianchi**, and the librettist, Cesare Oliveri. On p. 36–39 description, argument, and cast of "L'inaspettata consolazione nelle sventure, ballo eroicomico." The second ballet was called "Rinaldo nel giardino incantato d'Armida." Both were by Domenico Ricciardi and composed by Vittorio Amedeo Canavasso. SCHATZ 991

Il **trionfo della pace.** Dramma per musica da rappresentarsi per l'aprimento del nuovo Regio-Ducal Teatro in Mantova la primavera dell' anno 1783 . . .

Mantova, per l'erede di Alberto Pazzoni, n. d. 70 p. 16cm.

Two acts. Dedicatory poem, argument, cast, scenario, and names of Cesare Oliveri as author, of Giuseppe **Sarti** as the composer ("La musica sarà"). On p. [49]–70 prefatory note, argument, cast, scenario, and description of Innocenzo Gambuzzi's ballets (music by Antonio Bonazzi) "Enea nel Lazio ed Il pellegrinaggio o sia La vindemmia fiamminga, ballo piacevole—pantomimo."
First performed, as indicated, May 10, 1783. SCHATZ 9478

Il **trionfo della pazzia.** A. T. of Bernardini's Il fonte d'acqua gialla.

Il **trionfo della virtù.** Dramma per musica da rappresentarsi nel famosissimo Teatro Grimani di San Gio. Grisostomo l'autunno dell' anno MDCCXXIV . . .

Venezia, Marino Rossetti, n. d. 58 p. 16cm.

Three acts. As appears from the notice to the reader, altered and condensed to six characters from eight by unknown author from original text by Pietro d'Averara, who is not mentioned. Dedication, argument, cast, scenario, and name of Giovanni Francesco **Brusa.** SCHATZ 1375

Il **trionfo della virtù.** A. T. of von Schacht's La festa interotta.

Il **trionfo di Alessandro** o sia La disfatto di Dario, ballet. *See* Cimarosa's Oreste.

Il **trionfo di Alessandro** o sia La disfatta di Dario, ballet. *See* Sarti's Medonte.

Il **trionfo di Allesandro** ossia La prigionia di Dario, ballet. *See* Paisiello's Elfrida.

Il **trionfo di Alessandro** o sia La prigionia di Dario, ballet. *See* Piticchio's Il militare amante.

Il **trionfo di Alessandro** o sia La prigionia di Dario, ballet. *See* Zanetti's Didone abbandonata.

Il **trionfo di Amore e di Marte,** drama da rappresentarsi nel nobilissimo Theatro Zane di S. Moisè. L'anno 1689. Dell' abbate Paolo Emilio Badì, dottore de l'una, e l'altra legge . . .

Venetia, Zamaria Rossi, 1689. 5 p. l., 46 p. 14cm.

Three acts. Author's dedication, argument, scenario, and notice to the reader with name of Antonio **Lombardini** as composer. SCHATZ 5679

Il **trionfo di Arianna,** ballet. *See* Tarchi's La Virginia.

Il **trionfo di Bacco.**   A. T. of Bernardini's Il barone a forza.

Il **trionfo di Camilla, regina de' Volsci.**   Dramma per musica di Silvio Stampiglia, tra gl'Arcadi Palemone Licurio . . .

Napoli, Domenico Antonio Parrino e Michele Luigi Mutio, 1696. *2 p. l., 83 p.   13^{cm}.*

Three acts.   Argument.   T.-p. and list of characters have been supplied in ms., as above.   This was evidently done under the impression that the copy is one of the Naples ed. (1696) of Marc Antonio **Bononcini's** opera, but as Wotquenne's catalogue proves, this should have 6 p. l., 70 p., not 2 p. l., 83 p.!   Consequently, our imperfect copy belongs to some other edition.   It is distinctly different from the next entry.

SCHATZ 1206

— **Camilla, regina de' Volsci.**   Drama da rappresentarsi in musica nel famoso Teatro Vendramino l'anno 1698 . . .

Venetia, Girolamo Albrizzi, 1698.   59 p.   14½^{cm}.

Three acts.   Publisher's dedication, dated Venice, October 4, 1698, scenario, argument, and prefatory note, in which it is stated:
"E convenuto ridurlo con molta fatica à quella brevità, ch'e indispensabilmente necessaria al costume delle nostre scene."
Accordingly, the first act has 17 scenes, the second 15, the third 12, as against 15, 18, 15 in our imperfect copy.   Also, the text differs noticeably in scenes otherwise the same.   For instance, imperf. copy has, in Scene I, act I, *Camilla*, "Ma più di voi son' io misera figlia;"   Venice (1698) has, "O d'infelice rè misera figlia."   In the latter the opera ends with a quartet, "Amore nel mio core;" the imperf. copy with a chorus, "A tanto giubilo."   The opera became known under many titles besides the two here given: "Regina de' Volsci," "La fede in cimento o sia, Camilla, regina de' Volsci," "Amore per amore," "La rinovata Camilla."

SCHATZ 1208

— Il **trionfo di Camilla regina de' Volsci**, drama per musica di Silvio Stampiglia tra gl' Arcadi Palemone Licurio.   Da rappresentarsi nel Teatro da S. Sebastiano l'anno 1701 . . .

Livorno, Jacopo Valisi, 1701.   72 p.   13^{cm}.

Three acts.   Dedication, argument, scenario.   The composer, probably Marc' Antonio **Bononcini**, is not mentioned.

ML 50.2.T82B9

— **Camilla.**   An opera.   As it is perform'd at the Theatre Royal in Drury-Lane, by Her Majesty's servants.

London, Jacob Tonson, 1706.   3 p. l., 38, [2] p.   21½^{cm}.

On last (unnumb.) page, publisher's book list.
Three acts, prologue, and epilogue.   Cast and dedication by "Owen Swiny," which reads, in part:
"The mighty encouragement musick has lately met with in England, is not only an effect of the true taste our nobility and gentry entertain of that nice science, but an instance that we have some among us, who may be able in time to bring it into a setled reputation.   Hitherto it seem'd confin'd to the more Southern climates, as if it had been the peculiar product of those happier countries;   and languish'd, like tender exoticks, when remov'd into our colder region.   But some late attempts have made it appear, that the English genius is not so inharmonious, but that a publick encouragement may render us capable of contending for the mastery with the Italians themselves.
"This consideration made me ambitious of addressing the following essay to Your Ladyship [Lady Wharton], which is design'd to introduce a foreign composition, that may serve at present to give us a taste of the Italian musick, and in time prove a foil to the English . . ."
Owen MacSwiney mentions neither Stampiglia, whose "Il trionfo di Camilla" he simply translated, nor M. A. **Bononcini.**   Nor does he mention Niccolo Francesco Haym.   If Grove's Dictionary says:
"*Camilla* (adapted from Buononcini, to a libretto by Owen Mac Swiney) was Haym's first opera, produced at Drury Lane, April 30, 1706."
this information is partly misleading, partly incorrect, since a comparison between the score of "The songs . . . in Camilla" (London, Walsh) and the ms. score of Bononcini's opera proves that the latter was performed at London practically intact, without additions by Haym or any other composer.

LONGE 132

Il trionfo di Cesare in Egitto, ballet. *See* Monza's Cleopatra.

Il trionfo di Clelia. Dramma scritto . . . dall' autore in Vienna, e rappresentato nella Cesarea Corte la prima volta, con musica dell' Hasse . . . in occasione del felicissimo parto di S. A. R. l'arciduchessa Isabella di Borbone l'anno 1762.

pl., [3]–94 p. 26ᶜᵐ. (Metastasio, Opere, t. ix, Parigi, vedova Herissant, 1781.)

Three acts. Argument.   ML 49.A2M44

Il trionfo di Clelia. Dramma del celebre Signor abate Pietro Metastasio . . . da rappresentarsi per musica in Bologna nell primavera dell' anno 1763 in occasione della prima apertura del Nuovo Pubblico Peatro inventato dal celebre Sig. Cavaliere Antonio Galli Bibiena . . .

Bologna, Giam Battista Sassi, n. d. 79, [1] p. 21½ᶜᵐ.

Three acts. Argument, cast, scenario, and name of Cristoforo Gluk (**Gluck**) as the composer. With the opera were performed (composers of the music not mentioned) Augusto Hus's ballets. "Il riposo interotto" and "Le fontane incantate" briefly described in the libretto.

First performed, as indicated, May 14, 1763.   ML 48.M2E

Il trionfo di Clelia. Dramma per musica da rappresentarsi in occasione del felicissimo parto di S. A. R. l'arciduchessa Isabella . . . In Vienna l'anno MDCCLXII.

n. i., n. d. Unpaged. 21½ᶜᵐ.

At end: "Vienna, nella Stamperia di Ghelen 1762." Frontispiece, ornamental title page, head and tail pieces, etc., designed by different artists, engraved by A. Tischler.

Three acts. Argument, cast, scenario, and names of Metastasio as author, of Joh. Ad. **Hasse** as composer.

First performed at Vienna, Burgtheater, April 27, 1762.   Schatz 4566

— **Die triumphirende Claelia,** ein theatralisch-musicalisches schauspiel, so bey der gluecklich erfolgten entbindung Ihrer Koenigl. Hoheit . . . Isabella . . . in Wien aufgefuehret worden im jahr 1762. Verfasset von herrn abbate Metastasio . . . und in das teutsche uebersetzt von J. A. E. v. G.

[Wien], Gedruckt mit von Ghelischen schriften, n. d. Unpaged. 15½ᶜᵐ.

Three acts. Translated by Johann Anton, edler von Ghelen. Argument, cast, scenario, and name of **Hasse** as the composer.   Schatz 4567

Il trionfo di Clelia. Dramma per musica da rappresentarsi nel Real Teatro dell' Ajuda nel felicissimo giorno natalizio del fedelissimo monarca D. Giuseppe I . . . nel di 6. giugno, 1774.

[Lisbona], Stamperia reale, n. d. 70 p. 14ᶜᵐ.

Three acts. Argument, cast, scenario, and names of Metastasio as author, of Niccolò **Jommelli** as composer ("nuova composizione," consequently Abert's 1772 on p. 93 of his Jommelli biography would appear to be incorrect). The date in the score at Naples, San Carlo 1757, if correct, would mean that the Lissabon score was a second setting.   Schatz 4883

Il trionfo di Clelia. Dramma per musica da rappresentarsi nel nuovo Teatro di Corte . . . nel carnevale dell' anno MDCCLXXVI. La poesia è dell Sig. abbate Pietro Metastasio . . . La musica è del Sig. Giuseppe Michl . . .

Monaco, Francesco Giuseppe Thuille, n. d. 8 p. l., 145, [42] p. 15^cm.

Three acts. Argument, scenario, and cast. German title page, "Der sieg der Clelia," and text face Italian. The unpaged part contains in French and Italian cast and description of Trancart's ballets "Télémaque dans l'isle de Calypso" ("Telemach in der insel der Calipso") and "Venus et Adonis" ("Venus und Adonis"). The composers of the music are not mentioned. SCHATZ 6489

Il trionfo di Clelia. Dramma per musica da rappresentarsi nel Regio Teatro di Torino nel carnovale del 1768 . . .

Torino, Onorato Derossi, n. d. viii, 61, [1] p. · 16^cm.

Three acts. By Metastasio, who is not mentioned. Argument, cast, scenario, and name of Joseph **Misliweczek** as the composer. On p. 59–61 description of the ballets that were performed with the opera. Only the first "Egle e Dafni" had a special title. It was invented by Antonio Pitrot and Giuseppe Antonio Le Messier composed the music.

First performed, as indicated, December 26, 1767. SCHATZ 6531

Il trionfo di Clelia. Nuovo dramma del celebre Antonio Simone Sografi da rappresentarsi in musica nel Teatro grande alla Scala di Milano il carnevale del 1799. Correndo l'anno VII. Repubblicano.

Milano, Gio. Batista Bianchi, n. d. 53, [3] p. 16^cm.

Two acts. Impresario's and author's prefatory notes, cast, scenario, and name of Sebastiano **Nasolini** as the composer ("La musica è tutta nuova"). On p. [27]–36 argument, cast, and description of Urbano Garzia's "Il Bruto Milanese ossia La congiura contro Galeazzo Maria Sforza Visconti, ballo tragico-pantomimo," on p. [55]–56 of his ballet "L'oracolo." The composers of the music are not mentioned.

First performed, as indicated, December 26, 1798. SCHATZ 7028

Second copy. ML 48.A5 v.1

Il trionfo di Clelia, dramma per musica da rappresentarsi nel Regio Teatro di Torino nel carnovale del 1787 . . .

Torino, Onorato Derossi, n. d. viii, 72 p. 15½^cm.

Three acts. By Metastasio, who is not mentioned. Argument, cast, scenario, and name of Angelo **Tarchi** as the composer. On. p. 65–72 cast and description of Sebastiano Gallet's four-act "Il signore benefico, ballo pantomimo,' music by Vittorio Amedeo Canavasso.

First performed, as indicated, December 26, 1786. SCHATZ 10222

Il trionfo di Flavio Olibrio. Drama per musica da rappresentarsi nel famosissimo Teatro Grimani a S. Gio. Grisostomo. Nell' autunno 1726 . . .

Venezia, Marino Rossetti, 1726. 58 p. 15^cm.

Three acts. Later version of "Flavio Anicio Olibrio" by Apostolo Zeno and Pietro Pariati, who are not mentioned. Impresario's dedication dated Venice, November 23, 1726, argument, cast scenario, and name of Giovanni **Porta** as the composer.

SCHATZ 8382

Il trionfo di Gedeone. Dramma sacro per musica da rappresentarsi nel Regio Teatro di via della Pergola la quadragesima del 1798 . . .

Firenze, Stamperia Albizziniana . . . per Pietro Fantosini, 1798. 40 p. 16½^cm.

Two acts. Author not mentioned and unknown to Schatz. Argument, cast, and name of Giuseppe **Moneta** as composer. ("La musica è tutta nuova.")

SCHATZ 6553

Il trionfo di Giuditta o sia La morte d'Oloferne. *See* the A. T.

Il trionfo di Gustavo rè di Svezia, ballet. *See* Paër's Il nuovo Figaro.

Il trionfo di Maggio, vincitor della peste. Favola musicale.

Girolamo Bartolommei Smeducci, Drammi musicali morali, Firenze, 1656, v. i, p. [131]–181. 23^{cm}.

Prologue and three acts. Argument, allegoria, and dedication to Ferdinando II., Gran duca di Toscana, in which he says:
". . . m'avvisai, che potesse per avventura non dispiacere, se con poetico stile Io n'offerissi dipinto l'abbominoso mostro della peste; il quale n'afflisse la bell' Italia, non perdonando alla Toscana. Quindi composi la presente favoletta musicale del Trionfo di Maggio; già che cessò in un tal tempo l'infettante contagio."   ML 49.A2B3

Il trionfo di Pallade in Arcadia. Drama pastorale da rappresentarsi in musica nel carnovale dell' anno 1716 nel Teatro Marsiglj Rossi . . .

Bologna, Costantino Pisarri, 1715. 50, [1] p. 15^{cm}.

Three acts. By conte Otto Mandelli. Dedication dated December 26, 1715, argument, cast, scenario, and name of Floriano **Aresti**, composer, but not of librettist.
         SCHATZ 312

Il trionfo di Rodrigo, ballet. *See* Sarti's Giulio Sabino.

Il trionfo di Scipione in Cartagine. Dramma per musica da rappresentarsi nel Regio Teatro di via della Pergola il carnevale del MDCCXCV . . .

Firenze, Pietro Fantosini, 1795. 36 p.

Three acts. Argument and cast. "La poesia è tutta nuova del Sig. C. M. La musica è espressamente tutta nuova del celebre . . . Giuseppe **Curcio** . . ."
         SCHATZ 2307

Il trionfo improvviso, ballet. *See* Pugnani's Demetrio a Rodi.

A trip to Bath. A. T. of The snuff-box.

A trip to Jamaica. A. T. of The sailor's opera.

A trip to Portsmouth. A. T. of S. Arnold's Britain's glory.

The trip to Portsmouth; a comic sketch of one act, with songs.

London, T. Waller, T. Becket [etc.], n. d. 51 p. 19^{cm}.

Cast, prologue, and Advertisement, in which the author, George Alexander Stephens (not mentioned), says that "these detached scenes," "begun and finished in five days," were inspired "by the late naval review at Portsmouth." The composer, Charles **Dibdin,** is not mentioned.
First performed at London, Haymarket Theatre, August 11, 1773.   LONGE 40

A trip to the Nore. A musical entertainment in one act. As performed by Their Majesty's servants at the Theatre-Royal, Drury-Lane. By Andrew Franklin . . .

London, George Cawthorn, 1797. 22 p. 21^{cm}.

Cast and prefatory note, according to which the text was written in less than a day, "to pay a just tribute of respect and applause to those gallant heroes who distinguished themselves in the late glorious action against the Dutch." The text of the song, "Why, Jack, my fine fellow," is credited, as also the text of the song "O'er the rude rocks," to John Grubb. The final medley is one of four British national airs. The composer and arranger is not mentioned, and is unknown to Schatz, but **Dibdin** contributed "Why, Jack, my fine fellow."
First performed November 9, 1797.   LONGE 244

The **triple wedding.** A. T. of A pill for the doctor.

Gesaenge aus dem singspiele Der **triumpf der liebe,** in vier aufzuegen, von Jester. In musik gesetzt von C. D. Stegmann.

Hamburg, Freystatzky und Rabe, 1796. 72 p. 15½^cm.

First performed at Hamburg, Theater beim Gänsemarkt, April 4, 1796.

SCHATZ 10044

Il **triumfo del fato** oder Das maechtige geschick bei Lavinia und
Dido. Wie solches am 15. [25.] novembris als den glorwuerdigsten
nahmens-tag des . . . Keisers Leopolds in aller-unterthaenigstem
gehorsam auf dem Hamburgischen Schauplatz in einem singe-spiel
auffgefuehret worden im jahr 1699.

n. i., n. d. Unpaged. 16^cm.

Badly cut copy.

Three acts. Neither the translator, Gottlieb Fiedler, nor the composer, Agostino
Steffani, nor the original author, Ortensio Mauro, is mentioned. The original
Italian title was "I trionfi del fato," to which, in the same year, was added the A. T.
"Le glorie d'Enea."

First performed, as "I trionfi del fato," at Hanover, December, 1695.

SCHATZ 10037

Der **triumph der Ariadne.** Tr. of Righini's Il trionfo d'Arianna.

Triumph der grossmuth und treue oder Cleofida, koenigin von
Indien. Tr. of Händel's Poro rè d'Italia.

Der **triumph der liebe und bestaendigkeit.** Tr. of Conti's Il
trionfo dell' amore & della costanza.

Der **triumph der treue.** A. T. of P. Guglielmi's Robert und
Kalliste.

Der **triumph der tugend.** A. T. of von Schacht's Das unterbrochene fest.

Der **triumph des Amors.** A. T. of Jommelli's Endymione, 1759.

Der **triumph des Amors.** Tr. of Jommelli's Il trionfo d'amore,
1763.

Der **triumph des schoenen geschlechts.** Tr. A. T. of P. v.
Winter's Ogus.

The **triumph of beauty.** A. T. of The judgment of Paris, ballad
opera.

The **triumph of conjugal love.** A. T. of Noverre's ballet Alceste.

Airs, chorusses, etc in the **Triumph of mirth**; or, Harlequin's
wedding.

London, n. publ., 1782. 15 p. 20^cm.

Neither author nor composer, Thomas **Linley,** the elder, mentioned.

First performed at London, Drury-Lane, 1782.

ML 52.2.T81

The **triumph of nature.** A. T. of Markoe's libretto The reconciliation.

The **triumph of peace.** A masque, presented by the Foure Honourable Houses, or Innes of court . . . [mutilated] the King and Queenes Ma . . . [mutilated] the Banquetting-house at White Hall, [mutilated] February the third, 1633. Invented and written by James Shirley . . .

London, Printed by John Norton, for William Cooke, 1633. 1 p. l., 8, 24 p. 17ᶜᵐ.

Text contains 9 songs and detailed description. On the last page the note: "The scene and ornament, was the act of Inigo Jones . . . The composition of the musicke, was perform'd by Mr. William **Lawes,** and Mr. Simon **Ives,** whose art gave an harmonious soule to the otherwise languishing numbers." Grove adds Henry **Lawes** as composer.   LONGE 188

The **triumph of peace.** A masque. Perform'd at the Theatre Royal in Drury-Lane. On occasion of the general peace, concluded at Aix la Chapelle, October 7th, 1748. Written by R. Dodsley. Set to musick by Mr. Arne.

London, R. Dodsley, 1749. 15 p. 20ᶜᵐ.

One act. First performed, as indicated, February 21, 1749.   AC901.M5 v.519

Die **triumphirende Claelia.** Tr. of Hasse's Il trionfo di Clelia.

Den **troe bruud.** Tr. of P. Guglielmi's La sposa fedele.

Die **Trofonius hoehle.** Tr. of Paisiello's La grotta di Trofonio.

Trofons zauberhoele. Tr. of Salieri's La grotta di Trofonio.

Les **trois comeres.** Piece en trois actes. Par Mʳˢ Le S * *. & d'Or * *. Représentée à la Foire S. Germain 1723.

Le Théâtre de la foire, Paris, 1737, t. ix, [423]–568 p. 17ᶜᵐ.

By Le Sage and D'Orneval. Largely *en vaudevilles.* The airs, selected or composed and arranged by Jean Claude **Gillier,** are printed at the end of the volume in the "Table des airs."   ML 48.L2IX

Les **trois fermiers,** comédie en deux actes, en prose, et mêlée d'ariettes, représentée pour la premiere fois, par les Comédiens italiens ordinaires du roi, le 12 mai 1777. Par M. Monvel.

Paris, Vente, 1777. 2 p. l., 87, [1] p. 21ᶜᵐ.

Cast. **Dezède,** the composer, is not mentioned. On p. [1–4] a prefatory note in which Monvel refers to an anecdote in "Les Ephémérides du Citoyen, tome 2, année 1769" as source of his play in answer to imputations of his critics Correct date of first performance, according to Schatz, May 24, 1777.   ML 50.2.T83D2

— Les **trois fermiers,** comédie en deux actes et en prose, mêlée d'ariettes; représentée pour la premiere fois par les Comédiens italiens ordinaires du roi, le 16 mai 1777. Par Monsieur Monvel. Nouvelle édition.

Paris, N. B. Duchesne, 1781. 40 p. 20ᶜᵐ.

Dezède, the composer, is not mentioned.   ML 50.2.T83D3

Les **trois comeres**—Continued.

— Les **trois fermiers,** comédie en deux actes, en prose, et mêlée d'ariettes; représentée pour la première fois par les Comédiens italiens ordinaires du roi, le 16 mai 1777.   Par M. Monvel.

Paris, Vente, 1782.   64 p.   19½ᶜᵐ.

With cast and author's preface, in which he narrates the anecdote on which his plot is founded.   **Dezède,** the composer, is not mentioned.   On p. 57–64 "Airs des Trois fermiers.   No. 1. *Romance.*   Faut attendre avec patience . . .   No. 2. *Chanson.* Je le compare avec Louis . . .   No. 3. *Romance en rondeau.*   Dre's l'instant que je vis . . .   No. 4. *Vaudeville.*   Sans un petit brin d'amour."   SCHATZ 2523

— **Die drey paechter.**   Ein singspiel in zwey aufzuegen.   Aus dem franzoesischen des hrn. Monvel.   Uebersetzt von herrn Wilhelm Gottlieb Becker.   Aufgefuehrt im k. k. Hoftheater naechst dem Kaerntnerthor.

Wien, beym logenmeister, 1785.   72 p.   16ᶜᵐ.

First performed, as indicated, October 28, 1785; at Francfort o/M, Theater im Junghof, April 21, 1779.   SCHATZ 2524

Trois nouvelles entrées.   *See* Fragments de Mr. de Lully.

Les **trois souhaits.**   A. T. of Philidor's Le bucheron.

Les **trois sultanes.**   A. T. of Gilbert's Soliman Second.

Troja distrutta.   Dramma per musica da rappresentarsi nel Nuovo Regio Ducal Teatro di Milano per il secondo spettacolo nel suo primo aprimento nel corrente autunno dell' anno 1778 . . .

Milano, Gio. Batista Bianchi, n. d.   55, [1] p.   16½ᶜᵐ.

Three acts.   By Mattia Verazj, who is not mentioned.   His remarks addressed "Al rispettabilissimo pubblico di Milano" are very instructive reading and show, if nothing else, how authors dreaded the caprices and "inveterate" traditions of the Milanese public.   Dedication, argument, cast, and name of Michele **Mortellari** as the composer ("La musica è nuova composizione").   With the opera were performed the anonymous ballets "Calipso abbandonata" and "La gelosia."

First performed, as indicated, September 1, 1778.   SCHATZ 6687

Il **Trojano schernito in Cartagine nascente e moribonda.** Dramma per musica, nel Teatro a San Samuele.

Venezia, Antonio Mora, 1743.   2 p. l., 7–45 p.   15½ᶜᵐ.

Three acts.   Note on 2d p. l.: "Le parole sono d'autore incognito.   La musica è di quattro virtuosi maestri."   Wiel mentions Giuseppe Imer as author of this parody of Metastasio's "La Didone abbandonata."   ML 48.A5   v.10

Le **trompeur trompé,** ou La rencontre imprévue.   Opera comique en un acte, par M. Vadé.   Représenté pour la premiere fois sur le Théâtre de la Foire S. Germain, le 18 février 1754 . . .

Paris, Duchesne, 1754.   61, [3] p.   18½ᶜᵐ.

On the [3] p. a list of plays published since 1747.   *En vaudevilles.*   The arranger of the music unknown to me.   On p. 56–61 the same airs as below.   Not to be confused with Blaise's opera of the same title (1767), in which Vadé's text had been retouched by Framery.   ML 50.2.T835

—Le **trompeur trompé,** ou La rencontre imprevue.   Opera-comique en un acte, par M. Vadé.   Représentés pour la première fois sur le Théâtre de la Foire S. Germain le 18 février 1755.

La Haye, Pierre Gosse, 1759.   67 p.   16ᶜᵐ.   (Vadé, Oeuvres, La Haye, 1760, t. ii.)

One act, *en vaudevilles.*   On p. 61–67 the three *airs notés:* "De tous les coeurs," "De même qu'une étincelle," "Quand on se rend."   ML 49.A2V2

Les **trompeurs trompés,** divertissement en un acte, à l'occasion de la fête de Madame de la Garde, pour la veille de Sainte-Anne, sa patrone: représenté le 27 juillet 1772, au Château de la Cour-Neuve.

n. pl., Aux Vertus, 1772. 102 p. 20ᶜᵐ.

Cast. On p. 69–95 "Bouquet pour Annette," the romanza "Des bouquets le plus simple" (airs only), "Chanter pour l'aimable Annette" (with acc.), "Auprès d'Annette, rassemblons-nous" (air only), "Je rêve en vain" (with acc.)

Not recorded by Cl. & L., Schatz or Towers.   SCHATZ 11517

Tropotipo. Intermezzi per musica di Ortanio, Past. Arc. Da rappresentarsi nel Teatro Grimani di S. Samuele. Nell' autunno dell' anno presente 1726.

Venezia, Marino Rossetti, 1726. 21 p. 14ᶜᵐ.

Three parts. By Domenico Lalli. Cast and name of Giovanni Battista **Pescetti** as the composer.   SCHATZ 7963

Les **troqueurs,** en un acte. Par M. Vadé. Représentés pour la première fois sur le Théatre de la Foire S. Laurent le 30 juillet 1753. Suivi du Rien; parodie des parodies de Titon et L'Aurore.

La Haye, Pierre Gosse, 1759. 24 p. 16ᶜᵐ. (Vadé, Oeuvres, La Haye, 1760, t. ii.)

One act. The parody and the "Airs choisis des Troqueurs," which should follow according to the table of contents, are wanting. The composer, Antoine **Dauvergne,** is not mentioned.

The *Ms. de Munich,* published by Prod'homme (Sammelbände d. I. M. G. July–September, 1905), gives the date of first performance as July 29, 1753. ML 49.A2V2

— Les **troqueurs,** opéra bouffon, interméde. Par Mr. Dauvergne. 1761.

n. i., n. d. 17 p. 21ᶜᵐ.

One act. By Jean Joseph Vadé, who is not mentioned.   ML 50.2.T84D3

Les **troubadours.** *See* Floquet's L'union de l'amour et des arts.

Les **Troyennes en Champagne,** opera-comique en un acte. Par M. Vadé représenté pour la premiere fois sur le Théatre de l'Opera-comique du Fauxbourg St. Germain, le 1 février 1755.

La Haye, Pierre Gosse, junior, 1759. (Vadé, Oeuvres, La Haye, 1759, t. iii.) 52 p. 16ᶜᵐ.

En vaudevilles. Cast. On p. 49, the *air noté* of the rondo "Ne lisons jamais dans l'avenir." This was a parody of Châteaubrun's tragedy, "Les Troyennes" (1754).

Not recorded by Cl. & L., though entered (without name of composer) in "Anecdotes dramatique" by Clément and De Laporte.   ML 49.A2V2

True-blue. L. T. of Carey's Nancy.

Das tugendhaffte lieben. *See* Graupner's Berenice e Lucilla.

Tullia Superba. Drama per musica da rappresentarsi nel novo Teatro di S. Angelo. L'anno 1678 . . .

Venetia, Francesco Nicolini, 1678. 64 p. 13½ᶜᵐ

Three acts. Dedication dated Venice, January 29, 1678, and signed by the supposed author, Antonio Medolago. Notice to the reader, calling this libretto "le primizie del mio povero ingegno," and mentioning Domenico **Freschi** as the composer, argument, and scenario.   SCHATZ 3356

Tullo Ostilio. Drama per musica del Sig. Adriano Morselli da rappresentarsi nel famoso Teatro di Tor di Nona . . .

Roma, Buagni, 1694. 72 p. 13ᶜᵐ.

Three acts. Impresario's dedication, cast, scenario, and prefatory note, in which it is stated:

"Comparisce per la seconda opera su queste scene, il *Tullo Ostilio*, bensi in gran parte mutata per quello che risguarda all' arie da Palemone Licurio [=Silvio Stampiglia] havendovi levate, & aggiunte alcune scene con qualche poca variazione in diversi passi de' recitativi . . . La musica in pochi giorni l'ha partorita il fertile ingegno del Signor Gio. **Bononcini**."

Consequently the opening remark in the dedication that "il Tullo Ostilio, che sin ora con sommo applauso ha passeggiato i più famosi teatri d'Italia viene a far mostra di sì in questo di Roma," appears to apply to the libretto, with music by some other composer, possibly by Marc' Antonio Ziani, first performed at Venice in 1685. Bononcini's setting was first performed, as indicated, during carnival, 1694. Schatz 1201

Tullo Ostilio. Dramma in musica da rappresentarsi nel nobile Teatro di Torre Argentina il carnevale dell' anno 1784 . . .

Roma, Cannetti, 1784. 40 p. 17ᶜᵐ.

Three acts. Francesco Ballani is mentioned as the author, Giuseppe **Gazzaniga** as the composer. Argument, scenario, and cast. With the opera were performed Onorato Viganò's "ballo eroico tragico pantomimo Andromaca in Epiro" and "ballo semitragico pantomimo Il convitato di pietra," music for both by Luigi Marescalchi. Schatz 3685

Tullo Ostilio. O. T. of Pescetti's I tre difensori della patria.

Tullo Ostilio. Drama per musica da rappresentarsi nel ristaurato famoso Teatro Vendramino di S. Salvatore. L'anno MDCLXXXV . . .

Venetia, Francesco Nicolini, 1685. 64 p. 14ᶜᵐ.

Three acts. By Adriano Morselli. Neither he is not mentioned, nor the composer, Marc' Antonio **Ziani**. Publisher's dedication, argument, and scenario.

First performed, as indicated, carnival, 1685. Schatz 11195

Le turc généreux. Entrée in Rameau's Les Indes galantes.

La turca in cimento, ballet. *See* Andreozzi's Angelica e Medoro.

Gli Turchi amanti. L. T. of Cimarosa's I Traci amanti.

Turia Lucrezia. Dramma per musica da rappresentarsi nel Teatro di Sant' Angelo nel carnevale dell' anno MDCCXXVI . . .

Venezia, Marino Rossetti, 1726. 58 p. 16ᶜᵐ.

Three acts. Dedication by Domenico Lalli as author ("la presente mia opera"), and dated Venice, December 26, 1725, argument, cast, scenario, and name of Antonio **Pollaroli** as the composer. Schatz 8265

Turno Aricino. Drama per musica da rappresentarsi nel Teatro del Falçone . . .

Genoa, Gio. Battista Scionico, 1702. 4 p. l., 62, [4] p. 15ᶜᵐ.

Three acts. Argument, scenario, cast, and dedication by Giov. Batt. Scionico. Neither the author, Silvio Stampiglia, is mentioned, nor the composer, Giuseppe Antonio Vincenzo **Aldrovandini**. Schatz 140

Turno re de Rutoli. Dramma tragico per musica di Gio. Gastone Boccherini Lucchese . . .

Vienna, Giovanni Tommaso de Trattnern, 1767. 64 p. 21ᶜᵐ.

Three acts. Argument, scenario and dedication in which Boccherini says:

"L'ardente desio che ho di mostrare ogni mio poco ingegno, prima della mia destinata partenza da questa Dominante, mi fa risolvere a dare alla luce un' opera teatrale, senza aspettar l'occasione che si produca in scena."

No composer or performance recorded by Schatz. ML 50.2.T9

The **turnpike gate**; a musical entertainment, in two acts. Now performing with universal applause, at the Theatre Royal, Covent-Garden. By T. Knight.

London, G. G. and J. Robinson, 1799. 2 p. l., 52 p. 21½ᶜᵐ.

Cast and "advertisement for the use of the theatres" to the effect that the "old, but ridiculous" and contradictory "signs of P. S., meaning prompt side; and O. P. meaning opposite prompt" have been replaced by "R. H. meaning right hand; and L. H meaning left hand; (always supposing you are on the stage and facing the audience." The composers, Joseph **Mazzinghi** and William **Reeve**, are not mentioned.

First performed November 14, 1799.   LONGE 258

La **Tusnelda** o sia La disfatti di Vario, ballet. *See* Cimarosa's Artaserse.

Le **tuteur trompé** o sia Il maestro di musica, ballet. *See* Gelosia e pazzia.

Il **tutore.** Intermezzi . . . In Dresde, l'anno 1738.

See the 22 additional pages in **Hasse**'s Alfonso, (Dresda), 1738. He composed also these intermezzi, the author of which is unknown to Schatz.

First performed at Naples, Teatro di San Bartolomeo, 1730; at Dresden, Hoftheater, May 11, 1738.   SCHATZ 4510

— Il **tutore.** Intermezzi da rappresentarsi in musica.

n. i., n. d. 45 p. 16½ᶜᵐ.

Two parts. Cast and note: "In Dresda l'anno 1738." **Hasse** is not mentioned. German title page, "Der vormund" and text face Italian. Obviously issued for the convenience of a German audience for the same performance as above. SCHATZ 4569

— **Pandolfo.** Intermezzo a due voci.

Venezia, Marino Rossetti, 1739. 21 p. 15ᶜᵐ.

Two parts. Cast and name of Johann Adolph **Hasse** as composer. The text is that of "Il tutore." Was performed as intermezzi for Chiarini's opera "Achille in Sciro."   SCHATZ 4583

— Il **tutore e la pupilla.** Intermezzo per musica da rappresentarsi nel Teatro dell' Opera Pantomima de Piccoli Hollandesi sopra la Piazza de Cappuccini. A Vienna, la prima vera dell' anno MDCCXLVII.

n. i., n. d. Unpaged. 20ᶜᵐ.

Two parts. Cast and name of Joh. Ad. **Hasse** as the composer. Same text as the above.

First performed under this longer title at Hamburg, Opernhaus beim **Gänsemarkt**, November 26, 1744.   SCHATZ 4570

Il **tutore burlato.** A. T. of Accorimboni's Il podestà di Tufo antico.

Il **tutore burlato.** A. T. of Insanguine's opera La finta semplice.

Il **tutore burlato** o sia I matrimonii in maschera. L. T. of G. M. Rutini's I matrimoni in maschera.

Il **tutore deluso** o sia La semplice, intermezzo a quatro, da rappresentarsi nel Teatro di Ratisbona . . .

[Regensburg], Gedruckt mit Zunkelischen schriften, n. d.' 135, [1] p. 15½ᶜᵐ.

Two acts. Cast, name of Theodor, freiherr von **Schacht** as the composer, and his "avertissement":

"Cet opéra, qui peut être est un des anciens sortis d'Italie, avait pour titre *La Semplice.* C'est sous ce nom qu'il est connu et c'est sans contredit un des meilleurs

Il tutore deluso—Continued.

que nous ayons de ce pais là . . . Cependant ayant a representer un opéra devant un public, dont une grande partie s'attache au défaut de la langue, aux beautés d'un chant aisé et naturel, sans faire attention à des expressions trop recherchés et indispensables au musicien, lorsque les paroles les demande; j'ai donc fait changer par Monsieur Friggieri, presque tout le caractere du premier acteur Giacinto, qui, outre son ingénuité, était farci de ces expressions empoullés difficiles à saisir d'abord, même à des connoisseurs de la langue. J'ai de plus ajouté quelque airs du célèbre Metastasio . . ."

German title-page, "Der betrogene vormund oder Das einfaeltige maedgen," and text face Italian.

Must have been performed after 1780. SCHATZ 9564

Il tutore e la pupilla. L. T. of Hasse's Il tutore.

Il tutore in scompiglio, ballet. *See* Tarchi's Il matrimonio per contrattempo.

Il tutore ingannato, ballet. *See* Anfossi's Azor, rè di Kibinga.

Il tutore ingannato. Dramma giocoso per musica. Da rappresentarsi nel Teatro di San Samuelle il carnovale dell' anno 1774.

Venezia, Modesto Fenzo, 1774. 56 p. 17½cm.

Three acts. Author not mentioned and unknown to Schatz. Cast, scenario, and name of Luigi **Marescalchi** as the composer. With the opera were performed Onorato Viganò's ballets "Diana sorpresa" (described on p. 28–29) and 'Amore trionfator della magia." The composer of the music is not mentioned. SCHATZ 5945

Il tutore ingannato, ballet. *See* Paisiello's Il Sismano nel Mogol.

Il tutore sorpreso, ballet. *See* Tarchi's Giulio Sabino.

Tutto per amore. Dramma giocoso per musica da rappresentarsi nel Teatro di S. A. E. di Sassonia. Composto dal Sign. Caterino Mazzolà . . .

Dresda, n. publ., 1785. 131 p. 15cm.

Two acts. Johann Gottlieb **Naumann** is mentioned as the composer. German title page, "Alles aus liebe," and text face Italian.

First performed, as indicated, March 5, 1785. SCHATZ 7057

— Elskovs magt. Et syngespil i to acter, af Caterino Mazzola, hvortil musikken er componeret af Naumann. Oversadt af Lars Knudsen.

Kiøbenhavn, Sønnichsens forlag, 1791. 110 p. 16½cm.

First performed at Copenhagen, Kongelige Theater par Kongens Nytorv, April 12, 1791. SCHATZ 7063

De twee standbeelden; zangspel, met balletten door den burger Pieter Pypers.

Amsteldam, J. Helders en A. Mars, 1798. 4 p. l., [vi], 127, [1] p. 16½cm.

Four acts. Dedication by the author dated "Amsterdam, 14 van wintermaand, 1797," and "Voorrede," dated "30. van Louwmaand, 1798," with the name of Bartholomaeus **Ruloffs** as the composer.

First performed at Amsterdam, Nationale Schouwburg, 1798. SCHATZ 9150

2, 5, 3, 8. A. T. of Storace's The prize.

The **two harlequins.** A farce of three acts. Written by Mr. Noble. And acted by the King's Italian comedians at Paris. And now perform'd by the French comedians at the Theatre in Lincoln's Inn Fields.

London, W. Mears and W. Chetwood, 1718. (double) 43 p. 19cm.

French original, "Les deux arlequins" (by the elder Riccoboni), faces the English translation.

First performed at Paris, March 20, 1718!   LONGE 262

The **two misers**: a musical farce. As it is performed at the Theatre Royal in Covent-Garden. By the author of Midas, and the Golden pippin.

London, G. Kearsley, 1775. 3 p. l., 32 p. 19½cm.

Two acts. By Kane O'Hara. Cast and note:

"The following scenes are taken from a justly admired piece entitled, *Les deux avares* [by Fenouillot de Falbaire]. The bare out-line only of the finish'd characters, with just enough of the dialogue to connect the incidents, has been retain'd in order to reduce the whole within the compass of an English farce . . ."

The composer, Charles **Dibdin**, is not mentioned. How much, if any, of Grétry's music he borrowed, is unknown to me. In Johnston's vocal score of "The two misers" Dibdin is not mentioned, and the title page says "The music selected from the works of the most celebrated composers." In our copy the name of Dr. **Hayes** is added in pencil to the duet "Now gossip strike home" and that of [Felice] **Giardini** to the catch "Fill ev'ry man his cup."

First performed, as indicated, January 21, 1775.   LONGE 32

The **two queens of Brentford**: or Bayes no poetaster: A musical farce, or comical opera. Being the sequel of the famous Rehearsal, written by the late duke of Buckingham. With a comical prologue and epilogue.

London, William Chetwood, 1721. 88 p. 19cm.

Five acts. Neither Thomas Durfey, the author, is mentioned, nor the composer. Possibly the text was not composed. No performance recorded.   LONGE 169

The **two Sosias.** A. T. of Purcell's Amphitryon.

Two to one. A comic opera, in three acts. As performed at the Theatre-Royal, Hay-market, and Smock-alley. Written by George Colman, jun. . . . The music composed by Dr. Arnold.

Dublin, Printed for W. Wilson, 1785. 54 p., 1 l. 17cm. [Bound with Thompson, James. Edward and Eleonora.]

Most of the music was composed by **Arnold**, but, as Harrison & co.'s vocal score shows, he also utilized some ballad airs. For instance, for air IV, "Adzooks, old Crusty" he used "Yankee Doodle." "When cruel parents" is headed in the vocal score as composed by Philip **Hayes.**

First performed at the Haymarket June 19, 1784.   PR

Den **ubeboede** øe. Tr. of Traetta's L'isola disabitata.

Die **uber eyffersucht und list triumphirende bestaendige liebe,** aus der bekandten historie von Tamestris in ein drama zusammen gezogen.

Wittenberg, August Koberstein, n. d. Unpaged. 19cm.

Four acts. Dedication signed by the composer and author, Johann Paul **Kuntze,** and his apologies to the reader, who is informed that the text

"mit samt der composition binnen 3. tagen muessen ihr ende sehen . . . Es mangelt zwar den arien so viel an penséen, als die recitative an historien abundiren. Allein, was jenes verursachet, ist schon gemeldet. Hier aber hat, was sonst ein oeffentlicher schauplatz und die action der personen verrichtet, durch worte bedeutet werden muessen."

It would seem that the opera was first performed in concert-form about 1720, at Wittenberg, in the composer's Collegium musicum.   SCHATZ 5315

Gli uccellatori. Dramma di tre atti per musica. Rappresentato per la prima volta in Venezia nel 1759 con musica del Gazman [!].

Carlo Goldoni, Opere teatrali, Venezia, Zatta e figli, 1788–95, v. 42, [159]–206 p. 18^cm. PQ

Li uccellatori. Dramma giocoso per musica di Polisseno Fegejo, Pastor Arcade. Da rappresentarsi nel Teatro Giustinian di S. Moisè il carnovale dell' anno 1759 . . .

Venezia, Modesto Fenzo, 1759. 58 p. 15^cm.

Three acts. By Goldoni. Cast, scenario, and name of Florian Leopold **Gassmann** as the composer. SCHATZ 3617

— Gl'uccellatori. Dramma giocoso per musica da rappresentarsi ne' Teatri Privilegiati di Vienna l'autunno dell' anno 1768.

Vienna, Ghelen, n. d. 60 p. 16^cm.

Three acts. Goldoni is mentioned as author and Florian Leopold **Gassmann** as the composer. Schatz claims that this was his second setting of the text. This Vienna version of the libretto follows fairly closely that of the original, Venice, 1759. Still, a number of differences are noticeable. For instance, the aria "Tu sai cupido" (I, 11) has become "Roccolina bella, bella," "Amor per te mi stimola" (III, 5) has become "Per te sospiro," etc., etc. SCHATZ 3627

Gl'uccellatori, ballet. *See* Robuschi's Li raggiri fortunati.

L'uccellatrice. Intermezzi per musica da rappresentarsi nel **Teatro** di S. Samuele nella fiera dell' Ascensione dell' anno MDCCL.

Venezia, All' insegna della Scienza, n. d. 19 p. 16^cm.

Two parts. Author not mentioned and unknown to Schatz. Cast and name of Niccolò **Jommelli** as the composer.
First performed, as indicated, May 6, 1750. . SCHATZ 4873

— Intermezzo in musica, da representarsi nel Teatro Privileggiato del Signor Pietro Moretti, in Dresda nel mese di giugn. 1762 intitolato **Il matto Don Narciso.**

n. i., n. d. 22 p. 16^cm.

Two parts. Cast and note: "La musica è di diversi autori," among whom Schatz includes **Jommelli.** The text is that of "L'Uccellatrice," but with so many differences as to almost hide the identity. SCHATZ 4874

Die ueber die liebe triumphirende weissheit, oder Salomon, in einem singe-spiel auff dem grossen Hamburgischen Schau-platze vorgestellet im jahr 1703.

[Hamburg], mit Greflingischen schrifften, n. d. Unpaged. 18^cm.

Three acts. Scenario and "vorrede," according to which "Der . . . Koenig Salomon" "vor einigen jahren" was performed at Brunswick, but:
"Dass man aber dieses schauspiel durchaus geaendert; und so wohl die music, poesie als auch die invention und einrichtung anders und kuertzer gemacht, ist aus solchen ursachen geschehen, die ein jeder errathen kan, der die opern, das hiesige theatrum und den gout der leute verstehet. Die eintzige partie von Salomon ist, was die poesie und die music anbelanget, aus gewisser raison so geblieben; nur dass man wegen der weitlaeufftigkeit vieles ausgelassen, und zuletzt eine neue arie hinzugesetzet, welche wie auch eine andere arie des Salomons in der music neu ist, und will man selbige aus unnoehtiger sorgfalt nicht beschreiben, weil ein jeder den grossen unterschied der alten und neuen composition leicht verstehen wird. Imgleichen hat man auf vornehmen befehl, . . . diese arie in dem dritten actu mit eingeruecket: *Euch ihr schoenen augen muss ich lieben,* und es dem hochgeneigten leser berichten wollen, um nicht angesehen zu werden, als ob man sie vor die seinige ausgaebe . . ."
Neither the author, Christian Friedrich Hunold (called Menantes), is mentioned, nor the composer, Reinhard **Keiser.** SCHATZ 5113

Ulisse. Dramma per musica di Domenico Lalli da rappresentarsi nel Teatro di S. Angelo per l'ultim' opera del carnevale dell' anno MDCCXXV . . .

   Venezia, Marino Rossetti, n. d.   56 p.   15^{cm}.

Three acts. Author's dedication, cast, scenario, argument, and name of Giovanni **Porta** as the composer.   SCHATZ 8394

Ulisse al Monte Etna, ballet. *See* Bianchi's L'orfano cinese.

L'Ulisse errante. Opera musicale dell' Assicurato, Academico incognito . . .

   Venetia, Gio. Pietro Pinelli, 1644.   118 p.   13^{cm}.

Five acts. By Giacomo Badoaro, who in his long dedication (p. 5–18) gives what may be called his esthetic creed of dramas for music. In the course of his remarks he says:

"Feci già molti anni rappresentare il *Ritorno d' Ulisse in patria*, dramma cavato di punto da Homero, e raccordato per ottimo da Aristotile nella sua Poetica, e pur' anco all' hora udii abbaiar qualche cane, ma io non fui però tardo à risentirmene co' sassi alle mani. Hora fò vedere l' *Ulisse errante* . . . ho voluto rappresentare gli accidenti più gravi, occorsi ad Ulisse nel gir' in patria . . . Se dirassi, e questa opera sia un mostro, dirò di nò; se dirassi, che'l soggetto ecceda la commune dell' altre tragedie, dirò che è un gigante nato per eccesso di materia, e non contra la mia voluntà. Se vorrà affermar un bell' ingegno, che di questo soggetto poteva fare cinque opere; io le rispondo, ch'è vero, ma non le hò fatte, perche hò voluto, e saputo farne una sola . . . "Fù il *Ritorno d' Ulisse in patria* decorato dalla musica del Signor Claudio Monteverde soggetto di tutta fama, e perpetuità di nome, hora mancherà questo condimento; poiche è andato il gran maestro ad intuonar la musica degli angeli à Dio. Si goderanno in sua vece le gloriose fatiche del Signor Francesco **Sacrati**, e ben' era di dovere, che per veder gli splendori di questa luna, tramontasse prima quel Sole. Havremo per ordinator di machine, e di scene il nostro ingegnosissimo Torelli . . ."

Between this dedication and the argument there is a notice to the reader by Giacomo Torelli, which is of importance in another direction. He says:

"Io hebbi dalla mano dell' auttore l' *Ulisse errante*, con privilegiata auttorità di farlo stampare in grande con le figure doppò fornite le recite, & ciò intrapresi per **haver** occasione di mostrar al mondo quelle fatiche, che hò io incontrate per ben servire à questi cavalieri; Hora dalla pienezza di questa gratia è nato in mè nuovo ardire di farla anco stampar in questa forma per incontrar la sodisfattione di quelli, che godono più simili cose, quando sieno accompagnate dalla lettura . . ."   SCHATZ 9255

L'Ulisse in Feaccia. Drama da rappresentarsi in musica nel luoco ove era il Theatro Zane à San Moisè. L'anno MDCLXXXI.

   Venetia, Francesco Nicolini, 1681.   47 p.   14½^{cm}.

Three acts. Notice to the reader, argument and scenario. Neither the author, Filippo Acciajuoli, nor the composer, Antonio del **Gaudio**, is mentioned. One of those operas that were staged with "figure formate di cera."   SCHATZ 3634

Ulisses. A. T. of Keiser's Circe.

Ulisses, musicalische opera, welche auff dem Theatro zu Bresslau in october anno 1726 vorgestellet . . .

   n. i., n. d.   Unpaged.   17½^{cm}.

Three acts. Dedication, argument, scenario, and names of "Signore Teofilo Fedele—Theophilo **Treu**" as composer, of Domenico Lalli as author. German text faces Italian.   SCHATZ 10444

L'ultima che si perde è la speranza. O. T. of Zini's text Gli amanti della dote.

L'ultima, che si perde è la speranza. Commedia per musica di Saverio Zini da rappresentarsi nel Real Teatro del Fondo di Separazione per second 'opera di questo corrente anno 1790.

Napoli, n. publ., 1790. 44 p. 15½ᶜᵐ.

Two acts. Cast and name of Marcello di Capua (Marcello **Bernardini**) as composer. On p. 5–7, cast and argument of "Magia contro Magia. Ballo eroico favoloso. Composto e diretto dal Sig. Gio. Battista Giannini." Pietro Dutillieu is mentioned as the composer of the music. Schatz 841

— **L'ultima che si perde è la speranza.** Farsa di un atto solo da recitarsi per musica nel nobilissimo Teatro della nobil Donna Tron Veronese in San Cassiano, il carnovale dell' anno 1792.

Venezia, Modesto Fenzo, 1792. 56 p. 18½ᶜᵐ.

Cast and name of Marcello da Capua (Marcello **Bernardini**) as composer ("La musica è del tutto nuova"). This one-act farce is followed as "atto secondo" (with cast) by "*Il convitato di pietra*. Farsa di un atto solo . . . La musica è di vari celebri maestri," on p. 29–56. Schatz 836

Ulysse, tragedie représentée par l'Académie royale de musique l'an 1703. Les paroles de M. Guichard & la musique de M. Rebel. LVIII. opera.

n. i., n. d. pl., p. 57–110. 14ᶜᵐ. (Recueil général des opéra, t. viii, Paris, 1706.)

Detached copy. Five acts and prologue. Brief *avertissement*. First performed, as indicated, January 21, 1703. Schatz 8622
Second copy. ML 48.R4

Ulysse et Circé. Entrée in Duplessis' Les festes nouvelles.

Ulysses. In einem musicalischen Schau-spiele auf dem Hamburgischen Theatro vorgestellet im jahre 1721.

[Hamburg], Caspar Jakhel, n. d. Unpaged. 18ᶜᵐ.

Three acts. Author not mentioned, and unknown to Schatz. Argument. Composed by Johann Caspar **Vogler,** who is not mentioned. Schatz 10801

Ulysses rückkunft zur Penelope. Tr. of Alessandri's Il ritorno di Ulisse a Penelope.

Umor di principessa o sia L'ambizione castigata. *See* the A. T.

Gli umori contrari. Dramma giocoso per musica di un atto solo di Gio. Bertati . . . posto in musica dal maestro Sebastiano Nasolini da rappresentarsi nel nob. Teatro di S. Cassiano nella state 1798.

Venezia, Antonio Rosa, n. d. 27 p. 17½ᶜᵐ. Schatz 7030

Das unbekannte dienstmaedgen. A. T. of Roellig's Clarisse.

Die unbewohnte insel. Tr. of Jommelli's L'isola disabitata.

Die unbewohnte insel. Tr. of Gius. Scarlatti's L'isola disabitata.

De under masken sluttede giftermaale. A. T. of G. M. Rutini's Den bedragne formynder.

Die uneinigen brüder. Tr. of Graun's I fratelli nemici.

Die unentbehrlichen verraether ihrer herrschaften aus eigennutz. A. T. of Salieri's Der rauchfangkehrer.

Die **unerwartete abreise**.   Tr. of Salieri's La partenza inaspettata.

Den **unge grevinde**.   Tr. of Gassmann's La contessina.

Das **ungeheuer** oder Liebe aus dankbarkeit.   Tr. of Seydelmann's Il mostro ossia Da gratitudine amore.

Die **ungezwungene liebe**.   A. T. of Telemann's Adelheid.

Die **ungleiche heyrath zwischen Vespetta und Pimpinone** in dreyen intermediis auf dem Hamburger Theatro vorgestellt.

> *n. i., n. d.   Unpaged.   18^{cm}.*
>
> The Arias in Italian, the recitatives in German. Neither Pietro Pariati, the author of the Italian "Vespetta e Pimpinone," nor the translator, Johann Philipp Praetorius, nor the composer, Georg Philipp **Telemann**, is mentioned. Ottzenn enters this, possibly from the score parts, as "Pimpinone oder Die ungleiche heirat."
> First performed as indicated, 1725.   SCHATZ 10273

Die **unglueckselige Cleopatra, koenigin von Egyppten**.   A. T. of Mattheson's Die betrogene staatsliebe.

L'union de l'amour et des arts, ballet-héroïque en trois entrées; composé des actes de Bathile & Chloé, de Théodore, & de La cour d'amour: représenté, devant Sa Majesté, à Choisy-le-roi, le 9 février 1774.

> *[Paris], P. Robert Christophe Ballard, 1774.   61 p.   19^{cm}.*
>
> Cast and names of Pierre René "Le Monnier, commissaire des guerres" as author and of Etienne Joseph **Floquet** as composer. The third entrée has, in the text, the alternative title "Les troubadours," and "Théodore" is preceded by this note:
> "Le sujet de cet acte, est le même que celui qui a été traité par M. Roi [Roy], dans le Ballet des Grâces; on a supprimé le rôle d'Eudoxe, mère de Théodore, parce qu'on a cru qu'il faisoit longueur. Les vers marqués par des guillemets, sont de l'ancien opera."
> First performed at Paris, Académie royale de musique, September 7, 1773.
> ML 52.2.U5

Union of the clans.   A. T. of The highland fair.

Das **unnuetze bestreben**.   Ein singspiel in zween aufzuegen.

> *n. i., n. d.   [113]–176 p.   16^{cm}.   (F. L. Schmidel's Theatralische werke, Wien & Leipzig, 1785.)*
>
> Detached copy. The text is preceded by this protest:
> "Dieses singspiel wurde den 23 hornung [February] 1783 in dem k. k. National-hoftheater unter dem titel—*Die betrogene arglist*—aufgefuehrt. Da es in dieser gestalt, in der es aufgefuehrt wurde, gar nicht zu dieser absicht bestimmt war, sondern von dem herausgeber ohne mein wissen dazu gebraucht worden ist, so bin ich nie-manden, der ueber seine unwahrscheinliche und unvollkommene ausfuehrung unzu-frieden war, und es sein musste, rechenschaft schuldig. Was die gegenwaertige ausfuehrung betrifft, erwarte ich das urtheil eines jeden kunstrichters, der mich belehren will."
> The piece was written, and composed by Joseph **Weigl**, for the marionettes theater of friends of Schmidel.   SCHATZ 10958

— Die **betrogne arglist**, ein singspiel in einem aufzuge.   In musik gesetzt von Joseph Weigl.   Aufgefuehrt im kaiserl. koenigl. National Hoftheater.

> *Wien, beym Logenmeister, 1783.   28 p.   16^{cm}.*
>
> By Schmidel with alterations by unknown author (*see* the foregoing entry). The text is preceded by this odd prefatory note by Joseph Weigl:
> "Die Goetter sehen mit begluckender huld auf die opfer der erstlinge herab; Du erstes, bestes publikum Deutschlands sey du meine gottheit! empfange dies erst-lingsopfer aus meinen fast noch unmuendigen haenden, und schenke mir, wo nicht beyfall, wenigstens nachsicht."
> First performed, as indicated, February 23, 1783.   SCHATZ 10959

Die **unnütze vorsicht.** A. T. of André's Der barbier von Sevilien.

Die **unnütze vorsicht.** A. T. of Paisiello's Der barbier von Sevilla.

Die **unruhige nacht.** Tr. of Gassmann's La notte critica.

Der **unschuldige betrug,** oder Auf dem land kennt man die rache nicht. Eine laendliche operette in einem aufzug, fuer die Marinellische Kinderschule. Von herrn Leopold Huber . . . Die musik ist von herrn Ferdinand Kauer . . .

Wien, Schmidt, 1790. 92 p. 15½^{cm}.
Cast of the children who took the characters.
First performed, as indicated, June 22, 1790.   Schatz 5061

Die **unsichtbare braut.** Tr. of Fabrizj's La sposa invisibile.

Unter zwey streitenden siegt der dritte. Tr. of Sarti's Fra i due litiganti il terzo gode.

Unter zwey streitenden zieht der dritte den nutzen. Tr. of Sarti's I pretendenti delusi.

Das **unterbrochene fest** oder Der triumph der tugend. Tr. of von Schacht's La festa interotta.

Das **unterbrochene opferfest.** Eine heroisch-komische oper in zwey akten.
By Franz Xaver Huber. Music by Peter von **Winter.**
First performed at Vienna, Kaernthnerthor Theater, June 15, 1796.
L. of C. has the original version only in the edition of 1803.

— Gesaenge aus dem singspiele: **Myrrha und Elvira,** oder Das opferfest, in zwey aufzuegen. Die musik ist von dem kapellmeister Winter.
Hamburg, Rabe und Freystatzky wittwe, 1797. 39 p. 16^{cm}.
Huber's text in Christian August Vulpius version, neither of whom is mentioned.
First performed at Hamburg, Theater beim Gänsemarkt, September 1, 1797.
   Schatz 11060

— Il **sacrifizio interrotto.** Dramma eroicomico in due atti da rappresentarsi nel Teatro Elettorale di Sassonia.
Dresda, n. publ., 1798. 159 p. 16^{cm}.
The Italian translator is not known. Peter von **Winter** is mentioned as the composer. German title-page, "Das unterbrochene opferfest," and text face Italian.
First performed, as indicated, April 25, 1798.   Schatz 11061

— Gesaenge aus der oper: Das **opferfest,** in vier acten. Die musik ist vom kapellmeister Winter.
Hamburg, Friedrich Hermann Nestler, n. d. 39 p. 15½^{cm}.
The Huber-Vulpius version.
First performed with this title at Hamburg, December 12, 1798.   Schatz 11062

Die **unvermutete zusammenkunft,** oder Die pilger von Mecca (Mekka). Tr. of Gluck's La rencontre imprévue.

Die **unvermutheten zufaelle.** Tr. of Grétry's Les événements imprévues.

L'uomo effeminato, ballet. *See* Crippa's Le confusioni per somiglianza.

L'uomo femmina. Dramma giocóso per musica da rappresentarsi nel Teatro Giustiniani in S. Moisè il presente autunno MDCCLXII.

> *Venezia, Francesco Valvasense, n. d.   48 p.   15^{cm}.*
> Three acts. Author not mentioned, and unknown to Schatz. Cast, scenario, and name of **Galuppi** as the composer.   Schatz 3509

L'uomo indolente. Commedia per musica di Giuseppe Palomba da rappresentarsi nel Teatro Nuovo sopra Toledo per terz' opera del corrente anno 1795.

> *Napoli, n. publ., 1795.   44 p.   15½^{cm}.*
> Two acts. With cast and name of the composer, Giuseppe **Farinelli.**
>   Schatz 3017

Uranio e Erasitea. Favola pastorale di Eaco Panellenio vice-custode della Parmense colonia da rappresentarsi nel Regio-Ducal Teatro di Parma l'agosto dell' anno 1773 per la nascita del real primogenito di Ferdinando Borbone. Infante di Spagna e di Maria Amalia . . . [vignette].

> *Parma, Stamperia reale, n. d.   6 p. l., 31 p.   22^{cm}.*
> Two acts. By conte Jacopo Antonio Sanvitale, who signs the dedication with both his real and his Arcadian name. Argument, cast, name of the composer, Giuseppe **Colla,** and note:
> "Questa favola pastorale, con maggiore estensione in tre atti divisi, fu un' opera fino dall' anno 1720 esposta sul Ducal Teatro di Piacenza in occasione delle nozze del Serenissimo Sig. Duca di Modena. La traccia, la condotta, e i pessimi versi, che ne fanno arrossire l'autore, sono tutti diversi, come diversa è l'allegoria; onde l'argomento medesimo chiaramente si vede in quante nuove, e migliori maniere possa esser trattato. Quanti autori di tragedie, di commedie, e di drammi musicali non hanno trattato il medesimo argomento? Giudica bene, e vivi elice."   Schatz 2108

Urganostocor. *See* Latilla's L'opera in prova alla moda.

Urtado e Miranda, ballet. *See* Curcio's La Nitteti.

Das (urteil) urtheil des Midas. Tr. of Grétry's Le jugement de Midas.

Urtheil des Paris, ballet. *See* Bernasconi's Temistokles.

Das urtheil des Paris. Tr. of Graun's Il giudicio di Paride.

The useless precaution. A. T. of Mrs Griffith's text The barber of Seville.

Det uventede møde. Tr. of Gluck's La rencontre imprévue.

Les vacances de Cythere. A. T. of L'amour desoeuvré.

Il vagabondo fortunato. Commedia per musica di P. M. Da rappresentarsi nel Teatro de' Fiorentini nell' autunno di quest' anno 1773.

> *Napoli, Vincenzo Flauto, 1773.   2 p. l., 56 p.   15^{cm}.*
> Three acts. By Pasquale Mililotti. Cast and name of Niccolò **Piccinni** as the composer.   Schatz 8142

Li **vaghi accidenti fra amore e gelosia.** L. T. of Galuppi's La diavolessa.

Valasco e Vespetta, intermezzi. *See* Stratonica.

Valcour et Zéila. A. T. of Philidor's La belle esclave.

La **vallée de Montmorency,** ou Jean Jacques Rousseau dans son hermitage, opéra-comique en trois actes, en prose, mêlé de vaudevilles. Par les CC. Piis, Barré, Radet et Desfontaines. Représenté, pour la première fois, sur le Théâtre du Vaudeville, le 23 prairial, an 6. [June 11, 1798]

Paris, chez le libraire au Théâtre du vaudeville, an VII [1798–99]. *87 p. 21½cm.*

Cast. Many of the airs are printed in the text. They are by no means all vaudevilles in the sense of real folk-songs but in the technical sense. For instance, **Rousseau's** own "Dans ma cabane obscure" was used and **Paisiello** is expressly mentioned as the composer of the *fredon* "Je suis Lindor" for "Toujours ainsi, de mon champêtre asyle," as also "C.[itoyen] **Wicht**" as composer for the *fredons* of "Pour leur grosseur" and "Cueillons ces cerises." A note on p. 2 informs us that the title of the opera at its first performance was simply "La vallée de Montmorency."

ML 50.2.V2

Il **valore delle donne.** Dramma giocoso per musica da rappresentarsi in Casale nel Teatro degl' Illmi Signori cavalieri della società nel carnevale dell' anno 1783 . . .

Casale, Giovanni Meardi, n. d. 53, [1] p. 14½cm.

Reimprimatur dated February 8, 1783. Two acts. By Giovanni Bertati. Impresario's dedication, cast, scenario, and name of Pasquale **Anfossi** as composer, but not of librettist.

First performed at Turin, Teatro Corignano, fall of 1780. Schatz 268

Le **vane gelosie.** Commedia per musica da rappresentarsi nel Teatro grande alla Scala la primavera 1791 . . .

Milano, Gio. Batista Bianchi, n. d. 80, [8] p. 16cm.

Three acts. By Giambattista Lorenzi, who is not mentioned. Impresario's dedication, scenario, and name of **Paisiello** as the composer. The unnumbered p. contain argument and description of Giuseppe Herdlitzka's "La schiava americana, ballo pantomimo di mezzo carattere." Neither of this nor of his second, comic, ballet "La vindemmia" is the composer of the music mentioned.

First performed at Naples, Teatro de' Fiorentini, spring, 1790. Schatz 7701

Vanelia: or, The amours of the great. An opera. As it is acted by a private company near St. James's . . .

London, E. Rayner, 1732. vii, [1], 55 p. 19cm.

Three acts and introduction. Political satire in form of a ballad opera. Table of the 21 songs, the airs to which are indicated by title in the text. Author unknown to Clarence. Longe 191

Vanesio and Larinda. A. T. of Orlandini's Le bourgeois gentilhomme.

La **vanità corretta dal disprezzo,** ballet. *See* Monza's Erifile.

La **vanità delusa.** Drama giocoso per musica da rappresentarsi nel Teatro Giustiniano di S. Moisè nel carnovale dell' anno 1748.

Venezia, n. publ., 1747. 59 p. 14½cm.

Three acts. Scenario, cast. Author and composer not mentioned and unknown to Schatz. Perhaps identical with Antonio Gori's text of the same title.

Schatz 11373

La vanità delusa. Dramma per musica da rappresentarsi in Firenze nell' autunno dell' anno 1731 nel Teatro di via del Cocomero . . .

Firenze, Giuseppe Pagani e Melchiorre Alberighi, 1731. 90 p. 14½cm.

Three acts. Argument and name of the composer, Giovanni **Chinzer**. The author (unknown to Schatz) in the argument resents the attacks made on him by "maligni censori" and others and protests that his text is not intended as "una satira diretta contro la nobilità.'   SCHATZ 1865

The varietie, a comedy, lately presented by His Majesties servants at the Black-Friers.

London, Humphrey Moseley, 1649. 2 p. l., 87 p. 14cm.

Five acts. By William, duke of Newcastle, who is not mentioned. Considerably interspersed with songs.   PR 2729.N5

Vasco di Gama, dramma per musica con cori e balli analoghi composto da Antonio de' Filistri . . . da rappresentarsi nel Regio Teatro di Berlino il carnovale dell' anno 1792. Con musica di vari autori.

Berlino, Haude e Spener, n. d. 119 p. 15½cm.

Three acts. Argument, cast. German title page and text face Italian. Carl Spazier wrote a sarcastic review of this pasticcio in the Musikalisches Wochenblatt, 1792, p. 153–155, 161–162, from which it appears that not less than eighteen composers were represented, amongst them **Prati, Paisiello, Nasolini, Bianchi, Sarti, Righini, Naumann, Jommelli,** and the then court conductor Felice **Alessandri,** who furnished most of the recitatives for this monstrum.

First performed, as indicated, January 20, 1792.   SCHATZ 11374

I vecchi delusi. Commedia per musica di Giuseppe Palomba da rappresentarsi nel Teatro de' Fiorentini per second' opera di questo corrente anno 1793.

Napoli, Vincenzo Flauto, 1793. 48 p. 15½cm.

Two acts. Cast and name of Gaetano **Marinelli** as the composer.   SCHATZ 5960

— I vecchi burlati. Dramma giocoso per musica da rappresentarsi nel nobile Teatro di San Samuele l'autunno dell' anno 1795 . . .

Venezia, Casali, 1795. 55, [1] p. 17cm.

Two acts. Palomba's "I vecchi delusi," without many alterations. Impresario's dedication, cast, and name of Gaetano **Marinelli** as the composer.   SCHATZ 5966

Il vecchio amante. Dramma giocoso per musica da rappresentarsi in Torino nel Teatro di S. A. S. il Signor principe di Carignano nel carnovale dell' anno 1747.

Torino, Giuseppe Domenico Verani, n. d. 78 p. 14½cm.

Three acts. Cast and name of Gaetano **Latilla** as composer. The author, Giovanni Barlocci, is not mentioned. Schatz says that the original title of his text was "La commedia in commedia."   SCHATZ 5463

Il vecchio burlato. O. T. of the libretto Chi vuol non puole.

Il vecchio burlato. Dramma giocoso per musica da rappresentarsi nel nobile Teatro di San Samuele l'autunno dell' anno 1783.

Venezia, Gio. Battista Casali, n. d. 72 p. 18½cm.

Two acts. Author unknown to Schatz. Cast, scenario, and name of "Luigi Ceruso" (Luigi **Caruso**) as the composer. On p. 65–72, argument, and detailed description of "Zemira e Azor, ballo serio pantomimo in cinque atti," by Francesco Clerico. Of this and the second ballet, "Lo sposo burlato," he also composed the music.   SCHATZ 1664

Il vecchio capricioso in amore. *See* Il vecchio pazzo in amore.

Il vecchio geloso. Dramma giocoso per musica da rappresentarsi nel Teatro di S. A. Serenissima il Signor Principe di Carignano nell' autunno del 1782.

Torino, Onorato Derossi, n. d. 78, [2] p. 14ᶜᵐ.

Two acts. Cast, scenario, and name of Felice **Alessandri** as the composer. Librettist unknown to Schatz. With the opera were performed Filippo Beretti's ballets (composer of the music not mentioned), "Il pastor fido" and "La contadina filosofà."

First performed at the Teatro della Scala, Milan, fall season of 1781.   SCHATZ 151

Il vecchio geloso.   L. T. of Galuppi's L'amante di tutte.

Il vecchio pazzo in amore.   Da rappresentarsi nel Teatro Giustiniano di S. Moisè nel carnovale dell' anno 1731. Dalla Sig. Rosa Venturini . . . e dal Signor Pietro Michelli.

[Venezia], n. publ., n. d. 12 p. 14ᶜᵐ.

Three intermezzi, performed with Paganelli's "La caduta di Leone Imperator d'Oriente." Author and composer not mentioned, and unknown to Schatz.

SCHATZ 11376

— **Il vecchio capricioso in amor.**   Da rappresentarsi nel Teatro Giustiniano di S. Moisè nel carnovale dell' anno 1732. Dalla Sig. Maria Penna, e dal Sig. Matteo Bevilacqua Bolognesi.

Venezia, Steffano Valvasense, n. d. 12 p. 15ᶜᵐ.

Three intermezzi, performed with Albinoni's "Gli evenimenti di Rugero." The text is the same as of "Il vecchio pazzo in amore."   SCHATZ 11375

Veddemaalet eller Elskernes skole.   Tr. of Mozart's Cosi fan tutte.

La vedova.   Drama musicale rappresentato nel giardino del Signor marchese Bartolommeo Corsini alla Porta al Prato.

n. i., n. d. p. [299]–403. 15½ᶜᵐ.

Detached from the third part (not in L. of C.) of Moniglia's "Poesie drammatiche," 1690. Three acts. Argument and scenario. On p. 301: "Fu questo drama composto dall' autore per comandamento del Sereniss., e reverendiss. principe cardinale Gio. Carlo di Toscana, per doversi rappresentare nel solito Teatro de' Signori Accademici Immobili sotto la protezzione della medesima Altezza Reverendissima, e già era stato messo in musica dal famoso Sig. Jacopo **Melani**, e n'erano di già state distribuite le parti a i recitanti; ma sopravenendo la sempre lagrimevol morte di si gran principe, ne restò sospesa la recita; la quale dopo molti anni da una fiorita conversazione di nobilissimi cavalieri fu richiamata su le scene l'anno 1680 nel giardino del Sig. march. Bartolommeo Corsini" [at Florence].

SCHATZ 6289

La vedova accorta.   Dramma giocoso per musica da rappresentarsi nel Teatro di S. Cassano il carnevale dell' anno 1745[!] . . .

Venezia, Modesto Fenzo, 1746[!] 64 p. 15½ᶜᵐ.

Three acts. Argument, cast and scenario. Ferdinando Giuseppe **Bertoni** is mentioned only as the composer of the recitatives and of nine arias, marked with an asterisk, for instance, "Son rimasta vedovella" (I, 3), "Voi, che pietà provate" (II, 4). The author, Ambrosio Borghese, is not mentioned.   SCHATZ 927

According to Wiel 1745 is the correct year of performance.

La vedova bizzarra.   Commedia per musica da rappresentarsi nel Teatro de' Fiorentini per prim' opera di quest' anno 1788.

Napoli, n. publ., 1788. 45 p. 15ᶜᵐ.

Three acts. By Giovanni Bertati. Cast and name of composer, Pasquale **Anfossi**, but not of librettist.   SCHATZ 261

La vedova capricciosa. Commedia per musica di Giuseppe Palomba Napolitano. Da rappresentarsi nel Teatro Nuovo sopra Toledo nel carnevale di quest' anno 1765.

Napoli, Vincenzo Mazzola-Vocola, 1765. 93 p. 15^{cm}.

Three acts. Cast and name of "Giacomo **Insanguine** detto Monopoli" as composer, "a riserba dell' arie di Odoardo e Celidea che sono di D. Carlo **De Franchi.**" (*See* f.-n. on p. 93 below the aria "Ah dalla gioja oppresso" substituted for "Io veggo un' astro splendere" in I, 3.)   SCHATZ 4840

La vedova ingegnosa. Intermezzi per musica, rappresentati nel Regio Teatro alla corte di Dresda. L'anno 1747.

n. i., n. d. 79 p. 15½^{cm}.

Three acts. Cast. The author, Tommaso Mariani, is not mentioned, nor the composer. According to Schatz this was first performed as intermezzi to "Emira," July 12, 1735, Teatro S. Bartolomeo, with music by Leonardo **Leo.** Though the opera was by Leo, the intermezzi possibly were not. Florimo mentions Ignazio **Prota** as the composer, and Florimo's predecessor is said by Leo, the biographer of his ancestor, to have attributed the music to Giuseppe **Sellitti.** The original title seems to have been "Drusilla, vedova ingegnosa e D. Strabone, dottore in medicina." German title page, "Die listige wittwe," and text face Italian in the Dresden ed.

SCHATZ 5554

— **La vedova ingegnosa.** Intermezzi per musica rappresentati nel Regio Teatro alla Corte di Dresda. L'anno 1747.

n. i., n. d. 39 p. 17½^{cm}.

The same, but Italian text only.   ML 50.2.V25L2

La vedova ingegnosa ossiano Le bizzarie del bel sesso, ballet. *See* Tarchi's Ademira.

La vedova raggiratrice, o siano I due sciocchi delusi. Dramma giocoso per musica da rappresentarsi nel Teatro Elettorale.

Dresda, n. publ., 1795. 127 p. 16^{cm}.

Two acts. Author not mentioned and unknown to Schatz and Carvalhaes. Marcos **Portugal** is mentioned as the composer. German title-page, "Die schlaue wittwe oder Die beiden angefuehrten thoren," and text face Italian.

First performed 1795, at Dresden, as indicated; at Florence, Teatro della Pergola, spring of 1794.   SCHATZ 8421

La vedova scaltra, ballet. *See* Alessandri's Il matrimonio per concorso.

La vedova scaltra, ballet. *See* P. Guglielmi's La sposa fedele.

La vedova scaltra. Dramma giocoso per musica da rappresentarsi nel magnifico Teatro dell' illust. Academia degl' Erranti della città di Brescia per la fiera dell' anno 1778 . . .

Brescia, Francesco Ragnoli, 1778. 63 p. 16½^{cm}.

Two acts. Author not mentioned and unknown to Schatz. Impresario's dedication, cast, and name of Vincenzo **Righini** as the composer.

First performed, as indicated, August, 1778.   SCHATZ 8790

Il veglione, ballet. *See* Stabinger's L'astuzie di Bettina.

Il vello d'oro. Dramma per musica da rappresentarsi nel Teatro Tron di S. Cassiano. Nel carnovale dell' anno 1749 . . .

Venezia, Modesto Fenzo, 1749. 36 p. 15^{cm}.

Three acts. By Giovanni Palazzi, who is not mentioned. Argument, cast, scenario, and name of Giuseppe **Scolari** as the composer.   SCHATZ 9800

Venceslao.

Apostolo Zeno, Poesie drammatiche, Venezia, 1744, t v., 94 p. 19^{cm}.

Five acts and licenza. Argument. No composer is mentioned. In the "Catalogo" at end of t. x, date and place of first ed. is given as "in Venezia. 1703. E in Vienna. 1725." (*See* below.) ML 49.A2Z3

— Venceslao. Pubblicato per la prima volta in Venezia 1703.

Apostolo Zeno, Poesie drammatiche, Orleans, 1785–86, t. ii, p. 217–304. 21^{cm}.

Five acts and licenza. Argument. No composer is mentioned. ML 49.A2Z4

Venceslao. Dramma per musica da rappresentarsi nel Teatro di S. A. S. il Signor principe di Carignano . . .

Torino, Francesco Antonio Gattinara, 1721. 4 p. l., 60, [1] p. 15^{cm}.

Three acts. Impresario's dedication, argument, cast, scenario, and name of the composer, Giuseppe **Boniventi**, but not of the librettist, Apostolo Zeno.
First performed, as indicated, December 26, 1720. SCHATZ 1195

Venceslao. Dramma per musica, da rappresentarsi nella Cesarea Corte per il nome gloriosissimo della Sac. Ces. e Catt. Real Maestà di Carlo VI. imperadore de' Romani . . . La poesia è del Sig. Apostolo Zeno . . . La musica è del Sig. Antonio Caldara . . .

Vienna d'Austria, Gio. Pietro Van Ghelen, n. d. 4 p. l., 72 p. 14½^{cm}.

Five acts and licenza. Argument and scenario. The ballet music was composed by Niccola Matteis.
First performed at Vienna, as indicated, November 4, 1725. SCHATZ 1489

Venceslao. Drama per musica da rappresentarsi nel Teatro Tron di S. Cassiano nel carnovale dell' anno MDCCLII.

[Venezia], n. publ., n. d. 60 p. 14½^{cm}.

Three acts. By Apostolo Zeno, who is not mentioned. Argument, cast, scenario, and name of Antonio Gaetano **Pampani** as the composer. SCHATZ 7759

Venceslao. Drama da rappresentarsi per musica nel Teatro Grimani in S. Giò. Grisostomo . . .

Venezia, Giròlamo Albrizzi, 1703. 72 p. 14½^{cm}.

Five acts. Dedication, with the initials of the author, Apostolo Zeno, from which it appears that the drama was first privately performed for Signore Filippo Rangoni before it appeared before the public at the Grimani Theatre. Argument, cast, scenario, notice to the reader, and name of Carlo Francesco **Pollaroli** as the composer ("La musica è . . . ventesima sua fatica in questo solo Teatro"). SCHATZ 8322

Venceslao, drama per musica.—Wenceslaus . . .

Hamburg, Spiering, 1744. 95 p. 19½^{cm}.

Three acts. By Apostolo Zeno, who is not mentioned. Scenario, cast, argument, and name of Paolo **Scalabrini** as the composer "a risserva di alcune arie di diversi autori." Italian and German texts.
First performed at Hamburg, Theater beim Gänsemarkt, August 19, 1744; at the same theater previously, October 31, 1743, and at Linz, Theater im Ballhause, 1743. SCHATZ 9518

Venceslao. Musicalisches schauspiel, umb auf dem hohen nahmenstag Seiner Churfuerstl. Durchl. Maximilian Emanuel . . . in Muenchen den 12. octob. dess 1725 sten jahrs vorgestellet zu werden. Auss dem welschen uebersetzt.

[Muenchen], Johann Lucas Straub, n. d. 76 p. 13^{cm}.

Five acts. Neither Apostolo Zeno, the author, nor the translator, nor the composer, Pietro **Torri**, is mentioned. The Italian text of the arias and choruses is added to the German. SCHATZ 10367

Les **vendangeurs** ou Les deux baillis, divertissement en un acte et en vaudevilles; par MM. de Piis & Barré; représenté pour la première fois, à Paris, le mardi 7 novembre 1780, & à Versailles, devant Leurs Majestés, le vendredi suivant, par les Comédiens italiens ordinaires du roi.

Paris, Vente, 1781. 40 p. 19^{cm}.

Cast. Not recorded by Cl. & L. or Schatz. SCHATZ 11521

La **Vendemia** ossia La contadina impertinente, ballet. *See* Insanguine's Calipso.

La **vendemmia.** A. T. of the ballet Li due sindaci.

La **vendemmia.** Dramma giocoso per musica. Da rappresentarsi nel Teatro presso la porta d'Italia. Sotto l'impresa e direzzione di Giuseppe Bustelli. L'anno 1779.

Vienna, Giuseppe noble de Kurzböck, n. d. 56 p. 16$\frac{1}{2}$^{cm}.

Two acts. By Giovanni Bertati, who is not mentioned. Scenario and name of Giuseppe **Gazzaniga** as composer. This version has in I, 3, the aria "Del destino invan mi lagno," in I, 6, "Su bel bello, adagio," in I, 8, "Alle selve alle capanne."
First performed at Florence, Teatro in via della Pergola, May 12, 1778; at Venice, Teatro di San Moisè, fall of 1778. ML 50.2.V28G3

—La **vendemmia.** Dramma giocoso per musica, da rappresentarsi nel Piccolo Teatro Elettorale.

Dresda, 1783, n. publ. 127 p. 15$\frac{1}{2}$^{cm}.

Two acts. German title page, "Die weinlese," and text face Italian. **Gazzaniga** is mentioned as the composer. This edition of Bertati's text is very different from that below.
The latter has in I, 3, the aria "La donna ch'è amante," the Dresden libretto has no aria; the Lisbon ed. has "Su bel bello, adagio" in I, 6, the Dresden ed. has it in I, 7. Scene I, 9, in the latter is the same as I, 8, in the former, but this has the aria "Egli è ver che son villana" instead of "Alle selve, alle campanne." SCHATZ 3675

— La **vendemmia.** Dramma giocoso per musica da rappresentarsi nel Reggio Teatro di S. Carlo della Principessa . . . nel 24 di giugno dell' anno 1794.

Lisbona, Simone Taddeo Ferreira, 1794. 77 p. 14$\frac{1}{2}$^{cm}.

Two acts. By Giovanni Bertati, who is not mentioned. Cast, scenario, and name of the composer, Giuseppe **Gazzaniga.** SCHATZ 3674

La **vendemmia** ossia La contadina impertinente, ballet. *See* Anfossi's Il curioso indiscreto.

Li **vendemmiatori**, ballet. *See* Piccinni's La scaltra letterata.

I **vendemmiatori** ovvero I due sindaci. Farsa in prosa con musica alla francese che si rappresenta della Compagnia Accademica toscana di Pietro Andolfati addetta al Regio Teatro degli Infuocati di Firenze . . .

Livorno, Antonio Lami e comp., 1790. 44 p. 14$\frac{1}{2}$^{cm}.

One act. Neither the author (unknown to Schatz) is mentioned, nor the composer, Ferdinando **Rutini.**
First performed at Florence, Teatro di via del Cocomero, carnival, 1789. ML 48.A5v.13

Le **vendemmie** o sia La villanella rapita, ballet. *See* Sarti's Fra i due litiganti il terzo gode, Lisbona, 1793.

Le **vendemmie fiamminghe,** ballet. *See* Bianchi's Il disertore.

La **vendetta d'amore,** ballet. *See* Paër's La testa riscaldata.

La **vendetta di Armida vinta dall' amore.** A. T. of the ballet Il ritorno di Rinaldo presso Armida.

La **vendetta di Nino,** ballet. *See* the pasticcio Elena e Paride.

La **vendetta di Nino.** Dramma per musica da rappresentarsi nel Real Teatro di S. Carlo nel dì 12 di novembre 1790 . . .

> *Napoli, Vincenzo Flauto, 1790. 56 p. 15cm.*

Two acts. Impresario's dedication, argument, cast, scenario, and name of Francesco **Bianchi** as the composer. The text is by Ferdinando Moretti (not mentioned) who based it on Melchiore Cesarotti's translation of Voltaire's "Semiramis." Dedication dated November 12, 1790, with remark that the first performance had to be postponed from November 4. On p. 8–24 cast, argument, and description of "Gli sventurati amori di Cleide ed Almindo o sia Il trionfo de' Goti. Balloeroico pantomimo, inventata e composto dal Sig. Sebastiano Gallet" in five acts, music ("tutta nuova") by Giuseppe Ercolano. SCHATZ 985

La **vendetta di Nino.** A. T. of Borghi's La morte di Semiramide.

La **vendetta di Nino,** ballet. *See* Curcio's Emira e Zopiro.

La **vendetta di Nino.** A. T. of Nasolini's La morte di Semiramide.

La **vendetta di Nino.** Melodramma tragico per musica da rappresentarsi nel nobile Teatro de' Cinque Signori Condomini di Senigallia la fiera di luglio dell' anno 1786 . . .

> *Firenze, n. publ., 1786. front., 47 p. 18cm.*

Two acts. The author is not mentioned and unknown to Schatz. Impresario's dedication, prefatory note, cast, and name of Alessio **Prati** as the composer ("musica tutta nuova"). SCHATZ 8452

— La **morte di Semiramide.** Tragedia in musica da rappresentarsi nel nobilissimo Teatro Venier in San Benedetto l'autunno dell' anno 1791.

> *Venezia, Modesto Fenzo, 1791. 54 p. 18½cm.*

Three act version of "La vendetta di Nino" in which Seleuco has become Sesostri. Cast, scenario, and name of Giuseppe instead of Alessio **Prati** as the composer. On p. [23]–28 argument and cast of Paolino Franchi's "Inkle e Jariko, ballo eroico tragico pantomimo." The composer of the music is not mentioned. SCHATZ 8453

La **vendetta disarmata dall' amore.** Drama per musica da rappresentarsi in Venezia nel Teatro di S. Fantino. L'anno 1704 . . .

> *Venezia, Domenico Miloco, 1704. 48 p. 14cm.*

Three acts. Dedication with the initials of the author Francesco Passarini, scenario, argument, and notice to the reader. The composer, Girolamo **Polani,** is not mentioned. The dedication begins "Gl'applausi, che riportò in Rovigo l'autunno scorso il presente drama" but it was then given with the title "La costanza nell' Honore." SCHATZ 8253

[Venere, Amore, etc.]

Venere, Amore, Iride, Borea, Nettuno, Anfione, Museo are the characters used for the prologue and six intermedii in:

"HERO, E LEANDRO. Favola marittima del Bracciolino dell' Api. Con intermedii apparenti. E col Montano Egloga . . . In Roma, Appresso Guglielmo Facciotti. 1630 . . . Ad instanza d'Ottavio Ingrillani."

Ingrillani's dedication is dated Rome, April 20, 1630. PQ.

Venere con Adone ossia Le gelosie di Diana e di Marte, ballet. *See* Paër's Ero e Leandro.

Venere e Adone, ballet. *See* Anfossi's La contadina incivilita.

Venere ed Adone, ballet. *See* Monza's Sesostri.

Venere gelosa di Niccolò Enea Bartolini . . .

  Padova, Paolo Framo, 1643. 7 p. l., 92, [1] p. 14^{cm}.

  Three acts with prologue. Author's dedication dated Padua, January 11, 1643, lengthy prefatory note, and argument. Francesco Paolo **Sacrati**, the composer, is not mentioned.

  First performed at Venice, Teatro Novissimo alla Cavallerizza, carnival, 1643.

                                                    SCHATZ 9251

Venere placata. Componimento drammatico per le augustissime nozze delle Reali Altezze di Giuseppe arciduca d'Austria etc e della reale infanta Donna Isabella di Borbone etc   Da cantarsi nel Teatro di Livorno la sera de' v. ottobre MDCCLX . . . [vignette]

  Livorno, Gio. Paolo Fantechi, n. d.   xxvii, [1] p. 29$\frac{1}{2}$^{cm}.

  Vignettes by C. Coltellini, engraved by F. Violanti and others. At the end Marco Coltellini is mentioned as the author and Carlo Antonio **Campion** as the composer. The cast consisted of two characters only, Venere, sung by Maria Maddalena Parigi and Amore, sung by Tommaso Guarducci.   SCHATZ 1536

Venere placata. Dramma per musica da rappresentarsi nel Teatro Grimani di S. Samuele nella fiera dell' Ascensione dell' anno MDCCXXX.

  Venezia, Carlo Buonarigo, 1731. 47, [1] p. 15^{cm}.

  Three acts. By Claudio Niccolò Stampa, with impresario's dedication, argument, cast, scenario, and names of the author and of the composer, Francesco **Courcelle**. The additional p. contains Buonarigo's announcement of publication of "un esatto catalogo di tutti li drammi musicali recitati in Venezia."   SCHATZ 2284

I Veneziani a Costantinopoli, ballet. *See* Luigi Piccinni's L'amante statua.

I Veneziani a Costantinopoli, ballet. *See* Trento's La finta amalata.

La vengeance. A. T. of Gresnich's Les faux monnoyeurs.

La vengeance de l'amour ou Diane et Endimion. *See* Palmire.

La Venitienne, comedie-ballet, représentée par l'Academie royale de musique l'an 1705. Les paroles de M. de la Mothe & la musique de M. de la Barre. LXIV. opera.

  n. i., n. d. 14^{cm}. front., 393–436, [3] p. (Recueil général des opéra, t. viii, Paris, 1706.)

  Detached copy. Three acts, with prologue. Cast.

  First performed, as indicated, May 26, 1705.   SCHATZ 5345
                                                    Second copy. ML 48.R4

Venus, feste galante, chantée devant Monseigneur, le 27 janvier 1698.

  [1]–12 p. 17$\frac{1}{2}$^{cm}. (Antoine Danchet, Théâtre, t. ii, Paris, 1751.)

  One act. Not recorded by De La Vallière.   PQ 1972.D1

Venus and Adonis: A masque. And **Myrtillo**: A pastoral interlude. Performed at the Theatre-Royal. Written by Colley Cibber,
Esq., set to musick by Dr. Pepusch . . .

> *London, Henry Lintot, 1736. vii, (incl. front.), [8]–24 p. 16^cm.*

The first piece consists of two "interludes." "Myrtillo" begins on p. 25. Casts
and preface:

"The following Entertainment is an Attempt to give the Town a little good Musick
in a Language they understand: For no Theatrical Performance can be absolutely
Good, that is not Proper; and how can we judge of its Propriety, when we know not
one Word of the Voice's Meaning? But perhaps this is not all that the Italian Language has of late impos'd upon us; most of our Opera's being (if possible) as miserably
void of Common Sense in their Original, as the Translation: Nay, the Tyranny is carried yet farther; for the Songs are so often turn'd out of their Places, to introduce
some absurd favourite Air of the Singer, that in a few Days the first Book you have
bought, is reduc'd to little more than the Title-Page of what it pretends to; and as it
now stands, the whole Entertainment seems to be dwindled into a Concert of Instruments; for a Voice that is not understood, has in reality no more Meaning than the
Fiddle that plays to it: And thus, by slavishly giving up our Language to the despotick
Power of Sound only, we are so far from establishing Theatrical Musick in England,
that the very Exhibition or Silence of it seems entirely to depend upon the Arrival or
Absence of some Eminent Foreign Performer. By this sort of Conduct, the vast
Sums that have been levied for the Support of it, have only ended in its Abuse and
Prostitution. And (though the insolent Charms of the Opera seem to be above it)
why should we suppose that a little plain Sense should do Musick any more harm,
than Virtue does a Beautiful Woman? And 'tis but a melancholy Proof of its Power,
that it has been so long able to keep Nonsense in countenance.

"It is therefore hoped, that this Undertaking, if encourag'd, may in time reconcile
Musick to the English Tongue. And, to make the Union more practicable, it is
humbly moved, that it may be allow'd a less Inconvenience, to hear the Performer
express his Meaning with an imperfect Accent, than in Words, that (to an English
audience) have no Meaning at all: And at worst, it will be an easier Matter to instruct
two or three Performers in tolerable English, than to teach a whole Nation Italian.

"After having said so much of its Absurdities, it will be but just to allow the Excel-
lencies of the Italian Composition; the Manner of it being indisputably superior to
all Nations for a Theatre: And 'tis hoped this Entertainment will want nothing of
the Italian, but the Language."

"Venus and Adonis" was first performed at Drury Lane, as indicated, November
22, 1715; "Myrtillo" in 1716.   ML 52.2.V47

Venus et Adonis, tragedie en musique, representée par l'Academie
royalle de musique.

> *Amsterdam, chez les héritiers d'Antoine Schelte, 1699. 57 p. (incl.
> front.). 14½^cm.*

Prologue and five acts. Neither the author, J. B. Rousseau, nor the composer,
Henri **Desmarets,** is mentioned.

First performed March 17, 1697, as indicated.   ML 50.2.V3D2

— **Venus et Adonis,** tragedie. Représentée par l'Academie royale
de musique l'an 1697. Les paroles sont de M. Rousseau & la musique
de M. Desmarets. XLI. opera. Tome VI.

> *n. i., n. d. front., p. 1–62. •(Recucil général des opéra, Paris, 1703.)
> 14^cm.*

Detached copy. Prologue and five acts.   SCHATZ 2535
                                        Second copy. ML 48.R4

— **Venus und Adonis,** in einer, sowohl der poësie, als musique nach,
frantzoesischen opera, nebst einem teutschen comiquen vorspiel auf
dem Hamburgischen Schau-platz, im april der 1725 sten jahres vorgestellet.

> *n. i., n. d. [46] p. 16½^cm.*

With "Vorbericht," in which **Desmarets** and Rousseau are mentioned. Translator unknown to Schatz. French and German text.   SCHATZ 2536

Venus et Adonis, ballet. *See* Michl's Il trionfo di Clelia.

Venus et Adonis. *See* Mondonville's Les festes de Paphos.

Venus et Adonis, entrée in Quinault's Les amours des Déesses.

La **vera costanza.** Dramma giocoso per musica da rappresentarsi nel Teatro delle Dame nel carnevale dell' anno 1776 . . .

　　Roma, Giovanni Bartolomicchi, 1776.　12, 70 p.　15½ᶜᵐ.

　　Three acts.　By Francesco Puttini, who is not mentioned.　Publisher's dedication, argument, scenario, cast, and name of Pasquale **Anfossi** as the composer.
　　First performed, as indicated, January 3, 1776.　　　　　ML 50.2.V33A5

— La **vera costanza.** Dramma giocoso per musica da rappresentarsi nel Teatro di via della Pergola nella primavera del MDCCLXXVII . . .

　　Firenze, Gio. Risaliti, 1777.　48 p.　16ᶜᵐ.

　　Three acts.　By Francesco Puttini.　Name of Pasquale **Anfossi** as composer, but not of librettist, and cast of the ballets, but not of the opera.　　SCHATZ 249

— La **vera costanza;** drama giocoso per musica da rappresentarsi nel Regio Teatro.—Den sande bestandighed; et lystigt syngespill . . .

　　Kiøbenhavn, H. J. Graae, 1778.　163 p.　16½ᶜᵐ.

　　Three acts.　Argument, cast, and name of Pasquale **Anfossi** as composer.　Danish text faces Italian.
　　First performed, as indicated in the title, January 31, 1778.　　SCHATZ 250

— La **vera costanza.** Dramma giososo per musica.　Da rappresentarsi nel Piccolo Ducal Teatro di Bronsvic.

　　Bronsvic, n. publ., 1783.　159 p.　16ᶜᵐ.

　　Three acts.　Scenario and name of **Anfossi** as composer.　German title-page, "Die wahre beständigkeit," and text face Italian.　　SCHATZ 251

— La **pescatrice fedele.** Dramma giocoso per musica da rappresentarsi nel Teatro Giustiniani di San Moisè l'autunno dell' anno 1776.

　　n. i., n. d.　2 p. l., 80 p.　17ᶜᵐ.

　　Three acts.　Cast, scenario and name of Pasquale **Anfossi** as composer.　This is practically the same text as that of "La vera costanza," except that the third act of "La pescatrice fedele "has six scenes only instead of nine, that III, 1 is different, shorter and without the aria "Nò, non andrà l'indegna," and that the scene II, 11 "Perdona amato Ernesto" with aria "A questo bel segno" has been dropped.
　　First performed at Venice, as indicated, November 20, 1776.　　SCHATZ 248

La **vera costanza.** Dramma giocoso per musica da rappresentarsi nel Real Teatro dell' Ajuda nel felicissimo giorno natalizio di Sua Altezza Serenissima l'augusto Don Giovanni, principe del Brasile li 13. maggio 1789.

　　[Lisbona], Stamperia reale, n. d.　60 p.　15½ᶜᵐ.

　　Two acts.　By Francesco Puttini, who is not mentioned.　Scenario, cast, and name of Jeronymo Francisco de **Lima** as composer.
　　First performed at Lisbon, Theatro de Salvaterra, carnival, 1785.　　SCHATZ 5617

Die veraechter der schoenen oder Der wechsel in der liebe.　Tr. of Tritto's Li disprezzatori delle donne o sia Le vicende amorose.

Die an dem gluecklichen vermaehlungs-tage Ihr. Roemisch. und Ungar. Majestaet koenig Josephs mit der Durchl. printzessin Wilhelmina Amalia gebohrnen hertzogin zu Braunschw. und Lueneb. vorgebildete **Verbindung des grossen Hercules mit der schoenen Hebe,** wie solche in einem singe-spiel auf dem Hamburg. Schau-platz aufgefuehret worden.

[Hamburg], Nicolaus Spieringk, 1699. Unpaged. 18^{cm}.

Three acts. Historical preface by the author, Christian Heinrich Postel (not mentioned), with name of Reinhard **Keiser** as composer.

First performed, as indicated, February 14/24, 1699.   Schatz 5114

Die **verdammte staat-sucht,** oder Der verfuehrte Claudius, in einem sing-spiel auff dem Hamburgischen Schau-platz vorgestellet.

Hamburg, Nicolaus Spieringks wittwe, 1703. Unpaged. 19^{cm}.

Three acts. Neither the author, Hinsch, is mentioned, nor the composer, Reinhard **Keiser.** Some of the arias have Italian text only.   Schatz 5130

— **Claudius, roemischer kaeyser,** in einem sing-spiele auf dem Hamburgischen Schau-platze vorgestellet im jahr 1726.

[Hamburg], mit Stromerschen schrifften, n. d. Unpaged. 19^{cm}.

Three acts. Argument, scenario. Neither the author, resp. translator, Hinsch, nor the composer, Reinhard **Keiser,** is mentioned. Some of the arias have Italian text added to the German. Noticeably different from the edition of 1703. For instance, the aria "Wie sich die blauen flammen entzünden" has been dropped from I, 1, as also "Holde goettin glimmer hertzen" from I, 2, and the aria in I, 2, "Toedtliche eyffersucht," has been replaced by "Du grausame schoene."   Schatz 5083

Die **vereinigten mit-buhler** oder Die siegende Atalanta, in einem singe-spiel auff dem Hamburgischen Schau-platz vorgestellet 1698.

n. i., n. d. Unpaged. 18^{cm}.

Prologue and three acts. German version by Gottlieb Fiedler of Agostino **Steffani**'s "Le rivale concordi," text by Ortensio Mauro. As such, first performed at Hanover, February 10, 1692, not 1693 as Riemann incorrectly states in his Steffani bibliography.   Schatz 10035

Die **vereitelten raenke.** Tr. of Cimarosa's Le trame deluse.

Veremonda l'Amazzone di Aragona. Drama ridotto in nuova forma dal Signor Luigi Zorzisto, per esser honorato di musica dal Signor Francesco Cavalli . . .

Venetia, Giuliani, 1652. 93 p. (incl. front.) 15^{cm}.

Three acts with prologue. By conte Maiolino Bisaccioni. The dedication is signed by Gio. Battista Balbi, the director of the scenery, machinery, etc., is dated Venice, January 28, 1652, and deals with the machines, etc., only. The argument appears on p. 86–91.

First performed at Venice, Teatro a SS. Giovanni e Paolo, fall of 1652.

          Schatz 1742

Die **verfolgte unbekannte.** Tr. of Piccinni's L'incognita perseguitata.

Die **verfolgte und triumphirende liebe.** A. T. of Grüger's Hass und aussoehnung.

Der **verfuehrte Claudius.** A. T. of Keiser's Die verdammte staatsucht.

Die **vergebliche vorsicht.** A. T. of F. L. Benda's Der barbier von Seville.

La **vergine del sole.** A. T. of the ballet Cora.

La **vergine del sole.** Dramma per musica da rappresentarsi nel Regio Teatro degl' illustrissimi Signori Accademici Avvalorati in Livorno l'autunno dell' anno 1799.

> *Livorno, La Società tipografica, n. d.* 35 p. 17½*cm*.

Two acts. By Francesco Casòli. Prefatory note, argomento, cast, and names of composer, Gaetano **Andreozzi,** and author.

First performed at Palermo, Teatro di Santa Cecilia, fall of 1797. SCHATZ 203

La **vergine del sole.** A. T. of Sarti's L'Idalide.

La **vergine del sole.** Dramma per musica di Carlo Lanfranchi Rossi, gentiluomo toscano, tra gli Arcadi = Egesippo Argolide. Da rappresentarsi nel Real Teatro del Fondo di Separazione per quart' opera di quest' anno 1786 . . .

> *Napoli, n. publ., 1786.* 48 p. 14½*cm*.

Two acts. Impresario's dedication, notice to the public, in which this is called the last opera of the season, argument, scenario, cast, and name of Giacomo **Tritto** as the composer. On p. 41–48, argument and description, without name of the composer of the music, of Giambattista Giannini's "Il Tancredi, ballo eroico pantomimo." His second ballet was called "L'infedeltà sorpresa." SCHATZ 10464

La **vergine del sole** o sia Alonzo e Cora, ballet. *See* Prati's L'Ifigenia in Aulide.

Die **verhinderte grausamkeit.** A. T. of the ballet Raoul, herr von Crequi.

I **veri amici.** O. T. of Silvani's Candace libretto, as altered by Lalli.

I **veri amici.** Secondo drama per musica da rappresentarsi in occasione che si festeggiano le augustissime nozze de serenissimi sposi Carlo Alberto principe elettorale di Baviera etc e Maria Amalia, principessa elettorale, arciduchessa d'Austria etc l'anno MDCCXXII.

> *Monaco, Enrico Teodoro di Côllen.* 70 p. 14½*cm*.

Prologue and three acts. By Francesco Silvani and Domenico Lalli. Argument, cast, scenario, and name of Tommaso **Albinoni** as composer. With this opera were performed his intermezzi, "*Vespetta e Pimpinone*" (*see his* Pimpinone).

First performed, as indicated, October 24, 1722. SCHATZ 99

I **veri amici.** Drama per musica da rappresentarsi nel Teatro Tron di S. Cassano. Nel carnovale dell' anno 1713 . . .

> *Venezia, Marino Rossetti, 1713.* 70 p. 15*cm*.

Three acts. Dedication, argument, cast, scenario, and notice of the publisher, in which he says:

"L'idea del presente drama, è presa dalla famosa tragedia di Mons. Pietro Cornelio, intitolata l'Eraclio ["Héraclius"], ella fù appoggiata ad una storia egittia, cangiatevi perciò i nomi. Consegnato poi ad altro auttore perche la verseggiasse, questo si è creduto in debito di aggiugnervi diverse altre scene ancora per ridurre l'opera all uso italiano, che gusta vedere ad agire gl' interlocutori, e non solo sentirli parlare . . ."

This note does not seem to quite bear out Wiel and Schatz, who attribute the text to Francesco Silvani *and* Domenico Lalli. They both consider Andrea **Paulati** as the composer. SCHATZ 7786

La verità in cimento. Drama per musica da rappresentarsi nel Teatro di S. Angelo l'autunno dell' anno 1720 . . .

Venezia, Marino Rossetti, 1720. 48 p. 15^{cm}.

Three acts. By Giovanni Palazzi, who is not mentioned. Impresario's dedication, argument, cast, scenario, and name of Antonio **Vivaldi** as the composer.

SCHATZ 10782

La verità nell' inganno. O. T. of Francesco Silvani's text Attalo rè di Bitinia.

La verità nell' inganno. O. T. of Silvani's text I fratelli riconosciuti.

La verità nell' inganno. Drama per musica, da rappresentarsi nella Cèsarea Corte per il nome gloriosissimo della Sac. Ces. e Catt. Real Maestà di Carlo VI . . . L'anno MDCCXVII.

Vienna d'Austria, Gio. Van Ghelen, n. d. 95 p. 14½^{cm}.

Three acts and licenza. By Francesco Silvani, who is not mentioned, but who presumably also wrote the three intermezzi in three parts of *"Lisetta ed Astrobolo"* (p. 84–95). With argument, scenario, and name of the composer, Antonio **Caldara.** The ballet music was composed by Niccola Matteis.

First performed at Vienna, Hoftheater, November 4, 1717.   SCHATZ 1490

La verità nell' inganno. Drama per musica da rappresentarsi nel Teatro Tron di S. Cassano. Nel carnovale dell' anno 1713 . . .

Venezia, Marino Rossetti, 1713. 72 p. 14½^{cm}.

Three acts. By Francesco Silvani, who is not mentioned. Dedication dated Venice, February 7, 1713, argument, cast, scenario, name of Carlo Francesco **Gasparini,** and notice to the reader, who is informed that the libretto was written eight years previously, remained since then destined for performance, but now had to be cut, altered, and adapted "all' attività de' virtuosi, che devono rappresentarlo."

SCHATZ 3587

La verità raminga, e'l Disinganno. Drammi musicali. Di Francesco Sbarra. Di nuovo aggiunti alla moda.

Venetia, n. publ., 1664. 41 p. 13^{cm}.

On p. 28–41: "Il *Disinganno.* [2] Intremedi rappresentati in musica." This is preceded by "La verità raminga. Balletto in musica" in two parts (p. 3–27), but it is really a bizarre opera with ballets. The argument was delivered by "Il Tempo" in person, who "al suono d'una bizarra corrente comparve ballando grave d'anni non meno, che leggiero di piedi un vecchio alato . . ." No composer recorded by Allacci, Wotquenne, or Schatz.   ML 50.2.V35

Die verkehrte welt. Tr. of Galuppi's Il mondo alla roverscia.

Die verkehrte welt, in einer opera comique auf dem Hamburgischen Schau-platze vorgestellet. Im jahr 1728.

[Hamburg], Gedruckt mit Stromerschen schrifften, n. d. Unpaged. 18^{cm}.

Three acts. Cast, names of Johann Philipp Praetorius as author, of Georg Philipp **Telemann** as composer and "Vorbericht," in which Praetorius gives as his source Le Sage's "Le monde renversé," first performed 1718. The capable German translation then made could not be traced. Besides, it was mostly in prose:

"So hat der uebersetzer des gegenwaertigen sing-spiels, dem herrn Le Sage, *mutatis mutandis,* lediglich folgen, und nach dessen wohlgetroffenen original seine schlechte copie einrichten muessen."   SCHATZ 10267

Der verkleidete liebhaber oder Der verstellte gaertner. Tr. of Philidor's L'amant déguisé.

Die **verlassene Armide**.   Tr. of Prati's Armida abbandonata.

Die **verlassene Dido**.   Tr. of Hasse's La Didone abbandonata.

Die **verlassene Dido**.   Tr. of Jommelli's Didone abbandonata.

Die **verlassene Didone**.   Tr. of Fiorillo's La Didone abbandonata.

Der **verliebte eigensinn** oder Nannerl bei hofe.   Tr. of Favart's parody Le caprice amoureux.

Der **verliebte herr doctor**.   A. T. of Dieter's Der schulze im dorfe.

Der **verliebte herr doctor**.   A. T. of Lacher's Der schulze im dorfe.

Der **verliebte maler**.   Tr. of Duni's Le peintre amoureux de son modèle.

Die **verliebte taenzerin**.   Tr. of Cimarosa's La ballerina amante.

Gesaenge aus der oper Der **verliebte werber**, in zwey aufzuegen. Die musik ist von Carl Eule.
> *Hamburg, Peter Christian Heinrich Rabe, 1799. 32 p. 15½^{cm}.*
> Author unknown to Schatz.
> First performed at Hamburg, Theater beim Gänsemarkt, September 10, 1799.
> SCHATZ 2961

Die **verliebten bauernmaedchen**.   Tr. of Borghi's Le villanelle innamorate.

Die **verliebten poltergeister**.   Tr. of Mozart's Gli amanti folletti.

Het **vernietigd verdrag**.   Tr. of Gaveaux 'Le traité nul.

Il **vero amico**.   A. T. of the ballet Zeboschi ed Esing.

Il **vero amore**.   Da cantarsi nel Teatro privilegiato da S. M. C. e Cat. in Vienna.   Nell' anno MDCCXXXVI.   Nel mese di novembre.—Die wahre liebe . . .
> *Wien, Johann Peter v. Ghelen, n. d. 67 p. 15^{cm}.*
> Three acts. Argument. German text faces Italian. Author and composer not mentioned, and unknown to Schatz. Not recorded by von Weilen.   SCHATZ 11377

Il **vero amore**.   A. T. of Schuster's Rübenzahl.

Il **vero omaggio**.
> *Metastasio, Poesie, Parigi, vedova Quillau, 1755, t. vii, [363]–376 p. 16^{cm}.*
> One act. ML49.A2M42

— Il **vero omaggio**.   Questo breve drammatico componimento fu scritto in Vienna dall' autore, l'anno 1743, e cantato con musica del Bonno nel Palazzo del giardino di Schönbrunn, alla presenza de' sovrani, per festeggiare il giorno di nascita di S. A. R. l'arciduca Giuseppe, poi imperadore.
> *[405]–416 p. 26^{cm}. (Pietro Metastasio, Opere, t. ii, Parigi, vedova Herissant, 1780.)*
> One act. ML49.A2M44

Die **verschwoerung der Odaliken**[!] oder Die loewenjagd. Ein singspiel in drey aufzuegen, fuer die K. K. priv. Marinellische schaubuehne, von Karl Friedrich Hensler. In musik gesetzt, von herrn kapellmeister Müller.

> *Wien, mit Goldhannschen schriften, 1792.* 91 p. .16^{cm}.

Cast.

First performed, as indicated, May 3, 1792. Schatz 6974

Il **versillo della libertà.** *See* M. Curzio.

Der **verspottete geitzige.** Tr. of Paisiello's L'avaro deluso.

Der **verstellte gaertner.** A. T. of Philidor's Der verkleidete liebhaber.

Die **verstellte gaertnerin.** Tr. of Anfossi's La finta giardiniera.

Das **verstellte kammermaedgen.** Tr. of Galuppi's La finta cameriera.

Der **verstellte narr aus liebe.** Tr. of Sacchini's Il soldato per forza impazzito per amore.

Der **verstellte Policare.** Tr. of Conti's Il finto Policaro.

Die **verstellte Teutsche.** Tr. of Hasse's La finta Tedesca.

Vertunno e Pomona, ballet. *See* Anfossi's La forza delle donne.

Vertunno e Pomona, ballet. *See* Rust's Il conte Baccelone.

Die **verwaiste Amerikanerin.** Tr. of Gestewitz' L'orfanella americana.

Die **verwandelte Daphne.** *See* Händel's Der beglueckte Florindo.

Die **verwandelten weiber,** oder Der teufel ist los. Eine komische oper in drey aufzuegen. Zweyte auflage.

> *Leipzig, Dyckische buchhandlung, 1772.* 144 p. 15½^{cm}.

On p. [2], the note: "Nach dem *Devil to pay* or *The wives metamorphosed* des herrn Coffey." On October 6, 1752, Christian Felix Weisse's two-act "Der teufel ist los oder Die verwandelten weiber" was performed, with music by Johann **Standfuss,** at Leipzig. Later on Weisse rewrote the text in three acts, after Sedaine's "Le diable à quatre" and reversed the title, and Johann Adam **Hiller** revised Standfuss's music, replaced rejected portions of it by music of his own, and composed all new matter in the text. The libretto of 1772 mentions neither author nor composers. In the revised three-act version this practically first German comic opera was first performed at Koch's Theater am Rannstaedter Thore, Leipzig, May 28, 1766 (Calmus). Schatz 4732

— Arien und gesaenge aus der komischen oper Die **verwandelten weiber,** oder Der teufel ist los, in drey aufzuegen. Nach dem "Devil to pay or the Wives metamorphosed" des herrn Coffey. Die musik ist von Standfuss und Hiller.

> *Riga, Julius Conrad Daniel Mueller, 1794.* 16 p. 16^{cm}.

Schatz 4732a

Die **verwandelten weiber**—Continued.

— Die **verwandelten weiber** oder Der teufel ist los.　Eine komische oper in drey aufzuegen.

　　C. F. Weisse, Komische opern, Carlsruhe, 1778, th. ii, 5 p. l., 104 p. 18½ᶜᵐ.

　　Text preceded by the dedicatory poem to Anna Amalia duchess of Saxe-Weimar and Eisenach, as protectress of German dramatic and histrionic art.　On p. [2] the note: "Nach dem *Devil to pay, or, the Wives metamorphosed* des herrn Coffey."　Without names of **Standfuss** and **Hiller**.　　　　　　　　　　　　　　ML 49.A2W2

Die **verwandelten weiber**.　Tr. of Portugal's Le donne cambiate.

Verwirrung durch aehnlichkeit.　Tr. of Portugal's Le confusioni della somiglianza.

Il **Vespasiano.**　Drama per musica nel nuovo Teatro Grimano di S. Gio. Chrisostomo.　L'anno 1678.　Di Giulio Cesare Corradi . . .

　　Venetia, Francesco Nicolini, 1678.　72 p.　14½ᶜᵐ.

　　Three acts.　Author's dedication, notice to the reader with name of Carlo **Pallavicino** as the composer, argument, and scenario.　　　　　　　　　SCHATZ 7732

Vespetta e Milo.　Intermezzi by A. Scarlatti (I–II), and Conti (III) in Lotti's opera " Giove in Argo."　　　　　　　　　　　　SCHATZ 5719

[**Vespetta e Milo**]　Intermedi cantati dalli Signori Livia Constantini la Polachina, e Lucrezio Borsari, ambi virtuosi della Maestà Augusto Secondo rè di Polonia . . .—Traduction des intermedes italiens en françois . . .

　　Dresde, Jean Riedel, 1717.　31 p.　15ᶜᵐ.

　　A notice to the reader tells us that the first and second intermezzo were by Alessandro **Scarlatti**, the third by Francesco [Bartolommeo] **Conti**; also that the text of the first two was by Silvio Stampiglia, of the third by baron Francesco Ballerini and that

　　"Le arie che sono tradote in francese, di Vespetta e di Milo, si possono cantare come le italiane."

　　Not mentioned by Dent, unless I am much mistaken.　The libretto of these intermezzi forms also part of that to Antonio Lotti's opera "Giove in Argo," Dresda, (1717).　(Unpaged.　19cm.　See Schatz 5719.)

　　First performed at Dresden, Schlosstheater ("Sala di Ridotto"), October 25, 1717 (Schatz), though the dedication in the libretto of "Giove in Argo" is dated November, 1717.　　　　　　　　　　　　　　　　　　　SCHATZ 9522

Vespetta e Pimpinone.　L. T. of Albinoni's Pimpinone.

Vespetta e Valasco, intermezzi.　*See* Stratonica.

La **veuve.**　Entrée in Mouret's Les festes de Thalie.

La **veuve coquette.**　Entrée in Mouret's Les festes de Thalie.

La **veuve indécise.**　Parody of La veuve coquette.

Il **viaggiator ridicolo,** dramma giocoso per musica.　Da rappresentarsi nel Teatro privileggiato di Vienna nell' anno 1766.

　　[*Vienna*], *Ghelen, n. d.　56 p.　16½ᶜᵐ.*

　　Three acts.　Cast, scenario, and names of Goldoni as the author, and of Florian Leopold **Gassmann** as the composer.

　　First performed as indicated, Kaernthnerthortheater, May 25. 1766.

　　　　　　　　　　　　　　　　　　　　　　　　SCHATZ 3618

Il viaggiator ridicolo. Dramma giocoso da rappresentarsi nel Teatro Giustinian di S. Moisè il carnovale dell' anno 1761.

Venezia, Modesto Fenzo, 1761. 58 p. 14^{cm}.

Three acts. By Goldoni, who is not mentioned. Cast, scenario, and name of Salvatore **Perillo** as the composer.　　　　　　　　SCHATZ 7922

Il viaggiatore ridicolo. Dramma di tre atti per musica. Rappresentato per la prima volta in Parma nel carnovale dell' anno MDCCLVII con musica del Mazzoni.

Carlo Goldoni, Opere teatrali, Venezia, Zatta e figli, 1788–95, t. 40, [5]–56 p. 18^{cm}.　　　　　　　　　　　　　　　　　PQ

Il viaggiatore ridicolo. Dramma giocoso per musica del Signor dottor Carlo Goldoni da rappresentarsi nel magnifico Teatro dell' illustrissima Accademia degli Erranti di Brescia per la fiera di agosto dell' anno 1771 . . .

Brescia, Fratelli Pasini, n. d. 55 p. 17^{cm}.

Three acts. Dedication, cast, scenario, and name of the composer, Pietro **Caramanica.**　　　　　　　　　　　　　　　　SCHATZ 1619

Il viaggiatore ridicolo. Dramma giocoso per musica da rappresentarsi nel Teatro del Bairo Alto di Lisbona nell' estate del corrente anno 1770. Poesia del rinomato avvocato Carlo Goldoni . . .

Lisbona, Stamperia reale, n. d. 72 p. 14$\frac{1}{2}$^{cm}.

Three acts. Dedication, cast, scenario, and name of Giuseppe **Scolari** as composer, except for the arias: "Quant' è buono il cioccolato" (I, 1), "Se placate un dì vi miro" (I, 3), "Vous êtes le mon cher coeur" (I, 6), "Sò che gl'uomini han per uso" (I, 8), "Io sono un uomo docile" (II, 1), "Di sdegno m'accende (II, 2), "Astolfo poveretto" (II, 4), "Io conosco d'ogni amante" (II, 5), "Non sperar ch'io faccia pace" (III, 4). The composer of these is not mentioned.　　ML 50.2.V42S2

I viaggiatori. Commedia per musica di Pasquale Mililotti da rappresentarsi nel Teatro de' Fiorentini nella primavera del corrente anno 1776.

Napoli, n. publ., 1776. 48 p. 15$\frac{1}{2}$^{cm}.

Three acts. Cast and name of Niccolò **Piccinni** as composer. Florimo and Schatz state that the opera had been previously performed there in the fall of 1775.
　　　　　　　　　　　　　　　　　　　　SCHATZ 8134

I viaggiatori o siano I matrimoni in cantina. Dramma giocoso per musica da rappresentarsi nel nuovo Teatro de' nobili Signori fratelli Prini della città di Pisa il carnevale dell' anno 1786.

Pisa, Francesco Pieraccini, 1786. 49 p. 17$\frac{1}{2}$^{cm}.

Two acts. Author not mentioned, and unknown to Schatz. Cast and name of Michele **Neri Bondi** as the composer. ("La musica tutta nuova.")　SCHATZ 7079

I viaggiatori areostatici, ballet. *See* Pugnani's Demofoonte.

I viaggiatori felici. Dramma giocoso per musica da rappresentarsi nel Piccolo Teatro di S. A. E. di Sassonia.

Dresda, n. publ., 1781. 163 p. 15$\frac{1}{2}$^{cm}.

Two acts. By Filippo Livigne, who is not mentioned. Name of **Anfossi** as composer. German title-page, "Die gluecklichen reisenden," and text face Italian.

First performed at Dresden on November 21, 1781; at London in the same year (Schatz), and at Venice, Teatro di S. Moisè, fall of 1780.　　SCHATZ 255

I viaggiatori felici—Continued.

— I **viaggiatori felici**; a new comic opera, in two acts. As performed at the King's Theatre in the Hay-Market. The music entirely new, by the celebrated Signor Anfossi.

London, H. Reynell, 1782.   68 p.   17½ᶜᵐ.

Two acts. By Filippo Livigni, who is not mentioned.   Schatz 254

— I **viaggiatori felici.** Dramma giocoso per musica. Da rappresentarsi ne' Teatri privilegiati di Vienna l'anno 1783.

[Vienna], Giuseppe Nob. de Kurzbeck, (1783).   173 p.   16½ᶜᵐ.

Two acts. Name of **Anfossi** as composer. German title, "Die gluecklichen reisenden," and text face Italian.
First performed on December 29, 1783, as indicated in the title.   Schatz 256

La **viaggiatrice** o sia Le circostanze imbarazzanti, ballet.   *See* Bianchi's Briseide.

Le **vicende amorose.**   Dramma giocoso per musica del Timido da rappresentarsi nel Teatro Giustiniani di S. Moisè l'autunno dell' anno 1760.

Venezia, Modesto Fenzo, 1760.   59 p.   14½ᶜᵐ.

Three acts. Unknown author's preface, cast, scenario, and name of Ferdinando Giuseppe **Bertoni** as composer.   Schatz 928

Le **vicende amorose.**   O. T. of Tritto's Li disprezzatori delle donne o sia Le vicende amorose and of his I raggiri d'amore.

Le **vicende d'amor e di fortuna.**   Da rappresentarsi in musica nel Teatro di San Fantino il carnovale dell' anno 1709.

Venetia, Marino Rossetti, n. d.   46 p.   14ᶜᵐ.

Three acts. Argument, scenario. Author (Giov. Domenico Pallavicino, text originally called "Tiberio imperadore d'Oriente") and composer (unknown to Schatz) not mentioned.   Schatz 11378

Le **vicende d'amore.**   O. T. of the libretto L'impostura poco dura.

Le **vicende d'amore.**   Dramma in musica a cinque voci. Da rappresentarsi ne' Teatri privilegiati di Vienna l'anno 1784.

Vienna, Giuseppe nob. de Kurzbeck, n. d.   [9]–70 p.   17ᶜᵐ.

Two acts. Author not mentioned and unknown to Schatz. Pietro **Gugliemi** is mentioned as the composer. On p. 1–8 a "Capitolo burlesco sopra lo studio."
First performed, as indicated, June 16, 1784; at Rome, Teatro Valle, carnival, 1784.
          Schatz 4278

Le **vicende della sorte.**   Dramma giocoso per musica da rappresentarsi nel Teatro di S. A. Serenissima il Signor principe di Carignano nell' autunno dell' anno MDCCLXIV.

Torino, Gaspare Bayno, n. d.   46 p.   16ᶜᵐ.

Three acts. The author, Giuseppe Petrosellini, is not mentioned. Cast and name of Niccolò **Piccinni** as the composer.
First performed at Rome, Teatro Valle, January 3, 1761.   Schatz 8154

— Le **vicende della sorte.**   Dramma giocoso per musica da rappresentarsi nel Real Teatro dell' Ajuda in occasione di festeggiarsi il giorno natalizio del fedelissima monarca D. Giuseppe I. . . . nel di 6 giugno. MDCCLXVI.

Lisbona, Michele Maneschal da Costa, n. d.   63 p.   16ᶜᵐ.

Two acts. By Giuseppe Petrosellini, who is not mentioned. Cast, scenario, and name of Niccolò **Piccinni** as the composer.   Schatz 8143

Le **vicende della sorte**—Continued.

— Der **glueckswechsel,** oder Mutter Natur in ihren kindern. Ein komisches singspiel in zwey aufzuegen, nach Goldoni und Riccini[!], von Bock.

n. i., n. d.   78 p.   16^{cm}.

Is no. I in IIter theil of his "Komische opern der Italiener," Leipzig, 1782.
First performed at Leipzig, Theater b. Rannstädter Thore, June 30, 1780.
SCHATZ 8120

Victor, hertzog der Normannen.   Opera.

n. i., n. d.   Unpaged.   16½^{cm}.

Three acts. Argument. Neither the author, Hinsch, is mentioned, nor the composers, Johann Christian **Schieferdecker** (act I), Johann **Mattheson** (act II), and Georg **Bronner** (act III).
First performed at Hamburg, Theater beim Gänsemarkt, 1702.   SCHATZ 9605

Li **viecchie coffejate.** Commeddeia pe museca de col' Antuono Feralintisco pe lo triato de li Shiorentine nchist' anno 1710 . . .

Nuenezia, pe l'arede de Casparra Stuorto, 1710.   4 p. l., 61 p.   13½^{cm}.

Three acts. By Francesco Antonio Tulli, who is not mentioned. Dedication, cast, scenario, and notice to the reader, in which this is said about the anonymous and unknown composers:
"Fà ntennere a li benigne lejeture, ca chi à puosto nmuseca stà commedeja è no povero sorece nfus' all' uoglio no scuro prinzipiante, e no scolariello de chillo gra' mastrone, ch' hà fatto la primma, e farrà la terza; ed è uno nzomma, c'hà la varva peccerella, e perzò e sseno scarzo ancora de fonnamiento, mmereia d'essere compatuto, si non se vedea lè cose soje tutta la regola, e tutta la mellonia, che nc'abbesogna . . ."
SCHATZ 11381

Lo **viecchio avaro.** Commedia pe' museca, de col' Antuono Feralintisco. Da rappresentarese a lo Triato de li Shiorentine 'nchisto carnevale de ll'anno 1727 . . .

Napole, A spese de lo   mpresario, 1727.   60 p.   14½^{cm}.

Three acts. By Francesco Antonio Tulli. Scenario, notice to the reader, cast, name of Giuseppe de **Majo** as composer, and impresario's dedication, according to which the carnival season was to close with this opera.   ML 50.2.V41M2

La **vieillesse** ou L'amour enjoué. Entrée in Campra's Les ages, ballet.

La **vieillesse d'Annette et Lubin,** opéra. En un acte et en prose, mêlé de chant par M. A. L. d'Antilly. Réprésenté, pour la première fois, par les Comédiens italiens ordinaires du roi, le premier août 1789.

Paris, Prault, 1790.   47 p.   21^{cm}.

Cast. The composer, Pierre David Augustin **Chapelle,** is not mentioned.
ML 50.2.V45C3

Le **vieux chateau,** ou La rencontre, comédie en un acte, mêlée de chants; représentée pour la première fois sur le Théâtre Feydeau, le 25 ventose an 6 [March 15, 1798]; paroles du citoyen Alex. Duval, musique du citoyen Domenico Della Maria.

Paris, Au bureau dramatique, an VI. [1798–99]   46 p.   21^{cm}.

ML 50.2.V49D2

Le **village.** Entrée in Boismortier's Les voyageurs de l'amour.

The **village maid**; an opera. In three acts. By a young lady . . .
*London, Printed for the authoress, by William Innes, 1792. 4 p. l.,
90 p. 20½*^{cm}.

List of subscribers and Advertisement. Neither authoress, composer, or performance recorded by Clarence.   LONGE 220

The **village opera.** As it is acted at the Theatre-Royal, by His Majesty's servants. Written by Mr. Johnson . . . To which is added the musick to each song.

London, J. Watts, 1729. 3 p. l., 70 p. 20^{cm}. [*Bound with Gay,
John. The beggar's opera. London, 1728.*]

Three acts. Ballad opera. Cast and table of the 53 songs, followed by a one-page list of "Books lately publish'd and printed for J. Tonson and J. Watts." The corresponding airs are printed in the text with their titles. Air 40 ("Softer than the breath of May") is a "Minuet, by Mr. **Fairbank**."
First performed at Covent Garden, as indicated, February 6, 1729.   ML 50.5.B3

— The **village opera.** As it is acted at the Theatre-Royal, by His Majesty's servants. Written by Mr. Johnson . . . To which is added the musick to each song.

London, J. Watts, 1729. 4 p. l., 76 p. 20½^{cm}.

Three acts. Same cast and same book list, but the table of contents now has 63 not 53 songs and on recto of p. l. 4 appears "A new air": "If 'tis true, that once," sung by Miss Raftor in II, 3. The "Minuet by Mr. Fairbank" has now become Air 45.   ML 50.5.V45
Second copy of this edition, but of an issue which has this characteristic misprint in the heading of the book list: "O OKS lately publish'd . . ."   LONGE 32

The **village wedding:** or, The faithful country maid. A pastoral entertainment of music. As it is performed at the Theatre-Royal at Richmond.

London, M. Hingeston, 1767. 35 p. 19^{cm}.

Two acts. Cast. By James Love, who is not mentioned. Composer unknown to Schatz.   LONGE 198

La **villana riconosciuta.** Commedia per musica di Giuseppe Palomba da rappresentarsi nel Teatro di S. Ferdinando a Ponte nuovo.

Napoli, Domenico Sangiacomo, 1791. 48 p. 15^{cm}.

Two acts. Cast and name of **Cimarosa** as the composer. On p. 2 a notice to the effect that two arias, one of them "Rammenta alfin chi sono" (I, 10), were changed "per comodo de' cantanti" and that "per serbare la brevità si tralascia di rappresentare l'atto 3." On p. 48 the notice:
"Si avverte che mancava la composizione della musica dell' aria di Mad. nell' atto secondo scena x, p. 38 ("Misero pargoletto") e si è costituita la seguente: "*Che smania . . . che affanno. La rabbia m'opprime.*"
First performed at Naples, Teatro del Fondo, 1783.   SCHATZ 1987

La **villanella incostante.** Dramma giocoso per musica di Giovanni Bertati da rappresentarsi nel Teatro Giustiniani di S. Moisè l'autunno dell' anno 1773.

Venezia, Antonio Graziosi, 1773. 60 p. 17½^{cm}.

Three acts. Cast, scenario, and name of Johann Gottlieb **Naumann** as the composer.   SCHATZ 7058

La **villanella incostante**—Continued.

— **Le nozze disturbate.** Dramma giocoso per musica del Sigr. Giovanni Bertati da rappresentarsi nel Piccolo Teatro di S. A. S. E. di Sassonia.

Dresda, n. publ., l'anno 1774. 143, [1] p. 16½ᶜᵐ.

Three acts. Johann Gottlieb **Naumann** is mentioned as the composer. On the additional page the remark:

"Poichè nel finale dell' atto secondo è stato cangiato il Brindisi fatto per la città di Venezia, si avverte per il rispetto dovuto al celebre autore, che la variazione è seguita per adattarsi alle circostanze di questo teatro."

German title page, "Die gestoehrte hochzeit," and text face Italian.

First performed in 1774, as indicated. SCHATZ 7059

La **villanella ingentilita.** Commedia per musica di Saverio Zini da rappresentarsi nel Nuovo Teatro de' Fiorentini per terza opera del corrente anno 1779.

Napoli, n. publ., 1779. 68 p. 15ᶜᵐ.

Three acts. Cast and name of Pietro **Guglielmi** as the composer.

First performed, as indicated, November 8, 1779. SCHATZ 4292

— **Li fratelli Pappamosca.** Dramma giocoso per musica da rappresentarsi nel Real Teatro di Salvaterra nel carnovale dell' anno 1786.

[Lisbon], Stamperia reale, n. d. 83 p. 15½ᶜᵐ.

Three acts. Cast, scenario, and name of Pietro **Guglielmi** as the composer. This is Zini's "La villanella ingentilita" with noticeable differences. For instance, I, 3, has now the aria "Fiumicel, soave erbetta" instead of "Dormiva il mio pastore un dì nel prato" and II, 5, now begins "Fratello Sesto mio, mi dice il core" instead of "Oh che fussi ammazzata." SCHATZ 4283

La **villanella rapita.** A. T. of the ballet Le vendemmie.

La **villanella rapita.** Dramma giocoso per musica di Giovanni Bertati da rappresentarsi nel Teatro Giustiniani in San Moisè l'autunno dell' anno 1783 . . .

Venezia, Modesto Fenzo, 1783. 64 p. 17½ᶜᵐ.

Two acts. Impresario's dedication, cast, scenario, and name of composer, Francesco **Bianchi.** The two ballets were called "La pastorella fedele" by Federico Terrades, music ("tutta nuova") by Mattia Stantingher [Stabingher] and "Il barbiere di Siviglia, ballo comico" by the same author, the composer not being mentioned. SCHATZ 986

— **La villanella rapita.** Dramma giocoso per musica da rappresentarsi nel Teatro alla Scala l'autunno dell' anno 1785 . . .

Milano, Gio. Battista Bianchi, n. d. 64 p. 17ᶜᵐ.

Two acts. Cast, name of Francesco **Bianchi** as composer, scenario, and dedication, according to which the "vera malattia della principale attrice," the "Signora Giacinta Galli prima donna assoluta senza vicenda," had delayed the performances several days. They began in September. Bertati is not mentioned. With the opera were performed Sebastiano Gallet's ballets, "L'amor vincitore ossia Diana ed Endimione" and "Le pazzie amorose," the composers of the music not being mentioned.

ML 48.A5 v. 12

— **La villanella rapita.** Dramma giocoso per musica da rappresentarsi nel Teatro di S. A. E. di Sassonia.

Dresda, n. i.; 1785. 135 p. 15½ᶜᵐ.

Two acts. With name of Francesco **Bianchi** as composer. German title-page, "Das entfuehrte bauernmaedchen," and text face Italian.

First performed at Dresden in 1785. SCHATZ 987

La **villanella rapita**—Continued.

— La **villanella rapita**; a comic opera, in two acts, as performed at the Theatre Royal in the Hay Market. The music by Signor Bianchi, under the direction of Signor Federici.

London, H. Reynell, 1790. 71 p. 19^{cm}.

Two acts. The author, Bertati, is not mentioned.
First performed 1790, as indicated.   ML 48.M2N

— La **villanella rapita**, osia, Le gelosie di Pippo: Dramma giocoso per musica da rappresentarsi nel Regio Teatro di S. Carlo, della Principessa la primavera dell' anno 1796.

Lisbona, Taddeo Ferreira, 1796. 135 p. 14½^{cm}.

Two acts. Cast, argument, scenario, and name of the "celebre Sig. Adamo[!] Bianchi" as composer—of course, an error for Francesco **Bianchi**. The text is that by Bertati. Between the acts was performed "La villanella socorsa," ballet by Luigi Chiaveri, the composer not being mentioned. Portuguese text faces Italian.
                                                                    SCHATZ 990

— La **fedeltà tra le selve**. Dramma giocoso per musica a sette voci da rappresentarsi nel Teatro alla Valle degl' illm̃i Sigg. Capranica nell' anno 1789.

Roma, Michele Puccinelli, n. d. 58 p. 15^{cm}.

Two acts Cast and name of the composer, Francesco **Bianchi,** but not of the librettist, Giovanni Bertati. Four arias, marked with an asterisk, were by Valentino **Fioravanti**, as stated in the note: "Che giorno di contento" (I, 7), "Care selve amiche piante" (II, 15), etc. The text is that of "La villanella rapita."
                                                                    SCHATZ 992

La **villanella socorsa,** ballet. *See* Bianchi's La villanella rapita.

Le **villanelle astute**. Dramma giocoso per musica da rappresentarsi nel nobile Teatro di S. Samuele il carnovale dell' anno 1786.

Venezia, Modesto Fenzo, 1786. 45, [1] p. 18^{cm}.

Two acts. By unknown author. Cast, scenario, and name of Franesco **Bianchi,** as composer. The ballets, both by Eusebio Luzzi, the composers not being mentioned, were called "Giulietta e Romeo, ballo tragico in cinque atti" and "Il geloso in cimento."   SCHATZ 1010

Le **villanelle innamorate**. Azzione comica per musica da rappresentarsi nel Piccolo Teatro di S. A. S. E. di Sassonia l'anno 1778.

Dresda, Nella Stamperia elettorale, n. d. 79 p. 16½^{cm}.

Two acts. By unknown author. German title-page, "Die verliebten Bauernmaedchen," and text face Italian. Giov. Battista **Borghi** is mentioned as composer.
First performed as "L'amore in campagna" at Vienna, Hoftheater, June 19, 1774.
                                                                    SCHATZ 1238

Il **villano geloso**. O. T. of Bertati's text I finti eredi.

Il **villano geloso**. Dramma giocoso per musica da rappresentarsi nel Teatro Giustiniani di S. Moisè l'autunno dell' anno 1769 . . .

Venezia, Modesto Fenzo, 1769. 48 p. 16½^{cm}.

Three acts. By Giovanni Bertati, who is not mentioned. Impresario's dedication, scenario, and name of Baldassare **Galuppi** as composer.   SCHATZ 3472

Il **villano geloso.** Dramma giocoso per musica da rappresentarsi nel Piccolo Teatro di S. A. E. di Sassonia.

Dresda, n. publ., 1770. 125 p. 15^cm.

Three acts. By Giovanni Bertati, who is not mentioned. Scenario and name of Johann Gottlieb **Naumann** as the composer. The cast has been added in ink by a contemporary hand. German title page, "Der eyfersuechtige bauer," and text face Italian.

First performed 1770, as indicated. Schatz 7060

La **ville.** Entrée in Boismortier's Les vogages de l'amour.

Le **villeggiatrici ridicole.** Dramma comico per musica d'Antonio Bianchi Veneziano da rappresentarsi nel Teatro Tron di S. Cassiano nell' autunno dell' anno 1765.

Venezia, Modesto Fenzo, 1765. 59 p. 14½^cm.

Three acts. Cast, scenario, and name of the composer, Antonio **Boroni.**

Schatz 1253

La **villeggiatura.** A. T. of Cimarosa's L'apparenza inganna.

La **villeggiatura.** Dramma giocoso per musica. Da rappresentarsi nel Teatro di S. A. Serenissima il Signor principe di Carignano nell' autunno dell' anno MDCCLXIV.

Torino, Gaspare Bayno, n. d. 55 p. 15½^cm.

Three acts. Cast. Neither Niccolò **Piccinni,** the composer, nor the author (unknown to Schatz) is mentioned.

First performed at Bologna, Teatro Formagliari, carnival, 1764. Schatz 8155

La **villeggiatura di Mestre.** Farsa per musica da rappresentarsi dai Comici del Teatro Tron in S. Cassiano nel carnovale dell' anno 1770 . . .

Venezia, Gio. Battista Casali, n. d. 48 p. 15^cm.

Two acts. Dedication signed by the author, Giovanni Dolfin, and name of the composer, Salvatore **Perillo.** Schatz 7923

La **villeggiatura in scompiglio** ossia Il falso amico, ballet. *See* G. Giordani's Cajo Mario.

I **viluppi amorosi.** Commedia per musica di due atti di Giuseppe Mililotti. Da rappresentarsi nel Teatro Nuovo sopra Toledo per la prima opera di quest' anno 1778.

Napoli, n. publ., 1778. 60 p. 15^cm.

Two acts. Argument, cast, and name of Angelo **Tarchi** as the composer.

Schatz 10227

Il **vincitor di se stesso.** Dramma per musica del Sig. conte Antonio Zaniboni . . . da rappresentarsi nel Teatro di Sant' Angelo l'autunno dell' anno MDCCXLI . . .

Venezia, Marino Rossetti, 1741. 45 p. 15^cm.

Three acts. Impresario's dedication dated November 4, 1741, argument, scenario, cast, and name of the composer, Ignazio **Fiorillo.** Schatz 3204

Il vincitor generoso. Drama per musica da rappresentarsi nel famosissimo Teatro Grimani di S. Gio. Grisostomo il carnovale dell' anno MDCCVIII . . .

Venezia, Marino Rossetti, 1708.   70, [1] p.   15^cm.

The add. p. contains a list of "Opere musicali sin' ora stampate in Venezia da Antonio Bortoli."
Three acts. Dedication with the initials of the author, Francesco Brianni, who calls this his first drama and dates the dedication Venice, January 10, 1708, notice to the reader, cast, and scenario. The composer, Antonio **Lotti**, is not mentioned.
                                                            SCHATZ 5726
                                    Second copy.   ML 45.A5   v.12

La vindemmia, ballet.   *See* Paisiello's Le vane gelosie.

Vindemmia, ballet.   *See* Salieri's La partenza inaspettata.

La vindemmia o La contadina impertinente, ballet.   *See* Tarchi's Le Danaidi.

La vindemmia fiamminga.   A. T. of the ballet Il pellegrinaggio.

Vindice la pazzia della vendetta.   Favola pastorale da rappresentarsi in musica nel Teatro di S. Fantino l'anno 1707 in Venezia . . .

Venezia, Gio. Maria Rossi, 1707.   42 p.   15^cm.

Three acts. Dedication by the author, Bartolomeo Pedoni, argument, notice to the reader, cast, and scenario. The composer, Girolamo **Polani**, is not mentioned.
                                                            SCHATZ 8254

A Vingança da Cigana: drama jocoserio de hum so' acto, para se representar no Real Theatro de S. Carlos, pela companhia italiana, offerecido ao publico por Domingos Caporalini no dia do seu beneficio. Anno de 1794. A poesia he de Lereno Secinuntino Arcade Romano. A musica he do Sr. Antonio Leal Moreira, mestre do Real Seminario, e do mesmo theatro.

Lisboa, Simão Thaddeo Ferreira, n. d.   47 p.   14^cm.

Cast.   SCHATZ 6634
                                    Second copy.   ML 48.C6I

The vintner outwitted.   A. T. of Love and revenge.

Il vinto trionfante del vincitore.   Drama per musica da rappresentarsi nel Teatro di Sant' Angelo l'autunno dell' anno MDCCXVII . . .

Venezia, Marino Rossetti, 1717.   59 p.   14½^cm.

Three acts. Dedication by the author, Antonio Marchi, dated Venice, November 22, 1717, cast, argument, scenario, and notice to the reader, in which Marchi says:
    "Nel ristretto termine di pochi giorni sono stato obbligato ad alestire il presente mio drama. Questo è lo stesso sogetto, che hai compatito molti anni sono nel Teatro di Santi Giovanni e Paolo [as "Zenobia regina dei Palmireni"]; mà pero ora ridotto più uniforme al tuo genio, ed al gusto moderno, in guisa tale, che ti sembrerà al tutto diverso . . ."
Composer not mentioned and unknown to Schatz, who calls this a pasticcio.
                                                            SCHATZ 11379

La Violante.   O. T. of A. Palomba's text Don Saverio.

La violenza d'amore.   A. T. of Gasparini, Polaroli and Ballarotti's L'Alciade.

The **virgin prophetess.** A. T. of Cassandra.

The **virgin unmasked.** A. T. of An old man taught wisdom.

Virginia. Dramma per musica da rappresentarsi nel nobilissimo Teatro delle Dame nel carnevale dell' anno 1786 . . .

Roma, Gioacchino Puccinelli, n. d. 44 p. 16^cm.

Three acts. Dedication, argument, scenario, and name of Gioacchino **Albertini** as composer. The author is unknown to Schatz. The music ("tutta nuova") of the first ballet was by Francesco Giuliani. Schatz 86

Virginia. Tragedia per musica in tre atti del conte Alessandro Pepoli da rappresentarsi nel nobilissimo Teatro della Fenice al principio del carnevale dell' anno 1794.

Venezia, Modesto Fenzo, 1793. 88 p. 19^cm.

Three acts. Cast, scenario, and name of Felice **Alessandri** as composer. First performed December 26, 1793, as indicated in title. Schatz 156

La **Virginia.** Dramma per musica da rappresentarsi nel Nuovo Teatro dagli Armeni della città di Livorno l'autunno dell' anno 1786.

Livorno, Gio. Vinc. Falorni, n. d. 48 p. 15^cm.

Three acts. Author not mentioned, and unknown to Schatz. Impresario's dedication, argument, cast, scenario, and name of Angelo **Tarchi** as composer ("La musica è tutta nuova"). With the opera was performed (composers of the music not mentioned) Domenico Ballou's "Il trionfo di Arianna, ballo eroico pantomimo." As second ballet for later on was announced "Il cappellaro." First performed at London, Hay-market, May 4, 1786; at Florence, Teatro di via della Pergola, fall of 1785. Schatz 10232

Virginio consolo. Drama per musica da rappresentarsi nel Teatro in Sant' Angelo l'anno 1704. Di Matteo Noris.

Venetia, Gio. Battista Zuccato, 1704. 72 p. 15^cm.

Three acts. Scenario and prefatory note, in which Noris says: "Quando io credevo haver terminata la lunghissima mia carriera (ed' il perche già lo sai) di compor drami per musica, mi conviene di bel nuovo dar principio alla corsa in un teatro, dove l'augustia della scena non admette imperiali magnificenze nè pompose maestà . . ."

Antonio **Zannettini,** the composer, is not mentioned. Schatz 11145

Viriate. Dramma per musica da rappresentarsi nel Teatro Vendramino di San Salvatore nella fiera dell' Ascensione dell' anno 1762.

Venezia, Valvasense, 1762. 60 p. 15^cm.

Three acts. By Metastasio, who is not mentioned, and whose original title was "Siface" (Schatz). Argument, cast, scenario, and name of **Galuppi** as the composer. ("La musica sarà tutta nuova.")

First performed May 19, 1762, as indicated. Schatz 3511

Viriate. Dramma per musica da rappresentarsi nel famosissimo Teatro Grimani di S. Gio. Grisostomo nel carnovale del 1739 . . .

Venezia, Marino Rossetti, 1739. 60 p. 14½^cm.

Three acts. Metastasio's "Siface," altered by Domenico Lalli, who signs the dedication. Argument, cast, scenario, and name of Joh. Ad. **Hasse** as composer. Schatz 4581

La virtù al cimento.   Melodramma da rappresentarsi in Parma nel R. D. Teatro di Corte il carnevale dell' anno MDCCXCVIII . . .

     Parma, Carmignani, n. d.   58, [4] p.   18^{cm}.

     Two acts.   By Angelo Anelli, who is not mentioned, and whose original title was "Griselda."   Dedication, cast, scenario, and name of Ferdinando Pär (**Paër**) as the composer.   ("La musica è tutta nuova.")   With the opera were performed Francesco Clerico's ballets, "Ercole e Dejanira" and "Zemira e Azor," of which latter a description on the unnumbered pages.   The composers of the music are not mentioned.

     First performed in February, 1798.   SCHATZ 7545

La virtù de' strali d'amore.   Opera tragicomica musicale di Giovanni Faustini . . .

     Venetia, Pietro Miloco, 1642.   96 p.   13$\frac{1}{2}$^{cm}.

     Three acts, with prologue.   Author's dedication.   The composer, Pietro Francesco **Cavalli**, is not mentioned.

     First performed at Venice, Teatro di S. Cassiano, carnival, 1642.   SCHATZ 1729

La virtù nel cimento.   L. T. of Orlandini's Griselda.

La virtù premiata.   A. T. of Bianchi's Tarara.

La virtù premiata.   A. T. of Gardi's La semplice.

La virtù sublimata dal grande ovvero Il Macedone continente. L. T. of M. A. Ziani's Alessandro Magno in Sidone.

La virtù tra' nemici.   Drama per musica da rappresentarsi nel Teatro Giustiniano di San Moisè il carnovale dell' anno MDCCXVIII . . .

     Venezia, Marino Rossetti, 1718.   59 p.   14$\frac{1}{2}$^{cm}.

     Three acts.   Argument, notice to the reader, cast, scenario, and dedication signed by the author, Giovanni Battista Abbati, who calls this, in the prefatory note, "il secondo aborto della mia penna."   Giuseppe **Boniventi**, the composer, is not mentioned.   SCHATZ 1193

La virtù trionfante d'amore vendicativo.   Favola pastorale da recitarsi in musica nel Teatro di San Fantino l'anno 1708 . . .

     Venezia, Gio. Maria Rossi, 1708.   44 p.   14$\frac{1}{2}$^{cm}.

     Three acts.   Dedication by the author Bartolomeo Pedoni, briefest kind of scenario, argument and notice to the reader with the name of Girolamo **Polani** as the composer.   SCHATZ 8256

Virtù trionfante del vizio, La.   A. T. of Franceschini's Dionisio.

La virtù trionfante dell' amore e dell' odio.   O. T. of Silvani's text Tigrane.

La virtù trionfante dell' amore, e dell' odio: Drama per musica da recitarsi nel Teatro Vendramino di S. Salvatore, l'anno 1691.   Di Francesco Silvani.   Nova impressione . . .

     Venetia, Nicolini, 1681.   67 p.   14$\frac{1}{2}$^{cm}.

     Three acts.   Author's dedication, argument, scenario, and notice to the reader, in which Silvani says:

     "Voglio . . . che tù faccia smentire coloro che dicono, ch'il gusto di Venetia è corrotto, e che non piacciono oramai più che le barzelette, e che s'abborriscono sù le scene la gravità & il decoro.   Io ò lettore non ho di te tal sentimento, onde ti prego secondare la mia opinione, col frequentare un teatro, dove la virtù trionfa, sostenuta dalle musiche note del Signor Marc' Antonio **Ziani,** dall' arte de più virtuosi & insigni cantanti d'Italia . . ."   SCHATZ 11207

     First performed as indicated, carnival 1691.

Virtues of nature. A. T. of The American Indian.

La virtuosa alla moda. Dramma giocoso per musica da rappresentarsi nel Teatro della nobilissima Accademia Intronata di Siena nell' estate dell' anno 1777 . . .

> *Siena, Vincenzo Pazzini Carli e figli, 1777. 56 p. 16^{cm}.*
>
> Two acts. By Giovanni Bertati, who is not mentioned. Impresario's dedication, cast, and name of Luigi **Caruso** as the composer.
> First performed at Bologna, Teatro Marsigli Rossi, 1776; at Trieste, Teatro di San Pietro, carnival, 1776. SCHATZ 1648

— Li due amanti rivali. Dramma giocoso per musica da rappresentarsi nel nobile Teatro di San Samuele l'autunno dell' anno 1779.

> *Venezia, Modesto Fenzo, 1779. 47 p. 17^{cm}.*
>
> Two acts. Considerably different from the above. In this the character of the prima buffa, for instance, is called Isabellina, in "La virtuosa alla moda" Mirandolina. A note on p. 3 reads:
> "La musica è del Signor maestro Luigi Carusio [**Caruso**], escluse però le due arie della prima buffa, e quelle della seconda."
> Cast, scenario. SCHATZ 1653

La virtuosa bizzara. L. T. of P. Guglielmi's La virtuosa in Mergellina.

La virtuosa in Mergellina. Dramma giocoso in musica da rappresentarsi nel Regio Teatro nell' Accademia degli Avvalorati in Livorno il carnevale dell' anno 1793.

> *[Livorno], Tommaso Masi e comp., n. d. 61 p. 17^{cm}.*
>
> Two acts. By Saverio Zini, who is not mentioned. Impresario's dedication, cast, scenario, and name of Pietro **Guglielmi** as the composer.
> First performed at Naples, Teatro Nuovo, summer, 1785. SCHATZ 4279

— La virtuosa bizzara. Dramma giocoso per musica da rappresentarsi nel nobilissimo Teatro Giustiniani in San Moisè l'autunno dell' anno 1791.

> *Venezia, Modesto Fenzo, 1791. 52 p. 16½^{cm}.*
>
> Two acts. Cast and name of Pietro **Guglielmi** as the composer. This is Zini's "La virtuosa in Mergellina" text, but especially in the arias remarkably different from the Livorno, 1793, ed. SCHATZ 4280

— Chi la dura la vince ossia La finta cantatrice. Dramma giocoso per musica da rappresentarsi in Cremona nel Teatro della Nobile Associazione il carnevale dell' anno 1791.

> *Cremona, Lorenzo Manini, n. d. 59 p. 15^{cm}.*
>
> Two acts. Cast and name of Pietro **Guglielmi** as the composer. This is Zini's "La virtuosa in Mergellina" text, but with many alterations. SCHATZ 4299

Le virtuose bizzarre. Intermezzo per musica a cinque voci da rappresentarsi nel Teatro di Tordinona nel carnevale dell' anno 1779 . . .

> *Roma, Ottavio Puccinelli, 1778. 36 p. 15^{cm}.*
>
> Two parts. Author not mentioned and unknown to Schatz. Cast and name of Agostino **Accorimboni** as composer. Contains arias: "Se mai s'inalza al volo," "Se mi trovo in campo," "Sono amor giovane," "Se a cantar mi metto," etc.
> First performed as indicated, December 29, 1778. ML 50.2.V6A2

Le virtuose ridicole.

[219]–270 p. 16½ᶜᵐ. (Carlo Goldoni, Opere drammatiche giocose, t. ii, Torino, 1757.)

Three acts. First composed by *Galuppi* as below.   ML 49.A2G6

— **Le virtuose ridicole.** Dramma di tre atti in versi.

Carlo Goldoni, Opere teatrali, Venezia, Zatta e figli, 1788–95, v. 43, [123]–178 p. 18ᶜᵐ.   PQ

Le virtuose ridicole. Dramma giocoso per musica da rappresentarsi nel Teatro posto in contrada di San Samuele. Il carnovale dell' anno 1752.

Venezia, Giuseppe Bettinelli, 1752. 60 p. 15ᶜᵐ.

Three acts. Neither the author, Goldoni, nor the composer, **Galuppi,** is mentioned, whom at least Wiel does not positively identify with the music.

    Schatz 3512

The vision of the twelve goddesses, presented in a mask the 8th of Jan. at Hampton-Court, by the Queen's most excellent Majesty, and her ladies.

London, n. publ., 1717. [225]–245 p. 16ᶜᵐ.

Detached copy. The long dedication (p. [227]–235) by Sam. Daniel, the author, to Lady Lucy, countess of Bedford, begins:
"In respect of the unmannerly presumption of an indiscreet printer, who without warrant hath divulged the late show at Court, presented the 8th of January, by the Queen's Majesty and her ladies, and the same very disorderly set forth: I thought it not amiss, seeing it would otherwise pass abroad, to the prejudice both of the mask and the invention, to describe the whole form thereof, in all points as it was then perform'd . . ."
The composer not mentioned and unknown to Schatz.
First performed, as indicated, January 8, 1623.   Longe 201

I visionarj. Dramma giocoso per musica da rappresentarsi nel Teatro Giustiniani di S. Moisè l'autunno dell' anno 1772. Di Giovanni Bertati.

Venezia, Antonio Graziosi, 1772. 68 p. 16½ᶜᵐ.

Three acts. Cast, scenario, and name of Gennaro **Astaritta** as composer.

    Schatz 375

— **I visionarj.** Dramma giocoso per musica del Sigr. Giovanni Bertati da rappresentarsi nel Piccolo Teatro di S. A. S. E. di Sassonia.

Dresda, n. publ., 1774. 151 p. 17ᶜᵐ.

Three acts. Name of **Astaritta** as composer. German title-page, "Die lächerlichen gelehrten, ein lustiges singespiel," and text face Italian.
First performed, as indicated, September 3, 1774.   Schatz 376

— **I filosofi immaginarj.** Dramma giocoso per musica da rappresentarsi nel Real Teatro di Salvaterra nel carnovale dell' anno 1775.

[Lisbona], nella Stamperia reale, n. d. 78 p. 15½ᶜᵐ.

Three acts. Cast, scenario, and name of Gennaro **Astaritta** as composer. The text is Bertati's "I visionari."   Schatz 379

I visionari. L. T. of Paisiello's I filosofi immaginari.

La visione. *See* M. Curzio.

Les **visitandines,** comédie en deux acte [!] et en prose. Mêlée d'ariettes. Représentée sur le Théâtre de la rue Feydeau, le 7 août 1792. Par M. Picard.

Paris, Delalain, 1792. 31 p. 20cm.

Cast. The composer, **Devienne,** is not mentioned.
The printed full score has as date of first performance, July 7, 1792.

ML 50.2.V63D3

— De **visitandines,** zangspel in drie bedryven. Naar het fransch, door Hendrik Ogelwight, junior.

Amsteldam, J. Helders en A. Mars, 1796. 4 p. l., 63, [1] p. 16½cm.

With "Voorbericht." Translation of **Devienne's** "Les visitandines," text by Picard.

SCHATZ 2563

—Gesaenge aus der oper: **Liebe wagt alles,** in zwey aufzuegen. Dei musik ist von Devienne.

Hamburg, Rabe und Freystatzky wittwe, 1798. 24 p. 15cm.

Translation of "Les visitandines" by Heinrich Gottlieb Schmieder.
First performed at Hamburg, Theater beim Gaensemarkt, May 4, 1798.

SCHATZ 2556

De **visschers.** Tr. of Gossec's Les pêcheurs.

Il **vitio depresso, e la virtù coronata.** Drama per musica da rappresentarsi nel Teatro di S. Angelo l'anno 1687. Di Aurelio Aureli . . .

Venetia, Francesco Nicolini, 1687. 72 p. 13½cm.

Three acts. Author's dedication, dated Venice, November 24, 1686, argument, scenario, and author's notice to the reader, in which he mentions Teofilo **Orgiani** as the composer, and remarks:

"Questo drama, che leggi è il mio *Eliogabalo,* che già 18. anni rappresentar tù vedesti con tanto applauso nel famoso Teatro Grimano a Ss. Gio. e Paolo. È l'istesso personaggio, ma vestito in forma diversa . . ." SCHATZ 7299

La **vittoria d'Ercole contro Anteo,** ballet. *See* Draghi's opera Sulpitia.

La **vittoria d'Imeneo.** Festa da rappresentarsi nel Regio Teatro di Torino per le nozze delle A. A. R. R. di Vittorio Amedeo, duca di Savoia, e di Maria Antonia Ferdinanda, infanta di Spagna, l'anno MDCCL.

Torino, Pietro Giuseppe Zappata, e figliuolo, n. d. 68 p. 15½cm.

Three acts. By Giuseppe Bartoli. Cast, scenario, name of **Galuppi** as composer, and author's long dramaturgic preface by way of argument (p. 3–9), in which he says:

"In somma ho tentato di riunire le sorelle bene spesso divise, facendo sì che la poesia, la musica, la pittura, e la danza dirette in questa occasione senza violenza ad un solo fine, mostrassero la dipendenza loro da un solo principio. Giovò ancora questo incorporamento del ballo con l'azione per non altrepassare di molto a cagion de' versi il prescritto limite allo spettacolo."

First performed, as indicated, June 7, 1750. SCHATZ 3500

La **vittoria di Tamerlano contro Bajazette** ossia La Rossana, ballet. *See* Sacchini's Armida.

La vittoria nella costanza. Drama per musica da rappresentarsi nel Teatro di Sant' Angelo l'anno 1702 . . .

Venetia, Marino Rossetti, n. d. front., 54 p. 15ᶜᵐ.

Three acts. Dedication signed by the author, Francesco Passarini, argument, scenario, and notice to the reader, with name of Giuseppe **Boniventi** as composer, and in which Passarini says:

"hò invitato da Hannover il mio dramma à comparire sù le scene dell' Adria . . . L'hò vestito come ho potuto, non come dovevo e volevo, obligato à tenermi a quelle scene destinate già alla Briseide . . ." Schatz 1194

Vittorina. Dramma di tre atti per musica. Rappresentato per la prima volta in Londra l'anno MDCCLXXXII con musica del Piccini.

Carlo Goldoni, Opere teatrali, Venezia, Zatta e figli, 1788–95, v. 36, [249]–309 p. 18½ᶜᵐ.

Schatz dates the first performance London, Haymarket, 1779. PQ

Voilà ma journée. A. T. of Dalayrac's Ambroise.

Les voleurs. A. T. of Lesueur's La caverne.

Volodomiro. Dramma per musica da rappresentarsi nel Regio Teatro di Torino nel carnovale del 1787 alla presenza di S. S. R. M.

Torino, Onorato Derossi, n. d. viii, 80 p. 16ᶜᵐ.

Three acts. By Giandominico Boggio. Argument, cast, scenario, and names of the composer, Domenico **Cimarosa**, and the author. On p. 71–79, cast and description of "Ludovico Sforza detto Il Moro, ballo pantomimico in cinque atti." The second ballet was called "Chi ne fa ne aspetta." The third had no specific title. All three were by Sebastien Gallet, music by Vittorio Amedeo Canavasso. Schatz 2000

Vologeso. Dramma per musica da rappresentarsi nel nobillissimo Teatro di S. Benedetto nella fiera dell' Ascensione dell' anno MDCCLXX.

Venezia, Modesto Fenzo, 1770. 59 p. 17½ᶜᵐ.

Three acts. By Apostolo Zeno, a later version of his "Lucio Vero." Argument, cast, scenario, and name of the composer, Giuseppe **Colla.** Schatz 2111

Il Vologeso, ballet. *See* Gazzaniga's Circe.

Vologeso. Dramma per musica da rappresentarsi nel nobilissimo Teatro Venier in San Benedetto la fiera dell' Ascensione dell' anno 1796.

Venezia, Modesto Fenzo, 1796. 46 p. 18½ᶜᵐ.

Three acts. By Apostolo Zeno (originally his "Lucio Vero"), who is not mentioned. Argument, cast, scenario, and name of Ignazio **Gerace** as the composer. On p. 21–28 a description with argument and cast of "La morte d'Ippolito e Fedra, ballo tragico pantomimo."

First performed, as indicated, May 4, 1796. Schatz 3780

Vologeso. Dramma per musica da rappresentarsi nel Regio-Ducal Teatro di Milano per il carnevale dell' anno 1776 . . .

Milano, Giovanni Montani, n. d. 42, 23, 9 p. 15ᶜᵐ.

Three acts. A later version of "Lucio Vero" by Apostolo Zeno, who is not mentioned. Impresario's dedication dated Milan, December 22, 1775, argument, scenario, cast, and name of Pietro **Guglielmi** as composer. The additional pages contain cast and description of Noverre's "Les Horaces et les Curiaces, ballet tragique en cinq actes" and description of his "Les incidents, conte." The composers of the music are not mentioned.

First performed, as indicated, December 26, 1775. Schatz 4307

Il **Vologeso.** Dramma per musica da rappresentarsi nel Real Teatro di Salvaterra nel carnevale dell' anno 1769.

Lisbona, Michele Manescal da Costa, n. d. 62 p. 15cm.

Three acts. A later version of "Lucio Vero" by Apostolo Zeno, who is not mentioned. Argument, cast, scenario, and name of Niccolò **Jommelli** as the composer.
First performed at Ludwigsburg, Hoftheater, February 11, 1766. SCHATZ 4877

Vologeso. Dramma per musica da rappresentarsi nel Regio Teatro di Torino nel carnovale del 1783. Alla presenza delle Maestà Loro.

Torino, Onorato Derossi, n. d. viii, 52 p. 16½cm.

Three acts. A later version of "Lucio Vero" by Apostolo Zeno, who is not mentioned. Argument, cast, scenario, and names of Vincenzo Martin (**Martin y Soler**) as the composer of the opera, and of Vittorio Amedeo Canavasso as the composer of the music of Innocenzo Gambuzzi's ballets: "Le gelosie villane in Montefosco," "La sposa peruviana," and "Il macchinista ossia La susta matematica."
Performed as second opera of the season. SCHATZ 6024

Vologeso. Dramma per musica da rappresentarsi nel Teatro di S. Benedetto il carnevale dell' anno MDCCLXV.

Venezia, Giorgio Fossati, n. d. 62 p. 16cm.

Three acts. A later version of "Lucio Vero" by Apostolo Zeno, who is not mentioned. Argument, cast, scenario, and name of Giuseppe **Sarti** as the composer.
First performed at Copenhagen, Royal Theater, carnival, 1754. SCHATZ 9465

— **Vologeso.** Dramma per musica da rappresentarsi nel Teatro di Verona il carnovale dell' anno MDCCLXIX . . .

Venezia, Modesto Fenzo, 1769. 60 p. 15cm.

Three acts. By Zeno, who is not mentioned. Impresario's dedication, argument, scenario, cast and name of Giuseppe **Sarti** as the composer. ML 50.2.V7S3

Il **Vologeso.** Dramma per musica da rappresentarsi nel Nuovo Teatro alla Cavallerizza nella fiera di Pascha dell' anno MDCCLIII. In Lipsia.

n. i., 1753. 5 p. l., 123 p. 15mc.

Three acts. A later version of "Lucio Vero" by Apostolo Zeno, who is not mentioned. German text faces Italian. Argument, cast, and name of Francesco **Zoppis** as the composer. SCHATZ 11284

Vologeso rè de' Parti. Drama per musica da rappresentarsi nel Regio Teatro di Torino nel carnovale del 1744 . . .

Torino, Pietro Giuseppe Zappata e figliuolo, n. d. 4 p. l., 63 p. 15½cm.

Three acts. A later version of "Lucio Vero" by Apostolo Zeno, who is not mentioned. Argument, cast, scenario, and names of Leonardo **Leo** as composer of the opera, of Alessio Rasetti as composer of the three incidental ballets.
First performed, as indicated, December 26, 1743. SCHATZ 5562

I **volponi.** Dramma di tre atti per musica. Rappresentato per la prima volta in Parigi l'anno MDCCLXXVII.

Carlo Goldoni, Opere teatrali, Venezia, Zatta e figli, 1788–95, t. 39, [5]–66 p. 18cm.

Composer unknown to me. PQ

La **volubile,** ballet. *See* Andreozzi's **Argea.**

La **volubile,** ballet. *See* Basili's **Il ritorno d'Ulisse.**

Il **volubile.** L. T. of Piccinni's **L'incostante.**

Il **volubile assodato,** ballet. *See* Ottani's Arminio.

Die **von Amor beschuezten liebhaber,** ballet. *See* Salieri's Der geraubte eymer.

Der **von dem ackers-pflug zu den** [!] **thron erhabene kaeyser Justinus.** In einem sing-spiel auff den [!] grossen Hamburgischen Schau-Platze vorgestellet. Im jahr 1706.

n. i., n. d. Unpaged. $16\frac{1}{2}^{cm}$.

Three acts. Argument and scenario. Neither the author (unknown to Schatz) nor the composer, Johann Christian **Schieferdecker,** is mentioned.   SCHATZ 9604

Die **von Paris entfuehrte Helena.** A. T. of Keiser's Die macht der liebe.

Die **vorgeblichen grafen.** Tr. of Cimarosa's I due supposti conti.

Der **vormund.** Tr. of Hasse's Il tutore.

Die **vornehme schaeferin.** Tr. of Jommelli's La pastorella illustre.

Das **vornehme Suschen,** eine komische operette in drey aufzuegen.

1 p. l., 184 p. 16^{cm}. (Zwo komische operetten von G * * *, Chemnitz, 1773.)

In his prefatory note, the unidentified author says:

"Wuerdiget man mich seiner beurtheilung, so macht man sich einen juengling verbindlich, der die Musen, von seiner wiege an, unbeschreiblich liebte, und setzt ihn dadurch vielleicht in den stand, diese gesetzlosen taendeleyen dereinst durch correctere und wichtigere arbeiten der verzeyhung wuerdig zu machen."

Not recorded by Schatz. The "Zwo komische operetten" have been attributed (*see* Deutsches Anonymen Lexikon) to Carl Franz Henisch, 1745–1776, and to Wilhelm Kraus, but (1) the title page clearly points to a name beginning with the letter *G.*; (2) Kraus's earliest known publication dates from 1795, so that an interval of more than twenty years would lie between this and the "Zwo komische operetten;" (3) the dedicatory poem, with the motif of "Die erstlinge," ends:

"Und so auch heiligt Dir die dankbare Camoene
Die ersten ihrer toene."

This can not possibly apply to Henisch, who began to publish his Singspiele in 1770, and who would hardly, in 1773, have called himself a "Juengling." Neither this nor "Das Testament," the other operetta in the volume, is recorded by Schatz.

     SCHATZ 11655

Le **voyage an Mont-Bernard.** A. T. of Cherubini's Elisa.

Le **voyage en Grèce.** A. T. of Plantade's Palma.

Les **voyages de l'amour,** ballet représenté par l'Académie royale de musique, l'an 1736. Paroles de Mr de la Bruere. Musique de Mr Boismortier. CXXV. opera.

205–280 p. 14$\frac{1}{2}^{cm}$. (Recueil général des opera, Paris, 1745, t. xvi.)

Detached copy. Prologue and the acts, "Le village," "La ville," "La cour" (both versions), "Le retour," "La ville, acte nouveau."

First performed, as indicated, May 3, 1736.   ML 48.R4

Vulcan's revenge. A. T. of Noverre's The amours of Venus.

Vulcan's wedding. A. T. of Momus turn'd fabulist.

Arien aus den **Waescherinnen.** Eine komische operette von zwei aufzuegen.

n. i., n. d. 24 p. 15ᶜᵐ.

Translation of Mari's text, "Le lavarandine." Neither the translator, Johann Christoph Bock, is mentioned, nor the composer, Francesco **Zannetti.**
First performed under the above title at Dresden, Kleines Theater, 1779. The Italian original was first performed at Rome, Teatro Capranica, carnival, 1772.

SCHATZ 11139

— Die **waeschermaedchen.** Eine komische operette in zwey aufzuegen. (Nach einem italienischen text und Zanetti's komposition.)

n. i., n. d. [9]–76 p. 16ᶜᵐ. (Komische opern der Italiener, Zum gebrauch fuer die deutsche buehne herausgegeben von J. C. Bock, Erster th. Leipzig, 1781.)

Translation of Francesco Mari's text, "Le lavarandine," music by **Zannetti,** first performed Rome, Teatro Capranica, carnival, 1772.
First performed at Leipzig, Theater beim Rannstaedter Thor, October 6, 1779.

SCHATZ 11138

Der **waffenschmid.** Eine komische oper in zwey aufzuegen, nach herrn Ziegler's beliebtem lustspiele: Liebhaber und nebenbuhler in einer person. Als singspiel fuer die Marinellische Schaubuehne bearbeitet von Karl Friedrich Hensler. Die musik ist von Ferdinand Kauer . . .

Wien, Joseph Kamesina, 1797. 92 p. 16ᶜᵐ.

First performed, as indicated, July 25, 1797. SCHATZ 5065

Die **wahl des Herkules.** Ein lyrisches drama. In musik gesetzt von Anton Schweitzer. Am 17 ten geburtstage des damaligen herrn erbprinzen von Sachsen-Weimar und Eisenach auf dem Hoftheater zu Weimar im jahre 1773 aufgeführt.

n. i., n. d. p. [201]–223. 14ᶜᵐ.

Detached from an edition of Wieland's works, possibly 19th century.
First performed September 4, 1773, as indicated. SCHATZ 9775

Wahnsinn aus liebe. A. T. of Dalayrac's Nina.

Wahnsinn aus liebe. A. T. of Paisiello's Nina.

Die **wahre beständigkeit.** Tr. of Anfossi's La vera costanza.

Die **wahre liebe.** A. T. of Schuster's Der herr als bedienter.

Die **wahre liebe.** A. T. of Schuster's Ruebenzahl.

Der **wahre menschenfreund,** ein singspiel in zween aufzuegen, aufgefuehrt von der studirenden jugend des katholischen schulhauses zu Augsburg St. Salvator. Den 2. 3. und 6ten herbstmondes 1790.

[Augsburg], Joseph Anton Hueber, n. d. [15] p. 18ᶜᵐ.

Cast and "Vorbericht" mentioning "Matthaus **Fischer,** regulirter chorherr des Hl. Augustus beym Heil. Kreuze," as composer. At head of title: "Der gerechte koenig, ein schauspiel . . . und" SCHATZ 3226

Walder, ein laendliches schauspiel mit gesang in einem aufzuge. (Der inhalt ist aus Marmontels Silvain genommen, die musik von hrn. Georg Benda.)

Gotha, Carl Wilhelm Ettinger, 1778. 64 p. 15ᶜᵐ.

By Friedrich Wilhelm Gotter.
First performed at Gotha, Hoftheater, February 23, 1776. SCHATZ 778

Gesaenge aus dem singspiele Die **waldmaenner**, in drey aufzuegen. Die musik ist von Heneberg.

Hamburg, Freystatzky und Rabe, 1797. 24 p. 15½ᶜᵐ.

By Johann Emanuel Schikaneder, who is not mentioned.
First performed at Hamburg, Theater beim Gänsemarkt, May 31, 1797; at Vienna, Theater auf der Wieden, October 14, 1793.   SCHATZ 4631

Wallrad und Evchen oder Die parforsjagd, ein singspiel von L. Ph. Hahn. Mit musik von J. L. F. C. Maier, dem juengern.

Zweibruecken, P. Hallanzy, 1782. 67 p. 16½ᶜᵐ.

On p. 3–11 a "Vorbericht" dated "Zweibruecken, im Erndemond, 1782," which reads like a novel. According to this, a starving, old, retired actor by the name of Meyer came to the author with the request to cede to him some literary work which he would publish at his own expense and from the sale of which Meier expected to reap a profit. Hahn finally consented, found an old "Entwurf zu einem Hochzeit-gedicht," completed it as a singspiel in eight days, got a young, local musician, evidently Maier, to compose it, etc. The result, of course, was that Meyer did not even cover the printing expenses with this venture. A few years later he was dead and Hahn then decided to give the possible proceeds from the sale of the libretto, which seems to have at first been printed under the name of Meier, to the widow. Finally, Hahn says that the play is in certain respects local, the characters being designed after certain well-known persons of Zweibruecken.   SCHATZ 5844

Walmir und Gertraud, oder Man kann es ja probieren. Eine operette in drey aufzügen.

n. i., n. d. 75 p. 13½ᶜᵐ.

At head of title: I. Apparently a detached copy from the collected works of Johann Benjamin Michaelis, who says in his Vorbericht:
"Diese operette sollte ein versuch seyn, die rührende komödie in das lyrische drama ueberzutragen . . . Ubrigens ist diese kleinigkeit sein erster theatralischer ausflug, den er bereits 1766 gewagt."
The composer, Anton **Schweitzer**, is not mentioned.
First performed at Hanover, Schlosstheater, 1769.   SCHATZ 9776

Die **wankelmuethige**. Tr. of Portugal's La donna di genio volubile.

The **wanton countess:** or, Ten thousand pounds for a pregnancy. A new ballad opera, founded on true secret history . . .

London, Nichols, 1733. 40 p. 18½ᶜᵐ.

Three acts and introduction. The 22 airs used are indicated by title. Dedicated by "Mortimer" to "Sir T. Gaudy of Gaudy-Hall." Author unknown to Clarence.
                    LONGE 275

The **wanton Jesuit:** or, Innocence seduced. A new ballad opera. As it is acted at the New Theatre in the Hay-Market.

London, J. Millan and W. Shropshire, 1731. 5 p. l., [1], 48, [1] p. 19ᶜᵐ.

Three acts, introduction, and epilogue. Cast and preface beginning:
"The following ballad-opera is a faithful translation of the French original; nor is there one word added to the title, or any character omitted in the dramatis personæ . . . There is a strong presumption that it was wrote by a Hugonot to please the Jansenists, who abhor Jesuits . . . But it is not very material who was the author of it . . ."
The preface of the anonymous and unknown translator then goes on to say how the piece was privately performed, how the Jesuits caused it to be suppressed, etc.
                    LONGE 120

Was den damen gefaellt. A. T. of Die fee Urgele.

Was einem recht, ist dem andern billig. *See* Dezède's Julie.

Was erhaelt die maenner treu? Ein original singspiel in zwey aufzuegen vom herrn professor Zehnmark. Die musik ist vom herrn Ruprecht, mitgliede der k. k. Nationalschaubuehne. Aufgefuehrt auf dem k. k. Nationaltheater.

Wien, beym logenmeister, 1780. 36 p. 17½ cm.

First performed, as indicated, March 30, 1780. SCHATZ 9161

Was thut die liebe nicht. Tr. of Naumann's La dama soldato.

Was vermag die liebe nicht? A. T. of Dalayrac's Nina.

The waterman; or, The first of August. A ballad opera, in two acts. As performed at the Theatre-Royal, Hay-Market. A new edition.

London, R. Baldwin, 1783. v. [1], 40 p. 21 cm.

Original cast and 1783 Covent-Garden cast. In his preface the author-composer-compiler, Charles **Dibdin** (not mentioned) says:

"Finding among the different pieces I have composed for Ranelagh and the theatre, a number of ballads which I took great pains with, and which have been but little heard, I thought I could not better employ my leisure time than in furnishing, upon some familiar plan, the dialogue necessary to work up these materials into a ballad farce, a species of entertainment which has always been well received, and which; as it has lain dormant for some time, I thought would have so far the charms of novelty to recommend it.

"I had heard of a piece of this sort, which has the characters of a Waterman and a gardener in it; and the scene of which is laid at Battersea: This I enquired after, but was informed it was out of print; I nevertheless liked the idea of those two characters so well, that I determined to pursue the hint . . . I never read the piece in question. nor do I for a certainty at this moment know the title of it . . ."

First performed at the Haymarket August 17, 1774 (Clarence, but Genest "the 5th time"), July 14, 1774 (Schatz). LONGE 121

— **The waterman;** or, The first of August. A ballad opera, in two acts. By Charles Dibdin, Esq.

[83]–112 p. 19 cm. (Collection of the most esteemed farces and entertainments, t. vi, Edinburgh, 1792.)

Hay-Market and Covent-Garden casts. Music partly selected, partly composed by **Dibdin.** SCHATZ 11753

The weathercock. A musical entertainment of two acts; as performed at the Theatre-Royal, Covent-Garden.

London, T. Evans, 1775. 2 p. l., 37 p. 21 cm.

Two acts. Cast, table of the 19 songs, and prefatory note. By Theodosius Forrest, according to Clarence. Schatz does not record the composer.

First performed October 17, 1775, as indicated. LONGE 86

Der wechsel in der liebe. A. T. of Tritto's Die veraechter der schoenen.

The wedding: a tragi-comi-pastoral-farcical opera. As it is now acting at the Theatre-Royal, in Lincoln's-Inn-Fields. With an Hudibrastick Nimmington. By Mr. Hawker . . . To which is prefix'd, The overture, by Dr. Pepusch. With an addition of the musick to each song, engrav'd on copper plates.

London, Printed for W. Mears, . . . and sold by S. Birt, 1729. v, [1], 23 p. 19½ cm.

The last p. supplied in ms. The engraved music plates are missing.

One act. Cast and dedication of "The tender buddings . . . of an infant Muse," by Essex Hawker, who played the part of Rako. The 23 airs are indicated in the text by title.

First performed May 6, 1729. LONGE 33

The **wedding**—Continued.

— The **wedding**: a tragi-comi-pastoral opera. As it is acted at the Theatre-Royal in Covent-Garden. With an Hudibrastick Skimmington. Written by Mr. Hawker . . . With the overture by Dr. Pepusch. Also the music to each song, engraven on copper plates. The second edition.

*London, W. Mears, 1734. fold. front., 24 p.; (music) 8, 8 p. 19*cm.

One act. Same cast and same text as in the first edition, but without the dedication. The overture (8 p.) is followed by the 23 airs (8 p.) numbered, without titles, to correspond to those indicated by title in the text. Longe 306

— The **country-wedding, and Skimmington**: a tragi-comi-pastoral-farcical opera. As it is acted by His Majesty's servants at the Theatre-Royal in Drury Lane,

*London, W. Trott, 1729. 2 p. l., 24 p. 18½*cm.

One act. Cast and "Advertisement to the town," by "The Young company," dated Theatre-Royal, July 18, 1729. It appears that this libretto was published prior to the performances. The 25 airs used in this ballad opera are indicated by title.

Comparison shows that this is practically the same text as Essex Hawker's ballad opera "The wedding," notwithstanding noticeable differences. The cast is also different, Hawker having disappeared and the number of characters having been reduced from seven to five. Longe 275

The **wedding ring**, a comic opera. In two acts. As it is performed at the Theatre Royal in Drury Lane.

*London, T. Becket, 1773. 2 p. l., ii, 41 p. 20*cm.

Two acts. Cast and preface, dated February 8, 1773, by Charles **Dibdin**, in which he says:

"The reader will perceive at first sight that the hint of this piece is borrowed from an Italian Opera, entitled, *Il Filosofo di Campagna* [by Goldoni]. There is also a circumstance from Moliere, which, except about twenty lines taken from different publications, and thrown occasionally into the songs, are the only passages in it that have ever appeared either on the stage, or in print.

"Indeed conscious of my own inability, I should have collected all the materials, had it been practicable; but attempting this without success, and being unwilling to throw away a subject than which 'tis hardly possible to conceive any thing more operatical, I determined to make a tryal of what I could do to it myself, and this in no respect with a view of setting myself up for an author, but merely from a desire of assisting my reputation as a musician . . ."

First performed, as indicated, February 1, 1773 (Genest). Longe 28

Weibertreue oder Die maedchen sind von Flandern. Tr. of Mozart's Così fan tutte.

Die **weinlese**. Ein singspiel in zwei aufzeugen. Nach dem Erndte-kranz des herrn Weisse, fuer die Mannheimer National-schaubuehne eingerichtet von Meyer, mitgliede dieses theaters. Die composition ist von Herrn Becke, hauptmann eines schwaebischen Dragoner-regiments.

*Mannheim, C. F. Schwan, 1783. 110, [2] p. 16*cm.

Cast. The additional pages contain a biographical sketch of the librettist Wilhelm Christian Dietrich Meyer, who died on September 2, 1783, in his thirty-sixth year during the publication of his libretto.

First performed, as indicated, on December 10, 1782. Schatz 679

Die **weinlese**. Tr. T. of Gazzaniga's La vendemmia.

Arien und gesaenge aus Der **weinlese.** Eine laendlich-komische oper von Joh. Jacob Ihlee. Mit musik von herrn musikdirektor Kuntzen.

Frankfurt am Main, n. publ., 1793. 23 p. 16½ cm.

First performed at Frankfort on Main, Nationaltheater, May 3, 1793.

SCHATZ 5331

—Das **fest der winzer.** Komische oper in drei aufzuegen.

n. i., n. d. 120 p. 15 cm.

This is Ihlee's "Die weinlese," composed by **Kunzen.**

SCHATZ 5332

—Gesaenge aus der oper: Das **fest der winzer,** oder Wer fuehrt die braut nach hause? Die musik ist von herrn F. L. A. Kunzen.

n. i., n. d. 23 p. 16 cm.

Ihlee's "Die weinlese" with alterations.

SCHATZ 5333

Der **weiseste in Sidon,** in einer opera **auf dem** Hamburgischen Schau-platze vorgestellet. 1733.

Hamburg, gedruckt mit seel. Spieringks schrifften, n. d. Unpaged. 18 cm.

Three acts. Argument, cast, and names of Johann Georg Hamann as author, of Georg Philipp **Telemann** as composer.

First performed at Hamburg, Opernhaus beim Gänsemarkt, October 10, 1729.

SCHATZ 10268

Welche ist die beste nation? Ein lustspiel mit gesang in zwey aufzuegen. Aufgefuehrt im k. k. National-Hoftheater.

Wien, Joseph edler von Kurzbeck, 1782. 61 p. 16 cm.

By Ayrenhoff (Haas), who is not mentioned. He says in his "Vorerinnerung":

"Ein komisches singspiel, worin einem geschickten tonkuenstler auf eine natuerlich herbeygefuehrte art, gelegenheit verschaft wuerde, die verschiedenheiten des musikalischen geschmacks der verschiedenen europaeischen nationen auszudruecken, sollte in unserm gesangreichen zeitalter keine undankbare arbeit seyn—so dacht ich mir; und so enstund gegenwaertiger versuch . . ."

Ignaz **Umlauf** (not mentioned) composed the music. The piece was hissed. (Haas).

First performed at Vienna, Burgtheater, December 13, 1782.　SCHATZ 10528

The **Welsh opera:** or, The grey mare the better horse. As it is acted at the new Theatre in the Hay-Market. Written by Scriblerus, Secundus, author of the Tragedy of tragedies . . .

London, Printed by E. Rayner, and sold by H. Cook, n. d. 1 p. l., ii, ii, 39, [1] p. 19 cm.

Two acts and introduction. Cast and preface, in which the author, Henry Fielding, hints at the political basis of this piece, and says:

"As the performance of the Grub-street opera has been prevented, by a certain influence, which has been very prevailing of late years, we thought it would not be unacceptable to the town, if we communicated to them the *Welsh* opera, from which the other was not only originally borrow'd, but which is in effect the same, excepting some few additions, that were made only with a view to lengthen it . . ."

Ballad opera, the 30 airs used being indicated by title.

First performed in July, 1731, as indicated.　LONGE 262

The **Welsh opera**—Continued.

—The **genuine Grub-street opera.** As it was intended to be acted at the New Theatre in the Hay-market. Written by Scriblerus Secundus . . .

London, Printed and sold for the benefit of the comedians of the New Theatre in the Hay-market, 1731. vii, [1], 9–64 p. 19cm.

Three acts and introduction. Ballad opera. The 57 airs are indicated by title.

ML 50.5.G79

Die **welt im monde.** Tr. of Galuppi's Il mondo della luna.

Wenceslaus. Tr. of Scalabrini's Venceslao.

Wenzel ou Le magistrat du peuple. Opéra en trois actes, présenté à la Convention nationale le 2 germinal de la deuxième année républicaine [March 22, 1794], joué sur le Théâtre national le 21 du même mois: [April 10, 1794] Paroles de Pillet: musique de la Durner. [Ladurner.]

Paris, Maradan, Seconde année, [1794]. 2 p. l., 30 p. 20½cm.

SCHATZ 5375

Wer andern eine grube graebt, fällt selbst darein. A. T. of Die schatzgraeber.

Wer das glueck hat. A. T. of Paisiello's Der betrogene geizige.

Wer den schaden hat, darf fuer den spott nicht sorgen. Eine komische oper in zwey aufzuegen, nach Dorvigny, fuer die Marinellische schaubuehne von Karl Friedrich Hensler. Die musik ist von herrn Wenzel Mueller, kapellmeister.

Wien, Joseph Kamesina, 1798. 92 p. 16½cm.

First performed, as indicated, May 10, 1798.   SCHATZ 6976

Wer fuehrt die braut nach hause? A. T. of Kunzen's Das fest der winzer.

Wer wagt, gewinnt. A. T. of Accorimboni's Das herbstabentheuer.

Die **wette,** oder Maedchenlist und liebe. Tr. of Mozart's Così fan tutte.

What news now? A. T. of The humours of the time.

Who's afraid? A farce of one act: with songs.

[351]–410 p. (Select dramatic pieces, London, W. Lowndes, 1787.) 21cm.

By Dr. Jodrell, who is not mentioned. No performance recorded. LONGE 203

The **widow of Wallingford**; a comedy of two acts: (With songs) as it was performed in the neighbourhood of Wallingford, by a set of gentlemen and ladies; at whose request it is now published.

London, Printed for the author, n. d. 2 p. l., 32 p. 21cm.

Author not recorded by Clarence. No tunes indicated.   LONGE 102

Der **wiedererkannte Cyrus.** Tr. of Verocai's Il Ciro riconosciuto.

Die **wiedererkannte Medea.** Tr. of Vinci's Medea riconosciuta.

Die **wiedererkannte sclavin.** Tr. of Piccinni's La schiava ricon-osciuta.

Die **wiederhergestellte ruh,** oder Die gecroente tapferkeit des Heraclius, auff das ungarische kroenungs-fest . . . Caroli VI erwehlten roemischen kaeysers . . . in einem singe-spiel auf dem Hamburgischen Schauplatz vorgestellet im junio MDCCXII.

> *n. i., n. d. Unpaged. 19^{cm}.*

Five acts and prologue. Scenario, dedication by the author, Johann Ulrich König, and "vorrede." The composer, Reinhard **Keiser,** is not mentioned. Schatz 5115

Die **wiederkehr der gueldnen zeit,** bey hoechst-gluecklicher ver-maehlung Sr. Majestaet des roemischen und hungarischen koenigs Josephi I mit . . . Wilhelmina Amalia, gebohrne hertzogin zu Braunschweig und Lueneburg, vermittelst eines singe-spieles auff dem Hamburgischen Schauplatz vorgestellet.

> *[Hamburg], Nicolaus Spieringk, 1699. Unpaged. 19^{cm}.*

Three acts. "Vorbericht," without the name of the author, Friedrich Christian Bressand, or the composer, Reinhard **Keiser.**
First performed, as indicated, February, 1699. Schatz 5131

Die **wiedervereinigten freier.** Tr. of the ballet Les amans reunis.

A **wife of ten thousand.** A. T. of Dibdin's The cobler.

Die **wilddiebe,** eine operette in einem aufzuge.

> *Muenster in Westphalen, Heinrich Philipp Perrenon, 1774. Unpaged. 15½^{cm}.*

Neither the composer, Johann Gottlieb **Nicolai,** nor the authors, Wilhelm Stühle and Anton Matthias Sprickmann, are mentioned.
First performed at Muenster, Hoftheater, 1774. Schatz 7114

Die **wilden.** Tr. of Dalayrac's Azémia.

Der **wildfang.** Eine komische oper in zwey aufzuegen. Nach herrn v. Kotzebue frey bearbeitet von Franz Xaver Huber. Aufgefuehrt auf den K. K. Hof-Theatern in Wien.

> *[Wien], Mit von Kurtzbekischen schriften, 1797. 140 p. 16½^{cm}.*

"Vorbericht" dated Vienna, September, 1797, and name of Franz Xaver **Suess-mayr** as composer.
First performed October 4, 1797, as indicated. Schatz 10185

Willhelm und Roeschen, oder Die Hollandgaenger, eine operette in drey aufzuegen.

> *Zelle, Carl Gsellius, 1773. 72 p. 15^{cm}.*

On p. 2, the note:
"Das sujet dieser operette ist aus dem 85 und 86ten stuecke des Hannoverschen Magazins vom J. 1770 genommen, und soll eine wahre geschichte seyn. Aus der Clarisse des herrn Bocks sind ein paar sich passende arien, fast unveraendert, ein-geschaltet"
Not recorded by Schatz. Not found in "Deutsches Anonymen Lexikon."
Schatz 11468

William and Nanny; or, The cottagers. L. T. of The cottagers.

Windsor castle; or, The fair maid of Kent, an opera, as performed at the Theatre-Royal, Covent-Garden, in honour of the marriage of Their Royal Highnesses the Prince and Princess of Wales.　By the author of Hartford-Bridge . . .

London, T. N. Longman, 1795.　4 p. l. (incl. front.), 40 p.　20^{cm}*.*

Two acts.　By William Pearce.　Cast, dedication, dated London, May 4, 1795, and Advertisement, according to which

"it was the author's suggestion that the second act of this performance might exhibit a tournament, as the spectacle most apposite to the heroic character of the court of Edward the Third; Mr. Noverre, having, however, projected a ballet on an event in the classic mythology, the author withdrew his plan; and the episode of the *Marriage of Peleus and Thetis* [called a masque in the text] was adopted . . ."

"The music is principally by Mr. [Johann Peter] **Salomon**.　It is, however, a justice due to Mr. [Reginald] **Spofforth**, a young English composer, of very considerable promise, to state that the opening roundelay, the glee "Shades of Windsor," and Mr. Fawcett's song ["In throng from all parts"], at the end of the first act, were produced by him.

First performed, as indicated, April 6, 1795.　　　　　　LONGE 231

The wishes.　A. T. of Belphegor.

The wit of a woman.　A. T. of Love at first sight.

Der wittwer und die wittwe.　Tr. of Winter's I due vedovi.

Das witzige landmaedchen, oder Der geadelte landmann.　Tr. of Paisiello's Il matrimonio inaspettato.

The wives metamorphos'd.　A. T. of The devil to pay.

The wives revenged; a comic opera in one act.　As it is performed at the Theatre-Royal in Covent-Garden.

London, G. Kearsley, 1778.　36 p.　31^{cm}*.*

Cast and same prefatory note by the author-composer, Charles **Dibdin**, as in his "Rose and Colin."

First performed September 18, 1778, as indicated.　　　　LONGE 87

Der wohlthaetige, ein singspiel in zween aufzuegen, von der studirenden jugend des katholischen Schulhauses zu Augsburg bey St. Salvator aufgefuehrt den 3. 4. und 6ten herbstmondes 1799.

[Augsburg], Joseph Anton Hueber, n. d.　[15] p.　18^{cm}*.*

Cast and "Vorbericht" saying that the "tonverfassung" is by Matthäus **Fischer** and that the singspiel was first performed "vor sieben Jahren" [1792].　At head of the title: "Der fuerst auf der jagd, ein schauspiel . . . und"　　SCHATZ 3228

Der wohlthaetige derwisch oder Die schellenkappe.　O. T. of Schack's Die zaubertrommel oder Der wohlthaetige derwisch.

The women in an uproar.　A. T. of The commodity excis'd.

The wonder! An honest Yorkshireman.　*See* Carey's The honest Yorkshire-man.

Wonders in the sun, or The kingdom of the birds; a comick opera. With great variety of songs in all kinds, set to musick by several of the most eminent masters of the age.　Written by Mr. Durfey.

London, Jacob Tonson, 1706.　3 p. l., 69, [2] p.　21^{cm}*.*

Durfey's dedication, "Introduction to the prologue," "Dramatis personae," "Emblematical figures," prologue ("all sung"), four acts (spoken dialogue with

Wonders in the sun—Continued.

some incidental songs), and epilogue, of which the last page has been supplied in ms. in this copy. The words of the "Ode" (act I) "Groves and woods" were "made to a pretty, but very difficult tune of Mr. **Eccles**" and the "Dialogue" (act III) "Pray now John" was "made to a famous Sebel, of Seignour Baptist **Lully**." No other composers are mentioned. Tufts quoting Whincop says "It had several ballads in it that took very much with the common people," which leaves the question open whether or not "ballads" are meant in the sense of songs set to popular ballad airs.

First performed at London, Haymarket, April 5 not March 7, 1706.   LONGE 194

Songs, duets, trios, glees, choruses, etc. in the comic opera of the Woodman. As performed at the Theatre-Royal, Covent-Garden, Second edition. By Mr. Bate Dudley.

London, T. Cadell, 1791. 1 p. l., 28 p. 17½ cm.

Three acts. Cast and prefatory note dated February 26, 1791. The text, hastily put together, was written "to excite the admired talents of a musical friend," William **Shield**, but Longman & Broderip's vocal score says "composed *chiefly*" by Shield.

First performed February 26, 1791.   LONGE 218

— The woodman, a comic opera, in three acts; as performed at the Theatre-Royal, Covent-Garden, with universal applause. By Mr. Bate Dudley.

London, T. Cadell, 1791. 5 p. l. (incl. front.), 94 p. 18 cm.

Cast. Henry Bate Dudley's dedication dated Bradwell Lodge, April 30, 1791, and reprint of the prefatory statement.   LONGE 215

A world discovered. A. T. of Columbus.

The world in the moon; an opera. As it is perform'd at the Theatre in Dorset-Garden. By His Majesty's servants. By E. S. . . . The second edition.

London, Abel Roper, 1697. 4 p. l., 43, [1] p. 20½ cm.

Five acts, prologue, and epilogue. Cast and epistle dedicatory by Elkanah Settle, to Christopher Rich, which reads, in part:

"The feast being made under your own roof, I cannot choose so proper a patron for this entertainment as your self . . . So great an undertaking, I am sure, has never been on an English stage; and I am not traveller sufficient to make foreign comparisons. And here I think my self obliged to do the pencil this publick right, to tell the world that never was such a pile of painting rais'd upon so generous a foundation; especially under all the hardships of so backward a season of the year . . .

"As to the entertainment itself I hope I shall not be vain to say, that the model of the scenes of this play are something of an original: I am sure I have removed a long heap of rubbish, and thrown away all our old French lumber, our clouds of clouts, and set the theatrical paintings at a much fairer light . . ."

Not a real opera, but a play interspersed with some music composed in about equal parts by Jeremiah **Clarke** and Daniel **Purcell**.   LONGE 180

A worse plague than the dragon. A. T. of Margery.

Die wuensche. A. T. of Stegmann's Sultan Wampum and Schach Wampum.

Die wueste insel. Singspiel. Nach Metastasio, von A. G. Meissner. [vignette]

Leipzig, Dykische Buchhandlung, 1778. 7 p. l., 34 p. 16 cm.

One act. Dedicatory poem, "Dem barden Rhingulph geweiht," argument, and prefatory note, in which Meissner says:

"Dass ich bey vorliegender arbeit Metastasio ['L'isola disabitata'] zu meinem urbild gewaehlt, sagt der titel . . . Was mein singspiel selbst betrift; so hab' ich den

Die wueste insel—Continued.

inhalt der recitative so treu als moeglich uebergetragen, und bloss in den arien mir einige abweichungen, und zwar mit fleiss erlaubt. Denn freylich ist es ganz etwas andres, in reimfreye Jamben, als in gereimte musikalische Stanzen, getreu zu uebersetzen; und nachher sind selbst—so viel ehrfurcht ich sonst fuer Metastasio habe—seine arien, wenigstens nach meinem urtheil, immer mehr des herrlichen stoffes fuer die tonkunst, und ihres einsichtvollen baues und standpunkts, als ihres dichterischen styls wegen merkwuerdig. Oft erlaubt er sich sogar in ihnen taendeleyen, vor denen er sich in seinen recitativen sorgfaeltigst hueten wuerde . . .''

First performed at Leipzig, with music by Joseph **Schuster**, Theater beim Rannstaedter Thore, September 30, 1779. Schatz 9758

Das wuetende heer, oder: Das maedchen im Thurme. Ein heroisch-komisches singspiel in drey aufzuegen. Nach Bretznern, fuer das K. K. Opern Theater eingerichtet, und in musik gesetzt von herrn Ruprecht.

[*Wien*], *n. d., bey dem logenmeister.* *80 p.* *16ᶜᵐ.*

First performed at Vienna, Kaernthnerthor Theater, June 1, 1787. Schatz 9162

Das wütende heer, oder Das maedgen im thurme. Eine operette in drey akten. [silhouette] Componirt vom herrn kapellmeister Schweitzer in Weimar.

[*99*]*–192 p.* *16ᶜᵐ.* (*C. F. Bretzner, Operetten, bd. I, Leipzig, 1779.*)

The silhouette is a portrait of the actress Minna Brandes.
Date of first performance unknown to Schatz, but it must have occurred between 1772 and 1774. *The work is not mentioned by Maurer in his book on Schweitzer.*

Schatz 11680

—Das **wuetende heer**, oder Das maedgen im thurme. Eine operette in drey akten. Von C. F. Bretzner. Componirt vom herrn kapellmeister Schweitzer in Gotha.

Leipzig, Carl Friedrich Schneider, 1788. *79 p.* *15½ᶜᵐ.*

Schatz 9777

Die wunderbahr errettete Iphigenia (by Postel). *See* Graun's Iphigenia.

Die wunderbahr-errettete Iphigenia in einem singe-spiel auff dem Hamburgischen Schau-platz vorgestellet.

Hamburg, Nicolaus Spieringk, 1699. *Unpaged.* *19ᶜᵐ.*

Five acts. Argument and "vorbericht." Neither the author, Christian Heinrich Postel, is mentioned, nor the composer, Reinhard **Keiser.**
First performed, as indicated, 1699. Schatz 5132

Der wunderliche Franzos. Tr. of Astaritta's Il francese bizarro.

Die wunderschoene Psyche, zu hoechstem gedaechtniss des erfreulichsten gebuhrts-tages der aller-durchlauchtigsten, grossmaechtigsten koenigin in Preussen . . . Sophien Scharlotten, welcher einfiel den 20. octobris, in einem Singe-spiel auff dem Hamburgischen Schau-platz vorgestellet.

[*Hamburg*], *Nicolaus Spieringk, 1701.* *Unpaged.* *19ᶜᵐ.*

Three acts. "Vorbericht." Neither the author, Christian Heinrich Postel, nor the composer, Reinhard **Keiser,** is mentioned. Postel based the text on Marini's "Adone," on Corneille and Fontenelle's "Psyche," and on Matteo Noris's "L'Amor inamorato."

Schatz 5116

Xerse. Drama per musica nel Teatro a SS. Gio. e Paolo per l'anno MDCLIV . . .

Venetia, Matteo Leni, 1654. 6 p. l. (incl. front.) 71 p. 14ᶜᵐ.

Three acts with prologue. By conte Niccolò Minato, who signs the dedication with his initials and dates it Venice, January 12, 1654. Argument, scenario, and notice to the reader without name of Pietro Francesco **Cavalli** as composer.

SCHATZ 1743

—Il Xerse. Drama per la musica con aggionta dell' intermedii, e molte altre scene, & aggiustamenti, conforme si rappresentò nella città di Palermo. Data in luce ad instantia dell' Academia delli Musici di detta città . . .

Palermo, Andrea Colicchia, 1658. 5 p. l., 142 p. 13ᶜᵐ.

Prologue and three acts. Dedication and argument. No allusion to author or composer, except that the dedication says: "composto con felice vena di poesia d'autor famoso in tal materia." Comparison proved it to be conte Niccolò Minato's "Xerse," as set to music by Francesco **Cavalli**, Venice, 1654. The intermedii are of a comic character. ML 50.2.X3C2

Youth against magic. A. T. of Merlin in love.

L'yvrogne corrigé, opera-comique en deux actes; par Mrs. Anseaume & * * *; mis en musique par M. De la Ruette: représenté pour la premiere fois sur le Théâtre de l'Opéra-comique de la Foire Saint Laurent, le 23 juillet 1759.

Paris, Duchesne, 1759. 40 p. 20½ᶜᵐ.

Cast. On p. 35 the vaudeville "Un amant dans ses beaux discours" and on p. 38–40 "Sa tendresse pour moi chaque jour." For a German version of this, made for use of **Gluck**'s setting of the above, but providing in an appendix for use of Laruette's music, *see* Schatz 3909 under "L'ivrogne corrigé." SCHATZ 5434

Zaïde, reine de Grenade, ballet heroique, représenté par l'Academie royale de musique de Lyon, en juin 1749.

Lyon, Rigollet, 1749. 41 p. 19½ᶜᵐ.

Prologue and three acts. Neither the author, de La Marre, is mentioned, nor the composer, **Royer.** Cast.
First performed at Paris, Académie royale de musique, September 3, 1739.

ML 52.2.Z2R7

Zaira. Dramma nuovo per musica da rappresentarsi nel nobilissimo Teatro Venier in San Benedetto il carnovale dell' anno 1797.

Venezia, Modesto Fenzo, 1797. 44 p. 18½ᶜᵐ.

Two acts. Probably by Mattia Botturini. Cast, scenario, and name of Sebastiano **Nasolini** as the composer.
First performed, as indicated, February 22, 1797. SCHATZ 7018

Intermezzi di Zamberlucco, e Palandrana, da rappresentarsi nel Teatro Bonacossi da S. Stefano il carnovale dell' anno MDCCXXI.

[At end] Ferrara, Bernardino Pomatelli, n. d. 15, [1] p. 15ᶜᵐ.

Three intermezzi. Neither the author (unknown to Schatz) nor the composer, Carlo Francesco **Gasparini**, is mentioned.
First performed at Venice, Teatro di S. Cassiano, fall, 1709. SCHATZ 3591

La Zanina maga per amore. Dramma comico per musica da rappresentarsi nella terra di S. Giovanni in Persiceto nel Teatro de' Sig. Accademici Candidi Uniti l'autunno dell' anno MDCCXXXVII.

Bologna, Costantino Pisarri, n. d. 49, [2] p. 15ᶜᵐ.

Three acts. Attributed by Schatz to the composer, Giuseppe Maria **Buini**, who is not mentioned. Dedication, notice to the reader, and cast. *Imprimatur* dated August 29, 1737. SCHATZ 1398

La **Zanina maga per amore**—Continued.

—**Zanina maga per amore.** Dramma comico per musica da rappresentarsi in Cesena nel Teatro eretto nel Palazzo Spada il carnovale 1745.

*[At end] Bologna, Costantino Pisarri, 1745.   1 p. l., 50, [1] p.   14½*cm*.*

Exactly the same text as in 1737, though Schatz claims "con cambiamenti." With impresario's dedication dated Cesena, February, 1745, notice to the reader, and cast, but again without the names of the composer and the librettist. Schatz claims that **Buini** and "altri maestri" were responsible for the music, but this claim is apparently based on the libretto published by Modesto Fenzo for the performances at Venice, May, 1742. Wiel enters the opera under that year as "di vari autori."

SCHATZ 1399

Der **zauberer.** Ein singspiel in zween aufzuegen. Aufgefuehrt auf der hochfuerstl. Thurn und Taxischen schaubuehne.

*Regensburg, Breitfeld, 1781.   17*cm*.*

Imperfect.
Two acts. Cast. "Die poesie ist von herrn Poinsinet. Die musik von Henri **Croes** verfertigt." (p. [2]). This is a translation by Johann Heinrich Faber (Schatz) of Poinsinet's "Le sorcier." The missing pages (after p. 56) of the last scene have been added in manuscript.   SCHATZ 2294

Der **zauberer.** Tr. of Philidor's Le sorcier.

Die **zauberfloete.** Eine grosse oper in zwey aufzuegen. Von Emmanuel Schikaneder. Die musik dazu ist von herrn Wolfgang Amade Mozart . . .

*n. i., 1794.   96 p.   18*cm*.*

According to Schatz and Dent the text was (at least) planned in part by Gieseke.
First performed at Vienna, Theater auf der Wieden, September 30, 1791.

ML 50.2.Z25M7

—Die **zauberflöte.** Eine oper in drei aufzuegen, neubearbeitet von C. A. Vulpius. Die musik ist von Mozart. Aufgefuehrt auf dem herzoglichen Hoftheater zu Weimar zum erstenmal am 16. Januar 1794.

*Leipzig, Johann Samuel Heinsius, 1794.   front., 104 p.   16*cm*.*

The "Vorrede" dated "Weimar, den 30. Jan. 1794" reads:
"Es war uns schlechterdings unmoeglich, die *Zauberfloete* nach dem originale, welches Mozart durch seine himmlische komposition gleichsam veredelt hatte, vor unser delikates publikum hier auf das theater zu bringen. Es musste daher auf eine umarbeitung gedacht werden, und so enstand die meinige, welche nachher auch von der Mannheimer buehne angenommen wurde.
"Wer das original kennt, wird wissen, was ich geleistet habe, oder nicht. Den dialog habe ich ganz neu umgeschaffen. Die verse habe ich geaendert und wenigstens—vom nonsens gereiniget, wie ich hoffe! Dennoch wird man hier und da noch harte reime genug finden. Sie sind immer, bei arbeiten dieser art, ziemlich unvermeidlich. Es ist unendlich leichter *fuer* die musik, als *nach* einer schon vorhandenen komposition, zu arbeiten . . .
"Das originalstueck hat gar keinen plan. Die menschen gehen darinne nur, um wieder zu kommen, und kommen, um abgehen zu koennen. —Ich habe es versucht, einen plan hineinzudraengen . . . In dieser ruecksicht habe ich auch das stueck in *drei* aufzuege abgetheilt, weil der zwischenraum von nacht und tag mir dadurch bestimmter gemacht zu seyn schien, und weil ueberhaupt der zweite aufzug durch seine unverhaeltnissmaessige laenge, ermuedete . . ."   SCHATZ 6849

—Il **flauto magico.** Dramma eroicomico per musica in due atti tradotto dall' idioma tedesco nell' italiano. Da rappresentarsi nel Elettorale Teatro di Dresda.

*n. i., 1794.   94 p.   16½*cm*.*

Argument. Italian version, by Giovanni de Gamerra.
First performed, as indicated, April 2, 1794.   SCHATZ 6850

Der **zauber-hain**, oder Das land der liebe. Eine romantisch komische oper in drey akten von Th. Berling. Komponirt vom musikdirektor Bierei.

n. i., 1799. 31 p. 16½ᶜᵐ.

First performed at Dresden, Theater vor dem schwarzen thore, May 8, 1799.

SCHATZ 1032

Die **zauberharfe**. L. T. of Walter's Die harfe.

Die **zauberhoele des Trofonius**. Tr. of Salieri's La grotta di Trofonio.

Die **zauberinsel**. L. A. T. of Wenzel Müller's Der sturm.

Die **zauberinsel**. A. T. of Schack's Der stein der weisen.

Der **zaubernde soldat**. Tr. of Philidor's Le soldat magicien.

Der **zauberspiegel**. Tr. of Grétry's La fausse magie.

Arien zur **Zaubertrommel** oder Der wohlthaetige Derwisch. Eine[!] grosses komisches singspiel in drey aufzuegen. Die musik dazu ist von herrn Schak. Aufgefuehrt von der Mihuleschen Gesellschaft.

Augsburg, n. publ., 1793. 29 p. 16ᶜᵐ.

The author, Johann Emanuel Schikaneder, is not mentioned. The music was by **Schack, Gerl,** and others (Komorzynski).

First performed at Augsburg, Nationaltheater, 1793; at Vienna, Theater auf der Wieden, 1792, as "Der wohlthätige derwisch oder Die schellenkappe."

SCHATZ 9571

Die **zauberzither**. A. T. and L. T. of Wenzel Müller's Der fagottist.

Der **zaubrer**. Eine komische oper in einer handlung von Karl Franz Henisch.

Prag, n. publ., 1772. 48 p. 16½ᶜᵐ.

The composer, Franz Andreas **Holly,** is not mentioned.

First performed at Prague, Kgl. Theater i. d. Kotzen, 1772.   SCHATZ 4773

Zeboschi ed Esing, ossia Il vero amico, ballet. *See* P. C. Guglielmi's Dorval e Virginia.

Zefiro e Flora, ballet. *See* Manfredini's Armida.

Der **zeitvertreib auf dem lande**. Tr. of Astaritta's Il divertimento in campagna.

Zelia, drame en trois actes, mêlé de musique. Paroles de Dubuisson, musique de Deshaye.

Paris, et se trouve à Lille, Deperne, 1793. 71 p. 19ᶜᵐ.

First performed (music by Prosper Didier **Deshayes,** with the alternative title, "L'homme à deux femmes") at Paris, Théâtre de la rue de Louvois, 1791.

ML 50.2.Z33D2

La **Zelinda.** Dramma per musica da rappresentarsi nel Real Teatro del Fondo di Separazione per prim' opera di quest' anno 1786 . . .

Napoli, n. publ., 1786. 36 p. 14½ᶜᵐ.

Three acts. The author is not mentioned, and is unknown to Schatz. Impresario's dedication dated Naples, April 17, 1786, notice to the readers ("Vi taccio il nome dell' autore. Per una natural modestia giammai egli si è annunziato nelle sue produzioni"), argument, scenario, cast, and name of Giuseppe **Millico** as the composer. The first ballet was analogous to the opera; the second, by Giambattista Giannini (music by Capuzzi), was called "Annetta e Fierillo." SCHATZ 6499

Zelindor roi des Sylphes.

Opéra-ballet in one act, with prologue by Moncrif; music by **Rebel** and **Francoeur.** First performed at Versailles March 17, 1745; at Paris, l'Académie royale de musique, August 10, 1745, and revived there in 1754.
Not in L. of C.

—**Zéphire et Fleurette,** parodie de Zelindor, en un acte. Par Messieurs * * *. Representée pour la premiere fois, par les Comédiens italiens ordinaires du roi, le samedi 23 mars 1754.

Paris, veuve Delormel & fils, 1754. 27, 8, 4 p. 19ᶜᵐ. (*Theatre de M. Favart, Paris, Duchesne, 1763–77, t. ii.*)

Cast. *En vaudevilles.* No airs printed in the text, but the 8, and 4 p. at end contain nine engraved "Airs de Zephire et Fleurette" and "Vaudeville de Zephire et Fleurette." On p. [3] this Avertissement:
"Cette pièce d'abord en prose, & en couplets, fut présentée aux Comediens italiens en 1745. Ils se préparoient à la jouer, lorsque des circonstances momentanées les empechèrent de donner des parodies. Une copie de cet ouvrage tomba entre les mains d'un comedien de province, qui le fit imprimer après y avoir ajouté quelques couplets. Les auteurs le révendiquerent, en retranchèrent les augmentations, la pièce fut refondue & donnée dans la forme qui suit."
The authors were Laujon and Panard and the piece was "refondue" by Favart. The arranger of the music is not mentioned by Font. ML 49.A2F1

Zemine et Almanzor. *See* L'industrie.

Zemira. Dramma per musica da rappresentarsi nel nobilissimo Teatro di S. Benedetto il carnovale dell' anno 1782.

Venezia, Modesto Fenzo, 1782. 63, [1] p. 17ᶜᵐ.

Two acts. By Gaetano Sertor. Argument, cast, scenario, and names of composer, Pasquale **Anfossi,** and librettist.
On p. 27–42 "Descrizione del primo ballo Don Pietro, rè di Castiglia, ballo tragico pantomimo in cinque atti, inventato, e diretto dal Signor Paolino Franchi . . ." The second ballet was called "L'amore in contrasto." The composer of the music of the ballets is not mentioned. SCHATZ 272
First performed December 26, 1781, as indicated.

Zemira. Dramma per musica da rappresentarsi nel nob. Teatro nuovo della magnifica città di Padova la fiera del Santo l'anno MDCCLXXXVI.

Padova, Gio. Antonio Gonzatti, n. d. 32 p. 17ᶜᵐ.

Two acts. Argument, cast, scenario, and name of Francesco **Bianchi** as composer, but not of Gaetano Sertor, the author. The music is called "del tutto nuova." Consequently, the performances of a "Zemira" by Bianchi at Naples, Teatro di S. Carlo, November 4, 1781, as mentioned by Schatz, may have been an earlier setting of the same text. SCHATZ 1001

Zemira e Azor, ballet. *See* Andreozzi's Giovanna d'Arco.

Zemira e Azor, ballet. *See* Caruso's Il vecchio burlato.

Zemira e Azor, ballet. *See* Paër's La virtù al cimento.

Zemira e Azore. Tr. of Grétry's Zémire et Azor.

Zemire et Azor, comédie ballet, en vers et en quatre actes; mêlée de chants et de danses; représentée devant Sa Majesté, à Fontainebleau, le 9 novembre 1771, & sur le Théatre de la Comédie italienne, le lundi 16 décembre suivant. Par M. Marmontel . . . La musique de M. Gretry.

Paris, Vente, 1772. 56 p. 17½^{cm}.

Cast. On p. 50–56 three "Airs de Zemire et Azor": "Rose chérie, aimable fleur," "Des mains d'un pere," "Du moment qu'on aime." YUDIN PQ

— Zémire et Azor, comédie ballet, en vers et en quatre actes, mêlée de chants et de danse, représentée devant Sa Majesté à Fontainebleau, le 9 novembre 1771, & sur le Théatre de la Comédie italienne le lundi 16 décembre suivant. Par M. Marmontel . . . La musique de M. Gretry.

Paris, Vente, 1774. 56 p. 18^{cm}.

Cast. On p. 49–56 "Airs de Zemire et Azor": "Rose chérie, aimable fleur" (II, 2), and "Du moment qu'on aime" (III, 5). SCHATZ 4191

— Zemire et Azor, comédie-ballet.

p. 3–43. 20½^{cm}.

Caption title. Lacks title-page, etc. Approbation at end dated November 16, 1771.
Three acts. Text by Marmontel, music by **Gretry**. ML 52.2.Z45

— Zemire et Azor, comédie-ballet en vers et en quatre actes, mêlée de chants et de danses; par Mr. Marmontel . . . La musique est de Mr. Gretri.

Berlin [!], Le Moine, 1773. 56 p. 18½^{cm}.

On p. [2] the note:
"Représenté devant Sa Majesté, à Fontainebleau, le 9 novembre 1771, & sur le Théâtre de la Comédie italienne, le lundi 16 décembre suivant." SCHATZ 11709

— Zemira e Azore, a new comic opera; as performed at the King's Theatre, in the Hay-market. Translated into Italian by Signor Verazzi. And into English by Mrs. Rigaud. The music by the most celebrated composer, Signor Gretry.

London, G. Bigg, 1779. 65 p. 18½^{cm}.

Cast.
First performed as indicated, in 1779. Mattia Verazi's Italian version, according to Schatz, was first used at Mannheim, Hoftheater, January, 1776. SCHATZ 4196

— Zemire und Azor, ein singspiel in vier aufzuegen aus dem franzoesischen uebersetzt, mit musik.

Frankfurt am Mayn, mit Andreäischen schriften, 1775. 80 p., 16 p. (folded music). 16½^{cm}.

By Johann Heinrich Faber, who is not mentioned. The music (voice and bass) consists of "Jene geister, womit man schreckt" ("Les esprits dont on nous a fait peur," I, 1), "Ach! welche quaal! ach! welche schmerzen" ("Ah! quel tourment d'être sensible," III, 1), "Munter sieht man den vogel" ("La fauvette avec ses petits," III, 5). SCHATZ 4192

Zemire et Azor—Continued.

—**Zemire und Azor.** Eine romantisch komische oper in vier aufzuegen.　Nach dem franzoesischen des Marmontel.

　Breslau und Leipzig, Christian Friedrich Gutsch, 1779.　87 p.　15½ᶜᵐ.
　German version, by Karl Emil Schubert.　　　　　　　SCHATZ 4193

—Gesaenge aus **Zemire und Azor,** einem singspiele in vier aufzuegen, von herrn Gretry.

　Mitau, Johann Friedrich Steffenhagen, 1782.　24 p.　16½ᶜᵐ.
　German version by Heinrich August Ottokar Reichard.
　First performed at Gotha, Hoftheater, January 29, 1776.　　SCHATZ 4194

—**Zemire und Azor,** ein singspiel in vier aufzuegen aus dem franzoesischen uebersetzt.

　Muenster, Perrenon, 1777.　64 p.　17ᶜᵐ.
　　　　　　　　　　　　　　　　　　　　　　　　SCHATZ 4195

—Gesaenge zu der oper: **Zemire und Azor** in vier aufzuegen.　Aus dem franzoesischen uebersetzt.

　n. i., n. d.　22 p.　17½ᶜᵐ.
　Printed before 1800?　　　　　　　　　　　　　SCHATZ 11710

Zémire et Mélide, ou Les fausses infidélités.　O. T. of Philidor's Mélide ou Le navigateur.

Zemire und Azor, eine romantisch-komische oper in vier. aufzuegen Nach dem franzoesischen des Marmontel.

　Breslau, Johann Friedrich Korn d. ältere, 1775.　56 p.　15½ᶜᵐ.
　Lyrics by Karl Emil Schubert; dialogue by the composer, Gotthilf von **Baumgarten** (neither mentioned).
　First performed at Breslau, Schuch'sches Theater, May 18, 1776.　SCHATZ 658

Zemire und Azor.　Tr. of Grétry's Zémire et Azor.

Zemirens und Azors ehestand.　A. T. of Umlauf's Der ring der liebe.

Zenis et Almasie, ballet héroique, représenté devant Leurs Majestés, à Fontainebleau, le 2 novembre 1765.

　[Paris], Christophe Ballard, 1765.　22 p.　20½ᶜᵐ.　(Journal des spectacles, t. ii, Paris, 1766.)
　One act.　Cast and names of Chamfort as author of the text, of Benjamin Jean de **La Borde** and Bernard de **Bury** (*see* t. I, p. 15) as composers of the music, and of Laval père et fils as "composers" of the ballet.　　ML 48.J7

Zenobia.

　Metastasio, Poesie, Parigi, vedova Quillau, 1755, t. v, 93 p.　16ᶜᵐ.
　Three acts and licenza.　Argument.　　　　　ML 49.A2M42

— **Zenobia.**　Dramma scritto dall' autore l'anno 1740, e rappresentato la prima volta con musica del Predieri nel palazzo dell' Imperial Favorita . . . il dì 28 agosto dell' anno medesimo, per festeggiare il giorno di nascita dell' imperatrice Elisabetta . . .

　pl., [3]–96 p.　26ᶜᵐ.　(Metastasio, Opere, t. vi, Parigi, vedova Herissant, 1780.)
　Three acts and licenza.　Argument.　　　　　ML 49.A2Z44

Zenobia—Continued.

— **Zenobie.**

Metastasio, Tragedies-opera, Vienne, 1751, v. i, p. [137]–243. 14^{cm}.
Three acts. Richelet's translation of "Zenobia." ML 49.A2M47

La Zenobia. Drama per musica di Mattio Noris. Da rappresentarsi nel Teatro di San Cassano l'anno 1665 . . .

Venetia, Camillo Bortoli, 1666. 15 p. 13^{cm}.

Three acts. Author's dedication, dated Venice, January 10, 1666, argument, scenario, and notice to the reader ("Sono anni quattro in circa, che hò delineato questo, mio parto"). The composer, Giovanni Antonio **Boretti**, is not mentioned.
SCHATZ 1221

Zenobia. Dramma per musica da rappresentarsi nel Teatro Giustinian di S. Moisè. L'autunno dell' anno 1746.

Venezia, Modesto Fenzo, 1746. 52 p. 17^{cm}.

Three acts. By Metastasio, who is not mentioned. Argument, scenario, cast, and name of Girolamo **Michelli** as the composer. SCHATZ 6481

Zenobia. Dramma per musica, da rappresentarsi nel nobil Teatro del Bairo Alto la state dell' anno 1765. Per celebrare la riccorrenza del gloriosissimo compleannos di S. A. R. il Signor prencipe di Beira.

[Lisbona], n. publ., n. d. 12 p. l., 123 p. 14$\frac{1}{2}$^{cm}.

Three acts. By Metastasio, who is not mentioned. Impresario's dedication, argument, cast, scenario, congratulatory poem, and note:
"La musica tutta, ch'è quella stessa, cantata nel Regio Teatro di Milano in occasione delle gloriosissime feste celebrate l'anno 1752, è parto felice del celebre Sig. David **Perez** . . ."
but the opera was actually first performed there fall of 1751. Portuguese title page and text face Italian. ML 50.2.Z37P3

Zenobia. Festa teatrale per musica. Da rappresentarsi nel giorno del felicissimo, e gloriosissimo nome della Sac. Ces. e Catt. Real Maestà di Elisabetta Cristina imperadrice regnante . . . l'anno MDCCXXXII. La poesia è del Sig. abate Gio. Claudio Pasquini . . . La musica è del Sig. Giorgio Reütter il giovine . . .

Vienna d'Austria, Gio. Pietro Van Ghelen, n. d. Unpaged. 21$\frac{1}{2}$^{cm}.

One act and licenza. Argument.
First performed at Vienna, Hoftheater, November 19, 1732. ML 48.M2C

Zenobia. Dramma per musica da rappresentarsi nel Teatro di S. Angelo l'autunno dell' anno 1740 . . .

Venezia, Marino Rossetti, n. d. 60 p. 15^{cm}.

Three acts. By Metastasio, who is not mentioned. Impresario's dedication, argument, cast, scenario, and name of Guglielmo **Sbacci** as the composer.
SCHATZ 9512

Zenobia. Dramma per musica da rappresentarsi nel Nuovo Teatro di corte . . . nel carnevale dell' anno MDCCLXXIII. La poesia è dell' Sig abbate Pietro Metastasio . . . La musica e del Sig. Antonio Tozzi . . .

Monaco, Francesco Gioseppe Thuille, n. d. 173, [26] p. 15^{cm}.

Three acts. Argument, cast, and scenario. German title-page, "Zenobia," and text face Italian. The unnumb. 26 p. contain casts and descriptions in French and German of Canziani's "Le jugement de Paris, ballet heroique et pantomime—Das urtheil des Paris" and Regina's "L'Espagnol genereux, ballet pantomime—Der grossmuethige Spanier." The composers of the music are not mentioned.
First performed January, 1773, as indicated. SCHATZ 10384

Zenobia. Dramma per musica da rappresentarsi nel nobil Teatro di Torre Argentina nel carnovale dell' anno 1762 . . .

   Roma, Giovanni Giussani, 1762. 51 p. 15^{cm}.

Three acts. Dedicatory poem, cast, argument, scenario, names of composer, Tommaso **Trajetta**, and librettist, Metastasio, and *protesta:*
"Ciocchè si è variato, ed aggiunto nel dramma, si è fatto per accomodarlo al teatro presente: e per quanto è stato possibile, vi si sono adattate le ariette, ed i recitativi di altre opere dramatiche dello stesso autore: i di cui celebri originali restano sempre illesi nelle molte applaudite edizioni . . ."   SCHATZ 10398

Zenobia, dramma per musica, da rappresentarsi nel Regio Teatro Danese.—Zenobia, et syngespil . . .

   Kiøbenhavn, L. N. Svare, 1770. 87 p. 17½^{cm}.

Three acts. Argument and cast. Neither Metastasio, the author, nor Francesco Antonio Baldassare **Uttini**, the composer, is mentioned. Danish text faces Italian. First performed at the same theater, carnival, 1754.   SCHATZ 10551

Zenobia oder Das muster rechtschaffener ehelichen liebe. Tr. of Händel's Radamisto.

Zenobia in Palmira. Dramma serio per musica da rappresentarsi nel Regio Teatro dell' Accademia degli Avvalorati in Livorno l'autunno dell' anno 1796.

   [Livorno], presso Tommaso Masi, e compagno, n. d. 32 p. 17½^{cm}.

Two acts. By Gaetano Sertor. Cast, scenario, and name of composer, Pasquale **Anfossi**, but not of librettist.
With the opera were performed the ballo serio "Il Zorilan" and the ballo comico "Il pittor burlato," both invented by Gio. Batista Giannini. The composer of the music is not mentioned.
First performed at Venice, Teatro di S. Benedetto, December 26, 1789.
    SCHATZ 257

Zenobia in Palmira. Drama per musica da rappresentarsi nel Regio Teatro di Milano l'anno 1710 . . .

   Milano, Giuseppe Pandolfo Malatesta, n. d. 58 p. 13½^{cm}.

Three acts. Attributed by Schatz to Zeno (jointly with Pariati), but no such text appears in Zeno's collected works. The text is largely the same as that of the anonymous "L'amore eroico," 1725. Dedication, argument, scenario, and Reimprimatur. The composer, Fortunato **Chelleri**, is not mentioned.
First performed at Barcellona, 1709, Teatro en la casa de la Lonja.   SCHATZ 1818

Zenobia, regina de Palmireni. Dramma per musica da rappresentarsi nel Teatro Grimano de SS. Gio. e Paolo l'anno 1694. De Antonio Marchi . . .

   Venetia, Per il Nicolini, 1694. 71 p. 13½^{cm}.

Three acts. Author's dedication, argument, scenario, and notice to the reader, in which Marchi calls this his second drama and mentions Tommaso **Albinoni** as the composer.   SCHATZ 112

Zenobia regina dei Palmireni. O. T. of Marchi's text Il vinto trionfante del vincitore.

Zenobie. Tr. of Metastasio's Zenobia.

Zenocrate ambasciatore a' Macedoni. Drama per musica da rappresentarsi nel Teatro Zane di S. Moisè l'anno 1687. Del Gasparini . . .

   Venetia, Francesco Nicolini, 1687. 60 p. 14^{cm}.

Three acts. Dedication, argument, notice to the reader, scenario. The composer, Pietro **Porfiri**, is not mentioned.   SCHATZ 8356

Zenone, imperator d'Oriente. Drama per musica. Da rappresentarsi nel Teatro di San Casciano l'anno 1696. Di Antonio Marchi . . .

Venetia, Nocolini, 1696. 71 p. 14½^{cm}.

Pages 5–6 wanting.

Three acts. Dedication, argument, notice to the reader. Composed by Tommaso Albinoni, who is not mentioned. SCHATZ 101

Zéphire et Fleurette. Parody of Rebel and Francoeur's Zelindor.

Zephire et Flore, opera, representé par l'Academie royale de musique. Suivant la copie imprimée, a Paris.

[Amsterdam, Antoine Schelte], 1688. 47 p. (incl. front.) 13½^{cm}.

Prologue and three acts. For author and composer *see* next entry.

ML 50.2.Z4L9

— Zephire et Flore, opera, representé par l'Academie royale de musique.

Imprimé à Paris, & on les vend a Anvers, chez Henry van Dunewald, 1689. 36 p. 13½^{cm}.

Prologue and three acts. Neither the author, Michel Du Boulay, is mentioned, nor are the composers, Louis and Jean Louis de Lully.

First performed, as indicated, March 22, 1688. ML 50.2.Z4L9

— Zephire et Flore, opera representé par l'Academie royale de musique l'an 1688. Les paroles de M. Du Boulay, & la musique de Mrs Louis de Lully, & Jean Louis de Lully. XXIII. opera.

n. i., n. d. 14^{cm}. pl., 281–330 p. (Recueil général des opéra, t. iii, Paris, 1703.)

Detached copy. Three acts and prologue. SCHATZ 5784

Second copy. ML 48.R4

Das zerstoerte Troja, oder Der durch den tod Helenen versoehnte Achilles, wurde an dem theuren Carols-tage wegen des neulichen von Ihro Roem. Kays. und Cathol. Maj. unsern allergnaedigsten kayser und herrn, ueber die Tuercken befochtenen sieges, und der darauf hoechst gluecklich erfolgten eroberung der sehr wichtigen vestung Temeswar, [vignette] zu allerunterthaenigster bezeugung der hierob geschoepften freude in einem musicalischen singe-spiel auf dem Hamburgischen Schau-platz vorgestellet im novembre, 1716.

Hamburg, Fridrich Conrad Greflinger, n. d. Unpaged. 19^{cm}.

Five acts. Scenario and historical "vorbericht" by the author, Johann Joachim Hoë, who is not mentioned. He says:

"zur nachricht, dass einige gute freunde den verfasser der poetie, welcher die poetische feder nur bey einigen muessigen stunden ergriffen, veranlasset, gegenwaertige opera zu verfertigen, welche, wenn man die italiaenische entgegen zu halten beliebet, eben nicht fuer eine blosse ubersetzung wird zu schaetzen seyn. Fuernemlich aber hat ihn dazu angetrieben des grossen virtuosen, des hn. capell-meister Keisers extraordinaire composition . . ."

Many arias have the Italian text added to the German. Hoë based his text on Urbano Rizzi's "Achille placato."

As sixty-sixth opera, by Keiser, first performed, as indicated, November 4, 1716.

SCHATZ 5117

Die **zigeuner.** Ein lustspiel mit gesang, in fuenf aufzuegen, von Heinrich Ferdinand Moeller. Aufgefuehrt auf dem churfuerstl. Theater zu Muenchen. Die musik hierzu ist von herrn Joh. Chr. Kaffka, und bey selbigem in Augsburg zu haben.

n. i., n. d., 1778.   94 p.   16^{cm}.

First performed, as indicated, 1778.   SCHATZ 4988

Die **zigeuner.**   A. T. of Salieri's Der talisman.

Zima, ballet.   *See* P. Guglielmi's Lo sciocco poeta di campagna.

Zima, ballet.   *See* Zingarelli's La secchia rapita.

Li **Zingani in fiera,** ballet.   *See* Tritto's Nicaboro in Jucatan.

La **Zingara.**

Intermezzo in two parts.   Music by **Rinaldo di Capua.**   Author unknown.   Date of first performance unknown.

Not in L. of C. and no copy of the original edition had been traced by Spitta when he wrote his essay on Rinaldo di Capua for the Vierteljahrsschrift für Musikwissenschaft, 1887.   In this essay Spitta sought to reconstruct the original version of "La Zingara" (though without much success), principally on the basis of the somewhat altered score edited by Cosimi some time after the first performance of "La Zingara" on June 19, 1753, at the Académie royale de musique, Paris.   Compare Spitta also for the relationship between this score and that of Favart's French version of 1755.   Cosimi's score contains the following (arias in Italics):

(Int. I) *Con la speme del goder.*
Si taglia borse.
Tu non pensi.
Caro fratello mio.
Hò ragione, si signore.
Mancherebbe amor questa.
Ella può credermi.
E in breve sarò sposo.
Si, caro ben sarete.
E dove, dove l'orso n'andò (Rec. acc.)
Che orror che spavento.
Donde Signor tant ira.
Amor, oh che diletto.

(Int.II) Imaginar non puoi.
E specie di tormento (text Metastasio's Temistocle).
S'avvicina, Calcante.
O voi possenti Numi (Rec. acc.)
Voce, che flebile.
Nulla, nulla Signor.
Perfidi, che volete.
Non tante smanie.
O dell' Egitto Nume custode (= "Dea delle selve . . .   Tu il core intatto" in **Hasse's** Leucippo).
Io giuro rei.
Viverò se tu lo vuoi.
Oh Dio Nisa d'amore.
Ogni tromba, ogni tamburo.

—La **Bohémienne,** comedie en deux actes en vers, mêslée d'ariettes, traduite de la Zingara, intermede italien.

La Haye, H. Constapel, 1758.   40 p.   15½^{cm}.

Two acts.   By Favart, parodied from **Rinaldo di Capua's** "La Zingara," and first performed at Paris, Comédie italienne, July 28, 1755.   At the head of the arias are given the first words of the Italian arias used.   The cast is preceded by this impudent
"Avertissement

"Cette bagatelle est une traduction de l'intermède italien donné sur le Théâtre de l'Opéra.   Dans tous les endroits où l'on a suivi l'original à la lettre, on a dû nécessairement se rencontrer avec les auteurs qui ont traduit le même sujet.   On ne peut point être soupconné de plagiat, quand'il n'y qu'une façon de dire les choses."

SCHATZ 8797

La **Zingara**—Continued.

—La **Bohémienne**, comédie en deux actes et en vers, meslée d'ariettes, traduite de la Zingara, intermède italien. Représentée pour la premiere fois par les Comédiens italiens ordinaires du roi, le 28 juillet 1755.

Paris, N. B. Duchesne, 1759. 43, [5], [41]–96 p. 19ᶜᵐ. Theatre de M. Favart, Paris, Duchesne, 1763–77, t. ii.)

Cast. The [5] p. contain catalogues of plays; the p. [41]–96, seventeen "Ariettes de la Bohémienne." In the text which coincides with that of the published score the corresponding ariettes are headed by the first words of the Italian arias.

The seventeen ariettes are:

Dans l'espérance du plaisir (= "Con la speme del goder" in La Zingara).
Tu ne songes guère (= "Tu non pensi" in La Zingara).
Que t'importe que je reste (= "Hò ragione, si Signore" in La Zingara).
Ah! cette ligne désigne (= "Ella può credermi" in La Zingara).
Examinez sa grace (= "Tre giorni son che Nina." For a long time attributed to **Pergolesi**, though without proof. Radiciotti persists in attributing this song to Pergolesi on the strength of rather naïve "internal" evidence. His reading of Squire's articles on the song in "Musical Times," 1899, and Zeitschrift d. I. M. G. 1900/01 is curiously inaccurate. Squire adduced some contemporary evidence that the song was considered a composition by Legrenzio Vincenzo **Ciampi**, and he traced its first anonymous appearance in print to the year 1749 when it was printed (in April) by Walsh of London as one of the interpolated songs in a comic opera called "I tre cicisbei ridicoli," a *rifacimento* (London, Haymarket, March 14, 1749) perhaps by Ciampi, the accredited "maestro to the company" in London of Natale Resta's opera (text by Vasini), Venice, Teatro di Sant' Angelo, May 1748. Spitta was inclined, though without sound reasons, to attribute the song, which originally was comic, not tragic, to **Rinaldo di Capuā**. Pergolesi's name did not become attached to it until the sixth decade of the eighteenth century, *i. e.* if Gugler really saw an English sheet-edition of the song with Pergolesi's name, or otherwise not until the nineteenth century. Weckerlin, for instance, never saw an edition with Pergolesi's name older than 1847.)

Oui, vous serez sans cesse (= "Si, caro ben sarete" in La Zingara).
Ah! mon ours a pris la fuite (= "Maledetti quanti siete" in **Ciampi's** Bertoldo, Bertoldina e Cacasenno).
Oh! laissez donc mon coeur (= "Madam' lasciatemi" in **Resta's** I trè cicisbei ridicoli).
Mon coeur, o cher Calcante (as appears from a note in the score, this duet was by **Pergolesi**. Indeed it is "Per te io hò nel core" from his Flaminio).
(Int. II) *Je n'en puis plus* (= "Si ravviva" [nel mio core], which also appears in the "Giocatore" Paris).
Au piège il va se rendre (= "E specie di tormento" in La Zingara).
Je perds sans ressource (= Che orror! che spavento" in La Zingara).
O vous, démons celèbres (= O voi possenti Numi (in the text called an ariette, in the "Ariettes" a recitative and in the score correctly a "Recitatif accompagnè." It is from La Zingara).
Ta voix au noir séjour (= "Voce che lugubre" in La Zingara).
Au secours. Ah! je tremble (= "Perfidi che volete" in La Zingara).
Pauvre Nise! Tu chéris (= "Vedovella, poverella" in **Cocchi's** La scaltra governatrice).
Toujours preste, toujours leste (= "Ogni tromba, ogni tamburo" in La Zingara).

ML 49.A2F1

La **Zingara**.   L. T. of Vento's L'Egiziana.

Ziste et Zeste, ou Les importuns, folie en un acte et en vaudevilles, par les CC. Cailhava et Leger. Représentée pour la première fois, sur le Théâtre du Vaudeville . . . 27 Août 1796.

Paris, Au Théâtre du Vaudeville, [etc], An Vᵉ [1796–97]. 35 p. 8°.

Cast. On p. 34 the air of the "Vaudeville. Paroles et musique du citoyen **Leger.**—*Plein de la plus vive ardeur.*"

Not recorded by Cl. & L. or Schatz.

ML 48.M2E

Zoe. Dramma per musica da rappresentarsi nel Teatro novissimo di San Benedetto il carnovale dell' anno MDCCLVI.

Venezia, Angiolo Geremia, n. d. 52 p. 15½ cm.

Three acts. By Francesco Silvani, an altered version of whose "La forza del sanguine" this is, according to Schatz. Argument, cast, scenario, and name of Gioacchino **Cocchi** as composer.

First performed, as indicated, December 26, 1755.   SCHATZ 2047

La Zoe. Dramma per musica da rappresentarsi nel nobile Teatro Tron di S. Cassiano l'autunno dell' anno 1736 . . .

Venezia, Giuseppe Bettinelli, 1736. 71 p. 15 cm.

Three acts. A later version of "La forza del sangue" by Francesco Silvani, who is not mentioned. Dedication by Domenico Lalli, argument, cast, scenario, and name of Luca Antonio **Predieri** as composer.   SCHATZ 8459

Zon-Zon principe di Kibin-Kinka. Dramma giocoso da rappresentarsi nel Regio Ducal Teatro di Milano l'autunno dell' anno 1773 . . .

Milano, Gio. Batista Bianchi, n. d. 68, [2] p. 15½ cm.

Two acts. A considerably altered version of "L'inimico delle donne" by Bertati, who is not mentioned. Impresario's dedication, scenario, and name of Giuseppe **Gazzaniga** as the composer. With the opera was performed Gasparo Angiolini's "La partenza d'Enea, o sia Didone abbandonata," who possibly also composed the music for this ballet.   SCHATZ 3688

Zophilette. Conte de Mr. Marmontel mis en scènes & en ariettes, & représenté le 17 mai 1765.

Paris, n. publ., 1768. 2 p. l., 39 p. 19 cm.

One act. The anonymous author says in his preface:

"J'avais toujours imaginé qu'en travaillant d'après l'élégant Marmontel, la réussite était sure. Je m'amusai à mettre en scènes son Conte de Laurette. A peine eus-je achevé de compiler mon drame en faveur d'une société qui a bien voulu s'amuser de le représenter, que je crus qu'il n'y avait qu'à le faire mettre en musique. J'ai refais mes ariettes sur des airs italiens." J'entrevoyais déjà mon triomphe, & le plaisir d'avoir contribué à celui du public." However, he decided first to submit his play to a "femme charmante, pleine d'esprit & de goût" for her criticism which he expected to be in the form of a compliment. He quotes her not altogether flattering "réflexions" and suggestions for improvement and continues by saying:

"Me connaissant trop de paresse & point assez de talent pour suivre le conseil sage & honnête que renferme cette juste critique, j'abandonnai mon projet de me faire jouer sur le théâtre. Je me plaindrai peut-être bientôt de l'avoir été trop en société."

The "airs italiens" to which his ariettes were to be sung are indicated in every instance with the name of the composer. Accordingly the music formed an anthology of arias by **Galuppi, Ferrandini, Jommelli, Gluck, Bach, Piccinni, Traetta, Sarti** and others and includes a few Venetian canzonettas.

Not recorded by Schatz, Cl. & L., etc.   ML 50.2.Z6

Zoraime et Zulnar, opéra en trois actes, par le C. Saint-Just, musique du C. Boieldieu. Représenté pour la première fois sur le Théâtre de la rue Favart, le 21 floréal, an 6 de la République Française. [May 10, 1798]

Paris, Au bureau dramatique, an VI. [1797–98]. 67, [1] p. 21 cm.

Cast.   ML 50.2.Z65B6

Zorei e Ozai, ballet. *See* G. Giordani's Erifile.

Il **Zorilan,** ballet. *See* Anfossi's Zenobia in Palmira.

Zorilan, ballet. *See* Cimarosa's L'impegno superato.

Zorinski: a play, in three acts, as performed at the Theatre Royal, Hay-Market. By Thomas Morton . . .

London, T. N. Longman, 1795. 2 p. l., 73 p. 20^{cm}.

Cast. Considerably interspersed with songs, etc., composed by Samuel **Arnold** (not mentioned).

First performed June 20, 1795. Longe 232

Zoroastre, tragedie. Representée par l'Academie royale de musique, pour la premiere fois, le vendredy cinq décember 1749.

[Paris], Aux depens de l'Academie, 1749. 74, [2] p. 22$\frac{1}{2}$^{cm}.

Five acts. Cast, argument, and names of Louis de Cahusac as author, of Jean Philippe **Rameau** as composer. ML 50.2.Z7R2

Zoroastro, tragedia tradotta dal francese, da rappresentarsi nel Regio Elettoral Teatro di Dresda, dalla compagnia de comici italiani in attuale servizio di Sua Maestà nel carnovale dell' anno MDCCLII.

Dresda, Stamperia regia, n. d. 8 p. l., 64 p. 20^{cm}.

Five acts. Argument, synopsis of plot, cast. [Giacomo] Casanova [de Seignalt] is mentioned as author of this Italian version of Louis de Cahusac's tragedy, and "Signor [Johann August] **Adam,** musico di camera di S. M." as composer of the music including the ballets excepting the overture and the first chorus, which were by **Rameau,** and presumably taken from his "Zoroastre."

First performed, as indicated, February 7, 1752. Schatz 55

Il zotico incivilito. L. T. of Anfossi's Lo sposo disperato.

Zulima. Dramma per musica da rappresentarsi in Firenze nella primavera dell' anno 1796 nel Regio Teatro degli Intrepidi detto della Palla a corda . . .

Firenze, Ant. Gius. Pagani e comp., 1796. 39 p. 17^{cm}.

Two acts. By Francesco Gonella di Ferrara. Argument, name of Marco **Portogallo** as composer and note: "La poesia è tutta nuova dell' autore della Lodiska."

ML 48.A5 v.14

Zulima. Dramma per musica da rappresentarsi nel Teatro di via della Pergola nel carnevale del MDCCLXXVII . . .

Firenze, Gio. Risaliti, n. d. 39 p. 16$\frac{1}{2}$^{cm}.

Two acts. By Cesare Oliveri, who is not mentioned. Cast, argument, and name of Giovanni Marco **Rutini** as the composer. With the opera was performed Antonio Terrade's ballet "Il Francese in Londra," the composer of the music not being mentioned. Schatz 9189

Zulima o sia La famiglia riunita, ballo pantomimo. *See* Farinelli's Il nuovo savio della Grecia.

Die **zur meisterin gewordene schuelerin.** Tr. of Cingoni's La scolara fatta maestra.

Die **zurueckkunft aus Londen.** Tr. of Fischietti's La ritornata di Londra.

Die **zween Savoyarden.** Tr. of Dalayrac's Les deux petits Savoyards.

Die **zwey comtessinnen.** Tr. of Paisiello's Le due contesse.

Die **zwey geizigen.** A. T. of Joh. Ad. Hiller's Das grab des Mufti.

Die **zwey geitzigen.**   A. T. of Grétry's Das grab des Mufti.

Die **zwey schatzgraeber,** eine komische operette von einem aufzug.
  n. i., 1781.   55 p.   16½^{cm}*.*
  Not recorded by Schatz.   Not found in "Deutsches Anonymen Lexikon."
                                              SCHATZ 11665

Die **zwey vormuender.**   Tr. of Dalayrac's Les deux tuteurs.

Die **zwischenfälle.**   Tr. of Sarti's I contratempi.

Zwo komische operetten von G * *, nebst andern gedichten
zum anhange.
  Chemnitz, Joh. Dav. Stoessels erben u. Putscher, 1773.   4 p. l., 287 p.
  16^{cm}*.*
  Dedication and apology, "An den kunstrichter," followed by (p. 1–184) "Das
  VORNEHME SUSCHEN, eine komische operette in drey aufzuegen" and "Das TESTA-
  MENT, eine komische operette in einem aufzuge" (p. 185–246).   For further data *see*
  these under their titles.   SCHATZ 11655

Die **zwoelf schlafenden jungfrauen.**   Zweyter theil.   Ein schauspiel mit gesang in vier aufzuegen, nach der geistergeschichte des
herrn Spiess, fuer die Marinellische schaubuehne bearbeitet, von
Karl Friedrich Hensler.   Die musik ist vom hrn. Wenzel Mueller,
kapellmeister.
  Wien, Mathias Andreas Schmidt, 1798.   83 p.   16^{cm}*.*
  First performed, as indicated, July 24, 1798.   Of the Iter theil, the L. of C. has not
  the original ed. of 1797, but only Berlin, 1805, of the IIIter theil we have the
  original ed., Wien, 1800.   SCHATZ 6979

Die **zwölf schlafenden jungfrauen.**   Ein schauspiel mit gesang
in 4 aufzuegen, von Karl Ludwig Gieseke . . .   Die musik ist von
Matthaeus Stegmayr.   Fuer das K. K. Wiednertheater.
  Wien, Binzische Buchhandlung, 1798.   126 p.   16½^{cm}*.*
  First performed June 4, 1796, as indicated.   SCHATZ 10052